Hoover's Handbook of

Emerging Companies

2015

HOOVERS™

A D&B COMPANY

Austin, Texas

10 9 8 7 6 5 4 3 2 1

Publishers Cataloging-in-Publication Data
Hoover's Handbook of Emerging Companies 2015
    Includes indexes.
    ISBN: 978-1-63053-408-0
    ISSN 1073-6433

    1. Business enterprises — Directories. 2. Corporations — Directories.
HF3010 338.7

U.S. AND WORLD BOOK SALES

Mergent Inc.
580 Kingsley Park Drive
Fort Mill, SC 29715
Phone: 800-342-5647
e-mail: orders@mergent.com
Web: www.mergentbusinesspress.com

Mergent Inc.

Publisher: Jonathan Worrall

Executive Managing Director: John Pedernales

Executive Vice President of Sales: Fred Jenkins

Managing Director of Relationship Management: Chris Henry

Senior Product Manager: Neel Gandhi

Managing Director of Print Products: Thomas Wecera

Director Print Products: Charlot Volny

Quality Assurance Editor: Wayne Arnold

Production Research Assistant: Erin Keane

Mergent Customer Service

Support and Fulfillment Manager: Melanie Horvat

ABOUT MERGENT INC.

Mergent, Inc. is a leading provider of business and financial data on global publicly listed companies. Based in the U.S, the company maintains a strong global presence, with offices in New York, Charlotte, San Diego, London, Tokyo and Melbourne.

Founded in 1900, Mergent operates one of the longest continuously collected databases of: descriptive and fundamental information on domestic and international companies; pricing and terms and conditions data on fixed income and equity securities; and corporate action data. In addition, Mergent's Indxis subsidiary develops and licenses equity and fixed income investment products based on its proprietary investment methodologies. Our licensed products have over $9 billion in assets under management and are offered by major investment management firms. The Indxis calculation platform is the chosen technology for some of the world's largest index companies. Its index calculation and pricing distribution protocols are used to administer index rules and distribute real-time pricing data.

Abbreviations

AFL-CIO – American Federation of Labor and Congress of Industrial Organizations

AMA – American Medical Association

AMEX – American Stock Exchange

ARM – adjustable-rate mortgage

ASP – application services provider

ATM – asynchronous transfer mode

ATM – automated teller machine

CAD/CAM – computer-aided design/computer-aided manufacturing

CD-ROM – compact disc – read-only memory

CD-R – CD-recordable

CEO – chief executive officer

CFO – chief financial officer

CMOS – complementary metal oxide silicon

COO – chief operating officer

DAT – digital audiotape

DOD – Department of Defense

DOE – Department of Energy

DOS – disk operating system

DOT – Department of Transportation

DRAM – dynamic random-access memory

DSL – digital subscriber line

DVD – digital versatile disc/digital video disc

DVD-R – DVD-recordable

EPA – Environmental Protection Agency

EPS – earnings per share

ESOP – employee stock ownership plan

EU – European Union

EVP – executive vice president

FCC – Federal Communications Commission

FDA – Food and Drug Administration

FDIC – Federal Deposit Insurance Corporation

FTC – Federal Trade Commission

GATT – General Agreement on Tariffs and Trade

GDP – gross domestic product

HMO – health maintenance organization

HR – human resources

HTML – hypertext markup language

ICC – Interstate Commerce Commission

IPO – initial public offering

IRS – Internal Revenue Service

ISP – Internet service provider

kWh – kilowatt-hour

LAN – local-area network

LBO – leveraged buyout

LCD – liquid crystal display

LNG – liquefied natural gas

LP – limited partnership

Ltd. – limited

mips – millions of instructions per second

MW – megawatt

NAFTA – North American Free Trade Agreement

NASA – National Aeronautics and Space Administration

NASDAQ – National Association of Securities Dealers Automated Quotations

NATO – North Atlantic Treaty Organization

NYSE – New York Stock Exchange

OCR – optical character recognition

OECD – Organization for Economic Cooperation and Development

OEM – original equipment manufacturer

OPEC – Organization of Petroleum Exporting Countries

OS – operating system

OSHA – Occupational Safety and Health Administration

OTC – over-the-counter

PBX – private branch exchange

PCMCIA – Personal Computer Memory Card International Association

P/E – price to earnings ratio

RAID – redundant array of independent disks

RAM – random-access memory

R&D – research and development

RBOC – regional Bell operating company

RISC – reduced instruction set computer

REIT – real estate investment trust

ROA – return on assets

ROE – return on equity

ROI – return on investment

ROM – read-only memory

S&L – savings and loan

SEC – Securities and Exchange Commission

SEVP – senior executive vice president

SIC – Standard Industrial Classification

SOC – system on a chip

SVP – senior vice president

USB – universal serial bus

VAR – value-added reseller

VAT – value-added tax

VC – venture capitalist

VoIP – Voice over Internet Protocol

VP – vice president

WAN – wide-area network

Contents

Companies Profiled

Companies Profiled (continued)

Companies Profiled (continued)

About Hoover's Handbook of Emerging Companies 2015

Hoover's Handbook of Emerging Companies enters its 22nd year as one of America's premier sources of business information on younger, growth-oriented enterprises. Given our current economic realities, finding value in the marketplace becomes ever more difficult, and so we are particularly pleased to present this edition of Hoover's Handbook of Emerging Companies 2015 — the result of a search of our extensive database of business information for companies with demonstrated growth and the potential for future gains.

The 600 companies in this book were chosen from the universe of public US companies with sales between $10 million and $2.5 billion. Their selection was based primarily on sales growth and profitability, although in a few cases we made some rather subjective decisions about which companies we chose to include. They all have reported at least three years of sales and have sustained annualized sales growth of at least 7% during that time. Also, they are profitable (through year-end September 2014).

In addition to the companies featured in our handbooks, comprehensive coverage of more than 40,000 business enterprises is available in electronic format on our website, Hoover's Online (www.hoovers.com). Our goal is to provide one site that offers authoritative, updated intelligence on US and global companies, industries, and the people who shape them. Hoover's has partnered with other prestigious business information and service providers to bring you all the right business information, services, and links in one place.

Hoover's Handbook of Emerging Companies is one of our four-title series of handbooks that covers, literally, the world of business. The series is available as an indexed set, and also includes Hoover's Handbook of American Business, Hoover's Handbook of World Business, and Hoover's Handbook of Private Companies. This series brings you information on the biggest, fastest-growing, and most influential enterprises in the world.

We believe that anyone who buys from, sells to, invests in, lends to, competes with, interviews with, or works for a company should know as much as possible about that enterprise. Taken together, Hoover's Handbook of Emerging Companies 2014 and the other Hoover's products represent the most complete source of basic corporate information readily available to the general public.

How to use this book

This book has four sections:

1. "Using Hoover's Handbooks" describes the contents of our profiles.

2. "A List-Lover's Compendium" contains lists of the fastest-growing and most profitable companies. The lists are based on the information in our profiles, or compiled from well-known sources.

3. The company profiles section makes up the largest and most important part of the book — 600 profiles arranged alphabetically. Each profile features an overview of the company; some larger and more visible companies have an additional History section. All companies have up to five years of financial information, product information where available, and a list of company executives and key competitors.

4. At the end of this volume are the combined indexes from our 2014 editions of all Hoover's Handbooks. The information is organized into three separate sections. The first sorts companies by industry groups, the second by headquarters location. The third index is a list of all the executives found in the Executives section of each company profile. For a more thorough description of our indexing style, see page xii.

Using Hoover's Handbooks

ORGANIZATION

The profiles in this volume are presented in alphabetical order. This alphabetization is generally word by word, which means that Bridge Bancorp precedes Bridgepoint Education. You will find the commonly used name of the enterprise at the beginning of the profile; the full, legal name is found in the Locations section. If a company name starts with initials, such as BJ's Restaurants or U.S. Physical Therapy, look for it under the combined initials (in the above example, BJ or US, respectively).

Basic financial data is listed under the heading Historical Financials; also included is the exchange on which the company's stock is traded, the ticker symbol used by the stock exchange, and the company's fiscal year-end. The annual financial information contained in the profiles is current through fiscal year-ends occurring as late as September 2013. We have included certain nonfinancial developments, such as officer changes, through January 2013.

OVERVIEW

In the first section of the profile, we have tried to give a thumbnail description of the company and what it does. The description will usually include information on the company's strategy, reputation, and ownership. We recommend that you read this section first.

HISTORY

This extended section, which is available for some of the larger and more well-known companies, reflects our belief that every enterprise is the sum of its history and that you have to know where you came from in order to know where you are going. While some companies have limited historical awareness, we think the vast majority of the enterprises in this book have colorful backgrounds. We have tried to focus on the people who made the enterprises what they are today. We have found these histories to be full of twists and ironies; they make fascinating reading.

EXECUTIVES

Here we list the names of the people who run the company, insofar as space allows. In the case of public companies, we have shown the ages and pay of key officers. The published data is for the previous fiscal year, although the company may have announced promotions or retirements since year-end. The pay represents cash compensation, including bonuses, but excludes stock option programs.

Although companies are free to structure their management titles any way they please, most modern corporations follow standard practices. The ultimate power in any corporation lies with the shareholders, who elect a board of directors, usually including officers or "insiders," as well as individuals from outside the company. The chief officer, the person on whose desk the buck stops, is usually called the chief executive officer (CEO). Often, he or she is also the chairman of the board.

As corporate management has become more complex, it is common for the CEO to have a "right-hand person" who oversees the day-to-day operations of the company, allowing the CEO plenty of time to focus on strategy and long-term issues. This right-hand person is usually designated the chief operating officer (COO) and is often the president of the company. In other cases one person is both chairman and president.

A multitude of other titles exists, including chief financial officer (CFO), chief administrative officer, and vice chairman. We have always tried to include the CFO, the chief legal officer, and the chief human resources or personnel officer. Our best advice is that officers' pay levels are clear indicators of who the board of directors thinks are the most important members of the management team.

The people named in the Executives section are indexed at the back of the book.

The Executives section also includes the name of the company's auditing (accounting) firm, where available.

LOCATIONS

Here we include the company's full legal name and its headquarters, street address, telephone and fax numbers, and website, as available. The back of the book includes an index of companies by headquarters locations.

In some cases we have also included information on the geographic distribution of the company's business, including sales and profit data. Note that these profit numbers, like those in the Products/Operations section below, are usually operating or pretax profits rather than net profits. Operating profits are generally those before financing costs (interest income and payments) and before taxes, which are considered costs attributable to the whole company rather than to one division or part of the world. For this reason the net income figures (in the Historical Financials section) are usually much lower, since they are after interest and taxes. Pretax profits are after interest but before taxes.

PRODUCTS/OPERATIONS

This section lists as many of the company's products, services, brand names, divisions, subsidiaries, and joint ventures as we could fit. We have tried to include all its major lines and all familiar brand names. The nature of this section varies by company and the amount of information available. If the company publishes sales and profit information by type of business, we have included it.

COMPETITORS

In this section we have listed companies that compete with the profiled company. This feature is included as a quick way to locate similar companies and compare them. The universe of competitors includes all public companies and all private companies with sales in excess of $500 million. In a few instances we have identified smaller private companies as key competitors.

HISTORICAL FINANCIALS

Here we have tried to present as much data about each enterprise's financial performance as we could compile in the allocated space. Although the information varies somewhat from industry to industry, the following is generally present.

A five-year table, with relevant annualized compound growth rates, covers:

- Sales — fiscal year sales (year-end assets for most financial companies)
- Net income — fiscal year net income (before accounting changes)
- Net profit margin — fiscal year net income as a percent of sales (as a percent of assets for most financial firms)
- Employees — fiscal year-end or average number of employees
- Stock price — the fiscal year closing price
- P/E — high and low price/earnings ratio
- Earnings per share — fiscal year earnings per share (EPS)
- Dividends per share — fiscal year dividends per share
- Book value per share — fiscal year-end book value (common shareholders' equity per share)

The information on the number of employees is intended to aid the reader interested in knowing whether a company has a long-term trend of increasing or decreasing employment. As far as we know, we are the only company that publishes this information in print format.

The numbers on the left in each row of the Historical Financials section give the month and the year in which the company's fiscal year actually ends. Thus, a company with a September 30, 2010, year-end is shown as 9/10.

In addition, we have provided in graph form a stock price history for each company. The graphs, covering up to five years, show the range of trading between the high and the low price, as well as the closing price for each fiscal year.

Key year-end statistics in this section generally show the financial strength of the enterprise, including:

- Debt ratio (long-term debt as a percent of shareholders' equity)
- Return on equity (net income divided by the average of beginning and ending common shareholders' equity)
- Cash and cash equivalents
- Current ratio (ratio of current assets to current liabilities)
- Total long-term debt (including capital lease obligations)
- Number of shares of common stock outstanding
- Dividend yield (fiscal year dividends per share divided by the fiscal year-end closing stock price)
- Dividend payout (fiscal year dividends divided by fiscal year EPS)
- Market value at fiscal year-end (fiscal year-end closing stock price multiplied by fiscal year-end number of shares outstanding)

Per-share data has been adjusted for stock splits. The data for public companies has been provided to us by Morningstar, Inc. Other public company information was compiled by Hoover's, which takes full responsibility for the content of this section.

Hoover's Handbook of

Emerging Companies

A List-Lover's Compendium

The 200 Largest Companies by Sales in Hoover's Handbook of Emerging Companies 2015

Rank	Company	Sales ($ bil.)	Rank	Company	Sales ($bil.)	Rank	Company	Sales ($ bil.)
1	Wal-Mart Stores, Inc.	$476,294	61	Coca-Cola Co (The)	$46,854	121	AFLAC Inc.	$23,939
2	Exxon Mobil Corp.	$438,255	62	Sysco Corp.	$46,517	122	EMC Corp. (MA)	$23,222
3	Chevron Corporation	$228,848	63	Energy Transfer Partners LP	$46,339	123	Staples Inc	$23,114
4	Apple Inc	$182,795	64	Lockheed Martin Corp.	$45,600	124	Lilly (Eli) & Co.	$23,113
5	Berkshire Hathaway Inc.	$182,150	65	FedEx Corp	$45,567	125	Alcoa, Inc.	$23,032
6	Phillips 66	$174,809	66	Merck & Co., Inc	$44,033	126	Raytheon Co.	$22,826
7	General Motors Co.	$155,929	67	Johnson Controls Inc	$42,828	127	Time Warner Cable Inc	$22,812
8	General Electric Co	$146,045	68	CHS Inc	$42,664	128	Arrow Electronics, Inc.	$22,769
9	Ford Motor Co. (DE)	$144,077	69	Ingram Micro Inc.	$42,554	129	Baker Hughes Inc.	$22,364
10	CVS Health Corp	$139,367	70	Best Buy Inc	$42,410	130	Abbott Laboratories	$21,848
11	Valero Energy Corp.	$138,074	71	Plains GP Holdings, L.P	$42,249	131	Burlington Northern & Santa	$21,552
12	McKesson Corp.	$137,609	72	Plains All American Pipeline	$42,249	132	Fluor Corp.	$21,532
13	UnitedHealth Group Inc	$130,474	73	World Fuel Services Corp.	$41,562	133	National Oilwell Varco Inc	$21,440
14	AT&T Inc	$128,752	74	Prudential Financial, Inc.	$41,461	134	Xerox Corp	$21,435
15	Fannie Mae	$125,696	75	Goldman Sachs Group, Inc.	$40,874	135	U.S. Bancorp (DE)	$21,059
16	Verizon Communications	$120,550	76	Delta Air Lines, Inc. (DE)	$40,362	136	Freeport-McMoRan Inc	$20,921
17	AmerisourceBergen Corp.	$119,569	77	Honeywell International, Inc	$40,306	137	Icahn Enterprises L P	$20,682
18	Costco Wholesale Corp	$112,640	78	United Continental Holdings	$38,279	138	ManpowerGroup	$20,251
19	Hewlett-Packard Co	$111,454	79	Oracle Corp	$38,275	139	HollyFrontier Corp.	$20,161
20	JPMorgan Chase & Co	$106,283	80	Tesoro Corporation	$37,601	140	Kimberly-Clark Corp.	$19,724
21	Express Scripts Holding Co	$104,099	81	Tyson Foods, Inc.	$37,580	141	Global Partners LP	$19,590
22	Bank of America Corp.	$101,697	82	Morgan Stanley	$36,848	142	Cummins, Inc.	$19,221
23	Marathon Petroleum Corp.	$100,254	83	Sears Holdings Corp	$36,188	143	PBF Energy Inc	$19,151
24	International Business Machi	$99,751	84	Deere & Co.	$36,067	144	Danaher Corp.	$19,118
25	Kroger Co.	$98,375	85	Du Pont (E.I.) de Nemours	$36,046	145	AutoNation, Inc.	$19,109
26	Citigroup Inc	$92,543	86	Mondelez International Inc	$35,299	146	Nucor Corp.	$19,052
27	Cardinal Health, Inc.	$91,084	87	American Express Co.	$34,932	147	Kohl's Corp.	$19,031
28	Boeing Co.	$90,762	88	Allstate Corp.	$34,507	148	AbbVie Inc.	$18,790
29	Federal Reserve System	$90,540	89	HCA Holdings Inc	$34,182	149	Whirlpool Corp	$18,769
30	Archer Daniels Midland Co.	$89,804	90	INTL FCStone Inc.	$34,012	150	Amgen Inc	$18,676
31	Amazon.com Inc.	$88,988	91	Cigna Corp	$32,380	151	Southwest Airlines Co	$18,605
32	Wells Fargo & Co.	$88,069	92	Twenty-First Century Fox Inc	$31,867	152	Kraft Foods Group Inc	$18,218
33	Microsoft Corporation	$86,833	93	3M Co	$31,821	153	Progressive Corp. (OH)	$18,171
34	Procter & Gamble Co	$83,062	94	DIRECTV	$31,754	154	Goodyear Tire & Rubber Co.	$18,138
35	Freddie Mac	$81,221	95	General Dynamics Corp.	$30,852	155	CenturyLink, Inc.	$18,095
36	Philip Morris International	$80,029	96	Time Warner Inc	$29,795	156	Murphy USA Inc	$18,083
37	Home Depot Inc	$78,812	97	Halliburton Company	$29,402	157	General Mills, Inc.	$17,910
38	Target Corp	$72,596	98	Publix Super Markets, Inc.	$29,148	158	eBay Inc.	$17,902
39	Johnson & Johnson	$71,312	99	International Paper Co	$29,080	159	Lear Corp.	$17,727
40	Anthem Inc	$71,024	100	McDonald's Corp	$28,106	160	ConAgra Foods, Inc.	$17,703
41	American International Grp	$68,678	101	Macy's, Inc.	$27,931	161	Chesapeake Energy Corp.	$17,506
42	MetLife Inc	$68,199	102	NIKE, Inc	$27,799	162	Dollar General Corp	$17,504
43	Pepsico Inc.	$66,683	103	Avnet Inc	$27,500	163	TRW Automotive Hldngs Crp	$17,435
44	Google Inc	$66,001	104	Exelon Corp.	$27,429	164	United States Steel Corp.	$17,424
45	United Technologies Corp.	$65,100	105	TJX Companies, Inc.	$27,423	165	Colgate-Palmolive Co.	$17,420
46	Comcast Corp	$64,657	106	Travelers Companies Inc	$27,162	166	Supervalu Inc.	$17,155
47	ConocoPhillips	$58,248	107	Tech Data Corp	$26,822	167	Paccar Inc.	$17,124
48	Dow Chemical Co.	$58,167	108	American Airlines Group Inc	$26,743	168	PG&E Corp. (Holding Co.)	$17,090
49	Intel Corp	$55,870	109	Qualcomm, Inc.	$26,487	169	Southern Co.	$17,087
50	United Parcel Service Inc	$55,438	110	Hartford Financial Services	$26,236	170	PNC Financial Services Grp	$16,872
51	Caterpillar Inc.	$55,184	111	Occidental Petroleum Corp	$25,736	171	Sunoco Logistics Partners L.	$16,639
52	Lowe's Companies Inc	$53,417	112	Rite Aid Corp.	$25,526	172	Starbucks Corp.	$16,448
53	Pfizer Inc	$51,584	113	Duke Energy Corp	$24,598	173	Micron Technology Inc.	$16,358
54	Federal Reserve Bank of NY	$50,355	114	Emerson Electric Co.	$24,537	174	The Gap, Inc.	$16,148
55	Disney (Walt) Co. (The)	$48,813	115	Altria Group Inc	$24,466	175	Apache Corp.	$16,054
56	Humana, Inc.	$48,500	116	Hess Corp	$24,421	176	AES Corp.	$15,891
57	Energy Transfer Equity L P	$48,335	117	T-Mobile US Inc	$24,420	177	Bristol-Myers Squibb Co.	$15,879
58	Enterprise Products Partners	$47,727	118	Capital One Financial Corp	$24,176	178	Monsanto Co.	$15,855
59	Aetna Inc.	$47,295	119	Union Pacific Corp	$23,988	179	Jabil Circuit, Inc.	$15,762
60	Cisco Systems, Inc.	$47,142	120	Northrop Grumman Corp	$23,979	180	Bank of NY Mellon Corp	$15,701

SOURCE: HOOVER'S, INC., DATABASE, DECEMBER 2014

The 200 Largest Companies by Sales in
Hoover's Handbook of Emerging Companies 2015 (continued)

Rank	Company	Sales ($ bil.)
181	Exelon Generation Co LLC	$15,630
182	American Electric Power Co.,	$15,357
183	Omnicom Group, Inc.	$15,318
184	Baxter International Inc.	$15,259
185	NextEra Energy Inc	$15,136
186	Western Digital Corp.	$15,130
187	PPG Industries, Inc.	$15,108
188	Loews Corp.	$15,053
189	FirstEnergy Corp.	$15,049
190	Marathon Oil Corp.	$14,959
191	Aramark	$14,833
192	Kellogg Co	$14,792
193	Penske Automotive Grp Inc	$14,705
194	Oneok Inc.	$14,603
195	Anadarko Petroleum Corp	$14,581
196	EOG Resources, Inc.	$14,487
197	Illinois Tool Works, Inc.	$14,484
198	Land O' Lakes Inc	$14,236
199	Whole Foods Market, Inc.	$14,194
200	Genuine Parts Co.	$14,078

The 200 Largest Employers in
Hoover's Handbook of Emerging Companies 2015

Rank	Company	Employees	Rank	Company	Employees	Rank	Company	Employees
1	Wal-Mart Stores, Inc.	2200000	61	Emerson Electric Co.	115100	121	O'Reilly Automotive, Inc.	62533
2	Kelly Services, Inc.	548100	62	Caterpillar Inc.	114233	122	Nordstrom, Inc.	62500
3	Yum! Brands, Inc.	537000	63	Lockheed Martin Corp.	112000	123	MGM Resorts International	61700
4	McDonald's Corp	440000	64	American Airlines Group Inc	110400	124	Raytheon Co.	61000
5	International Business Machi	431212	65	Mondelez International Inc	107000	125	Baxter International Inc.	61000
6	United Parcel Service Inc	395000	66	Intel Corp	106700	126	Automatic Data Processing In	61000
7	Kroger Co.	375000	67	Tenet Healthcare Corp.	103711	127	Alcoa, Inc.	60000
8	Target Corp	366000	68	Bloomin' Brands Inc.	101000	128	Family Dollar Stores, Inc.	60000
9	Home Depot Inc	365000	69	Dollar General Corp	100600	129	Deere & Co.	59623
10	General Electric Co	307000	70	General Dynamics Corp.	99500	130	Icahn Enterprises L P	59565
11	Hewlett-Packard Co	302000	71	Apple Inc	97000	131	HanesBrands Inc	59500
12	CVS Health Corp	297800	72	L Brands, Inc	94600	132	Baker Hughes Inc.	59400
13	Pepsico Inc.	271000	73	Philip Morris International	91100	133	VF Corp.	59000
14	Aramark	269500	74	3M Co	89800	134	Bed, Bath & Beyond, Inc.	58000
15	Wells Fargo & Co.	264900	75	Rite Aid Corp.	89000	135	Parker Hannifin Corp.	57450
16	Lowe's Companies Inc	262000	76	Dollar Tree, Inc.	87400	136	DaVita HealthCare Partners I	57400
17	JPMorgan Chase & Co	251196	77	Whole Foods Market, Inc.	87200	137	Humana, Inc.	57000
18	Citigroup Inc	251000	78	United Continental Holdings	87000	138	Donnelley (R. R.) & Sons Co.	57000
19	Sears Holdings Corp	249000	79	Community Health Systems, In	87000	139	NIKE, Inc.	56500
20	AT&T Inc	243000	80	Western Digital Corp.	84072	140	Autoliv Inc.	56500
21	Bank of America Corp.	242000	81	Convergys Corp.	84000	141	Morgan Stanley	55794
22	Robert Half International In	225000	82	Staples Inc	83008	142	Brinker International, Inc.	55586
23	General Motors Co.	216000	83	Delta Air Lines, Inc. (DE)	80000	143	Time Warner Cable Inc	55170
24	HCA Holdings Inc	215000	84	Barrett Business Services, I	79315	144	Marsh & McLennan Companies	55000
25	United Technologies Corp.	211500	85	Computer Sciences Corp.	79000	145	Cummins, Inc.	54600
26	Darden Restaurants, Inc. (Un	206489	86	TRW Automotive Hldngs Corp	78200	146	PNC Financial Services Group	54433
27	Costco Wholesale Corp	195000	87	Pfizer Inc	77700	147	Google Inc	53600
28	TJX Companies, Inc.	191000	88	Halliburton Company	77000	148	Chipotle Mexican Grill Inc	53090
29	Starbucks Corp.	191000	89	Merck & Co., Inc	76000	149	Dow Chemical Co.	53000
30	Ford Motor Co. (DE)	187000	90	AutoZone, Inc.	76000	150	PetSmart, Inc.	53000
31	Starwood Hotels & Resorts	181400	91	Exxon Mobil Corp.	75000	151	Jones Lang LaSalle Inc	52700
32	Disney (Walt) Co. (The)	180000	92	Abercrombie & Fitch Co.	75000	152	Bank of New York Mellon Corp	51100
33	Verizon Communications Inc	176800	93	Cisco Systems, Inc.	74042	153	Stanley Black & Decker, Inc.	50700
34	Macy's, Inc.	172500	94	Omnicom Group, Inc.	74000	154	Sysco Corp.	50300
35	Cognizant Technology Solutio	171400	95	Cracker Barrel Old Country S	72000	155	Michaels Companies Inc	50200
36	UnitedHealth Group Inc	170000	96	Advance Auto Parts Inc	71867	156	Thermo Fisher Scientific Inc	50000
37	Johnson Controls Inc	168000	97	International Paper Co	69000	157	Ryder System, Inc.	49200
38	Publix Super Markets, Inc.	166000	98	Abbott Laboratories	69000	158	Illinois Tool Works, Inc.	49000
39	Boeing Co.	165500	99	Whirlpool Corp	69000	159	Brookdale Senior Living Inc	49000
40	FedEx Corp	162000	100	GameStop Corp	69000	160	Regis Corp.	49000
41	Amazon.com Inc.	154100	101	Caesars Entertainment Corp	68000	161	Aetna Inc.	48600
42	Hilton Worldwide Holdings In	152000	102	Goodyear Tire & Rubber Co.	67000	162	Las Vegas Sands Corp	48500
43	Corporate Resource Services	150800	103	Jacobs Engineering Group, In	66300	163	Anthem Inc	48200
44	Xerox Corp	143100	104	Ross Stores, Inc.	66300	164	L-3 Communications Holdings,	48000
45	Jabil Circuit, Inc.	142000	105	Universal Health Services, I	66100	165	Ascena Retail Group Inc	48000
46	Best Buy Inc	140000	106	Danaher Corp.	66000	166	Sykes Enterprises, Inc.	47900
47	Kohl's Corp.	137000	107	U.S. Bancorp (DE)	65565	167	Prudential Financial, Inc.	47355
48	The Gap, Inc.	137000	108	Brinks Co (The)	65100	168	Union Pacific Corp	47201
49	Comcast Corp	136000	109	MetLife Inc	65000	169	CenturyLink, Inc.	47000
50	Coca-Cola Co (The)	130600	110	Chevron Corporation	64600	170	Southwest Airlines Co	46278
51	Johnson & Johnson	128100	111	Northrop Grumman Corp	64300	171	Texas Roadhouse Inc	45700
52	Microsoft Corporation	128000	112	American International Group	64000	172	Ecolab, Inc.	45415
53	Honeywell International, Inc	127000	113	Synnex Corp	64000	173	Interpublic Group of Compani	45400
54	Lear Corp.	125200	114	Office Depot, Inc.	64000	174	Hyatt Hotels Corp	45000
55	Tyson Foods, Inc.	124000	115	EMC Corp. (MA)	63900	175	Cedar Fair, L.P.	44700
56	Marriott International, Inc.	123000	116	Fidelity National Financial	63861	176	Amphenol Corp.	44500
57	Oracle Corp.	122000	117	National Oilwell Varco Inc	63642	177	Federal-Mogul Holdings Corp	44275
58	Procter & Gamble Co	118000	118	Kindred Healthcare Inc	63300	178	CBRE Group Inc	44000
59	ABM Industries, Inc.	118000	119	Du Pont (E.I.) de Nemours &	63000	179	Foot Locker, Inc.	43518
60	Penney (J.C.) Co.,Inc. (Hold	117000	120	American Express Co.	62800	180	AECOM	43300

SOURCE: HOOVER'S, INC., DATABASE, DECEMBER 2014

The 200 Largest Employers in
Hoover's Handbook of Emerging Companies 2015 (continued)

Rank	Company	Employees
181	Sanmina Corp	43101
182	Burlington Northern & Santa F	43000
183	Kimberly-Clark Corp.	43000
184	General Mills, Inc.	43000
185	McKesson Corp.	42800
186	Lauder (Estee) Cos., Inc. (T	42400
187	Capital One Financial Corp	41951
188	PPG Industries, Inc.	41400
189	Quest Diagnostics, Inc.	41000
190	Barnes & Noble Inc	41000
191	TeleTech Holdings, Inc.	41000
192	Six Flags Entertainment Corp	40900
193	Panera Bread Co.	40100
194	T-Mobile US Inc	40000
195	Dillard's Inc.	40000
196	American Eagle Outfitters, I	40000
197	Waste Management, Inc. (DE)	39800
198	Allstate Corp.	39400
199	Apollo Education Group, Inc.	39000
200	United States Steel Corp.	38500

The Top 200 Companies by Net Income in
Hoover's Handbook of Emerging Companies 2015

Rank	Company	Net Income ($ bil.)
1	Fannie Mae	$83,963
2	Freddie Mac	$48,668
3	Apple Inc	$39,510
4	Exxon Mobil Corp.	$32,580
5	Microsoft Corporation	$22,074
6	Pfizer Inc	$22,003
7	Wells Fargo & Co.	$21,878
8	Chevron Corporation	$21,423
9	Berkshire Hathaway Inc.	$19,476
10	AT&T Inc	$18,249
11	JPMorgan Chase & Co	$17,923
12	International Business Machi	$16,483
13	Wal-Mart Stores, Inc.	$16,022
14	Google Inc	$14,444
15	Johnson & Johnson	$13,831
16	Citigroup Inc	$13,673
17	General Electric Co	$13,057
18	Intel Corp	$11,704
19	Procter & Gamble Co	$11,643
20	Verizon Communications Inc	$11,497
21	Bank of America Corp.	$11,431
22	Oracle Corp.	$10,955
23	ConocoPhillips	$9,156
24	American International Group	$9,085
25	Liberty Media Corp (DE)	$8,780
26	Coca-Cola Co (The)	$8,584
27	Philip Morris International	$8,576
28	Goldman Sachs Group, Inc.	$8,040
29	Qualcomm, Inc.	$7,967
30	Cisco Systems, Inc.	$7,853
31	Disney (Walt) Co. (The)	$7,501
32	Comcast Corp	$6,816
33	Pepsico Inc.	$6,513
34	United Technologies Corp.	$6,220
35	Occidental Petroleum Corp	$5,903
36	U.S. Bancorp (DE)	$5,836
37	UnitedHealth Group Inc	$5,619
38	McDonald's Corp	$5,586
39	Boeing Co.	$5,446
40	Visa Inc	$5,438
41	Home Depot Inc	$5,385
42	American Express Co.	$5,359
43	Union Pacific Corp	$5,180
44	Amgen Inc	$5,081
45	Hess Corp	$5,052
46	Hewlett-Packard Co	$5,013
47	3M Co	$4,956
48	Lilly (Eli) & Co.	$4,685
49	CVS Health Corp	$4,644
50	Altria Group Inc	$4,535
51	Twenty-First Century Fox Inc	$4,514
52	Merck & Co., Inc	$4,404
53	United Parcel Service Inc	$4,372
54	Burlington Northern & Santa F	$4,271
55	Honeywell International, Inc	$4,239
56	PNC Financial Services Group	$4,227
57	Capital One Financial Corp	$4,159
58	AbbVie Inc.	$4,128
59	General Motors Co.	$3,949
60	Mondelez International Inc	$3,915

Rank	Company	Net Income ($ bil.)
61	Dow Chemical Co.	$3,772
62	Annaly Capital Management In	$3,730
63	Phillips 66	$3,726
64	Caterpillar Inc.	$3,695
65	Travelers Companies Inc (The	$3,692
66	Time Warner Inc	$3,691
67	Du Pont (E.I.) de Nemours &	$3,625
68	MasterCard Inc	$3,617
69	Lockheed Martin Corp.	$3,614
70	Freeport-McMoRan Inc	$3,441
71	MetLife Inc	$3,368
72	PPG Industries, Inc.	$3,231
73	Ford Motor Co. (DE)	$3,187
74	Deere & Co.	$3,162
75	AFLAC Inc.	$3,158
76	Gilead Sciences, Inc.	$3,075
77	Micron Technology Inc.	$3,045
78	CBS Corp	$2,959
79	Illinois Tool Works, Inc.	$2,946
80	Facebook, Inc.	$2,940
81	Biogen Idec Inc	$2,935
82	Morgan Stanley	$2,932
83	BlackRock, Inc.	$2,932
84	EMC Corp. (MA)	$2,889
85	DIRECTV	$2,859
86	Monsanto Co.	$2,740
87	Valero Energy Corp.	$2,720
88	Kraft Foods Group Inc	$2,715
89	Danaher Corp.	$2,695
90	NIKE, Inc	$2,693
91	Duke Energy Corp	$2,665
92	Enterprise Products Partners	$2,607
93	Abbott Laboratories	$2,576
94	General Dynamics Corp.	$2,533
95	National Oilwell Varco Inc	$2,502
96	Anthem Inc	$2,490
97	Corning, Inc.	$2,472
98	Discover Financial Services	$2,470
99	Goodyear Tire & Rubber Co.	$2,452
100	Viacom Inc	$2,391
101	Franklin Resources, Inc.	$2,384
102	Chubb Corp.	$2,345
103	Las Vegas Sands Corp	$2,306
104	Apache Corp.	$2,288
105	Lowe's Companies Inc	$2,286
106	Allstate Corp.	$2,280
107	Raytheon Co.	$2,244
108	Colgate-Palmolive Co.	$2,241
109	EOG Resources, Inc.	$2,197
110	Texas Instruments, Inc.	$2,162
111	Emerson Electric Co.	$2,147
112	TJX Companies, Inc.	$2,137
113	State Street Corp.	$2,136
114	Halliburton Company	$2,125
115	Marathon Petroleum Corp.	$2,112
116	Bank of New York Mellon Corp	$2,111
117	FedEx Corp	$2,097
118	Northrop Grumman Corp	$2,069
119	Starbucks Corp.	$2,068
120	Costco Wholesale Corp	$2,058

Rank	Company	Sales ($bil.)
121	Time Warner Cable Inc	$2,031
122	Baxter International Inc.	$2,012
123	Bristol-Myers Squibb Co.	$2,004
124	Norfolk Southern Corp.	$2,000
125	Synchrony Financial	$1,979
126	Target Corp	$1,971
127	Constellation Brands Inc	$1,943
128	CSX Corp.	$1,927
129	Aetna Inc.	$1,914
130	NextEra Energy Inc	$1,908
131	ERP Operating L.P.	$1,906
132	Equity Residential	$1,905
133	Priceline Group Inc. (The)	$1,893
134	Express Scripts Holding Co	$1,845
135	Fifth Third Bancorp (Cincinn	$1,836
136	Weyerhaeuser Co.	$1,826
137	General Mills, Inc.	$1,824
138	Exelon Corp.	$1,820
139	Kellogg Co	$1,807
140	Precision Castparts Corp.	$1,777
141	Praxair, Inc.	$1,755
142	Marathon Oil Corp.	$1,753
143	BB&T Corp.	$1,729
144	Southern Co.	$1,710
145	Dominion Resources Inc	$1,697
146	Publix Super Markets, Inc.	$1,654
147	Cummins, Inc.	$1,651
148	Southern Copper Corp	$1,619
149	Western Digital Corp.	$1,617
150	Enable Midstream Partners L.	$1,615
151	HCA Holdings Inc	$1,556
152	Simon Property Group, Inc.	$1,552
153	Kimberly-Clark Corp.	$1,526
154	Kroger Co.	$1,519
155	Automatic Data Processing In	$1,516
156	Macy's, Inc.	$1,486
157	American Electric Power Co.,	$1,480
158	Ford Motor Credit Company LL	$1,479
159	Cigna Corp	$1,476
160	Reynolds American Inc	$1,470
161	CF Industries Holdings Inc	$1,465
162	PG&E Corp. (Holding Co.)	$1,450
163	Celgene Corp.	$1,450
164	SLM Corp.	$1,418
165	International Paper Co	$1,395
166	Yahoo! Inc.	$1,366
167	Plains All American Pipeline	$1,361
168	Marsh & McLennan Comp.	$1,357
169	Florida Power & Light Co.	$1,349
170	Suntrust Banks, Inc.	$1,344
171	Archer Daniels Midland Co.	$1,342
172	Ameriprise Financial Inc	$1,334
173	Motorola Solutions Inc.	$1,299
174	Waste Management, Inc. (DE)	$1,298
175	The Gap, Inc.	$1,280
176	Thermo Fisher Scientific Inc	$1,273
177	McKesson Corp.	$1,263
178	American Capital Agency Corp	$1,259
179	Lincoln National Corp.	$1,244
180	Public Service Enterprise Gr	$1,243

SOURCE: INC., SEPTEMBER 2014

The Top 200 Companies by Net Income in
Hoover's Handbook of Emerging Companies 2015 (continued)

Rank	Company	Net Income ($ bil.)
181	T Rowe Price Group, Inc.	$1,230
182	Cognizant Technology Solutio	$1,229
183	Johnson Controls Inc	$1,215
184	VF Corp.	$1,210
185	Lauder (Estee) Cos., Inc. (T	$1,204
186	Kinder Morgan Inc.	$1,193
187	Georgia Power Co.	$1,191
188	Lorillard, Inc.	$1,187
189	Becton, Dickinson & Co.	$1,185
190	Paccar Inc.	$1,171
191	Blackstone Group LP	$1,171
192	Cardinal Health, Inc.	$1,166
193	Progressive Corp. (OH)	$1,165
194	Eastman Chemical Co.	$1,165
195	Xerox Corp	$1,159
196	Regions Financial Corp	$1,155
197	Humana, Inc.	$1,147
198	Principal Financial Group, I	$1,144
199	M & T Bank Corp	$1,138
200	Virginia Electric & Power Co	$1,138

Hoover's Handbook of

Emerging Companies

2015

1st Century Bancshares, Inc.

Where would Jesus bank? Probably at 1st Century Bank the operating subsidiary of 1st Century Bancshares. Not to be confused with First Century Bank of West Virginia 1st Century Bank is a one-branch commercial bank located in western Los Angeles near Beverly Hills. It caters to small businesses entrepreneurs and high-net-worth professionals. 1st Century Bank offers checking money market accounts CDs trusts debit and credit cards and online banking to more than 2300 account holders. Commercial loans make up about half of its loan portfolio with real estate loans accounting for most of the rest. 1st Century Bancshares was founded in 2004 not the 1st century.

The bank targets middle-market businesses and professionals in west Los Angeles that typically borrow between $250000 and $5 million and also require account services and cash management. 1st Century Bancshares has a $7.1 million lending limit smaller than most banks and it arranges for loans from other banks when customers need to borrow more. West Los Angeles is home to many small businesses such as service firms merchandising distribution and support industries. The bank's customers include law firms medical practices and individual physicians business management and accounting firms and real estate agents.

Its portfolio of real estate loans include first and junior trust deeds on single- family residential properties undeveloped land multi-family residential properties commercial/industrial real estate and construction-in-process. Some three-fourths of its real estate loans have an outstanding balance of at least $1 million.

The company has recorded a net loss for all but two years of its operating history.

Chairman Alan Rosenberg owns 10% of 1st Century Bancshares.

EXECUTIVES

Vice President Business Development Ofc, Justin Weissman
Relationship Manager Vice President, Christopher Hoshek
Secretary, Donna Cromer
Auditors: Perry-SmithLLP

LOCATIONS

HQ: 1st Century Bancshares, Inc.
1875 Century Park East, Suite 1400, Los Angeles, CA 90067
Phone: 310 270-9500
Web: www.1cbank.com

PRODUCTS/OPERATIONS

2009 Sales

	$ mil.	% of total
Interest		
Loans	9.6	75
Investments	2.1	16
Other	0.1	1
Noninterest	1.0	8
Total	**12.8**	**100**

COMPETITORS

American Business Bank   Community Bank

Bank of America
Bank of the West
CalWest Bancorp
California Bank & Trust
Citibank
City National
Comerica
JPMorgan Chase
Kinecta FCU
MUFG Americas Holdings
NCAL Bancorp
Pacific Mercantile
Simplicity Bancorp
U.S. Bancorp
Wells Fargo

HISTORICAL FINANCIALS

Company Type: Public

Income Statement

FYE: December 31

	ASSETS ($ mil.)	NET INCOME ($ mil.)	INCOME AS % OF ASSETS	EMPLOYEES
12/13	538.1	6.8	1.3%	63
12/12	499.1	2.9	0.6%	56
12/11	405.2	1.0	0.3%	49
12/10	308.3	(1.9)	—	41
12/09	272.1	(7.8)	—	43
Annual Growth	**18.6%**	**—**	**—**	**10.0%**

2013 Year-End Financials

Return on assets: 1.3%
Return on equity: 13.1%
Long-term debt ($ mil.): —
No. of shares (mil.): 9
Sales ($ mil): 18
Dividends
Yield: —
Payout: —
Market value ($ mil.): 68

	STOCK PRICE ($) FY Close	P/E High/Low		PER SHARE ($) Earnings	Dividends	Book Value
12/13	7.15	10	6	0.76	0.00	5.84
12/12	4.61	14	10	0.33	0.00	5.38
12/11	3.54	37	28	0.11	0.00	4.97
12/10	4.10	—	—	(0.22)	0.00	4.77
12/09	3.45	—	—	(0.86)	0.00	5.02
Annual Growth	**20.0%**			**—**	**—**	**3.8%**

3D Systems Corp. (DE)

3D Systems helps product designers and engineers bring their concepts to life. The company's stereolithography apparatuses (SLAs) and other machines create 3-D prototypes of everything from toys to airplane parts. Its SLAs rapidly produce 3-D objects designed in CAD/CAM software in a process called solid imaging which uses a laser to sculpt plastic resin materials into physical models. Its ThermoJet solid object printer also fabricates plastic models using a modified ink jet printing system. Additionally 3D Systems sells the raw plastic and metal consumable material used in its machinery. Customers have included General Electric Hasbro and Texas Instruments.

Geographic Reach

The company does business in Europe the US and Asia. International clients account for about 45% of the company's business.

Sales and Marketing

3D Systems primarily sells via a direct sales force but it also uses distributors and resellers for select products and regions. The company targets manufacturers of automotive aerospace consumer dental electronics defense education and medical products; independent prototyping service providers; and universities and government agencies performing research activities. International clients account for more than half of its business.

3D Systems spent about $6 million on advertising and marketing expenses during fiscal 2013.

Financial Performance

The company's revenue increased by $160 up to $513.4 million in fiscal 2013 compared to $353.6 million in fiscal 2012. This spike in revenue was primarily due to a 234% increase in printer unit sales compared to the previous year along with increased sales of print materials and increased software and Quickparts revenue.

3D Systems reported a net profit of $44 million in fiscal 2013. That was an increase of $5.2 million (or 13%) from the net income the company claimed in fiscal 2012. The company's cash flow took a dip in fiscal 2013 because of acquisitions expenses.

Mergers and Acquisitions

3D Systems uses a steady stream of acquisitions to supplement the development of its products and services and expand its customer base. In early 2013 it acquired Geomagic which provides complementary 3-D design sculpt and scan software. It also brought COWEB that year a Paris start-up that makes custom 3-D printed products and Rapid Product Development Group a quick-turn manufacturer that expands 3D Systems' on-demand parts manufacturing capabilities. In 2012 the company bought VIDAR Systems and Z Corporation from Danish large format scanner maker Contex for more than $135 million. 3D Systems saw the companies as a natural fit with its own technologies with potential to accelerate its growth in the 3-D content-to-print market. The acquisitions also added complementary products to the company's portfolio and expand its distribution and market reach.

3D Systems also acquired direct manufacturing and product development services provider Paramount Industries that year to boost its ability to serve the aerospace and medical device industries. 3D Systems integrated Paramount's manufacturing facilities and advanced tooling and assembly operations with its on-demand direct manufacturing facilities.

Also in 2012 3D Systems expanded its reach in the consumer market with the purchase of Amsterdam-based FreshFiber a leading 3-D printed consumer electronics accessories brand sold online and in retail stores such as Apple Fnac and Gravis. 3D Systems plans to extend the company's customized products portfolio (including its flagship personalized iPhone cases) through its extensive manufacturing infrastructure and its Cubify.com platform. Cubify's Cube 3-D printer is a low-cost (under $1500) wireless printer geared toward the home market. 3D Systems boosted that acquisition with another buying Viztu Technologies which offers customers a way to make interactive and printable 3-D models from pictures and video. Also that year the company bought San Francisco-based startup Bespoke —adding scan design and print technology used to deliver custom fit prosthetics orthotics and orthopedic devices —and South Korea's Rapidform which offers complementary products and gives 3D Systems a foothold in South Korea and Japan.

HISTORY

3D Systems was founded in 1986 by Charles Hull a veteran of Bell & Howell and DuPont who pioneered the stereolithography modeling method. 3D Systems shipped its first product in 1988. It went public that year; Ciba-Geigy (now Ciba Specialty Chemicals) took a stake. The technology attracted attention but market reception was lukewarm. In 1991 3D Systems hired automation software executive Arthur Sims as CEO. Sims added system maintenance and outsourcing services but sales and earnings remained low.

In 1997 3D Systems bought the Stereos business of EOS a German maker of rapid prototyping systems. That year Hull became vice chairman and chief technology officer EVP Richard Balanson replaced him as president and COO. (Balanson resigned in 1999.)

3D Systems inked a pact with Sony in 1998 to make a version of 3D Systems' machines available in Asia. Hull retired in 1999; Walter Loewenbaum was elected chairman and Brian Service became CEO. Also in 1999 the company introduced its ThermoJet ink jet solid imaging device. Late that year Hull returned as CTO.

The company received its largest order ever in 2000 when a Hong Kong-based business group bought 100 ThermoJet systems. In 2001 3D Systems acquired Texas-based rapid prototyping systems builder DTM for about $45 million in cash. Also in 2001 3D Systems acquired OptoForm (metal and ceramic tooling technology) and RPC (stereolithography material).

Service resigned as CEO and director in 2003; Hull succeeded him as CEO on an interim basis. Later that year 3D Systems named former Sealed Air Corp. executive Abe Reichental president and CEO.

In 2004 3D Systems decided to outsource assembly of its products to manufacturing contractors. Also that year the company introduced a manufacturing-capable selective laser sintering system the Sinterstation HiQ SLS system. In 2005 the company moved its headquarters to Rock Hill South Carolina consolidating several US facilities.

In 2009 it acquired the assets of Acu-Cast Technologies a provider of rapid prototyping and manufacturing services for precision parts employing a variety of casting finishing and molding methods. Using the acquisition as a springboard the company launched 3Dproparts. The scope of that service soon expanded into the military/aerospace market with a subsequent purchase of assets from AdvaTech Manufacturing.

3Dproparts continued to grow in 2010 when 3D Systems made seven acquisitions for the division beginning with the assets of Moeller Design & Development adding aerospace medical device and mechanical CAD prototyping applications. It bought online rapid prototyping specialist Design Prototyping Technologies soon after to improve the ability of 3Dproparts to provide service via the Internet then acquired French prototyping and manufacturing service providers CEP (laser sintering manufacturing services) and Protometal (die cast metal parts) expanding its 3Dproparts' services in Europe.

Also that year it bought the assets of Express Pattern a rapid prototyper that served defense transportation and health care clients; UK-based Bits From Bytes Limited a maker of 3-D printers and accessories primarily for education and hobbyist applications; and Italy-based Provel a provider of rapid prototyping tooling and manufacturing services.

EXECUTIVES

President; Chief Executive Officer; Director,
Abraham N. (Avi) Reichental, age 57, $791,982 total compensation
EVP CTO and Director, Charles W. (Chuck) Hull, age 75, $340,961 total compensation
EVP Mergers and Acquisitions, Damon J. Gregoire, age 45, $389,276 total compensation

VP and Chief Marketing Officer, Cathy L. Lewis, $257,308 total compensation
CFO, Ted Hull
Vice President G Manager M Qast, Scott Turner
Vp Sales Us, John Beljan
Vp Of Alliances And Partnershi, Neal Orringer
Vice President, Scott Harmon
Vice President, Robby Hudson
Vice President, John Kawola
Vice President Global Customer Support Production Printer Solutions, Dennis Fogle
Vice President Software Engineering Operations, Martin Thomas
Senior Vice President Information Technology, Mike White
Vice President Global Branding And Marketing Comm, Wendy Pinckney
Vice President Engineering Research And Development, Kevin Williams
Vice President Of Information, Andrew Lamont
Vice President Advanced Development, Mark Cook
Vp Materials R&d Ink Jet, Don Titterington
Vice President Quickparts, Tony Moran
Vice President Of Business, Sameer Vachani
President; Chief Executive Officer; Director, Abraham N. (Avi) Reichental, age 57
Chairman, G. Walter Loewenbaum, age 69
Treasury Consultant, Michael Scott
Auditors: BDOUSALLP

LOCATIONS

HQ: 3D Systems Corp. (DE)
333 Three D Systems Circle, Rock Hill, SC 29730
Phone: 803 326-3900
Web: www.3DSystems.com

2013 Sales

	$ mil.	% of total
US	284.7	56
Europe		
Germany	51.2	10
Other	82.6	16
Asia/Pacific	94.9	18
Total	**513.4**	**100**

PRODUCTS/OPERATIONS

2013 Sales

	$ mil.	% of total
Printers and other products	227.7	44
Services	128.4	25
Materials	157.3	31
Total	**513.4**	**100**

COMPETITORS

DSM	SOGECLAIR
Dassault	Soligen 2006
Delcam	Stratasys
DuPont	Vero Software
ExOne	voxeljet

HISTORICAL FINANCIALS

Company Type: Public

Income Statement

FYE: December 31

	REVENUE ($ mil.)	NET INCOME ($ mil.)	NET PROFIT MARGIN	EMPLOYEES
12/13	513.4	44.1	8.6%	1,388
12/12	353.6	38.9	11.0%	1,010
12/11	230.4	35.4	15.4%	714
12/10	159.8	19.5	12.2%	484
12/09	112.8	1.0	0.9%	387
Annual Growth	**46.1%**	**153.6%**	**—**	**37.6%**

2013 Year-End Financials

Debt ratio: 1.7%	No. of shares (mil.): 103
Return on equity: 6.2%	Dividends
Cash ($ mil.): 306	Yield: —
Current ratio: 4.77	Payout: —
Long-term debt ($ mil.): 18	Market value ($ mil.): 9,592

	STOCK PRICE ($) FY Close	P/E High/Low	PER SHARE ($) Earnings	Dividends	Book Value
12/13	92.93	205 65	0.45	0.00	9.04
12/12	53.35	108 32	0.47	0.00	5.38
12/11	14.40	122 29	0.47	0.00	3.35
12/10	31.49	120 37	0.28	0.00	1.90
12/09	11.30	701233	0.02	0.00	1.54
Annual Growth	**69.3%**	**—**	**—127.8%**	**—**	**55.7%**

AAR Corp

On much more than a wing and a prayer AAR provides a wide variety of aviation services and technology products primarily for the aerospace and defense industries. The company supplies commercial customers and the US government and its contractors with aircraft components such as transportation pallets containers shelters mobility systems and control systems in support of the deployment of military and humanitarian activities. AAR also provides inventory management and parts distribution; aircraft maintenance repair and overhaul; and expeditionary airlift services. The company traces its historical roots to 1955 when it was founded as Allen Aircraft Radio.

Geographic Reach

AAR operates through more than 60 locations in 17 countries. It has a presence in the Americas EMEA (Germany France Sweden Norway the United Arab Emirates and the UK) the Asia/Pacific and Australia. Maintenance facilities reside in Indianapolis; Oklahoma City; Duluth Minnesota; and Miami.

Operations

In 2013 AAR streamlined its organizations from four segments into two. Aviation Services (its main segment representing more than 75% of total sales) provides inventory management and parts distribution; aircraft maintenance repair and overhaul; and expeditionary airlift services. It sells and leases new overhauled and repaired engine and airframe parts to commercial and defense customers. The segment also acts as a distributor for 80 aviation product manufacturers.

AAR's Technology Products segment makes and repairs transportation pallets containers shelters mobility systems and control systems in support of the deployment of military and humanitarian activities. The segment also makes transportation pallets and containers used by commercial airlines.

Sales and Marketing

Customers include airlines business aircraft operators cargo carriers aviation OEMs and militaries; the US government accounts for about 40% of sales.

Financial Performance

AAR's sales declined 5% in fiscal 2014 (ended May) versus the prior year to $2 billion on lower sales to commercial customers due to softness in maintenance repair and overhaul activity in its Aviation Services business. Sales of Technology Products fell 9% year over year on decreased demand for commercial cargo containers and precision machined parts. The decline in sales to government and defense customers was due to lower demand by the Department of Defense for expeditionary airlift services in Afghanistan and for mobility products. The slide in fiscal 2014 revenue reversed three consecutive years of growth for the company during which revenue peaked at $2.1 billion.

Despite the decline in revenue net income grew 33% to nearly $73 million in fiscal 2014 on the increased gross profit margin on sales to commercial customers. Cash flow from operations decreased by $23 million

Strategy

As sales to government and defense customers decrease but business with commercial customers rises AAR has been making acquisitions that boost its operations in the civilian sector. After acquiring Telair a maker of cargo loading systems for widebody and narrow-body Airbus and Boeing aircraft in 2011 and making it a subsidiary AAR has completed several bolt-on purchases including: Nordisk a maker of heavy-duty pallets and lightweight cargo containers for commercial airlines; and Airinmar which provides aircraft component repair management services.

AAR's Airlift division got a lift from the Department of the Navy in September 2014 when it was awarded a $49 million contract to provide personnel recovery airlift services in West Africa. AAR Airlift provides expeditionary airlift services in support of contingency operations worldwide in such areas as Afghanistan Africa and the Western Pacific.

Mergers and Acquisitions

In August 2014 AAR's Mobility Systems unit acquired the assets of Cool Containers a maker of temperature-controlled containers used to transport climate-sensitive pharmaceuticals and biological cargo. In December 2013 the company's Telair subsidiary purchased the cargo loading assets from Germany's PFW Aerospace GmbH thereby enhancing its position as a leading global supplier of cargo loading and baggage handling systems

HISTORY

Ira Allen Eichner began selling aircraft radios and instruments out of his car in 1951; in 1955 he incorporated his business as Allen Aircraft Radio. He opened a maintenance facility in Oklahoma City in 1959 and moved into aircraft overhaul. The firm entered Europe in 1965 became AAR in 1966 and went public the next year. AAR began selling commercial aircraft in 1973 and expanded into manufacturing with the 1981 acquisition of Brooks & Perkins. AAR flew high and fast during the late 1980s but lost altitude in the recession of the early 1990s as the airline industry hit a major air pocket.

The company restructured in 1993 and AAR rose again along with a resurgent airline industry. In 1997 AAR bought Cooper Aviation Industries Avsco Aviation Service and ATR International (composite structures and parts). It bought 14 used 747s from British Airways and inked maintenance deals with the US Air Force Hughes and GE. A loading systems contract with FedEx provided more lift. In 1998 AAR won a $67 million deal to maintain aircraft for the US Marshals Service and the Immigration and Naturalization Service. It also sold its floor maintenance equipment business (AAR PowerBoss) to Minuteman International.

AAR gained investment and technology potential in 1999 when it formed Aviation Inventory Management Co. with GE Capital Aviation and GE

Engine Services. The following year AAR announced a deal with Societe Internationale de Telecommunication Aeronautiques (SITA) an air-transport information technology cooperative to sell airline and aerospace products and services online but later in 2000 it decreased its stake in the venture (Aerospan.com).

Late in 2001 AAR formed a joint venture Spairwise L.L.C. with Air France Industries (AFI) to provide component management support to operators of Airbus A320 family of aircraft in North and Central America. In 2002 the company inked a three-year deal to supply American Airlines with parts. As sales slumped in 2003 AAR made several refinancing moves to improve liquidity.

AAR bolstered its MRO operations in early 2007 with the purchase of Reebair Aircraft. Based in Arkansas the business operates under the name AAR Aircraft Services —Hot Springs.

In 2008 the company acquired Avborne Heavy Maintenance which provides maintenance services for Airbus and Boeing aircraft; it is part of AAR's MRO operations. The prior year AAR bought Brown International a provider of engineering design manufacturing and systems integration services to the aerospace industry. Brown International is being integrated into AAR's Structures and Systems division. It also purchased Summa Technology a provider of machining fabrication welding engineering and test services. Some of Summa's projects have included the Space Shuttle Tomahawk cruise missiles air defense systems and even lawn tractors. Summa operates as part of AAR's Structures and Systems division. AAR exited its non-core industrial turbine business.

On the military front AAR became the exclusive provider of composite interiors for the Sikorsky S-92 and H-60 helicopter programs in 2010; the two-year contract deal is valued at $6 million. Multiply that amount by 100 and you'll know the value of AAR's largest deal in company history —in 2009 it was awarded a $600 million contract (over nine years) to provide supply chain and logistics services as well as maintenance operations for Northrop Grumman's KC-10 air-to-air tanker aircraft program. Northrop Grumman is the prime contractor for the US Air Force's project.

In April 2010 AAR purchased Aviation Worldwide Services (renamed AAR Airlift Group) a provider of expeditionary airlift services and aircraft modifications to the US Department of Defense. AAR Airlift brought a fleet of 58 aircraft which has been deployed in Afghanistan. The $200 million acquisition included two operating subsidiaries —Presidential Airways and STI Aviation. The acquisition expanded AAR's offerings to government customers engaged in national defense nation building efforts and humanitarian relief projects.

EXECUTIVES

Vice President Corporate Facilities, Douglas Hara
Group Vice President Aircraft Sales And Leasing, John Johnson
VP Marketing and Business Development, Peter K. Chapman
VP CFO and Treasurer, Timothy J. Romenesko, age 58, $499,272 total compensation
Chairman and CEO, David P. Storch, age 61, $906,449 total compensation
Vp-chief Info Systems Officer, John C Mache
Aviation Services Group VP Airlift, Randy J. Martinez, age 59, $360,447 total compensation
VP and CIO, Kevin M. Larson
VP General Counsel and Secretary, Robert J. (Bob) Regan, age 57, $391,586 total compensation

VP CFO and Treasurer, John C. Fortson, age 47, $400,000 total compensation
Vice President ‚Â– Cargo Systems, Axel P. Hauner
Vice President Of Manufacturing, Derek Sheedy
Group Vice President Supply Chain, John Holmen
Vice President Application Development, Scot Cerka
Vice President Operations, Dharmesh Patel
V Pres, Jack M Arehart
Vice President Government Programs, Robert B Vaneveld
Vice President Sales And Marketing, Christopher Aessup
Svp Supply Chain, Andrew J Schmidt
Vice President Information Technology, Eric Miles
Vice President Tax And Assistant, Mike Carr
Senior Vice President Operations, Ed Fernandez
Vice President Of Programs, Darrell Sims
Vice President Finance, Serge Dupuis
Vp And General Manager Aar Aircraft Services Indianapolis, Danny Martinez
Vice President, Ann T Baldwin
Vice President Strategy And Corporate Developement, James Ward
Vp Operations, Hudson Hardin
Senior Vice President, Harold Kugelman
Vice President Operations, Ramses Perez
Vice President Operations, Ken Hein
Group Vice President Maintenance Repair And Overhaul, Dany Kleiman, age 54
Vice President And General Manager, Toshifumi Hari
Vice President Sales And Marketing, Darren Spiegel
Vice President Business Development, Ben Williams
General Manager Senior Vice President, Pat Aherne
Vice President Employee Culture, Maryanne Cipperly
Vice President Supply Chain And Program, Robert Morris
Vice President, Jay Pereira
Vice President Finance, Bob Daly
Vice President Of Strategic Planning, Lee Hall
Vice President Supply Chain Information Technology, Kevin Deru
Vice President Finance For Atc, John Landman
Vp Of Operations, Jesus Banal
Vice President Defense Programs, David Prusiecki
Vice President Sales, Paul Richardson
Vice President, Robert Scoble
Vice President Commercial Business Development, Jon Butler
Gm Vice President Of Operations, Wayne Jamroz
Vice President And Chief Quality, Art Smith
Vice President Sales And Marketing, Pascal Parant
Vice President Engineering, Ron Eaton
Vice President Quality, Dennis Christen
Vp Process Improvement, Thomas Tanner
Vp, Bill Buck
Vice President Human Resources, Dub Dubois
Vice President Government Affairs, Cheryle Jackson
Vice President Quality, Noel Christen
Vice President And General Manager, Rick Uber
Vice President Of Program Management, Wayne Tackett
Senior Vice President Global Sales, Gary Hundley
Vp Asset Management And Trading, Steven McConnell
Vice President Finance, Bret Pryor
Vice President Maintenance Engineering, Larry Montford
Vice President Of Finance, Gregory Moore
Vice President Programs Business Development, Chris Fiddes
Vice President Of Planning, Robert Tate

Senior Vice President Product Line, Sal Marino
Vice President Finance, Karen Pepping
Vp Strategic Dev & Gov Pgms, Joe Ford
Vice President Marketing, Robert Laird
Vice President Human Resources, Kyle McGillivray
Vice President Engineering, Brian Meyer
Vice President Of Operations, Bob O'Brien
Vice President Operations, Ted Anderson
Vice President Engineering, Tom Patterson
Vice President Operations, Keith Johnson
Vice President Operations, John Carey
Vice President Sales, Johnny Williams
Vice President, Ram Krishnappa
Vice President Sales And Marketing Mro, Matt Eaton
Vice President, Kevin Burkhart
Vice President Finance And Information Technology, Thomas Zonneveld
Vice President Global Operations, Terry Stinson
Vp Of Quality, John Bannon
Vp Planning And Continuous Improvement, Chris Cook
Regional Vice President, Daniel Curci
Vice President Aviation Operations, Phil Adams
Vice President Technical Services, Daniel Martinez
Chairman and CEO, David P. Storch, age 61
VP General Counsel and Secretary, Robert J. (Bob) Regan, age 57
VP CFO and Treasurer, John C. Fortson, age 47
Auditors: KPMGLLP

LOCATIONS

HQ: AAR Corp
One AAR Place, 1100 N. Wood Dale Road, Wood Dale, IL 60191
Phone: 630 227-2000   Fax: 630 227-2019
Web: www.aarcorp.com

PRODUCTS/OPERATIONS

2014 Sales

	$ mil.	% of total
Aviation Services	1560	77
Technology Products	475	23
Total	2035	100

2014 Sales

	$ mil.	% of total
Products	1226.3	60
Services	808.7	40
Total	2035	100

Selected Products

Aircraft Sales and Leasing
Airframe Parts Supply
Aviation Worldwide Services
Cargo Handling Systems
Component Repair
Containers Shelters and Pallets
Engine Parts Supply
Engineering Services
Enterprise Applications Integration
Inventory Management Programs
Landing Gear Services
Maintenance Repair and Overhaul
Mobility Systems
Precision Machined Parts
Wheel and Brake Services

Selected Services

Aircraft maintenance and modification
Component repair
Logistics support
Parts distribution
Supply chain management

COMPETITORS

Airbus Americas	L-3 Vertex
Applied Industrial Technologies	LMI Aerospace
Aviall	Lufthansa Technik
Boeing	MSC Industrial Direct
Crane Co.	Midcoast Aviation
Cubic Corp.	Moog
Curtiss-Wright	Rockwell Collins
Esterline	Sequa
GECAS Asset Management Services	Spirit AeroSystems
HEICO	TIMCO Aviation
Hawker Pacific	Teledyne Technologies
Hexcel	TransDigm Group
Kaman	Triumph Group
Kennametal	United Technologies
	VAS Aero
	Willis Lease

HISTORICAL FINANCIALS

Company Type: Public

Income Statement   FYE: May 31

	REVENUE ($ mil.)	NET INCOME ($ mil.)	NET PROFIT MARGIN	EMPLOYEES
05/14	2,035.0	72.9	3.6%	6,400
05/13	2,137.3	55.0	2.6%	7,200
05/12	2,065.0	67.7	3.3%	7,600
05/11	1,775.7	69.8	3.9%	6,870
05/10	1,352.1	44.6	3.3%	6,340
Annual Growth	10.8%	13.1%	—	0.2%

2014 Year-End Financials

Debt ratio: 28.8%	No. of shares (mil.): 39
Return on equity: 7.6%	Dividends
Cash ($ mil.): 89	Yield: 0.0%
Current ratio: 2.78	Payout: 16.3%
Long-term debt ($ mil.): 564	Market value ($ mil.): 961

	STOCK PRICE ($) FY Close	P/E High/Low	PER SHARE ($) Earnings	Dividends	Book Value
05/14	24.30	17 11	1.83	0.30	25.27
05/13	20.06	15 7	1.38	0.30	23.33
05/12	12.05	19 7	1.65	0.30	21.47
05/11	26.39	16 9	1.73	0.08	21.01
05/10	19.70	22 12	1.16	0.00	18.92
Annual Growth	5.4%	— —	12.1%	—	7.5%

ABIOMED, Inc.

ABIOMED gives weary hearts a rest. The medical device maker has developed a range of cardiac assist devices and is developing a self-contained artificial heart. Its Impella micro heart pumps can temporarily take over blood circulation during surgery or catheterization. Its AB5000 ventricular assist device temporarily takes over the heart's pumping function and improves circulatory flow in patients with acute heart failure thus allowing their hearts to rest and recover. ABIOMED markets its products through both a direct sales force and distributors.

Operations

ABIOMED has also developed a battery-powered implantable replacement heart system called AbioCor which can be used to extend life for dying patients who aren't eligible for a heart transplant. ABIOMED developed the AbioCor system based on technology developed at Pennsylvania State University. However due to the limited number of patients that qualify for use of the AbioCor the

company places little emphasis on marketing efforts for this product line.

Geographic Reach

While many of ABIOMED's products are approved for use in in other countries international sales to Canada parts of Europe and the Middle East make up less than 10% of the company's revenues. The company intends to improve its international results with more sales and support teams in Europe. It manufactures its Impella products at a facility in Germany while the rest of its products are made in Massachusetts.

Financial Performance

After years of steady sales growth ABIOMED made its first profit in 2012. Previously its research and development expenditures had outpaced its sales income. That year's profit came from strong reorders of its Impella systems which accounted for more than 80% of company revenues.

In 2014 efforts to shore up its European sales force particularly in Germany paid off when the company reported a 16% increase in revenue up to $184 million from $158 million due to improved utilization of its products in the US and higher sales in Germany. However the higher costs of expanding its marketing efforts and sales personnel took a bite out of net income causing a 15% decrease from $15 million to $7 million. Cash flow also dropped but only $3 million taking it down to $23 million.

Strategy

The company's research efforts are focused on developing new products for acute heart failure patients as well as next-generation versions and support systems for its existing products. The company has shifted more of its development and sales efforts onto the Impella product line in order to expand its uses and variations while gradually discontinuing its other products.

In addition to expanding its product portfolio and approvals the company also dedicates personnel and financial resources to raising awareness of its products in the medical community. ABIOMED also continuously evaluates opportunities for strategic acquisitions. To that end it acquired a German heart catheter pump maker in 2014 expanding its product line and German sales efforts.

Mergers and Acquisitions

In 2014 as part of its plan to expand it product line and its German sales force ABIOMED purchased Berlin-based ECP Entwicklungsgesellschaft mbH for $14 million. ECP produces heart catheter pumps that use an external drive shaft to increase circulation.

HISTORY

Chairman David Lederman founded ABIOMED in 1981 to make products he had designed (such as artificial heart pumps and valves) as well as dental diagnostic products. ABIOMED went public in 1987. In 1988 it got about $1 million from the National Institutes of Health for heart replacement device (HRD) research and development. In 1990 it began working with Canada's World Heart on HRD technology. In 1992 ABIOMED launched BVS-5000.

In 1990 the company formed ABIODENT to consolidate its dental operations. It received FDA clearance to market the PerioTemp device in 1994. In 1996 it voluntarily recalled some of its BVS-5000 blood pumps citing component irregularities (it said no patients were affected).

To fund product development ABIOMED accepted government funding to finish testing its battery-powered HRD (1996) and to develop a laser-based tissue-welding system (1998). Biotech firm Genzyme invested about $15 million in ABIO-MED that year acquiring 14% of the firm.

In 1998 ABIOMED again recalled some lots of BVS-5000 this time for electrical problems. The company attributed 1998's losses to an increase in self-funding on the HRD project as well as to red ink in its now-discontinued dental business.

ABIOMED received funding from the National Heart Lung and Blood Institutes in 2000 to support the testing of its AbioCor product an implantable heart replacement device. The following year AbioCor became the first artificial heart implanted in a patient.

The FDA approved the use of the artificial hearts in five patients in 2001 all of whom were considered too sick to receive heart transplants. The first patient died the same year but the cause of death was not attributed to AbioCor.

The fifth patient to receive the device died early in 2002. By late 2002 seven patients had been fitted with the device but only one was living. A moratorium on recruiting new patients was imposed. ABIOMED wanted patients that were healthy enough to live long past the time of implantation but only patients that were extremely ill would be considered candidates for the device.

By January of 2003 the moratorium had been lifted and three more patients had received implants by March. Because of the troubles with finding qualified recipients for its AbioCor product the company began focusing on other products to sustain revenues. It got good news on that front that same year when the FDA approved ABIOMED's AB5000 Circulatory Support System Console a device that temporarily pumps the patient's blood when the heart has failed.

David Lederman stepped down as CEO in 2004 but remained chairman. He was replaced by then-37-year-old Michael Minogue.

The following year the company made good on its pledge to focus on other products when it purchased German firm Impella CardioSystems whose mini-heart pumps had already been approved in Europe.

In 2006 ABIOMED received FDA approval for its intra-aortic balloons (IABs) which are used in cardiac catheterization labs to assist heart functioning.

EXECUTIVES

VP CFO and Treasurer, Robert L. (Bob) Bowen, age 64, $315,946 total compensation
President CEO and Director, Michael R. Minogue, age 47, $519,663 total compensation
Chief Medical Officer, Karim Benali, age 48, $171,200 total compensation
VP Healthcare Solutions, Andrew J. Greenfield, age 42, $211,592 total compensation
CTO, Thorsten Siess
COO, David M. Weber, age 53, $341,844 total compensation
VP and General Manager Global Sales and Marketing, Michael G. Howley, age 50, $296,970 total compensation
Vice President Human Resources, Franky Leblanc
Vice President General Counsel, Steve McEvoy
Vice President Engineering, Doug Vincent
Vp Western Us Sales, Geoffrey Heldoorn
Chief Scientific Officer Senior Vice President, Robert Kung
Vice President Asia, Keisuke Suzuki
Executive Assistant To Sr Vp Global, Kristin Carroll
Vice President Western U S Sales, Geoffrey Heldoorn
Vice President Eastern U S Sales, Jim Dillon

President CEO and Director, Michael R. Minogue, age 47
Secretary, Peter M Rosenblum
Auditors: Deloitte&ToucheLLP

LOCATIONS

HQ: ABIOMED, Inc.
22 Cherry Hill Drive, Danvers, MA 01923
Phone: 978 646-1400   **Fax:** 978 777-8411
Web: www.abiomed.com

2014 Sales

	% of total
US	91
Other countries	9
Total	**100**

PRODUCTS/OPERATIONS

2014 Revenues

4 mil.		% of total
Impella products	167.0	91
Service & other revenue	10.9	6
Other products	5.4	3
Funded research & development	0.3	-
Total	**183.6**	**100**

COMPETITORS

CardiacAssist	St. Jude Medical
Edwards Lifesciences	Teleflex
Getinge	Terumo
HeartWare	Thoratec Corp
Medtronic	

HISTORICAL FINANCIALS

Company Type: Public

Income Statement

FYE: March 31

	REVENUE ($ mil.)	NET INCOME ($ mil.)	NET PROFIT MARGIN	EMPLOYEES
03/14	183.6	7.3	4.0%	511
03/13	158.1	15.0	9.5%	467
03/12	126.3	1.5	1.2%	397
03/11	101.1	(11.7)	—	374
03/10	85.7	(19.0)	—	365
Annual Growth	**21.0%**	—		**8.8%**

2014 Year-End Financials

Debt ratio: —	No. of shares (mil.): 39
Return on equity: 4.8%	Dividends
Cash ($ mil.): 20	Yield: —
Current ratio: 3.88	Payout: —
Long-term debt ($ mil.): —	Market value ($ mil.): 1,039

	STOCK PRICE ($) FY Close	P/E High/Low	PER SHARE ($) Earnings	Dividends	Book Value
03/14	26.04	158 86	0.18	0.00	4.22
03/13	18.67	65 32	0.37	0.00	3.55
03/12	22.19	605252	0.04	0.00	3.22
03/11	14.53	— —	(0.32)	0.00	2.78
03/10	10.32	— —	(0.52)	0.00	2.88
Annual Growth	**26.0%**	—	—	—	**10.0%**

Abraxas Petroleum Corp.

Abraxas is a mythical Gnostic symbol that represents the number 365 in Greek and Abraxas Petroleum is working hard as a 365-days-a-year oil and gas company. The independent energy company is engaged in natural gas and crude oil exploration development and production. It operates primarily in Texas (in the South along the Gulf Coast and in the Permian Basin) the Rocky Mountains and the Mid-Continent and in 2013 the company reported estimated proved reserves of 31 million barrels of oil equivalent. That year Abraxas Petroleum also owned interests in more than 132880 net acres (primarily in mature fields) and in 1059 gross producing wells.

Geographic Reach

The company has operations across the US Rocky Mountain Permian Basin and onshore Gulf Coast regions and in Alberta Canada. The company derived about 98% of its revenues from the US in 2013.Abraxas Petroleum's properties in the Rocky Mountain region are in the Williston Basin of North Dakota and Montana and in the Green River Powder River and Unita Basins of Wyoming and Utah. In the Permian Basin its assets are in the Delaware Basin and the Eastern Shelf. In the Delaware Basin its wells are in Pecos Reeves and Ward Counties Texas; in the Eastern Shelf its wells are in Coke Scurry Mitchell and Nolan Counties Texas. Its onshore Gulf Coast assets are located along the Edwards trend in DeWitt and Lavaca Counties Texas the Eagle Ford shale in Atascosa and McMullen Counties Texas and in the Portilla field in San Patricio County Texas. The company's properties in Canada are in Central Alberta in the Pekisko fairway and the Nordegg/Tomahawk area and in the Duvernay Shale.

Operations

Its business strategy is to focus on developing its conventional assets in Texas Wyoming Montana and North Dakota while acquiring leases in emerging unconventional resource plays (such as the Eagle Ford Shale in Texas and the Bakken Shale in North Dakota) that complement its core portfolio of assets.

Sales and Marketing

The company sells its oil and gas at current market prices under short-term arrangements. In2013 two purchasers accounted for about 49% of total its oil and gas sales.

Financial Performance

That year Abraxas Petroleum reported a 38% increase revenues in 2013 thanks to a 32% growth in oil sales volumes and prices. Gas sales volumes dropped 16% but were offset by higher realized gas prices. It also saw a significant rise in NGL sales volumes partially offset by lower prices. New production brought on line in 2013 led to an increase oil sales volumes offset by natural field declines and property sales. Gas sales volumes decreased due to natural field declines andthe emphasis on drilling oil wells as opposed to gas wells. NGL sales increased primarily due to increased gas production in West Texas Wyoming and North Dakota in areas that have a higher NGL content than its traditional gas production locations.The company reported net income of $38 million in 2013 compared to a net loss of $19 million in 2012. The increase was mainly due to higher revenues decreased impairment charges and an improved gain on the 2013 sale of properties in the Eagle Ford shale (which resulted in a $33 million gain). Abraxas Petroleum has seen a healthy revenue growth year over year since 2009 primarily due to increased volumes and as well as higher prices. However due to weak gas prices its focus during 2013 was primarily on higher yield oil and liquids projects resulting in increased volumes and record revenues in 2013.

Strategy

The company's business strategy is to focus on core operated basins maintain financial flexibility and grow production and reserves. As part of its efforts to focus its property portfolio it sells assets its deems as non-core. Abraxas Petroleum's capital expenditure budget for 2014 is $125 million 94% of which was targeted to be spent on unconventional horizontal oil wells in the Bakken/Three Forks in the Rocky Mountain region and in the Eagle Ford Shale play in South Texas with the remainder being used for leasehold acquisitions in these core basins.

In 2013 the company sold various non-operated properties through the auction process for $7 million and sold the Bakken and Three Forks rights on the company's Fairview Prospect in Richland County Montana and McKenzie County North Dakota for $11 million. It also sold non-operated properties in the Bakken for $38.3 million and a non-operated position in the Wycross area of the Eagle Ford for $71 million. That year it also agreed to sell its non-operated Bakken properties (13500 net Bakken acres) to Natural Resource Partners L.P. for $35.3 million.

In 2012 Abraxas Petroleum moved to dissolve its Eagle Ford joint venture Blue Eagle Energy LLC. following which Abraxas and its joint venture partner split the assets with Abraxas retaining a 100 percent interest in the Eagle Ford and shallower rights in Jourdanton Atascosa County (4401 net acres) a 100% interest in Yoakum DeWitt County (1868 net acres) a 25% interest in WyCross McMullen County (695 net acres) and a 25% interest in Nordheim DeWitt County (944 net acres). It received net proceeds of $22 million.

HISTORY

Abraxas was founded in 1977 by 26-year-old oil engineer and San Antonio native Robert Watson formerly a Tesoro Petroleum engineer. Over the next 13 years the company grew through the formation and operation of 23 limited partnerships. Vulnerable to the boom-and-bust cycles of the oil business including the 1986 oil crash the company went public in 1991 after which it began buying major oil and gas properties. In 1993 Abraxas purchased producing wells near Corpus Christi Texas from Mobil Oil for $20 million and in 1994 it acquired properties near Midland Texas for $28 million. The development of the Midland field helped the company post strong sales that year.

In 1996 the company acquired producing properties in Wyoming and Canada for more than $132 million (including the acquisition of a major stake in Grey Wolf Exploration) and spent $37 million expanding its assets in Texas. It raised $215 million in a private placement to help pay for the purchases. The first seven wells Abraxas drilled in its Wyoming property greatly boosted its production revenues.

In 1998 Abraxas failed in an attempt to buy an oil company active near its Rocky Mountain properties but the next year it acquired New Cache Petroleum which operates in western Canada. The company sold some of its undeveloped New Cache holdings in 1999.

To raise cash Abraxas sold some of its Wyoming properties for $34 million in 2000.

In 2003 Abraxas sold its Canadian subsidiaries to a royalty trust for approximately $138 million and reorganized its remaining Canadian assets as Grey Wolf Exploration Inc. In 2005 Abraxas spun off Grey Wolf Exploration in an IPO.

As part of its strategy to develop its core properties in 2008 Abraxas Petroleum acquired oil and gas properties in the Rockies and Mid-Continent regions from St. Mary Land & Exploration for $126 million.

In 2009 Abraxas Petroleum merged with Abraxas Energy Partners L.P in order to increase capital and simplify its overall organizational structure. (The company had held a 46% stake in Abraxas Energy Partners' operating unit which controlled lucrative assets in the Bakken play).

Accelerating its development of its Gulf Coast properties in 2010 Abraxas Petroleum formed a $100 million joint venture with Blue Stone Oil & Gas to exploit the Eagle Ford Shale play in South Texas.

To support the expansion of its Bakken activities in 2011 the company bought a drilling rig and hired an experienced rig operator.

EXECUTIVES

VP Exploration, Lee T. Billingsley, age 61, $232,750 total compensation

VP Land and Marketing and Secretary, Stephen T. Wendel, age 64, $182,510 total compensation

Chairman President and CEO, Robert L. G. (Bob) Watson, age 63, $415,000 total compensation

VP Operations, William H. Wallace, age 56, $232,750 total compensation

VP Engineering, Peter A. (Pete) Bommer, $230,000 total compensation

VP and CFO, Geoffrey R. King, $237,500 total compensation

VP Land and Marketing and Secretary, Stephen T. Wendel, age 64

Chairman President and CEO, Robert L. G. (Bob) Watson, age 63

Auditors: BDOSeidmanLLP

LOCATIONS

HQ: Abraxas Petroleum Corp.
18803 Meisner Drive, San Antonio, TX 78258
Phone: 210 490-4788
Web: www.abraxaspetroleum.com

2013 Sales

	$ mil.	% of total
US	92.3	98
Canada	2.0	2
Total	**94.3**	**100**

COMPETITORS

Apache	Devon Energy
Bill Barrett	EOG
BreitBurn	Encana
Cabot Oil & Gas	Exxon Mobil
Chesapeake Energy	FieldPoint Petroleum
Chevron	XTO Energy

HISTORICAL FINANCIALS

Company Type: Public

Income Statement

FYE: December 31

	REVENUE ($ mil.)	NET INCOME ($ mil.)	NET PROFIT MARGIN	EMPLOYEES
12/13	94.3	38.6	41.0%	112
12/12	68.5	(18.7)	—	101
12/11	64.6	13.7	21.3%	104
12/10	59.0	1.7	3.0%	74
12/09	52.7	(18.7)	—	70
Annual Growth	**15.6%**	**—**		**12.5%**

2013 Year-End Financials

Debt ratio: 19.6%	No. of shares (mil.): 92
Return on equity: 57.8%	Dividends
Cash ($ mil.): 5	Yield: —
Current ratio: 0.48	Payout: —
Long-term debt ($ mil.): 41	Market value ($ mil.): 303

	STOCK PRICE ($) FY Close	P/E High/Low		PER SHARE ($) Earnings	Dividends	Book Value
12/13	3.26	9	5	0.41	0.00	0.94
12/12	2.19	—	—	(0.20)	0.00	0.50
12/11	3.30	40	15	0.15	0.00	0.68
12/10	4.57	221	92	0.02	0.00	(0.20)
12/09	1.92	—	—	(0.34)	0.00	(0.24)
Annual Growth	**14.2%**			**—**	**—**	**—**

Acadia Healthcare Company Inc.

Acadia Healthcare help people to be mentally healthy. Acadia operates more than 45 behavioral health facilities with 3700 licensed beds in 21 US states and Puerto Rico. Its mental health and addiction treatment services include adult geriatric and adolescent inpatient residential and partial hospitalization programs. The company also offers treatment options for children with autism eating disorders fetal alcohol syndrome substance abuse and traumatic brain injury as well as for sexually abused children. Acadia offers services nationwide.

Sales and Marketing

Patients are referred to Acadia's behavioral healthcare facilities through healthcare workers public programs other treatment facilities managed care organizations unions emergency departments judicial officials social workers and police departments. It also gets patient referrals via word of mouth from previously treated patients and their families and other sources.

Financial Performance

The company's revenues spiked by 88% in 2012 thanks to new revenues from 2011 and 2012 acquisitions (including Youth & Family Centered Services PHC Haven Facilities Timberline Knolls and Park Royal). Same-facility revenues increased by $20.5 million or 9.3% primarily due to a higher patient enrollment. Medicaid accounted for more than 60% of Acadia's 2012 revenues.Acadia reported net income of $20.4 million in 2012 (compared to loss of $34.9 million in 2011) due to higher revenues in and a drop in transaction-related expenses (stemming from the absence of fees paid for the termination of professional services agreement investment banking advisory and bridge commitment fees and advisory fees) partially offset by a rise in salaries wages and benefits professional fees supplies interest expense and other operating expenses.

The increase in interest expense was primarily a result of borrowings under its senior credit facility and interest on the $150 million of senior notes issued in late 2011. Higher operating expenses were primarily due to a slight increase in other operating expenses.

Strategy

The company primarily grows through acquisitions.

Mergers and Acquisitions

In 2013 the company acquired nashville-based Behavioral Centers of America for $145 million. The firm operates three inpatient psychiatric facilities and one psychiatric hospital in Michigan Ohio and Texas.

In 2012 Acadia acquired three acute care inpatient psychiatric hospitals from Haven Behavioral Healthcare for $91 million in cash. The purchase added about 165 beds at facilities in Tucson; Wichita Falls Texas; and Ada Oklahoma and marked the company's entrance into the Oklahoma market. The company also entered Illinois in 2012 by acquiring a 122-bed inpatient behavioral health care facility in Lemont Illinois for about $90 million. It also picked up Park Royal Hospital a 76-bed acute inpatient psychiatric hospital in Ft. Myers Florida for $33.4 million.

In a major move the company merged with mental health services provider PHC in late 2011. Through all-stock transaction Acadia added more than a dozen mental health and substance abuse centers in six states. When the companies combined Acadia's existing shareholders including majority owner Waud Capital Partners wound up with nearly 80% of the combined firm. The acquisition also let formerly private Acadia take a place on the NASDAQ stock exchange while PHC's NYSE Amex stock was delisted. While PHC's dba Pioneer Behavioral Health continues to be used following the transaction the legal PHC entity was absorbed into a subsidiary of Acadia. The merger created a company with a strong foundation in services for special populations including armed forces police transportation and gaming employees.

Acadia already operated about 20 behavioral health centers in more than a dozen states prior to its acquisition of PHC. Many of these facilities were gained through an earlier 2011 acquisition the purchase of Youth & Family Centered Services (YFCS) for some $178 million. YFCS operated about a dozen centers in eight states primarily focused on providing adolescent services.

PHC had also been expanding its operations prior to its merger into Acadia. The firm purchased the MeadowWood Behavioral Health center in mid-2011 for about $21 million. With about 60 beds on an 11-acre campus MeadowWood moved the company into Delaware and geriatric care. Before the Acadia deal PHC planned to expand the facility. PHC also grew in 2011 through the opening of a newly constructed inpatient treatment center in Michigan. In addition to its inpatient facilities PHC operated outpatient centers through its Harmony Healthcare and North Point Pioneer subsidiaries.

Ownership

Waud Capital Partners owns 29% of Acadia.

Company Background

Acadia was founded in 2005 by Waud Capital Partners to acquire and operate behavioral health facilities. Its first centers were purchased in 2008 and 2009 in Georgia Louisiana and Tennessee.

EXECUTIVES

Chairman and CEO, Joey A. Jacobs, age 61, $660,000 total compensation
President, Brent Turner, age 49, $435,000 total compensation
EVP and General Counsel, Christopher L. (Chris) Howard, age 48, $420,000 total compensation
COO, Ron Fincher, age 61, $450,000 total compensation
CFO, David Duckworth, $327,000 total compensation
Director Of Nursing, X St Martin
Vice President Of Risk Management, Dule Mooney
Division President, Jeff Barnett
Vice President National Marketing, Randall Goldberg
Vice Chairman, Bruce A. Shear, age 60
Chairman and CEO, Joey A. Jacobs, age 61
Auditors: Ernst&YoungLLP

LOCATIONS

HQ: Acadia Healthcare Company Inc.
830 Crescent Centre Drive, Suite 610, Franklin, TN 37067
Phone: 615 861-6000
Web: www.acadiahealthcare.com

PRODUCTS/OPERATIONS

2012 Sales

	% of total
Medicaid	64
Commercial	20
Medicare	12
Self-pay	2
Other	2
Total	**100**

Selected Facilities

Arizona
  Parc-Place (residential adolescents ages 11-17)
Arkansas
  Ascent Children's Health Services (day treatment all ages)
  Millcreek of Arkansas (long-term residential ages 6-21 years with mental retardation and/or related developmental disabilities)
Delaware
  MeadowWood Hospital (in-patient and out-patient adults and seniors)
Florida
  Park Royal Hospital
  The Refuge
Georgia
  Blue Ridge Mountain Recovery
  Greenleaf Centers
  Lakeview Behavioral Health
  RiverWoods Behavioral Health System (outpatient and partial hospitalization adults and seniors)
Illinois
  Timberline Knolls (residential treatment)
Indiana
  Resolute Treatment Center (residential males ages 11-18)
  Resource Treatment Center (residential ages 8-20)
  Options Behavioral Health System (residential ages 8-18)
Louisiana
  Acadia Vermilion Hospital (inpatient and outpatient all ages)
  Acadiana Addiction Center (inpatient and outpatient adults)
Michigan
  Detroit Capstone Academy (residential adjudicated adolescents)
  Harbor Oaks Hospital (inpatient all ages)
  Harbor Oaks Outpatient Clinic (outpatient all ages)
  Pioneer Counseling Centers (outpatient all ages)
Renaissance Recovery (residential ages 12-17)
Wellplace Michigan (local call center clinical screening and access center)
Mississippi
  Millcreek of Magee (residential 21 years and younger)
  Millcreek of Pontotoc (residential ages 6-18)
Missouri
  Lakeland Regional Hospital (residential and long term ages 4-17)
Montana
  Acadia Montana (residential ages 5-18)
Nevada
  Harmony Healthcare (outpatient all ages)
  Seven Hills Behavioral Institute (outpatient ages 12 and up)
New Mexico
  Desert Hills of New Mexico (residential ages 5-18)
Ohio
  Ohio Hospital for Psychiatry (adults and seniors)
  Shaker Clinic (adults and seniors)
  Ten Lakes Center (adults ages 55 and up)
Oklahoma
  Rolling Hills Hospital (acute inpatient psychiatric care for adults geriatrics intellectually disabled patients as well as addiction treatment)
Pennsylvania
  Southwood Hospital (various programs ages 4-18)
  Wellplace (outpatient all ages)
Tennessee
  Dealt Medical Center
  The Village (residential ages 13-17)
Texas
  Acadia Abilene (residential all ages)
Utah
  Highland Ridge Hospital (inpatient all ages)
  Wellplace (employee assistance programs and 24 hour call center)
Virginia
  Mount Regis Center (inpatient and outpatient adults)
Puerto Rico
  Hospital San Juan Capestrano Rio Piedras Puerto (treatment services for mental health conditions and addiction problems of Puerto Rico)

COMPETITORS

Betty Ford	Horizon Health
CIGNA Behavioral Health	Magellan Health
	Mental Health Network
CRC Health	Northwestern Human Services
Comprehensive Care	
Devereux Foundation	Universal Health Services
HCA	
Hazelden Betty Ford	

HISTORICAL FINANCIALS

Company Type: Public

Income Statement

	REVENUE ($ mil.)	NET INCOME ($ mil.)	NET PROFIT MARGIN	EMPLOYEES
12/13	713.4	42.5	6.0%	11,000
12/12	407.4	20.4	5.0%	7,200
12/11	221.3	(34.8)	—	5,820
12/10	64.3	6.2	9.7%	4,857
12/09	51.8	2.8	5.6%	0
Annual Growth	**92.6%**	**96.1%**	**—**	**—**

FYE: December 31

2013 Year-End Financials

Debt ratio: 50.3%
Return on equity: 9.3%
Cash ($ mil.): 4
Current ratio: 1.27
Long-term debt ($ mil.): 601

No. of shares (mil.): 50
Dividends
  Yield: —
  Payout: —
Market value ($ mil.): 2,370

STOCK PRICE ($) FY Close	P/E High/Low	PER SHARE ($) Earnings	Dividends	Book Value
12/13	47.33	57 27	0.85	0.00	9.60
12/12	23.35	46 18	0.53	0.00	8.67
12/11	9.97	—	(1.86)	0.00	3.00
Annual Growth	117.9%	—	—	—	78.9%

Aceto Corp.

Distributor Aceto (pronounced "a-seat-o") is getting bigger through chemicals –primarily specialty chemicals and pharmaceuticals. It sources and distributes more than 1100 chemical products through three segments. Its largest segment is Performance Chemicals which sources and distributes specialty chemicals and agricultural protection products. Aceto's other business segments include Pharmaceutical Ingredients (active pharmaceutical ingredients or APIs and pharmaceutical intermediates) and Human Health (finished dosage form generic drugs and nutraceutical products). Aceto sources about two-thirds of its products from Asia mostly China and India and turns around to sell more than half of them in the US.

Geographic Reach

Aceto has operations in China France Germany Hong Kong India the Netherlands Singapore the UK and the US.

Financial Analysis

Aceto saw an increase in revenues of 8% in 2011 thanks to a 51% increase in Human Health segment revenues due to a $27703 increase in sales of Rising Pharmaceuticals products and a jump in sales of domestic nutritional supplements of $4869 due to new business development from existing customers and new projects from Aceto's pipeline. In addition the company recorded a 9% increase in Pharmaceutical Ingredients as a result of a growth in sales of APIs thanks to the reorders of existing products. In addition the Pharmaceutical Ingredients segment saw international sales rise $5963 over the prior year thanks to an increase in sales of APIs and pharmaceutical intermediates. However the Performance Chemicals segment revenues declined by 9% due to a drop of $5768 in sales of specialty chemicals sold outside the US as well as a decline in agricultural protection products sales of $20482 primarily due to lower glyphosate sales caused by poor market conditions.

Aceto's 2011 net income increased by 89% thanks to strong revenue growth an increase in gross profit and lower operating assets and liability costs.

Strategy

Leveraging its access local professionals in areas with lower pricing Aceto sources more than two-thirds of its products from Asia buying from about 500 companies in China and 200 in India.

In 2012 it reorganized from six segments to three to provide a simpler more efficient operational structure for customers suppliers employees and shareholders.

Customers include major and generic pharmaceutical makers as well as chemical companies. It works with makers of generics well in advance of the drugs coming off patent to ensure those customers are ready to go with their products as soon

as legally allowed to do so. In 2011 through a subsidiary Aceto acquired New Jersey-based Rising Pharmaceuticals in a transaction valued at $80 million. Buying Rising which manufactures and distributes generic prescription and over-the-counter drugs expands Aceto's reach into the pharmaceutical market.

In 2010 Aceto broke into new markets with the acquisition of Andrews Paper & Chemical which serves the paper films and electronics industries. Some of its products include diazos and couplers that are used in the manufacture of microfilm and printed circuit boards.

HISTORY

Chemical engineers Frankel and Seymour Mann set up Aceto Chemical Co. (the name relates to acetic acid an ingredient used in synthesizing plastics) in 1947. The two built the business around the reviving chemical industry in Europe during the 1950s by acting as the US agent for British chemical firms (including BP Chemical). Aceto began to import from Asia in the 1960s and it went public in 1962. In 1969 the company set up a manufacturing plant in Carlstadt New Jersey. Up until the late 1970s the company principally operated as a US sales agent for non-US companies.

The company changed its name to Aceto Corporation in 1985. President and CEO Seymour Mann died of a heart attack in 1989 and Frankel (then chairman and CFO) assumed the CEO position the next year.

During the 1990s Aceto purchased raw materials from Chinese and Indian suppliers at half the price of those produced by some European and Japanese makers. To ensure quality control from its suppliers Aceto hired field technicians including a team based in Shanghai. To lower capital costs and concentrate on distribution the company closed its two manufacturing plants.

Aceto sold its Pfaltz & Bauer subsidiary in 1996. Frankel stepped down as CEO in 1997 and company veteran and president Leonard Schwartz filled the position. Lower sales of agricultural chemicals and bulk pharmaceuticals led to a drop in revenues that year.

In 2001 Aceto acquired the Schweizerhall Pharma division of Schweizerhall Holding AG for about $25 million. The acquisition included facilities in Germany the Netherlands France Singapore India and Hong Kong. The acquisition strengthened its international operations and its pharmaceutical and nutraceutical businesses.

The company bolstered its biopharmaceutical distribution operations in 2004 with the acquisition of Pharma Waldhof from Roche. Aceto announced plans to exit the sanitary supplies segment late that year and it sold most of the assets of its CDC Products and Magnum Research subsidiaries the following year.

Albert Eilender was named CEO of Aceto in 2010. He replaced Vincent Miata who continued as president and COO of the company.

EXECUTIVES

Executive Vice President Global Pharmaceutical Strategy, Frank Debenedittis, age 61
Assistant Vice President And Director Transportation, Amy Rogers
President and CEO, Salvatore J. Guccione, age 51, $563,750 total compensation
SVP Nutritionals, Raymond Bartone
SVP and CFO, Douglas Roth, age 57, $341,250 total compensation
SVP Performance Chemicals, Carlos Restrepo

SVP Pharmaceutical Ingredients, Nicholas Shackley
VP Pharmaceutical Intermediates, Guillaume Saint-Clair
SVP Agricultural Protection Products, Terry Kippley
President and COO Rising Pharmaceuticals Inc., Satish Srinivasan, $338,462 total compensation
Sr V Pres Hr, Charles Alaimo
V Pres-regulatory Affairs, David Petrocine
Vice President International, Guillaume Saint Clair
Vice President Specialty Chemicals, Roy Goodman
Int'l Senior Vice President, Nick Shackley
Vice President Global Regulatory, Jean Poulos
Vice President Associate General Counsel Regulatory, Michael Dibello
Chairman, Albert L. Eilender, age 71
Advisory Board Member, Melissa Orlando
Auditors: BDOUSALLP

LOCATIONS

HQ: Aceto Corp.
4 Tri Harbor Court, Port Washington, NY 11050
Phone: 516 627-6000
Web: www.aceto.com

2011 Sales

	$ mil.	% of total
US	289.6	65
Europe		
Germany	82.6	19
France	33.2	7
Netherlands	13.7	3
Asia/Pacific	25.3	6
Total	**444.4**	**100**

PRODUCTS/OPERATIONS

2011 Sales

	$ mil.	% of total
Performance Chemicals	176.1	40
Pharmaceutical Ingredients	163.0	37
Human Health	105.3	23
Total	**444.4**	**100**

Selected Products

Performance Chemicals (specialty chemicals agricultural protection products and active ingredients for pharmaceuticals)
Pharmaceutical Ingredients (pharmaceutical intermediates and active pharmaceutical ingredients)
Human Health (finished dosage form generics and nutritionals)

COMPETITORS

Air Products	Sigma-Aldrich
American Vanguard	Synthomer
Brenntag	Univar USA
Farma International	Young Chemical Co.
K.A. Steel Chemicals	

HISTORICAL FINANCIALS

Company Type: Public

Income Statement

FYE: June 30

	REVENUE ($ mil.)	NET INCOME ($ mil.)	NET PROFIT MARGIN	EMPLOYEES
06/14	510.1	29.0	5.7%	270
06/13	499.6	22.3	4.5%	234
06/12	444.3	16.9	3.8%	233
06/11	412.4	8.9	2.2%	238
06/10	346.6	6.5	1.9%	216
Annual Growth	10.1%	44.9%	—	5.7%

2014 Year-End Financials

Debt ratio: 22.5%
Return on equity: 13.5%
Cash ($ mil.): 42
Current ratio: 2.33
Long-term debt ($ mil.): 97

No. of shares (mil.): 28
Dividends
Yield: 1.3%
Payout: 23.5%
Market value ($ mil.): 522

	STOCK PRICE ($) FY Close	P/E High/Low		PER SHARE ($) Earnings	Dividends	Book Value
06/14	18.14	24	13	1.02	0.24	8.12
06/13	13.93	17	10	0.81	0.22	6.99
06/12	9.03	16	8	0.63	0.20	6.24
06/11	6.71	27	15	0.34	0.20	6.04
06/10	5.73	28	19	0.26	0.20	5.49
Annual Growth	33.4%	—	—	40.7%	4.7%	10.3%

ACI Worldwide Inc

ACI Worldwide helps money go mobile. The company develops e-payment and electronic funds transfer (EFT) software for companies around the world. Customers use its software to process transactions involving ATMs credit and debit cards online banking and payment processing point-of-sale terminals smart cards and wire transfers. ACI also makes network integration software and it offers services such as design implementation and facilities management. The company serves the financial services and retail industries with more than 750 customers in some 80 countries.

Sales and MarketingThe company distributes products primarily through its own sales force but also utilizes third-party distributors in certain regions (primarily Asia and Latin America). Among those distributors are DataOne (Thailand) Optimisa (Chile) and Syscom Computer (China).

Geographic ReachACI generates more than half its sales from the Americas with the EMEA and Asia-Pacific regions contributing 35% and more than 10% respectively. The company saw revenues rise across all regions in 2011 with the Asia-Pacific region showing the strongest growth at nearly 20%.

Financial AnalysisACI has reported strong revenue growth since 2009 when sales fell amid the worst of the economic recession. The company's 2011 revenue hit $465 million which is up 11% from 2010 as it saw double-digit increases in software license and maintenance fees and smaller growth in service and software hosting fees.Net income was also up in 2011 jumping nearly 70% to $46 million on the increase in revenue as well as lower growth in maintenance fees general and administrative costs and other expenses. ACI also saw lower income tax expenses in 2011.

Mergers and AcquisitionsACI Worldwide has worked to strengthen its international presence and add new technology to its repertoire in part through acquisitions. In 2012 it bought rival S1 Corporation for about $540 million in cash and stock. The two companies had very similar product lines and customers and ACI Worldwide believed the merger would create significant cost savings and cross-selling opportunities as well as boost its profile among community financial and branch banking institutions. S1 was integrated into ACI's other operations. The deal added a consumer online banking division and a significant retail presence outside North America.Additionally that year ACI acquired payments software developer Distra to extend the feature set of its products to address mobile usage social channels and payment services hubs.In 2011 the company bought Dallas-based ISD Corporation to add functionality to its products for retailers. ISD's applications were designed to consolidate manage and route electronic transactions for authorization and settlement processing. ACI Worldwide integrated the acquired technology into its On-Demand hosted service and its Retail Commerce Server product to add flexibility for its customers.

HISTORY

oApplied Communications Inc. (ACI) was formed by computer programmer James Cody and two other men in 1975. ACI's electronic funds software for banks seemed to be so ahead of its time that Cody made one successful sales call in mismatched shoes. The company went public in 1983. Combining its software with Tandem computers also aided ACI's fortunes. ACI was acquired by Baby Bell U S WEST in 1986; it then formed ACIL a joint venture with Sema Group. In 1991 Tandem Computers (later acquired by Compaq which was itself bought by Hewlett-Packard) bought ACI and ACIL. Management led by president and CEO William Fisher bought the units in 1993. The company changed its name to Transaction Systems Architects (TSA) in 1994 and went public again the next year.

In the mid-1990s the company went on a buying spree. It acquired Open Systems Solutions a maker of Windows NT-based payment management software in 1996. The next year TSA expanded its presence in Europe by buying the software and service division of Italian firm Banksiel. With the acquisitions of Smart Card Integrators and Media Integration which were among TSA's half-dozen 1998 purchases the company further expanded its smart card product expertise.

In 1999 TSA bought SDM International a provider of electronic payment and electronic data interchange software. That year the company acquired and restructured Insession a maker of ICE network connectivity software. In 2000 TSA filed to spin off the subsidiary renamed Insession Technologies in a public stock offering (plans which were shelved in 2001 amid a weakening economy).

In 2001 TSA acquired MessagingDirect a provider of software for the delivery and processing of electronic statements and bills. The following year the company sold its Regency Systems subsidiary a provider of software for community banks to S1 Corporation.

The company bought S2 Systems a provider of electronic payments software with operations in Europe the Middle East and the Asia/Pacific region in 2005. Later that year the company implemented a reorganization which combined three of its subsidiaries (ACI Worldwide Intranet Worldwide and Insession Technologies) into one organization operating under the ACI Worldwide name; in 2007 the company officially changed its name to ACI Worldwide.

In 2006 the company acquired P&H Solutions for $150 million. Later that year the company completed the divestiture of its e-Courier and Work-Point product lines.

Its 2007 purchase of Visual Web Solutions expanded its presence in the Asia/Pacific region (and bolstered its product offerings by adding international trade finance and Web-based cash management capabilities) while its acquisition that year of Stratasoft Sdn. Bhd. added electronic payment offerings in Malaysia.

In 2009 the company purchased UK-based Euronet Essentis Limited a division of Euronet Worldwide that provided payment products and services for card issuing and merchant acquisition. ACI also began selling its products directly in some international markets instead of relying on distributors for sales as it had in the past.

EXECUTIVES

President and CEO, Philip G. (Phil) Heasley, age 64, $650,000 total compensation
Group President Strategic Products and Global Markets, Daniel J. (Dan) Frate, age 53
EVP and Chief Administrative Officer, Dennis P. Byrnes, age 50, $310,000 total compensation
SEVP and Chief Technology, Tony Scotto
EVP and Chief Risk Officer, David N. Morem, age 56, $275,000 total compensation
EVP Treasurer and Corporate Development Officer, Craig A. Maki, age 47, $275,000 total compensation
SEVP and CFO, Scott W. Behrens, age 42, $310,000 total compensation
Group President Customer Management and Maintenance, Carolyn Homberger
Group President ACI On-Demand, Apratim Purakayastha
Vice President Investor Relations And Strategic Analysis, John Kraft
Vice President Operations Asia Pacific, Erwin Chan
Vice President Of Marketing, Debbie Brookling
Vice President Global Product Business Operations, Craig Saks
Vp Corporate Development, David Diloreto
Vice President Product Management, Jyothsna Shetty
Vice President Retail Solution, Bob Koscheski
Vice President Human Resources Business Partner, Shirley Guidroz
Senior Vice President Implementation, Chris Scalia
Sr Administrative Assistant To Svp Gm, Leah Bedi
Vice President Software Engineering, Shelley Ahlers
Vp Engineering, John Mandel
Vp Software Engineering, Mitesh Mehta
Vice President Corporate Marketing, Shirley Macbeth
Vice President Engineering, Raj Vaidyanathan
Vice President Financial Planning, Kevin Long
Vice President Hosted Services, Kevin Blaser
Vice President Operations And Planning, J Elam
Vice President Account And Channel Development, John Acquaviva
Senior Vice President And General, William Proctor
Senior Vice President, Eric Labiak
Vice President Americas Sales Operations And Planning, Cliff Elam
Vice President Global Solutions And Product Marketing, Gabrielle Lukianchuk
Chairman, Harlan F. Seymour, age 65
Auditors: Deloitte&ToucheLLP

LOCATIONS

HQ: ACI Worldwide Inc
3520 Kraft Rd, Suite 300, Naples, FL 34105
Phone: 239 403-4600
Web: www.aciworldwide.com

2013 Sales

	$ mil.	% of total
Americas	541.9	63
EMEA	228.7	26
Asia/Pacific	94.3	11
Total	**864.9**	**100**

PRODUCTS/OPERATIONS

2013 Sales

	$ mil.	% of total
Software hosting fees	263.0	31
Maintenance fees	245.9	28
Software license fees	233.9	27
Services	122.1	14
Total	**864.9**	**100**

2013 Sales by Productline

	% of total
Retail payment processing	48
Online Banking and community financial services	26
Billers	12
Wholesale baking payments	4
Payment fraud management	4
Tools and infrastructure	4
Card and merchant management	2
Total	**100**

Selected Service Areas

Online banking and cash management
Payment fraud detection
Retail
Retail banking payments
Tools and infrastructure
Wholesale banking payments

COMPETITORS

Fair Isaac	Ingenico Corp.
Fidelity National Information Services	Intuit Financial Services
First Data	Total System Services
Fiserv	VeriFone
Fundtech	

HISTORICAL FINANCIALS

Company Type: Public

Income Statement

FYE: December 31

	REVENUE ($ mil.)	NET INCOME ($ mil.)	NET PROFIT MARGIN	EMPLOYEES
12/13	864.9	63.8	7.4%	4,329
12/12	666.5	48.8	7.3%	3,530
12/11	465.1	45.8	9.9%	2,131
12/10	418.4	27.2	6.5%	2,134
12/09	405.7	19.6	4.8%	2,114
Annual Growth	**20.8%**	**34.3%**	**—**	**19.6%**

2013 Year-End Financials

Debt ratio: 44.9%
Return on equity: 11.8%
Cash ($ mil.): 95
Current ratio: 1.26
Long-term debt ($ mil.): 708

No. of shares (mil.): 116
Dividends
  Yield: —
  Payout: —
Market value ($ mil.): 7,577

	STOCK PRICE ($) FY Close	P/E High/Low	PER SHARE ($) Earnings	Dividends	Book Value
12/13	65.00	119 79	0.53	0.00	4.66
12/12	43.69	111 67	0.41	0.00	4.52
12/11	28.64	83 55	0.45	0.00	3.14
12/10	26.87	104 57	0.27	0.00	2.56
12/09	17.15	107 69	0.19	0.00	2.31
Annual Growth	**39.5%**	**— —**	**29.4%**	**—**	**19.2%**

Acorda Therapeutics Inc

Acorda Therapeutics hopes its products really get on your nerves. The company is developing prescription drugs that aim to restore neurological function for patients with central nervous system disorders. The company's marketed drugs include Ampyra which enhances conduction in nerves damaged from multiple sclerosis (MS) and Zanaflex a muscle spasm controller. Acorda is working with Biogen Idec to market Ampyra outside the US. Acorda's other drug candidates include potential new therapies for MS and other central nervous system disorders as well as cardiac conditions.

Operations

Sales of its two commercial products have helped the company increase its product revenues in recent years with Ampyra as the company's main breadwinner that the firm hopes will drive growth in future years. The drug is the first to improve the functionality of damaged nerve fibers; other MS treatments generally treat symptoms or slow its progression. Biogen Idec holds rights to market Ampyra outside of the US and pays royalties to Acorda on the drug's sales. Biogen Idec has gained approval for Ampyra (known internationally as Fampyra) in areas including Australia Canada Israel and the European Union.

Zanaflex on the other hand is facing dwindling sales after Zanaflex capsules began facing generic competition in 2012 when its patent expired. (The Zanaflex tablets are still under patent protection.) Acorda launched an authorized generic capsule version with Actavis (formerly Watson Pharmaceuticals) that year to help offset losses. In addition Acorda is stepping up efforts to broaden its product offerings.

The company doesn't have its own manufacturing operations; it instead uses Patheon and Alkermes as its third-party manufacturers.

Sales and Marketing

The company markets its products in the US through a direct sales force that targets neurologists and other specialists as well as primary care physicians specialty pharmacies hospitals managed care companies and drug distribution companies.

Financial Performance

Though the company has products on the market it still invests heavily in R&D efforts for new candidates as well as to build up a marketing and sales support network for existing products. However Acorda experienced its first profitable year in 2011 when it reported a net income of $30 million. Its transition from a development-stage firm to a profitable drugmaker came primarily from increased revenues on sales of Ampyra in both 2010 and 2011 (the company more than doubled revenues both years).

Sales grew another 5% in 2012 to $306 million due to higher Ampyra sales and increased royalty revenues on both Ampyra and generic Zanaflex offset by lower sales of its branded Zanaflex offerings. Profits also increased by more than 400% in 2012 due to income tax over-provision benefits.

Strategy

The company is focused on increasing sales of Ampyra. It is also looking to add new uses for Ampyra which was first approved by the FDA in 2010 as a therapy to improve the ability to walk in people who suffer from MS. The firm is developing the drug for additional MS-related functional impairment indications as well as for potential use in cerebral palsy and chronic stroke treatment.

In its internal R&D programs Acorda is exploring applications for its nerve and tissue repair technologies in cardiology and neurology fields. For instance in addition to the Ampyra development programs the company has candidates for treatment of spinal cord injury stroke epilepsy and heart failure as well as a new potential treatment for MS.

Mergers and Acquisitions

In 2012 the company expanded its pipeline by acquiring development firm Neuronex in a deal worth some $9.3 million (plus potential future milestone payments) to gain access to Neuronex's nasal spray epilepsy candidate. It first paid $2.5 million to gain a minority stake in Neuronex and then exercised its option to purchase the rest for $6.8 million later in the year.

Ownership

Investment firm Blackrock owns an 11% stake in Acorda.

Company Background

The company was founded by CEO Ron Cohen in 1995 to develop therapies for multiple sclerosis and other neurological conditions.

EXECUTIVES

CFO, Michael W. Rogers
President and CEO, Ron Cohen, $690,000 total compensation
Chief Scientific Officer, Andrew R. Blight, $404,467 total compensation
Chief of Business Operations, David Lawrence, $293,683 total compensation
President International and General Counsel, Jane Wasman, $458,750 total compensation
EVP Commercial Development, Lauren M. Sabella
Chief Medical Officer, Enrique J Carrazana, $365,667 total compensation
Chief Technical Officer, Richard P. Batycky
National Account Manager, Shannon Diantonio
Vp Quality, Bonnie Pappacena
Vice President Of Drug Safety And Risk Management, Thomas Aquilina
Senior Vice President Medical Affairs, Adrian Rabinowicz
Vice President Sales, Kerry Clem
Vice President Trade Relations And Operations, Tara Stevens
Abm, Jim Mack
Assistant Treasurer, Elizabeth Keating
Vice Chairman, Pilar Colvin
Auditors: KPMGLLP

LOCATIONS

HQ: Acorda Therapeutics Inc
420 Saw Mill River Road, Ardsley, NY 10502
Phone: 914 347-4300   **Fax:** 914 347-4560
Web: www.acorda.com

PRODUCTS/OPERATIONS

2012 Sales

	$ mil.	% of total
Product sales	282.4	92
Royalty	14.4	5
License	9.0	3
Total	**305.8**	**100**

COMPETITORS

Actavis	Cephalon
Alseres	Cytokinetics

Pharmaceuticals
Apotex
Bayer HealthCare
  Pharmaceuticals
Bayhill
BioMarin
  Pharmaceutical
Biogen Idec
Catalyst
  Pharmaceutical

InVivo Therapeutics
Meda Pharmaceuticals
Mylan
Novartis
Sanofi
Shire
Teva
Upsher-Smith

HISTORICAL FINANCIALS

Company Type: Public

Income Statement

FYE: December 31

	REVENUE ($ mil.)	NET INCOME ($ mil.)	NET PROFIT MARGIN	EMPLOYEES
12/13	336.4	16.4	4.9%	421
12/12	305.8	154.9	50.7%	378
12/11	292.2	30.6	10.5%	328
12/10	191.0	(11.7)	—	305
12/09	54.6	(83.9)	—	249
Annual Growth	57.5%	—	—	14.0%

2013 Year-End Financials

Debt ratio: 0.7%
Return on equity: 3.9%
Cash ($ mil.): 48
Current ratio: 3.80
Long-term debt ($ mil.): 3

No. of shares (mil.): 40
Dividends
  Yield: —
  Payout: —
Market value ($ mil.): 1,194

	STOCK PRICE ($) FY Close	P/E High/Low		PER SHARE ($) Earnings	Dividends	Book Value
12/13	29.20	99	61	0.39	0.00	10.77
12/12	24.86	7	6	3.84	0.00	9.70
12/11	23.84	42	24	0.76	0.00	5.22
12/10	27.26	—	—	(0.31)	0.00	3.90
12/09	25.20	—	—	(2.22)	0.00	3.62
Annual Growth	3.8%	—	—	—	—	31.3%

Acuity Brands Inc (Holding Company)

And a booming voice cried out "Let there be light" and Acuity Brands replied "Okay sure." Acuity Brands through its subsidiaries manufactures and distributes a range of indoor/outdoor lighting fixtures and control systems. Applications include residential as well as commercial and institutional buildings industrial facilities and infrastructure projects (highways airports and tunnels). Its services provide wireless and network control-based lighting energy audits and turn-key labor renovation. The company's 13 plants in the US and Mexico one in Canada and two in Europe turn out offerings under such brands as Holophane Gotham Lithonia ROAM Sensor Switch and Tersen.

Sales and Marketing
About 90% of the company's sales are made in the US; Home Depot accounts for more than 10% of sales.

Financial Performance
Acuity has enjoyed steady growth over the last few years. From 2013 to 2014 its total sales increased by almost 15% from $2.09 billion to $2.39 billion its biggest revenue total in seven years. Prof-

its jumped 38% from $127 million in 2013 to $176 million in 2014 its highest total in the last 10 years.

The 2014 growth was driven by a 16% spike in sales from the US and a 2% increase in international sales. The company was also helped by higher demand for LED luminaires as sales of these products more than doubled compared to the last year.

The surge in profits for 2014 was due to an increase in gross profit attributed to higher sales volumes lower material and component costs and improved manufacturing productivity due in part to the elimination of $8 million of temporary manufacturing inefficiencies incurring during 2013.

Strategy
Acquisitions are also helping Acuity exploit a wide-spectrum of technologies intended to offer customers a one-stop source. In 2013 in a move to bolster its European footprint the company acquired eldoLAB Holding B.V. (eldoLED) a provider of high-performance drivers for LED lighting systems based in Eindhoven The Netherlands. To expand its wireless lighting controls portfolio in 2012 Acuity purchased Adura Technologies (Adura) a developer of radio frequency (RF) mesh networking technology that allows individual light fixtures to communicate in a wireless mesh network with switches sensors and system management software.

EXECUTIVES

Vice President Sourcing, Gary Wallpe
Vice President Controller, Karen J Holcom
Chairman CEO and President, Vernon J. (Vern) Nagel, age 57, $600,000 total compensation
EVP and CFO, Richard K. (Ricky) Reece, age 59, $421,750 total compensation
EVP, Mark A. Black, $395,000 total compensation
Vice President Information Technology, Karen Nocher
Vice President Internal Audit, Tom Wilson
Vice President And Associate Counsel, Barry Goldman
Vice President Finance, Tony Mezza
Vice President Of Sales, Eric Stewart
National Sales Manager, Eric Stevenson
Vice President Sales And Marketing, Bob Adamicki
Regional Sales Vice President, Michael Shatzkin
Vice President Global Corporate, Richard Albright
Regional Sales Vice President, Al Tyre
Vice President Vertical Mkt Streets, Troy Harms
Vice President Of Technical Marketing Services, Cheryl English
Vice President, Terry Utterback
Strategic Accounts Vice President, Leslie West
Vice President Architect, Scott Butler
Vice President Of Data Management, Blake Burroughs
Vice President Sales, Greg Parmley
Vice President Sourcing, Edwin Wright
Vice President Supply Chain, Tyler Moon
Vice President Showroom Sales Acuity Brands Inc, Jennifer Thorpe
Vice President Marketing, David Grimm
Vice President Of Agency Sales, Geoffrey Marlow
Vice President Financial Shared, Cynthia West
Vice President Strategy And Corporate Development, Pete Shannin
Vice President Of Sales, William Astary
Vice President Strategic Account Management, John Kimmel
Vice President Of It, Phil Kilgore
Vice President Oem Sourcing, Paul Foster
Senior Vice President General Manager, Steve Hire
Vice President F, Chris Tuttle
Vice President Sales Operations, Dave Nelson

Executive Vice President, Darnell Charles
Vice President Manufacturing, Nate Vanmeter
Senior Vice President Operations, Martin Carr
Vice President Of Marketing, Neil Tarallo
Senior Vice President Specialty, Chuck Meteer
Vp Sales, Mark Geiger
Vice President Northeast, Keith Keller
Vice President Of Lighting Technology, Jeffrey Quinlan
Vice President Strategic Services Group, Larry Smith
Regional Sales Vice President, Shawn Fentress
Chairman CEO and President, Vernon J. (Vern) Nagel, age 57
Board Member, Ray M Robinson
Auditors: Ernst&YoungLLP

LOCATIONS

HQ: Acuity Brands Inc (Holding Company)
1170 Peachtree Street, N.E., Suite 2300, Atlanta, GA 30309-7676
Phone: 404 853-1400   Fax: 404 853-1300
Web: www.acuitybrands.com

2014 Sales

	$ mil.	% of total
US	2155.0	90
Other countries	238.5	10
Total	2393.5	100

PRODUCTS/OPERATIONS

Selected Products and Brands

Controls products
  Lighting Controls & Design (LC&D) (digital lighting controls and software ranging from dimming and building interfaces to digital thermostats)
  ROAM (streetlight monitoring system)
  SensorSwitch (lighting controls and energy management systems)
  Synergy (control systems suitable for high-rise office buildings multi-building complexes manufacturing plants and sports facilities)
Indoor lighting products
  Gotham (architectural indoor lighting)
  Mark Architectural Lighting (specification manufacturer of lighting products)
  Peerless (commercial and institutional indoor lighting)
  SunOptics (high performance prismatic daylighting)
Indoor/Outdoor products
  Carandini (amenity flood industrial and street lighting)
  Holophane (industrial indoor and outdoor lighting)
  Lithonia Lighting (commercial industrial outdoor and residential lighting)
  RELOC Wiring Solutions (modular wiring indoor and outdoor)
Outdoor lighting products
  American Electric Lighting (outdoor lighting products for commercial government industrial and institutional applications)
  Antique Street Lamps (outdoor decorative lighting products)
  Hydrel (architectural and landscape lighting)
  Renaissance Lighting (solid-state light-emitting diode (LED) architectural lighting)
  Tersen (day and night-time outdoor lighting systems)
  Winona Lighting (architectural and high-performance indoor and outdoor lighting products)
Renovation products
  MetalOptics (fluorescent indoor lighting fixtures)

Selected Mergers and Acquisitions

FY2013
  eldoLAB Holding B.V. (Eindhoven The Netherlands; high performance drivers for LED lighting system)
FY2012
  Adura Technologies (developer of radio frequency mesh technology)
FY2011

Healthcare Lighting Inc. (Pennsylvania; light products for health care industry)
Horizon Control Inc. (Personal computer-based lighting control systems maker)
Pathway Connectivity Inc. (Alberta Canada; maker of networked data communications and interface equipment for lighting control systems)

COMPETITORS

Altman Lighting
Cree
Everbrite
GE
Hubbell
Juno Lighting
Litelab
OSRAM SYLVANIA
Orion Energy Systems
Philips Electronics
Professional Luminaires North America
Revolution Lighting Technologies
Schneider Electric

HISTORICAL FINANCIALS

Company Type: Public

Income Statement

FYE: August 31

	REVENUE ($ mil.)	NET INCOME ($ mil.)	NET PROFIT MARGIN	EMPLOYEES
08/14	2,393.5	175.8	7.3%	7,000
08/13	2,089.1	127.4	6.1%	6,500
08/12	1,933.7	116.3	6.0%	6,000
08/11	1,795.7	105.5	5.9%	6,000
08/10	1,626.9	79.6	4.9%	6,000
Annual Growth	10.1%	21.9%	—	3.9%

2014 Year-End Financials

Debt ratio: 16.3%
Return on equity: 16.3%
Cash ($ mil.): 552
Current ratio: 2.52
Long-term debt ($ mil.): 353
No. of shares (mil.): 42
Dividends
  Yield: 0.0%
  Payout: 12.8%
Market value ($ mil.): 5,310

	STOCK PRICE ($) FY Close	P/E High/Low		PER SHARE ($) Earnings	Dividends	Book Value
08/14	123.88	35	21	4.05	0.52	27.14
08/13	85.50	30	20	2.95	0.52	23.38
08/12	64.16	24	12	2.72	0.52	19.96
08/11	46.04	25	16	2.42	0.52	18.25
08/10	38.74	26	17	1.80	0.52	16.16
Annual Growth	33.7%	—	—	22.5%	(0.0%)	13.3%

Advanced Energy Industries Inc.

Advanced Energy Industries advances ordinary electrical power to the head of the high-tech class. The company's power conversion products transform raw electricity making it uniform enough to ensure consistent production in high-precision manufacturing. Semiconductor and solar manufacturing equipment maker Applied Materials (14% of sales) is its top customer. Advanced Energy's gear also is used in the production of solar panels and other thin-film products such as cell phones computers cars and glass panels for windows and elec-

tronic devices. The company gets around 70% of sales from the US.

Operations

Advanced Energy Industries operates in two divisions - Thin Films and Solar Energy. Each division accounts for about half of sales. Sales for the Solar Energy division rose 15% in 2012 as more large utility-scale projects use its high-efficiency inverters while sales of Thin Film products fell almost 30% as demand from semiconductor equipment makers and other OEMs decreased.

Geographic Reach

Advanced Energy Industries has manufacturing plants in Canada China South Korea and the US (in Washington state). Design facilities are located in the US and Switzerland while the company has sales and services offices in China Germany India Japan Singapore South Korea and Taiwan.

Sales and Marketing

Products are sold to more than 450 OEMs and integrators and directly to almost 1500 end users. It uses a direct sales force as well as independent sales representatives and distributors such as wholesaler Scientech in Taiwan. The company's 10 largest customers account for about half of sales.

Financial Performance

Overall sales fell 12% in 2012 to $451 million as semiconductor equipment makers and other OEMs didn't need to make as many products and didn't need Advanced Energy Industries' products to do so. The semiconductor market experienced excess manufacturing capacity which reduced demand while the company did see growth for its solar energy division. In 2012 profits also fell to $20 million down 43% from $36 million in 2011 even though the company was able to keep operating expenses down after 2011's restructuring.

Strategy

The company reorganized late in 2011 to reduce costs by aligning its R&D and manufacturing operations with the location of its customers. It cut its workforce by 12% closed facilities and transferred the production of solar inverter components to China.

Mergers and Acquisitions

Advanced Energy Industries has made two recent acquisitions for both its Thin Films and Solar Energy divisions. In 2013 it paid Â59 million ($79 million) for REFUsol Holding GmbH a Germany-based provider of three-phase string solar PV inverters for commercial applications. The year before it bought Solvix SA a Swiss company that makes power supplies for the surface treatment and thin films industry. Solvix's Switzerland office also became a new engineering and development center for its thin-film industrial products business.

HISTORY

Douglas Schatz (chairman) a veteran of Applied Materials and Brent Backman who had worked for Hughes Aircraft (sold to General Motors in 1986) founded Advanced Energy Industries in 1981. The company's first product replaced a refrigerator-sized power source with one the size of a bread box. Also during the 1980s the company introduced its first direct-current system for use in semiconductor deposition processes.

The company went public in 1995. The following year sales growth slowed as the chip industry went through one of its periodic slumps. To cushion its dependence on the volatile semiconductor market in 1997 and 1998 Advanced Energy acquired power supply firms Tower Electronics (products used in the telecommunications medical and non-impact printing industries) and MIK

Physics (power supplies used in industrial vacuum coating) among others. Advanced Energy also bought one of its main rivals RF Power Products. In 2000 Advanced Energy bought Noah Holding a privately held maker of temperature control systems.

In 2001 the company acquired Engineering Measurements Company (EMCO) a maker of flow meters and other precision measurement equipment. During 2001 the company twice cut its workforce —by a total of one-fourth —in response to a sharp decline in the worldwide electronics industry.

In 2002 Advanced Energy acquired Aera Japan (mass flow controllers) for about $80 million in cash and debt assumption. Later that year it acquired Germany-based Dressler HF Technik (power systems for plasma-based production equipment) and the e-diagnostics applications of privately held Symphony Systems (Web-based software used to control wafer manufacturing processes).

In 2005 Doug Schatz said he would retire as president and CEO once a successor could be found. Hans-Georg Betz CEO of West STEAG Partners (a German venture capital firm) and a director of Advanced Energy since 2004 was named president and CEO later that year. Schatz remained as nonexecutive chairman of the company.

Later that year Advanced Energy raised around $92 million in a secondary stock offering. The company marked its 25th anniversary in business during 2006.

The company closed its plant in Stolberg Germany in 2007. Manufacturing was shifted to Advanced Energy's high-volume plant in Shenzhen China and to its advanced manufacturing facility in Fort Collins Colorado. The company said the decision came down to deciding whether to expand the plants in Stolberg and Shenzhen with the Chinese facility getting the nod. Advanced Energy acquired the Stolberg location through the acquisition of Dressler HF Technik in 2002. The German plant employed about 65 people.

Bolstering its power conversion products for the solar market in 2010 Advanced Energy acquired PV Powered a maker solar inverters for the commercial residential and utility-scale markets. Later the same year the company sold its Aera mass flow control and related product lines to Hitachi Metals for about $44 million in order to focus on its core power product lines.

EXECUTIVES

Executive Vice President Corporate Development and General Counsel, Thomas O. (Tom) McGimpsey, age 52, $283,512 total compensation
President CEO and Director, Yuval Wasserman, age 60, $385,224 total compensation
President - Solar Energy, Gordon Tredger
Executive Vice President Human Resources, Randall S. Hester
Chief Accounting Officer, Bill Trupkiewicz
Vice President Of Finance And Controller, John McMahon
Senior Vice President Of Finance, Michael E Hillow
Senior Vice President, William Metz
Vice President Operations, Joan Summerford
Senior Vice President, Paul Martin
Chairman, Richard P. (Dick) Beck, age 81
President CEO and Director, Yuval Wasserman, age 60

Board Of Directors, Frederick A Ball
Board Of Directors, Edward Grady
Board Of Directors, Terry Hudgens
Auditors: GrantThorntonLLP

LOCATIONS

HQ: Advanced Energy Industries Inc.
  1625 Sharp Point Drive, Fort Collins, CO 80525
Phone: 970 221-4670
Web: www.advanced-energy.com

2012 Sales

	$ mil.	% of total
North America		
US	322.8	71
Canada	30.1	7
Asia/Pacific		
China	20.0	5
Other countries	54.8	12
Europe		
Germany	18.4	4
Other countries	5.8	1
Total	**451.9**	**100**

PRODUCTS/OPERATIONS

2012 Sales

	$ mil.	% of total
Solar energy	216.6	48
Thin films		
Semiconductor capital equipment	134.2	30
Non-semiconductor capital equipment	51.0	11
Global support	50.1	11
Total	**451.9**	**100**

Selected Products

Inductively coupled plasma sources
Ion sources
Optical fiber thermometers
Photovoltaic (PV) power inverters
  Bipolar transformerless inverters (Solaron)
  Grid-tie PV inverters (PV Powered)
Power control and conversion systems (used with wafer
  etching and vapor deposition equipment)
  AC power supply
  Direct-current (DC) products
  High-power products
  Low-frequency products
  Mid-frequency power supplies
  Radio-frequency generators
Radio-frequency power systems (cables generators
  instrumentation power supplies power delivery
  systems and variable frequency generators)

Selected Acquisitions

2013
  REFUsol Holding GmbH (Germany; solar inverters)
2012
  Solvix (Switzerland; arc detection and suppression)
2010
  PV Powered (Bend OR; solar inverters)

COMPETITORS

Acme Electric	Satcon Technology
BASF SE	Schneider Electric
MKS Instruments	Siemens AG
SMA Solar Technology	

HISTORICAL FINANCIALS

Company Type: Public

Income Statement

FYE: December 31

	REVENUE ($ mil.)	NET INCOME ($ mil.)	NET PROFIT MARGIN	EMPLOYEES
12/13	547.0	32.0	5.9%	1,504
12/12	451.9	20.5	4.6%	1,354
12/11	516.8	36.3	7.0%	1,471
12/10	459.4	71.1	15.5%	1,788
12/09	186.4	(102.7)	—	1,316
Annual Growth	**30.9%**	**—**	**—**	**3.4%**

2013 Year-End Financials

Debt ratio: 2.0%	No. of shares (mil.): 40
Return on equity: 7.5%	Dividends
Cash ($ mil.): 138	Yield: —
Current ratio: 3.41	Payout: —
Long-term debt ($ mil.): —	Market value ($ mil.): 926

	STOCK PRICE ($) FY Close	P/E High/Low	Earnings	PER SHARE ($) Dividends	Book Value
12/13	22.86	32 17	0.79	0.00	11.47
12/12	13.81	27 20	0.52	0.00	10.20
12/11	10.73	20 10	0.83	0.00	9.71
12/10	13.64	11 7	1.64	0.00	8.63
12/09	15.08	— —	(2.45)	0.00	6.62
Annual Growth	**11.0%**	**— —**	**—**	**—**	**14.7%**

Advent Software, Inc.

Advent Software manages investments from beginning to end. A provider of investment management software for advisers brokers funds and other financial firms Advent offers applications for managing everything from client relationships to trade order executions. The company's products (marketed under the APX Geneva Black Diamond and Tamale brands among others) are used to manage portfolio accounting trading and order execution hedge and venture fund allocation reconciliation and other functions. Advent also offers services such as consulting hosting support and maintenance. More than 80% of sales come from customers in the US including TIAA CREF Merrill Lynch and Wells Capital Management.

Geographic Reach

The company has operations in China Denmark Norway Singapore Sweden the UK the United Arab Emirates and the US. The US generates 83% of total revenues.

Sales and Marketing Advent sells its products directly to customers via one of five sales groups centered around product and/or geography. It primarily targets investment firms and institutions that include asset managers wealth managers registered investment advisers brokers fund managers pension funds and endowments.

Financial Performance The company has seen solid revenue growth over the last three years. Revenues jumped 10% from $326 million in 2011 to $359 million in 2012. Its profits hovered at the $30 million mark for both 2011 and 2012.

The growth for 2012 was the result of increased revenues of APX and Geneva products as well as contributions from Syncova and Black Diamond which were acquired in 2011. Its revenues from the US surged by 12% from 2011 to 2012 while international revenues spiked by 2%.

Mergers and Acquisitions The company has used acquisitions to expand its product lines and customer base as well as to grow its international operations. In 2011 Advent bought UK-based Syncova Solutions a developer of margin management and financing software for hedge fund operators and prime brokers. Advent cited its desire to diversify its product line with Syncova's margin calculation application Optima and its debit finance reconciliation and tool Abacus as the reason for the deal. The company bought Black Diamond Performance Reporting later that year for about $73 million. The deal extended Advent's ability to offer Web-based portfolio management and reporting tools to financial advisers. Ownership Chairman John Scully through hedge fund SPO Advisory owns about 30% of Advent Software.

HISTORY

Stephanie DiMarco was a financial analyst at a small investment bank when she sought to computerize the firm's back-office operations. The IBM PC soon came out and DiMarco foresaw a promising market; she started Advent in 1985 with programmer Steve Strand. The following year the company sold its first product Professional Portfolio designed to help smaller investment firms with accounting and record keeping.

Sales grew to more than $4 million by 1990. The company introduced Axys the first Windows-based portfolio management system software in 1993. That year DiMarco bought out Strand. Advent went public in 1995. The next year the company bought Data Exchange a maker of portfolio and trade order software designed for large regional broker/dealers and money managers.

In 1997 Advent released Geneva software for managing investments with international accounting requirements. The company bought the grants management operations of Blackbund and MicroEdge a provider of software for charitable trusts and other grant-giving organizations in 1998. New product releases that year included Advent Office a suite of applications for automating investment management.

DiMarco handed over the CEO post in 1999 to president Peter Caswell; DiMarco remained chairman. The company expanded into the UK in 2000 when it opened a London office.

In 2001 the company continued to expand its offerings branching out into not-for-profit software products through its purchase of privately held NPO Solutions. The next year Advent added wealth management software to its product line through its purchase of privately held Kinexus for about $68 million and it acquired portfolio management software provider Techfi for about $23 million.

As part of a larger restructuring designed to reduce costs and refocus on core markets Caswell resigned as president and CEO in 2003. DiMarco resumed the CEO position and handed over the chairman title to director John Scully.

In late 2008 the company acquired Tamale Software for about $28 million; the purchase expanded Advent's front office software applications and helps it establish a presence in the research management solutions niche market.

Advent sold its MicroEdge subsidiary in 2009 to Vista Equity Partners for about $30 million in cash. The deal enabled the company to focus on its core market of serving investment management industry clients. In early 2010 the company purchased Goya AS a Norway-based provider of software for fund managers and fund distributors in Europe and the Middle East. Goya's Tradex software was combined with Advent's Portfolio Exchange product which gave Advent an integrated product for managing front- and back-office tasks related to fund and asset management.

EXECUTIVES

President and CEO, David Peter F. (Pete) Hess, age 44, $493,750 total compensation
EVP Global Client Experience, Anthony Sperling, $308,125 total compensation
EVP and CTO, Todd Gottula, $297,500 total compensation

EVP Sales and Solutions Management, Christopher J. (Chris) Momsen, $365,700 total compensation
General Manager Europe Middle East and Africa, H Åkan Valberg, age 52
EVP and CFO, James S. (Jim) Cox, age 42, $342,500 total compensation
SVP and CIO, Doug Yokoyama
SVP and General Manager Black Diamond, Dave Welling
Vice President Strategic Accounts, Todd Honderd
Vice President Of Business Development, Thomas (Tom) Zdon
Vice President Solutions Marketing, Robert Oboyle
Senior Vice President Acquisitions, Reed Colley
Vice President Product Management And Solution Consulting, Daniel Eriksson
Vice President Of Marketing At Advent Software Inc, Susan Lundquist
Executive Vice President Of Information Technology, Chris Bendixen
Vice President, Tim Gill
Vice President Advisory Market Strategy And Channel Management, Cathy Clauson
Vp Global Client Services, Casey Keller
Vp Sales & Marketing, John Jones
Chairman and Interim CEO, Stephanie G. DiMarco, age 57
Auditors: PricewaterhouseCoopersLLP

LOCATIONS

HQ: Advent Software, Inc.
600 Townsend Street, San Francisco, CA 94103
Phone: 415 543-7696
Web: www.advent.com

2012 Sales

	$ mil.	% of total
US	299.0	83
Other countries	59.8	17
Total	**358.8**	**100**

PRODUCTS/OPERATIONS

2012 Sales

	$ mil.	% of total
Recurring revenues		
Term license revenues	159.9	44
Maintenance revenues	67.1	19
Other recurring revenues	97.6	27
Non-recurring revenues		
Professional services & other	31.3	9
Perpetual license fees	2.9	1
Total	**358.8**	**100**

Selected Brands

Advent
Axys
Black Diamond
Geneva
Moxy
Syncova
Tamale

COMPETITORS

Algorithmics	Eze Software Group LLC
Ariba	Fidessa
AspenTech	Fiserv
Blackbaud	Linedata
Broadridge	Misys
Charles River Systems	SS&C
Charles Schwab	SunGard
DST Systems	Thomson Reuters

HISTORICAL FINANCIALS

Company Type: Public

Income Statement

FYE: December 31

	REVENUE ($ mil.)	NET INCOME ($ mil.)	NET PROFIT MARGIN	EMPLOYEES
12/13	382.9	28.8	7.5%	1,151
12/12	358.8	30.4	8.5%	1,222
12/11	326.2	30.1	9.2%	1,201
12/10	283.5	24.1	8.5%	1,051
12/09	259.5	36.8	14.2%	998
Annual Growth	**10.2%**	**(6.0%)**	**—**	**3.6%**

2013 Year-End Financials

Debt ratio: 66.8%
Return on equity: 29.0%
Cash ($ mil.): 33
Current ratio: 0.58
Long-term debt ($ mil.): 285

No. of shares (mil.): 51
Dividends
Yield: 25.7%
Payout: 1,875.0%
Market value ($ mil.): 1,792

	STOCK PRICE ($) FY Close	P/E High/Low		PER SHARE ($) Earnings	Dividends	Book Value
12/13	34.95	64	38	0.54	9.00	(2.18)
12/12	21.38	47	35	0.58	0.00	6.14
12/11	24.36	107	34	0.56	0.00	5.55
12/10	57.92	122	79	0.44	0.00	5.27
12/09	40.73	58	27	0.70	0.00	4.87
Annual Growth	**(3.8%)**	**—**	**—**	**(6.1%)**	**—**	**—**

Advisory Board Company (The)

Here's where a hospital might go for a second opinion. The Advisory Board Company specializes in providing best practices consulting to member-clients in the health care and education industries. Members include more than 3700 hospitals pharmaceutical and insurance companies universities and related organizations. The Advisory Board offers more than 50 programs across three key areas: best practices research software tools and management and advisory services. Members buy subscriptions to its programs and participate in research efforts. Programs typically include research studies seminars customized reports and decision-support tools. The firm was founded in 1979 as the Research Council of Washington.

Operations

The company has counted among its members such industry leaders as The Cleveland Clinic Johns Hopkins Hospital Massachusetts General Hospital and Johnson & Johnson.

Advisory Board spinoff The Corporate Executive Board operates on a similar membership business model serving companies in a variety of industries. The Corporate Executive Board and The Advisory Board collaborate on projects and have agreed to refrain from competing in core business areas.

Geographic Reach

The Advisory Board Company has six regional offices in the US as well as offices in Europe and Asia serving international members.

Strategy

The Advisory Board hopes to grow not only by adding members particularly from outside the US but also by selling additional services to existing members. It also plans to continue to add to its list of programs. Since 2001 it has added almost 40 programs to its list of offerings and it plans to launch about three to four new programs each year.

The program-membership business model distinguishes The Advisory Board from many of its competitors —consulting firms that are hired on a job-by-job basis. Benefits for The Advisory Board include the ability to spread program costs over a growing membership base and the opportunity to involve members in identifying issues and conducting research.

Sales and Marketing

The company's sales force consists of more than 150 new business development teams that are responsible for selling new memberships. Each new business development team generally consists of two employees: one marketer who travels to prospective members to meet in person and one marketing associate who provides support from the office. The two-person new business development teams sell programs to new members as well as cross-sell additional programs to existing members of other programs. Separate member services teams are responsible for servicing and renewing existing memberships.

Financial Analysis

Revenue increased more than 30% and net income increased by more than 36% in 2012 compared to 2011. The increase in revenue was due to growth in the healthcare and education markets that year. Net income increased due to the growth in revenue as well as a gain on the sale of its OptiLink business.

The company's cash flow increased by $61.1 million in 2012 over 2011 thanks to financing activities including the exercise of stock options the issuance of common stock under its employee stock purchase plan and tax benefits resulting from the exercise of employee options.

Mergers and Acquisitions

In addition to rolling out new programs the company sees acquisitions as a means for achieving growth. In 2012 it purchased PivotHealth a physician practice management firm for nearly $20 million. It made the acquisition to to supplement its existing physician practice management capabilities while leveraging PivotHealth's expertise in long-term physician practice management.

The Advisory Board in 2011 acquired Cielo MedSolutions a provider of population management analytics and patient registry software in the ambulatory environment for nearly $12 million. It bought Cielo to enhance its existing suite of physician performance management solutions. The purchase added analytics and workflow tools that give providers visibility to patients and enable appropriate clinical decisions.

In 2010 it acquired Concuity the health care division of Trintech Group PLC. Concuity makes billing and recovery software catering to health care providers. The deal strengthened its revenue cycle management capabilities by allowing it to offer a more scalable Web-based software used for improving its customers' financial performance. The Advisory Board in 2009 obtained Southwind a consulting firm with expertise in physician employment clinical integration and information technology deployment practices.

EXECUTIVES

Executive Vice President Sales, Scott Schirmeier
President, David L. Felsenthal, age 43, $450,000 total compensation

CFO, Michael T. Kirshbaum, age 37, $320,833 total compensation
Chairman and CEO, Robert W. Musslewhite, age 44, $556,250 total compensation
CEO, David Kapaska
Medical Director, William Lynagh
Vice President Crimson Market Advantage, Kyle Rose
Vice President Information Technology, Steve Baxter
Vp Products, Jordan Silvergleid
Vice President Financial Operations, John Gallagher
Senior Vice President, Dennis Shin
Executive Vice President Member, Chris Denby
Southwind Vice President, Susan Neves
Executive Vice President Strategy, James C Bonnette
Vice President, Ken Keller
Executive Vice President Head Of Strategy Consulting, Jim Bonnette
Owner Senior Vice President, Shazad Razman
Chairman and CEO, Robert W. Musslewhite, age 44
Auditors: Ernst&YoungLLP

LOCATIONS

HQ: Advisory Board Company (The)
2445 M Street, N.W., Washington, DC 20037
Phone: 202 266-5600
Web: www.advisory.com

2014 Sales

	$ mil.	% of total
US	504.2	97
Other countries	16.4	3
Total	**520.6**	**100**

PRODUCTS/OPERATIONS

2014 Sales

	% of total
Healthcare	93
Education	7
Total	**100**

Selected Products and Services

Best practices installation and support
Business intelligence and analytics
Clinical research
Daily briefings and news
Executive education
Executive watches
Leadership development
Online advisory resources
Strategy and operations research
Workforce performance

COMPETITORS

Accenture	Huron Consulting
Accretive Health	IMS Health
Booz Allen	McKesson
Boston Consulting	McKinsey & Company
Conference Board	MedAssets
Deloitte Consulting	Navigant Consulting
Emdeon	Premier Inc.

HISTORICAL FINANCIALS

Company Type: Public

Income Statement

FYE: March 31

	REVENUE ($ mil.)	NET INCOME ($ mil.)	NET PROFIT MARGIN	EMPLOYEES
03/14	520.6	24.7	4.8%	2,800
03/13	450.8	22.1	4.9%	2,400
03/12	370.3	25.2	6.8%	1,850
03/11	290.2	18.5	6.4%	1,600
03/10	239.3	11.4	4.8%	1,100
Annual Growth	**21.4%**	**21.3%**	**—**	**26.3%**

2014 Year-End Financials

Debt ratio: —	No. of shares (mil.): 36
Return on equity: 8.0%	Dividends
Cash ($ mil.): 23	Yield: —
Current ratio: 0.89	Payout: —
Long-term debt ($ mil.): —	Market value ($ mil.): 2,334

	STOCK PRICE ($) FY Close	P/E High/Low		PER SHARE ($) Earnings	Dividends	Book Value
03/14	64.25	101	65	0.67	0.00	9.29
03/13	52.52	153	64	0.61	0.00	8.01
03/12	88.62	116	60	0.73	0.00	6.43
03/11	51.50	89	53	0.57	0.00	4.64
03/10	31.50	90	44	0.37	0.00	3.61
Annual Growth	**19.5%**	**—**	**—**	**16.4%**	**—**	**26.7%**

Aegion Corp

Aegion owns a legion of companies that aim to prop up aging highways bridges and pipes. Its energy- and mining-focused companies –Bayou Corrpro CCSI CRTS and United Pipeline —rehab pipelines and provide corrosion protection for pipes storage tanks and water treatment facilities. Insituform the water and wastewater unit refurbishes water distribution stormwater and wastewater pipes in situ that is without digging them up. Its commercial and structural reinforcement firm Fyfe makes the Tyfo and Fibrwrap brands of support and strengthening systems for masonry steel concrete and wooden structures. Aegion which has more than 20 global offices was formed in 2011 as a holding company.

Geographic Reach

The US is Aegion's largest market accounting of nearly 60% of its revenue. Canada accounts for more than 15% followed by Europe with less than 10%. The company's Energy and Mining segment is active in the US Canada Mexico South America the Middle East and Europe.

Operations

Aegion's largest business is Energy & Mining representing about 50% of total revenue. The global operation conducts business in the US through subsidiaries in Colorado Louisiana Texas and Oklahoma. Overseas Aegion's Hockway unit is located in the United Arab Emirates and the firm has other subsidiaries in the UK Portugal Argentina Brazil and Chile.

The company's North American Water and Wastewater unit (about 30% of revenue) has counterparts in Europe and Asia which combined contribute about 10% of sales. The firm's Commercial and Structural operations rehabilitate and strengthen pipelines buildings bridges tunnels and waterfront structures in the US and Canada. Aegion's Fyfe subsidiary provides product and engineering services in Latin America and the Asia-Pacific Region.

Financial Performance

Aegion's revenue topped $1 billion in 2012 a 10% increase compared with 2011. Net income rose 105% to $56.8 billion over the same period. 2012 marked the fourth consecutive year of increasing revenue for the firm. Growth of its Energy and Mining business drove Aegion's results in 2012 as did additional revenue from the acquisitions of CRTS Hockway and Fyfe. Partially offsetting the gains from Energy and Mining were losses across all of the company's Water and Wastewater operations.

Strategy

While about three-quarters of the company's revenue comes from North America it has been actively expanding into other regions since it feels the growth opportunities are low in the region due to its market penetration and the slow US economy. Australia India and Singapore are on Aegion's radar as potential growth markets for its water and wastewater group while energy and mining looks to Saudi Arabia Morocco and offshore in the Gulf of Mexico. Since its commercial and structural group is the smallest and newest the company sees great growth potential as the unit makes its fiber-reinforced polymer system known to engineers.

Mergers and Acquisitions

Aegion in June 2013 acquired oil-and-gas services provider Brinderson LP for $150 million. Brinderson provides maintenance construction engineering and turnaround activities for the upstream and downstream oil and gas markets primarily in California. The purchase bolstered Aegion's Energy and Mining business.

The 2011 purchase of the North American operations of Fyfe Group LLC contributed to the launch of Aegion's fast-growing Commercial and Structural business segment. The acquisition brought Fyfe's highway bridge and pipeline reinforcement systems into the Aegion fold. In 2012 the firm acquired Fyfe's operations in Asia Europe and Latin America.

In 2011 Aegion had added UK pipe coating maker Hockway and its Hockway Middle East unit to Corrpro.

EXECUTIVES

Vice President, Daniel Cowan, age 38
Svp And Treasurer, Kenneth L (Ken) Young, age 63
Vice President, Dorwin Hawn, age 68
EVP General Counsel and Chief Administrative Officer, David F. Morris, age 52, $377,000 total compensation
President Infrastructure Solutions, Thomas E. (Tom) Vossman, age 52
President and CEO, Charles R. (Chuck) Gordon, age 55
EVP and CFO, David A. Martin, $357,000 total compensation
President Corrosion Protection, Greta Senn
President Energy Services, Russell Conda
CTO, David H. Kroon
V Pres Hr, Laura Villa
Senior Vice President Human Resrcs Chro, Jack Owczarczak
Vp Business Integration, Dwane Ruiz
Vice President, Daniel Gamboa
Vp Business Integration, Justine Macdonald
Auditors: PricewaterhouseCoopersLLP

LOCATIONS

HQ: Aegion Corp
17988 Edison Avenue, Chesterfield, MO 63005-1195
Phone: 636 530-8000
Web: www.insituform.com

2012 Sales

	$ mil.	% of total
US	600.2	58
Canada	180.3	18
Europe	86.9	8
Other countries	160.6	16
Total	**1028.0**	**100**

PRODUCTS/OPERATIONS

2012 Sales

	$ mil.	% of total
Energy & mining	525.1	51
North American water &wastewater	317.3	31
Commercial & structural	74.5	7
European water &wastewater	72.6	7
Asia-Pacific water &wastewater	38.5	4
Total	**1028.0**	**100**

COMPETITORS

Aquarius Coatings	Northern Technologies
Bodycote	Praxair
Cohesant	RPM International
Daubert Industries	Severn Trent Services
Holloman	Sterling Construction
Jones Bros.	Willbros
MPW	

HISTORICAL FINANCIALS

Company Type: Public

Income Statement

FYE: December 31

	REVENUE ($ mil.)	NET INCOME ($ mil.)	NET PROFIT MARGIN	EMPLOYEES
12/13	1,091.4	45.5	4.2%	5,400
12/12	1,027.9	56.8	5.5%	3,400
12/11	938.5	27.6	2.9%	3,000
12/10	914.9	61.8	6.8%	3,200
12/09	726.8	26.1	3.6%	3,000
Annual Growth	**10.7%**	**14.9%**	**—**	**15.8%**

2013 Year-End Financials

Debt ratio: 28.5%	No. of shares (mil.): 37
Return on equity: 6.4%	Dividends
Cash ($ mil.): 158	Yield: —
Current ratio: 2.74	Payout: —
Long-term debt ($ mil.): 366	Market value ($ mil.): 831

	STOCK PRICE ($) FY Close	P/E High/Low	PER SHARE ($) Earnings	Dividends	Book Value
12/13	21.89	22 18	1.13	0.00	18.68
12/12	22.19	17 11	1.33	0.00	17.95
12/11	15.34	45 16	0.67	0.00	16.28
12/10	26.51	18 12	1.53	0.00	15.44
12/09	22.72	34 17	0.70	0.00	13.82
Annual Growth	**(0.9%)**	**— —**	**12.7%**	**—**	**7.8%**

Affiliated Managers Group Inc.

AMG knows a good asset when it sees one. Affiliated Managers Group (AMG) is an asset management company that owns interests in more than 30 boutique investment management firms in the North America Europe and Asia. Together the company's affiliates manage approximately $625 billion in assets and offer more than 400 investment products including more than 200 mutual funds. AMG typically acquires majority stakes in its affiliates which cater to institutional investors and wealthy individuals. The structure allows affiliates to retain partial ownership of their firms and operate with relative autonomy. AMG usually allocates a percentage of revenues to affiliates for operating expenses such as compensation.

Geographic Reach

Massachusetts-headquartered AMG has offices in Conshohocken Pennsylvania; Norwalk Connecticut; Chicago; Sydney Australia; Toronto; Zurich; Hong Kong; and Dubai.

Financial Performance

The buoyant stock market in 2013 helped propel AMG's revenue to a record high of nearly $2.2 billion. Indeed the company's revenue has more than doubled since 2009 when asset values tanked during the financial crisis. Revenue increased 21% in 2013 versus 2012 driven by an increase in assets under management from investment performance net client cash flows and the full-year impact of 2012 investments in new affiliates. The mutual fund channel outperformed other channels. Net income jumped 107% over the same period to $360.5 million on higher revenue and increased income from equity method investments.

AMG's assets under management increased 24% in 2013 over 2012 to $537.3 billion.

Strategy

Key to AMG's business strategy is growth in the US where it's focusing on the US retail market. To this end in early 2014 the company rebranded its US domestic retail distribution business as AMG Funds and the alignment of Aston Asset Management (acquired in 2010) within the AMG Funds business by acquiring the remaining equity of Aston that it didn't already own. (AMG purchased a majority interest in Chicago-based Aston Asset Management by acquiring Aston's parent company Highbury Financial. Aston is the principal adviser to the Aston Funds a family of about 25 mutual funds with some $6 billion of assets.)

In 2011 AMG diversified its service offerings by establishing a wealth management arm (10% of annual revenue). AMG Wealth Partners handles the needs of high-net-worth clients. The subsidiary intends to expand AMG's partnership strategy by acquiring boutique wealth management firms. In 2012 AMG made its first wealth management investment by taking an equity stake in Veritable L.P. which has $10 billion under management.

After entering the Asian market in 2009 with a modest 5% stake in Value Partners Group a Hong-Kong based boutique asset manager AMG is continuing to make acquisitions there. In 2014 it acquired Asian equity manager Veritas Asset Management. The company opened a sales and marketing office in Hong Kong and hired a director of business development for Europe's Nordic region. The following year AMG opened a sales and marketing office in Dubai to focus on the Mid-

dle East. AMG also has offices in London Sydney. Clients outside the US now account for more than half of AMG's assets under management and almost 40% its revenue.

Acquisitions have helped boost AMG's total assets under management and in turn its revenue from asset-based fees and transaction fees.

Mergers and Acquisitions

In June 2014 AMG acquired Louisville Kentucky-based River Road Asset Management from Aviva Investors North America Holdings Inc. (a subsidiary of Aviva plc). In March 2014 the firm purchased a majority equity stake in SouthernSun Asset Management LLC. With some $6 billion in assets under management SouthernSun manages long-term concentrated portfolios through a fundamental research-intensive investment process.

To further expand in the Asian market AMG in April 2014 purchased a majority equity interest in Veritas Asset Management LLC. With offices in London and Hong Kong Veritas manages approximately Â10 billion ($17 billion) across both funds and segregated portfolios for institutional and retail investors in the UK and around the world.

In July 2012 AMG acquired a majority stake in Austin Texas-based Yacktman Asset Management with approximately $17 billion of assets under management.

EXECUTIVES

Vice President Affiliate Development, Jennifer Borggaard
Vice President Finance, Peter Maceen
Vp Affiliate Mktg, Dean J Patenaude, age 52
Senior Vice President Finance And Accounting, Daniel Shea
Vice President Finance And Accounting, Aaron Galis
Vice President New Investments, Riz Jamal
Vp And Senior Counsel Legal And Compliance, Claire Manning
Vice President Affiliate Development, Benjamin Scott
President; Chief Operating Officer, Nathaniel Dalton, age 47, $500,000 total compensation
Chairman and CEO, Sean M. Healey, age 52, $750,000 total compensation
Chief Financial Officer, Jay C. Horgen, age 44, $500,000 total compensation
Executive Vice President and Head of Global Distribution, Andrew Dyson, $334,889 total compensation
EVP and General Counsel, David M. Billings
Vice President Corporate Strategy And Investor Relations, Alexandra Lynn
Senior Vice President, John Benvenuto
Vice President Affiliate Development, Jeff Murphy
Chairman and CEO, Sean M. Healey, age 52
Vice Chairman, John Kingston, age 48
Auditors: PricewaterhouseCoopersLLP

LOCATIONS

HQ: Affiliated Managers Group Inc.
600 Hale Street, P.O. Box 1000, Prides Crossing, Prides Crossing, MA 01965
Phone: 617 747-3300

PRODUCTS/OPERATIONS

2013 Sales by segment

	$ mil.	% of total
Mutual funds	1023.0	47
Institutional	948.7	43
High-net-worth clients	217.1	10
Total	**2188.8**	**100**

COMPETITORS

AllianceBernstein
Asset Alliance
Bank of America
Conning
FMR
Federated Investors
GAMCO Investors
National Financial
  Partners

Neuberger Berman
Nuveen
Old Mutual (US)
T. Rowe Price
The Vanguard Group
U.S. Trust
Virtus Investment
  Partners

HISTORICAL FINANCIALS

Company Type: Public

Income Statement

FYE: December 31

	REVENUE ($ mil.)	NET INCOME ($ mil.)	NET PROFIT MARGIN	EMPLOYEES
12/13	2,188.8	360.5	16.5%	2,500
12/12	1,805.5	174.0	9.6%	2,230
12/11	1,704.8	164.9	9.7%	2,020
12/10	1,358.2	138.6	10.2%	1,910
12/09	841.8	59.4	7.1%	1,580
Annual Growth	27.0%	56.9%	—	12.2%

2013 Year-End Financials

Debt ratio: 13.6%
Return on equity: 17.0%
Cash ($ mil.): 469
Current ratio: 2.35
Long-term debt ($ mil.): 865

No. of shares (mil.): 53
Dividends
  Yield: —
  Payout: —
Market value ($ mil.): 11,690

	STOCK PRICE ($) FY Close	P/E High/Low	PER SHARE ($) Earnings	Dividends	Book Value
12/13	216.88	32 19	6.55	0.00	39.60
12/12	130.15	39 29	3.28	0.00	38.67
12/11	95.95	35 23	3.11	0.00	34.62
12/10	99.22	35 20	2.81	0.00	33.37
12/09	67.35	51 20	1.38	0.00	24.23
Annual Growth	34.0%	— —	47.6%	—	13.1%

Air Lease Corp

Air Lease doesn't really lease air unless of course you include the air inside the cabins of its fleet of airplanes. An aircraft leasing company Air Lease buys new and used commercial aircraft from manufacturers and airlines and then leases to airline carriers in Europe the Asia-Pacific region and the Americas. Its fleet is primarily made up of about 45 narrowbody and widebody Boeing and Airbus passenger airplanes that it leases to Air China (15% of revenues) Air Italy (11%) Air France (10%) and other major carriers. In addition to leasing Air Lease also offers fleet management services such as lease management and sales.

Geographic Reach

Air Lease serves customers in Asia-Pacific Western Europe Eastern Europe South America and the Middle East. Weste Urope accounted for 40% of the company's 2013.

Sales and Marketing

Its customers include Air Canada; Sunwing Airlines; WestJet; AeroMexico; Aeromar; Interjet; Volaris; Hawaiian Airlines; Southwest Airlines; Spirit Airlines; Sun Country; United Continental Holdings; Liat Airline; and Caribbean-Airlines.

Financial Performance

In 2013 its sales increased by 31% driven by a 30% rise in flight equipment rental revenues due to increased aircraft count and the leasing of additional aircraft. Aircraft sales trading and other revenues also rose in 2013.Air Lease posted a 44% increase in net income in 2013 driven by increased sales and lower stock-based compensations partially offset by higher operating expenses (including interest expense and amortization of discounts and deferred debt issue costs).The company's cash from operating activities in 2013 was $654.2 million (compared to $491 million in 2012). This increase was driven by higher revenues and net income coupled with a decrease in stock-based compensation.

Strategy

Although the largest portion of its fleet is leased to customers in Western Europe Air Lease is setting its sights on markets in the Asia-Pacific region Eastern Europe South America and the Middle East where it predicts the travel industry will grow the fastest in coming years. It has also targeted carriers in stable but slower-growing travel markets such as North America.

The company has ordered new narrowbody and widebody commercial jet transport aircraft in bulk directly from the manufacturers to minimize the acquisition price while enhancing its technology and fuel efficiency.

In 2014 Air Lease and Air New Zealand announced an agreement for five new Airbus A320 aircraft.

Air Lease introduced its first ATR-600 in Mexico in 2013.

Company Background

Air Lease went public in 2011. Udvar-H¯zy and other Air Lease used a significant portion of the proceeds raised to acquire additional aircraft and for general corporate purposes. With sufficient capital and financing already in place Air Lease has placed orders for some 150 new aircraft to be delivered by 2017. While most of its fleet will consist of Boeing and Airbus passenger airplanes the company has ordered similar aircraft manufactured by Embraer and turboprops from Avions de Transport R gional (ATR).

Udvar-H¯zy had co-founded ILFC now one of the largest aircraft leasing companies in the industry in the 1970s. He stayed on after AIG bought ILFC in the 1990s and continued to head the company until 2010 when he retired in the wake of the ongoing financial trouble that hit AIG in 2008. Udvar-H¯zy subsequently founded Air Lease with the help of institutional investors including some that were large shareholders prior to the IPO's filing (Ares Management which held an 11% stake; Leonard Green & Partners 11%; and Commonwealth Bank of Australia 10%). Udvar-H¯zy maintained a 7% stake in Air Lease in 2013.

EXECUTIVES

Evp, Alex A Khatibi, age 54
President Chief Operating Officer, Molly Kostka
Svp Aircraft Procurement And Specification, John D Poerschke, age 53
Senior Vice President, Toby Maccary
Senior Vice President, Kishore Korde
Evp, Grant A Levy, age 52
Executive Vice President, Marc H Baer, age 50
Vice President Finance Chief Accounting Officer, Gregory B Willis, age 36
Assistant Vice President, Czar Vigil
Vice President Technical Asset Management, Pierce Chang
Executive Vice President Gen, Carol Forsyte
Assistant Vice President Controller, Ardy Ghanbar
Senior Vice President, Robert McNitt
Assistant Vice President, Sara Evans
Auditors: KPMGLLP

LOCATIONS

HQ: Air Lease Corp
  2000 Avenue of the Stars, Suite 1000N, Los Angeles, CA 90067
Phone: 310 553-0555
Web: www.airleasecorp.com

2013 Sales

	% of sales
Asia/Pacific	40
Europe	26
Central America South America & Mexico	15
US & Canada	10
The Middle East & Africa	9
Total	**100**

PRODUCTS/OPERATIONS

2013 Sales

	$ mil.	% of total
Flight equipment rentals	836.5	97
Interest & other	22.2	3
Total	**858.7**	**100**

COMPETITORS

AerCap
Aircastle
Aviation Capital Group
Boeing Capital
CIT Transportation
  Finance

Fly Leasing
GE Capital Aviation
  Services
ICON Capital
ILFC

HISTORICAL FINANCIALS

Company Type: Public

Income Statement

FYE: December 31

	REVENUE ($ mil.)	NET INCOME ($ mil.)	NET PROFIT MARGIN	EMPLOYEES
12/13	858.6	190.4	22.2%	63
12/12	655.7	131.9	20.1%	52
12/11	336.7	53.2	15.8%	47
12/10	58.3	(52.0)	—	34
Annual Growth	145.0%	—	—	22.8%

2013 Year-End Financials

Debt ratio: 62.7%
Return on equity: 7.8%
Cash ($ mil.): 270
Current ratio: 2.04
Long-term debt ($ mil.): 5,853

No. of shares (mil.): 101
Dividends
Yield: 0.3%
Payout: 5.8%
Market value ($ mil.): 3,165

	STOCK PRICE ($) FY Close	P/E High/Low		PER SHARE ($) Earnings	Dividends	Book Value
12/13	31.08	18	11	1.80	0.11	24.78
12/12	21.50	20	14	1.28	0.00	23.04
12/11	23.71	50	30	0.59	0.00	21.61
12/10	0.00	—	—	(1.32)	0.00	18.73
Annual Growth	—	—	—	—	—	9.8%

Air Methods Corp.

It's a bird it's a plane ... it's an ambulance! With a fleet of more than 400 medically equipped aircraft mainly helicopters Air Methods is the largest provider of emergency medical air-transportation services in the US. The company operates through three divisions. A community-based operating segment which represents roughly 60% of revenues offers transportation and in-flight medical care from hubs in some two dozen states. A hospital-based segment contracts with hospitals in 30 states to transport critically ill patients; the hospitals themselves provide in-flight medical personnel. The smallest division United Rotorcraft designs manufactures and installs aircraft medical-transport products.

Financial Analysis

Despite a slow economy Air Methods is maintaining a near three-decade-long positive trajectory. In 2010 the company posted more than a 50% year-over-year rise in earnings. The next year the company posted historic totals in both revenue (which increased by almost 18% to $660.5 million) and profits (spiking 9% to $46.7 million).

Its 2011 growth was driven by a 26% increase in flight revenues attributable to the company's mainstay business community-based services (CBS). CBS revenues which benefited from price increases the addition of bases and new service agreements helped to offset a 20% increase in flight center costs related to higher workers compensation and expenses made from acquisitions.

Strategy

Business acquisitions are part of the company's strategy to gain market share. It acquired Las Vegas helicopter tour operator Sundance Helicopters for $44 million in late 2012. Sundance offers helicopter services to support efforts in fire fighting natural resource agency operations vertical lifts

and news gathering and it generated $52 million in revenue for its fiscal year ended March 2012.

Air Methods spent approximately $200 million in mid-2011 to take over OF Air Holdings Corporation owned by Wind Point Partners. The move secured all of its subsidiaries including rival Omniflight Helicopters a Texas-based air medical transport service (comprising both community-based and hospital-based business) spanning 18 states and 75-base locations. On the heels of acquiring Omniflight Air Methods bought out Texas-based United Rotorcraft Solutions a full-service helicopter and fixed-wing completions and maintenance repair operation.

EXECUTIVES

CEO and Director, Aaron D. Todd, age 52, $521,655 total compensation
CFO Secretary and Treasurer, Trent J. Carman, age 53, $314,569 total compensation
President Domestic Air Medical Services, Michael D. Allen, $348,005 total compensation
VP Information Technology, Doni Perry
Director Operations, Dennis McCall
President Sundance Helicopters, Jay Francis
Interim President Tourism Division, Bob Engelbrecht
Senior Vice President Aviation Services, Archie Gray
Western I Vice President, John Heiskell
Vice President Safety, Ed Stockhausen
Vice President, Crystal L Gordon
Senior Vice President Western Operations, Jonathan Collier
Svp-process Improvement, Kevin Campbell
Svp-human Resources, Allison Farish
Vice President Of Operations Lifenet, Richard Frazer
Regional Vice President, Kevin Stanhope
Regional Vice President, Chris Burns
Vice President Human Resources, Joann Bailey
Vice President, Kyle Williams
Senior Vice President, Bill Smoot
Executive Assistant To Senior Vice President Of Aviation Services, Jennifer Peasley
Regional Vice President, Dan Keough
Vice President Clinical Services, Tina Giangrasso
Medical Director, Mike Presley
Vice President Of Corporate Development, Craig Yale
Senior Vice President Patient Business Services, Mark Keene
Board Member, Ralph Bernstein
CEO and Director, Aaron D. Todd, age 52
CFO Secretary and Treasurer, Trent J. Carman, age 53
Chairman, C. David Kikumoto, age 64
Board Member, David Roehr
Auditors: KPMGLLP

LOCATIONS

HQ: Air Methods Corp.
7301 South Peoria, Englewood, CO 80112
Phone: 303 792-7400
Web: www.airmethods.com

PRODUCTS/OPERATIONS

2011 Sales

	$ mil.	% of total
Community-based services (CBS)	432.0	63
Hospital-based services (HBS)	198.3	29
United Rotorcraft	57.4	8
Adjustments	(27.2)	-
Total	660.5	100

COMPETITORS

Acadian Ambulance Service Inc.
Bristow Group Inc
CHC Group
Evergreen Holdings
PHI Inc.

HISTORICAL FINANCIALS

Company Type: Public

Income Statement

FYE: December 31

	REVENUE ($ mil.)	NET INCOME ($ mil.)	NET PROFIT MARGIN	EMPLOYEES
12/13	881.6	62.3	7.1%	4,227
12/12	850.8	93.1	10.9%	3,961
12/11	660.5	46.5	7.1%	3,935
12/10	562.0	44.1	7.8%	2,960
12/09	510.6	28.9	5.7%	2,942
Annual Growth	14.6%	21.1%	—	9.5%

2013 Year-End Financials

Debt ratio: 54.0%
Return on equity: 18.6%
Cash ($ mil.): 9
Current ratio: 2.10
Long-term debt ($ mil.): 608

No. of shares (mil.): 39
Dividends
Yield: —
Payout: —
Market value ($ mil.): 2,276

	STOCK PRICE ($) FY Close	P/E High/Low		PER SHARE ($) Earnings	Dividends	Book Value
12/13	58.26	38	21	1.54	0.00	9.42
12/12	36.91	50	33	2.39	7.00	7.73
12/11	84.45	72	41	1.21	0.00	7.53
12/10	56.27	48	22	1.17	0.00	6.50
12/09	33.62	45	17	0.78	0.00	5.26
Annual Growth	14.7%	—	—	18.7%	—	15.7%

Akamai Technologies Inc

Akamai offers an accelerated course on digital delivery. The company's technology enables corporations and government agencies to deliver digital content and applications such as ads business transaction tools streaming video and websites over the Internet. It also offers applications that supply network data feeds and website analytics to customers. With a network of more than 137000 servers in 87 countries around the world Akamai analyzes and manages Web traffic transmitting content from servers that are geographically closest to end users. In addition to its 11 US offices the company has more than 25 international locations. Customers include Apple Hitachi and SAP.

Operations

The company has five different core products - AQUA Web Solutions AURA Network Solutions KONA Security Solutions SOLA Media Solutions and TERRA Enterprise Solutions - that provide application and cloud performance services digital media and software distribution and storage website optimization and security tools.

For example AQUA WEB Solutions speeds up applications using compression connection optimization dynamic caching and routing technologies. It is tailored for such online applications as airline reservation systems course planning tools customer order processing and human resources.

KONA is a suite of services and software used to guard against data theft and other Web attacks while SOLA enables streaming live or on-demand HD video to online viewers across several technologies including Adobe Flash Microsoft Silverlight and Apple iOS.

Geographic Reach

Akamai operates from about 40 offices in 25 countries across the Americas Asia and Europe. The US however is its largest market accounting for about 70% of sales. The company has about a dozen US locations.

Sales and Marketing

The comp any sells its products through a direct sales force as well as more than 100 channel partners such as AT&T IBM Verizon and Spain's top telco Telefonica. It does business with a large number of private and public sector customers; no one accounts for more than 10% of sales.

Financial Performance

Overall sales grew almost 20% in 2012 reaching a record $1.3 billion. That year the company cited robust growth in traffic from clients in the media and entertainment industries as they consume more bandwidth to feed increasing amounts of digital content to wireless devices. Akamai also saw sales to companies in a variety of other industries rise as more enterprises turn to hosted applications outsourced IT systems management and other cloud-based services.

Profits only increased slightly (2%) to $203 million as the company spent an additional $77 million on sales and marketing expenses - primarily from paying commissions to salespeople.

Mergers and Acquisitions

Akamai uses acquisitions to supplement its internal product development efforts particularly in the area of optimizing Web page and data delivery to the growing number of mobile devices tapping the Internet.

In 2012 it made four acquisitions. The largest was Cotendo a provider of Web and mobile acceleration services for about $268 million. It also bought Blaze Software a developer of Web optimization applications to complement its website acceleration products with technology designed to maximize the speed at which a Web page is rendered. Later in the year it bought network optimization software provider FastSoft and Verivue which offers licensed content delivery network (CDN) infrastructure services for network operators.

Also that year it sold its Advertising Decision Solutions (ADS) data cooperative to media-buying platform MediaMath. As part of the deal MediaMath has exclusive rights to its pixel-free technology for use within digital advertising and marketing applications.

In 2013 Akamai bought Velocius Networks a provider of quality of service (QoS) technology that optimizes traffic to keep networks from running slowing for remote end-users. The acquisition is expected to complement Akamai's hybrid cloud optimization strategy for optimizing IP application traffic.

EXECUTIVES

EVP; General Counsel and Secretary, Melanie Haratunian, age 54, $399,192 total compensation
President Products and Development, Rick M. McConnell, age 48, $499,031 total compensation
CEO, Tom (Tom) Leighton, age 57
President Worldwide Operations, Robert W. (Bob) Hughes, age 47, $499,054 total compensation
SVP and General Manager Web Experience Division, Michael M. (Mike) Afergan

VP and General Manager Carrier Products Division, Mick Scully
SVP and CIO, Kumud Kalia
SVP Networks and Operations, Robert Blumofe
EVP and CFO, Jim Benson, $392,731 total compensation
SVP and General Manager Americas, Jim Ebzery
SVP and General Manager APJ, Sanjay Singh
SVP and General Manager Emerging Products Division, Willie Tejada
SVP and General Manager Media Products Division, Bill Wheaton
SVP and General ManagerEMEA, Doug Tilford
SVP Networks and Chief Network Architect, Noam Freedman
SVP and General Manager Security Division, Stuart Scholly
Vice President, Sanjay Acharya
Regional Vice President And Country Manager Centra, Michael Heuer
Vice President Of Engineering Security, Ohad Parush
Vice President Of Marketing, John Tenore
Apj Vice President, Micheal McCollough
Vice President Digital Media, Dwight Rees
Vice President Media Platform Optmization, Keith Oslakovic
Vice Presidenthuman Resources Operations, Susan Lapointe
Vice Chairman, Paul L. Sagan, age 55
Chairman, George H. Conrades, age 76
Auditors: PricewaterhouseCoopersLLP

LOCATIONS

HQ: Akamai Technologies Inc
150 Broadway, Cambridge, MA 02142
Phone: 617 444-3000   **Fax:** 617 444-3001
Web: www.akamai.com

2014 Sales

	% of total
US	73
Other regions	27
Total	**100**

PRODUCTS/OPERATIONS

2014 Sales

% million		% of total
Media Delivery Solutions	917.4	47
Performance & Security Solutions	900.7	46
Service and Support Solutions	145.8	7
Total	**1963.9**	**100**

Selected Products

Terra
  Alta
Aqua
  Aqua Ion
  Aqua Ion Mobile
  Dynamic Site Accelerator
Sola
  Sola Media Experience
  Sola Software Distribution
Kona
  Site Defender
  Web Application Firewall
Aura
  Aura Accelerated Network Partner Program
  Managed CDN
  Licensed CDN

Selected Acquisitions

2013
Velocius Networks (Quality of Service (QoS) technology)
2012
Blaze Software ($19.3 million; frontend (FEO) technology)
Cotendo ($278 million; Web & mobile acceleration software)

FastSoft ($14.4 million; content acceleration software)
Verivue ($30.9 million; high-performance IP platforms)

COMPETITORS

Brilliant Digital Entertainment	Level 3 Communications
CDNeworks Co.	Limelight
Digital River	MediaMind
EyeWonder	Mirror Image Internet
Internap Network Services	NaviSite
	NeuStar
	Onstream Media

HISTORICAL FINANCIALS

Company Type: Public

Income Statement

FYE: December 31

	REVENUE ($ mil.)	NET INCOME ($ mil.)	NET PROFIT MARGIN	EMPLOYEES
12/13	1,577.9	293.4	18.6%	3,908
12/12	1,373.9	203.9	14.8%	3,074
12/11	1,158.5	200.9	17.3%	2,380
12/10	1,023.5	171.2	16.7%	2,200
12/09	859.7	145.9	17.0%	1,750
Annual Growth	**16.4%**	**19.1%**	**—**	**22.2%**

2013 Year-End Financials

Debt ratio: —
Return on equity: 11.8%
Cash ($ mil.): 333
Current ratio: 3.91
Long-term debt ($ mil.): —

No. of shares (mil.): 178
Dividends
  Yield: —
  Payout: —
Market value ($ mil.): 8,425

	STOCK PRICE ($) FY Close	P/E High/Low	PER SHARE ($) Earnings	Dividends	Book Value
12/13	47.18	32 20	1.61	0.00	14.72
12/12	40.91	36 24	1.12	0.00	13.19
12/11	32.28	48 17	1.07	0.00	12.15
12/10	47.05	56 25	0.90	0.00	11.67
12/09	25.34	30 15	0.78	0.00	10.15
Annual Growth	**16.8%**	**— —**	**19.9%**	**—**	**9.7%**

Akorn Inc

Akorn has its roots firmly planted in the pharmaceutical industry. The firm makes and sells branded and generic drugs in therapeutic and diagnostic categories including ophthalmology injectables and specialty therapeutics. Akorn's ophthalmic segment includes antibiotics steroids glaucoma treatments and diagnostic stains and dyes as well as prescription and OTC eye care products. The firm's injectable and hospital-administered therapeutics segment includes anti-infectives antidotes anesthesia agents pain management drugs and other specialty substances. Akorn also provides contract drug manufacturing services. Chairman John Kapoor is the company's largest shareholder owning a one-third stake in Akorn.

Geographic Reach

Akorn has manufacturing plants in the US (one in Illinois one in New York and one in New Jersey) and India and nearly all of its revenues come from sales in the US market. The company also operates a Research and Development center in Vernon Hills Illinois and a distribution warehouse in Gurnee Illinois.

Operations

The company's largest operating segment is ophthalmics which brings in about 36% of annual revenues followed by hospital drugs and injectables which together account for 57% of sales. Many of Akorn's products are generic drugs licensed from external sources though it is working to increase the number of internally developed products in both the branded and generic categories. The company manufactures a variety of pharmaceutical products for third party pharmaceutical customers based on their specifications. Contract services accounted for 7% of Akorn's revenues in 2013.Through subsidiary Advanced Vision Research the company makes and markets a line of over-the-counter (OTC) ophthalmic products for the treatment of dry eye under the TheraTears brand name as well as a portfolio of private label OTC ophthalmic products.

Sales and Marketing

Akorn's products are sold nationally to hospitals physicians optometrists group purchasing organizations pharmacies and wholesalers via direct sales representatives and independent distributors. The company's three biggest customers accounting for about two-thirds of its 2013 sales are wholesalers Cardinal Health(23%) McKesson(16%) and AmerisourceBergen(19%).

Financial Performance

The company has reported year-to-year revenue growth since 2009. Revenues rose by 24% in 2013 due to primarily from increased sales of new and revived products which accounted for $48.5 million of the increase. Its hospital drugs & injectables saw a surge in the sales of new and revived products with more than half of the increase attributable to progesterone capsules and Td vaccine. Ophthalmic segment revenues grew due to increase in OTC product sales of TheraTears branded products and private label products and sales of products acquired late in 2013 from Merck. Contract services revenue also increased due to a rise in US contract services.Akorn's net income increased by 48% in 2013 due to a bargain purchase gain and a decline in interest expense related to a debt discount and to the change in fair value of its additional consideration of $15 million payable to Lundbeck (related to its acquisition of various injectable products from that company in 2011).Operating cash flow increased by $31 million in 2013 due to a decline in cash used in trade accounts receivable and inventories.

Strategy

In addition to regular growth through acquisitions Akorn is working to increase its internal product development efforts to speed up the time it takes to bring a new product to market (as well as to reduce its dependence on licensing deals and acquisitions).

Mergers and Acquisitions

In 2014 Akon acquired the US NDA rights to Zioptan (a prescription ophthalmic eye drop indicated for reducing elevated intraocular pressure in patients with open-angle glaucoma or ocular hypertension) from Merck Sharp and Dohme Corp. and the NDA rights to Betimol (a prescription ophthalmic eye drop for the reduction of eye pressure in glaucoma patients) from Japan-based Santen Pharmaceutical Co. Ltd.

In 2013 the company acquired from Merck the US rights to three branded ophthalmic products (AzaSite Cosopt and Cosopt PF) for $52.8 million. It began selling Cosopt and Cosopt PF at the end of 2013 and began selling AzaSite in early 2014. This acquisition allows Akorn to leverage its exist-

ing ophthalmic sales force and physician relationships.

Also in 2013 Akorn agreed to acquire Hi-Tech Pharmacal for some $640 million. The purchase will expand Akorn's development pipeline as well as its offerings of generic and branded OTC and prescription products. Hi-Tech Pharmacal makes a number of dosage forms including liquid semi-solid oral topical nasal spray and sterile ointments and gels.

HISTORY

Joseph Yazbeck founded Akorn in Metairie Louisiana in 1971; the name was chosen so the firm would appear near the front of alphabetical listings. Akorn initially distributed eye care products from various suppliers. In 1988 the firm went public. In 1989 Yazbeck retired (replaced by John Kapoor) and Akorn bought its first manufacturing facility from Irish drug company Norbrook Holdings; two years later after product recalls and a push from the FDA to modernize Akorn closed the facility. The company resumed manufacturing operations in 1992 with the purchase of Taylor Pharmaceuticals.

Akorn diversified in 1995 starting a surgical instrument repair unit and boosted its line of injectable drugs the next year. Akorn moved its headquarters from Louisiana to Illinois in 1997 and introduced a generic version of Merck's antiglaucoma drug Timoptic.

In 1998 Akorn increased earnings by acquiring eight new products including worldwide rights to Allergan's Fluress stain. The purchase of a manufacturing facility in New Jersey decreased dependency on outside suppliers. In 1999 Akorn partnered with CIBA Vision to market a generic form of that company's Ocupress glaucoma treatment. In 2000 the company sought permission to begin testing a treatment for age-related macular degeneration a leading cause of blindness in elderly people.

That same year the FDA issued a warning about problems at the company's manufacturing facility in Decatur Illinois. Additional inspections in 2002 2003 and 2004 revealed other "deviations" at the facility which the company has since responded to and corrected. These difficulties prevented Akorn from developing new products at Decatur for several years which had a significant impact on its business.

Arthur Przybyl resigned as CEO in 2009. The board then appointed newcomer Raj Rai as CEO in mid-2009.

Akorn decided in 2009 to exit the market for flu vaccine distribution. Biologics and vaccines previously accounted for about 40% of Akorn's sales in 2009. The company discontinued the rest of the division's operations (tetanus-diphtheria vaccines) in early 2010. The exit didn't impact Akorn's revenues as it increased sales within its other segments during 2009 and 2010.

The company centralized its R&D operations in early 2010 by opening a focused R&D center in Skokie Illinois; previously the company's internal research was performed at its two manufacturing plants.

A major boost in the ophthalmics segment came when Akorn entered the OTC eye care market through the 2011 purchase of Advanced Vision Research for some $26 million in cash. The purchase added such brands as TheraTears and MacuTrition. Akorn is already familiar with the products having been their primary contract manufacturer for several years. To round out its offer-

ings it plans to manufacture private label eye care products and license new products.

The company's generic injectables division experienced increased demand in 2011 (due to shortages of certain products in the US market) and in response Akorn decided to ride that wave by growing the segment's operations. To expand its portfolio of proprietary branded products Akorn acquired manufacturing and marketing rights for three injectable drugs from Danish firm Lundbeck for some $50 million that year (plus potential future milestone payments). The drugs include Nembutal a controversial drug used in lethal injection executions; Cogentin for Parkinson's disease symptoms; and Diuril a diuretic and antihypertensive medicine. To focus on its most profitable growth offerings the firm sold its stake in a portfolio of injectable products marketed with Strides Arcolab to Pfizer in 2011.

To increase its production of injectables Akorn acquired a compound of contract manufacturing facilities for sterile injectables from India-based Kilitch Drugs in a deal worth some $60 million in 2012. The purchase expandedAkorn's capabilities in emerging international markets and the firm plans to apply for FDA certification of the facility to boost its US offerings as well. As portions of the India facility are still under construction the purchase also provided future capacity for additional products including new ophthalmics and expansion into cancer drugs in both the US and international markets.

EXECUTIVES

Vice President, Abu S Alam
Senior Vice President Regulatory, Sam Boddapati
EVP Operations Global Quality Assurance and Technical Services, Mark M. Silverberg, age 61, $280,160 total compensation
SVP Global Sales and Marketing and National Accounts, John R. Sabat, age 65, $280,160 total compensation
CEO, Raj Rai, age 47
CFO, Timothy A. (Tim) Dick, age 44, $309,000 total compensation
COO, Pharm.D. Bruce Kutinsky, $313,685 total compensation
Vice President Business Development, Sean Brynjelsen
Vice President Of Sales And Marketing, Brett Novak
Vice President Information Technology, Bill Bradford
Vice President Soln Technical Support, Georgette Frank
Executive Vice President, Ramesh Acharya
Vice President Information Technology, Bradford Greg
Vp, William Alexander
Vice President, Pat Castelluzzo
Vice President Research And Development, Pati Biswajit
Chairman, John N. Kapoor
Board Member, Adrienne Graves
Board Member, Steven J Meyer, age 59
Board Member, Aleksey Milenkov
Auditors: Ernst&YoungLLP

LOCATIONS

HQ: Akorn Inc
  1925 W. Field Court, Suite 300, Lake Forest, IL 60045
Phone: 847 279-6100
Web: www.akorn.com

PRODUCTS/OPERATIONS

2013 Sales

	$ mil.	% of total
Hospital drugs & injectables	179.6	57
Ophthalmic	114.5	36
Contract services	23.6	7
Total	**317.7**	**100**

COMPETITORS

Aerie Pharmaceuticals	Hospira
Allergan	InSite Vision
Apotex	Novartis
Bausch & Lomb	Patheon
Baxter International	Pfizer
CBL	Sagent Pharmaceuticals
Fresenius Kabi	Sun Pharmaceutical
Hikma	Teva

HISTORICAL FINANCIALS
Company Type: Public

Income Statement
FYE: December 31

	REVENUE ($ mil.)	NET INCOME ($ mil.)	NET PROFIT MARGIN	EMPLOYEES
12/13	317.7	52.3	16.5%	1,462
12/12	256.1	35.3	13.8%	767
12/11	136.9	43.0	31.4%	564
12/10	86.4	21.8	25.3%	410
12/09	75.8	(25.3)	—	329
Annual Growth	**43.0%**	**—**	**—**	**45.2%**

2013 Year-End Financials

Debt ratio: 25.1%	No. of shares (mil.): 96
Return on equity: 22.7%	Dividends
Cash ($ mil.): 34	Yield: —
Current ratio: 2.76	Payout: —
Long-term debt ($ mil.): 108	Market value ($ mil.): 2,378

	STOCK PRICE ($) FY Close	P/E High/Low	PER SHARE ($) Earnings	Dividends	Book Value
12/13	24.62	48 23	0.46	0.00	2.69
12/12	13.36	45 29	0.32	0.00	2.10
12/11	11.12	26 11	0.41	0.00	1.67
12/10	6.07	27 6	0.22	0.00	0.92
12/09	1.79	— —	(0.28)	0.00	0.43
Annual Growth	**92.6%**		**—**	**—**	**58.4%**

Alamo Group, Inc.

Remember the Alamo Group for tractor-mounted mowing equipment —rotary flail and sickle-bar! The company designs manufactures and distributes a slew of right-of-way maintenance and agricultural equipment. Its branded lines Alamo Industrial and Tiger hydraulically powered tractor-mounted mowers serve US government agencies. Rhino Products and M&W Gear subsidiaries sell rotary cutters and other equipment to farmers for pasture upkeep. UK McConnel and Bomford and France's S.M.A. subsidiaries market vegetation maintenance equipment such as hydraulic boom-mounted hedge and grass mowers. Alamo Group operates 18 plants in North America Europe and Australia garnering more than 60% of its sales in the US.

The Alamo Group's sales are impacted by a myriad of variables including global economic conditions pricing and availability of raw materials government budgets and policies interest rates and access to credit for capital. Even more directly demand for the company's products may teeter with a drop in farm incomes droughts and floods animal disease outbreaks and pest infestations of crops worldwide general demand for farm produce and limits on agricultural imports.

The company realized more than a 17% increase in sales in 2010 compared to the previous year (after suffering a 20% drop in sales in 2009). North American industrial sales improved just over 10% primarily due an uptick in the sales of replacement replacement parts-an indication that customers are electing to repair existing equipment rather than buy new machinery. The addition of Bush Hog a 2009 acquisition helped boost North American agricultural sales by more than 85%. Poor market conditions was a contributing factor in a 12% drop in European sales.

The Alamo Group has sought to counter the adverse events endemic to its industry by strategically cultivating its geographic presence and product portfolio primarily through acquisitions of businesses and branded lines that enhance dominate or promise to significantly rival competitors within their equipment markets. Since its start more than 40 years ago Alamo Group has invested in some two dozen companies.

Alamo Group was founded by chairman and former CEO Donald Douglass. Capital Southwest Venture Corporation owns more than a 20% interest in the company; it is led by chairman and CEO and president Gary Martin a director of Alamo Group.

EXECUTIVES

VP; Managing Director Alamo Group (EUR) Ltd., Geoffrey (Geoff) Davies, age 66, $327,753 total compensation
CEO and President, Ronald A. (Ron) Robinson, age 61, $504,265 total compensation
Vice President Of Information Systems, Terry Stevens
EVP and CFO, Dan E. Malone, age 53, $253,299 total compensation
VP; Manager Agricultural Division, Richard D. Pummell, age 68, $258,825 total compensation
Vice President Of Information, Keith Vinyard, age 65
VP; Manager Industrial Division, Jeffery A. Leonard, $275,606 total compensation
Vice President Information Technology, Keith Krichevsky
Executive Vice President And General, Ian Burden
Vice President Of Human Resources, Janet Pollock
Vice President Of Treasury, Robert H George, age 69
Chairman, James B. Skaggs, age 76
Auditors: KPMGLLP

LOCATIONS

HQ: Alamo Group, Inc.
1627 East Walnut, Seguin, TX 78155
Phone: 830 379-1480 **Fax:** 830 372-9683
Web: www.alamo-group.com

2010 Sales

	$ mil.	% of total
North America		
US	322.2	61
Canada	15.3	3
Europe		
France	93.1	18
UK	36.7	7
Australia	11.8	2
Other regions	45.4	9
Total	**524.5**	**100**

PRODUCTS/OPERATIONS

2010 Sales

	$ mil.	% of total
North American		
Industrial	192.4	37
Agricultural	173.4	33
European	158.7	30
Total	**524.5**	**100**

Selected Products
Boom mowers/power arms
Excavators
Flail mowers
Loader/backhoes
Rotary mowers
Snow removal equipment
Street sweepers
Vacuum trucks

COMPETITORS

AGCO	R.P.M. Tech
Art' s-Way	Scag Power Equipment
Deere	TYMCO
Elgin Sweeper Company	Tennant
MTD Products	Toro Company

HISTORICAL FINANCIALS
Company Type: Public

Income Statement
FYE: December 31

	REVENUE ($ mil.)	NET INCOME ($ mil.)	NET PROFIT MARGIN	EMPLOYEES
12/13	676.8	36.0	5.3%	2,550
12/12	628.4	28.9	4.6%	2,470
12/11	603.5	32.0	5.3%	2,500
12/10	524.5	21.1	4.0%	2,300
12/09	446.4	17.0	3.8%	2,340
Annual Growth	**11.0%**	**20.5%**	**—**	**2.2%**

2013 Year-End Financials

Debt ratio: 0.1%	No. of shares (mil.): 12
Return on equity: 10.9%	Dividends
Cash ($ mil.): 63	Yield: 0.4%
Current ratio: 4.18	Payout: 9.9%
Long-term debt ($ mil.): 0	Market value ($ mil.): 733

	STOCK PRICE ($) FY Close	P/E High/Low	PER SHARE ($) Earnings	Dividends	Book Value
12/13	60.69	20 11	2.96	0.28	29.03
12/12	32.64	14 11	2.40	0.24	25.89
12/11	26.93	11 7	2.68	0.24	23.33
12/10	27.82	16 10	1.79	0.24	21.41
12/09	17.15	10 6	1.65	0.24	20.04
Annual Growth	**37.2%**	**— —**	**15.7%**	**3.9%**	**9.7%**

Alexion Pharmaceuticals Inc.

Alexion Pharmaceuticals can't suppress its enthusiasm for treating immune functions gone awry.

The firm develops drugs that inhibit certain immune system functions that cause rare hematology nephrology oncology neurology inflammatory and metabolic disorders. The company's first marketed antibody product Soliris has won approval in the US Canada and some European and Asian countries for the treatment of two rare genetic blood disorders known as paroxysmal nocturnal hemoglobinuria (PNH) and atypical hemolytic uremic syndrome (aHUS). Alexion is also developing Soliris as a potential treatment for other kidney and neurology conditions and it has development programs for other disease-fighting antibodies.

Geographic Reach

Alexion has a manufacturing facility in Rhode Island where it makes a portion of its supply of biopharmaceuticals; it also relies on contract manufacturers (primarily Lonza) to make some of its Soliris supply. It also has service administration and research facilities in the US (Massachusetts) Switzerland and France as well as sales offices in Canada Australia Europe and Asia.

Alexion has expanded sales of Soliris into markets including the EU the US Australia Canada South Korea Japan and Switzerland; the drug has gained approval for treatment of PNH in more than 40 countries and is approved to treat aHUS in the US and European Union. In 2012 Europe surpassed the US for the largest geographic segment accounting for 37% of annual revenues.

Operations

Soliris is the first and only drug approved for the treatment of PNH a rare disorder in which the death of red blood cells can bring on conditions including blood clotting and organ damage. In 2011 the drug gained an additional indication when it was approved for the treatment of aHUS a rare genetic disease that causes blood clots leading to kidney failure in both the US and European markets. The drug is taken by relatively few and at a hefty cost: more than $400000 per patient per year (making it one of the world's most expensive drugs).

Sales and Marketing

Alexion markets the drug through a specialized direct sales force as well as through distribution partners in select geographic markets. In the US the company serves customers including specialty distributors and specialty pharmacies which in turn supply Solaris to physicians and clinics. Internationally its customers include hospitals pharmacies distributors and buying groups.

Financial Analysis

Revenues for Alexion have grown since its first commercial product Soliris gained regulatory approval in the EU and the US in 2007 increasing each year as the company has moved the drug into new territories. Profits have also steadily risen excluding a drop in 2010 caused by a sharp rise the previous year from a one-time tax benefit. In 2012 revenues increased by 45% to some $1.1 billion and net income rose 45% to $255 million primarily attributed to increased use of Soliris in new and existing markets.

Strategy

The company is pursuing regulatory approval to launch Soliris in new markets; for instance it introduced the drug in Japan in 2010 and in Australia in 2011. Alexion is also researching Soliris as a treatment for additional conditions including other rare blood disorders organ transplant rejection and eye and nerve conditions.

With the success of Soliris underway the company has laid out a strategy for research partnership and acquisition activities that capitalizes on its ability to develop and commercialize drugs for rare conditions. In addition to Soliris Alexion has can-

didates in its pipeline for the treatment of rare metabolic and inflammatory disorders.

Following increased sales of Soliris in 2012 the company announced plans to build a new global headquarters building in New Haven Connecticut. The facility is scheduled for completion in 2015.

Mergers and Acquisitions

The company expanded into metabolic disease treatment in 2011 by buying up the rights to an investigational drug for the treatment of Type A molybdenum cofactor deficiency (MoCD) a rare disorder that can cause severe brain damage in newborns from Orphatec Pharmaceuticals. In early 2012 it also paid $610 million to acquire Montreal-based Enobia Pharma; the purchase added a development candidate to treat an ultra-rare metabolic disease known as hypophosphatasia (HPP) which currently has no treatment options.

In 2011 Alexion acquired Taligen Therapeutics which had a drug in development stages that would have competed with Soliris for about $111 million. Taligen Therapeutic's pipeline also included a potential treatment for ophthalmic diseases.

Ownership

Investors in Alexion include Capital Research Global Investors with an 11% ownership stake and T. Rowe Price (10%).

EXECUTIVES

EVP and Chief Global Operations Officer, Stephen P. Squinto, age 57, $607,000 total compensation
CEO, David L. Hallal, age 48, $610,000 total compensation
EVP and Chief Human Resources Officer, Clare M. Carmichael, age 55
EVP and CFO, Vikas Sinha, age 50, $615,000 total compensation
EVP General Counsel, John Moriarty
EVP and Global Head Research & Development, Martin Mackay, $397,000 total compensation
Vice President, Jeremy Springhorn
Vice President Pdas, Yas Saotome
Senior Vice President Chief Development, Steven Ryder
Vice President Global Regulatory Affairs, Martine Zimmermann
Vice President Emea Commercial Operations Wec, Jordi Casals
Medical Director Pharmacovigilance, Suresh Mahabhashyam
Vice President Quality Assurance, Declan Kelly
Vice President Regulatory Affairs, Edward Miller
Vice President, Heidi Wagner
Chairman, Leonard Bell, age 56
Auditors: PricewaterhouseCoopersLLP

LOCATIONS

HQ: Alexion Pharmaceuticals Inc.
352 Knotter Drive, Cheshire, CT 06410
Phone: 203 272-2596
Web: www.alxn.com

2012 Sales

	$ mil.	% of total
Europe	418.3	37
US	400.5	35
Asia Pacific (mostly Japan)	161.5	14
Other regions & countries	153.8	14
Total	**1134.1**	**100**

PRODUCTS/OPERATIONS

Selected Products

Approved

Soliris (eculizumab paroxysmal nocturnal hemoglobinuria - PNH - and atypical hemolytic uremic syndrome - aHUS)
In development
ALXN 1007 (inflammatory disorders)
ALXN 1102/1103 (inflammatory disorders)
Asfotase alfa (hypophosphatasia)
cPMP (molybdenum cofactor deficiency - MoCD - type A)
Soliris (STEC-HUS myasthenia gravis neuromyelitis optica transplant rejection neuromyelitis optica other disorders)
TT30 (paroxysmal nocturnal hemoglobinuria)

COMPETITORS

Abbott Labs	Genentech
Allergan	Genzyme
Amgen	Gilead Sciences
Archemix	GlaxoSmithKline
AstraZeneca	Human Genome Sciences
Baxter International	Medicis Pharmaceutical
BioMarin	Millennium: The Takeda
Pharmaceutical	Oncology Company
Biogen Idec	MorphoSys
CSL Behring	Novo Nordisk
Celgene	Pfizer
Celldex Therapeutics	Pharming
ChemoCentryx	Regeneron
Cubist Pharmaceuticals	Pharmaceuticals
Dyax	Vertex Pharmaceuticals
Forest Labs	XOMA

HISTORICAL FINANCIALS

Company Type: Public

Income Statement

FYE: December 31

	REVENUE ($ mil.)	NET INCOME ($ mil.)	NET PROFIT MARGIN	EMPLOYEES
12/14	2,233.7	656.9	29.4%	2,273
12/13	1,551.3	252.9	16.3%	1,774
12/12	1,134.1	254.8	22.5%	1,373
12/11	783.4	175.3	22.4%	1,008
12/10	540.9	97.0	17.9%	792
Annual Growth	**42.6%**	**61.3%**	**—**	**30.2%**

2014 Year-End Financials

Debt ratio: 3.9%	No. of shares (mil.): 199
Return on equity: 23.1%	Dividends
Cash ($ mil.): 944	Yield: —
Current ratio: 4.61	Payout: —
Long-term debt ($ mil.): 116	Market value ($ mil.): 36,831

	STOCK PRICE ($) FY Close	P/E High/Low		PER SHARE ($) Earnings	Dividends	Book Value
12/14	185.03	60	39	3.26	0.00	16.59
12/13	132.88	103	65	1.27	0.00	12.09
12/12	93.74	88	52	1.28	0.00	10.12
12/11	71.50	109	46	0.91	0.00	6.12
12/10	80.55	151	83	0.52	0.00	4.70
Annual Growth	**23.1%**	**—**	**—**	**58.2%**	**—**	**37.1%**

Align Technology Inc

Brace-face begone! Align Technology produces and sells the Invisalign system which corrects malocclusion or crooked teeth. Instead of using metal or ceramic mounts that are cemented on the teeth and connected by wires (traditional braces) the system involves using an array of clear and removable dental Aligners to move a patient's teeth into a desired tooth alignment. The company markets its products to orthodontists and dentists worldwide. Align also provides training for practitioners to model treatment schemes using its online ClinCheck application which simulates tooth movement and suggests the appropriate Aligner. It also makes and sells orthodontic scanning and CAD (computer-assisted design) devices.

Operations

The company operates through two segments: Clear Aligner and Scanners and CAD/CAM Services ("SCCS"). Clear Aligner is the Invisalign product lines and it accounts for 93% of revenue. SCCS includes the iTero intra-oral 3D scanning system for orthodontic and restorative dentistry and OrthoCAD services.

Geographic Reach

Align Technology has administrative and manufacturing locations in Costa Rica Mexico Israel the Netherlands and the US. Its products are primarily marketed in North America (accounting for three-fourths of sales) and Europe. It also operates in areas of Latin America and the Asia/Pacific and is working to expand sales into Middle Eastern African and smaller European countries. Invisalign is available in 45 countries worldwide.

Sales and Marketing

Align Technology sells its products through a direct sales force in North America and select international markets as well as through distribution partners in other regions. The company primarily markets its products to orthodontist and dental practices who then commit to sell the products to consumers. It is targeting general practice dentists as a primary sales growth channel since general dentists have larger patient populations than orthodontists who traditionally treat malocclusion.

Financial Performance

Align Technology has seen several years of increasing revenue and 2013 was no exception. The company reported an 18% increase to $660 million as all products and geographic regions saw higher sales despite some lower average selling prices of Invisalign in the US due to customers switching to the less expensive Express product. Net income also improved growing 10% from $59 million to $64 million due to higher revenue lower expenses and interest earned on larger cash reserves. Revenue growth lead to improved cash from operations; it grew by $52 million to $186 million.

Strategy

To stay ahead of potential competitors looking to enter the clear alignment market Align Technology continuously tries to expand sales of its Invisalign system by increasing the number of dentists and orthodontists that are committed to selling the products. It also increases brand awareness through consumer marketing programs. Geographically the firm is looking to expand into new markets. For instance in 2012 it moved into the Russian market and select Middle Eastern markets through an existing distribution partner and in 2013 it transitioned Asian markets back to a direct sales model coordinated out of its new regional headquarters in Singapore. It also launched a branding campaign across Western Europe which lead to higher sales.

To widen use of its products Align Technology also develops new versions and variations of the Invisalign system as well as tools that make it easier for dentists to adopt use of the Invisalign offerings. In 2013 it launched the Invisalign G5 system which helps doctors manage treatment of patients with deep bites and rolled out the latest iterations for its ClinCheck and iTero products. In 2012 it in-

troduced the Express 5 system for minor treatment of orthodontic relapse crowding or spacing conditions. Some of the company's product development efforts are conducted through partnerships with other medical device firms such as Danaher.

EXECUTIVES

Vice President North American Sales, Daniel Ellis
CFO, David L. White, age 58, $153,846 total compensation
President and CEO Director, Thomas M. Prescott, age 59, $615,000 total compensation
VP Operations, Emory M. Wright, age 45, $330,288 total compensation
Vice President Manager Director, Arnel Alon
Vice President Research And Development, Zelko Relic
Vice President Marketing, Zach Lamppa
Vice President Information Technology, Roger George
Vice President Of Regulatory And Quality Assurance, John D'Angelo
Vice President And Chief Scientist, Avi Kopelman
Executive Vice President Operations, Rackel Madrigal
Vice President Marketing, Mohammed Khaishgi
Vice President Information Technology, Adefemi Defreitas
Vice President Of Finance, Eldon Bullington
Vice President Software, Eric P Costello
Vice President Software Development, Eric Meyer
Chairman, C. Raymond Larkin, age 65
Auditors: PricewaterhouseCoopersLLP

LOCATIONS

HQ: Align Technology Inc
2560 Orchard Parkway, San Jose, CA 95131
Phone: 408 470-1000
Web: www.aligntech.com

2013 Sales

	$ mil.	% of total
US	491.4	74
Netherlands	127.8	19
Other countries	41.0	7
Total	**660.2**	**100**

PRODUCTS/OPERATIONS

2013 Sales

	$ mil.	% of total
Clear Aligner	614.6	94
Scanners & CAD/CAM services	45.6	6
Total	**660.2**	**100**

Selected Products and Services

CAD/CAM services
Invisalign Assist
Invisalign Express 5
Invisalign Express 10
Invisalign Full
Invisalign G3
Invisalign G4
Invisalign G5
Invisalign Lite
Invisalign Teen
iTero scanners
OrthoCad iOC intra-oral scanners
Vivera Retainers

COMPETITORS

3M	Patterson Companies
Ceradyne	Sirona
DENTSPLY	Straumann
Henry Schein	Sybron Dental
National Dentex	Young Innovations
Nobel Biocare	

HISTORICAL FINANCIALS

Company Type: Public

Income Statement

FYE: December 31

	REVENUE ($ mil.)	NET INCOME ($ mil.)	NET PROFIT MARGIN	EMPLOYEES
12/13	660.2	64.3	9.7%	3,420
12/12	560.0	58.6	10.5%	3,176
12/11	479.7	66.7	13.9%	2,593
12/10	387.1	74.2	19.2%	2,097
12/09	312.3	(31.2)	—	1,895
Annual Growth	**20.6%**	**—**	**—**	**15.9%**

2013 Year-End Financials

Debt ratio: —
Return on equity: 10.5%
Cash ($ mil.): 242
Current ratio: 3.11
Long-term debt ($ mil.): —
No. of shares (mil.): 80
Dividends
Yield: —
Payout: —
Market value ($ mil.): 4,605

	STOCK PRICE ($) FY Close	P/E High/Low		PER SHARE ($) Earnings	Dividends	Book Value
12/13	57.14	73	32	0.78	0.00	7.87
12/12	27.75	54	31	0.71	0.00	7.21
12/11	23.73	30	17	0.83	0.00	6.23
12/10	19.54	22	14	0.95	0.00	4.94
12/09	17.82	—	—	(0.45)	0.00	3.66
Annual Growth	**33.8%**			**—**	**—**	**21.1%**

Allegiant Travel Company

Allegiant Travel pledges to serve the vacation needs of residents of more than 60 small US cities in 35 states. Through Allegiant Air the company provides nonstop service to tourist destinations such as Las Vegas Los Angeles and Orlando Florida from places such as Cedar Rapids Iowa; Fargo North Dakota; and Toledo Ohio. It maintains a fleet of about 50 MD-80 series aircraft. Besides scheduled service Allegiant Air offers charter flights for casino operators Caesars Entertainment (formerly Harrah's Entertainment) and MGM MIRAGE in addition to other customers. Sister company Allegiant Vacations works with partners to allow customers to book hotel rooms and rental cars along with their airline tickets.

The company hopes to thrive by sticking to what it believes to be an underserved niche: Allegiant Air is the only provider of nonstop service to its chosen destinations from most of the markets where it operates. Allegiant Travel has identified about 100 more small cities in the US and Canada as candidates for its services; it also plans to expand its list of leisure destinations. In addition to Las Vegas Los Angeles and Orlando Allegiant Travel offers service to Phoenix; and to two other Florida markets (Fort Lauderdale and Tampa/St. Petersburg).

Allegiant Travel believes the diversity of its revenue mix will help ensure the company's success. The long-term fixed-fee contract with Harrah's is a predictable and useful supplement to its scheduled airline service. Other sources of revenue include the fees it collects when customers arrange lodging and ground transportation via the Allegiant Air website and the charges for ancillary services such as advance seat assignments and in-flight food and beverages. The fees added up allowing the company to realize a whopping 50% increase in ancillary revenue in 2010; these additional fees played a great part in the company's overall revenue increase of 11%.

Even with these increases the company is still interested in controlling aircraft-related costs. Allegiant Travel has chosen to fly planes from the venerable MD-80 series which are readily available second-hand. (The average age of the company's MD-80s is just over 21 years.) The aircraft formerly an industry mainstay cost less than new planes and using a single type of plane makes maintenance simpler and thus less expensive. On the downside MD-80s are less fuel-efficient than newer aircraft.

In early 2010 the company shifted its business strategy slightly to include longer-haul transportation. It agreed to purchase six Boeing 757-200 aircraft in order to extend its services to Hawaii. Seeing Hawaii as an untapped leisure market ripe with growth Allegiant Travel plans to have all the new aircraft delivered by 2012. It will cost the company between $75 million and $90 million to acquire and prepare the fleet for service. Until it recieves regulatory approval for extended over water operations the company has leased two of the Boeing aircraft to a third party.

Just as the company's aircraft have been tested so has Allegiant Travel's management team. This isn't the first go-round in the airline industry for CEO Maurice Gallagher who helped found low-fare carrier ValuJet (now AirTran). Gallagher controls about 20% of Allegiant Travel.

EXECUTIVES

Chairman and CEO, Maurice J. (Maury) Gallagher, age 64
CIO, Scott M. Allard, age 46, $193,428 total compensation
SVP and CFO, D. Scott Sheldon, age 36, $195,000 total compensation
SVP Planning, Jude Bricker, $188,712 total compensation
Svp Marketing, Michael Reichartz
Vice President Application Development, Todd Cinnamon
Vice President People Services, Rebecca Henry
Vice President Sales, Chris Robinson
Vp Flight Operations, James Carr
Vice President Flight Operations, Greg Skelley
Chairman and CEO, Maurice J. (Maury) Gallagher, age 64
Auditors: Ernst&YoungLLP

LOCATIONS

HQ: Allegiant Travel Company
1201 North Town Center Drive, Las Vegas, NV 89144
Phone: 702 851-7300
Web: www.allegiant.com

2010 Selected Routes

Destination	No. of routes
Las Vegas	45
Orlando	29
Phoenix	27
Tampa Bay/St. Petersburg	20
Los Angeles/Lon Beach	17
Ft. Lauderdale	7
Other cities	15
Total	**160**

PRODUCTS/OPERATIONS

2010 Sales

	$ mil.	% of total
Scheduled service	427.8	64
Ancillary revenues		
Air-related charges	169.6	26
Third party products	24.4	4
Fixed fee contract revenues	40.6	6
Other	1.2	-
Total	**663.6**	**100**

COMPETITORS

AirTran Airways	Horizon Air
Alaska Air	JetBlue
American Airlines Group	Southwest Airlines
	US Airways
Delta Air Lines	United Continental
Frontier Airlines	

HISTORICAL FINANCIALS

Company Type: Public

Income Statement

FYE: December 31

	REVENUE ($ mil.)	NET INCOME ($ mil.)	NET PROFIT MARGIN	EMPLOYEES
12/13	996.1	92.2	9.3%	2,235
12/12	908.7	78.6	8.6%	1,938
12/11	779.1	49.4	6.3%	1,719
12/10	663.6	65.7	9.9%	1,826
12/09	557.9	76.3	13.7%	1,734
Annual Growth	**15.6%**	**4.9%**	**—**	**6.6%**

2013 Year-End Financials

Debt ratio: 25.1%
Return on equity: 23.7%
Cash ($ mil.): 108
Current ratio: 1.48
Long-term debt ($ mil.): 214

No. of shares (mil.): 18
Dividends
Yield: 2.1%
Payout: 48.1%
Market value ($ mil.): 1,955

	STOCK PRICE ($) FY Close	P/E High/Low	Earnings	Dividends	Book Value
12/13	105.44	23 15	4.82	2.25	20.26
12/12	73.41	19 12	4.06	2.00	20.71
12/11	53.34	21 15	2.57	0.00	18.42
12/10	49.24	17 11	3.32	0.75	15.67
12/09	47.17	15 9	3.76	0.00	14.71
Annual Growth	**22.3%**	**— —**	**6.4%**	**—**	**8.3%**

Alliance Fiber Optic Products Inc.

Alliance Fiber Optic Products (AFOP) unites with light. Communications equipment manufacturers incorporate AFOP's fiber-optic components into products used to build networks that connect cities regions within cities and telecommunications service providers with their individual customers. Its optical path integration and optical fiber amplifier components which include attenuators couplers depolarizers multiplexers and splitters account for most of sales. The company sells directly to telecom equipment makers primarily in North America where it gets about half of sales. AFOP has more than 200 customers.

Foxconn Holding/Hon Hai Precision Industry owns around 19% of AFOP; the world's largest contract electronics manufacturing services company is a customer and a supplier.

The company has a limited number of customers. Its top 10 account for nearly two-thirds of revenues. The fiber-optic components industry is growing more competitive as industry consolidation of vendors continues.

Alliance Fiber Optic Products has offices and manufacturing plants in China Taiwan and the US.

Chairman president and CEO Peter Chang owns 15% of Alliance Fiber Optic Products including stock options.

EXECUTIVES

Executive Vice President - Sales & Marketing, David A. Hubbard, age 54, $162,000 total compensation
Auditors: MarcumStonefieldadivisionofMarcumLLP

LOCATIONS

HQ: Alliance Fiber Optic Products Inc.
275 Gibraltar Drive, Sunnyvale, CA 94089
Phone: 408 736-6900   **Fax:** 408 736-2466
Web: www.afop.com

2009 Sales

	$ mil.	% of total
North America	14.7	49
Asia	8.0	27
Europe	7.1	24
Total	**29.8**	**100**

PRODUCTS/OPERATIONS

2009 Sales

	$ mil.	% of total
Connectivity products	18.6	63
Optical passive products	11.2	37
Total	**29.8**	**100**

Selected Products

Advanced optical devices
  All-fiber optical depolarizer
  Automatic variable optical attenuator
  Switchable optical drop/add module
Optical path management
  Amplifiers
  Couplers and splitters
  Customized integrated modules
  Optical interconnect devices
Wavelength management
  Fused fiber WDM couplers
  Multiplexing components and modules

COMPETITORS

Avago Technologies	Kotura
Cisco Systems	Oclaro
Corning Cable Systems	Oplink Communications
DiCon Fiberoptics	TE Connectivity
Finisar	Thorlabs Quantum
Gemfire	Electronics
JDS Uniphase	

HISTORICAL FINANCIALS
Company Type: Public

Income Statement
FYE: December 31

	REVENUE ($ mil.)	NET INCOME ($ mil.)	NET PROFIT MARGIN	EMPLOYEES
12/13	76.0	18.8	24.7%	1,514
12/12	46.6	9.6	20.7%	1,063
12/11	42.0	4.4	10.5%	1,037
12/10	45.4	6.0	13.2%	1,137
12/09	29.8	1.4	4.8%	870
Annual Growth	26.4%	90.3%	—	14.9%

2013 Year-End Financials

Debt ratio: —	No. of shares (mil.): 18
Return on equity: 26.6%	Dividends
Cash ($ mil.): 18	Yield: 1.0%
Current ratio: 4.08	Payout: 15.6%
Long-term debt ($ mil.): —	Market value ($ mil.): 277

	STOCK PRICE ($) FY Close	P/E High/Low		PER SHARE ($) Earnings	Dividends	Book Value
12/13	15.05	39	10	1.02	0.15	4.41
12/12	12.02	22	14	0.54	1.25	3.48
12/11	7.66	79	28	0.25	0.00	3.58
12/10	15.68	41	3	0.35	0.00	3.30
12/09	1.20	19	8	0.08	0.00	2.88
Annual Growth	88.2%	—	—	92.0%	—	11.2%

Alliance Holdings Group LP

When it comes to coal mining it takes more than one company to make this Alliance work. Alliance Holdings GP owns Alliance Resource Management GP which is the managing general partner of major coal mining company Alliance Resource Partners L.P. That operational company company has seven coal mining complexes in Illinois Indiana Kentucky and Maryland plus other coal interests in West Virginia. Alliance Holdings GP generates all of its revenues from its general partnership interest and its ownership stake in Alliance Resource Partners L.P.

Geographic Reach

The company's Alliance Resource Partners unit has coal mining operations in Illinois Basin Central Appalachia and Northern Appalachia.

Operations

Alliance Resource Partners has five reportable segments: the Illinois Basin Central Appalachia Northern Appalachia White Oak and Other and Corporate. In 2013 the Illinois Basin operations produced 30.7 million tons of coal; Central Appalachia 2 million rons; and Northern Appalachia 6.1 million tons.

Sales and Marketing

Alliance Resource Partners' two largest customers in 2013 were Louisville Gas and Electric Company and Tennessee Valley Authority which together accounted for 26.5% of that unit's total revenues. In 2013 it sold 94% of its total tons to electric utilities primarily to utility plants with installed pollution control devices.

The company's coal is transported to its customers by rail truck and barge.

Financial Performance

Alliance Holdings' revenues grew by 8% in 2013 due to increased tons of sold (38.8 million produced and sold) partially offset by the lower average coal sales prices (which decreased to $55.04 per ton from $56.28 per ton in 2012) as the result of reduced coal sales into the metallurgical coal export market. The increase in tons sold and produced came from increased production at the Tunnel Ridge mine the River View and Gibson North mines and the Onton mine (which was acquired in 2012). The company's net income increased by 19% in 2013 mainly due to higher revenues and as well as the absence of asset impairment charges (as the Pontiki mining complex ceased operations in 2013) partially offset by increased depreciation depletion and amortization expenses and equity in loss of affiliates.Cash provided by operating activities increased by $157 million in 2013 primarily due to higher net income and decreases in trade receivables coal inventory and certain prepaid expenses offset partially by lower accounts payable.Alliance Holdings has seen a growth in revenues since 2009 primarily due to higher volumes fueled by capacity expansion and acquisitions.

Strategy

The primary business objective of Alliance Holdings is to increase its cash distributions to unit holders by actively supporting its main operating unit (Alliance Resource Partners) in implementing its business activities.Mergers and Acquisitions

Growing its coal assets in 2013 Alliance Resource Partners acquired from and leased back to White Oak 89.9 million additional tons of proven and probable high-sulfur coal reserves. It 2012 it acquired Green River Collieries (coal mining business and operations in Webster and Hopkins Counties Kentucky).

Company Background

Chairman president CEO Joseph Craft owns 43% Alliance Holdings GP.

The Alliance companies were assembled by Joseph Craft.

EXECUTIVES

Executive Vice President - Marketing, Robert G. Sachse, age 65, $310,000 total compensation
EVP and Director, Charles R. Wesley, age 59, $236,280 total compensation
Chairman of the Board President and Chief Executive Officer, Joseph W. Craft, age 63, $334,828 total compensation
Senior Vice President and Chief Financial Officer, Brian L. Cantrell, age 54, $275,000 total compensation
Senior Vice President and Chief Operating Officer, Thomas M. Wynne, age 57, $359,000 total compensation
Vice President Information Technology, David Gilbert
EVP and Director, Charles R. Wesley, age 59
Chairman of the Board President and Chief Executive Officer, Joseph W. Craft, age 63
Auditors: Deloitte&ToucheLLP

LOCATIONS

HQ: Alliance Holdings Group LP
1717 South Boulder Avenue, Suite 400, Tulsa, OK 74119
Phone: 918 295-1415
Web: www.ahgp.com

2013 Sales

	$ mil.	% of total
Illinois Basin	1629.1	73
Northern Appalachia	377.6	17
Central Appalachia	169.5	8
Corporate & other	39.8	2
White Oak	2.2	-
Adjustments	(13.1)	-
Total	**2205.2**	**100**

PRODUCTS/OPERATIONS

2013 Sales

	$ mil.	% of total
Coal	2137.5	97
Transportation	32.6	1
Other	35.1	2
Total	**2205.2**	**100**

COMPETITORS

Alpha Natural Resources	Foresight Energy
Arch Coal	James River Coal
CONSOL Energy	Patriot Coal
Drummond Company	Peabody Energy

HISTORICAL FINANCIALS
Company Type: Public

Income Statement
FYE: December 31

	REVENUE ($ mil.)	NET INCOME ($ mil.)	NET PROFIT MARGIN	EMPLOYEES
12/13	2,205.2	233.8	10.6%	4,313
12/12	2,033.9	196.0	9.6%	4,345
12/11	1,843.2	214.1	11.6%	3,832
12/10	1,609.7	174.3	10.8%	3,558
12/09	1,230.6	114.2	9.3%	3,090
Annual Growth	15.7%	19.6%	—	8.7%

2013 Year-End Financials

Debt ratio: 41.6%	No. of shares (mil.): 59
Return on equity: —	Dividends
Cash ($ mil.): 98	Yield: 5.2%
Current ratio: 1.53	Payout: 81.0%
Long-term debt ($ mil.): 848	Market value ($ mil.): 3,510

	STOCK PRICE ($) FY Close	P/E High/Low		PER SHARE ($) Earnings	Dividends	Book Value
12/13	58.63	17	12	3.91	3.10	8.28
12/12	47.58	16	12	3.28	2.72	7.19
12/11	51.98	16	12	3.58	2.28	6.63
12/10	48.13	17	9	2.91	1.90	5.38
12/09	27.41	15	7	1.91	1.69	4.38
Annual Growth	20.9%	—	—	19.6%	16.4%	17.3%

Alliance Resource Partners LP

Coal is the main resource of Alliance Resource Partners which operates in the Illinois Basin Central Appalachia and Northern Appalachia. The company has 11 underground coal mining complexes in Illinois Indiana Kentucky Maryland Pennsylvania and West Virginia. Alliance controls about 650 million tons of reserves. Approximately 205 million tons of these reserves located in Hamilton County Illinois are leased to independent coal company White Oak Resources. Alliance produces about 32 million tons of coal annually nearly all of which is sold to electric utilities.

Geographic Reach

The company operates 11 underground mining complexes in five states (Illinois Indiana Kentucky Maryland and West Virginia) and also operates a coal-loading terminal on the Ohio River at Mt. Vernon Indiana.

Operations

Alliance's coal is transported from its mines to customers by rail truck and barge. In 2011 61% of its coal was shipped by rail 25% by barge and 14% by truck.

Sales and Marketing

The company's two largest customers in 2011 were Louisville Gas and Electric Company and the Tennessee Valley Authority.

Financial Perfomance

Alliance's revenues increased by 15% in 2011 due to higher average coal sales prices (contributing $151.2 million in coal sales) and increased tons sold (contributing $83.4 million in additional coal sales). Average coal sales price also increased primarily as a result of improved contract pricing across all regions.

The company's net income increased by 21% in 2011 due to higher revenues a decrease in interest expense (attributable to a nonrecurring adjustment to capitalized interest) and reduced interest expense resulting from annual principal repayments made during August 2011 and 2010 of $18.0 million on our original senior notes issued in 1999. Other factors included a decrease in transportation revenues and expenses primarily attributable to reduced tonnage in 2011.

Alliance saw an upward trend in revenue from 2007 to 2011. The year-over year upward trend was mainly attributable to the increased coal prices primarily as a result of improved contract pricing.

Strategy

In 2012 Alliance Coal expanded its holdings in the Illinois Basin coal basin by acquiring Kentucky-based Green River Collieries. The deal includes the Onton No. 9 mining complex which produces about 1.5 million tons of coal per year as well as the addition of an estimated 40 million tons of coal reserves in the West Kentucky No. 9 coal seam.

Ownership

President and CEO Joseph Craft III controls 42% of Alliance Resource Partners. Craft a coal industry veteran owns his stake in Alliance Resource Partners through Alliance Holdings GP a company he controls that went public in 2006.

EXECUTIVES

Vice President Operations, George Tichnell
Vice President Operations Technology, Justin Gaydamaka
Vice President Information Technology, Teil Blackshare
Treasurer, Julie Hober
Auditors: Deloitte&ToucheLLP

LOCATIONS

HQ: Alliance Resource Partners LP
1717 South Boulder Avenue, Suite 400, Tulsa, OK 74119
Phone: 918 295-7600
Web: www.arlp.com

PRODUCTS/OPERATIONS

2011 Sales

	$ mil.	% of total
Coal sales	1786.1	97
Transportation	32.0	2
Other	25.5	1
Total	**1843.6**	**100**

COMPETITORS

Alpha Natural Resources	Drummond Company
Arch Coal	James River Coal
CONSOL Energy	Peabody Energy

HISTORICAL FINANCIALS

Company Type: Public

Income Statement

FYE: December 31

	REVENUE ($ mil.)	NET INCOME ($ mil.)	NET PROFIT MARGIN	EMPLOYEES
12/13	2,205.5	393.4	17.8%	4,313
12/12	2,034.3	335.5	16.5%	4,345
12/11	1,843.5	389.3	21.1%	3,832
12/10	1,610.0	321.0	19.9%	3,558
12/09	1,231.0	192.1	15.6%	3,090
Annual Growth	**15.7%**	**19.6%**	**—**	**8.7%**

2013 Year-End Financials

Debt ratio: 41.7%	No. of shares (mil.): 73
Return on equity: —	Dividends
Cash ($ mil.): 93	Yield: 11.8%
Current ratio: 1.51	Payout: 125.7%
Long-term debt ($ mil.): 848	Market value ($ mil.): 5,692

	STOCK PRICE ($) FY Close	P/E High/Low		PER SHARE ($) Earnings	Dividends	Book Value
12/13	77.00	22	16	3.63	4.57	11.51
12/12	58.06	27	17	3.06	4.16	9.57
12/11	75.58	20	15	4.07	1.81	8.48
12/10	65.76	20	11	3.34	3.21	6.21
12/09	43.37	25	14	1.48	2.95	4.36
Annual Growth	**15.4%**	**—**	**—**	**25.3%**	**11.5%**	**27.5%**

Altra Industrial Motion Corp

Altra Industrial Motion likes to bring things to a stop. The company manufactures mechanical power transmission and motion control products. Altra specializes in industrial clutches and brakes gear drives couplings and bearings used in such diverse assemblies as elevator braking systems and wheelchairs. Its lineup is marketed under multiple brands including TB Wood's and Warner Electric both directly and through distributors to OEMs in material handling mining and transportation industries. The company also caters to customers engaged in energy food processing medical and turf and garden markets. North America accounts for more than 60% of sales.

Geographic Reach

In addition to its leased headquarters in Braintree Massachusetts Altra maintains 34 production facilities 15 of which are located in the US one in Canada 12 in Europe two in Brazil three in China and one in Mexico.

Sales and Marketing

Its global sales and marketing network includes more than 1000 direct OEM customers and over 3000 distributor outlets. Roughly 35% of its net sales from were generated through independent distributors in 2013. Altra works with industrial distributors such as Motion Industries Applied Industrial Technologies Kaman Industrial Technologies and W.W. Grainger.

Financial Performance

Altra reached a historic revenue milestone of $732 million in 2012 followed by marginal decline of 1% to $722 million in 2013. The slight revenue decline for 2013 was due to lower sales levels across all operating segments fueled by weak demand in all geographies as well as a decline in the mining energy and metals industries.

After experiencing a steep drop in profits during 2012 Altra posted a 66% surge in profits to peak at a record-setting $40 million in 2013. The profit growth was primarily due to a decline in interest expenses due to its debt refinancing efforts in November 2012. In addition Altra has experienced four straight years of steady growth from its operating cash flow.

Strategy

Altra's long-term strategy is to increase its sales through organic growth expand its geographic reach and product offerings through strategic acquisitions and improve its profitability through cost reduction initiatives. In 2013 it acquired Svendborg Brakes and S.B. Patent Holding ApS (together Svendborg) for $110 million. Svendborg has a major presence in Denmark in addition to a sales network in seven additional countries in Western Europe China South America Australia and the US. In 2012 Altra expanded its manufacturing presence in Asia beyond its current plant in Shenzhen China with the addition of its new manufacturing facility in Changzhou China.

EXECUTIVES

VP and CFO, Christian Storch, age 54, $382,500 total compensation
Chairman and CEO, Carl R. Christenson, age 55, $600,000 total compensation
Vp Global Sales, Gerald Ferris, age 66
National Accounts Manager, Mike Tibbets
National Accounts Manager, Annamarie Donaldson
National Account Manager, Michael Bunkley
Vice President Of Engineering, Robert Ryland
National Sales Manager, John Proven
Vp And General Manager Boston Gear Formsprag Steiber And Huco Business Units, Edward Novotny, age 62
Chairman and CEO, Carl R. Christenson, age 55
Executive Board Member, Gerhard Eschenr
Auditors: Deloitte&ToucheLLP

LOCATIONS

HQ: Altra Industrial Motion Corp
300 Granite Street, Suite 201, Braintree, MA 02184
Phone: 781 917-0600
Web: www.altramotion.com

2013 Sales

	$ mil.	% of total
North America	454.1	63
Europe	216.6	30
Asia & other regions	51.5	7
Total	**722.2**	**100**

PRODUCTS/OPERATIONS

Selected Products
Electromagnetic Clutches and Brakes
Engineered Bearing Assemblies
Engineered Belted Drives
Flexible Couplings
Gearing
Heavy Duty Clutches and Brakes
Linear Products
Overrunning Clutches
P.T. Components

Selected Brands
Ameridrives Couplings
Bauer Gear Motor
Bibby Turboflex
Boston Gear
Delroyd Worm Gear
Formsprag Clutch
Huco
Industrial Clutch
Inertia Dynamics
Kilian Manufacturing
Lamiflex Couplings
Marland Clutch
Matrix
Nuttall Gear
Stieber Clutch
Svendborg Brakes
TB Wood's
Twiflex
Warner Electric
Warner Linear
Wichita Clutch

COMPETITORS

Baldor Electric	Hitachi
Danaher	Regal Beloit
Emerson Electric	Rexnord
GE	Siemens AG
Harbin Electric	

HISTORICAL FINANCIALS

Company Type: Public

Income Statement

FYE: December 31

	REVENUE ($ mil.)	NET INCOME ($ mil.)	NET PROFIT MARGIN	EMPLOYEES
12/13	722.2	40.2	5.6%	3,810
12/12	731.9	24.2	3.3%	3,617
12/11	674.8	37.6	5.6%	3,466
12/10	520.1	24.5	4.7%	2,787
12/09	452.8	(2.3)	—	2,613
Annual Growth	12.4%	—	—	9.9%

2013 Year-End Financials

Debt ratio: 37.8%
Return on equity: 16.0%
Cash ($ mil.): 63
Current ratio: 2.49
Long-term debt ($ mil.): 261

No. of shares (mil.): 26
Dividends
  Yield: 1.1%
  Payout: 36.8%
Market value ($ mil.): 918

	STOCK PRICE ($) FY Close	P/E High/Low		PER SHARE ($) Earnings	Dividends	Book Value
12/13	34.22	23	15	1.50	0.38	10.08
12/12	22.05	24	16	0.91	0.16	8.73
12/11	18.83	19	7	1.41	0.00	7.83
12/10	19.86	22	11	0.92	0.00	6.22
12/09	12.35	—	—	(0.09)	0.00	5.33
Annual Growth	29.0%	—	—	—	—	17.3%

AMC Networks Inc

AMC Networks is now somewhere over the rainbow. Formerly Rainbow Media Holdings the company is a leading cable television broadcaster with a portfolio of popular TV networks anchored by American Movie Classics (AMC) the cable network airing such critical hits as Mad Men and Breaking Bad that reaches more than 95 million households. It also owns The Independent Film Channel (IFC) the Sundance Channel and WE: Women's Entertainment (WE tv) one of the top networks aimed at women viewers. The company was a former subsidiary of Cablevision Systems until mid-2011 when Cablevision spun off Rainbow Media Holdings into a publicly traded company and changed its name to AMC Networks.

Change in Company Type

Believing that both companies would operate more effectively if they were two distinct companies Cablevision Systems spun-off of Rainbow Media in order to focus on its core cable television service business.

Geographic Reach

Headquartered in New York City the company has a broadcasting and technology center in Bethpage New York. In addition the company has properties in California Illinois Georgia and Michigan. Its channels are distributed throughout the US Europe and Asia. amctv.com delivers more than 4 million unique browsers each month.

Operations

The company is comprised of two reportable segments: National Networks and International and other. The National Networks segment includes four nationally distributed programming networks: AMC WE tv IFC and Sundance Channel.

International and Other includes AMC/Sundance Channel Global (international programming business) IFC Films (independent film distribution business) and AMC Networks Broadcasting & Technology (network technical services business). It also includes VOOM HD Holdings LLC which the company is winding down and which continues to sell certain limited amounts of programming through program license agreements.

AMC Networks brought in about 92% of its revenue from its National Networks segment during fiscal 2012 while the remaining 8% of revenue came from the International and other segment.

AMC Networks also make its IFC Films library content available on third-party digital platforms such as Netflix and iTunes.

Financial Performance

The company's annual revenue increased by 14% while its profits increased by 8% in fiscal 2012 compared to fiscal 2011. The growth was powered by increased revenue from the National Networks segment while revenue from International and other segment decreased in fiscal 2012 compared to the previous year.

The company gets the majority of its revenue from distribution includes affiliation fees paid by distributors to carry its programming networks as well as the licensing of programming for digital foreign and home video distribution.

In fiscal 2012 distribution and other revenue accounted for 61% of the company's revenues while the remaining 39% of revenue came from its advertising sales.

Strategy

Like other cable network operators AMC Networks is constantly focused on developing or acquiring new programming to attract viewers to its television properties. It also targets the networks to specific demographic groups or niche interests such as women and film fans. By targeting the programming the company can deliver specific audiences that advertisers want to reach.

AMC Newtorks has used partnerships and licensing to grow its business. In 2013 Rogers Communications Canada's leading diversified communications company signed a multi-year agreement with AMC to continue to offer Rogers digital cable customers new seasons of hit original series including Breaking Bad Mad Men and The Walking Dead.

EXECUTIVES

President and CEO, Joshua W. Sapan, $1,280,000 total compensation
Vp Special Projects And Operations, Jason Zegel
Vice President Corporate Communicatns Marketing, Christine Bragan
Senior Vice President Broadband, Dave Evans
Senior Vice President And General, John Barbieri
Vice President Of Sales And Marketing, Gina Hughes
SVP Broadcasting Information Systems and Technology, Steven J. Pontillo
COO, Ed Carroll, $1,100,000 total compensation
EVP and General Counsel, James G. (Jamie) Gallagher, $520,000 total compensation
SVP Communications, Ellen Kroner
President AMC Network Distribution, Robert (Bob) Broussard
EVP Human Resources, Rob Doodian
EVP and CFO, Sean S. Sullivan, $655,000 total compensation
EVP Finance, John Huffman
Senior Vice President Gm Rainbow, Harold Gronenthal
Senior Vp, Paul Rehrig
Senior Vice President Programming Operations, Joshua Berger
Senior Vice President Production, Theresa Patiri
Vp On-demand/broadband Video Production And Delivery, Greg Varhely
Vice President Advertising Sales La, Danielle Pantages-baker
Senior Vice President Original, Lauren Gellert
Vp Finance We, Ruth Sandhass
Executive Vice President Original, Joel Stillerman
Senior Vice President Affiliate Marketing, Jan Diedrichsen
Vice President Technology Services, Carlos Rethana
Senior Vice President Unscripted, Eliot Goldberg
Senior Vice President Scripted, Ben Davis
Vice President Southeast Boston Region, Lee Freedman
Vice President Revenue Planning, Eric Sack
Vice President Product Development, Michael Cagnazzi
Vice President, Steve Wegienek
Vice President Operations And Program, Dave Alworth
Executive Vice President Content And Inventry Strategy, David Epstein
Area Vice President Media And Ent, Larry Keating
Svp Distribution, Stefanie Nimick
Senior Vice President Direct Sales, Pat Lucci
Vice President Finance Amc And We, Stefan Reinhardt

Senior Vice President And Secretary, Anne Gill Kelly

Vp Information Technology, Rob Rubino

Vice President Midwestern Sales, Dodi Bashan

Vice President Distribution, Elizabeth Mulholland

V P And Creative Director, Mike Walton

Vice President Event Marketing And Promotions, Lauren Burack

Senior Vice President Strategic, Michele Goldstein

Vice President Of Digital Media, Drew Pisarra

Senior Vice President Marketing, Monica Bloom

Vice President Unscripted Programming, Tracey Lentz

Vice President Distribution And Business Development Latin America, Gustavo Lopez

Senior Vice President Scripted, Christian Vesper

Vice President Business Affairs, Scott Stein

Senior Vice President Corporate, James Maiella

Vice President Corporate Communications, Elana Mandelup

Senior Vice President Business Affairs, Marci Wiseman

Vice President Public Relations, Katie Lanegran

Senior Vice President Financial, John Hsu

Vice President Corporate Communications, Jaime Saberito

Senior Vice President Public Relations, Marnie Black

Vice President Partnerships And Advertising Sales, Lee Sparer

Vice President Digital Partnerships And Operations, Kirk Linden

Vice President Pricing And Planning, Thomas Etheridge

Senior Vice President Corporate Legal, Cliff Bail

Vice President Programming Strategy, Ray Giacopelli

Svp Sales Revenue Management, Steve Luttinger

Vice President Research Digital, Lisa Ciancarelli

Vice President Of Ad Sales Wetv, Tim Philbin

Svp Sales, Vanessa Benfield

Vp Promotional Planning And Strategy, Kristen Oliver

Vice President Tax, Trisha Delorenzo

Vice President Assistant Controller, Philip Gong

Vp Strategic Planning, Mariela Condy

Vice President Direct Response, Ann Cashen

Administrative Assistant To The Svp, Alissa Alvino

Vice President Production And Advanced, John Khoury

Vice President Business Affairs, Aleksandar Stojkovic

Senior Vice President Ad Sales, Marc Krok

Vp Tax, Christopher Nordin

Sales And Marketing Vp, Lisa Schwartz

Senior Vice President Strategic Financial Planning And Operations, Mary Martin

Vice President Marketing, Melissa Wasserman

Vice President, Bob Bruno

Vice President Pricing And Planning, Shannon Frasier

Vice President Ad Sales Fin Operations, Dan Russo

Vice President Creative Director, Lauren Cassidy

Vice President Finance Corporate Ifce Voom, Robert Berju

Vice President Financial Systems, Michael Morales

Executive Chairman, Charles Dolan

Treasury, May Wong

Auditors: KPMGLLP

LOCATIONS

HQ: AMC Networks Inc
11 Penn Plaza, New York, NY 10001
Phone: 212 324-8500
Web: www.amcnetworks.com

PRODUCTS/OPERATIONS

2012 Sales

	% of total
National Networks	92
International and other	8
Inter-segment adjustments	—
Total	**100**

Selected Television Networks

American Movie Classics (classic films)
The Independent Film Channel
IFC Films
Sundance Channel (independent films)
WE tv (entertainment and information for women)

COMPETITORS

A&E Networks	MTV Networks
ABC Cable Networks	NBCUniversal
Discovery Communications	Scripps Networks
	Showtime Networks
HBO	Turner Broadcasting

HISTORICAL FINANCIALS

Company Type: Public

Income Statement

FYE: December 31

	REVENUE ($ mil.)	NET INCOME ($ mil.)	NET PROFIT MARGIN	EMPLOYEES
12/13	1,591.8	290.7	18.3%	2,197
12/12	1,352.5	136.5	10.1%	1,010
12/11	1,187.7	126.4	10.6%	956
12/10	1,078.3	80.1	7.4%	876
12/09	973.6	53.7	5.5%	0
Annual Growth	**13.1%**	**52.5%**	**—**	**—**

2013 Year-End Financials

Debt ratio: 82.3%
Return on equity: ***,***.*%
Cash ($ mil.): 521
Current ratio: 3.15
Long-term debt ($ mil.): 2,169

No. of shares (mil.): 72
Dividends
  Yield: —
  Payout: —
Market value ($ mil.): 4,923

	STOCK PRICE ($) FY Close	P/E High/Low		PER SHARE ($) Earnings	Dividends	Book Value
12/13	68.11	18	12	4.00	0.00	(7.91)
12/12	49.50	27	18	1.89	0.00	(12.19)
12/11	37.58	22	17	1.79	0.00	(14.41)
Annual Growth	**34.6%**			**—**	**49.5%**	**—**

Ameren Illinois Co

Ameren Illinois brings gas and electric services to customers across the Land of Lincoln. The Ameren subsidiary operates a rate-regulated electric and natural gas transmission and distribution business in Illinois serving more than 1.2 million electricity and 806000 natural gas customers in 85 of Illinois' 102 counties. The multi-utility has a service area of 43700 square miles. Ameren Illinois operates 4500 miles of transmission lines 45400 miles of power distribution lines and 18000 miles of gas transmission and distribution mains. It also has 12 underground natural gas storage fields.
Geographic Reach
The company serves customers in more than 1200 communities in central and southern Illinois.

Company Background

In 2010 parent Ameren consolidated its three Illinois gas and electric utilities —AmerenCILCO AmerenCIPS and AmerenIP —into one utility under the Ameren Illinois Company name. The move which made the company one of the top electric and gas distribution providers in the state gained efficiencies for customers and reduced operating costs.

The 2010 consolidation rationalized the Illinois utility acquisitions made by Ameren over a 13 year period. Ameren acquired CIPSCO Incorporated (parent company of Central Illinois Public Service which became known as AmerenCIPS) in 1997. AmerenCILCO was acquired by Ameren from AES in 2003; Ameren subsequently transferred substantially all of the utility's fossil-fueled power plants (1100 MW of capacity) and the related wholesale marketing operations to a nonregulated affiliate. In 2004 Ameren acquired Illinois Power Company which subsequently became AmerenIP.

EXECUTIVES

Vp And Treasurer Cilco And Ameren, Jerre E Birdsong, age 60
Senior Vice President; General Counsel; Secretary, Gregory L Nelson, age 55
Vice President Corporate Secretary, James Johnson
Svp General Counsel Secretary And Director; Svp General Counsel And Secretary Ameren Cips Aeg Ameren Services Union Electric And Ip, Steven R Sullivan, age 54
Board Member, Richard Lumpkin
Auditors: PricewaterhouseCoopersLLP

LOCATIONS

HQ: Ameren Illinois Co
6 Executive Drive, Collinsville, IL 62234
Phone: 618 343-8150

COMPETITORS

Alliant Energy	Dynegy
Berkshire Hathaway Energy	Integrys Energy Services
Commonwealth Edison	Nicor Gas

HISTORICAL FINANCIALS

Company Type: Public

Income Statement

FYE: December 31

	REVENUE ($ mil.)	NET INCOME ($ mil.)	NET PROFIT MARGIN	EMPLOYEES
12/13	2,311.0	163.0	7.1%	3,133
12/12	2,525.0	144.0	5.7%	2,994
12/11	2,787.0	196.0	7.0%	2,793
12/10	3,014.0	252.0	8.4%	2,752
12/09	869.0	29.0	3.3%	657
Annual Growth	**27.7%**	**54.0%**	**—**	**47.8%**

2013 Year-End Financials

Debt ratio: 25.6%
Return on equity: 6.7%
Cash ($ mil.): 1
Current ratio: 0.82
Long-term debt ($ mil.): 1,856

No. of shares (mil.): 25
Dividends
  Yield: 0.0%
  Payout: 68.7%
Market value ($ mil.): 628

	STOCK PRICE ($)	P/E		PER SHARE ($)	
	FY Close	High/Low	Earnings	Dividends	Book Value
12/13	24.63	— —	(0.00)	1.66	96.00
12/12	25.25	— —	(0.00)	1.66	94.16
12/11	25.65	— —	(0.00)	1.38	96.16
12/10	24.40	— —	(0.00)	1.66	101.02
12/09	23.40	— —	(0.00)	1.66	22.51
Annual Growth	1.3%	— —	—	(0.0%)	43.7%

America First Multifamily Investors, L.P.

Shout it from the rooftops of its properties: America First Tax Exempt Investors is indeed for the most part tax exempt. The company invests in federally tax-exempt mortgage revenue bonds which are issued by state and local governments to help fund construction of and provide financing for multifamily housing complexes; ultimately the bonds are designed to provide affordable mortgages to low- to middle-income homebuyers. Currently America First Tax Exempt Investors' portfolio consists of more than 15 tax-exempt bonds that fund about 20 multifamily properties. The firm is managed by America First Real Estate Group and is part of Burlington Capital Group.

Most of America First Tax Exempt Investors' funded properties are apartment complexes located in eight states including Indiana Kentucky Minnesota Florida and Texas. In addition to its investments in mortgage revenue bonds the firm also occasionally makes taxable mortgage loans and invests in tax-exempt securities that are not secured by real estate.

America First Tax Exempt Investors is itself tax exempt but it owns holding company subsidiaries that do pay taxes. It maintains its tax-exempt status because it passes the interest earned from the bonds on to its investors who in most cases do not pay taxes on the interest income.

EXECUTIVES

President, Niles Andersen
Regional Manager Director of Compliance, Sheri Stambaugh

LOCATIONS

HQ: America First Multifamily Investors, L.P.
1004 Farnam Street, Suite 400, Omaha, NE 68102
Phone: 402 444-1630   **Fax:** 402 930-3047
Web: www.ataxfund.com

COMPETITORS

AIMCO Properties	Goldman Sachs
Apartment Investment and Management	Oaktree Capital
	The Blackstone Group
Equity Residential	The Carlyle Group
Fortress Investment Group	

HISTORICAL FINANCIALS
Company Type: Public

Income Statement
FYE: December 31

	ASSETS ($ mil.)	NET INCOME ($ mil.)	INCOME AS % OF ASSETS	EMPLOYEES
12/13	534.2	17.7	3.3%	0
12/12	413.1	4.4	1.1%	0
12/11	297.9	(2.2)	—	0
12/10	241.6	(0.4)	—	0
12/09	190.7	23.8	12.5%	0
Annual Growth	29.4%	(7.2%)	—	—

	STOCK PRICE ($)	P/E		PER SHARE ($)	
	FY Close	High/Low	Earnings	Dividends	Book Value
12/13	6.29	18 16	0.40	0.50	3.98
12/12	6.67	50 36	0.14	0.50	4.25
12/11	4.94	— —	(0.04)	0.50	4.35
12/10	5.24	87 74	0.07	0.50	4.25
12/09	5.98	45 30	0.15	0.55	4.51
Annual Growth	1.3%	— —	27.8%	(2.1%)	(3.1%)

American Campus Communities Inc

American Campus Communities (ACC) actually does most of its business off campus. The self-managed real estate investment trust (REIT) owns and operates student housing properties located at or near colleges and universities in more than 25 states. The company leases the ground for on-campus properties from the schools which in turn receive half of the net cash flow from these properties. ACC also works with schools to develop new properties and renovate existing housing and provides third-party leasing and management services for other student housing owners. In all the REIT manages about 201 properties (with some 128700 beds) at more than 85 schools in the US and Canada.

Operations

The company is a fully integrated self-managed and self-administered equity real estate investment trust with expertise in the design finance development construction management and operational management of student housing properties. It has four reportable segments: Wholly-Owned Properties On-Campus Participating Properties Development Services and Property Management Services.

Many of ACC's properties feature resort-style amenities making them more desirable than your typical dorm facility. The company has been successful in establishing strong relationships with school systems which pays off in earning repeat business as various campuses seek to add new housing options. Among the REIT's developments are sites in Texas and New Mexico.

ACC owns 167 student housing properties containing approximately 102700 beds. Including its owned and third-party managed properties ACC's total managed portfolio consists of 201 properties with approximately 128700 beds.

Sales and Marketing

The company has been increased spending on marketing and advertising initiatives in recent years In 2013 it spent $18 million (up from $11 million in 2012).

Financial Performance

ACC's revenues have been restated due to divestiture of a number of properties (including Hawks Landing University Mills State College Park Campus Ridge Brookstone Village and Campus Walk and Pirates Cove). In 2013 its revenues grew by 34% primarily due to an increase in revenues from same store properties thanks to higher average rental rates for the 2013/2014 and 2012/2013 academic years offset by a slight decrease in average occupancy from 96.1% in 2012 to 96.0% in 2013. Third-Party Management Services revenues grew as a result of three newly awarded third-party management contracts and the recognition of incentive management fees from another third-party management contract.After taking a hit during the worst of the US recession in 2009 profits have been on the rise since 2010. In 2013 ACC's net income increased by 85% due to higher revenues and increased income from discontinued operations. The company's operating cash inflow in 2013 increased to $246.7 million from $195.1 million in 2012 primarily due to operating cash flows provided from the timing of the acquisition of 46 properties and an additional phase at an existing property in 2012 and 2013 and the completion of construction and opening of 11 owned development projects in August and September 2012 and seven owned development projects in August and September 2013.

Strategy

ACC has expanded its portfolio by both buying existing properties and developing new ones. It regularly buys properties in bulk adding thousands of beds at a time. In addition to buying and developing new housing communities the REIT also sells properties when they are no longer considered core to its long-term investment strategy.

In 2013 the company announced that two of its owned properties in Tampa entered into housing affiliation agreements with the University of South Florida Department of Housing & Residential Education. The Province and Avalon Heights both located within walking distance of the USF Tampa campus are popular housing choices among USF students. Under the agreements the USF housing office will refer eligible upper-division transfer and graduate students to the affiliated properties as alternative housing options should the demand for on-campus housing exceed the university's present capacity.

Mergers and Acquisitions

In 2013 ACC made a number of major acquisitions including: Cardinal Towne a 255-unit 545-bed wholly-owned property located near the University of Louisville campus for $59.2 million; U Centre at Fry Street a 194-unit 614-bed wholly-owned property located near the University of North Texas campus ($51.3 million); Park Point a 300-unit 924-bed wholly-owned property located near the Rochester Institute of Technology campus($100.3 million); and a 366-bed additional phase at an existing property The Lodges of East Lansing ($32.3 million).

Company Background

In 2012 ACC acquired 15 properties with nearly 6600 beds in several states for some $627 million. The previous year the REIT acquired four properties as well as shopping center it plans to redevelop into a mixed-use community. It also completed and opened four new communities.

EXECUTIVES

EVP CFO and Treasurer, Jonathan A. Graf, age 49, $350,000 total compensation

President and CEO, William C. Bayless, age 50, $515,000 total compensation

EVP and COO, James C. Hopke, age 53, $242,000 total compensation

EVP Chief Investment Officer, William Talbot, age 40, $280,000 total compensation

EVP Public and Private Transactions, James E. (Jamie) Wilhelm, age 51, $225,000 total compensation

SVP Capital Markets, Daniel Perry, age 41

SVP Leasing Administration, Jennifer Beese, age 41

SVP Chief Technology Officer, Jorge de C Årdenas

Vice President Investor Relations And Corporate Marketing, Gina Cowart

Vice President Public Private, Noel Brinkman

Senior Vice President Marketing And Business Development, Jason Wills

Vice President Facilities Management, Wayne Schrader

Vice President Risk Management, Jane Downing

Vice President Project Management And Construction, Heather Laney

Vice President Application Development, Jeff Barret

Assistant Vice President Of Marketing, Ashley Kelly

Vice President Of Marketing, Kimberly Kelly

Vice President Project Management, Xavier Garcia

Vice President Public Private Partnerships, Mark Rogers

Chief Information Officer Chief Technology Officer Vice President Information Technology, Katherine Peeples

Senior Vice President Information Technologies, Jorge De Cardenas

Svp Information Technologies, Jorge C De Rdenas

Vice President Or Director Of Management Information Systems Or Information Technology, Greg McCarty

Vice President Investor Relations, Ryan Dennison

Vice President Financial Reporting, Jason French

Vice President Corporate Partner Development, David Valentino

Vice President Project Management Construction, Aaron Armstrong

EVP CFO and Treasurer, Jonathan A. Graf, age 49

Chairman, R.D. (Dan) Burck, age 81

Board Of Directors, Winston Walker

Auditors: Ernst&YoungLLP

LOCATIONS

HQ: American Campus Communities Inc
12700 Hill Country Blvd., Suite T-200, Austin, TX 78738
Phone: 512 732-1000
Alabama
  Shelton State College
  Stillman College
  University of Alabama - Birmingham
  University of Alabama - Tuscaloosa
Alberta
  Southern Alberta Institute of Technology
Arizona
  Arizona State University
  Pima Community College
  University of Arizona
California
  American River Community College
  California State University - Fresno
  Fresno Pacific University
  San Diego State University
  Sierra College
Colorado
  Community College of Denver
  Front Range Community College
  Regis University

University of Denver
Florida
  Santa Fe Community College
  Seminole State College of Florida
  University of Florida - Gainesville
  Valencia Comunity College
Georgia
  Athens Technical College
  East Georgia College
  Georgia Gwinnett College
  Piedmont College - Athens Campus
  Wiregrass Georgia Technical College
Hawaii
  University of Hawaii - Manoa
Illinois
  Parkland College University of Illinois
Indiana
  Indiana/Purdue University
  Indiana University
Iowa
  Des Moines University
  Drake University
  Kaplin University
Kentucky
  Blue Grass Technical College
  Bowling Green Community College
  Western Kentucky University
Louisiana
  Baton Rouge Community College
  Louisiana State University
  Southern University
  University of New Orleans
Maryland
  Morgan State University
  University of Maryland
Michigan
  Central Michigan University
  Eastern Michigan University
  Kalamazoo Valley Community College
  Michigan State University
  University of Michigan
  Western Michigan University
Minnesota
  Art Institute International
  Minnesota State University
  University of Minnesota
Mississippi
  East Mississippi Community College
  Mississippi State University
Nebraska
  Nebraska Wesleyan University
  Southeast Community College
  University of Nebraska
Nevada
  University of Nevada at Reno
New Jersey
  Bloomfield College
  Essex County College
  Seton Hall University
New Mexico
  University of New Mexico
New York
  Buffalo State College
  Canisius College
  Medaille College
  State University of New York at Buffalo
North Carolina
  Central Piedmont Community College
  Durham Tech
  Johnson & Wales
  UNC Chapel Hill
Ohio
  Cleveland State University
  Owens Community College
  University of Toledo
Oklahoma
  Oklahoma City Community College
  Rose State College
  University of Oklahoma
Ontario
  Fanshawe College
  London College
  University of Western Ontario
Pennsylvania
  Drexel
  Penn State University
  Temple University
South Carolina
  Columbia College

Midlands Tech
Tennessee
  Daymar Institute
  East Tennessee State University
  Milligan College
  Pellissippi State Community College
  University of Tennessee
Texas
  Blinn College
  Lubbock Christian University
  Sam Houston State University
  Texas A&M University
  University of Houston - Victoria
Virginia
  Blue Ridge Community College
  Eastern Mennonite University
  New River Community College
  University of Virginia
  Virginia Tech
West Virginia
  Fairmont State College
  Marshall University
  Potomac State
  West Virginia University

PRODUCTS/OPERATIONS

2013 Sales

	$ mil.	% of total
Wholly owned properties	618.5	94
On-campus participating properties	26.3	4
Third-party management services	7.5	1
Third-party development services	2.6	1
Resident services	2.6	-
Total	**657.5**	**100**

COMPETITORS

AMLI Residential	Campus Apartments
Allen & O' Hara	Campus Crest
Alliance Residential	Education Realty
Apartment Investment and Management	Fairfield Residential
	JPI
Camden Property	Place Properties

HISTORICAL FINANCIALS

Company Type: Public

Income Statement
FYE: December 31

	REVENUE ($ mil.)	NET INCOME ($ mil.)	NET PROFIT MARGIN	EMPLOYEES
12/13	657.4	104.6	15.9%	3,059
12/12	491.2	56.6	11.5%	2,913
12/11	390.3	56.6	14.5%	2,387
12/10	344.9	16.2	4.7%	2,334
12/09	309.5	(12.8)	—	2,183
Annual Growth	20.7%	—	—	8.8%

2013 Year-End Financials

Debt ratio: 49.0%
Return on equity: 3.9%
Cash ($ mil.): 38
Current ratio: 1.28
Long-term debt ($ mil.): 2,744

No. of shares (mil.): 104
Dividends
  Yield: 4.4%
  Payout: 146.1%
Market value ($ mil.): 3,375

	STOCK PRICE ($) FY Close	P/E High/Low	PER SHARE ($) Earnings	Dividends	Book Value
12/13	32.21	48 32	0.98	1.42	25.05
12/12	46.13	72 61	0.65	1.35	25.30
12/11	41.96	52 38	0.80	1.35	18.90
12/10	31.76	124 91	0.26	1.35	18.15
12/09	28.10	— —	(0.28)	1.35	17.22
Annual Growth	3.5%	— —	—	1.2%	9.8%

American Capital Agency Corp

American Capital Agency is taking on the rocky real estate market. The real estate investment trust (REIT) was created in 2008 to invest in securities backed by single-family residential mortgages and collateralized mortgage obligations guaranteed by government agencies Fannie Mae Freddie Mac and Ginnie Mae. The company is externally managed and advised by American Capital Agency Management a subsidiary of US publicly traded alternative asset manager American Capital which spun off American Capital Agency in 2008 but retained about a 33% stake in the REIT.

American Capital Agency raised some $300 million from its 2008 IPO. The REIT used the proceeds from the offering to build and develop its investment portfolio.

EXECUTIVES

EVP and CFO; VP and Treasurer American Capital Agency Management, John R. Erickson, age 54
Chairman President and CEO; President American Capital Agency Management, Malon Wilkus, age 62
EVP and Secretary; VP and Secretary American Capital Agency Management, Samuel A. Flax, age 57
Senior Vice President - Agency Portfolio Investments, Christopher Kuehl
EVP and CFO; VP and Treasurer American Capital Agency Management, John R. Erickson, age 54
Chairman President and CEO; President American Capital Agency Management, Malon Wilkus, age 62
EVP and Secretary; VP and Secretary American Capital Agency Management, Samuel A. Flax, age 57
Auditors: Ernst&YoungLLP

LOCATIONS

HQ: American Capital Agency Corp
2 Bethesda Metro Center, 14th Floor, Bethesda, MD 20814
Phone: 301 968-9300
Web: www.AGNC.com

PRODUCTS/OPERATIONS

2009 Sales

	$ mil	% of total
Interest income	127.9	72
Gain on sale of agency securities	49.9	28
Adjustments	(4.2)	-
Total	**173.6**	**100**

COMPETITORS

ARMOUR Residential REIT	CIFC
Annaly Capital Management	Capstead Mortgage
	Chimera
Anworth Mortgage Asset	Hatteras Financial
Bimini Capital Management	JAVELIN Mortgage
	MFA Financial
	Redwood Trust

HISTORICAL FINANCIALS

Company Type: Public

Income Statement

FYE: December 31

	REVENUE ($ mil.)	NET INCOME ($ mil.)	NET PROFIT MARGIN	EMPLOYEES
12/13	1,440.0	1,259.0	87.4%	0
12/12	1,440.0	1,277.0	88.7%	0
12/11	850.6	770.4	90.6%	0
12/10	307.3	288.1	93.7%	0
12/09	130.0	118.6	91.2%	0
Annual Growth	**82.4%**	**80.5%**	**—**	**—**

2013 Year-End Financials

Debt ratio: 1.1%
Return on equity: 12.8%
Cash ($ mil.): 2,143
Current ratio: 0.13
Long-term debt ($ mil.): —
No. of shares (mil.): 356
Dividends
Yield: 19.4%
Payout: 62.0%
Market value ($ mil.): 6,871

	STOCK PRICE ($) FY Close	P/E High/Low		PER SHARE ($) Earnings	Dividends	Book Value
12/13	19.29	10	6	3.28	3.75	24.42
12/12	28.90	9	7	4.17	5.00	32.15
12/11	28.08	6	5	5.02	5.60	27.71
12/10	28.74	4	3	7.89	5.60	24.24
12/09	26.54	5	2	6.78	5.15	22.48
Annual Growth	**(7.7%)**	**—**	**—**	**(16.6%)**	**(7.6%)**	**2.1%**

American Public Education Inc

American Public Education (APE) promotes military intelligence. The company offers online post-secondary education to those in the military and other public servants such as police and firefighters. Its American Military University and American Public University make up the American Public University System which offers roughly 90 degree programs and 70 certificate programs in such disciplines as business administration criminal justice intelligence technology liberal arts and homeland security. Enrollment in the online university consists of more than 100000 students from all 50 states and about 100 foreign countries. More than 60% of APE's students serve in the US military on active duty.

APE's nationally and regionally accredited online education system offers associate's bachelor's and master's degrees. It is specifically geared toward adult students who are on call for rapid-response missions or extended deployment. APE has an open enrollment system accepting all applicants with a high school diploma or equivalent and it has some 1800 full- and part-time faculty members to support its students. For those with limited financial resources tuition assistance programs offered by the US Department of Defense constitute about half of the company's annual revenues.

APE is ramping up its outreach efforts focusing on retention of students in its core military market (which represents more than 2 million potential students) while marketing the availability of federal student aid grants and low-cost loans to the public service and civilian markets. It is also expanding the number and type of degrees offered based on demographic trends. In 2011 for instance APE received approval from the Higher Learning Commission to offer degree programs in eight new areas including retail management and accounting.

Its efforts have paid off with the company experiencing rapidly climbing revenues since 2007 including a 31% increase in 2011 to some $260 million. Profits have followed suit with APE reporting a 36% increase in net income in 2011 (to some $41 million). Its annual course registration rate increased more than 30% in both 2010 and 2011. APE attributes the increases to the cost and variety of its programs student referral and satisfaction rates new course accreditations and increasing acceptance of online learning as a viable alternative to bricks and mortar schooling.

APE was founded in 1991 as American Military University by a retired Marine Corps major. It went public in 2007 and used the proceeds to pay stockholders more than $93 million.

EXECUTIVES

EVP Chief Development Officer; CEO Hondros College of Nursing, Harry T. Wilkins, $314,533 total compensation
President and CEO, Wallace E. (Wally) Boston, $539,231 total compensation
EVP and CFO, Richard W. Sunderland
EVP Programs and Marketing, Carol S. Gilbert, $264,454 total compensation
Chief Information Officer, Michael P. Miotto
EVP and Provost, Karan H. Powell, $236,488 total compensation
EVP and COO, Sharon van Wyk, $314,631 total compensation
SVP Academic Operations Officer, Gwendolyn M. (Gwen) Hall
Chairman, Timothy T. (Tim) Weglicki
Auditors: McGladreyLLP

LOCATIONS

HQ: American Public Education Inc
111 West Congress Street, Charles Town, WV 25414
Phone: 304 724-3700
Web: www.americanpubliceducation.com

PRODUCTS/OPERATIONS

2011 Selected Programs

Programs	Number
Undergraduate certificates	35
Graduate certificates	34
Bachelor of Arts	24
Master of Arts	17
Associate of Arts	13
Bachelor of Science	12
Associate of Science	8
Master of Science	6
Master of Education	3
Master of Public Administration	1
Master of Public Health	1
Master of Business Administration	1
Bachelor of Business Administration	1
Total	**156**

Selected Degree Programs

Accounting
Business Administration
Communication
Computer Applications
Counter Terrorism
Criminal Justice
Database Application
Early Childhood Development
Emergency and Disaster Management
English
Environmental Services

COMPETITORS

Apollo Education
Bridgepoint Education
Capella Education
Career Education
Corinthian Colleges
DeVry Education Group
Embry-Riddle Aeronautical University
Grand Canyon Education
Heald College
ITT Educational
Kaplan
Strayer Education
Touro College
University of Maryland

HISTORICAL FINANCIALS

Company Type: Public

Income Statement

FYE: December 31

	REVENUE ($ mil.)	NET INCOME ($ mil.)	NET PROFIT MARGIN	EMPLOYEES
12/13	329.4	42.0	12.8%	3,492
12/12	313.5	42.3	13.5%	2,950
12/11	260.3	40.7	15.7%	1,790
12/10	198.1	29.8	15.1%	1,500
12/09	149.0	23.9	16.1%	1,480
Annual Growth	21.9%	15.1%	—	23.9%

2013 Year-End Financials

Debt ratio: —
Return on equity: 22.2%
Cash ($ mil.): 94
Current ratio: 2.15
Long-term debt ($ mil.): —

No. of shares (mil.): 17
Dividends
Yield: —
Payout: —
Market value ($ mil.): 764

	STOCK PRICE ($) FY Close	P/E High/Low		PER SHARE ($) Earnings	Dividends	Book Value
12/13	43.47	19	13	2.35	0.00	11.78
12/12	36.12	19	11	2.35	0.00	9.64
12/11	43.28	21	14	2.23	0.00	7.50
12/10	37.24	29	15	1.59	0.00	5.43
12/09	34.36	35	23	1.27	0.00	4.49
Annual Growth	6.1%	—	—	16.6%	—	27.3%

American Railcar Industries Inc

American Railcar Industries (ARI) doesn't make the little engine that could but it does make the cars that the engine pulls. A North American manufacturer of railcars and railcar components the company also provides maintenance and fleet management services to freight shippers railcar leasing companies and railroads. Its two Arkansas manufacturing facilities make several types of railcars including covered hoppers for grains cement and other dry bulk and tank cars for liquid and gas commodities. The company also serves non-rail industries with industrial products such as steel and aluminum casting machining stamping welding and fabrication.

Geographic Reach

Headquartered at Saint Charles Missouri ARI has two Arkansas-based railcar manufacturing plants; three sub-assembly and fabrication facilities; three railcar and industrial component manufacturing facilities; six railcar repair plants; and 10 mobile repair and mini-shop locations throughout in the US (primarily concentrated in Texas and Missouri) and Canada (Ontario).

Through its subsidiaries ARM I and ARM II (located in Mauritius) it holds a 50% interest in Amtek Railcar Private Limited an Indian joint venture.

Operations

ARI divides its operations across three segments: manufacturing (89% of total sales) railcar services (9%) and railcar leasing (2%).

Sales and Marketing

The company sells and markets its products and services through marketing personnel and sales representatives directly to its customers in North America. It serves primarily leasing companies industrial companies and clients that use railcars for freight transport or shippers and Class I railroads.

Its top 10 customers accounted for 83% of its total revenues in 2012; the top three include CIT Group (50%) American Railcar Leasing (10%) and AEP Leasing (8%).

Financial Performance

After suffering through the decline in demand for new railcars due to the economic downturn ARI has enjoyed exceptional growth over the last few years. Revenues surged 37% from $519 million in 2011 to $712 million in 2012 while its profits absolutely skyrocketed by more than 1000% from $4 million to $64 million.

The growth for 2012 was attributed to a 40% spike in manufacturing revenue driven by increased demand from the tank railcar market. ARI also experienced strong growth from railcar leasing from third parties.

The impressive jump in profits was driven by the higher revenue coupled with a steep decline in operating expenses and a $7.4 million dip affiliated with a joint venture loss.

Strategy

ARI is focused on growing its leasing operations. In 2012 it completed nearly $200 million in financing of its railcar lease fleet through a newly formed subsidiary Longtrain Leasing. These efforts seemed to have paid off as railcar leasing revenue skyrocketed by more than 1000% from 2011 to 2012.

Ownership

Chairman and billionaire financier Carl Icahn owns 56% of ARI.

EXECUTIVES

Sr Vice President Sales, Al Lullman
SVP CFO and Treasurer, Dale C. Davies, age 62, $205,000 total compensation
President and CEO, Jeffrey S. Hollister
SVP CFO and Treasurer, Umesh Choksi
Vice President Marketing, Jim Doty
Senior Vice President Marketing, Elise Brasel
Vice President Manufacturing, Rich Arnbruster
SVP CFO and Treasurer, Dale C. Davies, age 62
Chairman, SungHwan Cho, age 39
SVP CFO and Treasurer, Umesh Choksi
Secretary, Bonnie Cavender
Board Member, Hunter C Gary
Vice Chairman Of The Board Non Executive Director, Guofei Xu
Auditors: GrantThorntonLLP

LOCATIONS

HQ: American Railcar Industries Inc
100 Clark Street, St. Charles, MO 63301
Phone: 636 940-6000

PRODUCTS/OPERATIONS

Selected Products and Services

Industrial Products
  Aluminum Casting
  Custom Plate Burning
  Heat Treating
  Machining and Inspection
  Robotic Fabrication
  Roll Forming
  Specialty Welding
  Steel and Alloy Casting
  Structural Fabrication
Manufacturing
  Cement and Sand Railcars
  Grain Railcars
  Hopper railcars
  Ore Railcars
  Plastic Pellet Railcars
  Pressureable Railcars
  Specialized Railcars

2012 Sales	$ mil.	% of total
Manufacturing operations	633.5	89
Railcar services	64.7	9
Railcar leasing	13.5	2
Total	711.7	100

COMPETITORS

FreightCar America
GE Rail Services
Greenbrier Companies
Kawasaki Rail Car

Miner Enterprises
Trinity Industries
Union Tank Car

HISTORICAL FINANCIALS

Company Type: Public

Income Statement

FYE: December 31

	REVENUE ($ mil.)	NET INCOME ($ mil.)	NET PROFIT MARGIN	EMPLOYEES
12/13	750.5	86.9	11.6%	2,663
12/12	711.7	63.8	9.0%	2,643
12/11	519.3	4.3	0.8%	2,413
12/10	273.5	(27.0)	—	1,598
12/09	423.4	15.4	3.7%	1,335
Annual Growth	15.4%	54.0%	—	18.8%

2013 Year-End Financials

Debt ratio: 23.5%
Return on equity: 21.6%
Cash ($ mil.): 101
Current ratio: 2.53
Long-term debt ($ mil.): 188

No. of shares (mil.): 21
Dividends
Yield: 2.1%
Payout: 24.5%
Market value ($ mil.): 977

	STOCK PRICE ($) FY Close	P/E High/Low		PER SHARE ($) Earnings	Dividends	Book Value
12/13	45.75	12	7	4.07	1.00	20.32
12/12	31.73	12	7	2.99	0.25	17.30
12/11	23.93	142	70	0.20	0.00	14.53
12/10	22.13	—	—	(1.27)	0.00	14.44
12/09	11.02	17	9	0.73	0.09	15.76
Annual Growth	**42.7%**		**—**	**53.7%**	**82.6%**	**6.6%**

American Vanguard Corp.

American Vanguard Corporation (AMVAC) bugs bugs roots out roots out weeds and helps people take care of their health and personal appearance. The company makes specialty chemicals designed to protect the health of animals crops and people. Products made by its AMVAC Chemical subsidiary include pesticides plant-growth regulators herbicides and soil fumigants. Its GemChem subsidiary distributes the company's chemicals nationally to the cosmetic nutritional and pharmaceutical industries. AMVAC also has marketing subsidiaries in the UK and Mexico.

Operations

The company's SmartBox delivery system allows for controlled and regular dissemination of crop protection products. AMVAC pairs the SmartBox system with its own insecticides as well as with products of Bayer CropScience and Syngenta Crop Protection (through licensing agreements). This allows AMVAC to offer farmers multiple crop protection options thereby not allowing insects to develop resistance to any one pesticide.

Sales and Marketing

Tenkoz; Crop Production Services (formerly United Agri Products Western Farm Services and Crop Production Services); and Winfield accounted for 26% 18% and 11% respectively of AMVAC's revenues in 2011. The US accounted for 79% of 2011 revenues. The largest non-US customer Mexico accounted for 5% of total revenues that year.

Financial Analysis

AMVAC's revenues increased by 34% in 2011 due to a growth in sales of insecticides as a result of sales of granular soil insecticides which were up approximately 125% driven by a strong performance from primary corn soil insecticides - Aztec Smartchoice Counter and Force. This product group also benefitted from the newly acquired Mocap and Nemacur granular insecticides/nematicides which were purchased in December 2010 and net sales of herbicides were up by 5% over prior year whereas non-crop segment net sales were up by about 24%.

Net income increased by 101% in 2011 thanks to higher revenues offset in part by a 28% increase in operating expenses.

Strategy

The company has pursued a growth strategy of acquiring established product lines and companies that complement its core businesses. It also develops and commercializes new compounds through licensing arrangements.

AMVAC acquired the domestic segment of the cotton defoliant product Tribufos (sold under the trade name Def) and the global insecticide Ethoprophos (marketed as Mocap) from Bayer CropScience in 2010. The international segment was acquired in late 2011. The acquisition of Def complements AMVAC's existing cotton defoliant product Folex which it has marketed since 2002. Mocap is used globally to eradicate nematode species in a variety of crops.

In 2010 the company also acquired the Nemacur insecticide from Bayer CropScience which is used in more than 30 countries to fight above-ground sucking insects.

Ownership

Heartland Advisors Herbert A. Kraft (Co-Chairman) and T. Rowe Price Associates own 17% 10% and 10% of the company respectively.

EXECUTIVES

Chairman and CEO, Eric G. Wintemute, age 58, $592,000 total compensation
President GemChem, Robert F. (Bob) Gilbane, $230,022 total compensation
CFO, David T. Johnson, age 57, $306,500 total compensation
Managing Director AMVAC Netherlands BV, Ad de Jong
National Sales Manager Amvac, Jim Lehman
Senior Vice President Chief Administrative Officer Treasurer Assistant Secretary, James A (Jim) Barry, age 64
Chairman and CEO, Eric G. Wintemute, age 58
Board Member, Esmail Zirakparvar
Auditors: BDOUSALLP

LOCATIONS

HQ: American Vanguard Corp.
 4695 MacArthur Court, Newport Beach, CA 92660
Phone: 949 260-1200
Web: www.american-vanguard.com

2011 Sales

	$ mil.	% of total
US	241.0	79
Other countries	63.4	21
Total	**304.4**	**100**

PRODUCTS/OPERATIONS

2011 Sales

	$ mil.	% of total
Crops		
Insecticides	137.4	45
Herbicides	90.8	30
Other	47.2	15
Non-crop	29.0	10
Total	**304.4**	**100**

COMPETITORS

Aceto	DuPont Agriculture
Bayer CropScience	FMC
Dow AgroSciences	KMG Chemicals

HISTORICAL FINANCIALS

Company Type: Public

Income Statement

FYE: December 31

	REVENUE ($ mil.)	NET INCOME ($ mil.)	NET PROFIT MARGIN	EMPLOYEES
12/13	381.0	34.4	9.0%	499
12/12	366.1	36.8	10.1%	504
12/11	304.4	22.0	7.2%	390
12/10	229.6	10.9	4.8%	350
12/09	209.3	(5.7)	—	330
Annual Growth	**16.2%**	**—**	**—**	**10.9%**

2013 Year-End Financials

Debt ratio: 11.5%	No. of shares (mil.): 28
Return on equity: 14.2%	Dividends
Cash ($ mil.): 6	Yield: 0.9%
Current ratio: 2.26	Payout: 13.9%
Long-term debt ($ mil.): 51	Market value ($ mil.): 697

	STOCK PRICE ($) FY Close	P/E High/Low		PER SHARE ($) Earnings	Dividends	Book Value
12/13	24.29	28	18	1.19	0.22	8.98
12/12	31.07	28	10	1.28	0.22	7.91
12/11	13.34	18	10	0.79	0.08	6.78
12/10	8.54	24	15	0.40	0.03	6.06
12/09	8.30	—	—	(0.21)	0.06	5.60
Annual Growth	**30.8%**		**—**	**—**	**38.4%**	**12.5%**

American Woodmark Corp.

American Woodmark has more cabinet selections than the prime minister of Russia. A top maker of home cabinets in the US the company makes and distributes about 600 styles of low- to mid-priced kitchen cabinets and vanities. Styles vary by finish (oak cherry hickory maple as well as laminate) and door design. Brands include American Woodmark Shenandoah Cabinetry Timberlake and Waypoint. Targeting the remodeling and new home construction markets American Woodmark sells its lineup through home centers and independent dealers and distributors; it also sells directly to major builders. American Woodmark was established through a leveraged buyout of Boise Cascade's cabinet division.

Geographic Reach

Virginia-based American Woodmark operates nine manufacturing facilities in Arizona Georgia Indiana Kentucky Maryland Tennessee Virginia and West Virginia. Its coast-to-coast service centers expand its customer reach beyond the Sun Belt construction market.

Operations

Business is divided between two markets: Remodeling which accounted for 66% of sales in fiscal 2014 (ended April) and new home construction 44% of sales. Products are distributed through four assembly plants and a third party logistics network.

Through its nine service centers nationwide American Woodmark offers complete turnkey installation services to its direct builder customers.

The company keeps in stock about 85 door designs in about 20 colors.

Sales and Marketing

Together Lowe's and The Home Depot accounted for nearly 49% of the company's fiscal 2014 (ended April) sales. Advertising expenses for fiscal years 2013 2012 and 2011 were $36.5 million $37.4 million and $30 million respectively.

Through three primary channels –home centers builders and independent dealers and distributors —American Woodmark services the remodeling and new home construction markets.

Its brand names include American Woodmark Timberlake (sold to major home builders) Shenandoah Cabinetry (Lowe's) Potomac (Lowe's) and Waypoint Living Spaces.

Financial Performance

American Woodmark has enjoyed rising revenue since 2009. Following a steep decline in sales and profits when the US housing marketing tanked American Woodmark's sales have rebounded. Indeed in fiscal 2014 (ended April) the cabinet maker reported sales of more than $726 million a 15% increase versus the prior year. Net income rose sharply over the same period to about $20.5 million a 110% increase. Notably sales to the new home market increased more than 30%.

Strategy

Responding to the prolonged slump in housing activity that began back in 2007 the cabinet market closed two manufacturing facilities and suspended production at a third in late 2011. The company also redesigned its long-term employee benefit plans effective fiscal 2013.

Now that the outlook for housing in the US is improving American Woodmark expects that industry-wide cabinet remodeling sales will continue a trend that began in fiscal 2013 and improve at roughly a mid-single digit rate during fiscal years 2014 and 2015. The cabinet marker expects to continue to gain market share in its growing dealer business and to outperform its rivals. Indeed cabinet sales as reported by members of the Kitchen Cabinet Manufacturers Association increased by 11% during fiscal 2013. By comparison over the same period American Woodmark's sales grew 22%.

HISTORY

Alvin Goldhush in 1951 started cabinet company Form Laminates which lumber giant Boise Cascade acquired two decades later. Four senior managers of Boise Cascade's cabinet division — William Brandt Jeff Holcomb Al Graber and Donald Mathias —engineered an LBO of the unit in 1980 and named it American Woodmark after a popular line of cabinets. The company started selling cabinets nationwide through distribution centers and went public in 1986.

American Woodmark spent the first half of the 1990s diversifying its product and brands. In 1990 it introduced Timberlake a cabinet line for the construction industry. Other brands including Coventry and Case Crestwood and Scots Pine were added and quintupled its product line.

President and COO Jake Gosa became CEO in 1996. The sales cupboard was rather bare that year from a downturn in the closely linked home centers industry. The market surged in 1997 causing American Woodmark's profits to nearly triple and new equipment and manufacturing techniques boosted output. In 1998 the company began offering hickory cabinets (its first new wood species in a decade) kitchen accessories and high-quality ready-to-assemble framed cabinets (Flat Pack).

In 1999 American Woodmark expanded its hickory cabinet offerings (adding the Newport and Charleston brands). The company began operations at its new assembly facility in Gas City Indiana in 2000. To both preserve and increase market share in a slow-growth economy in 2001 American Woodmark initiated plans to expand two plants and open two more in Kentucky and Oklahoma.

As a result of the introduction of new products and increased shipments the company's net sales for fiscal 2002 increased 24%; the company's profits also increased due in part to lower freight and material costs and through its improved product mix.

The next year brought mixed results as the company continued to prosper in the first half of the year (sales growth of 16% and net income growth of 20%) but fell during the second half (sales growth of 10% and a 15% decline in net income). Contributing factors included weakened growth due to concerns about the economy and the impact of war in Iraq a temporary decline in business with The Home Depot (in support of its efforts to reformat many of its stores) the pricing of hardwood lumber as supply dropped below demand and higher costs associated with the company's increased capacity.

Shipments to both the remodeling and new home construction markets grew in fiscal 2004 and American Woodmark's sales increased by about 18% from the previous year. The company's gross profit (as a percentage of sales) dropped to about 20% due to higher materials costs per unit labor costs and shifts in the product mix. The company began producing wood cabinet components at its newly built plant in Hardy County West Virginia (its third plant there) in 2004 and it also built an assembly facility in Cumberland Maryland that began operations in 2005.

EXECUTIVES

Senior Vice President Manufacturing, Cary Dunston

Chairman and CEO, Kent B. Guichard, $636,346 total compensation

SVP and General Manager New Construction, R. Perry Campbell

EVP and COO, S. Cary Dunston, $356,633 total compensation

SVP Remodel Sales and Marketing, Bradley S. (Brad) Boyer, $258,173 total compensation

CFO, M. Scott Culbreth

Senior Vice President, Ian Sole

Vice President Manufacturing, David Blount

Vice President Of Market Research, Thomas Downy

Vp Manufacturing, Alan Davis

Vice President Of Value Stream Services, Bob Foote

Vice President Supply Chain Services, Mike Feighery

Vice President Of Marketing For, Max Caldas

Vice President Home Depot Sales, Jim Schaefer

Vice President Sales Lowes, Doug Boucher

Vice President New Construction, Boz Malik

Vice President Marketing And Sales, Mark Kovich

Vice President, Gary Wolf

Vice President Of Sales And Marketing, Al Graber

Vice President Of Timberlake Marketing, Don Repshas

Vice President Of Sales And Marketing, Tom Kline

Executive Vice President, Elizabeth Wters

Board Member, Rick Hardy

Chairman and CEO, Kent B. Guichard

Secretary, Donald Mathias

Auditors: KPMGLLP

LOCATIONS

HQ: American Woodmark Corp.
3102 Shawnee Drive, Winchester, VA 22601
Phone: 540 665-9100
Web: www.americanwoodmark.com
Allegany County MD
Gas City IN
Hardy County WV
Humboldt TN
Jackson GA
Kingman AZ
Monticello KY
Orange VA
Toccoa GA

Selected Service Centers

Berryville VA
Coppell TX
Houston TX
Huntersville NC
Kennesaw GA
Montgomeryville PA
Orlando FL
Phoenix AZ
Raleigh NC
Rancho Cordova CA
Tampa FL

PRODUCTS/OPERATIONS

2014 Sales

	% of total
Remodeling	56
New home construction	44
Total	**100**

Selected Brands

American Woodmark
Potomac
Shenandoah Cabinetry
Timberlake
Waypoint Living Spaces

COMPETITORS

Armstrong World Industries
Elkay Manufacturing
Masco
MasterBrand Cabinets
Norcraft Companies Inc.
US Home Systems

HISTORICAL FINANCIALS

Company Type: Public

Income Statement

FYE: April 30

	REVENUE ($ mil.)	NET INCOME ($ mil.)	NET PROFIT MARGIN	EMPLOYEES
04/14	726.5	20.4	2.8%	4,916
04/13	630.4	9.7	1.5%	4,537
04/12	515.8	(20.7)	—	3,791
04/11	452.5	(20.0)	—	3,693
04/10	406.5	(22.3)	—	3,401
Annual Growth	**15.6%**	**—**	**—**	**9.6%**

2014 Year-End Financials

Debt ratio: 6.5%
Return on equity: 12.1%
Cash ($ mil.): 135
Current ratio: 2.95
Long-term debt ($ mil.): 20
No. of shares (mil.): 15
Dividends
  Yield: 0.0%
  Payout: —
Market value ($ mil.): 464

	STOCK PRICE ($) FY Close	P/E High/Low		PER SHARE ($)	
			Earnings	Dividends	Book Value
04/14	30.01	30 23	1.31	0.00	12.31
04/13	33.65	54 24	0.66	0.00	9.86
04/12	17.95	— —	(1.45)	0.27	9.03
04/11	20.31	— —	(1.40)	0.36	10.77
04/10	23.11	— —	(1.58)	0.36	12.34
Annual Growth	6.7%	—	—	—	(0.1%)

Amsurg Corp

It's not quite an assembly line but AmSurg aims to make outpatient surgeries more efficient cost effective and up to date. The company operates ambulatory surgery centers that specialize in a few high-volume low-risk procedures with no overnight stays. Its specialties include gastroenterology (colonoscopy and endoscopy) orthopedics (knee scopes and carpal tunnel repair) ophthalmology (cataracts and laser eye surgery) otolaryngology (earn nose and throat) and urology. Each of its centers are affiliated with physicians practice group and offer either a single or multiple specialty.

Geographic Reach

AmSurg owns a majority interest in more than 240 outpatient centers in 35 US states and Washington DC.

Operations

In 2012 about 1.5 million surgical procedures were performed in its ambulatory surgery centers which have a total of 2000 physician partners.

Typically the local physician practice groups own 49% of each center while AmSurg holds 51%. Gastroenterology and ophthalmology procedures account for the bulk the company's revenues. Because colonoscopies and cataract surgeries are more common among older patients AmSurg is optimistic that the aging population will provide a lucrative revenue stream.

Outpatient surgery is generally less expensive than any hospital stay and managed care plans like to steer their customers to such facilities when possible. AmSurg negotiates to secure managed care contracts with health plan providers and also markets its centers to referring physicians.

Sales and Marketing

The company markets its surgery centers directly to patients referring physicians and third-party payors including health maintenance organizations (HMOs) preferred provider organizations (PPOs) and other managed care organizations.

Financial Performance

AmSurg's revenues grew by 18% in 2012 thanks to an increase in procedures performed in its ASCs as the result of the acquisition of additional centers. The company's net income increased by 25% in 2012 thanks to higher revenues partially offset by an increase in operating expenses.

AmSurg derived 27% of its 2012 revenues from Medicare and other government programs. Changes in reimbursement rates affect the company's revenues directly —up or down. Reforms in the health care law will also affect the company: for instance Medicare and other health plans are now required to completely cover certain preventive screening procedures including colonoscopies.

Strategy

AmSurg acquires develops and operates ambulatory surgery centers in partnership with physician practice groups throughout the US.

The US market is reaching a saturation point with ambulatory surgical centers and procedure volume at its existing centers is limited by facility capacity so AmSurg's primary revenue growth strategy involves acquiring new centers. Historically it has made small acquisitions of centers that already have minority physician ownership.

Mergers and Acquisitions

However in 2011 it bought National Surgical Care which included 17 centers for $135 million.

EXECUTIVES

Vice President Finance, Kevin Eastridge
EVP and Chief Development Officer, David L. Manning, age 66, $442,000 total compensation
EVP CFO Secretary and Director, Claire M. Gulmi, age 61, $442,000 total compensation
President CEO and Director, Christopher A. Holden, age 50, $736,450 total compensation
EVP Operations, Phillip A. Clendenin, age 51, $350,000 total compensation
SVP Corporate Services and Chief Compliance Officer, Shawn G. Strash
Vice President Facility Management, Daniel Buehler
Associate Vice President Ophthalmology Marketing, Sandy Smith
Division President, Kari Lindsey
Vice President Quality, Kathy Wilson
Division Vice President, Don Myers
Vice President Clinical Services, Bruce Bardall
Associate Vice President Information Technology, Andy Sisco
Vice President Of Strategic Planning, Todd Lunsford
Assistant Vice President Information Technology, Kimberly Franks
Director Of Clinical Services, B J Schott
Regional Vice President Operations, Warren Savitz
Associate Vice President Operations, Alan Roberts
Division President, Debby McMillin
Associate Vice President Clinical Risk Management, Debbie Cibulka
Operations Vice President, Eric Moss
Vice President Acquisitions, Michael Bone
Registered Nurse Vice President, Kevin Miller
Vice President Operations, Dakon Magers
Vice President Operations, Terry Hawes
Associate Vice President Information, Andy Sleppy
Registered Nurse Vice President, Colin Dunnigan
Regional Vice President Operations, James Ciutiis
Regional Vice President Operations, Trent Mattison
Regional Vice President Operations, Steven Loser
Vice President Market Development, Tim Smith
Regional Vice President Operations, Kim Walsh
Vp Business Operations Amsurg, Renee Judkins
Associate Vice President Operations, Eric Albrecht
Clinical Director Multi Ortho, Marie Slee
Regional Vice President Gastroenterology Division, Michele Toungette
Assistant Vice President Operations, Deb Work
Chairman, Steven I. Geringer, age 68
Treasurer Head Of Treasury, Rachel Lane
Auditors: Deloitte&ToucheLLP

LOCATIONS

HQ: Amsurg Corp
20 Burton Hills Boulevard, Nashville, TN 37215
Phone: 615 665-1283
Web: www.amsurg.com

PRODUCTS/OPERATIONS

Strategic Services

Advocacy
Anesthesia Management Services
Development
Information Technology
Marketing and Media Relations
Physician Recruitment
Quality
Operational Services
Business Operations
Clinical
Compliance
Contracting
Facilities Management and Construction
Finance
Human Resources
Materials Management

COMPETITORS

Community Health Systems	Symbion
Dynacq Healthcare	TLC Vision
HCA	Tenet Healthcare
LCA	United Surgical Partners
Surgical Care Affiliates Inc.	Universal Health Services

HISTORICAL FINANCIALS

Company Type: Public

Income Statement

FYE: December 31

	REVENUE ($ mil.)	NET INCOME ($ mil.)	NET PROFIT MARGIN	EMPLOYEES
12/13	1,079.3	72.7	6.7%	6,200
12/12	928.5	62.5	6.7%	6,100
12/11	786.8	50.0	6.4%	5,500
12/10	710.4	49.8	7.0%	3,100
12/09	668.7	52.1	7.8%	2,780
Annual Growth	12.7%	8.7%	—	22.2%

2013 Year-End Financials

Debt ratio: 27.7%	No. of shares (mil.): 32
Return on equity: 10.0%	Dividends
Cash ($ mil.): 50	Yield: —
Current ratio: 2.35	Payout: —
Long-term debt ($ mil.): 583	Market value ($ mil.): 1,486

	STOCK PRICE ($) FY Close	P/E High/Low		PER SHARE ($)	
			Earnings	Dividends	Book Value
12/13	45.92	21 13	2.28	0.00	23.62
12/12	30.01	16 12	1.98	0.00	21.59
12/11	26.04	17 12	1.60	0.00	19.70
12/10	20.95	14 10	1.62	0.00	18.17
12/09	22.02	14 8	1.69	0.00	16.47
Annual Growth	20.2%	— —	7.8%	—	9.4%

Anika Therapeutics Inc.

Anika Therapeutics uses hyaluronic acid (HA) a natural polymer extracted from rooster combs and other sources to make products that treat bone cartilage and soft tissue. Anika's Orthovisc treats osteoarthritis of the knee and other joints and is available in the US and overseas. (DePuy Mitek sells the product in the US.) The company also makes and sells products that maintain eye shape and protect tissue during eye surgery some of which are marketed by Bausch & Lomb. Other items include surgical anti-adhesive products veterinary osteoarthritis therapies and dermatology products. The US accounts for about three-fourths of sales.

Operations Orthopedic products make up more than 60% of the company's annual revenues. In addition to Orthovisc Anika markets two newer osteoarthritis drugs in international markets: Orthovisc mini (for treatment in small joints) and Monovisc a next-generation single-injection therapy. Anika is looking to move these products into new markets. For instance it received Canadian approval for Monovisc in 2009 and it hopes to gain FDA approval to market Monovisc in the US. It has additional osteoarthritis and joint health treatments under development.

Sales and Marketing As the exclusive marketer of eye surgery viscoelastic agent Amvisc Bausch & Lomb (B&L) has historically accounted for the bulk of Anika's ophthalmic revenues. However an agreement restricting Anika from marketing its own viscoelastic products expired at the end of 2010 after which the firm moved to commercialize its own product AnikaVisc. While Anika markets some products on its own a number are sold through additional partnering firms and distribution representatives. DePuy Mitek and B&L are Anika's largest customers accounting for 47% and 16% of product sales respectively.

Financial Analysis Anika has seen strong revenue growth over the past several years including a 17% jump to $65 million in 2011. Growth that year was led by a 30% year-over-year increase in joint health (orthobiologics) products including Orthovisc in the US and Monovisc internationally. On the back of its strong sales growth the company's net income nearly doubled to more than $8 million in 2011.

Mergers and Acquisitions The company expanded its orthobiologic offerings in 2009 when it acquired Fidia Farmaceutici Biopolymers (FAB) an Italian producer of HA-based products in a number of therapeutic areas including the regeneration of connective and structural tissues damaged by injuries aging or degenerative diseases. FAB's products which are primarily marketed in Europe include Hyalograft C for cartilage regeneration and Hyalofast for bone marrow support. The purchase of FAB also added commercialized products in a range of wound care and surgical areas which were added to Anika's existing dermatology and surgical product lines. Ownership Italian drugmaker Fidia Farmaceutici former parent of Fidia Farmaceutici Biopolymers (which Anika acquired in 2009) owns about 14% of the company.

EXECUTIVES

President and CEO, Charles H. Sherwood, $505,447 total compensation
Chief Scientific Officer, John W. Sheets
CFO, Sylvia Cheung
Vice President Of Operations, Randall Ilhoite
Senior Vice President, Sean Kinney
Vice President Of Clinical Regulatory And Quality Systems, Carol Pekar
Vice President Of Engineering, Victor Bovey
Vice President Business And Corporate, Michael O'Regan
Vice President Of Sales And Marketing, Roger Strikeleather
Senior Vice President Sales, Bob Tellis
Vice President Of Clinical Regulatory, Carol Soares
Auditors: PricewaterhouseCoopersLLP

LOCATIONS

HQ: Anika Therapeutics Inc.
32 Wiggins Avenue, Bedford, MA 01730
Phone: 781 457-9000
Web: www.anikatherapeutics.com

2011 Sales

	$ mil.	% of total
US	48.4	75
Europe	11.0	17
Other	5.4	8
Total	**64.8**	**100**

PRODUCTS/OPERATIONS

2011 Sales

	$ mil.	% of total
Product sales		
Orthobiologics	39.8	61
Opthalmic surgery	11.0	17
Surgical	5.0	8
Dermal	3.7	6
Veterinary	2.5	4
Licensing milestone & contract revenue	2.8	4
Total	**64.8**	**100**

Selected Products

Orthobiologics
Hyalofast (bone marrow support)
Hyaloglide (tenolysis)
Hyalograft C (autograft for cartilage regeneration)
Hyalonect (graft gauze wrap)
Hyaloss (bone regeneration)
Monovisc (osteoarthritis)
OrthoVisc (osteoarthritis marketed by DePuy Mitek)
OrthoVisc mini (osteoarthritis in small joints)
Dermal
Elevess/Hydrelle (aesthetic dermatology products)
Hyalograft 3D (skin regeneration)
Hyalomatrix (burn and ulcer treatment)
Ophthalmic
Amvisc (eye surgery product sold by Bausch & Lomb)
Amvisc Plus (eye surgery product sold by Bausch & Lomb)
AnikaVisc (eye surgery product)
Optivisc (formerly ShellGel ophthalmic product)
STAARVISC II (ophthalmic product sold by STAAR Surgical)
Surgical
Hyalobarrier (post-operative adhesion barrier)
Incert (post-surgical adhesion prevention product)
Veterinary
Hyvisc (equine osteoarthritis treatment distributed by Boehringer Ingelheim)

COMPETITORS

Allergan	Pathfinder Cell
Exactech	Therapy
Fibrocell Science	Pfizer
Genzyme Biosurgery	Quidel
Harvard Bioscience	RTI Surgical
ImmunoGen	Smith & Nephew
Integra LifeSciences	Solta Medical
Lifecore Biomedical	Stellar
Medicis Pharmaceutical	Pharmaceuticals
Merz Aesthetics	Stryker
Obagi Medical	XOMA
OrthoLogic	Zimmer Holdings

HISTORICAL FINANCIALS

Company Type: Public

Income Statement

FYE: December 31

	REVENUE ($ mil.)	NET INCOME ($ mil.)	NET PROFIT MARGIN	EMPLOYEES
12/13	75.0	20.5	27.4%	102
12/12	71.3	11.7	16.5%	106
12/11	64.7	8.4	13.1%	129
12/10	55.5	4.3	7.8%	114
12/09	40.1	3.6	9.2%	133
Annual Growth	**16.9%**	**53.7%**	**—**	**(6.4%)**

2013 Year-End Financials

Debt ratio: —
Return on equity: 16.8%
Cash ($ mil.): 63
Current ratio: 10.19
Long-term debt ($ mil.): —
No. of shares (mil.): 14
Dividends
Yield: —
Payout: —
Market value ($ mil.): 545

	STOCK PRICE ($) FY Close	P/E High/Low		PER SHARE ($) Earnings	Dividends	Book Value
12/13	38.16	26	7	1.39	0.00	9.49
12/12	9.94	20	10	0.82	0.00	7.86
12/11	9.80	17	8	0.62	0.00	6.95
12/10	6.67	23	15	0.32	0.00	6.32
12/09	7.63	28	10	0.32	0.00	6.12
Annual Growth	**49.5%**	**—**	**—**	**44.4%**	**—**	**11.6%**

Ansys Inc.

ANSYS helps designers and engineers around the world visualize their ideas. With the company's software product developers can see a simulation of their design concept on their desktop computer before a prototype is built. The computerized models are analyzed for their response to combinations of such physical variables as stress pressure impact temperature and velocity. Ranging from small consulting firms to multinational enterprises its customers come from a broad range of industries and have included Delphi Airbus Invensys and Plexus. ANSYS generates two-thirds of its revenues from outside the US with Japan and Germany among its leading international markets.

Geographic Reach

ANSYS has more than 75 sales offices around the world. The US only accounts for about one-third of revenue.

Sales and Marketing

The company sells its products directly and through channel partners worldwide. It uses distribution partners in more than 40 countries. Indirect sales accounted for about one-fourth of ANSYS' total revenues in 2012.

ANSYS also partners with hardware suppliers — including AMD Dell Cray Intel Microsoft and HP among others —to ensure that its products are compatible with technology upgrades. In addition it collaborates with CAD and electronic design automation (EDA) system providers such as Autodesk and Cadence to provide links between products and support data transfer between design packages and ANSYS' simulation portfolio. These strategic alliances provide additional marketing opportunities for the company.

Financial Performance

Sales for 2012 were up 15% to $798 million on increases in both software license and maintenance revenues. New sales also contributed to the year's revenue growth. Net income for 2012 rose to an all-time high of $203 million.

Mergers and Acquisitions

The company periodically makes acquisitions to bolster its product offerings. In 2014 it bought Reaction Design a California company whose CHEMKIN-PRO chemistry simulation software is used by more than 400 customers around the world. Chemistry simulation software is used by transportation and energy companies to develop products without having to rely solely on experiments which could be dangerous. The prior year it bought Evolutionary Engineering AG a Swiss provider of composite analysis to help automotive aerospace energy and marine companies find the best composite materials to build products.

In 2012 it bought French software developer Esterel Technologies for about $58 million. The deal will add Esterel's SCADE application a tool used by software and systems engineers to design simulate and produce embedded software for electronics in aircraft rail automotive and energy systems.

EXECUTIVES

Vice President World Wide Sales Support, Joe Fairbanks
Vice President General Manager Central Development Unit, Brian Drew
VP and CFO, Maria T. Shields, age 49, $299,874 total compensation
President and CEO, James E. (Jim) Cashman, age 60, $610,000 total compensation
Chief Product Officer, Walid Abu-Hadba, $225,417 total compensation
Vice President Mechanical Business Unit, Joe Solecki
Vice President Human Resources, Debra Burk
Sales Training Vice President, John Gilmore
Vice President And General Manager, Shane R Emswiler
Vice President, Paolo Colombo
Vice President Of U S Operations, Swaminathan Subbiah
Regional Vice President, Michael Smocer
Vice President Of North American Sales, Frank Bernieri
Vice President Sales North America, Wade Smith
Vice President, Andrew Yang
Non Executive Chairman, Ronald Hovsepian
Treasurer, Kristi Fenner
Board Member, Bradford Morley
Auditors: Deloitte&ToucheLLP

LOCATIONS

HQ: Ansys Inc.
275 Technology Drive, Canonsburg, PA 15317
Phone: 724 746-3304
Web: www.ansys.com

2014 Sales

	$ mil.	% of total
Europe		
Germany	99.7	11
Other countries	217.8	23
North America		
US	320.3	34
Canada	14.0	1
Japan	108.8	12
Other regions	175.4	19
Total	**936.0**	**100**

PRODUCTS/OPERATIONS

2014 Sales

	$ mil.	% of total
Software licenses	564.5	60
Maintenance & service	371.5	40
Total	**936.0**	**100**

Selected Acquisitions

FY 2015
Newmerical Technologies (simulation software for aircraft)
FY 2014
Reaction Design (California chemistry simulation software)
FY 2013
Evolutionary Engineering AG (Switzerland composite analysis)
FY 2012
Esterel Technologies (France critical systems simulation software)
FY 2011
Apache Design Solutions (semiconductor simulation software)
FY 2008
Ansoft (electronic design automation software)
FY 2006
Aavid Thermal Technologies
FY 2005
Century Dynamics

COMPETITORS

Altair Engineering	Kubotek USA
Autodesk	MSC Software
Bentley Systems	MathWorks
Cadence Design	Mentor Graphics
Dassault	PTC
Delcam	Siemens PLM Software

HISTORICAL FINANCIALS

Company Type: Public

Income Statement

FYE: December 31

	REVENUE ($ mil.)	NET INCOME ($ mil.)	NET PROFIT MARGIN	EMPLOYEES
12/13	861.2	245.3	28.5%	2,600
12/12	798.0	203.4	25.5%	2,400
12/11	691.4	180.6	26.1%	2,100
12/10	580.2	153.1	26.4%	1,660
12/09	516.8	116.3	22.5%	1,600
Annual Growth	**13.6%**	**20.5%**	**—**	**12.9%**

2013 Year-End Financials

Debt ratio: —
Return on equity: 12.0%
Cash ($ mil.): 742
Current ratio: 2.42
Long-term debt ($ mil.): —
No. of shares (mil.): 92
Dividends
  Yield: —
  Payout: —
Market value ($ mil.): 8,050

	STOCK PRICE ($) FY Close	P/E High/Low	PER SHARE ($) Earnings	Dividends	Book Value
12/13	87.20	34 25	2.58	0.00	23.14
12/12	67.34	34 26	2.14	0.00	20.94
12/11	57.28	32 23	1.91	0.00	18.94
12/10	52.07	32 23	1.64	0.00	16.69
12/09	43.46	33 14	1.27	0.00	14.64
Annual Growth	**19.0%**	**—**	**19.4%**	**—**	**12.1%**

Apollo Commercial Real Estate Finance Inc.

Apollo Commercial Real Estate Finance invests in buys and manages commercial real estate mortgage loans and other real estate-related debt investments. The company was formed in 2009 by Apollo Global Management to be a mortgage real estate investment trust (REIT). Externally managed by ACREFI Management (an indirect subsidiary of Apollo Global Management) the firm is using proceeds from its 2009 IPO to invest in performing non-distressed US commercial real estate loans; commercial mortgage-backed securities (CMBS); and other commercial real estate debt investments. Apollo Commercial Real Estate Finance expects its average investment to range between $25 million and $75 million.

The REIT raised $200 million from its initial public offering. While Apollo's priority is to invest in senior performing commercial mortgage loans CMBS and commercial real estate debt and loans it may choose to invest in short-term interest-bearing investments such as money market accounts.

EXECUTIVES

President CEO and Director, Stuart A. Rothstein, age 48, $33,333 total compensation
Chief Investment Officer, Scott Weiner
CFO Treasurer and Secretary, Megan Gaul, $150,000 total compensation
Chairman, Jeffrey M. (Jeff) Gault
Auditors: Deloitte&ToucheLLP

LOCATIONS

HQ: Apollo Commercial Real Estate Finance Inc.
c/o Apollo Global Management, LLC, 9 West 57th Street, 43rd Floor, New York, NY 10019
Phone: 212 515-3200
Web: www.apolloreit.com

COMPETITORS

Capital Trust	Resource Capital
Petra Real Estate	iStar Financial Inc

HISTORICAL FINANCIALS

Company Type: Public

Income Statement

FYE: December 31

	REVENUE ($ mil.)	NET INCOME ($ mil.)	NET PROFIT MARGIN	EMPLOYEES
12/13	77.4	52.4	67.8%	0
12/12	57.0	40.1	70.4%	0
12/11	52.9	25.8	48.9%	0
12/10	32.4	11.0	33.9%	0
12/09	0.6	(2.1)	—	0
Annual Growth	**237.8%**	**—**	**—**	

2013 Year-End Financials

Debt ratio: 22.2%
Return on equity: 8.5%
Cash ($ mil.): 50
Current ratio: 2.50
Long-term debt ($ mil.): 202
No. of shares (mil.): 36
Dividends
  Yield: 9.8%
  Payout: 145.4%
Market value ($ mil.): 599

	STOCK PRICE ($)	P/E	PER SHARE ($)		
	FY Close	High/Low	Earnings	Dividends	Book Value
12/13	16.25	15 12	1.26	1.60	18.51
12/12	16.23	11 8	1.64	1.60	19.50
12/11	13.13	13 9	1.35	1.60	16.39
12/10	16.35	21 18	0.87	1.50	16.97
12/09	17.99	— —	(0.21)	0.00	18.15
Annual Growth	(2.5%)	— —	—	—	0.5%

Approach Resources Inc

Approach Resources takes a different approach to natural gas and oil exploration development and production. Specializing in finding and exploiting unconventional reservoirs the company operates primarily in West Texas' Permian Basin. It also has operations in East Texas. The company's unconventional designation results from a focus on developing natural gas reserves in tight gas sands and shale areas necessitating a reliance on advanced completion fracturing and drilling techniques. In 2012 Approach Resources reported proved reserves of 95.5 million barrels of oil equivalent.

Geographic Reach

The company's operations are focused on the Wolfcamp oil shale resource play in the Permian Basin in West Texas; all of its proved reserves are located in Crockett and Schleicher Counties. It also has minor operations in the East Texas Basin in East Texas.

Operations

In 2012 Approach Resources owned and operated 594 producing oil and gas wells in the Permian Basin and had an estimated 2983 identified drilling and recompletion locations of which 359 were proved. Some 39% of the company's 2012 production was oil; 31% natural gas; and 30% NGLs.

Sales and Marketing

In 2012 Shell Trading (US) and BML each accounted for 22% of company's revenues. Belvan Partners DCP Midstream and Plains Marketing accounted for 20% 17% and 6% respectively.

Financial Performance

Approach Resources revenues increased by 19% in 2012 due to a growth in production volumes (the result of the development of its Pangea project in the Permian Basin) offset by a decrease in oil and gas prices. The average price received for production before the effect of commodity derivatives declined by 4%. The company reported a 12% drop in net income in 2012 as higher revenues were outpaced by higher expenses. Depletion depreciation and amortization expenses increased as the result of higher production and oil and gas property carrying costs.

Strategy

The markets for oil NGLs and gas are volatile and modest drops in prices can affect financial results. Prices for oil NGLs and gas fluctuate widely in response to relatively minor changes in the supply and demand for these commodities market uncertainty and other factors. As "growth-through-the-drillbit" company with limited capital all of the company's proved reserves and production have so far been limited to its core West Texas operations.

In 2013 Approach Resources reported that its production was temporarily negatively affected due to a power outage at the Phillips 66 Sweeny Texas refinery. In 2011 it acquired the remaining 38% working interest (for $76 million) in its Cinco Terry operating area in the Permian Basin Crockett County Texas from two non-operating partners boosting total working and net revenue interests in Cinco Terry to 100% and 76% respectively. That year it acquired additional acreage in Crockett County Texas (10900 contiguous net acres) from private parties. The new acreage (Pangea West) nine miles west of the company's existing acreage boosted Approach Resources' total Permian Basin holdings to 109000 net acres (148000 net acres by the end of 2012).

Ownership

First Manhattan Co. owns 11% of Approach Resources.

EXECUTIVES

Chairman President and CEO, J. Ross Craft, age 58, $525,000 total compensation
COO, Qingming Yang, $340,000 total compensation
EVP and CFO, Sergei Krylov
VP Land, John L. Harris
VP Reservoir Engineering, Troy A. Hoefer
Vice President, Ismael Arreola
Chairman President and CEO, J. Ross Craft, age 58

LOCATIONS

HQ: Approach Resources Inc
One Ridgmar Centre, 6500 West Freeway, Suite 800, Fort Worth, TX 76116
Phone: 817 989-9000
Web: www.approachresources.com
West Texas
Ozona Northeast field (Wolfcamp Canyon Sands Strawn and Ellenburger)
Cinco Terry project (Wolfcamp Canyon Sands and Ellenburger)
East Texas
(Cotton Valley Sands Bossier and Cotton Valley Lime)

PRODUCTS/OPERATIONS

2012 Sales

	$ mil.	% of total
Oil	82.1	64
NGLs	30.8	24
Gas	16.0	12
Total	**128.9**	**100**

COMPETITORS

Abraxas Petroleum	Halcǻn Resources
Anadarko Petroleum	Legacy Reserves
Chesapeake Energy	Occidental Permian
Clayton Williams Energy	Parallel Petroleum
Concho	Permian Basin
Freeport-McMoRan Oil & Gas LLC	Quicksilver Resources
	Whiting Petroleum

HISTORICAL FINANCIALS

Company Type: Public

Income Statement

FYE: December 31

	REVENUE ($ mil.)	NET INCOME ($ mil.)	NET PROFIT MARGIN	EMPLOYEES
12/13	181.3	72.2	39.9%	135
12/12	128.8	6.3	5.0%	95
12/11	108.3	7.2	6.7%	81
12/10	57.5	7.4	13.0%	55
12/09	40.6	(5.2)	—	45
Annual Growth	45.3%	—	—	31.6%

2013 Year-End Financials

Debt ratio: 21.8%
Return on equity: 10.7%
Cash ($ mil.): 58
Current ratio: 1.07
Long-term debt ($ mil.): 250
No. of shares (mil.): 39
Dividends
　Yield: —
　Payout: —
Market value ($ mil.): 754

	STOCK PRICE ($)	P/E	PER SHARE ($)		
	FY Close	High/Low	Earnings	Dividends	Book Value
12/13	19.30	17 10	1.85	0.00	18.20
12/12	25.01	214 125	0.18	0.00	16.31
12/11	29.41	134 61	0.25	0.00	14.13
12/10	23.10	69 18	0.34	0.00	11.80
12/09	7.72	— —	(0.25)	0.00	10.52
Annual Growth	25.7%	— —	—	—	14.7%

ArcBest Corp

ArcBest (formerly Arkansas Best) puts its best efforts on the road to provide freight transportation services in its home state and the rest of North America. Specializing in long-haul less-than-truckload (LTL) shipments of general commodities (no hazardous waste or dangerous explosives) subsidiary ABF Freight System accounts for nearly 75% of the company's sales. (LTL carriers combine freight from multiple shippers into a single truckload.) ABF Freight System operates a fleet of about 3700 tractors and 20000 trailers from about 270 terminals in the US Canada and Puerto Rico; it offers service into Mexico via alliances. The company changed its name in 2014.

Operations

ArcBest operates through five segments. Freight Transportation accounted for 75% of its total sales in 2013 and consists of ABF Freight System Panther Expedited Services and other subsidiaries. Its non-asset-based segments include Premium Logistics and Expedited Freight Services Truck Brokerage and Management Emergency and Preventative Maintenance and Household Good Moving Services.

ArcBest's subsidiaries support ABF's business. FleetNet America unit provides maintenance and emergency roadside services for the commercial trucking industry. ArcBest Technologies provides computer information services primarily to ABF while FreightValue works in association with ABF to provide alternative transportation options. Freight carried by the company includes chemicals food textiles apparel appliances and furniture.

Financial Performance

In 2013 ArcBest reported an 11% increase in revenue due to higher volume across all segments with Domestic & Global Transportation Management leading way when it posted a 58% revenue bump.

After posting a net loss of $8 million for 2012 ArcBest had net income of $16 million for 2013. (It has posted a net loss three out of the last four years.) The improvement was due to higher revenue and improved margins from cost reductions. Not surprisingly cash from operations also improved about 10% on the strength of better results from ABF Freight.

The 2012 net loss was primarily attributed to an increase in operating expenses and labor costs. Included in these operating expenses was an amount of $2 million in acquisition-related costs.

Strategy

ArcBest looks to maintain its traditional LTL services while expanding into the newer non-asset-based arena. To that end it purchased Panther Expedited Services in 2012 to complement ABF Freight.

Mergers and Acquisitions

In 2012 ArcBest acquired freight transportation and logistics firm Panther Expedited Services for about $180 million from Fenway Partners. The acquisition helped the company to service the end-to-end logistics needs of supply chains that are becoming more complex. Panther now operates as a sister company to ABF Freight System.

EXECUTIVES

President and CEO, Judy R. McReynolds, $575,000 total compensation
CFO, David R. Cobb, age 49
Chief Innovation Officer and President ArcBest Technologies, Michael E. Newcity, $277,667 total compensation
President and CEO ABF Freight System Inc., Roy M. Slagle, $375,000 total compensation
President ArcBest Technologies, David A. (Dave) Cogswell
President ABF Logistics, James A. (Jim) Ingram, age 46, $306,917 total compensation
President and CEO FleetNet America Inc., Gary W. Cummings
President and CEO Panther Expedited Services Inc., R. Louis (Lou) Schneeberger
Vice President Global Supply Chain Division, Carlos Martinez-tomatis
Senior Vice President Tax And Chief, Lavon Morton
Vice President Of Information, Stella Likhterman
Vice President Production And Quality, Ronald W Toothaker
Vice President Operations, William L Driscoll
Vice President Global Sales, Steve Biegacki
Chairman, Robert A. Young
Auditors: Ernst&YoungLLP

LOCATIONS

HQ: ArcBest Corp
3801 Old Greenwood Road, Fort Smith, AR 72903
Phone: 479 785-6000   **Fax:** 479 785-6004
Web: www.arkbest.com

PRODUCTS/OPERATIONS

2013 Sales

	$ mil.	% of total
Freight Transportation	1761.7	74
Premium Logistics & Expedited Freight Services	246.8	11
Emergency & Preventative Maintenance	137.5	6
Domestic & Global Transportation Management	137.5	5
Household Goods Moving services	82.2	4
Other & Eliminations	(33.9)	-
Total	**2299.5**	**100**

COMPETITORS

Averitt Express
Con-way Freight
Estes Express
Expeditors
FedEx Freight
Forward Air
J.B. Hunt
Landstar System
Old Dominion Freight
Premier Logistics
Roadrunner Transportation Systems
Saia
Schneider National
UPS Freight
Vitran
Werner Enterprises
YRC Worldwide

HISTORICAL FINANCIALS

Company Type: Public

Income Statement

FYE: December 31

	REVENUE ($ mil.)	NET INCOME ($ mil.)	NET PROFIT MARGIN	EMPLOYEES
12/13	2,299.5	15.8	0.7%	11,420
12/12	2,066.0	(7.7)	—	9,900
12/11	1,907.6	6.1	0.3%	10,800
12/10	1,657.8	(32.6)	—	10,750
12/09	1,472.9	(127.8)	—	10,347
Annual Growth	**11.8%**	**—**		**2.5%**

2013 Year-End Financials

Debt ratio: 12.4%
Return on equity: 3.2%
Cash ($ mil.): 105
Current ratio: 1.35
Long-term debt ($ mil.): 81

No. of shares (mil.): 25
Dividends
 Yield: 0.3%
 Payout: 20.3%
Market value ($ mil.): 870

	STOCK PRICE ($) FY Close	P/E High/Low		PER SHARE ($) Earnings	Dividends	Book Value
12/13	33.68	59	16	0.59	0.12	20.15
12/12	9.55	—	—	(0.31)	0.12	17.92
12/11	19.27	121	65	0.23	0.12	18.32
12/10	27.42	—	—	(1.30)	0.12	18.99
12/09	29.43	—	—	(5.12)	0.60	19.98
Annual Growth	**3.4%**		**—**	**—**	**(33.1%)**	**0.2%**

Arctic Cat Inc

Prowling over hard ground or snow Arctic Cat offers drivers a purrfect ride. The company manufactures and markets about 30 types of all-terrain vehicles (ATVs) and about 40 snowmobile models. Its four-wheel recreational and utility ATVs and snowmobiles are marketed under the Arctic Cat name. Arctic Cat also supplies replacement parts and Cat-branded protective clothing and riding gear to foster its drivers' experience and loyalty. The company produces and outsources parts to other vehicle OEMs too. Products are sold through a network of independent dealers throughout North America and through representatives of dealers worldwide. The US accounts for roughly half of Arctic Cat's sales.

Despite its reach the company has struggled against the impact of the economic recession and high unemployment coupled with tight credit mar-

kets. In 2011 Arctic Cat reported a slight improvement in sales over 2010. The increase its first since 2007 was attributable primarily to demand for snowmobiles and snow-related parts. Moreover after mounting losses in 2008 and 2009 the company broke the trend in 2010 and in 2011 managed to boost profits by nearly seven fold over the prior year.

Arctic Cat responded to the industry-wide decline in retail sales by implementing a number of cost controls including reducing ATV and snowmobile production. It also cut headcount at its Thief River Falls' plant where its products are designed manufactured and assembled. ATV engine-making was transitioned to a new facility in St. Cloud Minnesota. All told operating expenses as a percent of sales in 2011 were decreased by more than 15%.

New product introductions and marketing programs have also supported Arctic Cat's efforts to gain market share and counter its slump. In spring 2011 the company launched almost 25 new snowmobiles accounting for 75% of its 2012 model offerings. Roughly 90% of the company's sales are from products introduced within the prior three years. Concurrently Arctic Cat continues to target niche powersports environments as well as consumers seeking ride and handling power fuel efficiency and style. The company has signaled its entry into the growing market for side-by-side utility terrain vehicles (UTV) —which allow a passenger to sit next to the driver.

A new leadership plan is anticipated to continue the company's momentum. CEO Christopher Twomey retired at the end of 2010 succeeded by Claude Jordan. Twomey retains his post as chairman helping to smooth the transition for Jordan who joined Arctic Cat in 2008 as president and COO.

Suzuki which makes the company's snowmobile engines is Arctic Cat's largest stakeholder. The Japanese motorcycle and carmaker owns nearly 35% of the company.

HISTORY

The Arctic Cat snowmobile was introduced in 1961. The snowmobile industry expanded rapidly in the 1960s and early 1970s but by the late 1970s sales had declined as a result of high gasoline prices and high interest rates. Arctic Enterprises maker of Arctic Cat went bankrupt in 1981 but demand for its products remained strong from loyal customers. The company re-emerged in 1983 when a group of former employees distributors and dealers revived the product line under a licensing agreement. The group bought rights to all of Arctic Cat's trademarks equipment and manufacturing in 1986 and 1987 and the group went public as Arctco in 1990.

Snowmobile demand soared in the 1990s as US trails improved and consumers' thirst for excitement expanded. In 1993 the company started making personal watercraft under the Tigershark brand. However in 1994 Arctco with its Suzuki engines felt the scratch of higher costs related to a stronger Japanese yen. The following year its Tigershark PWC product line was increased to six models (including a three-person vehicle) and the company shipped its first ATV.

Arctc changed its name to Arctic Cat in 1996. The next year it introduced the first snowmobile with an electronic fuel-injection system (which doesn't require batteries). In 1998 Arctic Cat and Outboard Marine struck a long-term agreement to use Outboard's low-emission fuel systems in Arctic Cat's ATVs and personal watercraft.

In 1999 about 11500 Arctic Cat snowmobiles (14 models) were recalled due to possibly faulty drive clutches. The company's sales and profits dipped that year due to warmer weather and increased sales of lower-margin ATVs. Sinking sales of its personal watercraft business convinced the company to abandon those operations in 1999.

Arctic Cat inked a deal in 2000 with AGCO Corporation's Massey Ferguson subsidiary for that company to sell Arctic Cat ATVs in European agricultural markets. The following year the company became an official NASCAR sponsor for top-ranked Winston Cup driver Ricky Rudd. Fiscal 2003 brought record revenues for Arctic Cat mostly driven by its line of ATVs. The company announced in 2004 that it would design and build its first ATV engine.

It expanded internationally in 2005 by acquiring a European maker of ATVs for on-road use the choice of ATV enthusiasts in Europe. In 2006 the company partnered with the Piaggio Group to strengthen product development as well as distribution in Europe and North America. Concurrently Arctic Cat launched its workhorse the Prowler Utility Terrain Vehicle (UTV) —with a variety of company-made engines —into the utility ATV marketplace. The Prowler's success against sportier models was lack luster. (ATV sales tumbled more than 50% from 2007 to 2010.)

Arctic Cat sold its Madison South Dakota paint and subassembly facility in 2007 and relocated company headquarters to Minneapolis. It also rolled out the industry's first biodiesel-powered ATV and in 2008 an ATV with the largest displacement engine in the industry (the Thundercat 1000).

In the snowmobile industry Arctic Cat's product development includes the first model to use four-stroke engines (to reduce emissions). It later unveiled a version with a turbo charged four-stroke inter-cooled engine and in 2009 the most powerful production snowmobile engine in history a 177 horsepower turbo charged EFI four stroke engine.

The company in 2009 inked a deal with GE Capital enabling financing for Arctic Cat's US dealers as well as buoying sales against the impact of the economic recession.

EXECUTIVES

CEO, Christopher T. (Chris) Metz, age 49
CFO, Christopher J. Eperjesy, age 46
VP Operations, Paul A. Fisher, age 57, $236,830 total compensation
VP and General Manager Snowmobile, Brad Darling, $250,322 total compensation
VP and General Manager Parts Garments and Accessories, Tracy Crocker, $217,201 total compensation
V Pres, Bradley D Darling
V Pres Hr, William J Nee
Vice President, Joe Klosterman
Chairman, Chris Twomey
Board Member, Tony J Chriatianson
Board Member, Christian Koch
Board Member, Robert J Dondelinger
Board Member, Susan E Lester
Board Member, Masayoshi Ito
Auditors: GrantThorntonLLP

LOCATIONS

HQ: Arctic Cat Inc
505 Highway 169 North, Suite 1000, Plymouth, MN 55441
Phone: 763 354-1800
Web: www.arcticcat.com

2011 Sales

	$ mil.	% of total
US	218.5	47
Canada & other countries	246.1	53
Total	**464.6**	**100**

PRODUCTS/OPERATIONS

2011 Sales

	% of total
ATVs	39
Snowmobiles	39
Parts garments & accessories	22
Total	**100**

Selected Products

All-Terrain Vehicles
  Competition
  Recreation
  Utility
  Youth
Snowmobile Models and Brands
  2-stroke performance (Sno Pro)
  4-stroke performance (Turbo Sno Pro)
  Crossover sleds
  Mountain sleds
  Touring sleds
  Utility sleds
  Youth sled
Parts Garments and Accessories
  Brake Levers
  Caps
  Coats
  Fuel de-icer
  Fuel stabilizer
  Handlebar stands
  Heated seat kits
  Helmets
  Recoil handles
  Remote start kits
  Riding gear
  Sled lifts
  Suspension blocks
  Synthetic oil change kits
  Touring bags
  Tow straps
  Traction strips and flexi-skis
  Vehicle covers
  Windscreens and windshields

COMPETITORS

Bajaj Auto	Polaris Industries
Bombardier	TEAM Industries Inc.
E-Z-GO	Yamaha Motor
Honda	
Kawasaki Heavy Industries	

HISTORICAL FINANCIALS

Company Type: Public

Income Statement

FYE: March 31

	REVENUE ($ mil.)	NET INCOME ($ mil.)	NET PROFIT MARGIN	EMPLOYEES
03/14	730.4	39.4	5.4%	1,611
03/13	671.5	39.7	5.9%	1,508
03/12	585.2	29.9	5.1%	1,369
03/11	464.6	13.0	2.8%	1,323
03/10	450.7	1.8	0.4%	1,350
Annual Growth	**12.8%**	**114.1%**	**—**	**4.5%**

2014 Year-End Financials

Debt ratio: —	No. of shares (mil.): 12
Return on equity: 21.9%	Dividends
Cash ($ mil.): 22	Yield: 0.8%
Current ratio: 1.92	Payout: 15.2%
Long-term debt ($ mil.): —	Market value ($ mil.): 616

	STOCK PRICE ($) FY Close	P/E High/Low		PER SHARE ($) Earnings	Dividends	Book Value
03/14	47.79	20	13	2.90	0.40	14.36
03/13	43.70	15	11	2.89	0.00	13.21
03/12	42.84	24	7	1.72	0.00	10.61
03/11	15.55	24	10	0.70	0.00	10.00
03/10	10.85	125	34	0.10	0.00	9.18
Annual Growth	**44.9%**	—		**132.1%**	—	**11.8%**

Aspen Technology Inc

Aspen Technology (AspenTech) helps its customers scale mountains of supply chain and engineering challenges. It provides supply chain manufacturing and engineering process optimization software to some 1500 companies in the energy chemical construction and pharmaceutical industries among others. The company's software — which includes supplier collaboration inventory management production planning and collaborative engineering functions —is offered under its aspenONE subscription service. AspenTech which generates most of its sales outside the US also provides related technical and professional services such as technical support training and systems implementation and integration.

Geographic Reach Europe is the company's largest geographic segment accounting for about a third of sales (up from just over a quarter of sales in 2011). The US contributes 30% of sales. Other markets served include the Asia-Pacific region Canada Latin America and the Middle East.

Sales and Marketing AspenTech sells directly through resellers in non-core markets and by licensing to universities to encourage future demand. It continues to target global process manufacturers whose capital-intensive technologically advanced operations require more specialized software and services than are available in broader enterprise resource planning (ERP) applications. Financial Analysis In mid-2009 the company released its aspenONE subscription product and switched its revenue recognition model which resulted in a significant drop in revenue and net income. AspenTech's sales have risen since as customers are migrated to the new subscription model. In fiscal 2012 (ended June) the company reported $243 million in revenue a jump of nearly 25%. An expanded base of aspenONE customers was enough to counter drops in support training and professional services. The company expects software support and maintenance revenue to continue falling as those services are provided as part of the aspenONE subscription. AspenTech saw a net loss of nearly $14 million in 2012 (down from net income of $10 million the previous year when the company recognized a tax benefit of $54 million).

Strategy The company also targets global growth especially in emerging markets. As its customers move into China India Russia Latin America and the Middle East AspenTech is establishing customer support and sales operations in Russia and the Middle East with plans for more international locations. AspenTech is also focused on the continued adoption of its aspenONE subscription model by customers. The service which was launched in mid-2009 gives customers access to all applications within the software suite they license including upgrades and future products. The company believes this allows clients more flexibility to increase their usage of the software as needs change.

Mergers and Acquisitions AspenTech acquired Hamburg Germany-based flowsheet simulation software developer SolidSim Engineering in 2012. The purchase augmented the company's existing solids process modeling tools contained in its core aspenONE application.

In 2013 it purchased pipeline and dock scheduling software from Refining Advantage which will enhance the supply chain services AspenTech offers its petroleum customers.

Ownership Mutual fund manager Waddell & Reed owns 17% of the company.

HISTORY

Lawrence Evans was a chemical engineering professor at MIT in 1976 when he became the principal investigator for the Energy Department's ASPEN (Advanced System for Process Engineering) project to develop synthetic fuels. He was joined by Joseph Boston and Herbert Britt (both chemical engineers) in 1977. Four years later they formed Aspen Technology to develop and market computer-aided chemical engineering software for process manufacturers.

The company launched its first product in 1982 and introduced process simulation software the following year. Boston became AspenTech's president and Evans became chairman and CEO in 1984.

The company went public in 1994. A series of acquisitions followed —including the purchases of Industrial Systems in 1995 and Dynamic Matrix Control and Setpoint in 1996 —which gave the company operation control software. In 1997 it bought consultant Special Analysis & Simulation Technologies and intelligent software expert NeuralWare.

After reporting a drop in software license revenues AspenTech in 1999 cut 200 jobs (more than 10% of its workforce). In 2000 the company bought supply chain management systems specialist Petrolsoft for $60 million.

In 2001 the company launched its PetroVantage subsidiary a provider of Web-based software used by petroleum companies to manage supply chains and the transportation and trade of crude oil and refined products. The economic downturn that year brought reduced revenue and losses however forcing AspenTech to reverse course on spinning off PetroVantage.

The next year it acquired Hyprotech an engineering software provider for the petroleum industry from UK-based AEA Technology for about $100 million. The Hyprotech acquisition triggered an antitrust investigation by The Federal Trade Commission which claimed the deal boosted Aspen's share of the market for engineering simulation software to as much as 82%. (The FTC agreed in 2004 to a settlement whereby AspenTech sold its operator training services business and the rights to the Hyprotech product line retaining the right to continue selling and developing the engineering software purchased with Hyprotech.)

In 2003 Advent International invested $100 million in the company in exchange for a 32% stake.

A year later CEO David McQuillin was pushed out by the board when the company's audit committee raised questions about certain software license agreements mentioned on financial statements. Mark Fusco was named CEO at the beginning of 2005.

EXECUTIVES

Senior Vice President Corporate Strategy, Richard Packwood

EVP Products, Manolis E. Kotzabasakis, age 54, $348,000 total compensation

President and CEO, Antonio J. Pietri, age 49, $500,000 total compensation

EVP and CFO, Mark P. Sullivan, age 58, $370,000 total compensation

Sr Vp Human Rsrcs, Helen Moye

Vice President Strategy And Research, Joanna Nikka

Vice President Of Product Management E, Steve Williams

Vice President, Toni Rudnicki

Executive Vice President, Paul Taylor

Vice President, Qiliang Bo

Vice President Engineering, Boz Elloy

Vice President Corporate Sales, Greg Mason

Vp R&d, Bruce McFarlin

Vice President Of Sales And Operations, Walter Dedrick

Vice President Business Operations Planning And Sales Operations, Mark Holmes

Senior Vice President Research And De, Willie Chan

Vice President Worldwide Inside Sales, Allison Frank

Vice President Sales, Jim Boozer

Vice President Product Development, Steven Pringle

Vice President Worldwide Sales Operations And Business Development, Clint Clemans

Vice President Of Sales Operations, Quint Clemens

Senior Vice President Accounts, John Hague

Vp Program Management Office, Kenneth Young

Sales And Marketing Vp, Jasmine Lombardi

Svp Services, Michele Triponey

Sales Vice President, Henry Lau

Vice President Of Sales, David Haake

Vice President Technology, Basil Joffe

Vp Corporate Controller, Jim Steuterman

Vice President Marketing, Daniel Sapir

Vice President Sales Nala Chemicals, Ramsey McCreary

Vice President Professional Services, Kelly Harred

Vice President Product Marketing, Jim Bascom

Vice President Engineering Products, Philippe Muller

Vice President Market Development Supply Chain Division, Walt Beadling

Director And Vice President Of Finance, Frank Sansone

Vice President Professional Services Emea, Michel Beek

Vice President Regional Sales, Oscar Gutierrez

Vice President Of Technology, Ashok Subramanian

Board Of Directors, Steve Jennings

Treasurer, Roger Kuebel

Chairman, Robert M. Whelan, age 62

Treasurer Head Of Treasury, Anthony Cefalo

Auditors: KPMGLLP

LOCATIONS

HQ: Aspen Technology Inc
20 Crosby Drive, Bedford, MA 01730
Phone: 781 221-6400
Web: www.aspentech.com

2012 Sales

	% of total
Europe	34
US	26
Other	38
Total	**100**

PRODUCTS/OPERATIONS

2012 Sales

	$ mil.	% of total
License	166.7	69
Software maintenance and support training & other	54.0	22
Professional services	22.4	9
Total	**243.1**	**100**

Selected Products

Aspen Plus
Aspen HYSYS
Aspen Exchanger Design and Rating
Aspen Economic Evaluation
Aspen Basic Engineering
Aspen Info Plus.21
Aspen DMCplus
Aspen Collaborative Demand Manager
Aspen Petroleum Scheduler
Aspen PIMS
Aspen Plant Scheduler
Aspen Supply Chain Planner
Aspen Inventory Management & Operations Scheduling
Aspen Petroleum Supply Chain Planner
Aspen Fleet Optimizer

COMPETITORS

ABB	OSIsoft
Dassault	Oracle
GSE Systems	PTC
Honeywell	QAD
International	Rockwell Automation
Infor Global	SAP
JDA Software	Shell Global Solutions
KBC Advanced	Siemens AG
Technologies	Yokogawa Electric

HISTORICAL FINANCIALS

Company Type: Public

Income Statement

FYE: June 30

	REVENUE ($ mil.)	NET INCOME ($ mil.)	NET PROFIT MARGIN	EMPLOYEES
06/14	391.4	85.7	21.9%	1,344
06/13	311.3	45.2	14.5%	1,328
06/12	243.1	(13.8)	—	1,325
06/11	198.1	10.2	5.2%	1,269
06/10	166.3	(107.4)	—	1,289
Annual Growth	**23.9%**	**—**	**—**	**1.1%**

2014 Year-End Financials

Debt ratio: —
Return on equity: 92.4%
Cash ($ mil.): 199
Current ratio: 1.24
Long-term debt ($ mil.): —

No. of shares (mil.): 91
Dividends
　Yield: —
　Payout: —
Market value ($ mil.): 4,253

	STOCK PRICE ($) FY Close	P/E High/Low	PER SHARE ($) Earnings	Dividends	Book Value
06/14	46.40	51 31	0.92	0.00	0.91
06/13	28.79	68 46	0.47	0.00	1.09
06/12	23.15	— —	(0.15)	0.00	1.22
06/11	17.18	155 85	0.11	0.00	1.67
06/10	10.89	— —	(1.18)	0.00	1.53
Annual Growth	**43.7% (12.0%)**		**—**	**—**	**—**

Astronics Corp.

In the glare of its own lights but without histrionics Astronics Corporation displays its talents daily to a specialized audience. Astronics makes external and internal lighting systems as well as power generation and distribution technology for commercial general aviation and military defense aircraft. Products include cabin emergency lighting systems (escape path markers and exit locators) cockpit lighting systems (avionics keyboards ambient light sensors annunciator panels and electronic dimmers) external lights and military test equipment. Astronics operates subsidiaries include Astronics Advanced Electronic Systems Corp. Ballard Luminescent Systems and DME Corporation.

Operations

The company operates in two segments: Aerospace and Test Systems. The Aerospace segment designs and makes a range of products for the global aerospace industry. Its products include aircraft lighting airframe power avionics airfield lighting and cabin electronics. The Test Systems segment designs develops and manufactures communications and weapons test systems and training and simulation devices for military clients.

Sales and Marketing

Astronics' customers include the Department of Defense (DOD) Federal Aviation Administration and airport operators US military forces foreign military agencies and makers of military communication systems.

Financial Performance

The company's revenues grew by 17% in 2012 thanks to a 19% increase in Aerospace sales partially offset by lower sales volume in Test Systems segment. Sales growth was primarily driven by higher sales of cabin electronics to commercial airlines as well as the impact of the Ballard acquisition.

Astronics' net income bumped up by 1% in 2012 as the result of higher revenues partially offset by the increase in SG&A expenses (including higher legal expenses and cost related to the Ballard and Max-Viz acquisitions). It also benefited from the absence of an impairment loss (it carried one in 2011).

Strategy

The company continues to invest in new technologies and aircraft programs for each of its markets even while the aerospace industry as a whole is experiencing a slowdown along with the economy in general. In particular Astronics is developing an electrical power distribution system for the Learjet 85 that shows promise of becoming a standard component of business jets. Its products and technologies are also used in the F-35 Joint Strike Fighter the Airbus A380 XWB and the Boeing 787 to name a few.

Mergers and Acquisitions

Growing its Aerospace portfolio in 2012 Astronics acquired Max-Viz a designer and manufacturer of enhanced vision systems for defense and commercial aerospace applications. In 2011 Astronics bought Ballard Technology which designs and manufactures avionics databus solutions for aerospace applications.

Ownership

Astronics' Chairman Kevin Keane owns about 28% of the company.

Company Background

Astronics has become more dependent on the DoD since its 2009 acquisition of DME Corporation a provider of military test training and simulation equipment. The company is expected to make a substantial increase in product offerings sales and headcount due to the acquisition. The addition of DME gives Astronics a stronger foothold in the defense industry and is intended to provide balance to its core lighting systems business. In mid-2010 DME won a five-year $7.4 million contract with the US Air Force to install airfield lighting at bases across the country.

HISTORY

Founded in 1968 Astronics was originally involved in electroluminescent products until it began to diversify into the packaging and printing industries. The company acquired MOD-PAC a maker of paperboard packaging in 1972 and Krepe-Kraft a specialized printing company in 1987.

In 1995 Astronics bought Loctite Luminescent Systems and integrated it with E-L FlexKey Technologies which specialized in components used in the aerospace and military electronics industries. Later renamed Luminescent Systems the division was awarded two high-dollar Canadian contracts the following year. One contract was for cockpit lighting systems for Bombardier's long-range business jets; the other was for ruggedized keyboards for the control room of a Canadian nuclear power plant.

The US Air Force awarded Astronics a contract to manufacture night-vision lighting for the F-16 aircraft in 1998. The next year the company was awarded an additional contract that almost doubled the number of units it would provide for F-16s. Astronics' aerospace and electronics segment doubled its manufacturing capabilities with the addition of two new facilities.

The company further enhanced its ability to fulfill its F-16 contract with the acquisition of Canada-based CRL Technologies (lighted keyboards) in 2000. Also that year Astronics acquired illuminated indicators for use in aircraft cockpits from Aerospace Avionics. In late 2001 the company was awarded a contract from the US government to provide lighted control panels for the Bradley M2A3 infantry fighting vehicle. The following year it received a contract from the US Air Force valued at up to $30 million to develop spare parts for the F-16.

Astronics discontinued its electroluminescent lamp business in 2002 and spun off MOD-PAC in 2003. It entered the market for electrical power generation control and distribution systems for aircraft in 2005 by buying the assets of Airborne Electronics Systems from a unit of General Dynamics. Astronics paid $13 million for Airborne Electronics Systems which had revenues of about $25 million in 2004.

EXECUTIVES

Vice President Luminescent Systems, Richard C (Rick) Miller
Executive Vice President Luminescent Systems, James S. (Jim) Kramer, $242,000 total compensation
President and Chief Executive Officer, Peter J. Gundermann, age 52, $430,000 total compensation
VP and CFO, David C. Burney, age 52, $270,000 total compensation
Executive Vice President Astronics Advanced Electronic Systems, Mark Peabody, $310,000 total compensation
Vice President Luminescent Systems, Frank G Johns
Vice President Of Test Solutions Astronics Dme Corporation, Lou Salzano
Vice President Luminescent Systems, D Johns
Executive Vice President, Michelle Belcher
Executive Vice President, Donald Derrick
Vice President, Dave Freund
Chairman of the Board, Kevin T. Keane, age 81
Auditors: Ernst&YoungLLP

LOCATIONS

HQ: Astronics Corp.
  130 Commerce Way, East Aurora, NY 14052
Phone: 716 805-1599
Web: www.astronics.com

2010 Sales

	$ mil.	% of total
North America	168.6	86
Asia	13.0	7
Europe	11.3	6
South America	2.5	1
Other regions	0.4	-
Total	**195.8**	**100**

PRODUCTS/OPERATIONS

2012 Sales

	$ mil.	% of total
Aerospace	254.9	96
Test systems	11.5	4
Total	**266.4**	**100**

2012 Sales by Product Line

	$ mil.	% of total
Aerospace		
Cabin electronics	141.5	53
Aircraft lighting	69.6	26
Airframe power	18.8	7
Avionics	15.3	6
Airfield lighting	9.7	4
Test systems	11.5	4
Total	**266.4**	**100**

Selected Products:Aircraft lighting

Astronics Advanced Electronic Systems Corp
Ballard Technology Inc
DME Corporation
Luminescent Systems Canada Inc
Luminescent Systems Inc
Max-Viz Inc

COMPETITORS

AIM Aviation	L-3/IS
B/E Aerospace	Premium Aircraft
C&D Zodiac	Interiors Group
Ducommun	TransDigm Group
Honeywell Aerospace	Ultra Electronics
Indel	Zodiac Aerospace

HISTORICAL FINANCIALS

Company Type: Public

Income Statement

FYE: December 31

	REVENUE ($ mil.)	NET INCOME ($ mil.)	NET PROFIT MARGIN	EMPLOYEES
12/13	339.9	27.2	8.0%	1,715
12/12	266.4	21.8	8.2%	1,156
12/11	228.1	21.5	9.5%	1,081
12/10	195.7	14.9	7.6%	1,010
12/09	191.2	(3.8)	—	1,035
Annual Growth	15.5%	—		13.5%

2013 Year-End Financials

Debt ratio: 40.7%	No. of shares (mil.): 21
Return on equity: 18.3%	Dividends
Cash ($ mil.): 54	Yield: —
Current ratio: 2.48	Payout: —
Long-term debt ($ mil.): 188	Market value ($ mil.): 1,093

	STOCK PRICE ($) FY Close	P/E High/Low		PER SHARE ($) Earnings	Dividends	Book Value
12/13	51.00	41	18	1.24	0.00	8.00
12/12	22.88	34	19	1.01	0.00	6.01
12/11	35.81	31	16	1.16	0.00	5.79
12/10	21.00	24	8	0.92	0.00	4.90
12/09	8.55	—	—	(0.24)	0.00	3.87
Annual Growth	56.3%	—		—	—	19.9%

Atlantic American Corp.

Baseball apple pie and... insurance! Atlantic American sells a mix of property/casualty health and life insurance throughout the US. Its Bankers Fidelity Life Insurance subsidiary provides life and supplemental health insurance offerings with income primarily coming from sales of Medicare supplement policies. Its American Southern subsidiary offers commercial and personal property/casualty products including automobile insurance products targeted at large motor pools and fleets owned by local governments. The unit also offers general commercial liability coverage and surety bonds catering to niche markets such as school bus transportation and subdivision construction.

Operations

Sales of health insurance policies by the Bankers Fidelity division account for more than 60% of Atlantic American's annual revenues with most of the division's premiums coming from Medicare supplement policies. The company's American Southern division (more than 30% of total sales) earns most of its revenues on sales of auto insurance policies.

Non-insurance subsidiary xCalibre Benefits offers third-party administrator services for employee benefits programs.

Sales and Marketing

Atlantic American sells its products to individuals and businesses through a network of independent agents and brokers. It also while markets and sells to government corporate and municipal entities through a specialized force of independent agents. Overall the company has more than 2000 agents in its marketing network.

Financial Performance

The company's revenues grew by 18% in 2013 primarily due to an increase in insurance premiums attributable to a growth in the Medicare supplement business as well as a rise in the commercial automobile business (property and casualty) due to a major new state contract as well as an increase in realized investment gains. Atlantic American's net income increased by 148% from $4 million in 2012 to $11 million in 2013 due to higher revenues partially offset by a growth in insurance benefits and losses incurred and higher commissions and underwriting expenses.

While other life insurers get a significant amount of their income from investments Atlantic American gets nearly 90% of its revenues from actual premiums. This quirk didn't quite protect it from reporting losses during the depths of the economic recession but the resilient company increased revenues each year after a sharp drop in 2008 and returned to profitability in 2010. Since 2010 the company saw continuous growth in 2011 2012 and 2013.

Strategy

Atlantic American is focused on forming strong relationships with its exclusive independent agents. It also seeks to grow in core geographic and demographic markets as well as in its primary niche product areas of Medicare supplement policies and commercial fleet auto policies.

To expand its network base in 2012 the company formed a strategic partnership with BetterInvesting the premier nonprofit association serving retail investors.

Mergers and Acquisitions

In 2013 Atlantic American acquired Direct Life Insurance Company (DLIC) and changed its to Bankers Fidelity Assurance Company. The acquisition will allow Bankers Fidelity to offer additional similar products to those it already writes permitting greater diversification of product and pricing as well as opportunity for future expansion in other states.

Company Background

In 2011 the company's Bankers Fidelity Life purchased a block of Medicare supplement policies from American Community Mutual Insurance. The purchase expanded Atlantic American's Medicare operations in Michigan Indiana and Ohio.

Atlantic American's roots reach back to 1937 and the founding of the Dilbeck and Dominey Insurance Agency. J. Mack Robinson purchased the company in 1974. The family of J. Mack Robinson (who died in 2014) hold about 76% of the company.

EXECUTIVES

Vice Chairman, Harriett J Robinson, age 84
Board Of Directors, Edward E Elson, age 81
Auditors: BDOSeidmanLLP

LOCATIONS

HQ: Atlantic American Corp.
4370 Peachtree Road, N.E., Atlanta, GA 30319
Phone: 404 266-5500
Web: www.atlam.com

PRODUCTS/OPERATIONS

2013 Sales

	$ mil.	% of total
Life & health		
Bankers Fidelity	110.0	66
Property & casualty		
American Southern	54.0	33
Corporate & other	1.4	1
Total	**165.4**	**100**

2013 Sales

	$ mil.	% of total
Insurance premium	145.6	88
Investment income	10.8	7
Realized investment gains	8.8	5
Other	0.2	-
Total	**165.4**	**100**

Selected Products
Business Automobile Insurance
General Liability Insurance
Life and Health Insurance
Property Insurance
Surety Bonds

COMPETITORS

AIG	Penn Treaty
Aflac	Prudential
Alfa Mutual	Safeco
Blue Cross	State Farm
CNO Financial	Travelers Companies
Liberty Mutual	USAA
Nationwide	

HISTORICAL FINANCIALS
Company Type: Public

Income Statement FYE: December 31

	ASSETS ($ mil.)	NET INCOME ($ mil.)	INCOME AS % OF ASSETS	EMPLOYEES
12/13	319.3	11.0	3.5%	133
12/12	320.1	4.4	1.4%	122
12/11	302.1	3.2	1.1%	121
12/10	277.5	2.4	0.9%	117
12/09	262.0	(1.2)	—	125
Annual Growth	5.1%	—	—	1.6%

2013 Year-End Financials

Return on assets: 3.4%
Return on equity: 10.6%
Long-term debt ($ mil.): —
No. of shares (mil.): 21
Sales ($ mil): 165

Dividends
  Yield: 1.7%
  Payout: 15.5%
Market value ($ mil.): 86

	STOCK PRICE ($) FY Close	P/E High/Low		PER SHARE ($) Earnings	Dividends	Book Value
12/13	4.09	8	6	0.48	0.07	4.78
12/12	3.09	16	10	0.18	0.07	4.98
12/11	1.97	17	13	0.12	0.02	4.53
12/10	2.03	23	13	0.09	0.00	3.72
12/09	1.28	—	—	(0.08)	0.00	3.48
Annual Growth	33.7%	—		—	—	8.3%

Atlas Air Worldwide Holdings, Inc.

Atlas carried the weight of the world; Atlas Air Worldwide Holdings (AAWW) carries the freight of the world. The company leases cargo planes to customers mainly airlines under long-term ACMI (aircraft crew maintenance and insurance) contracts. The segment accounts for about 45% of AAWW's revenue. All told the company maintains a fleet of more than 35 Boeing 747 freighters. AAWW also offers dry leasing (aircraft and engines only) via its Titan division. Affiliates Atlas Air and 51% owned Polar Air Cargo provide charter services to charter brokers freight forwarders airlines and the US military (referred to as AMC) which accounts for 22% of sales.

Geographic Reach

AAWW provides global services with operations in Africa Asia Australia Europe the Middle East North America and South America operating more than 25500 flights serving 430 destinations in 124 countries.

Operations

During 2014 AAWW operated 35 Boeing 747 freighters four Boeing Large Cargo Freighters more than 10 Boeing 767 freighters six Boeing 777 freighters two Boeing 737 freighters and one Boeing 737 and Boeing 757 each.

Financial Performance

AAWW has enjoyed unprecedented revenue growth over the last few years with revenues peaking at a record-setting $1.66 billion in 2013. Profits however have fluctuated over the years increasing sharply in 2012 only to decline 28% to $94 million in 2013.

The company's historic growth for 2013 was driven by an impressive 200% surge in Dry Leasing revenue due to the acquisition of three 777-200LRF aircraft in 2013 that were leased to customers on a long-term basis. The company was also helped by a 10% increase in ACMI revenue for 2013.

The company's erosion of profits was 2013 was attributed to a lease termination charge of $17.8 million it paid in addition to increased depreciation and amortization expenses. AAWW's cash flow from operating activities has also seen an upward trend the last few years.

Strategy

Each year AAWW maintains a proper balance sheet by adjusting its cost structure and by extending its flight network reach. In 2013 it launched a daily nonstop 747-400 express freighter service between Cincinnati and Tokyo.

HISTORY

Michael Chowdry a pilot and aviation consultant credited the Persian Gulf War with the creation of his company. As he looked out of his Hong Kong hotel room one night in 1991 he noticed postwar terrorism threats had sharply reduced passenger flights from Kai Tak airport but air cargo plane traffic was still heavy. In 1992 with just one cargo plane he started Atlas Air.

The company leased cargo space to airlines typically for multiyear contracts providing 100% use of a plane and allowing for a few cancellations of hours (cancellations hurt the company in early 1997). Atlas lost money in 1992 and 1993 while building its fleet but was in the black by 1994. It went public a year later. Despite having to make the transition from startup carrier to one of the world's biggest cargo airlines Atlas Air doubled the size of its operations in 1996.

In 1996 the company agreed to buy six 747s from Thai Airways and to lease five more from FedEx. But high expenses for the FedEx planes cut into 1997 results. Chowdry responded by ordering 10 new Boeing 747-400s. He also replaced Mickey Foret as president after 14 months. Foret presided when Atlas Air bought its FedEx lemons.

In 1998 Atlas Air secured a cargo agreement with a new customer Alitalia. The next year the company announced that it was closing its offices in Golden Colorado and at New York City's JFK International Airport and moving operations to Harrison New York.

In anticipation of China's entry into the World Trade Organization Atlas strengthened its position in that country signing lease agreements in 2000 with Air China China Southern Airlines and Hong Kong-based Dragonair.

Tragedy struck Atlas the next year when founder Chowdry died in the crash of a private jet he was piloting. Later that year the company reorganized as a holding company renaming itself Atlas Air Worldwide Holdings.

Faced with a slump in demand for air freight services Atlas Air Worldwide Holdings announced plans to cut about 15% of its workforce in 2001. The company missed payments on some of its aircraft and over the course of the next year it became apparent that cost-cutting alone would not bring the company back into the black.

In addition Atlas Air Worldwide Holdings announced plans to re-audit its 2000 and 2001 financial results which had been certified by Arthur Andersen and the SEC began an investigation in 2002. (The investigation was closed in 2007 and Atlas Air Worldwide Holdings was not penalized. To address the SEC's concerns the company moved during the inquiry to improve its internal financial controls and reporting procedures.)

Amid the turmoil CEO Richard Shuyler was abruptly let go in March 2003 —less than two months after he had been tapped to be the company's next vice chairman. Three other officers left the company and board member John Blue stepped in as interim CEO. Later in 2003 Blue was replaced by Jeffrey Erickson.

Atlas Air Worldwide Holdings resolved to restructure through bankruptcy and the company spent much of 2003 negotiating deals with creditors; it filed for Chapter 11 bankruptcy protection early in 2004. The pre-filing negotiations helped smooth the restructuring process and Atlas Air Worldwide Holdings emerged from bankruptcy in July 2004.

Erickson retired as president and CEO in 2006 and former GeoLogistics CEO William Flynn was named to replace him.

EXECUTIVES

Vice President Sales Mkt Chief Exec Ofc, Kersti Krepp
Vp Flight Operations And Labor Relations, James R (Jim) Cato, age 60
Vice President Security Charles, Gary Wade
Vice President Strategic Development, Gregory T Guillaume
Vice President Procurement, Lawrence Gibbons
Vice President Safety And Regulatory Compliance, William E Kelley
Vice President System Operations, Kevin Sarubbe
Vice President Ground Operations, Bob Kiss
President and Chief Executive Officer, William J. (Bill) Flynn, age 60, $1,035,040 total compensation
Executive Vice President and Chief Operating Officer, John W. Dietrich, age 50, $632,524 total compensation
Executive Vice President and Chief Commercial Officer; President and CEO Titan Aviation Holdings, Michael T. Steen, age 48, $550,021 total compensation
EVP General Counsel Chief Human Resources Officer and Secretary, Adam R. Kokas, age 43, $488,769 total compensation
EVP and CFO, Spencer Schwartz, age 47, $425,016 total compensation
Vice President Information Technology, Richard Ross
Staff Vice President Of Taxation, Scott Roper
Senior Vice President And General, Vamshi Rokkam
Vice President Technical Operations, Mark S Swearingin
Vice President And Controller Finance, Keith Mayer
Vice President Flight Operations, Jeff Carlson
Chairman, Frederick McCorkle, age 70
EVP General Counsel Chief Human Resources Officer and Secretary, Adam R. Kokas, age 43
Auditors: PricewaterhouseCoopersLLP

LOCATIONS

HQ: Atlas Air Worldwide Holdings, Inc.
2000 Westchester Avenue, Purchase, NY 10577
Phone: 914 701-8000
Web: www.atlasair.com

PRODUCTS/OPERATIONS

2013 Sales

	$ mil.	% of total
ACMI	755.0	46
Commercial charter	496.1	30
AMC charter	356.3	22
Dry leasing	35.2	2
Other	14.3	1
Total	**1656.9**	**100**

COMPETITORS

AerCap	FedEx Freight
Air Atlanta	GE Capital Aviation
Aviation Capital Group	Services
CIT Transportation	ILFC
Finance	Kalitta Air
Castle Aviation	Lufthansa Cargo
Evergreen Holdings	

HISTORICAL FINANCIALS

Company Type: Public

Income Statement
FYE: December 31

	REVENUE ($ mil.)	NET INCOME ($ mil.)	NET PROFIT MARGIN	EMPLOYEES
12/13	1,656.9	93.8	5.7%	1,792
12/12	1,646.0	129.9	7.9%	1,744
12/11	1,398.2	96.0	6.9%	1,716
12/10	1,337.7	141.8	10.6%	1,532
12/09	1,061.5	77.7	7.3%	1,337
Annual Growth	**11.8%**	**4.8%**	**—**	**7.6%**

2013 Year-End Financials

Debt ratio: 45.6%	No. of shares (mil.): 25
Return on equity: 7.2%	Dividends
Cash ($ mil.): 321	Yield: —
Current ratio: 1.42	Payout: —
Long-term debt ($ mil.): 1,539	Market value ($ mil.): 1,030

	STOCK PRICE ($) FY Close	P/E High/Low		PER SHARE ($) Earnings	Dividends	Book Value
12/13	41.15	14	10	3.66	0.00	52.63
12/12	44.32	12	8	4.89	0.00	48.57
12/11	38.43	20	8	3.64	0.00	43.24
12/10	55.83	11	7	5.44	0.00	40.35
12/09	37.25	11	3	3.56	0.00	34.48
Annual Growth	**2.5%**			**0.7%**	**—**	**11.1%**

Atwood Oceanics, Inc.

Atwood Oceanics is at work in oceans all over the world. An offshore oil and gas drilling contractor the firm owns about a dozen drilling rigs including six semisubmersible rigs five jack-ups and one semisubmersible tender assist vessel (which places drilling equipment on permanent platforms). Its rigs operate in the Gulf of Mexico offshore Southeast Asia offshore West Africa offshore Australia and in the Mediterranean. Atwood Oceanics serves a limited number of customers at one time and generates nearly all of its sales internationally.

Geographic Reach Australia represents the company's largest market contributing about 45% of sales in fiscal 2012; Africa accounts for about a third. Australian revenue increased more than 80% year-over-year as 2012 marked the first full year of operation for the Atwood Osprey semisubmersible which is working for Chevron Australia.

Atwood Oceanics has offices in the US as well as Australia Malaysia Singapore and the UK.

Sales and Marketing The company provided services for 16 customers in fiscal 2012 including

Chevron Australia (34% of sales) Noble Energy (17%) and Kosmos Energy Ghana (11%). Other clients included Hess Apache Energy and CEC International.

Financial Performance With commodity prices bouncing back after the global recession in 2010 Atwood Oceanics posted a jump in revenues and net income. Revenue dropped slightly in 2011 but returned to growth in fiscal 2012 (ended September) rising 22% to $787 million.

Revenue from new rigs including the Condor in the Gulf of Mexico and the Osprey in Australia contributed positively to the results and offset flat or reduced sales in other areas as projects remained steady or ended. Net income in 2012 remained flat at $272 million as the rise in revenue was accompanied by an increase in contract drilling costs and depreciation expenses. Strategy The company is committed to upgrading its fleet to keep pace with the increasing demand for global offshore exploration. Its newest semisubmersible drilling rig began operating in fiscal 2012 in the Gulf of Mexico; Atwood Oceanics anticipates this rig (Condor) will increase its US revenue in coming years. In addition the company has three ultra-deepwater drillships and two-jack up rigs scheduled to come online between 2013 and 2015. Ownership Fellow drilling contractor Helmerich & Payne owns 12% of Atwood Oceanics. Its CEO Hans Helmerich serves as a director of Atwood Oceanics. Wellington Management owns about 10%.

EXECUTIVES

Vice President Human Resource, Luis Jimenez
Vice President, Glen Kelley
Vice President Controller, Michael A (Mike) Campbell, age 45
EVP and CFO, Mark L. Mey, age 49, $442,000 total compensation
SVP Technical Services, Barry M. Smith, age 55, $301,877 total compensation
President and CEO, Robert J. (Rob) Saltiel, age 51, $742,770 total compensation
SVP Operations, Arthur M. (Mac) Polhamus, age 60, $317,700 total compensation
Vp Gen Council And Corp Sec, Drew Baker
Chairman, George S. Dotson, age 74
Secretary, Shannon Treadway
Auditors: PricewaterhouseCoopersLLP

LOCATIONS

HQ: Atwood Oceanics, Inc.
15011 Katy Freeway, Suite 800, Houston, TX 77094
Phone: 281 749-7800   **Fax:** 281 492-7871
Web: www.atwd.com

2012 Sales

	$ mil.	% of total
Australia	363.4	46
Africa	252.0	32
Asia	84.0	10
South America	45.2	6
US	36.5	5
Middle East	6.3	1
Total	**787.4**	**100**

PRODUCTS/OPERATIONS

2012 Sales

	% of total
Chevron Australia	34
Noble Energy	17
Kosmos Energy Ghana	11
Other customers	38
Total	**100**

COMPETITORS

Diamond Offshore	Rowan Companies
Ensco	Saipem
Nabors Industries	Schlumberger
Noble	Seadrill
Oceaneering International	Transocean
Parker Drilling	Vantage Drilling

HISTORICAL FINANCIALS

Company Type: Public

Income Statement
FYE: September 30

	REVENUE ($ mil.)	NET INCOME ($ mil.)	NET PROFIT MARGIN	EMPLOYEES
09/14	1,173.9	340.8	29.0%	1,905
09/13	1,063.6	350.2	32.9%	1,830
09/12	787.4	272.1	34.6%	1,460
09/11	645.0	271.6	42.1%	1,300
09/10	650.5	257.0	39.5%	1,200
Annual Growth	**15.9%**	**7.3%**	**—**	**12.2%**

2014 Year-End Financials

Debt ratio: 38.9%	No. of shares (mil.): 64
Return on equity: 14.3%	Dividends
Cash ($ mil.): 80	Yield: —
Current ratio: 2.97	Payout: 4.7%
Long-term debt ($ mil.): 1,742	Market value ($ mil.): 2,812

	STOCK PRICE ($) FY Close	P/E High/Low		PER SHARE ($) Earnings	Dividends	Book Value
09/14	43.69	11	8	5.24	0.00	39.71
09/13	55.04	11	8	5.32	0.00	34.46
09/12	45.45	12	8	4.14	0.00	29.63
09/11	34.36	12	7	4.15	0.00	25.44
09/10	30.45	10	6	3.95	0.00	21.26
Annual Growth	**9.4%**	**—**	**—**	**7.3%**	**—**	**16.9%**

Autobytel Inc.

Autobytel puts cars on the information superhighway. Using the company's websites a potential car buyer can research make model fuel efficiency and more then complete an online request form for the desired new or used car. The form is forwarded to local auto dealers and manufacturers who contact the shopper within 24 hours. Car buyers can also research insurance financing and other related services. Autobytel generates most of its revenue through lead referral fees it charges dealers and manufacturers (car buyers pay no fees). However the company also operates advertising-driven consumer website Car.com which offers many of the same services.

Sales and Marketing
The company generates traffic to its website through search engine optimization or "SEO" paid search (search engine marketing or "SEM") direct marketing and partnering with other website publishers that provide links to its websites. During fiscal 2012 Autobytel spent some $1.2 million on advertising marketing and promotion.

Autobytel counts AutoNation General Motors Volkswagen and Volvo among its customers.

Financial Performance
The company's revenue increased by about 5% in fiscal 2012 compared with 2011. Revenue in-

creased primarily due to an increase in lead fees. Lead revenues increased 6% in fiscal 2012 compared to the previous year.

Autobytel's net income also increased in fiscal 2012 (up to $1.4 million from $.4 million in fiscal 2011) mainly because of increased revenue paired with decreased operating expenses. The company's sales and marketing expenses decreased 4% during the year while the company's technology spend decreased 3% in fiscal 2012 primarily due to lower computer software and maintenance costs along with decreased data content and licensing charges.

The bump in revenue and improved net income helped the company's net cash inflow increase by approximately $2 million in fiscal 2012 compared with the prior year.

Strategy
In 2012 the company launched the mobile version of Autobytel.com which gives consumers the opportunity to view photographs and videos read car reviews and check pricing from their mobile devices while on the go or when they are at dealerships shopping for vehicles. The mobile optimized website also has shopping tools that allow a consumer to find a local dealer browse inventory and request free dealer price quotes.

HISTORY

After his Southern California car dealership went under during an industry slump in the early 1990s Peter Ellis decided to work car sales from another angle. He teamed with John Bedrosian (co-founder of National Medical Enterprises which later became Tenet Healthcare the nation's #2 hospital chain) and founded Auto-By-Tel in 1995. The company launched its Web site for new car sales the same year and by the end of 1995 it had signed up more than 350 car dealers. Investors in an early round of private financing included General Electric unit GE Capital Services auto insurance company American International Group (AIG) and former HBO and Warner Music Group head Michael Fuchs.

Auto-By-Tel formed an agreement with Chase Manhattan's Chase Auto Finance unit in 1996 to provide car loan services. It also introduced Internet-based insurance services through an online link with AIG. In 1996 the company's services became available in Canada.

The company added used cars to its service in 1997. Poor market conditions for Internet stocks forced Auto-By-Tel to withdraw its IPO originally planned for April 1997. By the close of 1997 more than 1600 car dealers had signed up with the Auto-By-Tel service.

The company changed its name to autobytel.com in 1998 and Mark Lorimer replaced Ellis as CEO. The next year with market conditions improving autobytel.com went public. The same year the company launched its car auction service and expanded into Japan the UK and Sweden. autobytel.com later teamed with LendingTree (now Tree.com) to add a banking center to its Web site and launched an online automotive superstore. In early 2000 the company acquired A.I.N. Corporation owner of the CarSmart.com vehicle buying service.

The company also laid the groundwork for expansion into Australia and Europe and later purchased rival Autoweb.com. Jeffrey Schwartz joined Autobytel in 2001 as vice chairman after its purchase of Autoweb.com where he was president and CEO. He was elected Director and appointed President and CEO that year. Also that year the dot-com crash worsened and the company put an end to its buying spree. A sign of the times Autobytel.com ditched the suffix and changed its name to Autobytel Inc. In 2002 the company scaled back its international presence closing its Australian operations and reducing its stake in Autobytel.Europe to 49%.

In 2004 Autobytel acquired Stoneage Corporation operator of rival online auto site Car.com for about $50 million. That same year the company bought iDriveonline adding heft to its customer loyalty and retention marketing business.

Autobytel.Europe was dissolved in 2005. Also in 2005 Richard (Rick) Post replaced Schwartz as President and CEO. The following year James Riesenbach agreed to become President and CEO. The company sold its price and specification business Automotive Information Center to R. L. Polk & Co in 2007.

After pursuing a sale in 2008 Autobytel instead decided to continue to shed non-core assets. Later that year the company sold its AVV data extraction and customer relationship management software product to Dominion Enterprises for $22.75 million in cash plus a working capital payment. Also that year it cut about 35% of its workforce or some 75 jobs.

Riesnback left the company in 2008; he was replaced by Jeffrey Coats. The next year Autobytel implemented a second round of layoffs representing about 25% of its employees. In 2010 Autobytel bought proprietary content and search marketing firms Cyber Ventures and Autotropolis for nearly $17 million.

EXECUTIVES

Senior Vice President Advertising, Rick Szatkowski
President and CEO, Jeffrey H. Coats, age 56, $450,000 total compensation
SVP and CFO, Curtis E. DeWalt, age 60, $268,000 total compensation
EVP and President Dealer Services, Phillip W. DuPree
Evp Corp Dev, Dennis Benner
Vice President Marketing, Michael Rosenberg
Vice President Corporate Relations, John Steerman
Vice President Of Advertising Sales, Brian Hafer
Sales Vice President, Joshua N McCarter
Executive Vice President Product Marketing And Analytics, Jim Helberg
Sr V Pres Tech, John J Skocilic
Senior Vice President Consumer, William Ferriolo
Executive Vice President Chief Legal, Ariel Amir
Senior Vice President Marketing, Anne Benvenuto
Vice President Of Sales, Steve Ammons
Senior Vice President Web Business, Jonathan Veeramraju
National Sales Manager, Marvin Grimm
Senior Vice President And Chief, John Petrone
Vice President Dealer Sales, Tim Rogers
Vice President Of Marketing, Amy Simpson
Vp Of Marketing, Mike Broderick
Vp Marketing, Lisa Kra
Vice President Finance, Mike Bonk
Vice President Of Marketing, Jim Julow
Vice President Advertising, David Armitage
Senior Vice President, James Fabin
Vice President Market Development, Joe Van Winkle
Vice President Of Corporate Communications, Melanie Webber
Vice President, Brandi Slaughter
Executive Vice President And Chief Mkt, Andy Donchak
First Vice President, Maria Neece
Vice President Marketing, Frank Marchilena
Vice President, Gary Leek

Executive Vice President Finance, Cherie Dejarlais
Vice President Product Marketing, Russell Lbartlett
Chief Financial Officer Senior Vp, John Markovich
Vice President Lead Operations, Katherine Steerman
Vice President Product Development, Ian Shields
Vice President Of Product Planning, Jack Collins
Vice President Product Development, Claire Bentley
Vice President Finance, Anthony Fidaleo
Vice President Human Resources, Lorna Paugh
Executive Vice President President Dealer Services, Phil Dupree
Vice President Advertising Data And Traffic Sales, Kyle Pratt
Vice Chairman, Mark R Ross
Executive Vice President Chief Legal And Administrative Officer Secretary, Glenn E Fuller, age 60
Treasurer, Hoshi Printer
Chairman, Michael J. Fuchs, age 69
Secretary, Craig Frost
Auditors: Ernst&YoungLLP

LOCATIONS

HQ: Autobytel Inc.
18872 MacArthur Boulevard, Suite 200, Irvine, CA 92612
Phone: 949 225-4500
Web: www.autobytel.com

PRODUCTS/OPERATIONS

2012 Sales

	$ mil.	% of total
Lead fees	63.1	95
Advertising	3.5	5
Other	0.2	
Total	**66.8**	**100**

Selected brands

Autobytel.com (Internet car buying)
Autoweb.com (Internet car buying)
Autosite.com (resourse for entry level buyers)
CarSmart.com (vehicle data)
Car.com (Internet car buying)
MyRide.com (consumer-driven flagship auto portal)

COMPETITORS

ADP	Internet Brands
American Automobile Association (AAA)	Penske Automotive Group
AutoNation	Priceline
AutoTrader	Reynolds and Reynolds
CarMax	Robert Bentley
Cars.com	Sonic Automotive
Dealix Corporation	TeleTech
Edmunds.com	Trader Corporation
Experian Americas	eBay

HISTORICAL FINANCIALS

Company Type: Public

Income Statement

FYE: December 31

	REVENUE ($ mil.)	NET INCOME ($ mil.)	NET PROFIT MARGIN	EMPLOYEES
12/13	78.3	38.1	48.7%	159
12/12	66.8	1.3	2.1%	122
12/11	63.8	0.4	0.7%	118
12/10	51.5	(8.5)	—	119
12/09	52.9	(2.3)	—	120
Annual Growth	**10.3%**	**—**		**7.3%**

2013 Year-End Financials

Debt ratio: 10.4%
Return on equity: 84.2%
Cash ($ mil.): 18
Current ratio: 2.88
Long-term debt ($ mil.): 9
No. of shares (mil.): 8
Dividends
  Yield: —
  Payout: —
Market value ($ mil.): 135

	STOCK PRICE ($) FY Close	P/E High/Low		PER SHARE ($) Earnings	Dividends	Book Value
12/13	15.13	4	1	3.61	0.00	7.28
12/12	3.98	29	5	0.15	0.00	2.91
12/11	0.70	29	14	0.05	0.00	2.70
12/10	0.86	—	—	(0.95)	0.00	2.53
12/09	1.00	—	—	(0.25)	0.00	3.12
Annual Growth	**97.2%**	—	—	—	—	**23.6%**

AvalonBay Communities, Inc.

AvalonBay Communities has it down in the apartment department. The real estate investment trust (REIT) buys develops renovates and operates multifamily properties in the US. It specializes in upscale properties in high barrier-to-entry markets such as Boston Los Angeles New York City San Francisco Seattle and Washington DC. By providing luxury living in high-demand areas where apartment-zoned land is in low supply AvalonBay can also charge premium rent. The REIT owns about 180 apartment communities with more than 53000 units. It also has more than 30 properties under construction or redevelopment and owns rights to develop more than 30 additional ones.

Most of AvalonBay's properties are garden-style but the company also owns mid- and high-rise apartment buildings. Its core Avalon brand comprises upscale apartments with high-end amenities in urban and suburban markets. Its AVA brand consists of smaller apartments in urban areas near public transportation and entertainment options while Eaves by Avalon offers less expensive price points to renters in suburban settings.

The REIT handles its own leasing and management operations and usually acts as its own general contractor and construction manager for the development or renovation of properties. To attract and retain residents it offers amenities such as fully equipped kitchens with modern appliances patios and decks swimming pools fully equipped kitchens with modern appliances at many of its properties.

AvalonBay which is divesting most of its holdings in the Midwest sold about a dozen properties in 2011. The dispositions helped the REIT attain earnings of more than $441 million in 2011 which represented an increase of more than 150% compared to the previous year ($175.3 million). Meanwhile revenues rose from $874 million in 2010 to $968.7 million an increase of about 10%. The company benefitted from higher occupancy rates at its communities a continued decline in home ownership rates and a limited supply of new multifamily construction projects from competitors.

AvalonBay often sells non-strategic properties to fund new developments or acquisitions. The company has ramped up its development activity in anticipation of a further improving economy in order to capitalize on the aforementioned trends. It also expects to accelerate its acquisition activity which it put on hold during the recession.

EXECUTIVES

Ex Vp Human Resources, Charlene Rothkopf, age 63

Senior Vice President Development, Jonathan B Cox

Senior Vice President Development, Frederick Harris

Vice President, Ron Ladell

Vice President Property Operations, Deborah Coombs

Vice President Property Operations, Mona Stahlings

Vice President Systems, Shannon Brennan

Vice President Corporate Controller, Keri Shea

Chief Investment Officer, Matthew H. (Matt) Birenbaum, $395,192 total compensation

EVP and Chief Administrative Officer, Leo S. Horey, age 52, $420,192 total compensation

EVP Development and Construction Northeast, William M. (Bill) McLaughlin, age 50, $390,000 total compensation

Chairman President and CEO, Timothy J. (Tim) Naughton, age 53, $921,154 total compensation

Executive Vice President; General Counsel; Secretary, Edward M. Schulman, age 52, $319,282 total compensation

Executive Vice President - Development & Construction West Coast, Stephen W. (Steve) Wilson, age 58

COO, Sean J. Breslin, age 48, $418,269 total compensation

SVP Investment Management, Kevin P. O'Shea, age 48

EVP and Chief Construction Officer, Michael M. Feigin

Vice President Information Services, Karen A Hollinger

Vice President Engineering, Mike F Nootens

Vice President Marketing, Kevin Thompson

Vice President Of Operations, Heather Duffy

Sr Vp-construction, James R Liberty

Vice President For Mid And High Rise Construction, David Bellman

Senior Vice President Of Property, Bernard Ward

Vice President Of Information, Brian Brandt

Vice President Construction, Alfred Brockunier

Vice President And General Counsel, Michael Crehan

Svp And Chief Marketing Officer, George Henriques

Senior Vice President Development, Tom Javits

Vice President Investments, Pat Gniadek

Vice President Customer Care Center, Stephen Fabian

Vice President Sales And Marketing, Anthony Lupas

Executive Vice President, Darius Guerany

Vice President Sales And Marketing, Kurt Hesser

Vice President Property, Lisa Bongardt

Vice President, Andrew Kilbourne

Vice President Information Systems, Jim Graves

Vice President Of Construction, Janice Pope

Vice President Associate General, Alan Adamson

Executive Vice President Corporate, Birenbaum Matt

Vice President Construction, Steven Spiro

Chairman President and CEO, Timothy J. (Tim) Naughton, age 53

Treasurer, Craig Thomas

Board Member, Jay H Sarles

Board Member, Edward W Walter

Board Member, Alan B Buckelew

Auditors: Ernst&YoungLLP

LOCATIONS

HQ: AvalonBay Communities, Inc.
Ballston Tower, 671 N. Glebe Road, Suite 800, Arlington, VA 22203
Phone: 703 329-6300 **Fax:** 703 329-9130
Web: www.avalonbay.com

2011 Sales

	$ mil.	% of total
Established properties		
Metro New York/New Jersey	195.7	20
New England	169.9	18
Mid-Atlantic/Midwest	110.2	11
Northern California	103.0	11
Southern California	75.1	8
Pacific Northwest	37.7	4
Other stabilized properites	137.8	14
Development & redevelopment properties	129.7	13
Non-allocated	9.6	1
Total	**895.3**	**100**

PRODUCTS/OPERATIONS

2011 Sales

	$ mil.	% of total
Rental & other income	959.0	99
Management development & other fees	9.7	1
Total	**968.7**	**100**

COMPETITORS

AMLI Residential	Essex Property Trust
Apartment Investment and Management	Gables Residential Services
Camden Property	Home Properties
Equity Residential	UDR

HISTORICAL FINANCIALS

Company Type: Public

Income Statement

FYE: December 31

	REVENUE ($ mil.)	NET INCOME ($ mil.)	NET PROFIT MARGIN	EMPLOYEES
12/13	1,462.9	353.1	24.1%	0
12/12	1,038.6	423.8	40.8%	2,178
12/11	968.7	441.6	45.6%	2,095
12/10	895.2	175.3	19.6%	1,993
12/09	851.5	155.6	18.3%	1,877
Annual Growth	**14.5%**	**22.7%**	**—**	**—**

2013 Year-End Financials

Debt ratio: 40.0%
Return on equity: 4.5%
Cash ($ mil.): 281
Current ratio: 1.79
Long-term debt ($ mil.): 6,145

No. of shares (mil.): 129
Dividends
 Yield: 3.6%
 Payout: 211.8%
Market value ($ mil.): 15,301

	STOCK PRICE ($) FY Close	P/E High/Low	PER SHARE ($) Earnings	Dividends	Book Value
12/13	118.23	51 42	2.78	4.28	66.42
12/12	135.59	35 29	4.32	3.88	59.76
12/11	130.60	29 22	4.87	3.57	46.18
12/10	112.55	55 35	2.07	3.57	38.54
12/09	82.11	45 21	1.93	3.57	37.41
Annual Growth	**9.5%**	**— —**	**9.6%**	**4.6%**	**15.4%**

AZZ Inc

When companies need to power up or get "in zink" they give AZZ incorporated a buzz. The company has two business segments: galvanizing services and energy. To protect steel from environmental corrosion galvanizing services dip steel products into baths of molten zinc. The process is vital for steel fabricators who serve highway construction electrical utility transportation and water-treatment firms. Through subsidiaries AZZ makes electrical power distribution systems industrial lighting switchgear motor control centers bus duct systems and tubular goods. Industrial petrochemical and power generation and transmission companies use the company's products.

Operations

AZZ's energy segment (55% of total sales) is a manufacturer of specialty equipment focusing on the safe and reliable transmission of power from generation sources to end customers. Products include custom switchgear electrical enclosures medium and high voltage bus ducts explosion proof and hazardous duty lighting and tubular products. The company is also a third party supplier of safety related equipment for the nuclear industry. The galvanizing services segment (45%) provides hot dip galvanizing to the steel fabrication industry through facilities located throughout Canada and the US.

Financial Performance

AZZ has achieved dramatic growth over the last few years. Revenues surged 32% from $571 million in 2013 to reach $752 million in 2014 a historic milestone for the company. After posting a record-setting $60 million in profits in 2013 AZZ saw its profits hover around the same mark for 2014 due to increased expenses.

The strong growth in 2013 was driven by additional revenue from strategic acquisitions made during 2013. The company's operating cash flow increased by $14 million in 2013 due to cash generated from non-cash interest expense and accounts receivable.

Mergers and Acquisitions

AZZ has achieved explosive revenue growth over the years through the use of acquisitions. In 2014 it bought Zalk Steel & Supply Co. a Minnesota-based galvanizing company that targets customers in the Midwest. The acquisition added roughly 35 galvanizing plants to AZZ's galvanizing services segment. AZZ enhanced this segment previously with the $12 million 2013 acquisition of G3 Galvanizing Limited (G3) a company with operations in Halifax Nova Scotia.

In 2013 AZZ acquired Aquilex Holdings' Specialty Repair and Overhaul (SRO) business. The SRO unit added global maintenance revitalization and repair services to customers in the fossil fuel and nuclear power generation market as well as other energy and industrial customers. In mid-2012 it snatched up Nuclear Logistics a Texas-based provider of electrical and mechanical equipment and services used in promoting safety for nuclear facilities. The deal added a new portfolio of brands to AZZ's energy segment.

EXECUTIVES

Vice President - Manufacturing Strategies, Jim Stricklen

Svp-coo Energy Segment, Ashok E Kolady

President and CEO, Thomas E. (Tom) Ferguson, age 58, $214,205 total compensation

SVP Finance CFO and Secretary, Paul W. Fehlman,
age 50, $6,771 total compensation
SVP Galvanizing Services, Tim E. Pendley, age 53,
$330,000 total compensation
VP Information Technology, Matt Emery, age 46,
$220,000 total compensation
VP and Chief Accounting Officer, Robert J. Steines,
$64,167 total compensation
Vice President, Francis D Quinn, age 49
Vp, Christopher N Izzo
Vice President Of Human Resources, Trey Quinn
Vice President Electrical Industrial, John
  Chandragiri
Senior Vice President Electrical, John Petro
Vp Sales & Marketing, Will Mullendore
Vice President, Dixon Parker
Vp, R J Steines
Vice President, Gene Bazemore
**Senior Vice President And General Manager Sro
  Non Nuclear Services,** Doug Vail
Vice President, Brad Jeaurond
Vice President Sales And Marketing, Craig Irish
Chairman, Kevern R. Joyce, age 68
SVP Finance CFO and Secretary, Paul W. Fehlman,
age 50
Auditors: BDOSeidmanLLP

LOCATIONS

HQ: AZZ Inc
  One Museum Place, Suite 500, 3100 West Seventh
  Street, Fort Worth, TX 76107
Phone: 817 810-0095   **Fax:** 817 336-5354
Web: www.azz.com

PRODUCTS/OPERATIONS

2014 Sales

	$ mil.	% of total
Galvanizing services	416.1	55
Electrical & industrial products	335.6	45
Total	**751.7**	**100**

Selected Products and Services

Galvanizing Services
  Coordinated multi-plant operations
  Custom hot-dip galvanizing
  Duplex finishes
  Finished material warehousing
Electrical and Industrial Products
  Air and gas insulated bus duct
  Electrical power distribution centers
  Industrial hazardous-duty lighting
  Metal-clad outdoor switchgear
  Protective relay panels
  Tubular goods

COMPETITORS

ABB
Chamberlin
Earle M. Jorgensen
Energy Focus
Friedman Industries
GE
Gewiss
JJI Lighting
Jarden
LSI Industries
Legrand
Powell Industries
Professional Luminaires North America
SPX

HISTORICAL FINANCIALS

Company Type: Public

Income Statement

FYE: February 28

	REVENUE ($ mil.)	NET INCOME ($ mil.)	NET PROFIT MARGIN	EMPLOYEES
02/14	751.7	59.6	7.9%	2,927
02/13	570.5	60.4	10.6%	2,632
02/12	469.1	40.7	8.7%	2,154
02/11	380.6	34.9	9.2%	1,956
02/10	357.0	37.7	10.6%	1,530
Annual Growth	**20.5%**	**12.1%**	**—**	**17.6%**

2014 Year-End Financials

Debt ratio: 42.5%   No. of shares (mil.): 25
Return on equity: 16.7%   Dividends
Cash ($ mil.): 27   Yield: 1.2%
Current ratio: 2.06   Payout: 22.8%
Long-term debt ($ mil.): 384   Market value ($ mil.): 1,135

	STOCK PRICE ($) FY Close	P/E High/Low		PER SHARE ($) Earnings	Dividends	Book Value
02/14	44.37	21	15	2.32	0.56	14.70
02/13	44.66	28	13	2.37	0.53	13.16
02/12	50.20	33	23	1.61	0.50	11.43
02/11	42.66	32	23	1.39	0.50	10.24
02/10	31.41	28	11	1.51	0.13	9.22
Annual Growth	**9.0%**			**11.3%**	**45.5%**	**12.4%**

Balchem Corp.

Believe Balchem when they say they have it covered. The company has developed a technology that covers or encapsulates ingredients used in food and animal health products; the encapsulation improves nutritional value and shelf life and allows for controlled time release. Balchem also provides specialty gases such as ethylene oxide (used to sterilize medical instruments) propylene oxide (used to reduce bacteria in spice treating and chemical processing) and methyl chloride (a refrigerant). The company's unencapsulated feed ingredients unit (BCP Ingredients) supplies the nutrient choline chloride to poultry and swine farmers. Reashure an encapsulated choline product increases milk production in dairy cows.

Geographic Reach

Balchem operates two subsidiaries in the US: BCP Ingredients and Aberco. It also has three subsidiaries in Europe: Balchem BV and Balchem Trading in the Netherlands and Balchem Italia which has a manufacturing facility in Italy that makes and distributes methylamines (a building block for choline products) and choline.

Operations

Balchem's operations are divided into three main business segments. Its ARC Specialty Products segment offers re-packaging and distribution of select chemicals (including ethylene oxide and propylene oxide) to healthcare and other markets. Its Animal Nutrition and Health segment makes and supplies products (including choline chloride) to several animal health markets and also certain derivative chemical products for industrial use. Balchem's SensoryEffects segment provides human-grade choline and microencapsulation products for a range of applications in human food pharmaceutical and nutrition markets.

Sales and Marketing

The company sells its products through its own sales force independent distributors and sales agents.

Financial Performance

The company's revenues rose more than 9% in 2013 due to increased sales across all of its segments. Specialty Products' revenues were lifted by increased sales of propylene oxide products used in industrial applications and nutmeat fumigation and by ethylene oxide products used in medical device sterilization. The Food Pharma & Nutrition segment (now SensoryEffects) increased due to a 10% sales increase in the food sector due to higher volumes and product mix of encapsulated ingredients for baking and food preservation end markets. Also contributing was an increase in sales of 28% for VitaShure products for nutritional enhancement.The Animal Nutrition & Health segment's sales increased due to increased sales of ANH specialty ingredients largely targeted to the ruminant and companion animal markets; as a result of higher sales of non-AminoShure products and led by strong volume growth of ReaShure NitroShure and chelated minerals. This increase was partially offset by lower volumes of AminoShure products related mainly to the adverse impact of the suspension of sales of AminoShure-L 52% lysine in 2012.In addition global feed grade choline product sales increased by 5% due to price increases partially offsetting increased raw material costs. (Choline and choline derivative products are used for industrial applications predominantly in North America including use in fracking for natural gas). Industrial sales grew 20% in 2013 with the increase coming from higher volumes for use in the fracking process.Balchem's net income increased by 12% in 2013 due to higher revenues a more favorable product mix and operating efficiencies derived from higher volumes.

Strategy

The company is continuing to focus on leveraging its plant capabilities driving efficiencies from core volume growth broadening product applications of human and animal health specialty products as well as capitalizing on its varied choline production capabilities. It planned to invest $14 million to $15 million in capital expenditures in 2014.

In 2014 Taminco and Balchem agreed to build and operate a choline chloride facility in St. Gabriel Louisiana where both companies operate production facilities. Both parties will invest in expanding these assets into a world-scale choline chloride production unit which is expected to come on stream in 2015. In 2013 the company's capital expenditures were about $8.2 million out of which $3.3 million was invested in its new manufacturing facility in Covington Virginia. Balchem expanded production capacities to meet growing demand by opening the Covington plant in 2012 which doubled the output capacity for the Animal Nutrition and Health ruminant sector.

Mergers and Acquisitions

To accelerate the growth of its food and nutrition platforms with new product offerings in 2014 Balchem spent $567 million to acquire Missouri-based Performance Chemicals & Ingredients Company (aka SensoryEffects) a privately held supplier of customized food and beverage ingredient systems.

HISTORY

Herbert Weiss Leslie Balassa three ex officers of the Alcolac company and a group of Baltimore-based investors founded Balchem in 1967 in New

York City. The company focused on the development of encapsulated specialty ingredients (the coating of individual particles that allow precise control of nutrient delivery). Initially Balchem developed food ingredients used in meat processing flavor enhancement and dough leavening as well as in nutritional supplements. In 1971 the company won its first big order: encapsulating the ingredients in pudding mix for General Foods. Balchem later applied the same technology to foaming agents for plastics aquaculture supplements and animal feeds. It also developed a line of specialty gases.

In 1994 Balchem boosted its gas business with the purchase of AlliedSignal's sterilant gas business (used to sterilize medical devices). Weiss retired as CEO in 1996 and was succeeded by EVP Raymond Reber. Reber left the company a few months later and chemical industry veteran Dino Rossi replaced him. The next year Balchem developed a rumen-protected choline chloride for the animal nutrition market.

Balchem restructured its operations in 1998 away from aquaculture and towards animal nutrition and other growth markets. After successful university and field trials the company introduced Reashure its encapsulated choline product for dairy cows.

In 2000 Balchem was granted a patent for its technology that increases milk production in dairy cows. In 2001 the company acquired the choline and encapsulated product lines of DCV Inc. and its DuCoa L.P. affiliate which contributed to the company's increase in net sales by about 30% in 2002. In 2002 sales continued to build as the encapsulated/nutritional products segment introduced several new products and product applications for the enhancement of shelf-life and fortification of products in certain markets of the food industry.

Balchem's unencapsulated feed ingredients segment also referred to as BCP Ingredients got larger in 2007 when the company acquired two choline-related businesses. The first was in Italy from Akzo Nobel and the other deal was for a company called Chinook Global Limited whose operations were integrated into Balchem's business. Those deals nearly tripled the size of BCP Ingredients making it Balchem's largest unit.

In 2010 the company's growth increased again with the acquisition of Maryland-based Aberco a marketer and distributor of propylene oxide.

EXECUTIVES

VP Administration Treasurer and Assistant Secretary, Francis J. (Frank) Fitzpatrick, age 53, $255,500 total compensation

Chairman President and CEO, Dino A. Rossi, age 59, $653,352 total compensation

VP and General Manager ARC Specialty Products, David R. Ludwig, age 56, $248,000 total compensation

General Counsel and Secretary, Matthew D. Houston, age 50, $204,000 total compensation

CFO, William A. Backus

Chief Operating Officer, Richard A. Bendure, age 45, $446,000 total compensation

Vp Human Resources, Robert T (Bob) Miniger, age 61

Vice President Of Operations, John E Kuehner

Chairman President and CEO, Dino A. Rossi, age 59

General Counsel and Secretary, Matthew D. Houston, age 50

Auditors: McGladreyLLP

LOCATIONS

HQ: Balchem Corp.
52 Sunrise Park Road, New Hampton, NY 10958
Phone: 845 326-5600

2013 Sales

	$ mil.	% of total
US	227.7	68
Other countries	109.5	32
Total	**337.2**	**100**

PRODUCTS/OPERATIONS

2013 Sales

	$ mil.	% of total
Animal Nutrition & Health	238.5	71
Specialty Products	51.1	15
Food Pharma & Nutrition	47.6	14
Total	**337.2**	**100**

Selected Products

BCP Ingredients
  Choline chloride (essential nutrient for animal health)
  Choline chloride derivatives
Encapsulated/Nutritional Products
  Food Pharma & Human Nutrition Products
  Bakeshure (leavening agents dough conditioners fortifiers acidifiers and antimicrobials)
  Confecshure (acidulants for flavor)
  Flavorshure (taste and flavor masking)
  Meatshure (acidifiers antioxidants and flavors)
  Vitashure (vitamins nutraceuticals and botanicals)
  Animal Nutrition & Health Products
  Niashure
  Niacine (prevents niacin degradation)
  Urea (regulates nitrogen/carbohydrates ratio in proteins)
  Reashure (rumen-stable choline for dairy cows)
Specialty Products
  Ethylene oxide (sterilant gas for the health care industry)
  Methyl chloride (specialty herbicides)
  Propylene oxide (bacteria reduction in spices)

COMPETITORS

ABCO Laboratories	Coating Place
Air Products	Dow Chemical
Airgas	IGENE
BASF Corporation	Mitsubishi Chemical
BioDelivery Sciences	Praxair
International	Sigma-Aldrich
Clariant	

HISTORICAL FINANCIALS

Company Type: Public

Income Statement

FYE: December 31

	REVENUE ($ mil.)	NET INCOME ($ mil.)	NET PROFIT MARGIN	EMPLOYEES
12/13	337.1	44.8	13.3%	387
12/12	310.3	40.0	12.9%	376
12/11	291.8	38.7	13.3%	365
12/10	255.0	33.2	13.0%	351
12/09	219.4	26.7	12.2%	337
Annual Growth	**11.3%**	**13.8%**	**—**	**3.5%**

2013 Year-End Financials

Debt ratio: —
Return on equity: 14.8%
Cash ($ mil.): 208
Current ratio: 7.77
Long-term debt ($ mil.): —
No. of shares (mil.): 30
Dividends
  Yield: 0.4%
  Payout: 17.9%
Market value ($ mil.): 1,774

	STOCK PRICE ($) FY Close	P/E High/Low		PER SHARE ($) Earnings	Dividends	Book Value
12/13	58.70	39	24	1.45	0.26	10.96
12/12	36.45	30	19	1.32	0.22	9.27
12/11	40.54	34	24	1.28	0.18	7.95
12/10	33.81	29	15	1.12	0.15	6.52
12/09	33.51	35	19	0.93	0.11	5.24
Annual Growth	**15.0%**	**—**		**11.7%**	**24.0%**	**20.3%**

Barrett Business Services, Inc.

Barrett Business Services likes to put people to work. The company offers both temporary and long-term staffing to some 1750 small and mid-sized businesses. Its staffing services focus on light industrial clerical and technical businesses. Barrett also does business as a professional employment organization (PEO) providing outsourced human resource services such as payroll management benefits administration risk management recruiting and placement for more than 1500 clients. Established in 1965 Barrett operates through about 45 branch offices across 10 US states. Each year about 90% of its PEO revenue comes from customers residing in the states of California and Oregon.

Barrett depends mostly on the light-industrial sector for the majority of its staffing services revenue (the sector represented 86% of its total revenue in 20010). Its light-industrial workers operate machinery and perform manufacturing loading and unloading and construction-site cleanup tasks.

After experiencing declines in revenue and a net loss for 2009 Barrett bounced back by generating a 15.5% increase in revenue and a positive net income of $7.4 million at the end of 2010. The increase in PEO service fee revenue was mostly attributed to the signing of new customers while its staffing revenue levels rose because of increased demand for existing customers in its northwest and intermountain markets. Barrett's growth strategy involves diversifying its revenue mix by expanding (through acquisitions) outside of California and Oregon.

EXECUTIVES

VP Finance Treasurer and Secretary, James D. Miller, age 50, $265,000 total compensation

VP and COO -Corporate Operations, Gregory R. (Greg) Vaughn, age 58, $325,000 total compensation

President and CEO, Michael L. (Mike) Elich, age 48, $500,000 total compensation

VP and COO -Field Operations, Gerald Blotz

Board Member, Roger Johnson

VP Finance Treasurer and Secretary, James D. Miller, age 50

Chairman, Anthony Meeker, age 75

Auditors: MossAdamsLLP

LOCATIONS

HQ: Barrett Business Services, Inc.
8100 NE Parkway Drive, Suite 200, Vancouver, WA 98662
Phone: 360 828-0700   **Fax:** 360 828-0701
Web: www.barrettbusiness.com

PRODUCTS/OPERATIONS

2013 Sales

	$ mil.	% of total
PEO service fees	388.9	73
Staffing services	143.9	27
Total	**532.8**	**100**

Selected Services

PEO services
  Employee benefits
  Health insurance
  Human resource administration
  Drug testing
  Hiring
  Interviewing
  Placement
  Recruiting
  Regulatory compliance
  Payroll
  Workers' compensation coverage
  Workplace safety programs
Staffing services
  Contract
  Long-term
  Short-term

COMPETITORS

ADP TotalSource	ManpowerGroup
Adecco	Paychex
Insperity	TeamStaff
Kelly Services	TriNet Group

HISTORICAL FINANCIALS

Company Type: Public

Income Statement

FYE: December 31

	REVENUE ($ mil.)	NET INCOME ($ mil.)	NET PROFIT MARGIN	EMPLOYEES
12/13	532.8	17.8	3.4%	79,315
12/12	402.6	13.1	3.3%	64,315
12/11	314.8	14.3	4.5%	49,355
12/10	273.1	7.3	2.7%	40,935
12/09	236.4	(4.7)	—	34,725
Annual Growth	**22.5%**	**—**	**—**	**22.9%**

2013 Year-End Financials

Debt ratio: 1.6%
Return on equity: 28.3%
Cash ($ mil.): 93
Current ratio: 1.44
Long-term debt ($ mil.): 5
No. of shares (mil.): 7
Dividends
  Yield: 0.6%
  Payout: 23.6%
Market value ($ mil.): 664

	STOCK PRICE ($) FY Close	P/E High/Low		PER SHARE ($) Earnings	Dividends	Book Value
12/13	92.74	38	15	2.42	0.57	10.13
12/12	38.09	23	9	1.67	0.46	7.68
12/11	19.96	14	9	1.41	0.38	10.30
12/10	15.55	24	17	0.71	0.33	9.35
12/09	12.29	—	—	(0.46)	0.32	9.57
Annual Growth	**65.7%**			**—**	**15.5%**	**1.4%**

BCB Bancorp Inc

BCB Bancorp be the holding company for BCB Community Bank which opened its doors in late 2000. The independent bank serves Hudson County and the surrounding area from about 15 offices in New Jersey's Bayonne Hoboken Jersey City and Monroe. The bank offers traditional deposit products and services including savings accounts money market accounts CDs and IRAs. Funds from deposits are used to originate mortgages and loans primarily commercial real estate and multi-family property loans (which together account for more than half of the bank's loan portfolio). BCB Bancorp's branch network tripled in size when it added 10 locations through its 2010 acquisition of Pamrapo Bancorp.

EXECUTIVES

COO and Director; COO and CFO BCB Community Bank, Thomas M. Coughlin, age 54, $128,544 total compensation
Chairman, Mark D. Hogan, age 48
Director; Senior Lending Officer BCB Community Bank, James E. Collins, age 65, $131,222 total compensation
VP Commercial Lending BCB Community Bank, Amer Saleem, age 59, $94,500 total compensation
Independent Vice Chairman of the Board, Joseph Brogan, age 75
Chief Financial Officer of BCB Community Bank and BCB Bancorp, Kenneth Walter
COO and Director; COO and CFO BCB Community Bank, Thomas M. Coughlin, age 54
Director; Senior Lending Officer BCB Community Bank, James E. Collins, age 65
Independent Director, Robert Ballance, age 55
Independent Director, Judith Q. Bielan, age 49
Independent Director, Alexander Pasiechnik, age 52
Independent Director, Joseph Lyga, age 54
Independent Director, Gary Stetz
Independent Director, Robert Hughes
Independent Director, Spencer Robbins
Auditors: BeardMillerCompanyLLP

LOCATIONS

HQ: BCB Bancorp Inc
104-110 Avenue C, Bayonne, NJ 07002
Phone: 201 823-0700
Web: www.bcbbancorp.com

COMPETITORS

Bank of America	PNC Financial
City National Bancshares	Provident Financial Services
Hudson City Bancorp	Sterling Bank
Meridian Capital Group	Stewardship Financial
New York Community Bancorp	

HISTORICAL FINANCIALS

Company Type: Public

Income Statement

FYE: December 31

	ASSETS ($ mil.)	NET INCOME ($ mil.)	INCOME AS % OF ASSETS	EMPLOYEES
12/13	1,207.9	9.4	0.8%	249
12/12	1,171.3	(2.0)	—	269
12/11	1,216.9	6.0	0.5%	263
12/10	1,106.8	14.3	1.3%	174
12/09	631.5	3.7	0.6%	91
Annual Growth	**17.6%**	**25.9%**	**—**	**28.6%**

2013 Year-End Financials

Return on assets: 0.7%
Return on equity: 9.8%
Long-term debt ($ mil.): —
No. of shares (mil.): 8
Sales ($ mil): 60
Dividends
  Yield: 3.5%
  Payout: 52.7%
Market value ($ mil.): 112

	STOCK PRICE ($) FY Close	P/E High/Low		PER SHARE ($) Earnings	Dividends	Book Value
12/13	13.45	14	8	1.06	0.48	12.01
12/12	9.45	—	—	(0.23)	0.48	10.78
12/11	10.09	19	13	0.64	0.48	10.51
12/10	9.80	5	3	2.05	0.48	10.55
12/09	9.01	14	9	0.80	0.48	11.03
Annual Growth	**10.5%**			**7.3%**	**(0.0%)**	**2.1%**

Bel Fuse, Inc.

Bel Fuse manufactures electronic components for networking telecommunications high-speed data transmission and automotive and consumer electronics. Its magnetic products include discrete components power transformers and MagJack connector modules. It also offers power conversion modules for a variety of applications. Bel Fuse's miniature micro and surface-mounted fuses create supplementary circuit protection for consumer electronics. The company also makes passive jacks plugs and cable assemblies. Top customers include Hon Hai (14% of sales) and Flextronics (10% of sales).

Geographic Reach

Bel Fuse has more than two dozen manufacturing plants located in China Czech Republic Dominican Republic Mexico the UK and the US (in New York Pennsylvania Oklahoma and Texas.)

Asia (specifically Macao) accounts for more than half of sales; the US accounts for a third. Europe accounts for about 10% of sales.

Sales and Marketing

The company sells its products through one of three channels: direct strategic account managers regional sales managers working with independent sales reps or authorized distributors.

Financial Performance

Bel Fuse has experienced up and down sales over the past decade. 2013 was a good year and revenues grew 21% to $349 million driven largely by sales from acquisitions made in 2012. Profits shot up from $2 million in 2012 to a record $16 million in 2013 due to the higher revenues and lower expenses.

Strategy

The electronic components industry is highly competitive in good times and bad and increased competition from low-cost suppliers is one factor that drives the company to lower its average selling prices for products on a regular basis. Customers pressure Bel Fuse to cut prices and prices tend to decline rapidly over the life cycle of a product.

Mergers and Acquisitions

On the competitive front Bel Fuse continues to jockey for a bigger slice of the diversified electronics OEM market expanding its product and technology lineup and customer base through acquisitions.

Most recently it bought divisions of major manufacturers Emerson ABB and TE Connectivity. In 2014 it bought the Power One Solutions business from ABB for $117 million in cash. Power One Solutions makes power conversion products from two plants in China and Slovakia. It also agreed to buy the Emerson Network Power Connectivity Solutions (ECS) business of Emerson for $98 million in cash. ECS has plants in China the UK and the US. In 2013 it bought the transpower magnetics business from TE Connectivity for $22.4 million in cash. Renamed TRP International the company makes integrated connector module (ICM) products at its plant in China.

In 2012 it made several acquisitions: Powerbox Italia a supplier of AC/DC power supplies for broadcast communications and battery charging applications; GigaCom Interconnect a Swedish supplier of expanded beam fiber-optic technology and a developer of next-generation commercial aircraft standards; and Fibreco Limited a UK-based supplier of expanded beam fiber optic components used in broadcast communications military and offshore energy exploration applications.

EXECUTIVES

President and CEO, Daniel (Dan) Bernstein, age 60, $225,000 total compensation
VP Finance and Secretary, Colin Dunn, age 69, $190,000 total compensation
VP Operations, Dennis Ackerman, age 51, $175,000 total compensation
VP Asia Operations, Raymond Cheung, age 57, $170,000 total compensation
Auditors: Deloitte&ToucheLLP

LOCATIONS

HQ: Bel Fuse, Inc.
 206 Van Vorst Street, Jersey City, NJ 07302
Phone: 201 432-0463
Web: www.belfuse.com

2013 Sales

	% of total
Macao	55
US	33
Germany	5
UK	5
Italy	1
Czech Republic	1
Total	**100**

PRODUCTS/OPERATIONS

2013 Sales

	$ mil.	% of total
Magnetics	170.2	49
Interconnect	111.6	32
Modules	56.0	16
Circuit protection	11.4	3
Total	**349.2**	**100**

Selected Products

Magnetics
 Discrete components

Integrated connector modules (MagJack)
 Power transformers
Interconnect
 Cable assemblies
 Passive jacks
 Plugs
Modules
 Custom modules
 Integrated analog front end modules
 Power conversion modules (DC/DC converters)
Fuses (miniature micro and surface mount)

COMPETITORS

API Technologies	Littelfuse
Alcatel-Lucent	Pulse Electronics
CTS Corp.	S&C Electric
Curtis Instruments	Spang & Company
Digital Power	Standex
Espey Mfg.	TE Connectivity
Gowanda Electronics	Torotel
Hytek Microsystems	Yokogawa Electric

HISTORICAL FINANCIALS

Company Type: Public

Income Statement

FYE: December 31

	REVENUE ($ mil.)	NET INCOME ($ mil.)	NET PROFIT MARGIN	EMPLOYEES
12/13	349.1	15.9	4.6%	6,370
12/12	286.5	2.4	0.8%	4,166
12/11	295.1	3.7	1.3%	3,451
12/10	302.5	13.6	4.5%	4,161
12/09	182.7	(8.3)	—	2,674
Annual Growth	**17.6%**	**—**	**—**	**24.2%**

2013 Year-End Financials

Debt ratio: 4.1%
Return on equity: 7.1%
Cash ($ mil.): 62
Current ratio: 3.05
Long-term debt ($ mil.): —
No. of shares (mil.): 11
Dividends
 Yield: 1.3%
 Payout: 47.4%
Market value ($ mil.): 245

	STOCK PRICE ($) FY Close	P/E High/Low		PER SHARE ($) Earnings	Dividends	Book Value
12/13	21.31	17	10	1.32	0.28	19.87
12/12	19.55	123	86	0.17	0.28	18.65
12/11	18.75	94	49	0.28	0.28	18.72
12/10	23.90	23	15	1.10	0.28	18.83
12/09	21.49	—	—	(0.71)	0.28	17.95
Annual Growth	**(0.2%)**	**—**	**—**	**—**	**(0.0%)**	**2.6%**

Berkshire Hills Bancorp, Inc.

Berkshire Hills Bancorp is the holding company for Berkshire Bank which serves individuals and small businesses through some 60 branches in Massachusetts New York Connecticut and Vermont. Established in 1846 the bank provides standard deposit products such as savings checking and money market accounts CDs and IRAs in addition to credit cards investments private banking wealth management and lending services. Real estate mortgages make up nearly three-quarters of Berkshire Hills Bancorp's loan portfolio which also includes business and consumer loans. In addition to its banking activities the company also owns insurance agency Berkshire Insurance Group.

Geographic Reach

Berkshire Hills Bancorp also is eyeing further expansion into Connecticut and other parts of New England and New York by opening new branches and through acquisitions.

Financial Performance

Berkshire Hills Bancorp's revenue increased in fiscal 2013 compared to the prior year. It reported $262 million in revenue for fiscal 2013 up from $230 million in fiscal 2012. Net income also went up to $58 million in fiscal 2013 compared to the $47 million Berkshire Hills Bancorp reported for net income in fiscal 2012.

The company's cash on hand increased by more than $100 million in fiscal 2013 compared to fiscal 2012 levels.

Strategy

Berkshire Hills Bancorp which was established in 1846 believes one of its competitive advantages is the regional niche it serves which has been relatively unscathed by the recession compared to other parts of the country.

The bank's performance has been boosted by an increase in business development in the company's market area in addition to growth in its asset-based lending and private banking businesses. The bank also has grown its loans and deposits and has plans to grow its insurance and wealth management operations as well.

EXECUTIVES

Senior Vice President Commercial, Michael Ferry
Svp Retail Lending And Marketing, Charles A Bercury
Svp-commercial Reg Exec-ny Reg, Michael Carroll
President and CEO, Michael P. Daly, age 52, $575,000 total compensation
EVP HR, Linda A. Johnston
EVP Retail Banking, Sean A. Gray, $350,000 total compensation
EVP Commercial Banking, George F. Bacigalupo, $229,554 total compensation
EVP and Chief Risk and Administrative Officer, Richard M. Marotta, $350,000 total compensation
EVP and CFO, Josephine Iannelli, age 42, $177,404 total compensation
Vice President, Jim Hickson
Senior Management Senior Vice President, Scott E Schiff
Svp Comm'l Regional Leader, Sheryl L McQuade
Vice President, Maura Kelly
Svp Commercial Leader For Ber, Scott J Houghtaling
Assistant Vice President Mort Loan Ofc, Louann Harvey
Vice President, Yuki Cohen
Vice President Retail Banking, Tami Gunsch
Senior Vice President, Mark Foster
Assistant Vice President Branch Operations Officer, Dawne Cowhey
Vice President Loan Review Officer, George Austin
Vice President Od, Lauren Harvey
Vice President, Theresa Wituszynski
Chairman, William J. (Bill) Ryan, age 71
Treasurer, Mike Macy
Secretary Treasurer, Diane Taylor
Member Board Of Directors, Williar James
Board Member, Williar J Dunlaevy
Auditors: PricewaterhouseCoopersLLP

LOCATIONS

HQ: Berkshire Hills Bancorp, Inc.
24 North Street, Pittsfield, MA 01201
Phone: 413 443-5601
Web: www.berkshirebank.com

PRODUCTS/OPERATIONS

COMPETITORS

Bank of America
Citizens Financial
  Group
Hudson City Bancorp

KeyCorp
Pathfinder Bancorp
Sovereign Bank
TD Bank USA

HISTORICAL FINANCIALS

Company Type: Public

Income Statement

FYE: December 31

	ASSETS ($ mil.)	NET INCOME ($ mil.)	INCOME AS % OF ASSETS	EMPLOYEES
12/13	5,672.8	41.1	0.7%	939
12/12	5,296.8	33.1	0.6%	1,012
12/11	3,991.2	17.5	0.4%	760
12/10	2,880.7	13.7	0.5%	599
12/09	2,700.4	(16.0)	—	622
Annual Growth	20.4%	—		10.8%

2013 Year-End Financials

Return on assets: 0.7%
Return on equity: 6.1%
Long-term debt ($ mil.): —
No. of shares (mil.): 25
Sales ($ mil): 261

Dividends
  Yield: 2.6%
  Payout: 44.4%
Market value ($ mil.): 683

	STOCK PRICE ($) FY Close	P/E High/Low		Earnings	PER SHARE ($) Dividends	Book Value
12/13	27.27	18	14	1.65	0.72	27.08
12/12	23.86	16	14	1.49	0.69	26.53
12/11	22.19	24	18	0.98	0.65	26.17
12/10	22.11	23	17	0.99	0.64	27.56
12/09	20.68	—	—	(1.52)	0.64	27.64
Annual Growth	7.2%			—	3.0%	(0.5%)

BFC Financial Corp.

Holding company BFC Financial controls Florida-based BankAtlantic and investment firm Woodbridge Holdings (formerly Levitt Corporation) which has holdings in real estate companies Core Communities and Bluegreen Corporation and restaurant franchise Pizza Fusion. (Famous for constructing Levittown New York —widely regarded as the first planned community in the US —Levitt filed for Chapter 11 bankruptcy protection in 2007 and re-emerged the following year as Woodbridge.) BFC also owns a minority stake in Asian-themed restaurant chain Benihana. Chairman president and CEO Alan Levan and vice chairman Jack Abdo control BFC Financial.

The company has felt the sting of the economic downturn particularly in its real estate holdings and from its stake in BankAtlantic which operates in the hard-hit Florida market. Nonetheless BFC in 2009 upped its stakes in both the bank and Bluegreen and it acquired the remaining stock in

Woodbridge that it did not already own after abandoning plans for a similar deal two years earlier. The Bluegreen acquisition which was accounted for as a "bargain purchase" using fair-value estimates helped BFC return to profitability in 2009 after two years of losses. The company's Woodbridge subsidiary now plans to acquire the remaining 46% stake in Bluegreen it does not already own.

Its positive results were short-lived however and BFC reported losses of more than $100 million in 2010 as its subsidiaries continued to struggle. That year Pizza Fusion expressed doubts about its ability to continue as a going concern (for its part BFC said it would not make any new investments in the company after writing off its initial investment in 2009) and Benihana announced its intent to evaluate its strategic alternatives including a sale of the company.

In 2011 BankAtlantic entered into a Order to Cease and Desist with the Office of Thrift Supervision that stipulates that the bank improve its capital position. Later that year Southeast banking giant BB&T agreed to acquire BankAtlantic. Following the completion of the deal the bank's holding company BankAtlantic Bancorp will change its name to BBX Capital and continue to manage a portfolio of distressed assets transferred from the bank. It may eventually engage in real estate investment or specialty finance using proceeds from the sale of the assets.

There was a bright spot for BFC in 2011. Revenues were up and the company reported (only) a $12 million loss for the year mostly related to discontinued operations as its real estate business turned a profit.

EXECUTIVES

Chairman and CEO, Alan B. Levan, age 69,
  $1,500,000 total compensation
EVP and Director, Seth M. Wise, age 44, $472,662
  total compensation
CFO and Chief Accounting Officer, Raymond S.
  Lopez, age 39
EVP and Director, Jarett S. Levan, age 40, $750,000
  total compensation
Senior Vice President Finance, Amerisa Kornblum
Senior Vice President, Bruce Parker
Vice President And Manager Sales, Steve Deegan
Chairman and CEO, Alan B. Levan, age 69
Auditors: PricewaterhouseCoopersLLP

LOCATIONS

HQ: BFC Financial Corp.
  401 East Las Olas Boulevard, Suite 800, Fort
  Lauderdale, FL 33301
Phone: 954 940-4900
Web: www.bfcfinancial.com

PRODUCTS/OPERATIONS

2011 Sales

	$ mil.	% of total
Real Estate & Other		
Sales of real estate	170.0	24
Interest	88.1	13
Other resorts fee-based revenue	71.0	10
Other	74.4	11
Financial Services		
Interest	143.8	20
Service charges on deposits	42.6	6
Gain on sale of Tampa branches	38.6	5
Other service charges & fees	26.4	4
Other non-interest income	19.5	3
Other	25.4	4
Total	**699.8**	**100**

COMPETITORS

BKF Capital Group
Bank of America
H.I.G. Capital

Huizenga Holdings
St. Joe
Sun Capital

HISTORICAL FINANCIALS

Company Type: Public

Income Statement

FYE: December 31

	ASSETS ($ mil.)	NET INCOME ($ mil.)	INCOME AS % OF ASSETS	EMPLOYEES
12/13	1,441.3	29.0	2.0%	5,050
12/12	1,547.1	166.0	10.7%	4,445
12/11	4,778.1	(11.2)	—	5,119
12/10	5,813.0	(103.8)	—	5,084
12/09	6,047.0	25.7	0.4%	5,368
Annual Growth	(30.1%)	3.1%		(1.5%)

2013 Year-End Financials

Return on assets: 1.9%
Return on equity: 10.8%
Long-term debt ($ mil.): —
No. of shares (mil.): 78
Sales ($ mil): 563

Dividends
  Yield: —
  Payout: —
Market value ($ mil.): 227

	STOCK PRICE ($) FY Close	P/E High/Low		Earnings	PER SHARE ($) Dividends	Book Value
12/13	2.89	8	4	0.35	0.00	3.05
12/12	1.26	1	0	2.09	0.00	3.87
12/11	0.35	—	—	(0.16)	0.00	1.70
12/10	0.37	—	—	(1.39)	0.00	2.04
12/09	0.37	2	0	0.44	0.00	3.40
Annual Growth	67.2%			— (5.6%)	—	(2.7%)

BGC Partners, Inc.

BGC Partners provides inter-dealer brokerage services for banks investment firms and other institutional traders around the world through about 115 offices. Through its eSpeed and BGC Trader-branded platform it offers voice electronic and hybrid trade brokerage for a broad range of financial products including government and corporate bonds interest rate swaps foreign exchange derivatives and futures. The company also provides processing clearing and settlement services as well as market data and analytics products. BGC Partners was established by Cantor Fitzgerald which controls nearly half of the company. (BGC is named after Cantor Fitzgerald founder B. Gerald Cantor.)
Operations

The company has been entering new lines of business. In 2011 it launched BGC Environmental Brokerage Services following the acquisition of CantorCO2e from Cantor Fitzgerald. The subsequent acquisition of Newmark the US arm of global brokerage partnership Knight Frank added commercial real estate brokerage services. On the heels of its acquisition of Newmark BGC acquired the assets of bankrupt commercial real estate services firm Grubb & Ellis. The deal underscored BGC's commitment to build a strong position in the property services market. Upon the completion of that acquisition BGC launched Newmark Grubb Knight Frank a full-service commercial real estate platform. The move included BGC realigning its business under real estate services and financial services banners.

The Financial Services segment specializes offers fixed income securities interest rate swaps foreign exchange equities equity derivatives credit derivatives commodities futures and structured products. Real Estate Services serves commercial tenants owners investors and developers with a full range of services including consulting project and development management leasing and other consulting services along with investment sales debt placement appraisal and valuation services.

Geographic Reach

The company has been expanding worldwide including in the US. It has also established or added to existing operations in Brazil China Russia Turkey and other markets in recent years. BGC Partners plans to continue its global growth with Asia as a key target market.

Sales and Marketing

BGC markets its financial services through its salespeople and its real estate services through traditional advertising event sponsorship and sales collateral.

Financial Performance

The Grubb & Ellis acquisition pushed the company into a 21% revenue gain for 2012. An 11% decline in financial services offset the big real estate gains. Net income and cash flow also improved.

Strategy

BGC continues to expand through acquisitions technology investments and hiring new brokers.

Mergers and Acquisitions

In 2012 BGC Partners purchased real estate services firm Grubb & Ellis for about $47 million. Other purchases that year included Wolfe & Hurst Bond Brokers a municipal bonds interdealer broker in North America and totaled about $24 million.

Ownership

Cantor Fitzgerald L.P. and CF Group Management each own about 50% of the company.

Company Background

BGC lost nearly all of its US employees in the September 11 2001 terrorist attacks. Subsequently it set up funds for survivors and families of victims and paid healthcare for affected employees for 10 years.

EXECUTIVES

Evp And Chief Product Architect, Joseph C Noviello, age 49
Executive Vice President General Counsel Secretary, Stephen M. Merkel, age 56, $1,000,000 total compensation
Chairman and CEO, Howard W. Lutnick, age 53, $1,000,000 total compensation
Executive Managing Director North America; Global Head FX Products, Daniel M. LaVecchia, age 54
Executive Managing Director e-Commerce, Philip (Phil) Norton
Executive Managing Director and General Manager North America, Louis (Lou) Scotto, age 61
Executive Managing Director Asia, Mark E. Spring, age 56
President, Shaun D. Lynn, age 51, $1,000,000 total compensation
Executive Managing Director Global Head Listed Products and General Manager Continental Europe, Jean-Pierre Aubin
COO, Sean A. Windeatt, age 41, $594,338 total compensation

Executive Managing Director and General Manager Asia/Pacific, Leonard (Len) Harvey
CFO, A. Graham Sadler, age 58, $475,470 total compensation
Executive Managing Director and General Manager London, Mark Webster
Global Head of Real Estate, Michael Lehrman
Executive Managing Director and Director of BCG Market Data, Mark Benfield
CIO, Eric Hirschhorn
Head of Credit Repo and EGBs, Phil Cramp
Svp And Global Head Futures And Ecco Software Sales, David Hall
Vice President, Craig Vanzanten
Vice President, Charles Kergaravat
Senior Vice President, Tze Tan
Chairman and CEO, Howard W. Lutnick, age 53
Auditors: Ernst&YoungLLP

LOCATIONS

HQ: BGC Partners, Inc.
  499 Park Avenue, New York, NY 10022
Phone: 212 610-2200
Web: www.bgcpartners.com

PRODUCTS/OPERATIONS

2012 Sales

	$ mil.	% of total
Financial Services		
Non-interest income	1220.1	69
Interest income	1.3	-
Real Estate Services		
Non-interest income	454.2	26
Interest income	.4	-
Other	91.0	5
Total	**1767.0**	**100**

Selected Subusdiaries

Ameefi Services Inc.
Aqua Securities Holdings LLC
Aqua Securities L.P.
Aurel BGC
BGC Brokers Gp Limited
BGC Brokers Holdings L.P.
BGC Brokers Holdings LLC
BGC Brokers Investment L.P.
BGC Brokers L.P.
BGC Brokers Limited
BGC Brokers US Holdings LLC
BGC Brokers US L.P.
BGC Canada Securities Company
BGC Canada Securities Company Holdings L.P.
BGC Canada Securities Company Holdings LLC
BGC Capital Markets (Hong Kong) Limited
BGC Capital Markets (Japan) LLC
BGC Capital Markets (Switzerland) LLC
BGC Capital Markets And Foreign Exchange Broker (Korea) Limited
BGC Capital Markets L.P.
BGC China Holdings LLC
BGC China L.P.
BGC European GP Limited
BGC European Holdings L.P.
BGC Financial Group Inc.
BGC Financial L.P.
BGC France Holdings
BGC Global Holdings GP Limited
BGC Global Holdings L.P.
BGC Global Limited
BGC GP Limited
BGC GP LLC
BGC Holdings (Turkey) LLC
BGC Holdings II LLC
BGC Holdings U.S. Inc.
BGC Holdings L.P.
BGC Holdings LLC
BGC Information Holdings LLC
BGC Information L.P.
BGC International
BGC International GP Limited
BGC International Holdings L.P.

BGC International L.P.
BGC Mexico R.E. Holdings LLC
BGC Mexico R.E. Holdings S. de R.L. de C.V.
BGC Notes LLC
BGC Partners (Australia) Pty Limited
BGC Partners (Singapore) Limited
BGC Partners Menkul Degerler A.S.
BGC Partners L.P.
BGC Radix Energy L.P.
BGC Real Estate LLC
BGC Rie Holdings LLC
BGC SA Financial Brokers (Pty) Limited
BGC Securities (Hong Kong) LLC
BGC Securities (South Africa) Pty Limited
BGC Shoken Kaisha Limited
BGC Trading Holdings LLC
BGC USA Holdings LLC
BGC USA L.P.
BGCantor Market Data Holdings LLC
BGCantor Market Data L.P.
BGCCMHK Holdings LLC
ECCO LLC
ELX Futures Holdings LLC
eSpeed (Hong Kong) Limited
eSpeed Markets L.P.
eSpeed LLC
ESX Clearing Holdings LLC
Euro Brokers Holdings Ltd.
FHLP LLC
Freedom International Brokerage Company
G&E Management Services LLC
G&E Real Estate Inc.
Ginalfi Finance
Itsecco Holdings Limited
Jadestone Consultants Limited
Kleos Managed Services L.P.
MIS Holdings LLC
Newmark & Company Real Estate Inc.
Seminole Financial
Tower Bridge GP Limtied
Tradesoft Technologies Inc.
Treasuryconnect LLC

COMPETITORS

Bloomberg L.P.	Jones Lang LaSalle
CBRE Group	London Stock Exchange
Colliers International	MarketAxess
Cushman & Wakefield	NASDAQ OMX
Eastdil Secured	Thomson Reuters
GFI Group	Tradeweb
HFF	Tullett Prebon
ICAP	VIEL
Interactive Brokers	
Intercontinental Exchange	

HISTORICAL FINANCIALS

Company Type: Public

Income Statement

FYE: December 31

	REVENUE ($ mil.)	NET INCOME ($ mil.)	NET PROFIT MARGIN	EMPLOYEES
12/13	2,498.0	70.9	2.8%	6,386
12/12	1,766.9	23.8	1.4%	6,547
12/11	1,464.6	20.1	1.4%	4,129
12/10	1,331.1	21.1	1.6%	2,743
12/09	1,162.3	20.0	1.7%	2,524
Annual Growth	21.1%	37.2%	—	26.1%

2013 Year-End Financials

Debt ratio: 19.6%	No. of shares (mil.): 216
Return on equity: 15.0%	Dividends
Cash ($ mil.): 725	Yield: 7.9%
Current ratio: 1.91	Payout: 114.2%
Long-term debt ($ mil.): 408	Market value ($ mil.): 1,309

	STOCK PRICE ($)	P/E		PER SHARE ($)		
	FY Close	High/Low	Earnings	Dividends	Book Value
12/13	6.05	17 9	0.36	0.48	2.45
12/12	3.46	50 20	0.16	0.63	2.60
12/11	5.94	58 32	0.17	0.65	3.05
12/10	8.31	36 16	0.24	0.48	3.43
12/09	4.62	23 6	0.24	0.30	3.70
Annual Growth	7.0%	— —	10.7%	12.5%	(9.8%)

Bio-Reference Laboratories, Inc.

Bio-Reference Laboratories tests positive as the lab of choice for many in the Northeast. Primarily serving the greater New York Metropolitan Area the company offers routine clinical tests including Pap smears pregnancy tests cholesterol checks and blood cell counts. Through its GenPath business unit it also performs more sophisticated esoteric testing such as cancer pathology and molecular diagnostics. It gets most of its orders (close to 8 million per year) from doctors' offices collecting specimens at draw stations scattered throughout its primary service area in the New York area. Bio-Reference Laboratories also provides services in Connecticut Delaware Maryland New Jersey and Pennsylvania.

Operations

The company offers focused expertise in specialty areas through its various subsidiaries. It operates as a national oncology laboratory through its GenPath subsidiary. GenPath also houses Bio-Reference's women's health testing unit. GeneDX another wholly owned subsidiary performs testing of rare and ultra-rare genetic diseases nationally. Bio-Reference intends to build a marketing team to cross-sell its genetic testing and women's health testing capabilities to doctors who specialize in prenatal care.

Bio-Reference's specialty testing operations (both esoteric and for emerging markets) have been growing at a faster clip than its core routine testing business and now routine lab tests account for less than half of the company's sales.

Another Bio-Reference unit PSIMedica makes health informatics software that combines information from health care claims lab results and other sources and markets it to managed care organizations. The CareEvolve subsidiary markets the company's online connectivity software to other laboratories. Revenues from PSIMedica and CareEvolve contribute a negligible percentage of the company's overall sales.

Geographic Reach

The company's laboratory service in the New York Metro area is its core business but it is growing steadily and now offers some of its testing services nationwide.

Sales and Marketing

Bio-Reference's primary client base is composed of doctors employers clinics and governmental units.

Bio-Reference grows its services by tapping into emerging laboratory markets. The company is focused on developing its cardiology histology and women's health diagnostic testing capabilities to complement its existing hemostasis (process by which blood changes from fluid to a solid state) hematopathology (tests for congenital disorders) and correctional health care initiatives.

Still demand for the both its routine and esoteric lab testing is expected to increase thanks to a growing US trend of shorter inpatient stays at hospitals. With patients being discharged earlier some of the business that would typically go straight to the hospital-based lab is instead being sent to labs like Bio-Reference by the patients' after-care physicians.

Financial Analysis

The company has enjoyed an upward trend in revenue the past five fiscal years. Net revenues were $.5 million in fiscal 2011 $.66 million in fiscal 2012 and $.7 million in 2013. Bio-Reference's increase in revenue per patient was due to increases in specialized testing. The revenue increase lead to a 9% bump in net income. But cash flow from operations decreased $10 million as the company was slower to collect on accounts.

Strategy

Part of Bio-Reference's strategy for expanding its testing areas is to partner with medical providers whose expertise can help expedite the development process. In 2010 Bio-Reference entered into one such agreement with Massachusetts General Hospital to develop a line of clinical diagnostic tests designed to identify and help treat solid tumors. The test will make use of the emerging field of personalized medicine in which a patient's unique genetic make-up is used to help tailor testing and treatment to best address that patient's individual needs.

Doctors can place orders for lab tests and get test results using the company's proprietary CareEvolve online portal. Outside of its customer relationships with doctors' offices Bio-Reference serves government agencies large employers (for substance abuse testing for instance) and prison systems in the northeastern US.

In 2013 the company launched Spanish-language lab services in the US began offering genetic testing for cancer and expanded its R&D facilities. It also purchased genetic counseling service GeneTests.org from the University of Washington.

Mergers and Acquisitions

The company occasionally purchases other testing businesses to expand its reach. It acquired GeneTests.org in 2013 along with Hunter Laboratories in California for $15000 and genetic sequencing firm Edge BioServ for $2500. In 2012 it bought two lab companies for a total of about $25000.

HISTORY

Marc Grodman founded Med-Mobile in 1981 offering mobile medical examination services. In 1987 it opened a clinical laboratory in New Jersey. The purchase of Cytology and Pathology Associates a small specialized lab followed in 1988. Demand for tests rose leading the company to relocate all operations to a modern lab near New York City. It renamed itself Bio-Reference Laboratories in 1989 and went public in 1993.

The company moved into specialty testing to compensate for the industrywide drop in reimbursement rates that hit its general labs acquiring GenCare Biomedical Research (cancer testing 1995) Oncodec Labs (gene mutations 1995) and SmithKline Beecham's renal dialysis testing business (1996). Late in 1996 the firm sued SmithKline Beecham accusing it of fraud regarding the purchase.

In 1997 the company sold part of its GenCare oncology laboratory services division to IMPATH. To build its regional presence the company acquired Medilabs from Long Term Care in 1998. The next year it ventured into new frontiers opening and acquiring websites for online ventures and buying the Right Body Foods health foods business.

In 2000 Bio-Reference Laboratories expanded its Internet presence (including a business-to-business Web portal for health care professionals CareEvolve.com) and re-entered the oncology market resuming full-service testing to physicians and institutions.

In the following years the company was intent on expanding its geographic reach and adding services to its roster to make push itself into a leading position in the testing industry. Some of its key acquisitions include the 2006 purchases of Diagnostic Pathology Services a Maryland-based anatomic pathology lab serving the mid-Atlantic states and GeneDx which specializes in diagnosing rare genetic disorders using DNA sequencing technology. That buy fit with GeneDx' strategy to develop and its expand its genetic diagnostic testing capabilities.

EXECUTIVES

Senior Vice President, Scott Fein
Vp Of Finance, Warren Erdmann
Vice President, Dominick Cetani
Vice President, Maryann Amato-ferri
SVP and CFO, Sam Singer, age 71, $449,200 total compensation
EVP COO and Director, Howard Dubinett, age 63, $449,200 total compensation
Chairman President and CEO, Marc D. Grodman, age 63, $1,136,700 total compensation
SVP Sales and Marketing, Charles T. Todd, age 62, $594,000 total compensation
CIO; President PsiMedica, Richard L. Faherty, age 68, $547,528 total compensation
Chief Medical Officer, James Weisberger, age 59
President CareEvolve, Cory Fishkin
President and Clinical Director GeneDx, Sherri Bale
CEO and Scientific Director GeneDx, John Compton, age 65
Vice President Director Of Medilabs, Thomas Pasko
Vice President, Chris Smith
Vice President Information Technology, John Mooney
Vice President Of Sales And Marketing, Brian Jones
Vice President, Marsha Munson
Vice President Of Sales Genpath, Don Fowler
EVP COO and Director, Howard Dubinett, age 63
Chairman President and CEO, Marc D. Grodman, age 63

LOCATIONS

HQ: Bio-Reference Laboratories, Inc.
481 Edward H. Ross Drive, Elmwood Park, NJ 07407
Phone: 201 791-2600   **Fax:** 201 791-1941
Web: www.bioreference.com

PRODUCTS/OPERATIONS

Selected Products and Services
Routine testing (Performed in Elmwood Park New Jersey)
  Blood cell counts
  Cholesterol levels
  HIV tests
  Pap smears

Pregnancy tests
Substance abuse tests
Urinalysis
Esoteric testing (Performed in Elmwood Park Milford
Massachusetts and Gaithersburg Maryland)
  Endocrinology
  Genetics
  Immunology
  Microbiology
  Oncology
  Serology
  Toxicology
Other
  CareEvolve (physician-based connectivity portal for
  clinical laboratories)
  PSIMedica Clinical Knowledge Management System
  (health informatics software)

Selected Mergers and Acquisitions

FY2011
The Genetics Center Inc. (undisclosed price; Smithtown
  NY; clinical laboratory business)
FY2010
Lenetix Medical Screening Laboratory Inc. (undisclosed
  price; Mineola NY; clinical testing laboratory)

COMPETITORS

American Bio Medica	LabCorp
Athena Diagnostics	MEDTOX Laboratories
IDENTIGENE	Orchid Cellmark
Integrated Genetics	Quest Diagnostics
Kroll Background	Solstas
America	eScreen

HISTORICAL FINANCIALS

Company Type: Public

Income Statement

FYE: October 31

	REVENUE ($ mil.)	NET INCOME ($ mil.)	NET PROFIT MARGIN	EMPLOYEES
10/14	832.2	46.7	5.6%	4,347
10/13	715.3	45.8	6.4%	4,427
10/12	661.6	42.1	6.4%	3,564
10/11	558.6	36.3	6.5%	3,155
10/10	458.0	26.3	5.8%	2,424
Annual Growth	16.1%	15.4%	—	15.7%

2014 Year-End Financials

Debt ratio: 11.5%
Return on equity: 15.8%
Cash ($ mil.): 17
Current ratio: 2.43
Long-term debt ($ mil.): 15
No. of shares (mil.): 27
Dividends
  Yield: —
  Payout: —
Market value ($ mil.): 833

	STOCK PRICE ($) FY Close	P/E High/Low	PER SHARE ($) Earnings	Dividends	Book Value
10/14	30.04	22 14	1.68	0.00	11.50
10/13	32.41	20 14	1.65	0.00	9.81
10/12	27.76	21 8	1.51	0.00	8.20
10/11	20.04	19 13	1.29	0.00	6.79
10/10	21.56	51 19	0.94	0.00	5.47
Annual Growth	8.6%	— —	15.6%	—	20.4%

Biomed Realty Trust Inc

BioMed Realty knows its niche. A self-administered real estate investment trust (REIT) the firm acquires develops leases and manages laboratory and office space for biotechnology and pharmaceutical companies scientific research institutions government agencies and other life science tenants. BioMed owns more than 80 properties with around 185 buildings and more than 16 million sq. ft. of rentable space. The REIT's properties which span about a dozen states are often located near universities; its preferred markets include research and development hubs such as Boston New York San Diego San Francisco and Seattle. In 2013 BioMed acquired Wexford Science & Technology.

Geographic Reach

San Diego-based BioMed Realty's preferred markets include research and development hubs such as Boston San Francisco Maryland San Diego New York/New Jersey Pennsylvania Seattle and Cambridge in the UK. With nearly three million leased square feet of space Boston is the REIT's largest market and accounts for about a third of its annualized base rent.

Sales and Marketing

The REIT has more than 300 tenants. Its largest is Human Genome Sciences (owned by pharmaceutical giant GlaxoSmithKline plc) contributing 9% of its annual base rent. Vertex Pharmaceuticals and Regeneron Pharmaceuticals each account for about 8%.

Financial Performance

BioMed Realty's revenue increased 23% in 2013 compared with 2012 to $637.3 million. The strong rise in revenue came on the heels of an 18% gain in the previous annual comparison. The company credited the double-digit gain to its purchase of more than 2.9 million square feet of rentable lab and office space over the course of the year and rising revenue from previously owned properties due to higher leasing activity. Net income soared 295% in 2013 versus 2012 on higher sales and increased income from continued operations. Cash flow has tracked the steady rise in revenue since 2009 and acceleration over the past two years. Indeed cash flow from operations increased 60% between 2011 and 2013 from $175 million to almost $280 million.

At the end of 2013 the REIT had 309 tenants (up from 209 tenants in 2012) and its portfolio of properties was 91.4% leased.

Strategy

BioMed Realty Trust's growth strategy includes converting properties to higher-yielding laboratory space and developing new office and lab space. When considering acquisitions the REIT sometimes looks for properties with vacancies and utilizes its business contacts in the life science industry to fill them. Acquisitions and new development have boosted the REIT's revenue and cash flow in recent years. BioMed Realty Trust is banking on the continued growth of the life sciences industry because of an aging populace and rising health care costs.

The firm's leasing strategy is focused on leasing vacant space negotiating renewals for leases scheduled to expire during the year and identifying new tenants or existing tenants seeking additional space. In 2014 the REIT singed a long-term lease with Intertek USA Inc. for 46142 sq. st. at the company's Wateridge Summit property in San Diego. Also in 2014 the firm invested in two properties both in the growing life science community adjacent to the Yale School of Medicine in New Haven Connecticut.

Mergers and Acquisitions

In June 2013 BioMed acquired Wexford Science & Technology (WS&T) for about $672 million. The purchase of WS&T a private real estate and development company with about 2.5 million in square feet of rentable space furthers BioMed's position as a leading provider of real estate to the life science industry. As a wholly-owned subsidiary of BioMed WS&T will develop life science real estate for academic and medical research organizations with a specialization in urban development and redevelopment of life science properties. Also in the 2013 the firm acquired 99500 square feet of lab and office space in Cambridge Massachusetts for $52 million.

BioMed Realty entered the UK market with the 2012 acquisition of Granta Park a complex with 11 laboratory and office buildings in Cambridge. Other recent transactions include the 2011 acquisition of life science campus Ardsley Park in New York which included some 160500 sq. ft. of rentable space and another 500000 sq. ft. of developable space. In 2012 the REIT bought the three-building 80%-leased Cambridge Place boosting its presence in the Boston market. By acquiring leased properties the company is able to secure relatively stable revenue lines although the health of its tenants' businesses always has the ability to impact BioMed's bottom line.

EXECUTIVES

Chairman and CEO, Alan D. Gold, age 53, $760,000 total compensation
EVP and Director, Gary A. Kreitzer, age 59, $125,000 total compensation
CFO, Greg N. Lubushkin, age 62, $420,000 total compensation
EVP Asset Management, Karen A. Sztraicher, age 50
President and COO, R. Kent Griffin, age 44, $567,500 total compensation
SVP Leasing and Development, John P. Bonanno
VP Real Estate Legal, Kevin M. Simonsen
SVP Development Wexford Science and Technology, Daniel C. Cramer
President Wexford Science and Technology, James R. Berens
VP Information Technology, David Hsiao
Vice President Lega And Secretary, Jonathan P Klassen
Chairman and CEO, Alan D. Gold, age 53
Auditors: KPMGLLP

LOCATIONS

HQ: Biomed Realty Trust Inc
  17190 Bernardo Center Drive, San Diego, CA 92128
Phone: 858 485-9840   **Fax:** 858 485-9843
Web: www.biomedrealty.com
California
Colorado
Delaware
Maryland
Massachusetts
New Hampshire
New Jersey
New York
North Carolina
Pennsylvania
Washington

PRODUCTS/OPERATIONS

2013 Sales

	$ mil.	% of total
Rental income	446.0	70
Tenant recoveries	141.6	22
Other	49.7	8
Total	**637.3**	**100**

2013 Sales

	$ mil.	% of total
Same properties	537.2	84
New Properties	86.4	14
Development/redevelopment properties	7.3	1
Corporate	6.4	1
Total	**637.3**	**100**

COMPETITORS

Alexandria Real Estate Equities	HCP
Boston Properties	Health Care REIT
Equity Commonwealth	Liberty Property Trust
	PS Business Parks

HISTORICAL FINANCIALS

Company Type: Public

Income Statement

FYE: December 31

	REVENUE ($ mil.)	NET INCOME ($ mil.)	NET PROFIT MARGIN	EMPLOYEES
12/13	637.3	46.6	7.3%	235
12/12	518.1	11.8	2.3%	175
12/11	439.7	42.1	9.6%	166
12/10	386.4	38.8	10.0%	159
12/09	361.1	58.7	16.3%	132
Annual Growth	**15.3%**	**(5.6%)**	**—**	**15.5%**

2013 Year-End Financials

Debt ratio: 44.7%	No. of shares (mil.): 192
Return on equity: 1.7%	Dividends
Cash ($ mil.): 34	Yield: 5.2%
Current ratio: 0.14	Payout: 561.7%
Long-term debt ($ mil.): 2,671	Market value ($ mil.): 3,481

	STOCK PRICE ($) FY Close	P/E High/Low		PER SHARE ($) Earnings	Dividends	Book Value
12/13	18.12	115	90	0.20	0.96	15.30
12/12	19.33	—	—	(0.03)	0.88	16.05
12/11	18.08	109	81	0.19	0.80	16.89
12/10	18.65	102	71	0.19	0.63	17.58
12/09	15.78	36	13	0.45	0.70	18.33
Annual Growth	**3.5%**	—	—	**(18.4%)**	**8.3%**	**(4.4%)**

BJ's Restaurants Inc

The Windy City inspires the food and drink at BJ's. BJ's Restaurants owns and operates 130 restaurants in California and 14 other mostly western states under the names BJ's Restaurant & Brewhouse BJ's Restaurant & Brewery and BJ's Pizza & Grill. The casual-dining eateries offer Chicago-style pizza salads sandwiches pasta and the company's own hand-crafted beers. Its Restaurant & Brewery locations which feature an onsite microbrewery help supply beer to the rest of the chain. The Brewhouse locations sell beer from company breweries and from third-parties using the company's recipes. The smaller Pizza & Grill

shops have limited menus. The first BJ's opened in California in 1978.

Geographic Reach

The company has 130 restaurants in 15 states mostly concentrated in California Texas and Florida.

Financial Performance

BJ's has enjoyed unprecedented growth over the years. In 2012 its revenues increased 14% from $621 million in 2011 to peak at $708 million in 2012 a historic milestone for the company. Profits remained flat from 2011 to 2012 hovering around the $31 million mark.

Such growth has been the result of increases in both guest traffic and the average amount spent per guest. This was in part due to higher menu prices which were raised by about 3%. In addition BJ's opened 16 new restaurants in 2012 which added to the revenue spike.

Strategy

More than 80% of its locations operate under the Brewhouse brand which is similar to its Brewery restaurants except they do not manufacture beer. However the company will continue to build additional Brewery locations in certain areas where it is more appropriate to brew its own beer. It also opens smaller-format BJ's Pizza and Grill locations (the company's legacy format) in densely-populated urban areas or in smaller cities where a larger location is not feasible or appropriate.

EXECUTIVES

Svp Operations Talent Development, Lon F Ledwith, age 58
President and CEO, Gregory A. (Greg) Trojan, age 55
EVP CFO and Secretary, Gregory S. (Greg) Levin, age 47, $350,000 total compensation
EVP and Chief Development Officer, Gregory S. (Greg) Lynds, age 53, $325,000 total compensation
EVP and Chief Restaurant Operations Officer, Wayne L. Jones, age 55, $325,000 total compensation
Chief Supply Chain Officer, John D. Allegretto, age 51, $218,500 total compensation
V Pres Food & Beverage, Salvadore A Navarro
Vp Marketing, Melanie R Bruno-carbone
Vice President Purchasing, Rhonda Ridgers
Area Vice President Information Technology, Eric Berman
Vice President Restaurant Facilities, Don Gardner
Senior Vice President Touring, James Boland
Vice President Of Operations Services, Ame Kuyper
Vice President, Cindy Taunton
Vice President Marketing, Tim Hackbardt
Area Vice President Of Operations, Bob Salessi
Vice President Marketing, Kevin Sherman
Senior Vice President Of Brewing Operations, Alex Puchner
Senior Vice President Resturant Operations, Lon Ledwidth
Vice President Operations, Christopher Insak
Board Member, Peter A (Pete) Bassi, age 65
EVP CFO and Secretary, Gregory S. (Greg) Levin, age 47
Auditors: Ernst&YoungLLP

LOCATIONS

HQ: BJ's Restaurants Inc
7755 Center Avenue, Suite 300, Huntington Beach, CA 92647
Phone: 714 500-2400
Web: www.bjsrestaurants.com

2012 Locations

	No.
California	61
Texas	28
Florida	11
Arizona	6
Nevada	5
Colorado	4
Ohio	3
Oregon	3
Oklahoma	2
Washington	2
Indiana	1
Kansas	1
Kentucky	1
Louisiana	1
New Mexico	1
Total	**130**

PRODUCTS/OPERATIONS

Restaurant Brands
BJ's Restaurant & Brewery
BJ's Restaurant & Brewhouse
BJ's Pizza & Grill
BJ's Grill

Selected Menu Items
Appetizers
Desserts
Entrees
Microbrews
Pastas
Salads
Sandwiches
Soups

COMPETITORS

Applebee's International	Johnny Rockets
Brinker	OSI Restaurant Partners
California Pizza Kitchen	Pat & Oscars
Carlson Restaurants	Rock Bottom Restaurants
Darden	Round Table Pizza
Elephant Bar	Ruby Tuesday
Gordon Biersch	Uno Restaurants
Jerry's Famous Deli	

HISTORICAL FINANCIALS

Company Type: Public

Income Statement

FYE: December 31

	REVENUE ($ mil.)	NET INCOME ($ mil.)	NET PROFIT MARGIN	EMPLOYEES
12/13*	775.1	21.0	2.7%	18,695
01/13	708.3	31.4	4.4%	16,430
01/12	620.9	31.5	5.1%	14,360
12/10	513.8	23.1	4.5%	12,230
12/09	426.7	13.0	3.1%	11,130
Annual Growth	**16.1%**	**12.7%**	**—**	**13.8%**

*Fiscal year change

2013 Year-End Financials

Debt ratio: —	No. of shares (mil.): 28
Return on equity: 5.4%	Dividends
Cash ($ mil.): 23	Yield: —
Current ratio: 0.77	Payout: —
Long-term debt ($ mil.): —	Market value ($ mil.): 879

	STOCK PRICE ($) FY Close	P/E High/Low		PER SHARE ($) Earnings	Dividends	Book Value
12/13*	31.06	54	34	0.73	0.00	14.19
01/13	32.90	48	29	1.09	0.00	13.25
01/12	44.03	49	29	1.08	0.00	11.98
12/10	36.18	45	22	0.82	0.00	10.53
12/09	18.78	39	19	0.48	0.00	9.45
Annual Growth	**13.4%**	—	—	**11.1%**	**—**	**10.7%**

*Fiscal year change

Blackbaud, Inc.

Blackbaud provides financial fundraising and administrative software for not-for-profit organizations and educational institutions. Software offerings include The Raiser's Edge for fundraising management Blackbaud Enterprise CRM for customer relationship management The Financial Edge for accounting and The Education Edge for managing school admissions registration and billing. Blackbaud has about 30000 customers in 60 countries including colleges environmental groups health and human services providers churches and animal welfare groups. The company generates most of its sales in the US.

Operations

Blackbaud generates revenue for its software through product licenses subscriptions maintenance and services. Most of its software is sold on a subscription basis; product licensing revenue only accounts for about 3% of overall sales. Subscription revenue has experienced the most growth over the years; however it has substantially lower gross margins than product licensing. Services revenue accounts for nearly 25% of sales much of that from training. In addition the company makes about 28% of sales from ongoing support and maintenance for existing customers.

Geographic ReachThe US is its largest market accounting for 87% of sales. Canada and Europe each account for 5% of sales while the Asia/Pacific region generates 3%. Blackbaud has roughly 10 offices spanning the US and a handful of international offices in Australia Canada Hong Kong the Netherlands and the UK.

Financial PerformanceBlackbaud has experienced strong revenue growth over the past decade for its niche products with 2013 sales up 13% to peak at $504 million. The increase was driven by double digit growth from its Enterprise Customer Business Unit (ECBU) and its General Markets Business Unit (GMBU). The company also experienced single digit growth from its International Business Unit (IBU) and Target Analytics operations.

The overall growth for 2013 was attributed to a surge in subscriptions as a result of new product launches attributed to the company's 2012 Convio acquisition. Blackbaud was additionally helped by higher demand for its consultancy services and from its online and hosted fundraising services.While the company has been consistently profitable net income (profits) fell 80% to $6.5 million in 2012 due to increased financing expenses for its 2012 Convio acquisition. However net income skyrocketed by over 300% to $30 million in 2013 due to the additional revenue and lower general and administration expenses. Blackbaud's cash flow has been unstable over the past five years; however its cash flow climbed by $39 million during 2013 when compared to the prior year primarily due to an increase in earnings as adjusted for non-cash transactions.

StrategyBlackbaud is looking to expand its product offerings for the Internet. Online donations account for a growing percentage of charitable donations and marketing membership newsletters event management and volunteer recruitment can often be done over the Internet at a lower cost and a higher success rate. Its Sphere eMarketing Suite which facilitates online giving can be integrated into its most popular product The Raiser's Edge.The company's strategy also includes expanding geographically. Over the years it has es-

tablished a Hong Kong office and a Mexico City office which joined other international offices in Canada the UK and Australia.

Mergers and AcquisitionsBlackbaud has expanded its product line and its customer roster in part through acquisitions. In 2012 it acquired not-for-profit software maker Convio in a deal valued at about $275 million. The acquisition paired Blackbaud's strong CRM services with Convio's online fundraising services to create one of the largest Software-as-a-Service (SaaS) companies in the not-for-profit space.

HISTORY

The company bought eTapestry a software-as-a-service provider focused on fundraising tools for the not-for-profit sector for about $25 million in 2007 as well as Target Software. The acquisition supplemented Blackbaud's prospect research software for not-for-profits. In 2008 it purchased chief competitor Kintera for $46 million in cash. Blackbaud combined the Target and Kintera businesses and technology with its prospect research division to form a new unit known as Target Analytics. The division offers donor acquisition and related development tools and services including WealthPoint (database screening) and P!N Service (donor screening).

EXECUTIVES

President General Markets Business, Kevin W. Mooney, age 56, $370,150 total compensation
SVP and Chief Scientist, Charles L. (Chuck) Longfield, age 57, $226,667 total compensation
CFO and SVP Finance and Administration, Anthony W. (Tony) Boor, age 51, $352,475 total compensation
President CEO and Director, Marc E. Chardon, age 58, $608,925 total compensation
President International Business, Bradley J. (Brad) Holman, $369,220 total compensation
SVP Products and Marketing, Jana B. Eggers, $326,275 total compensation
Senior Vice President - New Business Development, Charlie Cumbaa, $330,075 total compensation
Vp And General Counsel, Jon Olson
Vice President Professional Services, Kevin Knight
Vice President Enterprise Professional Services, Esther Pomeleo-fowler
Vice President Product Specialists, Mark Davis
Vice President Of Customer Support, Marty North
Svp-global Product Dev, Kevin McDearis
Financial Sys Conslt Vice President Mkt, Mary Pat
Vice President Engineering, Tom Maszk
Vice President And Corporate Controller, Chad Anderson
Vice President Of Strategic Services, Dennis McCarthy
Chairman, Andrew M. Leitch, age 70
President CEO and Director, Marc E. Chardon, age 58
Treasurer Pay Services, Jim Cunningham
Treasurer, Mary Donnellon
Auditors: PricewaterhouseCoopersLLP

LOCATIONS

HQ: Blackbaud, Inc.
2000 Daniel Island Drive, Charleston, SC 29492
Phone: 843 216-6200   **Fax:** 843 216-6100
Web: www.blackbaud.com

2013 Sales

	$ mil.	% of total
US	439.9	87
Europe	24.1	5
Canada	23.3	5
Asia/Pacific	16.5	3
Total	**503.8**	**100**

PRODUCTS/OPERATIONS

2013 Sales

	$ mil.	% of total
General Markets Business Unit (GMBU)	225.3	45
Enterprise Customer Business Unit (ECBU)	195.6	39
International Business Unit (IBU)	41.5	8
Target analytics & other	41.4	8
Total	**503.8**	**100**

2013 Sales

	$ mil.	% of total
Subscriptions	212.7	42
Maintenance	138.7	28
Services	126.6	25
Licenses	16.7	3
Other	9.1	2
Total	**503.8**	**100**

Selected Products

Accounting software
  Blackbaud Forms (wealth identification)
  The Financial Edge (not-for-profit accounting)
Analytical services
  Prospect Management (prospect management and research)
  Wealth & Affluence Indicators (wealth identification and information)
Business intelligence software
  Altru (general admissions management)
  The Patron Edge (ticketing management for admissions)
Customer relationship management
  Blackbaud Enterprise CRM
  eTapestry
Education administration software
  The Education Edge (admissions registrar business office and development office software)
  Small Colleges (suite for colleges under 300 students)
  Student Billing
  Total Campus Solution (suite for colleges under 2000 students)
Fundraising management software
  The Raiser's Edge (fundraising management system)

COMPETITORS

Acorn Systems	Microsoft
Advanced Solutions	Oracle
Auctionpay	Sage Software
Campus Management Corp	SunGard
Intuit	salesforce.com
MicroEdge	

HISTORICAL FINANCIALS

Company Type: Public

Income Statement

FYE: December 31

	REVENUE ($ mil.)	NET INCOME ($ mil.)	NET PROFIT MARGIN	EMPLOYEES
12/13	503.8	30.4	6.0%	2,666
12/12	447.4	6.5	1.5%	2,705
12/11	370.8	33.2	9.0%	2,256
12/10	327.0	29.8	9.1%	2,065
12/09	309.3	28.4	9.2%	1,956
Annual Growth	**13.0%**	**1.7%**	**—**	**8.0%**

2013 Year-End Financials

Debt ratio: 21.6%		No. of shares (mil.): 46	
Return on equity: 19.7%		Dividends	
Cash ($ mil.): 11		Yield: 1.2%	
Current ratio: 0.64		Payout: 96.0%	
Long-term debt ($ mil.): 135		Market value ($ mil.): 1,737	

	STOCK PRICE ($)	P/E	PER SHARE ($)		
	FY Close	High/Low	Earnings	Dividends	Book Value
12/13	37.65	62 34	0.67	0.48	3.50
12/12	22.83	226 141	0.15	0.48	3.24
12/11	27.70	40 28	0.75	0.48	3.12
12/10	25.90	41 30	0.68	0.44	2.77
12/09	23.63	36 14	0.65	0.40	2.61
Annual Growth	12.4%	— —	0.8%	4.7%	7.7%

Blucora, Inc.

Why crawl the Web when others can do it for you? Blucora (formerly InfoSpace) operates through two businesses. Its InfoSpace unit consists of online search services that rely on its metasearch search technology. Owned and operated consumer websites include Dogpile.com WebFetch.com and MetaCrawler.com which query such leading search providers as Google and Yahoo! and then collate and rank those search results. InfoSpace also offers a private-label search product for businesses (which it calls distribution partners); it develops hosts and delivers search results for more than 100 distribution partners. Blucora acquired its other primary business online tax solutions provider TaxACT in 2012.

Sales and Marketing

About 80% of the company's search services revenue is generated through its distribution partners many of which are mobile app developers. It has distribution and partnership agreements with search giants Google and Yahoo! ensuring access to search results.

Financial Performance

The company has benefitted from increased distribution revenue and the addition of more than 40 new distribution partners (a result of the recent smartphone boom).

HISTORY

Indian immigrant Naveen Jain a veteran of Microsoft's online services unit set out to create an interactive "people and business finder" in 1996. Eschewing funding from venture capitalists (disdainfully calling them "vulture capitalists") the outspoken Jain launched his new enterprise dubbed InfoSpace with $250000 of his own money. Its online phone directory service debuted in May and a few months later it unveiled an online e-mail directory. Unlike most Internet players InfoSpace wasn't looking to lure users to its own website (though it did have one). Instead the company focused on supplying information to other sites.

By the beginning of 1997 InfoSpace had added industry stalwarts Lycos (now owned by South Korea's Daum Communications) and Microsoft to its customer list. That year it signed up @Home Network Playboy Dow Jones' Wall Street Journal Online and Go2Net. The company's content also found its way to cable TV that way by way of InfoSpace's alliance with Source Media's Interactive Channel. InfoSpace continued expanding beyond traditional Internet customers inking deals to feed its content to Motorola and SkyTel pagers the 3Com PalmPilot and the AT&T PocketNet service.

The company secured two vital customers in 1998 signing America Online (AOL) and Netscape (later acquired by AOL) to content distribution deals. To get the agreements however InfoSpace had to pay AOL and Netscape to carry its content. Also in 1998 the company set up shop in the UK through a joint venture with Thomson Directories. It went public later that year as InfoSpace.com.

After going public the company entered into e-commerce agreements with Cyberian Outpost and Multiple Zones (now known as just Zones). In 1999 it joined with Quote.com to create a financial content package. It later established a venture capital fund launched its comparison shopping application ActiveShopper and expanded into Canada and India. InfoSpace bolstered its wireless operations in 2000 through acquisitions of Saraide and Millet Software and signed agreements with GTE Wireless (now Cingular) and VeriSign. The company later dropped the ".com" from its name and Jain handed the CEO title to Arun Sarin.

In October InfoSpace expanded its infrastructure services and content offerings when it acquired online content company Go2Net for about $1.5 billion. The company's stock sank into the single digits however and a management shakeup led to the departures of its COO and CFO. Jain took back the CEO title from Sarin (who briefly served as vice chairman before resigning from the board) and realigned the company's focus on its core distribution products. The company later acquired Locus Dialogue a developer of speech recognition technologies. In late 2002 one of the company's directors Jim Voelker replaced Jain as chairman and CEO.

InfoSpace cut about 115 jobs and sold its Silicon Investor site in 2003. It also purchased mobile media company Moviso for some $25 million from the now defunct Vivendi Universal Net USA Group. The company formed a Media Studios business unit in order to house its Moviso acquisition.

Later that year Jain resigned from the board of directors after the company filed a lawsuit against him claiming his new company Intelius violated non-compete clauses. (The suit was dismissed the following year.) Also in 2003 in a separate case a US District Judge ruled that Jain violated federal law when he bought and sold millions of shares of InfoSpace stock within a six-month period. He was later ordered to pay a $247 million penalty. (Up until that point the largest award for that type of insider trading was $20 million.)

InfoSpace sold its payment solutions business to Lightbridge (later renamed Authorize.Net Holdings) in 2004 for $82 million and boosted its local directory offerings with the acquisition of Switchboard for $160 million. It also acquired mobile game creators Atlas Mobile and IOMO Limited.

In 2006 InfoSpace announced a restructuring plan as a response to revenue losses. The plan included 250 job cuts and the closing of its Hamburg Germany facility. Streamlining continued in 2007 with the company's sale of its online directory business including Switchboard to Idearc (now called SuperMedia) for $225 million. Also in 2007 InfoSpace sold Media Studios (including Moviso) to FunMobility Inc. of Pleasanton California for an undisclosed price and its mobile services business for $135 million to Motricity a provider of mobile content.

In 2008 it closed its European facilities. Jim Voelker retired as CEO early in 2009. InfoSpace acquired Internet shopping service Mercantila in 2010 only to divest the business a year later. John Cunningham became chairman in early 2011 and Bill Ruckelshaus was named CEO later that year.

The company changed its name from InfoSpace to Blucora in 2012 followng its acquisition of TaxACT for some $287.5 million.

EXECUTIVES

President CEO and Director, William J. (Bill) Ruckelshaus, age 50, $56,923 total compensation
CFO and Treasurer, Eric M. Emans, age 41, $170,654 total compensation
EVP Corporate Development, George Allen
President TaxACT, JoAnn Kintzel
President Monoprice, Bernard Luthi
President InfoSpace, Peter Mansour
Sr Vp-human Resources, Randy Massengale
Vp Strategic Dev, Chris Matty
Evp, Brian McManus
Vice President Of Product, Justin Law
Vice President And Chief Strategy, Anthony Stonefield
Vice President Wireless Product, Ron Pessner
Vice President Human Resources, Bill Mapel
Vice President Prod Management Wireline And Broadband Internet Services, Mike Quigley
Chairman, John E. Cunningham, age 57
Board Member, Lewis M Taffer
Board Member, Steve Hooper
Board Member Chair Audit Committee, Liz Huebner
Board Member, Richard D Hearney
Auditors: Deloitte&ToucheLLP

LOCATIONS

HQ: Blucora, Inc.
10900 N.E. 8th Street, Suite 800, Bellevue, WA 98004
Phone: 425 201-6100   Fax: 425 201-6150
Web: www.blucora.com

2014 Sales

	$mil.	% of total
United States	556.5	96
International	24.2	4
Total	580.7	100

PRODUCTS/OPERATIONS

Selected Operations

Infospace
  Owned and operated websites
  Dogpile.com
  InfoSpace.com
  MetaCrawler.com
  WebCrawler.com
  White label search services
TaxACT
Monoprice

2014 Sales

	$ mil.	% of total
Search and Content	326.3	56
E-Commerce	150.7	26
Tax Preparation	103.7	18
Total	580.7	100

COMPETITORS

AOL	Intuit
Answers Corporation	Jackson Hewitt
Ask.com	Local.com
Conversant	LookSmart
Daum Communications	MSN
Google	Marchex
H&R Block	Yahoo!

HISTORICAL FINANCIALS

Company Type: Public

Income Statement

FYE: December 31

	REVENUE ($ mil.)	NET INCOME ($ mil.)	NET PROFIT MARGIN	EMPLOYEES
12/13	573.9	24.4	4.3%	450
12/12	406.9	22.5	5.5%	225
12/11	228.8	21.5	9.4%	198
12/10	246.8	13.7	5.6%	174
12/09	207.6	7.4	3.6%	157
Annual Growth	28.9%	34.7%	—	30.1%

2013 Year-End Financials

Debt ratio: 30.9%
Return on equity: 5.2%
Cash ($ mil.): 130
Current ratio: 1.48
Long-term debt ($ mil.): 113

No. of shares (mil.): 42
Dividends
  Yield: —
  Payout: —
Market value ($ mil.): 1,227

	STOCK PRICE ($) FY Close	P/E High/Low	PER SHARE ($) Earnings	Dividends	Book Value
12/13	29.16	51 24	0.56	0.00	12.22
12/12	15.71	33 20	0.54	0.00	10.17
12/11	10.99	21 14	0.56	0.00	8.98
12/10	8.30	31 18	0.37	0.00	8.61
12/09	8.57	42 25	0.21	0.00	7.91
Annual Growth	35.8%	— —	27.8%	—	11.5%

Blue Nile Inc

Blue Nile helps tech-savvy Marc Antonys bejewel their Cleopatras. The leader in online jewelry sales Blue Nile offers luxury-grade jewelry at bluenile.com and sells loose diamonds settings engagement rings as well as non-bridal jewelry made of gold platinum and silver set with diamonds pearls emeralds rubies and sapphires. While engagement rings account for about 70% of its sales the e-tailer also sells watches and provides custom jewelry design services. Blue Nile's web sites serve customers in the US Canada Europe and the Asia-Pacific region —more than 40 countries in all. Chairman Mark Vadon and Ben Elowitz formerly of Fatbrain.com founded the site in 1999.

Geographic Reach

Based in Seattle Washington Blue Nile also operates in Dublin Ireland through its fulfillment center there as well as in Shanghai with a pair of facilities.

Operations

The bulk of Blue Nile's business or 70% comes from engagement rings while non-engagement revenue brings in 30%.

Sales and Marketing

Blue Nile relies on both online and offline initiatives to get its name in front of new and existing customers. These efforts include search engines online display affiliate programs direct online marketing social networking and public relations. To this end the jewelry retailer's marketing expenses came in at $24.3 million in 2013 up from $21 million in 2012 and $16.9 million in 2011.

Strategy

Since late 2011 when Blue Nile announced it will focus on non-bridal jewelry going forward Blue Nile has reversed its engagement-focused strategy. Indeed the retailer made its mark by selling dia-

mond engagement rings online at prices significantly less than brick-and-mortar jewelry stores. Engagement rings are often a customer's first purchase through the site. However declining margins on engagement rings and dim prospects for Millennials many of whom are either out of work or are delaying marriage altogether. Blue Nile will keep chasing after consumers who are ready to head to the altar through its 2014-inked agreement with Zac Posen for an exclusive collection of engagement rings and fine jewelry.

Another priority for the e-tailer is building its mobile business. To serve jewelry buyers on the go the company launched a mobile website designed for the iPhone iPod touch and Android mobile devices. The mobile version is smaller than the PC site in scope with quick tabs to find diamonds engagement rings and other gift ideas. To maintain its momentum Blue Nile is launching native language sites such as the one it rolled out in 2014 in Arabic to entice consumers in the United Arab Emirates to shop Blue Nile online. The site complements its existing versions in English French Spanish Japanese and traditional and simplified Chinese.

Financial Performance

Blue Nile's revenue has grown from more than $302 million in fiscal 2009 to $450 million in 2013. The jewelry retailer attributes the steady gains to growth across its three main categories specifically an increase in average order value offset in part by a drop in the number of orders. Engagement orders across all price points and higher-priced non-engagement orders led the 2013 sales increases dragged down by a decrease in non-engagement orders at lower price points. Blue Nile posted $10.9 million in net income in 2013 representing a 30% increase from 2012. The company logged $23.4 million in net cash from operations in 2013 vs. $34.4 million in 2012 thanks to greater cash flow from Q4 due to a noteworthy rise in revenue from holiday sales.

EXECUTIVES

Vice President Head Strategy At Blue, Jon Sainsbury
President and CEO, Harvey S. Kanter, $480,733 total compensation
CFO, David B. Binder, $254,376 total compensation
SVP Operations, Dwight Gaston, $264,817 total compensation
General Manager and President International, Vijay Talwar, $278,501 total compensation
Chief Merchandising Officer, Julie Yoakum, $135,751 total compensation
Vice President Of Regulatory Strategic Information Technology, Crystal McIntyre
Vice President Of Human Resources, Derek Mullens
Chairman, Mark Vadon
Auditors: Deloitte&ToucheLLP

LOCATIONS

HQ: Blue Nile Inc
411 First Avenue South, Suite 700, Seattle, WA 98104
Phone: 206 336-6700
Web: www.bluenile.com

2013 Sales

	$ mil.	% of total
US	376.8	84
International	73.2	16
Total	**450.0**	**100**

PRODUCTS/OPERATIONS

2013 Sales

	$ mil.	% of total
Engagement	314.7	70
Non-engagement	135.3	30
Total	**450.0**	**100**

Selected Products

Accessories
  Cuff links
  Desk accessories
  Frames
  Key rings
  Money clips
  Pens
Bracelets
Earrings
Necklaces and pendants
Watches
  Men's
  Women's
Wedding and anniversary rings

Selected Materials

Diamonds
Gemstones
  Emeralds
  Rubies
  Sapphires
Gold
Pearls
Platinum
Silver

COMPETITORS

Amazon.com	QVC
Cartier	Reeds Jewelers
Costco Wholesale	Ross-Simons
Gucci	Saks
H. Stern	Saks Fifth Avenue
HSN	Samuels Jewelers
Helzberg Diamonds	Signet
Lazare Kaplan	Tiffany & Co.
Mondera	Union Diamond
Neiman Marcus	Wal-Mart
Nordstrom	Zale
Overstock.com	eBay

HISTORICAL FINANCIALS

Company Type: Public

Income Statement

FYE: December 29

	REVENUE ($ mil.)	NET INCOME ($ mil.)	NET PROFIT MARGIN	EMPLOYEES
12/13	450.0	10.8	2.4%	291
12/12*	400.0	8.3	2.1%	253
01/12	348.0	11.3	3.3%	212
01/11	332.8	14.1	4.2%	193
01/10	302.1	12.8	4.2%	188
Annual Growth	10.5%	(4.0%)	—	11.5%

*Fiscal year change

2013 Year-End Financials

Debt ratio: 0.3%
Return on equity: 39.8%
Cash ($ mil.): 115
Current ratio: 1.17
Long-term debt ($ mil.): 0

No. of shares (mil.): 12
Dividends
  Yield: —
  Payout: —
Market value ($ mil.): 618

	STOCK PRICE ($) FY Close	P/E High/Low		PER SHARE ($) Earnings	Dividends	Book Value
12/13	47.78	55	35	0.85	0.00	3.14
12/12*	37.70	68	37	0.63	0.00	1.13
01/12	40.88	80	38	0.77	0.00	2.54
01/11	57.06	64	42	0.94	0.00	3.37
01/10	63.33	75	21	0.84	0.00	2.95
Annual Growth	(6.8%)	—	—	0.3%	—	1.5%

*Fiscal year change

BNC Bancorp

BNC Bancorp knows the ABCs of the financial world. The firm is the holding company for Bank of North Carolina which has about 35 locations in both North and South Carolina. The bank offers community-oriented services to local business and retail customers providing checking savings and money market accounts credit cards and certificates of deposit. Its loan portfolio is mainly composed of residential and commercial mortgages and construction loans. Bank of North Carolina also offers insurance retirement planning and other investment products and services. BNC Bancorp is buying First Trust Bank which has three branches in the Charlotte area for some $35 million.

The deal is the latest in a string of acquisitions for BNC Bancorp. In 2010 the company acquired the failed Beach First National Bank in an FDIC-facilitated transaction expanding Bank of North Carolina's branch network into South Carolina. The 2012 acquisitions of Regent Bank further extended the bank's reach in the state. BNC Bancorp acquired another failed bank in 2011 with assistance from the FDIC Blue Ridge Savings Bank in North Carolina. The following year it bought the single-branch KeySource Financial also in North Carolina.

In 2010 Aquiline Capital Partners a private equity firm specializing in the financial services industry invested nearly $35 million in BNC Bancorp. The transaction netted the investor approximately 10% of the bank holding company as well as convertible shares that could equate to an additional 15% stake.

EXECUTIVES

President CEO and Director; President and CEO Bank of North Carolina, W. Swope Montgomery, age 65, $345,200 total compensation
EVP COO and Director; EVP and COO Bank of North Carolina, Richard D. Callicutt, age 55, $268,650 total compensation
EVP and CFO BNC and Bank of North Carolina, David B. Spencer, age 51, $251,200 total compensation
Svp Bank Of North Carolina, Thomas N Nelson
Vice President And Operations Manager, Jenny Smith
Svp And Regional Executive Bank Of North Carolina, Mark N Lewis
Vice President, Jawn Scott
Vice President, Daren Fuller
Exec V Pres-cao, Ronald Gorczynski
Exec Vice President Chief Entp Risk Ofc, Bill McKendry

Vice President And Assistant Secretary, Bonnie Murdock
Vice President, Donna Brown
Senior Vice President City Executive, Heather Grossnickle
Assistant Vice President Dir Int Aud, Kristy Fyfe
Vice President Special Assets, Danny Broach
Senior Vice President, Janet Helms
Executive Vice President Director Human, Annette Rollins
Assistant Vice President Business Services Support Team Leader, Kristen Curtis
Senior Vice President Business Banking, Jimmie Bowman
Vice President Senior Loan Processor, Tassie Montgomery
Senior Vice President, Rob Ellenburg
Assistant Vice President Assistant Operations Manager, Diane Anderson
Vice President, Jim Tobin
Senior Vice President Raleigh City Exec, Mark Carlton
Senior Vice President Director Leasing, Curtis Weaver
Vice President, Mike Jacobs
Vice President Special Assets, Lance Miller
Senior Vice President Loan Operations, Pat Strickland
Vice President Learning And Development, Julie McMichael
Assistant Vice President Branch Manager, Lucy Ortiz
Senior Vice President City Executive, John Bencini
Vice President, Ann Walker
Vice President Business Development Ofc, Stan Lamb
Executive Vice President, Don Draughon
Vice President Information Systems, Mark Murphy
Chairman Emeritus, W. Groome Fulton, age 75
President CEO and Director; President and CEO Bank of North Carolina, W. Swope Montgomery, age 65
EVP COO and Director; EVP and COO Bank of North Carolina, Richard D. Callicutt, age 55
Chairman of the Board, Thomas R. Sloan, age 69
Auditors: CherryBekaert&HollandLLP

LOCATIONS

HQ: BNC Bancorp
3980 Premier Drive, High Point, NC 27265
Phone: 336 476-9200
Web: www.bankofnc.com

PRODUCTS/OPERATIONS

2008 Sales

	$ mil.	% of total
Interest		
Loans including fees	64.8	85
Debt securities	5.7	7
Other	0.5	1
Noninterest		
Service charges	3.0	4
Mortgage fees	0.8	1
Other	1.8	2
Total	76.6	100

COMPETITORS

BB&T	NewBridge Bancorp
Bank of America	Piedmont Federal
Bank of the Carolinas	Southern Community
Carolina Bank	Financial
CommunityOne Bancorp	Wells Fargo
First Bancorp (NC)	
First Citizens BancShares	

HISTORICAL FINANCIALS

Company Type: Public

Income Statement

FYE: December 31

	ASSETS ($ mil.)	NET INCOME ($ mil.)	INCOME AS % OF ASSETS	EMPLOYEES
12/13	3,229.5	17.2	0.5%	620
12/12	3,083.7	10.4	0.3%	564
12/11	2,454.9	6.9	0.3%	455
12/10	2,149.9	7.7	0.4%	372
12/09	1,634.1	6.5	0.4%	262
Annual Growth	18.6%	27.4%	—	24.0%

2013 Year-End Financials

Return on assets: 0.5%
Return on equity: 6.2%
Long-term debt ($ mil.): —
No. of shares (mil.): 27
Sales ($ mil): 161
Dividends
Yield: 1.1%
Payout: 32.7%
Market value ($ mil.): 468

	STOCK PRICE ($) FY Close	P/E High/Low		PER SHARE ($) Earnings	Dividends	Book Value
12/13	17.14	28	13	0.61	0.20	9.94
12/12	8.01	18	14	0.48	0.20	11.45
12/11	7.25	20	14	0.45	0.20	18.00
12/10	9.00	17	11	0.61	0.20	16.81
12/09	7.59	13	8	0.62	0.20	17.19
Annual Growth	22.6% (12.8%)	—	—	(0.4%)	(0.0%)	

Bofl Holding, Inc.

BofI Holding owns Bank of Internet USA a savings bank that operates online in all 50 states. The bank offers checking savings and money market accounts CDs and ATM and check cards. Multifamily real estate loans account for nearly two-thirds of the company's loan portfolio although the bank only offers them in selected states; it also acquires them on the secondary market. Offered nationwide single-family residential mortgages make up nearly 30% of its loan portfolio. Bank of Internet USA also issues home equity automobile and recreational vehicle loans. Officers and directors own more than 30% of BofI Holding's stock.

EXECUTIVES

EVP and CFO, Andrew J. Micheletti, age 55, $220,000 total compensation
President and CEO, Gregory Garrabrants, age 43, $375,000 total compensation
EVP Specialty Finance and Chief Legal Officer, Eshel Bar-Adon, $205,000 total compensation
EVP and Chief Credit Officer, Thomas Constantine, $205,000 total compensation
EVP and Chief Lending Officer, Brian Swanson, age 34, $185,000 total compensation
Senior Vice President Chief Risk, Thomas Williams
Senior Vice President, Jason W Kenoyer
Vice President Engineering, Barbara Fronek
Vice President Controller, Pete Bauer
Assistant Vice President Senior Commercial Analyst, Joshua Butensky
Vice President Secondary Marketing, Melissa Rowe
Chairman, Theodore C. (Ted) Allrich, age 68
Vice Chairman, Nicholas A. Mosich
Auditors: CroweHorwathLLP

LOCATIONS

HQ: BofI Holding, Inc.
4350 La Jolla Village Drive, Suite 140, San Diego, CA
92122
Phone: 858 350-6200
Web: www.bofiholding.com

COMPETITORS

Bank of America	ISN Bank
Citigroup	MUFG Americas Holdings
E*TRADE Bank	Steel Partners
First IB	Holdings
ING DIRECT USA	

HISTORICAL FINANCIALS

Company Type: Public

Income Statement
FYE: June 30

	ASSETS ($ mil.)	NET INCOME ($ mil.)	INCOME AS % OF ASSETS	EMPLOYEES
06/14	4,403.0	55.9	1.3%	366
06/13	3,090.7	40.2	1.3%	312
06/12	2,386.8	29.4	1.2%	230
06/11	1,940.0	20.5	1.1%	173
06/10	1,421.0	21.1	1.5%	90
Annual Growth	32.7%	27.6%	—	42.0%

2014 Year-End Financials

Return on assets: 1.4%	Dividends
Return on equity: 17.5%	Yield: —
Long-term debt ($ mil.): —	Payout: —
No. of shares (mil.): 14	Market value ($ mil.): 1,062
Sales ($ mil): 195	

	STOCK PRICE ($) FY Close	P/E High/Low		PER SHARE ($) Earnings	Dividends	Book Value
06/14	73.47	27	12	3.85	0.00	25.66
06/13	45.82	16	7	2.89	0.00	19.53
06/12	19.76	8	5	2.33	0.00	17.95
06/11	14.41	9	6	1.87	0.00	14.16
06/10	14.12	8	3	2.22	0.00	12.75
Annual Growth	51.0%	—	—	14.8%	—	19.1%

Bonanza Creek Energy, Inc.

Bonanza Creek Energy searches for a treasure of black gold. The independent oil and natural gas company has exploration and production assets in Arkansas California Colorado and Texas. Unlike many in the industry it operates nearly all of its projects and has an 89% working interest in its holdings. The company reported a 32% increase in proved reserves in 2013 to 69.8 million barrels of oil equivalent resulting primarily from the development of the Wattenberg Field in Colorado. Most of the company's proved reserves are in its Rocky Mountains (Niobara oil shale) and Arkansas (Cotton Valley sands) holdings.

Geographic Reach

The company's assets and operations are focused in the Rocky Mountains in the Wattenberg Field (primarily the Niobrara oil shale) and in Dorcheat Macedonia Field in southern Arkansas

(Cotton Valley sands).The Rocky Mountain region contributed 66% if the company's total production in 2013; the Mid-Continent region 34%.

Bonanza Creek also has field offices in Houston Texas; Bakersfield California; Stamps Arkansas; and Kersey Colorado.

Operations

In 2013 the company drilled 134 wells and completed 121 productive operated wells and participated in drilling 12 and completing 4 productive non-operated wells. The resulting production rates achieved by the drilling program boosted sales volumes by 72% over 2012 to 16219 barrels of oil equivalent per day (of which 72% was crude oil and natural gas liquids-NGLs).

In 2013 Bonanza Creek produced about 3.9 million barrels of oil 20 billion cu. ft. of natural gas and 352800 barrels of natural gas liquids.

That year the company reported about 73889 gross (62003 net) leasehold acres and 684 gross (616.2 net) productive wells.

Sales and Marketing

Though Bonanza Creek sells crude oil natural gas and associated NGLs the majority of sales come from oil. The marketing arm of Plains All American Pipeline accounted for 37% of the company's revenues in 2013; petroleum marketer Lion Trading & Transportation 29%; and Sierra Crude Oil & Marketing 15%.

Financial Performance

The company's revenues increased by 82% in 2013 fueled by higher crude oil natural gas and NGL production and higher crude oil and natural gas prices partially offset by lower NGL prices. Oil natural gas and NGL production increased as a direct result of the $447 million expended for drilling and completion during 2013.

Bonanza Creek's net income grew by 49% in 2013 thanks to higher revenues offset by an increase in lease operating expense related to the increased production volumes attributable to the drilling program and the operation of an additional gas plant (constructed during 2012). The increase in depreciation depletion and amortization expenses is due to a 55% rise in depreciable assets and a loss incurred on derivative contracts during 2013.The company has seen year over year growth in revenues since 2010 primarily due to its continuous investment in drilling activity which triggered the volume growth and as well through the expansion of its properties and by acquisitions.

Strategy

The company is concentrating on increasing production from existing unconventional assets in its core areas while making complementary acquisitions.

Bonanza Creek capital expenditures for 2014 arein the range of $575 million to $625 million. It is focused on the horizontal development of significant resource potential from the Niobrara and Codell formations in the Wattenberg Field expecting to invest approximately 85% of its 2014 capital budget in this project. The remaining 15% of its 2014 budget is allocated primarily to the vertical development of the Dorcheat Macedonia and McKamie Patton Fields in southern Arkansas targeting oil-rich Cotton Valley sands.

It invested 82% of its 2013 capital budget in the horizontal development in the Niobrara and Codell formations in the Wattenberg Field. While it has focused on the Niobrara B bench primarily using 4000 foot laterals it has begun to develop the Niobrara C bench and Codell formation as well as to test extended reach lateral drilling in the Wattenberg Field and down-spacing concepts in both of its core areas.It also intends to pursue bolt-on acquisitions in the Wattenberg Field and in southern

Arkansas where it can take advantage of its core operational and engineering competencies. In 2013 Bonanza Creek increased its 2013 capital budget to drill a "super-section" test of stacked laterals in multiple zones from multi-well pads in the Wattenberg Field and to drill additional wells in southern Arkansas during the fourth quarter. In addition the expanded budget accommodated increasing non-operated activity and infrastructure projects in the Wattenberg Field. It spent about $472 million in 2013. In order to focus on its core areas in 2012 the company sold most of its non-core properties in California for $9 million.

Mergers and Acquisitions

In 2012 Bonanza Creek bought leases in the Wattenberg Field from the State of Colorado State Board of Land Commissioners for $60 million.

Company Background

The company went public in 2011. It used its $251 million in IPO proceeds to repay debt and to fund the exploration and development of oil producing assets.

Bonanza Creek was formed in 2006.

EXECUTIVES

Executive Vice President General Counsel,
Christopher I Humber
President CEO and Director, Richard J. Carty, age 45
EVP and COO, Tony Buchanon
VP Rocky Mountain Operations, Kerry McCowen
VP Mid-Continent Operations, John Larson
EVP and CFO, Bill Cassidy
Vice President Es&rc, John Hess
Vice President Land, Michael McPhetridge
Chairman, James A. Watt, age 64
President CEO and Director, Richard J. Carty, age 45

LOCATIONS

HQ: Bonanza Creek Energy, Inc.
410 17th Street, Suite 1400, Denver, CO 80202
Phone: 720 440-6100   **Fax:** 720 305-0804
Web: www.bonanzacrk.com

PRODUCTS/OPERATIONS

2013 Sales

	$ mil.	% of total
Oil	357.0	85
Natural gas	46.5	11
Natural gas liquids	18.3	4
CO2	0.1	-
Total	**421.9**	**100**

COMPETITORS

Anadarko Petroleum	Exxon Mobil
Apache	Hunt Consolidated
BP	Noble Energy
Chesapeake Energy	Pioneer Natural
Chevron	Resources
ConocoPhillips	Royal Dutch Shell
Devon Energy	

HISTORICAL FINANCIALS

Company Type: Public

Income Statement

FYE: December 31

	REVENUE ($ mil.)	NET INCOME ($ mil.)	NET PROFIT MARGIN	EMPLOYEES
12/13	421.8	69.1	16.4%	236
12/12	231.2	46.5	20.1%	155
12/11	112.4	12.6	11.3%	96
12/10	1.7	(0.1)	—	71
Annual Growth	522.9%	—	—	49.2%

2013 Year-End Financials

Debt ratio: 32.9%
Return on equity: 11.2%
Cash ($ mil.): 180
Current ratio: 1.51
Long-term debt ($ mil.): 508

No. of shares (mil.): 40
Dividends
Yield: —
Payout: —
Market value ($ mil.): 1,751

	STOCK PRICE ($) FY Close	P/E High/Low	PER SHARE ($) Earnings	Dividends	Book Value
12/13	43.47	33 16	1.71	0.00	16.28
12/12	27.79	25 11	1.17	0.00	14.42
12/11	12.50	32 29	0.43	0.00	13.37
12/10	0.00	— —	(0.01)	0.00	12.23
Annual Growth	—	— —	—	—	10.0%

Boston Beer Co., Inc

A half-pint compared to megabrewers like the world's #1 beer maker Anheuser-Bush InBev The Boston Beer Company holds a distinction all its own –it is the US's largest craft brewer. The company produces more than 50 seasonal and year-round varieties of craft beers at breweries in Boston and four other states. Annually it sells around 2.7 million barrels of lagers and ales (including its flagship Samuel Adams Boston Lager and other Sam Adams brand beers) and Twisted Tea malt beverages. it also brews beer for third parties. Founded in 1984 by its chairman James Koch The Boston Beer Company has grown along with America's increasing thirst for better beer.

Geographic Reach

In addition to Boston The Boston Beer Company owns breweries in Breinigsville Cincinnati Breinigsville Pennsylvania and Los Angeles. The company distributes its brews primarily in the US but they are also sold in Canada the Caribbean Europe Israel Mexico and the Pacific Rim.

Operations

Beyond beer the company makes 10 flavored malt beverages under the Twisted Tea brand name and five hard ciders under the Angry Orchard brand. The Boston Beer Company's A&S Brewing Collaborative (dba Alchemy & Science) subsidiary (formed in 2011) makes five beers under two brand names. A&S recently formed House of Shandy (since renamed Traveler Beer Co.) which brews shandy style beers (beer mixed with citrus flavored soda carbonated lemonade ginger beer or cider).

In addition to production at its own breweries the company contracts some of its production to brewers among them Wisconsin-based City Brewing Company and New York-based Pleasant Valley Wine.

Sales and Marketing

The Boston-based brewer distributes its products through a network of some 340 wholesale distributors who in turn sell its beverages to retailers including pubs restaurants food and liquor stores and stadiums. Boston Beer employs a sales force of approximately 330 people.

The company's media campaigns include TV radio billboards and print. The brewer complements is media buying by sponsoring cultural and community events local beer festivals industry-related trade shows and promotional events at local establishments. Boston Beer reported spending on advertising and promotions of $78.3 million in 2012 versus $73.4 million in 2011 and $66.1 million in 2010.

Financial Performance

The Boston Beer Company's sales topped $580 million in 2012 a 13% increase versus 2011. The double-digit gain was driven primarily by an increase in core brand (Sam Adams Twisted Tea Angry Orchard) shipment volume and price increases levied in 2012 and capped a decade of steady and accelerating sales growth for the company. Indeed Boston Beer's five-year annual revenue growth rate exceeds 11%. Boston Beer shipped 2.7 million barrels during 2012 versus 2.5 million barrels in 2011.

Net income fell 10% in 2012 versus 2011 due to a one-time gain in 2011 related to a product recall.

Strategy

The domestic beer industry is dominated by two major brewers Anheuser-Busch InBev and Miller-Coors which together account for more than 90% of all US domestic beer production (excluding exports). Boston Beer –along with a growing number of craft brewers –competes in the Better Beer (as opposed to mass-produced) category. However with the domestic beer industry excluding Better Beers in decline the beer giants have begun developing their own specialty beers and acquiring craft brewers to compete in this small growth market. To keep adventurous drinkers brand-loyal Boston Beer follows a strategy of frequently offering new beverages and discontinuing others. During 2012 the company launched two specialty variety six-packs under the Samuel Adams IPA Hopology and Samuel Adams Hop Tour names.

Mergers and Acquisitions

In January 2012 the company acquired craft brewer Southern California Brewing Company (dba Angel City Brewing) for nearly $2 million. Tasked with finding unique brewing techniques and ingredients in 2012 A&S acquired Los Angeles-based Southern California Brewing Company a craft brewer doing business as Angel City Brewing Company.

Ownership

Founder and chairman James Koch owns about a third of the company's shares. Investment firm Neuberger Berman owns nearly 13%.

HISTORY

Management consultant James Koch started The Boston Beer Company with his former secretary Rhonda Kallman in 1983. With Koch's $100000 in life savings plus $300000 raised from family and friends the company contracted with Pittsburgh Brewing to make beer using Koch's great-great-grandfather's recipe. (Louis Koch had brewed beer in Germany before opening a St. Louis brewery in 1860.)

Koch and Kallman launched their premium beer in Boston in 1985 and four years later Boston Beer contracted with Blitz-Weinhard Brewing in

Oregon to make beer for distribution in the western US.

The company's rise to the top of the small hopmeister heap was driven by Koch's earnest radio spots and by the quality of the product. Boston Beer went public in 1995 while the craft-brewing sector was booming but by 1997 the market stopped growing soggy with competing brands.

Using recipes gleaned from a home-brewing contest the company briefly brewed the LongShot line of beers in 1996. The next year Boston Beer moved into the fledgling alcoholic cider market with HardCore Cider and it purchased a small-batch brewery in Koch's hometown of Cincinnati. In 1998 Boston Beer expanded distribution to Japan and Australia while 1999 saw the introduction of Millennium Ale.

In 2000 Boston Beer launched BoDean's Twisted Tea a malt-and tea-based beverage. In 2001 president Martin Roper was named CEO succeeding Koch who remains chairman.

Boston Beer began selling its first light beer Sam Adams Light in 2002 in most of its top US markets. The following year the company broke records with its 25% alcohol Utopia brew and in 2004 introduced Chocolate Bock. These offerings joined Millennium and Triple Bock under the heading Extreme Beers. Limited edition Samuel Adams Chocolate Bock which uses Scharffen Berger Chocolate was introduced in 2003.

In 2007 the company announced a brewing agreement with City Brewing to brew some of City's Latrobe brand beer. In order to add to its brewing capacity in 2008 Boston Beer acquired Pennsylvania Brewery from Diageo North America for $55 million.

In December 2010 the company introduced Infinium a limited-edition ale that was developed with Germany's Weihenstephan Brewery –recognized as the world's oldest brewery. Infinium was touted as the first new style of beer created under Reinheitsgebot purity standards in more than a century. (Reinheitsgebot purity laws dictate that only barley hops yeast and water may be used as ingredients in beer.) The ale was described by Boston Beer as tasting crisp and champagne-like.

EXECUTIVES

Vice President Of Marketing, John C Geist, age 54
VP Operations, Thomas W. Lance, age 61, $329,000 total compensation
VP Brewing, David A. Grinnell, age 56
President CEO and Director, Martin F. Roper, age 51, $686,750 total compensation
CFO and Treasurer, William F. Urich, age 58, $372,000 total compensation
VP Brand Development, Robert P. Pagano
National Account Manager, Carissa Sweigart
Senior Vice President, Deirdre Andiorio
National Account Manager, Whitney Stevenson
Vice President Information Technology, Paul Moss
National Account Manager, Barbara Silk
President CEO and Director, Martin F. Roper, age 51
Chairman, C. James (Jim) Koch, age 65
CFO and Treasurer, William F. Urich, age 58
Board Member, Paul Hill
Auditors: Ernst&YoungLLP

LOCATIONS

HQ: Boston Beer Co., Inc
One Design Center Place, Suite 850, Boston, MA 02210
Phone: 617 368-5000   **Fax:** 617 368-5500
Web: www.bostonbeer.com

PRODUCTS/OPERATIONS

Selected Brands and Year Introduced

Barrel Room Collection
  Samuel Adams American Kriek 2009
  Samuel Adams New World Tripel 2009
  Samuel Adams Stony Brook Red 2009
  Samuel Adams Thirteenth Hour 2011
Brewmaster's Collection
  Samuel Adams Black Lager 2005
  Samuel Adams Blackberry Witbier 2009
  Samuel Adams Boston Ale 1987
  Samuel Adams Cherry Wheat 1995
  Samuel Adams Coastal Wheat 2009
  Samuel Adams Cranberry Lambic 1990
  Samuel Adams Cream Stout 1993
  Samuel Adams Irish Red 2008
  Samuel Adams Latitude 48 IPA 2010
  Samuel Adams Pale Ale 1999
Core Focus Beers
  Samuel Adams Boston Lager 1984
  Sam Adams Light 2001
Flavored Malt Beverages
  Twisted Tea Backyard Batch Hard Iced Tea 2009
  Twisted Tea Half Hard Iced Tea & Half Hard Lemonade 2003
  Twisted Tea Hard Iced Tea 2001
  Twisted Tea Light Hard Iced Tea 2007
  Twisted Tea Peach Hard Iced Tea 2005
  Twisted Tea Raspberry Hard Iced Tea 2001
  Twisted Tea Blueberry Hard Iced Tea 2011
Hard Cider
  Angry Orchard Apple Ginger 2011
  HardCore Crisp Hard Cider 1997
Imperial Series
  Samuel Adams Double Bock 1988
  Samuel Adams Imperial Stout 2009
  Samuel Adams Imperial White 2009
  Samuel Adams Wee Heavy 2011
Limited Edition Beers
  Infinium 2010
  Samuel Adams Utopias 2001
Seasonal Beers
  Samuel Adams Octoberfest 1989
  Samuel Adams Summer Ale 1996
  Samuel Adams Winter Lager 1989
  Samuel Adams Alpine Spring 2011

COMPETITORS

Anchor Brewers	Michigan Brewing
Anheuser-Busch InBev	MillerCoors
Asahi Breweries	New Belgium Brewing
Bacardi	Pabst
Carlsberg	Pyramid Breweries
Craft Brew Alliance	Rogue Ales
Diageo	Shipyard Brewing
Grupo Modelo	Company
Heineken	Sprecher
Kirin Brewery of America	Stoudt's Brewing
	Victory Brewing
Lancaster Brewing Co.	Weyerbacher Brewing
Lion Brewery	

HISTORICAL FINANCIALS

Company Type: Public

Income Statement

FYE: December 28

	REVENUE ($ mil.)	NET INCOME ($ mil.)	NET PROFIT MARGIN	EMPLOYEES
12/13	739.0	70.3	9.5%	1,120
12/12	580.2	59.4	10.2%	950
12/11	513.0	66.0	12.9%	840
12/10	463.8	50.1	10.8%	780
12/09	415.0	31.1	7.5%	780
Annual Growth	15.5%	22.6%	—	9.5%

2013 Year-End Financials

Debt ratio: 0.1%	No. of shares (mil.): 12
Return on equity: 25.8%	Dividends
Cash ($ mil.): 49	Yield: —
Current ratio: 1.57	Payout: —
Long-term debt ($ mil.): 0	Market value ($ mil.): 3,086

	STOCK PRICE ($) FY Close	P/E High/Low		PER SHARE ($) Earnings	Dividends	Book Value
12/13	242.10	47	24	5.18	0.00	23.70
12/12	132.98	30	21	4.39	0.00	19.13
12/11	108.56	22	14	4.81	0.00	14.41
12/10	97.91	27	12	3.52	0.00	12.36
12/09	46.81	21	8	2.17	0.00	12.15
Annual Growth	50.8%	—	—	24.3%	—	18.2%

Boulder Brands Inc

Walking a nutrition tightrope? Boulder Brands (formerly Smart Balance) may help; its growing portfolio of food brands target the health conscious and those with health problems such as diabetes and glutin allergies. The company makes Smart Balance buttery spreads and other alternative food products including peanut butter popcorn and cooking oils. As the company has grown its Smart Balance business has been outweighed by its Natural foods segment including the Glutino and Gluten-Free Pantry Udi's Earth Balance and the EVOL brands of shelf-stable and frozen products. Boulder Brands' products are sold by food retailers throughout North America. Founded in 2005 the company became Boulder Brands in 2013.

Geographic Reach

Boulder-based Boulder Brands rings up nearly 90% of its sales in the US.

Financial Performance

Boulder Brands reported sales of $461.3 million in 2013 a 25% increase versus 2012. The double-digit gain was driven by increased sales of products in the company's Natural segment partially offset by declining Smart Balance sales. Net income increased a robust 148% over the same period to $10.4 million on higher sales lower marketing and other operating expenses related to restructuring acquisitions and integration-related costs.

Strategy

Fast-growing Boulder Brands has diversified its brand portfolio through acquisitions. Following its 2012 purchase of Udi's Healthy Foods the company changed its name from Smart Balance to Boulder Brands in January 2013 and relocated its corporate headquarters to Boulder Colorado in the summer. The name change is meant to reflect the company's multibrand focus following the acquisition of Udi's a maker of gluten-free bread and bakery products in mid-2012. The firm established two operating segments: Smart Balance (spreads butter grocery and milk); and Natural comprised of Earth Balance Glutino and Udi's branded products.

Since changing its name and moving to Boulder the company has continued its active acquisition schedule adding health-related food companies to its portfolio of products. Also it wound down its Bestlife spreads business although it retains a health and wellness subscription-based website (bestlife.com) under the Bestlife name.

The company has adopted a strategy to increase brand awareness through acquisition and diversification into new high-growth natural brands. To that end it has formed Boulder Brands Investment Group to target early-stage growth companies in the natural and organic food and beverage industries.

Mergers and Acquisitions

In December 2013 Boulder Brands acquired EVOL Foods from owner Phil's Fresh for about $48.9 million. Based in Boulder EVOL Foods makes and markets frozen foods that are antibiotic- hormone- and GMO-free and have no artificial preservatives or flavors. In July 2013 the company bought an 80% stake in GlucoBrands LLC the owner of Level Life foods for $2.4 million. (It has the right to acquire the remaining 20% beginning 2016.) Level Life makes diabetic-friendly convenience foods for the daily management of diabetes.

Spying the rapidly rising gluten-free food aisle in mid-2012 the company acquired $60-million-in-sales Udi's Healthy Foods for $125 million in cash from Hubson Acquisition (an affiliate of buyout specialist E&A Industries) and the family of founder Udi Bar-on and other minority stakeholders. Denver-based Udi's is primarily known for gluten-free bread and bakery products. A year earlier Boulder Brands took over another albeit smaller gluten-free foods purveyor Canada-based Glutino Food Group for $66.3 million. Glutino makes and sells premium-priced gluten-free snacks frozen baked goods and entrees and baking mixes. Both deals extend the company's footprint in the retail market and food service outlets as well as its distribution reach into Canada formerly a less significant market. Glutino's addition also bolts on one of only a few manufacturing facilities in North America that exclusively make gluten-free products.

EXECUTIVES

Chairman and CEO, Stephen B. (Steve) Hughes, age 60, $710,500 total compensation
President and COO, Terry Schulke, $375,000 total compensation
CFO and Treasurer, Christine Sacco, age 39
Senior Vice President Sales Services, Howard Seiferas
Senior Vice President Of Business Development, Carole Buyers
Vice President And General Manager, Howard Lazar
Vice President And General Manager, Jason Berry
Chairman and CEO, Stephen B. (Steve) Hughes, age 60

LOCATIONS

HQ: Boulder Brands Inc
1600 Pearl Street, Suite 300, Boulder, CO 80302
Phone: 303 652-0521
Web: www.boulderbrands.com

2013 Sales

	$ mil.	% of total
US	412.4	89
Foreign	48.9	11
Total	**461.3**	**100**

PRODUCTS/OPERATIONS

2013 Sales

	$ mil.	% of total
Natural	285.0	62
Smart Balance	176.3	38
Total	**461.3**	**100**

Selected Brands and Products

Bestlife
Earth Balance spreads
EVOL Foods
Glutino and Gluten-Free Pantry
Level Life
Nucoa spread
Smart Balance
  Buttery Spreads Sticks and Sprays
  Cooking Oil
  Cooking Sprays
  Enhanced Milks
  Omega Plus Light Mayonnaise
  Peanut Butters
  Popcorn
Udi' s Gluten Free Foods

COMPETITORS

Annie' s Inc.
ConAgra
Crystal Farms Refrigerated Distribution Company
Dairy Farmers of America
Dean Foods
Galaxy Nutritional Foods
Hain Celestial
Land O' Lakes
Lifeway Foods
Mondelez International
Smucker
Spectrum Organic Products
Unilever
Ventura Foods

HISTORICAL FINANCIALS

Company Type: Public

Income Statement

FYE: December 31

	REVENUE ($ mil.)	NET INCOME ($ mil.)	NET PROFIT MARGIN	EMPLOYEES
12/13	461.3	10.4	2.3%	720
12/12	369.6	4.2	1.1%	613
12/11	274.3	9.6	3.5%	203
12/10	241.9	(128.1)	—	69
12/09	239.5	3.4	1.4%	73
Annual Growth	17.8%	31.7%	—	77.2%

2013 Year-End Financials

Debt ratio: 38.2%
Return on equity: 3.0%
Cash ($ mil.): 16
Current ratio: 1.63
Long-term debt ($ mil.): 292

No. of shares (mil.): 60
Dividends
  Yield: —
  Payout: —
Market value ($ mil.): 955

	STOCK PRICE ($) FY Close	P/E High/Low	PER SHARE ($) Earnings	Dividends	Book Value
12/13	15.86	103 49	0.17	0.00	5.89
12/12	12.90	195 72	0.07	0.00	5.64
12/11	5.36	43 25	0.16	0.00	5.46
12/10	4.33	— —	(2.08)	0.00	5.23
12/09	6.00	139 81	0.06	0.00	7.04
Annual Growth	27.5%	— —	29.7%	—	(4.3%)

Bridge Capital Holdings

Bridge Capital Holdings helps its business clients get from here to there. It is the holding company of Bridge Bank which caters to small midsized and emerging businesses in California's Silicon Valley and San Francisco Bay area. The bank has re-gional branches in Palo Alto and San Jose; it also has Small Business Administration (SBA) loan production offices in Pleasanton and San Francisco. Additional SBA offices are located in Irvine California; Dallas; Boston; and Reston Virginia. The bank also has groups devoted to technology banking IPO services and international banking. Its Bridge Capital Finance unit provides factoring and asset-based lending services.

Operations

In addition to its specialized business services Bridge Bank also offers traditional retail services such as checking and savings accounts credit and debit cards home equity and improvement loans and auto loans. It finances residential and commercial construction projects as well.

Geographic Reach

Bridge Capital operates loan production offices in San Francisco Palo Alto Pleasanton and Newport Beach California as well as in Dallas and Boston and in Reston Virginia.

Financial Performance

In 2013 Bridge Capital reported a 12% revenue increase from $76 million to $85 million as a result of growth in its loan department. That growth lead to a 7% improvement in net income from $14 million to $15 million as cash flow held steady.

Strategy

Bridge Capital has been growing by expanding its network of loan offices to increase its loan portfolio. It has moved into San Francisco and Boston in recent years to offer more loans to more companies. Increasing overall revenue mostly tied to loan growth shows the strategy is working.

EXECUTIVES

Evp And Senior Loan Officer Bridge Bank, Lori Edwards
Evp And Sba Manager Sba Lending And Commercial Mortgage Banking Bridge Bank, Ralph W Barnett
Svp And Group Manager Capital Finance Group Bridge Bank, Lee A Shodiss
Evp And Manager International Banking Group, Jeannie Kao
Svp And Information Systems Manager Bridge Bank, John P Peckham
Svp And Market Manager Specialty Markets Bridge Bank, Jeff Whalen
Svp And Market Manager Technology Banking Group Bridge Bank, Paul E Gibson
Svp And Regional Sales Manager Sba Lending And Commercial Mortgage Banking Bridge Bank, Kenneth (Ken) Mannina
Svp And Credit Administration Officer Administration And Support Services Bridge Bank, George S Schmidt
Vp And Branch Services Manager Commercial Banking San Jose Bridge Bank, Manju Kamboj
Svp And Note Department Manager Bridge Bank, Linda Michaels
Svp And Operations And Documentation Manager Administration And Support Services Bridge Bank, Shelly Medina
Vp And Sba Note Department Manager Sba Lending And Commercial Mortgage Banking Bridge Bank, Barbara Johnson
Vice President Vendor Relationship Manager Vice President, Brian Simonson
Svp And Construction Loan Officer Bridge Bank, Kimberly Rysyk
Vp And Team Leader Commercial Banking San Jose Bridge Bank, Martin Kriegler
President and CEO, Daniel P. (Dan) Myers, age 53, $400,000 total compensation
CFO; Chief Risk Officer and Chief Strategy Officer Bridge Bank, Thomas A. Sa, age 52, $255,000 total compensation
EVP and COO, Timothy W. (Tim) Boothe, age 48, $230,000 total compensation
EVP and Chief Credit Officer, Allen (Al) Williams, $200,000 total compensation
EVP and Chief Banking Officer, Margaret Bradshaw, $200,000 total compensation
Senior Vice President Accounting & Financial Reporting Officer, Debra Bradford
Senior Vice President Manager, Tom Hoffman
Vice President Team Leader, Anthony Crisci
Senior Vice President Credit Administration Officer, Sarah Gill
Vice President Team Leader, Kelly McRitchie
Vice President Depository Services Officer, Bella Betsayad
Vice President Of Business Development, Joe Baker
Vice President Manager East Bay, Ryan Banta
Vice President Manager San, Melinda Clifford
Vice President Manager East Bay, Brian Schwarer
Senior Vice President Team Leader, Scott Reising
Senior Vice President Business Development Officer, Steven Chaker
Svp-market Mgr San Francisco, Bob D'Acquisto
Vice President Manager Domestic Funds Transfer, Alicia Lopez
Senior Vice President Manager, Larry Lacroix
Vice President Team Leader, Darla Auchinachie
Vice President Treasury Management Services Officer, Maha Banoub
Svp San Francisco Technology, Joel Gragg
Svp-southern Ca Region, Caroline Harkins
Svp And Controller Bridge Bank, Cathe Franklin
Chairman, Allan C. Kramer, age 77
Auditors: VavrinekTrineDay&Co.LLP

LOCATIONS

HQ: Bridge Capital Holdings
55 Almaden Boulevard, San Jose, CA 95113
Phone: 408 423-8500
Web: www.bridgebank.com
Boston
Dallas
Newport Beach
Palo Alto
Pleasanton
Reston
San Francisco
San Jose

PRODUCTS/OPERATIONS

2013 Sales

	$ mil.	% of total
Interest		
Loans	64.6	76
Investment securities and other	6.2	7
Noninterest		
Service charges on deposit accounts	3.7	4
International fee income	2.7	3
Gain on sale of SBA loans	2.7	3
Warrant income	1.2	1
Other	4.0	6
Total	85.1	100

Selected Services

Debit & Credit Cards
International Banking
Lending
Merchant Services
Online Services
Treasury Management

COMPETITORS

Bank of America   SVB Financial

Bank of the West
Comerica
Heritage Commerce

Tech CU
Wells Fargo

HISTORICAL FINANCIALS

Company Type: Public

Income Statement

FYE: December 31

	ASSETS ($ mil.)	NET INCOME ($ mil.)	INCOME AS % OF ASSETS	EMPLOYEES
12/13	1,604.1	14.7	0.9%	235
12/12	1,343.5	13.8	1.0%	207
12/11	1,161.0	7.8	0.7%	193
12/10	1,029.7	2.5	0.3%	170
12/09	844.0	1.4	0.2%	164
Annual Growth	17.4%	78.9%	—	9.4%

2013 Year-End Financials

Return on assets: 1.0%
Return on equity: 9.5%
Long-term debt ($ mil.): —
No. of shares (mil.): 15
Sales ($ mil): 85

Dividends
Yield: —
Payout: —
Market value ($ mil.): 326

	STOCK PRICE ($) FY Close	P/E High/Low	PER SHARE ($) Earnings	Dividends	Book Value
12/13	20.54	21 13	0.97	0.00	10.26
12/12	15.56	17 11	0.92	0.00	9.32
12/11	10.40	22 16	0.52	0.00	8.55
12/10	8.70	192114	0.06	0.00	9.81
12/09	7.25	— —	(0.42)	0.00	15.40
Annual Growth	29.7%	— —	—	—	(9.7%)

Bridgepoint Education, Inc.

Bridgepoint Education invites students from all walks of life to cross on over to the higher-education side. The for-profit company offers some 1400 courses and about 85 graduate and undergraduate degree programs online and at its bricks-and-mortar campuses: Ashford University in Iowa and University of the Rockies in Colorado. Academic disciplines include education business psychology and health and social sciences. Most of the company's campus-based revenues are derived from federal financial aid. About 99% of Bridgepoint Education's more than 90000 students are enrolled exclusively online.

Much like a community college Bridgepoint appeals to students who might find tuition costs credit transfer or work schedules to be barriers to attending traditional universities. Bridgepoint tries to remove those barriers by accepting a maximum number of prior credits to ease transferability by continuously expanding its online course offerings to increase accessibility and by structuring the price of its tuition to fall below Title IV loan limits so most students can afford to attend its schools. Title IV loans such as Stafford loans and Pell grants are generally easier to obtain than private loans and carry lower fixed interest rates. In 2011 both Ashford University and the University of the Rockies derived about 85% of their revenues from Title IV programs.

However Ashford University and University of the Rockies have been facing scrutiny over compliance issues from government agencies including the US Department of Education and two regional accreditation commissions that could put their administration of Title IV funds at risk. The difficulties come as online universities have increasingly been put under the magnifying glass by officials and are being required to enact extra academic integrity initiatives (such as changes in compensation policies and the enactment of student preparedness programs) to meet new regulatory standards. As a result of these changes as well as bad publicity related to government scrutiny of the industry Bridgepoint Education saw a downturn in new student enrollments during the second half of 2011.

Despite its troubles Bridgepoint Education's overall enrollment levels have grown exponentially in recent years including an 11% increase in 2011 causing the company to experience a coinciding rise in revenues. In 2011 for instance sales increase more than 30% to some $933 million and net income rose 35% to $173 million. The firm attributes much of its success to an increase in admissions staff and online advertising as well as to strong student satisfaction levels and its ability to balance operational costs as its revenue has grown.

Bridgepoint bases its growth strategy on expanding its academic offerings to attract more students. It identifies new programs by listening to student and faculty feedback as well as by researching macro market trends to identify which job areas will experience demand in coming years and introducing programs to educate students in those fields (such as health care and education).

In addition the firm enhances its technology capabilities to increase the quality and affordability of its programs. It introduced its proprietary Constellation platform in 2010 which allows students to access digital learning materials and textbooks from a variety of mobile devices. To enhance the Constellation platform it added the Thuze cloud-based collaborative learning environment in 2012.

The company also seeks to increase its student base by offering special programs for corporate employees and military personnel. Both of Bridgepoint's universities work with employers offering education reimbursement programs and Ashford University also offers educational opportunities to active-duty personnel and veterans of US armed forces branches with special tuition rates waived fees and free books and shipping costs. Nearly 20% of its students are with the military.

Warburg Pincus owns about two-thirds of the company. CEO and president Andrew Clark owns a 5% stake in Bridgepoint Education which he founded in 2004 with the assistance of other executives of the company and the backing of Warburg Pincus.

HISTORY

Ashford University was founded in 1918 as Mount St. Clare College by the Sisters of St. Francis. It became The Franciscan University in 2002 and was purchased in 2005 by Bridgepoint Education which changed the university's name. In 2007 Bridgepoint acquired University of the Rockies (formerly Colorado School of Professional Psychology) which focuses on offering graduate degrees in psychology.

Hoping to take advantage of the growing market for online and nontraditional schools the company went public in 2009. The IPO filing came on the heels of the public offerings of other education companies China Distance Education Holdings and

Grand Canyon Education. Bridgepoint raised roughly $141 million in its IPO; proceeds went to the company's investors as well as towards general corporate purposes. Principal investor Warburg Pincus retained majority ownership of Bridgepoint's shares after the IPO.

EXECUTIVES

Chief Financial Officer Executive Vp, Anthony J (Tony) Park, age 49
Vice President And President University, Charlita Shelton
President and CEO, Andrew S. Clark, age 48, $600,000 total compensation
EVP and CFO, Daniel J. Devine, age 49, $365,000 total compensation
EVP External Affairs and Chief Academic Officer, Jane McAuliffe, age 46, $330,000 total compensation
EVP and Chief Marketing Officer, Ross L. Woodard, age 47, $216,000 total compensation
EVP and Chief Administrative Officer, Rodney T. (Rocky) Sheng, age 47, $380,000 total compensation
EVP and CIO, Thomas (Tom) Ashbrook, age 48
EVP Strategy and Corporate Development, Douglas C. Abts
Executive Vice P, Brent Bickett
Vice President Vp, Kim Pham
Vice President Vp, Melissa Schulze
Vice President Vp, Natalie De Witte
Vice President Data Analytics, Jack Phadungtin
Named Vice President And Senior, Robert Wernli
Vice President Vp, Steve Wainwright
Vice President Vp, Judy Kwan
Associate Vice President Editor In, Erik Evans
Vice President Vp, Kenya Wilson
Vice President Vp, Lacy Stewart
Associate Vice President Of Investor, Paul Goodson
Chairman, Patrick T. Hackett, age 52
Senior Vice President Treasurer, Daniel K Murphy
Auditors: PricewaterhouseCoopersLLP

LOCATIONS

HQ: Bridgepoint Education, Inc.
13500 Evening Creek Drive North, San Diego, CA 92128
Phone: 858 668-2586
Web: www.bridgepointeducation.com

PRODUCTS/OPERATIONS

2013 Enrollment by Degree Type

No.		% of total
Bachelor's	49634	78
Master's	8377	13
Associate's	4182	7
Doctoral	919	1
Other	512	1
Total	**63624**	**100**

Selected Programs

Associate of Arts
  Business
Bachelor of Applied Science
  Accounting
  Computer
  Computer Graphic Design Core
Bachelor of Arts
  Accounting
  Business Administration
  Communication Studies
  Education
  Health Care Administration
  Liberal Arts
  Political Science and Government
  Psychology
  Social and Criminal Justice
  Social Science
  Sociology

Visual Arts
Bachelor of Science
  Biology
  Clinical Cytotechnology
  Health Science Administration
  Natural Science
Doctorate
  Psychology
Master of Arts
  Education
  Organizational Management
  Psychology
  Teaching and Learning with Technology
Master of Business Administration
Master of Public Administration

COMPETITORS

American Public Education
Apollo Education
Capella Education
Career Education
Corinthian Colleges
DeVry Education Group
Education Management
Grand Canyon Education
ITT Educational
International Scholarship and Tuition Services
Laureate Education
Lincoln Educational Services
Strayer Education

HISTORICAL FINANCIALS

Company Type: Public

Income Statement

FYE: December 31

	REVENUE ($ mil.)	NET INCOME ($ mil.)	NET PROFIT MARGIN	EMPLOYEES
12/13	768.6	41.0	5.3%	4,620
12/12	968.1	127.9	13.2%	5,620
12/11	933.3	172.7	18.5%	8,900
12/10	713.2	127.5	17.9%	3,000
12/09	454.3	47.1	10.4%	5,795
Annual Growth	14.0%	(3.4%)	—	(5.5%)

2013 Year-End Financials

Debt ratio: —
Return on equity: 9.7%
Cash ($ mil.): 249
Current ratio: 1.98
Long-term debt ($ mil.): —
No. of shares (mil.): 44
Dividends
  Yield: —
  Payout: —
Market value ($ mil.): 793

	STOCK PRICE ($) FY Close	P/E High/Low	PER SHARE ($) Earnings	Dividends	Book Value
12/13	17.71	27 13	0.74	0.00	7.77
12/12	10.30	11 3	2.29	0.00	9.17
12/11	23.00	9 5	3.02	0.00	6.84
12/10	19.00	12 5	2.14	0.00	4.51
12/09	15.02	25 12	0.74	0.00	2.48
Annual Growth	4.2%	— —	(0.0%)	—	33.0%

Brookline Bancorp Inc (DE)

Brookline Bancorp is the holding company for Brookline Bank Bank Rhode Island (BankRI) and First Ipswich Bank (formerly The First National Bank of Ipswich) which together operate more than 45 full-service branches in eastern Massachusetts and Rhode Island. Commercial and multifamily mortgages backed by real estate such as apartments condominiums and office buildings account for the largest portion of the company's loan portfolio followed by indirect auto loans commercial loans and consumer loans. Established in 1997 as Brookline Savings Bank the bank went public five years later and changed its name to Brookline Bank in 2003. Brookline Bancorp. has expanded by acquiring other regional banks.

Geographic Reach

Boston-based Brookline Bancorp operates 47 full-service branches in greater Boston and greater Providence Rhode Island.

Operations

The holding company also provides indirect automobile loans through Brookline Bank and equipment financing through its Eastern Funding and Macrolease Corp. subsidiaries. Eastern Funding LLC a majority-owned firm with more than $1 billion in in direct loans that specializes in financing coin-operated laundry dry cleaning and convenience store equipment in the New York City metropolitan area.

Financial Performance

The multi-bank holding company has $5.3 billion in assets. In 2013 Brookline Bancorp reported net income of $35.4 million compared with $37.1 million in 2012. Net earnings from operations were $36 million in 2013 compared to $41.1 million for 2012.

Strategy

Brookline has grown from a sleepy suburban community savings bank to a publicly-traded commercial lender with loan volumes that put it among Massachusetts' top banks. As it transitions to a commercial bank Brookline has also been growing geographically through acquisitions.

Mergers and Acquisitions

In January 2012 Brookline acquired Providence-headquartered Bancorp Rhode Island for $234 million in cash and stock adding 18 BankRI branches in that state. BankRI retained its brand and operates as a subsidiary of Brookline Bancorp.

In February 2011 it acquired The First National Bank of Ipswich a six-branch bank serving Massachusetts' North Shore. The $19.7 million transaction gave First National Bank of Ipswich a much-needed boost as that bank had been struggling with loan losses during the recession. It also expanded Brookline Bancorp's market area as there was no overlap between the two banks.

Brookline Bancorp's board rejected a takeover offer by an unnamed suitor in early 2010. Two directors had voted to accept the bid however including former longtime chairman Richard Chapman. Both resigned in the aftermath of the vote.

EXECUTIVES

President and CEO, Paul A. Perrault, age 63, $675,000 total compensation
COO, James M. Cosman, $250,000 total compensation
President and CEO Bank Rhode Island, Mark J. Meiklejohn, $310,000 total compensation
Chief Risk Officer General Counsel and Secretary, Michael W. McCurdy
Chief Credit Officer, M. Robert Rose, $272,000 total compensation
President and CEO The First National Bank of Ipswich, Russell G. Cole
CFO, Carl M. Carlson
Vice President Senior Operations, Joe Beck
Chairman, Joseph J. Slotnik, age 78
Auditors: KPMGLLP

LOCATIONS

HQ: Brookline Bancorp Inc (DE)
  131 Clarendon Street, Boston, MA 02117-9179
Phone: 617 425-4600
Web: www.brooklinebank.com

COMPETITORS

Bank of America	Eastern Bank
Boston Private	Sovereign Bank
Central Bancorp	TD Bank USA
Century Bancorp (MA)	
Citizens Financial Group	

HISTORICAL FINANCIALS

Company Type: Public

Income Statement

FYE: December 31

	ASSETS ($ mil.)	NET INCOME ($ mil.)	INCOME AS % OF ASSETS	EMPLOYEES
12/13	5,325.1	35.3	0.7%	720
12/12	5,147.5	37.1	0.7%	662
12/11	3,299.0	27.6	0.8%	358
12/10	2,720.5	26.8	1.0%	266
12/09	2,615.8	19.2	0.7%	245
Annual Growth	19.4%	16.5%	—	30.9%

2013 Year-End Financials

Return on assets: 0.6%
Return on equity: 5.7%
Long-term debt ($ mil.): —
No. of shares (mil.): 70
Sales ($ mil): 220
Dividends
  Yield: 3.5%
  Payout: 59.6%
Market value ($ mil.): 674

	STOCK PRICE ($) FY Close	P/E High/Low	PER SHARE ($) Earnings	Dividends	Book Value
12/13	9.55	20 16	0.51	0.34	8.70
12/12	8.50	18 14	0.53	0.34	8.70
12/11	8.44	24 15	0.47	0.34	8.50
12/10	10.85	25 19	0.46	0.34	8.39
12/09	9.91	37 23	0.33	0.54	8.26
Annual Growth	(0.9%)	— —	11.5%	(10.9%)	1.3%

Bruker Corp

The life sciences research field likes to put Bruker's equipment to the test. The company makes an array of scientific analysis instruments for pharmaceutical biotech industrial academic and government customers through four business units. Its Bruker MAT unit manufactures a portfolio of X-ray analysis products while Bruker CALID makes mass spectrometry equipment and chromatography instruments used for chemical testing and CBRNE detection. Bruker Energy & Supercon Technologies (BEST) offers superconducting systems and magnetic devices used in medical imaging and energy research. The company also makes magnetic resonance equipment through Bruker BioSpin. Bruker is owned by the Laukien family.

IPO

In 2010 the company's BEST subsidiary announced plans to go public through a $100 million IPO with proceeds going toward R&D and production expansion efforts as well as repaying loans to its parent company. Bruker would have remained the majority shareholder of BEST; however the IPO was delayed in 2011 and withdrawn in 2012 due to poor market conditions.

Geographic Reach

Bruker operates major manufacturing plants and technology centers in North America Europe and Japan. It also maintains a direct sales network in these operation regions and it markets its products through independent representatives and wholesale distributors in smaller markets.

Operations

The company operates through four business units: Bruker MAT a manufacturer of X-ray analysis products; Bruker CALID which makes mass spectrometry equipment and chromatography instruments; Bruker Energy & Supercon Technologies a manufacturer of superconducting systems and magnetic devices; and Bruker BioSpin which makes magnetic resonance equipment.

Sales and Marketing

Bruker maintains a direct sales network in its primary operation regions and it markets its products through independent representatives and wholesale distributors in smaller markets. It targets customers in the pharmaceutical biotechnology proteomics molecular diagnostics industrial agricultural government and academic sectors. Its advertising expenses were $7.5 million during fiscal year 2012.

Financial Performance

Bruker's revenue was up 8.5% in 2012 over 2011. Overall its revenue growth has been on the rise in recent years due to organic growth and acquisitions. The company's net income which has fluctuated in recent years with changes in acquisition-related expenses was up 16% in 2012.

Strategy

Bruker's growth strategy includes ramping up sales in emerging markets like Asia and pursing strategic acquisitions that enable it to sell in new markets and expand and build on its product offerings.

Mergers and Acquisitions

Bruker bolstered its X-ray analysis product offerings with the 2012 acquisition of X-ray analysis equipment maker Hecus X-Ray GmbH. The company also enhanced its imaging technologies business the same year after acquiring SkyScan N.V. a manufacturer of tomography systems for 3D X-ray imaging technologies.

Ownership

Frank Laukien and his brothers and fellow company executives Dirk Laukien and J rg Laukien together own more than 35% of Bruker.

Company Background

The company was formed in 2008 through the combination of several entities controlled by the Laukien family. Through the transaction publicly traded Bruker (then named Bruker BioSciences which held the AXS Daltonics and Optics units) purchased Bruker BioSpin a private company owned by the Laukiens in a cash and stock deal worth more than $900 million.

EXECUTIVES

Vice President For Nmr Applications And Training, Clemens Anklin
Vice President, Ulli Giessman
Vice President Life Science Sales, Ian Sanders
Chairman President and CEO, Frank H. Laukien, age 55, $547,562 total compensation
EVP and CFO, Charles F. (Charlie) Wagner, age 46, $490,631 total compensation
President Bruker Nano Inc., Mark R. Munch, $380,000 total compensation

President Bruker CALID Group, Juergen Srega, $371,896 total compensation
President Bruker BioSpin Group, Thomas W. Bachmann
Assistant Vice President Sales, Victor Fursey
Vice President - Finance; Chief Accounting Officer, Michael Knell
Vice President Process Technology, John Richmond
Vice President Compensation Benefits And Human Resources Technology Hris, Justin Fossbender
Chief Information Officer Chief Technology Officer Vice President Information Technology, Ken Ribeiro
Vice President Sales And Marketing, Ramaswami Ramanathan
Vice President Sales, Art Heiss, age 71
Secretary And Director, Richard M Stein, age 63
Chairman President and CEO, Frank H. Laukien, age 55
Auditors: Ernst&YoungLLP

LOCATIONS

HQ: Bruker Corp
40 Manning Road, Billerica, MA 01821
Phone: 978 663-3660
Web: www.bruker.com

2012 Sales

	$ mil.	% of total
Europe	706	39
Asia Pacific	570.6	32
US	377	21
Other regions & countries	137.4	8
Total	1791.4	100

PRODUCTS/OPERATIONS

2012 Sales

	$ mil.	% of total
Scientific instruments (BioSpin CALID & MAT)	1666.1	93
Energy & Supercon Technologies	136.2	7
Adjustments	(10.9)	-
Total	1791.4	100

COMPETITORS

ABB	PANalytical
AMETEK	PerkinElmer
Affymetrix	Renishaw
Agilent Technologies	Sequenom
Danaher	Shimadzu
GE Healthcare	Smiths Detection
Hitachi Medical	Sumitomo
Systems America	Thales
JEOL	Thermo Fisher
Mettler-Toledo	Scientific
Mitsubishi Electric	Toshiba
Olympus	Waters Corp.
Oxford Instruments	Zygo

HISTORICAL FINANCIALS

Company Type: Public

Income Statement

FYE: December 31

	REVENUE ($ mil.)	NET INCOME ($ mil.)	NET PROFIT MARGIN	EMPLOYEES
12/13	1,839.4	80.1	4.4%	6,200
12/12	1,791.4	77.5	4.3%	6,400
12/11	1,651.7	92.3	5.6%	6,000
12/10	1,304.9	95.4	7.3%	5,400
12/09	1,114.5	81.2	7.3%	4,500
Annual Growth	13.3%	(0.3%)	—	8.3%

2013 Year-End Financials

Debt ratio: 17.8%
Return on equity: 10.3%
Cash ($ mil.): 438
Current ratio: 2.21
Long-term debt ($ mil.): 354
No. of shares (mil.): 167
Dividends
Yield: —
Payout: —
Market value ($ mil.): 3,313

	STOCK PRICE ($) FY Close	P/E High/Low		Earnings	PER SHARE ($) Dividends	Book Value
12/13	19.77	44	32	0.48	0.00	5.05
12/12	15.24	35	24	0.46	0.00	4.24
12/11	12.42	38	21	0.55	0.00	3.75
12/10	16.60	30	19	0.58	0.00	3.18
12/09	12.06	25	7	0.49	0.00	2.54
Annual Growth	13.2%	—	—	(0.5%)	—	18.8%

Buffalo Wild Wings Inc

Hot sauce fuels the flight of this restaurateur. Buffalo Wild Wings (BWW) operates a chain of about 900 Buffalo Wild Wings Grill & Bar quick-casual dining spots that specialize in serving Buffalo-style chicken wings. The eateries found in about 40 states offer more than a dozen unique dipping sauces to go with the spicy wings as well as a complement of other items such as chicken tenders and legs. BWW's menu also features appetizers burgers tacos salads and desserts along with beer wine and other beverages. The company owns and operates more than 380 of the restaurants while the rest are operated by franchisees.

Geographic Reach

Buffalo Wild Wings has locations across 49 states in the US as well as in Canada. The majority of the company's restaurants are located in California Illinois Indiana Michigan Ohio and Texas. Many BWW locations are found in suburban areas typically near established retail and entertainment developments.

Operations

Typical in the casual dining industry the BWW chain comprises a mix of corporate-run and franchised locations. Its large estate of owned and operated eateries accounts for the greatest share of the company's sales (about 93% in fiscal 2012) and allows it to maintain control over the Buffalo Wild Wings dining experience while its franchising efforts help expand the chain with fewer construction and operating costs.

Food and nonalcoholic beverages accounted for about 78% of restaurant sales in fiscal 2012. The remaining 22% of restaurant sales was from alcoholic beverages.

Sales and Marketing

The BWW concept is designed to appeal to a broad mix of customers but the chain promotes itself as a place for groups and families to gather and watch sporting events. (Some locations have as many as 50 TV screens to give everyone a good view of the big game.)

Local franchise operators such as Michigan-based Diversified Restaurant Holdings typically pay the company royalties and other fees in order to use the Buffalo Wild Wings brand and marketing.

BWW competes broadly against other casual dining chains such as Applebee's and T.G.I. Friday's (owned by Carlson Restaurants Worldwide) but within its target audience the chain faces competition from Dave & Buster's the Fox & Hound chain of sports bars and of course Hooters.

Financial Performance

The company's revenue increased by 33% to $1.04 billion in fiscal 2012 up from $784 million in fiscal 2011 while its profits grow by 14% in fiscal 2012 compared to fiscal 2011. The spikes were powered by growth in both its Restaurant sales and Franchise royalties and fees.

Restaurant sales increased by 35% due to a $182.7 million increase associated with 69 company-owned restaurants that opened or acquired in 2012. A same-store sales increase of 7% accounted for $41.6 million of the increase in restaurant sales. Franchise royalties and fees increased by 14% primarily due to royalties related to additional sales at 12 more franchised restaurants in operation at the end of the period compared to prior year and an increase in same-store sales for franchised restaurants of 7% in 2012.

Strategy

The company is working toward the goal of eventually reaching about 1500 locations with plans calling for corporate-owned restaurants to make up about 40% of the chain. BWW opened its first international location in Toronto Canada in 2011 and plans to have 50 Canadian outposts of the restaurant up and running by 2016.

Company Background

Jim Disbrow and Scott Lowery opened the first Buffalo Wild Wings restaurant on the campus of Ohio State University in Columbus in 1982. (Legend has it that they started the eatery because they craved the style of chicken wings they had eaten in Buffalo New York.) Originally called Buffalo Wild Wings & Weck (a reference to the Kimmelweck brand rolls used for sandwiches) the chain became known as BW3 for short. Rapid expansion and financial mismanagement pushed Buffalo Wild Wings to the brink of bankruptcy by the mid-1990s. Sally Smith became CEO in 1996 and helped retool the chain's branding strategy to appeal more to families and non-students.

EXECUTIVES

Senior Vice President Franchise And Development, Mounir N (Mo) Sawda, age 58

EVP CFO and Treasurer, Mary J. Twinem, age 54, $375,000 total compensation

President CEO and Director, Sally J. Smith, age 57, $585,000 total compensation

EVP and President North America Buffalo Wild Wings, Judith A. (Judy) Shoulak, age 55, $330,000 total compensation

EVP Chief Strategy Officer and Business Development, Kathleen M. (Kathy) Benning, age 52, $285,000 total compensation

COO, James M. Schmidt, age 55, $375,000 total compensation

Vice President Of Marketing, Bob Ruhland

Executive Vice President, Craig W Donoghue

Vice President Food And Beverage, Andrew Dismore

Vice President Financial Planning And Analysis, Ben Nelsen

Vice President Information Technology, Karen Bird

Vice President Technology Operations, Chad Anderson

Vice President Marketing, Bill Hinz

Vice President International, Matt Brokl

Vice President Marketing, Robert Ruhland

Vice President Construction, Jay Allen

President CEO and Director, Sally J. Smith, age 57

Chairman, James M. Damian, age 63

Svp And General Counsel Secretary, Emily C Decker

Auditors: KPMGLLP

LOCATIONS

HQ: Buffalo Wild Wings Inc
5500 Wayzata Boulevard, Suite 1600, Minneapolis, MN 55416
Phone: 952 593-9943
Web: www.buffalowildwings.com

PRODUCTS/OPERATIONS

2012 Sales

	$ mil.	% of total
Restaurants	964.0	93
Franchising	76.5	7
Total	**1040.5**	**100**

2012 Locations

	No.
Franchised	510
Company-owned	381
Total	**891**

COMPETITORS

Applebee's International
Brinker
Carlson Restaurants
Damon's
Darden
Dave & Buster's
Famous Dave's
Fox & Hound Restaurant
Hooters
Houlihan's
Johnny Rockets
OSI Restaurant Partners
Rock Bottom Restaurants
Ruby Tuesday

HISTORICAL FINANCIALS

Company Type: Public

Income Statement

FYE: December 29

	REVENUE ($ mil.)	NET INCOME ($ mil.)	NET PROFIT MARGIN	EMPLOYEES
12/13	1,266.7	71.5	5.6%	31,700
12/12	1,040.5	57.2	5.5%	25,500
12/11	784.4	50.4	6.4%	21,000
12/10	613.2	38.4	6.3%	15,900
12/09	538.9	30.6	5.7%	14,000
Annual Growth	23.8%	23.6%	—	22.7%

2013 Year-End Financials

Debt ratio: —
Return on equity: 16.9%
Cash ($ mil.): 133
Current ratio: 1.10
Long-term debt ($ mil.): —
No. of shares (mil.): 18
Dividends
Yield: —
Payout: —
Market value ($ mil.): 2,747

	STOCK PRICE ($) FY Close	P/E High/Low		PER SHARE ($) Earnings	Dividends	Book Value
12/13	146.08	40	19	3.79	0.00	24.77
12/12	71.94	31	21	3.06	0.00	20.59
12/11	68.24	25	16	2.73	0.00	17.30
12/10	44.97	25	17	2.10	0.00	14.10
12/09	42.92	26	13	1.69	0.00	11.62
Annual Growth	35.8%	—	—	22.4%	—	20.8%

C&J Energy Services Inc.

Fracturing normally carries negative implications unless of course you're in the oil and gas industry. Serving oil and gas companies C&J Energy Services (C&J) provides hydraulic fracturing (fracking) services in geologically challenging areas in Texas Louisiana and Oklahoma. The company also provides coiled tubing and pressure pumping services which are used during well completion maintenance and other projects and it makes and repairs fraking pumping and other oilfield equipment. Major customers have included EOG Resources EXCO Resources Anadarko Petroleum Penn Virginia Apache Plains Exploration and Chesapeake.

Geographic Reach

C&J is headquartered in Houston and operates in major US oil producing regions including the Permian basin and the Eagle Ford Bakken and Marcelus shale formations.

Operations

The company is an independent provider of premium hydraulic fracturing coiled tubing wireline and other complementary services with a focus on complex technically demanding well completions. It also makes and repairs equipment to fulfill its internal needs as well as for third party companies in the energy services industry.

C&J operates in three segments. The Stimulation and Intervention group (73% of 2013 revenues) provides fracking and other well stimulation services fracking chemicals and drilling tools. Its Wireline Services unit (26%) provides equipment that helps drillers assess and test wells. The Equipment Manufacturing segment makes inspects and repairs oilfield equipment and provides parts and supplies to other C&J units and third-parties.

The Stimulation and Well Intervention Services segment has three related service lines providing hydraulic fracturing coiled tubing and other well stimulation services. Additionally with the development of the specialty chemicals business and strategic acquisitions during 2013 the company provides specialty chemicals for completion and production services as well as downhole tools and related directional drilling technology and data control systems. The Wireline Services segment provides cased-hole wireline services and other complementary services including logging perforating pipe recovery pressure testing and pumpdown services. The Wireline Services segment consists of 69 wireline units and 33 pumpdown units as well as pressure control and other ancillary equipment. It deployed six new wireline units and 14 pumpdown units during 2013; and planned to deploy an additional two new wireline units and four new pumpdown units in early 2014.The Equipment Manufacturing segment constructs equipment conducts equipment repair services and provides oilfield parts and supplies for third-party customers in the energy services industry as well as to fulfill the internal equipment demands of the Stimulation and Well Intervention Services and Wireline Services segments. Through subsidiary Total E&S Inc. C&J also manufactures and repairs hydraulic fracturing coiled tubing pressure pumping and other equipment used in the energy services industry.

Financial Performance

The domestic bonanza in oilfield operations due to fracking make be slowing. After several years of growth in 2013 C&J reported a 4% drop in revenue as the Stimulation and Intervention group saw lower utilization and prices for fracking services and Equipment Manufacturing revenue dropped due to excess supply. The bright spot was Wireline Services which improved due to a 2012 acquisition. Net income dropped 64% as a result of the decreased revenue along with higher costs associated with acquisitions and R&D. Cash from operations also fell by $67 million due to lower net income and a drop in receivables. The company has seen growth in revenues since 2009 primarily due to acquisition of businesses assets equipment and and units which lead to increased capacity. It declined in 2013 due to lower utilization and pricing for its hydraulic fracturing services.

Strategy

In an effort to get back on solid ground the company is focusing on growing its core service lines through the expansion of its assets customer base and its geographic reach.

As part of its future growth strategy the company plans to bolster its fleet of hydraulic fracturing units and expand its presence into other US regions. C&J has been expanding its fleet service lines and geographic footprint. It added hydraulic fracturing horsepower in Oklahoma opened an R&D center and established a presence in the Middle East by opening an office in Dubai in 2013.It also grew its coiled tubing and wireline businesses deploying six new coiled tubing units and six new wireline units during 2013. Through its wireline business it also increased its pumpdown operations with the deployment of 14 pumpdown units. During 2013 it added coiled tubing services to its existing wireline and pressure pumping operations in the Marcellus Shale and strengthened the presence of its coiled tubing wireline and pressure pumping operations in the Eagle Ford and Bakken Shales and in the Permian Basin.During 2013 C&J invested in a number of strategic initiatives to expand its business through vertical integration service line diversification and technological advancement. The strategic initiatives include the development of a specialty chemicals business for completion and production services; and investing in a new Research and Technology center.

Mergers and Acquisitions

In 2013 C&J bought a drilling equipment and tool company for $9 million and a data control instrument maker for $7 million. The instruments are used in its fracking operations.

To expand its portfolio and geographic coverage in 2012 C&J Energy bought Casedhole Holdings a manufacturer of well assessment equipment for $272.5 million. After the acquisition the company added another business segment named Wireline Services.

Company Background

Formed in 2006 C&J went public in 2011. The company used a portion of the $113 million in IPO proceeds to repay debt. The company also used some of the proceeds to fund capital expenditures and for general corporate purposes.

EXECUTIVES

Chairman and CEO, Josh Comstock, age 45, $740,000 total compensation
President and CFO, Randall C. McMullen, age 39, $485,000 total compensation
COO, Don Gawick, $375,000 total compensation
EVP General Counsel and Corporate Secretary, Ted Moore, $325,000 total compensation

Chief Strategy Officer, James H. Prestidge, $244,863 total compensation
SVP Hydraulic Fracturing, Billy Driver
SVP Coiled Tubing, Mike McCoy
SVP Sales and Marketing, Lance Dunn
President Research and Technology, Pat Bixenman
SVP Corporate Oilfield Operations, Ed Keppler
SVP Casedhole Solutions, Tim Wallace
President Total Equipment and Service, Barry Beadle
VP Wireline, Jeremy Kinslow
Vice President - Coiled Tubing, Brandon D Simmons, age 46
Vice President Tubingmichael, Michael A McCoy
Vice President And Controller, Mark Cashiola
Vice President - Hydraulic Fracturing, Patrick Schneider
Vice President Mena, Jeremy Alston
Vice President Pumping Operations, Chris Williams
Senior Vice President Casedhole Solutions, Timothy Wallace
Vice President Hydraulic Fracturing, Pat Schneider
Chairman and CEO, Josh Comstock, age 45

LOCATIONS

HQ: C&J Energy Services Inc.
3990 Rogerdale Rd, Houston, TX 77042
Phone: 713 325-6000
Web: www.cjenergy.com

PRODUCTS/OPERATIONS

2013 Sales

	$ mil.	% of total
Stimulation & well intervention services	783.4	73
Wireline services	278.8	26
Equipment manufacturing	8.1	1
Total	**1070.3**	**100**

COMPETITORS

Baker Hughes	Schlumberger
FTS International	Stewart & Stevenson
Halliburton	LLC
National Oilwell Varco	Weatherford
RPC	International

HISTORICAL FINANCIALS

Company Type: Public

Income Statement

FYE: December 31

	REVENUE ($ mil.)	NET INCOME ($ mil.)	NET PROFIT MARGIN	EMPLOYEES
12/13	1,070.3	66.4	6.2%	2,609
12/12	1,111.5	182.3	16.4%	1,989
12/11	758.4	161.9	21.4%	1,127
12/10	244.1	32.2	13.2%	831
12/09	67.0	(2.4)	—	0
Annual Growth	**99.9%**	**—**	**—**	**—**

2013 Year-End Financials

Debt ratio: 14.5%	No. of shares (mil.): 54
Return on equity: 10.2%	Dividends
Cash ($ mil.): 14	Yield: —
Current ratio: 2.05	Payout: —
Long-term debt ($ mil.): 164	Market value ($ mil.): 1,261

	STOCK PRICE ($) FY Close	P/E High/Low		PER SHARE ($) Earnings	Dividends	Book Value
12/13	23.10	20	14	1.20	0.00	12.75
12/12	21.44	7	5	3.37	0.00	11.29
12/11	20.93	10	4	3.19	0.00	7.61
Annual Growth	**5.1%**		**—**	**—(38.7%)**	**—**	**29.4%**

Cabot Oil & Gas Corp.

Like a cog on a gear in a well-oiled machine Cabot Oil & Gas (ticker symbol: COG) is very efficiently engaged in the oil and gas industry. It explores for and produces primarily natural gas (and some oil) and it sells gas to industrial customers local utilities and gas marketers. In 2012 Cabot Oil & Gas reported estimated proved reserves of more than 3.8 trillion cu. ft. of natural gas equivalent. About 96% of the company's reserves is in the form of natural gas. Its major areas of operation include gas shale plays in Pennsylvania Oklahoma Louisiana and Texas.

Geographic Reach

Cabot Oil & Gas is exploiting the Marcellus Shale play in Pennsylvania. It is also developing the Haynesville Shale play in East Texas and Louisiana (where the company has identified up to 1.8 trillion cu. ft. of estimated gas reserves) the Eagle Ford play in South Texas and the Marmaton in the Oklahoma and Texas Panhandle.

Sales and Marketing

The company's principal markets for their natural gas are in the northeastern and midwestern US and the Gulf Coast. In the Northeast Cabot Oil & Gas sells natural gas to industrial customers local distribution companies. In the Gulf Coast and the Midwest it sells natural gas to intrastate pipelines processors and marketing companies.

Financial Performance

Cabot Oil & Gas' revenues increased by 23% in 2012 primarily due to a 81% hike in crude oil and condensate sales thanks to higher production from the Eagle Ford and Marmaton plays coupled with higher oil prices. Natural gas revenues grew by 17% due to higher production in the Marcellus Shale partially offset by the sales of some oil and gas assets in the Rockies in 2011 and decreases in production primarily in Oklahoma Texas and West Virginia (due to a shift from natural gas to higher-return liquids drilling) and production declines as part of the natural life cycle of wells.Net income increased by 8% in 2012 as the result of higher sales and lower brokered natural gas costs (due to buying and selling natural gas using separate purchase and sale transactions whereby Cabot Oil & Gas and/or a counterparty takes title to the natural gas purchased or sold).

Increased production and higher oil prices helped the company to post an upward trend in revenues between 2009 and 2012.

Strategy

Cabot Oil & Gas is investing heavily in exploiting some of the US' major undeveloped gas assets —shale plays. In 2013 it allocated 65% of its capital program to the Marcellus Shale 30% to liquids-focused plays in south Texas and Oklahoma and the remaining 5% to other emerging plays and non-drilling expenditures.

In order to raise cash to pay down debt and invest in its core US properties in 2012 Cabot Oil & Gas sold a 35% non-operated working interest in the Pearsall Shale in 50000 leased acres in Atascosa Frio La Salle and Zavala counties of Texas for $250 million. It also sold oil and gas properties in South Texas to a private company for $29.9 million and various other Texas assets to other parties for $14.4 million.

In 2011 the company sold certain non-core proved oil and gas properties located in Colorado Utah and Wyoming to Breitburn Energy Partners L.P. for $285.0 million. It exited Canada in 2010 with the sale of its remaining assets there for $63.1 million.

In 2010 Cabot Oil & Gas sold its Pennsylvania-based midstream gas assets to Williams Partners for $150 million. Williams also agreed to a 25-year gathering agreement with Cabot for its Marcellus Shale gas production.

EXECUTIVES

VP Marketing, Jeffrey W. (Jeff) Hutton, age 59, $272,167 total compensation
VP CFO and Treasurer, Scott C. Schroeder, age 52, $377,500 total compensation
Chairman President and CEO, Dan O. Dinges, age 60, $641,667 total compensation
VP and Regional Manager South Region, Matt Reid
Vice President - Land And Business Development, Todd Liebl
VP CFO and Treasurer, Scott C. Schroeder, age 52
Chairman President and CEO, Dan O. Dinges, age 60
Auditors: PricewaterhouseCoopersLLP

LOCATIONS

HQ: Cabot Oil & Gas Corp.
Three Memorial City Plaza, 840 Gessner Road, Suite 1400, Houston, TX 77024
Phone: 281 589-4600   **Fax:** 281 589-4653
Web: www.cabotog.com

PRODUCTS/OPERATIONS

2012 Sales

	$ mil.	% of total
Natural gas		
Natural gas production	933.6	77
Brokered natural gas	34.0	3
Crude oil & condensate	227.9	19
Other	9.0	1
Total	**1204.5**	**100**

COMPETITORS

Anadarko Petroleum	Newfield Exploration
BP	Noble Energy
Belden & Blake	PDC Energy
Black Hills	Petrohawk Energy
Chesapeake Energy	Pioneer Natural
Chevron	Resources
Dominion Resources	Quicksilver Resources
EOG	Range Resources
EQT Corporation	Royal Dutch Shell
Exxon Mobil	SM Energy
Key Energy	Southwestern Energy

HISTORICAL FINANCIALS

Company Type: Public

Income Statement

FYE: December 31

	REVENUE ($ mil.)	NET INCOME ($ mil.)	NET PROFIT MARGIN	EMPLOYEES
12/13	1,746.2	279.7	16.0%	684
12/12	1,204.5	131.7	10.9%	589
12/11	979.8	122.4	12.5%	529
12/10	844.0	103.3	12.2%	409
12/09	879.2	148.3	16.9%	567
Annual Growth	18.7%	17.2%	—	4.8%

2013 Year-End Financials

Debt ratio: 23.0%
Return on equity: 12.9%
Cash ($ mil.): 51
Current ratio: 0.93
Long-term debt ($ mil.): 1,147

No. of shares (mil.): 416
Dividends
  Yield: 0.1%
  Payout: 10.3%
Market value ($ mil.): 16,140

	STOCK PRICE ($) FY Close	P/E High/Low	PER SHARE ($) Earnings	Dividends	Book Value
12/13	38.76	116 49	0.66	0.06	5.29
12/12	49.74	263 94	0.31	0.08	5.07
12/11	75.90	300 127	0.29	0.03	5.04
12/10	37.85	187 109	0.25	0.06	4.50
12/09	43.59	128 51	0.36	0.06	4.37
Annual Growth	(2.9%)	— —	16.8%	(0.0%)	4.9%

Cadence Design Systems Inc

Cadence Design Systems helps engineers pick up the development tempo. A leader in the market for electronic design automation (EDA) software Cadence sells and leases software and hardware products used to design integrated circuits (ICs) printed circuit boards (PCBs) and other electronic systems. Semiconductor and electronics systems manufacturers use its products to build components for wireless devices networking equipment and other applications. The company also provides maintenance and support and offers design and methodology consulting services. Customers have included Pegatron Silicon Labs and Texas Instruments. Cadence gets more than half of its sales from customers outside the US.

HISTORY

Cadence Design Systems arose from the 1988 merger of software firms ECAD (formed in 1982) and SDA Systems (founded 1983). The stock market crash of 1987 helped propel SDA Systems an EDA company that gave up its planned IPO in the wake of the crash into its merger with ECAD which was publicly held to form Cadence Design. Private venture capital investor and SDA chairman Donald Lucas became chairman of Cadence. Joe Costello the young charismatic and tall (6-foot-7) president and COO of SDA was named president and CEO of Cadence. It became the world's leading electronic design automation (EDA) software supplier by enlarging and improving the range of software it developed in-house and via such acquisitions as Tangent Systems (1989) and Valid Logic Systems (1991).

In 1995 the company bought Unisys' integrated circuit (IC) and electronic systems design group. In an effort to broaden its market Cadence began providing design consulting and services to makers of industrial products.

A protracted legal battle began in 1995 when Cadence sued rival Avant! accusing it of stealing software code and trade secrets.

Cadence acquired High Level Design Systems a Silicon Valley maker of IC design tools in 1996 and Cooper & Chyan Technology a designer of the connections between elements on computer chips in 1997.

CEO Joe Costello resigned in late 1997 after presiding over the company's growth from $79 million in annual sales to nearly $1 billion and was succeeded by Jack Harding who had previously been the president and CEO of Cooper & Chyan.

The company's 1998 purchases included system-on-a-chip software maker Ambit Design Systems and the semiconductor design group of Lucent's Bell Labs. Late that year Cadence began streamlining operations cutting its workforce by 12%. It ended 1998 by becoming the first EDA company to cross the $1 billion threshold for annual sales though the restructuring was partly responsible for a large drop in profits.

Facing lagging orders from semiconductor makers plus projected lower earnings CEO Harding resigned; he was replaced by CFO Bingham. That year Cadence bought rival Quickturn Design Systems (a $271 million deal) and printed circuit board design specialist OrCAD ($121 million).

Cadence beefed up its EDA services in late 1999 and early 2000 by acquiring private design firms Diablo Research and Westport Technologies. In mid-2000 the company filed to take its design services business public as Tality; after postponing its planned IPO Cadence continued to offer design services through Tality as a wholly owned subsidiary.

Cadence won a major legal victory in 2001 when it was awarded $195 million in restitution after Avant! and seven of its current and former executives pleaded no contest to criminal charges that they stole software code from Cadence. Later that year the company acquired virtual prototyping software provider Silicon Perspectives.

In the face of a broad economic downturn — which was particularly brutal for the global semiconductor industry —the company trimmed its workforce in late 2001 then again in 2002. Both reductions were centered on its Tality subsidiary which was absorbed into Cadence's Foundry Solutions unit later in 2002.

In 2002 Cadence accepted the offer of Avant! (and its new owner Synopsys) to settle the long-running civil suit between them in return for a $265 million payment to Cadence. That same year the company acquired the assets of mixed-signal design tool provider Antrim Design Systems.

In early 2003 Cadence acquired Celestry Design Technologies a start-up specializing in silicon modeling tools and full-chip circuit simulation software for about $64 million.

Looking to bridge the technological gap between chip designs and the photomask sets that actually produce integrated circuits Cadence in 2003 acquired K2 Technologies a supplier of software for mask data preparation. The K2 software became part of Cadence's Design for Manufacturing (DFM) business unit and was ported to the OpenAccess unified database for easier interaction with other design software.

In 2003 Cadence and competitor Mentor Graphics agreed to settle litigation over emulation and acceleration technology with Mentor paying $18 million to Cadence; in a sign of lawsuit fatigue in the EDA industry the two companies also agreed not to sue each other over that technology for seven years.

To better compete against Synopsys Cadence acquired Get2Chip in 2003 for about $77 million and later bought Verplex Systems a supplier of design verification software. The company also spent around $77 million in 2003 to acquire assets of its Japanese distributor Innotech.

In 2004 it acquired Neolinear a supplier of software for designing analog and mixed-signal semiconductors. Cadence also acquired rival Verisity in 2005.

In 2010 Cadence acquired Denali Software for $315 million in cash adding a mixture of computer memory software models design intellectual property (IP) and verification IP.

The following year the company bought Altos Design Automation to bolster its chip design product line. Altos specialized in software used in memory and standard cell libraries and in models for system-on-chip (SoC) implementation. Also in 2011 Cadence bought semiconductor design software maker Azuro to further extend its expertise in chip design applications.

EXECUTIVES

Senior Vice President Advanced Commercial Banking Systems, Christopher J (Chris) Tice
Vice President Of Finance, Jaswinder S Ahuja
SVP and CFO, Geoffrey (Geoff) Ribar, age 56, $380,000 total compensation
President CEO and Director, Lip-Bu Tan, age 55, $454,616 total compensation
Senior Vice President Worldwide Field Operations and System & Verification Group, Charlie Huang, age 49, $400,000 total compensation
President Cadence Japan, Ryoichi Kawashima
Senior Vice President IP Group, Martin Lund, $292,115 total compensation
VP Marketing, Pankaj Mayor
Senior VP Custom IC & PCB Group, Tom Beckley
Svp-product Mktg, Ajay Malhotra
Vice President Group Director World Wide Information Technology, Paul Rose
Executive Vice President Senior Advisor To The Exe, Ping Chao
Vice President, Alan H Lindstrom
Vice President Corporate Finance, James Haddad
Vice President Sales Global Accounts, Veronica Watson
Vice President Software Engineering Architect, Limin He
Vice President Technical Field, Matthew Macconnel
Vice President Operations, Colin McIntyre
Corporate Vice President And Chief Technlgy Advis, Anirudh Devgan
Vice President Finance And Operations Emea Worldwide Revenue Accounting, Nick Phillips
Vice President Research And Development, Emmanuelle Amouriaux
Vice President Of Sales Emea, Rick Darenberg
Senior Vice President, Diane Bradley
Corporate Vice President Research And Development, Daisuke Iida
Vice President Encounter Test, Sanjiv Taneja
Vice President Research And Development, Moshe Rubin
Vice President Strategic Marketing, Jamie Metcalf
Vice President Design For Manufacturing, Marc Levitt
Vice President Finance Europe, Mervyn Fernandez
Vice President Business Development Icd, Suk Lee
Vice President Engineering Blda, Hao Nham
Vice President Custom Layout Product, Jacques Olivier Piednoir
Vice President Product Marketing System, Micha Siwi Ski
Senior Vice President Development, Jim Miller
Vice President Engineering Performance, Neil Santos
Vice President Engineering, Nishath Verghese
Vice President, Jian Sun
Vice President Of Engineering, Mike Meyer
Vice President Research And Development, Diane Elieff
Vice President Research And Development, Sergio Silva
Vice President Of Operations, Sheila Noonan
Corporate Vice President Sales, Vikas Kumar
Vice President Sales Focus Accounts, Adi Navon

Vice President Research And Development, Narain Arora
Vice President Research And Development, Kamran Torabi
Vice Presicfent Software Development, James Ready
Vice President Research And Development, Mohamad Khouja
Svp And General Counsel Secretary, James J (Jim) Cowie, age 50
Chairman, John B. Shoven, age 66
President CEO and Director, Lip-Bu Tan, age 55
Board Member, Susan L (Sue) Bostrom, age 55
Board Member, George M Scalise, age 81
Board Member, Donald L (Don) Lucas, age 85
Secretary, Lars Hagan
Board Member, Alberto Sangiovanni
Auditors: KPMGLLP

LOCATIONS

HQ: Cadence Design Systems Inc
2655 Seely Avenue, Building 5, San Jose, CA 95134
Phone: 408 943-1234   **Fax:** 408 943-0513
Web: www.cadence.com

2012 Sales

	% of total
US	43
EMEA	20
Japan	16
Rest of Asia	19
Other	2
Total	**100**

Selected AcquisitionsFY 2010Denali Software (software $315 million)FY 2011Altos Design Automation (software)Azuro (software)FY 2012SigrityFY 2013Cosmic CircuitsTensilica

PRODUCTS/OPERATIONS

2012 Sales

	$ mil.	% of total
Product	839.1	36
Maintenance	373.3	28
Services	114.0	9
Total	**1326.4**	**100**

2012 Sales

	% of total
Functional verification & design IP	30
Digital IC design	23
Custom IC design	23
System interconnect design	9
Design for manufacturing	6
Service & other	9
Total	**100**

Selected Software

Analog simulators (Spectre)
Cycle-based simulators (SpeedSim)
Deep submicron design (Envisia)
Digital IC design (Encounter platform including First Encounter SoC Encounter and Nano Encounter)
Digital simulators (NC-simulator NC-Verilog NC-VHDL)
Editing and synthesis compaction device-level editing (Virtuoso family)
Equivalence checking (Affirma)
Hardware emulators (CoBALT Mercury)
Model checking (Affirma Formalcheck)
Place and routing (Envisia Silicon Ensemble)
Printed circuit board design and packaging (Allegro SPECCTRA)
Synthesis (Envisia Ambit BuildGates)
Verification (Assura line including Diva and Dracula; Incisive platform; Palladium)

Selected Services

Education
IC design services (Cadence Design Foundry)
IC implementation

Intellectual property (IP Gallery)
Methodology
Wireless design

COMPETITORS

ANSYS
Agilent EEsof
Altium
Atrenta
Intrinsix
Mentor Graphics
PDF Solutions
Synopsys
Zuken

HISTORICAL FINANCIALS

Company Type: Public

Income Statement

FYE: December 28

	REVENUE ($ mil.)	NET INCOME ($ mil.)	NET PROFIT MARGIN	EMPLOYEES
12/13	1,460.1	164.2	11.2%	5,700
12/12	1,326.4	439.9	33.2%	5,200
12/11*	1,149.8	72.2	6.3%	4,700
01/11	935.9	126.5	13.5%	4,600
01/10	852.6	(149.8)	—	4,400
Annual Growth	**14.4%**	**—**	**—**	**6.7%**

*Fiscal year change

2013 Year-End Financials

Debt ratio: 13.3%
Return on equity: 15.9%
Cash ($ mil.): 536
Current ratio: 1.06
Long-term debt ($ mil.): —
No. of shares (mil.): 288
Dividends
   Yield: —
   Payout: —
Market value ($ mil.): 4,014

	STOCK PRICE ($) FY Close	P/E High/Low		PER SHARE ($) Earnings	Dividends	Book Value
12/13	13.93	27	21	0.56	0.00	4.01
12/12	13.44	8	6	1.57	0.00	3.26
12/11*	10.40	43	30	0.27	0.00	1.51
01/11	8.26	18	11	0.48	0.00	1.04
01/10	5.99	—	—	(0.58)	0.00	0.40
Annual Growth	**23.5%**	**—**	**—**	**—**	**—**	**77.6%**

*Fiscal year change

CAI International Inc

Is it bigger than a breadbox? CAI International can pack it. The company leases large steel boxes to ship freight by plane train or truck around the world. More than 65% of its container fleet is owned by CAI and the balance owned by container investors is managed by CAI. The leasing segment offers 280-plus shipping companies short-term and long-term leases with some leases giving the lessees the option to purchase the container. The container management segment provides container investors with the ability to lease re-lease and dispose of their container portfolio; services also include container repair relocation and storage.

Geographic Reach

CAI caters to 280 customers from 16 offices spanning 12 countries. CAI purchases the majority of its containers in China and operates from offices in Belgium Hong Kong Japan Korea Singapore Taiwan the UK and the US among others.

Operations

CAI has two reportable business segments: equipment leasing (92% of sales) and container management (8%). The equipment leasing segment generates revenue from the ownership and leasing of containers to container shipping lines and freight forwarders.

The container management segment draws revenue from management fees earned from portfolios of containers and associated leases which are managed on behalf of container investors. In addition CAI derives revenue from the sale of containers to container investors who in turn enter into management agreements with the company.

Sales and Marketing

The top ten largest lessees accounted for about 60% of its total leasing segment sales (approximately 55% of total sales). Its largest customer CMA CGM accounted for 12% of sales.

Financial Performance

CAI has enjoyed three straight years of unprecedented growth. Revenues climbed 38% from $126 million in 2011 to reach a historic high of $174 million in 2012. Profits also surged 26% from $50 million in 2011 to $63 million 2012 another record high.

The growth was driven by a 45% spike in equipment leasing sales due to an increase in the average number of owned containers on lease. The company was also helped by a 100% surge in finance lease sales. This growth was offset by a 13% decrease in container management sales.

Ownership

Founder Hiromitsu Ogawa owns about 22% of the company while Columbia Wanger Asset Management owns 12%

Company Background

Founded by Hiromitsu Ogawa in 1989 CAI has evolved from solely an intermodal leasing concern to a more ambitious manager of containers owned by investors.

EXECUTIVES

President and CEO, Victor M. Garcia, age 46, $323,833 total compensation
VP Operations, Camille G. Cutino, age 55, $164,800 total compensation
CFO, Timothy Page
Vice President Business Development, Conrad Esposito
Auditors: KPMGLLP

LOCATIONS

HQ: CAI International Inc
Steuart Tower, 1 Market Plaza, Suite 900, San Francisco, CA 94105
Phone: 415 788-0100
Web: www.capps.com

PRODUCTS/OPERATIONS

2012 Sales

	$ mil.	% of total
Equipment leasing	160.6	92
Container management	13.3	8
Total	**173.9**	**100**

2012 Sales

	% of total
Rental revenue	88
Management fee revenue	7
Finance lease income	4
Gain on sale of container portfolios	1
Total	**100**

Selected Operations

Container leasing
  Container owned by CAI
  Full benefits of ownership

Placed on long- and short-term leases to shipping lines
Container management
  Container sold to investors
  Generate cash flow through management fee revenue and trading income
  Managed by CAI over expected life of asset

COMPETITORS

COSCO Group	Seaco
SeaCube Container	Touax
Seacastle	XTRA Corp.

HISTORICAL FINANCIALS

Company Type: Public

Income Statement

FYE: December 31

	REVENUE ($ mil.)	NET INCOME ($ mil.)	NET PROFIT MARGIN	EMPLOYEES
12/13	212.4	63.9	30.1%	85
12/12	173.9	63.4	36.5%	91
12/11	125.7	50.1	39.9%	83
12/10	77.9	28.3	36.4%	89
12/09	65.2	13.5	20.8%	83
Annual Growth	**34.3%**	**47.4%**		**0.6%**

2013 Year-End Financials

Debt ratio: 67.9%	No. of shares (mil.): 22
Return on equity: 16.7%	Dividends
Cash ($ mil.): 45	Yield: —
Current ratio: 0.83	Payout: —
Long-term debt ($ mil.): 1,061	Market value ($ mil.): 524

	STOCK PRICE ($) FY Close	P/E High/Low		PER SHARE ($) Earnings	Dividends	Book Value
12/13	23.57	10	7	2.82	0.00	18.64
12/12	21.95	7	5	3.18	0.00	15.73
12/11	15.46	10	4	2.55	0.00	11.92
12/10	19.60	13	5	1.56	0.00	9.31
12/09	9.03	12	3	0.76	0.00	7.21
Annual Growth	**27.1%**	—	—	**38.8%**	—	**26.8%**

Cal-Maine Foods, Inc.

Cal-Maine Foods' more than 26 million laying hens are some of its top performers. The nation's largest shell egg producer and marketer the company sells more than 880 million dozen eggs a year. It is also one of the top suppliers of specialty shell eggs (which are Omega-3 enhanced organic and cage free) that are marketed under the Egg-Land's Best Farmhouse and 4Grain brands. Cal-Maine's operations span all phases of shell egg production: hatching chicks making feed housing hens and distributing eggs. Customers include US grocery stores (such as Publix) superstores the likes of Wal-Mart and warehouse clubs (Sam's Club) as well as foodservice distributors and makers of egg products dotting 29 states.

Geographic Reach

The company's operations extend nationwide across nearly 30 states.

Mergers and Acquisitions

Cal-Maine continues to grow its share of the shell-egg market through acquisitions of existing production and processing operations. It has made nearly 20 acquisitions since 1989. Each added between 600000 to 7.5 million laying hens (called layers) and related facilities as well as expanded the company's portfolio of name brands. Such investments and acquisitions have boosted Cal-Maine's flock of layers pullets and breeders. The flock is likely the largest in the US.

The company acquired certain egg operations from Pilgrim's Pride in 2012. Cal-Maine gained two production facilities in Texas with capacity for some 1.4 million laying hens and stepped up its presence in the Southwest market as a result. Adding to its Texas holdings Cal-Maine in late 2012 acquired Maxim Production Co. The purchases complement its 2009 acquisition of Florida's Tampa Farms' 4Grain brand of specialty shell eggs.

Strategy

Cal-Maine also looks to shore up operations through construction of new more efficient egg production and processing plants paired with a pullet growing facility. It also regularly disposes of older less efficient facilities.

On several separate occasions the company was hit by a nationwide food recall. The 2011 and 2010 recalls were attributable to possible salmonella contamination from eggs produced by Hillandale Farms of Iowa as well as from other outside contractors. In addition Cal-Maine is under pressure from animal welfare advocates who argue for better treatment of its flock of hens including larger cages fewer beak trimmings and decreased forced molting practices (which put chickens under stress to lay more eggs). The Humane Society of the United States and the United Egg Producers agreed in 2011 to press toward new federal legislation which if passed will increase the production costs of housing and feeding hens.

Financial Performance

Net sales rose 18% in fiscal 2012 as compared to 2011 due in part to an 8% increase in total dozens of eggs sold and a boost in the average selling price of shell eggs. Cal-Maine's 48% increase in net income during the same reporting period is primarily attributable to the increase in net sales partially offset by the increase in cost of sales. Contributing to the cost of sales bump were the increase in dozens produced dozens purchased from outside shell egg producers and cost of feed ingredients.

Sales and Marketing

Cal-Maine markets its shell eggs through a distribution network serving a diverse group of customers. It caters to national and regional grocery store chains club stores foodservice distributors and egg product makers. Together Wal-Mart and Sam's Club account for 31% of sales and Publix Super Markets generates 10%.

The company's advertising costs totaled $4245 $5768 and $2098 in fiscal 2012 2011 and 2010 respectively.

Company Ownership

Cal-Maine also faces significant control by a small party. Founder and chairman emeritus Fred Adams Jr. owns about 53% of the company's voting power. The son-in-law of Adams Adolphus "Dolph" Baker is president and CEO and holds a 14% stake.

HISTORY

One can side with the chicken or the egg in the which-came-first argument but it was Fred Adams Jr. who came first at Cal-Maine. A former salesman with pet food giant Ralston Purina (now Nestl ꝗurina PetCare) Adams founded a poultry and egg business in Mendenhall Mississippi in 1957. He focused exclusively on egg sales in 1960 and merged his company in 1969 with Maine Egg Farms and Dairy Fresh Foods in California to form Cal-Maine Foods.

Cal-Maine cracked new markets through internal growth and the acquisition of rival egg firms. The company acquired Egg City (Arkansas 1989) Sunny Fresh Foods (Arkansas 1990) Sunnyside Eggs (North Carolina 1991) Wayne Detling Farms (Ohio 1994) A&G Farms (Kentucky 1995) and Sunbest Farms (Arkansas 1996). After going public in 1996 Cal-Maine bought two Georgia firms: Southern Empire Egg Farm (1997) and J&S Farms (1998).

In 1998 the company sold off its egg products division which provided food makers with egg whites and yolks and accounted for 4% of total sales.

In 1999 Cal-Maine bought two egg producers and processors: Kentucky-based Hudson Brothers and Texas-based Smith Farms. Declining supplies in the cyclical egg market and increasing demand in late 2000 raised the company out of the loss column for the first time in 18 months. In late 2001 Cal-Maine's board of directors voted to explore the possibility of the company becoming privately held but abandoned the idea because of a sagging egg market. Industry-wide overproduction helped to drive down egg prices pecking away at the company's profits in 2002.

In 2003 Cal-Maine's board of directors voted to take the company private. However as demand for eggs shot up so did Cal-Maine stock prices and shareholders were unconvinced such a move would benefit them. Faced with shareholder lawsuits in November of that year the board voted to terminate the proposal to take the company private.

After years of oversupply and weak prices starting in 2003 the entire egg industry enjoyed a boost from the popular protein-heavy Atkins diet. Cal-Maine's sales jumped as people chose hard-boiled eggs as snacks. However by 2004 its popularity had peaked leaving the market (and Cal-Maine) with an egg glut and plunging sales. In 2005 the company acquired egg supplier Hillandale Farms.

In 2006 the company formed a 50-50 joint venture (Green Forest Foods) with Pier 44 Properties to lease and operate Green Forest Egg's production assets which included about 1 million laying hens at facilities located in Arkansas. Cal-Maine's bought of Pier 44's interest in Green Forest in 2007 and purchased the shell-egg division of George's Inc. for which it paid $11 million in cash.

Fred Adams Jr. founder and chairman handed over the title of CEO to former COO Dolph Baker in late 2010.

EXECUTIVES

Vice President; Controller, Charles F Collins, age 70
Vice President Operations Production, Jack B Self, age 86
VP CFO Secretary Treasurer and Director, Timothy A. Dawson, age 60, $179,346 total compensation
Chairman President and CEO, Adolphus B. (Dolph) Baker, age 57, $320,000 total compensation
VP Feed Mill Division, Joe M. Wyatt, age 75, $134,553 total compensation
VP and COO, Sherman Miller
VP Egg Products, James (Jim) Hull
Vice President Operations, Christopher Myers
Vp-operations, Wil Webb
Vice President Human Resources, Don Long
Vice President Business Development Group, Christopher Anderson
Vice President, Steve Stallone
Vice President Operations, David Jenkins

Vice President Operations, Steve Storm
Chairman President and CEO, Adolphus B. (Dolph) Baker, age 57
Vice Chairman, Richard Looper
Auditors: Ernst&YoungLLP

LOCATIONS

HQ: Cal-Maine Foods, Inc.
3320 Woodrow Wilson Avenue, Jackson, MS 39209
Phone: 601 948-6813   **Fax:** 601 969-0905
Web: www.calmainefoods.com

PRODUCTS/OPERATIONS

2012 Sales

	% of total
Shell eggs	
Non-specialty shell eggs	73
Specialty shell eggs	23
Other shell eggs	—
Egg products	3
Incidental feed & feed ingredients	1
Total	

Selected Brands

4Grain
Cal-Maine
Egg-Land's Best (licensed from Egg-Land's Best Inc.)
Farmhouse
Rio Grande
Sunny Meadow
Sunups

COMPETITORS

Cargill Kitchen Solutions	Ise America
	Luberski
Chino Valley Ranchers	Michael Foods
ConAgra	Moark
Cooper Farms	National Food
Egg Innovations	Rose Acre Farms
Hickman's Family Farms	Wilson Farms

HISTORICAL FINANCIALS

Company Type: Public

Income Statement

FYE: May 31

	REVENUE ($ mil.)	NET INCOME ($ mil.)	NET PROFIT MARGIN	EMPLOYEES
05/14*	1,440.9	109.2	7.6%	2,645
06/13	1,288.1	50.4	3.9%	2,479
06/12	1,113.1	89.7	8.1%	2,175
05/11	941.9	60.8	6.5%	2,100
05/10	910.1	67.8	7.5%	1,950
Annual Growth 12.2%		12.6%	—	7.9%

*Fiscal year change

2014 Year-End Financials

Debt ratio: 7.5%
Return on equity: 19.7%
Cash ($ mil.): 14
Current ratio: 3.68
Long-term debt ($ mil.): 50

No. of shares (mil.): 48
Dividends
  Yield: 0.0%
  Payout: 22.5%
Market value ($ mil.): 3,374

	STOCK PRICE ($) FY Close	P/E High/Low		PER SHARE ($) Earnings	Dividends	Book Value
05/14*	69.76	31	20	2.26	0.51	12.28
06/13	44.74	44	33	1.05	0.64	10.74
06/12	34.84	22	15	1.88	0.42	10.01
05/11	28.93	27	21	1.27	0.52	8.78
05/10	32.37	26	16	1.42	0.40	7.93
Annual Growth 21.2%		—	—	12.3%	6.3%	11.6%

*Fiscal year change

CalAmp Corp

CalAmp adds a little boost even to the weakest of TV programs. The former military supplier makes microwave amplification and conversion components that improve reception in satellite television wireless cable and wireless broadband access systems. Its products include antennas amplifiers and transceivers and receivers for broadband wireless transmission. CalAmp's wireless datacom segment provides wireless network and mobile resource management products for state and local governments and industrial utility and transportation companies. The company's largest customer EchoStar accounted for 21% of consolidated annual sales in fiscal 2014.

Geographic Reach

Based in Oxnard California the company also operates wireless datacom locations in Virginia and Minnesota in the US and in Quebec Canada and Auckland New Zealand.

Operations

Some 79% of CalAmp's fiscal 2014 revenues came from wireless datacom's US customers while the remaining 21% came from Satellite services.

Sales and Marketing

CalAmp offers its wireless datacom through direct and indirect sales force in US and through sales personnel in Latin America Israel and the UK. Its Satellite segment sells its products primarily to EchoStar an affiliate of DISH Network which accounted about 21% 22% and 29% for the years 2014 2013 and 2012 respectively.

Financial Performance

The company's revenues have trended upward since 2010. In 2013 CalAmp reported revenue growth of 31% driven by higher wireless datacom revenues (up 34%) due to a) the revenue contribution of the newly acquired Wireless Matrix business and strong demand for the company's MRM products on the part of fleet management and asset tracking customers and b) a 19% increase in satellite revenues primarily due to the introduction of new home networking products.CalAmp's net income declined by 74% in fiscal 2014 driven by higher cost of revenues including products costs (which increased by $26 million) while its Application subscriptions and other services cost of revenue increased by $7 million. Another factor was an increase in operating expenses (including Research and development Selling expenses General and administrative and Intangible asset amortization expenses). Costs increases were partly offset by higher salesThe company's cash flow in operating activities reported $22.8 million in fiscal 2014 (compared to $16.6 million in fiscal 2013) due to lower deferred tax assets expenses which were offset by an increase in depreciation amortization and accounts payable expenses.

Strategy

The company plans to invest in new initiatives to drive revenues and earnings growth. In fiscal 2014 it announced a new product category for CalAmp the MDT7. In fiscal 2015 it also plans to launch the CalAmp private App Store to support the delivery of value added applications for the MDT7 whether developed and supplied by CalAmp third-party content providers or their customers. In 2014 it signed a supply agreement with Masternaut Europe's leading mobile resource management services company under which CalAmp will supply Masternaut with advanced telematics devices to enable trailer heavy equipment and industrial machinery tracking with Masternaut's Connect telematics platform.

In 2013 it teamed up with Swiss-based u-blox a global leader in cellular and positioning modules and integrated circuits as GPS receiver and cellular modem supplier for their new line of vehicle tracking anti-theft and insurance telematics devices designed especially for the Brazilian market.

Mergers and Acquisitions

To expand its product and service offerings within core vertical markets in 2013 the company acquired Wireless Matrix USA Inc. (which provides resource management software for the remote tracking and monitoring of vehicle fleets) for $52.9 million. It also bought Radio Satellite Integrators Inc. a privately-held provider of fleet management solutions primarily to city and county government agencies for applications involving public works waste management transit and public safety (for $6.5 million).

HISTORY

DISH Network substantially reduced its business with CalAmp during fiscal 2007 and fiscal 2008 due to a product quality problem that CalAmp blamed on its supplier of laminate material for printed circuit boards. DISH returned more than 1.2 million units to CalAmp for analysis and rework; it cut off all orders to the company in 2007 until CalAmp's products could be requalified for its use. Later that year CalAmp reached a settlement with DISH; the terms included issuing a $5 million note to the customer a $1 million credit against outstanding receivables 1 million shares of CalAmp's common stock and a warrant to purchase 350000 additional shares of common stock over three years. The company resumed shipments to DISH Network in 2008.

EXECUTIVES

Vice President Operations, Neil Friedlander
EVP CFO and Secretary, Richard K. (Rick) Vitelle, age 60, $295,000 total compensation
President and CEO, Michael J. Burdiek, age 54, $425,000 total compensation
Vice-president, Michael Jakab
Vice President, Michael Ferron
Vice President, Lasse Glassen
Vice President General Manager Aercept Business Unit, Michael Zachan
Vice President Sales And Marketing, Gallin Chen
Chairman, Frank Perna, age 76
EVP CFO and Secretary, Richard K. (Rick) Vitelle, age 60
Auditors: SingerLewakLLP

LOCATIONS

HQ: CalAmp Corp
   1401 N. Rice Avenue, Oxnard, CA 93030
Phone: 805 987-9000
Web: www.calamp.com

2014 Sales

	% of total
United States	81
International	19
Total	**100**

PRODUCTS/OPERATIONS

2014 Sales

	$ mil.	% of total
Wireless DataCom	187	79
Satellite	48.9	21
Total	**235.9**	**100**

2014 Sales

$ mil		% of total
Products	195.5	83
Application subscriptions and other services	40.4	17
Total	**235.9**	**100**

Selected Products

Satellite components
   Amplifiers
   Downconverters
   Feedhorns
Wireless access equipment
   Antennas
   Broadband analog scrambling/decoding systems (MultiCipher)
   Transceivers (passive planar stand-alone)

COMPETITORS

AML Communications	Motorola Solutions
Broadcast Microwave Services	Novatel Wireless
COM DEV	STC Microwave Systems
Cohu	Sharp Corp.
Enfora	Sierra Wireless
Filtronic	Trimble Navigation
Kratos Defense & Security Solutions	WebTech
	Wistron NeWeb

HISTORICAL FINANCIALS

Company Type: Public

Income Statement

FYE: February 28

	REVENUE ($ mil.)	NET INCOME ($ mil.)	NET PROFIT MARGIN	EMPLOYEES
02/14	235.9	11.8	5.0%	490
02/13	180.5	44.6	24.7%	380
02/12	138.7	5.2	3.8%	370
02/11	114.3	(3.2)	—	440
02/10	112.1	(10.8)	—	510
Annual Growth	**20.4%**	**—**	**—**	**(1.0%)**

2014 Year-End Financials

Debt ratio: 1.0%
Return on equity: 9.4%
Cash ($ mil.): 19
Current ratio: 2.19
Long-term debt ($ mil.): 0

No. of shares (mil.): 35
Dividends
   Yield: —
   Payout: —
Market value ($ mil.): 1,149

	STOCK PRICE ($) FY Close	P/E High/Low		PER SHARE ($) Earnings	Dividends	Book Value
02/14	32.04	98	27	0.33	0.00	3.71
02/13	10.95	7	3	1.49	0.00	3.35
02/12	4.30	27	14	0.19	0.00	0.87
02/11	3.05	—	—	(0.12)	0.00	0.63
02/10	2.81	—	—	(0.43)	0.00	0.69
Annual Growth	**83.8%**			**—**	**—**	**52.1%**

Cambrex Corp

Cambrex focuses on health. Providing products services and technologies which help to accelerate the development and commercialization of small molecule therapeutics the company develops products for the human health care market that include active pharmaceutical ingredients (APIs) and intermediates for over-the-counter and prescription branded and generic pharmaceuticals. It also makes intermediates used in cosmetics and food additives. Cambrex focuses on developing drug delivery technologies and the manufacture of high-potency compounds and controlled substances.

Geographic Reach

Cambrex has facilities in Estonia Germany India Italy Sweden and the US. R&D and specialty manufacturing facilities are located in Europe India and the US. In 2012 Europe accounted for 54% of sales North America 38%.

Sales and Marketing

The company sells its products through a combination of direct sales and independent agents. In 2012 Gyma Laboratories of America accounted for 13% of the company's sales. One active pharmaceutical ingredient (API) sold to multiple customers accounted for 12% of Cambrex's 2012 total revenues.

Financial Analysis

Cambrex's revenues grew by 8% in 2012 despite foreign currency exchange rate that unfavorably impacted sales by 3.4%. Excluding foreign currency sales volumes increased in most of the company's product lines including controlled substances generic APIs custom development and products using Cambrex's drug delivery technology. It also experienced a modest increase in its custom manufacturing product sales including APIs and pharmaceutical intermediates sold to innovative drug companies. Higher demand for certain APIs was partially offset by a newly approved product in which the customer built up inventory in 2011. In 2012 custom development and manufacturing product contributed 45% of Cambrex's total revenues; generic APIs 36%.

However net income spiked by 468% in 2012 thanks to higher revenues increased income from continuing operations the increased absorption of R&D expenses into inventory and the lower cost of goods sold as a result of increased revenue generating custom development activity.

Strategy

Cambrex's stated strategy is to grow its portfolio of customer development projects —primarily those in the latter stages of the clinical trial process —and secure long-term supply agreements to make APIs and intermediates for recently approved drug products. It also seeks to expand sales based on its technologies and to partner with generic drug manufacturers to expand the company's portfolio of APIs. It also drives growth in strategic business segments through the selective acquisition of businesses products product lines technologies and capabilities.

In 2013 Cambrex and Dow Chemical signed a deal for Cambrex to contract make Dow Hydroxypropyl Methylcellulose Acetate Succinate for Drug Solubility Enhancement. Dow's polymer science and application expertise coupled with Cambrex's capabilities positions Dow for rapid entry into the market using the AFFINISOL product platform.

In 2012 Cambrex also agreed to supply an active pharmaceutical ingredient for a customer's Phase 3 program during 2013 and 2014.

Mergers and Acquisition

The company acquired a 51% stake in Zenara Pharma in 2010 giving Cambrex a platform within India's growing pharmaceutical market and making it a global player in the nicotine replacement therapy market. Cambrex has an option to obtain the remaining 49% in 2016.

Ownership

Fund advisor BlackRock owns nearly 10% of Cambrex.

EXECUTIVES

Vice President Operations, Joe Nettleton

President and CEO, Steven M. (Steve) Klosk, age 57, $533,333 total compensation
Managing Director Cambrex Profarmaco, Aldo Magnini, $338,666 total compensation
EVP and CFO, Gregory P. (Greg) Sargen, age 49, $400,000 total compensation
EVP and COO, Shawn P. Cavanagh, $412,500 total compensation
Tax Director Vice President, Andrew Spada
Vice President Sales And Business Development, Eric Neuffer
Vice President Global Sales, Simon Edwards
Head Of Treasury, Donald Hardman
Auditors: PricewaterhouseCoopersLLP

LOCATIONS

HQ: Cambrex Corp
One Meadowlands Plaza, East Rutherford, NJ 07073
Phone: 201 804-3000   **Fax:** 201 804-9852
Web: www.cambrex.com

2012 Sales

	$ mil.	% of total
Europe	150.7	54
North America	105.4	38
Asia	12.8	5
Other & adjustments	7.6	3
Total	**276.5**	**100**

PRODUCTS/OPERATIONS

2012 Sales

	% of total
Custom development & manufacturing	45
Generic APIs	36
Controlled substances	14
Drug delivery	5
Total	**100**

Selected Mergers and Acquisitions2010Zenara Pharma (51%; India; nicotine replacement therapy)

COMPETITORS

Aceto	Valeant
Albany Molecular	Pharmaceuticals
Research	West Pharmaceutical
Boehringer Ingelheim	Services
Sigma-Aldrich	

HISTORICAL FINANCIALS

Company Type: Public

Income Statement

	REVENUE ($ mil.)	NET INCOME ($ mil.)	NET PROFIT MARGIN	EMPLOYEES
12/14	374.6	57.3	15.3%	1,117
12/13	318.1	25.9	8.1%	936
12/12	276.5	62.3	22.5%	891
12/11	255.6	10.9	4.3%	833
12/10	226.9	9.6	4.2%	829
Annual Growth	**13.3%**	**56.1%**	**—**	**7.7%**

FYE: December 31

2014 Year-End Financials

Debt ratio: 12.3%
Return on equity: 24.8%
Cash ($ mil.): 45
Current ratio: 2.30
Long-term debt ($ mil.): 60

No. of shares (mil.): 31
Dividends
  Yield: —
  Payout: —
Market value ($ mil.): 672

Stock Price / P/E / Per Share

	STOCK PRICE ($) FY Close	P/E High/Low		PER SHARE ($) Earnings	Dividends	Book Value
12/14	21.62	13	9	1.81	0.00	8.08
12/13	17.83	23	13	0.84	0.00	6.90
12/12	11.38	7	3	2.06	0.00	5.46
12/11	7.18	21	11	0.37	0.00	3.39
12/10	5.17	18	9	0.33	0.00	3.66
Annual Growth	**43.0%**	**—**	**—**	**53.0%**	**—**	**21.9%**

Cantel Medical Corp

Cantel Medical can tell you that cleanliness is second to nothing when it comes to medical and scientific equipment. Through its subsidiaries the firm sells infection prevention and control products to hospitals dentists drugmakers researchers and others in the US and abroad in the field of health care. Its diverse offerings include medical device reprocessing systems and disinfectants for dialyzers and endoscopes water purification equipment masks and bibs used in dental offices specialty packaging of biological and pharmaceutical products and therapeutic filtration systems. Fast-growing Cantel Medical employs an active acquisition strategy.

Operations
Cantel Medical's major subsidiary companies include: Mar Con Purification (water filtration and purification); Medivators (disposables disinfection sterilization); Crosstex (infection control and prevention); and Saf-T-Pak (packaging medical shipping systems). Endoscopy products account for about 40% of Cantel's sales followed by water purification/filtration with around 30%.Disposable products account for about a fifth of sales followed by dialysis with about 10%.

Geographic Reach
Cantel Medical rings up more than 80% of its sales in the US. Foreign markets include Canada Europe Africa the Middle East South America and the Asia-Pacific region.

Sales and Marketing
Cantel's customers include diagnostic clinical and university laboratories as well as pharma and biotech companies United States and Canadian government agencies hospitals and medical research facilities.

In the US the company uses its own sales force to market its products; in international markets it employs independent distribution companies.

Financial Analysis
Cantel Medical's fiscal 2014 (ends July) net sales rose 15% from $425 million to $489 million as demand increased across the board new acquisitions contributed and the company introduced new products. The uptick in revenue lead to a 9% increase in net income from $43 million to $39 million offset by an increase in operating expenses. Strong revenue and net income lead to a 25% jump in cash from operations; a change in the timing of the company's payments of vendor invoices and tax bills also helped.

Strategy
Cantel Medical has grown and diversified by employing an active acquisition strategy. Indeed the company has made nearly 20 purchases over the past decade. The firm targets companies in the infection prevention and control market healthcare disposable products and water purification and filtration markets among others. More recently it has focused on endoscopy. It supplements acquisitions with occasional product launches including 2013's new disinfectant for heat-sensitive materials and devices.

Mergers and Acquisitions
The acquisitive company made two purchased in 2013 dialysis water and colonoscopy tool companies and in 2014 it picked up a sterilization process monitoring firm. The biggest purchase of late however is Cantel's 2014 acquisition of UK endoscope and supply maker PuriCore for $27 million. PuriCore became Cantel Medical UK and joined its parent's endoscopy segment.

EXECUTIVES

Chief Financial Officer, Ann E. Berman, age 61
CEO and Director, Andrew A. Krakauer, age 59, $612,500 total compensation
EVP and General Counsel, Eric W. Nodiff, age 57, $346,857 total compensation
President and COO, Jorgen B. Hansen, age 48, $434,611 total compensation
Vice President Human Resources, Chris Geschickter
Vice President Of Infection Prevention, Chuck Hughes
Vice President Business Systems And Procurement, Lawrence Conway
Vice President, Matt Conlon
Vice Chairman, George L. Fotiades, age 61
Chairman, Charles M. Diker, age 79
CEO and Director, Andrew A. Krakauer, age 59
Assistant Secretary, Ann Gitin
Auditors: Ernst&YoungLLP

LOCATIONS

HQ: Cantel Medical Corp
150 Clove Road, 9th Floor, Little Falls, NJ 07424
Phone: 973 890-7220   **Fax:** 973 890-7270
Web: www.cantelmedical.com

2014 Sales

	$ mil.	% of total
US	403.9	83
Europe Africa & Middle East	32.6	7
Asia/Pacific	24.7	5
Canada	20.7	4
Latin America/South America	6.8	1
Total	**488.7**	**100**

PRODUCTS/OPERATIONS

2014 Sales

	$ mil.	% of total
Endoscopy	190.4	39
Water purification & filtration	159.5	33
Healthcare Disposables	101.8	21
Dialysis	30.9	6
Other	6.1	1
Total	**488.7**	**100**

Selected Acquisitions

FY2014
  PuriCore International Limited ($27 million; Somerset UK; endoscope products)
FY2013
  Jet Prep Ltd ($5 million; Herzliya Israel; developer of JET PREP Flushing device)
FY2012
  Byrne Medical Inc. ($100 million; Houston TX; infection control products)
FY2011
  ConFirm Monitoring Systems Inc. ($7.5 million; Denver Colorado; sterilization monitoring products)
  Gambro Medical Water Systems ($23.7 million; Colorado; production of medical grade water)

Selected Subsidiaries

Biolab Equipment Ltd.
Carsen Group Inc. (Canada)
Crosstex International Inc.
Medivators Inc.
Medivators Japan K.K.
Saf-T-Pak Inc. (Canada)
Strong Dental Products Inc.

COMPETITORS

3M Health Care	Getinge
CONMED Corporation	Johnson & Johnson
DENTSPLY	Kimberly-Clark Health
Danaher	Olympus
Ecolab	STERIS
Fresenius	Siemens AG
GE Water and Process	TIDI Products
Technologies	

HISTORICAL FINANCIALS
Company Type: Public

Income Statement
FYE: July 31

	REVENUE ($ mil.)	NET INCOME ($ mil.)	NET PROFIT MARGIN	EMPLOYEES
07/14	488.7	43.2	8.9%	1,534
07/13	425.0	39.2	9.2%	1,292
07/12	386.4	31.3	8.1%	1,198
07/11	321.6	20.4	6.4%	1,117
07/10	273.9	19.9	7.3%	883
Annual Growth	15.6%	21.4%	—	14.8%

2014 Year-End Financials

Debt ratio: 15.0%
Return on equity: 12.6%
Cash ($ mil.): 31
Current ratio: 2.46
Long-term debt ($ mil.): 80

No. of shares (mil.): 41
Dividends
  Yield: 0.2%
  Payout: 8.7%
Market value ($ mil.): 1,390

	STOCK PRICE ($) FY Close	P/E High/Low	PER SHARE ($) Earnings	Dividends	Book Value
07/14	33.53	36 25	1.04	0.09	8.81
07/13	26.54	39 26	0.95	0.09	7.81
07/12	26.12	42 25	0.77	0.09	6.79
07/11	24.93	53 26	0.52	0.05	6.03
07/10	15.88	41 25	0.52	0.04	5.52
Annual Growth	20.5%	— —	18.7%	19.3%	12.4%

Carbo Ceramics Inc.

CARBO Ceramics' proppants (tiny alumina-based ceramic beads) are a welcome release for natural gas and oil well operators. To increase well production operators often pump fluids down wells at high pressure to create fractures in the hydrocarbon-bearing rock formation (hydraulic fracturing). Proppants are suspended in the fluid to fill the channels and "prop" up the fissures so that natural gas and oil may flow to the surface. The company's products compete against guar bean and sand-based proppants. CARBO Ceramics also offers related software consulting services and specialty polymers.

Geographic Reach

Headquartered in Houston Texas CARBO Ceramics manufactures its products in Eufaula Alabama; New Iberia Louisiana; Toomsboro and McIntyre Georgia; Luoyang China; and Kopeysk Russia. The company has numerous storage and distribution facilities in North America (US and Canada) Europe and Asia (China).

The US is CARBO Ceramics largest market accounting for 77% of company's revenues in 2012.

Operations

CARBO Ceramics is the world's leading supplier of ceramic proppant the provider of the world's most popular fracture simulation software and a supplier of fracture design and consulting services. The company also offers a broad range of technologies for spill prevention containment and countermeasures.

The company's ceramic proppants are made from alumina-bearing ores (including clay bauxite bauxitic clay and kaolin). The main deposits of these ores in the US are in Arkansas Alabama and Georgia; other economically viable deposits are found in Australia Brazil China Gabon India Jamaica Russia and Surinam.

In North America the company leased 2100 rail cars to distribute its products and expected to add 250 more railcars by the end of 2013.

Its other operations include Falcon Technologies (high performance polymers) and StrataGen (reservoir stimulation technology).

Sales and Marketing

CARBO Ceramics supplies its customers with products on a just-in-time basis. Continuing sales of products depend on the company's direct customers and the well operators being satisfied with product quality availability and delivery performance. It also provides its software simulation products and consulting services directly to owners and/or operators of oil and gas wells and service companies.

The company's international marketing efforts are conducted through sales offices in Dubai UAE; Aberdeen Scotland; Beijing China; and Moscow Russia and through commissioned sales agents in China and South America.

Halliburton and Schlumberger each accounted for more than 10% of CARBO Ceramics' 2012 and 2011 revenues.

Financial Performance

CARBO Ceramics saw its revenues grow by 3% in 2012 due to 7% increase in proppant sales volume and an increase in sales from some other business units partially offset by a drop in proppant prices as a result of competitive pricing pressures. An increase in the oil rigs lifted North American demand as did the acceptance of the company's products in oily liquids-rich basins. International sales volumes grew led by increases in China Mexico and Russia partially offset by a decrease in Europe. The company reported a $105.9 million net income in 2012 down 18.6% over the previous year primarily due to increased operating expenses. Selling general and administrative expenses rose due to higher administrative spending. Other operating expenses consisted primarily of a loss on disposal of assets as the result of CARBO Ceramics winding down Applied Geomechanics its geotechnical monitoring operation. With the exception of a recession-driven revenue slump in 2009 the company reported an upward trend in revenues from 2008 through 2012.

Strategy

Growing its US manufacturing base in 2012 CARBO Ceramics began construction of a 600 million pound-per-year resin-coating plant in Marshfield Wisconsin. In 2011 the company acquired real estate and submitted environmental permit applications to construct a ceramic proppant plant in the Millen Georgia area. CARBO Ceramics believes this plant (due for completion in 2013) could support a manufacturing capacity of up to 500 million pounds of ceramic proppant per year.

Ownership

William C. Morris owns 12% of CARBO Ceramics.

Company Background

The company was incorporated in 1987.

EXECUTIVES

VP Chief Financial Officer, Ernesto Bautista, age 43, $305,000 total compensation
VP Operations, Mark L. Edmunds, age 59, $272,500 total compensation
President and CEO, Gary A. Kolstad, age 55, $700,000 total compensation
VP Marketing and Sales, David G. Gallagher, age 56, $283,750 total compensation
Managing Director Asia Pacific, Hongwei Wang
Managing Director Europe Middle East Africa, Paul Masseboeuf
VP of Marketing and Sales, Don P. Conkle, $94,053 total compensation
Vice President Sales, Jenna Richardson
Senior Vice President Operations, Jeffrey Chalmers
Vice President Operations, Mark Vessely
Vice President Of Sales, Peter Grace
Vice President Human Resources, Ellen Smith
Vice President Marketing Sales, David Kasal
Chairman, William C. Morris, age 75
President and CEO, Gary A. Kolstad, age 55
Secretary, R Sean Elliott, age 41
Auditors: Ernst&YoungLLP

LOCATIONS

HQ: Carbo Ceramics Inc.
  575 North Dairy Ashford, Suite 300, Houston, TX 77079
Phone: 281 921-6400
Web: www.carboceramics.com

2012 Sales

	$ mil.	% of total
US	500.1	77
Canada	30.9	5
Other countries	114.5	18
Total	**645.5**	**100**

COMPETITORS

China GengSheng Minerals	Halliburton
Core Laboratories	Hi-Crush
Fairmount Minerals	Saint-Gobain
	Unimin

HISTORICAL FINANCIALS
Company Type: Public

Income Statement
FYE: December 31

	REVENUE ($ mil.)	NET INCOME ($ mil.)	NET PROFIT MARGIN	EMPLOYEES
12/13	667.4	84.8	12.7%	1,025
12/12	645.5	105.9	16.4%	992
12/11	625.7	130.1	20.8%	961
12/10	473.0	78.7	16.6%	806
12/09	341.8	52.8	15.4%	741
Annual Growth	18.2%	12.6%	—	8.4%

2013 Year-End Financials

Debt ratio: —
Return on equity: 11.4%
Cash ($ mil.): 94
Current ratio: 6.55
Long-term debt ($ mil.): —

No. of shares (mil.): 23
Dividends
  Yield: 0.9%
  Payout: 31.3%
Market value ($ mil.): 2,690

	STOCK PRICE ($) FY Close	P/E High/Low	PER SHARE ($) Earnings	Dividends	Book Value
12/13	116.53	34 18	3.67	1.14	33.30
12/12	78.34	29 13	4.59	1.02	30.88
12/11	123.33	32 17	5.62	0.88	27.27
12/10	103.54	30 17	3.40	0.76	22.59
12/09	68.17	31 12	2.27	0.70	19.82
Annual Growth	14.3%	— —	12.8%	13.0%	13.9%

Cardtronics Inc

Cardtronics is the largest non-bank owner and operator of automated teller machines (ATMs) and related financial services equipment in the world. It maintains more than 111000 cash machines in Europe and North America including 93350 locations in the US many of which are branded by banks such as Chase SunTrust and Citibank. The company also leases and sells machines to airports convenience stores supermarkets malls and drug stores including Walgreen and Rite-Aid stores. Most clients pay the company to handle some or all of the maintenance services or operational services of their ATMs. Cardtronics also operates Allpoint which is the largest surcharge-free ATM network in the US with 55000 machines.

Geographic Reach

Houston-based Cardtronics operates in the US (including all 50 states and the territories of Puerto Rico and the Virgin Islands) the UK Germany Mexico and Canada. The US is the firm's largest market accounting for 75% of revenue in 2013. Europe (the UK and Germany) contributes about 20%.

Operations

ATM operating revenues account for more than 95% of Cardtronics' total revenue. The rest is generated by ATM product sales. In addition to dispensing cash and responding to balance inquiries some Cardtronics ATMs take bill payments cash checks and transfer money. In the UK the company operates its own armored courier operation Green Team Services with secure cash deposit facilities in London and Manchester England.

Financial Performance

Cardtronics reported revenue of $876.5 million in 2013 an increase of 12% versus 2012 driven by rising revenue in Europe as a result of acquisitions and higher interchange revenues resulting from unit growth. While the company's revenue has grown steadily in recent years its net income of $23.8 million in 2013 is off sharply from its $70 million peak in 2011. The company blamed rising operating expenses including payroll costs acquisition related expenses and taxes on the restructuring of its UK operations for the squeeze. Cash flow from operations increased by $47.2 million over 2012 to $183.6 million in 2013 on higher operating profits and a $13.4 million boost from an outstanding insurance receivable.

Strategy

Worldwide ATM network expansion is at the top of Cardtronics' strategy. The fast-growing company entered the highly-fragmented ATM market in Germany with the purchase of UK-based Cardpoint Limited in August 2013. The purchase more than doubled Cardtronics' ATM portfolio in the UK and expanded its footprint to Germany. It contin-

ues to seek opportunities in the UK and Mexico which are operated by its Bank Machine and Cardtronics Mexico subsidiaries. Cardtronics also entered Canada with the 2011 purchase of Mr. Cash ATM Network (renamed Cardtronics Canada). The deal added some 600 machines throughout the country. In late 2012 Cardtronics Canada acquired privately-held Can-Do-Cash Ltd. an ATM services company headquartered in Ottawa. Other target growth areas include Central and Eastern Europe Central and South America and the Asia/Pacific region.

Other growth initiatives include building the company's Allpoint surcharge-free network in the US and to introduce it in Cardtronics' international markets. Under the Allpoint model financial institutions pay Cardtronics for participation instead of users paying transaction fees. In 2010 Allpoint entered Australia's market through a partnership with that country's largest ATM operator Customers Limited. The following year Allpoint entered Mexico by adding more than 2500 ATMs across the country.

Cardtronics also has attracted new customers who use prepaid debit cards to make cash withdrawals. These unbanked or underbanked customers previously could not use ATMs. However increased use of prepaid cards have allowed those users access to Cardtronics' kiosks. In 2010 Cardtronics struck a deal with MasterCard to offer free ATM access for prepaid cards. Also that year Univision launched a prepaid card product utilizing the Allpoint Network. The company plans to go after other opportunities to work with financial institutions that issue stored-value debit cards.

In addition to growing its ATM network the company also is interested in expanding its service capabilities.

Mergers and Acquisitions

In October 2014 the company acquired Welch ATM adding 26350 US ATMs and growing Cardtronics' domestic portfolio to 93350 ATMs. The $160 million purchase created a combined Walgreens portfolio of 5100 ATMs giving Cardtronics a significant portion of the drugstore chain's national footprint. It also added 3100 ATMs in Ride-Aid stores. Also in February 2014 the firm acquired Arizona-based Automated Financial LLC adding 2100 merchant ATM contracts and a sales and service office in Arizona. (Previous acquisitions added regional hubs in New Jersey Minnesota Oregon and California.)

In June 2013 Cardtronics bought the Merrimak ATM Group an independent ATM deployer based in California. Merrimak provides ATM managed services to a nationwide network of some 4800 ATMS. In May 2013 the company acquired Portland Oregon-based Aptus Financial a leader in ATM sales ATM leasing and management services. In March its UK subsidiary bought i-design group plc a Scottish firm that provides technology and services that print ads on ATM screens and receipts for third-party advertisers.

EXECUTIVES

President U.S. Business Group, Rick Updyke, age 55, $309,679 total compensation
EVP of Network and Financial Services, Ben Psillas
President Global Services, Michael H. (Mike) Clinard, age 47, $400,582 total compensation
CEO, Steven A. (Steve) Rathgaber, age 61, $569,384 total compensation
President Enterprise Growth Group, David Dove

EVP and Division Executive ATM Services, Carleton K. (Tres) Thompson, age 45, $200,170 total compensation
EVP of Audit and Risk Management, Randy Rice
EVP of U.S, Tony Muscarello
EVP of Product Management, Bill Knoll
General Manager Mexico, Scott Abogado
EVP Corporate Development, Phillip Chin
SEVP Sales and Relationship Management, Todd Clark, age 47, $335,000 total compensation
EVP Global Operations, Jeffrey B. Keith
Chief Accounting Officer, Brad Conrad
Chief Information Officer, Mike McCarthy
EVP of Global Operations, Jeffery B. Keith
EVP of Human Resources, Debra Bronder
Executive Vice President - Global Procurement, Ric Davis
Managing Director - Cardtronics Europe, Jonathan SimpsonDent
Vice President Information Technology, Ernie Aurbor
Vice President Retail Sales, Tony Anthony
Senior Vice President Cash And Delivery, Dawn Alvarez
Senior Vice President Sales Financial Institutions, Tina Reese
Senior Vice President Management, David McCrary
Senior Vice President Customer Services, Adam Roark
Vice President Information Technology, Ernie Freudenthal
Senior Vice President Financial, Steve Lund
Vice President National Sales, Ralph Depp
Vice President National Accounts, Earl Jess
Vice President Tax, Christine Nguyen
Vice President Operation Analytics, Steve Miller
Vice President Information Technology, Ernie Arbour
Senior Vice President Solutions, Dillman Moree
Vice President Financial Services, John Dyer
Vice President Sales, Mike Hudkins
Senior Vice President Mexico Sales, Giovanni Locandro
National Sales Manager, Laine Cipolla
Vice President, Greg Rippey
Vice President Atm Solutions, Tom Gress
Executive Vice President International, Anthony Horne
Vice President Program Management, Laura Dallman
Vice President Field Operations, Joe Stevens
Vice President Sales, Jim Howe
Senior Vice President Customer Support, Susan Panya
Vice President Us Digital Marketing, Elizabeth Birenbaum
Vice President Operations, Maya Fuentes
Vice President Of Atm Technology, Henry Blades
Vice President Of Strategic Alliances, Dave Olender
Vice President Tax, Christine Murdock
Senior Vice President And Ciso, Doug Martin
Senior Vice President Corporate, Chris Mounts
Vice President Customer Care, George Someson
Vp Continuous Improvement, Kevin Barmettler
Vice President Client Executive, Mike Sears
Svp Eft, Jerry Gray
Evp Opns, Jim Bettinger
Vice President Financial Services, Laura Gleason
Vice President, Ken Bliss
Svp Pmo, Janene Budnik
Vp Fraud Prevention And Remediation, Henry Freyer
Svp North America Accounting, Alan Watson
Senior Vice President Retail Sales And Relationship Management, Chris Juetten
Vice President Corporate Development, Benjamin Bregman

Vp Relationship Management, Joseph Biener
National Sales Manager, Luke Doelle
Vice President Service, Glenn Olson
Svp Merchant Business Unit, Lloyd Nobles
Vice President Product Management, Wade Edwards
Vp Sales & Business Development, Joe Makarewicz
Vp Process Improvement, Melissa Justice
Vice President, Ken Gaston
Vice President, Robin Robicheau
Senior Vice President Indirect Business, Jeremy Inman
Vice President Global Procurement, Jeff Ude
Chairman, Dennis F. Lynch, age 65
Board Member, Mark Rossi
Auditors: KPMGLLP

LOCATIONS

HQ: Cardtronics Inc
  3250 Briarpark Drive, Suite 400, Houston, TX 77042
Phone: 832 308-4000
Web: www.cardtronics.com

2013 Sales by Region

	$ mil.	% of total
US	657.4	75
Europe	178.5	20
Other international	40.6	5
Total	**876.5**	**100**

PRODUCTS/OPERATIONS

2013 Sales

	$ mil.	% of total
ATM operating revenues	854.2	97
ATM product sales & other	22.3	3
Total	**876.5**	**100**

Selected Mergers & Acquisitions

2011
  Mr. Cash ATM Network Inc. (Letherbridge Alberta Canada; ATM network)
  EDC ATM Subsidiary LLC/Efmark Deployment I Inc. ($145 million; Walnut Creek California; ATM network)
  Access to Money Inc. (Cherry Hill New Jersey; merchant-owned ATMs
  LocatorSearch LLC (New York; location search technology)

COMPETITORS

BBVA Bancomer	HSBC Fianzas
Banamex	Lloyds Banking Group
Bank of America	NYCE Payments Network
Barclays Bank	PNC Financial
DirectCash	PayPoint
Electronic Cash Systems	Payment Alliance
Fifth Third	Payzone
First Data	Royal Bank of Scotland
Global Axcess	U.S. Bancorp
	WRG Services

HISTORICAL FINANCIALS

Company Type: Public

Income Statement

FYE: December 31

	REVENUE ($ mil.)	NET INCOME ($ mil.)	NET PROFIT MARGIN	EMPLOYEES
12/13	876.4	23.8	2.7%	1,070
12/12	780.4	43.2	5.5%	740
12/11	624.5	70.1	11.2%	643
12/10	532.0	41.1	7.7%	535
12/09	493.3	5.2	1.1%	460
Annual Growth	**15.5%**	**45.8%**	**—**	**23.5%**

2013 Year-End Financials

Debt ratio: 46.4%	No. of shares (mil.): 44
Return on equity: 12.0%	Dividends
Cash ($ mil.): 86	Yield: —
Current ratio: 0.96	Payout: —
Long-term debt ($ mil.): 489	Market value ($ mil.): 1,928

	STOCK PRICE ($) FY Close	P/E High/Low	PER SHARE ($) Earnings	Dividends	Book Value
12/13	43.45	85 45	0.52	0.00	5.61
12/12	23.74	32 23	0.96	0.00	3.30
12/11	27.06	18 10	1.58	0.00	2.54
12/10	17.70	19 10	0.96	0.00	0.99
12/09	11.06	94 7	0.13	0.00	(0.07)
Annual Growth	**40.8%**	**— —**	**41.4%**		

Carpenter Technology Corp.

The Tin Man never would have rusted had he been built with metal from Carpenter Technology. It processes basic raw materials such as cobalt nickel manganese and titanium to make various corrosion-resistant materials. Most sales come from stainless steel products and alloys that provide special heat- or wear-resistance or special magnetic or conductive properties. Finished products come in billet bar rod wire and other forms. Carpenter also produces certain metal powders. Markets include aerospace automotive medical and industrial companies. Aerospace and defense accounted for 46% of its total sales in fiscal 2014.

Geographic Reach

Carpenter has manufacturing plants in the US (Florida Ohio Pennsylvania Rhode Island and South Carolina) and in Sweden. In fiscal 2014 the US accounted for 71% of company's total revenues.

Operations

The company manufactures fabricates and distributes specialty metals. Its three operating segments were Specialty Alloys Operations (premium alloy and stainless steel manufacturing operations); Latrobe (the manufacturing and distribution operations of the Latrobe businesses acquired in 2012); and Performance Engineered Products (including Dynamet titanium Carpenter Powder Products Amega West and the Specialty Steel Supply distribution business that was gained in connection with the Latrobe Specialty Metals acquisition).

Carpenter changed its reportable segments in 2014 to reflect the completion of the integration of the Latrobe Specialty Metals businesses. As a result Carpenter has two reportable segments Specialty Alloys Operations and Performance Engineered Products.

Financial Performance

After experiencing sizable growth since 2009 in fiscal 2014 the company's revenues decreased by 4% reflect a drop in sales combined with higher shipment volume and an unfavorable shift in product mix. Sales to the aerospace and defense market declined by 8% as the result of supply chain destocking in the first half of fiscal year. Energy market sales decreased by 8% reflecting weak demand in materials used in oil and gas completions as well as the power generation sector. These de-clines were partially offset by a moderate increase in sales particularly rentals through in the Amega West oil and gas business.In fiscal 2014 Carpenter's net income decreased by 9% due to a decline in revenues and other income as the result of a decrease in earnings in the funding mechanisms for certain non-qualified retirement plans and the negative impacts of foreign exchange losses.That year the company's operating cash inflow increased to $239.6 million (compared to $188.5 million in 2013) primarily due to higher free cash flow (reflecting a drop in pension contributions –$6.3 million in 2014 compared to $144.9 million in 2013 as a result of the $75 million of discretionary pension contributions included in 2013 which significantly reduced the minimum contributions that were required in 2014).

Strategy

Carpenter grows through strategic partnerships organic expansion and complementary acquisitions.

Expanding its supply position in 2013 the company signed a multi-level agreement with United Technologies Corporation through its Pratt & Whitney Division. The deal includes the production of superalloy powders (and associated licensing technology) and a long-term supply agreement. Carpenter plans to build a $20 million superalloy powder facility. Additionally UTC's aerospace business units (Pratt & Whitney Pratt & Whitney Canada Corp. UTC Aerospace Systems and Sikorsky Aircraft Corporation) have agreed to purchase alloy steel bar/billet nickel superalloy billet stainless bar/billet and strip laminate products from Carpenter for a period of ten years. Carpenter currently supplies UTC's aerospace businesses with a portion of their overall demand for nickel stainless and strip laminate products.That year it also signed a supply deal to provide Rolls-Royce with advanced technology materials used in the manufacture of jet engine components including rings blades vanes and airfoils. Demand for the material will be generated by Rolls-Royce in the UK and the US and its global suppliers. Materials in support of this program will be manufactured at Carpenter's Reading Pennsylvania and Athens Alabama specialty steelmaking facilities.

That year Carpenter signed a deal with US Steel for the development of a new "lightweighting" steel for automotive applications. Carpenter's patented alloy TEMPER TOUGH specialized steel alloy is designed for use in flat-roll automotive applications as well as other demanding applications.

Responding to rapid growth in Asia in 2013 the company also announced plans to build a bar finishing plant in China.

Company Background

In order to keep a tight focus on manufacturing and selling specialty materials for the aerospace energy and other high-growth markets Carpenter began trimming in 2012 by announcing that it was commencing the process to sell its distribution businesses: Latrobe Specialty Steel Distribution (LSSD) which it gained as part of its 2012 Latrobe Specialty Metals acquisition and Aceros Fortuna Carpenter's Mexican distribution business. The proceeds will be reinvested into its core product businesses.

In 2012 Carpenter acquired rival Latrobe for $558 million. (Latrobe which filed for an IPO in 2011 made and distributed specialty metals and alloys used for landing gear oil valves turbine bolts and metal-cutting dies. The deal elevates Carpenter's position in the aerospace and energy markets. To gain approval by US antitrust authorities however Carpenter agreed to sell assets used in making alloys for two aerospace applications (MP159 and MP35N) to French metals manufacturer Eramet).

HISTORY

Engineer James Henry Carpenter founded Carpenter Steel in Pennsylvania in 1889. The company began making specialty steels after winning a US Navy contract to develop armor-piercing projectiles. Business declined after Carpenter's death in 1898 but former rival Robert Jennings took over and the company rebounded thanks to marketing savvy and the development of new steel grades. Carpenter first produced stainless steel in 1917.

The company went public in 1937 and continued to grow. It made huge expansions in its production capacity to meet the demands spawned by WWII. The company changed its name to Carpenter Technology Corporation in 1968.

Carpenter survived the 1981-82 recession largely because of its lucrative niche in specialty steel. Another recession led to a 1991 reorganization. Robert Cardy a 30-year company veteran became chairman president and CEO the next year.

In 1994 Carpenter established a joint venture in Taiwan with Walsin-Lihwa (a Taiwanese maker of cable and wire). It also acquired Aceros Fortuna (Mexico's largest distributor of specialty steel) and purchased Certech (structural ceramics). In 1997 the company bought Dynamet a producer of titanium bar and wire. It also purchased about 75% of diversified manufacturer Talley Industries for about $312 million acquiring the remainder of Talley the next year. Carpenter formed a joint venture with Kalyani Steels in 1999 to make and distribute specialty steels in India.

High natural gas prices forced the company to increase prices for its nickel- and cobalt-based high-temperature alloys in 2001. The following year Carpenter's sales decreased due to lower stainless steel shipments and an overall weakness in the manufacturing industry.

In 2003 Carpenter's president Robert Torcolini was named to the added positions of chairman and CEO after chairman Dennis Draeger's retirement. Because of broad-based demand on its products Carpenter raised prices primarily on its stainless bar premium-metal alloys and high-speed tool steel products in 2004.

The next year Carpenter sold its Special Products unit a manufacturer of precision engineered metal components and assemblies to investment firm WHI Capital Partners. The former Carpenter Special Products which served customers in the aerospace medical device and nuclear power generation businesses was renamed Veridiam. Carpenter continued to supply alloys to its former subsidiary.

Three years after he took on the added roles of chairman and CEO Torcolini announced his retirement. Carpenter went outside the company to find his replacement tabbing Ford veteran Anne Stevens to take on all three titles.

The company's former Special Products unit sold in 2005 now operates as Veridiam. Carpenter continues to supply alloys to Veridiam which serves customers in the aerospace medical device and nuclear power generation businesses.

William Wulfsohn a former SVP with PPG Industries was named president and CEO of Carpenter in 2010.

To strengthen its presence globally in high-alloy metal powder products Carpenter formed a joint venture in 2010 with Sweden-based Sandvik Powdermet designed to lock in access to each other's goods and services. Each company took a 40% stake in the other assuring Sandvik's supply of powder materials and Carpenter's access to global manufacturing and sales services. The partnership will facilitate joint development of powder metal products particularly for the energy sector.

In fiscal 2011 Carpenter's net revenues increased about 40% as net sales reached nearly $1.7 billion in 2011 compared to less than $1.2 billion in 2010. Carpenter cited improved product mix price increases and better performance for the jump in profit and sales. Net income also soared in 2011 reaching $71.7 million compared to $2.1 million in 2010.

In 2011 Carpenter acquired Amega West Services a Houston-based manufacturer and service provider of components for directional drilling equipment and Oilfield Alloys Pte. a Singapore-based directional drilling equipment company. The acquisitions helped Carpenter to expand its presence in the directional drilling equipment market.

EXECUTIVES

Vice President Financial Planning, Jaime Vasquez
Vp Manufacturing, Russell E Reber
Vice President Engineering, Bernard Mara
Chairman and CEO, Gregory A. Pratt, age 66, $296,528 total compensation
SVP and CFO, Tony R. Thene, age 54, $449,515 total compensation
VP and CIO, James A. Johnson
VP Coil Strip and Plate Products Business, Andrew T. Ziolkowski, age 49, $380,644 total compensation
VP Research and Product Commercialization, Timothy R. Armstrong
SVP Global Operations, David L. Strobel, age 53, $381,878 total compensation
VP Strategic Primes Group, Stephen Peskosky
SVP Performance Engineered Products, Gary Heasley, age 49, $350,077 total compensation
VP Manufacturing and Reading Operations, Matthew S. Enoch
VP Bar Wire Strip Business Unit, Jerold S. Leibensperger
Associate Vice President Customer, Tammy Koch
Vice President Investor Relations, Michael A (Mike) Hajost
Vp Investor Relations And Business Development, David A Christiansen, age 59
Vice-president, Carol Jackson
Senior Vice President And Regional, Paul Hartley
Vice President Market Development, Dudley Merchant
Executive Assistant To Sr Vp Chief, Cheryl Kuszyk
Executive Vice-president, Laurence Miller
Vice President, Bill Beible
Chairman and CEO, Gregory A. Pratt, age 66
Auditors: PricewaterhouseCoopersLLP

LOCATIONS

HQ: Carpenter Technology Corp.
P.O. Box 14662, Reading, PA 19610
Phone: 610 208-2000   **Fax:** 610 208-2361
Web: www.cartech.com

2014 Sales

	$ mil.	% of total
North America		
US	1537.9	71
Mexico	59.2	3
Canada	65.3	3
Europe	349.5	16
Asia/Pacific	137.1	6
Other regions	24.0	1
Total	**2173.0**	**100**

PRODUCTS/OPERATIONS

2014 Sales by Product

	$ mil.	% of total
Special alloys	917.0	42
Stainless steel	643.6	30
Alloy & tool steel	240.4	11
Titanium products	157.7	7
Powder metals	48.6	2
Distribution & other	165.7	8
Total	**2173.0**	**100**

2014 Sales by Market

	$ mil.	% of total
Aerospace	980.7	46
Industrial & consumer	481.6	22
Energy	310.4	14
Transportation	150.1	7
Distribution	137.6	6
Medical	112.6	5
Total	**2173.0**	**100**

COMPETITORS

AK Steel Holding Corporation	JFE Holdings
Allegheny Technologies	Nucor
Dofasco	Precision Castparts
Earle M. Jorgensen	RTI International Metals
Eramet	Titanium Metals
Essar Steel Algoma	United States Steel
Gerdau Ameristeel	

HISTORICAL FINANCIALS

Company Type: Public

Income Statement

FYE: June 30

	REVENUE ($ mil.)	NET INCOME ($ mil.)	NET PROFIT MARGIN	EMPLOYEES
06/14	2,173.0	132.8	6.1%	4,900
06/13	2,271.7	146.1	6.4%	4,800
06/12	2,028.7	121.2	6.0%	4,800
06/11	1,675.1	71.0	4.2%	3,500
06/10	1,198.6	2.1	0.2%	3,000
Annual Growth	**16.0%**	**182.0%**	**—**	**13.0%**

2014 Year-End Financials

Debt ratio: 19.7%	No. of shares (mil.): 53
Return on equity: 9.4%	Dividends
Cash ($ mil.): 120	Yield: 1.1%
Current ratio: 2.77	Payout: 28.4%
Long-term debt ($ mil.): 604	Market value ($ mil.): 3,361

	STOCK PRICE ($) FY Close	P/E High/Low		PER SHARE ($) Earnings	Dividends	Book Value
06/14	63.25	27	18	2.47	0.72	28.31
06/13	45.07	20	16	2.73	0.72	24.69
06/12	47.84	23	16	2.53	0.72	21.06
06/11	57.68	36	19	1.59	0.72	17.36
06/10	32.83	106	3422	0.04	0.72	13.04
Annual Growth	**17.8%**	**—**		**—180.3%**	**(0.0%)**	**21.4%**

Carrizo Oil & Gas, Inc.

Carrizo Oil & Gas sees its future in 3-D. An independent exploration and production company that explores for oil and gas in a handful of shale plays across the US and in proven onshore fields along the Gulf Coast of Texas and Louisiana Carrizo aggressively acquires 3-D seismic data and arranges land lease options in conjunction with conducting seismic surveys. As part of its shale strategy the company is exploiting the Marcellus play in Appalachia and the Eagle Ford and Barnett plays in Texas. Carrizo has additional properties in the Rockies Arkansas Kentucky Mississippi New Mexico and in the UK North Sea. In 2011 the firm reported proved reserves of 935.6 billion cu. ft. of natural gas equivalent.

Operations

Carrizo's oil and gas exploration and production operations are principally focused on developing proven producing oil and gas plays. In 2011 the company's proved reserves were 78% natural gas and 22% crude oil condensate and natural gas liquids.

Geographic Reach

The company focuses on the Eagle Ford Shale in South Texas the Niobrara Formation in Colorado the Barnett Shale in North Texas the Marcellus Shale in Pennsylvania New York and West Virginia and the Utica Shale in Ohio and Pennsylvania. Outside the US it is working in the UK North Sea in the Huntington Field.

Financial Analysis

Revenues from oil and gas production in 2011 increased 46% to $202.2 million from $138.1 million in 2010. Production volumes for oil and gas in 2011 increased 22% to 45.1 billion cu. ft. equivalent from 36.8 billion cu. ft. equivalent in 2010.

The increase in production from new oil wells in 2011 helped to lift revenues assisted by a jump in oil prices. Average oil prices increased 20% to $94.1 per barrel from $78.6 per barrel in 2010. By contrast average natural gas prices declined 11% to $2.98 per Mcf in 2011 from $3.33 per Mcf in 2010. Natural gas liquids prices increased 31% to $8.4 per Mcf in 2011 from $6.43 per Mcf in 2010 although lower production of NGLs led to a revenue decline in this segment.

In 2011 net income grew by 268% as surging revenues outpaced an increase in operating expenses and Carrizo did not have to carry the $31 million debt-related charge it carried in 2010.

Strategy

The company's strategy is focused on organic growth and to ramp up the development of shale plays (both in the US —Barnett Eagle Ford Marcellus Niobrara and Utica —and in the UK) which have become more commercially viable thanks to advances in drilling technology in recent years. It is pushing to develop higher return crude oil and liquids-rich shale assets (Eagle Ford Niobrara and Utica) to take advantage of high oil oil and NGL prices. The company also seeks capital influx from other companies (inclduing Indian oil companies) through joint ventures to help to develop its cost-intensive shale assets.

In 2012 Carrizo formed a joint venture with subsidiaries of OIL India Ltd. and Indian Oil to exploit Carrizo's assets in the Niobrara Formation oil development in Colorado. Carrizo sold its partners a 30% interest in the Colorado asset for $82.5 million.

In 2011 Carrizo and Avista Capital Partners formed a joint venture to acquire and develop acreage in the liquids rich region of the Utica Shale. In a similar move Carrizo also teamed up with India's GAIL Limited forming a joint venture to exploit assets in the Eagle Ford Shale.

In 2010 the company joined forces with Indian conglomerate Reliance Industries forming a joint venture which acquired 104400 undeveloped leasehold acres in the Marcellus Shale in Appalachia.

Selected Customers

DTE Energy Trading accounted for 43% of Carrizo's revenues in 2011.

EXECUTIVES

Vice President Of Information, Michael Hahn
President CEO and Director, S. P. (Chip) Johnson, age 59, $448,000 total compensation
VP and COO, J. Bradley (Brad) Fisher, age 54, $312,000 total compensation
Vice President of Exploration and Development, Gregory E. Evans, age 65, $303,000 total compensation
Vice President of Land, Richard H. Smith, age 57, $221,000 total compensation
CFO Chief Accounting Officer and Treasurer, David L. Pitts, age 48, $303,000 total compensation
VP Business Development (Marcellus), Jim Pritts
General Counsel and VP Business Development, Gerry Morton
Vice President, Kendall Trahan
Vice President, Jennifer Thompson
Vice President Of Business Development, Gary Uhland
Vice President Land, Jack Bayless
Vice President Internal Audit, Ben Verdina
Chairman, Steven A. Webster, age 62
President CEO and Director, S. P. (Chip) Johnson, age 59
CFO Chief Accounting Officer and Treasurer, David L. Pitts, age 48
Secretary, Lisa Gore
Board Member, Gardner F Parker
Auditors: KPMGLLP

LOCATIONS

HQ: Carrizo Oil & Gas, Inc.
500 Dallas Street, Suite 2300, Houston, TX 77002
Phone: 713 328-1000 **Fax:** 281 496-1035
Web: www.crzo.net

PRODUCTS/OPERATIONS

2011 Sales

	$ mil.	% of total
Natural gas	116.1	58
Oil & condensate	75.5	37
NGLs	10.6	5
Total	**202.2**	**100**

COMPETITORS

Abraxas Petroleum	Gastar Exploration
Adams Resources	Newfield Exploration
BP	Penn Virginia
Belden & Blake	Petrohawk Energy
Chesapeake Energy	Pioneer Natural
Chevron	Resources
Clayton Williams	Quicksilver Resources
Energy	Samson
Comstock Resources	Shell Oil
EnLink Midstream LLC	Statoil
Exxon Mobil	TOTAL
Forest Oil	

HISTORICAL FINANCIALS

Company Type: Public

Income Statement

FYE: December 31

	REVENUE ($ mil.)	NET INCOME ($ mil.)	NET PROFIT MARGIN	EMPLOYEES
12/13	520.1	43.6	8.4%	229
12/12	368.1	55.4	15.1%	208
12/11	202.1	36.6	18.1%	169
12/10	139.4	9.9	7.1%	132
12/09	114.0	(204.8)	—	111
Annual Growth	**46.1%**			**19.8%**

2013 Year-End Financials

Debt ratio: 42.6%
Return on equity: 6.1%
Cash ($ mil.): 157
Current ratio: 0.87
Long-term debt ($ mil.): 900
No. of shares (mil.): 45
Dividends
Yield: —
Payout: —
Market value ($ mil.): 2,036

	STOCK PRICE ($) FY Close	P/E High/Low	PER SHARE ($) Earnings	Dividends	Book Value
12/13	44.77	44 18	1.06	0.00	18.51
12/12	20.92	22 14	1.39	0.00	14.57
12/11	26.35	46 21	0.92	0.00	12.89
12/10	34.49	119 54	0.29	0.00	11.74
12/09	26.51	— —	(6.61)	0.00	7.96
Annual Growth	**14.0%**	— —	—	—	**23.5%**

Cascade Microtech Inc

In the foothills of the Cascade Range Cascade Microtech makes test systems for microelectronics. Semiconductor makers such as Broadcom Fujitsu Semiconductor IBM Intel Samsung and Toshiba use the company's probe cards probe stations and analytical probes to ensure the quality of their integrated circuits (ICs). Many of Cascade's customers use its tools to test their wireless broadband or other communications ICs at the wafer level before the wafers are cut into individual chips. The company has a development alliance with test equipment giant Agilent Technologies.

Geographic Reach

Cascade gets more than 70% of sales from outside the US primarily from customers in Asia.

Financial Performance

The company's revenue has been growing year-over-year. It reported revenue of $120 million for fiscal 2013 up from $113 million in fiscal 2012 and $104.6 million in fiscal 2011.

Cascade's net income has also been increasing every year. The company reported net income of $13.42 million in fiscal 2013 after clearing a little more than $6 million in fiscal 2012.

Cash flow also increased during fiscal 2013 compared to the prior fiscal period (by about $2 million).

EXECUTIVES

President and CEO; Director, Michael D. (Mike) Burger, age 55, $400,010 total compensation
Vp Advanced Development And Director Emeritus, K Reed Gleason, age 69
Chief Technical Officer; Director, Eric W. Strid, age 61, $203,231 total compensation

Executive Vice President, Steven L. (Steve) Harris, age 50, $272,234 total compensation

VP Marketing, Michael Kondrat, age 64, $163,846 total compensation

Vice President Finance and Chief Financial Officer, Jeff A. Killian, age 54, $252,582 total compensation

Vice President Operations, Steve Mahon, age 54

Vice President Corporate Development, Bruce McFadden

Vice President Corporate Techl, Ken Smith

Vice President Of Marketing, Ken Dawson

Vice President Of Marketing, Debbora Ahlgren

Vice President Sales, Robert Selley

Vice President Epd Technology Development, Reed Gleason

National Account Manager, Francis Lin

Vice President G (Financial Advisor), Joanne Phillips

Vp Sales, Paul Mara

President and CEO; Director, Michael D. (Mike) Burger, age 55

Chairman, F. Paul Carlson, age 75

Auditors: KPMGLLP

LOCATIONS

HQ: Cascade Microtech Inc
9100 S.W. Gemini Drive, Beaverton, OR 97008
Phone: 503 601-1000
Web: www.cascademicrotech.com

PRODUCTS/OPERATIONS

Selected Products

Analytical Probes
  Air coplanar probes and high-performance characterization (HPC) probes (transistors broadband chip packages)
Probe Stations
  Alessi series (general-purpose)
  S300 series (semi-automated with 300mm wafer testing capability)
  Summit series (transistor and chip measurements circuit element modeling)
Production Probe Cards
  LSI Pyramid probe cores (application-specific integrated circuits)
  Pyramid interface boards (all cores)
  RFC Pyramid probe cores (SONET and wireless chips optoelectronic devices)
  VLSR Pyramid probe cores (LCD driver chips)

COMPETITORS

Advantest	Interconnect Devices
Aehr Test Systems	KLA-Tencor
EG Systems	PDF Solutions
Everett Charles	Teradyne
Technologies	Xcerra
FormFactor	

HISTORICAL FINANCIALS

Company Type: Public

Income Statement

FYE: December 31

	REVENUE ($ mil.)	NET INCOME ($ mil.)	NET PROFIT MARGIN	EMPLOYEES
12/13	120.0	13.4	11.2%	426
12/12	112.9	6.1	5.4%	383
12/11	104.6	(5.8)	—	365
12/10	95.8	(10.3)	—	401
12/09	53.5	(7.6)	—	306
Annual Growth	22.4%	—	—	8.6%

2013 Year-End Financials

Debt ratio: —	No. of shares (mil.): 16
Return on equity: 16.4%	Dividends
Cash ($ mil.): 17	Yield: —
Current ratio: 4.20	Payout: —
Long-term debt ($ mil.): —	Market value ($ mil.): 151

	STOCK PRICE ($) FY Close	P/E High/Low	Earnings	PER SHARE ($) Dividends	Book Value
12/13	9.32	12 6	0.89	0.00	5.99
12/12	5.60	14 7	0.42	0.00	4.64
12/11	3.41	— —	(0.40)	0.00	4.19
12/10	4.35	— —	(0.72)	0.00	4.52
12/09	4.58	— —	(0.57)	0.00	5.30
Annual Growth	19.4%	— —	—	—	3.1%

Cash America International, Inc.

If cash is king then Cash America International is king of pawns. Cash America operates more than 960 stores under the banners Cash America Pawn SuperPawn and Pawn X-Change in the US and Cash America casa de empe ±o in Mexico. The company is one of the largest providers of secured non-recourse loans (also known as pawn loans). As part of its business Cash America also provides cash advances in half a dozen states through shops operating under the Cashland and Cash America Payday Advance banners. The company offers check cashing money orders and money transfers through about 90 owned and franchised Mr. Payroll stores in about 15 states.

Geographic Reach

Cash America operates through about two dozen US states as well as in Mexico. The US accounts for about 80% of its revenue. Its retail segment operates primarily in Texas and Ohio. Through its e-commerce business Cash America enjoys an extended reach into the UK Australia Canada and Mexico.

Operations

The company operates its business through two segments: Retail Services (63% of revenue) and E-commerce (37%).

Retail Services include pawn lending and consumer lending among other services. Its domestic retail services locations operate under the names Cash America Pawn SuperPawn Cash America Payday Advance Cashland and Mr. Payroll. The domestic retail services locations it has acquired were rebranded in 2013 as Cash America Pawn or SuperPawn. Its foreign retail services locations began operating exclusively under the name Cash America casa de empe ±o (previously operating under the name Prenda F´cil).

The E-commerce segment comprises its domestic and foreign online lending channels through which Cash America offers consumer loans. The segment operated in more than 30 US states and in three foreign countries. It offers a line of credit product in Mexico that is similar to the micro line of credit (MLOC). Consumer loan fees contribute about 43% of the company's revenue.

Financial Performance

Revenue rose by 17% in 2012 as compared to 2011. Growth in the UK and other foreign markets

helped Cash America log increases primarily due to consumer loan fees from higher average consumer loan balances in the e-commerce segment. Net income meanwhile dropped some 21% during the same reporting period thanks to increases in the cost of revenue from consumer loan loss provisions due to a mix of installment loans and line of credit accounts as a percentage of total consumer loan portfolio. The company's organic growth acquisitions and a $2.4 million spend on employee termination costs related to reorganizing its Mexico operations spurred rising expenses in its operations and administration unit.

Sales and Marketing

Cash America offers loans through retail stores. It offers consumer loans to customers in more than 30 US states through www.cashnetusa.com and www.netcredit.com. In the UK it operates www.quickquid.com.uk and www.poundstopocket.co.uk. In Australia Cash America runs www.dollarsdirect.com.au and in Canada it provides loans through www.dollarsdirect.ca.

Excluding lead purchase costs Cash America's marketing expenses reached $72.2 million in 2012 up significantly from $41.2 million in 2011 and $30.1 million in 2010. Its 2012 2011 and 2010 lead purchase expenses were $49.7 million $43.2 million and $40.5 million respectively.

The company's pawn and cash advance businesses carry a stigma whether justified or not of preying on the poor or uneducated. (For its part the company claims it attracts consumers who cannot or do not want to deal with traditional banks.) Several states have enacted legislation in recent years that put limits on loan amounts or the interest rates that pawn and payday lenders can charge. In these markets Cash America has either curtailed its operations or is concentrating on credit services such as arranging consumer loans through third-party lenders. The company has also increased it focus on gold-buying services and added stored-value cards.

Strategy

The company is working to expand where it already operates. Strategic markets include Tennessee North Carolina Kentucky and Arizona — states where the company already operates more than 80 pawn lending locations. As part of this push its Nevada subsidiary acquired a nine-store chain of pawn lending locations in Arizona for approximately $15.4 million. Cash America also purchased a 25-store chain of pawn lending locations in Kentucky North Carolina and Tennessee for about $55.1 million.

To streamline its business in Mexico Cash America reorganized its network of stores there to consist of only full-service pawn locations that offer pawn loans based on the pledge of general merchandise and jewelry-based collateral. To this end the company shuttered nearly 150 Mexico-based pawn locations that primarily offered pawn loans based on the pledge of jewelry-based collateral. The move involved buying a 20% minority interest in Creazione Estilo S.A. de C.V. for about $5.6 million and made it a wholly owned subsidiary of Cash America.

HISTORY

When Jack Daugherty was a student he hocked his guitar to finance dates. In 1970 after quitting school he opened a pawnshop that was so successful he used the proceeds to invest in oil. When oil took a downturn he returned to the pawn business incorporating Cash America in 1984; it went public in 1987.

Cash America bought UK-based Harvey & Thompson Ltd. in 1992; two years later the company acquired Sweden's Svensk Pantbel ning. As part of a low-cost expansion program the firm in 1997 introduced a Cash America franchise plan to independent pawnshop owners.

Over the next two years Cash America expanded further in Texas and Utah. In 1998 Mr. Payroll rolled out automated check-cashing machines that identified customers by their facial features; it formed an alliance with Crestar to supplement the bank's Virginia supermarket branches with the machines. Also that year the company launched its Rent-A-Tire subsidiary in Texas.

In 1999 Cash America expanded its automated check cashing business participating in InnoVentry a joint venture with Wells Fargo (InnoVentry ceased operations in 2001). In 2000 Cash America got lots of publicity (presumably unwanted) when its nine-story headquarters in downtown Fort Worth was slammed by a tornado; the building was later renovated.

In an attempt to focus on lending activities subsidiary Rent-A-Tire was sold off in 2002. The following year Cash America doubled its cash advance operations with the purchase of Cashland Financial Services.

With a desire to concentrate on US operations Cash America sold off its operations in Sweden and the UK in 2004 while at the same time expanding its presence in Southern California with the purchase of UrgentMoney and GoldX.

EXECUTIVES

EVP and CFO, Thomas A. Bessant, age 56, $448,846 total compensation
President and CEO, Daniel R. Feehan, age 63, $848,077 total compensation
EVP General Counsel and Secretary, J. Curtis Linscott, age 49, $336,923 total compensation
President & Chief Operating Officer Retail Services Division, Dennis J. Weese, age 51, $463,846 total compensation
CEO of the E-Commerce Division and CEO of ENOVA Financial, David A. Fisher
EVP and COO, T. Brent Stuart
Vice President Of Information Technology, Melody Smiley
Senior Vice President Public And Government Relations, Bill White
Vice President And Controller, Nina Vitagliano
Vice President Managing Associate General Counsel, Jacquie Hair
Vice President Chief Financial Officer And Treasurer, Roberto Martinez
Vice President Of Information Technology, Claudia Young
Vice President Of Public Affairs And Chief Legislative Officer, Mary Jackson
Chief Information Officer Chief Technology Officer Vice President Information Technology, Cliff Norman
Vice President Compensation And Benefits, Randy Blubaugh
Vice President Compensation And Benefits, Jodie Mooty
Vice President Learning And Development, Sandra Fulton
Senior Vice President Operations, Lovett Weems
President and CEO, Daniel R. Feehan, age 63
Chairman, Jack R. Daugherty, age 67
EVP General Counsel and Secretary, J. Curtis Linscott, age 49
Auditors: PricewaterhouseCoopersLLP

LOCATIONS

HQ: Cash America International, Inc.
1600 West 7th Street, Fort Worth, TX 76102-2599
Phone: 817 335-1100 **Fax:** 817 390-9333
Web: www.cashamerica.com

2012 Sales

	% of total
US	78
UK	17
Mexico	4
Other foreign countries	1
Total	**100**

PRODUCTS/OPERATIONS

Selected Services

Check Cashing & Other Financial Services
Consumer Loan Activities
Merchandise Disposition Activities
Pawn Lending

2012 Sales

	% of total
Retail Services	
Domestic	60
Foreign	3
E-commerce	
Domestic	19
Foreign	18
Corporate	—
Total	**100**

2012 Sales

	$ mil.	% of total
Consumer loan fees	781.5	43
Proceeds from disposition of merchandise	703.7	39
Pawn loan fees & service charges	300.9	17
Other	14.2	1
Total	**1800.4**	**100**

COMPETITORS

ACE Cash Express	EZCORP
Advance America	First Cash Financial
Cash Converters	Services
Cash Plus	Winmark
Check Into Cash	World Acceptance
DFC Global	Xponential
DGSE Companies	

HISTORICAL FINANCIALS

Company Type: Public

Income Statement

FYE: December 31

	REVENUE ($ mil.)	NET INCOME ($ mil.)	NET PROFIT MARGIN	EMPLOYEES
12/13	1,797.2	142.5	7.9%	7,637
12/12	1,800.4	107.4	6.0%	7,035
12/11	1,540.6	135.9	8.8%	6,619
12/10	1,293.3	115.5	8.9%	6,017
12/09	1,120.3	96.6	8.6%	5,445
Annual Growth	**12.5%**	**10.2%**	**—**	**8.8%**

2013 Year-End Financials

Debt ratio: 35.5%	No. of shares (mil.): 28
Return on equity: 13.7%	Dividends
Cash ($ mil.): 69	Yield: 0.3%
Current ratio: 5.80	Payout: 3.0%
Long-term debt ($ mil.): 717	Market value ($ mil.): 1,073

	STOCK PRICE ($) FY Close	P/E High/Low		PER SHARE ($) Earnings	Dividends	Book Value
12/13	38.30	11	7	4.66	0.14	38.64
12/12	39.67	13	9	3.42	0.14	34.34
12/11	46.63	13	8	4.25	0.14	30.88
12/10	36.93	11	8	3.67	0.14	26.95
12/09	34.96	11	4	3.17	0.14	23.10
Annual Growth	**2.3%**	**—**		**10.1%**	**(0.0%)**	**13.7%**

Cavco Industries Inc (DE)

Cavco's constructions keep customers covered whether they're at home work or vacation. Cavco Industries designs makes and sells manufactured homes (retail prices range from $26000 to more than $190000) under brands including Cavco Palm Harbor and Fleetwood. Its products include full-sized homes (about 500 sq. ft. to 3300 sq. ft.); park model homes (less than 400 sq. ft.) for use as recreational and retirement units; camping cabins; and commercial structures for use as portable classrooms showrooms and offices. Cavco operates about 15 factories in the West and Midwest; its homes are sold by more than 1000 independent retailers and company-owned outlets in the US Canada Mexico and Japan.

Operations
Cavco operates two business segments: factory-built housing accounting for more than 90% of sales; and a finance and insurance arm which represents the rest. Cavco's mortgage subsidiary CountryPlace Mortgage is an approved Fannie Mae and Ginnie Mae seller and servicer offering mortgages to buyers of the company's homes. Its insurances subsidiary Standard Casualty provides property and casualty insurance to owners of manufactured homes. Cavco owns 51% of Fleetwood Homes (acquired in 2009).

Financial Analysis
Cavco's fiscal 2012 (ends March) sales increased 158% vs. the prior year while net income rose 438% over the same period. The triple-digit increase in sales was driven by an 137% increase in sales of its factory-built homes and revenue growth from its financial services segment. The acquisition of the assets of bankrupt Palm Harbor Homes in 2011 increased sales and profits in fiscal 2012. Indeed Cavco sold 7860 homes in fiscal 2012 vs. 4786 in the previous year. Sales by company-owned stores increased dramatically although independent retailers sell more than three times as many Cavco homes.

Strategy
Cavco is the second-largest manufacturer of manufactured homes in the US. It markets a variety of brands styles floor plans and price ranges to appeal to a wide customer base. Cavco primarily targets the manufactured housing industry's mainstream market —high-value homes for entry-level and move-up buyers. It also targets specialty markets such as vacation homebuyers and developers of residential subdivisions and senior living communities. Cavco is one of the nation's largest producers of HUD-code manufactured homes which

account for some 80% of the manufacturer's homes.

The company has been successful at capitalizing on the woes of its competitors especially during the recent deep recession which led to consolidation of the industry. By acquiring assets of its former rivals Cavco has added production capacity especially for niche market opportunities. In 2009 acquired nine plants from failed competitor Fleetwood for $22 billion. The deal included mothballed facilities in California and Texas as well as operations in new states for Cavco: Idaho Georgia Oregon Tennessee and Virginia. Two years later Cavco went shopping for another ailing competitor. It formed a new subsidiary Fleetwood Homes which bought the assets of bankrupt Palm Harbor for more than $83 million. The deal included Palm Harbor's construction retail and finance units.

Ownership

Wells Fargo & Co. and Third Avenue Management each own about 13% of Cavco's shares. Columbia Wanger Asset Management owns 11% while T. Rowe Price Associates owns more than 10%.

HISTORY

Alfred Ghelfi and partner Bob Curtis began a part-time business in 1965 making pickup truck camper shells. The business Roadrunner Manufacturing became Cavalier Manufacturing in 1966 incorporated in 1968 and went public in 1969. The Cavalier name was already in use so in 1974 the company's name was changed to Cavco. After the 1970s oil crisis nearly wiped out the firm Ghelfi bought out Curtis' share and began making mobile homes. In time Cavco began leasing movable storage buildings but the only successful part of that business was the security container segment (the rest was sold in 1994). A mid-1980s housing market crash in Arizona spurred Cavco to enter a totally new field –health care utilization management –in 1987.

In 1995 Cavco partnered with Japan's Auto Berg Enterprises to begin selling modular housing in Japan. The next year Cavco teamed up with Arizona Public Service to develop solar-powered manufactured housing and it also sold its health care business. Centex acquired nearly 80% of Cavco for $75 million in 1997. The next year Cavco moved into Texas (one of the biggest markets for factory-built homes) acquiring Texas retailer Boerne Homes.

With demand shrinking and surplus inventory building up the company closed its Belen New Mexico factory in 2000 and moved its production to plants in Phoenix and Seguin Texas. That fall Centex tapped manufactured housing veteran Joseph Stegmayer as chairman of its manufactured housing segment.

In 2001 the company launched Factory Liquidators a new retail concept focusing on repossessed homes.

Centex's board of directors approved the tax-free distribution to its shareholders of all of Cavco's outstanding common stock in 2003. The spin-off was completed in June of that year. Continued weakness within the industry forced Cavco to close eight of its company-owned retail outlets in fiscal 2004 and seven more in 2005.

EXECUTIVES

Vice President Sales And Marketing, James S Parlette
Chairman President and CEO, Joseph H. (Joe) Stegmayer, age 63, $450,000 total compensation

EVP, William C. (Bill) Boor, age 48
VP CFO and Treasurer, Daniel L. Urness, age 46, $210,000 total compensation
President Fleetwood Homes; Inc, Charles E. Lott, age 66, $220,000 total compensation
Vice President, Daniel Blankenship
Vice President Operations, Dave Blank
Vice President, Iven Hargis
Vice President Chief Security Officer, Gerry Groundwater
Senior Vice President, Ruth Smith
Vice President Of Sales And Marketing, Paul Deroo
Chairman President and CEO, Joseph H. (Joe) Stegmayer, age 63
VP CFO and Treasurer, Daniel L. Urness, age 46
Auditors: Ernst&YoungLLP

LOCATIONS

HQ: Cavco Industries Inc (DE)
1001 North Central Avenue, Suite 800, Phoenix, AZ 85004
Phone: 602 256-6263
Web: www.cavco.com

PRODUCTS/OPERATIONS

2012 Sales

	$ mil.	% of total
Factory-built housing	406.9	92
Financial Services		
Consumer finance	22.2	5
Insurance	14.0	3
Total	**443.1**	**100**

2012 Sales Channels

No. of homes sold	
Independent retail outlets	1029
Company-owned retail centers	53
Total	**1082**

Selected Operations
Camping cabins
Commercial structures
Manufactured homes
Model homes and vacation homes
Park model homes

Selected Trademarks
AAA Homes
Catalina
Cavco
Cavco Cabins
Cavco Gold Key Guarantee
Cavco Home Center
Cavco Homes
Cedar Court
Desert Rose
Elite
Litchfield Limited
Nationwide Homes
Palm Harbor Homes
Saguaro
SmartBuilt
Sun Villa
Sunbuilt
Sunburst
Vantage
Villager
Westcourt
Winrock

COMPETITORS

All American Group	Fairmont Homes
American Homestar	Liberty Homes
Cavalier Homes	PulteGroup
Champion Home Builders	Skyline
Clayton Homes	Sunshine Homes

HISTORICAL FINANCIALS
Company Type: Public

Income Statement

FYE: March 29

	REVENUE ($ mil.)	NET INCOME ($ mil.)	NET PROFIT MARGIN	EMPLOYEES
03/14	533.3	16.2	3.0%	3,000
03/13	452.3	4.9	1.1%	2,600
03/12	443.0	15.2	3.4%	2,600
03/11	171.8	2.8	1.6%	1,250
03/10	115.6	(3.3)	—	1,300
Annual Growth 46.6%		—		23.3%

2014 Year-End Financials

Debt ratio: 14.9%	No. of shares (mil.): 8
Return on equity: 6.9%	Dividends
Cash ($ mil.): 81	Yield: —
Current ratio: 2.30	Payout: —
Long-term debt ($ mil.): 59	Market value ($ mil.): 696

	STOCK PRICE ($) FY Close	P/E High/Low	PER SHARE ($)		
			Earnings	Dividends	Book Value
03/14	78.64	42 21	1.94	0.00	32.84
03/13	47.57	74 59	0.71	0.00	25.39
03/12	46.58	24 13	2.19	0.00	24.43
03/11	45.16	114 74	0.41	0.00	22.10
03/10	34.14	— —	(0.52)	0.00	22.28
Annual Growth 23.2%		— —	—	—	10.2%

Century Casinos Inc.

In the 19th century people rushed to Cripple Creek Colorado seeking their fortune in gold. Today thanks to Century Casinos they can do basically the same thing (but via midsized regional casinos rather than through prospecting). The company's Womacks Casino & Hotel in Cripple Creek offers some 440 slot machines and video devices as well as a handful of gaming tables. It also owns the Century Casino & Hotel in Central City Colorado and another Century Casino & Hotel in Edmonton Canada. In addition it operate four cruise ship casinos and is the casino concessionaire for cruise lines run by TUI Cruises a joint venture between German travel operator TUI and #2 cruise ship operator Royal Caribbean.

Strategy

After a period of major expansion Century Casinos has been focused on upgrading its properties and making targeted acquisitions. In early 2010 the company acquired the Silver Dollar casino in Alberta Canada from struggling Evergreen Gaming for some $9.5 million. It spent nearly $2 million to renovate the gaming floor and dining area at Womacks during 2008.

Geographic Reach

Outside of North America Century Casinos continues to own a controlling stake in Casinos Poland Ltd. (CPL) owner and operator of eight casinos in Poland. Century Casinos owns 33% of CPL and in 2012 the company agreed to up its stake to 66.6%.

After a experiencing decreased gaming revenue at all of its properties during the global recession the company disposed of its properties in the Czech Republic and South Africa. It sold the Caledon Hotel Spa & Casino near Cape Town South Africa to Tsogo Sun Gaming in 2009. The deal included a 60% stake in Century Casino Newcastle.

Also that year it sold its Century Casino Millennium in the Marriott hotel in Prague to Viva Casino Group.

EXECUTIVES

Vice President Controller, Timothy Wright
Vice President, Niclas Schmiedmaier
Vp Of Finance, Larry Hannappel
Auditors: GrantThorntonLLP

LOCATIONS

HQ: Century Casinos Inc.
455 E. Pikes Peak Ave., Suite 210, Colorado Springs, CO 80903
Phone: 719 527-8300
Web: www.cnty.com

PRODUCTS/OPERATIONS

2009 Sales

	$ mil.	% of total
Century Casino & Hotel Alberta	20.4	41
Century Casino & Hotel Central City	16.7	34
Womacks	10.6	21
Cruise ships	2.0	4
Total	**49.7**	**100**

2009 Sales

	$ mil.	% of total
Gaming	46.5	82
Hotel food & beverage	8.4	15
Other	1.9	3
Adjustments	(7.1)	-
Total	**49.7**	**100**

Selected Properties

North America
Century Casino & Hotel (Century City Colorado)
Century Casino & Hotel (Edmonton Alberta Canada)
Womacks Casino & Hotel (Cripple Creek Colorado)
Poland
Casinos Poland Ltd. (33% 7 full casinos and one slot casino)

COMPETITORS

Global Casinos	Riviera Holdings
Herbst Gaming	Sun International
Isle of Capri Casinos	Limited
Majestic Star	Trans World
Nevada Gold & Casinos	Corporation

HISTORICAL FINANCIALS

Company Type: Public

Income Statement

FYE: December 31

	REVENUE ($ mil.)	NET INCOME ($ mil.)	NET PROFIT MARGIN	EMPLOYEES
12/13	104.5	6.1	5.9%	1,600
12/12	71.8	4.0	5.7%	1,000
12/11	70.8	3.0	4.3%	1,000
12/10	60.6	1.0	1.7%	876
12/09	49.7	10.8	21.9%	550
Annual Growth	**20.4%**	**(13.2%)**	**—**	**30.6%**

2013 Year-End Financials

Debt ratio: 17.8%	No. of shares (mil.): 24
Return on equity: 5.1%	Dividends
Cash ($ mil.): 27	Yield: —
Current ratio: 1.21	Payout: —
Long-term debt ($ mil.): 29	Market value ($ mil.): 127

	STOCK PRICE ($) FY Close	P/E High/Low		PER SHARE ($) Earnings	Dividends	Book Value
12/13	5.21	24	11	0.26	0.00	5.00
12/12	2.84	19	15	0.17	0.00	4.90
12/11	2.53	26	16	0.13	0.00	4.71
12/10	2.44	69	48	0.04	0.00	4.67
12/09	2.69	7	2	0.46	0.00	4.54
Annual Growth	**18.0%**	**—**	**(13.3%)**	**—**	**2.4%**

Chart Industries Inc

Chart Industries is charting its own miracle on ice campaign. The company designs equipment for low-temperature hydrocarbon and industrial gas production and storage including cryogenic systems that can operate near absolute zero. Chart vessels can process liquefy store and transport gases which are marketed to petrochemical and natural gas processors industrial gas producers satellite testing companies and restaurants and convenience stores. The company also offers engineered bulk gas installations and makes specialty liquid nitrogen end-use equipment used in the hydrocarbon processing and industrial gas industries.

Geographic Reach

Headquartered in Garfield Heights Ohio Chart has about 40 domestic operations located across the US and an international presence in Asia Australia and Europe. Although Chart products are sold worldwide the US generates about 70% of sales.

Operations

The company operates through three chief segments: energy and chemicals (32% of sales); distribution and storage (47%); and biomedical (21%).

The majority of Chart's products –including vacuum insulated containment vessels heat exchangers cold boxes and other cryogenic components — are used throughout the liquid gas supply chain for the purification liquefaction distribution storage and end-use of hydrocarbon and industrial gases.

Sales and Marketing

Chart's primary customers are large multinational producers and distributors of hydrocarbon and industrial gases and their suppliers. It sells its products and services to more than 2000 customers around the globe.

Financial Performance

Chart has successfully bounced back after a period of plunging profits and reduced revenue in 2010 when it was hurt largely by the struggling energy-related construction market. Revenues soared 28% from $795 million in 2011 to pass the $1 billion mark in 2012 the first time in its history.

The growth for 2012 was driven by a 58% spike in energy and chemicals sales due to increased demand across brazed aluminum heat exchanger and process systems product lines which included revenue recognized for several large LNG projects which ramped up production during the year. Distribution and storage sales also spiked 22% in 2012 due to higher volumes shipped from LNG applications including mobile equipment and bulk storage tanks especially in China. Both segments also benefited from acquisitions throughout the year.

Profits also jumped 61% from $44 million in 2011 to $71 million in 2012 as a result of the higher revenue coupled with a decline in interest expense.

Strategy

Acquisitions have helped maintain the momentum of its distribution and storage business now the company's largest in sales. Chart has specifically cast an eye towards expanding the segment's European footprint. To boost its BioMedical segment Chart in 2012 swallowed up AirSep which makes oxygen-generating systems for medical and industrial use for about $170 million in cash and some $10 million in assumed debt. The deal was one of Chart's largest in its history.

In late 2013 Chart announced it was acquiring the brazed aluminum heat exchanger (BAHX) business belonging to Wuxi City Zhongbo Heat Exchanger Co. Ltd in order to augment its energy and chemical segment. The agreement includes the construction of a newly built BAHX manufacturing and cold box fabrication facility in Wuxi China. Chart's existing cold box fabrication facility in Changzhou China will be integrated into the new facility in Wuxi which will open up more capacity for Chart's distribution and storage LNG business in Changzhou. The expansion projects are expected to be completed in the first half of 2014.

HISTORY

In 1986 Arthur Holmes teamed up with his brother Charles to purchase ALTEC International a struggling maker of brazed aluminum heat exchangers that dated to 1949. The brothers turned ALTEC around and used it to acquire undervalued companies. From 1986 to 1991 they purchased storage and transportation equipment for liquefied gases and high-pressure cryogenic equipment including Greenville Tube Corporation (stainless steel tubing 1987); Process Engineering Inc. (cryogenic tanks 1990); and Process Systems International (cold boxes 1991). The Holmes brothers finally established a public holding company in 1992 and named it Chart Industries (for CHarles and ARThur).

The company ran into trouble over the next few years trying to make its acquisitions profitable. Chart restructured its most troubled unit Process Engineering Inc. in 1994. It bought cryogenic vacuum pumps maker CVI to build systems for NASA. In 1995 the company began supplying vacuum equipment for the Laser Interferometer Gravitational-Wave Observatory project a research program searching for cosmic gravitational waves.

In 1997 Chart bought Cryenco Sciences which makes cryogenic road trailers. The next year the company acquired the Industrial Heat Exchanger division of UK-based IMI Marston (IMI sold the Marston aerospace business in 1999). In a move intended to increase foreign sales Chart in 1999 bought MVE Holding a cryogenic storage and transportation company with facilities in the US and Europe for $240 million in cash. The company also expanded its cryogenic equipment repair services across the US with the purchase of Northcoast Cryogenics.

Chart signed an agreement in 2000 to build and maintain a new liquid natural gas fueling station for Waste Management. The new refueling station will be the world's largest capable of refueling 120 trucks per four hours. In March 2002 the company announced it would place surcharges on its bulk storage tanks to offset the tariffs set by the US government on imported steel products which would increase manufacturing costs.

In 2003 the NYSE suspended trading of the company's shares after the company fell below continued listing standards and fell into bankruptcy protection. Later that year Chart Industries came out of bankruptcy protection with a new board membership and senior management. Chairman Arthur Holmes also resigned his post in 2003 but continued as a board member until 2005.

Chart Industries filed for another IPO in 2006 applying to list on the Big Board once more. The company had to settle for a Nasdaq listing but completed its IPO in mid-2006.

Also in 2006 the company acquired Cooler Service Company of Tulsa Oklahoma for nearly $16 million net of cash. Cooler Service makes custom air-cooled heat exchangers for hydrocarbon petrochemical and industrial gas processing and power generation. The firm became part of the Energy & Chemicals segment. In mid-2007 First Reserve sold its 48% equity stake in Chart Industries through a secondary offering receiving approximately $263 million. In 2009 Chart acquired Covidien's oxygen therapy business including its Companion and HELiOS brands.

In 2011 the company purchased GOFA Gocher Fahrzeugbau a Germany-based cryogenic and non-cryogenic mobile equipment manufacturer. The addition completed Chart's move to widen its liquefied natural gas (LNG) offerings as well as its opportunities in Europe's industrial gas energy chemical and other industries. The deal also helped Chart to capture a sizable share of the German market (the country accounted for 16% of its total sales in 2011).

At home in mid-2011 Chart acquired California-based Cryotech International (formerly VPS International). Cryotech added to its D&S manufacturing capacity for cryogenic injectors vacuum insulated piping systems and manifolds as well as branded design and service offerings. Its global customer base included defense semiconductor pharmaceutical biotechnology solar and electronics industry clients.

EXECUTIVES

Vice President Of Human Resources And Secretary, Mark H Ludwig
Vice President Information Technology, David Handal
EVP and CFO, Michael F. Biehl, age 59, $395,000 total compensation
Vice President Sales, Kurt J Breiling
Chairman President and CEO, Samuel F. Thomas, $735,000 total compensation
Vice President Sales And Marketing, Kevin Blount, age 53
Vice President And General Manager, Jeff G Sipes
Vice President Finance, Dave Tomashewski
Vice President Of Information Technology, William Moran
Vice President Manufacturing, Joel Guberud
Vice President Tax, Brent S Philo
Vice President For Operations, Chris Schmoeckel
Vice President Of Information Technology, Steve Lang
Vice President Operations, Douglas Lee
Vice President Of Engineered Systems, Tim Pettine
Vice President Of Dands Bulk Gas Products Group, Roger Hansen
Vice President Of Distribution And Storage Bulk Ga, Roger Dodd
National Sales Manager, Gary Degenhardt
Vice President Of Operations, Steve Harrold
Chairman President and CEO, Samuel F. Thomas
Vice Chairman, Ian Blackham
Auditors: Ernst&YoungLLP

LOCATIONS

HQ: Chart Industries Inc
One Infinity Corporate Centre Drive, Suite 300, Garfield Heights, OH 44125
Phone: 440 753-1490
Web: www.chartindustries.com

PRODUCTS/OPERATIONS

Selected Products

Cold boxes (reduce the temperature of gas mixtures to liquefy and separate them)
Cryogenic components (pumps valves vacuum-jacketed piping systems and specialty components)
Cryogenic storage tanks (tanks trailers intermodal containers and railcars)
Heat exchangers (facilitate cooling and liquefaction of air or hydrocarbons)
Space simulation systems (satellite and spacecraft testing)
Thermal vacuum systems (aerospace and research applications)
Vacuum insulated bulk liquid CO_2 containers (beverage carbonation)

COMPETITORS

Air Products	L' Air Liquide
Cobham	Matrix Service
Fives	Praxair
Flowserve	QualMark
Graham Corp.	Reliance Steel
Ingersoll-Rand	Senior plc
Kobe Steel	The Linde Group

HISTORICAL FINANCIALS

Company Type: Public

Income Statement

FYE: December 31

	REVENUE ($ mil.)	NET INCOME ($ mil.)	NET PROFIT MARGIN	EMPLOYEES
12/13	1,177.4	83.1	7.1%	5,086
12/12	1,014.1	71.3	7.0%	4,842
12/11	794.5	44.0	5.5%	3,831
12/10	555.4	20.1	3.6%	3,013
12/09	591.5	61.0	10.3%	2,517
Annual Growth	18.8%	8.1%	—	19.2%

2013 Year-End Financials

Debt ratio: 18.1%	No. of shares (mil.): 30
Return on equity: 11.4%	Dividends
Cash ($ mil.): 137	Yield: —
Current ratio: 1.30	Payout: —
Long-term debt ($ mil.): 64	Market value ($ mil.): 2,905

	STOCK PRICE ($) FY Close	P/E High/Low		PER SHARE ($) Earnings	Dividends	Book Value
12/13	95.64	47	23	2.60	0.00	24.85
12/12	66.69	32	23	2.36	0.00	23.18
12/11	54.07	42	22	1.47	0.00	20.63
12/10	33.78	49	20	0.69	0.00	17.31
12/09	16.52	11	2	2.11	0.00	16.70
Annual Growth	55.1%	—	—	5.4%	—	10.4%

Chase Corp.

Duct tape is great but when the job calls for higher-tech stuff Chase has it. The company has made and sold Chase & Sons branded protective tape and coatings including conducting and insulating products for cable and wire makers for more than 50 years. Chase processes almost any flexible material produced on a roll —films to fabrics. It makes laminates sealants and coatings for pipeline construction electronics as well as printing markets. Chase pipe coating tapes Tapecoat and Royston are sold to oil companies and gas utilities. The company also offers expansion/control joint systems and asphalt additives for roads bridges and stadiums. US customers represent about 84% of revenues.

Chase operates through two segments Industrial Materials and Construction Materials. Industrial Materials 62% of revenue provides products that are added to another company's products. The company's stalwart Chase & Sons trademark is included in this segment. Major product families in the segment include insulating and conducting materials moisture protective coatings laminated durable papers and flexible composites and laminates. Construction Materials are sold in final form for use in the transportation and architectural as well as construction markets. This segment's products include protective pipe coating tapes a polymer additive for waterproofing waterproofing sealants and expansion joints.

Revenue rose 4% in 2011 compared with 2010. Industrial Materials headed up 17% thanks mainly to demand from the electrical cable market for wire and cable products and demand from the industrial controls and automotive markets for electronic coatings products. Construction Materials fell 13% over the same period as the segment struggled with pipeline production problems at its UK facility that prevented the fulfillment of demand in the Middle East. The segment also contended with lower demand from the transportation and architectural markets. Lower sales of private label products additionally contributed to the segment's year-over-year revenue decline. The company's consolidated net income fell 13% in 2011 compared with 2010.

To consolidate manufacturing Chase is closing its Industrial Materials plant in Randolph MA which is one of the company's first plants making Chase & Sons electrical cable insulation tapes and other products for the wire and cable industries. The plant's operations are being transferred to other plants. The company had also moved its manufacturing operations at Webster MA to its Oxford MA plant and transferred its HumiSeal Europe manufacturing operations from Camberly in the UK to a more modern plant in Winnersh UK.

Acquisitions are included in Chase's strategy for growth. In 2012 Chase acquired NEPTCO which supplies engineered materials for producing copper cable and electronic packaging products for about $67 million. The acquisition broadens the menu of products offered by Chase and creates synergies between the markets targeted by Chase and Neptco. In 2010 Chase gained a cash infusion by divesting its contract circuit board assembler Chase Electronic Manufacturing Services (EMS) to contract manufacturer MC Assembly.

A trust controlled by heirs of the company's late founder Edward Chase owns about 12% of the company. Chase's son Peter who serves as company chairman and CEO holds nearly 15% of Chase.

HISTORY

Brothers Edward and Francis Chase founded Chase & Sons in 1946 to make rubberized power cable tape fabric. Under Francis' long tenure as president and CEO the company expanded into related markets. Purchases included Columbia Technical Corporation (electrical insulating varnish and laminates 1971) and Royston Laboratories (corrosion-resistant pipeline coating 1972). The company which by 1973 was called Columbia Chase (shortened to Chase in 1988) won a contract in 1975 to protect seams on the Alaska pipeline. Chase stumbled financially in the late 1980s after diversifying into non-petroleum energy markets. In 1988 Francis retired.

Chase sold its elastomeric materials and fuel technology divisions in 1991. Edward's son Peter became president in 1992 and CEO a year later. He oversaw the company's diversification into adhesives for water purification (Fluid Polymers 1995) and formed a joint venture with the Stewart Group to make products for fiber-optic cable production (sold to Owens-Corning 1997).

Chase entered the electronic manufacturing services market in 1996 by purchasing a 20% stake in DC Scientific. The company raised its interest to more than 50% then in 1999 bought DC Scientific and changed its name to Sunburst Electronic Manufacturing Solutions. Other acquisitions that year included RWA which offers electronic manufacturing and Northeast Quality Products (NEQP) a specialty printer of pressure-sensitive labels. The company boosted its electronic manufacturing service operations in 2000 with the addition of Netco Automation.

Late in 2001 Chase purchased the Tapecoat protective coatings assets of TC Manufacturing Co. The acquisition complemented Chase's Royston division a maker of waterproofing membranes asphalt additives tapes and accessories. Declining health forced co-founder Edward Chase to retire from the company in early 2003. Later in the year Chase sold its Sunburst Electronics Manufacturing Solutions subsidiary to the Edward L. Chase Revocable Trust.

In 2005 the company acquired UK-based Concoat Holdings for $9 million. The next year it bought New York-based Capital Services Joint Systems which made waterproofing sealants and expansion joints.

Looking to court global demand in 2007 Chase picked up UK-based Long Products a maker of corrosion protection and waterproofing systems. The acquisition increased Chase's presence in Europe the Middle East and Southeast Asia as well as its manufacturing capacity in weatherproofing and corrosion protection systems (used in the oil gas and water pipeline industries). In the same year Chase formed HumiSeal Europe via an acquisition of certain assets from Metronelec.

In 2009 Chase purchased the ServiWrap lineup of pipeline protection products from Grace Construction Products (a unit of W.R. Grace). The Â5.98 million ($9.7 million) deal picked up anti-corrosion systems that cater to global oil gas and water pipeline markets. On its heels Chase snatched up C.I.M. Industries a manufacturer of coating and lining systems. C.I.M.'s established presence in the liquid storage and containment industry opens up new avenues in the growing water and wastewater market.

Restructuring in 2009 the company moved work at a flexible composite and laminates manufacturing facility in Paterson New Jersey to locations in Webster Massachusetts and Taylorsville North Carolina. The company consolidated the sales administrative and research and development activities of two offices to one operation too. Also in 2009 NEQP went on the block sold to Label Tech Inc.

EXECUTIVES

President and CEO, Adam P. Chase, age 43, $326,000 total compensation
Vice-president Finance, Jacek Knop
Executive Chairman, Peter R. Chase, age 67
Auditors: PricewaterhouseCoopersLLP

LOCATIONS

HQ: Chase Corp.
26 Summer Street, Bridgewater, MA 02324
Phone: 508 819-4200
Web: www.chasecorp.com

2011 Sales

	$ mil.	% of total
US	103.3	84
Other countries	19.7	16
Total	**123**	**100**

PRODUCTS/OPERATIONS

2011 Sales

	$ mil.	% of total
Industrial Materials	75.7	62
Construction Materials	47.3	38
Total	**123**	**100**

2011 Sales

	$ mil.	% of total
Sales	120.9	98
Royalties & commissions	2.1	2
Total	**123**	**100**

Selected Products and Services

Electrical cable insulation tapes
Electrical splicing & terminating & repair tapes
Flexible composites & laminates for wire & cable
  aerospace & industrial laminate markets
Flexible packaging for industrial & retail use
Fluid applied coating & lining systems for the water &
  wastewater industry
Insulating & conducting materials for wire and cable
  manufacturers
Laminated durable papers
Moisture-protective coatings for electronics and printing
  services
Protectants for highway bridge deck metal supported
  surfaces
Protective conformal coatings
Protective pipe coating tapes
Slit film for the building wire market &
  telecommunication cable
Specialty tapes & related products for the electronic and
  telecommunications industries
Tapecoat® for anti-corrosion applications in the
  gas & oil & marine pipeline markets
Tapes & membranes for roofing & other construction
  applications
Waterproofing sealants expansion joints & accessories

COMPETITORS

3M	Iracore
American Biltrite	PPG Industries
Benchmark Electronics	Plymouth Rubber
Dow Corning	Praxair
ELANTAS PDG	Saint-Gobain
Flextronics	W. R. Grace

HISTORICAL FINANCIALS

Company Type: Public

Income Statement

FYE: August 31

	REVENUE ($ mil.)	NET INCOME ($ mil.)	NET PROFIT MARGIN	EMPLOYEES
08/14	224.0	26.6	11.9%	667
08/13	216.0	17.2	8.0%	666
08/12	148.9	9.3	6.3%	719
08/11	123.0	10.9	8.9%	324
08/10	118.7	12.5	10.5%	305
Annual Growth	**17.2%**	**20.8%**	**—**	**21.6%**

2014 Year-End Financials

Debt ratio: 23.9%
Return on equity: 21.3%
Cash ($ mil.): 53
Current ratio: 3.49
Long-term debt ($ mil.): 51

No. of shares (mil.): 9
Dividends
Yield: 0.0%
Payout: 15.7%
Market value ($ mil.): 323

	STOCK PRICE ($) FY Close	P/E High/Low		PER SHARE ($) Earnings	Dividends	Book Value
08/14	35.50	13	9	2.86	0.45	15.00
08/13	29.72	16	8	1.87	0.40	12.44
08/12	16.27	17	10	1.03	0.35	10.90
08/11	12.77	16	9	1.22	0.35	10.26
08/10	12.70	10	7	1.38	0.20	9.28
Annual Growth	**29.3%**	**—**		**20.0%**	**22.5%**	**12.7%**

Chefs' Warehouse Inc (The)

Before a gourmet chef can say "bon app ᴇt" he must first procure his ingredients. A distributor of specialty food products Chefs' Warehouse sells such gourmet food items as artisan charcuterie specialty cheeses hormone-free protein truffles caviar and chocolates as well as basic food ingredients like cooking oils flour butter milk and eggs. The company's core customers include chefs from independent restaurants fine dining establishments culinary schools hotels and country clubs. It is a leading gourmet ingredient distributor in culinary centers like New York City San Francisco Los Angeles and Washington DC. Tracing its roots back to 1985 Chefs' Warehouse went public in 2011.
IPO
Shares climbed following the company's market debut. The supplier for restaurants caterers and other foodservice businesses raised $135 million; the proceeds from the IPO were about $63.1 million after expenses which went to repay debt and fund general corporate activity. Company CEO Christopher Pappas Christopher's brother John Pappas and brother-in-law Dean Facatselis collectively retain control of Chefs' Warehouse.
Geographic Reach
Based in Connecticut Chefs' Warehouse operates in one segment —food product distribution — along the East and West coasts. It serves some of the nation's culinary hot spots including New York California Nevada and Washington as well as in Ohio Maryland Florida and Oregon.
Financial Performance

Except for revenue slump in 2009 due to the global economic recession Chefs' Warehouse has seen an upward trend in revenue from 2008 to 2012. The company has logged rising net income in all fiscal years from 2008-2012 due to increased net sales and decreased operating expenses. Chefs' Warehouse revenue jumped 20% in fiscal 2012 as compared to 2011 thanks to net sales increases resulting from organic sales growth and the acquisitions of Michael's and Praml in 2012 and Provvista in late 2011. The company's net sales growth was negatively impacted by Hurricane Sandy however during the fourth quarter of 2012 and the prior year impact of an extra week in 2011. Chefs' Warehouse reports $14.51 million in 2012 net income —an 88% increase —due to increased net sales in 2012 and reduced interest expenses.

Mergers and Acquisitions

Going forward Chefs' Warehouse's growth strategy continues to include acquisitions of small food distributors that beef up its entree offerings. In 2013 the company purchased Qzina Specialty Foods North America a Florida-based supplier of gourmet chocolate dessert and pastry products that serves pastry chefs in a deal worth some $32.7 million. In 2012 it bought out Michael's Finer Meats a Midwest distributor of meat and seafood for approximately $54.3 million. The deal was one of several; earlier in the year Chefs' Warehouse purchased Praml International a specialty foods importer and foodservice distributor founded in 1987. The acquisition extended the company's reach to some 500 locations in Las Vegas and Reno. Chefs' Warehouse expanded its operations into south Florida after acquiring Monique & Me Inc. (dba Culinaire Specialty Foods) for $3.7 million in 2010. The previous year it bought the San Francisco division of European Imports for $3.8 million. The transaction bolstered its California operations.

Strategy

Besides acquiring other companies Chefs' Warehouse is expanding its customer base in existing markets and bolstering its product offerings to its existing customers. It is also taking steps to control costs by improving its logistics and inventory management systems. In recent years Chefs' Warehouse has experienced significant financial growth due in large part to a rise in revenue generated by sales to both new and existing customers.

Sales and Marketing

Chefs' Warehouse works to cover a number of popular markets including Philadelphia Boston Napa Valley and Seattle. As part of its business the company serves chefs working in country clubs independent restaurants fine dining establishments culinary schools and hotels.

The company distributes its specialty food products to more than 12500 distinct customer locations from distribution centers located in New York San Francisco Los Angeles Las Vegas Miami Portland Columbus Cincinnati and Washington DC. Its products are sourced from more than 2700 different suppliers.

Company Ownership

Chefs' Warehouse is 17% owned by Christopher Pappas; John Pappas retains another 15% stake.

Company Background

The Pappas family originally founded the company in 1985 as Dairyland USA a specialty dairy product distributor that served chefs in the New York metropolitan area. The company later expanded into other large US markets through acquisitions of small specialty food products distributors.

EXECUTIVES

Chief Information Officer, Frank ODowd
CFO, John D. Austin
Vp Supply Chain, John Scott
Vp Operations, Ed Caulfeld
Board Member, Dean Facatselis, age 59
Vice Chairman, John Pappas, age 50
Board Member, Kevin Cox
Board Member, Stephen Hanson
Auditors: BDOUSALLP

LOCATIONS

HQ: Chefs' Warehouse Inc (The)
100 East Ridge Road, Ridgefield, CT 06877
Phone: 203 894-1345
Web: www.chefswarehouse.com

PRODUCTS/OPERATIONS

2012 Sales

	% of total
Center of Plate	27
Dry Goods	25
Cheeses	14
Pastries & other	13
Oils & vinegars	10
Dairy products	9
Kitchen supplies	2
Total	**100**

Selected Products

Baking
Beverages
Caviar
Cheese & dairy
Chocolate
Coffee & tea
Condiments
Dry goods
Foie gras & pate
Fruits & nuts
Gluten-free
Molecular gastronomy
Oil & vinegar
Organic
Pasta
Specialty meats
Specialty seafood
Spices
Regional

COMPETITORS

American Milk Products	European Imports
DPI Specialty Foods	World Finer Foods
Dole & Bailey Inc.	atalanta
Economy Foods	

HISTORICAL FINANCIALS

Company Type: Public

Income Statement

FYE: December 27

	REVENUE ($ mil.)	NET INCOME ($ mil.)	NET PROFIT MARGIN	EMPLOYEES
12/13	673.5	16.9	2.5%	1,160
12/12	480.2	14.5	3.0%	780
12/11	400.6	7.7	1.9%	600
12/10	330.1	15.8	4.8%	571
12/09	271.0	8.9	3.3%	0
Annual Growth	**25.6%**	**17.3%**	**—**	**—**

2013 Year-End Financials

Debt ratio: 41.6%
Return on equity: 19.8%
Cash ($ mil.): 20
Current ratio: 2.88
Long-term debt ($ mil.): 140

No. of shares (mil.): 25
Dividends
　Yield: —
　Payout: —
Market value ($ mil.): 729

	STOCK PRICE ($)	P/E		PER SHARE ($)		
	FY Close	High/Low	Earnings	Dividends	Book Value
12/13	29.14	37 19	0.77	0.00	5.28
12/12	15.40	36 18	0.69	0.00	1.87
12/11	17.86	42 27	0.43	0.00	1.13
Annual Growth 116.0%	**27.7%**	**— —**	**33.8%**	**—**	

Chesapeake Utilities Corp.

Chesapeake Utilities gasses up the Chesapeake Bay and then some. Chesapeake's regulated natural gas distribution divisions serve more than 1138000 customers in the Northeast and Florida. Another unit distributes electricity to about 31000 customers in Florida. On the unregulated side the company also serves more than 52000 retail propane customers in Delaware Florida Maryland and Virginia. Another subsidiary Xeron sells propane at wholesale to distributors industrial users and resellers throughout the US. In addition Chesapeake has interstate gas pipeline and gas marketing operations. Through BravePoint the company also offers data services consulting and software development.

Operations

The utility operates through three divisions: regulated energy unregulated energy and other. Regulated the largest consists of electricity and natural gas distribution. Unregulated includes propane distribution wholesaling and storage (3.6 million gallons of it) as well as natural gas marketing. Other covers a host of unrelated businesses including its IT services business BravePoint payment processor SkipJack and various real estate holdings.

Geographic Reach

Chesapeake Utilities provides its goods and services in Delaware Virginia Maryland and Florida.

Financial Performance

Revenue rose 13% to $444 million in 2013 as both regulated and unregulated saw growth due to an increase in customers and weather-related higher consumption respectively. Rising revenue lead to a 14% increase in net income to $32.8 million. Cash from operatios also rose by $6.3 million to $73 million due to improved revenue and net income as well as an increase in fuel costs that the company passed on to customers.

Strategy

Chesapeake Utilities' business strategy is to grow its core energy businesses while diversifying its portfolio to strengthen its range of revenue opportunities. In this regard in 2013 it expanded its natural gas distribution services in Delaware Maryland and Florida.

Mergers and Acquisitions

In 2013 Chesapeake Utilities purchased the propane assets of Glades Gas for $3 million to expand its Florida operations. It also bought three Maryland propane operations for a total of about $6.6 million.

Company Background

The company was founded in 1859 as the Dover Gas Light Company. It became Chesapeake Utilities Corporation in 1947. During 2003 Chesapeake began to exit the water services business selling six of its seven dealerships. The company sold the remaining water dealership in 2004. Chesapeake Utilities expanded into Florida through the acquisition of Florida Public Utilities Company in 2009.

EXECUTIVES

Vice President, William C Boyles, age 58
SVP CFO and Corporate Secretary, Beth W. Cooper, age 47, $256,250 total compensation
SVP; President Eastern Shore Natural Gas, Stephen C. (Steve) Thompson, age 53, $306,250 total compensation
President CEO and Director, Michael P. (Mike) McMasters, age 56, $387,500 total compensation
President and COO BravePoint, John R. Harlow, age 59
President Sharp Energy, S. Robert (Bob) Zola, age 63, $143,750 total compensation
President Florida Public Utilities, Jeffry M. Householder
President Xeron, Richard G. Garcia
Vice President - Business Development & Gas Operations, Kevin J Webber
Vice President Of Sales, Sean C Garguilo
Vp Business Development, John Lewnard
Vice President Eastern Shore Natural Gas Company, William B Zipf
Vice President Marketing, Joseph Cummiskey
Vice President, James Schneider
Vice President Technical Services, Donald Gillum
Vice President Business Development, Richard Ioia
SVP CFO and Corporate Secretary, Beth W. Cooper, age 47
Vice Chairman, John R. Schimkaitis, age 66
President CEO and Director, Michael P. (Mike) McMasters, age 56
Chairman, Ralph J. Adkins, age 71

LOCATIONS

HQ: Chesapeake Utilities Corp.
909 Silver Lake Boulevard, Dover, DE 19904
Phone: 302 734-6799
Web: www.chpk.com

PRODUCTS/OPERATIONS

2013 Sales

	$ mil.	% of total
Regulated energy	264.7	60
Unregulated energy	166.7	37
Other	12.9	3
Total	**444.3**	**100**

Selected Subsidiaries

Chesapeake Service Company
BravePoint Inc. (formerly United Systems Inc. information technology)
Chesapeake Investment Company (real estate investments)
Eastern Shore Real Estate Inc. (office building leases)
Skipjack Inc. (office building leases)
Eastern Shore Natural Gas Company (transmission)
Florida Public Utilities Company (gas power and propane distribution)
Flo-Gas Corporation
Peninsula Energy Services Company Inc
Peninsula Pipeline Company Inc.
Sharp Energy Inc. (propane distribution)
Sharpgas Inc.
Xeron Inc. (propane marketing)

COMPETITORS

Constellation Energy Group	JEA
Delmarva Power	New Jersey Resources
	NextEra Energy
Energy Transfer	Suburban Propane
Ferrellgas Partners	UGI

HISTORICAL FINANCIALS

Company Type: Public

Income Statement

FYE: December 31

	REVENUE ($ mil.)	NET INCOME ($ mil.)	NET PROFIT MARGIN	EMPLOYEES
12/13	444.3	32.7	7.4%	842
12/12	392.5	28.8	7.4%	738
12/11	418.0	27.6	6.6%	711
12/10	427.5	26.0	6.1%	734
12/09	268.7	15.9	5.9%	757
Annual Growth	**13.4%**	**19.8%**	**—**	**2.7%**

2013 Year-End Financials

Debt ratio: 28.0%
Return on equity: 12.2%
Cash ($ mil.): 3
Current ratio: 0.57
Long-term debt ($ mil.): 117
No. of shares (mil.): 14
Dividends
Yield: 3.8%
Payout: 67.2%
Market value ($ mil.): 868

	STOCK PRICE ($) FY Close	P/E High/Low		PER SHARE ($) Earnings	Dividends	Book Value
12/13	60.02	27	20	2.26	1.52	19.28
12/12	45.40	24	20	1.99	1.44	17.82
12/11	43.35	23	20	1.91	0.91	16.78
12/10	41.52	23	15	1.82	1.31	15.84
12/09	32.05	24	15	1.43	1.25	14.89
Annual Growth	**17.0%**	**—**	**—**	**12.1%**	**5.0%**	**6.7%**

Churchill Downs, Inc.

You might say this company has put its money on the sport of champions to win. Churchill Downs is a leading operator of horse racing tracks in the US with four major race courses including its namesake track that hosts the world-famous Kentucky Derby. Other tracks include Arlington Park (Illinois) Calder Race Course (Florida) and Fair Grounds Race Course (Louisiana). In addition to horse racing Churchill Downs has gaming assets. It operates a number of simulcast networks and off-track betting facilities as well as a TwinSpires wagering deposit service that allows punters to place bets online. Richard Duchossois who controls diversified holding company Duchossois Group owns about 20% of Churchill Downs.

Geographic Reach
Churchill Downs operates the racetracks in Florida Illinois Kentucky and Louisiana. The company's off-track betting facilities widen its reach.

Financial Performance
While still grounded in live horse racing Churchill Downs has been actively investing in new ventures —both gaming and non-gaming —to diversify its revenue stream. The company has enjoyed an upward trend in revenues during recent fiscal years. It reported $779.3 million in fiscal 2013 after bringing in $732.4 million in fiscal 2012 and $696.9 million in fiscal 2011.

Strategy
In addition to its emphasis on new technology Churchill Downs is focused on investing in its traditional horseracing and gaming sphere. In 2012

Churchill Downs entered into a 50% joint venture with Delaware North Companies Gaming & Entertainment to develop a new harness racetrack and video lottery terminal gaming facility in Lebanon Ohio. The project will involve the relocation of the current operations of Lebanon Raceway to a new location along the Interstate 75 corridor between Cincinnati and Dayton.

HISTORY

Inspired by a tour of European horse racing meets Colonel Lewis Clark founded the Louisville Jockey Club in 1874. The next year the first Kentucky Derby debuted at a site that by 1883 was called Churchill Downs (after Clark's uncles the Churchills who leased him the land). The track suffered financially until 1903 when it showed its first profit. Over the next 25 years the Jockey Club added four more tracks but when the Great Depression hit the company began selling and closing its tracks. Churchill Downs incorporated in 1937 and by 1952 the Kentucky Derby was televised. The company had never really prospered since the Depression and company executives thwarted a takeover bid by National Industries in 1969; two other takeovers were attempted in 1984.

Thomas Meeker who once had served as the company's lawyer took over as president and CEO of Churchill Downs in 1984. He sought to turn the track around and pitched a five-year $25 million renovation of the company's facilities. The investment to revitalize Churchill Downs drove earnings up for the company in the late 1980s.

During the 1990s Churchill Downs diversified into different states and media. Its first simulcast wagering facility opened in 1992 and in 1994 the company gained a majority interest in Hoosier Park (sold 2007). The company acquired a third racetrack Ellis Park in 1998. The following year it launched the Kentucky Derby Auction site on the Web which features the buying and trading of memorabilia related to the race. The firm moved into the technical side of gambling when it formed a joint venture (Charlson Broadcast Technologies LLC) with Charlson Industries to provide simulcast graphic software and video services to its racing and off-track betting sites. Also in 1999 Churchill Downs expanded its geographical base with the $86 million purchase of Calder Race Course in Miami and the Hollywood Park Race Track and adjacent card casino in Southern California.

The company bought Arlington International Racecourse near Chicago as well as five related off-track betting and pari-mutuel operations in Illinois from Duchossois Industries (later The Duchossois Group) in 2000. The next year it joined the New York Racing Association in its bid to buy New York City Off-Track Betting but the group failed to snag the OTB operation which was won by a consortium led by Magna Entertainment. Also in 2001 Churchill Downs sold a 15% stake in Hoosier Park to Centaur Racing for $4.5 million (the company still owned 62% of Hoosier Park with Centaur owning the rest). In 2002 Churchill Downs sold its 35% interest in EquiSource a procurer of equine industry supplies and services.

In 2004 Churchill Downs acquired the Fair Grounds Race Course in New Orleans from Fair Grounds Corporation for $47 million. It also acquired Video Services Inc. (VSI) that year. VSI runs the Louisiana poker business. A year later Churchill Downs sold its Hollywood Park track to Bay Meadows Land Company.

The company's Louisiana Fair Grounds and nearby betting facilities were closed in 2005 in the wake of Hurricane Katrina. Horse races scheduled for the Fair Grounds were moved to Bossier City's Louisiana Downs (operated by Harrah's (now Caesars Entertainment). The following year Robert Evans replaced longtime CEO Meeker. In 2007 Churchill Downs sold its stake in Hoosier Park to Centaur.

The company acquired interactive-betting technology company Youbet.com in 2010 in order to expand its online wagering capabilities; it combined the site with its Twinspires wagering deposit service. Later that year Churchill Downs acquired Harlow's Casino Resort & Hotel in Greenville Mississippi for about $138 million

EXECUTIVES

CEO, William C. (Bill) Carstanjen, age 46, $476,539 total compensation
SVP; President Churchill Downs Racetrack, T. Kevin Flanery, age 49
EVP and CFO, William E. (Bill) Mudd, age 42, $431,539 total compensation
SVP; President Fair Grounds Race Course and Slots, Timothy W. (Tim) Bryant
SVP and CTO, Ben Murr
EVP and General Counsel, Alan K. Tse, age 42, $297,692 total compensation
General Manager Arlington Park, Tony Petrillo
Senior Vice President, Kevin Flanery
Chief Financial Officer And Vice President Of Finance, John McCusker
Vice President Of Finance And Treasurer, Mike Anderson
Senior Vice President, William Tompkins
Vice President Corporate Development, Jeffrey Mainka
Vice President, Thomas Jenkins
Vp Sales And Operations Churchill Downs, Patrick Troutmn
Vice President Legal, Brad Blackwell
Chairman, Robert L. (Bob) Evans, age 62
Board Of Directors, Richard Duchossois
Assistant Treasurer, Karen Cecil
Board Of Directors, Robert Fealy
Auditors: PricewaterhouseCoopersLLP

LOCATIONS

HQ: Churchill Downs, Inc.
  600 North Hurstbourne Parkway, Suite 400, Louisville, KY 40222
Phone: 502 636-4400
Web: www.churchilldownsincorporated.com

PRODUCTS/OPERATIONS

Selected Operations

Racetracks
  Arlington Park (Arlington Heights IL)
  Calder Race Course (Miami)
  Churchill Downs (Louisville KY)
  Fair Grounds Race Course and Slots (New Orleans)
Gaming
  Calder Casino (slot machines Florida)
  Harlow' s Casino Resort & Hotel (casino Mississippi)
  Video Services (video poker machines Louisiana)
  Fair Ground Slots (slot machines Louisiana)
Online
  Bloodstock Research Information Services (equine industry information)
  Horse Racing TV (HRTV minority stake)
  TwinSpires (deposit wagering service)
Other operations
  Churchill Downs Simulcast Productions
  United Tote Company (pari-mutuel wagering systems)

COMPETITORS

Boyd Gaming
Caesars Entertainment
Daily Racing Form
Dover Downs Gaming
Equibase
Granite Real Estate
Jacksonville Greyhound Racing

MTR Gaming
Penn National Gaming
Pinnacle Entertainment
Seminole Tribe of Florida

HISTORICAL FINANCIALS

Company Type: Public

Income Statement

FYE: December 31

	REVENUE ($ mil.)	NET INCOME ($ mil.)	NET PROFIT MARGIN	EMPLOYEES
12/13	779.3	54.9	7.0%	2,600
12/12	732.3	58.2	8.0%	2,300
12/11	696.8	64.3	9.2%	2,000
12/10	585.3	16.3	2.8%	2,000
12/09	439.7	16.8	3.8%	1,300
Annual Growth	15.4%	34.4%	—	18.9%

2013 Year-End Financials

Debt ratio: 27.3%
Return on equity: 8.1%
Cash ($ mil.): 44
Current ratio: 0.75
Long-term debt ($ mil.): 369

No. of shares (mil.): 17
Dividends
  Yield: 0.9%
  Payout: 24.6%
Market value ($ mil.): 1,609

	STOCK PRICE ($) FY Close	P/E High/Low	PER SHARE ($) Earnings	Dividends	Book Value
12/13	89.65	29 21	3.06	0.87	39.27
12/12	66.45	20 15	3.34	1.32	36.93
12/11	52.13	14 10	3.76	0.60	34.00
12/10	43.40	42 29	1.05	0.50	30.55
12/09	37.35	34 18	1.21	0.50	29.74
Annual Growth	24.5%	— —	26.1%	14.9%	7.2%

Cimarex Energy Co

Cimarex Energy's energy is devoted to oil and natural gas exploration and production. The independent is focusing its operations developing assets in two regions —the Mid-Continent and the Permian Basin. The company reported proved reserves in 2012 of about 1.3 trillion cu. ft. of natural gas and 168 million barrels of oil and natural gas liquids (NGLs). Cimarex Energy's 2012 production averaged 626.5 million cu. ft. of natural gas equivalent per day. That year company-operated wells accounted for 68% of Cimarex Energy's total proved reserves and some 80% of its total production.

Geographic Reach
The company has locations in Colorado Oklahoma and Texas. Its operations are mainly located in Texas Oklahoma New Mexico and Kansas.

Sales and Marketing
Cimarex Energy's sells its oil at prices tied directly or indirectly to field postings. Company-produced natural gas is sold under pricing mechanisms related to either monthly index prices on pipelines carrying its gas or the daily spot market. In 2012 Sunoco Logistics Partners accounted for 22% of the company's revenues; Enterprise Products Partners 21%.

Financial Performance
Cimarex Energy's revenues decreased by 8% in 2012 a result of weaker commodity prices (gas was down 35%; NGLs 28%; and oil 4%). The company pointed to regional and worldwide economic and geopolitical activity weather and other variable factors that contributed to the volatility of commodity prices.Net income slumped by 33% in 2012 as a result of lower revenues from weaker commodity prices coupled with higher depreciation depletion and amortization expenses.

Strategy
Cimarex Energy's strategy is to select and develop properties from across its extensive acreage that give the best return on its investments. The company makes the occasional acquisition to enhance its assets in its core geographic areas.

The company is focusing on drilling in liquids-rich gas basins that produce more attractively priced NGL liquids such as ethane propane and butane rather than in gas basins that produce lower-priced dry gas alone.

In 201 and 2011 Cimarex Energy made oil and gas property acquisitions totaling $78.9 million. It bought $33.5 million of properties in 2012 the largest of which was the $21 million purchase of assets in Culberson County Texas. In 2011 the company acquired properties for $45.4 million of which $42.2 million added complementary assets to its Cana-Woodford shale play.

To raise cash in late 2012 the company agreed to sell some non-core oil and gas properties (with reserves of 9.4 million barrels oil equivalent) in Texas for $294 million. In 2011 to raise capital for reinvestment purposes Cimarex Energy sold its 57.5% operated working interest in the Riley Ridge Federal Unit and gas plant in southwestern Wyoming for $191 million.

Ownership
T. Rowe Price Associates and Capital World Investors own 10% and 9.6% of the company respectively.

Company Background
The company boosted its presence in the Permian Basin and the Mid-Continent in 2005 through the acquisition of Magnum Hunter Resources in a $2.1 billion stock purchase that doubled the size of the company and tripled its proved reserves.

EXECUTIVES

Vice President Human Resources, Richard S Dinkins, age 71
EVP Business Development, Stephen P. Bell, age 60, $364,292 total compensation
Chief Operating Officer; Executive Vice President; Director, Joseph R. Albi, age 56, $439,808 total compensation
Chairman President and CEO, Thomas E. Jorden, age 57, $477,625 total compensation
Chief Financial Officer; Senior Vice President, Paul J. Korus, age 58, $428,575 total compensation
VP Corporate Engineering, Gary R. Abbott, age 42
Vice President, Roger Burau
Ronco's Executive Vice President Of Sales And Marketing, Russell Worley
Chairman President and CEO, Thomas E. Jorden, age 57
Treasurer, Harold C Jones
Auditors: KPMGLLP

LOCATIONS

HQ: Cimarex Energy Co
1700 Lincoln Street, Suite 3700, Denver, CO 80203-4518
Phone: 303 295-3995   **Fax:** 303 295-3494
Web: www.cimarex.com

PRODUCTS/OPERATIONS

2012 Sales

	$ mil.	% of total
Oil	1027.8	63
Gas	340.7	21
NGLs	213.1	13
Gas marketing	(0.7)	–
Gas gathering & processing & other	43.0	3
Total	**1623.9**	**100**

Selected Subsidiaries

Brock Gas Systems & Equipment Inc.
Cimarex Energy Co. of Colorado
Key Production Company Inc.
Magnum Hunter Production Inc.
Prize Operating Company
Redhead Energy Inc.

COMPETITORS

Abraxas Petroleum	Newfield Exploration
Anadarko Petroleum	Noble Energy
BP	Pioneer Natural
Black Hills	Resources
Cabot Oil & Gas	QEP Resources
Chevron	Range Resources
Concho	Royal Dutch Shell
EOG	SM Energy
Exxon Mobil	Ultra Petroleum
Forest Oil	Unit Corporation
Linn Energy	Whiting Petroleum

HISTORICAL FINANCIALS

Company Type: Public

Income Statement

FYE: December 31

	REVENUE ($ mil.)	NET INCOME ($ mil.)	NET PROFIT MARGIN	EMPLOYEES
12/13	1,998.0	564.6	28.3%	908
12/12	1,623.9	353.8	21.8%	851
12/11	1,757.8	529.9	30.1%	824
12/10	1,613.6	574.7	35.6%	775
12/09	1,009.7	(311.9)	—	756
Annual Growth	**18.6%**	**—**	**—**	**4.7%**

2013 Year-End Financials

Debt ratio: 12.7%	No. of shares (mil.): 87
Return on equity: 15.0%	Dividends
Cash ($ mil.): 4	Yield: 0.5%
Current ratio: 0.69	Payout: 10.2%
Long-term debt ($ mil.): 924	Market value ($ mil.): 9,143

	STOCK PRICE ($) FY Close	P/E High/Low		PER SHARE ($) Earnings	Dividends	Book Value
12/13	104.91	17	9	6.47	0.54	46.15
12/12	57.73	21	12	4.07	0.46	40.13
12/11	61.90	19	9	6.15	0.38	36.50
12/10	88.53	13	7	6.70	0.30	30.62
12/09	52.97	—	—	(3.82)	0.24	24.40
Annual Growth	**18.6%**	**—**	**—**	**—**	**22.5%**	**17.3%**

Cirrus Logic, Inc.

Cirrus Logic's approach to computing is hardly wispy. The fabless semiconductor company long a leader in audio chips of all kinds develops integrated circuits (ICs) for specialized applications in consumer electronics energy and industrial equipment. Its more than 700 products include audio encoder/decoders (codecs) digital amplifiers digital audio converters and energy management devices. Cirrus Logic's audio chips are used in smartphones tablet and laptop computers Blu-ray Disc players gaming devices and digital TVs. Energy management products include LED driver ICs ADCs and DACs used to make LEDs digital utility meters and power supplies. The company gets most of its sales from customers in China.

HISTORY

Suhas Patil a professor who had developed a chip-level software system for controlling disk drives while at MIT founded Patil Systems in 1981. When his firm failed to find buyers for its advanced products Patil sought advice from semiconductor executive Michael Hackworth. Impressed with the products' possibilities Hackworth joined Patil Systems as CEO. In 1984 the company was renamed Cirrus Logic after the high-flying clouds.

The company initially focused on chips for computer peripherals but during the 1980s it also began making chips for PCs. It debuted the first controller chips small enough to be built directly into a disk drive unit an advance that prompted the PC industry's shift to smaller-profile disk drives. When IBM introduced its Video Graphics Array (VGA) graphics display standard in 1987 Cirrus Logic quickly followed with the market's first VGA controller chip.

Cirrus Logic went public in 1989. Its 1991 acquisitions of Crystal Semiconductor and Pixel Semiconductor provided it with access to audio and video technology for the multimedia and fax/modem markets. It bought PC graphics chip maker Acumos in 1992 and Pacific Communication Sciences (products for cellular communications) in 1993. The next year it bought PicoPower Technology a maker of system controller chips.

In 1996 Cirrus Logic sold its wireless infrastructure equipment unit to ADC Telecommunications. That year the company formed wafer fabrication joint venture Cirent with Lucent's microelectronics unit (which became Agere Systems later acquired by LSI Corp.).

An industry downturn led Cirrus Logic to cut its workforce by 13% in 1996 and by another 15% in 1997. That year Patil stepped away from the company's day-to-day operations (he continued to serve as chairman emeritus and a director) and Hackworth became chairman.

In 1998 continuing to expand its offerings Cirrus Logic debuted products for DVDs. In response to a prolonged slump in the semiconductor industry it eliminated its PC graphics and video accelerator product lines and sold voice compression technology subsidiary Nuera Communications to management. Also that year Cirrus Logic spun off its PC modem business as Ambient Technologies. Analog Devices VP/GM David French was named president and COO in 1998.

In 1999 about 500 more employees were laid off. In an effort to phase out more of its wafer fabrication operations the company that year handed over control of its MiCRUS joint venture (founded

in 1994) to partner IBM and transferred its ownership of Cirent to Lucent (now Alcatel-Lucent). Also that year French became CEO; Hackworth remained chairman.

In 2000 Cirrus Logic moved its headquarters from Fremont California to Austin Texas. The next year the company announced that it would focus growth efforts on semiconductors used in consumer entertainment devices. Despite historically dismal conditions in the chip industry Cirrus Logic took steps to pursue this strategy in 2001 when it acquired private chip makers Peak Audio (digital audio hardware and software) LuxSonor ($65 million DVD video processors) ShareWave ($92 million wireless home networking chips and software) and Stream Machine ($110 million digital video encoding chips).

Later in 2001 the company announced that it would lay off about 300 workers –30% of its staff –in the face of continued poor conditions in the global chip market. The next year Cirrus exited the magnetic storage chip business in order to focus on products for the consumer entertainment market. In 2003 the company announced more job cuts and discontinued the wireless product line acquired as part of the ShareWave acquisition. It also sold its chip testing facilities to ChipPAC (now part of STATS ChipPAC) which in turn supplied Cirrus Logic with assembly test and packaging services.

As conditions in the worldwide semiconductor market turned choppy again in 2004 Cirrus Logic had a 7% reduction in force more than 50 workers mostly affecting employees in California and Texas.

In 2005 the company received $25 million from a legal settlement with Amkor Technology Fujitsu and Sumitomo Bakelite. The litigation was over faulty semiconductors sold by Cirrus to Fujitsu. Cirrus and Fujitsu first sued each other in 2001; Amkor and Sumitomo were added as parties to the litigation (which shifted from federal court to state court) in 2003. The insurance carriers for the four vendors reached a settlement through arbitration in 2005.

That same year Cirrus Logic sold its digital video IC product line to Magnum Semiconductor an entity formed by investors led by Investcorp and August Capital Management. The company received a minority equity stake in Magnum Semi for the assets of the digital video line.

In 2006 Cirrus acquired Shanghai-based Caretta Integrated Circuits for about $10 million in cash. Caretta designed power management ICs for the large single-cell lithium-ion battery market.

David French resigned as president and CEO in 2007 after a special committee of the board investigated the company's past practices in granting stock options and found that French was significantly involved in backdating certain option grants. Chairman Michael Hackworth stepped in as acting president and CEO. VP/GM Jason Rhode a Cirrus Logic employee since 1995 was named to succeed French as president and CEO.

In 2007 the SEC's Division of Enforcement informed Cirrus Logic that its informal investigation of the company's historical stock option practices initiated a year earlier was elevated to a formal inquiry. The SEC later notified the company that the inquiry was concluded and the commission's staff was not recommending any enforcement action against the company.

Cirrus acquired Apex Microtechnology for $42 million in cash in 2007. Apex Micro developed precision high-power analog amplifiers for aerospace and industrial applications used in motors piezoelectrics programmable power supplies and other devices. Founded in 1980 the company (also known as Apex Precision Products) had some 1200 customers with about $20 million in annual sales and employed around 90 people.

In 2008 the company decided that things weren't working out with Caretta Integrated Circuits in terms of its long-term strategic plan. It shut down the subsidiary and laid off about 30 employees in China as a result.

The global financial crisis of 2008 which restricted the worldwide availability of credit destabilized the general economy and triggered a significant slowdown in orders for Cirrus Logic.

EXECUTIVES

Vp Marketing, Terry M Leeder, age 66
Senior Vice President; General Manager - Mixed-signal Audio Products, Scott A Anderson, age 61
President CEO and Director, Jason P. Rhode, age 44, $453,415 total compensation
Acting CFO, Thurman Case
Senior Vice President Ee, Mark Rygh
Vice President - Supply Chain, Randy Carlson
Vp Finance, W Patterson
Vice President Billing, Isa Card
Vice President, Yousef Palla
Vice President Engineering, Juergen Lutz
Vice President And General Manager, Darrel Mank
Vice President Of Marketing Communications, Stan Victor
Vice President Market Development, Michael Paquette
Vp General Manager Embedded Products, Keith Chny
Vice President Sales United States, Tom Lee
Vice President Engineering, Patrick Waddick
Vice President And General Manager Apex Precision Power, Gregory Brennan
Chairman, Alan R. Schuele
President CEO and Director, Jason P. Rhode, age 44
Auditors: Ernst&YoungLLP

LOCATIONS

HQ: Cirrus Logic, Inc.
800 W. 6th Street, Austin, TX 78701
Phone: 512 851-4000
Web: www.cirrus.com

2013 Sales

	$ mil.	% of total
China	700.0	87
US	38.7	5
UK	19.2	2
Taiwan	11.7	1
Japan	9.3	1
South Korea	9.0	1
Hong Kong	8.6	1
Rest of the World	13.3	2
Total	**809.8**	**100**

PRODUCTS/OPERATIONS

2013 Sales

	$ mil.	% of total
Audio products	754.8	93
Energy products	55.0	7
Total	**809.8**	**100**

Selected Products

Amplifier integrated circuits
Analog-to-digital converters
Digital amplifiers
Digital interface integrated circuits
Digital-to-analog converters
Linear amplifiers
Volume controls

COMPETITORS

AMD	Linear Technology
Actions Semiconductor	Macronix International
Analog Devices	Marvell Technology
Analogic	Maxim Integrated
Asahi Kasei	Products
Atmel	NXP Semiconductors
Broadcom	O2Micro
Conexant Systems	ON Semiconductor
Creative Technology	Power Integrations
Dialog Semiconductor	STMicroelectronics
Fairchild	Samsung Electronics
Semiconductor	Sigma Designs
Freescale	Sunplus
Semiconductor	Texas Instruments
Infineon Technologies	VIA Technologies
Integrated Device	Wolfson
Technology	Microelectronics
Intel	Yamaha
LSI Corp.	ams AG

HISTORICAL FINANCIALS

Company Type: Public

Income Statement

FYE: March 29

	REVENUE ($ mil.)	NET INCOME ($ mil.)	NET PROFIT MARGIN	EMPLOYEES
03/14	714.3	108.1	15.1%	751
03/13	809.7	136.6	16.9%	652
03/12	426.8	87.9	20.6%	676
03/11	369.5	203.5	55.1%	570
03/10	220.9	38.4	17.4%	505
Annual Growth	**34.1%**	**29.5%**	**—**	**10.4%**

2014 Year-End Financials

Debt ratio: —
Return on equity: 18.2%
Cash ($ mil.): 31
Current ratio: 5.76
Long-term debt ($ mil.): —
No. of shares (mil.): 61
Dividends
Yield: —
Payout: —
Market value ($ mil.): 1,209

	STOCK PRICE ($) FY Close	P/E High/Low		PER SHARE ($) Earnings	Dividends	Book Value
03/14	19.52	15	10	1.65	0.00	10.29
03/13	22.75	21	10	2.00	0.00	8.66
03/12	23.80	18	9	1.29	0.00	7.23
03/11	21.16	8	3	2.82	0.00	6.38
03/10	7.89	14	6	0.59	0.00	3.33
Annual Growth	**25.4%**			**29.3%**	**—**	**32.6%**

Clarcor Inc.

CLARCOR cleans up with filters. The company's industrial and environmental filtration unit makes air and antimicrobial filters for commercial industrial and residential buildings along with filters used in industrial processes. Brands include Airguard Facet and Purolator. Companies in CLARCOR's engine and mobile filtration business make products under brands such as Baldwin and Clark that filter the air oil fuel coolant and hydraulic fluids used in car truck heavy equipment and marine engines. CLARCOR's consumer packaging group makes custom-designed metal plastic and composite containers for food drug toiletry and chemical products.

Geographic Reach

CLARCOR makes and sells its products worldwide and about 30% of the company's sales come from outside the US.

Operations

CLARCOR operates in industry segments: Engine/Mobile Filtration; Industrial/Environmental Filtration; and Packaging.

The Engine/Mobile Filtration segment sells filtration products for engines used in stationary power generation and for engines in mobile equipment applications including trucks automobiles buses and locomotives and marine construction industrial mining and agricultural equipment.

The company's Industrial/Environmental Filtration segment centers around the manufacturing and marketing of filtration products used in industrial and commercial processes and in buildings and infrastructures of various types. Its liquid process filtration products include specialty industrial process liquid filters; filters for pharmaceutical processes and beverages; and filtration systems and filters for the oil and natural gas industry sewage treatment and water recycling and other industrial uses.

CLARCOR's Packaging segment is conducted by a wholly-owned subsidiary J.L. Clark which makes a wide variety of different types and sizes of containers and packaging specialties. Its metal plastic and combination metal/plastic containers and closures are used in packaging a wide variety of dry and paste form products such as food specialties smokeless tobacco products and lip balms.

Sales and Marketing

The company's filtration products are sold through independent distributors and dealers for OEMs as well as directly to end users. In the Packaging segment J.L. Clark uses an internal sales force and sells its products directly to customers for containers and packaging specialties.

Financial Performance

Revenues marginally decreased by 0.43% in 2012 due to a decline in sales in the Packaging segment driven by lower sales of smokeless tobacco and confection packaging products and lower sales of decorated flat sheet metal products and unfavorable changes in foreign currency exchange rates primarily due to the strengthening of the US dollar compared to the Euro.

CLARCOR's net income decreased by 1% in 2012 due to lower revenues a foreign currency loss of $0.8 million from the translation of cash accounts at certain foreign subsidiaries denominated in currencies other than their functional currency primarily driven by foreign holdings of US dollars.

Strategy

In 2013 the company announced plans to invest $40 million for subsidiary Baldwin Filters Inc. to build a new 400000 square foot warehouse and distribution center adjacent to Baldwin's current manufacturing facility in Kearney Nebraska. The project is due for completion in 2014 and will expand Baldwin's capacity to handle anticipated growth over the next decade.

In addition to organic growth CLARCOR has pursued a strategy of expanding through acquisitions. In 2013 the company inked a $265-million deal to purchase the air filtration business of General Electric's power and water division.

In 2012 the company acquired Modular Engineering Pty Ltd. an Australian manufacturer of natural gas filtration products as well as a distributor of aftermarket elements. Modular a longtime supplier to CLARCOR's PECOFacet division became part of the division. PECOFacet is included in the company's Industrial/Environmental Filtration segment. Modular produces skid-mounted equipment for the natural gas industry in the

Asia/Pacific region and expands CLARCOR's presence in that region in both manufacturing and aftermarket sales.

In 2011 the company purchased one of its suppliers of filtration media Transweb LLC. New Jersey-based Transweb manufactures and supplies media used in end-market applications including respirators and HVAC filters.

Ownership

Neuberger Berman Group LLC owns 13% of the company.

EXECUTIVES

Group President CLARCOR Engine Mobile, Sam Ferrise, age 58, $400,795 total compensation
VP Finance and CFO, David J. Fallon, age 44, $394,808 total compensation
Chairman President and CEO, Christopher L. Conway, age 58, $689,615 total compensation
Group President CLARCOR Industrial Air, Keith A. White, age 42
Sales And Marketing Vp, Kevin Nelson
Vice President Operations, Jay Geil
Vice President Tax, Christopher White
Senior Vice President Growth, Paul Marold
Vice President Information Technology, Sudhir Nair
Vice President Finance, Greg Resz
Vice President Of Operations, John Reuss
Vice President ??? Human Resources, Doug Griffin
Vphr, Bob Marion
Chairman President and CEO, Christopher L. Conway, age 58
Board Member, Mark A Emkes, age 62
Board Member, Arthur Laffer
Vice Chairman, William Walker
Treasury Manager, Mike Womack
Auditors: PricewaterhouseCoopersLLP

LOCATIONS

HQ: Clarcor Inc.
840 Crescent Centre Drive, Suite 600, Franklin, TN 37067
Phone: 615 771-3100   **Fax:** 615 771-5603
Web: www.clarcor.com

2014 Sales

	$ mil.	% of total
US	1027.0	68
Europe	165.5	11
Asia	146.9	10
Other countries	173.5	11
Total	**1512.9**	**100**

PRODUCTS/OPERATIONS

2014 Sales

	$ mil.	% of total
Industrial & environmental filtration	833.1	55
Engine & mobile filtration	603.8	40
Packaging	76.0	5
Total	**1512.9**	**100**

Selected Subsidiaries

Industrial and Environmental Filtration
CLARCOR Air Filtration Products Inc. (commercial and industrial air filters)
Facet USA Inc. (industrial filters advanced filtration and separation products and systems for the aviation marine and power generation markets)
Modular Engineering Pty Ltd. (skid-mounted equipment manufacturing Australia)
Newton Tool & Mfg. Company Inc. (synthetic fibers filtration)
Purolator Advanced Filtration Group Inc. (air filtration products for HVAC systems)
Martin Kurz & Co. Inc.
Purolator EFP (formerly United EFP)

Purolator Facet Inc. (high-end filter applications for the aeropower fluid processing and general industrial markets)
Total Filtration Services Inc. (filtration management services)
United Air Specialists Inc. (commercial and industrial air filters purification systems electrostatic fluid contamination control equipment and high-precision spray equipment)

Engine and Mobile Filtration
Baldwin Filters Inc. (aftermarket heavy-duty filters primarily for trucks construction and agricultural equipment)
Clark Filter Inc. (liquid and air filters for locomotives)
Sinfa SA (80% automotive and heavy-duty engine filters)

Packaging
J.L. Clark Inc. (plastic and metal containers)

COMPETITORS

Crown Holdings	EMD Millipore
Cummins	ESCO Technologies
Dana Holding	Pall Corporation
Delphi Automotive	Parker-Hannifin
Systems	Wårth Group
Donaldson Company	

HISTORICAL FINANCIALS

Company Type: Public

Income Statement

FYE: November 29

	REVENUE ($ mil.)	NET INCOME ($ mil.)	NET PROFIT MARGIN	EMPLOYEES
11/14	1,512.8	144.0	9.5%	6,015
11/13	1,130.7	118.0	10.4%	5,267
11/12*	1,121.7	122.9	11.0%	5,417
12/11	1,126.6	124.0	11.0%	5,447
11/10	1,011.4	96.0	9.5%	5,136
Annual Growth	**10.6%**	**10.7%**	**—**	**4.0%**

*Fiscal year change

2014 Year-End Financials

Debt ratio: 21.7%
Return on equity: 13.5%
Cash ($ mil.): 94
Current ratio: 3.25
Long-term debt ($ mil.): 411
No. of shares (mil.): 50
Dividends
Yield: 0.0%
Payout: 25.0%
Market value ($ mil.): 3,308

	STOCK PRICE ($) FY Close	P/E High/Low	PER SHARE ($) Earnings	Dividends	Book Value
11/14	65.89	24 19	2.83	0.71	21.99
11/13	60.53	26 19	2.34	0.58	20.49
11/12*	46.38	22 18	2.42	0.50	18.14
12/11	48.78	20 16	2.42	0.44	16.65
11/10	41.00	22 16	1.88	0.40	15.03
Annual Growth	**12.6%**		**10.8%**	**15.6%**	**10.0%**

*Fiscal year change

Clearwater Paper Corp

No pulp fiction here —the story of Clearwater Paper is clearly fact. The company produces solid bleach sulfate paperboard consumer tissue products lumber and hardwood and softwood pulp. Business is divided into two primary divisions: Its Pulp and Paperboard segment manufactures paperboard (used to make packaging for foods liquids pharmaceuticals and toiletries) and pulp (consumed internally to make paperboard and tissues).

A Consumer Products arm produces a private label tissue largely for grocery chains. Most of Clearwater sales are made in the US.

Geographic Reach

Clearwater has about 15 manufacturing locations and about 10 converting facilities spanning the US and Canada. The US accounted for 93% of its total revenues in 2013.

Operations

Clearwater's operations are divided into two primary segments: Consumer Products (around 60% of total sales) sells its line of at-home and away-from-home tissue products and Pulp and Paperboard (40%) makes its bleached paperboard used in packaging products.

Sales and Marketing

Clearwater's paperboard is sold to packaging converters domestically through sales offices located throughout the country with a smaller percentage channeled through distribution to commercial printers. International paperboard sales are conducted via sales agents. The company's largest client is Kroger which represents nearly 11% of total sales.

Financial Performance

In 2011 Clearwater achieved a historic milestone when it posted $1.9 billion in total revenue. After dipping slightly in 2012 revenues recovered to reach $1.89 during 2013. The slight growth in 2013 was due to increased shipments of paperboard and higher net selling prices for retail tissue which were favorably affected by a larger proportion of higher-priced through-air-dried TAD product sales.

Profits jumped 67% from $64 million in 2012 to $107 million in 2013 due to an income tax benefit received in addition to the higher revenue. Clearwater's operating cash flow has fluctuated over the last five years with continuous declines in 2010 and 2011 followed by growth in 2012 and another drop in 2013. The $62 million drop in 2013 was due to a decrease in working capital attributable to a build-up in inventory to support its through-air-dried (TAD) tissue program.

Strategy

Clearwater is continuing to grow its business and streamline its operations through business acquisitions capital investments and plant closings. In 2014 it shut down a tissue converting and distribution facility in Long Island New York. The year before it closed its Thomaston Georgia tissue converting and distribution facility. The closings are part of its strategy to consolidate regional plants to achieve short-term and long-term cost savings.

To bolster its wood fiber operations in late 2012 Clearwater purchased a wood chipping facility in Clarkston Washington for about $11 million.

Company Background

Clearwater was spun off from Potlatch Corporation a real estate investment trust in late 2008.

EXECUTIVES

President CEO and Director, Linda K. Massman, age 47, $700,000 total compensation
SVP and CFO, John D. Hertz, age 47, $416,667 total compensation
SVP and President Pulp and Paperboard, Danny G. (Dan) Johansen, age 63, $350,000 total compensation
CIO, David Edwards
SVP and President Consumer Products Division, Patrick T. Burke
Sr V Pres Hr, Jackson O Lynch
Senior Vice President Finance And Chief Financial Officer, David Morris

Executive Vice President Chief Supply Chain And
  Operations Officer, Beth Ford
Vice President Sales And Marketing, Joanne Shufelt
Vice President Labor Relations, Kari Moyes
Vice President Info System, Richard Kelly
Vice President, Pamela Mull
Vice President Manufacturing, Stephen Martineau
Vp Total Rewards, Linda McNally
National Accounts Manager, Mark Behling
National Accounts Manager, Mary Conwell
Chairman, Boh A. Dickey, age 69
President CEO and Director, Linda K. Massman,
  age 47
Corporate Controller And Treasurer, Johnathan D
  Hunter
Auditors: KPMGLLP

LOCATIONS

HQ: Clearwater Paper Corp
  601 West Riverside Avenue, Suite 1100, Spokane, WA
  99201
Phone: 509 344-5900
Web: www.clearwaterpaper.com

2013 Sales

	$ mil.	% of total
US	1751.0	93
Japan	67.7	4
Canada	26.2	1
Korea	10.9	1
Australia	7.9	-
China	5.4	-
Mexico	3.0	-
Taiwan	1.7	-
Other countries	16.0	1
Total	**1889.8**	**100**

PRODUCTS/OPERATIONS

2013 Sales

	$ mil.	% of total
Consumer Products	1149.7	61
Pulp & Paperboard	740.1	39
Total	**1889.8**	**100**

Selected Products

Paperboard Products
Commercial Print
Food Service
Packaging
Tissue Products
Away-From-Home
Machine Glazed
Parent Roll
Private Label

COMPETITORS

Georgia-Pacific	Procter & Gamble
International Paper	Rock-Tenn
Kimberly-Clark	Sonoco Products
MeadWestvaco	Tufco Technologies

HISTORICAL FINANCIALS

Company Type: Public

Income Statement

FYE: December 31

	REVENUE ($ mil.)	NET INCOME ($ mil.)	NET PROFIT MARGIN	EMPLOYEES
12/13	1,889.8	106.9	5.7%	3,860
12/12	1,874.3	64.1	3.4%	3,860
12/11	1,927.9	39.6	2.1%	3,710
12/10	1,372.9	73.8	5.4%	3,830
12/09	1,250.0	182.4	14.6%	2,500
Annual Growth	10.9%	(12.5%)	—	11.5%

2013 Year-End Financials

Debt ratio: 38.6%	No. of shares (mil.): 21	
Return on equity: 18.6%	Dividends	
Cash ($ mil.): 25	Yield: —	
Current ratio: 2.89	Payout: —	
Long-term debt ($ mil.): 674	Market value ($ mil.): 1,107	

	STOCK PRICE ($) FY Close	P/E High/Low		PER SHARE ($) Earnings	Dividends	Book Value
12/13	52.50	11	8	4.80	0.00	28.70
12/12	39.16	15	11	2.72	0.00	23.53
12/11	35.61	48	18	1.66	0.00	21.30
12/10	78.30	26	14	3.12	0.00	20.40
12/09	54.97	7	1	7.75	0.00	16.00
Annual Growth	(1.1%)	—	—	(11.3%)	—	15.7%

Cogent Communications Holdings, Inc.

Cogent Communications offers a compelling sales pitch: data at the speed of light. The company operates a fiber-optic data network that serves customers in North America Europe and Japan. It offers dedicated Internet access and data transport services to businesses through Ethernet connections that link its 44 data center facilities directly to customer office buildings. Clients include financial services companies law firms ad agencies and other professional services businesses. Cogent also sells access to its network and provides colocation and modem management services to ISPs hosting companies and other high-volume bandwidth users.

Operations

Cogent does business in 185 metropolitan markets serving almost 2000 connected office buildings most of which are multi-tenant. Its network is made up of in-building riser facilities metropolitan optical fiber networks metropolitan traffic aggregation points and inter-city transport facilities.

Geographic Reach

Cogent has offices data centers colocation facilities and points-of-presence across North America and Europe. North America (mostly the US) represents about 80% of sales; Europe makes up the other 20%.

Sales and Marketing

Cogent employs a direct sales approach that includes telemarketing. In 2014 it launched a channel partner program to leverage its relationships with national telecommunications master agents such as WTG and AB&T Telecom.

Financial Performance

The company generates most of its revenues from customers connected directly to its network (on-net customers) while clients served through other carriers' facilities (off-net customers) account for a quarter of revenues.

Cogent has enjoyed steady revenue growth over the past decade; overall sales increased 10% in 2013 to $347 million as its customer base grew from almost 35000 to 40000. Profits have been less consistent as its business is capital-intensive; however in 2013 net income grew to a record $56

million due to a $49 million one-time income tax benefit.

Strategy

The company has said that it is focusing on expanding its on-net customers; with multi-tenant office buildings the customer base is built in. It has also expanded its sales force to address a broader range of clients. Cogent is also investing in its network infrastructure to reach more clients in areas that represent significant concentrations of Internet traffic.

EXECUTIVES

Chairman and CEO, David (Dave) Schaeffer, age 57, $332,623 total compensation
CFO and Treasurer, Thaddeus G. (Tad) Weed, age 53, $257,262 total compensation
Vice President Sales, Stephanie Thomas
National Account Manager, George Sanchez
National Sales Manager, Brian Cappello
Senior Vice President Portfolio, Brian Shearrow
National Sales Manager, Robert Fogal
National Sales Manager, Matt Desing
National Sales Manager, Eric Christopher
Vice President Of Sales, Michael Kalina
Vice President Product Mgt, Charlie Cary
Vice President, Deborah Chitwood
National Account Manager, Gary Freitag
Vice President Tax, Steven McLernon
National Account Manager, Jonathan Emery
National Account Manager, Alain Turcot
National Account Manager, Dusty Fraser
National Accounts Manager, Jeremy Haskins
Chairman and CEO, David (Dave) Schaeffer, age 57
CFO and Treasurer, Thaddeus G. (Tad) Weed, age 53
Auditors: Ernst&YoungLLP

LOCATIONS

HQ: Cogent Communications Holdings, Inc.
  1015 31st Street N.W., Washington, DC 20007
Phone: 202 295-4200
Web: www.cogentco.com

2013 Sales

	$ mil.	% of total
North America	274.3	79
Europe	73.7	21
Total	**348.0**	**100**

PRODUCTS/OPERATIONS

2013 Sales

	% of total
On-net	74
Off-net	26
Total	**100**

COMPETITORS

AT&T	Level 3 Communications
Covad Communications Group	Verio
	Verizon
EarthLink	Wave2Wave
Everest Interlink	XO Holdings
Broadband	

HISTORICAL FINANCIALS

Company Type: Public

Income Statement

FYE: December 31

	REVENUE ($ mil.)	NET INCOME ($ mil.)	NET PROFIT MARGIN	EMPLOYEES
12/13	347.9	56.6	16.3%	707
12/12	316.9	(4.2)	—	605
12/11	305.5	7.5	2.5%	623
12/10	263.4	0.6	0.3%	568
12/09	235.8	(17.1)	—	577
Annual Growth	10.2%	—	—	5.2%

2013 Year-End Financials

Debt ratio: 65.7%	No. of shares (mil.): 47
Return on equity: 32.0%	Dividends
Cash ($ mil.): 304	Yield: 1.8%
Current ratio: 2.47	Payout: 844.4%
Long-term debt ($ mil.): 397	Market value ($ mil.): 1,913

	STOCK PRICE ($) FY Close	P/E High/Low		PER SHARE ($) Earnings	Dividends	Book Value
12/13	40.41	34	19	1.21	0.76	4.09
12/12	22.64	—	—	(0.09)	0.21	3.39
12/11	16.89	105	74	0.17	0.00	3.57
12/10	14.14	1429	703	0.01	0.00	3.31
12/09	9.86	—	—	(0.39)	0.00	3.22
Annual Growth	42.3%		—	—	—	6.1%

Cognex Corp.

Cognex machines see what the human eye cannot. The company is one of the world's largest producers of systems that linked to a video camera serve as eyes where human vision is insufficient. Semiconductor consumer goods health care and automotive companies among others use the company's machine vision and industrial identification systems to position and identify products gauge sizes and locate defects. Cognex serves three primary markets: factory automation semiconductor and electronics capital equipment and surface inspection. It also offers consulting and educational services as well as tech support for its products. Sales to customers based outside the US account for about two-thirds of sales.

Geographic Reach

The US and Europe each contributed nearly a third of Cognex's $324 million in sales in 2012. Japan accounted for 13%. Internationally Cognex has been expanding in China India Brazil and Eastern Europe.

Operations

Cognex operates two business segments. The largest is its Modular Vision Systems Division (MVSD) which accounts for about 85% of its sales. MVSD develops manufactures and markets modular vision systems and ID products that are used to automate the manufacturing and tracking of discrete items by locating identifying inspecting and measuring them during the manufacturing or distribution process. The smaller Surface Inspection Systems Division (SISD) develops makes and markets surface inspection vision systems that are used to inspect surfaces of materials processed in a continuous fashion such as metals papers plastics and glass to ensure that there are no defects on the surfaces.

Sales and Marketing

Cognex sells its MVSD products through a worldwide direct sales force and via a global network of integration and distribution partners. SISD. which is the smaller of the two businesses and has fewer customers in a concentrated group of industries sells its products primarily through a worldwide direct sales force.

Financial Performance

Cognex reported sales of $324.3 million in 2012 an increase of nearly 1% versus 2011. The modest uptick resulted from increased sales to factory automation and surface inspection customers partially offset by a decrease in sales to semiconductor and electronics capital equipment customers. Cognex's service revenue increased 17% on higher consulting services at MVSD as well as higher revenue from SISD spare part sales training services and maintenance and support contracts. On a geographic basis the US outperformed Europe and Japan. Indeed sales in the US increased 3% year over year while sales in Europe and Japan decreased 5% and 13% respectively. Sales to other countries jumped 17% to account for nearly a quarter of total sales.

Sales to customers in the factory automation market represented 75% of Cognex's total revenue in 2012. In the fourth quarter of 2012 revenue trends in Asia specifically in China were negatively impacted by a slowdown in the consumer electronics industry which overshadowed gains in the factory automation market in the Americas and Europe.

Strategy

Cognex's successful expansion into the factory automation market has significantly widened its customer base. The company is focusing on factory automation because it believes it provides the greatest potential for long-term sustainable revenue growth. To that end it's investing in new product development and functionality to make its machines vision products easier to use and more affordable. Cognex has opened sales offices in emerging markets such as China India and Brazil where it sees ample opportunity for the adoption of its factory automation products. Cognex's business strategy includes selective expansion into new machines vision applications through the acquisition of businesses and technologies.

Meanwhile Cognex has reduced its dependence on the highly-cyclical semiconductor and electronics industries which now account for less than 10% of sales down from 61% in 2000. Surface inspection customers represented 16% of sales in 2012. These customers use machine vision to examine materials including metals paper plastics and glass that are processed at high speeds in a continuous manner.

Ownership

Royce & Associates owns about 11% of Cognex's shares.

HISTORY

Robert Shillman and two MIT colleagues Marilyn Matz and William Silver started Cognex (short for "cognition experts") in 1981 to create vision replacement machines for factories. Competition and inadequate technology forced the firm to reevaluate its distribution strategy in 1986. Cognex began supplying machine vision technology to original equipment manufacturers. The company introduced the first custom vision chip in 1988 and went public the next year.

Cognex found success where human vision fails –in the high-speed detailed repetitive processes required in making semiconductors. The company

expanded by purchasing Acumen a developer of machine vision systems for semiconductor wafer identification (1995); Isys Controls a maker of quality control systems (1996); and Mayan Automation a maker of surface inspection systems (1997).

Low demand for semiconductor and printed circuit board manufacturing equipment in Asia hurt sales in 1998. Nonetheless the company boosted R&D by 10% and acquired some of Rockwell Automation's machine vision operations also becoming the preferred global supplier to Rockwell's plants. Orders picked up in early 1999 and Cognex invested $1 million in upstart Avalon Imaging (machine vision for the plastics industry) its first investment in such a company.

In 2000 Cognex acquired Komatsu's machine vision business. The Komatsu unit was one of the largest machine vision system suppliers in Japan. Also that year the company acquired additional machine vision products by purchasing UK-based Image Industries. In 2002 Cognex won an appeal in its ongoing patent lawsuit with the Lemelson Medical Education & Research Foundation. The company legally prevailed over the Lemelson trust again in 2005. In 2004 the company reached a legal settlement and licensing agreement with rival Electro Scientific Industries (ESI) with ESI paying a license fee to Cognex.

In 2003 the company acquired the wafer identification business of Siemens Logistics and Assembly Systems (formerly Siemens Dematic) expanding its presence in Europe. The same year it also bought the industrial parts identification business of Gavitec.

In 2005 Cognex bought DVT Corp. for $104 million in cash; DVT made vision sensors used on factory floors. Cognex celebrated its 25th anniversary in 2006 with a gala celebration at its corporate headquarters and in downtown Boston.

Also in 2006 Cognex acquired AssistWare Technology a developer of lane departure warning systems for vehicles. The experiment was short-lived as Cognex sold the the lane departure warning operations to Takata Corporation in 2008 saying the business did not fit the company's business model.

Reacting to the unfavorable business environment around the world Cognex took cost-cutting measures in 2008 and again in 2009. The latter reductions included laying off about 145 employees and contractors (a 17% cut in workforce) cuts in certain executive salaries adding more mandatory shutdown days and decreases in discretionary spending.

Seeking to expand its surface inspection system products Cognex in 2009 bought the SmartAdvisor web monitoring system product line from Monitoring Technology Corporation (MTC) for $5 million in cash.

EXECUTIVES

EVP Finance and Administration CFO and Treasurer, Richard A. Morin, age 65, $276,058 total compensation

President CEO and Director, Robert Willett, age 47, $351,346 total compensation

VP and Business Unit Manager ID Products, Carl Gerst

Senior Vice President Of Research And Development, John McGarry

Vice President Sales And Marketing, Sean Lett

Vice President Of Sales, Susanne Wasserboehr

Vice President Mvsd Sales And Service Europe, Dirk Rathsack

Vice President Operations, Herb Lade

Vice President Risk Management, Cy Marrion

Vp Marketing, Larry Baranauskas
Vice President Sales And Service Asia, Patrice
 Denizard
Vp Global Operations, Rocco Volpe
**EVP Finance and Administration CFO and
 Treasurer,** Richard A. Morin, age 65
Chairman and Chief Culture Officer, Robert J.
 (Bob) Shillman, age 68
President CEO and Director, Robert Willett, age 47
Treasury Manager, Patrick Thomas
Auditors: GrantThorntonLLP

LOCATIONS

HQ: Cognex Corp.
 One Vision Drive, Natick, MA 01760-2059
Phone: 508 650-3000
Web: www.cognex.com

2014 Sales

	$ mil.	% of total
Europe	205.1	42
US	147.4	30
Japan	43.4	9
Other	90.4	19
Total	**486.3**	**100**

PRODUCTS/OPERATIONS

2014 Sales

	$ mil.	% of total
Product	451.1	93
Service	35.2	7
Total	**486.3**	**100**

2014 Sales by Segment

	$ mil.	% of total
Modular Vision Systems	426.5	88
Surface Inspection Systems	59.8	12
Total	**486.3**	**100**

Selected Products

DataMan 100 and 200 Series (image-based ID readers)
DisplayInspect (LCD inspection software)
In-Sight 5000 (machine vision system)
SmartAdvisor (web monitoring technology)
SmartView Paper (paper web inspection system)
SmartView Metals (flat-rolled metals surface inspection
 system)

COMPETITORS

Adept Technology	KLA-Tencor
Camtek	National Instruments
Clemex	Orbotech
CyberOptics	PPT VISION
Data Translation	Panasonic Electric
Elbit Vision	Works UK
Electro Scientific	Perceptron
Industries	RoboGroup T.E.K.
Image Sensing Systems	Scanner Technologies
Integral Vision	

HISTORICAL FINANCIALS

Company Type: Public

Income Statement

FYE: December 31

	REVENUE ($ mil.)	NET INCOME ($ mil.)	NET PROFIT MARGIN	EMPLOYEES
12/13	353.8	73.5	20.8%	1,077
12/12	324.2	68.1	21.0%	984
12/11	321.9	69.8	21.7%	919
12/10	290.6	61.3	21.1%	824
12/09	175.7	(4.8)	—	729
Annual Growth	**19.1%**	**—**	**—**	**10.2%**

2013 Year-End Financials

Debt ratio: —	No. of shares (mil.): 86
Return on equity: 12.1%	Dividends
Cash ($ mil.): 40	Yield: —
Current ratio: 5.44	Payout: —
Long-term debt ($ mil.): —	Market value ($ mil.): 3,315

	STOCK PRICE ($) FY Close	P/E High/Low		PER SHARE ($) Earnings	Dividends	Book Value
12/13	38.18	76	35	0.83	0.00	7.42
12/12	36.79	56	38	0.78	1.54	6.65
12/11	35.79	44	30	0.82	0.18	6.55
12/10	29.42	41	21	0.76	0.25	5.76
12/09	17.71	—		(0.06)	0.30	4.97
Annual Growth	**21.2%**	**—**	**—**	**—**	**—**	**10.5%**

Collectors Universe Inc

Before you sell that silver dollar or those base-ball cards you might want to check with Collectors Universe. The company provides authentication grading and information services for sellers and buyers of trading cards event tickets vintage autographs and other memorabilia. The company charges a fee —usually between $4 and $200 per item —to determine the authenticity quality and worth of the collectible. Coins and sports cards account for most of the company's business; notable offerings include its Professional Coin Grading Service (PCGS). Collectors Universe also publishes price guides market reports rarity reports and other information in print form as well as on its website.

Geographic Reach

Collectors Universe does business primarily in the US. In 2010 the company's Professional Coin Grading Service (PCGS) opened an office in Paris as part of Collectors Universe's international expansion efforts. While expanding its geographic scope and its grading capabilities with an eye on the Asian market the company has also been cutting back in underperforming areas.

Operations

Collectors Universe three reportable service segments are coins trading cards and autographs and other high-end collectibles. The coin authentication and grading business represented about 66% of total revenues in both fiscal 2012 and 2011.

Sales and Marketing

Collectors Universe works directly with individual dealers who submit items to the company for authentication. It also maintains a presence at collectibles trade shows.

The company has enhanced its marketing programs to promote its services directly to the Internet other auction-related businesses and high-volume distributors of modern coins.

Because most collectibles are sold without being authenticated by a third party the company believes it has plenty of room for growth. Collectors Universe estimates that less than 10% of the vintage US coins less than 15% of vintage trading cards and less than 10% of valuable autographs have been authenticated and graded by independent providers of authentication and grading services.

Financial Analysis

The company's total revenue increased about 9% in fiscal 2012 to $48.3 million compared to

$44.4 million in 2011 thanks to a boost in the average service fees earned from grading authentication and related services. Except for a slump in 2009 the company has reported an upward trend in revenue from 2008 to 2012.

World coin authentication and grading revenues grew by approximately $1.7 million or 73% in fiscal 2012 compared to 2011. The windfall came from increased submissions of world coins including grading at the company's Paris facility.

Strategy

The company's growth strategy includes both acquisitions and new product launches. In 2010 Collectors Universe launched its PCGS Secure Plus service. The high-tech grading process uses laser scanning to help detect coins that have been artificially enhanced since their last certification. PCGS Secure Plus can also be used to help identify stolen coins.

Mergers and Acquisitions

Collectors Universe expanded its Web presence with the purchase of the precious metal and coin information website Coinflation.com in 2011 for $750000 in cash and stock. The acquisition complemented its existing Web holdings such as PCGSCoinFacts.com a source for historical US numismatic information and other related content.

Ownership

David G. Hall and Richard Kenneth Duncan Sr. each own about 13% and 12% of the company respectively.

EXECUTIVES

CEO, Robert G. (Bob) Deuster, age 64, $350,000 total
 compensation
President and COO, David G. Hall, age 67, $487,500
 total compensation
CFO, Joseph J. (Joe) Wallace, age 53, $260,000 total
 compensation
Vice President Professional Coin, Michael Sherman
Chairman, A. Clinton (Clint) Allen, age 70
Auditors: GrantThorntonLLP

LOCATIONS

HQ: Collectors Universe Inc
 1921 E. Alton Avenue, Santa Ana, CA 92705
Phone: 949 567-1234
Web: www.collectors.com

PRODUCTS/OPERATIONS

2012 Sales

	$ mil.	% of total
Grading & authentication fees	39.9	83
Other	8.5	19
Total	**48.4**	**100**

2012 Sales

	$ mil.	% of total
Coins	32.5	67
Cards & autographs	11.3	23
Other	4.6	10
Total	**48.4**	**100**

Selected Products & Operations

Coins
 Professional Coin Grading Service (PCGS)
 Certified Coin Exchange (CCE)
Trading Cards & Tickets
 Professional Sports Authenticator (PSA)
Autographs & Memorabilia
 PSA/DNA authentication services
Stamps
 Professional stamp experts
Expos
 Long Beach Expo
 Santa Clara Expo

Selected Mergers & Acquisitions

FY2011

Coinflation.com ($750000 in cash and stock; precious metal and coin information website)

COMPETITORS

Beckett Media
Christie's
F+W Media
H.R. Harmer

Leland's Auctions
Sotheby's
Spectrum Group

HISTORICAL FINANCIALS

Company Type: Public

Income Statement

FYE: June 30

	REVENUE ($ mil.)	NET INCOME ($ mil.)	NET PROFIT MARGIN	EMPLOYEES
06/14	60.5	7.3	12.1%	283
06/13	49.0	5.7	11.7%	256
06/12	48.3	6.7	14.0%	249
06/11	44.4	5.1	11.5%	241
06/10	39.7	16.7	42.0%	231
Annual Growth	11.1%	(18.5%)	—	5.2%

2014 Year-End Financials

Debt ratio: —
Return on equity: 35.7%
Cash ($ mil.): 19
Current ratio: 2.02
Long-term debt ($ mil.): —

No. of shares (mil.): 8
Dividends
  Yield: 6.6%
  Payout: 151.1%
Market value ($ mil.): 174

	STOCK PRICE ($) FY Close	P/E High/Low		Earnings	PER SHARE ($) Dividends	Book Value
06/14	19.59	26	15	0.89	1.30	2.33
06/13	13.25	21	13	0.71	1.30	2.42
06/12	14.68	21	15	0.84	1.30	3.03
06/11	14.82	25	18	0.66	1.28	3.16
06/10	13.41	7	2	2.19	0.80	3.59
Annual Growth	9.9% (10.2%)		—	—(20.2%)	12.9%	

Colony Financial Inc.

When most real estate investors are heading for the nearest exit Colony Financial is knocking on the doors of opportunity. The real estate investment and finance company which formed in 2009 and immediately filed for an initial public offering was established to acquire originate and manage commercial mortgage loans and other commercial real estate related debts. The firm's portfolio also includes real estate equity including single- and multifamily homes. It also has an interest in about 100 hotels acquired through foreclosure. Colony Financial is externally managed by affiliate Colony Financial Manager a wholly-owned subsidiary of the global real estate firm Colony Capital.

Geographic Reach

California-based Colony Financial's diversified portfolio of single- and multifamily homes and hotel properties spans about 20 states including Arizona California Florida Georgia and Texas.

Operations

The firm which has elected to be taxed as a real estate investment truest (REIT) for tax purposes has approximately 60 active investments repre-

senting $2 billion of invested equity at the end of 2013.

Financial Performance

Since its formation amid the global financial crisis in June 2009 the REIT has logged substantial revenue and profit growth. Indeed in 2013 revenue increased 68% compared with 2012 to more than $180 million. Net income was up 64% over the same period to $101.8 million. Cash flow from operations has kept pace with the steep rise in revenue and profits from negative cash flow in 2009 to $125.3 million in 2013. Colony Financial has a track record of delivering substantial returns portfolio-wide with limited use of leverage.

Strategy

The firm employs an opportunistic investment strategy that includes acquiring sub-performing and non-performing loans at a discount to par in the secondary market. The REIT's relationship with Colony Capital —one of the largest private equity real estate investors in the world —provides access to an extensive network of relationships worldwide. Despite the ongoing recovery of real estate assets since the depth of the financial downturn Colony Financial sees opportunity to acquire financial and real estate assets it believes are mispriced.

EXECUTIVES

CEO President and Director, Richard B. Saltzman
Chief Investment Officer, Kevin P. Traenkle, age 44
COO CFO and Treasurer, Darren J. Tangen, age 43, $350,000 total compensation
Chief Compliance Officer, David Palam Ⓐ©
Vice President Of Originations, Zachary Streit
Executive Chairman, Thomas J. Barrack
Auditors: Ernst&YoungLLP

LOCATIONS

HQ: Colony Financial Inc.
  2450 Broadway, 6th Floor, Santa Monica, CA 90404
Phone: 310 282-8820
Web: www.colonyfinancial.com

PRODUCTS/OPERATIONS

2013 Sales

	$ in mil.	% of total
Real Estate Debt investment	168.0	89
Other Real estate equity investment	19.9	11
Others	(7.7)	-
Total	**180.2**	**100**

2013 Hotel Properties

State	No. of Properties
Georgia	21
Alabama	18
Tennessee	12
North Carolina	12
South Carolina	10
Indiana	8
Florida	6
Mississippi	6
Kentucky	3
Louisiana	3
Virginia	2
Illinois	1
Total	**102**

COMPETITORS

Arbor Realty Trust
Bimini Capital
  Management
CIFC
Cousins Properties
Douglas Emmett

Macerich
Newcastle Investment
PS Business Parks
Pacific Office
  Properties Trust
Petra Real Estate

Institutional
  Financial Markets
JER Investors Trust

Redwood Trust
Starwood Property
Western Asset Mortgage

HISTORICAL FINANCIALS

Company Type: Public

Income Statement

FYE: December 31

	REVENUE ($ mil.)	NET INCOME ($ mil.)	NET PROFIT MARGIN	EMPLOYEES
12/13	180.2	101.7	56.5%	0
12/12	107.1	62.0	57.9%	0
12/11	65.4	43.3	66.2%	0
12/10	27.4	17.7	64.7%	0
12/09	1.0	(0.4)	—	0
Annual Growth	258.5%	—	—	—

2013 Year-End Financials

Debt ratio: 23.4%
Return on equity: 7.0%
Cash ($ mil.): 43
Current ratio: 0.24
Long-term debt ($ mil.): 477

No. of shares (mil.): 76
Dividends
  Yield: 6.9%
  Payout: 122.8%
Market value ($ mil.): 1,552

	STOCK PRICE ($) FY Close	P/E High/Low		Earnings	PER SHARE ($) Dividends	Book Value
12/13	20.29	20	16	1.20	1.40	22.02
12/12	19.50	15	12	1.32	1.44	23.04
12/11	15.71	15	8	1.46	1.31	18.48
12/10	20.02	17	14	1.18	0.97	19.16
12/09	20.37	—	—	(0.06)	0.07	18.68
Annual Growth	(0.1%)		—	—(111.5%)	4.2%	

Columbia Banking System, Inc.

Columbia Banking System (CBS) is the holding company for Columbia State Bank (also known as Columbia Bank). The regional community bank has about 155 branches in Washington from Puget Sound to the timber country in the southwestern part of the state as well as in northern Oregon where it also operates as Bank of Astoria. Targeting retail and small and medium-sized business customers the bank offers standard retail services such as checking and savings accounts CDs IRAs credit cards loans and mortgages. Commercial business and real estate loans make up more than 75% of the company's loan portfolio. CBS is increasing its presence in the Pacific Northwest through acquisitions of other community banks.

Geographic Reach

Tacoma-based Columbia Banking System has bank branches in 38 countries in Washington and Oregon.

Operations

The bank's Columbia Private Banking division offers customized financial services for businesses and affluent families. Subsidiary CB Financial Services provides investment products through a pact with third-party provider PrimeVest.

Financial Performance

Columbia Bank's revenue increased 17% in 2013 versus 2012 to $323.6 million. Net income rose 30% over the same period to $60 million. The bank's merger with West Coast Bank in early 2013 had a positive impact on its financial performance. Columbia's total assets at the end of 2013 were $7.16 billion compared with $4.9 billion at year end 2012 primarily due to the purchase of West Coast.

Strategy

Columbia Banking System has taken advantage of the rash of bank failures in recent years to increase its presence in the region. It added more than 30 branches in 2010 when it acquired most of the deposits and assets of failed banks Columbia River Bank and American Marine Bank a week apart. In similar transactions in 2011 it acquired most of the operations of the failed institutions Summit Bank First Heritage Bank and Bank of Whitman. Those deals added more than a dozen branches in Washington. More recently it acquired its smaller competitor West Coast Bank in spring 2013. Columbia plans to rebrand West Coast under its own name. Also Bank of Astoria will rebrand as Columbia State Bank to create a unified presence in the market.

Mergers and Acquisitions

In April 2013 Columbia acquired West Coast Bancorp —the parent company of West Coast Bank which operates nearly 60 bank branches in Oregon and Washington. The cash-and-stock deal included $264 million in cash and 12.8 million shares of its stock which were paid to West Coast shareholders. The purchase boosted Columbia's total assets to more than $7 billion and furthered Columbia's goal of becoming the leading regional community bank in the Pacific Northwest.

EXECUTIVES

Svp Special Credits, Elizabeth Anderson
President and CEO; President and CEO Columbia Bank, Melanie J. Dressel, age 62, $452,283 total compensation
EVP and COO, Mark W. Nelson, age 63, $253,073 total compensation
EVP and Chief Credit Officer, Andrew L. (Andy) McDonald, age 55, $209,998 total compensation
EVP and CFO, Clint E. Stein, $174,667 total compensation
EVP and COO, Hadley Robbins, age 54
Vice President, Terry Mehegan
Svp- Columbia Bank, Michael Drake
Vp/sr Financial Consultant, Tom Godwin
Senior Vice President And Eastern Washington Commercial Banking Regional Manager, Matt Duffy
Vice President, Anne Bopp
Avp-commercial Loan Support, Jodi Wunder
Vice President, Connie Pentecoast
Vice President & Program Manager, Nancy Almond
Assistant Vice President Treasury Management Officer, Jason Scott
Senior Vice President Olympia, Nina Maurer
Vice President Commercial Banking Officer, Rebekah Baze
Vice President, Kathy Peterman
Vice President Commercial Loan Officer, John Wallace
Senior Vice President And Manager Operations, Julie Tollkuehn
Senior Vice President Portland Team Leader, Andrew McKechnie
Vice President Commercial Banking, Frank Matulis
Vice President, Greg Todd
Vice President, Kit Gerwels
Chairman, William T. Weyerhaeuser, age 71
Auditors: Deloitte&ToucheLLP

LOCATIONS

HQ: Columbia Banking System, Inc.
1301 "A" Street, Tacoma, WA 98402-2156
Phone: 253 305-1900
Web: www.columbiabank.com

2013 Branches

	No.
Washington	86
Oregon	71
Total	**157**

COMPETITORS

BECU	JPMorgan Chase
Bank of America	KeyCorp
Banner Corp	U.S. Bancorp
Heritage Financial	Washington Federal
HomeStreet	Wells Fargo

HISTORICAL FINANCIALS

Company Type: Public

Income Statement

FYE: December 31

	ASSETS ($ mil.)	NET INCOME ($ mil.)	INCOME AS % OF ASSETS	EMPLOYEES
12/13	7,161.5	60.0	0.8%	1,695
12/12	4,906.3	46.1	0.9%	1,198
12/11	4,785.9	48.0	1.0%	1,256
12/10	4,256.3	30.7	0.7%	1,092
12/09	3,200.9	(3.9)	—	715
Annual Growth	**22.3%**	—		**24.1%**

2013 Year-End Financials

Return on assets: 0.9%	Dividends
Return on equity: 6.6%	Yield: 1.4%
Long-term debt ($ mil.): —	Payout: 33.8%
No. of shares (mil.): 51	Market value ($ mil.): 1,409
Sales ($ mil): 323	

	STOCK PRICE ($) FY Close	P/E High/Low		PER SHARE ($) Earnings	Dividends	Book Value
12/13	27.49	23	14	1.21	0.41	20.55
12/12	17.94	20	14	1.16	0.98	19.25
12/11	19.27	18	11	1.21	0.27	19.22
12/10	21.06	34	22	0.72	0.04	17.97
12/09	16.18	—	—	(0.38)	0.07	18.78
Annual Growth	**14.2%**		—	—	55.6%	2.3%

CommVault Systems Inc

CommVault Systems wants to have a lock on data management. The company provides software that customers use to store and manage enterprise data. Its Simpana software suite handles resource management backup archiving data replication disaster recovery and search. Altogether CommVault counts some 20000 customers that come from industries such as financial services health care manufacturing and utilities as well as from the public sector. CommVault's strategic partners include systems integrators and professional services firms distributors and resellers and technology providers. About 40% of its revenues are generated outside the US.

Geographic Reach

The company operates from 20 offices in the US. It has another 40 locations scattered across the Americas Asia and Europe. The US however is its largest market accounting for almost 60% of sales.

Sales and Marketing

CommVault primarily uses a direct sales force to sell its Simpana software to businesses and government agencies of all sizes. Partnerships are also an essential component of its sales strategy. Companies such as Dell Hitachi Data Systems and NetApp resell Simpana and in some cases incorporate the software into their own hardware. (For example Simpana is integrated with NetApp SnapShot and NetApp SnapProtect.) In addition distributor Arrow Electronics holds a distribution agreement with CommVault and provides around 30% of sales.

Simpana's software licenses are typically sold on a capacity basis which allows customers unlimited use based on the amount of terabytes of data under management. Only about 20% of sales come from a per-copy basis or as site licenses.

Financial Performance

CommVault has enjoyed a decade of straight revenue growth. In fiscal 2014 (year-end March) sales increased 18% to $586 million. The year the average amount of one of its software implementations was $272000 up from $266000 in 2013. Sales of both software and service are split 50-50. Profits also grew 20% in 2014 to $64 million.

Strategy

With the growth of big data comes the need to securely protect manage and access it and CommVault sees substantial opportunities for its data management capabilities. Still in order to keep up with technological advances the company continually updates the Simpana line (Simpana 10 was released in 2013) in order to keep pace with evolving industry technologies. The company spent $55 million on research and development in 2014 (9% of sales) and maintains two software development centers in India.

Company Background

The company was founded as an independent segment of Bell Laboratories in 1988; senior management (backed in part by funding from Sprout Group) purchased the company's assets from Lucent Technologies in 1996.

EXECUTIVES

Senior Vice President Worldwide Sales, Ron Miiller, age 49
Vice President Of Sales Operations, Brian D McAteer
Vice President, Rob Stroud
Chairman President and CEO, N. Robert (Bob) Hammer, age 72, $595,154 total compensation
EVP COO and Director, Alan G. (Al) Bunte, age 61, $481,308 total compensation
SVP Marketing and Business Development, David R. (Dave) West, age 49, $300,773 total compensation
VP Finance and CFO, Brian Carolan, age 43, $301,385 total compensation
VP Worldwide Technical Services, Robert Kaloustian
VP Product Management, Brian Brockway
VP Worldwide Alliances, Brian J. Allison
Vp Product And Segment Marketing, Michael Marchi
Vp-worldwide Sales Oprtns, Alistair Clark
Vice President North America Channels, Scott Skidmore
Regional Vice President Professional Services, Bob Carapezzi
Ea Vp Business D, Kathy Phillips

Vice President Operations, Janet Cropper
National Account Manager, Jeff Lockhart
Vp Emea, Steven Rose, age 58
Vice President Worldwide Partners And Programs, Ralph Nimergood
Area Vice President, Marty Turek
Vice President Dod Sales, Jon Teunis
Vice President Operations, Brigitte Shoemaker
Fifth Vice President Docent Manager, Bharani Surineni
Vice President Federal, Matt Galligan
Vp Finance Chief Accounting Officer, Gary Merrill, age 40
Vice President Worldwide Sales Operations, Rick Donnelly
Vice President Western Us, Rick Baumgart
National Account Manager, Kari Edgar
National Account Manager, Logan Sutterfield
Vice President Of Worldwide Sales, Michael McGuire
Vice President Human Resources, Joanne Bamforth
Vp Services And Technical Support Emea And Apac, Suresh P Reddy, age 53
Vice President Marketing And Business, Richard Conrad
Vice President Strategic Relations Deputy Chief Genealogy Officer, Ed Donakey
Vp Mkt, Mike Imanov
Area Vice President Sales, Rick Theiler
Chairman President and CEO, N. Robert (Bob) Hammer, age 72
Board Member, Jeff Moyer
Auditors: Ernst&YoungLLP

LOCATIONS

HQ: CommVault Systems Inc
1 CommVault Way, Tinton Falls, NJ 07724
Phone: 732 870-4000
Web: www.commvault.com

2014 Sales

	$ mil.	% of total
US	333.7	57
Other	252.6	43
Total	**586.3**	**100**

PRODUCTS/OPERATIONS

2014 Sales

	$ mil.	% of total
Software	294.4	50
Services	291.9	50
Total	**586.3**	**100**

COMPETITORS

CA Inc.	Microsoft
EMC	NetApp
Hewlett-Packard	Quantum Corporation
IBM Software	Symantec

HISTORICAL FINANCIALS

Company Type: Public

Income Statement

FYE: March 31

	REVENUE ($ mil.)	NET INCOME ($ mil.)	NET PROFIT MARGIN	EMPLOYEES
03/14	586.3	64.0	10.9%	1,973
03/13	495.8	53.2	10.7%	1,740
03/12	406.6	31.9	7.9%	1,437
03/11	314.7	21.0	6.7%	1,268
03/10	271.0	18.4	6.8%	1,154
Annual Growth	21.3%	36.6%	—	14.3%

2014 Year-End Financials

Debt ratio: —
Return on equity: 15.6%
Cash ($ mil.): 457
Current ratio: 2.59
Long-term debt ($ mil.): —
No. of shares (mil.): 47
Dividends
  Yield: —
  Payout: —
Market value ($ mil.): 3,059

	STOCK PRICE ($) FY Close	P/E High/Low		PER SHARE ($) Earnings	Dividends	Book Value
03/14	64.95	66	46	1.29	0.00	9.82
03/13	82.00	72	34	1.10	0.00	7.63
03/12	49.64	76	43	0.68	0.00	5.16
03/11	39.88	84	36	0.45	0.00	4.28
03/10	21.35	55	23	0.41	0.00	3.68
Annual Growth	32.1%	—	—	33.2%	—	27.8%

Computer Programs & Systems Inc

The general-sounding Computer Programs and Systems Inc. (CPSI) is focused on a very specific market - providing administrative software and hardware systems and outsourcing services to acute care community hospitals. CPSI develops and supports electronic health records (EHR) as well as financial and clinical information management software and IT systems for small and mid-sized hospitals in the US. The company boasts a client base of more than 650 hospitals across 45 states. CPSI's software enables users to manage their patients staff finances and facilities. Subsidiary TruBridge offers manged IT services and business office outsourcing services.

Operations

CPSI products form an integrated data management system so the company markets its various applications as a single system. Among the various functions its electronic health record (EHR) system covers the basic necessary system includes patient management and financial accounting along with the hardware needed to run those programs. The other applications available to customers are patient care clinical record keeping and reporting and enterprise applications. Enterprise applications include such functions as system backups integrated fax document scanning and more.

Sales and Marketing

Nearly all of CPSI's customers are organizations with 100 or fewer acute care beds but its target market includes hospitals with up to 300 such beds. The company serves less than 15% of the estimated size of its larger target market and less than one-quarter of its core market giving it room to continue the growth it has enjoyed so far.

For the most part CPSI lands new customers through referrals from existing customers. It also attracts potential customers with presentations at industry seminars and tradeshows and advertisements in publications for the healthcare industry. The company's typical sales cycle can be anywhere from six to 18 months.

Financial Performance

CPSI continued to grow revenue and profits in 2012 the former rising 5% to $183 million while net income climbed 16% to $29 million. The government incentives for health care organizations to move to electronic records continue to drive sales.

It installed systems at 34 new hospitals in 2012 (up from 17 in 2011). The TruBridge business management services segment continued to grow and now accounts for a fifth of total revenue.

Strategy

CPSI named its outsourcing division TruBridge in early 2013. TruBridge offers include network management and monitoring server and storage management hosted email firewall management malware protection data center services and help desk support and more. Business management services include electronic billing patient statement processing payroll processing website hosting and others.

EXECUTIVES

Vice President Sales, Troy D Rosser, age 50
Vice President Information Technology, Patrick A Immel, age 44
Vice President Product Development, Robert D Smith, age 44
President CEO and Director, J. Boyd Douglas, age 48, $521,154 total compensation
EVP Corporate and Business Development, Victor S. Schneider, age 55, $442,454 total compensation
SVP Software Services, Robert D. Hinckle, age 44
SVP Product Development Services, Michael K. Muscat, age 40
President TruBridge, Christopher L. Fowler, age 38
VP Information Technology Services, J. Scott Littrell, age 39
Executive Vice President General Mgt, John Larson
Vice President Purchasing, Don Goeke
Vice President Operations, Philip Walker
Vice President Sales, Lyle Hutchison
Vice President - Financial Support, Pamela Phillips
Vice President - Implementation, Lamar Cowart
V Pres Fin-controller-cao, James Britain
Vp Marketing, John Ohara
Vice President Of Business Development, Morgan Gillion
Vice President Information Technology Services, Scott Littrell
Vice President Of Marketing, Dennis Blakeley
Vice President Information Technology, Frank Malangone
Vice President Product Development, Robert Dreyer
Vice President Business Services Trubridge, Gregory Leatherbury
Vice President, Mark S Walker
Chairman of the Board; Chief Financial Officer; Treasurer; Secretary, David A. Dye, age 45
Board Member, William R Seifert, age 66
Board Member, John C Johnson, age 64
Board Member, Justin Arnold
Board Member, Austin W Mulherin
Auditors: GrantThorntonLLP

LOCATIONS

HQ: Computer Programs & Systems Inc
6600 Wall Street, Mobile, AL 36695
Phone: 251 639-8100
Web: www.cpsi.com

PRODUCTS/OPERATIONS

2012 Sales

	$ mil.	% of total
System sales	72.5	40
Support & maintenance	73.0	40
Business management services	37.8	20
Total	**183.3**	**100**

Selected Products

Clinical information systems

Anatomic pathology
  Cardiopulmonary
  Laboratory information systems
  Blood inventory
  Microbology
  Quality control
  Laboratory instrument interfaces
  Medical image management systems
  Pharmacy
  Physical therapy
  Radiology information systems
Enterprise applications
Financial accounting applications
  Accounts payable applications
  Budgeting
  Electronic direct deposit
  Executive information
  Fixed asset information
  General ledger applications
  Human resources
  Payroll and personnel
  Time and attendance applications
Home health
Patient care
  Care plans
  Core measures system
  Medication management
  Order entry/results reporting
  Patient activity
Patient management applications
  Contract management
  Electronic file management
  Health information management
  Patient accounting
  Quality improvement applications
  Registration systems

Selected Services
Application services
Internet services
Outsourcing services
  Business office management
  Electronic billing
  Statement processing
Support
System implementation and conversion
Training

COMPETITORS

Cerner	QuadraMed
Global Med	Quality Systems
Healthland	Siemens Healthcare
MEDHOST	Streamline Health
MEDITECH	Solutions
McKesson	

HISTORICAL FINANCIALS

Company Type: Public

Income Statement

FYE: December 31

	REVENUE ($ mil.)	NET INCOME ($ mil.)	NET PROFIT MARGIN	EMPLOYEES
12/13	200.8	32.7	16.3%	1,378
12/12	183.3	29.9	16.4%	1,420
12/11	173.4	25.8	14.9%	1,341
12/10	153.2	18.7	12.2%	1,194
12/09	127.7	15.1	11.9%	1,077
Annual Growth	12.0%	21.2%	—	6.4%

2013 Year-End Financials

Debt ratio: —	No. of shares (mil.): 11
Return on equity: —	Dividends
Cash ($ mil.): 11	Yield: 3.3%
Current ratio: 3.39	Payout: 69.1%
Long-term debt ($ mil.): —	Market value ($ mil.): 690

	STOCK PRICE ($) FY Close	P/E High/Low	PER SHARE ($) Earnings	Dividends	Book Value
12/13	61.81	21 16	2.95	2.04	6.19
12/12	50.34	23 17	2.71	2.84	5.16
12/11	51.11	31 18	2.34	1.44	5.19
12/10	46.84	29 21	1.71	1.44	4.24
12/09	46.05	36 16	1.39	1.44	3.89
Annual Growth	7.6%	— —	20.7%	9.1%	12.3%

Computer Task Group, Inc.

Computer Task Group (CTG) uses its IT expertise to take clients' computer systems to task. Serving primarily technology service providers health care manufacturing and financial services clients the company offers a wide range of professional technology services including IT staffing custom application development and systems integration. It also provides strategic consulting services to assess its clients' technology needs as well as project management and application outsourcing management services. It counts about 300 clients in North America and Western Europe; its largest client IBM accounts for more than 25% of revenues. The company was founded in 1966.

Geographic Reach

The company has facilities in about a dozen US states Belgium Canada Luxembourg and the UK. Customers in the US generate the bulk of revenue (about 84%) European revenue represented roughly 16% of total revenue in fiscal 2012.

Operations

CTG operates in only one segment: providing IT services to its clients. The company does have six operating subsidiaries.

Financial Performance

The company's revenues increased by about 7% and its net income increased 35% in fiscal 2012 compared with 2011. Net cash inflow increased by $11 million in fiscal 2012 compared with the prior year.

The increase in revenues during fiscal 2012 was attributed to an increase in revenue in North America due to strong demand for the company's IT solutions services. IT solutions revenue increased 18% primarily driven by an increase in the company's EMR work for providers in the healthcare vertical market in North America. The increase in year-over-year revenue in the company's European operations was primarily due to strength in the company's European IT solutions business.

The increase in net income during fiscal 2012 was primarily attributed to the increase in operating income as a percentage of revenues. The increase in operating income was primarily due to the favorable change in business mix to more solutions services in 2012 and lower SG&A costs as a percentage of revenue.

Strategy

The IT services market is heavily saturated and CTG can't compete with global IT service providers such as Accenture nor can it compete with offshore providers in India like Infosys. Staffing offers a lower profit margin but the company is a preferred

vendor with large technology service providers that require a lot of people with a specific expertise.

One way CTG plans to grow its IT services division is to target the health care industry specifically to assist companies in adopting electronic medical records (EMR). Its CTG HealthCare Solutions offers a range of services for hospitals and clinics with administration billing infrastructure regulatory compliance security and vendor management.

The push for EMR contracts is paying off as health care organizations are receiving federal incentives from the Health Information Technology for Economic and Clinical Health (HITECH) Act as part of the American Recovery and Reinvestment Act of 2009.

Mergers and Acquisitions

In January 2013 the company acquired etrinity a provider of IT services to the healthcare market in Belgium and the Netherlands. The strategic acquisition came as the European market is starting to move toward adopting US electronic medical records (EMR) systems that enhance the delivery of healthcare from a cost and outcomes perspective. The acquisition also gains significance as CTG plans to step up the growth of its healthcare IT business which contributes about one-third of its revenue.

Ownership

CTG's major shareholder is a trust overseen by an attorney. Trustee Thomas R. Beecher owns an 18% stake; other significant shareholders include Bank of America (11%) and Heartland Advisors (10%). Mr. Beecher is a partner at the Buffalo law firm of Phillips Lytle.

HISTORY

Former IBM employees Randy Marks and David Baer founded Computer Task Group (CTG) in 1966 as Marks-Baer. The company offered programming and other technical services to firms that lacked in-house expertise in these areas. Marks-Baer's first market was the medical industry but the company soon branched out. By 1968 sales reached $471000. That year it opened a New York City branch and changed its name to CTG.

The company went public in 1969 and spent the next decade collecting some prestigious clients including IBM Chemical Bank (now part of J.P. Morgan Chase) the City of Buffalo and the New York State Job Bank which accounted for half of CTG's sales in 1970.

Throughout the 1980s and 1990s CTG expanded through acquisitions buying professional services firm Neoterics (1980) software consulting business Shubrooks International (UK 1986) and computer services company Rendeck (1990).

The 1990s also saw the company move away from a one-time project model and toward a long-term contract approach. In 1998 CTG inked a $3 million deal to provide year 2000 compliance services for FBL Financial Group. The next year CTG bought Elumen Solutions an IT services provider to the health care industry for $89 million.

Kaiser Permanente hired CTG in 2001 to implement patient accounting systems at more than 100 medical facilities in Southern California.

CTG renewed its service contract with IBM its largest customer in 2003. Early in 2004 the company sold its Netherlands subsidiary.

EXECUTIVES

Vice President Solutions Development, Mike Colson

SVP and General Manager CTG Europe, Filip J. L. Gyde, age 53, $281,854 total compensation

CFO, Brendan M. Harrington, age 49, $305,000 total compensation
SVP CTG Health Solutions, Ted Reynolds
President and CEO, Cliff Bleustein
Vice President Western Region Strategic Staffing Services, Rick Sullivan
Sr Vice President Logistics Solutions, Paul Dimouro
Senior Vice President Strategic Staffing Services, Bud Crumlish
Interim Chairman, Daniel J. (Dan) Sullivan, age 67
Treasurer, Rhodie Ruminski
Auditors: KPMGLLP

LOCATIONS

HQ: Computer Task Group, Inc.
  800 Delaware Avenue, Buffalo, NY 14209
Phone: 716 882-8000
Web: www.ctg.com

2012 Sales

	$ mil.	% of total
US	355.0	84
Europe		
Belgium	42.0	10
Other countries	26.7	6
Other regions	.7	-
Total	**424.4**	**100**

PRODUCTS/OPERATIONS

Selected Services

Application management outsourcing
Business process modeling
E-business strategies
Help desk operation and support
Information technology assessment and consulting
Internetworking
Joint technology selection
Network development
Project management
Software development
Staffing
Supply chain assessment
Systems integration
Testing
Training

COMPETITORS

Accenture	Ernst & Young Global
Analysts International	Getronics
CDI	HP Enterprise Services
Capgemini	Info Technologies
Computer Sciences	KPMG
Corp.	Kelly Services
CorSource Technology	Robert Half
Group	TEKsystems
Deloitte	Volt Information

HISTORICAL FINANCIALS

Company Type: Public

Income Statement

FYE: December 31

	REVENUE ($ mil.)	NET INCOME ($ mil.)	NET PROFIT MARGIN	EMPLOYEES
12/13	419.0	15.6	3.7%	3,700
12/12	424.4	16.1	3.8%	3,900
12/11	396.2	11.9	3.0%	3,700
12/10	331.4	8.3	2.5%	3,400
12/09	275.5	5.9	2.2%	2,900
Annual Growth	**11.0%**	**27.5%**	**—**	**6.3%**

2013 Year-End Financials

Debt ratio: —	No. of shares (mil.): 18
Return on equity: 14.4%	Dividends
Cash ($ mil.): 46	Yield: 1.0%
Current ratio: 2.38	Payout: 19.8%
Long-term debt ($ mil.): —	Market value ($ mil.): 349

	STOCK PRICE ($) FY Close	P/E High/Low	PER SHARE ($) Earnings	Dividends	Book Value
12/13	18.83	25 16	0.92	0.20	6.14
12/12	18.23	18 11	0.96	0.00	5.48
12/11	14.08	19 12	0.71	0.00	4.81
12/10	10.88	21 11	0.52	0.00	4.32
12/09	8.01	21 7	0.38	0.00	3.95
Annual Growth	**23.8%**	**—**	**24.7%**	**—**	**11.7%**

Concho Resources Inc

Concho Resources has more than a hunch that a lucrative resource lies under its feet in Southeastern New Mexico and West Texas. The company explores and develops properties (more than 604370 net acres) located primarily in the Permian Basin region in which it produces oil and natural gas. The bulk of the company's reported 502.9 million barrels of proved reserves in 2013 is crude oil while the rest is natural gas. Concho Resources gets more than 80% its revenues from crude oil which is priced much higher than natural gas. The company drilled 392 net wells in 2013.

Geographic Reach

The company's core oil and gas exploration and production operating areas are the New Mexico Shelf Delaware Basin and Texas Permian in the Permian Basin region of Southeast New Mexico and West Texas. The New Mexico Shelf represented 45% of Concho Resources' total reserves in 2013; Texas Permian 28%; and the Delaware Basin 27%.

Operations

The company's core operations are focused in the Permian Basin which underlies a 250 miles wide and 300 miles long area of Southeast New Mexico and West Texas. In 2013 substantially all of its estimated proved reserves were located in its core operating areas and consisted of approximately 61 percent oil and 39 percent natural gas.

The company has assembled a multi-year inventory of vertical and horizontal development drilling and exploration projects including projects to further evaluate the areal extent of the Yeso formation and the Wolfberry play; the Brushy Canyon Bone Spring and Wolfcamp formations in the Delaware Basin; and the Spraberry and Wolfcamp formations in the Texas Permian.

Sales and Marketing

The company's major customers include HollyFrontier Refining and Marketing and Enterprise Crude Oil which accounted for 30% and 13% respectively of Concho Resources' revenues in 2013.

Financial Performance

The company's revenues increased by 27% primarily due to higher oil prices and a rise in production due to successful drilling efforts during 2012 and 2013 and production from the Three Rivers Acquisition which closed in July 2012. The company increased its average daily production from 84700 barrels of oil equivalent during the fourth quarter of 2012 to 97000 barrels of oil

equivalent during the fourth quarter of 2013.Concho Resources' net income decreased by 42% in 2013 thanks to increased depreciation and depletion expenses associated with new wells (drilled and completed in 2012 and 2013) and acquisitions in 2012 and higher depletion rates. Other factors included an increased loss on derivatives not designated as hedges. Its Exploration and abandonments expenses rose due to its increased drilling and exploration activity in the Delaware Basin area. Operating cash flows during 2013 grew by $124.5 million primarily due to an increase in oil and natural gas revenues offset in part by cash increases in oil and natural gas production costs cash increases in general and administrative expense and interest expense and negative variances in operating assets and liabilities.

Acquisitions and the increased demand for oil and gas have helped to lift Concho Resources' revenues each year from 2008 through 2013.

Strategy

The company has focused on expanding its holdings through medium- and large-sized complementary acquisitions primarily in the Permian Basin. Concho Resources is reinvesting high-margin cash flows into projects with robust rates of return and pursuing acquisitions that enhance existing portfolio. It intends to grow its reserves and production through development drilling and exploration activities on its multi-year project inventory and through acquisitions that meet its strategic and financial objectives. In 2013 it drilled 44% of its wells horizontally (an advanced drilling technology that usually produces more oil per well than the traditional vertical method) and it continues to evaluate converting its identified vertical locations to horizontal opportunities where possible.

It had a 2014 capital budget of $2.3 billion focused on drilling in the Delaware Basin and Midland Basin. It planned to spend 70% of it on drilling and completion costs on the Delaware Basin assets with which it expects to drill 281 (191 net) wells; and 23% on the Texas Permian assets with which it expects to drill 190 (99 net) wells.

To raise cash to help fund acquisitions in 2012 Concho Resources sold some non-core Permian Basin oil and natural gas properties to Legacy Reserves for $520 million.

Mergers and Acquisitions

In 2012 the company acquired interests in the Wolfberry trend in the Permian Basin from Petroleum Development Corporation for $189.2 million. The acquisition added about 10200 net acres to Concho Resources' holdings in the region and estimated proved oil reserves of about 10 million barrels of oil equivalent.

The company boosted its Permian holdings further in 2012 by buying all of the oil and gas assets of Three Rivers Operating Company for $1 billion. Three Rivers has estimated proved reserves of 45.5 million barrels of oil equivalent and 200000 net acres in a handful of Permian plays.

Concho Resources acquired three entities affiliated with OGX Holdings II LLC for $252 million. The OGX deal included producing and non-producing acreage in the Delaware Basin of Southeast New Mexico and West Texas representing about 5.7 million barrels of of proved oil equivalent reserves.

Company Background

It also sold its Bakken assets in North Dakota in 2011 to focus on its core Permian properties.

EXECUTIVES

EVP, Jack F. Harper, age 43, $280,000 total compensation

SVP CFO and Treasurer, Darin G. Holderness, age 50, $425,000 total compensation

SVP Exploration, Matthew G. Hyde, age 58, $425,000 total compensation

Chairman CEO and President, Timothy A. Leach, age 55, $850,000 total compensation

EVP Chief Commercial Officer and Corporate Secretary, C. William Giraud, $425,000 total compensation

EVP and COO, E. Joseph Wright, age 54, $500,000 total compensation

VP Land, Mona D. Ables

VP Texas, Clay Bateman

VP New Mexico, Gayle L. Burleson

VP Drilling, M. Ray Peterson

Director Information Technology, Kang Chen

Vice President Engineering And Operations, Joseph Wright

Senior Vice President Corporate, Steven H Pruett

Svp-business Operations & Eng, Steve Guthrie

Vice President Capital Markets Strategy, Price Moncrief

Vice President Of Administration, Kyle Rose

Information Technology Vice President, James Caputo

Executive Assistant To Senior Vp, Lisa Fields

Vice President General Counsel Corporate Secretary, William Giraud

SVP CFO and Treasurer, Darin G. Holderness, age 50

Chairman CEO and President, Timothy A. Leach, age 55

EVP Chief Commercial Officer and Corporate Secretary, C. William Giraud

Auditors: GrantThorntonLLP

LOCATIONS

HQ: Concho Resources Inc
One Concho Center, 600 West Illinois Avenue, Midland, TX 79701
Phone: 432 683-7443   **Fax:** 432 683-7441
Web: www.conchoresources.com

PRODUCTS/OPERATIONS

2013 Sales

	$ mil.	% of total
Oil	1938.4	84
Natural gas	381.5	16
Total	**2319.9**	**100**

COMPETITORS

Abraxas Petroleum	PDC Energy
Apache	Parallel Petroleum
Chaparral Energy	Permian Basin
Chevron	SM Energy
Cimarex	SandRidge Energy
Encore Energy	Treaty Energy
Exxon Mobil	Vanguard Natural
Legacy Reserves	Resources
Occidental Petroleum	Whiting Petroleum

HISTORICAL FINANCIALS

Company Type: Public

Income Statement

FYE: December 31

	REVENUE ($ mil.)	NET INCOME ($ mil.)	NET PROFIT MARGIN	EMPLOYEES
12/13	2,319.9	251.0	10.8%	868
12/12	1,819.8	431.6	23.7%	745
12/11	1,739.9	548.1	31.5%	592
12/10	972.5	204.3	21.0%	443
12/09	544.4	(9.8)	—	284
Annual Growth	**43.7%**	**—**	**—**	**32.2%**

2013 Year-End Financials

Debt ratio: 37.8%	No. of shares (mil.): 105
Return on equity: 6.9%	Dividends
Cash ($ mil.): 0	Yield: —
Current ratio: 0.69	Payout: —
Long-term debt ($ mil.): 3,630	Market value ($ mil.): 11,350

	STOCK PRICE ($) FY Close	P/E High/Low	PER SHARE ($) Earnings	Dividends	Book Value
12/13	108.00	51 34	2.39	0.00	35.76
12/12	80.56	28 19	4.15	0.00	33.14
12/11	93.75	21 13	5.28	0.00	28.74
12/10	87.67	40 19	2.18	0.00	23.19
12/09	44.90	— —	(0.12)	0.00	15.56
Annual Growth	**24.5%**	**— —**	**—**	**—**	**23.1%**

Connecticut Water Service, Inc.

The operations of Connecticut Water Service (CWS) consist of managing a lot of water in its namesake state and more recently in Maine as well. CWS's regulated subsidiaries —Connecticut Water Company Maine Water and Biddeford & Saco Water —provide water supply and services to 120000 customers in 76 municipalities in Connecticut and Maine. The non-operating holding company's subsidiaries gather water from yield from its 235 active wells and 25 surface water supplies and produce 72 million gallons daily. Other subsidiaries offer fire protection other water-related services and real estate services.

Geographic Reach

CWS operates in Connecticut and Maine.

Operations

Of the company's six key operating subsidiaries its regulated subsidiaries are the Connecticut Water the Maine Water and Biddeford & Saco Water. These businesses own and operate 30 water filtration facilities (a combined treatment capacity of 52 million gallons per day). Their transmission and distribution systems consists of 2100 miles of main and a reservoir storage capacity of 8.5 billion gallons. Connecticut Water CWS' largest subsidiary supplies water to about 300000 people in 56 towns in Connecticut. Unregulated companies include Chester Realty (real estate in Connecticut) and New England Water Utility Services (contract water and sewer operations and other water related services).

Financial Performance

CWS' revenues increased by 21% in 2012 due to added revenues associated with the acquisitions of Maine Water and Biddeford and Saco Water (which contributed about 87% of increased revenues). In addition rate increases and higher late payment fees lifted revenues by 4%.The company's net income increased by 21% in 2012 due to the acquisitions as well as increased non-water sales earnings and a higher gain on real estate transactions. That year the unregulated companies together with real estate transactions within Connecticut Water contributed about 17% of the CWS' net income through real estate transactions (and services and rentals).

Strategy

In recent years the company has grown primarily through acquisitions.

In 2013 CWS' Connecticut Water unit signed an agreement with state authorities to voluntarily return the benefit of an IRS tax law change to customers through a rate reduction over a 2 year period starting from April 2014 and to delay the filing of its next general rate case. The arrangement provides a rate reduction for customers while allowing for continued investment in the infrastructure.

Mergers and Acquisitions

In 2012 the company acquired Aqua America's Maine operations for $54 million.

The acquisition of Aqua Maine allowed the company to expand into New England. The regional company now known as The Maine Water Company and Connecticut Water received $33.7 million more in additional rates and increased its customer base by 16000. The transaction also made Connecticut Water the largest publicly traded water utility company in New England with 106000 customers in Connecticut and Maine.

That year it also acquired Biddeford and Saco Water (15500 customers in the Maine communities of Biddeford Saco Old Orchard Beach and Scarborough) for $12 million.

In 2011 the company acquired Green Springs Water Company (Madison Connecticut) which serves about 12000 people.

EXECUTIVES

VP Finance CFO and Treasurer Connecticut Water Service and Connecticut Water Company, David C. Benoit, age 57, $264,653 total compensation

Chairman President and CEO, Eric W. Thornburg, age 55, $424,000 total compensation

President The Maine Water Company, Judy E. Wallingford

VP Service Delivery, Craig J. Patla

Chairman President and CEO, Eric W. Thornburg, age 55

Auditors: PricewaterhouseCoopersLLP

LOCATIONS

HQ: Connecticut Water Service, Inc.
93 West Main Street, Clinton, CT 06413
Phone: 860 669-8636
Web: www.ctwater.com

PRODUCTS/OPERATIONS

2012 Sales

	$ mil.	% of total
Residential	50.8	60
Fire protection	15.6	19
Commercial	10.1	12
Industrial	3.1	4
Public authority	2.7	3
Other	1.5	2
Total	**83.8**	**100**

2012 Sales

	% of total
Water	92
Services & rentals	6
Real estate	2
Total	**100**

COMPETITORS

American Water	United Water Inc.
Aquarion	Veolia Water North
Pennichuck	America

HISTORICAL FINANCIALS

Company Type: Public

Income Statement

FYE: December 31

	REVENUE ($ mil.)	NET INCOME ($ mil.)	NET PROFIT MARGIN	EMPLOYEES
12/13	91.4	18.2	20.0%	259
12/12	83.8	13.6	16.3%	259
12/11	69.4	11.3	16.3%	198
12/10	66.4	9.8	14.8%	204
12/09	59.3	10.2	17.2%	225
Annual Growth	11.4%	15.7%	—	3.6%

2013 Year-End Financials

Debt ratio: 28.4%
Return on equity: 9.5%
Cash ($ mil.): 18
Current ratio: 2.06
Long-term debt ($ mil.): 175

No. of shares (mil.): 11
Dividends
Yield: 2.7%
Payout: 59.0%
Market value ($ mil.): 392

	STOCK PRICE ($) FY Close	P/E High/Low		PER SHARE ($) Earnings	Dividends	Book Value
12/13	35.51	21	17	1.66	0.98	17.99
12/12	29.78	21	17	1.53	0.96	17.01
12/11	27.13	22	18	1.29	0.94	13.59
12/10	27.88	24	18	1.13	0.92	13.13
12/09	24.77	21	14	1.19	0.90	12.75
Annual Growth	9.4%	—	—	8.7%	2.2%	9.0%

Conrad Industries, Inc.

Like the story of Noah's Ark Conrad Industries starts anew by rescuing the things its likes. Conrad Industries builds converts and repairs small to midsized vessels for commercial and government customers. More than half of the company's work is in constructing barges liftboats towboats and tugboats. Its boat-conversion projects mainly involve lengthening vessel mid-bodies or modifying vessels to perform different functions. Conrad Industries operates shipyards along the Gulf Coast in Louisiana and Texas. Conrad also offers fabrication of modular components used on offshore drilling rigs as well as storage and offloading of vessels. Established in 1948 the company is led by the founding Conrad family.

EXECUTIVES

Chief Financial Officer; Executive Vice President; Director, Cecil A. Hernandez, age 54, $150,000 total compensation
Co-Chairman President and CEO, John P. (Johnny) Conrad Jr., age 68, $197,096 total compensation
Co-Chairman, J. Parker Conrad, age 95, $216,920 total compensation
VP and COO, Terry T. Frickey
VP CFO and Director, Cecil A. Hernandez, age 53
Co-Chairman President and CEO, John P. (Johnny) Conrad Jr., age 68
Co-Chairman, J. Parker Conrad, age 94
Director, Michael J. Harris, age 61
Director, Ogden U. Thomas Jr., age 65
Auditors: DarnallSikesGardes&Frederick

LOCATIONS

HQ: Conrad Industries, Inc.
1100 Brashear Avenue, Suite 200, P.O. Box 790, Morgan City, LA 70381
Phone: 985 702-0195 **Fax:** 985 702-1126
Web: www.conradindustries.com

PRODUCTS/OPERATIONS

2013 Sales

	$mil.	% of total
Vessele Construction	224.8	74
Repair and conversions	78.5	26
Total	303.3	100

Selected Services

Vessel construction
Large and small deck cargo barges
Lift boats
Offshore supply vessels
Offshore tug boats
Push boats and towboats
Single and double hull tank barges
Repair and conversion
Conversions
Dry dock repairs
Underwater and topside repairs

COMPETITORS

Bollinger Shipyards
General Dynamics
Northrop Grumman
Quality Shipyards
RPC
Vigor Shipyards

HISTORICAL FINANCIALS

Company Type: Public

Income Statement

FYE: December 31

	REVENUE ($ mil.)	NET INCOME ($ mil.)	NET PROFIT MARGIN	EMPLOYEES
12/13	303.3	28.6	9.4%	616
12/12	233.6	20.8	8.9%	549
12/11	246.4	19.1	7.8%	492
12/10	138.8	10.2	7.4%	442
12/09	144.1	12.8	8.9%	454
Annual Growth	20.4%	22.2%	—	7.9%

2013 Year-End Financials

Debt ratio: 0.6%
Return on equity: 26.1%
Cash ($ mil.): 54
Current ratio: 2.44
Long-term debt ($ mil.): 0

No. of shares (mil.): 5
Dividends
Yield: 5.4%
Payout: 45.1%
Market value ($ mil.): 220

	STOCK PRICE ($) FY Close	P/E High/Low		PER SHARE ($) Earnings	Dividends	Book Value
12/13	36.92	8	4	4.80	2.00	19.81
12/12	18.50	6	4	3.46	2.00	17.06
12/11	14.90	5	3	3.01	0.00	15.53
12/10	9.75	6	4	1.60	0.00	12.48
12/09	7.55	4	2	1.99	0.00	10.86
Annual Growth	48.7%	—	—	24.6%	—	16.2%

Consolidated Communications Holdings Inc

Consolidated Communications is just what its name implies. The rural local exchange carrier (RLEC) encompasses operations in Illinois Kansas Missouri Pennsylvania Texas and California providing voice and data telecommunications to business and residential customers. It operates RLECs that offer local access and long-distance Internet and TV business phone systems and related services through about 256000 local access lines 123000 voice connections and about 255000 data and Internet connections. The company also offers directory publishing and carrier services. Operating subsidiaries include Illinois Consolidated Telephone Company (ICTC) Consolidated Communications of Fort Bend Company and Consolidated Communications of Texas Company.

Geographic Reach
In its home base of Illinois (the headquarters is in Mattoon) Consolidated operates 35 incumbent local exchanges serving primarily small towns and rural areas mostly in the central part of the state. It also has operations in East Texas western Pennsylvania around Sacramento Calif. and around Kansas City in Missouri and Kansas.

Sales and Marketing
Consolidated markets services individually and in bundles such as the "triple-play" of voice data and video services. The company boosted its advertising spending to $7.6 million in 2013 from $5.1 million in 2012.

Financial Performance
It's a sure bet that Consolidated's acquisition of SureWest in 2012 had something to do with the nearly 20% increase in revenue and the 446% increase in net revenue in 2013. Consolidated reported revenue of $601 million for the year up from $503 million in 2012. SureWest contributed in all areas. Otherwise Consolidated would have posted revenue decreases across the board except in data video and Internet connections.

The revenue brought in from SureWest helped pump up Consolidated's profit to almost $31 million in 2013 from just under $6 million in 2012. The company also gained from the sale of discontinued operations its business serving correctional facilities in Illinois.

The higher revenue spilled over into cash from operations which rose to $164 million from $123 million in 2012. It also has cash generated from account receivables and income tax receivables.

Strategy
One way to view Consolidated's strategy is to look at a map. Starting in Illinois the company has expanded to Pennsylvania Texas Missouri and Kansas and California gobbling up similar telecoms that serve small towns and rural areas. It's tweaking that approach with its move to the Kansas City area and into the Dallas-Fort Worth suburbs.

As the company's wireless business decreases (as it has with most telecom companies) Consolidated is moving to add more Internet data and video services to its lineup. The company is expanding its services in a big way in the Dallas-Fort Worth area where it has 30000 miles of fiber ready to light up with Internet access wide area networks and hosted iPBX for commercial customer. The network had been used for wholesale and carrier customers.

Consolidated also is expanding its services to provide carrier hotel space and data center space in its markets and to support fiber backhaul services to cell sites. It is to have nearly 700 cell tower sites completed by the end of 2014.

Mergers and Acquisitions

Acquisitions play a key role in Consolidated Communications growth strategy and the company continued in 2014 with a deal in the upper Midwest. It bought Enventis which has service in Iowa Minnesota North Dakota South Dakota and Wisconsin for about $350 million. Enventis brings about 39000 access lines 21000 high-speed Internet customers 12000 digital TV customers and 90 fiber-to-the tower sites as well as $123 million in revenue.

In 2012 Consolidated bought SureWest Communications a provider of residential and commercial communications and broadband services in the Sacramento California and Kansas City markets in a deal valued at $324 million excluding debt.

EXECUTIVES

Senior Vice President And President Texas Telephone Operations, Bob Udell
CIO, Christopher A. (Chris) Young, age 59, $228,692 total compensation
CFO, Steven L. (Steve) Childers, age 59, $249,885 total compensation
SVP and Corporate Secretary, Steven J. (Steve) Shirar, age 56, $238,346 total compensation
President and CEO, C. Robert (Bob) Udell, $295,654 total compensation
CTO, Tom White
Vice President Of Ir, Stephen Jones
Vice President Marketing, William Daw
Secretary Vice President, Edward Sheehan
Vice President Application Development, Brenda Fenley
Vice President Public Services And Network Services Consolidated Communications Illinois H, Brian Carr
Vice President Product Development, Philip Cleary
Vice President Product Development, Philip Midkiff
Executive Chairman, Robert J. (Bob) Currey, age 69
SVP and Corporate Secretary, Steven J. (Steve) Shirar, age 56
Treasurer, Steve Griom
Treasurer Secretary, Joyce Walters
Secretary, Nancy Ammirato
Auditors: Ernst&YoungLLP

LOCATIONS

HQ: Consolidated Communications Holdings Inc
121 South 17th Street, Mattoon, IL 61938-3987
Phone: 217 235-3311
Web: www.consolidated.com

PRODUCTS/OPERATIONS

2013 Sales

	$ mil.	% of total
Telephone		
Data Internet & video	270.0	44
Network access	112.4	19
Local calling	106.5	18
Subsidies	52.0	9
Long distance	19.3	3
Other services	41.4	7
Total	**601.6**	**100**

COMPETITORS

AT&T	Suddenlink
Comcast	Communications
Mediacom	Time Warner Cable
Communications	Verizon
Sprint Communications	

HISTORICAL FINANCIALS

Company Type: Public

Income Statement

FYE: December 31

	REVENUE ($ mil.)	NET INCOME ($ mil.)	NET PROFIT MARGIN	EMPLOYEES
12/13	601.5	30.8	5.1%	1,521
12/12	503.4	5.6	1.1%	1,632
12/11	374.2	26.4	7.1%	963
12/10	383.3	32.6	8.5%	991
12/09	406.1	24.9	6.1%	1,213
Annual Growth	**10.3%**	**5.5%**	**—**	**5.8%**

2013 Year-End Financials

Debt ratio: 69.9%	No. of shares (mil.): 40
Return on equity: 22.0%	Dividends
Cash ($ mil.): 5	Yield: 7.8%
Current ratio: 0.75	Payout: 203.8%
Long-term debt ($ mil.): 1,212	Market value ($ mil.): 786

	STOCK PRICE ($) FY Close	P/E High/Low		PER SHARE ($) Earnings	Dividends	Book Value
12/13	19.63	26	21	0.76	1.55	3.69
12/12	15.91	132	90	0.15	1.55	3.31
12/11	19.05	23	19	0.88	1.55	1.42
12/10	19.30	18	15	1.09	1.55	2.25
12/09	17.48	21	9	0.84	1.55	2.52
Annual Growth	**2.9%**			**(2.5%)**	**(0.0%)**	**10.0%**

Constant Contact Inc

Constant Contact makes sure businesses never lose touch with their prospects and customers. The company provides small businesses with Web-based marketing software and services for managing e-mail and social media campaigns as well as offering local deals managing digital storefronts and creating online surveys. Its offerings include tools for creating implementing tracking managing and analyzing marketing materials. Customers include retailers restaurants and other businesses as well as non-profit organizations alumni associations and churches; two-thirds of its clients have fewer than 10 employees. It claims more than 555000 customers for its products.

Geographic Reach Constant Contact has offices in Massachusetts Colorado Florida California and New York as well as in London. It serves clients in some 180 countries although the US accounts for nearly 90% of sales.

Sales and Marketing Of course Constant Contact uses digital marketing techniques to attract customers. Its products are marketed through its own advertising and referral efforts as well as through partnerships with more than 9500 local and national small business service providers.

It focuses on small businesses and organizations most of which pay a fixed monthly subscription fee based on the number of e-mail addresses in their account. Subscriptions to its e-mail marketing tools typically cost between $15-$150 per month which allows Constant Contact to serve a market that is typically ignored by larger CRM and marketing software competitors such as Oracle SAP and salesforce.com. The company has seen rapid organic growth in recent years with its customer base growing 20-fold from the 25000 it reported in 2004.

Financial Performance Constant Contact's revenue has risen steadily along with its customer base. In 2012 sales were up 18% to $252 million driven by a 12% increase in the number of average monthly customers and a 5% rise in revenue per customer. Now in its third year of profitability the company took in $12.7 million in net income for 2012 down 46% from $23 million in 2011. The decrease in profits was due to increases in operating expenses as well as costs for acquisitions the company has made.

Strategy The company continues to enhance its offerings with new services and tools and throughout 2012 it expanded its product suite from three products to six. CardStar provides mobile applications for loyalty cards and coupons. SaveLocal manages group coupons for small businesses and SinglePlatform offers a digital storefront for mobile formats. Previous product launches include online surveys (2007) event marketing (2009) and social media (2010) tools. It is also looking for growth in new geographic markets. Although international operations are a small part of Constant Contact's business today it sees opportunity in international markets. Its email marketing templates are also offered in Spanish and the company opened its first office outside the US in the UK in 2011.

Mergers and Acquisitions In 2012 Constant Contact paid $5.7 million for CardStar which provides mobile applications for loyalty cards and coupons. Also that year the company acquired SinglePlatform a developer of marketing software used by small businesses to improve their visibility to consumers on the Web. SinglePlatform's application enables businesses to use a single interface to distribute content to such online venues as Foursquare YP and UrbanSpoon as well as on social networks and other websites. In 2011 Constant Contact had added social CRM capabilities with the acquisition of Bantam Networks for $15 million in cash. Its Bantam Live application gives small businesses a place to launch and monitor customer engagement campaigns across social media platforms. In 2010 the company acquired NutshellMail giving its customers a tool for engaging social media networks from their e-mail inbox.

EXECUTIVES

EVP CFO and Treasurer, Harpreet S. Grewal, age 47, $325,000 total compensation
Vice President Constant Contact Labs, Daniel Richards
Vice President And Chief Human Resources Officer, Bob Nicoson
Svp-strategy & Corp Dev, Joel Hughes, age 51
Chairman President and CEO, Gail F. Goodman, age 53, $450,000 total compensation
CTO, Stefan Piesche
Senior Vice President Sales and Marketing, Christopher M. Litster, age 44, $200,000 total compensation
Vice President and General Manager SinglePlatform, Wiley Cerilli
Vice President Product, Ken Surdan
Vice President Sales And Marketing, Richard Lynn
Vice President Of Sales, Connie Hawk

Cooper Companies, Inc. (The)

From eye care to lady care The Cooper Companies has its customers covered. The global company makes specialty medical devices in two niche markets: vision care and gynecology. Its CooperVision subsidiary makes specialty contact lenses including toric lenses for astigmatism multifocal lenses for presbyopia and cosmetic lenses. The company also offers spherical lenses for more common vision problems such as nearsightedness and farsightedness. Subsidiary CooperSurgical specializes in women's health care; its wide range of products includes bone densitometers (for diagnosing osteoporosis) contraceptive devices surgery instruments and fetal monitors. Cooper's products are sold in more than 100 countries.

Geographic Reach

California-based Cooper rings up nearly half of its sales in the US and about 30% in Europe. The company has manufacturing and distribution facilities for optical products in the US (New York and Puerto Rico) the UK Australia and Japan. Its medical device and surgical instrument products are manufactured and distributed from facilities in Germany and the US (California Connecticut and Texas).

Sales and Marketing

Cooper markets its products through its own sales representatives in North America and through a mix of direct sales and distributors elsewhere. The company boosted its direct sales presence in international markets through acquisitions in Japan Mexico and the Czech Republic in 2010 and 2011.

Operations

The Cooper Companies operates through two business units: CooperVision the larger of the two (80% of annual sales) is one of the largest contact lens manufacturers in the world: CooperSurgical provides diagnostic and therapeutic products used by obstetricians and gynecologists. It has been a consolidator in the fragmented women's medical device market acquiring more than 30 niche companies since its inception in 1990. Trends that it is taking advantage of include the increase in laparoscopic procedures and a shifting of procedures done in doctor's offices rather than in hospital settings.

Financial Performance

The Cooper Companies' fiscal 2013 (ended October) sales increased 10% versus the prior year to $1.6 billion. Net income grew 19% over the same period to $296.1 million. The smaller of its two businesses CooperSurgical (CSI) out performed its sister company with CSI posting a 25% increase in annual sales while CooperVision's (CVI) sales rose a more modest 7%. Revenue from the acquisition of Origio propelled SCI's growth in fiscal 2013. The sale of more contact lenses and new products primarily silicone hydrogel lenses drove growth at CVI. The Cooper Companies has posted steady and significant growth in sales and profits in recent years as a result of organic growth and the purchase of other companies.

Sales gains in Europe (up 17%) outpaced growth in the US (up 9%) in fiscal 2013 compared with the prior year.

Strategy

CooperVision (CVI)is working to expand internationally by increasing operations in various high-growth geographic markets. It is building a plant in Costa Rica. The lens maker is attempting to expand its market share by launching new products. Its R&D team is working on several new products using its Proclear moisturizing technology. It is also developing new products using silicone hydrogel a more breathable lens material that is healthier and more comfortable for the eye including single-use (throwaway) toric and multifocal lenses. For instance CooperVision launched the new Biofinity multifocal and Avaira toric lens lines in the US in 2011. In 2013 CVI sold Aime its rigid gas-permeable contact lens and solutions business in Japan to Nippon Contact Lens. The sale was consistent with CVI's strategy to focus on its core soft contact lens business.

CSI is growing by acquiring complementary technologies products and businesses.

Mergers and Acquisitions

CooperSurgical paid some $44 million in late 2014 for EndoSee Corporation developer of an office-based disposable hysterectomy system. The unit plans to launch the system in the US in 2015.

In July 2012 Cooper acquired Denmark-based Origio an in-vitro fertilization (IVF) medical device company for approximately $189 million.

HISTORY

Cooper Labs (medical devices founded in 1958 and dissolved 1985) created CooperVision as a subsidiary in 1980. CooperVision diversified into diagnostic equipment and drugs; by 1987 (when it was renamed The Cooper Companies) debt had increased sixfold and creditors came knocking.

Two scandal-tainted families (the Sturmans and the Singers —fraud/organized crime and Medicaid fraud respectively) then bought their way onto the board. Proxy fights cronyism nepotism indictments and lawsuits ensued. Meanwhile cash-strapped Cooper sold most of its international and part of its US contact lens business as well as its ophthalmic surgical products and medical diagnostics businesses. Co-chairman Gary Singer took a leave of absence after being indicted in 1992.

Cooper bought Hospital Group of America and its hospitals that year. Singer resigned shortly before being convicted on 21 counts including racketeering mail and wire fraud and money laundering in 1994. Pharmaceutical industry veteran Thomas Bender joined the board that year and was named CEO in 1995. He was elected chairman in 2002.

Cooper rebuilt its contact business and turned to the women's health field in the early 1990s. In 1996 it bought a line of disposable gynecological products and worked to boost lens-making capacity. The next year it bought a line of colored contact lenses a minimally invasive gynecological surgical and disposable products company and a UK lens maker.

In 1998 The Cooper Companies discontinued its Hospital Group of America operations. It sold the group's hospitals treatment centers and clinics to Universal Health Services in 1999. In 2000 the company made three acquisitions including two makers of gynecological instruments. In 2002 The Cooper Companies bought Biocompatibles Eye Care one of the world's largest contact lens manufacturers.

The company's acquisitions in 2003 included Avalon Medical Corporation (distributor of female sterilization system) and Prism Enterprises (manufacturer of medical devices for the women's health care markets). The Cooper Companies bought gynecology products manufacturer Milex Products in 2004.

It nearly doubled its revenue with the 2005 acquisition of leading contact lens maker Ocular Sciences. The purchase strengthened its presence in the spheric (non-specialty) lens market; it also opened up new geographic markets particularly Germany and Japan. It also purchased NeoSurg Technologies and Inlet Medical in 2005 both of which made devices used in laparoscopic surgeries.

In 2006 it purchased Lone Star Medical Products adding a line of gynecological surgical products. The following year it added medical instrument maker Wallach Surgical Devices.

CooperVision faced some patent issues with CIBA over its silicone hydrogel Biofinity lenses (first launched in 2006); it settled with CIBA in 2007 agreeing to pay royalties on the lenses.

When chairman Thomas Bender chose to step down as CEO in 2007 company veteran Robert Weiss was tapped to fill that role. The Cooper Companies launched its Proclear daily lens in the US and Europe that year followed by the Avaira sphere two-week silicone hydrogel lens in 2008.

The company discontinued operations at its lens manufacturing plant in Norfolk Virginia in 2009 as part of a restructuring of the CooperVision division. It also relocated some of its Australian lens manufacturing operations to Puerto Rico and the UK to streamline and reduce expenses in the organization.

EXECUTIVES

EVP Secretary Chief Administrative Officer and Chief Governance Officer, Carol R. Kaufman, age 65, $419,661 total compensation
President and CEO, Robert S. Weiss, age 68, $800,000 total compensation
President and CEO CooperSurgical Inc., Paul L. Remmell, age 57, $295,000 total compensation
VP and Chief Strategy Officer, Albert G. White, age 45
EVP COO; President CooperVision Inc., Daniel G. (Dan) McBride, age 50, $367,744 total compensation
VP; CFO and Chief Risk Officer, Gregory W. Matz, $367,744 total compensation
Vice President And Corporate Controller, Rodney E Folden, age 67
Vice-president, Larry Bienati
Vice-president, Randy Harman
Vice President Of Surgical Sales, Mark Curtis
Vice President Engineering, Kerry Blair
Vice President, Mark Drury
Vice President, Russell Hanover
Vice Chairman, Allan E. Rubenstein, age 70
Chairman, A. Thomas Bender, age 76
Assistant Treasurer, Brian Andrews
Board Of Directors, Marvin Garrett
Auditors: KPMGLLP

LOCATIONS

HQ: Cooper Companies, Inc. (The)
6140 Stoneridge Mall Road, Suite 590, Pleasanton, CA 94588
Phone: 925 460-3600   **Fax:** 925 460-3648
Web: www.coopercos.com

2013 Sales

	$ mil.	% of total
US	742.2	47
Europe	479.1	30
Rest of world& other	366.4	23
Total	**1587.7**	**100**

PRODUCTS/OPERATIONS

2013 Sales

	$ mil.	% of total
CooperVision		
Toric lens	388.1	24
Single-use sphere soft lens	271.0	17
Multifocal lens	121.7	8
Non single-use sphere other eye care products& other	487.5	31
CooperSurgical	319.4	20
Total	**1587.7**	**100**

COMPETITORS

Abbott Medical Optics	Gyrus ACMI
Alara	Hoya Corp.
Alcon	Johnson & Johnson
Bausch & Lomb	Luxottica
Boston Scientific	Marchon Eyewear
Carl Zeiss	Orthometrix
Essilor International	Shamir Optical
Femcare	

HISTORICAL FINANCIALS

Company Type: Public

Income Statement

FYE: October 31

	REVENUE ($ mil.)	NET INCOME ($ mil.)	NET PROFIT MARGIN	EMPLOYEES
10/14	1,717.7	269.8	15.7%	9,460
10/13	1,587.7	296.1	18.7%	8,000
10/12	1,445.1	248.3	17.2%	7,800
10/11	1,330.8	175.4	13.2%	7,400
10/10	1,158.5	112.8	9.7%	6,800
Annual Growth	**10.3%**	**24.4%**	—	**8.6%**

2014 Year-End Financials

Debt ratio: 31.0%	No. of shares (mil.): 48	
Return on equity: 10.8%	Dividends	
Cash ($ mil.): 25	Yield: 0.0%	
Current ratio: 1.79	Payout: 0.9%	
Long-term debt ($ mil.): 1,280	Market value ($ mil.): 7,891	

	STOCK PRICE ($) FY Close	P/E High/Low	PER SHARE ($) Earnings	Dividends	Book Value
10/14	163.90	29 21	5.51	0.06	53.38
10/13	129.21	22 15	5.96	0.06	50.10
10/12	95.98	19 11	5.05	0.06	45.27
10/11	69.30	22 13	3.63	0.06	40.49
10/10	49.34	20 11	2.43	0.06	36.37
Annual Growth	**35.0%**	— —	**22.7%**	**(0.0%)**	**10.1%**

Copart, Inc.

What happens after cars are totaled in wrecks or natural disasters? How about stolen cars recovered "after" the insurance settlement? Perhaps Copart happens —it takes junked cars and auctions them for insurers auto dealers and car rental agencies. The buyers are mostly rebuilders licensed dismantlers and used-car dealers and exporters. It's replaced live auctions with Internet auctions using a platform known as Virtual Bidding Second Generation (VB2 for short). Copart also provides services such as towing and storage to buyers and other salvage companies as well as an online database and search engine for used parts. Copart has more than 150 storage facilities throughout North America Europe and Brazil.
Geographic Reach
The US is by far Copart's largest market accounting for more than 75% of sales. Europe accounts for about 20%. Copart operates about 135 storage facilities in the US four in Canada and 15 in the UK. It entered Brazil Germany and the Middle East in 2012 via acquisitions.
Sales and Marketing
Copart is going the extra mile to market its brand to car enthusiasts. The company produces Sold in Seconds a weekly TV program that highlights purchases from Copart.com and follows up with buyers to see what they've done with their vehicles. The show which started airing in 2010 complements Copart's racing sponsorships in the NASCAR Nationwide Series and NHRA Top Fuel Series.
Financial Performance
Copart's sales increased 6% in fiscal 2012 (ends July) vs. the prior year while net income grew by more than 9%. The online vehicle auction firm's sales and profits has increased steadily since fiscal 2009 when they slipped due to the falling US dollar-Great Britain pound exchange rate lower unit volumes and declining revenues per transaction. Indeed 2012's $924 million in sales and $182 million in net income were all-time highs for fast-growing Copart. Sales growth was driven by increases in service and vehicle sales up 6% and 5% respectively with growth in the US outpacing growth in Canada and the UK.
Strategy
An aggressive acquisition program at home and abroad has made Copart a leader in its industry. Buoyed by the recovery at home Copart is on a global hunt for junked vehicles and vehicle parts. Indeed in 2012 the company made several acquisitions in international markets including Brazil Canada Germany and Dubai UAE. Indeed the UAE is the second-largest international destination for cars sold at Copart's North American salvage yards.

Copart is also expanding its customer base beyond the traditional salvage market by launching new services such as CopartDirect. Launched in 2008 the program allows the company to sell cars to the general public using its VB2 application so that individuals can avoid the inconvenience of selling a vehicle themselves. Other services include Copart Dealer Services which sells trade-ins for franchises and independent dealerships using VB2 and CoPartfinder which enables customers to bid on a vehicle search for parts from Keystone Automotive Industries and receive e-mail notifications when cars matching their criteria come up for sale.
The majority of the vehicles Copart processes are auctioned under an incentive program in which

Copart gets a percentage of the proceeds; the rest are auctioned under a fixed-fee consignment basis (generally $50 to $175). Insurance company suppliers represent the firm's largest customer segment and account for about 80% of the vehicles Copart processes each year.

Mergers and Acquisitions

In 2012 Copart expanded into Germany (the world's fourth largest auto market) with the purchase of WOM Wreck Online Marketing a leading European salvage vehicle auction platform there. Earlier in the year it bought Canada's Diamond Auto Bids and Disposals a privately-held automotive auction that gives Copart a foothold in Western Canada specifically Calgary and Edmonton. It also extended the reach of its business into South America through its purchase of Central de Leiloes LTDA based in Sao Paulo Brazil. Central serves the Brazilian market through five facilities located in Sao Paulo states.

In 2011 Copart also purchased the Indiana-based auto auction firm Barodge Auto Pool expanding its presence in Indiana and surrounding states. The company also broadened its existing range of farming equipment in the UK when it acquired Hewitt International an auctioneer of agricultural vehicles and equipment based in central England in 2011. Copart's previous acquisitions have included D Hales an operator of five auto auction sites and parts centers in England in 2010.

Ownership

Founder and former-CEO Willis Johnson owns about 11% of Copart's shares.

HISTORY

Copart was co-founded in 1982 by Willis Johnson who had owned and operated an auto dismantling business for more than 10 years. After buying out his partner in 1986 he became CEO and used his own money to expand the company into a network of four California salvage yards by 1991. In the next two years Copart nearly tripled the number of salvage operations it owned by acquiring companies throughout the US. HPB Associates a private investor group came on board in 1993 buying 26% of the firm for $10 million and the company went public the next year.

Copart doubled its total facilities in 1995 with the acquisition of NER Auction Systems the largest privately held salvage auction company in the US. The firm acquired or opened more than 30 facilities between 1995 and 1997. In 1998 the company started an online auction site; expanded through acquisitions into Alabama Iowa Michigan and South Carolina and opened new locations in California and Minnesota. The next year rival Insurance Auto Auctions spurned its merger overtures.

In 2000 Copart opened three new salvage vehicle auction facilities and acquired eight more. That year the company also signed an agreement to sell Keystone Automotive Industries' parts through its Web site. In 2001 and 2002 the company acquired or opened 13 new locations. Continuing its acquisition strategy the company opened or acquired five more facilities in 2004.

In 2005 the company made two acquisitions for about $4.5 million: Kentucky Auto Salvage Pool a 25-acre salvage facility in Lexington Kentucky; and Insurance Auctions of Missouri. In November Copart acquired the salvage pool assets of Central Penn Sales a vehicle salvage disposal company with four sites in Pennsylvania and Maryland totaling 255 acres. In December the company opened a second salvage facility in Michigan.

In June 2007 Copart acquired Universal Salvage the operator of about 10 salvage yards in the UK

and a vehicle remarketer to the insurance and automotive industries for about $120 million. Adding to its UK holdings in August Copart purchased Century Salvage Sales Limited which has three salvage yards and AG Watson which has four salvage yards in England and Scotland.

During 2008 the company launched CopartDirect. The service allows Copart to sell cars to the general public using its VB2 application so that individuals can avoid the inconvenience of selling a vehicle themselves.

In February 2010 Willis Johnson relinquished the CEO's title to A. Jayson Adair who formerly served as president of Copart. Johnson continued as chairman of the company.

EXECUTIVES

Chief Executive Officer; Director, A. Jayson Adair, age 44, $553,849 total compensation
National Sales Manager, James S Miller
SVP and CRO, William E. Franklin, age 58, $300,000 total compensation
President; Director, Vincent W. Mitz, age 51, $375,000 total compensation
Vice President Of Human Resources, Rory Seidens
Vice President Sap Sys Glbl Bus, Diane Yassa
Vice President Development Delivery, David Fung
Senior Vice President Secy Gen Counsel, Paul Styer
Vice President Technology Infrastructure, Lisa Canada
Senior Vice President And Chief Technology Officer, Rama Prasad
Senior Vice President Human Resources, Tom Wylie
Chairman, Willis J. Johnson, age 67
Auditors: Ernst&YoungLLP

LOCATIONS

HQ: Copart, Inc.
  14185 Dallas Parkway, Dallas, TX 75254
Phone: 972 391-5000
Web: www.copart.com

2012 Sales

	$ mil.	% of total
US	724.9	78
UK	192.7	21
Canada	6.6	1
Total	**924.2**	**100**

PRODUCTS/OPERATIONS

2012 Sales

	$ mil.	% of total
Services	757.3	82
Vehicles	166.9	18
Total	**924.2**	**100**

Selected Services

Copart Access (online vehicle information retrieval)
Copart Dealer Services (online trade-in vehicle sales)
Copart Direct (online used car sales)
CoPartfinder (online used-parts search engine)
DMV processing (title document processing)
Monthly reporting (summary of all vehicles processed by company for suppliers)
Online bidding (online auctions)
Salvage brokerage network (coordination of vehicle disposal outside areas of current operation)
Salvage Lynk (software providing online information on vehicles being processed)
Transportation services (fleet of transport trucks)
Vehicle inspection stations (central locations for insurance companies to inspect vehicles)
Vehicle preparation and merchandising (cleaning and weather protection direct mailings to buyers)

COMPETITORS

Advance Auto Parts	KAR Auction Services
Columbus Fair Auto Auction	LKQ
Cox Enterprises	Manheim
Ford Motor	Pittsburgh Independent Auto Auction

HISTORICAL FINANCIALS

Company Type: Public

Income Statement

FYE: July 31

	REVENUE ($ mil.)	NET INCOME ($ mil.)	NET PROFIT MARGIN	EMPLOYEES
07/14	1,163.4	178.6	15.4%	4,179
07/13	1,046.3	180.0	17.2%	3,875
07/12	924.1	182.1	19.7%	2,981
07/11	872.2	166.3	19.1%	2,825
07/10	772.8	151.6	19.6%	2,834
Annual Growth	**10.8%**	**4.2%**	**—**	**10.2%**

2014 Year-End Financials

Debt ratio: 20.1%
Return on equity: 20.2%
Cash ($ mil.): 158
Current ratio: 1.69
Long-term debt ($ mil.): 223

No. of shares (mil.): 126
Dividends
  Yield: —
  Payout: —
Market value ($ mil.): 4,211

	STOCK PRICE ($) FY Close	P/E High/Low	PER SHARE ($) Earnings	Dividends	Book Value
07/14	33.38	26 22	1.36	0.00	7.96
07/13	32.51	26 16	1.39	0.00	6.08
07/12	23.76	38 16	1.39	0.00	4.51
07/11	43.45	43 29	1.09	0.00	4.21
07/10	36.44	43 36	0.89	0.00	6.44
Annual Growth	**(2.2%)**	**— —**	**11.2%**	**—**	**5.4%**

Core Molding Technologies Inc

The core business of Core Molding Technologies is fiberglass reinforced plastic and sheet molding composite materials. Through compression molding sprayup hand layup and vacuum-assisted resin infusion molding the company makes truck components (air deflectors fenders hoods) and personal watercraft parts (decks hulls and engine hatches). It divides its operations into two segments: Products and Tooling. Navistar International accounts for one-third sales and other major customers include heavy-duty truck manufacturers Volvo and PACCAR. The company's sales are confined to North America.

Geographic Reach

Core Molding operates plants in Columbus and Cincinnati Ohio; Gaffney South Carolina; and Matamoros Mexico.

Sales and Marketing

With Navistar and PACCAR collectively representing 68% of sales and the medium and heavy-duty truck market accounting for more than 80% it's an understatement to say that Core Molding Technologies has a limited number of customers.

Financial Performance

After posting $162 million in 2012 (a company milestone) Core Molding saw its revenues decline

11% to $144 million in 2013. Profits also slipped 16% from $8.2 million in 2012 to $6.9 million in 2013 due to a spike in selling general and administrative expenses.

The revenue decline for 2013 was driven by lower demand for its products from customers in the medium and heavy-duty truck market. In particular Core Molding experienced an overall decline in demand from Navistar. After experiencing two straight years of growth Core Molding saw its operating cash flow decrease by $8 million in 2013.

Company Background

Core Molding evolved in 1996 from the Columbus Plastics unit of International Truck & Engine (now Navistar Inc.).

EXECUTIVES

President CEO and Director, Kevin L. Barnett, age 51, $409,519 total compensation
VP Sales and Marketing, Terrence J. (Terry) O'Donovan, age 54, $197,481 total compensation
VP CFO Secretary and Treasurer, John P. Zimmer, age 50, $31,633 total compensation
VP Operations, William R. Ringling
Vice President Manufacturing, Douglas Spangler
Vice President Marketing Sales, Terrence Klotz
President CEO and Director, Kevin L. Barnett, age 51
Chairman, James L. Simonton, age 73
VP CFO Secretary and Treasurer, John P. Zimmer, age 50
Auditors: CroweHorwathLLP

LOCATIONS

HQ: Core Molding Technologies Inc
  800 Manor Park Drive, Columbus, OH 43228-0183
Phone: 614 870-5000
Web: www.coremt.com

2013 Sales

	$ mil.	% of total
US	95.0	66
Mexico	45.1	31
Canada	4.0	3
Total	**144.1**	**100**

PRODUCTS/OPERATIONS

2013 Sales

	$ mil.	% of total
Product	134.1	93
Tooling	10.0	7
Total	**144.1**	**100**

Selected Services

Assembly Machining and Paint Products
Closed molding
Compression Molding
Glass Mat Thermoplastic Compound
Open Molded Products
Post Molding
Product Development
Reaction Injection Molding
Resin Transfer Molding
Sheet Molding Compound

COMPETITORS

Clarion Technologies	Magna International
Crane Composites	Molded Fiber Glass
Flex-N-Gate	Primex Plastics
Industrial Molding	Sigma Industries
Corp.	Toledo Molding and Die
Lacks Enterprises	

HISTORICAL FINANCIALS

Company Type: Public

Income Statement

FYE: December 31

	REVENUE ($ mil.)	NET INCOME ($ mil.)	NET PROFIT MARGIN	EMPLOYEES
12/13	144.1	6.8	4.8%	1,458
12/12	162.4	8.1	5.0%	1,373
12/11	143.4	10.5	7.3%	1,596
12/10	100.2	2.4	2.4%	1,014
12/09	83.3	1.0	1.2%	813
Annual Growth	**14.7%**	**61.2%**	**—**	**15.7%**

2013 Year-End Financials

Debt ratio: 5.9%
Return on equity: 10.9%
Cash ($ mil.): 2
Current ratio: 1.84
Long-term debt ($ mil.): 2
No. of shares (mil.): 7
Dividends
  Yield: —
  Payout: —
Market value ($ mil.): 100

	STOCK PRICE ($) FY Close	P/E High	P/E Low	PER SHARE ($) Earnings	PER SHARE ($) Dividends	PER SHARE ($) Book Value
12/13	13.70	15	7	0.92	0.00	9.22
12/12	6.62	9	6	1.11	0.00	8.13
12/11	8.09	6	4	1.44	0.00	7.11
12/10	5.76	17	8	0.34	0.00	5.53
12/09	2.87	26	8	0.15	0.00	4.29
Annual Growth	**47.8%**	—	—	**57.4%**	—	**21.0%**

CoreSite Realty Corp.

CoreSite Realty leases data center space to those with data center needs. The real estate investment trust (REIT) owns develops and operates these specialized facilities which require enough power security and network interconnection to handle often complex IT operations. Its property portfolio includes about 15 operating data center facilities with more space under development. These properties comprise more than 2.7 million rentable sq. ft. and are located in major US tech hubs including Silicon Valley. Tenants include enterprise organizations communications service providers media and content companies government agencies and schools. The REIT has grown along with demand for data center space.

Geographic Reach

Denver-based CoreSite Realty operates 14 data center campuses in nine North American markets including: three facilities in Silicon Valley; two each in Los Angeles northern Virginia/Wasington DC and the New York area. Other sites include Boston Chicago Denver and Miami.

Sales and Marketing

The REIT boats a global customer base of more than 750 tenants including ISPs (Internet Service Providers) and CDNs (Content Delivery Networks). CoreSite's top 10 customers account for about a third of its annual rental revenue.

Financial Performance

CoreSite's 2012 sales increased 20% versus 2011 to $207 million. Indeed the company's sales and have ballooned since 2008 increasing more than 1000%. Cash flow from operations has also soared. Significantly the company swung from four years in the red to profitability in 2012 posting net income of $5 million.

Strategy

The properties in CoreSite's portfolio are strategically located in major metropolitan cities known for being high-tech hotbeds such as Boston Chicago Los Angeles New York City and the San Francisco Bay and Northern Virginia areas. Data centers especially outsourced ones (which are cheaper than in-house ones) are growing in these cities and others because they meet specific technology needs with specialized infrastructures that supply multiple network connectivity uninterruptible power backup generators cooling equipment fire suppression systems and physical security.

The company hopes to capitalize on demand that is outpacing supply for outsourced data centers in these markets. Supply of new data center facilities has been hampered in part by industry consolidation and lack of capital to develop additional space. CoreSite intends to market its existing portfolio —coupled with its development capabilities and the network interconnection services it offers —to attract more quality tenants.

The company's first data center was purchased in 2000. Acquisitions of these properties throughout its history have been funded and held through real estate funds affiliated with global private equity firm The Carlyle Group.

Company Background

CoreSite Realty Corp. started in 2001 as CRG West a portfolio company of The Carlyle Group. CoreSite Realty went public in September 2010 with an offering worth $270.4 million. CoreSite used the proceeds of its IPO to develop and redevelop additional data centers and to retire debt.

EXECUTIVES

President CEO and Director, Thomas M. (Tom) Ray, age 51, $540,000 total compensation
CFO, Jeffrey S. Finnin, age 50
SVP Marketing and Business Development, David W. Dunn, age 34, $152,578 total compensation
Svp Data Centers, Billie R Haggard, age 49
Svp-sales, Steven Smith
Vice President Controller, Mark Jones
Senior Vice President, Tom Guinn
Vice President Of Product Management, Brian Warren
Vice President Facilities, Matt Gleason
Vice President Carrier Sales, Eric Bell
Vice President Of Internal Audit Risk And Compliance, Ron Lester
Vice President Finance, Jeff Dorr
Vice President Strategy And Business Development, Brian Rieck
Vice President Cloud Market Development, Ted Chamberlin
Auditors: KPMGLLP

LOCATIONS

HQ: CoreSite Realty Corp.
  1001 17th Street, Suite 500, Denver, CO 80202
Phone: 866 777-2673
Web: www.coresite.com
Boston
Chicago
Denver
Los Angeles
Miami
New York/New Jersey
Northern Virginia/Washington DC
Silicon Valley (San Jose Milpitas Santa Clara)

PRODUCTS/OPERATIONS

2012 Sales

	$ mil.	% of total
Rental	123.4	60

Power	53.5	26
Interconnection	20.9	10
Tenant reimbursement &other	9.1	4
Total	**206.9**	**100**

COMPETITORS

AT&T	Internap Network
Brandywine Realty	Services
CenturyLink	QTS Realty Trust Inc.
CyrusOne	SAVVIS
Digital Realty	Telx Group
DuPont Fabros	Terremark Worldwide
Equinix	Zayo Group
Equity Office	

HISTORICAL FINANCIALS

Company Type: Public

Income Statement

FYE: December 31

	REVENUE ($ mil.)	NET INCOME ($ mil.)	NET PROFIT MARGIN	EMPLOYEES
12/13	234.8	18.8	8.0%	363
12/12	206.9	5.0	2.4%	316
12/11	172.8	(10.7)	—	224
12/10*	38.3	(10.7)	—	179
09/10	35.5	(1.5)	—	0
Annual Growth 60.3%				

*Fiscal year change

2013 Year-End Financials

Debt ratio: 23.5%
Return on equity: 5.6%
Cash ($ mil.): 5
Current ratio: 0.20
Long-term debt ($ mil.): 239
No. of shares (mil.): 21
Dividends
  Yield: 3.6%
  Payout: 263.6%
Market value ($ mil.): 688

	STOCK PRICE ($) FY Close	P/E High/Low		PER SHARE ($) Earnings	Dividends	Book Value
12/13	32.19	77	55	0.49	1.16	15.54
12/12	27.66	126	83	0.22	0.81	15.95
12/11	17.82	—	—	(0.24)	0.57	11.22
12/10*	13.64	—	—	(0.17)	0.00	11.82
09/10	16.00	—	—	(0.00)	0.00	(0.00)
Annual Growth 19.1%		—	—	—	—	—

*Fiscal year change

Corporate Executive Board Co.

Don't fear the competition; learn from it. So says The Corporate Executive Board Company (CEB) a provider of business research and analysis services to more than 5700 companies worldwide. Its program areas cover "best practices" in such topics as finance human resources information technology operations and sales and marketing. Unlike consulting firms which engage with one client at a time CEB operates on a membership-based business model. Members subscribe to one or more of the company's programs and participate in the research and analysis thus sharing expertise with others. Besides reports on best practices CEB offers seminars customized research briefs and decision-support tools.

CEB's health relies on adding more clients to its network and persuading existing clients to subscribe to more research programs. As the economy turned the corner and began to stabalize in 2011 CEB's client renewal rate made a modest climb. It also added more than 500 new clients in 2011.

That year revenues increased about 12% to $484.7 million from $432.4 million in 2010 while 2011 net income was $52.7 million up from $40.4 million in 2010. Gains were in part due to an increase in bookings to new and existing members and an ability to implement price increases. Earnings also improved thanks to the absence of an impairment loss that the company recorded in 2010 related to its Toolbox.com asset. CEB sold Toolbox.com a group of websites dedicated to online networking and information development at the close of 2011 to Ziff Davis and reported the asset as discontinued operations.

The company has been on the look-out for acquisitions in order to strengthen its existing programs. In 2012 it purchased global talent measurement firm SHL Group. Earlier in the year it acquired Valtera a global talent management company. Both deals are designed to boost HR services that help clients with hiring engaging and developing talent.

The previous year CEB improved its presence throughout Europe when it obtained Germany-based Baumgartner & Partner an advisory firm with expertise in providing HR finance and accounting process benchmarking data. And in 2010 CEB acquired Iconoculture a research company that provides behavior patterns and trends on Gen-Xers Baby Boomers and various multicultural markets.

CEB was spun off in 1999 from The Advisory Board Company which offers similar research and analysis services for clients in the health care industry. A non-compete agreement that prevented CEB from seeking health care clients and kept The Advisory Board from operating outside that industry expired in 2007; subsequently the companies agreed to collaborate on selected projects and to continue not competing in core businesses.

EXECUTIVES

Chairman and CEO, Thomas L. (Tom) Monahan, age 48, $841,250 total compensation
CFO, Richard S. Lindahl, age 51, $467,500 total compensation
Group President, Haniel Lynn
Group President, Warren Thune
Managing Vice President Financial Services Practice, Bruce Young
Vice President Global Oem Sales, Laura McKenna
Vice President, Shelley Dipper
Associate Vice President L Investments, Laura Wilson
Executive Vice President Wholesale, Jonathan Guidroz
Senior Vice President And Chief Information Officer, Carolina Valencia
Vice President, Andy Patel
Chair Department Of Security, Nagendra Veeranna
Vice President Of Engineering, Mike Mall
Vice President Relationship Mgr East, Deb Wenstrom
Senior Vice President, Woody Barela
Vice President Global Engine Oem Sales, Priscilla Destefano
Executive Vice President And Chief Operating Officer, Kanika Singal
Board Member, Gregor S Bailar, age 51
Chairman and CEO, Thomas L. (Tom) Monahan, age 48

Board Member, Kimberley Wadsworth
Board Member, Rowena Paskell
Board Member, Shana Greatman
Board Member, Jonathan Corrie
Board Member, Nicholas Toman
Advisory Board Member, Ryan Fay
Auditors: Ernst&YoungLLP

LOCATIONS

HQ: Corporate Executive Board Co.
  1919 North Lynn Street, Arlington, VA 22209
Phone: 571 303-3000   **Fax:** 571 303-3100
Web: www.executiveboard.com

2011 Sales

	$ mil.	% of total
US	326.9	67
Europe	71.9	15
Other regions	85.9	18
Total	**484.7**	**100**

PRODUCTS/OPERATIONS

Selected Practice Areas

Communications
Financial services
General management
Human resources
Information technology
Legal and compliance
Operations and procurement
Sales and marketing
Strategy and research and development

COMPETITORS

Accenture	Conference Board
Booz Allen	Kantar Group
Boston Consulting	McKinsey & Company

HISTORICAL FINANCIALS

Company Type: Public

Income Statement

FYE: December 31

	REVENUE ($ mil.)	NET INCOME ($ mil.)	NET PROFIT MARGIN	EMPLOYEES
12/13	820.0	31.9	3.9%	3,900
12/12	622.6	37.0	6.0%	3,400
12/11	484.6	52.6	10.9%	2,093
12/10	438.9	40.3	9.2%	1,879
12/09	442.9	45.6	10.3%	1,742
Annual Growth 16.6%		(8.5%)	—	22.3%

2013 Year-End Financials

Debt ratio: 37.2%
Return on equity: 25.0%
Cash ($ mil.): 119
Current ratio: 0.80
Long-term debt ($ mil.): 505
No. of shares (mil.): 33
Dividends
  Yield: 1.1%
  Payout: 113.9%
Market value ($ mil.): 2,604

	STOCK PRICE ($) FY Close	P/E High/Low		PER SHARE ($) Earnings	Dividends	Book Value
12/13	77.43	82	50	0.94	0.90	4.16
12/12	47.46	49	31	1.10	0.70	3.46
12/11	38.10	29	18	1.53	0.60	2.39
12/10	37.55	33	18	1.17	0.44	2.41
12/09	22.82	20	10	1.33	0.74	1.47
Annual Growth 35.7%		—	—	(8.3%)	5.0%	29.6%

CoStar Group, Inc.

CoStar has all the dirt on the commercial real estate industry. A provider of commercial real estate information CoStar has a proprietary database of some 4 million properties in the US the UK and France. The database contains information on more than 10 billion square feet of sale and lease listings. It also has more than 12 million digital images of buildings floor plans and maps. Its hundreds of data fields include location ownership and tenant names. CoStar additionally offers marketing and analytic services. Clients include government agencies real estate brokerages real estate investment trusts (REITs) and property owners and managers. Most of CoStar's sales come from subscription fees.

Geographic Reach

The company's sales teams are located in 30 field sales offices throughout the US and in offices located in London England; Manchester England; Glasgow Scotland and Paris France. Sales in the US accounted for about 95% of total revenues in fiscal 2012.

Operations

The company employs a team of more than 1000 research professionals and contractors who collect and analyze commercial real estate information. Its subscription-based services consist primarily of CoStar Property Professional (comprehensive inventory) CoStar Tenant (tenant information) CoStar COMPS Professional (comparable sales information) FOCUS (data on UK market) and Propex (UK market info for professional investors). It does business in England through CoStar UK.

Sales and Marketing

The company draws its customers from commercial real estate and related business community. Commercial real estate brokers have traditionally formed the largest portion of CoStar clients. The company also provides services to owners landlords financial institutions retailers vendors appraisers investment banks governmental agencies and other parties involved in commercial real estate.

CoStar sells its products and services through a direct sales force located in field sales offices. Its E-commerce advertising expenses were approximately $3 million in fiscal 2012.

Financial Performance

CoStar's revenue has spiked nearly 40% in fiscal 2012 compared to the previous year. The company brought in almost $350 million in revenue during fiscal 2012 after reporting about $251.7 million in fiscal 2011 and $226.3 million back in fiscal 2010.

The increase in revenues during fiscal 2012 was primarily attributable to additional revenue from the acquisition of LoopNet the penetration of the subscription-based information services and successful cross-selling of the company's services to its customers in existing markets combined with continued high renewal rates.

Net income decreased in fiscal 2012 mainly due to the increase in income tax expense and the impact of costs related to the LoopNet acquisition that are not deductible for tax purposes.

Mergers and Acquisitions

In 2012 the company significantly expanded its holdings with the $860 million purchase of Loop-Net a complementary provider of online commercial real estate information. The deal doubled the size of CoStar's paid subscriber base to some 160000. The previous year CoStar enhanced its real estate brokerage offerings when it obtained Virtual Premise a provider of real estate management software and lease abstraction services. Each month Virtual Premise manages over $1 billion in rent payments for its customers.

EXECUTIVES

President CEO and Director, Andrew C. Florance, age 50, $456,560 total compensation
Chief Information Officer, Frank Simuro, age 47
CFO, Brian J. Radecki, age 43, $249,600 total compensation
EVP Sales, Max Linnington
Managing Director CoStar UK, Paul Marples, age 52, $224,966 total compensation
EVP of Operations, Francis Carchedi
President Apartments.com, Brad Long
Vice President Customer Service, Susan Jeffress
Vice President Product Development, Grady Bryant
Vice President Finance, Scott Yinger
Vice President Of Business Development, Alexander Greenwell
Vice President Software Development, William Bryant
Vice President Major Accounts, Gerry Perrine
Chairman, Michael R. Klein, age 72
CFO, Brian J. Radecki, age 43
Corporate Treasurer, Charles Colligan
Auditors: Ernst&YoungLLP

LOCATIONS

HQ: CoStar Group, Inc.
1331 L Street, N.W., Washington, DC 20005
Phone: 202 346-6500   **Fax:** 877 739-0486
Web: www.costar.com

2012 Sales

	$ mil.	% of total
US	330.8	95
International	20.6	5
Adjustments	(1.5)	-
Total	**349.9**	**100**

PRODUCTS/OPERATIONS

Selected Subscription Products

CoStar COMPS Professional (comparable sales information)
CoStar Property Professional (flagship real estate database)
CoStar Tenant (tenant information)
FOCUS (UK real estate information)

Selected Data

Building characteristics
Contact information
Demographic information
For-sale information
Historical trends
Income and expense histories
Lease expirations
Mortgage and deed information
Number of retail stores
Ownership
Retail sales per square foot
Sales and lease comparables
Site and zoning information
Space availability
Tax assessments
Tenant names

COMPETITORS

First American	Reed Business
Market Leader	Information
Move Inc.	Reis
PropertyInfo	Zillow

HISTORICAL FINANCIALS

Company Type: Public

Income Statement
FYE: December 31

	REVENUE ($ mil.)	NET INCOME ($ mil.)	NET PROFIT MARGIN	EMPLOYEES
12/13	440.9	29.7	6.7%	2,046
12/12	349.9	9.9	2.8%	1,965
12/11	251.7	14.6	5.8%	1,514
12/10	226.2	13.2	5.9%	1,389
12/09	209.6	18.6	8.9%	1,438
Annual Growth	**20.4%**	**12.3%**	**—**	**9.2%**

2013 Year-End Financials

Debt ratio: 12.1%
Return on equity: 3.3%
Cash ($ mil.): 255
Current ratio: 2.77
Long-term debt ($ mil.): 129
No. of shares (mil.): 28
Dividends
  Yield: —
  Payout: —
Market value ($ mil.): 5,325

	STOCK PRICE ($) FY Close	P/E High/Low	PER SHARE ($) Earnings	Dividends	Book Value
12/13	184.58	174 83	1.05	0.00	32.16
12/12	89.37	242 153	0.37	0.00	29.15
12/11	66.73	116 74	0.62	0.00	25.93
12/10	57.56	89 58	0.64	0.00	18.37
12/09	41.77	47 26	0.94	0.00	17.41
Annual Growth	**45.0%**	**— —**	**2.8%**	**—**	**16.6%**

CPI Aerostructures, Inc.

To build an aircraft some assembly is required and CPI Aerostructures is ready. CPI Aero delivers contract production of structural aircraft subassemblies chiefly for the US Air Force and other US military customers. Military products include skin panels flight control surfaces leading edges wing tips engine components cowl doors and nacelle and inlet assemblies. The lineup is used on military aircraft such as the C-5A Galaxy and C-130 Hercules cargo jets E-3 Sentry AWACs jet and T-38 Talon jet trainer. As a subcontractor to OEMs CPI Aero also makes aprons and engine mounts for commercial aircraft such as business jets. Government prime and subcontracts represent a majority of CPI Aero's sales

Operations

CPI Aero is a U.S. manufacturer of structural assemblies for fixed wing aircraft helicopters and airborne Intelligence Surveillance and Reconnaissance pod systems in both the commercial aerospace and national security markets.

In conjunction with its assembly operations CPI Aero provides engineering program management supply chain management and MRO services. Among the key national security programs that CPI Aero supplies are the E-2D Advanced Hawkeye surveillance aircraft the A-10 Thunderbolt attack jet the UH-60 BLACK HAWK helicopter the MH-53/CH-53 variant helicopters the MH-60S mine countermeasure helicopter the AH-1Z ZULU attack helicopter the DB-110 reconnaissance pod and the ALMDS mine detecting pod. In the commercial aviation market CPI Aero manufactures products for the Gulfstream G650 ultra-large cabin business jet the HondaJet advanced light jet the Embraer Phenom 300 business jet the new Cessna Citation X+ and the S-92 helicopter.

Sales and Marketing

CPI Aero is a prime contractor to the US Department of Defense (primarily the Air Force). Its military customers have included Defense Supply Center Richmond Wright-Patterson Air Force Base (AFB) Warner Robins AFB Tinker AFB NAVICP Hill AFB and the US Army Redstone Arsenal. Its commercial customers have included NGC Lockheed Spirit Sikorsky Bell Helicopter Boeing Military Nordam Hupp UTAS Embraer Cessna and Honda.

Financial Performance

CPI Aero reported a 7% decline in revenues in 2013 due to a drop in prime government contracts. It also saw a decline in government subcontracts and commercial contracts.In 2013 net income decreased by 30% due to a decline in revenues and an increase in interest expense as the result of a rise in the average amount of outstanding debt.The company saw a cash inflow from operating activities of $3.3 million (compared to an outflow in $22.1 million in 2012) due to a decline in cash used in Tax benefit for stock options a decrease in accounts receivable higher costs and estimated earnings in excess of billings on uncompleted contracts and cash provided by a decrease in other assets.

Strategy

CPI Aero's performance has depended on winning government and military work coupled with commercial contracts (although in 2013 the company announced plans to transition away from being a prime government contractor). In 2014 the company received orders totaling $14 million from Northrop Grumman for Outer Wing Panel (OWP) kits. In 2013 it received an extension through 2015 to its existing General Ordering Agreement with Bell Helicopter.

EXECUTIVES

Vice President Operations, Charles Munna
Auditors: J.H.CohnLLP

LOCATIONS

HQ: CPI Aerostructures, Inc.
 91 Heartland Boulevard, Edgewood, NY 11717
Phone: 631 586-5200   **Fax:** 631 586-5840
Web: www.cpiaero.com

PRODUCTS/OPERATIONS

Selected Products

Cowl doors
Engine components
Flight control surfaces
Inlet assemblies
Leading edges
Nacelle assemblies
Skin panels
Wing tips

COMPETITORS

Boeing
Lockheed Martin
NORDAM
Northrop Grumman
Triumph Aerostructures - Vought Aircraft Division

HISTORICAL FINANCIALS

Company Type: Public

Income Statement

FYE: December 31

	REVENUE ($ mil.)	NET INCOME ($ mil.)	NET PROFIT MARGIN	EMPLOYEES
12/13	82.9	7.7	9.3%	268
12/12	89.2	11.0	12.3%	201
12/11	74.1	7.4	10.0%	157
12/10	43.9	0.5	1.2%	127
12/09	43.9	3.9	9.0%	91
Annual Growth	17.3%	18.3%	—	31.0%

2013 Year-End Financials

Debt ratio: 19.7%
Return on equity: 9.1%
Cash ($ mil.): 2
Current ratio: 3.79
Long-term debt ($ mil.): 2
No. of shares (mil.): 8
Dividends
 Yield: —
 Payout: —
Market value ($ mil.): 126

	STOCK PRICE ($) FY Close	P/E High/Low		PER SHARE ($) Earnings	Dividends	Book Value
12/13	15.04	16	9	0.91	0.00	10.58
12/12	10.01	11	7	1.40	0.00	9.63
12/11	11.87	14	9	1.04	0.00	7.78
12/10	14.08	177	75	0.08	0.00	6.58
12/09	6.01	12	6	0.64	0.00	6.38
Annual Growth	25.8%	—	—	9.2%	—	13.5%

Cray Inc

Cray makes computers that aren't just good — they're super. Its massively parallel and vector supercomputers provide the firepower behind research ranging from weather forecasting and scientific research to design engineering and classified government projects. The company also provides maintenance and support services and it sells its own and third-party data storage products primarily from NetApp and DataDirect Networks. Cray's largest customer is the US government which accounts for about two-thirds of sales. Cray also targets academic institutions and industrial companies. Around 80% of sales come from customers in the US.

Operations

All of its engineering and manufacturing facilities are located in the US (in California and Wisconsin) though the company uses subcontractors to produce the majority of its components. Of course all of its high-performance computers are built to order.

Cray has supercomputers installed at more than 100 sites worldwide. Its supercomputers run on the company's Cray Linux Environment (CLE) operating system. Cray is one of the only companies left that exclusively makes supercomputers. Competitors such as IBM are traditional PC companies that also custom-design high-performance models for customers.

Sales and Marketing

Cray has a direct sales force that operates from sales and service facilities in Australia Canada China France Germany Hong Kong India Italy Japan South Korea Spain Switzerland Taiwan the UK and the US. Only about 20% of sales come from outside the US.

Financial Performance

With supercomputer price tags often at $10 million and up the company's annual results can fluctuate dramatically. In 2012 overall sales jumped to $421 million up 78% from the $236 million earned in 2011. The increase was due a project with the National Center for Supercomputing Applications (NCSA) at the University of Illinois to build its supercomputer named Blue Waters as well as upgrades to the supercomputer at the Oak Ridge National Laboratory.

After years of losses Cray has been profitable since 2010 and 2012's profits skyrocketed 1000% to $161 million after it sold its interconnect hardware development program and related intellectual property to Intel for $140 million in cash.

Strategy

In 2013 Cray expanded its line of midrange supercomputers which have price tags between $200000 and $500000. The lower priced systems expand the company's market reach and potential for growth. In another strategic move in 2012 Cray formed YarcData a division focused solely on providing systems and services to the big data market. That year it also acquired California-based Appro International for about $21.8 million in cash. Appro International provides supercomputing services.

Company Background

Formerly Tera Computer the company bought Cray Research from Silicon Graphics and changed its name to Cray in 2000. In 2004 Cray acquired Canadian supercomputer developer OctigaBay Systems which became Cray Canada. The company's name comes from the late Seymour R. Cray the "father of supercomputing" although Mr. Cray never worked for Cray Inc.

EXECUTIVES

EVP and CFO, Brian C. Henry, age 57, $352,500 total compensation
Vp-hr, Linda J Howitson
President and CEO, Peter J. Ungaro, age 45, $475,000 total compensation
SVP and CTO, Steven L. (Steve) Scott, age 48, $323,077 total compensation
VP Field Operations, Charles A. (Chuck) Morreale, age 52
VP Asia-Pacific, Andrew Wyatt
President Cray Japan, Mamoru Nakano
VP Americas Sales, Larry Hoelzeman
SVP Cluster Products and Corporate Strategy and Planning, Daniel G.B. Kim
Director EMEA Operations, Dominik Ulmer
Sales & Marketing, Rene Copeland
Senior Vice President Hpc Systems, Margaret A (Peg) Williams, age 56
Vp-govt Programs, Jill Y Hopper
Vice President Of Worldwide Sales, John Josephakis
Senior Vice President Operations, Ly Pham
Vice President, Eddie Smith
Assistant To Senior Vice President Ops, Nancy Yeske
Vice President Software Engineering, Peter Young
Executive Vice President, Mike Inglis
Vice President Field Operations, Chuck Morreale
Vice President Cluster Solutions, James Yi
Chairman, Stephen C. Kiely, age 68
Auditors: PetersonSullivanP.L.L.C.

LOCATIONS

HQ: Cray Inc
 901 Fifth Avenue, Suite 1000, Seattle, WA 98164
Phone: 206 701-2000
Web: www.cray.com

2012 Sales

	% of total
US	82
Other countries	18
Total	**100**

PRODUCTS/OPERATIONS

2012 Sales

	% of total
High-performance computers	71
Maintenance & support	15
Storage & data management	12
Engineering services & other	2
Total	**100**

2012 Sales

	% of total
Products	84
Services	16
Total	**100**

COMPETITORS

Bull	Lockheed Martin
California Digital	NEC
Corp.	NetApp
Cirrascale	Northrop Grumman
Dell	Oracle
EMC	Panasas
Fujitsu	Penguin Computing
General Dynamics	SRC Computers
Hewlett-Packard	Silicon Graphics
Hitachi	International
IBM	Teradata
LexisNexis	

HISTORICAL FINANCIALS

Company Type: Public

Income Statement

FYE: December 31

	REVENUE ($ mil.)	NET INCOME ($ mil.)	NET PROFIT MARGIN	EMPLOYEES
12/13	525.7	32.2	6.1%	1,042
12/12	421.0	161.2	38.3%	929
12/11	236.0	14.3	6.1%	860
12/10	319.3	15.0	4.7%	885
12/09	284.0	(0.6)	—	872
Annual Growth	**16.6%**	—	—	**4.6%**

2013 Year-End Financials

Debt ratio: —	No. of shares (mil.): 40
Return on equity: 9.0%	Dividends
Cash ($ mil.): 192	Yield: —
Current ratio: 2.97	Payout: —
Long-term debt ($ mil.): —	Market value ($ mil.): 1,111

	STOCK PRICE ($) FY Close	P/E High/Low	PER SHARE ($) Earnings	Dividends	Book Value
12/13	27.46	33 19	0.81	0.00	9.28
12/12	15.95	4 1	4.27	0.00	8.64
12/11	6.47	20 12	0.40	0.00	4.54
12/10	7.17	17 10	0.43	0.00	4.04
12/09	6.42	— —	(0.02)	0.00	3.53
Annual Growth	**43.8%**	— —	—	—	**27.3%**

Credit Acceptance Corp. (MI)

In the world of Credit Acceptance Corporation (CAC) to purchase a car is not an impossible dream for problem borrowers. CAC makes the effort a reality. Working with more than 55000 independent and franchised automobile dealers in the US CAC provides capital for auto loans to people with substandard credit. The company also provides other services to dealers including payment servicing receivables management marketing and service contracts. CAC which concentrates its operations in a handful of US states typically funds about 1.5 million auto loans per year.

Geographic Reach

Michigan-based CAC serves consumers nationwide. Its largest markets include New York Texas Ohio and Pennsylvania.

Sales and Marketing

CAC caters to and partners with some 56000 independent and franchised automobile dealers throughout the US.

Operations

CAC steps in to help finance auto purchases for those whose credit histories aren't ideal. Auto dealers in turn benefit from the vehicle sales and from repeat and referral sales generated by these customers.

Strategy

The company funds loans in two ways: It advances money to its dealer-partners in exchange for the servicing rights to the underlying loan or it purchases loans directly from dealers. CAC earns most of its revenues from finance charges servicing fees and monthly program fees it charges its dealer partners. Indeed finance charges in 2013 accounted for 87% of revenue.

Financial Performance

The company's revenue has been growing for several years. In fiscal 2013 CAC posted 12% increases in revenue to $682.1 million as compared to 2012's $609.2 million. CAC points to a 10% boost in finance charges due to an increase in the average net loans receivable balance for the 2013 gains. These were offset however by a drop in the average yield on loan portfolio. Thanks to a new profit-sharing arrangement CAC entered in 2012 with third party providers (TPPs) other income jumped some 68% during the reporting period. Helping other income was an increase in GPS-SID fee income due to rising fee earned per unit purchased primarily resulting from new the new profit-sharing agreement. CAC's net income has been on the same trajectory. In 2013 net income rose some 15% to $253.1 million vs. 2012's $219.7 million bolstered by the company's higher revenue offset in part by an increased provision for income tax. Cash flow from operations also rose in 2013 — from $308.6 million in 2012 to $325.7 million in 2013 —attributable to higher net income a decrease in the provision for credit losses and a change in working capital.

HISTORY

Donald Foss was a used-car dealer in Detroit where to make sales he sometimes financed cars out of his own pocket. As Foss' chain of dealerships grew so did his financing business. In 1972 he established it as a separate company and 20 years later took it public.

For most of its history CAC stood alone in the field of subprime auto lending but stagnating salaries made it a competitive growth business in the early 1990s. At mid-decade the company entered Canada and the UK to tap similar markets there. In 1996 CAC acquired Montana Investment Group a credit reporting service.

Even as rising consumer debt and bad credit continued to pump buyers into CAC's loan pipeline the economic boom of the mid-1990s paradoxically made used cars less desirable. The soft used-car market squeezed several of CAC's competitors out of business; a staggering default rate —nearing 40% —also pressured CAC whose auditors insisted it increase reserves to cover losses. The subsequent earnings dive spurred a shareholder lawsuit accusing CAC of hiding its poor fiscal health. Although bad loans had damaged its bottom line the company adopted more stringent lending policies to reduce risk. Consumers filed class-action suits alleging unethical practices in 1998 but many claims were dismissed.

To pay off debt acquired through bad loans CAC sold Montana Investment Group in 1999. In 2000 it launched CAC Leasing to further offset losses from a decrease in subprime lending but in 2002 the company exited that line deciding the lending field was more profitable. CAC stopped originating new loans in the UK and Canada in 2003.

In 2005 the SEC investigated CAC's accounting methods specifically related to its loan portfolio and the company restated portions of its past financial results.

The company found itself in hot water again in 2008 when it agreed to pay some 15000 Missouri customers to settle a class action lawsuit. The lawsuit filed more than a decade prior alleged that CAC overcharged customers for fees and interest on their loans. As part of the settlement CAC said it would write off $39 million in outstanding accounts and distribute another $13 million to customers.

EXECUTIVES

Senior Vice President; Treasurer, Douglas W Busk, age 54
CEO, Brett A. Roberts, age 47, $1,025,000 total compensation
President, Steven M. Jones, age 50, $625,000 total compensation
CFO, Kenneth S. Booth, age 46, $414,792 total compensation
CIO, John S. Soave, age 50
Vice President, Steve Dion
Senior Vice President Risk, Art Smith
Vice President Of Portfolio Management, Keith Shields
Vice President Of Human Resources, Kristie Karr
Vice President Of Sales, Jeffrey Brock
Vice President Sales East Region, David Wall
Vice President Information Technology, Rael Mussell
Senior Vice President Analytics, David Perrine
Vice President Of Sales, Patrick Norris
Senior Vice President Dpsc, Jonathan Lum
Vice President Of Finance, Wendy Rummler
Chairman, Donald A. Foss, age 69
Auditors: GrantThorntonLLP

LOCATIONS

HQ: Credit Acceptance Corp. (MI)
25505 West Twelve Mile Road, Southfield, MI 48034-8339
Phone: 248 353-2700

PRODUCTS/OPERATIONS

2013 Sales

	$ mil.	% of total
Finance charges	590.4	87
Premiums earned	51.5	8
Other	40.2	5
Total	**682.1**	**100**

Selected Subsidiaries

Arlington Investment Company
Auto Funding America Inc.
Auto Lease Services LLC
AutoNet Finance Company.com Inc.
Buyers Vehicle Protection Plan Inc.
CAC Leasing Inc.
CAC Reinsurance Ltd.
CAC Warehouse Funding Corp. II III IV
Credit Acceptance Motors Inc.
Credit Acceptance Wholesale Buyers Club Inc.
Vehicle Remarketing Services Inc.
VSC Re Company

COMPETITORS

Ally Financial
American Honda Finance
Bank of America
Capital One Auto Finance
First Investors Financial Services
Ford Motor Credit
GM Financial
Mercedes-Benz Credit
Mercedes-Benz Financial Services USA
Toyota Motor Credit
Volkswagen Financial Services
Volvo Car Finance

HISTORICAL FINANCIALS

Company Type: Public

Income Statement

FYE: December 31

	REVENUE ($ mil.)	NET INCOME ($ mil.)	NET PROFIT MARGIN	EMPLOYEES
12/13	682.1	253.1	37.1%	1,317
12/12	609.2	219.7	36.1%	1,264
12/11	525.1	188.0	35.8%	1,037
12/10	442.1	170.0	38.5%	862
12/09	380.6	146.2	38.4%	911
Annual Growth	**15.7%**	**14.7%**	**—**	**9.7%**

2013 Year-End Financials

Debt ratio: 57.2%
Return on equity: 36.9%
Cash ($ mil.): 4
Current ratio: 1.27
Long-term debt ($ mil.): 1,392

No. of shares (mil.): 22
Dividends
Yield: —
Payout: —
Market value ($ mil.): 2,982

	STOCK PRICE ($) FY Close	P/E High	P/E Low	PER SHARE ($) Earnings	PER SHARE ($) Dividends	PER SHARE ($) Book Value
12/13	129.99	12	9	10.54	0.00	32.69
12/12	101.68	12	9	8.58	0.00	25.79
12/11	82.28	13	8	7.07	0.00	21.07
12/10	62.77	11	7	5.67	0.00	17.38
12/09	42.10	9	3	4.62	0.00	15.99
Annual Growth	**32.6%**	—	—	**22.9%**	—	**19.6%**

Cree, Inc.

Cree has its name in lights. Its blue green and near-ultraviolet light-emitting diodes (LEDs) — made from silicon carbide (SiC) and gallium nitride (GaN) —are used in dashboard lights architectural light fixtures market tickers and video screens. Cree also sells SiC wafers which work better at higher temperatures and voltages than other silicon devices and SiC and GaN materials. In addition it offers lighting systems (both LED and traditional) as well as power and radio-frequency (RF) products such as Schottky diodes and transistors. The company makes most of its products at plants in the US (North Carolina Wisconsin) and China. More than 50% of sales come from outside the US.

OperationsLED products (chips components and SiC wafers) account for about 50% of Cree's sales but that's down from more than 60% in previous years. Boosted by the acquisition of Ruud Lighting the lighting systems segment grew to nearly 40% of sales in 2014 from single digits in previous years. Power and RF products round out the company's segments.

Geographic ReachThe US is Cree's largest geographic market and its impact has increased substantially having grown from less than 20% of sales in fiscal 2010 to nearly 50% in fiscal 2014. China which has been declining in recent years contributes about 30%; all Asian countries together represent about 40% of total revenue.

Sales and MarketingMore than 50% of Cree's sales are made to distributors; in fiscal 2014 Arrow Electronics and Home Depot accounted for 13% and 11% of total sales respectively.

Financial PerformanceCree has enjoyed extraordinary revenue growth over the last several years. Revenue surged by 19% from $1.39 billion in 2013 to $1.65 billion in 2014 a company milestone. The historic growth for 2014 was due to higher sales across all three of its reportable segments. This was lead by a 43% increase in lighting products sales which was fueled by new product introductions

Profits were up by 43% from $87 million in 2013 to $124 million in 2014. This was due to the higher revenue coupled with a decrease in its loss on disposal or impairment of long-lived assets charge. Cree's operating cash flow has risen sharply the last two years increasing to $319 million in 2014 from $285 million in 2013.

StrategyCree created the first blue LED which when combined with red and yellow LEDs creates a full spectrum of colors. The technology has become an industry standard and expands the applications of LED lighting. To leverage this core technology Cree has introduced the XLamp family of high-power packaged LEDs for specialty lighting applications hoping to stay one step ahead of the competition. Cree's XLamp products have a wide array of residential and commercial uses including appliance lighting and reading lamps as well as backlighting for large flat-panel and retail displays.The trends towards increased energy-efficient and environmental lighting and the growing number of standard lighting products that use LEDs have helped Cree weather a challenging economic environment better than many in the electronics industry. The company has combined external acquisitions and internal R&D to broaden its offerings –and increase its sales and market reach –into LED lighting fixtures power switching and RF products.

HISTORY

Cree started at North Carolina State University where brothers Eric and Neal Hunter and Calvin Carter researched silicon carbide (SiC) applications in part with US government funding. In 1987 the trio founded Cree Research to continue their research. The company shipped its first-to-market blue light-emitting diode (LED) in 1991 and went public in 1993.

In 1995 the company began developing blue lasers –a project that continued for years to follow –via a 1999 pact with Microvision. Also that year Cree and Siemens formed a development and manufacturing agreement for blue and green LEDs. In 1997 Cree began supplying SiC crystals to gemstone manufacturer C3.

Cree in 1998 signed or extended pacts with Kansai Electric Power Siemens and Asea Brown Boveri (now ABB Ltd.). The next year the company shortened its name to Cree Inc. and released its first radio-frequency transistor.

In 2000 Cree acquired semiconductor R&D boutique Nitres for $233 million and to close out the year purchased the UltraRF division of Spectrian (a maker of linear power amplifiers) for $113.5 million. (It later renamed the unit Cree Microwave.)

In 2004 Cree acquired the gallium nitride substrate and epitaxy assets of Advanced Technology Materials a subsidiary of ATMI for about $10 million boosting its materials business and IP portfolio.

Co-founder Neal Hunter who served as CEO of Cree from 1994 to 2001 resigned as chairman in 2005 after a decade in that post and left the company's board of directors. Charles Swoboda who had succeeded Hunter as CEO in 2001 succeeded him as chairman as well.

Cree phased out its silicon-based RF and microwave semiconductor business in 2005 citing losses by its Cree Microwave subsidiary. The company refocused on its wide-bandgap RF and microwave devices fabricated on SiC and GaN substrates.

In 2006 the company opened a new engineering and production facility in Research Triangle Park measuring 230000 sq. ft. for making SiC and GaN devices.

That same year Cree acquired INTRINSIC Semiconductor for around $46 million including $43.6 million in cash. INTRINSIC Semiconductor made low-defect-density SiC substrates enabling high-power semiconductor devices and lower-cost LEDs.

In 2007 Cree acquired Hong Kong-based COTCO Luminant Device for about $200 million giving Cree a broader range of LED components access to a lower cost manufacturing facility and established sales channels in the fast growing China market.

EXECUTIVES

Vice President Operations, Robert C Glass
Vice President Cree Lighting Company, Mike Dunn
Vice President Corporate Marketing, Greg Merritt
President CEO and Chairman, Charles M. Swoboda, age 47, $742,308 total compensation
EVP Lighting, Norbert W.G. Hiller, age 54, $379,231 total compensation
EVP and CFO, Michael E. McDevitt, age 50, $391,923 total compensation
Vp Supply Chain, Lee Hudgins
Sr V Pres Sales & Business Dev, Bruce Renouard
Led Lighting Vice President Of Sales, Craig Lofton
Vice President Americas Sales, Vince Feorenzo
Vice President Of Global Channels, Mark Despotes

Vice President Business Developement, Bob Roller
Vice President Distribution Sales, John Spencer
National Account Manager, Randy Gaines
Vice President Marketing Business Dev, David Elien
Vice President Global Sales, Christopher Ruud
Vice President Global Sales Operations Lighting, Keith Karczewski
Vp & Director Strategic National, Steve Friedman
Vice President Of Marketing Lighting, Tami Timperio
Executive Vice President Manufacturing, Francis Wong
Vice President Strategic Marketing, Luka Lojk
National Account Manager, Brian Pillizzi
Vice President Of Finance Led, Carlos Gomez
National Sales Manager, Brett Hilkemann
Vice President Marketing, Chris James
Vice President Corporate Marketing, Mike Watson
National Account Manager Financial Services, Kate Hite
Secretary, Adam H Broome
President CEO and Chairman, Charles M. Swoboda, age 47
Director and Vice Chairman Lighting, Alan Ruud
Treasurer Head Of Treasury, Karl Steffen
Auditors: Ernst&YoungLLP

LOCATIONS

HQ: Cree, Inc.
4600 Silicon Drive, Durham, NC 27703
Phone: 919 407-5300 **Fax:** 919 313-5615
Web: www.cree.com

2014 Sales

	% of total
US	49
China	27
Europe	9
Japan	6
South Korea	2
Malaysia	1
Taiwan	1
Other countries	5
Total	**100**

PRODUCTS/OPERATIONS

2014 Sales

	$ mil.	% of total
LED products	833.7	51
Lighting systems	706.4	43
Power & RF products	107.5	6
Total	**1647.6**	**100**

Selected Products

Blue and green light-emitting diodes (LEDs; used in displays and indicators)
High-power packaged LEDs (XLamp)
Gallium nitride (GaN) products
  High electron mobility transistors (HEMT)
  Monolithic microwave integrated circuits (MMIC)
LED light fixtures (architectural lay-in bulbs downlights housings narrow beam spotlight)
Silicon carbide (SiC) products
  Radio-frequency and microwave transistors (used in communications applications)
  Rectifiers
  Switches
  Wafers (used in research programs)

COMPETITORS

Acuity Brands
Avago Technologies
Cooper Lighting
EPISTAR CORPORATION
GE
Hitachi
Hubbell
Infineon Technologies
Kopin
LG Electronics
Lighting Science Group
NEC
Nichia
OSRAM SYLVANIA
Orion Energy Systems
Panasonic Corp
Philips Lumileds
Philips Solid-State Lighting Solutions Inc.
Planar Systems
RF Micro Devices
ROHM
Revolution Lighting Technologies
Samsung Semiconductor
Sanken Electric
Sony
Sumitomo Electric Device Innovations
Toyoda Gosei
TriQuint
Zhejiang BOE Display

HISTORICAL FINANCIALS

Company Type: Public

Income Statement

FYE: June 29

	REVENUE ($ mil.)	NET INCOME ($ mil.)	NET PROFIT MARGIN	EMPLOYEES
06/14	1,647.6	124.1	7.5%	7,130
06/13	1,385.9	86.9	6.3%	6,120
06/12	1,164.6	44.4	3.8%	5,555
06/11	987.6	146.5	14.8%	4,753
06/10	867.2	152.2	17.6%	4,298
Annual Growth	**17.4%**	**(5.0%)**	**—**	**13.5%**

2014 Year-End Financials

Debt ratio: — No. of shares (mil.): 120
Return on equity: 4.3% Dividends
Cash ($ mil.): 1,162 Yield: —
Current ratio: 5.78 Payout: —
Long-term debt ($ mil.): — Market value ($ mil.): 5,823

	STOCK PRICE ($) FY Close	P/E High/Low	PER SHARE ($) Earnings	Dividends	Book Value
06/14	48.48	74 44	1.01	0.00	24.89
06/13	63.83	88 30	0.74	0.00	23.46
06/12	24.45	95 52	0.39	0.00	22.09
06/11	33.96	56 25	1.33	0.00	20.63
06/10	65.06	56 18	1.45	0.00	18.78
Annual Growth	**(7.1%)**	**— —**	**(8.6%)**	**—**	**7.3%**

Crocs Inc

Crocs has taken a bite out of the footwear industry. The company's shoe collection has grown by leaps and bounds from its ubiquitous colorful slip-on shoe to mainstream fashion. Branded as Crocs its shoes are made of proprietary closed-cell resin and designed for men women and children; its collection includes 300-plus four-season footwear styles. Jibbitz are their decorative add-on charms. The company sells its products in more than 90 countries operating distribution centers worldwide and manufacturing plants in Mexico and Italy. Crocs sells through retailers such as Dillard's Nordstrom and Dick's Sporting Goods as well as through about 250 of its own stores and kiosks worldwide.

Geographic Reach
Based in Colorado Crocs enjoys a global reach doing business in more than 90 countries. It maintains additional offices in Hong Kong England Brazil and Amsterdam.
Operations
The company has three operating segments: Americas Asia and Europe. Its Other segment comprises its manufacturing operations in Mexico and Italy.
The Americas segment generating 44% of sales consists of product sales in North and South America. Across the US and Canada it operates about 200 stores. Bringing in 41% of sales the Asia segment comprises revenue for product sales throughout Asia Australia New Zealand the Middle East and South Africa. The company's about 240 stores in the segment span Korea Taiwan Japan China and Hong Kong. Revenues and expenses related to product sales throughout Europe and Russia appear in the Europe segment which accounts for 15% of revenue. The segment operates nearly 100 stores in Russia Germany and Great Britain. The remaining stores are located throughout Asia Europe Australia the Middle East South America and South Africa.
As part of its business Crocs relies on third parties for its distribution centers which are located in the US China Japan Hong Kong Australia Korea Singapore India Taiwan the United Arab Emirates Russia Brazil Argentina Chile Puerto Rico and Italy.
Strategy
For the first time in company history Crocs reached $1 billion in revenue in 2011. Despite a continued difficult selling environment industry-wide it had boosted sales by more than 26% as compared to the same period in 2010.
Crocs has worked in recent years to transform its brand from what Crocs calls its clog silhouette to an all-season footwear brand. It's also looking at licensing to further diversify its revenue. The company's products fall into four categories: Core-Comfort Active Casual and Style. The footwear maker partners with the likes of Disney Marvel and Viacom to sell Crocs-licensed shoes and Jibbitz-branded shoe charms. Crocs in 2011 began to license certain trademarks to third parties.
Sales and Marketing
The company sells its products through three primary channels: wholesale (57% of sales) retail (33%) and Internet (10%). Wholesale customers include national and regional retail chains department stores sporting goods stores independent footwear retailers and family footwear retailers such as Dick's Sporting Goods Famous Footwear Academy Kohls Nordstrom Xebio and Murasaki Sports as well as online retailers the likes of Zappos.com and Amazon.com. Additionally Crocs has nearly 540 branded retail locations worldwide.
Crocs boasts sales offices in the US Canada South America Taiwan Hong Kong Australia Korea China the United Arab Emirates India and Europe.
In 2012 the company spent $39.8 million in total advertising marketing and promotional activities. It taps digital social and traditional media outlets for its campaigns. The company's in-house digital marketing team oversees digital marketing programs and platforms that include paid-and-organic search display re-targeting email and affiliate marketing.
Financial Performance
Crocs logged a 12% increase in sales in 2012 as compared to 2011 benefited by a 5% boost in global footwear unit sales and an 8% rise in footwear average selling price. It attributes most of

the gains to its retail channel (a 22% rise) which logged strong demand across its three reportable segments. Crocs also opened an impressive 107 net new stores in 2012 while shuttering some kiosks in favor of branded stores which offer customers its full line. Wholesale sales in the Americas and Asia spurred an 8% increase in 2012 sales. Revenues from its Internet channel also helped Crocs increasing 7% due to stronger brand awareness in the Americas and Asia. The company posted increased profits in both fiscal 2011 and 2012. Profits rose 17% in 2012 due to higher operating results and to a lesser extent a lower effective tax rate.

Mergers and Acquisitions

To reach into the accessories and sports businesses Crocs looks for add-on products (such as its purchase of Jibbitz) and technologies. Buying EXO Italia maker of ethylene vinyl acetate-based finished products has given Crocs the tools to compete in the popular performance footwear market against rivals the likes of Teva.

EXECUTIVES

Svp Retail Division, Peter S Case, age 54
Vp Global E-commerce, Chris Ladd
Vp Global Tax, Stephen Keating
CFO, Jeffrey (Jeff) Lasher, age 51, $400,000 total compensation
CEO, Gregg Ribatt, age 44
COO, Scott Crutchfield, age 53, $400,000 total compensation
President and Principal Executive Officer Crocs Inc., Andrew Rees, age 48
General Manager Asia Africa and Middle East Businesses, David Thomson
Vice President Global Creative Director, Becky Gebhardt
Vice President Europe, Vince Gunn, age 44
Vice President Global Marketing, Andy Sackmann
Vp Global Sales, Mike D Bell
Vp Finance, Dave Fargnoli
Vice President, Michael Brown
Vice President Global Ecommerce, Harvey Bierman
Vice President Direct To Consumer Channels Asia, Steve Castledine
Vice President Of Sales, Mike White
Vice President Finance, Thomas Grant
Vice President Operations, Todd Van Selus
Senior Vice President Of Sales, Harry Tanaka
Executive Vice President Of Sales, Robert Cilia
Senior Vice President Of Sales, Mike Thorne
Senior Vice President Of Sales, Martin Child
Executive Vice President Of Sales, Rick Case
Vice President Of Marketing, James Lentz
Vice President Of Product Line, Jeff Cross
Senior Vice President Global Supply Chain, Chap Kistler
National Accounts Manager, Matt Hoffman
Vice President Customer Care, Carin Wagner
Vice President Product Management, Christy Saito
Vice President General Manager Americas, Doug Hayer
Vice President Of Marketing, Glenda Ray
Chairman, Thomas J. Smach, age 53
Board Member, Doreen A Wright
Treasury Director, Mario Pasquale
Treasury Manager, Keith Love
Vice President Finance And Treasurer, Michael Kruteck
Board Member, Stephen W Cannon
Auditors: Deloitte&ToucheLLP

LOCATIONS

HQ: Crocs Inc
7477 East Dry Creek Parkway, Niwot, CO 80503
Phone: 303 848-7000
Web: www.crocs.com

2012 Sales

	$ mil.	% of total
Americas	495.8	44
Asia	457.4	41
Europe	169.4	15
Other	0.6	—
Total	**1123.3**	**100**

PRODUCTS/OPERATIONS

2012 Sales

	% of total
Wholesale	57
Retail	33
Internet	10
Total	**100**

2012 Sales

	$ mil.	% of total
Footwear	1076.2	96
Other	47.1	4
Total	**1123.3**	**100**

2012 Stores

	No.
Retail	287
Outlet	129
Kiosk	121
Total	**537**

COMPETITORS

Birkenstock USA	Skechers U.S.A.
Columbia Sportswear	São Paulo
Deckers Outdoor	Alpargatas
Heelys	Timberland
L.L. Bean	Wolverine World Wide
NIKE	adidas
R. Griggs	

HISTORICAL FINANCIALS

Company Type: Public

Income Statement

FYE: December 31

	REVENUE ($ mil.)	NET INCOME ($ mil.)	NET PROFIT MARGIN	EMPLOYEES
12/13	1,192.6	10.4	0.9%	5,000
12/12	1,123.3	131.3	11.7%	4,900
12/11	1,000.9	112.7	11.3%	4,157
12/10	789.7	67.7	8.6%	4,000
12/09	645.7	(42.0)	—	3,560
Annual Growth	**16.6%**	**—**	**—**	**8.9%**

2013 Year-End Financials

Debt ratio: 1.9%
Return on equity: 1.6%
Cash ($ mil.): 317
Current ratio: 3.42
Long-term debt ($ mil.): 11

No. of shares (mil.): 88
Dividends
  Yield: —
  Payout: —
Market value ($ mil.): 1,408

	STOCK PRICE ($) FY Close	P/E High/Low		PER SHARE ($) Earnings	Dividends	Book Value
12/13	15.92	149	101	0.12	0.00	7.06
12/12	14.39	15	8	1.44	0.00	6.96
12/11	14.77	25	11	1.24	0.00	5.48
12/10	17.12	25	7	0.76	0.00	4.27
12/09	5.75	—	—	(0.49)	0.00	3.36
Annual Growth	**29.0%**			**—**	**—**	**20.4%**

CSG Systems International Inc.

CSG Systems International tries to make life a little easier for CSRs (customer service representatives). Its customer care and billing software and services are designed for clients handling a high volume of transactions. The company offers outsourced transaction processing and customer service systems that are used to establish customer accounts process orders manage and mail monthly statements and perform marketing analysis among other functions. The company serves primarily North American cable TV direct broadcast satellite online services and telecom companies such as AT&T Time Warner Comcast and Verizon.

Geographic Reach CSG has some three dozen offices in about 25 countries although most of its sales (about 85%) are generated in the US. The company is seeing strong growth in its European and Asian operations however as those regions grew nearly 1000% and 2000% respectively year-over-year.

Sales and Marketing CSG markets its products directly via dedicated account teams. Its largest customers include Comcast (nearly 20% of sales) DISH Network (13%) and Time Warner (10%).

Financial Performance CSG has seen substantial revenue growth since 2005. In 2011 it reported a nearly 35% jump in sales to $735 million almost entirely the result of the acquisition of UK business services software provider Intec which boosted the company's software and maintenance segment by about 300%. Along with the strong 2011 sales net income nearly doubled to $42 million. Mergers and Acquisitions CSG uses acquisitions as one means of expanding. In 2012 it acquired Swedish software developer Ascade a provider of trading and routing applications to telecommunications companies worldwide for approximately $19 million in cash to extend its reach into the wholesale telecommunications wholesale market and expand its geographic reach. In 2010 the company bought Intec Telecom a UK-based business support systems software provider in a deal valued at about $376 million. CSG used the purchase to expand its customer base into international markets and broaden its portfolio of products used to interact with customers in real-time. By integrating Intec's retail billing mediation and wholesale business management systems with its customer interaction management software suite CSG was able to provide a more complete customer interaction platform to telecommunications companies outside of its core cable and satellite markets.

EXECUTIVES

Senior Vice President, Dwayne Ruffin
President and CEO, Peter E. Kalan, age 54, $530,400 total compensation
SVP Corporate Development and General Counsel, Joseph T. (Joe) Ruble, age 53, $316,200 total compensation
EVP and CFO, Randy R. Wiese, age 54, $367,200 total compensation
CTO and SVP product management and software development, Ken Kennedy
EVP and COO, Bret C. Griess, age 45, $372,300 total compensation
Svp Management, Sean Brown

Vice President Professional Services, Shaun Whalon
Vice President R&d Ascade, Ann Sofie Hansson
Vp Special Projects Csg Invotas, Paul Smith
Chairman, Donald B. Reed, age 69
Auditors: KPMGLLP

LOCATIONS

HQ: CSG Systems International Inc.
9555 Maroon Circle, Englewood, CO 80112
Phone: 303 200-2000
Web: www.csgi.com

2011 Sales

	$ mil	% of total
Americas	627.2	85
Europe Middle East and Africa	75.9	10
Asia Pacific	31.6	4
Total	**734.7**	**100**

PRODUCTS/OPERATIONS

2011 Sales

	$ mil.	% of total
Processing & related services	524.7	71
Software maintenance & services	210.0	29
Total	**734.7**	**100**

Selected Services

Revenue Management
  Cable & Satellite Care & Billing
  Convergent Rating & Billing
  Charging & Policy
  Total Service Mediation
  Partner Management Billing & Settlement
Customer Interaction Management
  Customer Communication Center
  Interactive Messaging
  Output Solutions
  Marketing Services
Analytics & Intelligence
  Customer Intelligence

COMPETITORS

Alcatel-Lucent	Huawei Technologies
Amdocs	Oracle
Convergys	Synchronoss
DST Systems	

HISTORICAL FINANCIALS

Company Type: Public

Income Statement

FYE: December 31

	REVENUE ($ mil.)	NET INCOME ($ mil.)	NET PROFIT MARGIN	EMPLOYEES
12/13	747.4	51.3	6.9%	3,398
12/12	756.8	48.8	6.5%	3,542
12/11	734.7	42.2	5.8%	3,352
12/10	549.3	22.4	4.1%	3,512
12/09	500.7	43.3	8.7%	2,061
Annual Growth	**10.5%**	**4.3%**	**—**	**13.3%**

2013 Year-End Financials

Debt ratio: 30.5%	No. of shares (mil.): 33
Return on equity: 14.8%	Dividends
Cash ($ mil.): 82	Yield: 1.5%
Current ratio: 2.30	Payout: 25.1%
Long-term debt ($ mil.): 250	Market value ($ mil.): 992

	STOCK PRICE ($) FY Close	P/E High/Low		PER SHARE ($) Earnings	Dividends	Book Value
12/13	29.40	19	11	1.56	0.45	10.85
12/12	18.18	15	9	1.51	0.00	9.68
12/11	14.71	17	10	1.28	0.00	8.12
12/10	18.94	35	26	0.67	0.00	6.95
12/09	19.09	15	10	1.26	0.00	6.04
Annual Growth	**11.4%**	**—**	**—**	**5.5%**	**—**	**15.8%**

CubeSmart

CubeSmart (formerly U-Store-It Trust) is a real estate investment trust (REIT) that owns more than 375 self-storage facilities with some 25 million sq. ft. of rentable space in about 25 states and Washington DC. The company also manages more than 100 self-storage facilities for third parties. Amenities at its properties include security systems and wider aisles for larger vehicles as well as climate-controlled units and outdoor storage for vehicles and boats at selected sites. The REIT also sells storage-related items such as packing supplies and locks to tenants who typically rent units on a month-to-month basis. As part of a re-branding initiative U-Store-It changed its name to CubeSmart in 2011.

In 2009 the REIT entered into an agreement with independent self-storage facility operators to provide management services in areas where it doesn't have a strong presence. CubeSmart expanded its facilities management operations the following year with the acquisition of some 85 contracts from United Stor-All Management. The company continues to pursue relationships with other self-storage owners.

Increased property management fees and more importantly additional rental income from properties acquired in 2010 and 2011 contributed to a nearly 10% rise in revenues for the latter year. However CubeSmart remained in the red for the third consecutive year though it was able to cut its losses to some $1.6 million in 2011 compared to nearly $7.4 million the year before.

CubeSmart believes the self-storage industry to be relatively recession proof as demand is driven by consumer mobility which increases during economic expansions as well as contractions. The industry also benefits from declining home ownership rates since renters which represent more than half of self-storage customers move more frequently. CubeSmart also believes that the fragmented nature of the self-storage sector also provides more acquisition opportunities.

When purchasing properties the company seeks out facilities in what it considers to be high-growth markets particularly Florida Illinois Texas and parts of the Northeast. (Combined California Florida Texas and Illinois account for approximately half of its revenues.) In 2011 CubeSmart acquired more than 20 self-storage facilities in the New York City metropolitan area from Storage Deluxe. In separate deals it added properties in attractive markets such as Atlanta Houston Miami and Washington DC.

Meanwhile CubeSmart is divesting properties in what it considers to be non-core markets. It sold nearly 20 storage facilities in the Canton Ohio; Cleveland; and Indianapolis areas in 2011.

Institutional investor Cohen & Steers owns nearly 15% of CubeSmart's stock. Vanguard holds more than 10%.

EXECUTIVES

CEO, Christopher P. (Chris) Marr, age 49, $410,000 total compensation
CFO, Timothy M. (Tim) Martin, age 44, $315,000 total compensation
SVP and CIO, Ajai Nair
SVP Operations, Joel Keaton
VP Third-Party Management, Guy Middlebrooks
Vice President, Carol Shipley
Chairman, William M. Diefenderfer, age 69
Auditors: KPMGLLP

LOCATIONS

HQ: CubeSmart
5 Old Lancaster Road, Malvern, PA 19355
Phone: 610 535-5000
Web: www.cubesmart.com

	No.
Florida	53
Texas	45
California	44
Illinois	27
New York	27
Arizona	24
Tennessee	24
Ohio	23
Connecticut	18
New Jersey	16
Georgia	9
New Mexico	9
Colorado	8
Virginia	7
North Carolina	6
Maryland	5
Massachusetts	4
Utah	4
Louisiana	3
Michigan	3
Pennsylvania	3
Nevada	2
Washington DC	2
Alabama	1
Indiana	1
Mississippi	1
Wisconsin	1
Total	**370**

PRODUCTS/OPERATIONS

2011 Sales

	$ mil.	% of total
Rental income	212.1	89
Property management fees	3.8	2
Other property-related income	21.7	9
Total	**237.6**	**100**

COMPETITORS

AMERCO	PODS Enterprises
Extra Space	Public Storage
Mobile Mini	Sovran

HISTORICAL FINANCIALS

Company Type: Public

Income Statement

FYE: December 31

	REVENUE ($ mil.)	NET INCOME ($ mil.)	NET PROFIT MARGIN	EMPLOYEES
12/13	318.4	41.4	13.0%	1,442
12/12	283.0	1.8	0.6%	1,409
12/11	237.6	(0.4)	—	1,276
12/10	216.8	(7.3)	—	1,172
12/09	217.2	(0.9)	—	953
Annual Growth	10.0%	—	—	10.9%

2013 Year-End Financials

Debt ratio: 48.2%
Return on equity: 3.9%
Cash ($ mil.): 3
Current ratio: 0.17
Long-term debt ($ mil.): 1,138

No. of shares (mil.): 139
Dividends
  Yield: 2.8%
  Payout: 418.1%
Market value ($ mil.): 2,221

	STOCK PRICE ($) FY Close	P/E High/Low		PER SHARE ($) Earnings	Dividends	Book Value
12/13	15.94	75	55	0.26	0.46	7.84
12/12	14.57	—	—	(0.03)	0.35	7.51
12/11	10.64	—	—	(0.02)	0.28	7.83
12/10	9.53	—	—	(0.08)	0.10	7.35
12/09	7.32	—	—	(0.01)	0.10	7.50
Annual Growth	21.5%	—	—	—	46.5%	1.1%

Cumulus Media Inc.

Cumulus Media reigns over an empire of radio stations. The company is the #2 radio station ownership group in the US (behind Clear Channel) with more than 525 owned or operated stations in about 110 markets throughout the country. In many of its markets Cumulus has built clusters of stations that realize cost savings through shared administrative and sales operations. In addition to its core mid-market stations Cumulus through a partnership with a private equity firm Crestview Partners owns about 30 stations in large markets including Atlanta Dallas and San Francisco. Crestview Partners controls about 40% of Cumulus.

Operations

The company's radio network serves more than 5500 affiliates nationwide.

Geographic Reach

In addition to its 525 stations Cumulus owns 45 studio facilities and has corporate offices in Atlanta New York and Dallas.

Financial Analysis

Cumulus' revenue doubled in 2012 based on the contribution of new acquisitions Cumulus Media Partners and Citadel as well as increased political advertising in conjunction with elections. Despite the big jump in revenue the company's increased operating expenses depreciation impairment charges and interest expense contributed to an overall loss in 2012.

Strategy

Not surprisingly the company's plans include improving the performance of its existing stations to generate internal growth. It also intends to continue acquiring broadcast companies and individual stations in larger markets and regional clusters.

Mergers and Acquisitions

In 2012 Cumulus purchased two stations in Kansas City for about $11 million. It also unloaded 55 stations in eleven markets it considered nonstrategic including Maine upstate New York North Dakota South Dakota and Alabama. The unloading was actually a swap with Townsquare Media. In exchange for the 55 non-strategic staions Cumulus received 10 stations in Bloomington and Peoria Illinois and about $115 in cash.

In 2011 Cumulus Media purchased Citadel Broadcasting. The deal was valued at roughly $2.5 billion.

Ownership

Chairman and CEO Lewis Dickey along with his family controls about 14% of Cumulus Media and Crestview Radio Investors holds about 41%.

HISTORY

Milwaukee investor Richard Weening and Atlanta-based radio consultant Lewis Dickey met in early 1996 while Dickey was working for some Caribbean radio stations owned by Weening. Seeing an opportunity to capitalize on the loosened ownership regulations of the Telecommunications Act of 1996 they formed Cumulus Media in 1997. With backing from investors such as the State of Wisconsin Investment Board and NationsBank Capital the two men began buying radio stations in small and midsized markets gaining on more than 50 stations to the tune of about $75 million. Cumulus Media went public in 1998. Its portfolio mushroomed to 195 stations (including pending acquisitions) by the end of that year.

In 1999 the company was forced to restate earnings for three quarters of 1999 which resulted in 11 shareholder lawsuits. (Several of the lawsuits were settled in 2001 for about $13 million.) In 2000 Cumulus bought 35 stations in nine Midwestern markets from Connoisseur Communications for about $266 million. The company also sold 30 stations to rival Clear Channel Communications. Dickey was later named CEO and Cumulus moved its headquarters to Atlanta. In 2002 the company completed its purchase of the 18-station company Aurora Communications and three stations in Nashville owned by DBBC. Later that year the company bought eight stations in Georgia for $35 million.

In 2003 Cumulus added another 25 stations to its stable at a total cost of $185 million. The next year the company acquired an additional 25 radio stations for a total of $94 million.

Cumulus' aggressive acquisition strategy left the company burdened with a heavy debt load forcing the company to slow its buying spree. In 2006 however it joined with private equity groups Bain Capital and The Blackstone Group to buy about 30 big-market stations from holding company Susquehanna Pfaltzgraff for about $1.2 billion.

Amid a rash of private equity media buyouts Dickey in 2007 formed an investment group that included other family members and executives as well as backing from Merrill Lynch to take the company private for more than $500 million. The buyout effort which valued the entire company at $1.3 billion was shelved the following year however.

Cumulus Media acquired Citadel Broadcasting in late 2011.

EXECUTIVES

EVP Content and Programming, John W. Dickey, age 47, $875,000 total compensation

Chairman President and CEO, Lewis W. (Lew) Dickey, age 51, $1,450,000 total compensation

SVP Secretary and General Counsel, Richard S. Denning, age 47, $500,000 total compensation

SVP CFO and Treasurer, Joseph P. (J.P.) Hannan, age 42, $550,000 total compensation

VP Sales Operations & Digital Media, Bill Hansen

SVP Affiliate Sales Broadcast Ops, Dennis Green

SVP Programming, Mike McVay

CIO, Alfred Lutter

President Westwood One, Steve Shaw

Vice President Finance, David McKeever

Vice President Social Commerce, Daniel Caplin

Vice President Finance, Eric Richards

Vice President Information Systems, Jason Hutchinson

National Account Manager, Jim Devine

Chairman President and CEO, Lewis W. (Lew) Dickey, age 51

SVP Secretary and General Counsel, Richard S. Denning, age 47

SVP CFO and Treasurer, Joseph P. (J.P.) Hannan, age 42

Auditors: PricewaterhouseCoopers LLP

LOCATIONS

HQ: Cumulus Media Inc.
3280 Peachtree Road, N.W., Suite 2300, Atlanta, GA 30305
Phone: 404 949-0700
Web: www.cumulus.com

COMPETITORS

CBS Radio	Liberman Broadcasting
Clear Channel	Morris Communications
Cox Radio	Radio One Inc.
Emmis Communications	SIRIUS XM
Entercom	Salem Communications
GAP Broadcasting	

HISTORICAL FINANCIALS

Company Type: Public

Income Statement

FYE: December 31

	REVENUE ($ mil.)	NET INCOME ($ mil.)	NET PROFIT MARGIN	EMPLOYEES
12/13	1,026.1	176.0	17.2%	6,002
12/12	1,076.5	(32.7)	—	6,483
12/11	549.5	63.8	11.6%	6,323
12/10	263.3	29.4	11.2%	2,318
12/09	256.0	(126.7)	—	2,255
Annual Growth	41.5%	—	—	27.7%

2013 Year-End Financials

Debt ratio: 67.8%
Return on equity: 42.3%
Cash ($ mil.): 32
Current ratio: 2.41
Long-term debt ($ mil.): 2,620

No. of shares (mil.): 214
Dividends
  Yield: —
  Payout: —
Market value ($ mil.): 1,656

	STOCK PRICE ($) FY Close	P/E High/Low		PER SHARE ($) Earnings	Dividends	Book Value
12/13	7.73	10	3	0.75	0.00	2.39
12/12	2.67	—	—	(0.33)	0.00	1.82
12/11	3.34	11	5	0.46	0.00	2.69
12/10	4.31	8	3	0.69	0.00	(8.13)
12/09	2.28	—	—	(3.13)	0.00	(8.95)
Annual Growth	35.7%	—	—	—	—	—

CVR Partners LP

Farmers dreaming of fertile fields can turn to CVR Partners. The company makes nitrogen fertilizers. From its fertilizer manufacturing facility in Kansas CVR Partners produces ammonia and urea ammonia nitrate (UAN). The company sells ammonia to agricultural and industrial customers such as Brandt Consolidated Interchem and National Cooperative Refinery Association and provides UAN products to retailers and distributors. To lower production costs CVR Partners uses petroleum coke instead of the more expensive natural gas. It obtains the majority of its petroleum coke from parent company CVR Energy which founded CVR Partners in 2007. CVR Partners went public in April 2011 raising $307 million.

EXECUTIVES

Evp And Fertilizer General Manager, Kevan A Vick, age 60
Vp Environmental Health And Safety, Christopher G Swanberg, age 57
Evp Bus Dev Cvr Gp Llc, Randal Maffett
Board Member, Frank M Muller, age 73
Auditors: KPMGLLP

LOCATIONS

HQ: CVR Partners LP
2277 Plaza Drive, Suite 500, Sugar Land, TX 77479
Phone: 281 207-3200

COMPETITORS

CF Industries
PCS Nitrogen
Rentech Nitrogen

HISTORICAL FINANCIALS

Company Type: Public

Income Statement

FYE: December 31

	REVENUE ($ mil.)	NET INCOME ($ mil.)	NET PROFIT MARGIN	EMPLOYEES
12/13	323.6	118.6	36.6%	133
12/12	302.3	112.2	37.1%	134
12/11	302.8	132.4	43.7%	124
12/10	180.4	33.3	18.5%	122
12/09	208.3	57.8	27.8%	0
Annual Growth	11.6%	19.6%	—	—

2013 Year-End Financials

Debt ratio: 21.0%
Return on equity: —
Cash ($ mil.): 85
Current ratio: 4.96
Long-term debt ($ mil.): 125
No. of shares (mil.): 73
Dividends
Yield: 10.6%
Payout: 120.3%
Market value ($ mil.): 1,203

	STOCK PRICE ($) FY Close	P/E High/Low	PER SHARE ($) Earnings	Dividends	Book Value
12/13	16.46	18 9	1.62	1.75	6.02
12/12	25.24	20 13	1.53	2.21	6.11
12/11	24.82	18 11	1.48	0.98	6.70
Annual Growth	(18.6%)	— —	4.6%	33.5%	(5.3%)

Cyberonics, Inc.

It may sound futuristic but Cyberonics is all about treating an age-old neurological disorder. The company is the maker of the first medical device to gain clearance by the FDA for treating epilepsy. Its Vagus Nerve Stimulation Therapy system (VNS Therapy) is a pacemaker-like device that is implanted under the collarbone with a lead that connects it to the vagus nerve in the neck. The device delivers intermittent signals to the brain to control epileptic seizures. Physicians can program the signals by computer and patients can start or stop signals with hand-held magnets. VNS Therapy is also used for treating depression that has been treatment-resistant. Cyberonics sells its systems worldwide.

Operations

The company's dependence on insurance reimbursement means that shifts in standard rates paid by the Centers for Medicaid & Medicare Services(CMS) which many other insurers follow have the potential to impact revenues in a positive or negative manner. At least that applies to the VNS Therapy system when it is used for treating epilepsy. Medicare has denied coverage for those seeking VNS Therapy for depression although some state Medicaid agencies cover it for depression as do a few private payers. Cyberonics has not given up obtaining more federal and private insurance coverage for VNS Therapy for depression and is engaged in further studies it hopes will convince Medicare and other third-party payers of its efficacy as a therapy for depression that is resistant to medication and other treatment efforts.

Geographic Reach

Cyberonics has facilities in Houston (manufacturing and corporate offices) and Austin Texas (warehousing and distribution) and administrative and sales offices in Europe China and Hong Kong. It is planning to build a second manufacturing plant in Costa Rica to provide for international markets. The plant is expected to be operational in fiscal year 2015.

The company has distribution agreements with distributors covering other parts of North and South America Asia and the Middle East. It market its products in more than 70 countries but the US accounts for 80% of revenue.

Sales and Marketing

Cyberonics employs a direct sales force in the US and in some European countries and it utilizes distributors elsewhere. Its marketing efforts target neurologists surgeons hospitals insurance companies and patients. The VNS Therapy system has been implanted in more than 89000 patients globally. The company relies on reimbursement from private and government insurance entities for more than three-fourths of its device sales; the Centers for Medicaid & Medicare (CMS) alone account for 25% of sales.

Financial Performance

Cyberonics has enjoyed increasing revenue for the past several years. In 2014 it rose from $254 to $282 an 11% increase due to higher unit sales and higher prices per unit; sales were up in the US and internationally. The revenue bump helped move net income up 18% from $46 million to $55 million with an assist from interest income. Cash from operations took a hit though due to increased accounts receivables balances; it fell 54% from $79 million to $54 million.

Strategy

As a result of its dependence on reimbursement for its financial health Cyberonics' strategic focus is on widening the use of its products through marketing research and technology enhancement efforts. The company also introduces next-generation versions of its VNS Therapy system. For example in 2011 its fifth-generation of VNS Therapy technology - the AspireHC generator (for use with the VNS Therapy system) - was approved and in fiscal 2012 the device was commercially launched. Each "next-generation" system is meant to incorporate greater functionality and ease of use. Improvements with the AspireHC version include longer battery life improved electronics and simplified programming features.

Other strategic initiatives for Cyberonics are increasing market penetration in the US and increasing international sales; sales outside the US grew to more than 20% of total product sales in 2013 with the largest markets being the UK France and Germany. The company also seeks opportunities for licensing its technology to third parties as an additional source of revenue.

EXECUTIVES

Vice President General Counsel, David S Wise
Vice President Sales And Marketing General Manager International, James Reinstein
SVP Finance and CFO, Gregory H. (Greg) Browne, age 62, $334,077 total compensation
President and CEO, Daniel J. (Dan) Moore, age 54, $613,654 total compensation
VP Clinical Quality and Regulatory, Bryan D. Olin, age 47
VP Emerging Therapies, Bruce H. KenKnight, age 53
SVP and COO, Rohan Hoare, $186,589 total compensation
Vp-business & Technology Dev, Burke T Barrett
Vice President Sales Business Development, Jeff Fostey
Vice President Finance, Pam Solomon
Vice President Of Client Engagements, Noel Wong
Vice President Manufacturing, Randy Simpson
Vice President Worldwide Operations, George Barby
Vice President Business Development, Sherrie Simpson
Chairman, Hugh M. Morrison, age 68
Auditors: KPMGLLP

LOCATIONS

HQ: Cyberonics, Inc.
100 Cyberonics Boulevard, Houston, TX 77058
Phone: 281 228-7200
Web: www.cyberonics.com

2014 Sales

	$ mil.	% of total
US	226.9	80
Other countries	55.1	20
Total	**282.0**	**100**

PRODUCTS/OPERATIONS

Selected VNS Therapy System Components

Equipment to assist with implant procedures
Equipment to assist treating physicians with setting the stimulation parameters for each patient
Implantable pulse generator (provides stimulation to the vagus nerve)
Lead (connects the generator to the vagus nerve)
Magnets (to manually suspend or induce stimulation on a temporary basi
Other
Instruction manuals

COMPETITORS

Brainsway	Pfizer
Cephalon	Sanofi
EnteroMedics	Shire
GlaxoSmithKline	St. Jude Medical
Meda Pharmaceuticals	Taro
Medtronic	Teva
Novartis	UCB

HISTORICAL FINANCIALS

Company Type: Public

Income Statement

FYE: April 25

	REVENUE ($ mil.)	NET INCOME ($ mil.)	NET PROFIT MARGIN	EMPLOYEES
04/14	282.0	54.8	19.5%	639
04/13	254.3	46.3	18.2%	581
04/12	218.5	36.0	16.5%	536
04/11	190.4	46.7	24.5%	484
04/10	167.7	78.4	46.8%	465
Annual Growth	13.9%	(8.5%)	—	8.3%

2014 Year-End Financials

Debt ratio: —	No. of shares (mil.): 26
Return on equity: 22.5%	Dividends
Cash ($ mil.): 103	Yield: —
Current ratio: 7.37	Payout: —
Long-term debt ($ mil.): —	Market value ($ mil.): 1,605

	STOCK PRICE ($) FY Close	P/E High/Low		PER SHARE ($) Earnings	Dividends	Book Value
04/14	60.02	36	21	2.00	0.00	9.69
04/13	42.99	33	22	1.66	0.00	8.36
04/12	38.58	30	18	1.28	0.00	6.66
04/11	35.59	21	10	1.64	0.00	6.20
04/10	19.53	8	4	2.67	0.00	4.00
Annual Growth	32.4%	—	—	(7.0%)	—	24.7%

Darling Ingredients Inc

A rather dainty name for a messy and stinky business Darling Ingredients (formerly Darling International) is the largest publicly traded rendering operation in the US; it collects and recycles animal by-products used cooking grease and bakery waste and offers grease-trap cleaning services. It counts restaurants butcher shops grocery stores and independent meat and poultry processors among its customers. Darling's rendering unit which accounts for most of its sales produces yellow grease tallow and meat bone and blood meal. The company sells its products nationwide and overseas to makers of soap rubber oils pet and livestock feed and chemicals.

Geographic Reach

Texas-based Darling Ingredients rings up more than 85% of its sales in the US. Export markets include Asia the European Union Mexico North Africa the Pacific Rim and South America. The company operates more than 120 processing and transfer facilities in 42 US states.

Operations

Darling operates two business segments: Rendering (more than 80% of sales) and Bakery which accounts for the rest. The company's rendering business processes animal by-products and used cooking oil into fats protein and hides. The Bak-

ery operation collects bakery residual and used cooking oil from poultry and meat processors commercial bakeries grocery stores butcher shops and food service establishments and provides grease trap cleaning services to many of the same establishments.

The company operates a fleet of trucks trailers and railcars for collection of its raw materials.

Financial Performance

Darling Ingredients' 2012 sales dipped 5% vs. 2011 while net income fell 23% over the same period. The sale decline followed a banner year in 2011 when sales rose to nearly $1.8 billion vs. about $723 million during 2010. The surge resulted from the 2010 acquisition of Griffin Industries the largest purchase in Darling's history. Darling attributed the sale dip in 2012 to a sales decline in its rendering segment. Price competition from rivals to Darling's BFT (bleachable fancy tallow) and PG (poultry grease) products depressed the company's pricing power. Results from the bakery segment were about flat. Sales in the US fell nearly 3% in 2012 vs. 2011 while foreign sales toppled 20%.

Darling's profits have suffered in recent years due to rising raw-material costs and high fuel prices. Raw material availability has declined too amid a weak economy coupled with a drop in US meat consumption that caused the company's suppliers to reduce slaughter volume. Restaurant grease volume dropped as well driven by fewer consumers choosing to dine out.

Strategy

For Darling competition comes mostly from obtaining its raw materials. Large meat-packing companies usually handle their own rendering in-house. As the meat industry has consolidated fewer independent meat and poultry processors are left from whom to collect scraps; however until the economic recession Darling had been seeing growth in its restaurant-services division even though collecting spent grease from restaurants is highly competitive. When it comes time to sell its commodity-grade products Darling competes with vegetable-oil producers as well as other rendering operations.

Mergers and Acquisitions

Nevertheless Darling has remained true to its growth through acquisition strategy. In 2012 it purchased RVO BioPur a provider of grease trap and used cooking oil collection services. RVO BioPur's customers are primarily restaurants and foodservice operators along the East coast. Although relatively small the acquisition followed Darling's buyout of fellow rendering company Griffin Industries. It picked up the Kentucky-based company in a deal valued at $840 million in late 2010. The purchase boosted the number of Darling's processing and transfer facilities to 120 adding Griffin's 55 locations that include a dozen rendering plants about 10 bakery by-product plants and a lone bio-diesel facility.

Prior to the Griffin buy Darling purchased the Indiana and Ohio operations of rival renderer Sanimax in 2010. The deal included a number of Sanimax collection routes in Pennsylvania and the lower part of Michigan. In mid-2010 the renderer purchased Nebraska By-Products extending its reach in Colorado Kansas Nebraska and South Dakota.

EXECUTIVES

Vp And Manager National Accounts Oil Collections Division, Bill Borrelli
EVP and CFO, John O. Muse, $500,000 total compensation

EVP General Counsel and Secretary, John F. Sterling, age 50, $335,000 total compensation
Chairman and CEO, Randall C. Stuewe, age 51, $850,000 total compensation
EVP and Co-COO Darling North America, Martin W. Griffin, $760,907 total compensation
COO, Dirk Kloosterboer
EVP Ecoson Rendac and Sonac, Jan van der Velden
EVP and Chief Strategy Officer, John Bullock, $309,000 total compensation
Vice President And President Asia Pacific, Shirley Elliott
Vice President Of Information Technology, Jim Hollenbaugh
Vice President Research And Technology, James Coalson
Vice President Of Marketing, Mitchell Kalinowski
Chairman and CEO, Randall C. Stuewe, age 51
Auditors: KPMGLLP

LOCATIONS

HQ: Darling Ingredients Inc
251 O' Connor Ridge Blvd., Suite 300, Irving, TX 75038
Phone: 972 717-0300   **Fax:** 972 717-1588
Web: www.darlingii.com

2012 Sales

	$ mil.	% of total
Domestic	1485.2	87
Foreign	216.2	13
Total	**1701.4**	**100**

PRODUCTS/OPERATIONS

2012 Sales

	$ mil.	% of total
Rendering	1406.0	83
Bakery	295.4	17
Total	**1701.4**	**100**

Selected Subsidiaries

Craig Protein Division Inc.
Darling Green Energy LLC
Darling National LLC
Griffin Industries LLC

COMPETITORS

ADM	Prosper De Mulder
Ag Processing Inc.	Restaurant
Baker Commodities	Technologies
Birchwood Meat &	Sanimax
Provision	Smithfield Foods
Maple Leaf Foods	Tyson Foods
North State Rendering	Valley Proteins
Company	

HISTORICAL FINANCIALS

Company Type: Public

Income Statement

FYE: December 28

	REVENUE ($ mil.)	NET INCOME ($ mil.)	NET PROFIT MARGIN	EMPLOYEES
12/13	1,723.5	108.9	6.3%	10,000
12/12	1,701.4	130.7	7.7%	3,400
12/11*	1,797.2	169.4	9.4%	3,320
01/11	724.9	44.2	6.1%	3,330
01/10	597.8	41.7	7.0%	1,820
Annual Growth	30.3%	27.1%	—	53.1%

*Fiscal year change

2013 Year-End Financials

Debt ratio: 27.3%	No. of shares (mil.): 164	
Return on equity: 7.0%	Dividends	
Cash ($ mil.): 870	Yield: —	
Current ratio: 6.38	Payout: —	
Long-term debt ($ mil.): 866	Market value ($ mil.): 3,412	

	STOCK PRICE ($) FY Close	P/E High/Low	PER SHARE ($) Earnings	Dividends	Book Value
12/13	20.77	26 17	0.91	0.00	12.30
12/12	15.54	17 12	1.11	0.00	9.02
12/11*	13.29	13 8	1.47	0.00	7.86
01/11	13.28	26 13	0.53	0.00	5.02
01/10	8.38	16 6	0.51	0.00	3.46
Annual Growth	25.5%	— —	15.6%	—	37.3%

*Fiscal year change

Datalink Corp

Datalink builds and implements high-end custom-designed data storage systems for large corporations. Its storage systems include disk- and tape-based storage devices storage networking components and data management software. The company employs an open-system standard building networks from products made by leading manufacturers such as Brocade EMC and Hitachi Data Systems. Datalink also provides ongoing support and maintenance services. The company markets its products directly to customers in the US. It has designed systems for clients including AT&T Harris Corporation NAVTEQ and St. Jude Medical. It has about 35 locations across the US.

Operations

Datalink breaks down its offering into four categories: datacenter virtualization which allows for shared resources; data protection and storage; network infrastructures; and business continuity and disaster recovery.

Geographic Reach

The company's 36 locations are spread across the US.

Sales and Marketing

Datalink sells it products through a number of suppliers including EMC Corporation Hitachi Data Systems Oracle Cisco and Dell.

Financial Performance

Revenue from products and services both rose in 2013 helping the company to a 17% improvement. Net income however dipped slightly due to increased costs of sales and operating expenses as well as costs related to the StraTech acquisition. Ups and downs in accounts receivable have lead to erratic movement in the company's cash flow. An increase in deferred customer support contracts lead to an upswing in cash flow for 2013.

Strategy

Going forward Datalink plans to improve its training process for new sales hires increase its geographic reach through acquisitions and offer a group of managed services to "free up" its customers IT teams.

HISTORY

Founded in 1963 as Stan Clothier Datalink was originally a manufacturers' representative for technology products and components. Its name change to Datalink in 1987 reflected the company's growing role as a distributor of data storage products. Datalink opened a Chicago office in 1989 and expanded beyond the Midwest in 1992 with an office in Seattle. Greg Meland formerly the company's VP of sales was named president and CEO in 1993.

In 1995 with the introduction of its DataCare program the company began to reposition itself as a provider of information management services rather than strictly a value-added distributor. Two years later Datalink began offering its consulting services to customers in the information management industry.

In 1998 Datalink initiated an IPO which it later withdrew. That year the company expanded throughout the US opening offices in Massachusetts New Jersey and California and adding five offices in the Southeast US with the acquisition of Georgia-based rival Direct Connect Systems. Datalink successfully went public in 1999. Its expansion continued in 2000 with additional offices opening in North Carolina and Oregon. In 2001 the company moved its headquarters from Edina Minnesota to Chanhassen a Minneapolis suburb.

Datalink raised more than $5 million in a 2002 private placement of stock with institutional investors buying the shares.

Charlie Westling previously the company's VP of market development was promoted to president and COO in 2003 (he joined Datalink in 2001) and was named CEO of the company in 2005; Meland was made chairman. Director Paul Lidsky took over as CEO in 2009.

Datalink expanded its operations by acquiring systems integrator Midrange Computer Solutions for $14 million in 2007. The purchase extended Datalink's operations in the northeastern and midwestern regions as well as in California.

EXECUTIVES

Chief Financial Officer; Vice President - Finance; Secretary, Gregory T. Barnum, age 60, $262,000 total compensation
President CEO and Director, Paul F. Lidsky, age 61, $375,000 total compensation
Chief Technology Officer, Scott D. Robinson, age 55
EVP of Field Operations, Shawn O'Grady, age 51, $289,000 total compensation
EVP of Field Operations, Shawn Grady
EVP of Field Operations, Shawn OGrady
Vice President Sales Regional Sales Dir, Bob Hebrink
Vice President Solutions Architecture, Phil Okonski
Vice President Technology, Christopher Feaver
Senior Vice President Michigan, Craig Armstrong
Vice President, Michael Schwartz
National Account Manager, Marion Mosley
Senior Vice President Business Dev, Chris Wilkes
Area Vice President, Stephen Lurie
Vp Finance, David Sharp
Vice President, Leonard Klemencic
Executive Vice President Co Founder, Gary Henderson
Senior Vice President Strategic, Barry Andersen
Vice President Sales, Kevin Powers
Vice President And General Manager, Rino Petricola
Senior Vice President Business, Darrell Royal
Vice President, Roman Alexander
Vice President Business Development, Geoff Jordan
Senior Vice President, Philippe Monrougie
Vice President Operations Front Porch, Bob Young
Senior Vice President Operations, Mike Parsons
Vice President Of Marketing, Boyd Clarke

Vice President Of Operations, Larry Knipple
Vice President Operations And Admin, Michael Graham
Vice President, Dick Domann
Vice President Services And Engineering, Jay Holt
Vice President Technical Services, Todd Sylvester
Vice President International Sales, Gracia Erazo
Vice President Marketing, Joe Robinson
Senior Vice President Of Marketing, Suzanne Gallagher
Vice President Sales And Marketing, Stephen Lacy
Vice President Sales, Jim Presley
Senior Vice President Corporate, Matt Richman
Vice President Operations, Mike Coar
Vice President Sales, Mike Degyansky
Senior Vice President Enterprise Sales, Tracy Hawkey
Excecutive Vice President, Misty Skinner
Vice President Sales Americas Front, Glen Green
Vice President Operations, Mary Stewart
Vice President Sales And Marketing, Tony Copeland
Vice President Of Business Development, Mitch Lemons
Vice President Of Finance, Terri Marine
Senior Vice President Strategic, John Dardick
Vice President Consulting Vp, Gregory Laird
Chairman, Greg R. Meland, age 61
Vice Chairman, James E. (Jim) Ousley, age 69
Treasurer, Valerie Whewell
Treasurer, Harry Radcliffe
Secretary, Nick Santoro
Auditors: McGladreyLLP

LOCATIONS

HQ: Datalink Corp
10050 Crosstown Circle, Suite 500, Eden Prairie, MN 55344
Phone: 952 944-3462

PRODUCTS/OPERATIONS

2013 Sales

	$ mil.	% of total
Products	373.0	63
Services	221.2	37
Total	**594.2**	**100**

Selected Services

Advanced Services
Architecture & Deployment
Capacity Services
Cloud Enablement Services
Cloud Service Management
Data Center Transformation
Managed Services
Reporting & Management
Residency Services
Support Services

COMPETITORS

Cisco Systems	InterVision Systems
Cranel	Technologies
Dell	NetApp
Dot Hill	Presidio Inc.
EMC	Qualstar
Forsythe Technology	Sirius Computer
Fujitsu	Solutions
Hewlett-Packard	Symantec
Hitachi Data Systems	VMware
IBM	

HISTORICAL FINANCIALS

Company Type: Public

Income Statement

FYE: December 31

	REVENUE ($ mil.)	NET INCOME ($ mil.)	NET PROFIT MARGIN	EMPLOYEES
12/13	594.1	10.0	1.7%	510
12/12	491.2	10.5	2.1%	459
12/11	380.0	9.8	2.6%	389
12/10	293.6	2.3	0.8%	299
12/09	178.0	(0.5)	—	307
Annual Growth	35.2%	—	—	13.5%

2013 Year-End Financials

Debt ratio: 4.6%
Return on equity: 8.3%
Cash ($ mil.): 76
Current ratio: 1.40
Long-term debt ($ mil.): —

No. of shares (mil.): 22
Dividends
Yield: —
Payout: —
Market value ($ mil.): 248

	STOCK PRICE ($) FY Close	P/E High/Low	PER SHARE ($) Earnings	Dividends	Book Value
12/13	10.90	27 16	0.52	0.00	6.40
12/12	8.55	18 12	0.60	0.00	5.09
12/11	8.26	17 7	0.61	0.00	4.48
12/10	4.67	27 16	0.18	0.00	3.50
12/09	4.33	— —	(0.04)	0.00	3.27
Annual Growth	26.0%	— —	—	—	18.2%

Dealertrack Technologies, Inc.

DealerTrack keeps auto dealers lenders OEMs and car buyers on track with its Web-based software and services. Using a Software-as-a-Service (SaaS) model the company offers a suite of dealer management system (DMS) vehicle inventory management and merchandising sales and financing compliance and processing (including e-registration and titling application) tools that provide real-time on-demand data for auto dealers to operate more efficiently and cost effectively. DealerTrack also operates the largest online credit application network in the US and Canada.

Operations

DealerTrack makes roughly the same amount of money through transaction services (23%) subscription services (25%) and other products and services (23%). The company operates through a number of subsidiaries including DealerTrack AAX DealerTrack Aftermarket Services DealerTrack Canada DealerTrack Digital Services and DealerTrack Processing Solutions.

Geographic Reach

DealerTrack operates in the US and Canada. About 91% of its revenue comes from the US. It is expanding outside of North America with its acquisition of Germany-based incadea.

Sales & Marketing

DealerTrack primarily sells to franchised and independent auto dealers through subscription agreements. It had about 18500 subscribing dealers in 2013 up from 17600 in 2012. The company also sells to lenders including national and regional

lenders local banks and credit unions. It had more than 1400 active lender customers. Other client pools include aftermarket providers OEMs and other service and information providers.

Financial Analysis

DealerTrack's revenue sped higher in 2013 reaching a record $481 million from about $389 million in 2012. Transaction revenue increased 23% from 2012 driven by greater auto sales more applications and better credit availability. The acquisitions of Casey & Casey and Vintek during the year also contributed. Subscription revenue also rose boosted by acquisitions made in 2012 and 2013.

The company set no net income records in 2013 with profit tumbling to about $5. 9 million from $20 million in 2012. Higher costs for product development and corporate expenses ate into the net profit. DealerTrack reported greater operating cash flow in 2013. It was about $82 million compared to about $70 million in 2012.

Strategy

With its Project Fusion DealerTrack is integrating its products including those from acquisitions into a common platform. The move will help auto dealers plug the company's products and services into their workflows.

Adding a first mobile product DealerTrack introduced eMenu for the iPad. It is to allow car buyers to move on their own to obtain financing and insurance. In 2014 the company was to launch a mobile version of its dealer management system.

Mergers and Acquisitions

A big part of DealerTrack's strategy is to acquire companies whose products fill out its offerings. Late in 2014 the company stepped into the international market with a $190 million offer to acquire incadea a Germany-based provider of dealer management software and services to the global automotive retail market. The acquisition would give DealerTrack a much bigger market. Incadea's customers include BMW Toyota Volkswagen Peugeot/Citro ën Ford Bosch Scania and Mercedes-Benz.

Earlier in 2014 the company finalized its acquisition of Dealer.com a provider of automotive marketing and operations software and services. The stock and cash ($620 million) deal enables DealerTrack to offer a more comprehensive range of services and products.

Other acquisitions include: Casey & Casey which expanded DealerTrack's registration titling and electronic lien businesses in Louisiana; Customer Focused Marketing which bring customer relations management services; Vintek which adds to DealerTrack's automotive collateral management electronic lien and title (ELT) and consumer automotive finance processing services; and Nexteppe Business Solutions expands the commpany's offering for dealer websites.

EXECUTIVES

Vice President For Marketing And Digital Services, Mark Brown

Chairman and CEO, Mark F. O'Neil, age 55, $591,667 total compensation

EVP CFO and Chief Administrative Officer, Eric D. Jacobs, age 48, $322,250 total compensation

Co-President, Rajesh (Raj) Sundaram, age 48, $322,500 total compensation

EVP Technology and Service Solutions; CIO, Richard McLeer, age 50, $315,000 total compensation

EVP Lender Solutions, Mark Furcolo, $265,167 total compensation

Co-President, Rick Gibbs

SVP Corporate Strategy Business Development and OEM Relations, Amit Maheshwari

Senior Vice President Chief Information Officer, Charles Giglia

Senior Vice President Customer Development, Rick Pusch

Executive Vice President, Barry Zwarenstein

Vice President Corporate Strategy, Chester Han

Executive Assistant To Sr Vp, Karen D'Andrea

Vice President Information Technology Architecture, Greg Bauer

Senior Vice President Information Technology, Patricia Young

Vice President Operations, Lisa Oelsner

Vice President Sales Strategy And Operations, Jane Dalzell

Chairman and CEO, Mark F. O'Neil, age 55

Auditors: PricewaterhouseCoopersLLP

LOCATIONS

HQ: Dealertrack Technologies, Inc.
1111 Marcus Avenue, Suite M04, Lake Success, NY 11042
Phone: 516 734-3600
Web: www.dealertrack.com

2011 Sales

	% of total
US	91
Canada	9
Total	100

PRODUCTS/OPERATIONS

2013 Sales

	$ mil.	% of total
Transaction services	276.9	57
Subscription services	181.7	38
Other	22.9	5
Total	481.5	100

COMPETITORS

ADP	Experian
American Honda Finance	Microsoft Dynamics
Arkona	Reynolds and Reynolds
AutoSoft	RouteOne
Compli	TransUnion
Equifax	

HISTORICAL FINANCIALS

Company Type: Public

Income Statement

FYE: December 31

	REVENUE ($ mil.)	NET INCOME ($ mil.)	NET PROFIT MARGIN	EMPLOYEES
12/13	481.5	5.8	1.2%	2,500
12/12	388.8	20.4	5.3%	2,000
12/11	353.2	65.1	18.4%	1,900
12/10	243.8	(27.8)	—	1,200
12/09	225.6	(4.3)	—	1,200
Annual Growth	20.9%	—	—	20.1%

2013 Year-End Financials

Debt ratio: 18.0%
Return on equity: 1.0%
Cash ($ mil.): 122
Current ratio: 2.37
Long-term debt ($ mil.): 172

No. of shares (mil.): 44
Dividends
Yield: —
Payout: —
Market value ($ mil.): 2,115

STOCK PRICE ($)		P/E		PER SHARE ($)		
	FY Close	High/Low		Earnings	Dividends	Book Value
12/13	48.08	344	190	0.13	0.00	13.67
12/12	28.72	66	50	0.46	0.00	13.33
12/11	27.26	18	9	1.53	0.00	11.82
12/10	20.07	—	—	(0.69)	0.00	10.05
12/09	18.79	—	—	(0.11)	0.00	10.41
Annual Growth	26.5%	—	—	—	—	7.0%

Deltic Timber Corp.

Money doesn't grow on trees? Deltic Timber might beg to differ. The company annually grows and harvests some 605000 tons of timber from the more than 450000 acres of timberland that it owns primarily in Arkansas and northern Louisiana. The company's two sawmills convert the timber (mainly Southern Pine) into softwood lumber products; this is then sold to wholesale distributors lumber treaters and truss manufacturers for use in residential construction to make roof trusses laminated beams and decking. In addition to its timber and lumber businesses Deltic Timber develops real estate in central Arkansas and manufactures medium density fiberboard (MDF) through Del-Tin Fiber.

Operations

Arkansas-based Deltic Timber operates sawmills in Ola and Waldo Arkansas and is engaged in real estate development in Little Rock and Hot Springs. Mills account for nearly 80% of the company's revenue with woodlands and real estate contributing 16% and 5% respectively. The company's Woodlands business is engaged in the harvesting and sale of timber and timberland sales and acquisitions. In addition to its core pine timberlands Deltic owns some 6700 acres of hardwood forest which is sold to manufacturers of railroad ties flooring and pallets. This business segment also earns income from hunting licenses and mineral lease rentals and royalties.

Deltic's Mills segment processes logs into lumber for a variety of lumber products and for a few third parties. Sawmill residuals such as chips shavings and sawdust are used primarily by Del-Tin Fiber. Den-Tin comprises a MDF manufacturing plant in Arkansas one of the largest of its kind in the world. MDF is most often used in the furniture and flooring industries.

Deltic's real estate business consists of three development areas: the Chenal Valley development (a 4900-acre upscale master-planned community in Little Rock Arkansas that includes two championship golf courses designed by Robert Trent Jones Jr.); Chenal Downs (a 400-acre development near Chenal Valley with an equestrian center); and Red Oak Ridge in Hot Springs which features estate-sized homes and garden houses as well as two Deltic-built lakes and a community park.

Financial Performance

Deltic Timber reported revenue of $200 million in 2013 up 42% versus 2012. Net income rose 183% over the same period to $26.2 million. Since a steep decline in revenue and profits in 2011 the company has had two strong years of rising sales profits and cash flow. Increased housing starts and repair and remodeling projects has increased demand for Deltic's lumber as the economy recovers and gains momentum. Rising real estate prices are also benefiting the company's real estate development arm.

Strategy

Vertically-integrated Deltic uses much of its own timber in its own sawmills and MDF facilities.

Mergers and Acquisitions

In April 2013 Deltic purchased the remaining 50% interest in Del-Tin Fiber from its joint venture partner International Paper for $20 million in cash and debt.

HISTORY

A longtime subsidiary of Murphy Oil Corporation Deltic Timber's roots reach back to 1907 when C. H. Murphy Sr. first bought investment land. A great deal of acreage was added in the 1920s and again in 1957 when Murphy acquired 85000 acres through a public land trade. The company started mill operations in the 1970s; to fuel growth in this area Murphy bought 138000 more acres between 1976 and 1984. The company's move into real estate began in 1989 with the sale of residential lots in the Chenal Valley west of Little Rock.

To concentrate on its core oil and gas exploration business Murphy Oil bundled its real estate timber and agricultural operations in 1996 and spun them off as Deltic Timber. That year Deltic Timber ventured into commercial real estate. In 1997 the company pushed for expansion in key markets by increasing its acreage harvest levels mill capacity and real-estate development operations.

In 1998 Deltic Timber's 50%-owned Del-Tin Fiber began producing medium-density fiberboard. (Temple-Inland Forest Products owns the remaining 50% of the joint venture.) The company stopped raising cotton and wheat in favor of corn and soybeans. Considering itself primarily a timberland company Deltic Timber bought an additional 30000 acres of forest in southern Arkansas.

Deltic Timber completed a $10.4 million stock buyback plan in 1999 believing that the worth of its holdings was not properly reflected in its stock price. The following year the company exited its agricultural operations selling most of its farmland in Arkansas and Louisiana that year and completing the sale of its remaining Louisiana farmland by the end of 2001. The company used the proceeds to buy approximately 37000 acres of southern pine timberland.

Deltic Timber recorded a non-cash write-off (of about $19 million pretax) on its Del-Tin Fiber investment during 2002. Also that year Deltic Timber sold about 3420 acres of non-strategic timberland and higher- and better-use lands. In 2003 the company closed on the purchase of almost 6700 acres of timberland.

EXECUTIVES

President and CEO, Ray C. Dillon, age 58, $515,000 total compensation
Vice President Treasurer Chief Financial Officer, Kenneth D. Mann, age 54, $240,000 total compensation
Vice President Operations, Kent L Streeter, age 54
Vice President, Cless Vaughn
Vice President Of Operations, Zachary Streeter
Vice President, W Rowe
Board Member, Christoph Keller, age 60
Chairman, Robert C. Nolan, age 72
Vice President Treasurer Chief Financial Officer, Kenneth D. Mann, age 54

Vice President General Counsel Secretary, Jim F Andrews, age 51
Board Of Directors, Randolph C (Randy) Coley, age 68
Auditors: KPMGLLP

LOCATIONS

HQ: Deltic Timber Corp.
210 East Elm Street, P.O. Box 7200, El Dorado, AR 71731-7200
Phone: 870 881-9400
Web: www.deltic.com

PRODUCTS/OPERATIONS

2013 Sales

	$ mil.	% of total
Mills	168.0	79
Woodlands	33.8	16
Real estate	11.7	5
Adjustments	(13.8)	-
Total	**199.7**	**100**

Selected Products

Hunting land leases
Oil and gas lease rentals and royalties
Real estate
Residual wood products
Softwood lumber products
Timber
Timberland

COMPETITORS

Acadian Timber Corp	Pope Resources
Anthony Forest	Potlatch
Products	Rayonier
Canfor	Tembec
CatchMark	West Fraser Timber
Georgia-Pacific	Western Forest
International Paper	Products
Louisiana-Pacific	Weyerhaeuser
Plum Creek Timber	

HISTORICAL FINANCIALS

Company Type: Public

Income Statement — FYE: December 31

	REVENUE ($ mil.)	NET INCOME ($ mil.)	NET PROFIT MARGIN	EMPLOYEES
12/13	199.7	26.1	13.1%	537
12/12	140.9	9.2	6.6%	438
12/11	121.8	2.6	2.2%	438
12/10	141.6	12.4	8.8%	454
12/09	112.0	3.6	3.3%	464
Annual Growth	15.6%	63.2%	—	3.7%

2013 Year-End Financials

Debt ratio: 21.8%	No. of shares (mil.): 12
Return on equity: 10.5%	Dividends
Cash ($ mil.): 4	Yield: 0.5%
Current ratio: 1.25	Payout: 19.4%
Long-term debt ($ mil.): 90	Market value ($ mil.): 861

	STOCK PRICE ($)	P/E		PER SHARE ($)		
	FY Close	High/Low		Earnings	Dividends	Book Value
12/13	67.94	36	28	2.05	0.40	21.00
12/12	70.62	98	74	0.73	0.30	18.33
12/11	60.39	350	232	0.21	0.30	18.02
12/10	56.34	62	39	0.99	0.30	18.39
12/09	46.18	173	93	0.30	0.30	17.37
Annual Growth	10.1%	—	—	61.7%	7.5%	4.9%

DepoMed, Inc.

For comedians and Depomed it's all about the delivery. The drug company makes proprietary drug therapies using its patented delivery technology AcuForm an extended-release technology that stretches out the time a pill stays in the stomach thus reducing the number of necessary doses and potential side effects. Depomed's internal development efforts have yielded three FDA-approved and marketed products: Gralise to treat nerve pain; Glumetza an extended-release formulation of common diabetes drug metformin; and ProQuin XR an extended-release version of antibiotic ciprofloxacin used to treat urinary tract infections.

Gralise (gabapentin) was approved by the FDA for postherpetic nerve pain (such as that caused by shingles) in 2011. Depomed launched the medication later that year and has since been focused on increasing commercialization efforts for the drug which it hopes will bring increased revenues in future years. Concurrent with its FDA approval the company received a $48 million milestone payment with (now-former) development partner Abbott Laboratories. Later that year the company ended its licensing agreement with Abbott regaining full rights to Gralise and gaining a $40 million settlement payment from Abbott in the process.

To complement sales efforts on Gralise in 2012 Depomed acquired another pain medication Zipsor which is used for mild to moderate acute pain. The drug was purchased from Xanodyne Pharmaceuticals for some $26 million plus potential future milestone payments. Zipsor will be marketed by the company's direct sales force which targets its marketing efforts towards pain specialists neurologists and primary care physicians.

Depomed's other commercialized products are primarily licensed out to third parties; for instance Valeant Pharmaceuticals markets Glumetza in Canada. Santarus co-promoted Glumetza in the US with Depomed until 2011 when Depomed sold Santarus full rights to market the drug. Depomed also no longer manufactures or markets Proquin XR due to declining demand and has exited its licensing agreements for the drug.

In addition to its marketed products Depomed has several drug candidates in clinical development including Serada another variation on gabapentin in late-stage clinical trials as a treatment for menopausal hot flashes. Other products in development include a drug to treat Parkinson's disease.

Depomed's internal development activities focus on creating new formulations of off-patent drugs (such as metformin) that could benefit from AcuForm's extended-release delivery. It also forms licensing and development partnerships for its product candidates once they have been formulated and are in clinical development; some companies also license Depomed's Acuform technology. Partnering pharmaceutical companies have included Boehringer Ingelheim Covidien Janssen Pharmaceutical and Merck.

Contract manufacturer Patheon actually makes the company's marketed product Gralise. Depomed's manufacturing capacity is limited to making supplies for its clinical trials. The company also outsources its US sales organization for Gralise to Ventiv Commercial Services.

Due to the commercialization of Gralise and the milestone and settlement payments from Abbott Depomed's revenues jumped 65% to some $133 million in 2011. It also reported a profit in both 2011 and 2010 due to collaboration and milestone fees; however the firm doesn't expect to remain profitable in the following years as its commercialization costs rise. Such fluctuation in revenues and net income levels is typical for development-stage pharmaceutical companies.

EXECUTIVES

Senior Vice President General Counsel, Matthew M Gosling, age 44
President and CEO, James A. Schoeneck, $567,000 total compensation
VP Research and Development; Chief Medical Officer, Michael M. Sweeney, $363,989 total compensation
SVP and CFO, August J. Moretti, $353,521 total compensation
VP Pharmaceutical Development, Gerd Kochendoerfer
Vice President Managed Markets And Trade, Cindy Atha
Vice President Of Business Development, David Wibbelsmann
Chairman, Peter D. Staple, age 62
Auditors: Ernst&YoungLLP

LOCATIONS

HQ: DepoMed, Inc.
7999 Gateway Boulevard, Suite 300, Newark, CA 94560
Phone: 510 744-8000

PRODUCTS/OPERATIONS

2011 Sales

	$ mil.	% of total
License & collaborative revenue		
Gralise (Abbott)	60.6	45
Boehringer Ingelheim	10.9	8
Other license & collaborative revenue	10.3	8
Product sales		
Glumetza	40.7	31
Gralise	0.5	—
Royalties	10.0	8
Total	**133.0**	**100**

COMPETITORS

Actavis	Pfizer
Bionovo	Ranbaxy Laboratories
Bristol-Myers Squibb	SkyePharma
Flamel Technologies	Takeda Pharmaceutical
GlaxoSmithKline	Teva
Johnson & Johnson	Valeant
Merck	Pharmaceuticals
Mylan Pharmaceuticals	

HISTORICAL FINANCIALS

Company Type: Public

Income Statement

FYE: December 31

	REVENUE ($ mil.)	NET INCOME ($ mil.)	NET PROFIT MARGIN	EMPLOYEES
12/13	134.2	43.3	32.3%	308
12/12	90.8	(29.7)	—	267
12/11	132.9	70.7	53.2%	110
12/10	80.7	3.9	4.8%	69
12/09	57.7	(22.0)	—	73
Annual Growth	**23.5%**	**—**	**—**	**43.3%**

2013 Year-End Financials

Debt ratio: —	No. of shares (mil.): 57
Return on equity: —	Dividends
Cash ($ mil.): 244	Yield: —
Current ratio: 2.15	Payout: —
Long-term debt ($ mil.): —	Market value ($ mil.): 607

STOCK PRICE ($) FY Close	P/E High/Low		Earnings	PER SHARE ($) Dividends	Book Value
12/13	10.58	14 7	0.75	0.00	2.40
12/12	6.19	— —	(0.53)	0.00	1.49
12/11	5.18	8 3	1.26	0.00	1.91
12/10	6.36	94 34	0.07	0.00	0.44
12/09	3.35	— —	(0.43)	0.00	0.30
Annual Growth	**33.3%**	**— —**	**—**	**—**	**67.9%**

Diamond Hill Investment Group Inc.

Diamond Hill Investment Group takes a shine to investment management. Operating through flagship subsidiary Diamond Hill Capital Management the firm oversees some $11.5 billion in assets most of it invested in mutual funds. Serving institutional and individual clients the company administers several mutual funds and sells them mainly through independent investment advisers brokerdealers financial planners investment consultants and third-party marketing firms. The firm hews to a value-based investment philosophy and takes a long-term perspective to investing. Formed in 1990 Diamond Hill Investment Group also manages separate accounts and hedge funds.

Operations

Diamond Hill Investment Group operates through its subsidiaries: Diamond Hill Capital Management; and Beacon Hill Fund Services and BHIL Distributors collectively known as Beacon Hill. Beacon Hill provides fund administration and statutory underwriting services to various clients including Diamond Hill Funds.

Financial Performance

Diamond Hill Investment Group's revenue rose 4% in 2012 versus 2011 to $66.6 million. The increase was due to a 13% rise in fees from mutual fund administration while investment advisory fees rose a more modest 3%. Net income rose 18% over the same period to $16.9 million. Assets under management at the end of 2012 exceeded $9.4 billion an increase of nearly 9% over the prior year. The firm's revenue and profits have increased steadily since 2008 after taking a hit during the financial crisis as investors retreated from the market.

EXECUTIVES

President and CEO; Director, Roderick H. (Ric) Dillon, age 57, $360,000 total compensation
Chief Financial Officer and President of Diamond Hill Funds; Director, James F. (Jim) Laird, age 57, $200,000 total compensation
Co-Chief Investment Officer, Christopher A. (Chris) Welch
Managing Director - Investments, Chuck Bath
Co-Chief Investment Officer, Christopher (Chris) Bingaman
President and CEO; Director, Roderick H. (Ric) Dillon, age 57
Chief Financial Officer and President of Diamond Hill Funds; Director, James F. (Jim) Laird, age 57
Auditors: Plante&MoranPLLC

HQ: Diamond Hill Investment Group Inc.
325 John H. McConnell Blvd., Suite 200, Columbus, OH 43215
Phone: 614 255-3333
Web: www.diamond-hill.com

PRODUCTS/OPERATIONS

2012 Sales

	$ mil.	% of total
Investment advisory	57.8	87
Mutual fund administration	8.8	13
Total	**66.6**	**100**

Selected Products

Diamond Hill Small Cap Fund
Diamond Hill Small-Mid Cap Fund
Diamond Hill Large Cap Fund
Diamond Hill Select Fund Fund
Diamond Hill Long-Short Fund
Diamond Hill Strategic Income Fund

COMPETITORS

AllianceBernstein	GAMCO Investors
American Century	Janus Capital
Calamos Asset	Legg Mason
Management	MFS
Cohen & Steers	Putnam
Columbia Management	Pzena Investment
Davis Advisers	Management
Duncan-Hurst	Raymond James
Eaton Vance	Financial
Edelman Financial	SEI Investments
Edward Jones	T. Rowe Price
Epoch	The Vanguard Group
FMR	Waddell & Reed
Franklin Templeton	Westwood Holdings

HISTORICAL FINANCIALS

Company Type: Public

Income Statement

FYE: December 31

	REVENUE ($ mil.)	NET INCOME ($ mil.)	NET PROFIT MARGIN	EMPLOYEES
12/13	81.4	22.1	27.2%	98
12/12	66.6	16.9	25.4%	79
12/11	63.8	14.3	22.5%	73
12/10	56.7	12.4	21.9%	77
12/09	43.5	11.3	26.1%	66
Annual Growth	**16.9%**	**18.1%**	**—**	**10.4%**

2013 Year-End Financials

Debt ratio: —	No. of shares (mil.): 3
Return on equity: 66.4%	Dividends
Cash ($ mil.): 33	Yield: 2.5%
Current ratio: 1.52	Payout: 47.4%
Long-term debt ($ mil.): —	Market value ($ mil.): 385

	STOCK PRICE ($) FY Close	P/E High/Low	Earnings	PER SHARE ($) Dividends	Book Value
12/13	118.34	18 10	6.94	3.00	13.80
12/12	67.86	15 12	5.44	8.00	6.86
12/11	73.98	17 14	4.86	5.00	6.03
12/10	72.34	19 11	4.48	13.00	2.68
12/09	64.23	16 7	4.40	10.00	8.58
Annual Growth	**16.5%**	—	**12.1%**	**(26.0%)**	**12.6%**

Dice Holdings Inc

Dice Holdings doesn't think recruiting and hiring or job-seeking should be left to a roll of the dice - unless that means using the company's websites devoted to employee recruiting and career development. Through its flagship website Dice.com it provides job postings and career-related resources for technology professionals. Dice also operates ClearanceJobs.com for people with US government security clearances; eFinancialCareers.com aimed at financial workers; AllHealthcareJobs.com targeting health care workers; and WorldwideWorker.com and Rigzone.com for professionals in the energy sector. It also puts on job fairs. Most of the company's revenue comes from employers who pay to post job listings and view resumes.

Operations

Dice slices its business into six categories five of which are the industries for which Dice has job listings. Listings for jobs in technology and workers with security clearances accounts for 61% of the company's revenue. The next biggest are financial listings 16% and energy 11%. The other segments are healthcare and hospitality. The corporate segment includes Dice's media properties such as Slashdot.com SourceForge.net and Freecode.com technology news sites supported by advertising.

Geographic Reach

About 80% of Dice's revenue comes from the US but it has customers around the world. Besides nine offices in the US and Canada it has offices in Singapore Germany the Netherlands Dubai Australia China and the UK. The company's IT Job Board provides listings for the UK Germany Belgium and the Netherlands for technology jobs as well as news for IT decision makers. The eFinancialCareers website operates in three languages in 19 markets including the UK Asia Continental Europe North America Australia and the Middle East.

Sales and Marketing

Dice has more than 15000 customers ranging from small businesses to some of the biggest firms in technology finance and energy. Customers include Amazon IBM JP Morgan Chase UBS Saudi Aramco Shell and British Petroleum. Dice markets to job seekers via targeted ads on websites. Its field sales staff approaches companies seeking workers.

Financial Performance

Dice rolled to its fourth straight year of revenue growth hitting $213 million in 2013 up from $195 million in 2012. Acquisitions fueled some of the revenue growth including $3.2 million from the European-focused The IT Job Board acquired in mid-2013. Revenue for the finance segment declined 9% affected by slower hiring at European institutions in the face of a debt crisis and UK recession. Smaller segments such as energy and healthcare had robust growth.

Despite the 9% rise in revenue the company's net income dropped 57% to $16 million in 2013 from $38 million in 2012. While acquisitions helped raise revenue they also raised the cost of gaining revenue in the technology and healthcare segments. Technology also spent $1.4 million toward an integrated enterprise platform which included software personnel and consulting services. Cash flow has declined for three straight years dropping to $49 million in 2013. It stood at about $55 million in 2012 and $64 million in 2011. The decrease was blamed on a slowdown in sales and timing in payments from customers and tax payments.

Mergers and Acquisitions

Dice's longtime strategy is to buy or create job sites that extend its reach in sectors where there is a scarcity of qualified professionals and expand into new ones. In 2014 Dice acquired oilcareers.com a job site for oil and gas professionals in Europe for $26 million. In the past two years Dice has acquired The IT Job Board onTargetjobs and FINS.com (now eFinancialCareers.com). To counter the effects of the sluggish economy the company's growth strategy includes developing career websites tailored for new industry niches. For example Dice Holdings is active in the burgeoning health care industry job search market through its AllHealthcareJobs.com website which attracts around 300000 visitors and has about 14000 job postings. The 2012 acquisition of the online media business of Geeknet a provider of Web content for open source software developers and other technology enthusiasts rolled sites such as Slashdot SourceForge and Freecode into Dice. The company bets that it can push traffic from these popular sites (which each attract about 1 million unique viewers per month) to its related career sites.

EXECUTIVES

President and CEO Director, Michael P. Durney, age 52, $432,923 total compensation
President Dice.com, Shravan Goli, $318,462 total compensation
Managing Director The IT Job Board, Alex Farrell
Global Managing Director eFinancialCareers, James E. Bennett, $275,808 total compensation
Co-Founder and Managing Director ClearanceJobs, Evan Lesser
SVP Technology, Klavs Miller
President Rigzone, Bob Melk
Managing Director OilCareers, Mark Guest
Managing Director BioSpace, Josh Goodwin
Founder and Managing Director HEALTHeCAREERS, Bryan Bassett
Managing Director Hcareers, Jim Finn
Managing Director SourceForge and Slashdot.org, Gaurav Kuchhal
VP Finance, Greg Schippers
Chairman, Peter Ezersky, age 54
Auditors: Deloitte&ToucheLLP

LOCATIONS

HQ: Dice Holdings Inc
1040 Avenue of the Americas, 8th Floor, New York, NY 10018
Phone: 212 725-6550
Web: www.diceholdingsinc.com

2010 Sales

	$ mil.	% of total
US	99.0	77
Other	30.0	23
Total	**129.0**	**100**

PRODUCTS/OPERATIONS

2013 Sales

	$ mil.	% of total
Tech & Clearance	131.9	61.8
Finance	34.9	16.4
Energy	23.5	11
HealthcareHospitalityOther	5.61.416.1	2.607.5
Total	**213.4**	**100**

Selected Operating Units

Tech and Clearance

Dice.com (recruiting and career development website for technology and engineering professionals in the US)

ClearanceJobs.com (recruiting and career development website for professionals with active US government security clearances)

Finance

eFinancialCareers.com (UK global recruiting and career development website for capital markets and financial services professionals)

Energy

WorldwideWorker.com (online recruitment for energy industry)

Rigzone.com (online recruitment for oil and gas industry)

Other

Health Callings (Job site for US healthcare professionals)

BioSpace (Site for biotechnology careers news and resources)

Hcareers (Site for hospitality jobs across North America)

Targets Job Fair (Produces job fairs for technology energy and security-cleared workers)

COMPETITORS

CareerBuilder
Google
LinkedIn

Monster Worldwide
craigslist

HISTORICAL FINANCIALS

Company Type: Public

Income Statement

FYE: December 31

	REVENUE ($ mil.)	NET INCOME ($ mil.)	NET PROFIT MARGIN	EMPLOYEES
12/14	262.6	27.6	10.5%	831
12/13	213.4	16.2	7.6%	755
12/12	195.3	38.0	19.5%	534
12/11	179.1	34.1	19.0%	396
12/10	129.0	18.9	14.7%	338
Annual Growth	19.4%	9.9%	—	25.2%

2014 Year-End Financials

Debt ratio: 25.8%
Return on equity: 15.9%
Cash ($ mil.): 26
Current ratio: 0.73
Long-term debt ($ mil.): 108

No. of shares (mil.): 54
Dividends
  Yield: —
  Payout: —
Market value ($ mil.): 542

	STOCK PRICE ($) FY Close	P/E High/Low		PER SHARE ($) Earnings	Dividends	Book Value
12/14	10.01	22	13	0.51	0.00	3.28
12/13	7.25	35	24	0.27	0.00	3.07
12/12	9.18	18	11	0.59	0.00	3.23
12/11	8.29	35	14	0.49	0.00	3.22
12/10	14.35	49	19	0.28	0.00	2.75
Annual Growth	(8.6%)	—	—	16.2%	—	4.6%

Digital Realty Trust, Inc.

Technically Digital Realty Trust puts its chips in real estate. The real estate investment trust (REIT) owns properties that are leased to firms in the technology sector. Its portfolio includes more than 100 properties in the US Europe and Asia including data communications hubs electronic storage and processing centers tech manufacturing facilities and offices of tech companies. All told the REIT owns more than 18 million sq. ft. of rentable space including space held for redevelopment. Digital Realty Trust focuses on hot tech markets such as Chicago Dallas Phoenix New Jersey New York northern Virginia and California's San Francisco Bay area and Silicon Valley (its largest market).

Digital Realty Trust's occupancy rate stood at nearly 95% at the end of 2011. Its largest tenant Century Link accounts for more than 10% of its annualized rent; other major tenants include Equinix AT&T Level 3 Communications and Facebook.

The REIT's growth strategy includes real estate acquisitions and redevelopment of its existing properties. It has approximately 2 million sq. ft. of space under development. The company believes that upgrades to its properties lead to low tenant turnover and longer lease terms.

Digital Realty Trust acquired 15 properties in 2010 (the busiest that the company had been since 2007) including some in new markets. The REIT added its first property in Asia when it bought a data center in Singapore. It entered Massachusetts and Connecticut with the acquisition of three data centers there.

Digital Realty Trust continued its acquisition activity into 2011 and 2012 when it purchased more than a dozen properties including some in new markets such as London and Sydney. The latter deals added to the company's international presence in Dublin Melbourne Paris and Singapore.

The acquisitions in 2010 and 2011 also helped to boost the company's revenues and net income for both years. Digital Realty Trust reported a more than 50% increase in net income from fiscal 2010 to 2011 ($105.4 million to $162.1 million) and a nearly 25% gain in operating income ($865.4 million to nearly $1.1 billion).

EXECUTIVES

CEO and Director, A. William Stein, age 60, $457,979 total compensation
Chief Investment Officer, Scott E. Peterson, age 52, $437,396 total compensation
CTO, Jim Smith
SVP Portfolio Management, David J. Caron, $285,833 total compensation
SVP EMEA, Bernard Geoghegan
Senior Vice President; Regional Head; Asia Pacific, Kris Kumar
Senior Vice President Capital Markets, Wendy Will
Vice President Portfolio Manager, Glenn Benoist
Vice President Sales Europe, Adam Levine
Vice President Human Resources, Rita Luz
Sr V Pres Technical Operations, David Schirmacher
Vice President Sales Northeast, Brian Doricko
Vice President Acquisitions, Michael Darragh
Vp Investor Relations And Corporate Marketing, Pamela Matthews Garibaldi
Vice President Investor Relations, Krupal Raval
Vice President Human Resources, Rita Da Luz
Vice President Of Sales And Mid Markets, John Hanko
Vice President Tax, Brian Keyser
Vice President Sales, Brent Buckles
Vice President Portfolio Management, Bryan Marsh
Vice President Of Sales, Joe Goldsmith
Vice President, Ed Scott
Vice President Design And Construction, Steve Kundich
Vice President Corporate Counsel, Jeannie Lee
Vice President Portfolio Management, Mark Luz
Vice President Corporate Assistant Controller, Joe Hegstrom
Vice President Design, Kevin Dalton
Assistant To Senior Vice President, Melissa Bendana

Vice President Portfolio Management, Fergal Creed
Vice President Engineering, Robert Bath
Vice President International Accounting, David Glennane
Vice President Portfolio Operations, Dana Stuart
Vice President Design Apac, Peter Adcock
Vice President Of Construction North, Anthony Caracino
Vice President Portfolio Operations, Tamara Budec
Vice President Portfolio Manager, Bob Holmes
Vp Portfolio Management, Dana Adams
Vice President, Bob Stephens
Vice President Of Sales For The Asia, Grant Yabsley
Vice President Sales Engineering, Roche Donough
Senior Vice President Sales, Matt Miszewski
Vice President Global Procurement, Jen Weitzel
Senior Vice President Of Corporate Services And Human Resources, Ellen Jacobs
CEO and Director, A. William Stein, age 60
Chairman, Dennis E. Singleton, age 69
Board Member, Laurence A Chapman, age 65
Treasury Manager, Kevin Lazenby
Senior Treasury Analyst, Sienna Wei
Treasury Manager, Declan Murtagh
Auditors: KPMGLLP

LOCATIONS

HQ: Digital Realty Trust, Inc.
Four Embarcadero Center, Suite 3200, San Francisco, CA 94111
Phone: 415 738-6500   **Fax:** 415 738-6501
Web: www.digitalrealty.com

PRODUCTS/OPERATIONS

2011 Sales

	$ mil.	% of total
Rental	820.7	77
Tenant reimbursements	211.8	20
Construction management	29.3	3
Other	0.9	-
Total	1062.7	100

COMPETITORS

Brandywine Realty
CenterPoint Properties
CoreSite
DuPont Fabros
Duke Realty
EastGroup Properties
First Industrial Realty

Kilroy Realty
Mack-Cali
Prologis
QTS Realty Trust Inc.
Vornado Realty

HISTORICAL FINANCIALS

Company Type: Public

Income Statement

FYE: December 31

	REVENUE ($ mil.)	NET INCOME ($ mil.)	NET PROFIT MARGIN	EMPLOYEES
12/13	1,482.2	314.4	21.2%	784
12/12	1,279.0	210.3	16.4%	702
12/11	1,062.7	156.2	14.7%	532
12/10	865.4	102.2	11.8%	454
12/09	637.1	87.6	13.8%	264
Annual Growth	23.5%	37.6%	—	31.3%

2013 Year-End Financials

Debt ratio: 51.2%
Return on equity: 8.8%
Cash ($ mil.): 56
Current ratio: 0.36
Long-term debt ($ mil.): 4,961

No. of shares (mil.): 128
Dividends
  Yield: 6.3%
  Payout: 146.4%
Market value ($ mil.): 6,310

	STOCK PRICE ($)	P/E	PER SHARE ($)		
	FY Close	High/Low	Earnings	Dividends	Book Value
12/13	49.12	35 21	2.12	3.12	28.11
12/12	67.89	54 40	1.48	2.92	27.72
12/11	66.67	50 38	1.32	2.72	23.79
12/10	51.54	93 68	0.68	2.02	21.53
12/09	50.28	80 42	0.62	1.47	20.30
Annual Growth	(0.6%)	— —	36.0%	20.7%	8.5%

Diodes, Inc.

Diodes Incorporated knows how important it is to be discrete in business. The company makes discrete semiconductors —fixed-function devices that are much less complex than integrated circuits. Diodes' products include diodes transistors and rectifiers; they are used by computer and consumer electronics manufacturers in products such as notebooks LCD monitors smartphones and game consoles. Other applications include power supplies climate control systems GPS devices and networking gear. Cisco LG Electronics Samsung Flextronics and Hon Hai are among its 150 OEM and contract manufacturing customers. The company's products are sold throughout Asia Europe and North America.

Geographic Reach
Asia is the Texas-based company's largest market accounting for more than 75% of its annual sales. China is its single largest market contributing 35% of sales followed by Taiwan (20%). Together Germany and the UK contribute about 9% of sales as does the US.

Operations
The semiconductor manufacturer operates design marketing and engineering centers in the US the UK Germany and Taiwan as well as a joint venture manufacturing plants in China and other manufacturing facilities in Neuhaus Germany and Taiwan.

Sales and Marketing
The company markets and sells its products worldwide through direct sales and marketing personnel independent sales representatives and distributors in the US Europe and Asia. Customers include about 150 leading OEMs as well as major electronic manufacturing service (EMS) providers. Additionally Diodes has about 65 distributor customers including Arrow Electronics and Avnet through which it indirectly serves more than 10000 customers worldwide. End users for the company's semiconductors include the: consumer electronics (33% of net sales); computing (28% of sales); Industrial (about 20% of sales); communications (about 15%) and automotive industries.

Financial Performance
The semiconductor maker's sales were flat in 2012 compared with 2011 at about $634 million. The company attributed the weak sales growth to a 10% increase in units sold offset by a 10% decrease in average selling price (ASP). ASP came under pressure from customers competitors and product mix. Asia was Diodes' best performing market in 2012 with sales there up 5% year over year on increased demand from China and South Korea.

Net income declined 52% in 2012 versus 201 to $24.1 million on margin pressure partially offset by a $4 million gain on asset sales in Europe and Taiwan. Manufacturing and raw materials costs particularly gold costs squeezed margins as did lower equipment utilization. 2012 marked the second consecutive year of steeply declining net income.

Strategy
Diodes is under continuous pressure from customers and competitors to reduce the prices of its products which can result in lower sales and profits for the company. The company has countered by expanding into higher-margin proprietary product lines such as high-density arrays and ultraminiature switching diodes used in mobile applications. It also continues to become more vertically integrated which brings down cost and increases efficiency of operations. Diodes is looking to expand manufacturing capacity R&D capabilities product development and its sales and marketing organization in part through acquisitions. It's also looking to reduce its gold consumption.

In 2013 Diodes enhanced its general-purpose low-voltage CMOS (complementary metal-oxide-semiconductor) logic family for wide application range by adding shift registers. It also expanded its power-circuit densities with integrate high-voltage regulator transistors.

Mergers and Acquisitions
In 2013 the company acquired BCD Semiconductor Manufacturing Limited for about $151 million in an effort to broaden its reach in Asia particularly China where BCD is strong. Previously Diodes purchased Power Analog Microelectronics a provider of advanced analog and high-voltage power ICs for $16 million in 2012. The purchase strengthened its position in analog products.

Ownership
Lite-On Semiconductor a company that is part of Taiwan's Lite-On Technology is Diodes largest shareholder with about 18% the stock. Lite-On Semiconductor is also Diodes' biggest customer and its biggest supplier. Investment firm T. Rowe Price owns about 13% of Diodes' shares.

EXECUTIVES

President and CEO, Keh-Shew Lu, age 68, $482,958 total compensation
SVP Operations, Joseph Liu, age 72, $294,167 total compensation
SVP Sales and Marketing, Mark A. King, age 55, $291,792 total compensation
VP Worldwide Discrete Products, Francis Tang, age 60, $245,292 total compensation
CFO Treasurer and Secretary, Richard D. White, age 67, $278,125 total compensation
VP Corporate Supply Chain/Planning Outsourcing and Quality, Clemente (Clay) Beltran
VP and Senior General Manager Worldwide Analog Products, Chieh Chang
Chairman, Raymond Soong, age 73
Vice Chairman, C. H. Chen, age 71
Auditors: MossAdamsLLP

LOCATIONS

HQ: Diodes, Inc.
4949 Hedgcoxe Road, Suite 200, Plano, TX 75024
Phone: 972 987-3900
Web: www.diodes.com

2012 Sales

	$ mil.	% of total
Asia	497.9	78
Europe	68.6	11
North America	67.3	11
Total	**633.8**	**100**

2012 Sales by Customer Location

	$ mil.	% of total
China	223.5	35
Taiwan	126.4	20
Switzerland	57.2	9
US	54.9	9
South Korea	50.9	8
UK	28.6	5
Singapore	27.0	4
Germany	24.4	4
Other countries	40.9	6
Total	**633.8**	**100**

PRODUCTS/OPERATIONS

2012 Sales by Market

	% of total
Consumer electronics	33
Computing	28
Industrial	19
Communications	16
Automotive	4
Total	**100**

Selected Products

Diodes
  Schottky diodes
  Switching diodes
  Zener diodes
High-density arrays
Metal oxide semiconductor field-effect transistors (MOSFETs)
Rectifiers
  Bridge rectifiers
  Schottky rectifiers
  Standard fast superfast and ultrafast recovery rectifiers
Transient voltage suppressors
  Thyristor surge protection devices
  Zener transient-voltage suppressors
Transistors
  Bipolar transistors
  Darlington transistors
  Prebiased transistors

COMPETITORS

Advanced Photonix	ON Semiconductor
BCD Semiconductor	ROHM
Fairchild Semiconductor	STMicroelectronics
IXYS	Sanken Electric
Infineon Technologies	Shindengen Electric Manufacturing
International Rectifier	Siliconix
Microsemi	Toshiba Semiconductor & Storage Products
NXP Semiconductors	Vishay Intertechnology

HISTORICAL FINANCIALS

Company Type: Public

Income Statement

FYE: December 31

	REVENUE ($ mil.)	NET INCOME ($ mil.)	NET PROFIT MARGIN	EMPLOYEES
12/13	826.8	26.5	3.2%	6,151
12/12	633.8	24.1	3.8%	4,605
12/11	635.2	50.7	8.0%	4,499
12/10	612.8	76.7	12.5%	3,986
12/09	434.3	7.5	1.7%	3,501
Annual Growth	17.5%	37.1%	—	15.1%

2013 Year-End Financials

Debt ratio: 16.2%
Return on equity: 3.8%
Cash ($ mil.): 196
Current ratio: 4.14
Long-term debt ($ mil.): 182
No. of shares (mil.): 46
Dividends
  Yield: —
  Payout: —
Market value ($ mil.): 1,100

	STOCK PRICE ($) FY Close	P/E High/Low	PER SHARE ($) Earnings	Dividends	Book Value
12/13	23.56	49 30	0.56	0.00	15.05
12/12	17.35	51 25	0.51	0.00	14.72
12/11	21.30	31 15	1.09	0.00	13.95
12/10	26.99	16 8	1.68	0.00	12.12
12/09	20.41	121 31	0.17	0.00	10.08
Annual Growth	3.7%	— —	34.7%	—	10.6%

Dorchester Minerals LP

The stakeholders of Dorchester Minerals are enjoying the benefits of three natural resource exploitation enterprises which came together as one. The oil and gas exploration company was formed by the 2003 merger of oil trust Dorchester Hugoton with Republic Royalty and Spinnaker Royalty. Dorchester Minerals' holdings include about 141600 net acres in Texas and 62850 net acres in Montana. The company holds assets (producing and nonproducing mineral royalty overriding royalty net profits and leasehold interests) in properties in 574 counties in 25 states. In 2009 Dorchester Minerals reported proved reserves of 60.3 billion cu. ft. of natural gas and 3.3 million barrels of oil and condensate.

In a major expansion of its asset base in 2010 the company acquired stakes in nonproducing properties in 206 counties and parishes in 17 states. The transaction added about 700000 gross acres primarily Texas and North Dakota.

EXECUTIVES

COO; Manager Dorchester Minerals Management GP LLC; COO Dorchester Minerals Operating GP LLC, James E. Raley, age 71, $96,000 total compensation

CEO; Manager Dorchester Minerals Management; CEO Dorchester Minerals Operating GP LLC, William Casey McManemin, age 50, $96,000 total compensation

CFO; Manager Dorchester Minerals Management GP LLC; CFO Dorchester Minerals Operating GP LLC, H. C. Allen Jr., age 72, $96,000 total compensation

Independent Member of the Board of Managers, C. Russell

Chief Financial Officer; Member of the Board of Managers, H. Allen

Independent Member of the Board of Managers, Pretson Peak

Chief Executive Officer; Member of the Board of Managers, William McManemin

COO; Manager Dorchester Minerals Management GP LLC; COO Dorchester Minerals Operating GP LLC, James E. Raley, age 71

Manager, Preston A. Peak, age 88

Manager, Buford P. Berry, age 75

CEO; Manager Dorchester Minerals Management; CEO Dorchester Minerals Operating GP LLC, William Casey McManemin, age 50

CFO; Manager Dorchester Minerals Management GP LLC; CFO Dorchester Minerals Operating GP LLC, H. C. Allen Jr., age 72

Manager, Robert C. Vaughn, age 58

Manager, C. William (Bill) Russell, age 69

Director, Ronald P. Trout, age 71

Auditors: GrantThorntonLLP

LOCATIONS

HQ: Dorchester Minerals LP
3838 Oak Lawn Avenue, Suite 300, Dallas, TX 75219
Phone: 214 559-0300
Web: www.dmlp.net

PRODUCTS/OPERATIONS

2009 Sales

	$ mil.	% of total
Royalties	33.4	77
Interest	9.4	21
Lease bonus	0.7	2
Other	0.1	-
Total	**43.6**	**100**

COMPETITORS

Anadarko Petroleum	Occidental Petroleum
BP	Pioneer Natural
Cabot Oil & Gas	Resources
Chesapeake Energy	Royal Dutch Shell
Devon Energy	Southwestern Energy
Exxon Mobil	Unit Corporation
Noble Energy	XTO Energy

HISTORICAL FINANCIALS

Company Type: Public

Income Statement

FYE: December 31

	REVENUE ($ mil.)	NET INCOME ($ mil.)	NET PROFIT MARGIN	EMPLOYEES
12/13	65.8	43.5	66.2%	21
12/12	63.2	38.0	60.2%	26
12/11	69.4	42.2	60.8%	28
12/10	61.0	34.8	57.1%	20
12/09	43.6	21.6	49.7%	19
Annual Growth	10.8%	19.1%	—	2.5%

2013 Year-End Financials

Debt ratio: —	No. of shares (mil.): 30
Return on equity: —	Dividends
Cash ($ mil.): 15	Yield: 6.6%
Current ratio: 29.68	Payout: 123.7%
Long-term debt ($ mil.): —	Market value ($ mil.): 797

	STOCK PRICE ($) FY Close	P/E High/Low	PER SHARE ($) Earnings	Dividends	Book Value
12/13	25.98	19 15	1.37	1.73	3.65
12/12	20.33	22 17	1.20	1.79	4.02
12/11	22.66	22 16	1.33	1.65	4.63
12/10	27.47	26 19	1.11	1.65	4.97
12/09	21.28	36 20	0.72	1.50	5.09
Annual Growth	5.1%	— —	17.4%	3.6%	(8.0%)

Dorman Products Inc

Got parts? Dorman does. From its stock of more than 130000 products Dorman Products (formerly R&B Inc.) is a leading supplier of automotive replacement parts (including brake parts) fasteners and service line products to the automotive aftermarket. It also provides household hardware and organization items to mass merchants. About 85% of revenue comes from parts sold under Dorman's sub-brands which include AutoGrade FirstStop and OE Solutions. Dorman sells to auto aftermarket retailers and warehouse distributors (such as AutoZone CARQUEST) as well as to parts manufacturers for resale under private labels. Dorman distributes its products in the North America Asia Europe and the Middle East.

Geographic Reach

Pennsylvania-based Dorman Products has about 15 warehouse and office facilities throughout North America and overseas in China and India. Dorman purchases about 80% of its products from international suppliers primarily in China. More than 90% of the company's sale come from customers in North America.

Sales and Marketing

About half of Dorman's products are primarily sold through automotive aftermarket retails such as AutoZone Advance Auto Parts and O'Reilly Automotive. Distributors such as CARQUEST NAPA account for more than 40% of the company's sales. International customers sales to mass merchants (including Wal-Mart Stores) and salvage yards represent the rest. In 2012 AutoZone Advance Auto Parts O'Reilly and Genuine Parts each accounted for more than 10% of sales and 57% of total sales.

Financial Performance

Dorman's sales grew 8% in 2012 versus 2011 to $570 million. Net income increased 33% over the same period to $71 million. The company credited strong demand for its products and higher new product sales for the gains. Indeed sales profits and cash flow have risen steadily since 2008 as tough economic times across North America drove demand in the automotive aftermarket and in turn Dorman's own business because drivers kept their cars longer and took a do-it-yourself approach to auto maintenance.

Strategy

Introducing new products to the automotive aftermarket has been central to Dorman's strategy. The company attributes its growth over the years to its development of a wide assortment of parts and accessories many of which Dorman believes may not have been easily available otherwise and which improve upon the original parts being replaced. As such the firm has made increased investments in product development resources and marketing programs to strengthen its ties to customers. Indeed spending on research and development has more than doubled from $4.6 million in 2010 to $10.5 million in 2012.

As its business in North America continues to grow the company cut its losses overseas with the sale of its ScanTech subsidiary in Sweden in late 2011. ScanTech distributed a line of Volvo and Saab replacement parts worldwide.

Mergers and Acquisitions

In October 2013 Dorman acquired North Carolina-base Re-Involt Technologies an aftermarket leader in hybrid battery remanufacturing technology. The purchase enables Dorman to refine its process for remanufacturing hybrid drive batteries develop new hybrid products for the aftermarket and ultimately capture sales of replacement batteries for hybrid vehicles a growing segment of the vehicle market.

Ownership

Chairman and CEO Steven Berman and his family control the company through their ownership of 31% of Dorman's common stock. Formerly COO of the company Steven succeeded his late brother Richard as CEO in 2011. The Berman brothers founded Dorman Products in 1978. Royce & Associates owns about 10% of the shares.

EXECUTIVES

President and Director, Mathias J. Barton, age 54, $368,745 total compensation

Chairman CEO Secretary Treasurer and Director, Steven L. Berman, age 55, $596,489 total compensation

Vice President Sales, Ronald R Montgomery, age 74

CFO, Matthew Kohnke, $220,000 total compensation

Vice President Supply Chain, David Lynch

Vice President National Accounts, Jeff Darby

Vice President Of National Accounts, Bob Castellani

Chief Learning Officer Vice President Director Manager Of Corporate Education, Susan Wheeler

Vice President National Accounts, Cliff Green

Vice President Engineering And Quality, Kevin Gallagher

Senior Vice President Human Resources And Organizational Development, Rebecca Kreitsek

National Account Manager, Jamie Dolder

Vice President Strategic Product Planning, Remy De Vlieghere

Vice President New Products, William Lawson

Vice President Corporate Operations, Clinton Shultz

Vice President Procurement, Michael Dempsey

Vice President Shared Services, Joe Weaver

Vice President, Joe Taik

Vice President Talent Management, Hope Bailey

Vice President, Alyssa Herman

Chairman CEO Secretary Treasurer and Director, Steven L. Berman, age 55

Board Treasurer, Rickie Locke

Auditors: KPMGLLP

LOCATIONS

HQ: Dorman Products Inc
3400 East Walnut Street, Colmar, PA 18915
Phone: 215 997-1800
Web: www.dormanproducts.com

PRODUCTS/OPERATIONS

2012 Sales

	% of total
Automotive aftermarket	49
Warehouse distributors	43
International & special markets (includes mass merchants & salvage yards)	8
Total	**100**

2012 Sales

	% of total
Power-train	33
Automotive body	30
Chassis	26
Hardware	11
Total	**100**

Selected Subsidiaries

Allparts Inc.
RB Distribution Inc.
RB Management Inc.
RB Vest Inc.

COMPETITORS

Canadian Tire	General Parts
Federal-Mogul	Genuine Parts
Ford Motor	Hahn Automotive
General Motors	Uni-Select

HISTORICAL FINANCIALS

Company Type: Public

Income Statement

FYE: December 28

	REVENUE ($ mil.)	NET INCOME ($ mil.)	NET PROFIT MARGIN	EMPLOYEES
12/13	664.4	81.9	12.3%	1,452
12/12	570.4	70.9	12.4%	1,321
12/11	529.2	53.2	10.1%	1,265
12/10	455.7	46.1	10.1%	1,185
12/09	377.3	26.5	7.0%	997
Annual Growth	**15.2%**	**32.6%**	**—**	**9.9%**

2013 Year-End Financials

Debt ratio: —
Return on equity: 22.0%
Cash ($ mil.): 60
Current ratio: 4.71
Long-term debt ($ mil.): —

No. of shares (mil.): 36
Dividends
Yield: —
Payout: —
Market value ($ mil.): 2,009

	STOCK PRICE ($) FY Close	P/E High/Low		PER SHARE ($) Earnings	Dividends	Book Value
12/13	55.09	25	15	2.24	0.00	11.34
12/12	34.15	26	11	1.94	1.50	9.13
12/11	36.93	29	19	1.47	0.00	8.77
12/10	35.99	36	12	1.28	0.00	7.36
12/09	15.76	22	9	0.74	0.00	6.09
Annual Growth	**36.7%**	**—**	**—**	**32.1%**	**—**	**16.8%**

Drew Industries, Inc.

Drew Industries makes wanderlust –in comfort and style –a possibility. The company manufactures aluminum and vinyl windows and doors and other products (furniture and slide-out walls) for travel trailers and fifth-wheel recreational vehicles (RVs) (some 85% of sales) and manufactured housing (MH). Drew does business via two subsidiaries: Kinro produces windows doors and screens and Lippert Components churns out axles ramps and chassis parts as well as specialty trailers for hauling boats and snowmobiles. Brands include Equa-Flex Happijac RV Lock Solera Ground Control and Level Up.

HISTORY

Drew Industries was founded as Drew National Corp. in 1962. Drew purchased Kinro a maker of aluminum primary and storm windows for the manufactured-housing industry in 1980. The company reincorporated as Drew Industries in 1984. Under the leadership of Kinro president David Webster investor (and chairman) Edward Rose and CEO Leigh Abrams (who all took up their leadership positions in 1984) Drew pursued a strategy of diversifying within its niche market of supplying components to the RV and manufactured-home industries. Kinro subsequently acquired makers of aluminum windows for manufactured homes and manufacturers of doors and windows for recreational vehicles and in 1993 it began production of vinyl windows in addition to aluminum windows.

In 1996 Drew acquired Shoals a maker of axles and a distributor of refurbished axles and new and refurbished tires for manufactured homes. The next year Drew purchased Lippert which makes

chassis and chassis parts and galvanized roofing for manufactured homes. Lippert CEO Douglas Lippert gained about a 19% stake in Drew as part of the deal. Drew bought Coil Clip (specialty steel parts supplier) in 1998. The company added five plants in 2000 to accommodate its booming RV chassis business.

In April 2001 the company gave a boost to its MH sales by acquiring rival Kevco's Better Bath division (bath fixtures). The next year Drew gained higher quarter sales numbers due to its implementation of cost-cutting measures and lower-than-normal product inventories.

Drew's Lippert Tire & Axle subsidiary sold its one remaining operation which engaged in refurbishing used axles and distributing used tires for manufactured homes in January 2003. Mid-year Drew expanded its RV segment through the purchase of LTM Manufacturing; later in the year Drew boosted its chassis manufacturing business into specialty chassis when subsidiary Lippert Components paid $3.6 million to acquire certain business and assets of specialty chassis manufacturer ET&T Frames Inc. of Elkhart Indiana.

Also in 2003 Drew transferred its stock listing to the New York Stock Exchange from the American Stock Exchange and began trading on the NYSE under the ticker DW in December of that year.

In 2004 the company's Better Bath division a part of its Kinro subsidiary entered into an equipment lease and license agreement with the buyer of certain of its intellectual property rights related to a process used in manufacturing a new composite material for use in fiberglass bathtubs. The $4 million sale included a five-year payoff period. Drew also acquired privately held Zieman Manufacturing Company a Whittier California-based manufacturer of trailers for equipment hauling boats personal watercrafts and snowmobiles; chassis and chassis parts for manufactured homes and RVs (mainly travel and fifth-wheel trailers); and specialty chassis for modular offices. Zieman became a part of Drew's Lippert Components business.

Lippert Components acquired the Venture Welding division of Banks Corporation for about $19 million in May 2005. Venture Welding manufactures chassis and chassis parts in Elkhart Indiana.

In 2004 and into 2005 a California state court rendered a verdict in favor of a former employee of Drew's Lippert Components subsidiary in connection with a workplace injury. The former employee was awarded $4 million in punitive damages and compensatory damages of $464000.

The hurricane extravaganza of 2005 was good to Drew Industries. Although not a FEMA supplier the company estimated a 6% increase in sales of both RVs and manufactured homes as dealers sold off inventory to meet demand. The increase offset to a certain extent slowing sales of RVs due to high gas prices.

In 2006 Lippert acquired recreational vehicle and manufactured home chassis supplier SteelCo Inc. for $4.5 million and Happijac which supplies bed-lift systems for RVs for $29.5 million. The following year Lippert purchased sister businesses Trailair and Equa-Flex makers of suspension systems used in towable RVs. In addition it bolted on Coach Step which produces electric steps for motor homes and Extreme Engineering and its affiliate Pivit Hitch specialty trailer makers (primarily for luxury boats).

Over a five-year period through 2010 Drew Industries acquired more than a dozen manufacturers as well as a slew of patent-pending designs used in manufactured homes RVs and specialty (such as horse cargo and utility) trailers. Deals included the purchase of Sellers Mfg. Inc. The half-a-million dollar deal snagged the assets for retrofitting chassis built by motor home RV bus and commercial truck OEMs and for producing the E-Z Cruise (an enhanced suspension system for motor homes and buses). The largest acquisition of 2010 targeted former rival Schwintek. Its purchase for $20 million included assets for an RV wall slide-out mechanism an aluminum cylinder integral to leveling motor homes and a power roof-lift used in tent campers. Separately Drew Industries spent for $1.4 million to pocket a patent-pending six-point leveling system for towable RVs.

EXECUTIVES

CEO, Jason D. Lippert, age 42, $800,000 total compensation
CFO and Treasurer, Joseph S. Giordano, age 45, $340,000 total compensation
President and COO, Scott T. Mereness, age 42, $550,000 total compensation
Chairman, James F. Gero, age 70
Auditors: KPMGLLP

LOCATIONS

HQ: Drew Industries, Inc.
3501 County Road 6 East, Elkhart, IN 46514
Phone: 574 535-1125
Web: www.drewindustries.com

PRODUCTS/OPERATIONS

2013 Sales

	$ mil.	% of total
Recreational vehicles	893.7	88
Manufactured housing	121.9	12
Total	**1015.6**	**100**

Selected Products

Manufactured housing (MH) products
  Aluminum and vinyl patio doors
  Axles
  Entry doors
  Steel and fiberglass entry doors
  Steel chassis
  Steel chassis parts
  Replacement windows doors thermoformed bath products
  Thermoformed bath and kitchen products
  Vinyl and aluminum windows and screens
Recreational vehicle (RV) products (travel trailers and fifth-wheel RVs)
  Aluminum windows and screens
  Chassis components
  Entry and baggage doors
  Entry steps
  Furniture and mattresses
  Manual electric and hydraulic stabilizer and lifting systems
  Patio doors
  Slide-out mechanisms
  Specialty trailers for hauling boats personal watercraft snowmobiles and equipment
  Thermoformed bath kitchen and other products
  Towable axles and suspensions
  Towable steel chassis
  Toy hauler ramp doors

COMPETITORS

Atwood Mobile	Meritor
Coast Distribution	Patrick Industries
Elixir Industries	Quality Trailer
Euramax	Products
Featherlite	Tuthill
LaSalle Bristol	Wozniak Industries

HISTORICAL FINANCIALS

Company Type: Public

Income Statement

FYE: December 31

	REVENUE ($ mil.)	NET INCOME ($ mil.)	NET PROFIT MARGIN	EMPLOYEES
12/13	1,015.5	50.1	4.9%	5,109
12/12	901.1	37.3	4.1%	5,179
12/11	681.1	30.0	4.4%	4,130
12/10	572.7	28.0	4.9%	3,016
12/09	397.8	(24.0)	—	3,054
Annual Growth	**26.4%**	**—**	**—**	**13.7%**

2013 Year-End Financials

Debt ratio: —
Return on equity: 16.7%
Cash ($ mil.): 66
Current ratio: 1.91
Long-term debt ($ mil.): —

No. of shares (mil.): 23
Dividends
  Yield: 3.9%
  Payout: 107.5%
Market value ($ mil.): 1,197

	STOCK PRICE ($) FY Close	P/E High/Low		PER SHARE ($) Earnings	Dividends	Book Value
12/13	51.20	25	15	2.11	2.00	13.42
12/12	32.25	20	15	1.64	2.00	12.53
12/11	24.53	20	13	1.34	2.00	12.52
12/10	22.72	22	14	1.26	1.50	11.05
12/09	20.65	—	—	(1.10)	0.00	11.11
Annual Growth	**25.5%**			**—**	**—**	**4.8%**

Dril-Quip, Inc.

Dril-Quip equips the folks who operate the expensive drills –the global deepwater oil and gas industry. The company specializes in deepwater harsh-environment and/or severe-condition equipment. Its products include drilling and production riser systems subsea and surface wellheads and production trees mudline hanger systems (which support the weight of each casing string at the mudline) and specialty connectors and pipe. Dril-Quip's offshore rig equipment includes drilling and completion riser systems wellhead connectors and diverters. The company also provides reconditioning tool rental and technical advisory services. It had work or service contracts with more than offshore rigs in 2012.

Geographic Reach

Dril-Quip's operations are organized into three geographic segments: Western Hemisphere (including North and South America; headquartered in Houston) Eastern Hemisphere (including Europe and Africa; headquartered in Aberdeen Scotland) and Asia/Pacific (including the Pacific Rim Southeast Asia Australia India and the Middle East; headquartered in Singapore).

Each of these segments sells similar products and services and the company has major manufacturing facilities in all three of its headquarter locations as well as in Macae Brazil. Dril-Quip has sales service and reconditioning facilities in Australia China Denmark Egypt Ghana the Netherlands Nigeria Norway Qatar and the US. In 2012 the company generated 74% of its total revenues outside of the US.

Sales and Marketing

Dril-Quip markets its products through its offices and sales representatives in the world's major energy markets. It markets its products and serv-

ices directly through its sales personnel in two US and 19 international locations. In addition in some international markets where the company does not maintain offices it sells through independent sales representatives. The company has sales representatives in Brazil China India Indonesia Malaysia Saudi Arabia and the UAE. Sales are geared at major integrated large independent and foreign national oil and gas companies. A portion of its customer base consists of offshore drilling contractors and engineering and construction companies.

Dril-Quip advertises its products and services in trade and technical publications and participates in industry conferences and trade shows to enhance industry awareness of its products.

The company is not dependent on any one customer; its top 15 customers represented 62% of total revenues in 2012; Brazil's PETROBRAS accounted for about 12%. Keppel Fels is also a major customer.

Financial Performance

Dril-Quip reported 22% rise in revenues in 2012 compared to FY 2011 was primarily as a result of increased revenues in subsea equipment and surface equipment partially offset by lower in offshore rig equipment revenues. The reduction in the number of long-term projects with offshore rig equipment components dragged down offshore rig equipment sales. However product revenues increased in each of is geographic segments reflecting strong industry demand for the company's equipment. Increased service revenues in the Western Hemisphere and the Eastern Hemisphere helped to lift overall service revenues despite a slight decrease in the Asia-Pacific region. The bulk of revenue growth in services came from increased demand for technical advisory services and installation tool rentals.Net income increased by 25% in 2012 primarily due to higher revenues and lower special items expenses. Interest income increased due to good returns from its short-term investments and reduced interest expenses.

In 2012 ATP Oil & Gas filed for bankruptcy owing Dril-Quip $1.4 million in receivables.

Dril-Quip reported a year-over-year increase in revenues between 2008 and 2012 thanks to growing oil and gas industry demand with higher oil prices and growing energy consumption prompting oil and gas companies to make capital expenditures on exploration drilling and production operations offshore.

Strategy

The company continually introduces new products and product enhancements and sees its ability to develop new products and maintain technological advantages as key to its future success. Dril-Quip has introduced multiple new products including liner hangers subsea control systems and subsea manifolds.

Dril-Quip's product development work is conducted at its facilities in Houston Texas and Aberdeen Scotland. The company's application engineering staff provides engineering services to customers in connection with the design and sales of its products. The company's global manufacturing and servicing locations allow it to have short supply lines and delivery times for its clients in far-flung oil and gas fields worldwide.

Taking advantage of its strong manufacturing presence in Brazil in 2012 Dril-Quip secured a $650 million four-year contract from PETROBRAS to supply subsea wellhead systems and associated tools to be used in the drilling of deepwater wells offshore Brazil.

Expanding its manufacturing base in 2011 Dril-Quip opened a new manufacturing plant in Singapore valued at $33.2 million.

Company Background
Dril-Quip was founded in 1981.

EXECUTIVES

VP Finance and CFO, Jerry M. Brooks, age 63, $367,654 total compensation

President and CEO, Blake DeBerry, $634,423 total compensation

SVP and COO, James A. Gariepy, $579,423 total compensation

Chairman, John V. Lovoi, age 53

Auditors: BDOUSALLP

LOCATIONS

HQ: Dril-Quip, Inc.
6401 N. Eldridge Parkway, Houston, TX 77041
Phone: 713 939-7711   **Fax:** 713 939-8063
Web: www.dril-quip.com

2012 Sales

	$ mil.	% of total
Western Hemisphere	367.8	50
Eastern Hemisphere	233.6	32
Asia/Pacific	131.6	18
Total	**733.0**	**100**

PRODUCTS/OPERATIONS

2012 Sales

	$ mil.	% of total
Products		
Subsea equipment	518.6	71
Offshore rig equipment	53.1	7
Surface equipment	38.5	5
Services	122.8	17
Total	**733.0**	**100**

Selected Products and Services

Products Group
  Diverters
  Drilling riser systems
  Mudline hanger systems
  Platform production trees
  Platform wellheads
  Production risers
  Specialty connectors
  Subsea production trees
  Subsea wellheads
  Surface wellheads
  Wellhead connectors
  Valves
  Well systems
Services Group
  Field installation
  Reconditioning
  Rental

COMPETITORS

ABB	Hornbeck Offshore
Aker Solutions	McDermott
Atwood Oceanics	Newpark Resources
Cameron International	Oceaneering
FMC Technologies	International
GE Oil	Parker Drilling
Global Power Equipment	Siem Offshore
GulfMark Offshore	Superior Energy
Helix Energy Solutions	Tesco Corporation
Hercules Offshore	

HISTORICAL FINANCIALS

Company Type: Public

Income Statement

FYE: December 31

	REVENUE ($ mil.)	NET INCOME ($ mil.)	NET PROFIT MARGIN	EMPLOYEES
12/13	872.3	169.8	19.5%	2,637
12/12	733.0	119.2	16.3%	2,451
12/11	601.3	95.2	15.8%	2,194
12/10	566.2	102.2	18.1%	2,127
12/09	540.2	105.1	19.5%	2,130
Annual Growth	**12.7%**	**12.7%**	—	**5.5%**

2013 Year-End Financials

Debt ratio: —	No. of shares (mil.): 40
Return on equity: 14.7%	Dividends
Cash ($ mil.): 384	Yield: —
Current ratio: 7.56	Payout: —
Long-term debt ($ mil.): —	Market value ($ mil.): 4,471

	STOCK PRICE ($) FY Close	P/E High/Low	PER SHARE ($) Earnings	Dividends	Book Value
12/13	109.93	29 17	4.16	0.00	30.54
12/12	73.05	26 20	2.94	0.00	26.35
12/11	65.82	34 21	2.36	0.00	23.03
12/10	77.72	32 16	2.55	0.00	20.68
12/09	56.48	22 7	2.66	0.00	17.78
Annual Growth	**18.1%**	— —	**11.8%**	—	**14.5%**

DSW Inc

While you don't have to watch out for trees in this jungle you may want to watch your back. DSW (short for Designer Shoe Warehouse) sells discounted brand-name footwear for style-conscious men women and kids through some 430 stores in 40-plus US states and Puerto Rico as well as online at dsw.com. DSW stores average 22000 square feet and stock about 23000 pair of dress casual and athletic shoes as well as a complementary array of handbags hosiery and accessories. The company also operates about 370 leased departments inside stores operated by other retailers. The discount footwear giant is dipping its toe in the luxury shoe market. DSW was founded in 1969.

Geographic Reach
Fast-growing DSW operates shoe stores in 42 US states the District of Columbia and Puerto Rico. Its two largest markets are California and Texas home to nearly 20% of its stores.

Operations
In addition to its historically-fast-growing retail operation DSW operates leased departments inside more than 260 stores operated by Stein Mart 90-plus Gordmans stores and one Frugal Fannie's Fashion Warehouse store. Leased departments accounted for 6% of DSW's fiscal 2014 (ended January) sales.

Sales and Marketing
DSW's marketing expenses totaled $56.2 million $55.9 million $50.9 million in fiscal years 2014 2013 and 2012 respectively.

Financial Performance
DSW's fiscal 2014 (ended January) sales topped $2.3 billion a 5% increase versus the prior year. The increase was driven by the addition of new company-owned retail stores and a small increase in comparable sales at existing ones. Sales at the company's leased departments rose 4% year over year on comparable sales growth and the addition of 12 new shoe departments and nine Loehmann's locations.

Net income grew 3% over the same reporting period to $151.3 million on higher sales declining interest expenses and the absence of expenses incurred in fiscal 2013.

Strategy
The historically fast-growing company has returned to a more aggressive growth strategy after a hiatus during the deep recession and its aftermath. (DSW was a relatively-strong performer throughout the recession which left many other retailers struggling with falling sales.) In fiscal 2014 the chain opened 30 new stores including its first in Canada with an ultimate goal of 450 to 500 stores. The company entered the Canadian market in spring 2014 with the purchase of a minority stake in that country's largest footwear retailer Town Shoes for about $62 million. Under the terms of the deal DSW has the right to purchase the rest of Town Shoes after four years.

The discount shoe retailer is also testing the luxury waters with a test (characterized by the company as "unsuccessful") of an expaned luxury assortment online. DSW's future approach to luxury sales will depend on its ability to buy products that will allow it to at least break even.

To further grow its online business the shoe seller will offer styles sizes and widths not available in local stores. DSW is also looking for new partner retailers for its leased department business. The company targets fashion-focused men and women from wide-ranging socioeconomic and demographic backgrounds. It looks to capture these shoppers by offering a broad selection of in-season styles at prices that rival the sales deals found in department stores.

Mergers and Acquisitions
In May 2014 DSW entered Canada with the purchase of a 44% stake in that country's largest footwear retailer Town Shoes for about $62 million. Under the terms of the deal DSW has the right to purchase the rest of Town Shoes after four years. Town Shoes operates 182 locations across Canada and reported sales of C$291 million. DSW's initial stake provides 50% voting control and board representation.

Ownership
DSW chairman Jay Schottenstein owns nearly 69% of the combined voting power of all classes of DSW's common stock.

Company Background
DSW was founded in 1969 and merged with its majority shareholder Retail Ventures in 2011. In May 2011 DSW bought out its majority shareholder Retail Ventures in an all-stock deal valued at about $773 million. Retail Ventures whose only operating business was its 62% stake in DSW became a subsidiary of DSW following the tax-free exchange of shares. The deal allowed Retail Ventures shareholders to become shareholders in DSW and eliminated the expenses associated maintaining Retail Venture's listing on the New York Stock Exchange.

EXECUTIVES

President and CEO, Michael R. (Mike) MacDonald, age 62, $1,050,000 total compensation

Vice President Human Resources, Kathleen C Maurer

Vice Chairman and Chief Merchandising Officer, Deborah L. Ferr Ae, age 60, $997,981 total compensation

EVP and Chief Administrative Officer, William L. (Bill) Jordan, age 42
EVP and Chief Supply Chain Officer, Harris Mustafa, age 60, $646,635 total compensation
CFO, Mary Meixelsperger
EVP and Chief Innovation Officer, Roger L. Rawlins
EVP and COO, Carrie McDermott
EVP and Chief Marketing Officer, Kelly N. Cook
V Pres-dsw-oper, Dave Disque
Vice President Human Resources, Todd S Cordell
Vice President Treasurer, Kurt Gatterdam
Vice President Store Planning, Dave Crawford
Executive Vice President Chief Operating Officer, Kevin Longergan
Vice President Information Technology Operations, Mark Delcher
Vice President Planning And Allocation, Linda Canada
Hr Director & Vp, Bob Drury
Senior Vice President General, Ray Blanton
Vice President Human Resources, J Roomsburg
Executive Vice President Of Business, Jon Ricker
Vice President Tax, Marla Walters
Chairman, Jay L. Schottenstein, age 60
Vice Chairman and Chief Merchandising Officer, Deborah L. Ferr Ã€, age 60
Board Member, Roger S Markfield
Board Member, Heywood Wilanksy
Board Member, Joanna T Lau
Board Member, Henry Aaron
Auditors: Deloitte&ToucheLLP

LOCATIONS

HQ: DSW Inc
810 DSW Drive, Columbus, OH 43219
Phone: 614 237-7100
Web: www.dswinc.com

2014 Stores

	No.
California	38
Texas	34
New York	28
Florida	26
Illinois	21
Pennsylvania	19
Michigan	17
Ohio	17
New Jersey	16
Massachusetts	15
Virginia	15
Georgia	14
Maryland	14
Colorado	11
Minnesota	10
Indiana	9
Arizona	8
North Carolina	8
Connecticut	7
Washington	7
Tennessee	6
Wisconsin	6
Missouri	5
Alabama	4
Louisiana	4
Oregon	4
Kentucky	3
Nevada	3
Oklahoma	3
Kansas	2
Nebraska	2
New Hampshire	2
Rhode Island	2
South carolina	2
Utah	2
District of Columbia	2
Arkansas	1
Delaware	1
Idaho	1
Iowa	1
Maine	1
Mississippi	1
North Dakota	1
Puerto Rico	1
Total	**394**

PRODUCTS/OPERATIONS

2014 Sales

	% of total
Women's shoes	62
Men's shoes	17
Athletic shoes	12
Accessories & other	9
Total	**100**

2014 Sales

	$ mil.	% of total
DSW stores	2231.0	94
Leased departments	137.7	6
Total	**2368.7**	**100**

COMPETITORS

Belk	Ross Stores
Brown Shoe	Sears
Dillard' s	Shoe Carnival
Foot Locker	Steven Madden
Iconix Brand Group	TJX Companies
J. C. Penney Company	Target Corporation
Kenneth Cole	The Gap
Kohl' s	Wal-Mart
Macy' s	Zappos.com
Payless ShoeSource	shoebuy.com
Rack Room Shoes	

HISTORICAL FINANCIALS

Company Type: Public

Income Statement

FYE: February 1

	REVENUE ($ mil.)	NET INCOME ($ mil.)	NET PROFIT MARGIN	EMPLOYEES
02/14	2,368.6	151.3	6.4%	11,000
02/13*	2,257.7	146.4	6.5%	11,000
01/12	2,024.3	174.7	8.6%	10,800
01/11	1,822.3	107.6	5.9%	10,500
01/10	1,602.6	54.7	3.4%	10,000
Annual Growth	**10.3%**	**28.9%**	**—**	**2.4%**

*Fiscal year change

2014 Year-End Financials

Debt ratio: —
Return on equity: 16.3%
Cash ($ mil.): 112
Current ratio: 2.86
Long-term debt ($ mil.): —
No. of shares (mil.): 90
Dividends
Yield: 0.0%
Payout: 22.7%
Market value ($ mil.): 3,416

	STOCK PRICE ($) FY Close	P/E High/Low		PER SHARE ($) Earnings	Dividends	Book Value
02/14	37.65	53	22	1.65	0.38	11.01
02/13*	67.55	43	30	1.62	1.44	9.54
01/12	49.49	22	13	2.27	1.15	9.08
01/11	33.28	33	18	1.20	0.00	7.25
01/10	24.10	43	11	0.62	0.00	5.98
Annual Growth	**11.8%**	**—**	**—**	**28.0%**	**—**	**16.5%**

*Fiscal year change

DTS Inc

DTS (formerly Digital Theater Systems) surrounds movie lovers with sound. The company's multi-channel audio systems are used in consumer electronic devices such as audio/video receivers DVD and Blu-ray HD players PCs car audio products video game consoles and home theater systems. DTS has licensing agreements with major consumer electronics manufacturers (Sony Samsung and Philips). It also provides DTS-encoded soundtracks in movies TV shows and music content. The firm was founded in 1990 as Digital Theater Systems by scientist Terry Beard. It received initial funding from Universal Pictures in 1993 and used that relationship to debut its audio system in the soundtrack to Universal's Jurassic Park.

Geographic Reach

While DTS is headquartered in the US it has a plethora of international offices including locations in the UK Japan and China. Nearly 90% of DTS's revenues were derived internationally in fiscal 2011 and fiscal 2012. Specifically Japan is a significant source of revenues accounting for more than 40% of the company's business.

Sales and Marketing

Sony and Samsung accounted for 13% and 11% respectively of the company's revenues in fiscal 2012.

Financial Performance

The company has enjoyed increasing revenues in recent fiscal years. It reported about $100.6 million in revenues for fiscal 2012 after claiming about $96.9 million in fiscal 2011 and $87.1 million in fiscal 2010. However the company's net income took a nosedive in fiscal 2012 partly as a result of amortization of intangibles from acquisitions.

Strategy

DTS' key strategy in the broadcast market is to actively work with broadcasters operators international standards organizations and manufacturers to expand the penetration of its solutions and capitalize on the increasing demand for high-definition audio delivery. The company has recently expanded its presence in Asia opening offices in Singapore and Shenzhen China.

Mergers and Acquisitions

In 2012 DTS acquired SRS Labs a provider of audio processing and enhancement technologies. The transaction worth about $148 million combined two complementary product and technology portfolios —DTS' suite of audio solutions and SRS Labs' audio processing technologies. DTS has also used the deal to expand its audio-related intellectual property holdings to more than 1000 registered and pending patents and trademarks. Such assets are designed to help it expand into the market for mobile phones and other Internet-connected devices.

Ownership

Janus Capital Management LLC owns about 20% of the company. Brown Capital Management Inc. and The Brown Capital Management Small Company Fund each own about 16% while Sarbit Advisory Services Inc. and Royce & Associates LLC each own about 10% of the company.

EXECUTIVES

Chairman and CEO, Jon E. Kirchner, age 46, $500,000 total compensation
EVP Finance and CFO, Melvin L. (Mel) Flanigan, age 55, $320,000 total compensation

EVP General Counsel and Corporate Secretary, Blake A. Welcher, age 52, $328,000 total compensation
EVP Corporate Strategy and Development, Patrick J. Watson, age 53, $232,308 total compensation
EVP and COO, Brian D. Towne, age 49, $350,000 total compensation
EVP and CTO, Frederick (Fred) Kitson, $345,000 total compensation
EVP Human Resources, Kris M. Graves
EVP and Chief Marketing Officer, Kevin Doohan
Vice President, Ton Kalker
Vice President Global Sales Operations, Matt Byrne
Corporate Vice President, Roy Law
Corporate Vice President And Managing, Len Lloyd
Vice President Business Development, Bob Lyle
Senior Vice President Product, Mat Hans
Vice President Business Development, Surya Jayaweera
Chair Department Of Media Arts, Reg Grant
Vice President Operations, Vincent Ting
Vice President Technology, Mark Randolph
Vice President Home A And V, Keith Burnett
Vice President Corporate Strategy, Benn Carr
Vice President Business Development, Sho Izaki
Vice President Sales Japan, Kaz Nieda
Vice President Business Development, John Hallman
Vice President Professional Audio, Ronny Katz
Vp Of Finance, Rachel Cahn
Vice President Finance And Accounting, Jason Boling
Vice President Marketing, Alan Cohen
Chairman and CEO, Jon E. Kirchner, age 46
Board Member, Daniel Slusser
Auditors: GrantThorntonLLP

LOCATIONS

HQ: DTS Inc
5220 Las Virgenes Road, Calabasas, CA 91302
Phone: 818 436-1000
Web: www.dts.com

2012 Sales

	$ mil.	% of total
Japan	41.2	41
South Korea	27.1	27
US	11.7	12
Other countries	20.6	20
Total	**100.6**	**100**

PRODUCTS/OPERATIONS

Selected Mergers and Acquisitions
FY2012
SRS Labs ($148 million; Santa Ana CA; provider of audio processing and enhancement technologies)

Selected Consumer Technology Licensing Applications
Audio/video receivers
Blu-ray HD DVD players
Car audio products
Home theater systems
Personal computers
Standard definition DVD players
Video game consoles

Selected Customer Segments
Consumer electronics manufacturers
Semiconductor manufacturers
Content providers

COMPETITORS

Dolby	QSound Labs
ILM	Sony
Microsoft	THX
Philips Electronics	Technicolor

HISTORICAL FINANCIALS

Company Type: Public

Income Statement

FYE: December 31

	REVENUE ($ mil.)	NET INCOME ($ mil.)	NET PROFIT MARGIN	EMPLOYEES
12/13	125.1	15.7	12.6%	373
12/12	100.6	(15.9)	—	369
12/11	96.9	18.2	18.8%	258
12/10	87.1	16.0	18.4%	228
12/09	77.7	10.6	13.6%	203
Annual Growth	**12.6%**	**10.4%**	**—**	**16.4%**

2013 Year-End Financials

Debt ratio: 12.4%
Return on equity: 8.6%
Cash ($ mil.): 66
Current ratio: 3.84
Long-term debt ($ mil.): 30
No. of shares (mil.): 17
Dividends
  Yield: —
  Payout: —
Market value ($ mil.): 413

	STOCK PRICE ($) FY Close	P/E High/Low	PER SHARE ($) Earnings	Dividends	Book Value
12/13	23.91	28 18	0.87	0.00	10.60
12/12	16.70	— —	(0.91)	0.00	9.94
12/11	27.24	46 22	1.08	0.00	8.82
12/10	49.05	53 28	0.90	0.00	8.52
12/09	34.21	56 22	0.60	0.00	8.09
Annual Growth	**(8.6%)**	**— —**	**9.7%**	**—**	**7.0%**

Ducommun Inc.

Too common? Not at all Ducommun. The company designs and makes aerostructures and electromechanical components for commercial and military aircraft as well as for missile and space programs. Ducommun AeroStructures (DAS) engineers and manufactures structures and assemblies such as aircraft wing spoilers and helicopter blades using aluminum composites and titanium. Ducommun LaBarge Technologies (DLT) makes electromechanical components such as switch assemblies actuators keyboard panels and avionics racks. Its Miltec subsidiary designs missile and aerospace systems. Products for military and space applications accounted for 54% of 2013 sales. Boeing accounted for 18% of 2013 revenues; Raytheon 10%.

Geographic Reach

The company has facilities in Alabama Arizona Arkansas California Kansas Mississippi Missouri New York Oklahoma Pennsylvania and Wisconsin Ducommun also operates plants in Mexico and Thailand.

Operations

DAS' production techniques include stretch-forming (the creation of large structural shapes from aluminum sheet metal extrusions) and hot-forming (metal working at high temperature) and computer-controlled machining. The segment also provides chemical milling (the removal of material to reduce weight) services. Commercial aerospace account for 57% of DAS' sales while military and space applications represent the rest.

Besides making electronic electromechanical and interconnect systems and components DLT offers services that include design integration and testing for advanced weapons and missile defense systems. Military and space applications account

for 58% of the segment's sales while commercial aerospace natural resources industrial medical and other markets represent the rest.

Sales and Marketing

The company serves the aerospace defense industrial natural resources and medical industries. The aerospace and defense markets represented 83% of Ducommun's revenues in 2013.

Financial Performance

Ducommun saw several years of revenue growth in revenue (until 2012) followed by marginal 1% decline in 2013. The decline in 2013 was due to a drop in the Ducommun LaBarge Technologies sales reflecting a 23% decrease in non-aerospace and defense revenues partially offset by a 4.5% increase in commercial aerospace sales in the Ducommun AeroStructures segment.After a net loss of more than $47 million in 2011 as the result in part of expenses related to its acquisition activity and greater interest demands. It bounced back to a $16 million profit due to absence of goodwill and impairment expenses. In 2013 Ducommun's net income dropped by 43% to $9 million due to forward loss provision and asset impairment expenses.Operating cash flow has followed net income trend. In 2013 operating cash flow decreased by some $2 million due to lower net income partially offset by abetter working capital management (primarily in inventory and accounts receivable).

Strategy

The company focuses on further expansion within the commercial airplane market and growing on growing its non-A&D business as expeditiously as possible. Acquisitions and joint venture partnerships are major elements of Ducommun's strategy.

In 2014 Ducommun signed a long-term agreement with AgustaWestland Philadelphia Corporation to continue producing specialized complex wiring harnesses for the AW139 multi-mission helicopter. The three-year agreement extends Ducommun's support of the program at its Joplin Missouri operation through 2016. The company has also been awarded several contracts by Spirit AeroSystems to produce structural assemblies for the Boeing 737 MAX commercial jetliner

Company Background

DLT was created in 2011 when the company's Technologies segment was merged with newly acquired LaBarge a St. Louis-based electronics component manufacturer.

Considered the oldest company in California with a founding date of 1849 Ducommun is dedicated to new technologies for the aerospace industry. It was the first to make all-composite rotor blades for Sikorsky S-61 helicopters; traditional blades were made of a mixture of metal and composite materials.

HISTORY

Swiss immigrant Charles Ducommun walked from Arkansas to California to take part in the California Gold Rush in 1849. He soon started a small watch-repair shop and then expanded his business to include general supplies. In the early 1900s the firm moved into the metals business as Ducommun Hardware Company and started making parts for California's aviation industry. The firm profited from increased demand during both World Wars and by the 1960s Ducommun had expanded into the electronics industry. It sold its metals business in 1981 and used the proceeds to buy aerospace companies.

The semiconductor business went bust in the early 1980s hurting Ducommun's sales. In 1986 the "Challenger" space shuttle explosion also took its toll on the company as the government scaled back on the space program. In 1987 Ducommun sold its electronics companies to Arrow Electronics the world's leading electronics distributor.

In 1988 the company began cutting costs and restructuring and by 1990 had made a small profit. In 1994 Ducommun began to remake itself as an aerospace component supplier. It bought Brice (aircraft seating 1994) 3dbm (telecommunications 1995) and MechTronics (radar enclosures 1996). A revived aerospace industry took off in 1997 fueling Ducommun's growth. Focusing on the aerospace industry the company sold 3dbm to COM DEV International (1998) and bought Jordan Industries' titanium components unit (1999).

In 2001 Ducommun announced the creation of Ducommun AeroStructures a combination of three of its subsidiaries (AHF-Ducommun Incorporated Aerochem Inc. and Parsons Precision Products Inc.) in an effort to reduce costs. Later in the year the company combined Ducommun AeroStructures with Composite Structures LLC. Ducommun sold Brice Manufacturing Company its airline seating manufacturer in 2002. The next year Ducommun acquired DBP Microwave a maker of radio frequency and microwave switches and incorporated those operations into its Technologies sector.

Ducommun went on a buying spree in 2006 spending roughly $66 million to acquire three new operations. Those were Miltec which provides missiles and aerospace systems; WiseWave a maker of microwave and millimeter-wave products; and CMP Display Systems a light-emitting diode (LED) edge-lit panel manufacturer. All three acquisitions were incorporated into Ducommun Technologies as part of an effort to bolster sales for that segment which served primarily military customers.

In late 2008 Ducommun paid more than $45 million in cash and notes to acquire privately held DynaBil Industries of Coxsackie New York. DynaBil broadened Ducommun's product line by making titanium and aluminum structural components and assemblies for commercial and military aerospace applications.

In 2011 the company expanded its capabilities by paying about $325.3 million to acquire LaBarge. LaBarge's products —including circuit board assemblies —served customers in the aerospace and defense industries as well as the medical energy and industrial markets. The deal added more than 10 manufacturing sites in six states to Ducommun's assets.

EXECUTIVES

VP Treasurer and CFO, Joseph P. (Joe) Bellino, age 63, $378,965 total compensation

Chairman and CEO, Anthony J. (Tony) Reardon, age 64, $628,269 total compensation

President and COO, Joel H. Benkie, $412,115 total compensation

Vice President Operations, Chuy Gonzalez

Chief Fin Officer Vp Sec Treas, James Heiser

Vice President Business Development, Tim Shumate

Vice President Corporate Quality, Jens Hauvn

Chairman and CEO, Anthony J. (Tony) Reardon, age 64

Auditors: PricewaterhouseCoopersLLP

LOCATIONS

HQ: Ducommun Inc.
23301 Wilmington Avenue, Carson, CA 90745-6209
Phone: 310 513-7200
Web: www.ducommun.com

PRODUCTS/OPERATIONS

2013 Sales

	$ mil.	% of total
LaBarge Technologies	421.4	57
AeroStructures	315.2	43
Total	**736.6**	**100**

2013 Sales

	$ mil.	% of total
Military & space	397.7	54
Commercial aerospace	213.2	30
Industrial	46.6	6
Medical & other	40.0	5
Natural resources	39.1	5
Total	**736.6**	**100**

2013 Sales

	% of total
Boeing	18
Raytheon	10
Next top eight customers	29
Other	43
Total	**100**

Selected Capabilities

Ducommun Aerostructures
  Assembly
  Bonding
  Forming
  Machining
  Tooling
Ducommun LaBarge Technologies
  Assembly
  Prototyping
  System integration
Ducommun Miltec
  Acoustics
  Aerodynamics
  Aviation and UAV sensors
  Configuration design
  Explosives testing & handling
  Infrasound sensor technology
  Mine detection
  Training & logistics

COMPETITORS

AIM Aviation
B/E Aerospace
Barnes Group
CPI Aerostructures
Esterline
GE
Kreisler Manufacturing
L-3 Avionics
LMI Aerospace
Lockheed Martin
Magellan Aerospace
Orbit International
Spirit AeroSystems
Triumph Aerostructures - Vought Aircraft Division

HISTORICAL FINANCIALS

Company Type: Public

Income Statement

FYE: December 31

	REVENUE ($ mil.)	NET INCOME ($ mil.)	NET PROFIT MARGIN	EMPLOYEES
12/13	736.6	9.3	1.3%	3,264
12/12	747.0	16.4	2.2%	3,294
12/11	580.9	(47.5)	—	3,541
12/10	408.4	19.8	4.9%	1,815
12/09	430.7	10.1	2.4%	1,872
Annual Growth	**14.4%**	**(2.1%)**	**—**	**14.9%**

2013 Year-End Financials

Debt ratio: 43.5%
Return on equity: 4.0%
Cash ($ mil.): 48
Current ratio: 3.19
Long-term debt ($ mil.): 332
No. of shares (mil.): 10
Dividends
  Yield: —
  Payout: —
Market value ($ mil.): 322

	STOCK PRICE ($) FY Close	P/E High/Low		PER SHARE ($) Earnings	Dividends	Book Value
12/13	29.81	36	17	0.86	0.00	22.16
12/12	16.17	11	5	1.55	0.00	21.02
12/11	12.75	—	—	(4.52)	0.08	19.38
12/10	21.78	13	9	1.87	0.30	24.19
12/09	18.71	21	12	0.97	0.30	22.38
Annual Growth	**12.3%**		**—**	**(3.0%)**	**—**	**(0.2%)**

DuPont Fabros Technology Inc

DuPont Fabros Technology's server farms corral a lot of data. The company owns develops operates and manages 10 wholesale data centers — the facilities that house power and cool computer servers for such technology companies as Facebook Rackspace Microsoft and Yahoo! Other tenants come from the media communications health care and financial services industries. Organized as a real estate investment trust (REIT) DuPont Fabros is exempt from paying federal income tax as long as it makes quarterly distributions to shareholders.

Operations

The company establishes its rental rates based on the amount of power reserved for tenant use and the square footage they occupy. As a wholesale provider the company targets clients with high power requirements and a preference for long-term leases. DuPont Fabros Technology develops its wholesale data centers to compete with more traditional colocation models in which managed services are bundled with power and cooling. Wholesale customers typically install and maintain their own servers.

Geographic Reach

DuPont Fabros Technology owns and operates 10 data centers —seven in northern Virginia one in suburban Chicago one in New Jersey and one in California - totaling 1.2 million square feet of server space. It has another five in development primarily expansion projects at existing sites and three undeveloped land sites.

Sales and Marketing

The company's four largest tenants —Facebook Microsoft Rackspace and Yahoo! —account for about two-thirds of rental revenue. Former tenant Google now operates its own data centers.

Financial Performance

DuPont Fabros Technology has experienced six straight years of revenue growth as demand for data centers continues to increase. Overall sales were up 12% in 2013 to $375 million as it signed several new leases. The company has also been consistently profitable. After posting record profits in 2011 it experienced a decline in 2012 and 2013 mostly due to property operating costs real estate taxes and insurance and depreciation and amortization.

Strategy

The company's primary focus for 2014 is to lease its available vacant space. In 2013 only two of its data centers had vacant space and more space will become available by 2015 when it expands two more sites. (One new California site is already 50% pre-leased.)

EXECUTIVES

V Pres, Maria Kenny, age 48
Chief Accounting Officer, Jeffrey H. Foster, age 51, $231,750 total compensation
EVP Operations, Scott A. Davis, age 54
EVP General Counsel, Richard A. (Rick) Montfort, age 53, $284,000 total compensation
President and CEO, Christopher (Chris) Eldredge
Vice President, Cantrell Tate
Vice President Essential Infrastructure, Bob Rosenberger
Vice President Client Infrastructure And Technology, Doug Steinberg
Board Member, Thomas D Eckert, age 67
Chairman, Lammot J. du Pont, age 47
Board Member, John T Roberts, age 51
Auditors: Ernst&YoungLLP

LOCATIONS

HQ: DuPont Fabros Technology Inc
1212 New York Avenue N.W., Suite 900, Washington, DC 20005
Phone: 202 728-0044
Web: www.dft.com

PRODUCTS/OPERATIONS

2013 Sales

	$ mil.	% of total
Base rent	265.7	71
Recoveries from tenant	104.3	28
Other revenues	5.1	1
Total	**375.1**	**100**

COMPETITORS

AT&T	QTS Realty Trust Inc.
CoreSite	Rackspace
CyrusOne	SAVVIS
Digital Realty	Terremark Worldwide
Equinix	Verizon
Internap Network Services	

HISTORICAL FINANCIALS

Company Type: Public

Income Statement

FYE: December 31

	REVENUE ($ mil.)	NET INCOME ($ mil.)	NET PROFIT MARGIN	EMPLOYEES
12/13	375.1	48.3	12.9%	92
12/12	332.4	53.0	16.0%	93
12/11	287.4	64.9	22.6%	91
12/10	242.5	30.4	12.6%	83
12/09	200.2	1.7	0.9%	70
Annual Growth	**17.0%**	**129.2%**	**—**	**7.1%**

2013 Year-End Financials

Debt ratio: 32.4%	No. of shares (mil.): 65
Return on equity: 2.8%	Dividends
Cash ($ mil.): 38	Yield: 3.8%
Current ratio: 0.49	Payout: 380.0%
Long-term debt ($ mil.): 869	Market value ($ mil.): 1,611

	STOCK PRICE ($) FY Close	P/E High/Low	Earnings	Dividends	Book Value
12/13	24.71	86 67	0.32	0.95	25.14
12/12	24.16	71 49	0.41	0.62	27.16
12/11	24.22	37 27	0.71	0.48	26.53
12/10	21.27	54 31	0.51	0.44	25.86
12/09	17.99	445 52	0.04	0.08	24.88
Annual Growth	**8.3%**	**— —**	**68.2%**	**85.6%**	**0.3%**

DXP Enterprises, Inc.

DXP Enterprises (DXP) knows that distribution is the quickest way to a customer's doorstep. The company is a distributor of industrial products and services through its three main segments Service Centers Supply Chain Services and Innovative Pumping Solutions. Generating the majority of sales the company's service centers offer bearing rotating fluid power and power transmission products and safety equipment as well as technical design and logistics services. Industries served include agriculture chemical construction food and beverage mining and municipal government. DXP operates from about 150 locations throughout North America.

Geographic Reach

DXP serves 50000 customers from more than 150 locations in 38 states seven provinces from Canada and one state in Mexico. The US generates 95% of its total sales while Canada accounts for the remainder.

Operations

The Service Centers segment 71% of sales operates more than 120 outlets and seven distribution centers. The segment distributes more than a million primarily MRO (maintenance repair operating) items. More than 60000 of them are stock keeping units.

Managing customers' supply chains including inventory the Supply Chain Services segment 15% of sales operates through outlets at more than 50 of its customers' facilities. It offers several software programs to help customers manage their supply chains including SmartAgreement for procuring items from service centers and SmartStore an e-Catalog.

With eight facilities in Arizona Colorado Louisiana Nebraska and Texas the Innovative Pumping Solutions segment 14% of sales helps clients with capital equipment by offering such services as fabrication and technical design.

Financial Performance

DXP has enjoyed unprecedented growth over the years. Revenues increased 36% in 2012 to reach the $1 billion mark for the first time in its history. Profits also skyrocketed 62% from $31 million in 2011 to peak at a record high of $51 million in 2012.

The growth for 2012 was fueled by a 58% rise in Supply Chain Services sales. Services Centers also experienced growth of 30%; Innovative Pumping Solutions 8%. The company also generated an additional 5% of its total revenue from Canada marking the first time it had ever generated sales from that country.

These rises were the result of previous acquisitions the company has made coupled with a surge in sales of pumps bearings safety products and industrial supplies for customers in the oil and energy sectors.

Strategy

Unlike many of its smaller competitors DXP benefits from having a comprehensive product inventory. It operates as a first-tier distributor getting its products directly from manufacturers which typically allows it to offer very competitive pricing on the goods that it distributes. With more product offerings the company is able to serve a diverse range of industries and to reduce dependence on any one customer base.

Mergers and Acquisitions

DXP acquires smaller niche businesses that strengthen its offerings geographic presence and profitability. The company quickly integrates acquired products and reaps their accretive earnings. Since 2004 DXP has completed more than 25 acquisitions ranging in value from $2.2 million to $106 million and it continues to gobble up market share in Canada.

In 2013 DXP entered a new market for rotating equipment through the purchase of Alaska Pump & Supply a provider and distributor of pump products and process equipment based in Alaska. The company also purchased National Process Equipment (Natpro) a Canadian distributor of pumps and Tucker Tool Company a distributor of abrasives coolants and machine shop supplies.

In 2012 DXP expanded its offerings by acquiring Canadian industrial safety services company HSE Integrated for about $85 million. HSE provides such services as gas detection air quality monitoring and fire protection. Other 2012 purchases included the acquisitions of Pump & Power Equipment Aledco and Force Engineered Products. All three firms are distributors of pump products process equipment and related services and the buy-outs allowed DXP to boost its rotating equipment product division.

Ownership

DXP executive David Vinson owns more than 20% of the company. Chairman and CEO David Little and FMR LLC each own 10%.

EXECUTIVES

SVP Finance; CFO; and Secretary, Mac McConnell, age 60, $170,000 total compensation
Chairman of the Board; President; Chief Executive Officer, David R. Little, age 62, $448,000 total compensation
SVP Innovative Pumping Solutions, David C. Vinson, age 63, $140,000 total compensation
Senior Vice President - Supply Chain Services and Marketing, John J. Jeffery, age 46, $140,000 total compensation

Senior Vice President - Service Centers, Todd
  Hamlin
Senior Vice President - Information Technology,
  Wayne Crane
Vice President Human Resources, Tracey Palak
Senior Vice President Corporate Dev, Kent Yee
Senior Vice President; General Counsel, Gary
  Messersmith
Vice President Of Operations, Aaron Haggerty
Regional Sales Vice President, Bill Kiefer
Vice President Of Marketing And Sales Strategy,
  Tom Atkinson
Vice President Operations, Jerry Ones
Vice President, Perry Pellman
**Chairman of the Board; President; Chief
  Executive Officer,** David R. Little, age 62

LOCATIONS

HQ: DXP Enterprises, Inc.
  7272 Pinemont, Houston, TX 77040
Phone: 713 996-4700
Web: www.dxpe.com

2012 Sales

	% of total
US	95
Canada	5
Total	**100**

PRODUCTS/OPERATIONS

2012 Sales

	$ mil.	% of total
Service Centers	779.0	71
Supply Chain Services	161.8	15
Innovative Pumping Solutions	156.3	14
Total	**1097.1**	**100**

COMPETITORS

Applied Industrial	Kaman
Technologies	MSC Industrial Direct
Dillon Supply	Production Tool Supply
DoALL	W.W. Grainger
Industrial	
Distribution Group	

HISTORICAL FINANCIALS

Company Type: Public

Income Statement

FYE: December 31

	REVENUE ($ mil.)	NET INCOME ($ mil.)	NET PROFIT MARGIN	EMPLOYEES
12/13	1,241.5	60.2	4.9%	3,207
12/12	1,097.1	50.9	4.6%	2,817
12/11	807.0	31.4	3.9%	2,093
12/10	656.2	19.3	3.0%	1,772
12/09	583.2	(42.4)	—	1,697
Annual Growth 20.8%		—	—	17.2%

2013 Year-End Financials

Debt ratio: 30.6%	No. of shares (mil.): 14
Return on equity: 23.8%	Dividends
Cash ($ mil.): 5	Yield: —
Current ratio: 2.11	Payout: —
Long-term debt ($ mil.): 168	Market value ($ mil.): 1,650

	STOCK PRICE ($) FY Close	P/E High/Low		PER SHARE ($) Earnings	Dividends	Book Value
12/13	115.20	27	12	3.94	0.00	20.69
12/12	49.07	14	9	3.35	0.00	14.92
12/11	32.20	15	8	2.08	0.00	11.10
12/10	24.00	17	8	1.32	0.00	8.82
12/09	13.07	—	—	(3.24)	0.00	6.97
Annual Growth 72.3%		—	—	—	—	31.2%

Dycom Industries, Inc.

The telecommunications industry dials up Dycom Industries for construction and engineering assistance. Operating through more than 30 subsidiaries the company primarily designs builds and maintains coaxial copper and fiber-optic cable systems for local and long-distance phone companies and cable television operators. Dycom also provides wiring services for businesses and government agencies installs and maintains electrical lines for electric and gas utilities and locates underground wires and pipelines for excavators. Dycom operates in the US and Canada.

Sales and Marketing As a specialty contractor Dycom is dependent upon the needs of telecom and utility companies. It has a limited number of customers with the top five representing about 60% of sales. AT&T CenturyLink and Comcast are its top customers together accounting for 40% of sales. Work for telecom companies make up the majority of revenue; utility companies account for about 10%.

Financial Performance Revenue in fiscal 2012 (ended July) rose 16% to $1.2 billion the second consecutive year of growth for Dycom after the recession led to a decline in sales in 2009 and 2010. Net income also grew that year jumping about 145% to $39 million. The company's largest segment construction services to telecommunications providers increased nearly 20% due to some significant new customer contracts and enhancements to existing contracts. It also saw an increase in sales to utility and other customers. Dycom reported a drop in the underground facility locating segment (as it has the past several years) amid a planned pullback on technician intensive customer contracts.

Strategy Dycom has benefited from the growing demand for converged voice video and data services a trend that requires the expansion and enhancement of telecommunications networks. It is also poised to take advantage of the continued need for mobile broadband as more consumers turn to smartphones and tablets.

Mergers and Acquisitions Dycom has a history of growth through strategic acquisitions. In late 2012 the company purchased the telecommunications infrastructure services business of Quanta Services for $275 million. The deal expands its rural engineering and construction operations and enhances its technical services customer roster and geographic scope. In 2010 Dycom acquired Georgia-based NeoCom Solutions for $27.5 million in cash. NeoCom provided engineering services such as tower construction for telecom government and energy companies.

HISTORY

Floyd Younkin (who died in 1997) founded Mobile Home Dynamics in 1969 to sell mobile homes. In 1981 Thomas Pledger who had a background in utility services joined the firm which began providing services to the electrical and telecommunications industries. The shift prompted the firm to change its name to Dycom short for "dynamic communications." Pledger was named president and CEO in 1984.

Dycom grew through acquisitions in the 1980s when it mainly installed fiber-optic cable for long-distance carriers. During the early 1990s the company suffered from management feuding lost contracts and shareholder lawsuits. However it continued to make acquisitions including North Carolina-based Globe Communications (1992). In 1993 a $24.3 million write-off for the earlier acquisitions of Ansco and Ivy H. Smith Company led to a loss and massive layoffs.

In 1997 Dycom acquired the Communications Construction Group bringing the company more business in the cable TV industry. The purchase also strengthened Dycom's presence in the Midwest Northeast and Mid-Atlantic states. The next year the firm bought Missouri-based Installation Technicians and Georgia-based Cable Com. In 1999 Steven Nielsen took the helm as CEO (Pledger became chairman then retired in 2001). Also that year Dycom acquired companies in Kentucky North Carolina and Washington.

Dycom's business expanded in the late 1990s mainly as a result of telecom deregulation and the rise of the Internet. But the new millennium brought new challenges.

Acquiring telecommunication infrastructure and construction services companies across the US Dycom broadened its customer base in 2000. The purchase of Louisiana-based Point to Point Communications gave Dycom access to Point's two biggest customers: WorldCom and Genuity. Also that year the company acquired Utah-based Niels Fugal Sons which serves the western US.

Despite making five acquisitions during its 2001 fiscal year a slowing economy forced Dycom to temporarily ease off its aggressive buying spree. Nielsen took on the additional title of chairman the next year following Pledger's retirement. After a few of its top customers reduced spending Dycom was forced to reduce its 7200-member workforce by 1000 in an effort to cut costs. In 2002 the company acquired Arguss Communications.

Later that year however Adelphia Communications which was one of Dycom's largest customers filed for bankruptcy protection and halted construction adding to Dycom's financial woes. To cut costs after its top customers pulled back on spending it once again looked to workforce reductions. The company continued to make acquisitions though purchasing Arguss Communications in 2002 and First South Utility Construction and underground utility locator UtiliQuest in 2003. In 2005 it bought customer premise equipment (CPE) installer Prince Telecom and in 2006 it acquired CPE installer Cable Express Holding from H.I.G. Capital for about $63 million.

In late 2010 Dycom bought the assets of Communications Services Inc. (CSI) a provider of outside plant construction services for around $10 million. CSI primarily provides its services to telecom companies in the southeastern and south central US.

EXECUTIVES

Chairman President and CEO, Steven E. Nielsen, age 51, $793,743 total compensation
EVP and COO, Timothy R. Estes, age 60, $542,391 total compensation
SVP and CFO, H. Andrew (Drew) DeFerrari, age 46, $376,065 total compensation
Vice President Of Internal Audit, Adair Barton
Chairman President and CEO, Steven E. Nielsen, age 51
Treasury Manager, Linda Klein
Auditors: Deloitte&ToucheLLP

LOCATIONS

HQ: Dycom Industries, Inc.
11770 US Highway 1, Suite 101, Palm Beach Gardens, FL 33408
Phone: 561 627-7171   **Fax:** 561 627-7709
Web: www.dycomind.com

PRODUCTS/OPERATIONS

2012 Sales

	$ mil.	% of total
Telecommunications	1015	84
Underground facility locating	131	11
Electric utilities & other	55	5
Total	**1201**	**100**

Selected Services

Construction maintenance and installation
Electric and gas utilities and other construction and maintenance
Engineering
Premise wiring
Underground facility locating

Selected Subsidiaries

Ansco & Associates LLC (North Carolina)
Broadband Express LLC (Ohio)
C-2 Utility Contractors LLC (Oregon)
CableCom LLC (Washington)
Cable Connectors LLC (South Carolina)
Can-Am Communications Inc. (Washington)
CAVO Broadband Communications LLC (Illinois)
Communications Construction Group LLC (Pennsylvania)
Ervin Cable Construction LLC (Kentucky)
Globe Communications LLC (South Carolina)
Installation Technicians LLC (Tennessee)
Ivy H. Smith Company LLC (North Carolina)
Lambert' s Cable Splicing Company LLC (North Carolina)
Locating Inc. (Georgia)
Midtown Express LLC (New York)
Nichols Construction LLC (Virgina)
Niels Fugal Sons Company LLC (Utah)
Point to Point Communications Inc. (Florida)
Precision Valley Communications of Vermont LLC (Vermont)
Prince Telecom LLC (Delaware)
RJE Canada ULC (Alberta Canada)
RJE Telecom LLC (Florida)
Star Construction LLC (Tennessee)
Stevens Communications LLC (Georgia)
S.T.S. LLC (Georgia)
TCS Communications LLC (Colorado)
Tesinc LLC (Florida)
Triple-D Communications LLC (Kentucky)
Underground Specialties LLC (Oregon)
UtiliQuest LLC (Georgia)
White Mountain Cable Construction LLC (New Hampshire)

COMPETITORS

Comm-Works	MDU Construction
EMCOR	Services
Fortress International	MYR Group
Group	MasTec
Goldfield	Pike Corporation

Henkels & McCoy
Integrated Electrical Services
LCC International
Quanta Services
Sirti
WPCS International
Willbros

HISTORICAL FINANCIALS

Company Type: Public

Income Statement

FYE: July 26

	REVENUE ($ mil.)	NET INCOME ($ mil.)	NET PROFIT MARGIN	EMPLOYEES
07/14	1,811.5	39.9	2.2%	10,592
07/13	1,608.6	35.1	2.2%	10,822
07/12	1,201.1	39.3	3.3%	8,111
07/11	1,035.8	16.1	1.6%	8,320
07/10	988.6	5.8	0.6%	8,897
Annual Growth	**16.3%**	**61.7%**	**—**	**4.5%**

2014 Year-End Financials

Debt ratio: 37.7%
Return on equity: 8.7%
Cash ($ mil.): 20
Current ratio: 3.08
Long-term debt ($ mil.): 446

No. of shares (mil.): 33
Dividends
  Yield: —
  Payout: —
Market value ($ mil.): 981

	STOCK PRICE ($) FY Close	P/E High/Low	PER SHARE ($) Earnings	Dividends	Book Value
07/14	28.85	28 21	1.15	0.00	14.27
07/13	26.48	25 12	1.04	0.00	12.88
07/12	17.68	20 11	1.14	0.00	11.70
07/11	17.04	40 16	0.45	0.00	10.51
07/10	9.05	95 52	0.15	0.00	10.21
Annual Growth	**33.6%**	**— —**	**66.4%**	**—**	**8.7%**

Dynex Capital, Inc.

Dynex Capital is a real estate investment trust (REIT) that invests in loans and fixed-income securities backed by single-family residential and commercial mortgage loans. The company isn't too picky investing in both investment-grade and subprime loans and adjustable-rate and fixed-rate loans. However citing competition and a "lack of compelling opportunities" in a volatile marketplace the company makes few new investments and has been slimming down its balance sheet by selling off assets including all of its manufactured home lending and delinquent property-tax receivable portfolios.

Operations
The company's residential mortgage-backed securities (MBS) operations accounted for more than 60% in 2012 followed by commercial MBS which accounted for 25%.

Financial Performance
Dynex Capital has enjoyed strong steady growth in the wake of the recession. Its revenues increased 47% from $83 million in 2011 to $122 million in 2012 due to growth within its Agency MBS portfolio. An increase in Non-Agency MBS also contributed to growth as a result of a higher average balance as well as a favorable increase in interest income for 2012. The company's net income also skyrocketed 86% to $74 million in 2012 from $40 million in 2011 due to the revenue surge and a rise in the gain on sale of investments.

Strategy

During 2012 Dynex Capital sold about 2.3 million shares of stock for a total of $56 million. It used the proceeds to cover expenses to acquire additional investments and for general corporate purposes.

EXECUTIVES

Vice President Information Systems, John Goodhue
Assistant Vice President Investor Relations, Alison G Griffin
Vice President Controller And Principal Accounting Officer, Jeffrey Childress
Vp Risk Management, Robert M Nilson
VP and Treasurer, Stephen J. Benedetti, age 52, $375,000 total compensation
President CEO and Co-Chief Investment Officer, Byron L. Boston, age 55, $600,000 total compensation
EVP and Co-Chief Investment Officer, Smriti L. Popenoe
Vp Portfolio, Wayne E Brockwell
Vice President Portfolio, Todd Kuimjian
Chairman, Thomas B. (Tom) Akin, age 63
Auditors: BDOSeidmanLLP

LOCATIONS

HQ: Dynex Capital, Inc.
4991 Lake Brook Drive, Suite 100, Glen Allen, VA 23060-9245
Phone: 804 217-5800

PRODUCTS/OPERATIONS

2012 Sales

	% mil.	% of total
Agency MBS	77.7	64
Non Agency MBS	30.0	25
Gain on sale of investments	8.4	7
Securitized mortgage loans & others	6.0	4
Total	**122.1**	**100**

COMPETITORS

BRT Realty	Redwood Trust
Capstead Mortgage	Starwood Property
Duff & Phelps	Triangle Capital
Hercules Technology	iStar Financial Inc
Impac Mortgage	
Holdings	

HISTORICAL FINANCIALS

Company Type: Public

Income Statement

FYE: December 31

	REVENUE ($ mil.)	NET INCOME ($ mil.)	NET PROFIT MARGIN	EMPLOYEES
12/13	127.1	68.0	53.5%	18
12/12	113.5	74.0	65.2%	17
12/11	83.3	39.8	47.7%	15
12/10	48.7	29.4	60.4%	15
12/09	39.2	17.5	44.8%	13
Annual Growth	**34.2%**	**40.3%**	**—**	**8.5%**

2013 Year-End Financials

Debt ratio: 0.3%
Return on equity: 11.3%
Cash ($ mil.): 69
Current ratio: 0.04
Long-term debt ($ mil.): 12

No. of shares (mil.): 54
Dividends
  Yield: 14.0%
  Payout: 103.7%
Market value ($ mil.): 434

STOCK PRICE ($)		P/E		PER SHARE ($)		
	FY Close	High/Low		Earnings	Dividends	Book Value
12/13	8.00	10	7	1.10	1.12	10.79
12/12	9.44	8	7	1.35	1.15	11.36
12/11	9.13	11	7	1.03	1.09	9.20
12/10	10.92	7	6	1.41	0.98	9.64
12/09	8.73	9	6	1.02	0.92	12.11
Annual Growth	(2.2%)	—	—	1.9%	5.0%	(2.9%)

Eagle Bancorp Inc (MD)

For those nest eggs that need a little help hatching holding company Eagle Bancorp would recommend its community-oriented EagleBank subsidiary. The bank serves businesses and individuals through more than 15 branches in Washington DC and its suburbs. Deposit products include checking savings and money market accounts; certificates of deposit; and IRAs. Commercial real estate and construction real estate loans combined represent about 70% of its loan portfolio. The bank which has significant expertise as a Small Business Administration lender also writes business consumer and home equity loans. EagleBank offers insurance products through an agreement with The Meltzer Group.

Financial Performance

Eagle Bancorp's revenue and net income have been trending up year-over-year. Its annual revenue increased in fiscal 2013 compared to the prior year. Eagle Bancorp reported $182 million in revenue for fiscal 2013 up from $163.3 million in fiscal 2012.

The company's net income also increased in fiscal 2013 versus the previous fiscal period. It reported $47 million in net income for fiscal 2013 up from $35 million in fiscal 2012.

Eagle Bancorp's cash on hand spiked from $15 million in fiscal 2012 up to more than $258 million by the end of fiscal 2013.

Strategy

The company has been focused on growing within its existing markets. Its strategy for further growth includes continuing to seek opportunities to open or acquire new banking locations while waiting out record low interest rates. Eagle's strict loan underwriting standards —it didn't write subprime residential mortgages and didn't buy securities backed by subprime mortgages —has helped it have fewer problem loans the downfall for many banks.

EXECUTIVES

Vp Marketing, Janette Shaw
Senior Vice President, Matthew Leydig
EVP and CFO, James H. Langmead, $300,500 total compensation
EVP, Susan G. Riel, $365,500 total compensation
President Community Banking of EagleBank, Thomas D. Murphy, $289,200 total compensation
Chairman President and CEO, Ronald D. Paul, $667,000 total compensation
EVP and COO, Michael T. Flynn, $236,080 total compensation
EVP and General Counsel, Laurence E. Bensignor
Vice President And Team Leader, John A Beck

Executive Vice President Chief Deposit, Steven A Reeder
Vice President Wire And Cash Room, Joan Grant
Vice President And Operations, Terry Clarke
Vice President Commercial Loan Ofc, Lisa Knapp
Vice President Branch Operations, Susan Lewis
Vice President Commercial Loan Officer, Scott Kinlaw
Assistant Vice President, Michele Capone
Assistant Vice President Loan Officer, Christine Andrukitis
Senior Vice President And Controller, Terry Weber
Vice President, Michael Brooks
Vice President Officer Cmcl Lending, Rob Powell
Vice President Commercial Real Estate Lender, Timothy Annett
Vice President Workout Recovery Lqd Ofc, Jodee Lichtenstein
Sr Vice President Mgr Res Lending Div, Roshan Alavi
Vice President, Jacqueline Ames
Senior Vice President And Director, Lisa Punt
Vice President Of Marketing, Jane Cornett
Senior Vice President, John Bettini
Assistant Vice President Cash Management Officer, Alexis Santin
Vice President Deposit Operations, Judy Callaway
Assistant Vice President, Christie Washington
Executive Vice President, Wayne Schisler
Vice President Senior Mortgage Banker, Raj Mahajan
Assistant Vice President Accounting, Linda Collins
Vice President Commercial Lending Deposit Officer Ii, Linda Dawkins
Assistant Vice President, Samantha Perry
Vice President, Clarice Ribeiro
Assistant Vice President Branch Relationship Manager Ii, Christian Videla
Assistant Vice President Commercial, Niki Sabir
Vice President Treasury Management Officer, Deborah Cabala-moshides
Vice Chairman, Robert P. Pincus
Chairman President and CEO, Ronald D. Paul
Auditors: Stegman&Company

LOCATIONS

HQ: Eagle Bancorp Inc (MD)
7830 Old Georgetown Road, Third Floor, Bethesda, MD 20814
Phone: 301 986-1800
Web: www.eaglebankcorp.com

PRODUCTS/OPERATIONS

Selected Subsidiaries
EagleBank
　Bethesda Leasing LLC
　Eagle Insurance Services LLC
　Fidelity Mortgage Inc.
Eagle Commercial Ventures LLC

COMPETITORS

BB&T	OBA Financial Services
Bank of America	PNC Financial
Capital One	Sandy Spring Bancorp
First Mariner Bancorp	SunTrust
M&T Bank	

HISTORICAL FINANCIALS

Company Type: Public

Income Statement

FYE: December 31

	ASSETS ($ mil.)	NET INCOME ($ mil.)	INCOME AS % OF ASSETS	EMPLOYEES
12/13	3,771.5	47.0	1.2%	386
12/12	3,409.4	35.2	1.0%	393
12/11	2,831.2	24.5	0.9%	338
12/10	2,089.3	16.6	0.8%	292
12/09	1,805.5	10.4	0.6%	235
Annual Growth	20.2%	45.7%	—	13.2%

2013 Year-End Financials

Return on assets: 1.3%
Return on equity: 12.6%
Long-term debt ($ mil.): —
No. of shares ($ mil.): 25
Sales ($ mil): 182

Dividends
　Yield: —
　Payout: —
Market value ($ mil.): 793

STOCK PRICE ($)		P/E		PER SHARE ($)		
	FY Close	High/Low		Earnings	Dividends	Book Value
12/13	30.63	18	11	1.76	0.00	15.22
12/12	19.97	14	10	1.46	0.00	13.86
12/11	14.54	14	11	1.04	0.00	12.15
12/10	14.43	21	14	0.70	0.00	9.45
12/09	10.47	22	11	0.50	0.00	8.76
Annual Growth	30.8%	—	—	37.0%	—	14.8%

Eagle Materials Inc

Eagle Materials is perched near the top of the building materials business. The company manufactures and distributes cement and gypsum wallboard which together account for nearly 75% of its total sales. Eagle Materials also produces ready-mix concrete aggregates and recycled paperboard. Its products are sold to residential commercial and industrial construction customers throughout the US. The company operates about 25 plants and manufacturing facilities. It also has about 140 railcars for shipping its wallboard products to customers across the country. Founded in 1963 Eagle Materials was spun off by homebuilder Centex Corporation in 2004.

Geographic Reach

Dallas-based Eagle Materials sells its gypsum wallboard throughout the US focusing on markets nearest its production facilities. The company sells cement in four regional markets including northern Nevada and California the greater Chicago area the Rocky Mountain region and Texas.

Operations

Cement is Eagle's largest business accounting for nearly 40% of its sales. In addition to wholly-owned plants in Illinois Wyoming and Nevada Eagle owns a 50% stake in Texas Lehigh Cement Co. in Buda Texas. Eagle manufactures gypsum wallboard at five plants representing about 35% of sales. Republic Paperboard Co. the company's paperboard business is located in Oklahoma and accounts for about 20% Eagle's sales. Concrete and aggregates make up the rest.

Financial Analysis

Eagle's sales rose 7% in fiscal 2012 (ends March) vs. the prior year with net income up 26% over the same period. The sales gain was the company's first in five years following the downturn in construction during the financial and housing crises. Still the $495 million Eagle rang up in fiscal 2012 was well below the more than $922 million it brought in in fiscal 2007. The uptick in 2012 sales was due to increases in average sales prices for all of Eagle's products and increased sales volumes for all of its businesses except gypsum wallboard and aggregates. Cement sales climbed 8% due to increased sales volumes in 2012 vs. 2011.

Strategy

Despite the recent uptick in sales and profits Eagle continues to struggle with softness in the building materials and construction products businesses. Commercial and residential construction activity remains at low levels and infrastructure spending has failed to take off. Indeed the company isn't forecasting a significant increase in government spending for infrastructure in the near term.

Nevertheless Eagle's Audubon Materials subsidiary agreed in late 2012 to purchase a pair of cement plans in Missouri and Oklahoma from rival Lafarge North America for about $446 million in cash. The pending purchase which also includes six distribution terminals two aggregates quarries eight ready-mix concrete plants and a fly ash business marks Eagle's return to acquisition mode. Prior to the recession the firm had designs on expansion especially in its core wallboard and cement business. The company opened a fifth gypsum wallboard plant in 2007 to increase production capacity but the addition proved untimely.

EXECUTIVES

Vice President, Rodney Cummilkez
President and CEO, Steven R. (Steve) Rowley, age 61, $885,000 total compensation
EVP Strategy Corporate Development and Communications, Robert S. (Bob) Stewart, age 60, $212,020 total compensation
VP Engineering and Technology, Franklin D. (Frank) Green, age 45
EVP General Counsel and Secretary, James H. (Jim) Graass, age 56, $365,000 total compensation
EVP Cement Aggregates and Concrete, Gerald J. (Gerry) Essl, age 64, $375,000 total compensation
EVP Gypsum, David B. (Dave) Powers, age 64, $375,000 total compensation
President Northern White Sand LLC, Kerry G. Gannaway, age 55
EVP Finance and Administration and CFO, D. Craig Kesler, age 38, $330,000 total compensation
COO, Michael Haack
Vice President Cement, Rahul Desai
Vice President Controller, Bill Devlin
Vice President Tax, Patrick Smith
Chairman, Laurence E. (Larry) Hirsch, age 68
Auditors: Ernst&YoungLLP

LOCATIONS

HQ: Eagle Materials Inc
3811 Turtle Creek Blvd., Suite 1100, Dallas, TX 75219
Phone: 214 432-2000   **Fax:** 214 432-2100
Web: www.eaglematerials.com

PRODUCTS/OPERATIONS

2012 Sales

	$ mil.	% of total
Cement	244.0	39
Gypsum wallboard	217.6	35
Recycled paperboard	118.8	19
Concrete & aggregates	45.5	7
Adjustments	(130.9)	
Total	**495**	**100**

Selected Subsidiaries
American Gypsum Company
Centex Materials
Illinois Cement Company
Mathews Readymix
Mountain Cement Company
Nevada Cement Company
Republic Paperboard Company
Texas Leigh Cement Company (50%)
Western Aggregates

COMPETITORS

BPB	Lehigh Hanson
Boral	Martin Marietta
CEMEX Inc.	Materials
Caraustar	New NGC
Georgia-Pacific	TXI
Holcim (US)	U.S. Concrete
Lafarge North America	USG

HISTORICAL FINANCIALS
Company Type: Public

Income Statement
FYE: March 31

	REVENUE ($ mil.)	NET INCOME ($ mil.)	NET PROFIT MARGIN	EMPLOYEES
03/14	898.4	124.2	13.8%	1,800
03/13	642.5	57.7	9.0%	1,800
03/12	495.0	18.7	3.8%	1,350
03/11	462.1	14.8	3.2%	1,350
03/10	467.9	28.9	6.2%	1,350
Annual Growth	17.7%	43.9%	—	7.5%

2014 Year-End Financials

Debt ratio: 25.2%	No. of shares (mil.): 50
Return on equity: 16.2%	Dividends
Cash ($ mil.): 6	Yield: 0.4%
Current ratio: 2.82	Payout: 18.3%
Long-term debt ($ mil.): 371	Market value ($ mil.): 4,438

	STOCK PRICE ($) FY Close	P/E High/Low		PER SHARE ($) Earnings	Dividends	Book Value
03/14	88.66	36	24	2.49	0.40	16.61
03/13	66.63	58	24	1.22	0.40	14.06
03/12	34.75	85	37	0.42	0.30	10.44
03/11	30.26	96	64	0.34	0.40	10.34
03/10	26.54	45	34	0.66	0.40	10.16
Annual Growth	35.2%	—	—	39.4%	(0.0%)	13.1%

Ebix Inc

Ebix knows a lot about the insurance biz. The company sells insurance industry software products and professional services to property/casualty insurers brokerages and individuals in Asia Australia Europe and North America. The company's EbixExchange service acts as an online auction house where buyers and carriers can exchange bids for auto home health life and other types of insurance while paying Ebix a fee on each transaction. Ebix also provides agency management software that includes workflow and customer relationship management (CRM) capabilities as well as other back-office functions for insurance brokers and insurance carriers. The company generates most of its sales in North America.

Geographic Reach

Atlanta-based Ebix's #1 market is the US accounting for about two-thirds of its sales. Australia accounts for nearly 20%. The firm's international operations are managed from Singapore. The Company has more than 35 offices across the US Australia Singapore New Zealand Canada China Japan and India.

Operations

About 80% of Ebix's revenue is generated by on-demand insurance Exchanges including life insurance annuity employee benefits and property and casualty exchanges. In addition to its insurance exchanges and software products Ebix also offers custom software development and business process outsourcing (BPO) services.

Financial Performance

Ebix has experienced impressive growth over the past decade with its revenue more than doubling since 2009. The company reported sales of $204.7 million in 2013 an 2% increase versus 2012. Net income declined 16% over the same period to $59.2 million mainly due to increases in operating expenses and a $4 million payment for litigation settlement.

The company has always been profitable and a handful of recent acquisitions have expanded its service offerings and geographic footprint as well as doubling its headcount since 2009. In 2012 Forbes ranked Ebix as the sixth fastest-growing technology company in the US with three-year average sales growth of 32% per year.

Strategy

Ebix recently experienced a failed bid by an affiliate of Goldman Sachs to take it private. In May 2013 Goldman Sachs offered to buy Ebix for $820 million but decided to nix the deal a month later after Ebix was notified about an investigation into allegations of intentional misconduct over a pending shareholder class action lawsuit. Ebix had been transparent about the lawsuit which was filed before the proposed acquisition. In 2014 the lawsuit was settled.

Mergers and Acquisitions

Ebix is an acquisitive company that buys others to expand its product lines customer base and geographic footprint. Most recently in May 2014 it bought Healthcare Magic whose "Ask a Doctor" service allows patients to pose a question to a network of 15000 physicians. In April 2013 it paid $5 million for UK-based Qatarlyst Limited an electronic trading exchange for the global insurance and reinsurance industry.

In 2012 it made four acquisitions beginning with Taimma Communications a developer of applications used by the pharmaceutical and biotech industries for medical training purposes. Next it bought Fintechnix a supplier of Web-based e-commerce applications for the life insurance and wealth management industries in Australia to boost its profile in the Asia/Pacific region. Then came PlanetSoft a developer of data exchange applications for the insurance industry for $40 million which expanded its operations in India and the US. Ebix also acquired London-based TriSystems an online insurance trading hub that enables commercial insurance and reinsurance transactions between London intermediaries and insurance companies expanding its presence in Europe. TriSystems' products and services became part of the EbixExchange division in Europe.

In 2011 Ebix paid about $66 million to buy Atlanta-based A.D.A.M. The deal gave it a boost in the health care and insurance markets. Later that year the company bought Connecticut-based health insurance and benefits online network exchange HealthConnect Systems which it integrated into the EbixHealth division. The purchase furthered Ebix's strategy to become a health information exchange (HIE).

EXECUTIVES

Chairman President and CEO, Robin Raina, age 48, $1,300,000 total compensation

CFO, Robert F. (Bob) Kerris, age 60, $175,000 total compensation

SVP Agency Systems, Graham Prior, $171,893 total compensation

SVP EbixExchange, Dan Delity

SVP Ebix Health, Jim Senge, $200,000 total compensation

Managing Director Ebix Singapore, Andy Wakefield

Managing Director Ebix Australia Group Head, Leon d'Apice, $199,665 total compensation

Managing Director Ebix New Zealand, Tony Wisniewski

Vice President Human Resources, Darren Joseph

Vp Sales, Sharon Greener

Vice President Product Development, Valerie Troffer

Vice President Of Technology, Ashley Franco

Sales Vice President, Doug Massey

Senior Vice President, Dale Okuno

Vice President Content, Cyndi Logan

Vice President Property Casualty Div, Jon Mayo

Vice President, Val Moeller

Vice President Operations Ebix Bpo, Jennifer Madsen

Vice President Health Exchange Solutions Governmen, Ellen Milantoni

Vice President Ebix Latin America, Mario Nogueira

Vice President, Thierry Semoff

Vice President, Jeffrey A Howard

Senior Vice President, Steve Isaac

Vice President Insurance Technologies, Ken Leibow

Vp It, Jan Ruffing

Vice President, Morgan Humphries

Assistant Vice President, Joan Hayes

Vice President Of Business Solutions, Bob Seese

Vice President Of Operations, Ronda Kerr

Vice President, Sherri Isaacson

Chairman President and CEO, Robin Raina, age 48

Secretary Treasurer, Bob Sanchez

Treasurer Secretary Systems Data, Don Campbell

Auditors: HabifArogeti&WynneLLP

LOCATIONS

HQ: Ebix Inc
5 Concourse Parkway, Suite 3200, Atlanta, GA 30328
Phone: 678 281-2020
Web: www.ebix.com

2013 Sales

	$ mil.	% of total
US	139.5	67
Canada	7.4	4
Latin America	5.5	3
Australia	38.2	19
Singapore	3.1	2
New Zealand	2.3	1
India	0.6	-
Europe	7.9	4
Total	**204.7**	**100**

Selected Subsidiaries

Ebix.com International Inc. a Delaware corporation
Ebix International LLC a Delaware limited liability company
Ebix BPO Division - San Diego a California corporation
Jenquest Inc. a California corporation
FACTS Services Inc. a Florida corporation
E-Z Data Acquisition Sub LLC a California limited liability company

Peak Performance Solutions Inc. a Delaware limited liability company
ADAM Inc. a Georgia corporation
Agency Solutions.com LLC (d.b.a. HealthConnect Systems) a Delaware limited liability company
Benefit Software Incorporated a California corporation
PlanetSoft Holdings Inc. a Delaware corporation
Ebix Software India Private Limited
Ebix Software India SEZ Private Limited
Premier Ebix Exchange Software Private Ltd.
Ebix Australia Pty. Ltd.
Ebix Australia (VIC) Pty. Ltd.
Ebix Exchange-Australia PTY LTD
Ebix New Zealand
Ebix New Zealand Holdings

PRODUCTS/OPERATIONS

2013 Sales

	$ mil.	% of total
Exchanges	163.9	80
Broker systems	18.4	9
Business process outsourcing	15.7	8
Carrier systems	6.7	3
Total	**204.7**	**100**

COMPETITORS

Answer Financial	Guidewire Software
Applied Systems	InsWeb
BenefitMall	Intuit
CCC Information	Life Quotes
Computer Sciences Corp.	SunGard
	The Hartford
Cover-All	TriZetto
Crawford & Company	Vertafore
Datamonitor	

HISTORICAL FINANCIALS

Company Type: Public

Income Statement

				FYE: December 31
	REVENUE ($ mil.)	NET INCOME ($ mil.)	NET PROFIT MARGIN	EMPLOYEES
12/13	204.7	59.2	29.0%	1,927
12/12	199.3	70.5	35.4%	1,903
12/11	168.9	71.3	42.2%	1,426
12/10	132.1	59.0	44.6%	1,179
12/09	97.6	38.8	39.7%	958
Annual Growth	**20.3%**	**11.2%**	**—**	**19.1%**

2013 Year-End Financials

Debt ratio: 10.2%
Return on equity: 15.0%
Cash ($ mil.): 56
Current ratio: 1.54
Long-term debt ($ mil.): 42
Dividends
  Yield: 1.5%
  Payout: 13.8%
No. of shares (mil.): 38
Market value ($ mil.): 560

	STOCK PRICE ($) FY Close	P/E High/Low		PER SHARE ($) Earnings	Dividends	Book Value
12/13	14.71	13	6	1.53	0.23	10.99
12/12	16.12	14	8	1.80	0.19	9.90
12/11	22.10	16	7	1.75	0.00	8.69
12/10	23.67	30	8	1.51	0.00	6.42
12/09	48.83	53	14	1.03	0.00	4.96
Annual Growth	**(25.9%)**	—	—	**10.4%**	—	**22.0%**

ECA Marcellus Trust I

EXECUTIVES

Ceo, Jon S Brumley

LOCATIONS

HQ: ECA Marcellus Trust I
The Bank of New York Mellon, Trust Company, N.A., Trustee, Global Corporate Trust, 919 Congress Avenue, Austin, TX 78701
Phone: 512 236-6555

HISTORICAL FINANCIALS

Company Type: Public

Income Statement

				FYE: December 31
	REVENUE ($ mil.)	NET INCOME ($ mil.)	NET PROFIT MARGIN	EMPLOYEES
12/13	30.5	29.4	96.5%	0
12/12	36.4	35.6	97.8%	0
12/11	43.5	41.8	96.2%	0
12/10	22.6	21.0	92.7%	0
Annual Growth	**10.4%**	**11.9%**	**—**	**—**

2013 Year-End Financials

Debt ratio: —
Return on equity: 11.7%
Cash ($ mil.): 1
Current ratio: 0.23
Long-term debt ($ mil.): —
No. of shares (mil.): 17
Dividends
  Yield: 25.9%
  Payout: 100.1%
Market value ($ mil.): 135

	STOCK PRICE ($) FY Close	P/E High/Low		PER SHARE ($) Earnings	Dividends	Book Value
12/13	7.67	11	4	1.67	1.99	13.32
12/12	15.27	11	6	2.48	2.39	15.16
12/11	25.58	14	10	2.38	2.29	17.32
12/10	26.55	23	16	1.19	0.69	19.18
/0.00	—	—	(0.00)	0.00	(0.00)	
Annual Growth	**—**	—	—	**—**	**—**	**—**

Echo Global Logistics Inc

By land air or sea Echo Global Logistics can help you deliver the goods. The company provides a wide range of transportation and logistics services such as carrier management rate negotiation freight bill audit and payment routing compliance and shipment execution and tracking. In addition its Evolved Transportation Manager (ETM) software analyzes clients' transportation needs and helps reduce costs as well as manages all procedures in shipping. Established in 2005 Echo Global Logistics customer base are primarily companies in the manufacturing and consumer products industries.

Geographic Reach

Echo is stationed in Chicago and has about 20 business development locations spanning 15 US states.

Operations

About 24000 transportation providers make up Echo's carrier network which consists of small and midsized fleets trucking companies and single-truck owners. Less-than-truckload and truckload services collectively account for about 90% of its total revenue.

Sales and Marketing

The company caters to nearly 28500 clients which are divided into two types: enterprise (under multiyear contracts) and transactional (services provided on a shipment-by-shipment basis). For 2012 transactional clients represented 70% of its total revenue.

Financial Performance

Echo has experienced unprecedented growth over the last few years. Revenues jumped 26% from $603 million in 2011 to reach $758 million in 2012 a historical milestone.

The growth was attributed to a major increase in its number of customers coupled with the uptick in shipment volumes. Revenue from enterprise clients jumped 19% in 2012 while revenue from transactional clients spiked 29%. Echo was also helped by $41 million in additional revenue generated in from acquisitions.

Profits also spiked 2% to reach a record high of $12.3 million in 2012 due to the recent surge in revenues and lower interest expenses.

Strategy

Although Echo's focus is on truckload (TL) less than truckload (LTL) and small parcel delivery; the company also offers intermodal (combination of rail and truck) air delivery. The company will continue to expand its geographic reach both through air and ocean modes of delivery; this strategy involves both the launching of new services and the purchasing of other businesses.

In 2013 Echo obtained Open Mile a truckload brokerage stationed in Boston. Echo enhanced its expertise in cloud computing as a result of the purchase. Throughout 2012 the company made several acquisitions including Sharp Freight Systems Purple Plum Logistics and Shipper Direct Logistics.

In 2011 the company gobbled up Rochester New York-based Trailer Transport Systems (TTS). TTS is a non-asset provider of intermodal transportation management and freight brokerage services. Its operations were integrated into the Echo Global Logistics as a regional hub.

Ownership

A group of company executives including directors Richard Heise Eric Lefkofsky and Bradley Keywell control 32% of Echo Global Logistics.

EXECUTIVES

COO, David B. (Dave) Menzel, age 52, $461,731 total compensation
CEO, Douglas R. (Doug) Waggoner, age 55, $650,000 total compensation
CTO, Nitin Kapoor
CFO, Kyle Sauers, $271,424 total compensation
Svp Human Resources, Julie Knudson
Evp-operations, Tyler Ellison
Regional V Pres, Lane Turner
Svp Talent, Cheryl Johnson
National Account Manager, Max Elias
National Account Manager, Bill Brown
Vice President Sales, John Mooney
National Account Manager, Aria Farmand
National Account Manager, Adam Russell
National Account Manager, Jordan Pinkelman
National Account Manager, Mike Decker
National Account Manager, Dustin Gale
National Account Manager, Jonathan Locke
National Accounts Manager, Brian Godla
Vice President Of Sales, Todd Muchow
National Account Manager, Ryan Haggerty
National Account Manager, Brandon Gardner
National Account Manager, Rick Cosmen
Vice President Application Development, C J Montano
National Account Manager, Eric Shahtaji
Vice President Of Truckload, Jon Fox
National Account Manager, Justin Bright
National Accounts Manager, Mike Ruane
National Account Manager, Andy Golitko
National Account Manager, Jimi Yu
National Account Manager, Joe Babcock
Vice President Of Marketing, Joseph Fahey
National Accounts Manager, Blake Dyer
National Account Manager, Gary Roycroft
National Account Manager, Cory Reiners
National Account Manager, Jared Rames
National Account Manager, Matt Fulton
Senior Vice President Aquistions, Michael Bloss
National Account Manager, Kyle Simpson
Vice President Of Pricing, Mark Redini
Vice President Of Finance Financial Controller, Pete Rogers
National Account Manager, Mark Baginski
National Accounts Manager, Sarah Embree
National Account Manager, Bernard Hurley
Vice President Technical Services, Todd Keating
National Account Manager, Erica Randle
National Account Manager, Stephanie Johnson
National Account Manager, Rea-ann Fuzy
National Account Manager, Ben Boelter
National Account Manager, Patrick Jackson
Regional Vice President, Greg Sanossian
National Account Manager, Daniel Kanter
Vice President Truckload, Andreas Katsaros
Regional Vice President, Joe Larson
National Account Manager, John Keating
National Account Manager, Josh Kemmerer
National Account Manager, Bob Poltzer
National Account Manager, Alex Fitzpatrick
National Accounts Manager, Dylan Brown
National Account Manager, Courtney Jones
National Account Manager, Ashley Knickrehm
National Account Manager, Conor Ryan
National Account Manager, Natalie Benedettini
National Account Manager, Andrew Callan
National Account Manager, Chad Ziegler
National Account Manager, Christopher Lorey
National Account Manager, Jesse Redmon
National Account Manager, Dustin Williams
National Accounts Manager, Jonathan Payne
National Account Manager, Alex Rossi
National Account Manager, Matthew Damhauser
National Account Manager, Chris Silungan
National Account Manager, Jon Carroll
National Account Manager, Matthew Kuhn
National Account Manager, Derek Jarrell
National Account Manager, Shane Kohler
National Account Manager, Richard Acuna
Board Member, Peter J Barris
Non-Executive Chairman, Samuel K. Skinner, age 75
Board Member, John R Walter
Board Member, John F Sandner
Auditors: Ernst&YoungLLP

LOCATIONS

HQ: Echo Global Logistics Inc
600 West Chicago Avenue, Suite 725, Chicago, IL 60654
Phone: 800 354-7993   **Fax:** 888 796-4445
Web: www.echo.com

PRODUCTS/OPERATIONS

2012 Sales

	% of total
LTL	45
TL	44
Small parcel	5
Intermodal	5
Other	1
Total	**100**

Selected Services

Domestic Air and Expedited Services
Flex TMS (a fee-based "software-as-a-service" transportation management system)
Inter-Modal
International air and ocean transportation services
Less than Truckload (LTL)
Small Parcel
Truckload

COMPETITORS

ABF Freight System
C.H. Robinson Worldwide
Con-way Inc.
Expeditors
FedEx
J.B. Hunt
MIQ Logistics
Ozburn-Hessey Logistics
Roadrunner Transportation Systems
Ryder System
Schneider Logistics
Total Quality Logistics
Transplace
UPS

HISTORICAL FINANCIALS

Company Type: Public

Income Statement

FYE: December 31

	REVENUE ($ mil.)	NET INCOME ($ mil.)	NET PROFIT MARGIN	EMPLOYEES
12/13	884.1	14.2	1.6%	1,297
12/12	757.6	12.3	1.6%	1,364
12/11	602.7	12.0	2.0%	913
12/10	426.3	8.4	2.0%	709
12/09	259.5	5.2	2.0%	663
Annual Growth	**35.9%**	**28.6%**	**—**	**18.3%**

2013 Year-End Financials

Debt ratio: 0.5%   No. of shares (mil.): 22
Return on equity: 9.4%   Dividends
Cash ($ mil.): 52   Yield: —
Current ratio: 2.10   Payout: —
Long-term debt ($ mil.): 1   Market value ($ mil.): 492

	STOCK PRICE ($) FY Close	P/E High/Low		PER SHARE ($) Earnings	Dividends	Book Value
12/13	21.48	36	28	0.61	0.00	6.95
12/12	17.97	35	29	0.54	0.00	6.21
12/11	16.15	33	21	0.53	0.00	5.39
12/10	12.04	42	26	0.38	0.00	4.76
12/09	12.69	51	40	0.29	0.00	4.31
Annual Growth	**14.1%**	**—**	**—**	**20.4%**	**—**	**12.7%**

Edgewater Technology Inc

Edgewater Technology tries to stay on the cutting edge of technology management consulting. The company provides management consulting designs customized software applications implements third-party software and helps enterprises optimize business processes. Its managed services division allows clients to outsource management and maintenance of IT facilities. Edgewater Technology has expertise in such markets as financial services health care insurance and higher education and targets middle-market clients and divisions of large (Global 2000) firms located mostly in the US. Edgewater counts more than 400 customers and its consultants work onsite at clients' facilities.

Operations In addition to management and technology consulting Edgewater specializes in developing enterprise performance management (EPM) systems including budgeting financial consolidation reporting and analytics and scorecarding applications.

Sales and Marketing As part of its sales and marketing efforts Edgewater maintains strategic partnerships with hardware software and tech services firms such as Informatica Google Microsoft Oracle and SAP. The partnerships include joint marketing initiatives discount pricing and sales lead sharing.

Financial Analysis Edgewater's revenue has suffered some rocky patches since 2008 when the global economic recession hit but the company saw sales jump more than 15% in 2011 to $102 million. The results are due primarily to organic growth in service revenue (more than three-fourths of overall sales) as demand for enterprise performance management (EPM) and enterprise resource planning (ERP) product-related services increased. The company eeked out a small profit in 2011 its first since 2007 on the strong revenue growth as well as a reduction in amortization and other expenses.

Mergers and Acquisitions Edgewater uses acquisitions to expand its customer base and consulting expertise. In 2010 the company bought the assets of Meridian Consulting International a Chicago-based consulting firm specializing in implementations of Oracle's Hyperion Strategic Finance product for about $4 million. The purchase helps fill out Edgewater's suite of Oracle EPM offerings and strengthens its presence in the upper Midwest region. Meridian has clients in energy health care higher education and retail. At the end of 2009 the company acquired Fullscope a consulting firm specializing in Microsoft Dynamics software. Edgewater paid $12.5 million in cash plus potential earnout payments. Fullscope provides technology consulting services and software as a national systems integrator with Microsoft in Canada and the US. In 2012 Edgewater sold Fullscope's Process Industries 2 (PI2) software to Microsoft for $3.25 million. As part of the agreement Fullscope will provide development and training support services while the PI2 module is integrated into Microsoft's enterprise ERP offering Microsoft Dynamics AX.

Ownership GAMCO Investors owns 20% of Edgewater.

HISTORY

Edgewater Technology was founded as StaffMark in 1996 when Clete Brewer and his father Jerry merged six regional staffing companies (Brewer Personnel Services founded by Clete Brewer; Prostaff Personnel; Maxwell Companies; Blethen Group; First Choice Staffing; and Human Resources Associates). The company went public in 1996 and embarked on an aggressive acquisition campaign.

In 1997 StaffMark acquired among others Structured Logic Co. a leading New York City-based IT recruiting firm. Among its acquisitions in 1998 were clinical trials support company ClinForce legal services firm Strategic Legal Resources and IT group Independent Software Services. StaffMark also branched into the UK with the purchase of placement firm Robert Walters. The next year it acquired Edgewater Technology a Boston-based Internet consulting and system integration firm founded in 1992.

With its debt load growing and its market value sinking the company decided to put its focus on the Internet and sold its Commercial Services Division (along with the StaffMark name) in 2000. Adopting the Edgewater Technology name it later spun off staffing firm Robert Walters on the London Stock Exchange and sold its IntelliMark division.

In 2001 Edgewater sold the rest of its staffing-related businesses including its ClinForce unit. In 2003 Edgewater acquired Virginia-based software and systems integration development company Intelix.

Ranzal & Associates acquired in 2004 helped companies develop business intelligence systems based primarily on Hyperion software applications.

In 2006 Edgewater acquired Connecticut-based consulting firm National Decision Systems a strategic business process consulting specialist. The acquired company brought expertise in such industry verticals as hospitality consumer goods and financial services; it also added merger and acquisition consulting and research advisory services to Edgewater's service offerings. The following year Edgewater bought three more firms with the primary goal of expanding its enterprise performance management (EPM) offerings.

EXECUTIVES

Vice President Busn Dev, Betsy Norris
Vice President, Marshall McCausland
Svp Edgewater Fullscope, Russell Smith
Corporate Vice President Enterprise Technology, Jim Wright
Managing Director, Bruce Lundie
Vice Presidetn Sap Erm, James Bushnell
Auditors: Deloitte&ToucheLLP

LOCATIONS

HQ: Edgewater Technology Inc
200 Harvard Mill Square, Suite 210, Wakefield, MA 01880-3209
Phone: 781 246-3343   **Fax:** 781 246-5903
Web: www.edgewater.com

PRODUCTS/OPERATIONS

2011 Sales

	$ mil.	% of total
Services	79.2	77
Software	13.1	13
Reimbursable expenses	7.4	7
Royalties	2.7	3
Total	**102.4**	**100**

Selected Services

Business advisory services
  Business Strategy
  Cloud
  Best Practices
  Transformational Change
Product-based consulting services
  Enterprise Performance Management (EPM)
  Enterprise Resource Planning (ERP)
  Customer Relationship Management (CRM)
Technology consulting services
  IT Strategy
  Analysis & Design
  Custom Development
  Web Solutions
  Enterprise Information Management (EIM)
  Infrastructure Services
Enterprise information management services
Analytics services

COMPETITORS

Accenture	Infosys
Bain & Company	Mattersight
Booz Allen	McKinsey & Company
Boston Consulting	Official Payments
Business & Decision SA	Holdings
CIBER	Oracle
Cognizant Tech	Perficient
Solutions	SAP
HP Enterprise Services	Sapient
Hackett Group	Tata Consultancy
Hitachi Consulting	Ventyx
IBM Global Services	Wipro

HISTORICAL FINANCIALS

Company Type: Public

Income Statement

FYE: December 31

	REVENUE ($ mil.)	NET INCOME ($ mil.)	NET PROFIT MARGIN	EMPLOYEES
12/13	103.5	34.7	33.5%	407
12/12	100.8	1.4	1.4%	395
12/11	102.4	0.3	0.3%	380
12/10	88.5	(23.5)	—	380
12/09	50.0	(3.8)	—	237
Annual Growth	**19.9%**	**—**		**14.5%**

2013 Year-End Financials

Debt ratio: —	No. of shares (mil.): 11
Return on equity: 68.5%	Dividends
Cash ($ mil.): 20	Yield: —
Current ratio: 2.53	Payout: —
Long-term debt ($ mil.): —	Market value ($ mil.): 77

	STOCK PRICE ($) FY Close	P/E High/Low		Earnings	PER SHARE ($) Dividends	Book Value
12/13	6.99	2	1	2.88	0.00	6.21
12/12	3.80	33	23	0.13	0.00	3.00
12/11	2.76	111	73	0.03	0.00	2.80
12/10	2.35	—	—	(1.93)	0.00	2.67
12/09	2.97	—	—	(0.32)	0.00	4.54
Annual Growth	**23.9%**	—	—	—	—	**8.1%**

Edwards Lifesciences Corp

Edwards Lifesciences has its heart in the right place. Named for the co-inventor of the first artificial heart valve Miles "Lowell" Edwards its main products are still heart valve devices including valves made from animal tissue annuloplasty rings that repair damaged valves and transcatheter heart valves for minimally invasive procedures. The company also makes monitoring systems that measure heart function during surgery; embolectomy catheters that remove blood clots from peripheral arteries; and various types of cannulae (surgical tubes used for drainage delivery or filtration) and other surgical supplies. Edwards Lifesciences markets its products worldwide.

Operations

Edwards Lifesciences' products fall into three main categories. Its surgical heart valve therapy segment makes tissue valve and valve repair items and accounts for about 40% of sales. The division also offers various items used in minimally invasive surgeries; cannulae and embolectomy catheters used to treat peripheral vascular disease; and disposable items used in cardiac and other major surgeries.

The critical care products segment includes patient monitoring systems such as the EV1000 for hemodynamic monitoring (cardiovascular performance heart pressure and oxygen saturation) using integrated sensors and catheters during and after surgeries. Other critical care offerings include disposable pressure transducers and various catheters (including central venous pulmonary artery and balloon). The rapidly growing transcatheter heart valve segment makes catheter-based treatment systems for heart valve disease that negate the need for open-heart surgery. The critical care and transcatheter divisions account for some 25% and 35% of sales respectively.

Geographic Reach

Edwards Lifesciences sells its products in roughly 100 countries worldwide with key operations in Australia Canada China Japan the US and numerous countries in Europe (including France Germany Italy the Netherlands Spain and the UK). The company makes most of its sales in the US (more than 45%) Europe and Japan.

US manufacturing plants are located in the in Irvine California; and Draper Utah; the company also has plants in the Dominican Republic Puerto Rico Singapore and Switzerland. Research labs are located in Israel the Netherlands and the US.

Sales and Marketing

Edwards Lifesciences markets its products around the globe through a direct sales force and independent distributors. The company's clients include doctors nurses and other hospital or medical facility staff members (such as purchasing managers and administrators).

Financial Performance

Despite challenges in the medical device market due to regulatory and economic factors Edwards Lifesciences has managed to steadily increase revenues and profits over the years by providing innovative products that are essential to modern cardiovascular procedures. (Such products are typically not subject to negative spending or coverage decisions by consumers or insurers.) Revenues increased 8% in 2013 to some $2.1 billion largely due to an increase in the US market (in

which sales grew by 16%) but partially offset by a 17% decline in Japan. Transcatheter heart valve sales rose 28% –driven primarily by sales of the Edwards SAPIEN valve –while other segments remained relatively flat.

Profits increased 34% to $391.7 million in 2013 as a result of the revenue growth; an $83.6 million payment from Medtronic for patent infringement damages related to the Andersen transcatheter heart valve also contributed to the rise in net income.

Cash flow from operations has also been on an upswing for the past five years. In 2013 the company's operating cash flow increased 27% to $472.7 million. In addition to the $83.6 million Medtronic settlement improved operating efficiency and increased collection of accounts receivable led to the cash inflow.

Strategy

Much of the firm's growth can be attributed to a key aspect of its business strategy: The development of new and next-generation medical devices. Over the past few years Edwards Lifesciences has increased its R&D spending. The company invested $323 million (or more than 15% of net sales) in R&D during 2013 up from $291 million in 2012 with a special focus on the high-growth field of minimally-invasive devices which aim to treat and monitor patients in a less traumatic way.

Edwards Lifesciences is focused on the development of next-generation transcatheter heart valves (designed to provide less invasive surgical options). The successful launch of the Edwards SAPIEN transcatheter heart valve in 2011 led Edwards Lifesciences to form a new transcatheter heart valve operating segment the following year. In 2013 the company received approval to market its SAPIEN 3 valve in Europe; the following year it received US approval for its SAPIEN XT valve (for the treatment of high-risk patients suffering from symptomatic aortic stenosis). The company is developing additional transcatheter systems.

The company is also creating new versions of its core Carpentier-Edwards PERIMOUNT pericardial tissue valves (for aortic and mitrial valve replacement). It gained approval for its Edwards INTUITY minimally invasive aortic heart valve system in Europe in 2012.

In the critical care segment Edwards Lifesciences is focused on the development of new hemodynamic monitoring systems. The firm is also developing minimally invasive automated glucose monitoring systems.

In addition to developing new technologies to better serve patients Edwards Lifesciences is dedicated to expanding its presence in expanding markets. In 2013 it doubled the size of its heart valve manufacturing plant in Singapore to meet growing worldwide demand.

Alongside its growth measures the company has also been known to downsize product segments that have been slow to grow.

Mergers and Acquisitions

Acquisitions can also serve as an effective way for the company to feed its development pipeline and expand its product offerings. In late 2014 Edward Lifesciences led a group that invested $50 million in CardioKinetix developer of the Parachute ventricular partitioning device. The investment will help CardioKinetix as it works to bring the device to the US and international markets; it also gives Edwards Lifesciences the right to purchase CardioKinetix at a later date.

Company Background

Edwards Lifesciences' roots can be traced back to about 1960 when the invention of the artificial heart helped spawn a company that was then

called Edwards Laboratories. The company was spun off from former parent Baxter International in 2000.

EXECUTIVES

Chairman and CEO, Michael A. Mussallem, $879,808 total compensation
Corporate Vice President Europe, Patrick Verguet
Corporate Vp Global Corporate Operations, Paul C Redmond, age 51
Vp Of Information Technology, Stuart Foster
CIO, Sal Chiovari
President and CEO Percutaneous Valve Technology, Stanton J. Rowe
Corporate VP and CFO, Scott B. Ullem, age 48
Corporate Vice President Human Resources, Christine McCauley
Vice President Tax, Edward Tarle
Vice President It, Julie Hubbard
Vice President Chief Intellectual Property Counsel, Keith Newburry
Vice President Government Affairs (2007), Dirksen Lehman
Vice President Customer Service, Dolores Tavares
Vice President Global Marketing, Terri Burke
Vice President Corporate Services, Tom Porter
Vice President Ra Edwards Lifesciences Corporation, Scott Beggins
Vice President Global Operations, Andrew Tymkiw
Vice President And General Manager, Carlos Vlez
Vice President Thv Manufacturing, Jose Aguirre
V Pres-corp Contrl, Robert W Sellers
Vp Clinical & Regulatory Affairs, Sally Maher
Vice President Business Development, Arlene Campbell
Vice President Process Excellence, Margie O'Jea
Chairman and CEO, Michael A. Mussallem
Secretary, Iris Motte
Auditors: PricewaterhouseCoopersLLP

LOCATIONS

HQ: Edwards Lifesciences Corp
One Edwards Way, Irvine, CA 92614
Phone: 949 250-2500
Web: www.edwards.com

2014 Sales

	$ mil.	% of total
US	1047.3	45
Europe	744.5	32
Japan	257.9	11
Other regions	273.2	12
Total	**2322.9**	**100**

PRODUCTS/OPERATIONS

2014 Sales

	$ mil.	% of total
Transcatheter heart valves therapy	943.6	41
Surgical heart valve therapy	826.1	35
Critical care	553.2	24
Total	**2322.9**	**100**

Selected Products

Surgical heart valve therapy
  Carpentier-Edwards Physio (mitral valve)
  Carpentier-Edwards Physio Tricuspid (annuloplasty ring)
  Carpentier-Edwards Perimount (aortic ease and mitral ease surgical heart valves)
  Cosgrove-Edwards (mitral valve)
  Edwards Intuity (minimally invasive aortic valve surgery system)
Critical care (for hemodynamic monitoring)
  Closed-loop blood sampling systems
  Disposable pressure monitors
  EV1000 (clinical monitoring platform)

FloTrac (continuous cardiac output monitoring system)
PediaSat (oximetry catheter)
PreSep (central venous oximetry catheter)
Swan-Ganz (pulmonary artery catheter)
VolumeView (sensor-catheter set)
Transcatheter heart valves
Edwards Sapien (transcatheter heart valve)
Edwards Sapien XT (transcatheter heart valve)
Cardiac surgery systems
IntraClude (aortic occlusion device)
Protection cannulae (for drainage venting and cardioplegia delivery)
ThruPort (minimal incision valve surgery platform)
Vascular
Fogarty embolectomy catheters
Surgical clips and clamps

COMPETITORS

ABIOMED	Johnson & Johnson
B. Braun Melsungen	LeMaitre Vascular
Becton Dickinson	LiDCO
Boston Scientific	Medtronic
CAS Medical	Sorin
Cook Group	St. Jude Medical
CryoLife	Stereotaxis
Hospira	Terumo
ICU Medical	W.L. Gore

HISTORICAL FINANCIALS

Company Type: Public

Income Statement

FYE: December 31

	REVENUE ($ mil.)	NET INCOME ($ mil.)	NET PROFIT MARGIN	EMPLOYEES
12/13	2,045.5	391.7	19.1%	8,600
12/12	1,899.6	293.2	15.4%	8,200
12/11	1,678.6	236.7	14.1%	7,800
12/10	1,447.0	218.0	15.1%	7,000
12/09	1,321.4	229.1	17.3%	6,400
Annual Growth	11.5%	14.3%	—	7.7%

2013 Year-End Financials

Debt ratio: 21.7%
Return on equity: 25.7%
Cash ($ mil.): 420
Current ratio: 4.99
Long-term debt ($ mil.): 593
No. of shares (mil.): 109
Dividends
Yield: —
Payout: —
Market value ($ mil.): 7,188

	STOCK PRICE ($) FY Close	P/E High/Low		PER SHARE ($) Earnings	Dividends	Book Value
12/13	65.76	27	18	3.44	0.00	14.27
12/12	90.17	43	27	2.48	0.00	12.94
12/11	70.70	44	30	1.98	0.00	11.73
12/10	80.84	55	26	1.83	0.00	11.38
12/09	86.85	43	26	1.95	0.00	10.19
Annual Growth	(6.7%)	—	—	15.2%	—	8.8%

Electro Rent Corp.

Electro Rent isn't the electronic version of the popular Broadway musical but it is a company that rents leases and resells electronic test and measurement equipment computers servers and related equipment. The company's test instruments come from suppliers that include Agilent Technologies and Tektronix while its computers and workstations are primarily sourced from from such manufacturers as Apple Dell Hewlett-Packard

and Toshiba. Electro Rent provides new and used equipment to government agencies and companies in the aerospace and defense electronics semiconductor and telecommunications industries.

True to its name Electro Rent gets more than half of its revenues from rentals and leases; the rest comes from selling equipment. The company's test and measurement unit accounts for some 90% of sales.

The company gets more than 85% of its sales in the US but also has key operations in Canada China and Europe.

Overall sales for Electro Rent were $248 million in fiscal 2012 about an 8% increase over the prior year. The higher sales were due to rental and lease revenues that were up nearly 10% on increased demand and rental rates for test and measurement equipment in North America and Europe partially offset by a decline in revenues related data products for the year also related to demand. Equipment sales and other revenues were up 7% for the year on increases in sales of new equipment and finance leases offset by lower sales of used equipment. Electro Rent is looking to flexible financing alternatives to drive growth in its lease and rental business. The company's net income was also 8% higher for the year due in part to bargain purchase gains related to acquisitions even though operating profit was lower on higher operating expenses.

In 2011 Electro Rent acquired Las Vegas-based Equipment Management Technology (EMT) which specializes in the sale and rental of electronic test equipment to companies in the aerospace and defense sectors. In 2010 the company bought the assets of Telogy for nearly $25 million in cash. Telogy (which had filed for bankruptcy protection from creditors) leased rented and sold electronic test equipment.

Chairman and CEO Daniel Greenberg and his brother Phillip own about 30% of Electro Rent outright and through a family trust.

HISTORY

Formed in 1965 to lease high-tech instruments Electro Rent was bought in 1973 by Telecor. That year Daniel Greenberg joined Electro Rent; he became chairman and CEO in 1979. Electro Rent was spun off and went public in 1980 and continued to thrive during the growth of the defense industry in the early 1980s. In 1985 the company formed a joint venture in Japan. Then sales began to slip as a result of cutbacks in federal spending for defense and aerospace. Greenberg overhauled the company which branched into the leasing of PCs and workstations in 1987. It worked. A surge in demand for PCs and workstations helped to offset the decline in revenues from test and measurement equipment.

Electro Rent's revenues rebounded in 1994 as growth in the communications industry helped boost demand for complex test equipment. Also that year Electro Rent bought rival Genstar Rental Electronics of Canada. In 1996 the company bought LDI Computer Rentals and the following year it doubled in size when it acquired General Electric Technology Management Services another computer and test equipment rental business. To cut costs the company reduced its workforce by 8% in 1998 and sold its Japanese operations.

Because of slipping demand for PC rentals in 2000 the company shifted focus to its test and measurement equipment rentals and began to offer telecommunications and fiber-optic test equipment in 2001.

It opened its rental center in China in 2005. That same year the company established a Euro-

pean outpost through its relationship with a Belgian rental firm Everest ES. Electro Rent later acquired Everest ES and made it part of its ER Europe subsidiary.

Electro Rent completed its acquisition of Rush Computer Rentals in 2006 and its acquisition of Telogy in 2010. In 2011 Electro Rent acquired Las Vegas-based Equipment Management Technology (EMT) which specializes in the sale and rental of electronic test equipment to companies in the aerospace and defense sectors.

EXECUTIVES

VP and CFO, Craig R. Jones, age 69, $246,897 total compensation
VP Product Management, Richard E. Bernosky, age 56
President and COO, Steven Markheim, age 62, $341,453 total compensation
Chairman and CEO, Daniel Greenberg, age 74, $499,047 total compensation
VP and General Manager Data Products, Dennis M. Clark, age 58, $135,000 total compensation
VP Administrative Services and Management Information Systems and Secretary, Meryl D. Evans, age 55
SVP North American Sales, Herb Ostenberg, age 65, $219,555 total compensation
Vice President Sales, John Hart
Auditors: Deloitte&ToucheLLP

LOCATIONS

HQ: Electro Rent Corp.
6060 Sepulveda Boulevard, Van Nuys, CA 91411-2501
Phone: 818 787-2100
Web: www.electrorent.com

2012 Sales

	$ mil.	% of total
US	214.4	86
Other countries	34.2	14
Total	248.6	100

PRODUCTS/OPERATIONS

2012 Sales

	$ mil.	% of total
Rentals & leases	129.8	52
Sales of equipment & other	118.8	48
Total	248.6	100

2012 Sales

	$ mil.	% of total
Test & measurement	230.0	93
Data products	18.6	7
Total	248.6	100

Selected Products

Test and Measurement
Cellular mobile and satellite
Data acquisition
Digital design
Electronic
Insulation
Network analyzers
Optical spectrum analyzers
Power monitors
Synthesized signal sources
Telecommunications
Test equipment calibration
Transformer
Video broadcasts
Wavelength meters
Data Products
Desktop computers
Hubs routers and switches
Peripherals
PCs
PC displays

Projection devices
Network devices
Notebook computers
Servers
UNIX workstations

COMPETITORS

CalFirst	ORIX
Continental Resources	Transcat
McGrath RentCorp	Trek Equipment
MetricTest	

HISTORICAL FINANCIALS

Company Type: Public

Income Statement

FYE: May 31

	REVENUE ($ mil.)	NET INCOME ($ mil.)	NET PROFIT MARGIN	EMPLOYEES
05/14	241.1	20.4	8.5%	420
05/13	248.7	22.7	9.1%	417
05/12	248.5	25.7	10.4%	393
05/11	228.7	23.7	10.4%	371
05/10	145.8	11.6	8.0%	335
Annual Growth	13.4%	15.2%	—	5.8%

2014 Year-End Financials

Debt ratio: —
Return on equity: 8.8%
Cash ($ mil.): 5
Current ratio: 1.88
Long-term debt ($ mil.): —

No. of shares (mil.): 24
Dividends
  Yield: 0.0%
  Payout: 95.2%
Market value ($ mil.): 388

	STOCK PRICE ($) FY Close	P/E High/Low		PER SHARE ($) Earnings	Dividends	Book Value
05/14	16.15	25	18	0.84	0.80	9.62
05/13	17.01	20	15	0.94	1.80	9.52
05/12	13.84	18	12	1.07	0.80	10.34
05/11	15.34	18	12	0.99	0.60	10.02
05/10	13.59	31	18	0.48	0.60	9.60
Annual Growth	4.4%	—		15.0%	7.5%	0.1%

Electronics for Imaging, Inc.

Electronics For Imaging (EFI) wants to take control of your color. The company makes hardware and software systems for commercial and enterprise digital printing and print management. EFI's Fiery line includes print servers as well as print controllers that copier and printer vendors such as Ricoh Xerox Canon Epson and Konica Minolta integrate into their equipment. EFI's Print MIS (management information systems) software provides supply chain and customer relationship management from job submission to fulfillment. Its Inkjet segment products include super-wide format (VUTEk) and industrial printers (Jetrion). It's also the world's largest manufacturer of digital UV ink.

Geographic Reach

The company has manufacturing plants in Michigan and New Hampshire and international manufacturing operations in Ontario Canada (for Entrac brand products) and Spain (for Cretaprint brand products).

It has sales and software design offices in Belgium Brazil Canada China Germany India New Zealand the Netherlands the UK and the US.

Sales and Marketing

Its industrial inkjet printers and software are primarily sold through a direct sales force. It also uses the annual EFI Connect trade show and other trade shows (such as Ceramics China Guangzhou for its Cretaprint products for the ceramic tile industry) to generate sales leads.

Its Fiery line of products are sold through printer manufacturers that act as distributors such as Canon/Oce Epson Konica Minolta Kyocera Mita OKI Data Ricoh Sharp Toshiba and Xerox.

Customers include Fedex Office Staples retail copy and print stores hotel business centers college campuses and libraries commercial photo labs large sign shops graphic screen printers and commercial printers.

Financial Performance

Overall sales grew 11% in 2013 to a record $727 million. Profits grew 30% to $109 million.

Strategy

Targets for development include scalable digital print controllers and software platforms. Among the company's recent product innovations is PrintMe Mobile which allows direct printing from mobile devices to any networked printer.

Mergers and Acquisitions

EFI has used acquisitions to build its business in recent years including big buys overseas. In 2012 it made five acquisitions - Technique Online Print Solutions (OPS) Metrics FX Colors and Cretaprint - for a combined $60.6 million in cash.

Out of those the largest acquisition was Spanish inkjet printer maker Cretaprint which serves the ceramic tile printing market. The $31 million purchase better enabled EFI to enter the Chinese ceramic tile industry. Sao Paulo-based Metrics Sistemas de Informacao (Metrics) which develops ERP systems for the printing and packaging industries in Latin America helped EFI gain better access to that region.

In 2011 it bought Alphagraph Prism Entrac Technologies and Streamline for a combined $33.7 million in cash.

HISTORY

Efi Arazi an MIT-trained engineer started Electronics For Imaging (EFI) in 1989. Arazi one of Israel's high-tech magnates had earlier founded Scitex Corp. a digital printer manufacturer; he later established Imedia a maker of routing systems for digital video; Imedia was acquired by cable modem provider Terayon.

Arazi acquired exclusive rights to an MIT patent that formed EFI's core technology. The company shipped its first Fiery server in 1991 and went public the next year. Its secondary strategy —selling its EfiColor and Cachet Color Editor software alone —failed so in 1993 the company scrapped Cachet making the development and marketing of the Fiery series top priority.

COO Dan Avida became CEO in 1995 replacing Arazi who remained chairman. That year EFI introduced the Fiery XJ series which doubled the speed of its predecessor and allowed easier upgrades. In 1996 EFI formed an alliance with Netherlands-based Oc ©and introduced a system for Oc © high-speed printers.

Boosting its software development EFI in 1997 bought Pipeline Associates a specialist in PostScript hypertext markup language (HTML) and printer control language interpreter technologies. During the next two years EFI partnered with AlphaGraphics Agfa and Fuji Xerox and nearly dou-

bled its customer base. It struck deals to incorporate Fiery controllers in Hewlett-Packard laser printers and Fiery servers in ENCAD's ink jet printers. In 1998 EFI released 40 new products including its Fiery ZX (for wide-format printers) and X2 (for pre-press devices) platforms. That year Avida replaced Arazi as chairman.

To secure a place in the digital market EFI in 1999 acquired competitor Management Graphics a Minnesota-based developer of digital imaging products. In 2000 president Guy Gecht who was credited with developing three-quarters of the company's products replaced Avida as CEO; Avida remained chairman. Later that year in an effort to expand its presence and keep pace with the color print market EFI acquired rival Splash Technology Holdings.

In 2001 EFI introduced an Internet-based printing service called PrintMe Networks. The following year the company acquired wireless messaging software provider Unimobile. EFI spun off its eBeam business which offered a system for electronically capturing whiteboard images in 2003. VeriSign acquired the assets of Unimobile in 2004.

EFI augmented its software line with its 2003 acquisitions of Best GmbH T/R Systems and Printcafe Software (for which it outbid rival Creo). The following year it acquired service automation software maker ADS Communications. (It spun off the ADS product line in 2006.)

In 2005 EFI acquired VUTEk for about $281 million in cash. EFI spun off its mobile workforce automation product line in 2006. Later that year EFI acquired Jetrion a maker of inkjet printers for the packaging and label industries for about $40 million.

EFI bought two companies in 2008 Raster Printers a maker of wide-format graphics printers and Pace Systems Group a developer of print management software.

Selling part of its headquarters campus in 2009 to Gilead Sciences brought in approximately $137 million during a harsh year for EFI. The company also contracted out production of its Fiery controllers that year in a bid to contain manufacturing costs.

EXECUTIVES

CEO, Guy Gecht, age 50, $620,000 total compensation
SVP Worldwide Sales and Marketing, Frank Mallozzi
CTO, Ghilad Dziesietnik
COO and Interim CFO, Marc Olin, age 50, $293,332 total compensation
VP and CIO, Calvin Do
SVP and General Manager Fiery Division, Toby Weiss
SVP and General Manager Inkjet Solutions, Scott Schinlever
SVP and General Manager Productivity Software, Gabriel (Gaby) Matsliach
Hr Director & Vp, Beverly Rubin
Vice President Of Marketing Fiery Division, John Henze
Vice President Of Customer Advocacy, Vicki Sam
Vice President Stategic Development, Roy Douglass
Sales Dvpt Specialist Direct Sales, Bill Mayer
Vice President Of Engineering, Michael Skowron
Vice President Marketing, Mark Lesperance
Director, Gill Cogan, age 63
Director Treasurer, Rene Felice
Auditors: PricewaterhouseCoopersLLP

LOCATIONS

HQ: Electronics for Imaging, Inc.
6750 Dumbarton Circle, Fremont, CA 94555
Phone: 650 357-3500
Web: www.efi.com

2012 Sales

	% of total
Americas	54
EMEA	30
Asia	16
Total	**100**

Selected Mergers

FY2012
  Cretaprint
  FX Colors
  Metrics
  Online Print Solutions (OPS)
  Technique
FY2011
  Alphagraph
  Entrac
  Prism
  Streamline Development

PRODUCTS/OPERATIONS

2012 Sales

	$ mil.	% of total
Inkjet	320.2	49
Fiery	228.4	35
Productivity software	103.5	16
Total	**652.1**	**100**

Selected Products and Brands

Fiery
  Embedded controllers
  External print servers (Fiery)
  Stand-alone servers
Inkjet products
  Industrial printers for packaging and labeling (Jetrion)
  Super-wide format printers for billboards and other large displays (VUTEk)
Advanced Professional Print Software (APPS)
  Color proofing
  E-commerce
  Job tracking
  Supply chain management
  Workflow management

Selected Suppliers

Intel (CPUs chip sets)
Toshiba (Application-specific integrated circuits ("ASIC") & inkjet print heads)
Open Silicon (ASICs)
Altera (ASICs & programmable devices)
Tundra (chip sets)
Avnet (contract manufacturing (Fiery))
Nazdar (contract manufacturing (solvent ink))
Columbia Tech (inkjet sub-assemblies)
Roberts Tool (inkjet sub-assemblies)
SEI S.p.A (inkjet sub-assemblies & laser finishing)
Shenzen Runtianzhi Tech (inkjet sub-assemblies)
Seiko (inkjet print heads)
Fuji (inkjet print heads)
Xaar (inkjet print heads)
Dimatix (inkjet print heads)
Progress Software (Monarch and Radius operating system)

COMPETITORS

Agfa	Konica Minolta
Canon	Océ
Dainippon Screen	Oki Data
Eastman Kodak	Peerless Systems
Fuji Xerox	Ricoh Company
Heidelberger Druckmaschinen	Sharp Corp.
Hewlett-Packard	Toshiba
	Xerox

HISTORICAL FINANCIALS

Company Type: Public

Income Statement

FYE: December 31

	REVENUE ($ mil.)	NET INCOME ($ mil.)	NET PROFIT MARGIN	EMPLOYEES
12/13	727.6	109.1	15.0%	2,523
12/12	652.1	83.2	12.8%	2,393
12/11	591.5	27.4	4.6%	2,142
12/10	504.0	7.4	1.5%	1,886
12/09	401.1	(2.1)	—	1,827
Annual Growth	**16.1%**	**—**		**8.4%**

2013 Year-End Financials

Debt ratio: 1.1%
Return on equity: 15.3%
Cash ($ mil.): 177
Current ratio: 2.99
Long-term debt ($ mil.): 11

No. of shares (mil.): 46
Dividends
  Yield: —
  Payout: —
Market value ($ mil.): 1,819

	STOCK PRICE ($) FY Close	P/E High/Low		PER SHARE ($) Earnings	Dividends	Book Value
12/13	38.73	17	8	2.26	0.00	16.34
12/12	18.99	11	8	1.74	0.00	14.10
12/11	14.25	32	22	0.58	0.00	12.39
12/10	14.31	92	58	0.16	0.00	11.88
12/09	12.97	—	—	(0.04)	0.00	11.74
Annual Growth	**31.5%**			**—**	**—**	**8.6%**

Ellie Mae Inc

Ellie Mae might sound like Fannie Mae's backwoods cousin but they're just in related industries not bloodlines. The company provides automation software and operates the Ellie Mae Network that facilitates the residential mortgage origination and funding process. Its Encompass software suite combines loan origination with CRM (customer relationship management) to gather review and verify data from a single database. Other programs handle regulatory compliance appraisal and title services underwriting tax transcripts and document preparation and management. More than 90000 mortgage professionals use its software and network to process more than 3 million new mortgages an estimated 20% of its addressable market.

Geographic Reach

Ellie Mae only operates in the US from offices in California Nebraska (technical support) and New Jersey.

Sales and Marketing

The company's sales force is divided into four teams that handle account management new account acquisition sales development and solution engineering. Customers include American Home Bank HighTechLending Skyline Financial and Supreme Lending.

Mortgage originators that use Encompass software pay for it either as a service with monthly fees based on the number of users and mortgages funded or through licensing and recurring subscription fees. Lenders and service providers that use the Ellie Mae Network pay fees per transaction for business received from Encompass users.

Financial Performance

Sales grew more than 80% in 2012 jumping from $55 million to $101 million year-over-year. The substantial increase was primarily due to En-

compass users adopting the on-demand Software-as-a-Service model. The company has grown its base of active SaaS users from about 24000 in 2011 to 41000 in 2012. Profits jumped from $3 million in 2011 to almost $20 million in 2012.

Mergers and Acquisitions

In 2013 the company offered to buy Massachusetts-based MortgageCEO which offers on-demand CRM and marketing automation software with marketing software being a new product in its software suite. In 2011 it bought Mortgage Pricing System with which it created its product and pricing service. Also that year it picked up Del Mar Datatrac which made the DataTrac origination software.

Strategy

A major part of Ellie Mae's SaaS focus is its "success-based" pricing model that allows customers to pay at the time loans are closed. Besides its objectives to add new Encompass users and cross-sell to existing ones the company plans to enhance its Ellie Mae Network with increased functionality and services and expand the use of settlement services on the system. Industry trends are also influencing strategy. The software industry has gone cloud crazy over the past few years and Ellie Mae has not been immune. A key part of its strategy is to emphasize the software-as-a-service (SaaS) incarnations of its Encompass offerings.

Company Background

Ellie Mae was founded in 1997 and launched the first version of its transaction network in 2000. The Encompass software suite came out in 2003.

EXECUTIVES

Senior Vice President Of Client, Joseph Tyrrell
EVP and CTO, Limin Hu, age 52, $270,000 total compensation
EVP and CFO, Edgar A. (Ed) Luce, age 62, $280,000 total compensation
President and CEO, Jonathan H. Corr, age 47, $310,000 total compensation
SVP HR and Operations, Lisa Bruun
Executive Vice President General Counsel Corporate Secretary, Elisa Lee, age 39, $225,000 total compensation
SVP and CIO, David Robbins
Vp Document Services, Lucille Johnson
Vice President Product Strategy, Jonas Moe
Vice President Customer Care, Ed Thompson
Vice President Financial Planning Anls, Michelle Gable
Svp Marketing, Susan C Scarth
Vice President North Coast Mortgage, Chris Solle
Vice President Of Legal Affairs, Wendy Nemeroff
Vice President Lender Business Dev, Lisa Schreiber
Executive Vice President Of Lender, Jerome Selitto
Vice President Mid Market Sales, John Aslanian
Senior Vice President Sales And Client, Cathleen Schreinergates
Vice President, Michael Bauschelt
Vice President Technical Operations, Robert Baca
Vice President Lender Relations, E Roof
Vice President Professional Services, Kathleen Haley
Vice President Of Compliance, Holly Spencer
Board Member, Carl Buccellato, age 73
Board Member, Craig S Davis, age 64
Chairman, Sig Anderman
Board Member, Frank Schultz, age 76
Board Member, Barr A Dolan
Auditors: GrantThorntonLLP

LOCATIONS

HQ: Ellie Mae Inc
4155 Hopyard Road, Suite 200, Pleasanton, CA 94588
Phone: 925 227-7000   **Fax:** 925 227-9030
Web: www.elliemae.com

PRODUCTS/OPERATIONS

2012 Sales

	% of total
On-demand	87
On-premise	13
Total	**100**

Selected Products

Ellie Mae Network
Encompass 4506 T-Service (income verification)
Encompass Appraisal Service (appraisals)
Encompass CenterWise (web and electronic document management)
Encompass Compliance Service (compliance)
Encompass EDM (electronic document management)
Encompass Flood Service (flood certifications)
Encompass WebCenter (creates customized websites)

COMPETITORS

D+H USA	Prymak
Davis + Henderson	Verisk
Dexma	Wolters Kluwer
FirstPoint Inc	WowTools
Fiserv	Xerox
ISG Novasoft	eLynx
MGIC Investment	
McCracken Financial Solutions	

HISTORICAL FINANCIALS

Company Type: Public

Income Statement

FYE: December 31

	REVENUE ($ mil.)	NET INCOME ($ mil.)	NET PROFIT MARGIN	EMPLOYEES
12/13	128.4	12.5	9.8%	407
12/12	101.8	19.4	19.1%	308
12/11	55.4	3.6	6.5%	270
12/10	43.2	0.7	1.8%	190
12/09	37.7	1.6	4.4%	0
Annual Growth	**35.9%**	**65.9%**	—	—

2013 Year-End Financials

Debt ratio: —
Return on equity: 6.7%
Cash ($ mil.): 33
Current ratio: 4.74
Long-term debt ($ mil.): —

No. of shares (mil.): 27
Dividends
Yield: —
Payout: —
Market value ($ mil.): 742

	STOCK PRICE ($) FY Close	P/E High/Low	PER SHARE ($) Earnings	Dividends	Book Value
12/13	26.87	70 40	0.44	0.00	7.49
12/12	27.75	35 7	0.76	0.00	6.40
12/11	5.65	32 17	0.18	0.00	3.75
Annual Growth	**118.1%**	— —	**56.3%**	—	**41.3%**

Ellington Financial LLC

Mortgage-related assets are music to Ellington Financial's ears. The specialty finance company manages a portfolio of primarily non-agency residential mortgage-backed securities valued at more than $366 million. It also seeks to acquire other target assets such as residential whole mortgage loans commercial mortgage-backed securities commercial real estate debt and asset-backed securities. Riskier residential whole mortgage loans which are generally not guaranteed by the US government include subprime non-performing and sub-performing mortgage loans. Founded in 2007 Ellington Financial went public in 2010 in hopes of taking advantage of the current credit environment.

The company is using a substantial portion of the proceeds from its initial public offering to acquire more target assets. It plans to use the balance for interest-bearing short-term investments — such as money market accounts —as well as for working capital and general corporate expenses.

In its attempt to acquire target assets Ellington Financial will compete with other specialty finance companies mortgage REITs public and private funds and commercial and investment banks. Keeping its portfolio diverse may help it weather downturns among certain geographic regions or property types that are subject to higher risk of foreclosure.

Ellington Financial executive officers and directors together own about a quarter of the company's stock.

EXECUTIVES

Director, Edward (Ed) Resendez, age 57
Chairman and Co-Chief Investment Officer, Michael W. Vranos, age 52
President CEO and Director, Laurence E. Penn
Co-Chief Investment Officer, Mark Tecotzky
Chief Financial Officer, Lisa Mumford
Director, Ronald I. Simon, age 76
Director, Thomas F. Robards, age 67
Director, Edward (Ed) Resendez, age 57
President CEO and Director, Laurence E. Penn
Auditors: PricewaterhouseCoopersLLP

LOCATIONS

HQ: Ellington Financial LLC
53 Forest Avenue, Old Greenwich, CT 06870
Phone: 203 698-1200
Web: www.ellingtonfinancial.com

COMPETITORS

Annaly Capital Management	MFA Financial
Chimera	MFResidential
Galiot Capital	Sutherland
	Western Asset Mortgage

HISTORICAL FINANCIALS

Company Type: Public

Income Statement

FYE: December 31

	REVENUE ($ mil.)	NET INCOME ($ mil.)	NET PROFIT MARGIN	EMPLOYEES
12/13	85.7	49.6	57.9%	130
12/12	63.8	24.1	37.9%	100
12/11	63.5	44.7	70.3%	100
12/10	45.6	24.7	54.3%	100
12/09	51.7	18.3	35.5%	0
Annual Growth	**13.5%**	**28.3%**	—	—

2013 Year-End Financials

Debt ratio: 0.0%
Return on equity: 8.8%
Cash ($ mil.): 183
Current ratio: 0.48
Long-term debt ($ mil.): 0

No. of shares (mil.): 25
Dividends
Yield: 16.8%
Payout: 217.6%
Market value ($ mil.): 576

	STOCK PRICE ($) FY Close	P/E High/Low	PER SHARE ($) Earnings	Dividends	Book Value
12/13	22.67	13 10	2.11	3.83	24.40
12/12	22.46	17 13	1.35	2.50	24.86
12/11	17.17	9 6	2.71	2.51	22.55
12/10	22.24	12 11	1.91	0.80	24.47
Annual Growth	**0.6%**	— —	—	**3.4%**	**68.5% (0.1%)**

Encore Capital Group Inc

Credit junkies beware: Encore Capital Group has your number. The firm and its Midland Credit Management subsidiary purchase at a discount defaulted consumer receivables that banks credit unions consumer and auto finance companies credit card issuers telecommunications firms retailers and other lenders have given up on. The group then does its best to collect the money via phone direct mail third-party collection agencies and legal action; it employs skip-tracing to track down stubborn debtors. Subsidiary Ascension Capital Group provides bankruptcy support services to the financial services industry. Encore collects debts in the US the UK and Ireland and now Colombia and Peru.

Geographic Reach

The San Diego-headquartered collection company's largest market is the US home to nearly 90% of its revenue. The UK accounts for the remainder. Encore operates call centers in the US (California Arizona Minnesota Texas) Costa Rica and another in India. The company considers its operations in India where the annual attrition rate for experienced account managers is well the below industry average in the US key to its future growth.

Operations

Encore Capital operates two business segments: portfolio purchasing and recovery (98% of revenue) and tax liens (2%) through Propel Financial Services (acquired in 2012). San Antonio Texas-based Propel acquires and services residential and commercial tax liens on property. the firm is the largest tax lien company in Texas.

The company boasts one of the debt collection industry's largest financially distressed consumer databases. Volume is important for Encore Capital as the company pursues collections on only a fraction of accounts and generates payments from less than 1% of them. Practicing a "friendly but firm approach" its account managers evaluate customers' ability to pay then develop tailored payment programs. The company utilizes proprietary statistical and behavioral models account-level valuation methods customized software applications and purchased credit bureau information to determine its collection strategies.

Strategy

Encore Capital has ramped up its acquisition of new portfolios of card telecom and consumer bankruptcy charge-offs amid continued stagnant job growth in the aftermath of the recession. As Encore's portfolio swells its gross collections are also increasing (by 35% in 2013 alone); not coincidentally its revenue and income are rising as well. The firm is also expanding its international reach through acquisitions in Europe and Latin America. Indeed Encore Capital opened a call center in Costa Rica in 2012 and may consider business acquisitions to expand its geographic presence in other parts of the world.

Financial Performance

Encore Capital reported revenue of $773.4 million in 2013 an increase of 39% versus the prior year. Net income rose 8% to $75.3 million over the same period. The fast-growing firm's revenue and profits have risen in tandem since 2009 and revenue has more than quadrupled over the past decade. Growth has been fueled by acquisitions at home and more recently abroad and an explosion of bad debt as a result of the financial crisis and the downturn in the housing market.

Mergers and Acquisitions

In 2014 Encore acquired a controlling stake in Grove Capital Management a purchaser of credit portfolios specializing on UK insolvencies and Spanish assets. The purchase broadened Encore's reach in the UK following its July 2013 purchase of Cabot Credit Management a debt management firm that operates in England and Ireland for Â115 million ($177 million). Under Encore's ownership Cabot went on to acquire Marlin Financial Group an acquirer of non-performing consumer debt in the UK for Â295 million ($481 million).

Other recent acquisitions include: Atlantic Credit & Finance (ACF) a collector of fresh higher-balance accounts for approximately $70 million in cash in 2014. (Encore also made additional payments totaling about $126 million to retire certain indebtedness and obligations of ACF.); and Refinancia S.A. a manager of non-performing loans in Colombia and Peru in December 2013. Refinancia also offers portfolio management services to banks for non-performing loans. In June 2013 Encore acquired Asset Acceptance Capital Corp. a debt recovery firm in the US.

Also Encore Capital acquired Propel Financial Services which specializes in tax lien transfers in 2012.

EXECUTIVES

Vp And Controller, Glen V Freter, age 52
Senior Vice President And Chief Information Officer, Olivier Baudoux
Group Executive International and Corporate Development, Paul J. Grinberg, age 53, $435,102 total compensation
President and CEO, Kenneth A. (Ken) Vecchione, age 59, $571,154 total compensation
SVP IT and CIO, Carl Eberling
President Propel Financial Services, Jack Nelson
EVP Encore India, Manu Rikhye
EVP U.S. Operations, Ashish Masih, $286,656 total compensation
SVP and COO India Operations, Anupam Arun
SVP Legal Collections Operations, Ryan Bell
EVP CFO and Treasurer, Jonathan Clark
Vice President Business Development, Amy Anuk
Vice President Operations, Iliana Gonzalez
Senior Vice President Chief Scientific Officer, Christopher Trepel
Vice President Human Resources, Steve Gonabe
Vice President Global Operations, Shailendra Kumar

Assistant Vice President Call Center Technology, Deepak Cherukuri
Vice President Strategy And Analytics, Kaushik Kundu
Vice President Tax, Mark Warner
Vice President Legal Outsourcing, Serdar Dincaslan
Vice President Credit Risk, John Chalekian
Vice President Finance, Greg Moy
Vice President Legal And Business, Andrew Asch
Senior Vice President Human Resources, Barbara Kennedy
Chairman, T. Willem (Will) Mesdag, age 61
EVP CFO and Treasurer, Jonathan Clark
Board Member, Warren Wilcox, age 57
Board Member, Francis Quinlan
Board Member, Christopher Teets
Board Member, Ronald Weissman
Board Member, Willem Mesdag
Auditors: BDOUSALLP

LOCATIONS

HQ: Encore Capital Group Inc
3111 Camino Del Rio North, Suite 103, San Diego, CA 92108
Phone: 877 445-4581
Web: www.encorecapital.com

2013 Sales

	$ mil.	% of total
United States	677.9	88
United Kingdom	95.5	12
Total	**773.4**	**100**

PRODUCTS/OPERATIONS

2013 Sales

	$ mil.	% of total
Portfolio purchasing and recovery	756.3	98
Tax lien business	17.1	2
Total	**773.4**	**100**

Selected Subsidiaries

Ascension Capital Group Inc.
Cabot Financial (UK Ireland)
Grove Financial (UK)
Marlin Financial Group (UK)
MCM Midland Management Costa Rica S.r.l.
Midland Credit Management Inc.
Midland Credit Management India Private Limited
Midland Funding LLC
Midland Funding NCC-2 Corporation
Midland India LLC
Midland International LLC
Midland Portfolio Services Inc.
MRC Receivables Corporation
Propel Financial Services (US)
Refinancia S.A. (Colombia Peru)

COMPETITORS

Asset Acceptance Capital
Asta Funding
Expert Global Solutions
FirstCity Financial
GC Services
Genesis Financial Solutions
Leland Scott & Associates
Nationwide Recovery Systems
Portfolio Recovery

HISTORICAL FINANCIALS

Company Type: Public

Income Statement

FYE: December 31

	REVENUE ($ mil.)	NET INCOME ($ mil.)	NET PROFIT MARGIN	EMPLOYEES
12/13	773.3	75.3	9.7%	5,300
12/12	555.8	69.4	12.5%	2,800
12/11	467.3	60.9	13.0%	2,200
12/10	381.3	49.0	12.9%	1,900
12/09	316.4	33.0	10.4%	1,500
Annual Growth	**25.0%**	**22.9%**	**—**	**37.1%**

2013 Year-End Financials

Debt ratio: 68.9%
Return on equity: 15.4%
Cash ($ mil.): 126
Current ratio: 3.03
Long-term debt ($ mil.): 1,850
No. of shares (mil.): 25
Dividends
  Yield: —
  Payout: —
Market value ($ mil.): 1,279

	STOCK PRICE ($) FY Close	P/E High/Low		Earnings	PER SHARE ($) Dividends	Book Value
12/13	50.26	17	9	2.87	0.00	22.47
12/12	30.62	11	8	2.80	0.00	17.50
12/11	21.26	13	8	2.37	0.00	15.15
12/10	23.45	12	7	1.95	0.00	12.61
12/09	17.40	14	2	1.37	0.00	10.41
Annual Growth	**30.4%**			**20.3%**	**—**	**21.2%**

Encore Wire Corp.

Encore Wire likes to keep customers applauding and calling for more —more wire that is. A low-cost manufacturer of copper electrical building wire and cable Encore produces NM-B cable a sheathed cable used to wire homes apartments and pre-fabricated housing and UF-B cable an underground feeder cable for outside lighting and remote residential building connections. Its inventory of stock-keeping units include THWN-2 cable an insulated feeder circuit and branch wiring for commercial and industrial buildings and other wires like armored cable. The company sells to wholesale electrical distributors and select retail home-improvement centers. It is the only public copper building wire company in the US.

Geographic Reach

Encore primarily maintains its product inventory at its plant in McKinney Texas. Additional product inventories are maintained at the warehouses of independent manufacturers' representatives located in Chattanooga Tennessee; Norcross Georgia; Cincinnati Ohio; Canton Michigan; Edison New Jersey; Louisville Kentucky; Greensboro North Carolina; Pittsburgh Pennsylvania; Santa Fe Springs California; Hayward California; and Lakeland Florida.

Sales and Marketing

Encore mainly provides interior electrical wiring in commercial and industrial buildings homes apartments and manufactured housing. It sells its products primarily through nearly 30 independent manufacturers' representatives located throughout US and to a lesser extent through its own direct in-house marketing efforts.

Financial Performance

Encore's revenues and profits have been up and down over the past few years. After declining from

2011 to 2012 revenues climbed 8% to $1.16 billion in 2013. Profits also fell from 2011 to 2012 only to skyrocket by more than 135% to $47 million in 2013.

The growth for 2013 was due to a 4% spike in copper wire sales driven by a 10% increase in copper wire pounds shipped. It was also helped by a 105% surge in aluminum wire sales driven by a near 117% spike in aluminum wire pounds shipped. The company's operating cash flow has also steadily risen the last few years climbing by $17 million to $476 million in 2013.

Strategy

A number of strengths have enabled Encore build its market share over some two decades. Among them the company's manufacturing operations are highly automated and production lines tightly integrated. Its low-cost efficient production processes allow for competitive product pricing as well as prompt order fulfillment. In addition Encore has continued to upgrade its expansive mix of products. Product offerings include color-coded commercial and residential wire and cable and an armored cable line. These goods feature easier installation increased accuracy and safety resulting in reduced operating costs for customers. Encore also takes advantage of cross-selling opportunities by buying small quantities of complementary wire products to resell along with its own lineup.

HISTORY

Industry veterans Vincent Rego and Donald Spurgin founded Encore Wire in 1989 to make wire for residential use after their previous company Capital Wire was bought out by Penn Central in 1988. Encore rolled through the homebuilding recession of the early 1990s gathering market share along the way. The company went public in 1992. Proceeds from the offering bought additional manufacturing equipment and paid off debt.

The firm began manufacturing commercial wire in 1994 following completion of a major plant expansion. A strong housing market helped charge the company's sales in 1996 prompting it to build a fabrication and reprocessing plant for copper rod (completed in 1998). Encore started to manufacture polyvinyl chloride (used in wire sheaths) in 1999. The company also restructured that year transferring its operations to Encore Wire Limited a limited partnership.

In 2000 the company introduced NONLEDEX a proprietary lead-free building wire. In 2002 the company built an $18 million manufacturing facility adjacent to its McKinney Texas headquarters.

EXECUTIVES

Chairman President and CEO, Daniel L. Jones, age 50, $685,000 total compensation

VP Finance and CFO, Frank J. Bilban, age 57, $335,000 total compensation

Vice President Of Information Technology, Darin Riggs

Vp Operations, David K Smith, age 55

Vice President Of New Product Development And Enviro, Gary Bliss

National Sales Manager, Jon Heiges

Vice President Facilities And Maintenance, Melvin Debord

Executive Vice President And General, Bert Cornelison

Executive Vice President, Theodore Pincus

Chairman President and CEO, Daniel L. Jones, age 50

Board Of Directors, Alan Bennett

Auditors: Ernst&YoungLLP

LOCATIONS

HQ: Encore Wire Corp.
1329 Millwood Road, McKinney, TX 75069
Phone: 972 562-9473   **Fax:** 972 562-4744
Web: www.encorewire.com

PRODUCTS/OPERATIONS

Selected Products

Armored Cable (multiple conductors insulated with PVC and coated with nylon used primarily as feeder circuit and branch wiring in commercial and industrial buildings)

NM-B Cable (non-metallic sheathed cable for interior wiring in homes)

Photovoltaic Cable (used by the solar industry providing connections between PV panels colllector boxes and inverters)

THWN-2 Cable (single conductor insulated with PVC and coated with nylon used primarily as feeder circuit and branch wiring in commercial and industrial buildings)

UF-B Cable (underground feeder cable for conducting power underground to outside lighting and other remote residential applications)

USE-2 Cable (general purpose applications; conduit or installed in underground sites or in recognized raceways for service feeders and branch-circuit wiring)

XHHW-2 Cable (used as feeder circuit and branch wiring in commercial and industrial buildings)

COMPETITORS

Belden	Madeco
Cerro Wire	Southwire
Freeport-McMoRan	Superior Essex
General Cable	Thomas & Betts
International Wire	Volex
Legrand	

HISTORICAL FINANCIALS

Company Type: Public

Income Statement

	REVENUE ($ mil.)	NET INCOME ($ mil.)	NET PROFIT MARGIN	EMPLOYEES
12/13	1,158.2	46.9	4.1%	1,108
12/12	1,072.3	19.8	1.8%	998
12/11	1,180.4	50.1	4.2%	886
12/10	910.2	15.2	1.7%	737
12/09	649.6	3.6	0.6%	669
Annual Growth	15.6%	89.5%	—	13.4%

FYE: December 31

2013 Year-End Financials

Debt ratio: —
Return on equity: 10.8%
Cash ($ mil.): 36
Current ratio: 6.89
Long-term debt ($ mil.): —

No. of shares (mil.): 20
Dividends
  Yield: 0.1%
  Payout: 4.0%
Market value ($ mil.): 1,122

	STOCK PRICE ($) FY Close	P/E High/Low		PER SHARE ($) Earnings	Dividends	Book Value
12/13	54.20	24	13	2.26	0.08	22.06
12/12	30.31	36	26	0.91	0.08	19.85
12/11	25.90	13	9	2.14	0.08	19.54
12/10	25.08	39	27	0.66	0.08	17.55
12/09	21.07	152	99	0.16	0.08	16.97
Annual Growth	26.6%	—	—	93.9%	(0.0%)	6.8%

EnerNOC Inc

EnerNOC knocks on the door of large energy customers and kindly asks them to dim the lights. Not literally of course but the company has added its technology to utility companies' traditional demand response model. Rather than manually calling up their largest end users EnerNOC's Network Operations Center (NOC) through its DemandSMART program remotely monitors their customers' energy assets and has the capability to adjust their electrical use. It caters to commercial industrial and institutional organizations as well as electric power grid operators and utilities. EnerNOC operates across the US and in Australia Canada New Zealand and the UK.

Geographic Reach

The company's commercial and industrial sales group sells energy intelligence software and solutions to commercial and industrial customers in major electricity regions throughout the US including New England New York the Mid-Atlantic Texas Florida California Idaho and internationally in Australia Canada Germany Ireland Japan New Zealand and the UK.

Operations

EnerNOC is a provider of cloud-based energy intelligence software (EIS) and services to thousands of enterprise customers and utilities globally. EIS for enterprise includes supply management utility bill management facility optimization visibility and reporting project management demand management and demand response. EnerNOC Demand Resource and EnerNOC Demand Manager are designed to address the needs of electric power grid operators and utilities across three different types of demand response programs: reliability-based demand response; price-based demand response; and short-term reserve resources (ancillary services).

Sales and Marketing

EnerNOC's electric power grid operator and utility customers include PJM Southern California Edison ISO New England Tennessee Valley Authority Australian Independent Market Operator Wholesale Electricity Market Electric Reliability Council of Texas Alberta Electric System Operator and OPA among others. In 2014 the company's sales to PJM accounted 45% of total sales.

Financial Performance

After experiencing a slight revenue decrease in 2012 the company saw a revenue increase of 38% in 2013 due to an increase in DemandSMART revenues thank to an increase in pricing and high enrollment in US-based demand response programs. The increase was also due to revenues recognized from participation in other international demand response programs including OPA Alberta Canada and New Zealand. After experiencing two straight years of losses EnerNOC posted a net income of $22.1 million in 2013 primarily due to higher revenues and increased income from continuing operations. In 2013 the company's operating cash inflow increased to $79.5 million (compared to $31.01 million in 2012) due to net income improvement tax benefits and increased working capital.

Strategy

EnerNOC's strategy is to capitalize on its established track record substantial operating experience and scalable and proprietary energy intelligence software platform as well as its market leading position in the USs to continue providing energy intelligence software and services to its commercial and industrial electric power grid operators and utility customers. The company is seeking to respond to the industry trends of increasing automation of power grids and stricter environmental controls on power production. In 2014 the company has that it has made a strategic investment in Boston-based WeSpire a software-as-a-service (SaaS) company for businesses seeking an innovative approach to measure and track the positive business impact of engaging employees in sustainability through technology.

That year Boston Properties a real estate investment trust and one of the largest owners managers and developers of commercial office properties in the US (and an EnerNOC customer since 2006) expanded its deployment of EnerNOC's software to include utility bill management across its portfolio. Boston Properties' portfolio consists of 180 properties (with 46.6 million square feet of space). In 2014 the company formed a joint venture with Marubeni to provide demand response applications and services in Japan. EnerNOC Japan K.K. which will have an exclusive license to market EnerNOC DemandSMART throughout Japan is working on a government-sponsored pilot demand response program with the Tokyo Electric Japan's largest utility.

Mergers and AcquisitionsIn 2014 the company acquired Dublin-based Activation Energy DSU Limited the leading provider of demand response software and services in Ireland. This acquisition gave EnerNOC an immediate presence in Ireland and further strengthens its ability to deliver its full suite of energy intelligence software applications throughout Europe. That year the company bought Germany-based Entelios AG or Entelios a leading provider of demand response in Europe. The deal accelerates EnerNOC's entry into continental Europe. (Germany is one of Europe's largest potential markets for demand response and energy intelligence software.)

As part of the company's strategy to diversify beyond demand response that year it also agreed to buy EnTech the leading provider of global utility bill management software. EnTech's software is deployed in more than 100 countries including many of the world's fastest growing economies such as China India and Brazil.

EXECUTIVES

VP Engineering, Hugh Scandrett
Chairman and CEO, Timothy G. (Tim) Healy, age 45, $602,931 total compensation
President, David B. Brewster, age 42, $527,489 total compensation
SVP Marketing and Sales, Gregg M. Dixon, age 42, $83,488 total compensation
VP Product Strategy and Technology, Micah Remley
CIO, Gerry Wilson
COO and CFO, Neil Moses, $346,500 total compensation
Vice President Of Enterprise Sales, Matthew Maloney
Vice President Of Candi Marketing And Communications, Cecilia Zhou
Vice President, Doug Chamberlin
Chairman and CEO, Timothy G. (Tim) Healy, age 45
Auditors: Ernst&YoungLLP

LOCATIONS

HQ: EnerNOC Inc
One Marina Park Drive, Suite 400, Boston, MA 02210
Phone: 617 224-9900
Web: www.enernoc.com

PRODUCTS/OPERATIONS

2013 Sales

	$ mil.	% of total
Demand response solutions (DemandSMART)	342.2	89
Energy management solutions (CarbonSMART EfficiencySMART SupplySMART)	41.3	11
Total	**383.5**	**100**

COMPETITORS

Ambient Corp.	Itron
Comverge	National Grid USA
ESCO Technologies	eMeter

HISTORICAL FINANCIALS

Company Type: Public

Income Statement

FYE: December 31

	REVENUE ($ mil.)	NET INCOME ($ mil.)	NET PROFIT MARGIN	EMPLOYEES
12/13	383.4	22.0	5.8%	716
12/12	277.9	(22.2)	—	685
12/11	286.6	(13.3)	—	599
12/10	280.1	9.5	3.4%	484
12/09	190.6	(6.8)	—	418
Annual Growth	19.1%	—	—	14.4%

2013 Year-End Financials

Debt ratio: —
Return on equity: 8.6%
Cash ($ mil.): 149
Current ratio: 2.16
Long-term debt ($ mil.): —
No. of shares (mil.): 29
Dividends
Yield: —
Payout: —
Market value ($ mil.): 515

	STOCK PRICE ($) FY Close	P/E High/Low		PER SHARE ($) Earnings	Dividends	Book Value
12/13	17.21	23	14	0.76	0.00	9.01
12/12	11.75	—	—	(0.84)	0.00	8.27
12/11	10.87	—	—	(0.52)	0.00	9.07
12/10	23.91	94	60	0.37	0.00	8.99
12/09	30.39	—	—	(0.32)	0.00	8.05
Annual Growth	(13.3%)	—	—	—	—	2.9%

Enersys

EnerSys' batteries are there when industrial-strength power is needed. The company makes stationary industrial batteries that provide uninterruptible power and backup power for electronic systems and motive power batteries for big equipment such as forklifts. Other products include battery chargers and accessories and batteries used for industrial and military applications. The battery manufacturer sells directly and through distributors to more than 10000 customers in more than 100 countries. It serves distributors warehouse operators retailers airports and mine operators as well as customers in the telecom electric utilities emergency lighting security systems and space satellites markets.

Geographic Reach

The company has manufacturing facilities in the following locations: Longmont Colorado; Hays Kansas; Richmond Kentucky; Warrensburg Missouri; Cleveland; Horsham Pennsylvania; Sumter South Carolina; and Ooltewah Tennessee.

International locations reside in Monterrey and Tijuana Mexico; Buenos Aires Argentina; and Sao Paulo. The EMEA region has locations in Targovishte Bulgaria; Hostimice Czech Republic; Arras France; Hagen and Zwickau Germany; Bielsko-Biala Poland; Newport Culhman and Thurso UK; Port Elizabeth South Africa; and Tunis Tunisia.

Locations in Asia include Jiangsu Chaoan and Chongqing in the People's Republic of China and Andhra Pradesh in India.

Operations

EnerSys distributes its battery products through two product lines: reserve power products and motive power products. Reserve power batteries are marketed under the ABSL ABSL Power ABSL Space ArmaSafePlus Cyclon DataSafe Genesis Hawker Huada Odyssey Oerlikon Battery PowerSafe and SuperSafe brands; motive power batteries under the Douglas Battery Express Fiamm Motive Power General Battery Hawker Huada and Ironclad brands.

Each segment contributes half of the company's sales each year. EnerSys operates globally through three geographic regions of the world: Americas (headquarters in Pennsylvania) Europe (Switzerland) and Asia (Singapore).

Sales and Marketing

The company distributes sells and services reserve and motive power products throughout the world principally through company-owned sales and service facilities as well as through independent manufacturers' representatives.

Financial Performance

With the manufacturing sector finally rebounding from the painful effects of the recession EnerSys has prospered significantly over the last few years. Net sales for 2014 reached $2.47 billion a historic milestone for the company. It attributes most of the growth to an increase in organic sales its ongoing cost savings programs price increases for its products and a boost from previous acquisitions. Sales from Asia spiked 7% in 2014.

After achieving a profit milestone of $167 million in 2013 the company saw its profits dip 10% to $150 million in 2014. This was due to legal proceedings charges in connection with an adverse arbitration result and a goodwill impairment charge affiliated with the fair value of its subsidiary in India.

EnerSys' operating cash flow increased largely during 2011 through 2013 but it dropped by $51 million in 2014 due to an increase in cash used in deferred income taxes accounts receivable and accounts payable.

Strategy

EnerSys' growth strategy centers around strategic joint ventures and acquisitions. It purchased Purcell Systems a maker of thermally managed electronic equipment and battery cabinet enclosures for $115 million in late 2013. Also that year EnerSys picked up Quallion LLC a manufacturer of lithium ion cells and batteries for high integrity applications including implantable medical devices defense aviation and space.

In early 2012 it established a new joint venture in India to produce batteries for industrial applications. EnerSys has majority ownership in the joint venture with Energy Leader Batteries India Limited an industrial battery produced based in India. The company established previous joint ventures located in Germany (EAS Germany GmbH which produces large format lithium-ion cells) and South Africa (Powertech Batteries producer of batteries for industrial uses).

Company Background

Like rival Exide Technologies EnerSys traces its corporate roots back to the formation of The

Electric Storage Battery Company (ESB) in the late 19th century. The corporate predecessors of EnerSys came out of ESB's industrial battery business.

HISTORY

EnerSys formed in 2000 when company management and Morgan Stanley acquired Yuasa's Motive Power and Stationary Power operations. It bought Invensys' Energy Storage products group in 2002.

The company went public in 2004; the next year it expanded its Australian operations with the acquisition of First National Battery a distributor of motive power batteries and chargers. Also in 2005 EnerSys acquired the motive power business of Italy's FIAMM for Å25 million.

In 2006 EnerSys purchased the assets of Alliant Techsystems' lithium primary battery business. The business known as the Power Sources Center has made batteries for aerospace and military equipment for more than four decades. Alliant Techsystems signed a five-year supply agreement with EnerSys as part of the transaction. The Power Sources Center manufactures ambient-temperature lithium reserve and active primary batteries. Also in 2006 EnerSys acquired the assets of Chaozhou Xuntong Power Source Company Limited (CFT) a Chinese manufacturer of valve-regulated lead-acid batteries.

In 2008 EnerSys created a joint venture in Tunisia with automotive battery manufacturer Accumulateur Tunisie Assad SA. The company owns 51% of the JV EnerSys-Assad SARL which makes industrial batteries. Also that year EnerSys completed a $350 million refinancing and launched its EcoSafe line of batteries for renewable energy storage applications.

EnerSys expanded its European presence through the acquisition of a metal fabricating facility in the Czech Republic to serve its industrial battery customers. In 2007 it bought Energia AD a Bulgarian producer of industrial batteries for approximately Å13 million and acquired the lead-acid battery business of Leclanch Ca Swiss firm. EnerSys restructured its European operations integrating Energia while reorganizing certain commercial and production operations on the Continent.

In early 2009 EnerSys expanded its niche battery operations by acquiring Keystone Mountaineer Power Systems a supplier of batteries and chargers to the mining industry. Keystone Mountaineer primarily sells to northern Appalachian coal mines. Later that year EnerSys bought the Oerlikon Battery business of Switzerland-based Accu Holding. The business consisted of OEB Traction Batteries and Oerlikon Stationary Batteries —both makers of industrial batteries used in telecom utilities rail and material handling applications —along with a Swedish sales subsidiary.

EnerSys in 2010 swallowed up industrial battery maker Douglas Battery. The acquisition added a strong brand and battery designs along with established distribution channels and customer base. Douglas Battery products included motive power and stationary batteries used in construction medical and telecommunications applications. EnerSys retained the Douglas brand sales team and distributors.

In 2011 EnerSys purchased ABSL Power Solutions a UK-based manufacturer of lithium-ion batteries. ABSL Power Solutions supplies lithium-ion cells and batteries for defense and aerospace applications such as satellite systems to Europe and the US. Also that year EnerSys obtained battery

manufacturing assets from Greece-based partner Ergon Batteries. That deal bolstered the company's distribution and services operations in the region.

EXECUTIVES

Chairman and CEO, John D. Craig, age 64, $960,000 total compensation
EVP, Richard W. (Dick) Zuidema, age 66, $480,000 total compensation
SVP Finance and CFO, Michael J. Schmidtlein, age 54, $420,000 total compensation
President and COO, David M. Shaffer, $375,000 total compensation
President Americas, Todd M. Sechrist, $375,000 total compensation
President Asia, Mark C. Tough
Vice President Global Operations, Kelly Sierakowski
Vice President Information Technology And Finance Projects, Eric Trupin
Chairman and CEO, John D. Craig, age 64
Assistant Treasurer, Robert Marley
Auditors: Ernst&YoungLLP

LOCATIONS

HQ: Enersys
2366 Bernville Road, Reading, PA 19605
Phone: 610 208-1991
Web: www.enersys.com

2014 Sales

	$ mil.	% of total
Americas	1267.6	51
EMEA	966.1	39
Asia	240.7	10
Total	**2474.4**	**100**

PRODUCTS/OPERATIONS

2014 Sales

	$ mil.	% of total
Motive power	1239.9	50
Reserve power	1234.5	50
Total	**2474.4**	**100**

Selected Products and Brands

Diesel engine starting batteries
  LMUD-500
  UB-510
Flooded batteries
  General
  Heritage
Lift truck batteries
  Exide
  Hup
Rail signal batteries
  EMF-R
Sealed gel maintenance-free batteries
  Renegade
  Smarthog
Valve-regulated lead-acid batteries
  Independence
Wet-cell batteries
  Loadhog
  Superhog
  Workhog

COMPETITORS

AMARA RAJA BATTERIES LIMITED
Beacon Power
C&D Technologies
China Shoto
Chloride Group
Coslight Technology International Group Limited
Crown Battery
Delphi Automotive Systems
East Penn Manufacturing
Exide

GS Yuasa
General Motors
Hitachi
Johnson Controls
Johnson Controls Power Solutions
Leoch International Technology Limited
Lithium Technology
Micro Power Electronics
Panasonic Corp
Ritar Power
SAFT
Schumacher Electric

HISTORICAL FINANCIALS

Company Type: Public

Income Statement

FYE: March 31

	REVENUE ($ mil.)	NET INCOME ($ mil.)	NET PROFIT MARGIN	EMPLOYEES
03/14	2,474.4	150.3	6.1%	9,500
03/13	2,277.5	166.5	7.3%	9,000
03/12	2,283.3	144.0	6.3%	9,200
03/11	1,964.4	113.4	5.8%	8,400
03/10	1,579.3	62.3	3.9%	7,800
Annual Growth	**11.9%**	**24.6%**	**—**	**5.1%**

2014 Year-End Financials

Debt ratio: 13.8%
Return on equity: 12.4%
Cash ($ mil.): 240
Current ratio: 2.24
Long-term debt ($ mil.): 288
No. of shares (mil.): 46
Dividends
  Yield: 0.7%
  Payout: 14.1%
Market value ($ mil.): 3,253

	STOCK PRICE ($) FY Close	P/E High/Low		PER SHARE ($) Earnings	Dividends	Book Value
03/14	69.29	23	13	3.02	0.50	26.76
03/13	45.58	13	9	3.42	0.00	24.44
03/12	34.65	14	9	2.93	0.00	21.59
03/11	39.75	17	9	2.27	0.00	19.47
03/10	24.66	19	9	1.28	0.00	16.05
Annual Growth	**29.5%**	**—**	**—**	**23.9%**	**—**	**13.6%**

Ensign Group Inc

The Ensign Group hangs its insignia at more than 125 senior living facilities. Most of its facilities are skilled nursing homes but it also operates a number of assisted-living and independent-living facilities as well as combination nursing assisted and independent-living centers. Some locations also offer rehabilitation hospice and physical therapy services. Ensign's facilities are either owned by the company or operated under lease agreements. The health care provider operates some 120 long-term care centers (it owns three-fourths of them) with a capacity of some 13200 beds in about a dozen states in the southwestern and western US. Ensign also operates home health and hospice agencies.

Geographic Reach
California-based Ensign has facilities in California Arizona Texas Washington Utah Idaho Colorado Nevada Iowa Nebraska Oregon and Wisconsin. California and Texas are the company's largest markets home to more than 50% of its beds.

Operations

Ensign is a holding company that counts among its operations more than 125 facilities nine hospice companies and nearly a dozen home health businesses. The company has a decentralized operating structure with its portfolio of homes organized into five regional operating companies. Each home operates under local —and largely independent — management. As part of its business the company relies on reimbursement from government and commercial health insurance plans as well as sales to private pay customers. It generates about three-fourths of its revenues from Medicaid and Medicare programs.

Financial Performance

Ensign reported revenue of $904.6 million in 2013 an increase of 10% versus 2012 on rising Medicare Medicaid managed care and private revenue. (The Medicare and Medicaid programs are Ensign's biggest payors contributing 72% of revenue in 2013.) Despite the double-digit rise in revenue net income declined 41% over the same period to $24 million due to US government settlement expenses incurred and an increase in the loss from discontinued operations. Some of Ensign's subsidiaries were the subject of an investigation (launched in 2006 and eventually settled in 2013) by the Department of Justice regarding claims submitted to the Medicare program.

Strategy

The company split its health care and real estate business into two separate publicly-traded companies in June 2014. Ensign continued to provide health care services through its existing operations while the underlying real estate became owned by CareTrust REIT Inc.

The company's growth strategy —and an growing population of increasingly infirm patients —has resulted in a decade of steady and significant revenue growth. Ensign primarily expands its operations by snapping up underperforming nursing homes in existing or new territories and turning them around both in terms of operating performance and clinical quality. In addition to acquiring new facilities and establishing local leadership teams the company works to boost patient occupancy at its existing facilities especially those facing financial troubles and extremely low occupancy rates. It does this by developing quality staff and clinical processes and through facility upgrades as well as by adding services such as outpatient therapy services. It is also focused on attracting more high-acuity patients who require higher levels of medical and rehabilitative care and for whom the company is generally reimbursed at higher rates.

Ensign branched out into a new area of operations in 2012 when it formed a joint venture with a group of physicians to establish or acquire urgent care centers in select communities. The Immediate Clinic venture intended to provide walk-in medical care to fill the gap between primary care doctor's offices and hospital emergency rooms which the company sees as a growing area of need as health reform measures take effect in the US. Its first acquisition in 2012 was Doctors Express which boasts about 50 franchised urgent care centers nationwide. However Immediate Clinic turned around and sold the Doctors Express business to American Family Care in 2013 while retaining five urgent care clinics in the greater Seattle area; Immediate Clinic plans to expand in that market.

Mergers and Acquisitions

In late 2014 Ensign purchased nine skilled nursing and assisted living facilities in the San Diego area from Shea Family Care. The closing of the Shea Family deal brought Ensign's growing portfolio to 136 healthcare facilities (nine of which will

be owned) nine hospice companies 12 home health agencies two home care businesses and 14 urgent care clinics in 12 states. Also that year the company bought Sherwood Village Assisted Living and Memory Care a 135-unit assisted living facility in Tucson Arizona for $4.8 million.

In 2012 2013 and 2014 Ensign added skilled nursing facilities assisted living facilities and independent living facilities in Idaho Texas Nevada Arizona and Washington.

EXECUTIVES

President CEO and Director, Christopher R. Christensen, age 46, $425,159 total compensation
EVP and Secretary, Gregory K. (Greg) Stapley, age 55, $354,299 total compensation
President Keystone Care, Barry R. Port, age 40, $300,000 total compensation
President Bandera, John P. Albrechtsen, age 37, $164,687 total compensation
CFO, Suzanne D. Snapper, age 40, $257,500 total compensation
President Cornerstone, Daniel H. (Danny) Walker
President Touchstone Care, Matthew Hueffner
President Northern Pioneer Healthcare, Matt Rutter
President Pennant, Owen Hammond
President Milestone Healthcare, Brian Newberry
President Gateway Healthcare, Michael Clegg
President Bridgestone Living, John Guerreri
President Keystone North, Rick Forscutt
President Keystone South, Jorge Rojas
President Paragon, Steve Burningham
Vice President General Counsel, Beverly B Wittekind, age 50
Vice President Finance, Gail Natale
Director Of Nursing, Janice Funk
Vice President Human Resources, Cynthia Hopkins
Vice President Of Agricultural Operations, Gregg Simonds
President CEO and Director, Christopher R. Christensen, age 46
EVP and Secretary, Gregory K. (Greg) Stapley, age 55
Chairman, Roy E. Christensen, age 81
Board Member, Van R Johnson, age 70
Auditors: Deloitte&ToucheLLP

LOCATIONS

HQ: Ensign Group Inc
27101 Puerta Real, Suite 450, Mission Viejo, CA 92691
Phone: 949 487-9500
Web: www.ensigngroup.net

2013 Beds

	No.
California	3973
Texas	3353
Arizona	1902
Utah	1413
Washington	555
Colorado	505
Idaho	477
Nebraska	366
Iowa	356
Nevada	304
Total	**13204**

PRODUCTS/OPERATIONS

2013 Facilities

	No.	% of total
Owned	96	81
Leased (without a purchase option)	21	18
Leased (with a purchase option)	2	1
Total	**119**	**100**

2013 Facilities

	No.
Skilled nursing	11124
Assisted living	1603
Independent living	477
Total	**13204**

2013 Sales

	% of total
Medicaid - custodial	36
Medicare	32
Medicaid - skilled	4
Managed care	13
Private & other	15
Total	**100**

COMPETITORS

Amedisys	Five Star Quality Care
American Baptist Homes of the West	Golden Horizons
	HCR ManorCare
Apria Healthcare	HealthSouth
Brookdale Senior Living	Kindred Healthcare
	Life Care Centers
Covenant Care	RehabCare
Dignity Health	SavaSeniorCare
Diversicare Healthcare Services	Skilled Healthcare Group
Enlivant	Sunrise Senior Living

HISTORICAL FINANCIALS

Company Type: Public

Income Statement

FYE: December 31

	REVENUE ($ mil.)	NET INCOME ($ mil.)	NET PROFIT MARGIN	EMPLOYEES
12/13	904.5	24.0	2.7%	11,372
12/12	824.7	40.5	4.9%	10,371
12/11	758.2	47.6	6.3%	9,433
12/10	649.5	40.5	6.2%	8,382
12/09	542.0	32.4	6.0%	7,718
Annual Growth	**13.7%**	**(7.3%)**	**—**	**10.2%**

2013 Year-End Financials

Debt ratio: 34.1%
Return on equity: 7.0%
Cash ($ mil.): 65
Current ratio: 1.88
Long-term debt ($ mil.): 251

No. of shares (mil.): 22
Dividends
　Yield: 1.1%
　Payout: 45.3%
Market value ($ mil.): 979

	STOCK PRICE ($) FY Close	P/E High/Low		PER SHARE ($) Earnings	Dividends	Book Value
12/13	44.27	42	25	1.07	0.27	16.10
12/12	27.15	16	13	1.85	0.25	15.03
12/11	24.50	15	9	2.21	0.23	13.10
12/10	24.87	13	8	1.92	0.21	10.96
12/09	15.37	12	8	1.55	0.19	9.09
Annual Growth	**30.3%**	**—**	**—**	**(8.8%)**	**9.4%**	**15.4%**

Entegris Inc

Entegris makes products integral to the manufacture of semiconductors and computer disk drives. The company makes more than 17000 standard and custom products used to transport and protect semiconductor and disk drive materials during processing. Its semiconductor products include wafer carriers storage boxes and chip trays as well as chemical delivery products such as pipes fittings and valves. Its disk drive offerings include shippers stamper cases and transport trays. Top customers include Applied Materials ASML MEMC Siltronic Tokyo Electron and Taiwan Semiconductor Manufacturing. More than 70% of Entegris' sales come from customers located outside the US primarily in the Asia/Pacific region.

Geographic Reach

Entegris has manufacturing and research and development facilities in France Japan Malaysia South Korea Taiwan and the US. It also has sales and service offices throughout Asia and Europe.

Operations

Entegris identifies its products as capital-driven (dependent on capital spending to expand manufacturing capacity) and unit-driven and consumable (products that are used or consumed in the manufacturing process). Unit-driven products which make up nearly two-thirds of sales include liquid filters specialized graphite components and wafers shippers. They provide some protection against industry cycles by providing a recurring source of revenue. Capital-driven products which include wafer process carriers and gas microcontamination control systems give the company access to more capital when chip makers retrofit or expand production facilities.

Sales and Marketing

The company sells its products through a direct sales force and strategic distributors serving a range of markets including Semiconductor Flat Panel Display Manufacturing Compound Semiconductor Disk Data Storage Aerospace Solar/Clean Energy Life Sciences Emerging Technologies and Water Treatment industries.

Financial Performance

Entegris reported a 3% decline in 2013 sales due to continued softness in semiconductor industry spending with lower demand from leading edge fabricators. Fab utilization rates remained well below peak levels and semiconductor industry capital spending remained restrained together with unfavorable foreign currency translation of $18.6 million.In 2013 the company's profits rose by 8% driven by lower cost of sales selling general and administrative expenses and lower amortization of intangible assets partially was offset by a decrease in revenues.Entegris reported $109.4 million cash flow in operating activities for 2013 (compared to $115.2 million in 2012) due to cash generated by the company's operations including net income of $74.5 million adjusted for the impact of various non-cash charges primarily depreciation and amortization of $38.8 million and share-based compensation expense of $7.9 million.

Strategy

In order to counter the cyclicality of the semiconductor industry Entegris has expanded into adjacent and ancillary markets including applications in solar flat-panel displays and high-purity chemicals. Non-semiconductor industries include the aerospace biomedical glass container and electrical discharge machining markets. Its focus includes strategic acquisitions and partnerships and related transactions that enable it to complement its product markets and broaden its technological capabilities and product offerings.

In 2013 it increased its R&D spending and invested in two of the largest infrastructure projects in Entegris' history (the i2M Center in Massachusetts and the ATC Center in Colorado)It expanded its operations in Taiwan to provide manufacturing capabilities to support important customers in the region and also established sales and service offices in China in anticipation of a growing semiconductor manufacturing base in that region and expanded its presence in Singapore to enhance its

global and regional management of supply chain and manufacturing processes.In 2013 Entegris partnered with SEMATECH to advance surface conditioning and wafer cleaning technology for semiconductor device manufacturing. In the same year it also Collaborated with Imec to advance the development and broaden the adoption of 3D integrated circuits followed by the partnership of 3S Korea Co. Ltd a leader in wafer shipping solutions for the sale of 450 mm wafer handling products to customers in Korea.

Mergers and Acquisitions

In an effort to position itself for larger orders Entegris bought fellow semiconductors materials supplier ATMI for some $1.15 billion in mid-2014 creating a leading supplier of products and materials for semiconductor and other advanced manufacturing products.

In 2013 it acquired Jetalon Solutions Inc. (a California-based supplier of fluid metrology products for $13.4 million) and also acquired remaining 50% of shares in its EPT joint venture in Taiwan.

Company Background

In 2008 Entegris acquired privately held Poco Graphite adding materials science technology and a new line of products used in front-end chip manufacturing to its portfolio. Poco supplies consumables and finished products made from graphite and silicon carbide to the aerospace medical optoelectronic and semiconductor industries among others.

EXECUTIVES

EVP and Chief Administrative Officer, Bertrand Loy, age 49, $625,000 total compensation

EVP and CFO, Gregory B. (Greg) Graves, age 53, $321,826 total compensation

SVP and COO, Todd Edlund, age 51, $291,577 total compensation

Vice President Manufacturing, Fred Faulkner

Vice President Human Resources, Jim Geller

Vice President Product And Technology, Jieh Shyu

Vice President Production, Bob Lipsky

Vice President Of Information Technology, Gary Bowman

Vice President Of Information Technology, Rina Vaissman

Vice President, Jean Marc

Executive Vice President Chief Financial Officer, Greg Graves

Chairman, Paul L. H. Olson, age 64

Auditors: KPMGLLP

LOCATIONS

HQ: Entegris Inc
129 Concord Road, Billerica, MA 01821
Phone: 978 436-6500   **Fax:** 952 556-1880
Web: www.entegris.com

2013 Sales

	$ mil.	% of total
US	201.4	29
Taiwan	128.2	19
Japan	101.5	15
South Korea	76.4	11
China	36.3	5
Singapore	30.9	4
Germany	23.3	3
Other countries	95.5	14
Total	**693.5**	**100**

PRODUCTS/OPERATIONS

2013 Sales

	$ mil.	% of total
Contamination Control Solutions	447.5	64
Microenvironments	178.2	26
Specialty Materials	67.8	10
Total	**693.5**	**100**

COMPETITORS

3M	Pall Corporation
Air Products	Parker-Hannifin
Brooks Automation	Peak International
Donaldson Company	SAES Getters
Illinois Tool Works	Saint-Gobain
L' Air Liquide	Schweiter Technologies
Mersen Group	Shin-Etsu Chemical
Mirae	Tokai Carbon

HISTORICAL FINANCIALS

Company Type: Public

Income Statement

FYE: December 31

	REVENUE ($ mil.)	NET INCOME ($ mil.)	NET PROFIT MARGIN	EMPLOYEES
12/13	693.4	74.5	10.7%	3,200
12/12	715.9	68.8	9.6%	3,050
12/11	749.2	123.8	16.5%	2,765
12/10	688.4	84.3	12.3%	2,975
12/09	398.6	(57.7)	—	2,760
Annual Growth	**14.8%**	**—**	**—**	**3.8%**

2013 Year-End Financials

Debt ratio: —	No. of shares (mil.): 138
Return on equity: 10.2%	Dividends
Cash ($ mil.): 384	Yield: —
Current ratio: 6.27	Payout: —
Long-term debt ($ mil.): —	Market value ($ mil.): 1,608

	STOCK PRICE ($) FY Close	P/E High/Low		PER SHARE ($) Earnings	Dividends	Book Value
12/13	11.59	21	17	0.53	0.00	5.46
12/12	9.18	20	15	0.50	0.00	5.02
12/11	8.73	11	7	0.91	0.00	4.48
12/10	7.47	12	6	0.63	0.00	3.46
12/09	5.28	—	—	(0.49)	0.00	2.66
Annual Growth	**21.7%**	**—**	**—**	**—**	**—**	**19.6%**

Epam Systems, Inc.

How do you say "offshoring" in Russian? Just ask EPAM. The IT outsourcing company provides software development and other IT services to US and European customers primarily from development centers in Russia Belarus Hungary Ukraine Kazakhstan and Poland. In addition to software product development the company offers services in such areas as e-commerce support data warehousing customer relationship management and application integration. EPAM also offers its own hosted and stand-alone enterprise software for sales force automation content management order management and other business processes. More than half of sales come from North America. EPAM went public in 2012.

IPO

The company plans to use the proceeds from its IPO to acquire facilities and to make acquisitions of businesses or technologies that complement its expansion strategies.

Strategy

The company is looking to extend its expertise in targeted industry verticals which include independent software vendors banking and financial services business information and media hospitality and travel and retail and consumer. To do this

EPAM continues to recruit IT professionals with specific industry knowledge and to pursue acquisitions that add to its service portfolio and customer base. Another part of EPAM's growth strategy is to make acquisitions of companies that have a significant presence in China Latin America and other emerging markets.

Mergers and Acquisitions

It found an acquisition in 2012 to further its expansion plans when it agreed to buy Toronto-based IT consultancy and software provider Thoughtcorp in a deal worth more than $17 million. The acquisition ticks a number of boxes: it bolsters EPAM's presence in North America improves the company's opportunities for growth in the telecommunications sector and brings in greater delivery capabilities in areas such as agile development enterprise mobility and business intelligence.

EPAM strengthened its presence in the business information and media industry when it bought New York-based Web data management services provider Instant Information in 2010. The purchase expanded its operations in Belarus. The acquisition of Rodmon Systems in 2009 added a large client in the business information and media industry along with operations in Belarus.

Financial Analysis

In 2010 revenues were up 48% over 2009 driven by a more than 150% increase in sales to the banking and financials services market and revenues from the business information and media industry that were 60% higher. Geographically most of EPAM's growth was from clients in Europe. In Switzerland revenues were up more than 300% and the UK saw a 74% increase in sales; both countries have strong banking and financial services industries. Though its profits dipped somewhat during the global economic downturn the company's net income in 2010 was double that reported in 2009.

Geographic Reach

The company has expanded geographically by adding client management offices in locations that are close to customers –including the US UK Germany Sweden Switzerland Russia and Kazakhstan –and by adding new development centers. Its development center in Poland was opened in 2011. The company's acquisition of PLUS MICRO in 2008 expanded EPAM's operations in Kazakhstan. In certain cases (such as Russia and Kazakhstan) EPAM has both development centers and client management offices in the same country.

Ownership

EPAM's investors include Renaissance Investment Management and Da Vinci Capital. Its clients include Barclays Thomson Reuters The Coca-Cola Company Expedia Google and Sberbank.

EXECUTIVES

President and CEO, Arkadiy Dobkin, age 54, $300,000 total compensation
President EPAM Systems Europe; EVP EPAM Systems, Karl Robb, age 52, $3,572 total compensation
Global Head Banking and Financial Services Industry Business Unit, Balazs Fejes, age 39, $190,973 total compensation
CTO, Sam Rehman
CFO, Anthony J. Conte
Global Head Media Entertainment and Publishing Business Unit, Alexey Vitashkevich
Global Head Travel and Consumer Industry Business Unit, Elaina Shekhter‎
Head Global Delivery Organization, Sergey Yezhkov

Head North American Business Unit, Victor Dvorkin
Head Commonwealth of Independent States Business Unit, Vasily Agafonov
Head Global Operations, Alex Lyashok
Vp And Head Of Esp, Valeri Makovik
Vice President Of Cloud Solutions, Eli Feldman
Senior Vice President Of Business, Isaak Karaev
Svp, David Scott
Vice President E Commerce, Ron Lankin
Vice President Technology Solutions, Michael Gavronsky
Vice President And Global Head Talent, Rajeev Bhat
Senior Vice President Of Business Information Service, Isaak Eisenberg
Vice President Marketing, Joseph King
Executive Vice President, John Fontana
Vice President, Darryl Hassell
Vice President Marketing, Beth Parker
President Eu Operations Executive Vp, Karl Jaruseski
Vice President Product Development, Lokesh Seth
Vice President Technology Solutions, Robert Olsson
Vice President Sales, John Shane
Vice President, Ramesh Karunakaran
Vp Experience Design, Jonathan Lupo
Vice President Application And Cloud, Kamesh Chetty
Vice President Of Technology Solutions, Igor Nys
Vice President Of Technology Solutions, Michael Seeley
Vice President Technology, Slava Lazebnikov
Board Member & Chairman Of Nominating, Bob Segert
Board Of Directors, Ronald Vargo
Auditors: Deloitte&ToucheLLP

LOCATIONS

HQ: Epam Systems, Inc.
41 University Drive, Suite 202, Newtown, PA 18940
Phone: 267 759-9000
Web: www.epam.com

2010 Sales by Customer Location

	$ mil.	% of total
North America	117.0	53
Europe		
UK	32.6	14
Other countries	26.0	12
CIS		
Russia	31.5	14
Other countries	10.9	5
Reimbursable expenses & other revenues	3.8	2
Total	**221.8**	**100**

PRODUCTS/OPERATIONS

2010 Sales

	$ mil.	% of total
Software development	149.6	67
Application testing services	44.5	20
Application maintenance & support	19.3	9
Infrastructure services	2.8	1
Licensing	1.8	1
Reimbursable expenses & other revenues	3.8	2
Total	**221.8**	**100**

2010 Sales by Industry

	$ mil.	% of total
Independent software vendors & technology	68.7	31
Business information & media	45.7	21
Banking & financial services	42.8	19
Travel & hospitality	18.8	8
Retail & consumer	17.7	8
Other verticals	24.3	11
Reimbursable expenses & other revenues	3.8	2
Total	**221.8**	**100**

Selected Services

Application development
Application maintenance and support
Application testing
Business intelligence
Business process management
Content management
Customer Relationship Management (CRM)
Data warehousing and business intelligence
E-commerce
Enterprise application integration
Enterprise resource planning
Infrastructure and hosting
Knowledge management
Localization
Offshore software development
Quality assurance consulting and testing strategy transformation
Server and network management

COMPETITORS

Accenture	Infosys
Atos	MindTree
Camelot Information	Pactera
Capgemini	Sapient
Cognizant Tech Solutions	Symphony Technology Group LLC
Computer Sciences Corp.	Tata Consultancy
GlobalLogic	VanceInfo
HCL Technologies	Wipro
IBM Global Services	iSoftStone

HISTORICAL FINANCIALS

Company Type: Public

Income Statement

FYE: December 31

	REVENUE ($ mil.)	NET INCOME ($ mil.)	NET PROFIT MARGIN	EMPLOYEES
12/13	555.1	61.9	11.2%	11,056
12/12	433.8	54.4	12.6%	10,043
12/11	334.5	44.3	13.3%	8,125
12/10	221.8	28.3	12.8%	6,168
12/09	149.9	13.5	9.0%	4,432
Annual Growth	**38.7%**	**46.3%**	**—**	**25.7%**

2013 Year-End Financials

Debt ratio: —   No. of shares (mil.): 46
Return on equity: 18.7%   Dividends
Cash ($ mil.): 169   Yield: —
Current ratio: 6.05   Payout: —
Long-term debt ($ mil.): —   Market value ($ mil.): 1,629

	STOCK PRICE ($) FY Close	P/E High/Low		PER SHARE ($) Earnings	Dividends	Book Value
12/13	34.94	29	13	1.28	0.00	8.07
12/12	18.10	18	11	1.17	0.00	6.44
Annual Growth	**93.0%**	**—**	**—**	**9.4%**	**—**	**25.3%**

EPIQ Systems Inc

Epiq Systems wants to make legal discovery and bankruptcy proceedings as quick and painless as possible (for attorneys that is). The company provides case and document management software for bankruptcy class action mass tort and other legal proceedings. Its software automates tasks including electronic discovery legal notice claims management and government reporting. Epiq's software line includes products for Chapter 7 liquidations as well as Chapter 13 and 11 reorganizations. The company which caters to law firms and bankruptcy trustees also offers consulting and case management services and software for class action mass tort and bankruptcy case administration. Epiq operates primarily in the US.

Geographic Reach

Kansas City-based Epiq Systems' primary market is the US representing more than 90% of its sales. The firm has offices in about 10 US cities including New York Chicago Dallas and Los Angeles. Overseas it has offices in London and Hong Kong.

Operations Epiq's largest and fastest-growing segment is electronic discovery or eDiscovery which provides collections and forensics processing search and review and document review services for corporate legal departments and law firms. Its bankruptcy division focuses on products for Chapter 7 and 13 filings as most bankruptcies fall under these models. As part of an effort to cover the entire bankruptcy spectrum however Epiq maintains its services to the Chapter 11 market. The company's smallest segment is settlement administration services which includes corporations administering the settlement of class action cases.

Financial Performance Revenue increased 32% in 2012 versus 2011 to $373 million on the strength of Epiq's eDiscovery business which posted a year-over-year gain of 48% as a result of the Encore and De Novo acquisitions in 2011. The firm's Settlement Administration businesses grew 64% due to a large legal notification engagement in 2012. The bankruptcy unit posted a 4% decline in annual sales. Net income rose 86% in 2012 versus 2011 to $22.4 million on higher sales and acquisition-related income from Encore. Mergers and Acquisitions Epiq which has traditionally grown organically acquired two eDiscovery businesses in 2011 to strengthen that segment. It purchased De Novo Legal in late 2011 for $68 million and Encore Discovery Solutions for $100 million earlier in the year. The company also made an acquisition in 2010 with the $60 million purchase of Jupiter eSources. Jupiter specializes in software (known as AACER) used by creditors to automate the processing of loans in bankruptcy cases. With the acquisition Epiq expanded its product line and added clients in such segments as banking and mortgage lending. Ownership The company was founded in 1988 by chairman and CEO Tom W. Olofson. He and his family own (both directly and through a family foundation) a 13% stake in the company. President and COO Christopher Olofson owns about 5% of the shares. St. Denis J. Villere & Co. owns 13% of the company's shares while investment firm T. Rowe Price holds 11%.

EXECUTIVES

Vice President Of Human Resources, Kathy Murry
Chairman and CEO, Tom W. Olofson, age 73,
$900,000 total compensation
SVP and CTO, Chris Jutkiewicz
EVP and CFO, Karin-Joyce S.F. (KJ) Tjon
Senior Vice President General Manager Class Action and Claims Solutions, Andrew Shimek
President and COO, Brad D. Scott
Vice President Info Technology R D, Rich Miller
Vice President, James Prutsman
Senior Vice President, Laura Kibbe
Senior Vice President Bankruptcy Services, Richard Arbuckle
Vice President New Product Development, Jayne Menard

Vice President And Senior Consultant, Joseph Wharton
Vice President, Tauheed Williams
Vice President Human Resources, Terry Gaylord
Senior Vice President Software, Bob Spike
Vice President Special Projects, Stephen Doherty
Vice President, Greg Lutz
Vice President Senior Consultant, Edward Kosmowski
Vice President And Senior Consultant, Jason Horwitz
Vice President Business Solutions, Alan Kays
Vice President Engineering, Gregory Jackson
Vice President Ediscovery Solutions, Lisa Schofieldsenior
Vice President Product Management, Kealani Tosh
Vice President Finance, Scott Hanson
Senior Vice President Business, Robert Patti
Vice President Legal Services, Richard Pentimonti
Vice President Finance, Bruce Wakefield
Executive Vice President Executive, Tom Bride
Vice President Of Business Development, Randall Burkholder
Vice President Of Marketing, Shane Lennon
Senior Vice President Bankruptcy, Patty Radovan
Vice President, Lance Lickel
Vice President, Shannon Wheatman
Vice President And Director Of Client Services, Robert Seraceni
Chairman and CEO, Tom W. Olofson, age 73
Treasurer, Alicia Lopez
Auditors: Deloitte&ToucheLLP

LOCATIONS

HQ: EPIQ Systems Inc
501 Kansas Avenue, Kansas City, KS 66105-1300
Phone: 913 621-9500
Web: www.epiqsystems.com

2012 Sales

	$ mil.	% of total
US	346.5	93
Other countries	26.6	7
Total	**373.1**	**100**

PRODUCTS/OPERATIONS

2012 Sales

	$ mil.	% of total
Electronic discovery	197.0	57
Bankruptcy	88.3	26
Settlement administration	59.5	17
Reimbursed expenses	28.3	-
Total	**373.1**	**100**

Selected Products

Case Power (Chapter 13 administration)
ClaimsMatrix (case management software to administer class action settlements)
DebtorMatrix (Chapter 11)
DocuMatrix (Hosted discovery management platform)
eDataMatrix (electronic discovery)
IQ Review (document indexing)
TCMS (Chapter 7 trustee case management system)
TCMSWeb (Web-based trustee case management system)

COMPETITORS

Applied Discovery	JPMorgan Chase
Clearwell Systems	Kroll Ontrack
Cricket Technologies	Kurtzman Carson
Daegis	Consultants
Dolan Company	LexisNexis
FTI Consulting	Misys
Fios	Recommind
Fiserv	SunGard
Hewlett-Packard	Symantec
Huron Consulting	Xerox

HISTORICAL FINANCIALS

Company Type: Public

Income Statement

FYE: December 31

	REVENUE ($ mil.)	NET INCOME ($ mil.)	NET PROFIT MARGIN	EMPLOYEES
12/13	482.0	11.1	2.3%	1,000
12/12	373.0	22.4	6.0%	1,000
12/11	283.3	12.0	4.3%	1,000
12/10	247.1	13.9	5.6%	550
12/09	239.0	14.6	6.1%	550
Annual Growth	**19.2%**	**(6.6%)**	**—**	**16.1%**

2013 Year-End Financials

Debt ratio: 41.7%
Return on equity: 3.3%
Cash ($ mil.): 40
Current ratio: 2.55
Long-term debt ($ mil.): 299

No. of shares (mil.): 34
Dividends
 Yield: 2.7%
 Payout: 109.7%
Market value ($ mil.): 566

	STOCK PRICE ($) FY Close	P/E High/Low	PER SHARE ($) Earnings	Dividends	Book Value
12/13	16.17	54 37	0.30	0.45	9.32
12/12	12.75	22 17	0.61	0.35	9.56
12/11	12.02	45 31	0.33	0.16	9.31
12/10	13.73	37 30	0.36	0.07	9.18
12/09	13.99	45 30	0.38	0.00	9.02
Annual Growth	**3.7%**	**— —**	**(5.7%)**	**—**	**0.8%**

ePlus Inc

ePlus wants to rate an A-plus from its customers by meeting their hardware and software needs. ePlus is a holding company and operates through two business segments that deal in technology sales and financing. Its ePlus Technology subsidiary resells and leases products from top IT infrastructure providers. Offerings include security storage and networking products as well as consulting and systems integration services. It also offers supply chain management software and services; its proprietary applications include procurement asset management spend analytics and document management tools. The company's Leasing and Financial Services arm offers lease financing and leases IT and medical equipment.

Geographic Reach

Virginia-based ePlus rings up 99% of its sales in the US. The firm which operates from 30-plus offices across the US also has operations in Canada and Iceland.

Sales and Marketing

ePlus markets its products and services to mid-sized and large businesses state and municipal government agencies and institutions of higher education. Its largest customer is Verizon Communications which represented about 11% and 14% of its total revenues in fiscal 2014 and 2013 respectively.

Products manufactured by Cisco Systems and HP represented 48% and 11% of ePlus's sales of product and services in 2014.

Financial Performance

The company's sales topped $1 billion in fiscal 2014 (ended March) an increase of nearly 8% versus the prior year and an all-time high for the company. ePlus credited the rise to higher product and service sales by its Technology subsidiary as well as increased fees and other income partially offset by a decline in financing revenue. (Indeed its sales of products and services has doubled over the past four years.) Net earnings increased 1% to $35.3 million over the same period. ePlus's technology segment accounted for approximately 97% of its total revenues and 85% of its consolidated earnings before taxes for the year.

Strategy

ePlus which focuses exclusively on middle market and larger enterprises is gaining market share by focusing on fast growing segments within its market including virtualization collaboration and security. The firm in fall 2014 was named an HP Gold Cloud Builder Specialist partner for its expertise in the design implementation and maintenance of HP Cloud computing environments.

ePlus' strategy includes expanding its professional services offerings organically —through the opening of new service centers —and via acquisitions. In 2014 the firm opened a new managed services center in Raleigh North Carolina adding to its existing presence in the state. In 2013 it opened offices in Scottsdale Arizona; Providence Rhode Island; and Portland Maine. Since going public it has acquired more than 15 businesses.

Mergers and Acquisitons

In August 2014 the company acquired Granite Business Solutions Inc. (dba Evolve Technology Group) a provider of IT products and services in Sacramento California. The purchase expanded ePlus's presence in the Golden State. In November 2013 the firm expanded its footprint in the New York area with the purchase of AdviStor Inc. a storage-focused provider in Pittsford New York. Previous purchases include: California-based Pacific Blue Micro (PBM) in 2012; and NCC Networks a provider of managed security services with a Security Operations Center (SOC) located in Chicago in 2011. With the SOC acquisition ePlus extended its security offerings for cloud-based networks and data centers adds a sales branch in Chicago and expands its customer base.

The company also developed and began offering eCloud a private cloud computing service which can be tailored to the needs of customers in 2011. ePlus believes customers will continue to focus on costs savings and will utilize technologies such as virtualization and cloud computing.

EXECUTIVES

Vice President Finance, George Fox
EVP; President ePlus Group, Bruce M. Bowen, $330,000 total compensation
Chairman President and CEO, Phillip G. Norton, $560,000 total compensation
COO; President ePlus Technology, Mark P. Marron, $450,000 total compensation
President ePlus Systems and ePlus Content Services, Kenneth G. Farber
CFO, Elaine D. Marion, $358,333 total compensation
CTO, Mark C. Melvin
President ePlus Group, Chad Fredrick
EVP Technology Sales, Darren Raiguel
Vice President Operations And Strategic Alliances, Bert Gastonguay
Vp-healthcare Practice, Robert Filaski
Vice President O, Kleyton L (Kley) Parkhurst, age 51
Senior Vice President Of International Information Technology, Ronnie Angello
Vice President, Andrew Norton
Regional Vice President Energy Manager, Jim Murray
Vice President Of Human Resources, Jim Solomone
Vice President Of Sales, Mark Gonzalez

Vice President And Corporate Controller, Jim Belger
Regional Vice President, Lisa Neal
Chairman President and CEO, Phillip G. Norton
Auditors: Deloitte&ToucheLLP

LOCATIONS

HQ: ePlus Inc
  13595 Dulles Technology Drive, Herndon, VA 20171-3413
Phone: 703 984-8400
Web: www.eplus.com

2014 Sales

	$ in mil	% of total
United States	1042.4	
99		
International	15.1	
1		
Total	**1057.5**	
100		

PRODUCTS/OPERATIONS

2014 Sales

	$ mil.	% of total
Technology sales	1021.4	97
Financing	36.1	3
Total	**1057.5**	**100**

Selected Subsidiaries

ePlus Canada Company
ePlus Capital inc.
ePlus Document Systems inc.
ePlus Group inc.
ePlus Iceland inc.
ePlus Jamaica inc.
ePlus Technology inc.

COMPETITORS

American Express
CDW
CSI Leasing
Citibank
CompuCom
Dell
Deutsche Bank
En Pointe
FAEF
Forsythe Technology
General Dynamics Information Technology
Hewlett-Packard
IBM Global Financing
IBM Global Services
Insight Enterprises
JPMorgan Chase
Leidos
Meridian Group
Microsoft
PC Connection
PC Mall
Pomeroy IT
Red River Computer
Systemax
UNICOM Government
Unisys
Zones

HISTORICAL FINANCIALS

Company Type: Public

Income Statement

FYE: March 31

	REVENUE ($ mil.)	NET INCOME ($ mil.)	NET PROFIT MARGIN	EMPLOYEES
03/14	1,057.5	35.2	3.3%	934
03/13	983.1	34.8	3.5%	904
03/12	825.5	23.3	2.8%	833
03/11	863.0	23.7	2.7%	725
03/10	684.2	12.7	1.9%	661
Annual Growth	**11.5%**	**29.0%**	**—**	**9.0%**

2014 Year-End Financials

Debt ratio: 12.4%   No. of shares (mil.): 8
Return on equity: 13.9%   Dividends
Cash ($ mil.): 80   Yield: —
Current ratio: 1.74   Payout: —
Long-term debt ($ mil.): 36   Market value ($ mil.): 448

	STOCK PRICE ($) FY Close	P/E High/Low		PER SHARE ($) Earnings	PER SHARE ($) Dividends	PER SHARE ($) Book Value
03/14	55.76	15	9	4.37	0.00	33.15
03/13	46.21	11	7	4.32	2.50	29.23
03/12	31.97	12	8	2.84	0.00	27.45
03/11	26.61	10	6	2.82	0.00	24.93
03/10	17.55	11	7	1.50	0.00	22.83
Annual Growth	**33.5%**	**—**	**—**	**30.6%**	**—**	**9.8%**

EQT Corp.

Integrated natural gas company EQT Corporation (formerly Equitable Resources) hopes to get its fair share of the natural gas market. EQT Production exploits proved reserves of 6 trillion cu. ft. of natural gas equivalent in the Appalachian region operating some 14000 active wells and drilling more than 700 new wells a year. EQT Production sells its natural gas products to Appalachian-area utilities and industrial customers and to marketers including EQT Energy its own gas marketing affiliate. EQT's Distribution unit provides gas to about 277400 customers in Pennsylvania West Virginia and Kentucky. EQT Midstream Partners operates more than 11000 miles of gathering pipeline and 770 miles of transmission lines.

Geographic Reach

EQT's distribution unit provides gas to about 276500 customers in Pennsylvania West Virginia and Kentucky. EQT's natural gas exploration and production companies are active in the Appalachian Basin with operations in Pennsylvania West Virginia Kentucky and Virginia.

Sales and Marketing

EQT's produced natural gas is sold to marketers utilities and industrial customers mainly in Appalachia. The company sells NGLs from its own production through EQT Production and from gas marketed for third parties by EQT Midstream Partners. The EQT Distribution segment provides natural gas distribution services to 277400 customers consisting of 258500 residential customers and 18900 commercial and industrial customers in southwestern Pennsylvania municipalities in northern West Virginia and field line sales in eastern Kentucky and West Virginia.

Customers of EQT Midstream's gas transportation storage risk management and related services are affiliates and third parties in the northeastern US including Dominion Resources NiSource PECO Energy and UGI.

EQT Energy's operations include gas processing and transportation storage marketing and trading.

Financial Performance

The company's revenues increased by $1.6 million in 2012 as a result of increased production from the 2011 and 2012 drilling programs in the Marcellus play. This increase was partially offset by the normal production decline of EQT's producing wells.

EQT's net income dropped by 62% in 2012 due to additional expense from the company's November 2011 issuance of senior notes (due in 2021) and a payment to close a forward-starting interest rate swap offset by a decrease in operating expenses.

Except for a revenue slump in 2009 and 2010 company saw an upward trend in revenues from 2008 to 2012. The sales decline in 2009 and 2010 was due to an increased in gas sales volumes across the industry and lower gas prices.

Strategy

EQT's overall strategy is to build up production and midstream gas businesses. It has a substantial acreage position (where it focuses on long-lived low-risk wells) extensive gas gathering and transmission assets low cost structure and proximity to northeastern US consumer markets.

Seeking capital investment in 2012 the company spun off EQT Midstream Partners as a public company; it retained a 63% limited partner interest in the company.

To raise cash to reinvest in production and midstream activities that year it also agreed to sell its natural gas distribution business Equitable Gas Company LLC to Peoples Natural Gas for $720 million. In the deal EQT Corporation will receive some Marcellus midstream assets including 200 miles of regulated transmission pipelines and four storage pools with a 15.1 billion cu. ft. working gas capacity.

In 2014 the company agreed to sell its Jupiter natural gas gathering system announced to EQT Midstream Partners for $1.2 billion.

In order to raise cash to invest in production activities in its shale areas in 2011 the company sold a Kentucky-based natural-gas processing complex and pipeline to MarkWest Energy Partners for $230 million. It also sold its 70-mile natural gas pipeline (Big Sandy Pipeline) in eastern Kentucky to Spectra Energyfor $390 million.

EXECUTIVES

Chairman President and Chief Executive Officer, David L. Porges, age 56, $725,962 total compensation
Senior Vice President and Chief Financial Officer, Philip P. (Phil) Conti, age 55, $390,520 total compensation
Senior Vice President and President Midstream Distribution & Commercial, Randall L. Crawford, age 51, $406,673 total compensation
Vice President; President - Midstream Operations, Martin A. Fritz, age 50
Vice President; President - Commercial Operations, M. Elise Hyland, age 55
Senior Vice President and President Exploration & Production, Steven T. Schlotterbeck, age 49, $406,673 total compensation
Senior Vice President Land Business, James E Crockard
Vice President Planning And Process, Paul Omasits
Vice President Marketing, Heejun Park
Sr Vice President, Steve Rafferty

Vp Land Midstream, Ralph Deer
Vice President Business Development, Patrick McGonagle
Vp Or Senior Vp, Michael Conn
Vice President And General Counsel, Sandra Fraley
Vice President Drilling And Water, Mike Butcher
Senior Vice President Human Resources, Carol Caracciolo
Group Senior Vice President Engineering, Shawn Rohowsky
Evp Commercial, Blue Jenkins
Senior Vice President Geosciences, Lindell Bridges
Senior Vice President Of Eris Parent, Edward Meyer
Vice President Engineering, David Elkin
Vp Or Senior Vp, Gregory Cummings
Senior Vice President Engineering, David Schlosser
Vice President Business Development, Marc Weaver
Vice President Construction, Jay Brandli
Vice President Operations, Lester Zitkus
Senior Vice President, Ted O'Brien
Vice President Midstream Construction, P Brandli
Asst Vice President Staffing Diversity, Jacob Bezeck
Vice President Geoscience, Joe Morris
Senior Vice President, Chris Akers
Sr Vice President, Mike Provencher
Vice President President Midstream, Martin Strong
Senior Vice President President, Randall McCormick
Vice President, Christopher Willian
Vice President Automation Controls, William Sybert
Vice President Completion Operations, Jim Helmick
Vice President Commercial Operations, Cliff Baker
Chairman President and Chief Executive Officer, David L. Porges, age 56
Treasury Specialist, Heidi Berkley
Treasury Specialist, Anna Leatherow
Treasurer, Maurice Royster
Assistant Treasurer, Daniel Greenblatt
Assistant Treasurer, Janice Brenner
Board Member, Michael Bryson
Auditors: Ernst&YoungLLP

LOCATIONS

HQ: EQT Corp.
625 Liberty Avenue, Suite 1700, Pittsburgh, PA 15222
Phone: 412 553-5700
Web: www.eqt.com

PRODUCTS/OPERATIONS

2012 Sales

	$ mil.	% of total
EQT Production	793.8	49
EQT Midstream	505.5	31
Distribution	314.0	20
Adjustments	28.3	-
Total	**1641.6**	**100**

COMPETITORS

AEP	Dominion Resources
Alliant Energy	Miller Energy
Belden & Blake	Resources
Berkshire Hathaway	NiSource
Energy	ONEOK
Cabot Oil & Gas	Range Resources
Chevron	

HISTORICAL FINANCIALS

Company Type: Public

Income Statement

FYE: December 31

	REVENUE ($ mil.)	NET INCOME ($ mil.)	NET PROFIT MARGIN	EMPLOYEES
12/14	2,469.7	386.9	15.7%	1,750
12/13	1,862.0	390.5	21.0%	1,621
12/12	1,641.6	183.4	11.2%	1,873
12/11	1,639.9	479.7	29.3%	1,835
12/10	1,322.7	227.7	17.2%	1,815
Annual Growth	**16.9%**	**14.2%**	**—**	**(0.9%)**

2014 Year-End Financials

Debt ratio: 24.7%
Return on equity: 8.9%
Cash ($ mil.): 1,077
Current ratio: 2.28
Long-term debt ($ mil.): 2,822

No. of shares (mil.): 151
Dividends
  Yield: 0.1%
  Payout: 3.5%
Market value ($ mil.): 11,476

	STOCK PRICE ($) FY Close	P/E High/Low		PER SHARE ($) Earnings	Dividends	Book Value
12/14	75.70	43	30	2.54	0.12	30.23
12/13	89.78	36	22	2.57	0.12	26.74
12/12	58.98	51	36	1.22	0.88	24.01
12/11	54.79	21	14	3.19	0.88	24.04
12/10	44.84	30	21	1.57	0.88	20.64
Annual Growth	**14.0%**	**—**	**—**	**12.8%**	**(39.2%)**	**10.0%**

Equinix, Inc (New)

Equinix provides data and network hosting and colocation facilities (it calls them Internet Business Exchanges or IBXs) where ISPs telecommunications carriers and content providers can locate equipment and interconnect networks and operations. The company also offers colocation-related services to provide clients with cabinets operating space and storage. Customers include network and mobility providers (such as AT&T BT and Comcast); cloud and IT services (Amazon.com Microsoft and Salesforce.com); and content providers (DIRECTV Facebook). Altogether Equinix operates more than 100 data centers around the world and international customers make up about one-third of sales.

Operations

The market for colocation facilities has been served by large telecom carriers that bundle telecommunications and managed services with their colocation offerings. But telecom customers still outsource their critical interconnection relationships to Equinix especially as more companies need data center space for bandwidth-intensive services such as video voice over IP (VoIP) social media mobile data gaming data-rich media Ethernet and wireless services. In addition the company has gained many customers that have outgrown their existing data centers.

Geographic Reach

Equinix has more than 100 data centers located in 15 countries around the world. Customers in the Americas however account for more than half of sales. The EMEA region makes up another quarter while Asian customers account for the remaining 15% of revenues.

Sales and Marketing

The company employs a direct sales force to serve its 4500 existing customers and attract new ones. It also actively promotes the brand around the world through industry conferences business and trade publications online media and sponsored activities.

Financial Performance

Equinix has enjoyed consistent revenue growth every year and overall sales increased 14% in 2013 reaching $2.1 billion. The boost was attributable to a growing international customer base driven by acquisitions and organic expansion of its global facilities network. The company has also been consistently profitable however net income fell 34% in 2013 to $95 million after it paid off $108 million in debt. In line with the reduced profits cash flow fell slightly to $604 million.

Mergers and Acquisitions

In anticipation of a steady demand for commercial data center services Equinix is expanding its infrastructure around the world. In 2013 it paid $50 million for a property in Frankfurt Germany that it was already leasing. That year it also added and/or expanded data centers in Brazil Japan Switzerland the UK and the US. In 2014 it spent $23 million expanding its third data center in Hong Kong which is used by many financial services companies.

In 2012 it bought the assets including five data centers and a disaster recovery center of Asia Tone for about $230 million in cash. The facilities are located in Hong Kong Shanghai and Singapore and expanded Equinix's footprint in China.

Also that year it completed its acquisition of Germany-based colocation and interconnection services provider ancotel GmbH which tacked on one more data center to Equinix's existing four in Frankfurt. With edge nodes (smaller more mobile data centers) not only in London but also Hong Kong and Miami the deal also expanded Equinix's geographical reach and it added 400 new customers.

In 2011 the company acquired 90% of ALOG Data Centers of Brazil for $83 million in cash $15 million of which was slated for future data center expansion. The deal extended the company's reach to South America bringing its total number of data centers to about 100 in 38 markets in 13 countries worldwide. ALOG has data centers in Rio de Janeiro and Sao Paolo.

Strategy

As part of an ongoing effort to deploy new resources internationally as it works to solidify the presence of its brand the company announced an investment of about $100 million in 2012 to build an additional data center in Washington DC to support expansion in the area. Late the previous year Equinix expanded its presence in Hong Kong spending $63 million to establish second data center there in support of growing demand in the region. This was part of a pattern of Asia-Pacific investment that also saw the company opening a third data center in both Sydney and Tokyo in 2011.

As it focuses on core markets the company is also divesting some data centers. In late 2012 it sold more than 15 centers exiting such markets as Cleveland Detroit and St. Louis. Equinix received $76 million from the sale.

EXECUTIVES

Vice President Human Resources, Garry Ronco
Chief Financial Officer, Keith D. Taylor, age 53, $470,577 total compensation
Managing Director United Kingdom, Russell Poole
President Equinix Asia-Pacific, Samuel Lee

COO, Charles Meyers, age 44, $440,400 total compensation
Managing Director France, Michel Brignano
Chief Global Operations Officer, Sushil (Sam) Kapoor, age 68, $256,833 total compensation
VP Strategy and Services, Eric Schwartz, age 47, $358,174 total compensation
Managing Director Equinix South Asia, Clement Goh
CEO & President; Director, Stephen M. (Steve) Smith, age 58, $764,615 total compensation
Regional Operating Chief Americas, Raouf F. Abdel, age 47
Chief Information Officer, Brian Lillie
Managing Director The Netherlands, Michiel Eielts
Managing Director Equinix Japan, Kei Furuta
Managing Director Switzerland, Marco Dottarelli
Managing Director Equinix Hong Kong, Alex Tam
Country Manager Australia, Jeremy Deutsch
Managing Director Equinix China, Sainti Li
Managing Director Germany, Donald Badoux
President Americas, Karl Strohmeyer, $15,385 total compensation
Vp Business Operations, Herb Kirchner
Vice President Of Information, Andy Castle
Vice President Finance, Ronald Khoo
Vice President Marketing, Ravi Ravishankar
Vice President Of Marketing And Mid, Kevin Young
National Account Manager, Lou Amato
Vice President Global Marketing Commo, Lisa Hempel
Vice President Technology Development, Teri Francis
National Account Manager, Chad Durham
Vice President Global Finance Operations, David Wilson
Assistant Vice President Strategy And Advanced Services, Marianne Arnautou
Applications Vice President, David Nale
Vice President Global Deal Desk, Biju Baby
Vice President Marketing, Chris Reid
Vice President Global Talent Management, Larry McAlister
European Financial Systems Vp, Elmar Van Dijk
Vice President Sales Europe, Michael Winterson
Vice President Indirect Channels, A Walker
National Account Manager, David Karchmer
National Account Manager, Jason Girardi
Vice President Sales Financial Services, Rich O'Dea
Vice President Corporate Strategy, Kaushik Joshi
Vice President Global Marketing Strategy And Operations, Bill Dembinski
Vice President Enterprise Sales, Jim Reilly
Vice President Ibx Operations Engineering, Fluke Pickut
Vice President Marketing Asia Pacific, Michele Felder
Finance Vice President, Arnaud Legay
Vice President Controller, Minnie Geronimo
Vice President Ap Legal, Yolande Goh
Vice President Global Product, John Harmon
Vice President Global Network, Andy Suydam
National Account Manager, Carrie Butler
Assistant Vice President Human, Sanford Anstey
Executive Vice President Of Sales, Buster Brown
Vice President North America Ibx, David Morgan
Co Founder And Vice President, Sandy Jen
National Account Manager, Michelle Pohndorf
Vice President Construction Management, Diraj Bamola
Vice President Of Interconnection Product Management, Bill Long
Vice President, Marianne Stanke
Vice President, Mitch Ferro
Vice President, Greg Maclean
Svp Sales United States, Daniel C (Dan) Walker

Vice President Finance, Wee Ong
National Account Manager, Shay Flavin
Senior Vice President Sales Americas, Peter Galanis
Chief Marketing Officer Vp Marketing, Todd Handcock
Vp Finance Emea, Kathryn Herrick
Vice President Services Product, John Shultz
Vice President Of Business Development, Brett Johnson
National Account Manager, Hank Bartels
Vp Ibx Global Operations Support, Benjamin Holeman
Executive Chairman, Peter F. Van Camp, age 59
CEO & President; Director, Stephen M. (Steve) Smith, age 58
Senior Treasury Analyst, Lin Wang
Treasury Consultant, Jeanne Castro Schmidt
Board Member, Christopher Paisley
Vp Tax & Treasury, Cathryn Arnell
Auditors: PricewaterhouseCoopersLLP

LOCATIONS

HQ: Equinix, Inc (New)
One Lagoon Drive, Fourth Floor, Redwood City, CA 94065
Phone: 650 598-6000
Web: www.equinix.com

2013 Sales

	$ mil.	% of total
Americas	1264.8	59
Europe Middle East & Africa	525.0	24
Asia-Pacific	363.0	17
Total	**2152.8**	**100**

PRODUCTS/OPERATIONS

2013 Sales

	% of total
Colocation	75
Interconnection	15
Managed infrastructure	5
Other	5
Total	**100**

Selected Mergers and Acquisitions

FY 2012
ancotel (Germany $85 million)
Asia Tone ($230 million)
FY 2011
ALOG Data Centers (Brazil $83 million)
FY 2010
Switch and Data Facilities ($683 million)

COMPETITORS

AT&T	Level 3 Communications
COLT Group	NTT
CenturyLink	NaviSite
CoreSite	Rackspace
CyrusOne	SAVVIS
Digital Realty	SingTel
DuPont Fabros	SunGard Availability
Everest Interlink	Services
Broadband	TeleCity
Hostway	Telx Group
InterXion	Terremark Worldwide
Internap Network	Verio
Services	Zayo Group

HISTORICAL FINANCIALS

Company Type: Public

Income Statement

FYE: December 31

	REVENUE ($ mil.)	NET INCOME ($ mil.)	NET PROFIT MARGIN	EMPLOYEES
12/13	2,152.7	94.6	4.4%	3,500
12/12	1,895.7	144.6	7.6%	3,153
12/11	1,606.8	94.0	5.9%	2,709
12/10	1,220.3	36.8	3.0%	1,921
12/09	882.5	69.4	7.9%	1,301
Annual Growth	25.0%	8.1%	—	28.1%

2013 Year-End Financials

Debt ratio: 55.5%	No. of shares (mil.): 49
Return on equity: 3.9%	Dividends
Cash ($ mil.): 261	Yield: —
Current ratio: 1.63	Payout: —
Long-term debt ($ mil.): 4,087	Market value ($ mil.): 8,800

	STOCK PRICE ($) FY Close	P/E High/Low	PER SHARE ($) Earnings	Dividends	Book Value
12/13	177.45	120 81	1.89	0.00	49.59
12/12	206.20	68 34	2.92	0.00	47.88
12/11	101.40	60 46	1.72	0.00	41.83
12/10	81.26	130 84	0.82	0.00	40.73
12/09	106.15	60 23	1.75	0.00	30.08
Annual Growth	13.7%	— —	1.9%	—	13.3%

Equity Lifestyle Properties Inc

Snow birds and empty nesters flock to communities developed and owned by Equity LifeStyle Properties. The real estate investment trust (REIT) owns and operates lifestyle-oriented residential properties aimed at retirees vacationers and second home owners. Other properties provide affordable housing for families. Equity LifeStyle Properties leases lots for factory-built homes cottages cabins and recreational vehicles. Available homes range in size and style. The REIT's portfolio includes more than 380 properties containing some 141000 lots in about 30 states and Canada. Properties are similar to site-built residential subdivisions with centralized entrances utilities gutters curbs and paved streets.

Many of Equity LifeStyle's communities include club houses swimming pools game courts and other amenities. The company mainly focuses on developing properties in large metro areas near retirement and vacation spots.

Subsidiary Realty Systems leases or finances homes at communities owned by Equity LifeStyle Properties. While home sales have dropped in recent years more customers are choosing to lease a home in light of uncertain economic conditions. The company has adjusted its strategy accordingly and significantly reduced its new home sales activities. Instead of selling new manufactured homes it rents them. Equity LifeStyle Properties also has bumped up rental rates in order to boost revenues. The company hopes to convert its home renters to buyers in the future as the economy recovers. Equity LifeStyle also is focused on offering smaller

more energy efficient and affordable homes which are in high demand.

The REIT which was founded in 1992 has significantly grown its portfolio over the years and continues to acquire properties located in high growth urban and resort areas such as Florida (which accounts for about 38% of revenues) Arizona and California. In 2011 the company acquired 74 manufactured home communities and one RV resort from Hometown America for some $1.5 billion. The deal added more than 31000 home sites in 16 states mostly in Florida and the northeastern US.

The company also looks to expand existing properties to accommodate more tenants. It focuses on attracting customers and extending their stays by providing attractive amenities (cable TV laundry rooms) and common facilities (swimming pools tennis courts clubhouses) that foster a social atmosphere for tenants and keep occupancy turnover low.

Equity LifeStyle Properties has been working to improve its membership business which gives members passes to certain properties within geographic zones in exchange for an annual fee. In 2008 it acquired Privileged Access an RV and vacation membership business which helped grow Equity LifeStyle Properties' client base. The deal added to Equity LifeStyle's other membership-based subsidiary Thousand Trails which has more than 130000 dues-paying members that have special access to campgrounds.

Chairman Sam Zell (the so-called "Grave Dancer" of Equity Office Properties and Equity Residential fame) controls about 9% of the REIT.

EXECUTIVES

EVP of Asset Management, Roger A. Maynard, age 56, $311,428 total compensation
Vice President And Treasurer, Paul Seavey
Vice President Customer Relations, David Kozy
Executive Vice President, Jim Phillips
Vice President Information Technology, Paul Jessie
Auditors: Ernst&YoungLLP

LOCATIONS

HQ: Equity Lifestyle Properties Inc
Two North Riverside Plaza, Suite 800, Chicago, IL 60606
Phone: 312 279-1400
Web: www.equitylifestyle.com

2011 Properties

	No.
US	
Florida	119
California	49
Arizona	41
Michigan	15
Texas	15
Washington	15
Pennsylvania	15
Colorado	10
Oregon	9
North Carolina	8
Delaware	7
Indiana	7
New York	7
Nevada	7
Virginia	7
Maine	5
Massachusetts	5
Wisconsin	5
Idaho	4
Illinois	4
New Jersey	4
Minnesota	4
South Carolina	3
Utah	3
Maryland	2

	No.
Ohio	2
Tennessee	2
New Hampshire	2
North Dakota	2
Ohio	2
Alabama	1
Connecticut	1
Kentucky	1
Canada	
British Columbia	1
Total	**382**

PRODUCTS/OPERATIONS

2011 Sales

	$ mil.	% of total
Community base rentals	318.9	54
Resort base rentals	130.5	22
Right-to-use annual payments	49.1	8
Utility and other	53.8	9
Right-to-use contracts current period gross	17.9	3
Home sales	**6.1**	
1		
Right-to-use contracts defeered net of prior period amortization	(11.9)	-
Other	15.7	3
Total	**580.1**	**100**

COMPETITORS

American Land Lease	Outdoor Resorts
Hometown America	Sun Communities
International Leisure	UMH Properties
Kampgrounds of America	

HISTORICAL FINANCIALS

Company Type: Public

Income Statement

FYE: December 31

	REVENUE ($ mil.)	NET INCOME ($ mil.)	NET PROFIT MARGIN	EMPLOYEES
12/13	728.3	125.9	17.3%	3,700
12/12	709.8	74.4	10.5%	3,600
12/11	580.0	42.5	7.3%	3,500
12/10	511.3	60.4	11.8%	3,600
12/09	489.9	56.2	11.5%	3,200
Annual Growth	10.4%	22.3%	—	3.7%

2013 Year-End Financials

Debt ratio: 64.6%	No. of shares (mil.): 83
Return on equity: 14.3%	Dividends
Cash ($ mil.): 58	Yield: 2.7%
Current ratio: 0.54	Payout: 78.1%
Long-term debt ($ mil.): 2,192	Market value ($ mil.): 3,018

	STOCK PRICE ($) FY Close	P/E High/Low	PER SHARE ($) Earnings	Dividends	Book Value
12/13	36.23	66 26	1.28	1.00	10.72
12/12	67.29	110 96	0.66	1.75	10.33
12/11	66.69	225171	0.32	0.75	11.28
12/10	55.93	94 74	0.63	1.20	3.67
12/09	50.47	83 49	0.61	1.10	3.60
Annual Growth	(8.0%)	— —	20.4%	(2.4%)	31.4%

Essex Property Trust, Inc.

Essex Property Trust acquires develops redevelops and manages apartment communities focusing on the metropolitan areas of Los Angeles San Diego San Francisco and Seattle. The self-managed and self-administered real estate investment trust (REIT) owns more than 230 residential communities —mostly in Southern California —and 15 properties under development. Essex also owns a handful of office buildings in its home state and has partial stakes in several apartment communities through joint ventures. The REIT adds to its portfolio through acquisitions and through the development and renovation of properties. In 2014 Essex acquired BRE Properties in a big deal valued at approximately $4.3 billion.

Mergers and Acquisitions

In April 2014 Essex Property Trust acquired California-based BRE Properties forming a combined company in which former Essex shareholders hold about 63% of the combined company's stock and former BRE shareholders hold 37%. (The combined company retained the name Essex Property Trust.) The deal valued at about $4.3 billion greatly bolstered the REIT's presence in the multifamily market on the West Coast.

In 2013 Essex acquired ownership interests in eight communities comprising 1472 units for $462.5 million. The acquired apartment complexes are in San Francisco (2) Los Angeles Mountain View and San Diego California and in Kirkland and Seattle (2) Washington.

Geographic Reach

Palo Alto-based Essex Property's portfolio derives more than 40% of its revenue from Southern California about 35% from Northern California and nearly 20% from the Seattle metro area. The REIT has offices in Woodland Hills Irvine and San Diego California and in Bellevue Washington.

Financial Performance

Buoyed by acquisitions and rising rents the REIT reported revenue of $613.7 million in 2013 an increase of 13% versus the prior year. Average rental rates increased 6% from $1502 per unit in 2012 to $1597 per unit in 2013. Rent contributes the vast majority of the REIT's revenue. Additional revenue came from the acquisition of 15 communities.

Net income rose 25% year over year to $156.3 million on higher revenue and income from discontinued operations.

Strategy

When making acquisitions Essex usually targets multifamily properties with more than 100 units and spends from $300 million to $500 million per transaction. It likes to be active in supply-constrained markets with populations of at least one million and drives rent growth through high occupancy rates (approximately 96% at year-end 2013). The REIT continually monitors its existing markets and isn't afraid to exit if the housing supply increases too much. The company sells off assets if they no longer fit into its strategy and often uses the money raised to buy newer communities.

As the economic recession settled over the US West Coast Essex remained flexible and began pursuing non-traditional investments such as parcels of land. In 2009 the company shifted its focus from building and acquiring apartments to resident retention and occupancy. However as rental income dipped during the economic downturn Essex looked again towards acquisitions to pick up the slack.

EXECUTIVES

First Vice President Of Asset Management, Mark J Mikl
1St Vp Div Mgr- Soutern Ca, Erik J Alexander
Vice President Acquisitions, Jeff S Rowerdink
Vice President Internal Audit, Gale H Hansrajh
Senior Vice President, Dan Keyser
EVP Acquisitions, Craig K. Zimmerman, age 63, $325,000 total compensation
EVP Development, John D. Eudy, age 59, $325,000 total compensation
President and CEO, Michael J. (Mike) Schall, age 56, $450,000 total compensation
VP Fund Manager, John F. Burkart, $275,000 total compensation
Vice President Portfolio Management, Angela L Kleiman
Vice President, Jared Ruger
Marketing Vice President, Donald Kinney
Vice President Of Operations, James Ponder
Vice President Internal Audit, Gale Hanseniorajh
Vice President Training Marketing, Deborah Ross
Vice President, Kevin Grani
Vice President Of Training, Casey Adams
First Vice President, Gerald Kelly
Vice Chairman, Keith R. Guericke, age 65
Chairman, George M. Marcus, age 73
Board Member, Byron Scordelis
Board Member, Claude Zinngrabe
Board Member, Janice Sears
Auditors: KPMGLLP

LOCATIONS

HQ: Essex Property Trust, Inc.
925 East Meadow Drive, Palo Alto, CA 94303
Phone: 650 494-3700
Web: www.essexpropertytrust.com

PRODUCTS/OPERATIONS

2013 Sales

	$ mil.	% of total
Rental & other property revenues		
Southern California	265.2	43
Northern California	214.4	35
Seattle Metro	107.6	18
Other real estate assets	14.8	2
Management & other fees from affiliates	11.7	2
Total	**613.7**	**100**

COMPETITORS

Apartment Investment and Management
AvalonBay
Camden Property
Colonial Properties
Equity Residential
Fairfield Residential
Irvine Apartment Communities
UDR

HISTORICAL FINANCIALS

Company Type: Public

Income Statement

FYE: December 31

	REVENUE ($ mil.)	NET INCOME ($ mil.)	NET PROFIT MARGIN	EMPLOYEES
12/13	613.7	156.2	25.5%	1,173
12/12	543.4	125.2	23.1%	1,144
12/11	475.5	47.0	9.9%	1,099
12/10	415.7	35.9	8.6%	1,039
12/09	411.3	37.1	9.0%	938
Annual Growth	10.5%	43.3%	—	5.7%

2013 Year-End Financials

Debt ratio: 58.4%
Return on equity: 8.5%
Cash ($ mil.): 53
Current ratio: 1.69
Long-term debt ($ mil.): 3,033
No. of shares (mil.): 37
Dividends
Yield: 3.3%
Payout: 119.8%
Market value ($ mil.): 5,370

	STOCK PRICE ($) FY Close	P/E High/Low		PER SHARE ($) Earnings	Dividends	Book Value
12/13	143.51	42	35	4.04	4.84	50.48
12/12	146.65	47	40	3.41	4.40	48.55
12/11	140.51	118	89	1.24	4.16	42.55
12/10	114.22	103	68	1.14	4.13	36.85
12/09	83.65	29	17	2.91	4.12	36.65
Annual Growth	14.4%	—	—	8.5%	4.1%	8.3%

Evercore Partners Inc

Evercore Partners provides advisory services on mergers and acquisitions restructurings divestitures and financing to corporate clients. The firm's investment management business principally manages and invests capital for clients including institutional investors such as corporate and public pension funds endowments insurance companies and high net-worth individuals. Evercore also makes private equity investments. All told Evercore Partners has some $13 billion of assets under management. In addition to its US operations the company is active around the world through subsidiaries such as Protego in Mexico and Evercore Europe in London. Evercore also has offices in Brazil Hong Kong and Scotland.

Geographic Reach

While Evercore Partners operates globally the US accounts for more than 70% of the firm's revenue. Europe contributes about a fifth while Latin America accounted for 6% in 2011.

Operations

Investment banking is the company's core business accounting for about 80% of its revenue in 2011. (Evercore's Institutional Equities services offering equity research and securities trading for institutional clients resides under the Investment banking umbrella.) The firm's Investment Management segment which focuses on asset management for institutions wealthy individuals and private equity clients accounts for most of the remainder. Evercore Trust (formed via the 2009 purchase of Bank of America's Special Fiduciary Services division) provides investment management and trustee services to employee benefits plans.

Financial Analysis

Evercore's revenue increased by about 35% in 2011 vs. 2010 to a record $543 million. Net income fell 22% over the same period while cash flow increased by more than 100%. The firm's investment banking activities generated more than $430 million and included about $15 million and nearly $9 million in commissions and underwriting revenues respectively. Evercore served 245 advisory clients in 2011 94 of which exceeded $1 million in revenue compared with 183 clients in 2010. Fee-based revenues earned from the management of client portfolios and other investment advisory services increased by a third vs. the prior year. The decline in net income was due to increased operating expenses related to higher compensations costs and other expenses.

Strategy

As an independent investment banking firm that isn't involved in commercial banking or proprietary trading Evercore has avoided the controversy swirling around competitors such as Goldman Sachs that results from the conflicts of interest that may occur at larger firms that both underwrite and invest in their clients. Evercore also appears to be capitalizing on the turmoil in the financial industry that has seen some of its bulge-bracket competitors go bankrupt (Lehman Brothers) or get acquired (Merrill Lynch Bear Stearns). Recent high-profile transactions include the 2012 breakup of Kraft Foods (now Mondelez International) the recapitalizations of GM and CIT Group and the acquisition of Lubrizol by Berkshire Hathaway.

Evercore is expanding its Investment Banking business by diversifying geographically and through sectors served. Indeed in 2012 it formed a partnership with VTB Capital to develop cross-border transactions between Russia and North America. In 2011 the firm bought UK-based investment bank Lexicon Partners which provides advisory services for large and midsize corporations from offices in London Hong Kong New York and Aberdeen Scotland. Evercore also acquired a 45% stake in ABS Investment Management.

Evercore has also been growing internally expanding its coverage of the chemicals and energy and mining minerals and materials sectors and adding financial institutions and technology telecommunications and media groups.

Ownership

Investment firm FMR LLC owns about 10% of the shares of Evercore Partners.

Company Background

Evercore was launched in 1996 (it went public 10 years later) by Roger Altman who formerly led investment banking and merger advisory practices at Lehman Brothers and The Blackstone Group. Altman resigned as CEO in 2009 and was succeeded by Ralph Schlosstein co-founder of asset management giant BlackRock; Altman remained executive chairman.

EXECUTIVES

Senior Managing Director and Co-Head Private Equity, James R. Matthews

Senior Managing Director Mexico, Pedro Aspe, age 63, $500,000 total compensation

CEO Evercore Wealth Management, Jeffrey S. (Jeff) Maurer

Senior Managing Director and Co-Head Private Equity, Neeraj Mital

Co-Vice Chairman Corporate Advisory Business, Eduardo G. Mestre, age 66, $500,000 total compensation

CEO and Director Protego Asset Management Business, Sergio Sanchez

CFO, Robert B. Walsh, age 58, $500,000 total compensation

Senior Managing Director and Head Equities Division, Charles Myers

Senior Managing Director and CEO Europe Investment Banking, Andrew Sibbald, age 47

Senior Managing Director and Head Real Estate Advisory, Martin J. Cicco, age 58

Senior Managing Director Mining Metals and Materials Advisory, F. Perkins (Perk) Hixon, age 55

Executive Vice President Process Equipment, William J. Miller

Managing Director, Mark Finkelstein

Senior Managing Director, Angus Winther

Chief Information Officer, Dean A. Ward

Vp Privatge Equity, Justin W Steil

Vp Corporate Advisors, Gus Christensen

Executive Chairman and Co-Chairman, Roger C. Altman, age 69

Auditors: Deloitte&ToucheLLP

LOCATIONS

HQ: Evercore Partners Inc
  55 East 52nd Street, 38th Floor, New York, NY 10055
Phone: 212 857-3100   **Fax:** 212 857-3101
Web: www.evercore.com

2011 Sales

	% of total
US	73
Europe & other	21
Latin America	6
Total	**100**

PRODUCTS/OPERATIONS

2011 Sales

	$ mil.	% of total
Investment banking	430.6	80
Investment management	99.2	18
Other	13.9	2
Total	**543.7**	**100**

COMPETITORS

Allen & Company	Greenhill
Bank of America	JPMorgan Chase
Barclays Capital	Lazard
Blackstone Group	Merrill Lynch
Citigroup Global	Morgan Stanley
Markets	Rothschild North
Credit Suisse	America
Deutsche Bank	UBS Investment Bank
Goldman Sachs	

HISTORICAL FINANCIALS

Company Type: Public

Income Statement

FYE: December 31

	REVENUE ($ mil.)	NET INCOME ($ mil.)	NET PROFIT MARGIN	EMPLOYEES
12/13	765.4	53.2	7.0%	1,000
12/12	642.3	28.8	4.5%	900
12/11	524.2	6.9	1.3%	800
12/10	378.9	8.9	2.4%	610
12/09	313.1	(1.5)	—	443
Annual Growth	25.0%	—	—	22.6%

2013 Year-End Financials

Debt ratio: 8.7%	No. of shares (mil.): 33
Return on equity: 11.4%	Dividends
Cash ($ mil.): 317	Yield: 1.5%
Current ratio: 1.89	Payout: 59.0%
Long-term debt ($ mil.): 103	Market value ($ mil.): 1,977

	STOCK PRICE ($) FY Close	P/E High/Low		PER SHARE ($) Earnings	Dividends	Book Value
12/13	59.78	37	18	1.38	0.91	15.20
12/12	30.19	31	21	0.89	0.82	14.49
12/11	26.62	142	81	0.23	0.74	14.59
12/10	34.00	85	49	0.39	0.63	15.05
12/09	30.40	—	—	(0.10)	0.51	16.30
Annual Growth	18.4%	—	—	—	15.6%	(1.7%)

Excel Trust Inc.

Excel Trust likes to buy retail space off the clearance rack. Based in San Diego the self-managed self-administered real estate investment trust (REIT) has a penchant for acquiring high-value retail properties at a reduced cost —including value-oriented community and "power" shopping centers grocery anchored neighborhood centers and freestanding retail properties —located in California Arizona Texas and about a dozen other states. Excel owns about 35 retail and office properties totaling more than 5.8 million sq. ft. of leasable space. Tenants include chain stores Bed Bath & Beyond and PetSmart among many others and health care systems operator Kaiser Permanente.

Geographic Reach

The San Diego-based REIT has holdings in more than a dozen states. Its largest markets are California Arizona Texas and Virginia which represented approximately 23% 18% 12% and 12% of the REIT's total revenue. In addition to its San Diego headquarters Excel has an office in Salt Lake City.

Sales and Marketing

The REIT counts many of the nation's largest retailers among its tenants. Its three largest retail tenants are Publix Super Markets discount apparel retailer Ross Stores and home improvement giant Lowe's which together accounted for about 9% of its total annualized base rent (ABR). Major office tenants include Kaiser Permanente Fitch and Buchalter Nemer which combined contributed 45% of total ABR.

Operations

The REIT derives nearly 90% of its revenue from its retail holdings. Office properties contribute about 7% while multi-family properties represent 5% of annual revenue. Excel's multi-family holdings consist of 339 apartment units above its West Broad Village retail shopping center in Richmond Virginia.

Financial Performance

The REIT's revenue increased 29% in 2013 versus 2012 to $112.5 million. Net income soared 948% over the same period to $19.5 million. Driving the revenue gain was increased rent from the firm's multi-family property in Virginia due to a full year of operations (versus just 3 months in 2012) and the purchase of 16 retail operating properties and one development property in 2013. Gains from asset sales (including the disposition of its Walgreens and Grant Creek Towne Center properties) buoyed net income in 2013.

Strategy

When buying retail properties the REIT targets those with anchor tenants that sell necessities such as groceries and value-oriented goods that are less sensitive to fluctuations in consumer spending during lean times as well as being located in high-traffic areas with substantial population and income growth. Geographically Excel targets the West and East Coasts and the Sunbelt region for their favorable demographic and property trends. Excel was an opportunistic buyer during the recession when many property owners needed to unload high-quality retail property investments at lower prices to avoid foreclosure.

IPO

Excel in April 2010 went public with an offering worth $210 million. The company used to proceeds to retire debt fund operations and to acquire properties.

EXECUTIVES

Chairman and CEO, Gary B. Sabin, age 60, $370,000 total compensation

SVP Acquisitions and Chief Investment Officer, Mark T. Burton, age 54, $200,000 total compensation

CFO and Treasurer, James Y. Nakagawa, age 49, $200,000 total compensation

President and COO, Spencer G. Plumb, age 39, $200,000 total compensation

SVP Capital Markets, Matthew S. Romney, age 43

Executive Vice President, William J Stone, age 72

Vice President Capital Markets And Communications, Greg Davis

Vice President Acquisitions And Dispositions, John Langford

Vice President Asset Management, Daniel Haslam

Chairman and CEO, Gary B. Sabin, age 60

Auditors: Deloitte&ToucheLLP

LOCATIONS

HQ: Excel Trust Inc.
Excel Centre, 17140 Bernardo Center Drive, Suite 300, San Diego, CA 92128
Phone: 858 613-1800
Web: www.ExcelTrust.com

PRODUCTS/OPERATIONS

2013 Sales

	$ in mil.	% of total
Rental revenue	92.3	82
Tenant recoveries	18.9	17
Other income	1.3	1
Total	**112.5**	**100**

2013 Sales

	$ in mil.	% of total
Retail properties	98.5	88
Office properties	8.6	7
Multi-family properties	5.4	5
Total	**112.5**	**100**

COMPETITORS

Cedar Realty Trust	Glimcher Realty
Colonial Properties	Kimco Realty
Donahue Schriber	Trade Street
Equity One	Residential

HISTORICAL FINANCIALS

Company Type: Public

Income Statement

FYE: December 31

	REVENUE ($ mil.)	NET INCOME ($ mil.)	NET PROFIT MARGIN	EMPLOYEES
12/13	112.5	19.5	17.3%	67
12/12	87.1	1.8	2.1%	45
12/11	55.2	0.4	0.8%	38
12/10*	15.9	(3.7)	—	31
04/10	1.5	(0.1)	—	0
Annual Growth	**191.1%**	—	—	—

*Fiscal year change

2013 Year-End Financials

Debt ratio: 43.5%	No. of shares (mil.): 48
Return on equity: 3.2%	Dividends
Cash ($ mil.): 3	Yield: 6.0%
Current ratio: 1.05	Payout: 570.8%
Long-term debt ($ mil.): 530	Market value ($ mil.): 551

	STOCK PRICE ($) FY Close	P/E High/Low	PER SHARE ($) Earnings	Dividends	Book Value
12/13	11.39	90 67	0.17	0.69	12.72
12/12	12.67	— —	(0.26)	0.65	13.23
12/11	12.00	— —	(0.15)	0.61	12.01
12/10*	12.10	— —	(0.24)	0.20	11.97
04/10	13.00	— —	(0.00)	0.00	(0.00)
Annual Growth	**(3.3%)**	— —	—	—	—

*Fiscal year change

ExlService Holdings Inc

Have an extra-large task you'd rather not take on? Outsource it to ExlService Holdings. The company known as EXL offers business process outsourcing (BPO) research and analytics and consulting services. EXL's BPO offerings which generate most of its sales include claims processing collections customer support and finance and accounting. Customers come mainly from the banking financial services and insurance industries as well as from the utilities and telecommunications sectors. EXL operates offices around the world including the US and countries in Eastern Europe and Asia. The company was established in 1999.

Geographic Reach

EXL operates through six offices in the US 15 offices in India as well as through a half-a-dozen locations in the Czech Republic Bulgaria Romania Malaysia and the Philippines. The company also has a sales office in the UK and networking and telecommunications centers in California New Jersey and New York.

Sales and Marketing

EXL earned revenue from more than 270 clients in 2012 with its top three clients generating 26% of its revenue. Major clients include The Travelers Indemnity Company which accounted for 10% of the company's total revenue in 2012 and natural gas supplier Centrica. The company hopes to grow primarily by selling more services to existing customers and by adding more Global 1000 companies to its client list.

Financial Performance

Revenue growth in its outsourcing services segment combined with revenue from its Landacorp and other acquisitions helped drive the company's profits up 20% in 2012 over 2011 results. EXL's overall revenue was up 23% during the same period.

Mergers and Acquisitions

EXL continues to evaluate acquisition opportunities; it has its eye fixed on BPO firms in Eastern Europe or the US with capabilities in insurance utilities compliance and risk management. In 2012 it acquired collaborative care management software subsidiary Landacorp from SHPS to strengthen its capabilities in healthcare process analytics and technology.

In 2011 EXL acquired Outsource Partners International (OPI) a provider of finance and accounting outsourcing services serving about 80 clients. OPI has expertise in such areas as payroll and tax compliance SEC financial reporting and risk management. The deal substantially bolstered EXL's existing finance and accounting offerings and allowed it to better cater to CFOs. It also enhanced its footprint in the Asia/Pacific and in Europe.

Ownership

FMR LLC owns a 13% stake in of EXL Blackrock Inc owns 12% and Columbia Wanger Asset Management LLC owns 10%.

EXECUTIVES

Vice Chairman and CEO, Rohit Kapoor, age 49, $553,904 total compensation

President and COO, Pavan Bagai, age 52, $225,475 total compensation

EVP and Business Head Insurance, Vikas Bhalla, age 42

EVP and Business Head Health Care, Rembert de Villa, age 57, $382,534 total compensation

EVP and CFO, Vishal Chhibbar, $250,119 total compensation

EVP and General Counsel, Nancy Saltzman

President Global Business and Marketing, Henry Schweppe

Vice President Finance And Accounting Coe, Vincent R Sparrow

Svp-head Uk & Europe, Leo Curran

Vp It, Raju Taneja

Vice President Operations, Madhavi Dahanukar, age 42

Vice President, Dean Forcucci

Vice President Operations, Rakesh Sachdeva

Assistant Vice President Business Innovation, Abhishek Midya

Vice President And Head Strategic Finance Initiatives, Sanghamitra Sarcar

Assistant Vice President Leadership, Parul Kataria

Asst Vice President Human Resrcs Trvl, Indu Kapoor

Vice President Human Resources, Aabha Nanda

Vice President Business Development, Tom Organ

Vice President Sales, Anthony Brock

Assistant Vice President Operations, Samy Kapoor

Vice President And Global Head Tax, Deepak Dhanak

Vice President Operations, Samy Sachdeva

Vice President Recruitment And Training, Rajesh Nandanwar

Assistant Vice President Operations, Kim Jagdev

Assistant Vice President Operations, Janet Rao

Vice President Sales, Lisa Chancellor

Vice President Product Management, Ashish Rustagi

Vice President Uk Operations, Mohit Manchanda

Vice President Transportation, Rajat Bhatnagar

Executive Vice President And Global, Aditya Mohan

Vice President Information Technology, Rex Fox

Vice President Channels, Renee Montcalm

Vice President And Principal, Mark Weber

Vice President 3 Trumbull Common, Bradley Burdick

Vice President, Pradeep Vachani

Vice President Analytics, Rupak Venugopal

Assistant Vice President Exl Decision Analytics, Lee Slutz

Svp-chief Human Resources, Nalin Miglani

Engagement Manager Avp Decision, Tomas Larsson

Vice President Human Resources Gcs, Robyn Burke

Assistant Vice President, Lakshmi Satydass

Assistant Vice President Operations Consulting, Braden Robinson

Assistant Vice President Client Services Operations, Mohit Tandon

Senior Assistant Vice President Legal Support Outsourcing, Mamta Mittal

Vice President, Kapil Arora

Savp Marketing Analyst Relations And Market Research, Cindy Carpenter
Assistant Vice President Operations, Pratap Rao
Vice President / Transformation, Jagmeet Singh
Vice President And Head Of Business Excellence Migration, Amardeep Mallik
Chairman, Garen K. Staglin, age 69
Vice Chairman and CEO, Rohit Kapoor, age 49
Board Member, Kiran Karnik
Auditors: Ernst&YoungLLP

LOCATIONS

HQ: ExlService Holdings Inc
280 Park Avenue, 38th Floor, New York, NY 10017
Phone: 212 277-7100
Web: www.exlservice.com

2012 Sales

	$ mil.	% of total
US	320.2	72
UK	89.5	20
Other countries	33.2	8
Total	**442.9**	**100**

PRODUCTS/OPERATIONS

2012 Sales

	$ mil.	% of total
Outsourcing services	366.7	83
Transformation services	76.2	17
Total	**442.9**	**100**

COMPETITORS

Accenture	Infosys
Genpact	Tata Consultancy
HP Enterprise Services	WNS (Holdings)
IBM Global Services	Wipro

HISTORICAL FINANCIALS

Company Type: Public

Income Statement

FYE: December 31

	REVENUE ($ mil.)	NET INCOME ($ mil.)	NET PROFIT MARGIN	EMPLOYEES
12/13	478.4	48.1	10.1%	22,200
12/12	442.9	41.8	9.4%	21,000
12/11	360.5	34.7	9.6%	18,900
12/10	252.7	26.5	10.5%	12,700
12/09	191.0	15.6	8.2%	10,700
Annual Growth	**25.8%**	**32.4%**	**—**	**20.0%**

2013 Year-End Financials

Debt ratio: 0.5%
Return on equity: 13.5%
Cash ($ mil.): 154
Current ratio: 3.32
Long-term debt ($ mil.): 1

No. of shares (mil.): 32
Dividends
  Yield: —
  Payout: —
Market value ($ mil.): 889

	STOCK PRICE ($) FY Close	P/E High/Low	PER SHARE ($) Earnings	Dividends	Book Value
12/13	27.62	22 16	1.42	0.00	11.38
12/12	26.50	23 16	1.26	0.00	10.70
12/11	22.37	23 16	1.10	0.00	8.93
12/10	21.48	24 17	0.88	0.00	8.44
12/09	18.15	34 11	0.53	0.00	7.09
Annual Growth	**11.1%**	**— —**	**27.9%**	**—**	**12.6%**

Exterran Partners LP

Exterran Partners is the largest operator of contract compression equipment in the US. Its services include designing installing operating repairing and maintaining compression equipment. The company operates a fleet of more than 3950 compressor units comprising almost 1.6 million horsepower. Exterran Holdings a global leader in full-service natural gas compression equipment and services controls Exterran Partners. Exterran Partners and Exterran Holdings manage their respective US compression fleets as one pool of compression equipment in order to more easily fulfill their respective customers' needs. (North American contract sales accounted for about 25% of Exterran Holdings' total revenues in 2010.)

Exterran Partners grows through accretive acquisitions of compression assets (including business lines and contracts) from its parent company third-party compression providers and natural gas producers or transporters.

In 2009 the company reported a growth in revenues as the properties gained from earlier acquisitions came into service. However increased costs brought down income that year.

Growing its portfolio in 2010 Exterran Partners acquired contracts serving 43 customers and 580 related compressor units from Exterran Holdings for $214 million. The growth in assets (a 21% increase in horsepower over 2009) lifted the company's revenues in 2010 but lower pricing and increased field operating expenses resulted in a net loss for the year.

In 2011 Exterran Partners acquired compression and processing assets (contracts serving 34 customers and 407 compressor units) from its parent for $228 million. It follow this up in 2012 buying another contract serving 40 customers (400 compressor units) for about $183 million.

Universal Compression Holdings held a 50% stake in the company (spun off in 2006) until Universal Compression merged with Hanover Compressors to form Exterran Holdings in 2007.

EXECUTIVES

Senior Vice President, Ronaldo Reimer
Director; Vp And Cfo Eastern Hemisphere, David S Miller, age 51
Ref Jonal Vice President, Robert Rice
Chief Financial Officer; Executive Vice President, William Austin
Executive Vice Chairman Of The Board, Mark R Sotir
Auditors: Deloitte&ToucheLLP

LOCATIONS

HQ: Exterran Partners LP
16666 Northchase Drive, Houston, TX 77060
Phone: 281 836-7000
Web: www.exterran.com

COMPETITORS

Cameron International	Enerflex
Compressor Systems	J-W Operating
Dresser-Rand	

HISTORICAL FINANCIALS

Company Type: Public

Income Statement

FYE: December 31

	REVENUE ($ mil.)	NET INCOME ($ mil.)	NET PROFIT MARGIN	EMPLOYEES
12/13	466.1	64.0	13.7%	0
12/12	387.4	10.5	2.7%	0
12/11	308.2	6.0	2.0%	0
12/10	237.6	(23.3)	—	0
12/09	181.7	14.7	8.1%	0
Annual Growth	**26.6%**	**44.3%**	**—**	**—**

2013 Year-End Financials

Debt ratio: 55.4%
Return on equity: —
Cash ($ mil.): 0
Current ratio: 3.82
Long-term debt ($ mil.): 757

No. of shares (mil.): 50
Dividends
  Yield: 6.8%
  Payout: 158.7%
Market value ($ mil.): 1,524

	STOCK PRICE ($) FY Close	P/E High/Low	PER SHARE ($) Earnings	Dividends	Book Value
12/13	30.23	27 17	1.18	2.08	11.74
12/12	20.27	179133	0.14	2.00	10.18
12/11	20.15	345202	0.09	1.92	11.14
12/10	26.86	— —	(0.90)	1.86	10.71
12/09	22.22	33 16	0.68	1.85	10.61
Annual Growth	**8.0%**	**— —**	**14.8%**	**3.0%**	**2.6%**

Extra Space Storage Inc

When closets are bursting at the seams and garages are overflowing Extra Space Storage gives its customers room to breathe. One of the largest operators and managers of self-storage properties in the US the self-administered self-managed real estate investment trust (REIT) wholly-owns owns in joint-venture partnerships or operates for third parties about 1030 facilities with some 680000 units totaling nearly 76 million sq. ft. of rentable space. Active in metropolitan areas in nearly 35 states and Washington DC the company also offers business boat and RV storage and leases to nearly 600000 tenants nationwide.

Geographic Reach

Utah-based Extra Space Storage operates its business throughout the US in 35 states Puerto Rico and Washington DC.

Operations

Extra Space Storage operates through three segments: rental operations; tenant reinsurance; and property management acquisition and development.

The rental operations segment focuses on rentals of the self-storage facilities it owns. Tenant reinsurance covers the reinsurance of risks relating to the loss of goods stored by tenants in the company's self-storage facilities. Its last segment — property management acquisition and development —manages acquires develops and sells self-storage facilities.

Strategy

The REIT has relied on acquisitions in growing markets to expand its business. In 2014 Extra

Space Storage acquired a self-storage portfolio of 17 assets located in Virginia for about $200 million. The deal gave the company 1.5 million sq. ft. of net rentable space across 14000 units. The company also has another five properties under contract for an approximate purchase price of $58 million. In 2012 Extra Space Storage added to its holdings with the acquisition of 21 properties in about a dozen states from a joint venture partner. It acquired a noteworthy 55 properties in 2011.

Extra Space Storage is also looking to expand Extra Space Management its third-party property management subsidiary.

Financial Performance

The storage company's revenue rose some $111.22 million in fiscal 2013 or 27% to $520.6 million continuing several years of incremental growth. It attributes the increases to a boost in property rental and tenant reinsurance revenue. Property rental revenue rose thanks to its purchase of 78 properties during 2013 and 91 properties during 2012.

Extra Space Storage logged $172.1 million in net income in fiscal 2013 representing a $54.78 million increase and a 47% jump overall. Higher revenues a gain on the sale of real estate assets and the purchase of a joint venture partners' interest all contributed to the spike.

Cash flow from operations also increased —by $55.38 million in 2013 —to $271.26 million from higher net income and the net change in working capital.

EXECUTIVES

Senior Vice President Chief Financial Officer, Kent W Christensen

EVP and COO, Karl T. Haas, age 62, $315,000 total compensation

Vice President Information Technology, Antonio Ceriud

CEO, Spencer F. Kirk, age 53, $387,500 total compensation

EVP Chief Legal Officer and Secretary, Charles L. Allen, age 64, $290,000 total compensation

SVP Accounting, Scott Stubbs

Vice President Information Technology, Bob Strother

Vice President Information Technology, Gerard Vega

Senior Vice President Capital Asset, Brent Hardy

Svp It, Bill Hoban

Senior Vice President Operations, Timothy Arthurs

Vice President, Samrat Sondhi

Svp Marketing And Corporate Communications, James Overturf

Vice President Business Development Mkt, John Bilton

Senior Vice President Development, Richard Keeler

Senior Vice President Development, Richard Tanner, age 63

Vice President Information Technology, Barbara Sharon

Vice President, Dean Anderson

Vice President, Gerald Valle

Vice President Acquisitions, Bret Durfee

Vice President Information Technology, Bill Hinkley

Division Vice President, Kenneth Speegle

Vice President Information Technology, Daun Ventura

Vice President Information Technology, Trevar Parker

Vice President Property Development, Todd Lucas

Vice President Information Technology, Tammi Cascone

Vice President Finance And Information Technology, Garrett Southworth

Vice President Information Technology, Gary Bloch

Vice President Information Technology, Erik Walsh

Vice President Information Technology, Ellie Casanova

Vice President Information Technology, James Collier

Vice President Information Technology, Darlene Zamora

Vice President Information Technology, Amy Gilliam

Vice President Information Technology, Trisha James

Vice President Information Technology, Stephanie Taylor

Vice President Information Technology, Amanda Bunton

Vice President Of Construction, Joseph Capasso

Vice President Information Technology, Steve Panza

Vice President Information Technology, Bob Porter

Senior Vice President Senior Legal, Charles Aen

Vice President Information Technology, Jacob Burkhart

Vice President Treasury And Risk, Stephen Blake

Executive Vice President, Cindy Lomeli

Chairman, Kenneth M. Woolley, age 67

Auditors: Ernst&YoungLLP

LOCATIONS

HQ: Extra Space Storage Inc
2795 East Cottonwood Parkway, Suite 400, Salt Lake City, UT 84121
Phone: 801 365-4600
Web: www.extraspace.com

PRODUCTS/OPERATIONS

2013 Sales

	$ mil.	% of total
Property rental	446.7	86
Tenant reinsurance	47.3	9
Management & franchise fees	26.6	5
Total	**520.6**	**100**

2013 Properties

	No.
Wholly-owned	506
Owned through joint venture partnerships	273
Managed	250
Total	**1029**

COMPETITORS

AMERCO	PODS Enterprises
CubeSmart	Public Storage
Mobile Mini	Sovran

HISTORICAL FINANCIALS

Company Type: Public

Income Statement

FYE: December 31

	REVENUE ($ mil.)	NET INCOME ($ mil.)	NET PROFIT MARGIN	EMPLOYEES
12/13	520.6	185.5	35.6%	2,584
12/12	409.4	127.6	31.2%	2,283
12/11	329.8	58.4	17.7%	2,239
12/10	281.5	33.3	11.9%	2,125
12/09	280.4	39.0	13.9%	2,001
Annual Growth	**16.7%**	**47.6%**	**—**	**6.6%**

2013 Year-End Financials

Debt ratio: 49.0%	No. of shares (mil.): 115
Return on equity: 11.4%	Dividends
Cash ($ mil.): 126	Yield: 3.4%
Current ratio: 3.06	Payout: 121.8%
Long-term debt ($ mil.): 1,948	Market value ($ mil.): 4,877

	STOCK PRICE ($) FY Close	P/E High/Low		PER SHARE ($) Earnings	Dividends	Book Value
12/13	42.13	32	24	1.53	1.45	15.19
12/12	36.39	32	21	1.14	0.85	13.47
12/11	24.23	45	32	0.54	0.56	10.75
12/10	17.40	59	37	0.30	0.40	10.06
12/09	11.55	33	14	0.37	0.38	10.20
Annual Growth	**38.2%**	**—**	**—**	**42.6%**	**39.8%**	**10.5%**

F5 Networks, Inc.

F5 Networks wants to help your network take a load off. The company's products include application delivery controllers (ADC) and software that are used for network load balancing availability assurance and security assessment. The company also provides file virtualization WAN optimization and remote access products. It additionally offers such services as network monitoring performance analysis and training. F5 targets a variety of industries including telecommunications manufacturing and financial services. The company gets more than half of its sales from the Americas.

Geographic ReachThe company saw solid growth of between 10%-15% across all geographic regions in fiscal 2013. The Americas accounts for nearly 60% of sales with the EMEA and Asia-Pacific (including Japan) regions contributing most of the other 40%.Sales and MarketingThe company sells primarily through distributors systems integrators and resellers although it also maintains a direct sales force for major enterprise accounts. Distribution giants Avnet Technology Solutions and Ingram Micro together account for more than 40% of the company's sales.

F5 Networks spent about $3 million on advertising in fiscal 2013.

Financial PerformanceThe company's revenue was about $1.5 billion in fiscal 2013. That was an 8% increase compared to fiscal 2012. The spike was primarily driven by increased service revenues as a result of their increased installed base of products and growth in sales of consulting and training offerings.

The company's net income has been increasing year-over-year. In fiscal 2013 it reported net income of $277 million after reporting net income of $275 million in fiscal 2012.

F5 Networks' operating cash flow increased by $4.2 million in fiscal 2013 compared to the previous period primarily from cash generated from net income.

StrategyF5 Networks operates in a highly competitive market bumping up against tech powerhouses Cisco Systems and EMC. F5 outsources the majority of its hardware manufacturing with Flextronics International making its ADC product line and Sanmina-SCI producing the ARX line.The company's broader strategy for growing sales includes delivering products as integrated software modules; focusing product development on software as well as hardware and keeping an eye out for gaining new technologies through acquisitions; developing strategic technology partnerships with such vendors as Oracle and SAP; and using the company's online community of network architects and developers known as DevCentral for product development.

In 2013 it formed a long-term partnership with Websense to develop a suite of network security products.

Mergers and AcquisitionsIn 2014 the company acquired Defense.Net Inc. for an undisclosed price. Defense.Net was a privately-held provider of cloud-based security services for protecting data centers and Internet applications from distributed denial-of-service (DDoS) attacks.

Back in 2013 F5 Networks acquired LineRate Systems for about $125 million. LineRate Systems was a privately-held developer of software defined network service solutions for packet core operators and cloud and web service providers.

EXECUTIVES

Senior Vice President And Corporate, John Rodriguez, age 54
Senior Vice President Worldwide Sales, Mark Anderson
President CEO and Director, John McAdam, age 62, $796,722 total compensation
EVP Business Operations, Edward J. Eames, age 55, $356,354 total compensation
EVP Product Development and CTO, Karl D. Triebes, age 46, $479,569 total compensation
Executive Vice President Marketing and Business Development, Dan Matte, age 47, $241,214 total compensation
EVP and CFO, Andy Reinland, age 49, $191,180 total compensation
EVP and General Counsel, Jeffrey A. (Jeff) Christianson, age 56, $340,772 total compensation
SVP Marketing, Dean Darwin
EVP Worldwide Sales, David Feringa, $352,141 total compensation
EVP Strategic Solutions, Manuel F. Rivelo, $347,081 total compensation
Vice President Product Development, Tom Sweeney
Vice President Of Sales, M Hull
Senior Vice President Of Business Operations And Global Services, Julian Eames
Senior Vice President Human Resources, Laurie Likai
Executive Vp, Pat Brennan
Vice President Global Ps Consulting, Ian Jones
Vice President Product Development, Patrick Jenny
Vice President Data System Architecture, Rick Gillett
Vice President Of Information, Andre Nurwono
Vice President Emea, John Williams
Executive Vice President, Chris Smith
Vice President Sales Country Mgr Canada, Nicole Wengle
Senior Vice President Finance, Cooper Werner
Vice President Global Customer Support, Mark Kramer
Rvice President Sales, Hwa Wong
Vice President Product Development, Ron Talmor
Rvp Sales, Yi Qiang Zhang
Vice President Marketing, Todd Callaway
Vice President Global Services Emea, Jim Tickner
Vice President Sales Operations, Dave Janssen
Regional Vice President Sales Cen Reg, Kevin Hollenbach
Vice President Customer Care, Andrew Markham
Vice President Atlantic Federal Sales, Charles Robertello

Regional Vice President Of Channel Sales For The Americas, Keith McManigal
Vice President Of Product Development, Brett Helsel
Vice President Engineering, Les Watson
Vice President Service Provider Sales, Jim Labovites
Vice President Tax, Steve Grieger
Vice President Product Management Core, Indrajit Roy
Vice President Mobility Cloud And Service Provider Solutions, Mallik Tatipamula
President CEO and Director, John McAdam, age 62
Chairman, Alan J. Higginson, age 67
Board Member, Jonathan Chadwick
Board Member, James Hockley
Auditors: PricewaterhouseCoopersLLP

LOCATIONS

HQ: F5 Networks, Inc.
401 Elliott Avenue West, Seattle, WA 98119
Phone: 206 272-5555
Web: www.f5.com

2013 Sales

	$ mil.	% of total
Americas	852	58
Europe Middle East & Asia	327.1	22
Asia/Pacific		
Japan	83	6
Other Asia/Pacific	219.2	14
Total	**1481.3**	**100**

PRODUCTS/OPERATIONS

2013 Sales

	$ mil.	% of total
Products	798.9	54
Services	682.4	46
Total	**1481.3**	**100**

Selected Products

Application delivery controllers (BIG-IP)
File virtualization (ARX)
Management console (Enterprise Manager)
SSL/VPN access appliances (FirePass)
WAN optimization (WANJet)

COMPETITORS

Array Networks	Imperva
Barracuda Networks	Juniper Networks
Blue Coat	NetApp
Brocade Communications	Nokia
Checkpoint Systems	Radware
Cisco Systems	Riverbed Technology
Citrix Systems	SonicWALL
EMC	Symantec
Extreme Networks	Tekelec
Fortinet	

HISTORICAL FINANCIALS

Company Type: Public

Income Statement

FYE: September 30

	REVENUE ($ mil.)	NET INCOME ($ mil.)	NET PROFIT MARGIN	EMPLOYEES
09/14	1,732.0	311.1	18.0%	3,834
09/13	1,481.3	277.3	18.7%	3,356
09/12	1,377.2	275.1	20.0%	3,029
09/11	1,151.8	241.4	21.0%	2,488
09/10	881.9	151.1	17.1%	2,012
Annual Growth	**18.4%**	**19.8%**	—	**17.5%**

2014 Year-End Financials

Debt ratio: —	No. of shares (mil.): 73
Return on equity: 21.4%	Dividends
Cash ($ mil.): 281	Yield: —
Current ratio: 1.57	Payout: —
Long-term debt ($ mil.): —	Market value ($ mil.): 8,714

	STOCK PRICE ($) FY Close	P/E High/Low		PER SHARE ($) Earnings	Dividends	Book Value
09/14	118.74	31	19	4.09	0.00	18.66
09/13	85.81	30	19	3.50	0.00	19.70
09/12	104.64	40	20	3.45	0.00	16.89
09/11	71.05	48	23	2.96	0.00	13.97
09/10	103.81	55	20	1.86	0.00	12.49
Annual Growth	**3.4%**	—	—	**21.8%**	—	**10.6%**

FAB Universal Corp

Wizzard Software has a lot to say. The company provides podcast hosting services and develops computer software products that focus on speech recognition and text-to-speech technology. The company's technology products serve as the basis for computer telephones other devices to to listen to spoken commands and respond with synthetic speech. Wizzard's Voice Tools suite enables programmers to integrate the company's speech technologies in their applications. The company also offers podcast hosting and operates a speech technology consulting services division that offers custom programming training and support services.

Wizzard acquired MedivoxRX Technologies in April 2004. MedivoxRx makes medicine bottles equipped with a microprocessor that allows pharmacists to record instructions describing to patients what type of medication is in the bottle and how and when to take it.

Wizzard augmented MedivoxRX when it acquired home health care provider Interim Healthcare in 2005. It purchased a second health care staffing agency Professional Nursing Personnel Pool (PNPP) in 2007.

Wizzard entered the podcast hosting business with the purchase of Switchpod.com in 2006 and expanded in 2007 when it acquired Webmayhem the parent company of podcast distributor Liberated Syndication (Libsyn) in 2007.

The company also operates Interim HealthCare of Wyoming a health care staffing and home health agency.

EXECUTIVES

Vp Podcaster Relations Wizzard Media, Rob Walch
Auditors: Gregory&AssociatesLLC

LOCATIONS

HQ: FAB Universal Corp
5001 Baum Boulevard, Suite 770, Pittsburgh, PA 15213
Phone: 412 621-0902 **Fax:** 412 621-2625
Web: www.fabuniversal.com

PRODUCTS/OPERATIONS

2007 Sales

	$ mil.	% of total
Health care	3.3	65
Software	1.8	35
Total	**5.1**	**100**

COMPETITORS

Alcatel-Lucent	Fonix
Apple Inc.	Maxim Healthcare
Apria Healthcare	Services Inc.
Audible Inc.	Nuance Communications
Cross Country	
Healthcare	

HISTORICAL FINANCIALS

Company Type: Public

Income Statement
FYE: December 31

	REVENUE ($ mil.)	NET INCOME ($ mil.)	NET PROFIT MARGIN	EMPLOYEES
12/13	110.8	20.6	18.6%	193
12/12	27.4	(4.0)	—	215
12/11	6.5	(9.9)	—	150
12/10	5.5	(4.1)	—	110
12/09	5.1	(6.5)	—	110
Annual Growth	**115.0%**	**—**		**15.1%**

2013 Year-End Financials

Debt ratio: 10.1%
Return on equity: 14.0%
Cash ($ mil.): 99
Current ratio: 3.06
Long-term debt ($ mil.): 16
No. of shares (mil.): 20
Dividends
  Yield: —
  Payout: —
Market value ($ mil.): 64

	STOCK PRICE ($) FY Close	P/E High/Low		PER SHARE ($) Earnings	Dividends	Book Value
12/13	3.07	10	3	0.99	0.00	7.68
12/12	3.22	—	—	(0.34)	0.00	6.54
12/11	0.13	—	—	(1.31)	0.00	1.70
12/10	0.25	—	—	(0.72)	0.00	3.30
12/09	0.34	—	—	(1.56)	0.00	4.13
Annual Growth	**73.3%**	**—**	**—**	**—**	**—**	**16.8%**

FARO Technologies Inc.

FARO Technologies is arming companies with a means to inspect the world around them. With the touch of its mechanical arm FARO's measuring systems can facilitate reverse engineering of an undocumented part or a competitor's product. The portable FaroArm FARO Laser ScanArm and FARO Gage are jointed devices that simulate the human arm's movement. Along with the FARO Laser Scanner LS and Laser Tracker inspections and measurements are integrated with 3-D software. Aerospace automotive consumer goods and heavy equipment companies such as Boeing Honda GM GE and Johnson Controls use FARO Arm units in their factories. Customers located outside the Americas account for more than 60% of sales.

Geographic Reach

FARO has some 13000 customers worldwide and manufactures from facilities located in Ger-

many Singapore Switzerland and the US. The company also has sales offices located in Brazil China France Germany India Italy Japan Malaysia the Netherlands Poland Singapore South Korea Spain Thailand Turkey the UK and Vietnam.

The US generates around 35% of its revenue while Germany is its second largest country market representing nearly 15%.

Operations

FARO's computer-aided measurement hardware and software offer portability and a link to its computerized measurement processing system giving customers improved speed and precision. In addition to manufacturing applications its products are used in accident and crime scene reconstruction as well as to create digital scans of historic sites.

Sales and Marketing

FARO conducts its sales and marketing efforts on a decentralized basis in three main regions around the world: Americas Europe/Africa and Asia/Pacific. The regional headquarters for the Americas resides in Lake Mary Florida; the Europe/Africa regional headquarters is located in Stuttgart Germany; and the headquarters for Asia/Pacific s located in Singapore.

The company also sells its products —primarily its FARO Focus Laser Scanner —through distributors although this channel represents a small portion of sales.

Financial Performance

FARO has enjoyed exceptional growth over the last three years. Revenues rose 8% from $254 million in 2011 to reach $273 million in 2012 a historic milestone for the company.

The growth for 2012 was attributed to a 13% spike in sales from the Asia/Pacific region and an 11% jump in the Americas due to increases in warranty revenue.

Profits stayed consistent from 2011 to 2012 hovering around the $23 million mark.

Strategy

FARO's strategy primarily revolves around the launching of new innovative measurement products to attract additional customers. In 2012 it introduced its smallest lightest and longest range laser tracker: the FARO Vantage. Also that year it introduced the FARO Prime a high-accuracy contact-only measurement arm.

EXECUTIVES

Senior VP and CFO, Keith S. Bair, age 59, $235,192 total compensation
President CEO and Director, Jay W. Freeland, age 44, $416,154 total compensation
Senior VPManaging Director Asia Pacific, Joseph (Joe) Arezone, age 48, $150,000 total compensation
SVP and Managing Director Europe, Ralf Drews
Chief Technology Strategist and Evangelist, Bernd Becker
Svp And Managing Director, Kathleen J Hall
Vice President Human Resources, Wes Warner
Vice President Marketing Americas, Rob Pietsch
Vice President Of Finance And Accounting Europe, Robert King
Chairman of the Board, Simon Raab, age 61
President CEO and Director, Jay W. Freeland, age 44
Auditors: GrantThorntonLLP

LOCATIONS

HQ: FARO Technologies Inc.
  250 Technology Park, Lake Mary, FL 32746
Phone: 407 333-9911
Web: www.faro.com

2012 Sales

	$ mil.	% of total
Americas		
US	97.9	36
Other	10.7	4
Europe		
Germany	42.4	15
Other	57.7	21
Asia	64.7	24
Total	**273.4**	**100**

PRODUCTS/OPERATIONS

2012 Sales

	$ mil.	% of total
Product	227.9	83
Service	45.5	17
Total	**273.4**	**100**

Products
Computer-Aided Design (CAD)
  Articulated measuring devices
  FaroArm
  FARO Laser ScanArm
  FARO Gage
  Inspection (factory-level statistical process control and high-density surveying)
  FARO Laser Scanner LS
  FARO Laser Tracker
  FARO Laser Tracker ION (large-volume portable laser tracker)
  CAM2 software (computer-aided measurement)

COMPETITORS

ANSYS	MKS Instruments
Autodesk	MTS Systems
Carl Zeiss	Nanometrics
Cimatron	PTC
Cognex	Perceptron
Cohu	ROFIN-SINAR
Dassault	RadiSys
Delcam	Renishaw
Hexagon AB	Rudolph Technologies
IPG Photonics	Stratasys
Ixia	X-Rite
Keithley Instruments	Xcerra
Leica Geosystems	Zygo

HISTORICAL FINANCIALS

Company Type: Public

Income Statement
FYE: December 31

	REVENUE ($ mil.)	NET INCOME ($ mil.)	NET PROFIT MARGIN	EMPLOYEES
12/13	291.7	21.5	7.4%	1,078
12/12	273.4	23.0	8.4%	961
12/11	254.1	23.3	9.2%	885
12/10	191.7	11.0	5.8%	781
12/09	147.7	(10.5)	—	734
Annual Growth	**18.6%**			**10.1%**

2013 Year-End Financials

Debt ratio: 0.0%
Return on equity: 7.1%
Cash ($ mil.): 124
Current ratio: 5.32
Long-term debt ($ mil.): 0
No. of shares (mil.): 17
Dividends
  Yield: —
  Payout: —
Market value ($ mil.): 1,002

	STOCK PRICE ($) FY Close	P/E High/Low		PER SHARE ($) Earnings	Dividends	Book Value
12/13	58.30	48	25	1.25	0.00	18.38
12/12	35.68	44	24	1.34	0.00	16.66
12/11	46.00	35	21	1.39	0.00	14.84
12/10	32.84	47	25	0.38	0.00	13.10
12/09	21.44	—	—	(0.66)	0.00	12.20
Annual Growth	**28.4%**	**—**	**—**	**—**	**—**	**10.8%**

Federated National Holding Co.

Trashed trailer crashed car damaged dwelling? Federated National Holding Company (formerly 21st Century Holding Company) has a policy to cover that. Through Federated National Insurance and other subsidiaries it underwrites a variety of personal property/casualty insurance lines in Florida. Products include homeowners flood liability and nonstandard automobile coverage. Its American Vehicle Insurance subsidiary offers commercial general liability insurance in nine southeastern states. Its Assurance MGA and Superior Adjusting subsidiaries underwrite policies and handle claims for third-party insurers. The firm distributes its products through independent agents and its Insure-Link agency.

Since its insurance subsidiary generates most of its business the company changed its name from 21st Century Holdings to Federated National Holding Company in 2012. The name change coincidently helps to eliminate some confusion between the company and the much larger auto insurer 21st Century Insurance group which is not related to the company.

The firm's independent agency Insure-Link (formed in 2008) distributes all of the company's products. Such vertical integration is unusual for small regional insurers but is part of Federated National's strategy to control all aspects of the insurance underwriting distribution and claims process.

American Vehicle Insurance is licensed to underwrite in more than a dozen states but only has operations in nine. In 2008 it extended its reach into the important Florida market when it was granted approval to write commercial multi-peril inland marine and surety insurance. It intends to continue similar expansion into other states.

EXECUTIVES

CFO Treasurer and Director, Peter J. Prygelski, age 45, $192,946 total compensation
President CEO and Director; Interim Chairman, Michael H. Braun, age 46, $229,824 total compensation
CFO Treasurer and Director, Peter J. Prygelski, age 45
President CEO and Director; Interim Chairman, Michael H. Braun, age 46
Treasurer Head Of Treasury, Faye Henry
Auditors: DeMeoYoungMcGrath

LOCATIONS

HQ: Federated National Holding Co.
14050 N.W. 14th Street, Suite 180, Sunrise, FL 33323
Phone: 954 581-9993
Web: www.21stcenturyholding.com

PRODUCTS/OPERATIONS

2009 Premiums

	% of total
Homeowners	81
Commercial general liability	15
Federal flood insurance	3
Personal auto	1
Total	**100**

2009 Revenue

	$ mil.	% of total
Net premiums earned	47.9	81
Net investment income	3.4	6
Other income	7.5	13
Total	**58.8**	**100**

COMPETITORS

Allstate	Safeco
AssuranceAmerica	Safeway Insurance
Bankers Financial	State Farm
GEICO	Universal Insurance
Main Street America	Holdings
Progressive	
Corporation	

HISTORICAL FINANCIALS

Company Type: Public

Income Statement

FYE: December 31

	ASSETS ($ mil.)	NET INCOME ($ mil.)	INCOME AS % OF ASSETS	EMPLOYEES
12/13	316.7	12.7	4.0%	153
12/12	185.8	4.3	2.3%	116
12/11	179.9	(0.4)	—	112
12/10	184.0	(8.0)	—	127
12/09	202.8	(10.2)	—	121
Annual Growth	**11.8%**	—	—	**6.0%**

2013 Year-End Financials

Return on assets: 5.0%	Dividends
Return on equity: 14.6%	Yield: 0.8%
Long-term debt ($ mil.): —	Payout: 11.6%
No. of shares (mil.): 10	Market value ($ mil.): 160
Sales ($ mil): 121	

	STOCK PRICE ($) FY Close	P/E High/Low		PER SHARE ($) Earnings	Dividends	Book Value
12/13	14.67	10	4	1.45	0.13	9.95
12/12	5.35	12	6	0.53	0.02	8.26
12/11	2.96	—	—	(0.05)	0.00	7.32
12/10	3.18	—	—	(1.01)	0.18	7.29
12/09	4.02	—	—	(1.29)	0.36	8.48
Annual Growth	**38.2%**	—	—	—	**(22.5%)**	**4.1%**

FEI Co.

FEI makes instruments to find very small defects. The company makes structural process management systems that use ion beams to analyze and diagnose submicron structures in integrated circuits (ICs) data storage components and biological and industrial compounds. FEI makes focused ion beam and dual beam electron microscopes that analyze ICs. It also makes scanning and transmission electron microscopes that detect defects in ICs and analyze biological specimens and materials. FEI targets applications in nanotechnology R&D but still gets significant sales from the semiconductor and data storage markets.

Operations

The company's products include transmission electron microscopes (TEMs) scanning electron microscopes (SEMs) focused ion beam system (FIBs) DualBeam systems that combine a SEM and a FIB and high-performance optical microscopes. Its products range in price from $100000 to more than $5 million.

Its operations focus on three areas in nanotechnology: nanobiology nanoelectronics and nanoresearch. Nanotech essentially means making things that have dimensions as small as 1 to 100 nanometers with a nanometer being one-billionth of a meter or about one-80000th the thickness of a human hair. Nanotech has applications in a variety of industries from consumer products like clothing and golf balls to electronics and health care.

Geographic Reach

In addition to sales and service offices located in some 50 countries FEI has R&D and manufacturing facilities in the Czech Republic Germany the Netherlands and the US (in Oregon).

Sales and Marketing

FEI sells its products through independent agents and distributors. Its sales cycle typically ranges from three months to a year and a half.

Financial Performance

Overall sales grew 4% in 2013 to $927 million despite cyclical downturns in the semiconductor capital equipment industry. (Because its equipment is used in labs for new process development and yield improvement FEI is less affected by cyclical swings than some other equipment suppliers.) Profits were up 10% to a record $126 million.

Strategy

FEI expects to see continued growth in 2014 driven by several factors. Emerging economies in Asia/Pacific (particularly China) continue to invest in the equipment that will make them more competitive in global technology and research offsetting some weakness in the US and European markets.

Mergers and Acquisitions

FEI periodically makes acquisitions to expand its product offerings and international presence. In 2013 it bought its Australian distributor nanoTechnology Systems Pty. Ltd.

In 2012 it made three acquisitions —ASPEX Corporation AP Tech and Visualization Sciences Group. It paid $30 million for ASPEX Corporation which makes rugged scanning electron microscopes for the materials science and natural resources business. It established a direct sales presence in South Korea with the $12 million purchase of sales and service agent AP Tech. Finally it bought France-based Visualization Sciences Group (VSG) for $55 million. VSG provides high-performance 3D visualization software products and tools to a range of markets.

Late in 2011 the company bought TILL Photonics a maker of digital light microscopes and imaging systems used for live-cell microscopy. FEI paid about $20 million for the German company to expand its products for life sciences market and extend its reach in Europe.

Company Background

The company was founded in 1971 as Field Emission Inc. referring to its use of field emission and ion technology.

EXECUTIVES

Vice President General Counsel, Bradley J (Brad) Thies, age 55
Vp Science Group, Paul Scagnetti
President CEO and Director, Don R. Kania, age 60, $620,839 total compensation
Sr Vp-sales-semiconductor, Joseph Robinson
EVP and CFO, Anthony L. Trunzo, age 52
EVP and COO, Benjamin Loh, age 51, $373,167 total compensation

VP Research and Chief Technology Officer, Michael R. (Mike) Scheinfein
Vice President Global Quality, Keith Price
Vice President New Businesses And Field Operations, Baertlein Tom
Vice President Sales North America, George Scholes
Vice President Sales And Service Europe, Rod Shipley
Vice President Manufacturing, Jiri Ocadlik
Vice President Sales & Service North, Greg Redinbo
Peter Campbell Vice President, Campbell Peter
Vice President And General Manager, Steve Bircher
Executive Vice President Of Information Technology, Alexander Rudolph
Vice President And General Manager, Peter Fruhstorfer
Chairman, Gerhard H. (Gerry) Parker, age 71
President CEO and Director, Don R. Kania, age 60
Board Member, Arie Huijser
Secretary, Alex McLin
Auditors: KPMGLLP

LOCATIONS

HQ: FEI Co.
5350 NE Dawson Creek Drive, Hillsboro, OR 97124-5793
Phone: 503 726-7500
Web: www.fei.com

2012 Sales

	$ mil.	% of total
North America	291.7	33
Europe	244.7	27
Asia/Pacific & other	355.3	40
Total	**891.7**	**100**

PRODUCTS/OPERATIONS

2012 Sales

	$ mil.	% of total
Materials science	315.5	35
Electronics	293.1	33
Service & components	200.2	22
Life sciences	82.9	9
Total	**891.7**	**100**

Selected Products

Dual beam defect characterization workstations
Electron and ion emitters
Focusing columns
Focused ion beam (FIB) workstations
Scanning electron microscopes (SEMs) and environmental SEMs
Transmission electron microscopes (TEMs)

COMPETITORS

Applied Materials	KLA-Tencor
Carl Zeiss	Rudolph Technologies
Dainippon Screen	Seiko Instruments
Hitachi	Tokyo Electron
High-Technologies	Veeco Instruments
JEOL	

HISTORICAL FINANCIALS

Company Type: Public

Income Statement

FYE: December 31

	REVENUE ($ mil.)	NET INCOME ($ mil.)	NET PROFIT MARGIN	EMPLOYEES
12/13	927.4	126.6	13.7%	2,611
12/12	891.7	114.9	12.9%	2,518
12/11	826.4	103.6	12.5%	2,074
12/10	634.2	53.5	8.4%	1,813
12/09	577.3	22.6	3.9%	1,781
Annual Growth	**12.6%**	**53.8%**	**—**	**10.0%**

2013 Year-End Financials

Debt ratio: —
Return on equity: 13.2%
Cash ($ mil.): 384
Current ratio: 3.40
Long-term debt ($ mil.): —

No. of shares (mil.): 42
Dividends
Yield: 0.4%
Payout: 14.4%
Market value ($ mil.): 3,765

	STOCK PRICE ($) FY Close	P/E High/Low	PER SHARE ($) Earnings	Dividends	Book Value
12/13	89.36	29 18	3.01	0.40	25.57
12/12	55.47	19 14	2.80	0.16	21.83
12/11	40.78	16 10	2.51	0.00	18.40
12/10	26.41	19 12	1.34	0.00	16.54
12/09	23.36	44 19	0.60	0.00	14.99
Annual Growth	**39.9%**	**— —**	**49.7%**	**—**	**14.3%**

Fidelity Southern Corp

Fidelity Southern Corp. is the holding company for Fidelity Bank which operates more than 25 branches mostly in and around Atlanta and another location in Jacksonville Florida. The bank offers traditional deposit services such as checking and savings accounts CDs and IRAs. Consumer loans primarily indirect auto loans which the company purchases from auto franchises and independent dealers throughout the Southeast make up more than 50% of its loan portfolio. Real estate construction commercial real estate business residential mortgage and other consumer loans round out Fidelity Southern's lending activities. Subsidiary LionMark Insurance Company offers consumer credit-related insurance products.

Financial Analysis

Fidelity Southern Corp. (FSC) saw its revenue increase by 5% in 2011 vs. 2010 while net income was up 12% for the year. It was the third consecutive year of rising revenue for FSC which does business in one of the regions hit hardest by the financial crisis that reached its peak in 2008. FSC reported some $12 million in net losses that year largely due to bad loans. The bank has worked to unload some of those loans and raise capital through investment and other asset sales; it also received a $48 million injection of Troubled Asset Relief Program money from the government.

FSC attributed the rise in revenue in 2011 to an increase in noninterest income of more than 15% due to an increase in revenues from Small Business Administration (SBA) lending and other income. Loan income fell by nearly 2%.

Strategy

Fidelity Southern has focused on building and diversifying its loan portfolio including originating more residential mortgages and consumer install-

ment loans. It has added more than 100 loan officers to its staff to increase its origination activity. Loan losses and charge-offs have declined and in 2010 FSC netted its first gains in three years. The following year the company acquired five branches as well as most of the loans and deposits of the shuttered Decatur First Bank. In 2012 Fidelity Southern acquired the assets and branches of Security Exchange Bank in an FDIC-assisted transaction. The deal added two branches in Marietta Georgia.

Ownership

Chairman and CEO James Miller Jr. owns about 24% of Fidelity Southern.

HISTORY

WWII veteran Clark Harrison and five others founded Fidelity National Bank in 1973. The first office opened in downtown Decatur Georgia the next year. Fidelity National Bank opened its second branch and formed Fidelity Southern Corporation as a holding company in 1979; it formed Fidelity National Mortgage a year later. In 1984 the company received trust powers opened two new branches and began a major credit card marketing program.

The acquisition of two branches from the Resolution Trust Corporation in 1992 brought the number of branches to 10 and increased assets to $257 million. Fidelity National Capital Investors a retail brokerage was incorporated that year. In 1993 Fidelity National Bank began a consumer sales finance department to buy auto loans from car dealers.

The company opened an office in Jacksonville in 1995 to offer mortgage car and construction lending. Also that year the firm changed the name of its holding company to Fidelity National Corporation.

Fidelity National acquired Friendship Community Bank in Florida and bought six branches from First Union and NationsBank in 1996; rapid expansion and unexpectedly high credit card chargeoffs that year slashed earnings and prevented Fidelity National from opening three of its newly acquired branches. Under the scrutiny of federal regulators the bank discontinued its high-default card program the next year and shored up its finances raising capital through a stock offering.

In 1998 Fidelity National focused on maintaining capital levels and recovering from its losses while other banks expanded. Fidelity National Bank finally gained regulatory approval to open the three remaining branches acquired from NationsBank and First Union later that year. Regulators released the bank from capital and dividend restrictions in 1999 but Fidelity National had to restate its earnings for 1997 citing overestimation of an asset's value.

Fidelity National experienced moderate growth in 2001. Inspections by the Federal Reserve Board in 2000 and 2001 led to Fidelity National's adoption of a resolution that prohibits Fidelity National from redeeming its capital stock paying dividends on its common stock or incurring debt without prior approval of the Federal Reserve Board. In light of a softening economy in 2001 Fidelity National placed greater significance on credit risk management and building the secured portion of its consumer loan portfolio. The company sold its credit card business to Bank One in December.

In 2003 the company changed its name back to Fidelity Southern Corporation and its branches converted to the shortened Fidelity Bank; the bank also switched from a national to a state charter.

EXECUTIVES

Vice President Marketing, Sue Cole
President; Secretary and Treasurer LionMark Insurance Company, H. Palmer Proctor, age 46, $500,000 total compensation
Chairman and CEO, James B. Miller, age 74, $750,000 total compensation
VP; EVP Fidelity Bank; President LionMark Insurance Company, David Buchanan, age 56, $400,000 total compensation
CFO, Stephen H. Brolly, age 51, $250,000 total compensation
Senior Vice President, Palmer Proctor
Vice President Sba Lending, John Jones
Senior Vice President Senior Credit Administrator, Leann Massey
Senior Vice President Technology, Sam Mathis
Vice President Retail Construction Manager, Scott Jackson
Assistant Vice President, Tim White
Senior Vice President Commercial Banking, David Fentress
Senior Vice President, Danny Preston
Assistant Vice President Manager Collections, Sheila White
Senior Vice President Mid Atlantic, Mike Onufrychuk
Senior Vice President Commercial Banking, Erik Bykat
Vice President Branch Assistant Manager, Tanya Kirwan
Vice President Commercial Banking, Marquietta Snyder
Vice President Cra Risk Management, Lorna Crawford
Vice President Senior Sba Analyst, Claire Huse
Vice President Dealer Operations Manager, Elaine Roesch
Vice President Construction Lending, Curtis Smith
Vice President Commercial Banker, Bob Elliott
Commercial Banking Vice President, Phillip Edwards
Branch Manager / Vice President, Sam Crowe
Vice President, Jackie Dennard
Senior Vice President Dealer Services Department, Bob Ciangi
Branch Manager Vice President, Neha Amin
Vice President Commercial Lender, Daniel Baker
Vice President Branch Manager, Pete Sereno
Senior Vice President Credit Administration, Tesula Miller
Vice President Residential Construction Lending, Steve Felske
Senior Vice President Commercial Banking, Benjy Thibodeaux
Regional Manager Vice President, Cory Jackson
Assistant Vice President Dealer Services Marketing Rep, Laura Roof
Vice President Marketing, Rich Staver
Chairman and CEO, James B. Miller, age 74
Board Member, Virginia Roberson
Abm, Hadley Heaton
Auditors: Ernst&YoungLLP

LOCATIONS

HQ: Fidelity Southern Corp
3490 Piedmont Road, Suite 1550, Atlanta, GA 30305
Phone: 404 639-6500
Web: www.fidelitysouthern.com

PRODUCTS/OPERATIONS

2011 Sales

	$ mil.	% of total
Interest		
Loans including fees	86.7	60
Investment securities	6.8	5
Federal funds sold & bank deposits	0.2	-
Noninterest		
Mortgage banking activities	24.7	17
SBA lending activities	8.4	6
Indirect lending activities	5.9	4
Service charges on deposit accounts	4.1	3
Bank owned life insurance	1.3	1
Securities gains	1.1	1
Other fees & charges	2.6	2
Other	3.3	2
Total	**145.1**	**100**

COMPETITORS

BB&T	SunTrust
Bank of America	Synovus
Citizens Bancshares	Wells Fargo
Regions Financial	

HISTORICAL FINANCIALS

Company Type: Public

Income Statement

FYE: December 31

	ASSETS ($ mil.)	NET INCOME ($ mil.)	INCOME AS % OF ASSETS	EMPLOYEES
12/13	2,564.1	27.6	1.1%	890
12/12	2,477.2	25.3	1.0%	774
12/11	2,234.8	11.4	0.5%	174
12/10	1,945.3	10.1	0.5%	559
12/09	1,851.5	(3.8)	—	488
Annual Growth	**8.5%**	**—**	**—**	**16.2%**

2013 Year-End Financials

Return on assets: 1.1%
Return on equity: 12.8%
Long-term debt ($ mil.): —
No. of shares (mil.): 21
Sales ($ mil): 194

Dividends
Yield: 0.3%
Payout: 3.6%
Market value ($ mil.): 355

	STOCK PRICE ($) FY Close	P/E High/Low		PER SHARE ($) Earnings	Dividends	Book Value
12/13	16.61	13	7	1.21	0.05	11.07
12/12	9.55	7	4	1.34	0.00	13.05
12/11	6.08	13	9	0.59	0.02	12.56
12/10	6.98	14	5	0.57	0.00	13.04
12/09	3.60	—	—	(0.71)	0.00	12.89
Annual Growth	**46.6%**	—	—	—	—	**(3.7%)**

Fifth Street Finance Corp

Fifth Street Finance works to put the companies it lends money to on easy street. A business development firm Fifth Street lends capital to and invests in small and midsized firms with annual revenues between $25 million and $250 million. The company typically invests $10 million to $100 million in the form of senior debt or equity per transaction. It favors established firms over start-ups and prefers to participate actively in its investments as advisors. Fifth Street's portfolio comprises more than 85 companies many of which operate in the health care manufacturing IT services and business services sectors. Formed in 2007 the specialty finance company boasts about $2 billion in assets under management.

Geographic Reach

Based in New York Fifth Street Finance operates in Connecticut Illinois California and Texas.

Sales and Marketing

Fifth Street Finance serves several customer types including financial advisors individual investors institutional investors and corporate finance professionals.

The firm has focused on advertising having spent $155 million in 2013 up significantly from $54 million in 2012.

Operations

Since inception Fifth Street Finance has originated $3.3 billion of funded debt and equity investments. Its portfolio which comprises $1.9 billion at fair value effective September 30 2013 consists of 99 investments 86 of which are in operating companies and 13 of which are in private equity funds. Additionally Fifth Street Finance holds equity investments consisting of common stock preferred stock or other equity interests in nearly half of its portfolio companies.

Fifth Street Finance is externally managed and advised by Fifth Street Management LLC.

Strategy

As a business development company Fifth Street Finance's overarching strategy includes infusing debt capital in businesses that show growth potential and then exiting its investments after businesses repay their debt or go through recapitalization.

As part of its own growth strategy the company intends to continue doing what has helped it grow so far: Focusing its lending activity on small and midsized companies which it believes to be underserved by many finance companies. Fifth Street Finance will also continue to originate its own loans to maintain control over the structuring of its investments and generate revenue from origination and exit fees.

Financial Performance

Fifth Street Finance has posted increases in both revenue and net income during the past five years.

Thanks to logging nearly $174 million in interest income from its portfolio investments and about $46 million in fee income Fifth Street Finance's 2013 revenue rose some 40% to nearly $222 million in fiscal 2013 as compared to $165 million in 2012. Increases in the firm's total investment income came from higher average levels of outstanding debt investments helped by a net increase of 18 debt investments and fees related to debt payoffs. Net income also increased by 28% to $102 million in 2012 vs. $79 million in 2012.

Mergers and Acquisitions

In 2013 the investment firm agreed to acquire Healthcare Finance Group planning to invest some $110 million.

EXECUTIVES

CEO and Director, Leonard M. Tannenbaum, age 42
President, Todd G. Owens
CEO and Director, Leonard M. Tannenbaum, age 42
Chairman Fifth Street Finance Corp. and Fifth Street Senior Floating Rate Corp., Bernard D. Berman, age 43
Auditors: PricewaterhouseCoopersLLP

LOCATIONS

HQ: Fifth Street Finance Corp
777 West Putnam Avenue, 3rd Floor, Greenwich, CT 06830
Phone: 203 681-3600
Web: www.fifthstreetfinance.com

PRODUCTS/OPERATIONS

Selected Portfolio Companies
ADAPCO
Advanced Pain Management Holdings Inc.
Caregiver Services
Cenegenics
CRGT Inc.
DISA Inc.
Dominion Diagnostics LLC
Eagle Hospital Physicians
Enhanced Recovery Corporation
Epic MedStaff Services Inc.
Filet of Chicken
Fitness Edge
Flatout
HealthDrive
idX
IZI
JTC Education Holdings
Lighting by Gregory
MedKnowledge Group
Miche Bag LLC
NDS Surgical Imaging
Nicos Polymers & Ginding
O' Currance Teleservices
Pacific Production Technologies
Premier Trailer Leasing
Rail Acquisition Corp.
ReBath
Specialty Bakers LLC
Tegra
Traffic Control and Safety Corporation
Trans-Trade
Welocalize Inc.
Western Emulsions
WhatCounts

COMPETITORS

American Capital	MCG Capital
Ares Capital	MVC Capital
Gladstone Capital	Solar Capital

HISTORICAL FINANCIALS
Company Type: Public

Income Statement
FYE: September 30

	REVENUE ($ mil.)	NET INCOME ($ mil.)	NET PROFIT MARGIN	EMPLOYEES
09/14	293.9	142.5	48.5%	0
09/13	221.6	114.9	51.9%	0
09/12	165.1	88.0	53.3%	0
09/11	125.1	67.1	53.6%	0
09/10	70.5	43.0	61.0%	0
Annual Growth	42.9%	34.9%	—	—

2014 Year-End Financials

Debt ratio: 31.2%	No. of shares (mil.): 153
Return on equity: 10.0%	Dividends
Cash ($ mil.): 86	Yield: 10.8%
Current ratio: 0.43	Payout: 102.0%
Long-term debt ($ mil.): 834	Market value ($ mil.): 1,408

	STOCK PRICE ($) FY Close	P/E High/Low		PER SHARE ($) Earnings	Dividends	Book Value
09/14	9.18	10	9	0.99	1.00	9.64
09/13	10.29	11	9	1.01	1.15	9.85
09/12	10.98	10	8	1.07	1.18	9.92
09/11	9.32	13	8	1.01	1.28	10.07
09/10	11.14	14	10	0.95	0.99	10.43
Annual Growth	(4.7%)	—	—	1.0%	0.2%	(2.0%)

Financial Engines Inc

Like the little engine that could Financial Engines provides financial advice portfolio management and retirement assessment services. The company serves US retirement-plan participants sponsors and service providers across a wide range of industries that includes more than 100 FORTUNE 500 companies and several of the largest retirement plan operators. It delivers its services online as well as by telephone. Financial Engines boasts more than $88 billion in assets under management and serves some 9 million individual retirement-plan participants. The company went public in 2010 with an offering worth $127.2 million.

Geographic Reach

Based in California Financial Engines serves US investors.

Operations

Financial Engines provides independent portfolio management services investment advice and retirement services. It delivers its services to both plan sponsors and plan participants through agreements with retirement plan providers. The firm also supports plan sponsors through an alliance with Charles Schwab.

Sales and Marketing

The financial advisor primarily serves participants in employer-sponsored defined contribution plans such as 401(k) plans. Through direct marketing and promotional efforts Financial Engines works to encourage plan participants and individual investors to enroll in its professional management service.

Clients include the likes of Aon Hewitt Charles Schwab Fidelity Mercer T. Rowe Price and Xerox. It maintains sub-advisory relationships with Vanguard ING and JPMorgan Chase.

Strategy

Financial Engines generates revenue from professional management fees and subscription-based platform fees –that is fees paid for access to its online information and services. It markets itself to new employers through existing relationships with plan administrators. Financial Engines also markets its management services to passive plan participants to beef up fee revenues.

In 2013 the firm began managing Individual Retirement Accounts (IRAs) for 401(k) participants from select sponsors.

In addition to adding new clients through a marketing push Financial Engines plans to grow by adding new services. It is investing in R&D to expand its investment research capabilities.

Financial Performance

As demand for retirement planning increases as the population ages the company has seen its business expand. As such revenues have more than doubled during the past five years. In fiscal 2013 Financial Engines' earnings increased $53.14 million or 29% from the year prior to $238.9 million primarily driven by growth in the company's professional (34%) and platform revenue.

Net income rose by 61% to $29.95 million in 2013 as compared to $18.57 million in 2012 thanks to higher revenue and a boost in income from operations. Operating cash flow also increased to $59.26 million vs. 2012's $38.09 million. It attributes these gains to net income growth and changes in the company's working capital.

Company Background

Co-founder Bill Sharpe is a notable innovator in the analysis and valuation of investments and has written books on topics including portfolio theory and investment fundamentals. He received the Nobel Prize in Economics in 1990.

HISTORY

Financial Engines was founded in 1996 by Nobel laureate William (Bill) Sharpe (Sharp was the recipient of the 1990 Nobel Prize in Economic Sciences); former SEC Commissioner Joseph Grundfest; and the late Craig Johnson then chairman of the Venture Law Group.

Its initial services included providing individual investors with online advice regarding tax-deferred accounts and taxable investments. In 1998 the company began providing advice and assessment on retirement portfolios which consisted of a personalized printed retirement assessment. In 2004 it expanded to offer professional management services to retirement-plan participants

EXECUTIVES

Executive Vice President Technology, Hallee Garry
Executive Vice President of Investment Management and Chief Investment Officer, Christopher L. (Chris) Jones, age 47, $323,250 total compensation
EVP and CFO Chief Risk Officer, Raymond J. (Ray) Sims, age 64, $277,440 total compensation
President and CEO, Lawrence M. (Larry) Raffone, age 51, $325,000 total compensation
Director and Acting General Counsel, Anne S. Tuttle Cappel, age 53
EVP Corporate and Institutional Marketing, Kelly S. O'Donnell, age 46
EVP Technology, Michael J. Campbell
EVP Product and Consumer Marketing, Chung Meng Cheong
EVP Service Delivery, Mark P. Costello
EVP and General Counsel, Anne Tuttle Cappel
Vice President, Steve Rubino
Executive Vice President Technology, Frank Garry
Vice President Technical Operations, David Smith
Vice President Of Client Services, Sally Golding
Vice President Of Client Services, Sa Bradley-goldberg
Chairman of the Board, Paul G. Koontz, age 54
Board Member, David Yoffie
Board Member, John Shoven
Auditors: KPMGLLP

LOCATIONS

HQ: Financial Engines Inc
   1050 Enterprise Way, 3rd Floor, Sunnyvale, CA 94089
Phone: 408 498-6000   **Fax:** 408 498-6010
Web: www.financialengines.com

PRODUCTS/OPERATIONS

2013 Sales

	$ mil.	% of total
Professional management	202.8	85
Platform fees	33.5	14
Other	2.7	1
Total	**239.0**	**100**

COMPETITORS

Ameriprise	Fidelity Financial
BlackRock	Merrill Lynch
Charles Schwab	Morningstar
FMR	The Vanguard Group

HISTORICAL FINANCIALS

Company Type: Public

Income Statement

FYE: December 31

	REVENUE ($ mil.)	NET INCOME ($ mil.)	NET PROFIT MARGIN	EMPLOYEES
12/13	238.9	29.9	12.5%	442
12/12	185.8	18.5	10.0%	380
12/11	144.0	15.1	10.5%	355
12/10	111.7	63.5	56.9%	303
12/09	84.9	5.6	6.7%	264
Annual Growth	29.5%	51.5%	—	13.8%

2013 Year-End Financials

Debt ratio: —
Return on equity: 10.2%
Cash ($ mil.): 126
Current ratio: 7.21
Long-term debt ($ mil.): —

No. of shares (mil.): 50
Dividends
  Yield: 0.2%
  Payout: 38.4%
Market value ($ mil.): 3,536

	STOCK PRICE ($) FY Close	P/E High/Low		PER SHARE ($) Earnings	Dividends	Book Value
12/13	69.48	115	45	0.57	0.20	6.33
12/12	27.74	70	45	0.37	0.00	5.50
12/11	22.33	84	47	0.31	0.00	4.80
12/10	19.83	12	7	1.30	0.00	4.30
Annual Growth	51.9%	—	—	(24.0%)	—	13.8%

Finisar Corp

Finisar helps put the "work" in network with optical components and subsystems that enable high-speed data communications over LANs or metro-area and storage-area networks (MANs/SANs). The company's subsystems include transmitters receivers transceivers transponders optical cables and wavelength selective switches. Its components consist primarily of packaged lasers photodetectors and passive devices. The company sells products to manufacturers of storage systems networking equipment and telecom equipment. Customers have included such tech giants as Alcatel-Lucent Brocade Cisco Systems and EMC Ericcson HP Huawei Technologies and IBM.

Geographic Reach

The company has manufacturing plants in Ipoh Malaysia and in Shanghai and Wuxi China. Its offices are located in Australia Germany India Israel Singapore Sweden and the US (in California Illinois Pennsylvania and Texas). The US is its largest single market accounting for about 30% of sales; China counts for 20% and Malaysia another 15%.

Sales and Marketing

Finisar uses a direct sales force augmented by distributors and manufacturers' representatives. Its optical subsystems and components are sold to a broad base of original equipment manufacturers (OEMs) distributors and system integrators. Products for data communication applications represent about 70% of sales while products for telecommunication applications represent 30%. Customers of the company in turn sell their systems to their own customers which consist of wireline and wireless telecom service providers and cable TV operators.

Financial Performance

Finisar became a billion-dollar company in fiscal 2014 (year-end April). That year overall sales grew 24% to $1.16 billion due to strong sales for datacom products offset by a slight decline for telecom products. The company sold another $230 million in datacom products are more companies upgraded their technology infrastructure with 10 Gbps and higher Ethernet transceivers. After recording a net loss in fiscal 2013 Finisar quickly returned to profitability in 2014 with $111 million in profits. Its cash flow from operations fell to $99 million from increased spending on working capital (accounts receivable inventory etc.)

Strategy

In order to maintain its position as a leading supplier of fiber optic subsystems and components Finisar's stated growth strategy is to continuing to invest in or acquire technologies to further its vertical integration capabilities; expand its product line; sell its products to other growth markets such as high performance computing military medical and consumer electronics products; and continue to strengthen its manufacturing capabilities.

Mergers and Acquisitions

Finisar has grown in part through an aggressive acquisition strategy. In early 2014 it paid $20 million for u2t Photonics AG a German company that makes optical components for high-speed telecom applications. With this acquisition Finisar added u2t's Indium-Phosphide-based 100 Gbps high-speed receivers and photodetectors to its portfolio of high-speed optics technologies.

In 2012 it bought optical amplification company RED-C Optical Networks for its telecom applications and Norwegian optical components maker Ignis to expand in the Nordic region of Europe and ensure a supply of tunable laser products. Tunable lasers are a vital component of Finisar's products and securing an internal supply is essential to its vertical integration strategy.

EXECUTIVES

Svp Operations And Engineering, Mark Colyar, age 52
Executive Vice President; General Counsel; Secretary, Christopher E Brown, age 47
EVP Global Operations, Joseph A. Young, age 58, $367,562 total compensation
CEO and Director, Eitan Gertel, age 52, $459,711 total compensation
EVP Sales and Marketing, Todd Swanson, age 42, $284,031 total compensation
EVP and CFO, Kurt Adzema, age 45, $292,385 total compensation
EVP Technology and Global Research and Development, John H. Clark
EVP and Chief Counsel, Chris Brown
Vice President Engineering, Bobby Hawthorne
Vice President Of Digital Systems Engineering, Mark Farley
Vice President Global Supply Chain Management, Barry Kasarda
Vice President, Wen Li
Vice President Of Sales Aoc Division, Greg Hart
Vice President Global Quality, Raj Cornelius
Vice President Corporate Development, Eric Bentley
Vice President Optical Engineering, Jan Lipson
Co Founder Vice President Sales, Kerry Craven
Vice President R&d, Roni Dadon
Vice President Of Marketing, Rafik Ward
Vice President Corporate Development, Eric Shami
Vice President Global Tax, Bill Bridgeman
CEO and Director, Jerry S. Rawls, age 70
CEO and Director, Eitan Gertel, age 52
Auditors: Ernst&YoungLLP

LOCATIONS

HQ: Finisar Corp
  1389 Moffett Park Drive, Sunnyvale, CA 94089
Phone: 408 548-1000
Web: www.finisar.com

2014 Sales

	$ mil.	% of total
US	339.4	29
China	229.2	20
Malaysia	185.2	16
Other countries	403.0	35
Total	1156.8	100

PRODUCTS/OPERATIONS

2014 Sales by Market

	$ mil.	% of total
Datacom	822.0	71
Telecom	334.8	29
Total	1156.8	100

COMPETITORS

ADVA	Intel
ARRIS	JDS Uniphase
Agilent Technologies	MRV Communications
Alliance Fiber Optic Products	McAfee
Avago Technologies	Mitsubishi Electric
Brocade Communications	Molex
Cisco Systems	NeoPhotonics
EMC	Oclaro
EMCORE	Oplink Communications
IBM	Sumitomo Electric
IMC Networks	Teledyne LeCroy
	Xyratex

HISTORICAL FINANCIALS

Company Type: Public

Income Statement

FYE: April 27

	REVENUE ($ mil.)	NET INCOME ($ mil.)	NET PROFIT MARGIN	EMPLOYEES
04/14	1,156.8	111.7	9.7%	13,000
04/13	934.3	(5.4)	—	9,720
04/12	952.5	42.9	4.5%	8,910
04/11	948.7	88.1	9.3%	8,065
04/10	629.8	14.1	2.2%	6,893
Annual Growth	16.4%	67.7%	—	17.2%

2014 Year-End Financials

Debt ratio: 16.8%
Return on equity: 12.3%
Cash ($ mil.): 303
Current ratio: 4.32
Long-term debt ($ mil.): 212

No. of shares (mil.): 97
Dividends
  Yield: —
  Payout: —
Market value ($ mil.): 2,682

	STOCK PRICE ($) FY Close	P/E High/Low		PER SHARE ($) Earnings	Dividends	Book Value
04/14	27.57	25	11	1.09	0.00	10.44
04/13	12.89	—	—	(0.06)	0.00	8.60
04/12	16.52	58	27	0.46	0.00	8.44
04/11	28.09	39	11	1.00	0.00	7.78
04/10	14.96	77	2	0.22	0.00	4.60
Annual Growth	16.5%	—	—	49.2%	—	22.8%

First Cash Financial Services Inc

First Cash Financial Services is the original pawn star. The company operates more than 1000 pawnshops and cash advance stores in about a dozen US states and nearly 30 states in Mexico. First Cash lends money secured by such personal property as jewelry electronics tools sporting goods musical equipment and firearms (in select markets). Its First Cash Pawn and Famous Pawn shops sell merchandise forfeited by borrowers. The company's Fast Cash Advance locations offer short-term and payday loans. The company exited the check cashing business in late 2014 when it discontinued its Cash & Go joint venture. Founded in 1988 fast-growing Fast Cash has acquired about 500 stores over the past five years.

Geographic Reach

Texas-based First Cash operates more than 1000 pawn shops in 13 US states including Colorado and Texas as well as 29 states in Mexico. The company which rings up about 55% of its revenue in Mexico is looking for further growth there.

Mergers and Acquisitions

In October 2014 First Cash acquired a chain of 15 large-format pawn stores located in Kentucky Missouri Tennessee and South Carolina. The purchase came on the heels of its purchase of 47 pawn shops in Mexico Colorado and Texas in August.

In 2012 First Cash announced a larger US deal with the acquisition of a 24-store chain of pawn stores operating under the Mister Money brand. The $25.5 million transaction expanded First Cash's geographic footprint in Colorado Kentucky Wyoming and Nebraska. The company later arranged to purchase 16 pawn stores operating as Fast Cash Pawn in the Denver area. That deal carried an approximately $46 million price tag.

Financial Performance

Fast-growing First Cash rang up $660.9 million in sales in 2013 an increase of 11% versus 2012. Net income rose 4% over the same period to $83.9 million on higher sales and lower taxes. Sales and profits have been rising in recent years as the company expands. Driving the revenue rise in 2013 was higher sales of retail merchandise at First Cash's growing number of pawn shops. Sales of consumer electronics appliances and power tools in Mexico bolstered sales.

First Cash Financial earns most of its revenue from pawn operations (more than 90%) while short term consumer loans account for the rest. The money-making pawn business is driven by pawn merchandise sales in addition to statutory service charges on pawns which reach up to 300% of the loan amount. However those service fees vary from state to state depending on the law. The company's average pawn loan amount in the US is about $171 and $71 in Mexico.

Strategy

To reduce its risk to new regulations associated with payday lending First Cash has exited the short term loan and credit business in the US through the discontinuation of Cash & Go which operates 37 check cashing and financial services kiosks located inside convenience stores in Texas.

The company is looking south of the border to grow business. First Cash operates about 600 pawn shops and payday advance stores in Mexico and it is looking to increase that number by opening new stores and through acquisitions. The company first expanded its presence in the country in 2008 with the acquisition of Presta Max a chain of 16 pawn shops in southern Mexico. In early 2012 it acquired a 29-store chain in western Mexico. First Cash is also looking to open new stores in Mexico where many people don't have bank accounts and have limited access to credit. The company also continues grow in the US by opening new shops or buying two or three individual pawn shops at a time.

HISTORY

First Cash grew from a single pawnshop in Dallas. John Payne traded some land in Colorado for the store after selling his Dallas bank in 1979. He and his wife ran the shop until 1985 when they sold it and built a new shop in the suburbs aiming to achieve the ambience of a video store.

It was an opportune moment: The Texas economy particularly the banking industry was just beginning its slide. Payne (who later left the company) incorporated First Cash in 1988 and brought in professional management under former banker Rick Powell in 1990.

Eight-store First Cash went public in 1991. Acquisitions and expansions included the 1994 purchase of a Baltimore/Washington DC area chain. The next year First Cash upgraded its computers to improve inventory control and loan valuations and became the first major pawn chain to stop selling or making loans on handguns.

In 1996 and 1997 First Cash added stores in Maryland and Texas. The next year it bought 10-store chain JB Pawn (from a brother of First Cash director Richard Burke) and about 20 individual shops. First Cash also moved into check-cashing buying 11-store Miraglia.

To reflect the diversification the company changed its name to First Cash Financial Services in early 1999. That year First Cash joined other pawnbrokers and short-term lenders in moving into Mexico. In 2000 First Cash partnered with Pawnbroker.com to provide online financial and support services to pawn shops.

First Cash discontinued its auto loan operations in 2008 two years after purchasing dealer and lender Auto Master. In the midst of a worldwide credit crunch First Cash sold Auto Master to Minneapolis-based Interstate Auto Group (dba CarHop).

EXECUTIVES

Chairman President and CEO, Rick L. Wessel, age 55, $850,000 total compensation
Chief Financial Officer; Executive Vice President; Treasurer; Secretary, R. Douglas (Doug) Orr, age 53, $400,000 total compensation
COO, Stephen O. Coffman, age 52, $420,000 total compensation
Vp Director It Is, Danny Allison
Vice President Of Operations Product, Chris Forbes
Chairman President and CEO, Rick L. Wessel, age 55
Chief Financial Officer; Executive Vice President; Treasurer; Secretary, R. Douglas (Doug) Orr, age 53

LOCATIONS

HQ: First Cash Financial Services Inc
690 East Lamar Blvd., Suite 400, Arlington, TX 76011
Phone: 817 460-3947
Web: www.firstcash.com

2013 Sales

	$ in mil.	% of total
Mexico	363.0	55
US	297.8	45
Total	**660.8**	**100**

2013 Locations

	No.
Mexico	597
US	
Texas	198
Colorado	29
Maryland	28
South Carolina	18
Indiana	10
Kentucky	7
Missouri	4
Oklahoma	4
Virginia	4
Wyoming	3
District of Columbia	3
Nebraska	1
Total	**906**

PRODUCTS/OPERATIONS

2013 Sales

	$ mil.	% of total
Retail merchandise	367.2	56
Pawn loan fees	181.5	27
Wholesale Scrap jewelry	68.3	10
Consumer loan and credit services fees	43.8	7
Total	**660.8**	**100**

Selected Subsidiaries

All Access Special Events LLC
American Loan Employee Services S.A. de C.V. (Mexico)
Cardplus Inc.
College Park Jewelers Inc.
Famous Pawn Inc.
FCFS MO Inc.
FCFS OK Inc.
FCFS SC Inc.
First Cash Corp.
First Cash Credit Ltd.
First Cash Inc.
First Cash Credit Management LLC
First Cash Ltd.
First Cash Management LLC
First Cash S.A. de C.V. (Mexico)
King Pawn Inc.
King Pawn II Inc.
Maryland Precious Metals Inc.
SHAC LLC
T.J. Unlimited LLC

COMPETITORS

ACE Cash Express	EZCORP
Cash America	World Acceptance
Check Into Cash	Xponential

HISTORICAL FINANCIALS

Company Type: Public

Income Statement

FYE: December 31

	REVENUE ($ mil.)	NET INCOME ($ mil.)	NET PROFIT MARGIN	EMPLOYEES
12/13	660.8	83.8	12.7%	7,100
12/12	595.9	80.3	13.5%	6,400
12/11	521.3	77.7	14.9%	5,300
12/10	431.1	57.6	13.4%	4,700
12/09	365.9	49.7	13.6%	4,200
Annual Growth	**15.9%**	**13.9%**	**—**	**14.0%**

2013 Year-End Financials

Debt ratio: 28.8%
Return on equity: 21.8%
Cash ($ mil.): 70
Current ratio: 5.95
Long-term debt ($ mil.): 187
No. of shares (mil.): 28
Dividends
Yield: —
Payout: —
Market value ($ mil.): 1,790

	STOCK PRICE ($) FY Close	P/E High/Low		PER SHARE ($) Earnings	Dividends	Book Value
12/13	61.84	22	17	2.84	0.00	14.31
12/12	49.62	18	12	2.70	0.00	12.11
12/11	35.09	20	12	2.47	0.00	10.48
12/10	30.99	17	11	1.86	0.00	9.56
12/09	22.19	14	7	1.65	0.00	7.12
Annual Growth	29.2%	—	—	14.5%	—	19.1%

First Community Bancshares, Inc. (NV)

First Community Bancshares doesn't play second fiddle to other area banks. The firm is the holding company for First Community Bank which serves communities in Virginia West Virginia North Carolina and Tennessee. Through some 75 branches the bank provides traditional services such as checking and savings accounts CDs and credit cards. The bank is mainly a real estate lender with residential loans and mortgages accounting for about half of its portfolio and commercial loans accounting for most of the remainder. First Community Bancshares also provides insurance through subsidiary Greenpoint Insurance and investment advisory services through First Community Wealth Management.

Over the past few years First Community has made a number of acquisitions across its various business lines. Its nonbanking purchases include Investment Planning Consultants GreenPoint Insurance and Carr & Hyde Insurance. The company also added five North Carolina banking locations with its acquisitions of Coddle Creek Financial (parent of Mooresville Savings Bank) and TriStone. After slowing its acquisition activity during the economic downturn First Community resumed in 2012 buying Peoples Bank of Virginia which added four branches in the Richmond area. The company also acquired the failed Waccamaw Bank in a FDIC-facilitated transaction. That deal brought in 16 branches in North Carolina.

The downturn hit First Community hard in 2009. That year it reported more than $90 million in losses related to nonperforming assets and loans. The company rebounded in 2010 with earning levels near those of previous years but in 2011 First Community saw its revenues shrink by some 10% to $123 million. Profits also slipped some 8% to $20 million as both interest and noninterest earnings went down. Construction and development levels in the markets it serves are still in decline and as a result lending remains a challenge. Regulatory limits to banking fees have had relatively little impact on First Community though as its customers increasingly turn to card-based payments; the company's revenues from overdraft fees and debit card interchange income rose in 2011.

EXECUTIVES

VP and Secretary; President and Director First Community Bank, Robert L. Buzzo, age 64, $225,800 total compensation

Chief Operating Officer; EVP; COO; CIO of First Community Bank; N.A., E. Stephen (Steve) Lilly, age 56, $247,000 total compensation
Chairman of the Board; Chief Executive Officer, William P. Stafford, age 51
Chief Financial Officer of the Company and First Community Bank; N. A., David D. Brown, age 40, $160,000 total compensation
Vice President Director Of Operations, Garry Stutts
Vice President Finance, Jason Belcher
Assistant Vice President Credit Adm, Jeff Noble
Senior Vice President And Director, Stephen Warden
Regional President, Milton Campbell
Senior Vice President, Mark Evans
Vice President Director Of Network, Brian Broyles
VP and Secretary; President and Director First Community Bank, Robert L. Buzzo, age 64
Auditors: DixonHughesGoodmanLLP

LOCATIONS

HQ: First Community Bancshares, Inc. (NV)
P.O. Box 989, Bluefield, VA 24605-0989
Phone: 276 326-9000　　**Fax:** 276 326-9010
Web: www.fcbinc.com

PRODUCTS/OPERATIONS

2011 Sales

	$ mil.	% of total
Interest		
Loans including fees	80.6	61
Securities	13.3	10
Deposits in banks	0.3	-
Noninterest		
Service charges on deposit accounts	13.2	10
Insurance commissions	6.2	5
Net gains on sales of securities	5.3	4
Wealth management	3.5	3
Other service charges commissions & fees	5.7	4
Other	3.9	3
Adjustments	(2.3)	-
Total	**129.7**	**100**

COMPETITORS

BB&T	Huntington Bancshares
Bank of America	SunTrust
City Holding	United Bankshares
First Citizens BancShares	WesBanco
Highlands Bankshares Inc.	

HISTORICAL FINANCIALS

Company Type: Public

Income Statement　　　　　　　FYE: December 31

	ASSETS ($ mil.)	NET INCOME ($ mil.)	INCOME AS % OF ASSETS	EMPLOYEES
12/13	2,602.5	23.3	0.9%	729
12/12	2,728.8	28.5	1.0%	760
12/11	2,164.7	20.0	0.9%	633
12/10	2,244.2	21.8	1.0%	683
12/09	2,274.8	(38.2)	—	646
Annual Growth	3.4%	—	—	3.1%

2013 Year-End Financials

Return on assets: 0.8%	Dividends
Return on equity: 6.8%	Yield: 2.8%
Long-term debt ($ mil.): —	Payout: 38.4%
No. of shares (mil.): 18	Market value ($ mil.): 309
Sales ($ mil): 139	

	STOCK PRICE ($) FY Close	P/E High/Low		PER SHARE ($) Earnings	Dividends	Book Value
12/13	16.70	16	13	1.11	0.48	17.75
12/12	15.97	11	8	1.40	0.43	17.77
12/11	12.48	14	9	1.07	0.40	17.13
12/10	14.94	14	9	1.23	0.40	15.11
12/09	12.05	—	—	(2.72)	0.58	14.29
Annual Growth	8.5%	—	—	—	(4.6%)	5.6%

First Niagara Financial Group, Inc.

A lot of water and a few barrels have gone over Niagara Falls since First Niagara Bank was founded. Tracing its roots to 1870 the flagship subsidiary of acquisitive First Niagara Financial operates about 430 branches in upstate New York Connecticut Massachusetts and Pennsylvania. The bank offers financial services like deposits loans insurance investments and wealth management. Commercial real estate loans business loans and residential mortgages account for most of the bank's loan portfolio. Subsidiary First Niagara Risk Management offers risk management employee benefits consulting and investment services while First Niagara Commercial Bank accepts municipal deposits.

First Niagara has been expanding rapidly via transformative acquisitions. In 2012 the company bought nearly 200 HSBC branches in upstate New York and Connecticut for some $1 billion. To satisfy antitrust concerns it is selling more than 35 locations included in the deal to KeyCorp and nearly 30 more to Community Bank System and Financial Institutions in separate transactions. The company is also consolidating 35 branches with nearby locations. In addition to expanding First Niagara's branch network the HSBC acquisition will boost the company's commercial business and credit card portfolio as well.

First Niagara previously entered Pennsylvania in a big way acquiring more than 50 branches from PNC Financial in 2009 and buying bank holding company Harleysville National the next year. The PNC acquisition which expanded First Niagara's operations into western Pennsylvania included locations that PNC was compelled to divest to satisfy antitrust concerns regarding its takeover of National City. The purchase of Harleysville National Bank added some 80 branches in central and eastern Pennsylvania.

First Niagara expanded its insurance business in Pennsylvania in 2010 with the acquisitions of employee benefits risk management and investment services firm Banyan Consulting and Summit Insurance Group's operations in the state. The new businesses were combined with previous acquisitions RTI Insurance Services and Three Rivers Financial Services and took the First Niagara Risk Management name.

To facilitate its expansion First Niagara Financial converted from a thrift holding company to a bank holding company and First Niagara Bank converted from a savings institution to a commercial bank in 2010 moves that gave the company more flexibility in making acquisitions.

In 2011 the company completed its $1.5 billion acquisition of NewAlliance Bancshares adding some 90 bank branches and extending its franchise into Connecticut and Massachusetts. The addition along with organic growth in First Niagara's commercial loan portfolio contributed to a nearly 25% increase in net income for the company that year.

Prior to its latest round of acquisitions First Niagara Financial had already more than doubled its size with an earlier spree of smaller deals. It had fewer than 50 branches operating under its banner at the end of 2003. That year the company acquired Finger Lakes Bancorp. It bought Troy Financial in 2004 and Hudson River Bancorp the following year. In 2008 the company bought Great Lakes Bancorp the parent of Greater Buffalo Savings Bank.

EXECUTIVES

Vice President, Frank Polino
Vice President Risk Management, Charlie Epes
Senior Executive Vice President and Chief Banking Officer, Daniel E. Cantara, age 55, $511,058 total compensation
Interim President and Chief Executive Officer, Gary M. Crosby, age 61, $587,716 total compensation
Executive Vice President Retail Banking, Mark R. Rendulic
Senior Executive Vice President and Chief Financial Officer, Gregory W. Norwood, $511,058 total compensation
Executive Vice President - Corporate Development, Oliver H. Sommer, age 45, $488,462 total compensation
Executive Vice President; Chief Risk Officer, Richard M. Barry
Executive Vice President Consumer Finance, Andrew D. Fornarola
Vice President, Deborah Cotton
First Vice President, Bobby Huddleston
Svp-customer Experience Exec, Ricky Otey
Senior Vice President Chief Credit Officer, Liam Brickley
Vice President Relationship Manager, Randall Cornelius
Svp-central Underwriting Credi, John Kenefick
Evp Managing Director Of Oper, Julie Signorille
Evp-comml Financial Services, Joseph Saffire
Vice President, Gail Maccleverty
Vice President And Department Manager, Daniel Ustach
First Vice President Regional Team Leader Hudson Valley, Sara Tucker
Vice President Relationship Manager Commercial Business Banking, Peter Hart
Vice President Manager Portfolio Credit Risk Management, Fred Lapple
First Vice President And Practice Leader Health And Welfare, John Kosciusko
Vice President Information Technology, Paul Ferguson
Vice President Financial Consultant, Joseph Murphy
Vice President Recruitment Manager And Human Resources, Beata Fijakowski
Vice President Application Development And Applica, Carl Taylor
First Vice President Technology Relationship Manager, Jennifer Holcomb
Vice President Secondary Marketing, Jim McEvoy
Vice President Solution Platform Architect, Amy Rech
Assistant Vice-president, Christopher Thomas
Vice President Of Information Security Manager, Kelly Hampton

Vice President Sourcing Manager, Nancy Pietras
Assistant Vice President Human, Becky Smith
Vice President, Barry Callahan
Vice President Corporate Banking, William Checkosky
Vice President Online Banking And Ecommerce, Anthony Parisi
Vice President Marketing Segment Manager, Charles Fashana
Assistant Vice-president, Kara Sciarra
Assistant Vice-president, Marie Zdanowicz
Vice President Commercial Real Estate Finance, Ryan Crouthamel
Project Manager Vice President, Tom Messman
Vice President And Regional Sales, Tanya Frye
Vice President Information Technology, Marcial Feliciano
Vice President Senior Information, Lesley Harrigan
First Vice President Wny Team Leader, Anthony Rizzo
Vice President Information Technology Client Services, Michael Sucharski
Senior Vice President Retail Bank, Joseph Tedesco
Vice President And Manager Sales Coach Brand Cultu, Carl Abate
Fvp Manager Product Strategy And Analytics, David Cushing
First Vice President Underwriting, Edward Dridge
Area Sales Manager Vice President, Terri Vertalino
Sr Vice President Dir Risk Analytics, Bob Macdonald
Vice President Consumer Finance, Wayne Morlock
Assistant Vice-president, Lindsay Waiss
Executive Vice President And Chief, Peter Babiarz
Executive Vice President And Chief, Robert McKnight
Assistant Vice-president, Brian Rochford
Senior Vice President Governance, Kevin Ruhl
Senior Vice President Compliance, Gary Pacos
Vice President, Joy Rogers
Vice President Area Sales Manager, Ronald Byers
Vice President Solution Delivery Manager, Calvin Robol
First Vice President, David Kavney
Vice President Human Resources, Patty Swan
Solutions Architect Vice President, Krishnam Penumetcha
Vice President Of Small Business Banking, Nick Capanna
Assistant Vice-president, Aaron Berger
Vice President Relationship Manager, Nick Walsh
Vice President Operations Risk Management, Mary Wilkie
Senior Vice President Corporate, David Lanzillo
Assistant Vice President Commercial, Brandon Exley
Vice President, Eric Seestedt
Vice President Commercial Banking, Bob Bazargan
First Vice President And Team Leader, Steven Weeks
First Vice President, John Allenson
Assistant Vice-president, Teresa Spadafora
First Vice President, Lura Bechtel
First Vice President Central Underwriting Manager, David Squire
Assistant Vice-president, Anne Tedstone
Assistant Vice President, Lori Pascuzzi
Vice President Corporate Banking, Dante Fazzina
Assistant Vice-president, Mark Hudson
Senior Vice President Commercial Bank, Lewis Cyr
Assistant Vice President Information Technology Vendor Management, Jason Cwiklinski
Vice President Special Assets, Herbert Ochoa
Senior Vice President, R Sears
Assistant Vice President Ofac Sanctions Manager, Richard McDermott

Vice President Enterprise Web Architect Informatio, David Hannes
Vice President Digital Product Management, Julie Rinard
Vice President Enterprise Project, Paul Gardner
Vice President And Assistant General Counsel, Michael Kozlowski
Fvp Compliance Intelligence And Analytics Manager, Gary Smith
Senior Vice President Information, Lesley Norris
Vice President, Robert Brewer
Vice President Commercial Lending, Chad Stewart
Vice President Business Development, Bill Kuhn
Vice President Senior Portfolio Officer, Michael Schwartz
First Vice President Business Banking Team Leader, David Gorny
Assistant Vice President Branch Manager, Deborah Cole
Vice President, Maria Barth
Vice President, Bennet Dunlap
Vice President, Gus Kasparis
Vice President Graphic Designer, Randy Jack
Vice President Senior Manager Human Resources Technology And Payroll, Sue Labelle
Vice President Director Of Operations, Rick Kuhn
Vice President Solutions Delivery, Susan Wells
Assistant Vice-president, Jodie Alexander
First Vice President And Financial Advisor, Christopher Dent
Vice President Capital Markets, Troy Jones
Executive Vice President And Chief, Jamel Perkins
Vice President, Traci Stadler
Senior Vice President Support Services, David Desanits
Senior Vice President And Corporate, Kenneth Segarra
First Vice President Learning, Debra Sayre
Vice President Area Sales Manager, Maddalena Prohaska
First Vice President Senior Portfolio, Charles Wyrwa
Vice President, David Baker
Vice President Of Organization, Elizabeth Davidson
Senior Vice President Head, Ross Marrazzo
Application Development Vice President, Carl Kessler
Vice President And Treasurer, Jane Cordts
Vice President Sr Info Tech Bus Anls, Kimberly Davis
Information Technology Vice President, Dawn Cato
Senior Vice President And Director, Patrick Killeen
Senior Vice President, Keith Broyles
Vice President Of Business Management, Adam Desmond
First Vice President Retail Sales, Robert Mills
Associate Counsel And Vice President, John Fenski
Vice President, Frank Cipriano
Vice President Commercial Real Estate, Stephen Olsavsky
First Vice President Consumer Finance, Matthew Wagner
Assistant Vice President Credit Analyst, Christopher Roy
Vice President Corporate Accounting, Theodore Buonanno
Vice President, Terence Sullivan
First Vice President And Wny Regional, Joseph Donofrio
Vice President Business Banking, Gardner Abbott
First Vice President Retail Cmpl Ofc, Jeffrey Delepine
Senior Vice President And Head Of Human, Valerie Deberry
Vice President Employee Benefits, Maryann Sansone

Senior Vice President Corporate, David Dodman
Vice President Organizational Development Consultant, Sarah Gilson
Vice President, Miranda Ronke-czarniecki
First Vice President, Donald Rotzien
Vice President, Christopher Wilson
Assistant Vice-president, James Jackson
Vice President Senior Portfolio Underwriter, Lorraine Hance
Assistant Vice-president, Deborah Henninger
Vice President, Michael Borowy
Assistant Vice-president, Dan Giannuzzi
Vice President International Trade Finance, Ralph Bocchino
Vice President, Robert Scarpello
Vice President, John Bodine
First Vice President And Team Leader, Marc Wegener
Vice President, Jeff Merrill
Vice President, Dawn Pellegrino
Vice President Commercial Lending, Michael McKelvey
Vice President, Tim Glass
Vice President And Senior Relationship Manager, Stephen Boyd
Vice President, Noreen O'Neill
Assistant Vice-president, Shane Sclichter
Vice President, John Berry
Assistant Vice-president, Jack Finkle
Vice President Commercial Relationship Manager, Michael Giancursio
Vice President, Jason Dewitt
Vice President Corporate Banking, Steve Yantz
Senior Vice President And Director Of Mortgage Operations, Nanette Gross
Vice President, Maurice Fry
Assistant Vice-president, Lynn Conway
Vice President, Peter Hausherr
First Vice President, Don Mishler
Vice President, Ivan Hicks
Vice President, Michael Danforth
Complex Asset Specialist And Vice President, Franz Ross
Vice President Senior Commercial Underwriter, Jeffrey Gorrell
Vice President, Frederick Parker
Vice President, Patrick Rowland
Vice President, Frederick Holmes
Vice President And Relationship Manager, Larry Alampi
Vice President Small Business Banker, Jayson Schmidt
Vice President / Relationship Manager Business Banking, Daniel Lent
Vice President And Corporate Banking, Sheila Studebaker
First Vice President Wny Team Leader, John Wright
Assistant Vice President Information, Jason Menton
Assistant Vice President Information, Gregg Allen
Vice President Program Manager, Erin Parenteau
Vice President And Associate Counsel, David Aldous
Vice President, Sharon Stockton
Assistant Vice President Information, Nick Farmer
Senior Portfolio Reviewer Vp, Diana Harrison
Vice President And Wealth Manager, Gina Dimonda
Vice President, Robert Drelick
Vice President Human Resources, Jennifer Kopf
Assistant Vice President And Senior, Tracey Pollard
Vice President Strategy Markets, Jason Sorensen
Vice President Information Technology, Richard Good
Vice President Enterprise Web Architect, David Januchowski
Vice President, Grace Dalton

First Vice President, Gary Danis
Vice President, Robert Cook
Vice President And Team Leader, Peter Vero
Vice President, Art Aramino
Vice President, Jim Rykowski
Assistant Vice-president, Eric Drylie
Regional Vice President New England, D Mulwani
Vice President Municipal Relationship, Carol Martini
Marketing Vice President, R Sears
Vice President, Daniel Hooper
Regional President, Juliet Bonetto
Board Member, Barbara S Jeremiah
Chairman, G. Thomas Bowers, age 71
Board Of Directors, Christa Hall
Treasurer, Devon Fik
Board Of Directors, Roxanne Coady
Board Member, Carlton L Highsmith
Board Member, Peter B Robinson
Board Member, Nathaniel D Woodson
Board Of Director, Nancy Freischlag
Auditors: KPMGLLP

LOCATIONS

HQ: First Niagara Financial Group, Inc.
726 Exchange Street, Suite 618, Buffalo, NY 14210
Phone: 716 819-5500
Web: www.firstniagara.com

PRODUCTS/OPERATIONS

2013 Sales

	$ mil.	% of total
Interest		
Loans & leases	845	54
Investment securities & other	365	23
Noninterest		
Deposit service charges	104	7
Insurance commissions	67	4
Wealthmanagement services	58	4
Merchant and card fees	49	3
Capital markets income	22	1
Others	64	4
Total	**1574**	**100**

COMPETITORS

Capital One	KeyCorp
Citigroup	M&T Bank
Citizens Financial Group	NBT Bancorp
Community Bank System	PNC Financial
HSBC USA	SEFCU
JPMorgan Chase	TD Bank USA

HISTORICAL FINANCIALS

Company Type: Public

Income Statement

FYE: December 31

	ASSETS ($ mil.)	NET INCOME ($ mil.)	INCOME AS % OF ASSETS	EMPLOYEES
12/13	37,628.0	295.0	0.8%	5,807
12/12	36,806.2	168.4	0.5%	5,927
12/11	32,810.6	173.9	0.5%	4,827
12/10	21,083.8	140.3	0.7%	3,791
12/09	14,584.8	79.3	0.5%	2,816
Annual Growth	**26.7%**	**38.8%**	**—**	**19.8%**

2013 Year-End Financials

Return on assets: 0.7%
Return on equity: 5.9%
Long-term debt ($ mil.): —
No. of shares (mil.): 353
Sales ($ mil): 1,574

Dividends
Yield: 3.0%
Payout: 45.7%

Market value ($ mil.): 3,759

	STOCK PRICE ($) FY Close	P/E High/Low	PER SHARE ($) Earnings	Dividends	Book Value
12/13	10.62	15 10	0.75	0.32	14.11
12/12	7.93	26 18	0.40	0.32	13.97
12/11	8.63	24 13	0.64	0.64	13.64
12/10	13.98	21 16	0.70	0.57	13.22
12/09	13.91	35 21	0.46	0.56	12.61
Annual Growth	**(6.5%)**	**— —**	**13.0%**	**(13.1%)**	**2.8%**

First Republic Bank (San Francisco, CA)

No not the original Roman Republic but rather a modern-day haven for the elite. Founded in 1985 First Republic Bank offers private banking wealth management trust and brokerage services for businesses and high-net-worth clients though about 70 branches. Its main geographic focus is on urban markets including San Francisco Los Angeles New York Boston Portland and San Diego. The bank's lending focuses on commercial and residential real estate and personal loans including vacation home mortgages and aircraft and yacht financing. Trust services are offered through the bank's First Republic Trust Company division. First Republic Bank has some $41.6 billion of assets under management.

Geographic Reach

The company operates 73 offices 66 of which are Preferred Banking locations in Boston; Los Angeles; New York; Newport Beach California; Palm Beach Florida; Palo Alto California; Portland Oregon; San Diego San Francisco and Santa Barbara California. In 2014 it opened an additional Preferred Banking office in downtown San Diego. The other seven locations offer lending wealth management or trust services.

Sales and Marketing

First Republic Bank advertises via digital media and newspaper and radio ads; its primary marketing goal is to attract deposits in its Preferred Banking offices. In 2013 the company spent $25.5 million on advertising and marketing slightly up from $25.1 million in 2012 (but down from $28.8 million in 2011).

Financial Performance

The bank has seen stable growth in earnings since 2010. In 2013 revenue grew 10% to $1.6 billion (compared to $1.5 billion in 2012) as both interest and noninterest income rose. Higher interest rates brought added income on both loans and investments while fees increases on investment advisory services net loan servicing deposits and foreign exchanges also contributed to the revenue growth. However a decline in gains on sales of loans slightly offset those improvements.

Net income which has also been on the rise grew 15% to $462.1 million in 2013 (versus $401.2 million in 2012) primarily as a result of the year's higher revenues. In turn the profit growth helped contribute to a rise of cash flow from operations which grew 28% to $562.2 million.

Strategy

A conservative lender First Republic has been relatively unscathed by the financial problems plaguing the banking industry. The company has a solid asset portfolio with few delinquencies. First Republic is focused on growing its business banking and wealth management business which spurs fee income. The bank is expanding its wealth management unit through hiring and cross-selling. The bank also caters to film and television companies by offering lending deposit and wealth management services.

EXECUTIVES

EVP Secretary and General Counsel, Edward J. Dobranski, age 63
President, Katherine August-deWilde, age 63
Chairman and CEO, James H. Herbert
EVP and Chief Credit Officer, David B. Lichtman
EVP Deposit Sales Product and Strategy, Joseph M. (Joe) Petitti
President First Republic Securities Company, David Tateosian
COO, Mike Selfridge, age 46
President First Republic Trust Company, Michael J. Harrington
President Private Wealth Management, Bob Thornton
EVP and Chief Marketing Officer, Dianne Snedaker
SVP Chief Investment Officer and Co-Chief Risk Officer, Gaye Erkan
EVP and CFO, Mike Roffler
EVP; Chief BSA and AML and Security Officer, Bill Ward
EVP and CIO, Dale A. Smith
EVP and Chief Administrative Officer, Jason C. Bender
Executive Assistant To Executive Vice President And Chief Information Officer, Brenna Souza
Vice President Wealth Management, Chris Rusk
Vice President Foreign Exchange, Shelley Gill
Vice President Compensation, James Reeve
Vice President, Brent Chapman
Vice President Technology Operations, Michael Nakamoto
Chairman and CEO, James H. Herbert
Auditors: KPMGLLP

LOCATIONS

HQ: First Republic Bank (San Francisco, CA)
   111 Pine Street, 2nd Floor, San Francisco, CA 94111
Phone: 415 392-1400
Web: www.firstrepublic.com

PRODUCTS/OPERATIONS

2013 Sales

	$ in mil.	% of total
Interest income other	1356.0	85
Noninterest income	244.4	15
Total	**1600.4**	**100**

Selected Affiliates

First Republic Investment Management Inc.
First Republic Securities Company LLC
First Republic Trust Company

COMPETITORS

Bank of Marin	City National
Bank of New York Mellon	JPMorgan Private Bank
	MUFG Americas Holdings
Boston Private	Morgan Stanley
Citigroup Private Bank	TriState Capital

HISTORICAL FINANCIALS

Company Type: Public

Income Statement

FYE: December 31

	ASSETS ($ mil.)	NET INCOME ($ mil.)	INCOME AS % OF ASSETS	EMPLOYEES
12/13	42,112.7	462.0	1.1%	2,388
12/12	34,387.6	402.4	1.2%	2,110
12/11	27,791.8	352.0	1.3%	1,821
12/10*	22,377.6	142.3	0.6%	1,502
06/10	0.0	128.8	—	0
Annual Growth	**—**	**37.6%**	**—**	**—**

*Fiscal year change

2013 Year-End Financials

Return on assets: 1.2%
Return on equity: 12.2%
Long-term debt ($ mil.): —
No. of shares (mil.): 132
Sales ($ mil): 1,600

Dividends
   Yield: 0.8%
   Payout: 11.6%
Market value ($ mil.): 6,950

	STOCK PRICE ($) FY Close	P/E High/Low	PER SHARE ($) Earnings	Dividends	Book Value
12/13	52.35	16 10	3.10	0.46	31.33
12/12	32.78	12 10	2.76	0.30	25.89
12/11	30.61	13 8	2.65	0.00	19.46
12/10*	29.12	26 24	1.12	0.00	16.59
Annual Growth	**21.6%**	**— —**	**40.4%**	**—**	**23.6%**

*Fiscal year change

FirstMerit Corp

FirstMerit Corporation is the holding company for FirstMerit Bank which provides retail and commercial banking services through more than 400 branches in five US states primarily in the Midwest. Serving local consumers and small to midsized businesses the bank provides standard services such as deposit accounts credit and debit cards and loans as well as wealth management and trust services. Subsidiaries offer investment and brokerage services financial planning commercial lease financing life and title insurance annuities and mortgage servicing.

Geographic Reach
About three-fourths of FirstMerit's bank branches are located in Ohio and Michigan. It has 40-plus branches in both Wisconsin and Illinois (the Chicago area) as well as four branches in Western Pennsylvania.

Financial Performance
After a few years of flat or declining revenue FirstMerit reported growth of more than 40% in 2013 as revenue hit $1 billion. In addition net income was up almost an equal amount topping $180 million. Those results were powered primarily by the 2013 acquisition of Citizens Republic Bancorp which doubled the bank's number of branches and extended its reach into new markets. On the strength of the acquisition total interest income rose 50% year-over-year; non-interest income grew by a slightly more modest 20%.

The company's net income has been on a strong growth trajectory over the past five years more than doubling since 2009. Cash flow from operations has been on a similar path jumping from about $90 million in 2009 to $173 million in 2013.

Strategy

FirstMerit emphasizes relationship banking and local decision-making with credit authority appropriate to specific markets and branches staffed by bankers with deep community ties. In 2013 it was focused on both organic growth and acquisitions. Organically that year the company saw commercial loan production in legacy markets grow 14%. The transformational event of the year however was the purchase of Citizens Republic.

Mergers and Acquisitions
In April 2013 FirstMerit completed the acquisition of Flint Michigan-based Citizens Republic Bancorp for $912 million in stock. The deal which is the largest in FirstMerit's history doubled its branch locations and ATM network strengthened its presence in northeastern Ohio and expanded its operations into Michigan and Wisconsin. The company completed its brand roll-out by mid-2013 and had converted operating systems in the new branches by year's end.

EXECUTIVES

Executive Vice President Human, Christopher J (Chris) Maurer, age 65
Executive Vice President; Chief Risk Officer, Judith A (Judy) Steiner, age 52
Senior Executive Vice President & Chief Financial Officer, Terrence E. Bichsel, age 64, $387,125 total compensation
President and CEO Akron Region, Nicholas V. Browning
Executive Vice President; Treasurer, Mark N. DuHamel
Chairman President and CEO FirstMerit and FirstMerit Bank, Paul G. Greig, age 58, $791,250 total compensation
President and CEO Columbus Region, Sue E. Zazon
SVP and Chief Marketing Officer, Julie C. Tutkovics
EVP & CIO, Mark D. Quinlan, age 53
EVP and Chief Credit Officer, William P. (Bill) Richgels, age 63, $387,125 total compensation
EVP of Retail, N. James (Jim) Brocklehurst
Senior Executive Vice President Chief Commercial Banking Officer, David G. Goodall, $326,000 total compensation
Executive Vice President Wealth Management Services, Michael G. Robinson
Vice Chairman FirstMerit Corporation; Chairman and CEO FirstMerit Michigan, Sandra L. Pierce
Assistant Vice President Database Network Infrastructure, Eric Kruse
Svp; Head Asset-based Lending And Secured Lending, Douglas K Winget
Vp Commercial Banking Toledo, Rob A Thomas
Vp Relationship Manager Cleveland Commercial Region, Anthony J Yannucci
Executive Vice President, Joseph Dolan
Exec V Pres-chief Legal Office, Carlton Langer
Assistant Vice President Branch Mgr, Victor Navarro
Assistant Vice President Manager, Jeffrey Lane
Senior Vice President, Michael Amon
Senior Vice President And Team Leader Commercial Banking, James Eckelberry
Vice President, Michael Mason
Vice President, Manjit Khuban
Vice President And Client Advisor, Linda Litman
Vice President It Project Management Office, Sharon Sciaulino
Senior Vice President Regional Business Banking Team Leader, Mike Kramer
Vice President Network Services, John Diller
Treasury Management Vice President, Marc Cesere
Assistant Vice President Portfolio, Donna Ditirro
Vice President Financial Reporting, Terry Rogers

Senior Vice President, Mary Patton

Vice President, Mona Sarkar

Senior Vice President Manager Hc Finance Group, Ken Sinha

Vice President Associate Legal Counsel, Stephen Macek

Assistant Vice President, Cheryl Uher

Vice President Director Of Commercial Marketing Channel Management, Jay Dobkowski

Vice President Systems Manager Strategic Information Group, Douglas Turner

Vice President Client Advisor, Annita Bradley

Executive Vice President Director Of Retail Banking, Jim Brocklehurst

Senior Vice President, Daniel Waldeck

Vice President, Mark Seryak

Senior Vice President, James Rudolph

Vice President Assistant Counsel, Elizabeth Curtis

Vice President Abl Relationship Manager, Lynn Gruber

Vice President Compliance, Benjamin Flaker

Senior Vice President Private Banking, Kristine Movsesian

Senior Vice President, Dave Izzo

Vice President Financial Reporting, Mike Woods

Vice President Finance, Steven Lick

Senior Vice President, Timothy Fossa

Vice President, Norman Lange

Assistant Vice President Of Marketing, Deborah Ross

Assistant Vice President Dealer Wi, David Oswald

Group Manager Senior Vice President, June Courtney

Assistant Vice President, Phil Long

Vice President Business Banking, Steve Vandette

Vice President Private Banker, Mark Blaser

Vice President Mgr Consumer, Murray James

Vice President And Manager Direct Marketing And Corporate Sponsorships, Beth Rimmel

Vice President Treasury Management, Lindsey Devar

Vice President Customer Service, Lynn Myers

Vice President Sales, Jane McKean

Senior Vice President District Manager, Tom Jalette

Vice President Corporate Accounting, Carol Baskey

Executive Vice President, Sheldon Bernstein

Senior Vice President, Dave Humbel

Executive Vice President, Robert Morlan

Vice President Buy Here And Pay Here, John Zelenka

Senior Vice President, Robert Stark

Vice President Total Rewards, Jennifer Steffes

Senior Vice President Govt Banking Div, Jack Bolender

Vice President Treasury Management, Alison Kavulich

Vice President, Thomas Heidy

Senior Vice President, Tom Maxwell

Vice President, Michelle Del Rio-keller

Vice President, Joleen Cicchinelli

Vice President, Joe Pelle

Senior Vice President Of Marketing, Eugene Lucci

Vice President Business Banking Relationship Manager, Donna Wells

Senior Vice President Risk Management, Michelle Holman

Senior Vice President And Compliance Manager, Tina Shaver

Vice President Systems Development Group, Amy Fadeley

Assistant Vice President Private Banker, Heather Schlegel

Vice President Corporate Accounting, Jane Litz

Senior Vice President Cmcl Banking, Matthew Stefani

Sr Vice President Corp Cmny, Norman Bliss

Senior Vice President ?? Managed Assets, Sterling Morris

Vice President Commercial Banking, Phillip Hohler

Vice President, Dennis Hodges

Vice President Commercial Ptflo Mgr, Robb Lightell

Vice President Firstmerit Bank, Mark Freeman

Vice President Manager Direct Consumer Underwriting, Michael Gulitz

Vice President Commercial Banking, Christopher Greco

Senior Vice President Franchise Finance, Merrilee Rojas

Branch Manager Asst Vice President, Jamie Patrasso

Vice President, Anil A Merrani

Senior Vice President Total Rewards, Matthew Majernik

Assistant Vice President Treasury, Noreen Ajmal

Assistant Vice President, Kenneth Gla

Vice President, Keith Creech

Senior Vice President Business Banking, Ronald Hongosh

Vice President Business Development, Jason Hanes

Senior Vice President, Doug Houser

Branch Manager Assistant Vice President, Michelle Johnson

Senior Vice President, Wendy Bolas

Vice President, Linda Kemp

Senior Vice President Director Of Operations, W Manning

Vice President Ccc Inbound Team Leader, Kelli Olsick

Retail Communications Manager Vp, Julie Hungerford

Senior Vice President Commercial Real, Jeffrey Schuman

Senior Vice President, Karl Durant

Senior Vice President Regional Managed, Mark Hunt

Vice President Branch Manager And Small, Stephen Miles

Senior Vice President Commercial, Helen Pennington

Executive Vice President And Division, William Stoll

Vice President Small Business Credit, Doug Fleenor

Senior Vice President Commercial, Kenneth Kosin

Executive Vice President, Joe Palazzolo

Vice President Retail Lending Midwest, Norma Fabela

Senior Vice President Commercial Real, John Spear

Senior Vice President Human Resources, Mary Ceas

Vice President And Banking Center, Mike Hutton

Senior Vice President Operations, David Steinhoff

Senior Vice President Commercial, David Natzke

Assistant Vice President, Eva Cryan

Vice President Of Marketing And Retail, Christian Schoenberger

Branch Manager Vice President, Todd Crysler

Vice President, Donald Woods

Senior Vice President Retail Credit, Thomas Lundberg

Senior Vice President, Robert Rood

Vice President Specialty Loan Servicing, Debra Dombos

Vice President Of Network Services, Joe Vincent

Executive Vice President, Tom O'Malley

Branch Manager Iii Vice President, Jaime Darwin

Senior Vice President, Jillian Price

Vice President, Michael Sommerfeld

Chairman President and CEO FirstMerit and FirstMerit Bank, Paul G. Greig, age 58

Vice Chairman FirstMerit Corporation; Chairman and CEO FirstMerit Michigan, Sandra L. Pierce

Auditors: Ernst&YoungLLP

LOCATIONS

HQ: FirstMerit Corp
III Cascade Plaza, 7th Floor, Akron, OH 44308
Phone: 330 996-6300
Web: www.firstmerit.com

2013 Branch Locations

	No.
Ohio	156
Michigan	153
Wisconsin	47
Illinois	44
Pennsylvania	4
Total	**404**

PRODUCTS/OPERATIONS

2013 Sales

	$ mil.	% of total
Interest		
Loans	635.9	61
Investment securities	129.9	13
Noninterest		
Service charges on deposits	74.4	7
Credit card fees	50.5	5
Trust department	34.8	3
Loan sales & servicing	23.1	2
ATM & other service fees	19.1	2
Bank-owned life insurance	16.9	2
Investment services & insurance	12.8	1
Other	41.5	4
Investment securities losses net	(2.8)	—
Total	**1036.1**	**100**

Selected Subsidiaries

Citizens Savings Corporation of Stark County
FirstMerit Bank National Association
   FirstMerit Advisors Inc.
   FirstMerit Equipment Finance Inc.
   FirstMerit Financial Services Inc.
   FirstMerit Insurance Agency Inc.
   FirstMerit Insurance Group Inc.
   FirstMerit Mortgage Corporation
   FirstMerit Mortgage Reinsurance Company Inc.
   FirstMerit-Moss Creek Ventures LLC
   FirstMerit Securities Inc.
   FirstMerit Title Agency Ltd.
   Midwest Financial and Investment Services Inc.
FirstMerit Community Development Corporation

COMPETITORS

Associated Banc-Corp	PNC Financial
Fifth Third	Park National
First Midwest Bancorp	Peoples Bancorp (OH)
Harris	TFS Financial
Huntington Bancshares	U.S. Bancorp
JPMorgan Chase	Wells Fargo
KeyCorp	Wintrust Financial
MB Financial	

HISTORICAL FINANCIALS

Company Type: Public

Income Statement

FYE: December 31

	ASSETS ($ mil.)	NET INCOME ($ mil.)	INCOME AS % OF ASSETS	EMPLOYEES
12/13	23,909.0	183.6	0.8%	4,570
12/12	14,913.0	134.1	0.9%	2,836
12/11	14,441.7	119.5	0.8%	3,177
12/10	14,136.9	102.9	0.7%	3,058
12/09	10,539.9	82.1	0.8%	2,495
Annual Growth	22.7%	22.3%	—	16.3%

2013 Year-End Financials

Return on assets: 0.9%
Return on equity: 8.4%
Long-term debt ($ mil.): —
No. of shares (mil.): 165
Sales ($ mil): 1,036

Dividends
Yield: 2.8%
Payout: 53.7%
Market value ($ mil.): 3,669

	STOCK PRICE ($) FY Close	P/E High/Low		PER SHARE ($) Earnings	Dividends	Book Value
12/13	22.23	20	12	1.18	0.64	16.38
12/12	14.19	14	11	1.22	0.64	15.00
12/11	15.13	18	9	1.10	0.64	14.33
12/10	19.79	24	16	1.02	0.64	13.86
12/09	20.14	24	14	0.90	0.77	12.25
Annual Growth	2.5%	—	—	7.0%	(4.5%)	7.5%

FleetCor Technologies Inc

Helping companies manage motor fleets is at the core of FleetCor's mission. The company is a leading provider of fleet cards and payment processing services aimed at commercial and government fleets. Its cards carry the names Fuelman CFN Mannatec Keyfuels CCS and Fuelcard. The fleet cards function like typical charge cards and can be used to purchase fuel and lodging. FleetCor tracks purchases in order to help manage employee spending. The company serves more than 500000 accounts and has more than 2 million cards active in Africa Asia Europe and North America. Major customers include oil giants BP Chevron and Shell. FleetCor is expanding rapidly at home and abroad via acquisitions.

Geographic Range

North America accounts for about half of Georgia-based FleetCor's sales. Beyond North America the company does business in some 40 countries in Africa Europe (including Russia) Latin America Australia and New Zealand.

Financial Performance

FleetCor's sales jumped 27% in 2013 versus 2012 to $895.2 million. Net income rose by nearly a third over the same period to $284.5 million. The fast-growing company credited the double-digit gain to growth in payment programs driven primarily by increases in both volume and revenue per transaction. The North American business segment's revenue increased due to the impact of higher fuel spread margins partially offset by lower fuel prices in the US. International revenue increased due to organic growth in payment programs and the impact of multiple acquisitions completed during 2013 and 2012.

Indeed since FleetCor went public in 2010 it has posted steep and steady gains in sales and profits while cash flow from operations has fluctuated significantly.

Strategy

The rapidly expanding company plans to consolidate the industry further by targeting smaller and regional fleet service providers in markets it currently serves and in new markets overseas. Indeed FleetCor is on an international acquisitions spree snapping up companies in growing markets in Europe Asia and Latin America. (Over the past two years International sales have grown from about a third of total revenue to account for nearly half.) After entering Russia and Brazil in 2012 the company entered Australian and New Zealand in 2013 via acquisitions in those two countries.

Mergers and Acquisitions

In August 2014 FleetCor purchased Comdata Inc. from Ceridian LLC for $3.45 billion to expand in payments. The deal allows FleetCor to dramatically expand in North America and enter the business of virtual bank-card payments.

In October 2013 the fuel card company purchased NexTraq a US-based provider of telematics services to small and medium-sized businesses. Atlanta-based NexTraq's Internet-based system seeks to enhance workforce productivity through real time vehicle tracking route optimization job dispatch and fuel usage monitoring. In September 2013 FleetCor acquired VB Servicos Comercio e Administracao LTDA (VB) a provider of transportation cards and vouchers in Brazil.

In 2012 the company entered the Brazil market with its acquisition of CTF Technologies for $180 million. CTF provides fuel payment processing in Brazil.

IPO

Founded in 2000 FleetCor went public in December 2010 via an initial public offering that raised about $290 million. The proceeds went to FleetCor's private equity shareholders Advent International Bain Capital and Summit Partners.

EXECUTIVES

Evice President Strategic Partnerships, H S Smith
Chief Executive Officer Chairman of the Board of Directors, Ronald F. (Ron) Clarke, age 58
CFO, Eric R. Dey, age 54
President - North American Partner Business, William J. (Bill) Schmit, age 57
President Petroleum Marketer Private Label Programs, Benton C. Routh
CEO FleetCor Europe, Andrew Blazye
Chief Operating Officer; President - U.S. Direct Business, Todd W. House, age 42
Executive Vice President Global Universal ProductsRobert, Robert P. Brandes, age 53
President - Corporate Lodging Consultants, Timothy J. Downs, age 56
President, Charles R. Freund
EVP of Global Products, Jeffrey D. Lamb
Executive Vice President Corporate Development, John S. Coughlin
Chief Information Officer, John A. Reed
Managing Director FleetCor Canada, Patrick Ducharme
CEO FleetCor Brazil, Armando Netto
EVP Corporate Development, Ali Ashurov
Senior Vice President Business Development, Scott Ruoff
Vice President Development And Strategy, Keith Lynn
Vice President Of Marketing Fuelman, Pamela Bartz
Senior Vice President Strategic Marketing, Ron Rogers
Vice President Us Infrastructure, Donald Basemore
Vice President Strategic Marketing, Krystl Black
Vice President Merchant Services, Jim Prantl
Vice President Global Credit Strategy, Ashley Thekkekara
National Account Manager, Barbara Mitchell
Vice President Of Strategic Relationships, John Leitner
Vp, H Smith
Senior Vice President Central Operations, Ken Grenway

Vice President Online And Direct Marketing, Susan Fischer
National Sales Manager, Brett Whitlock
Senior Vice President Sales, Andrea Pearson
Vice President Marketing, Robin Gregg
Vice President New Product Development, John Antos
Vice President Global Human Resources, Crystal Williams
Vice President Of Information Technology, Erik Hymel
Senior Vice President Sales And Marketing, Paul Citarella
Vice President Business Development, John Ryan
Senior Vice President Product Management And Engineering, Oliver Chang
Vice President Call Centers, Ken Kliment
Vice President Product Management, John Young
Vice President Corporate Development, James Howle
Vice President Business Development, Steve Greene
Vice President Product Management, Wes Williams
Vice President Of Partner Business Solutions International Corporate Development, David Jones
Auditors: Ernst&YoungLLP

LOCATIONS

HQ: FleetCor Technologies Inc
5445 Triangle Parkway, Norcross, GA 30092
Phone: 770 449-0479
Web: www.fleetcor.com

2013 Sales

	$ mil.	% of total
North America	460.7	51
Other	434.5	49
Total	**895.2**	**100**

PRODUCTS/OPERATIONS

Selected Brands and Subsidiaries

CCS
CFN Holding Co.
CLC Group
Corporate Lodging Consultants Inc.
FleetCards
FleetNet
Fuelman
The Fuelcard Company
Fuel Vend Limited
Keyfuels
Mannatec Inc.
Transit Card

COMPETITORS

Arval
Comdata
Edenred
Multi Service

Retail Decisions
Sodexo USA
U.S. Bancorp
WEX

HISTORICAL FINANCIALS

Company Type: Public

Income Statement

FYE: December 31

	REVENUE ($ mil.)	NET INCOME ($ mil.)	NET PROFIT MARGIN	EMPLOYEES
12/13	895.1	284.5	31.8%	3,500
12/12	707.5	216.2	30.6%	2,650
12/11	519.5	147.3	28.4%	2,130
12/10	433.8	107.9	24.9%	1,197
12/09	354.0	89.0	25.2%	1,130
Annual Growth	**26.1%**	**33.7%**	**—**	**32.7%**

2013 Year-End Financials

Debt ratio: 28.9%	No. of shares (mil.): 82	
Return on equity: 26.3%	Dividends	
Cash ($ mil.): 338	Yield: —	
Current ratio: 0.71	Payout: —	
Long-term debt ($ mil.): 474	Market value ($ mil.): 9,663	

	STOCK PRICE ($) FY Close	P/E High/Low	PER SHARE ($) Earnings	Dividends	Book Value
12/13	117.17	35 15	3.36	0.00	15.08
12/12	53.65	21 12	2.52	0.00	11.28
12/11	29.87	20 14	1.76	0.00	9.91
12/10	30.92	10 9	1.34	0.00	7.86
Annual Growth	**55.9%**	—	**35.9%**	—	**24.3%**

Flotek Industries Inc

Flotek Industries works to keep oil and gas flowing. The company provides the chemicals and logistical services required in the cementing and stimulation of oil and gas wells. (Cementing holds well casings in place; stimulation opens up cracks in the earth to allow for the easier flow of oil.) Flotek also provides drilling equipment used in cementing and stimulation as well as Petrovalve downhole pump valves (used to pump off the liquids in gas wells in a process known as artificial lift) and Spidle Turbeco (drilling tools motors and casing accessories). The company markets its products throughout the US and is expanding into international markets.

Geographic Reach

The company operates 30 manufacturing and warehouse facilities in eight US states. The US is Flotek's largest single market accounting for 87% of the company's revenue in 2012.

Operations

Flotek operates in three segments: Chemical and Logistics Drilling Products and Artificial Lift. In the Chemical and Logistics segment Specialty Chemicals makes and markets specialty chemicals used in oil and gas well cementing stimulation acidizing drilling and production. The Logistics unit manages automated material handling loading facilities and blending capabilities for oilfield services firms.

The Drilling segment rents inspects makes and markets downhole drilling equipment used in energy mining water well and industrial drilling activities.

Artificial Lift sells artificial lift equipment including rod pump components electric submersible pumps gas separators valves and services that support oil and gas production.

Sales and Marketing

Products are marketed directly to customers through Flotek's own direct sales force and contractual agency arrangements. The company markets products and services through third party agents as well as via direct sales in Asia Canada Central America Mexico the Middle East and South America.

Financial Performance

Flotek's revenues increased by 21% in 2012 due to increased sales to new and existing chemical customers of patented complex nano-fluidᴬᵐ (CnFᴬ®) technologies (which increased sales volumes of stimulation additives) and a growth in market share of centralizer products and float

equipment. A key driver in the increase of sales was growing customer demand for Flotek's oil tools resulting from the continued shift away from gas-focused drilling in North America to oil-directed drilling in response to low gas prices.

Net income grew by 88% in 2012 primarily due to higher sales a gain on the disposal of long-lived assets and increased interest expense.

With the exception of a recession-driven revenue slump in 2009 Flotek saw an upward trend in revenues from 2008 to 2012.

Strategy

With a eye towards growing its position as a global provider of oilfield specialty chemicals and logistics drilling and production tools to the energy and mining industries Flotek seeks to expand into new geographic markets and keep offering innovative products.

In 2013 the company signed a Letter of Intent with an affiliate of Gulf Energy LLC a leading Oman-based diversified oil and gas entity to build an advanced oilfield chemistry production plant and create a modern research and development organization to address the growing need for advanced oilfield chemistry and analysis in the Middle East and North Africa.

In 2011 Flotek introduced a hydraulic fracturing chemical (in strong demand in the burgeoning shale oil and gas developments across the US) that replaces traditional chemicals with an extract from orange peels turning the toxins/water mixture into a sweet-smelling blend.

Growing its international profile in 2011 Flotek chemicals were used in unconventional gas completions in France Poland and Turkey.

EXECUTIVES

Chairman President and CEO, Jerry D. Dumas, age 79, $450,000 total compensation
President, John W. Chisholm, age 59, $5,538 total compensation
EVP of Operations, Steven A. (Steve) Reeves, age 63, $275,000 total compensation
President Chemical and Logistics Segment, Todd Sanner
EVP and CFO, H. Richard Walton
Chief Information Officer, Robert Bodnar
Vice President Sales Mkt For Cesi Chem, Richard Fox
Senior Vice President Of Operations, Beth Thibodeaux
Vice President Strategic Chemical Innovations, Jeff Chang
Executive Vice President Research And Development, Joshua Snively
Vice President Of Business Development For Florida Chemical And Fc Pro Division, David Acker
Senior Vice President Of Sales And Product Development For Florida Chemical Division, Mark Henneberry
Senior Vice President Sales Downhole Tool Group, Don Bellinger
Vice President Human Resources, J Kulina
Vice President And Corporate Controller, Robert Schmitz
Senior Vice President Flavors And Fragrances Florida Chemical Division, Jon Leonard
Chairman President and CEO, Jerry D. Dumas, age 79
Auditors: UHYLLP

LOCATIONS

HQ: Flotek Industries Inc
10603 W. Sam Houston Parkway N., Suite 300, Houston, TX 77064
Phone: 713 849-9911 **Fax:** 713 896-4511
Web: www.flotekind.com

2012 Sales

	$ mil.	% of total
US	272.9	87
Other countries	39.9	13
Total	**312.8**	**100**

PRODUCTS/OPERATIONS

2012 Sales

	$ mil.	% of total
Chemicals & Logistics	184.0	59
Drilling Products	116.7	37
Artificial Lifts	12.1	4
Total	**312.8**	**100**

Selected Products

Specialty Chemicals
  Acidizing cementing and fracturing chemicals for oil and gas wells
Equipment Manufacturing
  Acid pump vehicles
  Bulk material handling facilities contracting
  Cement mixing units
  Hydraulic fracturing blenders
  Nitrogen equipment units
Downhole Equipment
  Downhole pumps valves
  Rigid centralizers
Chemical and Logistics
CESI Chemical
  Stimulation Chemicals
  Cementing Chemicals
  IOR
Sooner Energy Services
  Production Chemicals
  Drilling Chemicals
  Coil Tubing Chemicals
MTI
  Logistics Management
  Drilling Products
Teledrift
  Survey & Measurement Drilling Tools
Spidle Turbeco
  Downhole Drilling Tools
  CAVO Drilling Motors
  Casing Accessories
Galleon Turbeco
  Blast Hole Drilling Tools
  Underground
Artificial Lift
Flotek Pump Services
  Electrical Submersible Pumps
  Sucker Rod Pumps
  Oilfield Products
Petrovalve
  Rod Pump Valve
  Traveling Valve
  Cages
  Standing Valve

COMPETITORS

Baker Hughes	Lubrizol
CARBO Ceramics	Nalco Energy Services
Cameron International	Natural Gas Services
Champion Technologies	Schlumberger
FMC Technologies	Weatherford
FTS International	International
GE Oil	

HISTORICAL FINANCIALS

Company Type: Public

Income Statement

FYE: December 31

	REVENUE ($ mil.)	NET INCOME ($ mil.)	NET PROFIT MARGIN	EMPLOYEES
12/14	449.1	53.6	11.9%	561
12/13	371.0	36.1	9.7%	487
12/12	312.8	49.7	15.9%	405
12/11	258.7	31.4	12.1%	379
12/10	146.9	(43.4)	—	312
Annual Growth	32.2%	—	—	15.8%

2014 Year-End Financials

Debt ratio: 10.4%	No. of shares (mil.): 53
Return on equity: 19.2%	Dividends
Cash ($ mil.): 1	Yield: —
Current ratio: 2.74	Payout: —
Long-term debt ($ mil.): 25	Market value ($ mil.): 999

	STOCK PRICE ($) FY Close	P/E High/Low		PER SHARE ($) Earnings	Dividends	Book Value
12/14	18.73	33	16	0.97	0.00	5.73
12/13	20.07	34	17	0.67	0.00	4.82
12/12	12.20	14	8	0.97	0.00	3.12
12/11	9.96	18	7	0.56	0.00	1.59
12/10	5.45	—	—	(1.94)	0.00	(0.10)
Annual Growth	36.2%	—	—	—	—	—

Fonar Corp.

SONAR finds objects hidden under the water using sound waves; FONAR uses magnetic resonance imaging (MRI) to find disease or injury hidden inside the body. The company was the first to market a commercial MRI scanner in 1980 and it is trying to stay at the forefront of the field. Its primary products include the Upright MRI which scans patients in sitting standing or bending positions and the FONAR 360 a room-sized MRI. Both systems do away with the claustrophobia-producing enclosed tubes of traditional machines. Additionally FONAR's Health Management Corporation of America (HMCA) subsidiary provides management services to more than 20 diagnostic imaging centers primarily in Florida and New York.

Operations

The company divides its operations between medical equipment and managing imaging centers. Though it touts its MRI machines the most center management actually brings the bulk of revenue - 70%.

Despite being first to market the company has struggled against larger competitors (such as GE Healthcare and Toshiba). The company is banking on the success of its Upright MRI and marketing the product aggressively to hospitals and private imaging centers. It is especially touting the machine's ability to image weight-bearing conditions that are not apparent when patients lie down.

Geographic Reach

FONAR has its headquarters in New York with operations in the Netherlands Germany the UK Libya Spain Puerto Rico Switzerland Canada Australia and Greece. Its MRIs are installed across the globe in North America Europe and Asia. The majority of its revenues come from the US.

Financial Performance

In 2013 FONAR's revenue increased 25% based on a bump in patient fees after it acquired MRI center manager Health Diagnostic Management in 2013. Net income also climbed by 50% due to the increase in revenue.

Strategy

The company has primarily been focused on software upgrades for its MRI scanners. It also plans to upgrade and expand the imaging centers it manages. FONAR has also been growing its practice management business.

Mergers and Acquisitions

As part of its strategy to expand its management business in 2013 FONAR purchased Health Diagnostic Management. The company includes about a dozen MRI imaging centers in New York and Florida.

Background

Dr. Raymond V. Damadian —the company's chairman president and founder —is widely acknowledged as one of the inventors of medical MRI technology.

EXECUTIVES

Senior Vice President, Jay Butterman
Vice President Advertising, Tom Attea
Auditors: Marcum&KliegmanLLP

LOCATIONS

HQ: Fonar Corp.
110 Marcus Drive, Melville, NY 11747
Phone: 631 694-2929
Web: www.fonar.com

PRODUCTS/OPERATIONS

2013 Sales

	$ mil.	% of total
Imaging center management	34.2	70
Medical equipment	14.9	30
Total	49.1	100

COMPETITORS

Esaote	RadNet
GE Healthcare	Siemens Healthcare
Hitachi	Toshiba
Philips Electronics	

HISTORICAL FINANCIALS

Company Type: Public

Income Statement

FYE: June 30

	REVENUE ($ mil.)	NET INCOME ($ mil.)	NET PROFIT MARGIN	EMPLOYEES
06/14	68.5	10.4	15.2%	430
06/13	49.1	8.6	17.7%	411
06/12	39.4	5.7	14.6%	244
06/11	33.1	3.1	9.5%	214
06/10	31.8	(3.0)	—	238
Annual Growth	21.1%	—	—	15.9%

2014 Year-End Financials

Debt ratio: 14.8%	No. of shares (mil.): 6
Return on equity: 52.7%	Dividends
Cash ($ mil.): 9	Yield: —
Current ratio: 2.02	Payout: —
Long-term debt ($ mil.): 8	Market value ($ mil.): 78

	STOCK PRICE ($) FY Close	P/E High/Low		PER SHARE ($) Earnings	Dividends	Book Value
06/14	12.20	16	3	1.58	0.00	3.94
06/13	6.56	6	2	1.34	0.00	2.22
06/12	4.10	7	2	0.91	0.00	0.79
06/11	1.96	5	2	0.55	0.00	(0.24)
06/10	1.47	—	—	(0.61)	0.00	(1.08)
Annual Growth	69.7%	—	—	—	—	—

Forestar Group Inc

Forestar Group aims to make five-star investments in real estate mineral resources and wood fiber resources. The company owns approximately 150000 acres of real estate most of it undeveloped land in high-growth markets in about 10 states. It sells residential lots primarily to national or regional home builders for mid-priced single-family homes. The company has about 90 residential and commercial properties completed under development or in the entitlement process mostly in Texas and in the Atlanta area. The company also owns a handful of income-producing multifamily properties. In addition Forestar owns some 600000 net acres of oil and gas mineral interests in Texas Louisiana Alabama and Georgia.

Forestar also holds a significant minority interest in groundwater drawn for commercial purposes on some 1.5 million acres in those states.

The company's real estate segment accounts for about 80% of sales. Its real estate earnings come from land and property sales —by taking land from its raw state through the entitlement and development process the company is able to earn a premium on sales —as well as from income-producing properties. Mineral resources the second-largest segment accounts for nearly 20% of sales. The company's fiber resources segment the smallest encompasses the sale of wood fiber taken from the company's land holdings and the leasing of land for recreational uses.

Forestar's revenues grew 34% in 2011 to $135.6 million while profits rose 40% to $7.2 million. The growth was primarily attributed to an increase in land sales although offset by $45.2 million of non-cash impairment charges related to certain acquisitions. Mineral resources earnings were largely flat and fiber resource earnings declined as a result of lower harvests after sales of more than 200000 acres of timberland since 2008.

In 2012 Forestar bought oil and gas exploration company CREDO Petroleum for $146 million in a deal that more than doubled its proven oil and natural gas reserves holdings. Most of CREDO's revenues come from lease payments and royalties from some 470 producing wells owned by third parties. The acquisition includes significant holdings in North Dakota's Bakken and Three Forks considered among the hottest oil fields in the US.

In 2011 Forestar sold some 50000 acres of timberland in Georgia and Alabama to Plum Creek Timber Company for $75 million. The firm has been selling off noncore land in those areas in order to boost shareholder value in the company. In total Forestar sold about 169000 acres raising $270 million. The company also sold more than 1000 developed residential lots nearly 40% more than sold in 2010.

On the other hand the firm competes with other investors to buy develop and sell real estate. Forestar seeks to buy land in areas that are expected to see population growth in the future. In terms of mineral interests the company works to move its land holdings up the value chain by increasing acreage leased and the size of royalty interests.

EXECUTIVES

Chief Real Estate Officer, Bruce F. Dickson, age 61, $312,500 total compensation

CFO and Treasurer, Christopher L. (Chris) Nines, age 42, $278,000 total compensation

President CEO and Director, James M. (Jim) DeCosmo, age 55, $550,000 total compensation

Chief Investment Officer Real Estate, Craig A. Knight, age 66, $350,000 total compensation

EVP Real Estate Acquisitions, John Pierret

EVP Western Region Investment and Development, Tom Burleson

EVP Chief Administrative Officer General Counsel and Secretary, David M. Grimm, age 54, $257,000 total compensation

EVP Oil and Gas Business Administration, Charles D. (Chuck) Jehl, age 46

EVP Eastern Region Investment and Development, Michael Quinley

Chief Oil and Gas Officer, Flavious J. Smith, $333,333 total compensation

EVP Multifamily, Charles T. (Tom) Etheredge, age 52, $225,000 total compensation

EVP Water Resources; Chairman Real Estate Investment Committee, Phillip J. (Phil) Weber, $310,000 total compensation

SVP Fiber Resources Land Management, Jeff Portwood

Svp-corporate Affairs, Anna E Torma

Vice President - Multifamily Construction, Greg Schmittou

Vp, Tavia McCuean

Executive Vice President, Shelly Ro

Vice President Land Northern Division, Kevin Donohue

Vice President, Larry Long

Vice President Multifamily Construction, Dwayne Brown

Vice President Of Engineering And Development, Randy McCuistion

Vice President Legal And Senior Real Estate Counsel, Chuck Olderman

Vice President Accounting And Principal, Sabita Reddy

Senior Vice President Land Management, Charles J Portwood

Senior Vice President - Multifamily Acquisitions, Wayne McDonald

Vice President Multifamily Development, Brad Walters

Vice President Environmental Assets And Compliance, William Goodrum

Chairman, Kenneth M. (Kenny) Jastrow, age 67

President CEO and Director, James M. (Jim) DeCosmo, age 55

EVP Chief Administrative Officer General Counsel and Secretary, David M. Grimm, age 54

Board Member, Carl Thomason

Auditors: Ernst&YoungLLP

LOCATIONS

HQ: Forestar Group Inc
6300 Bee Cave Road, Building Two, Suite 500, Austin, TX 78746
Phone: 512 433-5200
Web: www.forestargroup.com

PRODUCTS/OPERATIONS

2011 Sales

	$ mil.	% of total
Real estate		
Sales	77.9	57
Income-producing properties & other	28.3	21
Mineral resources	24.6	18
Fiber resources & other	4.8	4
Total	**135.6**	**100**

COMPETITORS

Belz	Hines
Cencor Realty	LGI Development
Crescent Resources	Schlosser Development
Hillwood	

HISTORICAL FINANCIALS

Company Type: Public

Income Statement

FYE: December 31

	REVENUE ($ mil.)	NET INCOME ($ mil.)	NET PROFIT MARGIN	EMPLOYEES
12/13	331.0	29.3	8.9%	145
12/12	172.5	12.9	7.5%	130
12/11	135.5	7.1	5.3%	101
12/10	101.3	5.1	5.1%	92
12/09	146.2	59.1	40.4%	93
Annual Growth	22.7%	(16.1%)	—	11.7%

2013 Year-End Financials

Debt ratio: 30.4%
Return on equity: 4.7%
Cash ($ mil.): 192
Current ratio: 2.81
Long-term debt ($ mil.): 357

No. of shares (mil.): 34
Dividends
Yield: —
Payout: —
Market value ($ mil.): 739

	STOCK PRICE ($) FY Close	P/E High/Low	Earnings	PER SHARE ($) Dividends	Book Value
12/13	21.27	30 21	0.80	0.00	20.43
12/12	17.33	49 30	0.36	0.00	15.29
12/11	15.13	102 50	0.20	0.00	14.72
12/10	19.30	167 98	0.14	0.00	14.37
12/09	21.98	14 4	1.64	0.00	14.22
Annual Growth	(0.8%)	— —	(16.4%)	—	9.5%

Fortinet Inc

Fortinet secures the fortress against Internet marauders. The company makes network security appliances (sold under its FortiGate line) and software that integrate antivirus firewall content filtering intrusion prevention systems (IPS) and antispam functions to protect against computer viruses worms and inappropriate Web content. Its FortiGuard subscription services offer continuous updates on all new threats to provide real-time network protection. The company also offers complementary products that include its FortiManager security management and FortiAnalyzer event analysis systems.

Geographic Reach

Fortinet's largest geographic segment is the Americas which accounts for about 40% of revenues. The EMEA (Europe Middle East and Africa) segment accounts for about 35% of sales while the Asia/Pacific region accounts for the remainder.

The company operates sales and service offices in about 30 countries worldwide.

Operations

While service revenues –an important source of recurring income –account for a little more than half of sales product revenues have taken an increasingly important place in Fortinet's earnings as well. The company's products and services are used by companies in a variety of industrie including retail education telecom health care manufacturing and financial services.

Sales and Marketing

Through more than 10000 channel partners (distributors and resellers) Fortinet estimates that it has shipped more than 1.1 million appliances to 150000 end-user customers (including small businesses enterprises government entities and service providers) from its inception through the end of 2012. The company directly sells its products to distributors including Arrow Electronics Ingram Micro and Tech Data.

Financial Performance

Fortinet has experienced exponential revenue growth in recent years due to increased sales within its services and product segments. A 23% increase in revenues to $534 million in 2012 was driven by higher sales of the FortiGate products due to increased demand from small businesses large enterprises and service providers. Service revenues also increased due to Fortinet's larger customer base for subscription and support contracts.

Fortinet which first achieved profitability in 2008 has grown net income alongside revenues in the year since. Profits in 2012 increased 7% to $67 million on higher revenues and interest income.

Strategy

Fortinet sells its products to distributors and resellers who have significant purchasing power and deployment capabilities while at the same time strengthening its customer support network in high-growth regions. It also works to build a solid base of subscription and service customers.

In addition to expand its product offerings Fortinet conducts research and development efforts to create new software and hardware offerings for customers. The company employs about 600 R&D employees in Canada China and the US and spends some $80 million annually on research projects.

Mergers and Acquisitions

Fortinet acquired enterprise Internet telephony systems maker TalkSwitch in 2011 to expand its product selection and boost its profile in the multiservice gateway market. The company also extended the reach of its sales organization with the purchase; TalkSwitch has relationships with resellers and distributors worldwide. Past acquisitions included the purchase of the assets of IPLocks in 2008 a deal that expanded Fortinet's database security and compliance technologies.

Ownership

Fortinet was founded in 2000 by CEO Ken Xie who also founded leading firewall appliance provider NetScreen Technologies (acquired in 2004 by Juniper Networks). Xie holds an equity stake of nearly 16% in the company. CTO Michael Xie a co-founder of Fortinet and Ken Xie's younger brother owns about 11% of the company.

Fortinet used the proceeds from a 2009 IPO for general corporate purposes product development and to pursue potential acquisitions.

EXECUTIVES

President and CEO, Ken Xie, age 51, $359,375 total compensation

President and CTO, Michael Xie, age 45, $318,800 total compensation
Vice President Marketing, John Maddison
VP International Sales and Support, Patrice Perche
VP Services, Michael Anderson
CFO, Andrew (Drew) Del Matto
Vice President Product Marketing, Patrick Bedwell
Vice President Of Latin America Sales, Pedro Paixao
Vice President Of Enterprise Sales, Pete Brant
Vice President Us Channel Sales, Bryan Woods
Vice President Corporate Development, Rob Atherton
Vice President International, Gerald Delplace
Vice President Financial Services, Francine Panza
Vice President Marketing At Fortinet Inc, Tamir Hardof
National Account Manager, Jackie Kruger
Vice President Us Enterprise Sales, Scott Lewis
President and CEO, Ken Xie, age 51
Board Member, George Hara
Auditors: Deloitte&ToucheLLP

LOCATIONS

HQ: Fortinet Inc
899 Kifer Road, Sunnyvale, CA 94086
Phone: 408 235-7700

2012 Sales

	$ mil.	% of total
Americas	217.0	41
Europe Middle East & Africa (EMEA)	184.2	34
Asia/Pacific	132.4	25
Total	**533.6**	**100**

PRODUCTS/OPERATIONS

2012 Sales

	$ mil.	% of total
Services	274.0	51
Product	249.0	47
Ratable & other	10.6	2
Total	**533.6**	**100**

Selected Products

Database security appliance (FortiDB)
E-mail antispam (FortiMail)
Endpoint security software (FortiClient)
Endpoint vulnerability management appliance (FortiScan)
Network event correlation and content archiving (FortiAnalyzer)
Network security appliances (FortiGate)
Secure wireless access product (FortiAP)
Security management (FortiManager)
Spam and virus control subscription (FortiGuard)
Support (FortiCare)
Web application firewall appliance (FortiWeb)

COMPETITORS

Bivio Networks	Palo Alto Networks
Blue Coat	SRA International
CA Inc.	SonicWALL
Check Point Software	SteelCloud
Cisco Systems	Symantec
F5 Networks	Trend Micro
Fortrex	VeriSign
Infoblox	WatchGuard
Juniper Networks	Technologies
McAfee	e-DMZ Security
Microsoft	zvelo
NetWolves	

HISTORICAL FINANCIALS

Company Type: Public

Income Statement

FYE: December 31

	REVENUE ($ mil.)	NET INCOME ($ mil.)	NET PROFIT MARGIN	EMPLOYEES
12/13	615.3	44.2	7.2%	2,308
12/12	533.6	66.8	12.5%	1,954
12/11	433.5	62.4	14.4%	1,583
12/10	324.7	41.2	12.7%	1,336
12/09	252.1	60.1	23.9%	1,223
Annual Growth	**25.0%**	**(7.4%)**	**—**	**17.2%**

2013 Year-End Financials

Debt ratio: —
Return on equity: 8.0%
Cash ($ mil.): 115
Current ratio: 1.78
Long-term debt ($ mil.): —

No. of shares (mil.): 161
Dividends
  Yield: —
  Payout: —
Market value ($ mil.): 3,090

	STOCK PRICE ($) FY Close	P/E High/Low		PER SHARE ($) Earnings	Dividends	Book Value
12/13	19.13	93	61	0.26	0.00	3.63
12/12	21.02	68	42	0.40	0.00	3.19
12/11	21.81	121	40	0.38	0.00	2.31
12/10	32.35	113	51	0.27	0.00	1.56
12/09	17.57	19	17	0.39	0.00	1.07
Annual Growth	**2.1%**	**—**	**—**	**(9.6%)**	**—**	**35.8%**

Fortress Investment Group LLC

Fortress Investment Group protects its investments. The global investment firm manages private equity and hedge funds for institutional investors wealthy individuals and on its own behalf. Its private equity arm buys long-term controlling stakes in undervalued or distressed companies and credit assets; it also manages real estate investors Newcastle Investment and Eurocastle Investment. The hedge fund arm invests in liquid markets. Fortress offer traditional asset management through Logan Circle Partners. Fortress earns fees performance-based incentive revenues and investment income on its own investments. The firm has more than $62 billion in assets under management (effective April 2014).

Formerly focused solely on alternative investment vehicles Fortress diversified in 2010. It entered the fixed income asset management business when it acquired bond investor Logan Circle Partners. The deal added some $12 billion in assets under management; and allowed Fortress to begin offering its clients a broader range of investments. Now Logan Circle is considered Fortress' traditional asset management arm. It is focused on the organic growth of its existing fixed income business.

Fortress in late 2013 agreed to buy more than 50 senior-housing properties from Holiday Acquisition Holdings for more than $1 billion. It anticipates that rent for the portfolio of 5885 units will equal 6.5% of the purchase price.

In the private equity segment Fortress is known as a garbage collector of sorts; picking up the pieces of companies and assets that no one really wants. Fortress has taken advantage of opportunities to buy bargain assets from troubled firms during the economic downturn. In 2010 alone it purchased the European mortgages and operations of Ally Financial subsidiary ResCap including some 6000 good and bad loans; and about 80% of consumer lender American General Finance from AIG. Fortress also acquired commercial real estate loan servicer CW Financial Services in the hopes of profiting from a recovery in the US real estate market. It then purchased a $7 billion distressed portfolio of life settlement insurance policies from KBC. Fortress is eyeing new investments in the transportation senior living and financial services sectors.

In addition to buying assets Fortress also has been selling. Improvements in the equity markets have allowed Fortress Private Equity to spin off a few of its portfolio companies through IPOS. Nationstar SeaCube Container Leasing and RailAmerica recently entered the public markets. Fortress also has sold its positions in other publicly traded securities as the market improved. The proceeds helped Fortress refinance exisiting debt and obtain other debt financing.

The firm's growth strategy is centered on global expansion. Fortress which was founded in 1998 has 15 offices in North America Europe Australia and Asia. Most recently Fortress has grown in Asia. It has launched new private equity funds there and opened new offices in Singapore and Shanghai.

Fortress weathered the recession and in 2010 it reported strong results thanks to its diversification efforts and improved incentive fee income based on better fund performance. It has been raising capital across all of its funds and in 2011 invested in the regional aircraft asset management operations of defense manufacturer BAE Systems. The deal included 151 regional aircraft and is valued at $187 million.

However market volatility had an impact on Fortress' performance in 2011. Revenues declined by nearly 10% due to lower incentive income and a decrease in other revenues. Profits also declined. But Fortress is focused on the long term. Despite the challenging market the company continued to attract new capital commitments and new clients thanks to its diversified business model. In 2011 Fortress invested more than $3.5 billion on its investors' behalf and began marketing new funds in each of its business lines.

In addition to the challenging market Fortress' walls have been shaken by personnel troubles. Former CEO and board member Daniel Mudd resigned from Fortress in early 2012 while fighting SEC allegations that he'd misled investors during his prior position as CEO of Fannie Mae. The SEC alleged that Mudd hadn't sufficiently disclosed Fannie Mae's risky investments in the subprime market leading up to the housing crash. Mudd had taken the helm of Fortress in 2009 shortly after being ousted from Fannie Mae. Mudd took a leave of absence in late 2011 but stepped down a month later to dedicate his time to the lawsuit.

Fortress' core principals and founders remain at the helm. Co-chairmen Peter Briger and Wesley Edens each own around 13% of the company. Principal and director Michael Novogratz owns more than 12% of Fortress. While interim Interim CEO Randal Nardone and principal and director Robert Kauffman each own about 10%

EXECUTIVES

Managing Director Fortress Investment Group LLC Chief Executive Officer and Chief Investment Officer Logan Circle Partners, Jude T. Driscoll, age 50

Managing Director Fortress Investment Group LLC (UK), Jonathan Ashley, age 48

Managing Director Shanghai, Lilly H. Donohue

Vice President, Youssef M Hayek

Chief Executive Officer Co-Founder Principal and Director, Randal A. Nardone, age 59, $200,000 total compensation

Principal and Director; Co-Chief Investment Officer of the Fortress Macro Fund and the Drawbridge Global Macro Fund, Michael E. Novogratz, age 50, $200,000 total compensation

President Liquid Markets; Senior Managing Director Strategy, Stuart H. (Stu) Bohart, age 48

Managing Director Private Equity Group, Joseph P. Adams, age 57

CFO, Daniel N. Bass, age 48, $200,000 total compensation

Managing Director Chief Executive Officer and Chief Investment Officer Fortress Partners Funds Fortress Investment Group LLC, Alexander M. Cook

Managing Director Co-Chief Investment Officer of the Credit Funds at Fortress Investment Group LLC, Constantine M. (Dean) Dakolias

Managing Director Private Equity and Chief Operating Officer Permanent Capital Business Group, Andrew P. Dempsey

Managing Director President and Chief Operating Officer Credit Funds at Fortress Investment Group LLC, Marc K. Furstein

Managing Director Capital Formation Group, A. Todd Ladda

Managing Director Singapore and Chief Investment Officer Fortress Asia Macro Funds Co-Chief Investment Officer Fortress Macro Funds and Chief Executive Officer Fortress Investment Group (Singapore) Pte. Ltd., Adam J. Levinson

Managing Director San Francisco, Andrew A. McKnight

Managing Director Tokyo Chief Investment Officer Fortress Real Estate (Asia) GK, Thomas W. Pulley

Managing Director Deputy President and Chief Risk Officer Fortress Liquid Markets, Sherif Sweillam

Managing Director Global Chief Operating Officer Liquid Markets Hedge Fund, Louis D. Thorne

Managing Director Credit Funds, Anthony B. Tufariello

Vice President And Senior Asset Manager, Ron Cobb

Vice President Client Service Manager, Michael Greene, age 66

Vice President Vice President, Susan Givens

Vice President Controller, Avi Dreyfuss

Vice President Senior Tax Manager, Dora Dragomanova

Vice President, Randall Shy

Spqrea Vice President, Dana D'Ascoli

Vice President, Peter Leibman

Senior Vice President Head Of Expense Management And Operations, Scott Min

Vice President, James Rous

Vice President Compensation Controller, Paul Petrsoric

Vice President Tax Director, Douglas McKay

Vice President, Nils Wilson

Vice President, Rudy Siva

Vice President, Dan Perkins

Vice President Compensation And Benefits Counsel, Wonda Quinn

Vice President, Lance Sherer

Vice President, Robyn Gewanter

Vice President, Rory Vandamme

Vice President Info Tech Pgm Mgr Pe, Todd Gilbert

Vice President, Maggie Rosengarten

Vice President Regulatory Counsel And Allocations, James Wulffleff

Vice President, Mark Rambler

Vice President, Joe Gould

Senior Vice President Human Resources, Aimee Quick

Vice President Fund Controller Private, Christian Kurtz

Senior Vice President Vice President, Kevin Krieger

Vice President, Ana Fratila

Vice President, Scott Silvers

Vice President, Suvin Malik

Vice President, Paul Mrockowski

Vice President, Mario Rivera

Vice President Vice President, Kurt Winslow

Vice President Vice President, Kay Khoo

Vice President, Daniel Rodriguez

Vice President, Misty Shores

Vice President Payroll Manager, Brian Morazzini

Vice President Controller, Michael Sabatell

Senior Vice President And Portfolio, Daniel McFarlane

Vice President, Sergey Dyakin

Vice President Vice President, Richard Beecher

Vice President Vice President, Kevin Richardson

Vice President, Marc Sottile

Senior Vice President Director Of Operations, Daniel Ross

Vice President, Josh Bonacci

Vice President Tax Counsel, Jenifer Marsh

Vice President Vice President, Thomas Garbaccio

Vice President Asset Manager, Keith Caldwell

Senior Controller And Vice President, Jill Chanes

Vice President, Kenneth Blackman

Vice President, Paul Stockamore

Vice President Fund Counsel, Christine Putek

Vice President Senior Accountant, Maritza Munoz

Vice President, Rhonda Ramparas

Senior Vice President Portfolio Manager, Todd Howard

Vice President Asset Manager, Mari Subburathinam

Vice President, Adam Bodenstein

Vice President, Adrian Foo

Vice President Asset Manager, Jeff Casad

Vice President Credit Funds And Information Technology Program Manager, Armando Conde

Vice President, Judy Khuntaweetep

Vice President Of Tax Compliance Credit Funds, Johnery Laurimore

Senior Vice President And Controller, Scott Desiderio

Vice President, Christopher Frey

Senior Vice President Co Head, David Sharpe

Vice President, Solange Tsutsui

Vice President And Controller, Kristina Samuelsen

Vice President, Michael Richman

Vice President Treasury Supervisor, Alexander Keel

Vice President, Madhu Kutty

Senior Vice President, Jim Daly

Vice President Vice President, Tracy Dolan

Senior Vice President, Andrew Miller

Vice President, Scott Schwarmann

Vice President, Carrie Sin

Vice President, Peter Kobliska

Vice President, Leigh Maranuk

Vice President Senior Business Analyst, Todd Mangel

Vice President, Jason Okeefe

Vice President Vice President, Joseph Noce

Vice President Credit Info Tech Pm, Pankaj Jain

Vice President Vice President, Jonathan Schechter

Vice President, Noam Zur

Vice President Derivatives Counsel, Marc Finkelstein

Vice President, David Prael

Vice President Controller, Junko Nakamura

Vice President Vice President, Ryan Bell

Vice President, Yoni Shtein

Vice President, Brittain Rogers

Vice President Private Equity Global Sourcing, Jeanmarie Rall

Vice President Senior Business Analyst, Alex Etinger

Vice President Senior Accountant, Sean Hessle

Vice President Equity Analyst, David Rentschler

Vice President Vice President, Karen Braswell

Vice President Vice President, Brannen McElmurray

Vice President Vice President, Radhika Hulyalkar

Vice President Financial Planning, Jonathan O'Keeffe

Vice President Controller Value, Brad Flood

Vice President Senior Accountant, Mariko Inoue

Vice President Software Engineer, Maciek Samsel

Vice President Vice President, Ken Ikeo

Senior Vice President And Managing, Joseph Sciortino

Senior Vice President Counsel, Alex Gillette

Vice President Vice President, Greg Kleczek

Vice President, Laura Bevill

Vice President Fund Controller, Melissa Lorenz

Vice President Controller, Michael Cangelosi

Senior Vice President Controller, William Covino

Vice President Vice President, Sydney Goff

Vice President Senior Tax Associate, Peter Rosen

Vice President, Linh Ha

Vice President Vice President, Peter Su

Senior Vice President Senior Tax, Fran Benoit

Vice President Controller, Miki Ortiz

Vice President, Erin Imarisio

Vice President Controller, Timothy Chizak

Vice President, Jennifer Story

Vice President Operations, Robert Colacurto

Vice President Controller, Tracy Fojas

Vice President Financial Analyst, Paul Lyons

Vice President Controller, Eileen Kavanagh

Vice President Senior Portfolio Manager, Nikolai Walter

Vice President Operations Analyst, John Zinter

Vice President Tax Counsel, Dexter Samida

Vice President Transportation, Yan Khamish

Vice President Software Engineer, Jay Cheng

Vice President, Britt Rogers

Vice President Trader And Research, Kimberley Slough

Vice President, James Daly

Vice President, Ed Montolio

Vice President Sales And Marketing, Judy Godinho

Vice President, Timothy Bailey

Principal and Co-Chairman, Wesley R. (Wes) Edens, age 52

Principal and Co-Chairman, Peter L. Briger, age 51

Chief Executive Officer Co-Founder Principal and Director, Randal A. Nardone, age 59

Principal and Director; Co-Chief Investment Officer of the Fortress Macro Fund and the Drawbridge Global Macro Fund, Michael E. Novogratz, age 50

Board Member, George W Wellde, age 62

Treasury, Raymond Lee

Secretary, Marisol Sanchez

Auditors: Ernst&YoungLLP

LOCATIONS

HQ: Fortress Investment Group LLC
1345 Avenue of the Americas, New York, NY 10105
Phone: 212 798-6100

PRODUCTS/OPERATIONS

2012 Sales

	$ mil.	% of total
Management fees	501.7	52
Incentive income	272.6	28
Expense reimbursements from affiliates	189.3	19
Other	6.3	1
Total	**969.9**	**100**

COMPETITORS

American Capital	Investcorp
Apollo Investment	PineBridge Investments
Bessemer Trust	RREEF Funds
Blackstone Group	Schroders
Integrated Asset	Soros Fund Management
Management	

HISTORICAL FINANCIALS

Company Type: Public

Income Statement

FYE: December 31

	ASSETS ($ mil.)	NET INCOME ($ mil.)	INCOME AS % OF ASSETS	EMPLOYEES
12/13	2,674.4	200.4	7.5%	2,324
12/12	2,161.4	78.2	3.6%	1,996
12/11	2,220.6	(431.5)	—	979
12/10	2,076.7	(284.6)	—	900
12/09	1,660.2	(254.6)	—	819
Annual Growth	**12.7%**	—	—	**29.8%**

	STOCK PRICE ($) FY Close	P/E High/Low		Earnings	PER SHARE ($) Dividends	Book Value
12/13	8.56	11	5	0.79	0.24	1.68
12/12	4.39	16	10	0.27	0.20	1.35
12/11	3.38	—	—	(2.36)	0.00	0.98
12/10	5.70	—	—	(1.83)	0.00	0.88
12/09	4.45	—	—	(2.08)	0.00	0.58
Annual Growth	**17.8%**	—	—	—	—	**30.7%**

Forum Energy Technologies Inc

There is a proper forum for everything; for oil and natural gas drilling and control equipment it would be Forum Energy Technologies. The company designs makes and sells equipment for global customers including drilling contractors oilfield service businesses equipment rental companies and assemblers of drilling and well servicing equipment. Drilling products include tubular handling equipment and drilling data-management systems. Flow control products include expendable fluid end-components for mud and centrifugal pumps valves choke and kill manifolds and pressure control equipment. It also makes remote operating vehicles (ROVs) for subsea work.

IPO

Forum Energy Technologies went public in 2012 raising $258 million to pay down debt. Concurrently with the IPO Company sold 2.7 million shares of stock in a private placement to Tinicum L.P. a private equity fund for $50 million. Prior to the conclusion of the IPO L. E. Simmons controlled 75% of Forum Energy Technologies through investment entity SCF Partners. Following the IPO it held 47% through SCF-V L.P. and related entities.

Geographic Reach

A global player Forum Energy Technologies has manufacturing operations in Texas. It has sales and distribution centers in the US and Canada as well in Singapore the UAE and the UK. It also has regional representative offices in Chile Colombia Mexico and Peru.

The US accounted for 63% of the company's revenues in 2012; Europe & Africa 14%.

Operations

The company operates in two segments: Drilling and Subsea (drilling subsea and well construction completion and intervention product design and manufacture and related services); and Production and Infrastructure (the provision of equipment and services to the well stimulation completion production and infrastructure markets).

Financial Performance

Forum Energy Technologies' revenues increased by 25% in 2012 largely due to a Drilling and Subsea revenues jump of 25% as a result of increased sales of hydraulic catwalk units and blowout preventers (Drilling Technologies product line) and higher sales of ROVs in the Subsea Technologies product line. Production and Infrastructure revenues grew by 26% due to higher market demand for production equipment and valves as well as because of orders from new customers. The 2011 expansion of existing facilities and the addition of new facilities in Pennsylvania enabled higher shipments in the Production Equipment segment in 2012. Net income increased by 62% in 2012 thanks to higher revenues and decreased interest expenses due to lower debt levels as a result of repaying a portion of Forum Energy Technologies' debt from the net proceeds of the IPO and concurrent private placement. With the exception of 2009 when the global economic recession stymied demand and caused revenues to slump the company saw an upward trend in revenues from 2008 to 2012.

Strategy

The company has forged a strategy centered on acquiring complementary companies to enable its its ability to supply both expendable drilling products and capital products for the drilling rig refurbishment market to a global client base.

In 2013 Forum Energy Technologies' signed deals with Helix Energy Solutions Group's Canyon Offshore subsea robotics business unit to supply it with a PerryTM XT1500 Trenching system and two PerryTM XLX 200HP ROVs. In 2012 it signed a deal with Technip Odebrecht PLSV CV to supply that company with four PerryTM XLX Generation 2 150 horsepower ROVs.

Boosting its subsea assets in 2012 Forum Energy Technologies acquired Syntech Technology Inc. a Virgina-based manufacturer of syntactic foam buoyancy materials used for ROVs and other deepwater flotation applications and Dynacon Inc. a Bryan Texas-based provider of launch and recovery systems used for the deployment of ROVs and specialized cable and umbilical handling equipment. (In 2011 it acquired UK-based Specialist ROV Tooling Services Ltd. a provider of intervention tooling and custom engineered products).

Expanding its production and infrastructure portfolio in 2012 the company acquired Texas-based Wireline Solutions LLC a manufacturer of downhole completion tools including composite plugs used for plug perforate and fracture applications and wireline flow control products and Merrimac Manufacturing Inc. a maker of consumable parts for drilling well servicing and pressure pumping applications including mud pump parts power swivel parts and valves and seats for hydraulic fracturing pumps. In 2011 it acquired high pressure flow control equipment maker Phoinix Global.

Moving into the downhole product market in 2011 the company acquired downhole completion control lines and cable protection systems maker Cannon Services and SVP Products a provider of high-pressure flow control equipment for oil and gas wells. In a related move that year it acquired downhole cementing and casing products maker Davis-Lynch. Other accretive purchases in 2011 included Wood Flowline Products LLC (pressure control and flow equipment products) base in Oklahoma and Arkansas; and UK-based AMC Global Group Ltd. (specialized torque equipment for tubular connections) and PQuip Ltd. a leading manufacturer of proprietary mud pump fluid end assemblies.

Company Background

Seeking to grow in 2010 Forum Oilfield Technologies merged with a handful of other oilfield equipment and services companies (Subsea Services International Global Flow Technologies Allied Technology all based in Houston and Triton Group of the UK) to form Forum Energy Technologies. The $750 million in annual revenue business is led by former Halliburton executive Chris Gaut who is the managing director of SCF Partners a Houston-based private equity fund that was majority owner of all five companies.

EXECUTIVES

Executive Vice President; President - Drilling And Subsea Division, Charles E (Charlie) Jones, age 56
Senior Vice President General Counsel, James L McCulloch, age 62
SVP and CFO, James W. Harris, age 55, $363,940 total compensation
Chairman and CEO, C. Christopher ("Cris) Gaut, age 58, $626,720 total compensation
EVP and COO, Prady Iyyanki
Vice President Corporate Administration, Tom Simms
Svp-subsea Technologies, William Boyle
Svp Drilling Technologies, James Bement
Executive Vice President Of Business, E Hottle
Manufacturing Unit Vice President, Roy May
Vice President Of Corporate Development, Chris Dorros
Western Hemisphere Vice President, Miron Bertsch
Senior Vice President, Carl Daniel
Vice President Marketing, Rem Moreland
Senior Vice President Downhole Technologies, Sidney Smith
Vice President Engineering, David Greathouse
Vice President Strategic Development, Patrick Connelly
Vice President Systems And Processes, Adam Szczepanski
Vice President Of Sales And Marketing, Graham Adair
Vice President Of Marketing, Don Stark
Senior Vice President Downhole Technologies, Sid Smith
Vice President Investor Relations, Mark Traylor
Vice President Sales And Market????????ng, David Wolfe

Chairman and CEO, C. Christopher ("Cris) Gaut, age 58
V Pres Corp Strategy-treas, Pablo G Mercado
Auditors: PricewaterhouseCoopersLLP

LOCATIONS

HQ: Forum Energy Technologies Inc
920 Memorial City Way, Suite 1000, Houston, TX 77024
Phone: 281 949-2500   **Fax:** 281 949-2554
Web: www.f-e-t.com

2012 Sales

	$ mil.	% of total
North America		
US	895.0	63
Canada	114.2	8
Europe & Africa	196.8	14
Asia/Pacific	100.9	7
Latin America	58.4	4
Middle East	49.6	4
Total	**1414.9**	**100**

PRODUCTS/OPERATIONS

2012 Sales

	$ mil.	% of total
Drilling & Subsea	826.2	58
Production & Infrastructure	588.7	42
Total	**1414.9**	**100**

2012 Sales

	% of total
Drilling Technologies	30
Subsea Technologies	18
Production Equipment	16
Vale Solutions	15
Flow Equipment	11
Downhole Technologies	10
Total	**100**

Selected Mergers and Acquisitions

2012
Syntech Technology Inc. (Virgina; syntactic foam buoyancy materials used for ROVs and other deepwater flotation applications)
Dynacon Inc. (Bryan Texas; launch and recovery systems used for the deployment of ROVs and specialized cable and umbilical handling equipment)
Wireline Solutions LLC (Texas; downhole completion tools including composite plugs used for plug perforate and fracture applications and wireline flow control products)
2011
Specialist ROV Tooling Services Ltd (UK; intervention tools and custom engineered products)
Cannon Services (downhole completion control lines and cable protection systems)
Wood Flowline Products LLC (pressure control and flow equipment products)
AMC Global Group Ltd. (UK; specialized torque equipment for tubular connections).

COMPETITORS

Cameron International	Halliburton
Canrig Drilling Technology	National Oilwell Varco
	Pason Systems
Double Life	Schlumberger
Exterran	Weatherford
FMC Technologies	International
Fugro	Weir SPM

HISTORICAL FINANCIALS
Company Type: Public

Income Statement
FYE: December 31

	REVENUE ($ mil.)	NET INCOME ($ mil.)	NET PROFIT MARGIN	EMPLOYEES
12/13	1,524.8	129.5	8.5%	3,500
12/12	1,414.9	151.4	10.7%	3,400
12/11	1,128.1	93.3	8.3%	3,150
12/10	747.3	23.9	3.2%	0
12/09	677.3	19.3	2.9%	0
Annual Growth	**22.5%**	**60.9%**	**—**	**—**

2013 Year-End Financials

Debt ratio: 23.6%	No. of shares (mil.): 89
Return on equity: 10.4%	Dividends
Cash ($ mil.): 39	Yield: —
Current ratio: 3.68	Payout: —
Long-term debt ($ mil.): 512	Market value ($ mil.): 2,521

	STOCK PRICE ($) FY Close	P/E High/Low	PER SHARE ($) Earnings	Dividends	Book Value
12/13	28.26	22 17	1.37	0.00	14.91
12/12	24.75	14 10	1.74	0.00	13.80
Annual Growth	**14.2%**	**—**	**(21.3%)**	**—**	**8.1%**

Forward Air Corp

When it's time to haul freight Forward Air never looks back. The company transports deferred airfreight by truck —cargo that requires specific-time delivery but is less time-sensitive than airfreight. Forward Air typically receives freight that has been transported by plane sends it to a sorting facility then dispatches it by truck to a terminal near its destination. The company has nearly 2800 trailers and more than 400 tractors and straight trucks in its fleet. It operates from about 85 terminals at or near airports in the US and Canada including about a dozen regional hubs. It also provides services such as warehousing and local pick-up and delivery.

Operations
The company markets its services to airfreight forwarders air cargo carriers and airlines rather than directly to shippers. Although Forward Air does facilitate overnight delivery of freight the company doesn't compete in the parcel delivery market because it handles larger shipments.

Besides its expedited transportation business the company offers pool distribution services through a second business segment Forward Air Solutions. (Pool distribution involves combining goods from multiple shippers into loads headed to the same location.) Forward Air Solutions maintains about 20 terminals near airport in major cities. Because the segment's customers tend to be retailers located in malls and outlet-based chains revenues are dependent upon the health of the retail industry.

As with its competitors Forward Air uses a fuel surcharge as a way to compensate for fluctuating fuel prices. The rates are based upon the national average price of diesel per gallon and tonnage delivered.

Financial Performance

Forward Air has enjoyed three straight years of unprecedented growth. Revenues spiked by 9% from $536 million in 2011 to $584 million in 2012. Profits also jumped 12% from $47 million in 2011 to $53 million in 2012. Both these totals represented historic milestones for the company.

The growth for 2012 was driven by a 13% surge in airport-to-airport sales coupled with an 8% increase in logistics sales. Within its Froward Air Solutions segment pool distribution also recognized growth of 15%.

Strategy
The company intents to grow by adding new services to its lineup and by acquiring other transportation services companies. In 2013 Forward Air acquired Total Quality a provider of temperature-controlled logistics services serving the life science and pharmaceutical sector for $66 million. The deal added a new service to Forward Air's logistics portfolio and widened its client base.

EXECUTIVES

Chairman President and CEO, Bruce A. Campbell, age 63, $500,000 total compensation
EVP of Operations, Chris C. Ruble, age 52, $317,949 total compensation
Executive Vice President; Chief Legal Officer; Secretary, Matthew J. Jewell, age 48, $268,070 total compensation
Chief Financial Officer; Senior Vice President; Treasurer, Rodney L. Bell, age 52, $268,070 total compensation
Vice President Of Operations, Russ Buffaloe
Vice President International Logistics, Joe Tirone
Vice President International Department, F A Greenville
Executive Vice President Chief Legal, Matthew Hamilton
Senior Vice President Operations, David Qun
Executive Vice President Operations, Chris Stewart
Vice President, Hilda Verdayes
Vice President Sales, Walt Weid
Vice President Sales And Marketing, Jerry Cooper
Chairman President and CEO, Bruce A. Campbell, age 63
Chief Financial Officer; Senior Vice President; Treasurer, Rodney L. Bell, age 52
Board Member, Eric Scott
Auditors: Ernst&YoungLLP

LOCATIONS

HQ: Forward Air Corp
430 Airport Road, Greeneville, TN 37745
Phone: 423 636-7000
Web: www.forwardair.com

PRODUCTS/OPERATIONS

2012 Sales

	$ mil.	% of total
Forward Air		
Logistics	390.7	67
Airport-to-airport	83.8	14
Other	26.1	5
Forward Air Solutions	83.8	14
Total	**584.4**	**100**

COMPETITORS

Alliance Air	Old Dominion Freight
CRST Expedited	Panther Expedited
CRST International	Services
Daylight Transport	Schneider National
FedEx Freight	Towne Air Freight
New Penn Motor Express	XPO logistics

HISTORICAL FINANCIALS
Company Type: Public

Income Statement
FYE: December 31

	REVENUE ($ mil.)	NET INCOME ($ mil.)	NET PROFIT MARGIN	EMPLOYEES
12/13	652.4	54.4	8.3%	3,537
12/12	584.4	52.6	9.0%	2,128
12/11	536.4	47.2	8.8%	3,136
12/10	483.9	32.0	6.6%	2,717
12/09	417.4	9.8	2.3%	2,755
Annual Growth	11.8%	53.5%	—	6.4%

2013 Year-End Financials

Debt ratio: 0.0%	No. of shares (mil.): 30
Return on equity: 13.8%	Dividends
Cash ($ mil.): 127	Yield: 0.9%
Current ratio: 6.37	Payout: 22.1%
Long-term debt ($ mil.): 0	Market value ($ mil.): 1,340

	STOCK PRICE ($) FY Close	P/E High/Low		PER SHARE ($) Earnings	Dividends	Book Value
12/13	43.91	24	19	1.77	0.40	14.28
12/12	35.01	21	16	1.78	0.34	12.05
12/11	32.05	22	15	1.60	0.28	10.05
12/10	28.38	27	20	1.10	0.28	8.82
12/09	25.03	76	41	0.34	0.28	7.75
Annual Growth	15.1%		—	51.1%	9.3%	16.5%

Foster (L.B.) Co.

L. B. Foster can help keep you on track whether you're riding the rails or cruising the open road. The company manufactures new and relay rail and trackwork used in railroad and mass transit systems as well as in industrial markets such as mining. L. B. Foster also supplies pipe coatings for oil and natural gas industries and pipe products for industrial utility and agricultural water wells. It taps federal state and local infrastructure markets too selling and renting steel sheet piling and earth wall systems necessary in highway and levee construction and repair. Foster's products have been used for the construction and rehabilitation of such projects as the Brooklyn Bridge and Panama Canal.

Geographic Reach

North America is Pittsburgh-based L. B. Foster's largest market accounting for about 90% of annual sales. The UK represents about 3%. The company has plants in Alabama Arizona Colorado Ohio Pennsylvania Texas and Washington in the US as well as rail technologies plants in Canada and the UK.

Operations

About 60% of the company's revenue is generated from rail products including heavy and light new and used (relay) rail mainly to transit authorities industrial customers and and rail contractors. Its product list of rail accessories includes trackwork track spikes bolts angle bars and other products used to install or repair rail lines. The company's Construction Products business (about a third of sales) supplies piling fabricated products and precast concrete buildings. Tubular Products contribute more than 5% of sales and include coated pipe and threaded products. Foster owns a 45% interest in a joint venture (formed in 2009)

L B Pipe & Coupling that manufactures and sells precision couplings and various other products for the energy utility and construction markets.

Sales and Marketing

The company markets its rail construction and tubular products directly in the US Canada and the UK through a sales force of about 80 people. To supplement its internal sales force Foster relies on a network of agents across Europe South America and Asia to reach customers.

Financial Performance

Foster rang up sales of $598 million in 2013 an increase of nearly 2% versus 2012. Driving the revenue gain was a 67% increase in sales of construction products partially offset by declines of 6% and 29% of rail and tubular products segments respectively. Net income rose 81% over the same period to $29.3 million on rising sales and lower costs of good sold and decreased interest expense.

Strategy

In 2013 Foster expanded its steel pipe coating facility in Birmingham Alabama to improve manufacturing through-put and increase production capacity. Also in 2013 the company began delivery of their largest contract for steel grid bridge decking for the rehabilitation of the New York State Bridge Authority's Newburgh-Beacon span. The company established an larger international presence in the rail products market with the acquisition of Portec Rail Products Inc. (in 2010)

Looking for highway road and bridge construction funding L. B. Foster has broadened its offerings with a pipe pile featuring material and transportation savings. Its lineup of precast concrete structures used in pre-fabricated utility buildings has also been expanded.

Mergers and Acquisitions

Foster in October 2014 agreed to acquire the railroad tuning unit FWO of Balfour Beatty Rail GmbH. The German business provides track lubrication and switch roller equipment for international railways.

In November 2013 the company purchased Ball Winch LLC a privately-held company that applies specialty pipe coatings and provides field services for the oil and gas mining water and waste water industries.

EXECUTIVES

VP Rail Products, Samuel K. Fisher, age 61, $220,833 total compensation
SVP CFO and Treasurer, David J. Russo, age 55, $288,837 total compensation
SVP Rail Business, John F. Kasel, age 49, $276,683 total compensation
VP Tubular Products, Merry L. Brumbaugh, age 57
VP Rail Technologies, Konstantinos Papazoglou
President and CEO, Robert P. Bauer, $592,250 total compensation
VP Concrete Products, Steve Burgess
Vice President Global, Kostas Papazoglou
National Sales Manager, Mark Hammons
Vice President Technology And Business, Kevin Oldknow
Chairman, Lee B. Foster, age 68
Auditors: Ernst&YoungLLP

LOCATIONS

HQ: Foster (L.B.) Co.
415 Holiday Drive, Pittsburgh, PA 15220
Phone: 412 928-3400

2013 Sales

	$ mil.	% of total
US	495.7	83
Canada	37.3	6
UK	16.5	3
Other countries	48.5	8
Total	598	100

PRODUCTS/OPERATIONS

2013 Sales

	$ mil.	% of total
Rail products	363.7	61
Construction products	191.8	32
Tubular products	42.5	7
Total	598	100

2013 Sales

	$ mil.	% of total
Rail distribution products	144.9	24
Piling products	140.3	23
Rail technologies products	88.7	15
CXT concrete tie products	44.1	7
Transit products	41.9	7
CXT cocrete building products	33.0	6
Other products	105.1	18
Total	598	100

Selected Products

Rail
 Concrete ties
 Heavy and light rail
 Insulated rail joints
 Rail accessories
 Relay rail
Construction
 Fabricated highway products
 Precast concrete products
 Sheet and bearing piling
Tubular
 Column pipe
 Corrosion protection coatings
 Couplings
 Water well casing

COMPETITORS

ACF Industries	Greenbrier Rail
ALSTOM	Services
American Railcar	Harsco
Industries	Insteel
Amsted Industries	Trinity Industries
GATX	Westinghouse Air Brake

HISTORICAL FINANCIALS
Company Type: Public

Income Statement
FYE: December 31

	REVENUE ($ mil.)	NET INCOME ($ mil.)	NET PROFIT MARGIN	EMPLOYEES
12/13	597.9	29.2	4.9%	830
12/12	588.5	16.1	2.8%	820
12/11	590.9	22.9	3.9%	845
12/10	475.0	20.4	4.3%	866
12/09	381.9	15.7	4.1%	593
Annual Growth	11.9%	16.8%	—	8.8%

2013 Year-End Financials

Debt ratio: 0.0%	No. of shares (mil.): 10
Return on equity: 9.7%	Dividends
Cash ($ mil.): 64	Yield: 0.2%
Current ratio: 3.28	Payout: 4.3%
Long-term debt ($ mil.): 0	Market value ($ mil.): 482

	STOCK PRICE ($) FY Close	P/E High/Low	PER SHARE ($) Earnings	Dividends	Book Value
12/13	47.29	17 14	2.85	0.12	31.05
12/12	43.44	27 16	1.58	0.10	28.33
12/11	28.29	19 8	2.22	0.10	29.88
12/10	40.94	20 13	1.98	0.00	27.03
12/09	29.81	23 13	1.53	0.00	25.18
Annual Growth	12.2%	— —	16.8%	—	5.4%

Franklin Covey Co.

Franklin Covey publisher of the popular book The 7 Habits of Highly Effective People knows a thing or two about performance improvement. Targeted at individuals teams and organizations the company is a global provider of training programs consulting services books and planning products designed around seven practice areas: leadership productivity trust execution sales performance education and customer loyalty. Franklin Covey's more than 4200 clients include about 90% of the FORTUNE 100 75% of the FORTUNE 500 and thousands of small and midsized businesses. In addition to companies it serves government entities and educational institutions mostly in the US.

Geographic Reach

Franklin Covey has some 46 direct and licensee offices providing professional services in more than 140 countries. It has subsidiaries in Australia Japan and the UK.

Operations

The company delivers its services and products through professional Franklin Covey consultants that offer training on site at client locations. Client employees that have received specialized training can also deliver content as certified Franklin Covey facilitators. The company additionally provides its services through international licensees public workshops and a series of online offerings.

Financial Performance

The company's revenue increased in fiscal 2014 compared to the prior year. It reported $205.2 million in revenue for fiscal 2014 up from $190.9 million in revenue for fiscal 2013. Franklin Covey's net income also went up in fiscal 2014 compared to the previous fiscal period. It reported net income of $18 million for fiscal 2014 after clearing $14 million in net income during fiscal 2013.

Franklin Covey's cash flow increased by about $3 million in fiscal 2014 compared to fiscal 2013 levels.

Strategy

The company continues to expand its offerings beyond its flagship 7 Habits of Highly Effective People introducing new programs in order to boost sales.

Mergers and Acquisitions

In March 2013 Franklin Covey acquired Florida-based NinetyFive 5 LLC adding its Sales Enablement Consulting and Coaching Execution System (SUCCESS) which includes a subscription-based online tool set sales coaching and live and virtual training to Franklin Covey's Sales Performance Practice —doubling that business' size. The deal also brings NinetyFive 5's social media assets a cloud-based learning practice and execution platform called 5 Online and a client base of FORTUNE 1000 companies.

HISTORY

Hyrum Smith a former insurance agent founded H.W. Smith and Associates in 1982 to give time-management seminars. With help from Dennis Webb the business became the Franklin Institute (named after efficiency proponent Benjamin Franklin) in 1983. The next year it introduced the Franklin Day Planner. The company was renamed Franklin Quest and went public in 1992. It added new product lines through acquisitions including Productivity Plus (planning materials for military customers) and TrueNorth (corporate training) in 1996 and Premier Agendas (planners for students) in 1997.

That year Franklin Quest acquired Covey Leadership Center for $160 million. Stephen Covey a former professor at Brigham Young University formed his company in 1980. He wrote best-seller "The 7 Habits of Highly Effective People" in 1989 and followed it up with "The 7 Habits of Highly Effective Families" in 1997.

Renamed Franklin Covey Co. in 1998 the company dropped its fitness seminars teamed up with planner competitor At-A-Glance to sell products directly to employers and began a short-lived unsuccessful attempt at selling products through retail giant Office Depot.

Jon Rowberry named CEO in 1998 left the company just 15 months later as it struggled to integrate the operations of Franklin Quest and Covey Leadership Center. Robert Whitman became chairman in 1999 when Franklin Covey sold $75 million in stock to his Dallas investment company; Franklin Covey earmarked the proceeds for online ventures and acquisitions. Under Whitman Franklin Covey cut about 600 jobs and shut its Provo Utah office taking a restructuring charge of $16.3 million for fiscal 1999.

Whitman became CEO in 2000. Also that year the company simplified its product lines eliminating thousands of redundant offerings and sold its commercial printing division. In 2001 Franklin Covey sold its Premier Agendas and Premier School Agendas subsidiaries to School Specialty. In 2002 Mellon Financial's HQ Solutions group acquired a Franklin Covey unit that provides outsourced training operations. Also that year the company discontinued its online planning services unit (FranklinPlanner.com) and terminated a joint venture (Franklin Covey Coaching).

Continuing its strategy of closing unprofitable operations the company shuttered 22 US and 10 international retail stores during 2003 about 20 in 2004 and another 30 in 2005.

Wanting to focus on its consulting and training side of the business Franklin Covey sold its unprofitable Consumer Solutions business (including about 90 stores catalogs a website and licensed operations) to Peterson Partners in 2008 for $32 million. Peterson Partners controls the consumer business now called Franklin Covey Products while Franklin Covey retained a 20% stake.

EXECUTIVES

Vice President General Mgr Southeast, Mark Josie
Chief Financial Officer; EVP - Finance; Chief Accounting Officer; Corporate Secretary, Stephen D. (Steve) Young, age 60, $250,000 total compensation
SVP Innovation and Products, M. Sean Covey, age 50, $270,000 total compensation
Executive Vice President Chief People & Operations Officer, C. Todd Davis, age 56
VP U.S. Domestic Operations, Colleen Dom
President General Manager, Brian Martini

General Manager Government Services, Shawn D. Moon, age 46, $250,000 total compensation
EVP of Business Development and Marketing, Scott Miller
Managing Director, Sandy Rogers
Head of Corporate and Global Marketing, Curtis J. Morley
Vice President Of Human Resources Manager Services, Todd Davis
Vp Finance, Boyd Roberts
Vice President And Ptsa Fundraising, Maria Tiatia
Vice President Of Communications, Sara Myers
Vice President Operations, Richard Bridges
Vice President Of Product Management, Cherell Jordin
Vice President International Business, William McIntyre
Vice President Human Resources Manager Services, Clifton Davis
Executive Vice President And Chief Human Resources Manager Officer, Ctodd Davis
Vice President Sales Performance Group, Mahan Khalsa
Vice Chairman, Stephen R. Covey, age 82
Treasurer Head Of Treasury, Richard Putnam
Auditors: KPMGLLP

LOCATIONS

HQ: Franklin Covey Co.
2200 West Parkway Boulevard, Salt Lake City, UT 84119-2099
Phone: 801 817-1776
Web: www.franklincovey.com

PRODUCTS/OPERATIONS

Selected Programs
Core Program Offerings
  The 7 Habits of Highly Effective People Signature Program
  Leadership: Great Leaders Great Teams Great Results
  FOCUS: Achieving Your Highest Priorities
  The 4 Disciplines of Execution
  The xQ Service
Publications
  The 7 Habits of Highly Effective People by Dr. Stephen R. Covey
  The 8th Habit: From Effectiveness to Greatness by Dr. Stephen R. Covey
  Everyday Greatness by Dr. Stephen R. Covey
  The Ten Natural Laws of Successful Time and Life Management by Hyrum W. Smith
  The 7 Habits of Highly Effective Families by Dr. Stephen R. Covey
  The 7 Habits of Highly Effective Teens by Sean Covey
  The 6 Most Important Decisions You' ll Ever Make by Sean Covey
  Principle-Centered Leadership by Dr. Stephen R. Covey
  First Things First by Dr. Stephen R. Covey
  The Power Principle: Influence with Honor by Blaine Lee

COMPETITORS

American Management Association	Maritz
Bain & Company	Mission Control Productivity
Booz Allen	Organizational Dynamics
CCL	
Dale Carnegie	PRTM Management
Development Dimensions International	The Forum Corporation
IIR	Wilson Learning

HISTORICAL FINANCIALS

Company Type: Public

Income Statement

FYE: August 31

	REVENUE ($ mil.)	NET INCOME ($ mil.)	NET PROFIT MARGIN	EMPLOYEES
08/14	205.1	18.0	8.8%	825
08/13	190.9	14.3	7.5%	660
08/12	170.4	7.8	4.6%	630
08/11	160.8	4.8	3.0%	590
08/10	136.8	(0.5)	—	600
Annual Growth 10.6%		—	—	8.3%

2014 Year-End Financials

Debt ratio: 13.3%
Return on equity: 15.4%
Cash ($ mil.): 10
Current ratio: 2.17
Long-term debt ($ mil.): 26

No. of shares (mil.): 16
Dividends
Yield: —
Payout: —
Market value ($ mil.): 320

	STOCK PRICE ($) FY Close	P/E High/Low	PER SHARE ($) Earnings	Dividends	Book Value
08/14	19.07	21 15	1.07	0.00	7.55
08/13	15.71	20 12	0.80	0.00	6.54
08/12	10.35	24 15	0.43	0.00	5.12
08/11	9.52	43 22	0.27	0.00	4.49
08/10	6.10	— —	(0.04)	0.00	4.17
Annual Growth 33.0%		— —	—	—	16.0%

Franklin Electric Co., Inc.

When it comes to making pumps and motors Franklin Electric would make Old Ben proud. The company keeps things flowing by making and distributing submersible and specialty electric motors electronic drives and controls and related items. Its fueling system products include electronic tank monitoring equipment fittings flexible piping nozzles and vapor recovery systems. Franklin Electric's products are used by OEMs that incorporate them in underground petroleum pumping systems sewage pumps vacuum pumping systems and freshwater pumping systems. Some customers such as independent distributors and repair shops buy the company's products as replacement motors. Franklin Electric was founded in 1944.

Franklin Electric operates through its two segments of water systems and fueling systems. Water systems is the company's bread and butter typically representing around 80% of total sales each year. The company has operations in Australia Botswana Brazil Canada China the Czech Republic Germany Italy Japan Mexico South Africa Turkey and the US. The US represents about 45% of its total sales.

Franklin Electric has enjoyed healthily growing sales over the years coupled with rising profits. From 2010 to 2011 its revenue increased by 15% from around $714 million to $821 million. It's net income also surged by almost 62% from $39 million to $63 million the highest total it has achieved in at least 10 years. The company attributes much of this growth to acquisitions estimating it gained about $43 million (or 6%) in additional revenue

from acquired businesses in 2011. Due to the dry and hot weather that has engulfed the Midwest and Southwest US it has also benefited from higher sales of its pumping systems within the industrial and irrigation sectors.

Another factor contributing to the company's growth has been its rising international sales which accounted for 55% of its total revenue in 2011. Water systems sales in Europe the Middle East and Africa grew by 29% in 2011. Sales for this segment in Latin America grew by 14% and in the important growth region of China sales spiked by 25%.

Franklin Electric continues to expand its pumping business through acquisitions. In 2012 it raised its stake in Pioneer Pump Holdings a maker of pumps used for dewatering by the oil and gas municipal construction and mining industries from 35% to 70%. The year before it upped its presence in the Middle East by acquiring an 80% share of a groundwater pumping equipment supplier based in Turkey.

EXECUTIVES

Vp International, Peter C Maske
President and Chief Operating Officer, Gregg C. Sengstack, age 55, $407,005 total compensation
Chairman and CEO, R. Scott Trumbull, age 65, $689,594 total compensation
Senior Vice President and President International Water Systems, Robert J. Stone, age 50, $326,676 total compensation
Vice President Global Water Products Supply, Daniel J. (Dan) Crose, age 66
Vice President Chief Financial Officer and Secretary, John J. Haines, age 50, $317,515 total compensation
Vice President and President North America Water Systems, DeLancey W. (Dee) Davis, age 48, $298,762 total compensation
Vice President Global Water Systems Engineering, Steven (Steve) Aikman
VP and President Energy Systems, Don Kenney
Vice President Engineering, Todd Thomas
Vice President Marketing North America Water Systems, Diann Scott
Vice President Asia Pacific Water Sys, Melanie Dansby
Vice President Business Unit Manager, Brett Thompson
Vp Operations, Bob Lisco
Vp Of Engineering, Scott Leonard
National Sales Manager, Sean Murray
Vice President Global Water Systems Engineering, Steve Aikman
Vice President Of Sales, Matthew Venancio
Chairman and CEO, R. Scott Trumbull, age 65
Vice President Chief Financial Officer and Secretary, John J. Haines, age 50
Board Of Directors, Thomas Young
Board Of Directors, David Wathen
Treasury Supervisor, Joy Conrad
Board Member, Jerome D Brady
Auditors: Deloitte&ToucheLLP

LOCATIONS

HQ: Franklin Electric Co., Inc.
9255 Coverdale Road, Fort Wayne, IN 46809
Phone: 260 824-2900
Web: www.franklin-electric.com

2013 Sales

	$ mil.	% of total
US	460.5	48
Other countries	505	52
Total	**965.5**	**100**

PRODUCTS/OPERATIONS

2013 Sales

	$ mil.	% of total
Water systems	766.4	79
Fueling systems	199.1	21
Total	**965.5**	**100**

Selected Products

Fuel pumping systems
Load control monitors
Motor leads and couplings
Submersible electric motors
Water pressure drives

Selected Subsidiaries

Advanced Polymer Technology Inc.
Coverco S.r.l. (Italy)
EBW Inc.
FE Petro Inc.
Franklin Electric (Australia) Pty. Ltd.
Franklin Electric B.V. (Netherlands)
Franklin Electric Europa GmbH (Germany)
Franklin Electric International Inc.
Franklin Electric Manufacturing Inc.
Franklin Electric (South Africa) Pty. Limited
Franklin Electric spol s.r.o. (Czech Republic)
Franklin Electric (Suzhou) Co. Ltd. (China)
Franklin Fueling Systems GmbH (Germany)
Healy Systems Inc.
Intelligent Controls Inc.
Little Giant Pump Company
Motores Franklin S.A. de C.V. (Mexico)
Servicios De Mesmex (Mexico)

COMPETITORS

A. O. Smith	Interpump
American Manufacturing and Machine	Lincoln Electric
Baldor Electric	Magnetek
Charter International	Meggitt (North Hollywood)
Danaher	Pentair
Dover Corp.	Power Conversion
Dresser-Rand	Regal Beloit
EXX	SPX
Emerson Electric	TECO-Westinghouse
Grundfos	WEG Electric
Hayward Industries	Xylem
ITT Corp.	

HISTORICAL FINANCIALS

Company Type: Public

Income Statement

FYE: December 28

	REVENUE ($ mil.)	NET INCOME ($ mil.)	NET PROFIT MARGIN	EMPLOYEES
12/13	965.4	81.9	8.5%	4,400
12/12	891.3	82.8	9.3%	4,200
12/11*	821.0	63.1	7.7%	3,800
01/11	713.7	38.9	5.5%	3,470
01/10	625.9	25.9	4.2%	3,500
Annual Growth 11.4%		33.3%	—	5.9%

*Fiscal year change

2013 Year-End Financials

Debt ratio: 18.0%
Return on equity: 14.8%
Cash ($ mil.): 134
Current ratio: 3.41
Long-term debt ($ mil.): 174

No. of shares (mil.): 47
Dividends
Yield: 0.0%
Payout: 18.1%
Market value ($ mil.): 2,172

	STOCK PRICE ($) FY Close	P/E High/Low	PER SHARE ($) Earnings	Dividends	Book Value
12/13	45.51	40 18	1.68	0.31	12.48
12/12	60.05	35 25	1.73	0.29	10.91
12/11*	43.56	38 25	1.33	0.27	9.60
01/11	38.92	49 30	0.83	0.26	8.98
01/10	29.05	60 31	0.56	0.25	8.39
Annual Growth	11.9%	— —	31.6%	5.1%	10.4%

*Fiscal year change

Franklin Street Properties Corp

A real estate investment trust (REIT) Franklin Street Properties acquires finances leases and manages office properties in about 15 states throughout the US. It owns some 40 properties located mainly in suburban areas and manages about 15 others; Dallas Denver Houston and Washington DC are its largest markets. The company's FSP Investment unit is an investment bank and brokerage that organizes REITs that invest in single properties and raises equity for them through private placements. Another subsidiary FSP Property Management manages properties for Franklin Street as well as for some of the REITs sponsored by FSP Investments.

Geographic Reach

Massachusetts-based Franklin Street Properties' five largest markets are Atlanta Dallas Denver Houston and Minneapolis.

Sales and Marketing

Franklin Street's properties consist of approximately 9.7 million sq. ft. of leasable space. The firm serves a diverse mix of tenants. Major tenants include Primary PhysicianCare Headway Technologies The American Red Cross and Comcast of ColoradoX LLC.

Financial Performance

The firm reported $213.6 million in revenue in 2013 an increase of 30% versus 2012 on increasing rents from properties acquired in 2012 and 2013 and to a lesser extent higher occupancy rates. Net income jumped 160% over the same period to $19.8 million primarily due to the double-digit increase in revenue partially offset by rising expenses.

Strategy

Franklin Street Properties looks to buy office properties in select urban infill and central business districts with a primary emphasis on its top five markets: Atlanta Dallas Denver Houston and Minneapolis. The office REIT seeks value-oriented investments with an eye toward long-term growth and appreciation as well as current income. Other markets on the firm's radar include San Diego and Silicon Valley Greater Boston Raleigh-Durham and the greater Washington D.C. area.

Mergers and Acquisitions

Recent acquisitions include two properties in Denver's central business district for a combined total of $400 million as well as a 621000-square-foot office property in midtown Atlanta for $157.9 million both in 2013. In 2012 the firm acquired one property in Georgia and another in Texas.

EXECUTIVES

Vice President And Finance, Andrew J Klouse
EVP and CFO, John G. Demeritt, age 54, $204,750 total compensation
CEO President Chairman of the Board, George J. Carter, age 66, $225,000 total compensation
EVP COO Treasurer Secretary and Director; COO FSP Investments, Barbara J. Fournier, age 59, $227,500 total compensation
VP and Director; President FSP Property Management, Janet Prier Notopoulos, age 67, $193,375 total compensation
VP; VP and Regional Director Southeast Asset Management, Leo H. (Toby) Daley
Vice President, John F. Donahue
Vice President, William S. Friend
VP; VP and Regional Director Northeast & Northwest Asset Management, Patricia A. McMullen
Vice President And Asset Manager, Toby Daley
Executive Vice President Franklin Street Properties And Fsp Investments, Scott R Macphee
CEO President Chairman of the Board, George J. Carter, age 66
EVP COO Treasurer Secretary and Director; COO FSP Investments, Barbara J. Fournier, age 59
Auditors: Ernst&YoungLLP

LOCATIONS

HQ: Franklin Street Properties Corp
  401 Edgewater Place, Suite 200, Wakefield, MA 01880
Phone: 781 557-1300
Web: www.franklinstreetproperties.com

California
Colorado
Florida
Georgia
Illinois
Indiana
Maryland
Minnesota
Missouri
North Carolina
Ohio
South Carolina
Texas
Virginia
Washington

PRODUCTS/OPERATIONS

2013 Sales

	$ mil.	% of total
Rent	207.0	97
Management fees & interest income	6.7	3
Total	**213.7**	**100**

Selected Properties

Addison Circle One (Dallas TX)
Blue Lagoon Drive (Miami FL)
Centennial Technology Center (Colorado Springs CO)
Hillview Center (San Jose CA)
Legacy Tennyson Center (Dallas TX)
One and Two River Crossing (Indianapolis IN)
Park Seneca (Charlotte NC)
Satellite Place (Duluth GA)
TCF Tower and Bank Building (Minneapolis MN)

COMPETITORS

Boston Properties
Brandywine Realty
Corporate Office
  Properties Trust
Cousins Properties
Investors Real Estate
  Trust
Liberty Property Trust
Washington Real Estate

HISTORICAL FINANCIALS

Company Type: Public

Income Statement

FYE: December 31

	REVENUE ($ mil.)	NET INCOME ($ mil.)	NET PROFIT MARGIN	EMPLOYEES
12/13	213.6	19.8	9.3%	37
12/12	162.8	7.6	4.7%	35
12/11	139.4	43.5	31.2%	32
12/10	123.1	22.0	17.9%	42
12/09	128.3	27.8	21.7%	43
Annual Growth	13.6%	(8.2%)	—	(3.7%)

2013 Year-End Financials

Debt ratio: 45.3%
Return on equity: 2.0%
Cash ($ mil.): 19
Current ratio: 1.32
Long-term debt ($ mil.): 926
No. of shares (mil.): 100
Dividends
  Yield: 6.3%
  Payout: 380.0%
Market value ($ mil.): 1,197

	STOCK PRICE ($) FY Close	P/E High/Low	PER SHARE ($) Earnings	Dividends	Book Value
12/13	11.95	73 56	0.21	0.76	10.48
12/12	12.31	137106	0.09	0.76	10.43
12/11	9.95	29 19	0.53	0.76	11.11
12/10	14.25	56 39	0.28	0.76	11.32
12/09	14.61	40 27	0.38	0.76	11.76
Annual Growth	(4.9%)	— —	(13.8%)	(0.0%)	(2.8%)

Fresh Market, Inc.

When it comes to food fresh is best. The Fresh Market operates about 160 full-service upscale specialty grocery stores in some 25 US states from Florida to Wisconsin. As the name suggests the chain specializes in perishable goods (two-thirds of sales) including fruits and vegetables meat and seafood. The stores average 21000 square feet about a third to half the size of a conventional supermarket. However customers won't find the non-food items sold in most grocery stores these days such as cleaning and cooking supplies. Founded by husband-and-wife team Ray and Beverly Berry who opened their first store in 1982 The Fresh Market which went public in 2010 is expanding in the Southeast.

IPO

The Berry family and other company officers were the selling shareholders and received all the proceeds from the November 2010 initial public offering which raised about $290 million. With the economy rebounding the Berrys apparently felt it was time to cash out.

Geographic Reach

The fast-growing chain operates grocery stores in 26 states primarily located in the Southeast Midwest Northeast and Mid-Atlantic region. New markets include California and Texas. However established markets Florida North Carolina and Georgia are home to more than half of The Fresh Market's stores.

Sales and Marketing

The Fresh Market spends far less on advertising than its conventional competitors relying primarily on word-of-mouth publicity to attract customers. Indeed the grocery chain reported advertising costs of only $3862 in fiscal 2013 (ended January) or just 0.3% of annual sales up from $2652 in the previous year. In-store marketing activities include cooking classes and demonstrations tours and product demonstrations. It also distributes a weekly online newsletter named "Fresh Idea" to promote new products seasonal produce recipes and weekly specials.

Financial Performance

Fueled by the addition of new stores The Fresh Market's fiscal 2013 (ended January) sales increased 20% versus the prior year to more than $1.3 billion. Net income rose 25% over the same period to about $64 million due to higher sales and decreased interest expanse. Same-store sales at Fresh Market stores increased 6% year over year. Indeed fiscal 2013 marked the fifth consecutive year of rising sales and the second consecutive year of rising profits (since the 2010 IPO).

Strategy

The Fresh Market's recipe for growth is to continue to open stores at a rapid pace in new and existing markets and to increase sales at older stores. Indeed the grocery chain has announced plans to double its store count in the Southeast to more than 200 locations. Currently 104 of its 160 stores are located in the region. In fiscal 2014 it plans to open a record 22 locations. Ultimately management believes the US can support at least 500 of its upscale grocery stores. The Fresh Market is forecasting same-store sales to increase 4% to 6% in the coming year. The chain caters to its affluent customers by offering high-margin specialty foods such as hand-trimmed aged steaks fresh seafood hand-stacked fresh produce and a high level of customer service. Its smaller store footprint gives the retailer more flexibility in picking locations.

Ownership

The investment firms FMR LLC and Wells Fargo & Company each own about 11% of the company's shares. T. Rowe Price Associates owns about 10%. Founder and company chairman Ray Berry and his son vice chairman Brett Berry together own about 7% of the company stock.

EXECUTIVES

Senior Vice President Merchandising And Marketing, Maurus Anderson

EVP and COO; Interim CEO, Sean Crane, age 46, $293,162 total compensation

SVP Merchandising and Marketing, Marc Jones, age 42

EVP and CFO, Jeffrey (Jeff) Ackerman

Vice President Of Merchandising, Lee Arthur

Vice President, Steve Showalter

Vice President Finance, Jeffrey B Short

Vice President Non Perishables And Private Label At The Fresh Market, Karen Stout

Vice President Human Resource Operations, Matthew Bianchino

Vice President Meat And Seafood, Ross Reynolds

Vice President, Harold Lloyd

Vice President Deli Bakery, Mark Wolowitz

Vice President Of Real Estate, Rob Koch

Senior Vice President Real Estate And Development, Randall Young

Department Head, Luke Fontenot

Chairman, Ray Berry, age 73

Vice Chairman, Brett Berry, age 47

Board Member, David Rea

Board Of Director, Marco Brughera

Board Member, Meg Wheeler

Auditors: Ernst&YoungLLP

LOCATIONS

HQ: Fresh Market, Inc.
628 Green Valley Road, Suite 500, Greensboro, NC 27408
Phone: 336 272-1338
Web: www.thefreshmarket.com

2013 Stores

	No.
Florida	31
North Carolina	15
Georgia	12
Virginia	8
Illinois	7
Tennessee	7
Ohio	6
Alabama	5
South Carolina	5
Indiana	4
Louisiana	4
Maryland	4
Kentucky	3
Pennsylvania	3
Arkansas	2
Connecticut	2
New York	2
Wisconsin	2
California	1
Kansas	1
Massachusetts	1
Mississippi	1
New Hampshire	1
New Jersey	1
Oklahoma	1
Total	**129**

PRODUCTS/OPERATIONS

2013 Sales

	% of total
Perishable	66
Nonperishable	34
Total	**100**

COMPETITORS

Earth Fare	Trader Joe's
Food Lion	Wal-Mart
Kroger	Wegmans
Publix	Weis Markets
Safeway	Whole Foods
Sprouts	Winn-Dixie
Target Corporation	

HISTORICAL FINANCIALS

Company Type: Public

Income Statement

FYE: January 26

	REVENUE ($ mil.)	NET INCOME ($ mil.)	NET PROFIT MARGIN	EMPLOYEES
01/14	1,511.6	50.8	3.4%	11,700
01/13	1,329.1	64.1	4.8%	10,000
01/12	1,108.0	51.4	4.6%	8,500
01/11*	78.1	2.6	3.4%	7,300
12/10	974.2	22.9	2.4%	7,300
Annual Growth	**11.6%**	**22.0%**	**—**	**12.5%**

*Fiscal year change

2014 Year-End Financials

Debt ratio: 10.8%	No. of shares (mil.): 48
Return on equity: 22.4%	Dividends
Cash ($ mil.): 11	Yield: —
Current ratio: 0.79	Payout: —
Long-term debt ($ mil.): 50	Market value ($ mil.): 1,744

	STOCK PRICE ($) FY Close	P/E High/Low		PER SHARE ($) Earnings	Dividends	Book Value
01/14	36.13	54	34	1.05	0.00	5.31
01/13	47.64	47	32	1.33	0.00	4.11
01/12	44.74	43	29	1.07	0.00	2.64
01/11*	36.29	737	534	0.06	0.00	1.50
12/10	41.20	92	67	0.48	1.00	1.44
Annual Growth	**(3.2%)**	**— —**		**21.6%**	**—**	**38.5%**

*Fiscal year change

Fuller (H.B.) Company

H.B. Fuller has stuck with glue for more than a century. Long known for making adhesives sealants and specialty chemicals the company markets its products in some 40 countries. Industrial adhesives are its core product offering and customers include companies in the assembly packaging automotive woodworking and nonwoven textiles industries. Other products include construction materials principally ceramic tile installation products (such as grouts mortars and sealers) and HVAC insulating coatings (duct sealants fungicidal coatings and weather barriers).

HISTORY

In 1887 armed with a wood stove and an iron kettle Harvey Benjamin Fuller Sr. began making wet paste to sell to paperhangers in St. Paul Minnesota. The company became incorporated as the Fuller Manufacturing Company with $600 in capital from three Minneapolis lawyers. It began marketing glue to shoe companies bookbinders and other customers and producing ink for the city's schools. In 1888 Fuller's son Albert joined his father instantly doubling the firm's workforce.

After the 1892 acquisition of competitor Minnesota Paste Company Fuller grew largely through sales spurred by a series of inventions. Fuller's two cold-water products a dry wall cleaner and dry paste proved wildly successful. In 1905 the company was shipping to Australia Germany and the UK. Fuller's son Harvey Jr. joined the company in 1909.

In 1915 Fuller reincorporated as the H.B. Fuller Company. During WWI it supplied adhesives for canned goods shipped to the troops but business fell off after the war. Harvey Sr. died in 1921. Despite facing possible bankruptcy Harvey Jr. made a fateful decision to hire a full-time chemist. With Ray Burgess' inventions the company achieved record sales by the end of the 1920s.

After the stock market crashed Fuller acquired the Selvasize Company makers of a combination wallpaper- and plaster-adhesive. Fuller rode out the Depression with the success of new products such as Ice Proof (a glue resistant to cold water) and Nu-Type Hot Pick-Up (used in automated labeling). However in 1937 the company learned that three salespeople had been undercutting orders through a phantom firm which they then claimed to represent. Fuller's sales dropped almost $50000 the following year. In 1939 Harvey Jr. suffered a stroke.

In 1941 competitor Paisley Products of Chicago offered to buy the company for $50000. Instead Elmer Andersen (a business whiz who had joined the company as a salesman in the mid-1930s) persuaded Harvey to turn the reins over to him and give him a majority stake. WWII began bringing numerous government contracts to the company. During and after the war H.B. Fuller decentralized operations by opening branch plants beginning with Kansas City in 1943. By 1950 H.B. Fuller was the fourth-largest adhesives company in the US.

Andersen went on to become a state senator and eventually governor of Minnesota. Under the leadership of Al Vigard in the 1950s and 1960s the company expanded into Canada Costa Rica Panama and other countries. H.B. Fuller went public in 1968. In 1971 Tony Andersen (Elmer's son) took over and further pushed international sales. From 1971 to 1980 the company made some two dozen acquisitions –about half in foreign countries –and increased sales fivefold. In 1980 Andersen began revamping the company which had become inefficient because of its geographic expansion. By 1985 earnings were solid again.

In 1991 the company suffered adverse publicity after social activists accused it of marketing its Resistol glue in Latin America while knowing that street kids were sniffing the glue. In 1997 H.B. Fuller entered a joint venture with Switzerland's EMS-Chemie Holding AG to combine their automotive coatings sealants and adhesives businesses. CEO Walter Kissing whose efforts to reduce costs in the 1990s failed to improve margins retired in 1998.

The next year Andersen retired as chairman and Al Stroucken a former Bayer executive took the helm. Stroucken quickly announced a restructuring that would reduce the company's plant operations and lay off 10% of its workforce. From 2001-2003 the company eliminated 20% of its manufacturing plants and cut more than 550 employees. It restructured its adhesives business which was run through four geographic regions into one global unit. The company also reduced its product offerings by half allowing it to deliver products on time more consistently.

While H.B. Fuller did increase sales in 2003 over the previous year that improvement was due mainly to the weakened dollar (against the Euro and other foreign currencies) and the resulting exchange differences. Sales volume decreased as did prices. Revenues increased again in 2004 partly due to the same trend; however the company also benefited from the increased sales volume of global adhesives and specialty products and from its February 2004 acquisition of the adhesives business of Portugese chemical firm Probos.

Due to accounting irregularities during 1999 through 2004 H.B. Fuller conducted an internal investigation into the finances of its Chilean operations in 2005. As a result the company made minor adjustments in its 2004 financial statements.

Also in 2005 the firm combined its Chinese and Japanese adhesives businesses with those of Sekisui Chemical through joint ventures. Three years later H.B. Fuller acquired a business in Egypt called Egymelt to establish a presence in North Africa.

The company reorganized its business segments in 2007. H.B. Fuller rearranged its operations along geographic lines merging the former Global Adhesives and Full Valu/Specialty segments into regional operations. The new segments are Asia/Pacific Europe Latin America and North America. The move followed a gradual coming-together of the company's product groups. Fuller had worked to make its adhesive products more specialized and less of a commodity.

Jim Owens was named president and CEO of H.B. Fuller in 2010. He replaced Michele Volpi

who resigned from the company. Owens was previously SVP of H.B. Fullers' Americas operations.

In 2011 the company bought a 20% stake that Sekisui Chemical had held in its Chinese operations for $8.6 million.

The company acquired the global industrial adhesives business of Forbo in 2012. The $394 million cash deal expanded H.B. Fuller's position in the international adhesives industry. The business represented about 80% of revenues for the Forbo Bonding Systems division of Forbo Group. It is expected to increase H.B. Fuller's business in China by as much as 50% and strengthen its position in such markets as packaging and durable assembly.

In 2012 the firm bought Engent Inc. a provider of manufacturing research and development services to the electronics industry based in Norcross Georgia. The deal added development capabilities testing resources and technical support infrastructure increasing H.B. Fuller's capabilities in a wide range of microelectronic assembly technologies.

In 2012 the company sold its Central American paints business to Colombia-based paints company Compania Global de Pinturas (Pintuco) part of Grupo Mundial for $120 million. Pintuco has a strong market position in Central America and H.B. Fuller wanted to focus on its core adhesives operations.

EXECUTIVES

EVP and CFO, James R. (Jim) Giertz, age 57, $519,236 total compensation
President and CEO, James J. (Jim) Owens, age 50, $839,135 total compensation
SVP EMEA and India, Steven Kenny, age 53, $433,104 total compensation
SVP Americas Adhesives, Traci L. Jensen, $404,423 total compensation
VP Asia Pacific, Heather Campe
VP Global Operations, Elin Gabriel
CIO, David Moorman
CTO and Chief Innovation Officer, Hassan Rmaile
Vp Global Operations, Kevin M Gilligan, age 48
Vice President, Jorge W Bolanos
Sr V Pres, Alan R Longstreet
Vice President Of Information, Dan Piteleski
Executive Vice President, Dennis Hahn
Vice President, Jim Schmidt
Vice President Customer Service, Jim Vergin
Vice President Ecommerce, Paul Satre
National Sales Manager, David Santamaria
Vice President General Counsel, Timothy Keenan
Chairman, Lee R. Mitau, age 66
Auditors: KPMGLLP

LOCATIONS

HQ: Fuller (H.B.) Company
1200 Willow Lake Boulevard, St. Paul, MN 55110-5101
Phone: 651 236-5900 **Fax:** 651 236-5161
Web: www.hbfuller.com

PRODUCTS/OPERATIONS

2014 Sales

	$ mil	% of total
Americas Adhesives	920.7	44
EIMEA	719.8	34
Asia Pacific	275.8	13
Construction Products	188.2	9
Total	**2104.5**	**100**

Markets and Applications
Packaging
Building and Construction
Paper Converting
Woodworking Adhesives
General Assembly Adhesives and Laminates

Personal Hygiene and Nonwovens
Tile and Floor Adhesive Products
Polymers
Adhesive Technologies
H.B. Fuller Hot Melt Technology
H.B. Fuller Solvent-Based Technology
H.B. Fuller Urethane's Epoxies and other Reactive Chemistries
H.B. Fuller Water-Based Adhesive Technology
Innovative Solutions
Advantra Encore™ Packaging Adhesive
New Liquamelt® packaging adhesive system
New Flextra Quiet™ flexible packaging adhesive
Patent Information
Flextra Fast™ Solventless Laminating Adhesive System
PlyABLE™ Adhesive
Performance Products
Products: Liquamelt® Packaging Adhesive System
Products: Advantra Encore™
Products: Advantra®
Brands and Affiliates
Advantra Encore™
Advantra®
Clarity™
Clean Melt®
Flextra®
Full-Care™
Liquamelt®
LiquiLoc®
Rakoll®
Rapidex®

COMPETITORS

3M	Henkel
ADCO Global	SABIC Innovative
ADM Tronics	Plastics
Akzo Nobel	Sherwin-Williams
Bostik	Super Glue
Cytec	Valspar
Dow Corning	

HISTORICAL FINANCIALS

Company Type: Public

Income Statement

FYE: November 29

	REVENUE ($ mil.)	NET INCOME ($ mil.)	NET PROFIT MARGIN	EMPLOYEES
11/14	2,104.4	49.7	2.4%	3,700
11/13*	2,046.9	96.7	4.7%	3,700
12/12	1,886.2	125.6	6.7%	3,700
12/11	1,557.5	89.1	5.7%	3,500
11/10	1,356.1	70.8	5.2%	3,300
Annual Growth	**11.6%**	**(8.5%)**	**—**	**2.9%**

*Fiscal year change

2014 Year-End Financials

Debt ratio: 30.7%
Return on equity: 5.4%
Cash ($ mil.): 77
Current ratio: 2.41
Long-term debt ($ mil.): 547

No. of shares (mil.): 50
Dividends
  Yield: 0.0%
  Payout: 47.4%
Market value ($ mil.): 2,173

	STOCK PRICE ($) FY Close	P/E High/Low		PER SHARE ($) Earnings	Dividends	Book Value
11/14	43.19	53	37	0.97	0.46	17.69
11/13*	51.23	26	17	1.89	0.39	18.52
12/12	32.85	13	8	2.48	0.33	15.60
12/11	22.37	14	9	1.79	0.30	14.26
11/10	21.07	17	13	1.43	0.28	12.85
Annual Growth	**19.7%**	**—**	**—**	**(9.2%)**	**13.4%**	**8.3%**

*Fiscal year change

Furmanite Corp

Furmanite thrives under pressure. The specialty contractor provides a variety of technical services for petroleum refineries chemical plants nuclear power stations and other clients in the power generation manufacturing and processing industries. Furmanite specializes in sealing leaks in valves pipes and other flow-process systems often under emergency conditions involving exposure to high temperatures and pressures potential contact with dangerous materials explosion hazards and environmental contamination. It also provides onsite machining and custom engineering services and through Xtria consulting and support services for government agencies. Furmanite has about 75 offices around the world.

In addition to its pressure services Furmanite provides repair machining and other treatments for offline piping systems. The company has worked on fast-turnaround and custom engineering projects for such customers as Alcoa GlaxoSmithKline and PacifiCorp.

Furmanite is active around the world and has offices across six continents. The Americas represents about half of the company's annual sales. Europe Middle East and Africa makes up about 40%.

The company has been working to recover from the global recession which created lower demand for some of Furmanite's services and hurt revenues. The company implemented a $16 million cost-cutting plan that included consolidations and workforce reductions. The cost cutting in conjunction with economic recovery and higher demand helped Furmanite return to profitability by 2010.

Revenues increased by more than 10% in 2011. Furmanite attributed that growth to an increase in leak sealing line stopping bolting and composite repair services. Net income also increased tremendously that year. Profits grew thanks to higher sales and lower costs.

Furmanite continued to cut costs in 2012 and announced plans to further reduce administrative expenses and streamline its European operations. Furmanite also is focused on growing its geographic footprint and expanding its specialty industrial services capabilities. It achieved those goals mainly through acquisitions. In early 2011 Furmanite expanded its global operations when it acquired frequent partner Self Leveling Machines a machining specialist with operations in the US and Australia. The deal boosted Furmanite's global onsite machining capabilities especially those involving solutions for large-scale equipment and operations.

In 2012 Furmanite acquired Crane Energy Flow Solutions' Houston Service Center. The service center repairs certain Crane products and services all makes of valves. The deal came after Furmanite's move to Houston.

HISTORY

Kaneb Services which became Xanser in 2001 was founded in 1953 as a pipeline company. It built its first pipeline between Kansas and Nebraska. As its pipeline advanced through the Midwest Kaneb moved into offshore drilling coal production and banking. Profits sprung a leak during the Texas oil and banking bust and new CEO John Barnes inherited $574 million in debt when he came aboard in 1986. Barnes sold all of Kaneb's energy-related businesses except the pipeline company restruc-

tured Kaneb's debt and in 1989 took the pipeline public forming Kaneb Pipeline Partners (KPP).

The company bought debt-laden Furmanite in 1991. Furmanite was founded in the 1920s by Clay Furman who developed methods of sealing steam leaks.

In 1993 KPP bought Support Terminal Services one of the largest US liquid-storage firms. KPP purchased 550 miles of pipeline from Wyco two years later giving the company a presence in the Rocky Mountain area. That purchase and other terminal acquisitions in 1996 boosted Kaneb's sales.

Furmanite expanded internationally in 1997 with the acquisition of a longtime licensee serving Australia and New Zealand. In 1998 Furmanite teamed up with Yarway a steam trap inspection unit of diversified manufacturer Tyco International to offer service and repair to the hydrocarbon-processing industry. That year the company diversified further through the acquisition of a products-marketing firm that offers wholesale fuel-marketing services in California the Great Lakes region and the Rockies.

In 1999 KPP acquired six storage terminals in the UK. Kaneb also moved into information technology in a big way by acquiring Ellsworth Associates a major IT service provider to the US government. That year Kaneb won a multiyear multimillion-dollar contract with the US Army to produce more than 2 million solid-state wearable medical data storage devices.

Kaneb's information services unit formed an alliance with Datakey in 2000 to make Datakey's smart cards for US government agencies. The next year the company integrated four information technology services units into a new subsidiary Xtria.

Restructuring in 2001 the company spun off its stake in KPP and its fuel marketing operations to shareholders as Kaneb Services LLC. To reflect its shift in focus Kaneb changed its name to Xanser that year. Also that year subsidiary Furmanite Worldwide along with BAE Systems produced equipment for maintenance of Tornado fighter aircraft. In 2003 Xanser closed unprofitable operations in its Xtria subsidiary.

Furmanite's 2005 acquisition of Flowserve's General Services Group (GSG) added valve-repair and hot-tapping capabilities to the group's capabilities and effectively doubled the size of its business. The company in 2006 exited its health care-focused business (honoring existing contracts); these discontinued services included training and maintenance of digital radiology imaging systems known as picture archival and communication systems (PACS) which are used in connection with MRI (magnetic resonance imaging) ultrasounds digital X-rays and other radiology techniques.

Furmanite opened an office in West Africa in 2008 to expand its service lines to customers in the region.

EXECUTIVES

Chairman of the Board; Chief Executive Officer, Charles R. Cox, age 71, $333,333 total compensation
President and CEO, Joseph E. (Joe) Milliron, age 59, $350,000 total compensation
Vice President, Peter Casey
Evp Geographical, Clint Jordan
Senior Vice President Financial, Glenn Dinetz
Senior Vice President Operations Ess, Billy Peterson
Vice President Process Intervention Prccess Infervenhbn, Gary Gains
Vice President Information Technology, Francisco Callegari

Vice President Sales And Marketing, Jeffrey Wolf
Vice President Of Information Technology, Jay Goodyear
Vice President, Henia Leibman
Vice President Of Marketing, Scott Wiseman
Vice President Process Integrity, Julian White
Vice President Inflight Services, Mike Hafner
Vice President Valve Products, Tony Morris
Vice President Latin America And Caribbean Region, G Carrillo
Vice President Of Process Intervention, Gary Goins
Non Executive Director and Chairman, Sangwoo (Bill) Ahn
Assistant Treasurer, Charles Van Ravensyaay
Board Member, Ralph Patitucci
Secretary, Steve Lee
Auditors: UHYLLP

LOCATIONS

HQ: Furmanite Corp
10370 Richmond Avenue, Suite 600, Houston, TX 77042
Phone: 713 634-7777
Web: www.furmanite.com

2011 Sales

	$ mil.	% of total
Americas	158.5	50
Europe Middle East Africa	118.6	38
Asia/Pacific	39.0	12
Total	**316.2**	**100**

PRODUCTS/OPERATIONS

Selected Subsidiaries and Affiliates

Advance Integrity Solutions Inc.
CMS: Corrision Monitoring Services AS
Furmanite AB
Furmanite America Inc.
Furmanite Aruba N.V.
Furmanite A/S
Furmanite Australia Pty Ltd.
Furmanite BVBA
Furmanite BV
Furmanite Canada Corp
Furmanite Equipment Leasing Company LLC
Furmanite Germany Inc.
Furmanite GSG Limited
Furmanite Holding AS
Furmanite Holding BV
Furmanite Holding (Norway)
Furmanite International Finance Limited
Furmanite International Limited
Furmanite Offshore Services Inc.
Furmanite Limited
Furmanite Malaysia LLC
Furmanite Mechanical Technology Services (Shanghai) Co. Ltd.
Furmanite Middle East SPC
Furmanite NZ Limited
Furmanite SAS
Furmanite Singapore PTE Ltd.
Furmanite Technische Dienstleistengen GmbH
Furmanite US GSG BV
Furmanite US GSG LLC
Furmanite West Africa Limited
Furmanite Worldwide
Furmatec Limited
Furmanite 1986
Kaneb Financial Corporation
Management Services Furmanite Holding GmbH
Metaholding BV
Metalock BV
Self Leveling Machines Inc.
Specialty Industrial Services Sdn. Bhd.
Xanser Investment
Xanser Services LLC
Xtria LLC

Selected Mergers & Acquisitions
2012

Crane Energy Flow Solutions (Houston Texas valve service assets and operations)
2011
Self Leveling Machines International Pty Ltd and Self Leveling Machines Inc. (Melbourne Australia large-scale equipment operations)

COMPETITORS

Computer Sciences Corp.	National Oilwell Varco
Halliburton	Schlumberger
ITT Corp.	Sterling Construction
Kinder Morgan Management	T. D. Williamson
	Team

HISTORICAL FINANCIALS

Company Type: Public

Income Statement

FYE: December 31

	REVENUE ($ mil.)	NET INCOME ($ mil.)	NET PROFIT MARGIN	EMPLOYEES
12/13	427.2	14.0	3.3%	3,110
12/12	326.4	0.8	0.2%	1,833
12/11	316.2	23.9	7.6%	1,529
12/10	285.9	9.4	3.3%	1,521
12/09	275.9	(2.8)	—	1,737
Annual Growth	11.6%	—	—	15.7%

2013 Year-End Financials

Debt ratio: 22.9%	No. of shares (mil.): 37
Return on equity: 11.1%	Dividends
Cash ($ mil.): 33	Yield: —
Current ratio: 3.15	Payout: —
Long-term debt ($ mil.): 63	Market value ($ mil.): 399

	STOCK PRICE ($) FY Close	P/E High/Low	PER SHARE ($) Earnings	Dividends	Book Value
12/13	10.62	31 14	0.37	0.00	3.56
12/12	5.37	401 186	0.02	0.00	3.19
12/11	6.31	13 8	0.64	0.00	3.20
12/10	6.91	28 12	0.26	0.00	2.66
12/09	3.81	— —	(0.08)	0.00	2.33
Annual Growth	29.2%	— —	—	—	11.2%

FutureFuel Corp

FutureFuel's future may be in biofuels but for now it still relies on chemicals. The company manufactures biodiesel and other biofuels; however its core business is specialty chemicals which include a bleach activator and detergent additives a proprietary herbicide and chlorinated polyolefin adhesion promoters (used in coatings for the automotive industry). It synthesizes custom chemicals for a variety of industries and applications. Selling its products primarily in North America FutureFuel markets to customers that include industrial and consumer goods manufacturers as well as pharmaceutical companies and agribusinesses. It manufactures its biofuels and chemicals at a single plant in Arkansas.

Geographic Reach

Missouri-based FutureFuel has manufacturing plants laboratories an on-site liquid waste treatment site and other infrastructure and a warehouse in Batesville Arkansas. It sells primarily to customers in the US and Mexico.

Operations

FutureFuel divides its operations into two main segments: Biofuels and Chemicals. It splits its Chemicals segment further into Custom Manufacturing and Performance Chemicals (which include its own brands of specialty chemical products).

Its Biofuels segment produces biodiesel from feedstock with high fatty acids. The company which makes its biodiesel from organic products like soybean oil animal lard and cooking oils intends to continue growing its biofuels business by broadening its production and distribution capabilities. In 2011 the company redesigned its production line to achieve a capacity of about 35 million gallons of biodiesel per year. Additional debottlenecking increased the capacity to more than 45 millions gallons per year. The redesigned line enables it to make biodiesel from lower quality and less expensive feedstock. FutureFuels distributes its biofuels as well as its chemical products through its own tanker-truck fleet as well as leased vehicles.

The company's chemical products are used in a range of end uses including agrochemical automotive coatings detergents nutrition photographic imaging and polymer additives. About half of its total revenues comes from custom manufacturing specialty or performance chemicals for specific customers and a smaller portion comes from producing specialty chemicals or performance chemicals for several customers. The company also sells an intermediate anode powder which is used to produce lithium-ion batteries. Its Performance Chemicals unit includes polymer (nylon and polyester) modifiers and some specialty chemicals and solvents for various applications.

Financial Performance

FutureFuel's revenues grew by 14% in 2012 due to a 35% increase in the Biofuels results caused by higher biodiesel production ans sales Revenues from their biofuels also been benefited by sales to a refined petroleum products shipper on a common carrier pipeline. These gains were offset by 5% decline in chemical segment revenues. The company's net income of $351.8 million (14% up on 2011) was the result of higher net sales increased interest and dividend income and a gain on marketable securities.

With the exception of the revenue slump in 2009 (when the global recession and weakened demand for oil and gas products) FutureFuel has reported an upward trend in revenue between 2008 and 2012.

Strategy

FutureFuel's long-term strategy seeks to grow both its chemicals and biofuels businesses. The company also wants to commercialize other products such as building block chemicals. It is seeking to establish new markets for its biofuels business and hopes to accelerate marketing efforts to serve fleets and regional/national customers.

FutureFuel has had a multiyear contract with The Procter & Gamble Co. (which ends in 2016) to sell all of its bleach activator product. However Procter & Gamble notified FutureFuels in 2011 that it was reducing the quantities of bleach activator it purchases. FutureFuel also sells its proprietary herbicide and certain intermediates used in its production to Arysta LifeScience North America. Arysta reduced its purchase volumes of the herbicide by half in 2012.

Ownership

Paul A. Novelly who has been the company's chairman since its formation owns about 44% of the company. He is also chairman and CEO of Apex Oil.

HISTORY

The company's biofuels revenues dropped from 27% in 2009 to 18% in 2010. Despite a hit on profitability because of a hike in biodiesel feedstock prices and the loss of an industry-wide federal tax credit at the end of 2009 FutureFuel continued its renewable fuels business. Although it continues to work on improving this production line FutureFuel has been able to produce what it considers a high-quality biodiesel by using feedstock such as yellow grease tallow and crude corn oil.

With the reinstatement of the federal blender's credit in December 2010 FutureFuel expects to exceed biodiesel activity in 2011. However the tax credit is scheduled to expire again at the end of the year which would impact the profitability of biodiesel production.

EXECUTIVES

Executive Chairman and CEO, Paul A. (Tony) Novelly, age 70
COO and Director, Paul G. Lorenzini, age 74
EVP and General Manager, Samuel W. Dortch, age 65, $207,431 total compensation
Principal Financial Officer and Secretary, Rose Sparks, $145,045 total compensation
EVP Business and Marketing, Paul Flynn
Executive Chairman and CEO, Paul A. (Tony) Novelly, age 70
Auditors: RubinBrownLLP

LOCATIONS

HQ: FutureFuel Corp
8235 Forsyth Blvd., Suite 400, St. Louis, MO 63105
Phone: 805 565-9800
Web: www.futurefuelcorporation.com

2012 Sales

	$ mil.	% of total
US	338.3	96
Other countries	13.5	4
Total	351.8	100

PRODUCTS/OPERATIONS

2012 Sales

$ mil		% of total
Biofuels	191.4	54
Chemicals	160.4	46
Total	351.8	100

COMPETITORS

ADM	Exxon Mobil
BASF SE	Green Brick Partners
Cargill	Louis Dreyfus
Chemtura	Commodities
Dow Chemical	Renewable Energy Group
DuPont	UOP
Ecolab	

HISTORICAL FINANCIALS

Company Type: Public

Income Statement

FYE: December 31

	REVENUE ($ mil.)	NET INCOME ($ mil.)	NET PROFIT MARGIN	EMPLOYEES
12/13	444.9	74.0	16.6%	500
12/12	351.8	34.3	9.8%	500
12/11	309.8	34.5	11.1%	500
12/10	219.1	23.0	10.5%	500
12/09	196.7	16.9	8.6%	464
Annual Growth	22.6%	44.5%	—	1.9%

G-III Apparel Group Ltd.

G-III Apparel Group is into leather but not exclusively. The company is best known for making leather jackets under the G-III Marvin Richards Black Rivet Winlit Siena Studio and other labels (such as Andrew Marc) as well as under licensed names. It also makes pants skirts and sportswear from leather and other materials. More than two-thirds of G-III's sales are generated from licensed apparel it makes for the NFL NBA NHL and MLB teams as well as for Jones New York Nine West and Kenneth Cole. The company's customers include department stores such as Macy's Nordstrom Lord & Taylor and Kohl's.

Additionally Buckingham Capital Management and FMR each hold about a 12% stake.

The company formed a joint venture with The Camuto Group to develop a chain of stores devoted to footwear and accessories operating under the Vince Camuto banner. The chain leverages G-III's retail infrastructure (real estate distribution information and administrative systems) with Camuto providing its growing family of big-name brands including Vince Camuto Jessica Simpson BCBG Max Azria BCBGeneration Kensiegirl Lucky Brand and Arturo Chiang. The first Vince Camuto store opened in early 2011.

Having been big in licensing for a decade the company has inked several deals that maintain its strategy and revenue mix of licensed and non-licensed products. A particular purchase it has used as a foundation for this effort is its acquisition of Andrew Marc for $42 million in 2008. The deal gave G-III handbags and upscale specialty and department store distribution. Andrew Marc then entered a licensing agreement with Camuto to make and market women's footwear under the Andrew Marc and Marc New York brands. G-III's Jessica Howard license extends its reach into dresses with its Jessica Howard and Eliza J names. G-III's purchase of Industrial Cotton also expanded its junior denim products. The purchases also gave G-III a foothold in new retail outlets with the brands selling in Dillard's Nordstrom Sears Kohl's and Coldwater Creek among others.

Beyond the department store channel G-III operates about 120 retail stores most of which are outlet stores. The company's retail business generated about 16% of its sales in 2010. G-III had extended its reach into retail in 2008 when the apparel wholesaler acquired the Wilsons The Leather Experts' outlet stores as well as the Wilsons brand name and distribution center operations for about $22 million. The move represented G-III's effort to boost its retail presence.

G-III conducts most of its business in the US with 98% of its revenue generated within the country's borders. Its products are produced by independent manufacturers however located primarily in China as well as in India Indonesia Sri Lanka Taiwan Thailand Vietnam and Central and South America. Some of its garments are made in the US.

Ownership

Chairman and CEO Morris Goldfarb and investment firm FMR LLC each own about 15% of G-III's shares. Royce & Associates owns about 10%.

EXECUTIVES

COO, Wayne S. Miller, age 56, $500,000 total compensation
CEO President and Chairman, Morris Goldfarb, age 64, $1,000,000 total compensation
CFO and Treasurer, Neal S. Nackman, age 54, $375,000 total compensation
Vice President Of Credit Collections, Joanne Longo
National Sales Manager, Yaphet Smallwood
Vice President Of Sales, Kyle Sanborn
CEO President and Chairman, Morris Goldfarb, age 64
Vice Chairman, Sammy Aaron, age 54
Auditors: Ernst&YoungLLP

LOCATIONS

HQ: G-III Apparel Group Ltd.
512 Seventh Avenue, New York, NY 10018
Phone: 212 403-0500
Web: www.g-iii.com

2012 Sales

	$ mil.	% of total
US	1185.8	96
Other countries	45.4	4
Total	**1231.2**	**100**

PRODUCTS/OPERATIONS

2012 Sales

	$ mil.	% of total
Wholesale licensed apparel	840.7	68
Wholesale non-licensed apparel	277.6	23
Retail	164.3	13
Adjustments	(51.4)	(4)
Total	**1231.2**	**100**

Selected Divisions

Outerwear
  Andrew Marc
  Black Rivet
  Calvin Klein
  Cole Haan
  Dockers
  Ellen Tracy
  Guess
  Jones New York
  Kenneth Cole
  Levi's
  Marc New York
  Nine West
  Sean John
  Tommy Hilfiger
Ready to Wear
  Andrew Marc Dresses
  Calvin Klein Dresses
  Calvin Klein Performance Wear
  Calvin Klein Sportswear
  Calvin Klein Women Suits
  Eliza J Dresses
  Ellen Tracy Dresses
  Jessica Howard Dresses
  Jessica Simpson Dresses
  Marc New York Dresses

Sports
  G-III for Her
  G-III Sports by Carl Banks
  Major League Baseball
  National Basketball Association
  National Football League
  National Hockey League
  Officially Licensed Collegiate Products
  Touch by Alyssa Milano
Retail
  Wilsons Outlets

Selected Licenses

Men's and Women's
  Calvin Klein
  Cole Haan
  Guess?
  Jessica Simpson
  Kenneth Cole NY
  Levi's
  Vince Camuto
Sports
  Major League Baseball
  Major League Soccer
  National Basketball Association
  National Football League
  National Hockey League

COMPETITORS

Amerex	L.L. Bean
Armani	NIKE
Burberry	North Face
Burlington Coat Factory	Phat Fashions
Columbia Sportswear	Roc Apparel
Diesel SpA	Sean John
FUBU	Tandy Leather
J. Crew	The Gap
	Wal-Mart

HISTORICAL FINANCIALS

Company Type: Public

Income Statement

FYE: January 31

	REVENUE ($ mil.)	NET INCOME ($ mil.)	NET PROFIT MARGIN	EMPLOYEES
01/14	1,718.2	77.3	4.5%	6,631
01/13	1,399.7	56.8	4.1%	3,109
01/12	1,231.2	49.6	4.0%	2,592
01/11	1,063.4	56.6	5.3%	2,154
01/10	800.8	31.7	4.0%	1,880
Annual Growth	**21.0%**	**25.0%**	**—**	**37.0%**

GAIN Capital Holdings Inc

There is plenty to lose in the foreign currency exchange market but this company would like you to focus on the potential gains. GAIN Capital Holdings provides over-the-counter foreign exchange (forex) services to retail traders (responsible for about 97% of the company's trading volume) and institutional investors and through financial intermediaries such as broker-dealers banks and futures commission merchants. The company's FOREXTrader platform provides online trading tools and educational resources to help individual investors deal in forex trading online. It has 133000 funded retail accounts.

Geographic Reach

GAIN provides services to retail and institutional customers in more than 180 countries worldwide conducting business from offices in New York; Bedminster New Jersey; Chicago; Powell Ohio; Grand Rapids Michigan; London; Tokyo; Sydney; Beijing; Hong Kong; and Singapore.

Financial Performance

GAIN achieved explosive growth in 2013 as revenues skyrocketed 76% from $152 million in 2012 to $268 million in 2013 a historic milestone for the company. The impressive growth for 2013 was attributed to a spike in commission revenue due to an additional $15 million from its GTX business as well as an increase of $14 million from its futures business. GAIN's sales trader acquisition also generated an additional $10 million in commission. Trading revenue increased due to higher volatility levels in the foreign exchange markets.

Profits significantly shot up from $3 million in 2012 to $31 million in 2013 due to the higher revenue coupled with an income tax benefit of roughly $14 million received in 2013. GAIN's operating cash flow fell dramatically from 2011 to 2012; however it increased by $18 million in 2013.

Strategy

GAIN in 2013 achieved historic revenue growth through the use of acquisitions. Continuing to adhere to this strategy in 2014 it purchased Galvan Research a UK-based Contract for Difference (CFD) advisory business. The deal gave GAIN a solid foundation on which to build a comprehensive advisory service for its clients in support of its FX & CFD offering.

In 2013 GAIN bought Global Futures & Forex LTD (GFT). The combined company boasts a deeper global footprint a robust offering of more than 12500 financial products and industry-leading trading technology. GAIN is using GFT's broad product offering tools and educational capabilities to further strengthen its competitive position while realizing significant synergies.

EXECUTIVES

EVP Chief Commercial Officer and Chief Marketing Officer, Samantha Roady, age 44, $300,000 total compensation
EVP General Counsel and Corporate Secretary, Diego A. Rotsztain, $325,000 total compensation
COO, Jeffrey A. (Jeff) Scott, $325,000 total compensation
EVP and CFO, Jason E. Emerson, $62,500 total compensation
President and CEO, Glenn H. Stevens, $650,000 total compensation

Senior Vice President Marketing, Michael Thwaite
Senior Vice President Brand Marketing, Dina Grochowski
Vice President Financial Engineering, Alexander Peterhansl
Vice President, Concepcion Arena
Vice President Treasury, Chris Tavaglione
Vice President Retail Trading Platforms, Evangelos Tzoulafis
Vice President Application Architecture, Ramesh Srinivas
Vice President Trading Systems Dev, Keith Ginder
Vice President Configuration Release, Neil Wilkinson
Vice President Of Ecn Technologies, Alfred Oakes
Treasury Manager, Manuel Riveiro
Auditors: Deloitte&ToucheLLP

LOCATIONS

HQ: GAIN Capital Holdings Inc
Bedminster One, 135 Route 202/206, Bedminster, NJ 07921
Phone: 908 731-0700
Web: www.gaincapital.com
Bedminster NJ
Hong Kong
London
New York City
Seoul
Sydney
Tokyo
Woodmere OH

PRODUCTS/OPERATIONS

2013 Sales

	$ mil.	% of total
Non-interest income		
Trading revenue	205.1	77
Commission revenue	60.7	23
Others	1.2	-
Interest income	0.8	-
Total	**267.8**	**100**

COMPETITORS

FX Solutions	ISE
FXCM Inc.	Newedge
GFT	Rosenthal Collins
INTL FCStone	

HISTORICAL FINANCIALS

Company Type: Public

Income Statement

FYE: December 31

	REVENUE ($ mil.)	NET INCOME ($ mil.)	NET PROFIT MARGIN	EMPLOYEES
12/13	266.3	31.3	11.8%	551
12/12	151.3	2.6	1.7%	363
12/11	181.4	15.7	8.7%	364
12/10	189.1	37.8	20.0%	333
12/09	153.3	27.9	18.3%	361
Annual Growth	**14.8%**	**2.8%**	**—**	**11.2%**

2013 Year-End Financials

Debt ratio: 5.8%	No. of shares (mil.): 39
Return on equity: 15.7%	Dividends
Cash ($ mil.): 779	Yield: 2.6%
Current ratio: 1.35	Payout: 25.3%
Long-term debt ($ mil.): 65	Market value ($ mil.): 296

	STOCK PRICE ($) FY Close	P/E High/Low		PER SHARE ($) Earnings	Dividends	Book Value
12/13	7.51	17	5	0.79	0.20	5.95
12/12	4.09	86	49	0.07	0.20	4.69
12/11	6.70	22	11	0.40	0.05	4.81
12/10	9.20	1	1	1.00	0.00	4.81
Annual Growth	(6.5%)	—	—	(7.6%)	—	7.3%

GAMCO Investors Inc

Investing is anything but a game for "Super Mario" Gabelli the self-made billionaire investor and founder and CEO of GAMCO Investors. The firm oversees the mutual fund- and securities-related portion of Gabelli's financial empire. It provides advisory services to some 20 mutual funds and 10 closed-end funds under the Gabelli GAMCO and Comstock brands. Most of the company's approximately $34 billion in assets under management are invested in stocks though company also has a well-performing money-market fund. GAMCO also offers wealth management services for private clients and institutional investors such as pension plans endowments and municipalities. Gabelli controls the firm.

Geographic Reach

The company has five research offices in the US as well as offices overseas in London Hong Kong Shanghai and Tokyo.

Operations

As with many money managers GAMCO derives most of its revenue from investment advisory and incentive fees (82% in 2011) which are directly linked to its assets under management. Despite market uncertainty the company was able to grow its assets under management in most of its segments during 2011 including mutual funds closed-end funds institutional and private wealth management and investment partnerships. As a result its revenues and net income were up as well.

Financial Analysis

GAMCO's revenue increased by nearly 17% in 2011 vs. 2010 while net income was up about 1% over the same period. 2011 marked the second consecutive year of rising revenue following two years of decline during the financial crisis. Indeed GAMCO's $327 million in revenue in 2011 was an all-time high for the firm.

GAMCO's investment advisory business posted a 16% increase in revenue in 2011 vs. 2010 while distribution fees and other income rose nearly 38% over the same period. The firm's institutional research services segment posted a 14% decline.

Strategy

GAMCO which strives for long-term returns based on proprietary fundamental research is dependent on its flamboyant founder and his legendary gift for picking stocks particularly those of media and communications companies. A brand unto himself Gabelli is the chief investment officer for the firm's Value Portfolios which represent nearly 90% of GAMCO's assets under management and he gets paid tens of millions of dollars per year for his troubles. Gabelli is also the portfolio manager of Teton Advisors; GAMCO spun off the asset management firm in 2009 but retained ownership of more than 40% of the company.

GAMCO is expanding its mutual fund distribution network through agreements with brokerage firms and other third-party channels. It has traditionally reached out to prospective clients through direct marketing but is increasingly courting financial consultants who in turn offer GAMCO funds to their clients. The company focuses on households with more than $1 million to invest.

GAMCO also grows through acquisitions of and alliances with other asset managers. In 2010 the company's institutional and private wealth operations absorbed the client base of NMF Asset Management in Florida. It continues to seek out additional acquisition opportunities.

Ownership

Frederick J. Mancheski owns about 26% of GAMCO's class A shares. Gabelli owns 99% of the firm's class B shares.

HISTORY

Mario Gabelli displayed his flair early. He bought his first stocks when he was 13 years old and read stock market reports in his free time. After college he worked at Wall Street firms Loeb Rhodes and William D. Witter.

He founded institutional broker/dealer Gabelli & Company in 1976 and moved into separate account management —today the nucleus of the company's business —in 1977. Gabelli's first mutual fund debuted in 1986. Gabelli Fund affiliates acquired diversified holding company (now LGL Group) with operations in manufactured housing telecommunications services and TV stations.Through the 1980s the firm added investment vehicles. In 1988 it incorporated as Alpha G. By the 1990s assets had grown enormously but Alpha G suffered management turmoil frequently attributed to Gabelli's temper. By 1995 the Gabelli funds were in a slump; some analysts thought Gabelli was overextended.

He roared back with the Gabelli Global Opportunity Fund (global equities) and the Gabelli/Westwood Mighty Mites Fund (micro cap equities). To boost his funds' investment clout Gabelli used "rights offerings" asking investors to buy more fund shares at a discount —in effect forcing them to pony up or face dilution.

After trying to sell 25% of his firm in 1996 and 1997 Gabelli planned a 1998 IPO of the mutual fund businesses. But it was delayed until the next year because of issues relating to Gabelli's pay. In 1999 Gabelli halved his salary (putting the company on the hook for a compensatory $50 million payout in 2002). In 1999 and 2000 Gabelli Asset Management widened distribution of the funds and despite a static stock price bought up others including the Comstock family of funds. The company also opened a London office to boost its European presence.

The company adopted the name of one of its subsidiaries GAMCO Investments in 2005 and renamed that subsidiary GAMCO Asset Management.

EXECUTIVES

Vice President, Ronald S Eaker
Chairman CEO and Chief Investment Officer Value Portfolios, Mario J. Gabelli, age 72
President and COO, Douglas R. Jamieson, age 60, $300,000 total compensation
EVP and CFO, Robert S. Zuccaro, age 57, $300,000 total compensation
CFO Gabelli Funds, Agnes Mullady
President CEO of Teton Advisors, Nicholas F. Galluccio

Executive Vice President General Counsel Secretary, Kevin Handwerker
Senior Vice President, John D Gabelli, age 71
Svp; Evp And Coo Gabelli Funds, Bruce N Alpert, age 63
Assistant Vice President, David Rabin
Senior Vice President, Edward Wagner
Assistant Vice President, Robert Venezia
Regional Vice President, Jeff Tate
Assistant Vice President And Director Of Proxy Services, George Maldonado
Vice President Equity Trading, Marco Sampellegrini
Research Analyst Vice President, Anne Morrissy
Assistant Vice President, Annmarie Zingaro
Vice President Of Billing, Nina Lobozza
Assistant Vice President, Tara Morizio
V P, Edith Cook
Chairman CEO and Chief Investment Officer Value Portfolios, Mario J. Gabelli, age 72
Auditors: Deloitte&ToucheLLP

LOCATIONS

HQ: GAMCO Investors Inc
  One Corporate Center, Rye, NY 10580-1422
Phone: 914 921-3700
Web: www.gabelli.com
Chicago
Greeenwich CT
Hong Kong
London
Minneapolis
New York
Palm Beach FL
Reno NV
Shanghai
St. Louis

PRODUCTS/OPERATIONS

2011 Sales

	$ mil.	% of total
Investment advisory & incentive fees	268.0	82
Institutional research services	14.3	4
Distribution fees & other	44.8	14
Total	**327.1**	**100**

Selected Funds

Comstock Capital Value Fund
Gabelli ABC Fund
Gabelli Asset Fund
Gabelli Dividend Growth Fund
Gabelli Equity Income Fund
Gabelli Small Cap Growth Fund
Gabelli SRI Green Fund
Gabelli U.S. Treasury Money Market Fund
Gabelli Utilities Fund
Gabelli Value Fund
Gabelli Woodland Small Cap Value Fund
GAMCO Global Growth Fund
GAMCO Global Opportunity Fund
GAMCO Global Telecommunications Fund
GAMCO Gold Fund
GAMCO Growth Fund
GAMCO International Growth Fund
GAMCO Mathers Fund
GAMCO Vertumnus Fund
GAMCO Westwood Balanced Fund
GAMCO Westwood Equity Fund
GAMCO Westwood Income Fund
GAMCO Westwood Intermediate Bond Fund
GAMCO Westwood Mighty Mites Fund
GAMCO Westwood SmallCap Equity Fund

COMPETITORS

AllianceBernstein	Prudential
Capital Group	Raymond James
FMR	Financial
Franklin Templeton	T. Rowe Price
Legg Mason	The Vanguard Group
Old Mutual (US)	

HISTORICAL FINANCIALS

Company Type: Public

Income Statement

FYE: December 31

	REVENUE ($ mil.)	NET INCOME ($ mil.)	NET PROFIT MARGIN	EMPLOYEES
12/13	397.5	116.8	29.4%	228
12/12	344.2	75.5	21.9%	224
12/11	327.1	69.6	21.3%	218
12/10	280.3	68.7	24.5%	222
12/09	218.1	55.5	25.5%	194
Annual Growth	**16.2%**	**20.4%**	**—**	**4.1%**

2013 Year-End Financials

Debt ratio: 16.5%
Return on equity: 28.3%
Cash ($ mil.): 210
Current ratio: 3.48
Long-term debt ($ mil.): 117
No. of shares (mil.): 26
Dividends
  Yield: 0.2%
  Payout: 18.3%
Market value ($ mil.): 2,269

	STOCK PRICE ($) FY Close	P/E High/Low	PER SHARE ($) Earnings	Dividends	Book Value
12/13	86.97	19 10	4.54	0.72	17.53
12/12	53.07	18 14	2.86	2.88	14.28
12/11	43.49	20 14	2.61	1.15	15.10
12/10	48.01	20 13	2.52	1.82	14.27
12/09	48.29	27 13	2.02	2.12	15.93
Annual Growth	**15.8%**	**— —**	**22.4%**	**(23.7%)**	**2.4%**

Gartner, Inc.

You might not know IT but Gartner does. The company helps clients understand the information technology (IT) industry and make informed decisions about IT products. It provides more than 12400 client organizations with competitive analysis reports industry overviews market trend data and product evaluation reports. Its GartnerG2 Gartner Dataquest and other research services are made available through subscriptions primarily to CIOs and other IT professionals. Gartner also offers technology and management consulting services and it produces a number of conferences seminars and other events aimed at the technology sector.

Geographic Reach

The company operates in about 85 countries. Canada and the US represent almost 60% of its overall sales. The EMEA region contributes nearly 30% while other regions account for the remaining amount.

Financial Performance

During the recession Gartner's research and consulting segments (which together account for about 90% of the company's revenue each year) were hurt as corporate spending on IT infrastructure dried up. However the company has reversed this trend after enjoying three straight years of sizable growth.

From 2011 to 2012 its total sales increased by 10% and its profits surged by 21%. This was driven by double-digit growth in both its Research and Events segments and revenue increases across all its geographic regions (with a double-digit increase in Research revenues in every region).

Both its client retention and wallet retention remained strong during 2012 peaking at 83% and 99% respectively. Events revenues increased due to the 62 events in 2012 compared to 60 in 2011. It also experienced higher exhibitor volumes at its ongoing events.

Strategy

Gartner uses acquisitions to extend its geographic reach and penetrate fast-growing markets. In 2012 it acquired Ideas International Limited a publicly-owned Australian corporation that provided intelligence on IT infrastructure configurations and pricing data to IT professionals and vendors. Gartner paid around $19 million in cash for the company in order to introduce Ideas International's products and services to its much larger end user client base and to further penetrate the technology vendor market. Ideas International's business operations have been integrated into Gartner's Research segment.

Ownership

Investment advisor T. Rowe Price Associates owns about 16% of Gartner.

HISTORY

Computer analyst Gideon Gartner founded Gartner Group in 1979. Two years after its 1986 IPO the company was acquired by ad agency Saatchi & Saatchi in that firm's futile bid to become a business services powerhouse. A management buyout backed by Dun & Bradstreet forced Gideon Gartner out in 1990. Gartner Group went public again in 1993 and Dun & Bradstreet's stake was transferred to its spinoff Cognizant in 1996.

The firm bought complementary companies to stay on top of the IT market and round out its training capabilities. Though late to the Internet Gartner started hosting @vantage —a Web site featuring industry outlooks and research –in 1996 and developed data-intensive intranets for key customers.

Gartner bought computer market researchers Datapro and Northern Business Information from McGraw-Hill in 1997. It also bought a third of Jupiter Communications an Internet research business based in New York. (Jupiter eventually went out of business in 2002.) The company sold its Gartner Learning IT business to Harcourt General (now Houghton Mifflin Harcourt) in 1998. Michael Fleisher became CEO the following year and the company acquired telecommunications consulting firm Rendall and Associates.

Gartner Group acquired TechRepublic in 2000 an operator of Web communities for IT professionals. The company didn't keep TechRepublic long: it sold the business to CNET Networks for $23 million in 2001. Also that year the company shortened its name to Gartner and reduced its staff by 8%. Later in 2001 longtime chairman Manuel Fernandez announced he would retire (he was named chairman emeritus); Fleisher took over as chairman and CEO.

Fleisher continued to realign Gartner's operations in response to the worsening tech recession during 2002 and 2003.

Investment vehicle Silver Lake Partners which had acquired about $300 million of the company's debt in 2000 converted its debt equity to stock in 2003. Because the investment group's limited partners included tech heavyweights Michael Dell (Dell) Bill Gates (Microsoft) and Larry Ellison (Oracle) the transaction raised a few eyebrows and drew concerns that Gartner's research might somehow become tainted. The company moved quickly to reassure its clients that its research would remain independent of the interests of its shareholders and board members.

In 2004 Fleisher resigned from the company and ADP executive Gene Hall was appointed as the new CEO.

Gartner expanded when it acquired AMR Research for $63 million back in 2009. AMR Research's expertise in consulting event planning and supply chain management software analysis enhanced Gartner's product portfolio. Not long after acquiring AMR Research Gartner absorbed Burton Group for $56 million in cash.

EXECUTIVES

CEO and Director, Eugene A. (Gene) Hall, age 57, $817,143 total compensation
Senior Vice President Global Sales, Diane Julian
Senior Vice President End User Programs, Ken Davis
Executive Vice President Worldwide Sales, Steve Tait
Vice President Research Events Programs, Mark Atwood
SVP, Dale Kutnick, age 64, $391,151 total compensation
Sr Vp Worldwide Consulting, Madeline Hanewinckel
Vice President, Ian Weitzman
SVP High Tech and Telecom Programs, Michael Yoo
SVP Gartner Research, Peter Sondergaard, age 49, $318,270 total compensation
SVP High Tech and Telecom Programs, Kendall B. (Ken) Davis, age 45
SVP and CIO, Darko Hrelic, age 57
SVP Gartner Consulting, Per Anders Waern, age 52, $391,151 total compensation
Group VP Sales Asia/Pacific, Alwyn Dawkins, $283,800 total compensation
SVP Executive Programs, Chris Thomas
CFO, Craig Safian
Vice President Risk, John W Riley
Managing Vice President, Ray Laracuenta
Vice President, Bruce Ventriglia
Vice President And Chief Analyst, Ken Newbury
Senior Vice President Chief Information, Scott Fertig
Svp Global Sales, David Godfrey
Gvp It Infrastructure And Operations, Rick Ryan
Group Vice President Executive Programs, Roger Kemp
Area Vice President Greater China, Daniel Shieh
Vice President Executive Partner, Bart Stanco
Vice President, Peter Shores
Group Vice President, Bill Kumagai
Vice President Of Sales, Dan Holmes
Research Vice President, Scott Morrison
Research Vice President, Michele Caminos
Mvp, Edmond Murray
Vice President, Didier Boschmans
Vice President And Analyst, Massimo Pezzini
Research Vice President, Matthew Goldman
Vice President Enterprise Information Technology Leader, Yvonne Hyland
Vice President Of Product Development And Education, Lisa Lawlor
Vice President Consulting, Toshiyuki Zamma
Vice President Multimedia, Daniel Milikow
Sr Vice President Strategy Dev Exec, Moira Collins
Regional Vice President Sales, Nathaniel Swan
Vice President Utility Operations, Sahil Ghuman
Vice President, Kyoko Taneda
Regional Vice President Gartner Asia Pacific Sales, Derek Seow
Vice President Market Development, Alexa McCloughan
Research Vice President Erp And Supply Chain Manageme, Andrew White
Vice President And Gartner Fellow, Tina Nunno

Vice President Executive Partner, Ronei Dasilva
Global Vice President Talent Acquisition, Kathleen Gioffre
Vice President, Stephen Prior
Vice President Publishing Operations, Jackie Ryan
Vice President, Stewart Buchanan
Research Vice President, Dean Freeman
Vice President, Roger Hockenberry
Executive Vice President And Subsidiary Board Member, Marie Rhodes
Vice President Us Defense And Intelligence Sector, Tracey Haber
Group Vice President, Gary Hein
Managing Vice President, Ken Ruggles
Regional Vice President Sales, Marcio Krug
Vice President Executive Partner, Bill Jenks
Group Vice President Enterprise Content Management, Debby Gildersleeve
Vice President Consulting, Carlton Joiner
Managing Vice President Performance Optimization, Christopher Renn
Managing Vice President Product Marketing, Peter Guy
Senior Vice President, Colette Gardner
Vice President Sales, Gert Buelens
Research Vice President, Jim Duggan
Vice President, Paola Farina
Vice President And Chief Analyst, Denny Waylan
Gvp, Marc Miller
Managing Vice President, Debra Hofman
Group Vice President, Tom Hayes
Vice President Business Development, Peter Shaw
Research Vice President, Jeffrey Mann
Vice President And Research Director, Annemarie Earley
Vice President Rsrch Fellow At Gartner, Mark Raskino
Vice President Content And Methodologies, David Black
Vice President, Jose Ruggero
Vice President Executive Partner, Thijs Koppen
Research Vice President Of Enterprise Communications Applications, Drew Kraus
Vice President Canada, Peter Krasa
Regional Vice President Sales, Katie Roberts
Managing Vice President, Joe Beck
Vice President And Analyst On Social, Carol Rozwell
Vice President High Tech And Telecommunications Programs, James Stanton
Vice President, Moacyr Gomes
Regional Vice President, Liz Reynolds
Reg Vice President Sales, Moe Ali
Managing Vice President, Stephen Smith
Research Vice President Information, Earl Perkins
Regional Vice President, Antti Keino
Vice President, Peter Persico
Vice President Infrastructure Solutions, Megan Taylor
Regional Vice President Cpg, Mark Frederick
Vice President Cfc, Robert Symonds
Vice President Channel Marketing, Mona Kosseim
Vice President Distinguished Analyst, Bill Rosser
Managing Vice President Of Client Computing, Christopher Smulders
Group Vice Presiderlt And Director Of Research, Nell Macdonald
Managing Vice President, Michael Di Pietro
Research Vice President, James Browning
Research Vice President And Distinguished Analyst, Gene Phifer
Managing Vice President, Hideaki Horiuchi
Vice President And Distinguished Analyst, Betsy Burton
Gvp, Ann Laffaye
Managing Vice President, Kevin Knox
Vice President Of Mobile Computing, Ken Dulaney

Vice President Analyst, Andrew Johnson
Vice President Consulting Gartner Consulting, Tom Larson
Vice President, Tom McClure
Vice President Information Technology, Van Wyngene
Assistant Vice President Cpg, Matt Lewis
Vice President And Distinguished Analyst, Ted Friedman
Managing Vice President Gartner Research, Alvin Park
Vice President Of Executive Programme, Judi Edwards
Mvp, Laura Wilhelm
Vice President Consulting, Nino Moscardini
Research Vice President, John-david Lovelock
Vice President Consulting Sourcing, Kyle Hardy
Vice President Distinguished Analyst, Bill Hostmann
Vice President Of Consulting, Michael Pedersen
Vice President And Executive Partner, Michel Dubosqueille
Vice President, Nancy Shah
Group Vice President, David Howe
Group Vice President, Magnus Eriksson
Research Vice President, Tiffani Bova
Vice President, Pam Riccio
Team Lead Vice President And Executive Partner, Elizabeth Holden
Vice President, Tirath Mehta
Research Vice President, John Radcliffe
Research Vice President It Management, Frances O'Brien
Vice President Distinguished Analyst, Donna Scott
Vice President Research, John Van Decker
Vice President, Steve Kleynhans
Group Vice President Stg Operations, Joe Sacchi
Research Vice President, Ian Finley
Managing Vice President, Michael Uskert
Assistant Vice President Cpg, Moolee Wong
Managing Vice President, Kevin Gollogly
Executive Vice President Chief Strategy And Transformation Officer, Gail Hurry
Managing Vice President, Richard Cockcroft
Vice President Of Research With Amr Supply Chain, Jane Barrett
Vice President Information Technology Management Sector Gartner Research, Robert Goodwin
Vice President Executive Partner, Carol Hardcastle
Vice President And Research Director Gartner Research, Patrick Meehan
Vice President Healthcare Practice, Greg Hardin
Vice President Consulting, Catherine Peyralbe
Vice President Client Partner, Charles Burns
Research Vice President, Tom Eid
Vice President And Analyst In Executive Leadership And Innovation Team, Kathy Harris
Vice President, Dan Chong
Vice President And Gartner Fellow, David Cearley
Vice President And Distinguished Analyst, Donald Feinberg
Research Vice President Application Development And I, Dale Vecchio
Research Vice President, Matthew Cain
Managing Vice President, Ed Rashbrooke
Gvp Public Relations And Marketing Communications, Andrew Spender
Vice President, Philip Koh
Group Vice President Executive Programmes, Mary Maxwell
Vice President Marketing, Ann Marshman
Vice President At Gartner, Rakesh Kumar
Vice President, Michael Samsen
Executive Vice President, Adam Rin
Vice President Human Resources, Michael Leckie

Research Vice President Business Process Services, Cecilia Choong
South Valley Assistant Vice President, Frank Rahim
Vice President Accounting, Adrian Martin
Vice President Management Consulting, K Knutsen
Vice President Capital Appreciation Plans, Jane Lucas
Vice President Executive Partner, Rowan Snyder
Vice President Sales Representative, Erik Persson
Vice President And Research Fellow, Ken McGee
Vice President Product Management, Kate Russell
Vice President Executive Programs, Roger Acton
Regional Vice President, Andy Muench
Vice President, Martin Gutberlet
Vice President, Di Maio
Area Vice President, Mark Waldheim
Vice President Consulting, Marc Kindermans
Vice President Vertical Markets, Nick Portaro
Vice President Executive Partner, Brian Schade
Research Vice President, Philip Dawson
Vice President Consulting, Patrick Sullivan
Vice President Operations And Srv Training, Mark Deacon
Vice President Business Operations, Audrey Apfel
Managing Vice President, Bertrand Bidaud
Managing Vice President, Lori Robinson
Vice President Cfc, Henrik Lund
Vice President, Atilla Mukan
Vice President, Allen Weiner
Research Vice President, Ian Keene
Vice President And Research Group Director Gartner Research, Vincent Oliva
Regional Vice President, Ray Small
Vice President Industries Research, Don Scheibenreif
Regional Vice President Sales, Tim Phillips
Vice President Sales Operations, Brian Martin
Vice President, Philip Allega
Vice President, Linda Price
Consulting Group Vice President, Tsuneo Saito
Vice President Proposal And Deliverable Service, Laura Cascio
Wireless Analyst And Vice President, Kevin Dulaney
Vice President And Research Director, Rita Knox
Group Vice President, Jack Mazza
Research Vice President, Ant Allan
Vice President, Dan Karlsson
Managing Vice President, Marita Hume
Group Vice President Digital Marketing Products, John Flynn
Vice President Executive Programs, Elias Bayeh
Vice President Consulting, Ken Bergstrom
Vice President Executive Partner, Mark Bartram
Vice President, David Pack
Vice President, Andy Gartner
Research Vice President, Jonathan Edwards
Research Vice President, Paul Debeasi
Vice President, Lindsay McRory
Vice President Software Management, Roy Schulte
Senior Vice President, Kristen Bodelsen
Managing Vice President At Gartner Inc, John Davison
Managing Vice President, Richard Buchanan
Vice President And Research Area Director Of Network Technology, Dave Capuccio
Executive Vice President Business Development, Alvina Usher
Managing Vice President, Frank Fabricius
Group Vice President, Michael Chalk
Vice President Sales, John Gallant
Research Vice President, Alexa Bona
Managing Vice President, Debra Curtis
Research Vice President Software Infrastructure And Architecture, Jess Thompson

Executive Vice President Government Banking, Marianela Molinos
Vice President And General Manager, Heather Levy
Ideassvp Product Development And Information Services, Peter Cullen
Vice President Of Product Strategy And Marketing, Andrew McCauley
Vice President Campaign Marketing, Sarah McCurdy
Vice President Business Development, Carol Quinn
Vice President Consulting, Anthony Henderson
Regional Vice President Sales, Jeff Savino
Vice President, Jim Shepherd
Regional Vice President Sales, Larry Free
Vice President Distinguished Analyst, Robert Desisto
Executive Vice President, Peter Kalligher
Research Vice President, Carolina Milnesi
Vice President Finance And Operations, Jack Pranzo
Group Vice President Global Tax, Brent Gregoire
Amr Executive Vice President, Nancy Gendron
Research Vice President Chief Information Officer Research Group, Andrew Rowsell-jones
Vice President Product Management, Dharmesh Shah
Research Vice President, Ian Glazer
Vice President Research Area Director Gartner Research, Jim Sinur
Vice President, Gregg Menell
Vice President Human Resources Sales And Client Operations, Tessie Massa
Vice President Distinguished Analyst, Richard Hunter
Vice President Reasearch, Ricvhard Matlus
Managing Vice President Human Resources, Maria Warnken
Managing Vice President, Klaus Rinnen
Managing Vice President, Steven Lefebure
Vice President And Research Fellow, Martin Reynolds
Research Vice President, Paul Proctor
Vice President And Distinguished Analyst, Andrew Butler
Vice President Consulting, David Kish
Managing Vice President Of Semiconductor Research, Andrew Phillips
Vice President, Dean Daniels
Vice President Information Tech Rsrch, Scott Bittler
Vice President Of Corporate Systems, Sanjeev Porter
Vice President Distinguished, Mark Beyer
Information Technology Vice President, Doug Henry
Vice President Product Strategy, Cheryl Morones
Managing Vice President, Ian Bertram
Vice President Canada Executive Programs, Robert Langlois
Group Vice President, Alissa Stayn
Vice President And Director Of Research At Gartner, Lars Mieritz
Vice President Executive Partner, Duncan Chapman
Managing Vice President Finance, Sal Oppedisano
Vice President Executive Partner, Jean-marc Lejeune
Vice President Service Delivery, Peter Adler
Vice President And Client Director, Julie Tenwolde
Research Vice President, Jeff Woods
Regional Vice President Sales, Jeremy Shearn
Vice President And Principal Consultin, Chris Boyd
Vice President, Ewan Thompson
Vice President Service Delivery, Jan Soderberg
Regional Vice President Sales, Geraldine Crawford
Senior Vice President Marketing And Business Development, David West

Research Vice President, Carsten Casper
Gvp, Mike Parrish
Vice President Application Development, Andre
 Pienczykowski
Vice President Gartner Multimedia, Roger Grannis
Gvp, Gina Formichelli
Group Vice President Global Tax, Steve Baumann
Group Vice President And Research Fellow, Jim
 Popkin
Ideas_vp And Senior Analyst, Wally Katz
Group Vice President Compensation And
 Benefits, Jim Crane
Vice President Information Technology
 Longmont, Sabrina Moskovitz
Mvp Consulting, Paul Hertroys
Vice President Executive Partner, Alexander
 Hohnjec
Vice President Of Operations, Julie Dallieres
Research Vice President, Simon Mingay
Analyst Vice President Mgc, Michael Rollings
Research Vice President, Joseph Bugajski
Vice President Distinguished Analyst, Claudio Da
 Rold
Gvp, Shinji Hasejima
Vice President Information Technology, Lew
 Schwratz
Research Vice President, Catherine Tornbohm
Research Vice President, Kathryn Hale
Regional Vice President Sales, Struckman Mark
Vice President And Global Ibm Client Director,
 Dan Snelwar
Research Vice President For Smb Business
 Applications, Robert Anderson
Managing Vice President, Phil Schacter
Vice President Consulting, Thomas McClure
Vice President Business And Technology
 Operations, Pamela Riccio
Vice President Engineering, Steve Auerbach
Vice President And Gartner Fellow, David
 Furlonger
Research Vice President, David Coyle
Analyst Vice President Ads, Doug Laney
Vice President Vertical Markets, Nicholas Portaro
Vice President Disruptive Technology, Bart Mellink
Vice President, Dave McClure
Information Technology Vice President, Michael
 Blechar
Area Vice President Smb, Jonathan Pione
Research Vice President, Jane Dosbrow
Research Vice President, Stephen Kleynhans
Vice President And Head Gartner Executive
 Programs Researcher, Michael McDonald
Vice President Consulting, Christer Forsberg
Vice President Cfc, Chris Moore
Vice President And Distinguished Analyst, Frank
 Schlier
Regional Vice President, Nik Daruwala
Research Vice President, Hung Lehong
Managing Vice President, Lisa Pierce
Senior Vice President Exp, T Christopher
Chairman, James C. Smith, age 73
Board Member, Antti Paajanen
Board Member, Ellen McSweeney
Board Member, Paul Stropko
Assistant Treasurer, Matthew Albanese
Treasurer, John Halligan
Board Member, Antonia Boiano
Auditors: KPMGLLP

LOCATIONS

HQ: Gartner, Inc.
 56 Top Gallant Road, Stamford, CT 06902-7700
Phone: 203 316-1111
Web: www.gartner.com

2014 Sales

	$ mil.	% of total
US & Canada	1204.5	60
EMEA	570.3	28
Other regions	246.6	12
Total	2021.4	100

PRODUCTS/OPERATIONS

2014 Sales

	$ mil.	% of total
Research	1445.3	72
Consulting	348.4	17
Events	227.7	11
Total	2021.4	100

Selected Products and Services

Research
 Gartner Dataquest
 GartnerG2
 Publications
 Monthly Research Review
Consulting
 Enterprise process management
 Enterprise risk management
 Human capital management
 Information technology architecture
 Information technology strategy and management
 Market and business strategy
 Public sector consulting
 Sourcing
Events
 Best practice groups
 Conferences
 Executive programs
 Symposium/ITxpo
Other
 Assessment services
 Decision support software
 Performance management services

COMPETITORS

Aberdeen Group	Ipsos
Accenture	McKinsey & Company
Bain & Company	Millward Brown
Booz Allen	Nielsen
Boston Consulting	Penton Media
Datamonitor	SYS-CON Media
Forrester Research	TNS Custom
HP Enterprise Services	UBM TechWeb
IBM	WebMediaBrands
IDC	

HISTORICAL FINANCIALS

Company Type: Public

Income Statement

FYE: December 31

	REVENUE ($ mil.)	NET INCOME ($ mil.)	NET PROFIT MARGIN	EMPLOYEES
12/13	1,784.2	182.8	10.2%	5,997
12/12	1,615.8	165.9	10.3%	5,468
12/11	1,468.5	136.9	9.3%	4,975
12/10	1,288.4	96.2	7.5%	4,461
12/09	1,139.8	82.9	7.3%	4,305
Annual Growth	11.9%	21.8%	—	8.6%

2013 Year-End Financials

Debt ratio: 11.4%
Return on equity: 54.7%
Cash ($ mil.): 423
Current ratio: 0.94
Long-term debt ($ mil.): 136

No. of shares (mil.): 91
Dividends
 Yield: —
 Payout: —
Market value ($ mil.): 6,534

	STOCK PRICE ($) FY Close	P/E High/Low	PER SHARE ($) Earnings	Dividends	Book Value
12/13	71.05	36 23	1.93	0.00	3.93
12/12	46.02	29 19	1.73	0.00	3.28
12/11	34.77	30 23	1.39	0.00	1.95
12/10	33.20	33 18	0.96	0.00	1.95
12/09	18.04	23 10	0.85	0.00	1.17
Annual Growth	40.9%	— —	22.8%	—	35.3%

Gas Natural Inc.

Gas Natural (formerly Energy Inc.) does what comes naturally –it distributes markets transports and produces natural gas. Its Energy West Inc. unit has natural gas distribution operations in Maine Montana North Carolina and Wyoming. Gas Natural also owns Orwell Natural Gas and Northeast Ohio Natural Gas which distribute gas in Ohio and Pennsylvania. All told Gas Natural serves about 63500 customers. The company's energy marketing subsidiary Energy West Resources primarily sells natural gas and power to customers in Maine Montana North Carolina and Wyoming. It owns the Shoshone interstate and the Glacier gathering natural gas pipelines in Montana and Wyoming. It also has stakes in 160 gas wells.

In a move to expand its gas distribution base into Virginia in 2011 the company acquired Independence Oil & LP Gas which supplies heating oil liquid propane and kerosene to 4500 customers.

The company changed its name from Energy Inc. to Gas Natural Inc. in 2010 to more accurately reflect its primary focus.

Gas Natural had been a seller of propane but in the increasingly consolidated business the company felt outgunned by the larger national distributors. Consequently the company sold its Arizona division (which distributed propane to 7500 residential and business customers) to SemStream L.P. in 2007 and exited the propane business.

Energy West was originally incorporated in Montana in 1909.

EXECUTIVES

Chairman of the Board CEO and Director, Richard
 M. Osborne, age 68
VP CFO and Director, Thomas J. Smith, age 70
President and COO, Kevin J. Degenstein, age 55,
 $186,550 total compensation
VP Administration, Jed D. Henthorne, age 54,
 $103,250 total compensation
Corporate Secretary, Rebecca Howell
General Manager Bangor ME, Jerry Livengood
Gas Marketing Bangor ME, Jonathan W. Kunz
Director Operations Great Fall MT, Edward J.
 Kacer
General Manager Elkin NC, Ray Fischer
Marketing Manager Elkin NC, Ernest C. McGuire Jr.
Sales Elkin NC, Leeann Nixon
District Manager Cody Wyoming, Bradley J.
 Samuels
Senior Marketing Representative Cody WY, Steven
 A. Miller
VP Eastern Operations, David C. Shipley, age 53,
 $136,350 total compensation
VP EWR Great Falls MT, Nick J. Bohr
CIO, Dean A Ward

VP CFO and Director, Thomas J. Smith, age 70
Director, W. E. (Gene) Argo, age 72
Director, Gregory J. Osborne, age 34
Director, James R. Smail, age 66
Director, Ian J. Abrams, age 68
Director, Michael T. Victor, age 52
Independent Director, John Male
Independent Director, Nicholas Fedeli

LOCATIONS

HQ: Gas Natural Inc.
8500 Station Street, Suite 100, Mentor, OH 44060
Phone: 800 570-5688
Web: www.ewst.com

PRODUCTS/OPERATIONS

2009 Sales

	$ mil.	% of total
Natural gas	58.8	82
Wholesale gas & electric	12.2	17
Pipeline	0.5	1
Total	**71.5**	**100**

COMPETITORS

Black Hills	TransCanada
MDU Resources	Williams Companies
NorthWestern	Xcel Energy
Southwest Gas	

HISTORICAL FINANCIALS

Company Type: Public

Income Statement

FYE: December 31

	REVENUE ($ mil.)	NET INCOME ($ mil.)	NET PROFIT MARGIN	EMPLOYEES
12/13	118.8	6.6	5.6%	291
12/12	93.8	3.7	4.0%	244
12/11	99.2	5.3	5.4%	240
12/10	91.5	5.8	6.3%	191
12/09	71.4	6.8	9.5%	172
Annual Growth	13.6%	(0.5%)	—	14.0%

2013 Year-End Financials

Debt ratio: 34.4%
Return on equity: 7.6%
Cash ($ mil.): 13
Current ratio: 0.91
Long-term debt ($ mil.): 42

No. of shares (mil.): 10
Dividends
 Yield: 6.7%
 Payout: 81.8%
Market value ($ mil.): 84

	STOCK PRICE ($) FY Close	P/E High/Low	PER SHARE ($) Earnings	Dividends	Book Value
12/13	8.03	15 11	0.71	0.54	9.33
12/12	9.33	25 19	0.46	0.54	9.12
12/11	11.42	18 16	0.66	0.54	9.17
12/10	10.52	13 11	0.92	0.54	9.04
12/09	10.30	7 4	1.58	0.53	8.16
Annual Growth	(6.0%)	—	(18.1%)	0.7%	3.4%

Gastar Exploration Inc. (New)

Like many of its peers Gastar Exploration has hitched its star to exploring for natural gas (and some oil) in the US. The company's primary area of exploration and production is the Appalachian Basin ad its gas-bearing shale formations. Once active in Australia Gastar Exploration is now focusing exclusively on lucrative US properties primarily the Marcellus Shale play in northern West Virginia and southwestern Pennsylvania. It also owns oil and gas assets in Oklahoma. In 2012 the company had proved reserves of 248.9 billion cu. ft. of natural gas equivalent. Chesapeake Energy owns 10% of the company.
Geographic Reach
Gastar Exploration has exploration and production activities in Oklahoma Pennsylvania and West Virginia.
Operations
In addition to the Marcellus Shale holdings (85% of the company's total proved reserves in 2012) the company holds assets in Oklahoma. It has leases on 33000 gross (17000 net) acres in the Bossier play in the Hilltop area of East Texas in Leon and Robertson Counties but these were sold in 2013.
Sales and Marketing
In 2012 SEI Energy LLC and Clearfield Appalachian purchased the bulk of the company's Marcellus Shale production.
Financial Performance
Gastar Exploration's revenues grew by 24% in 2012 thanks to higher condensate and oil NGLs and natural gas sales as the result of a 72% increase in production. This was partially offset by a 15% drop in prices. The company's net income decreased by more than 9000% in 2012 primarily due to higher impairment charges of natural gas and oil properties as a result of a 33% decline in the 12-month average natural gas price. Strategy
The company focuses most of its drilling activity in the liquids-rich area of the Marcellus Shale (64% of its 2013 capital budget) although it also seeking to diversify its geographic portfolio by developing another core area (in the Mid-Continent).
To raise cash in 2013 Gastar Exploration sold its East Texas properties to Cubic Energy for $44 million. Mergers and Acquisitions
As a part of its long term strategy to develop a Mid-Continent horizontal oil play in 2013 the company acquired proven reserves and undeveloped leasehold interests in Kingfisher and Canadian counties Oklahoma from Chesapeake Energy. The assets includes drilling rights on 157000 net acres that adjoin Gastar's existing Mid-Continent acreage and 2.8 million barrels of oil equivalent of proved reserves. To recover costs later in the year the company sold its interests in 76000 of net undeveloped acres in Kingfisher and Canadian counties.
In an effort to balance its production profile between liquids and natural gas while also expanding its presence in the Hunton play in Oklahoma in 2013 Gastar Exploration spent $188 million for a 80.5% net revenue interest in 24000 acres of the West Edmund Hunton Lime Unit in Kingfisher Logan Oklahoma and Canadian counties. The acquired property produces at a daily rate of 1200 barrels of oil 2.7 million cubic feet of natural gas and 428 barrels of natural gas liquids. Company Background
In order to raise cash to pay down debts in 2009 Gastar Exploration sold its Australian assets (primarily coabed methane fields in New South Wales) to oil giant Santos for $240 million. It also sold its stake in the Hilltop Resort Gathering System in East Texas to US Infrastructure LP for $21.7 million.
In 2010 the company formed a joint venture with South Korea-based investment firm Atinum Partners to develop Marcellus Shale assets in West Virginia and Pennsylvania. In December 2010 the company bought 62000 net acres of Marcellus Shale from private sellers.
The company was incorporated in 1987 as CopperQuest Inc. It changed its name to Gastar Exploration in 2000. The company pursues a strategy of balancing high-risk deep natural gas exploration with low-risk coal bed methane development.

EXECUTIVES

President CEO and Director, J. Russell Porter, age 52, $500,000 total compensation
SVP and CFO, Michael A. Gerlich, age 59, $300,000 total compensation
VP Land, Henry J. Hansen, age 58
VP Exploration Manager, Keith R. Blair, age 59
SVP and COO, Michael McCown, $300,000 total compensation
Chairman, John M. Selser, age 56
Auditors: BDOSeidmanLLP

LOCATIONS

HQ: Gastar Exploration Inc. (New)
1331 Lamar Street, Suite 650, Houston, TX 77010
Phone: 713 739-1800   **Fax:** 713 739-0458
Web: www.gastar.com

PRODUCTS/OPERATIONS

2012 Sales

	$ mil.	% of total
Natural gas	33.8	61
Condensate & oil	12.4	22
NGLS	9.2	17
Unrealized natural gas hedge	(5.6)	-
Total	**49.9**	**100**

COMPETITORS

Abraxas Petroleum	Pioneer Natural
Anadarko Petroleum	Resources
Belden & Blake	Range Resources
Cabot Oil & Gas	Vanguard Natural
Goodrich Petroleum	Resources
Miller Energy	
Resources	

HISTORICAL FINANCIALS

Company Type: Public

Income Statement

FYE: December 31

	REVENUE ($ mil.)	NET INCOME ($ mil.)	NET PROFIT MARGIN	EMPLOYEES
12/13	87.7	49.3	56.2%	63
12/12	49.9	(153.7)	—	41
12/11	40.2	(0.7)	—	42
12/10	42.7	(12.4)	—	36
12/09	32.8	48.8	148.6%	24
Annual Growth	27.8%	0.3%	—	27.3%

2013 Year-End Financials

Debt ratio: 53.0%
Return on equity: 74.1%
Cash ($ mil.): 32
Current ratio: 1.02
Long-term debt ($ mil.): 312

No. of shares (mil.): 61
Dividends
 Yield: —
 Payout: —
Market value ($ mil.): 424

	STOCK PRICE ($) FY Close	P/E High/Low		PER SHARE ($) Earnings	Dividends	Book Value
12/13	6.92	10	2	0.63	0.00	1.36
12/12	1.21	—	—	(2.53)	0.00	0.75
12/11	3.18	—	—	(0.03)	0.00	3.21
12/10	4.30	—	—	(0.25)	0.00	3.23
12/09	4.79	5	0	1.06	0.00	3.30
Annual Growth (19.9%)	9.6%	—	—	(12.2%)	—	

Generac Holdings Inc

Perfect storms make good business for Generac Power Systems. That's because the company manufactures engine-driven standby and portable generators for homes businesses hospitals and recreational vehicles. The company also makes industrial power generation equipment automatic transfer switches switch gear and controls and remote monitoring software. Brands include Generac Magnum Ottomotores and Tower Light. Generac sells its products through retailers as well as through wholesale distributors. The US and Canada represent nearly 90% of the company sales.

Operations

Generac divides its operations into two primary segments: residential power products (57% of sales); and commercial and industrial power products (38%). Other products account for the remainder of revenue.

Sales and Marketing

The company targets the residential light commercial industrial and construction markets. Products are sold into these regions through a broad network of independent dealers retailers wholesalers catalogs e-commerce merchants and equipment rental companies under the Generac Magnum Ottomotores and Tower Light brand names. Generac also sells direct to certain national and regional account customers that are the end users of its products.

Financial Performance

Generac has achieved extraordinary revenue growth the last few years with revenues surging 26% from $1.18 billion in 2012 to peak at a record-setting $1.49 billion in 2013. Profits skyrocketed 87% from $93 million in 2012 to $175 million in 2013. The company's operating cash flow has also steadily increased over the last five years.

The exceptional growth for 2013 was fueled by double digit growth across all its segments: residential power products (20%) commercial and industrial power products (39%) and other products (19%). One chief reason for the increase was an uptick in home standby generators as a result of more power outages occurring throughout the year. Generac also received additional revenues through the use of acquisitions and increased sales from power washer products.

Strategy

The company plans to expand its presence in under-served North American regions by continuing to build its dealer network. Latin America Russia and China represent favorable opportunities for the company and have piqued Generac's interest in seizing growth opportunities in international

markets. The company is pursuing partnerships with established international companies and has built a network of 34 distributors in 16 international markets —primarily in Central and South America and Mexico —to handle its industrial and light-commercial generators.

Boasting a North American market share of 70% for residential standby generators a broad distribution network (direct dealers catalog wholesale and retail) a comprehensive product line and specialized engineering and manufacturing capabilities Generac continues to invest in innovation and product development as well as technician training to ensure the repair and maintenance of its products.

Mergers and Acquisitions

Generac has grown through the help of acquisitions. In 2014 the company acquired North Dakota-based MAC a manufacturer of premium-grade commercial and industrial mobile heaters within the US and Canada. The acquisition of MAC expanded its growing mobile products platform by adding a strong brand of industrial heaters. It also enhanced its access to the projected long term up-cycle in the oil and gas market.

In 2013 the company obtained Tower Light Srl and its wholly-owned subsidiaries. Tower Light is a developer and supplier of mobile light towers throughout Europe the Middle East and Africa. Also that year Generac purchased the generator division of Baldor Electric Company a wholly-owned subsidiary of ABB Group.

EXECUTIVES

Exec V Pres, Roger Pascavis, age 55
COO, Dawn Tabat, age 62, $450,000 total compensation
President and CEO, Aaron Jagdfeld, age 42, $496,438 total compensation
CFO, York A. Ragen, age 43, $246,500 total compensation
Senior Vice President Of Engineering, Allen Gillette, age 59
National Sales Manager, Ed Zamorski
Vice President Global Sourcing, Brian Michael
National Account Manager, Jeremy Demaa
Vice President Sales, John Quast
Vice President Andndash; Service Operations, Paul Cannestra
Vice President Corporate Litigation Counsel, Rod Rogahn
National Sales Manager, William Slavik
Vice President Of Sales Latin America, Saul Urrutia
National Account Manager, Robin Christ
Vice President Sales, Adam Soliman
Executive Vice President, Terry Dolan
Senior Vice President Operations, Rob Stoppek
National Account Manager, Andy Myers
Executive Vice President Residential Products, Russ Minick
Auditors: Ernst&YoungLLP

LOCATIONS

HQ: Generac Holdings Inc
S45 W29290 Hwy. 59, Waukesha, WI 53189
Phone: 262 544-4811

PRODUCTS/OPERATIONS

2013 Sales

	$ mil.	% of total
Residential power products	843.7	57
Industrial & commercial products	569.9	38
Other	72.2	5
Total	**1485.8**	**100**

Selected Products and Brands

Generators
Commercial (QuietSource)
Industrial (gaseous diesel bi-fuel modular power systems (MPS) Gemini)
Portable (GP XG XP iX)
Recreational vehicle (gasoline propane diesel)
Residential (QuietSource Guardian)

Selected Markets

Agricultural/mining
Business office
Commercial/retail
Data center
Education
Healthcare
Manufacturing
Municipal
Research
Residential
Telecom

COMPETITORS

Aggreko	Doosan Corp
Atlas Copco USA	Honda
Holdings	Kohler
Briggs & Stratton	Multiquip
Power Products	Taylor Group
Caterpillar	Techtronic
Cummins Power	Terex
Generation	Westerbeke Corp.

HISTORICAL FINANCIALS

Company Type: Public

Income Statement

FYE: December 31

	REVENUE ($ mil.)	NET INCOME ($ mil.)	NET PROFIT MARGIN	EMPLOYEES
12/13	1,485.7	174.5	11.7%	3,380
12/12	1,176.3	93.2	7.9%	3,048
12/11	791.9	324.6	41.0%	2,223
12/10	592.8	56.9	9.6%	1,444
12/09	588.2	43.0	7.3%	1,354
Annual Growth	26.1%	41.9%	—	25.7%

2013 Year-End Financials

Debt ratio: 66.5%
Return on equity: 44.7%
Cash ($ mil.): 150
Current ratio: 2.61
Long-term debt ($ mil.): 1,175
No. of shares (mil.): 68
Dividends
 Yield: 19.4%
 Payout: 497.7%
Market value ($ mil.): 3,886

	STOCK PRICE ($) FY Close	P/E High/Low		PER SHARE ($) Earnings	Dividends	Book Value
12/13	56.64	22	13	2.51	11.00	4.62
12/12	34.31	28	15	1.35	6.00	6.79
12/11	28.03	6	3	4.79	0.00	11.37
12/10	16.17	—	—	(1.65)	0.00	6.53
Annual Growth (10.9%)	51.9%	—	—	—	—	

Genesee & Wyoming Inc.

Genesee & Wyoming (GWI) once relied on the salt of the earth —hauling salt on a 14-mile railroad for one customer. Now however the company owns stakes in more than 110 short-line and regional freight railroads that operate over a total of more than 18000 miles of track including 15000 miles of track owned and leased by the company and another 3300 miles additional miles under contractual track access arrangements to 37 ports in North America Europe and Australia. Freight transported by GWI railroads includes coal forest products and pulp and paper.

Geographic Reach

GWI owns short line and regional freight railroads in the US Australia Canada the Netherlands and Belgium. Within the US the company has eight regions: Rail Link (which includes industrial switching and port operations) Pacific Mountain West Central Southern Midwest Ohio Valley and Northeast.

Operations

GWI's rolling stock consists of some 1041 locomotives of which 941 are owned and 100 are leased. It also maintains 21622 railcars of which 3904 are owned and 17718 are leased. The company generates non-freight revenues from its railcar switching car hire and rental services demurrage and storage car repair services railroad construction and fuel sales to third-parties. Freight revenues represent 75% of total sales while nonfreight revenues generate 25%.

Financial Performance

GWI achieved extraordinary growth in 2013 with revenues skyrocketing nearly 80% from $875 million in 2012 to $1.57 billion in 2013 a company milestone. Profits increased more than fivefold from $52 million in 2012 to peak at a record-setting $271 million in 2013 primarily due to the absence of an expense associated with a previous acquisition.

The considerable growth for 2013 was primarily attributed to its 2012 RailAmerica acquisition. With help from that transaction the company experienced a 103% surge in carloads. Metallic ores revenues and petroleum products revenues increased in 2013 due to new contracts while nonfreight revenues spiked by 57% due to additional construction revenues. Largely due to all these factors GWI's operating cash flow surged from $171 million in 2012 to $413 million in 2013.

Strategy

The company which has expanded over the years via acquisitions continues to grow by buying railroads not only in North America and Australia but also in European markets. Its $1.4 billion milestone deal to purchase RailAmerica in 2012 created the largest short-line railroad operator in the US with about 110 railroads and 15000 miles of track. The transaction helped to skyrocket GWI's revenues by nearly 80% from $875 million in 2012 to $1.57 billion in 2013.

In addition to that significant deal GWI expects freight business in Australia to pick up as the grain harvest in that country increased over the previous year's totals. To that end GWI purchased Australia's FreightLink rail network for about $332 million Australian dollars ($319 million). FreightLink which serves general freight and mining customers in South Australia will operate as part of Genesee & Wyoming Australia (GWA). GWA has managed FreightLink's rail services and operations and provided it with locomotives and crews since its inception.

EXECUTIVES

EVP International Business Development, Mark W. Hastings, $252,000 total compensation
Sr V Pres, Martin D Lacombe

President and CEO, John C. Hellmann, age 44, $824,000 total compensation
SVP Information Technology, Mike Meyers
CFO, Timothy J. Gallagher, age 51, $440,406 total compensation
SVP Southern Region Railroads, Bill Jasper
Managing Director Netherlands Region, Arnoud de Rade
SVP Coastal Region Companies, James E. Irvin
SVP Central Region Railroads, Dewayne Swindall
COO, David A. Brown, $391,400 total compensation
SVP Northeast Region Railroads, Dave Ebbrecht
SVP Canada Region Railroads, Louis Gravel
SVP Pacific Region Railroads, Joel N. Haka
SVP Midwest Region Railroads, Gary R. Long
SVP Ohio Valley Region Railroads, Charles E. McBride
SVP Mountain West Region Railroads, J. Bradley Ovitt
Managing Director Genesee and Wyoming Australia Pty Ltd, Greg Pauline
Vice President Transportation Ohio, Leonard M Wagner
Vice President Engineering, David Baer
Assistant Vice President Sales And Marketing, Sherrie Motley
V P Sales & Marketing, Albert Abruzzese
Vice President Rail Link North, Dave Bordner
Vice President Marketing And Sales, Bill Sclater
Assistant Vice President Sales, Roy Budgell
Senior Vice President, Richard Regan
Vp, Kathi Maness
Vice President Transportation, Todd Bjornstad
Asst Vice President Eng Fuel Invst Rcvr, Kristine Storm
Senior Vice President Operations, Ryan Ratledge
Avp Engineering Design, Larry Romaine
Vice President Transportation, Bret Strickland
Vice President Transportation Southern, Giles Perry
Vice President ?? Commercial Counsel, Kenneth Charron
Assistant Vice President Government, Patrick Kerr
Senior Vice President Ny And Pa Region, Ray Goss
Vice President Commercial, Marty Pohlod
Srvp Southern Region, Gerry Gates
Vp Southern Region, Chuck McBride
Vice President Engineering, Jeffrey Watson
Senior Vice President Engineering, Scott Linn
General Counsel Secretary, Allison Fergus
Chairman and CEO, Mortimer B. Fuller, age 72
Board Member, Savannah Port
Treasurer Systems Data Processing, Yvonne Chan
Vice President Corporate Dev Treasurer, Thomas Savage
Auditors: PricewaterhouseCoopersLLP

LOCATIONS

HQ: Genesee & Wyoming Inc.
20 West Avenue, Darien, CT 06820
Phone: 203 202-8900   **Fax:** 203 661-4106
Web: www.gwrr.com

2013 Sales

	$ mil.	% of total
North America		
US	1083.7	56
Canada	145.4	9
Australia	325.2	33
Europe	14.7	2
Total	**1569.0**	**100**

PRODUCTS/OPERATIONS

2013 Sales

	$ mil.	% of total
Freight		

Agricultural products	130.6	9
Chemicals & plastics	128.9	8
Metals	127.8	8
Metallic ores	125.9	8
Pulp & paper	112.7	7
Coal & coke	110.8	7
Imtermodal	98.7	6
Minerals & stone	96.8	6
Lumber & forest products	79.1	5
Petroleum products	65.2	4
Food ot kindred products	32.0	2
Autos & auto parts	26.4	2
Waste	22.8	1
Other	19.7	1
Non-freight		
Railcar switching	161.9	11
Demurrage & storage	58.3	4
Construction revenue	41.7	3
Car hire & rental income	34.7	2
Car repair services	21.1	1
Fuel sales to third parties	0.4	—
Other	73.5	5
Total	**1569.0**	**100**

COMPETITORS

Anacostia Rail Holdings
Arkansas & Missouri Railroad
Burlington Northern Santa Fe
CSX
Canadian National Railway
Canadian Pacific Railway
Dakota Minnesota & Eastern Railroad

Iowa Interstate Railroad
Kansas City Southern
Montana Rail Link
Norfolk Southern
OmniTRAX
Pan Am Railways
Pinsly Railroad
Pioneer Railcorp
Providence and Worcester Railroad
Union Pacific
Watco Companies

HISTORICAL FINANCIALS

Company Type: Public

Income Statement

FYE: December 31

	REVENUE ($ mil.)	NET INCOME ($ mil.)	NET PROFIT MARGIN	EMPLOYEES
12/13	1,569.0	272.0	17.3%	4,800
12/12	874.9	52.4	6.0%	4,600
12/11	829.1	119.4	14.4%	2,620
12/10	630.2	81.2	12.9%	2,502
12/09	544.8	61.3	11.3%	2,481
Annual Growth	**30.3%**	**45.1%**	**—**	**17.9%**

2013 Year-End Financials

Debt ratio: 30.5%   No. of shares (mil.): 53
Return on equity: 13.4%   Dividends
Cash ($ mil.): 62   Yield: —
Current ratio: 1.20   Payout: —
Long-term debt ($ mil.): 1,540   Market value ($ mil.): 5,143

	STOCK PRICE ($) FY Close	P/E High/Low	PER SHARE ($) Earnings	Dividends	Book Value
12/13	96.05	20 15	4.79	0.00	40.11
12/12	76.08	68 43	1.02	0.00	40.23
12/11	60.58	21 15	2.79	0.00	22.63
12/10	52.95	25 14	1.94	0.00	19.53
12/09	32.64	20 10	1.57	0.00	16.79
Annual Growth	**31.0%**	**—**	**32.2%**	**—**	**24.3%**

Gentex Corp.

Gentex would agree that competitors never look better than when they are in the rearview. The company focuses on designing making and marketing interior and exterior auto-dimming rearview mirrors and camera-based driver-assist systems for the automotive market. It serves customers worldwide but its largest base includes big carmakers such as Toyota General Motors and Volkswagen. Its products are found as standard or optional features on hundreds of vehicle models. To a lesser degree Gentex also makes dimmable aircraft windows found on commercial aircraft and fire protection products —including smoke detectors fire alarms and signaling devices —primarily for commercial buildings.

Geographic Reach Operating through five manufacturing facilities in Michigan Gentex has additional offices in the US Korea Canada France Mexico China Japan Sweden Hungary and the UK. Unsurprisingly the company's largest markets are the leading car production countries of the US (a third of sales) Germany (about a quarter) and Japan (nearly 10%).

Operations

The company's fire protection products are primarily sold to domestic distributors and OEMs of fire and security systems. Within the aerospace industry Gentex has delivered dimmable aircraft windows to the production line of Boeing's new 787 Dreamliner series and to Hawker Beechcraft for its business-class Beechcraft King Air 350i airplane. Gentex's dimmable window systems are marketed by PPG Aerospace under the brand name Alteos Interactive Window Systems.

Sales and Marketing The company's top customers are Volkswagen (15% of sales) General Motors and Toyota (each accounting for 12%) and Hyundai and Mercedes (both coming in at 11%). Other clients include BMW Ford Chrysler and Nissan. Gentex markets its products directly to OEMs as well as through Tier 1 suppliers.

Financial Performance The company's revenue jumped 25% in 2011 surpassing $1 billion for the first time in its history. It kept this momentum going in 2012 when revenue jumped by 7% from $1.02 billion to $1.1 billion. On the strength of the company's rising revenue net income increased by 2% in 2012 to hit $169 million the highest in the company's history.

Gentex was helped by a 32% surge in sales in Japan for 2012 and a 14% spike in sales in the US. It also experienced an 11% rise in auto-dimming mirror shipments reflecting the increase in light vehicle production in the North American market and increased penetration of those products on 2012 and 2013 model year vehicles.

Strategy To boost production capacity and support growth in its core geographic territories Gentex is busy making investments in its facilities. It constructed a new technology center adjacent to its headquarters in Zeeland Michigan and it is making a number of facility upgrades and renovations. The investments support the company's optimistic sales forecast and anticipated growing demand for high-tech camera-based automotive products such as Gentex's rear camera displays which consist of a liquid crystal display (LCD) that works with a rear-mounted video camera to provide a rear view while backing up and its SmartBeam high-beam assist system which uses a camera-on-a-chip to maximize forward lighting while eliminating the task of turning the high beams on and off manu-

ally. Both are integrated into Gentex auto-dimming mirrors.

HISTORY

At 23 Fred Bauer had already started and sold one company before founding Gentex in 1974. A maker of dual-cell photoelectric smoke detectors Gentex found its niche with products that had fewer false alarms and could detect slow smoldering fires. The company went public in 1981.

The next year Gentex entered the automotive market with the first electromechanical dimming mirror to beat the glare of nighttime driving. (Electrochromic technology uses electricity to darken a material.) The product was soon snapped up by Ford and General Motors to the tune of 200000 units a year. Five years later Gentex debuted the interior Night Vision Safety (NVS) electrochromic automatic-dimming mirror. Exterior NVS mirrors were introduced in 1991.

Gentex entered an agreement in 1992 with Japan's Ichikoh Industries to market mirrors in Asia. The following year it established a European office. Returning to its roots Gentex in 1993 introduced an AC/DC smoke detector. That year rival Donnelly paid $3.6 million in damages for infringing on Gentex's electrochromic mirror patent. Gentex formed a German subsidiary Gentex GmbH in 1994 and two years later opened an $8 million plant near its Michigan headquarters.

In 1997 Gentex developed a compass mirror a headlamp control mirror and a mirror that displays outside temperature. The next year it bought a stake in Photobit a developer of pixel sensor technology and sold more than 3.3 million NVS mirrors. In 1999 DaimlerChrysler agreed to equip all its models with Gentex mirrors.

Adding to its manufacturing capacity Gentex in 2000 completed the construction of a $12 million mirror manufacturing plant in Zeeland Michigan and made plans to build a factory in Europe. Adding more equipment to rearview mirrors paid off when GM announced that it would place the OnStar communications system in Gentex's interior mirrors in 1 million automobiles.

In 2002 Gentex announced that it would bring its new SmartBeam product to market by mid-2004. SmartBeam allowed drivers to use their bright lights more easily because the high beam self-dimmed when it detected an oncoming car. SureBeam came to market in 2004 the same year Gentex finished constructing a sales and engineering facility in Erlenbach Germany. The facility was intended to help Gentex better serve its European customers by offering greater logistics sales and engineering support.

EXECUTIVES

Vice President Sales, Dennis Alexejun
Vp Human Resources, Bruce Los, age 60
Chairman and CEO, Fred T. Bauer, age 72, $464,031 total compensation
SVP, Mark Newton, age 55, $257,040 total compensation
VP Operations, Paul Flynn, $153,273 total compensation
VP Europe, Brad Bosma
CFO and VP of Finance, Steve Downing
Vice President Of Marketing, Scott Chamberlain
Vice President, Robert Steel
Vp Quality, Ken Horner
Vice President Marketing, Keiffer Sestric
Chairman and CEO, Fred T. Bauer, age 72
Board Member, Eric Domke
Treasurer, Mike Hoffmann
Treasurer, Bill Tonar
Auditors: Ernst&YoungLLP

LOCATIONS

HQ: Gentex Corp.
600 N. Centennial Street, Zeeland, MI 49464
Phone: 616 772-1800   Fax: 616 772-7348
Web: www.gentex.com

2012 Sales

	$ mil.	% of total
Automotive products		
US	382.3	35
Germany	239.1	22
Japan	100.4	9
Other countries	355.2	32
Other products	22.6	2
Total	**1099.6**	**100**

PRODUCTS/OPERATIONS

2012 Sales

	$ mil.	% of total
Automotive products	1077.0	98
Other	22.6	2
Total	**1099.6**	**100**

Selected Products

Automotive
  Auto-dimming mirrors
  Curved glass mirrors
  Custom sensors (for detecting velocity rain and humidity)
  Interior lighting
  Microphones
  Mirror-based displays
  Side blind zone indicators
  SmartBeam (automatic high beam system integrated into auto-dimming mirror)
  Telematics systems
  Razor (turn signal lights)
  Rear camera display (LCD display integrated into auto-dimming mirror that works with a video camera mounted at rear of vehicle)
Fire protection
  Audio and visual signaling appliances
  Bells and speakers
  Carbon monoxide alarms
  Photoelectric smoke alarms and detectors
Other
  Dimmable aircraft windows

COMPETITORS

Ficosa
Guardian Industries
Ichikoh
Ingersoll-Rand Security Technologies
Magna Mirrors
Murakami Corp.
Safety Vision
SimplexGrinnell
UTC Climate Controls & Security
Universal Security Instruments
Visteon

HISTORICAL FINANCIALS

Company Type: Public

Income Statement

FYE: December 31

	REVENUE ($ mil.)	NET INCOME ($ mil.)	NET PROFIT MARGIN	EMPLOYEES
12/13	1,171.8	222.9	19.0%	3,801
12/12	1,099.5	168.5	15.3%	3,605
12/11	1,023.7	164.6	16.1%	3,481
12/10	816.2	137.7	16.9%	2,908
12/09	544.5	64.6	11.9%	2,371
Annual Growth	21.1%	36.3%	—	12.5%

2013 Year-End Financials

Debt ratio: 15.4% No. of shares (mil.): 291
Return on equity: 18.2% Dividends
Cash ($ mil.): 309 Yield: 3.3%
Current ratio: 5.01 Payout: 70.9%
Long-term debt ($ mil.): 265 Market value ($ mil.): 9,602

	STOCK PRICE ($) FY Close	P/E High/Low	PER SHARE ($) Earnings	Dividends	Book Value
12/13	32.98	43 24	0.78	0.55	4.56
12/12	18.85	53 25	0.59	0.51	3.92
12/11	29.59	58 38	0.57	0.47	3.56
12/10	29.56	60 34	0.49	0.44	3.14
12/09	17.85	77 31	0.24	0.44	2.66
Annual Growth	16.6%	— —	34.8%	5.7%	14.4%

Gentherm Inc

Don't worry TED can keep your car seat cool ... or warm. Gentherm (formerly Amerigon) develops thermoelectric device (TED) technology and incorporates it into its branded climate-control seat (CCS) which allows year-round temperature control and ventilation of car and truck seats on more than 50 vehicle models available in North America and Asia that are made by Ford General Motors and Nissan. Gentherm also provides heated and cooled cup holder and cable systems in addition to mattress systems. In late 2012 the company changed its name from Amerigon to Gentherm.

Geographic Reach

Gentherm has facilities in Germany Mexico China Canada Japan England Korea Malta Hungary the Ukraine and the US. The US accounts for 42% of its total sales while Germany generates 12% and China accounts for 10%. Korea and Japan collectively account for nearly 15% of Gentherm's total sales.

Sales and Marketing

Gentherm's largest customers include Johnson Controls (22% of total sales) Lear Corporation (18%) and Bosch Automotive (10%). Other major clients include General Motors Volkswagen Ford Hyundai Fiat and BMW.

Financial Performance

From 2011 to 2012 Gentherm recognized explosive growth ($370 million to $555 million) primarily due a 78% spike in sales from its previous W.E.T. acquisition and overall increases in new program launches for its climate-control seat (CCS) technology.

Strategy

The company has transformed its business structure in the wake of its 2011 milestone purchase of W.E.T. Automotive Systems a German-based firm that manufactures thermal systems for automotive seat applications. In June 2012 Amerigon began doing business as Gentherm and updated its trading symbol to better represent its new capabilities and extensive global reach now that W.E.T. Automotive Systems and itself have been officially integrated. (The name change became official after the company's shareholder meeting later in September 2012.)

EXECUTIVES

VP CFO and Treasurer, Barry G. Steele, age 44, $266,260 total compensation

President Automotive Business Unit, Frithjof Oldorff, $442,370 total compensation
President and CEO, Daniel R.Coker, $530,400 total compensation
VP Product Development, Darren A. Schumacher
VP Product Strategy and Business Planning, John Marx
VP Electronics Business Unit, Greg Steinl, $241,439 total compensation
Chairman, Oscar B. (Bud) Marx, age 75
Auditors: GrantThorntonLLP

LOCATIONS

HQ: Gentherm Inc
21680 Haggerty Road, Ste. 101, Northville, MI 48167
Phone: 248 504-0500
Web: www.gentherm.com

2012 Sales

	$ mil.	% of total
US	233.7	42
Germany	67.1	12
China	55.7	10
Korea	42.9	8
Japan	35.3	6
Canada	17.6	3
Czech Republic	15.4	3
Mexico	15.0	3
UK	13.2	2
Other	59.1	11
Total	**555.0**	**100**

PRODUCTS/OPERATIONS

2012 Sales

% mil.		% of total
W.E.T.	422.7	76
CCS	132.3	24
Total	**555.0**	**100**

Selected Services

Advancing core technology
Noise vibration and airflow management
Program management
Testing
Thermoelectric applications

COMPETITORS

Delphi Automotive Systems
Leggett & Platt
Magna International
Robert Bosch
Toyota Boshoku
Visteon

HISTORICAL FINANCIALS

Company Type: Public

Income Statement

FYE: December 31

	REVENUE ($ mil.)	NET INCOME ($ mil.)	NET PROFIT MARGIN	EMPLOYEES
12/13	662.0	33.8	5.1%	7,403
12/12	554.9	17.8	3.2%	116
12/11	369.5	10.3	2.8%	110
12/10	112.4	9.9	8.9%	93
12/09	60.9	0.7	1.2%	68
Annual Growth	81.6%	161.5%	—	223.0%

2013 Year-End Financials

Debt ratio: 17.0% No. of shares (mil.): 34
Return on equity: 16.2% Dividends
Cash ($ mil.): 54 Yield: —
Current ratio: 1.76 Payout: —
Long-term debt ($ mil.): 60 Market value ($ mil.): 936

	STOCK PRICE ($) FY Close	P/E High/Low	PER SHARE ($) Earnings	Dividends	Book Value
12/13	26.81	27 14	0.94	0.00	6.64
12/12	13.30	45 26	0.39	0.00	6.18
12/11	14.26	200113	0.09	0.00	4.83
12/10	10.88	25 15	0.44	0.00	2.61
12/09	7.94	307 75	0.03	0.00	2.24
Annual Growth	35.6%	—	—136.6%	—	31.2%

Geospace Technologies Corp

Geospace Technologies (formerly OYO Geospace) analyzes the spaces below the earth's surface to help companies find gas and oil. It makes instruments and equipment used by seismic contractors and oil and gas companies to gather and process seismic data to zero in on hydrocarbons. The company's geophones detect energy from the earth's subsurface and its hydrophones detect changes in pressure and gather seismic data in water. Other products include seismic leader wire geophone string connectors seismic telemetry cable and thermal imaging equipment; all are compatible with most seismic data-acquisition systems. Geospace also makes its thermal printers available for the commercial graphics industry.

Operations

The company has two business lines: seismic products (its largest segment) and thermal solutions products. Geospace's seismic product lines consist of land and marine nodal seismic data acquisition systems high-definition reservoir characterization products and services geophones and hydrophones (including multi-component geophones and hydrophones) seismic leader wire geophone string and acquisition system connectors seismic telemetry cables marine seismic cable retrieval and steering devices and specialized data acquisition systems targeted at conventional and niche markets.

Geospace's thermal printers include both thermal imagesetters for graphics applications and thermal plotters for seismic applications. In addition its thermal solutions products include direct-to-screen systems thermal printheads dry thermal film thermal transfer ribbons and other thermal media. The company also distributes private label high-quality dry thermal media for use in its thermal printers and direct-to-screen systems.

Geographic Reach

Geospace sells products to customers around the world. It is headquartered in Houston Texas. International offices are located in Canada China Russia and the UK. International manufacturing facilities are located in Canada and Russia.

Sales and Marketing

The company's principal seismic customers are seismic contractors and major independent and government-owned oil and gas companies that either operate their own seismic crews or specify seismic instrument and equipment preferences to contractors. Geospace's customers deepwater reservoir characterization products are generally large international oil and gas companies that operate long-term offshore oil and gas producing properties. The company's thermal imaging customers are direct users of its equipment as well as specialized resellers that focus on the newsprint silkscreen and corrugated box printing industries.

Financial Performance

Revenue increased by 11% in fiscal year 2012 due to higher customer demand for seismic products and particularly robust demand for sales and rentals of land-based wireless (or nodal) data acquisition systems driven by strong oil and gas exploration activities throughout the world.

Geospace's net income grew by 18% in fiscal year 2012 thanks to higher revenues and an increase in gross profits resulting from improved sales and rentals of seismic products.

Except for the revenue slump in 2009 the company saw an upward trend in revenues from fiscal year 2008 to 2012. The slump in 2009 was because of a decrease in sales stemming from the decline in customer demand for seismic products as a result of the effects of the worldwide economic slowdown and its impact on energy exploration activities.

Strategy

Geospace relies on a broad base of customers in a wide swath of countries to protect it from dramatic downturns in particular markets. While it has about 50 seismic contracting companies (about 20 of which specialize in marine activities) it also sells thermal printer products as part of its product diversification strategy.

In 2011 the company sold to Dawson Geophysical Company 14850 channels of its galvanic skin response (GSR) wireless data acquisition system for $15.6 million. This transaction aids Geospace's plans of making GSR wireless technology available to their customers under a rent-to-own strategy.

The company dropped OYO from its corporate name in 2012 following the sale of Japanese conglomerate OYO Corporation's 21% stake in the company.

Ownership

Eagle Asset Management owns 18% of Geospace.

EXECUTIVES

SVP and CTO, Michael J. Sheen, age 66, $272,250 total compensation

Chairman President and CEO, Gary D. Owens, age 67, $302,500 total compensation

EVP and Chief Project Engineer, Robbin B. Adams, $160,000 total compensation

EVP and COO, Walter R. Wheeler, $175,000 total compensation

Senior Vice President Administrative Assistant, Joan Wheeler

Vice President, Lacey Rice

Chairman President and CEO, Gary D. Owens, age 67

Auditors: UHYLLP

LOCATIONS

HQ: Geospace Technologies Corp
7007 Pinemont Drive, Houston, TX 77040-6601
Phone: 713 986-4444
Web: www.geospace.com

2012 Sales

	$ mil.	% of total
North America		
US	216.7	85
Canada	23.8	9
Russian Federation	9.8	4
Europe		
UK	4.1	2
Adjustments	(62.7)	
Total	**191.7**	**100**

PRODUCTS/OPERATIONS

2012 Sales

	$ mil.	% of total
Seismic	178.2	92
Thermal Solutions	12.7	7
Corporate	0.8	1
Total	**191.7**	**100**

Selected Products

Seismic
Data-acquisition systems
Geophone string connectors
Geophones
High-definition reservoir characterization equipment
Hydrophones
Marine seismic cable retrieval devices
Seismic leader wire
Seismic telemetry cable
Thermal Solutions
Dry thermal film (distribution)
Thermal imaging equipment (wide-format thermal printers for newsprint and other commercial applications)

COMPETITORS

Amphenol	Mitcham Industries
Bolt Technology	Petroleum Geo-Services
CGG	Ricoh Company
Core Laboratories	ShawCor
Dawson Geophysical	WesternGeco
ION Geophysical	Xantê©

HISTORICAL FINANCIALS

Company Type: Public

Income Statement

FYE: September 30

	REVENUE ($ mil.)	NET INCOME ($ mil.)	NET PROFIT MARGIN	EMPLOYEES
09/14	236.9	36.9	15.6%	1,149
09/13	300.6	69.5	23.1%	1,333
09/12	191.6	35.1	18.3%	1,164
09/11	172.9	29.7	17.2%	1,008
09/10	128.5	14.0	11.0%	891
Annual Growth	**16.5%**	**27.2%**	**—**	**6.6%**

2014 Year-End Financials

Debt ratio: —
Return on equity: 11.9%
Cash ($ mil.): 53
Current ratio: 10.45
Long-term debt ($ mil.): —

No. of shares (mil.): 13
Dividends
　Yield: —
　Payout: —
Market value ($ mil.): 462

	STOCK PRICE ($) FY Close	P/E High/Low		PER SHARE ($) Earnings	Dividends	Book Value
09/14	35.15	37	13	2.81	0.00	25.04
09/13	84.29	26	12	5.38	0.00	22.33
09/12	122.41	44	19	2.74	0.00	16.79
09/11	56.29	46	24	2.37	0.00	13.94
09/10	57.88	48	20	1.14	0.00	11.16
Annual Growth	**(11.7%)**	**—**	**—**	**25.4%**	**—**	**22.4%**

Globe Specialty Metals Inc

Globe Specialty Metals is an apt name for a company that peddles its metals around the world. The specialty metals manufacturer sells silicon metal and silicon-based alloys to customers in the Americas Asia and Europe from facilities in the US Argentina China and Poland. Its silicon metal and alloys are used to make a variety of industrial products from aluminum and automotive parts to steel and semiconductors. It holds about one-fifth of the Western market share for magnesium ferrosilicon. Globe also recycles by-products such as silica fume (a dustlike material known as microsilica that is collected in air filtration systems) which it sells for use as a concrete additive.

Operations

The company produces silicon foundry alloys steelmaking alloys electrodes and silica fume through its subsidiaries. Its principal operating companies are Globe Metallurgical Inc. Alden Resources LLC and Core Metals Group LLC Solsil Inc. in the U.S.; Globe Metales S.A. in Argentina; and Ningxia Yonvey Coal Industry Co. Ltd. in China.

Financial Analysis

Globe's revenues grew by 10% in 2011 the result of an 8% increase in average selling prices due to higher silicon-based alloys pricing primarily caused by higher magnesium ferrosilicon pricing spurred by strong demand from the automotive industry and a pass through of higher rare earth costs.

Globe Metais and Solsil sales decreased to $0 due to the timing of the sale of the company's Brazilian manufacturing operations and termination of BP Solar technology license joint development and supply agreement.

The company saw its 2011 net income increase by 2% thanks to higher revenues and a 33% decrease in the provision for income taxes due to reduced state taxes and reduced foreign losses.

Strategy

Globe's strategy is to focus on its core silicon businesses rationalizing costs to meet market demand levels (ramping up or scaling down plants as needed) while making strategic complementary acquisitions.

In 2012 the company expanded its silicon assets again when subsidiary QSI was declared winning bidder for certain assets of Bencacour Silicon. QSI acquired Bencacour's 51% stake in Quebec Silicon which owns a silicon metal plant in Becancour Quebec for $34 million. The plant produces about 47000 metric tons of silicon metal per year.

In 2011 Globe acquired Alden Resources a miner processor and supplier of specialty coal to the silicon and silicon-based alloy industries and thermal coal to the power industry. Alden operated several underground mines in Kentucky and Tennessee that had a combined 32 million tons of coal reserves.

Globe acquired Core Metals Group from Ospraie Funds for $52 million in 2010. Core is a Pennsylvania-based firm that produces and markets high-purity ferrosilicon and other specialty steel ingredients. The move enhanced Globe's ferrosilicon business and helped diversify its product line.

Ownership

In 2012 Globe chairman Alan Kestenbaum held 16.4% of the company Royce & Associates LLC 11.7%.

EXECUTIVES

CEO and COO, Jeff Bradley, age 54, $700,000 total compensation
Executive Director Globe Metales S.A., Delfin Rabinovich, age 65
Chief Financial Officer, Joe Ragan
Vice President Merger And Acquisitions And Corporate Development, Gilad Amozeg
Chairman, Alan Kestenbaum, age 52
Auditors: KPMGLLP

LOCATIONS

HQ: Globe Specialty Metals Inc
600 Brickell Ave, Suite 1500, Miami, FL 33131
Phone: 786 509-6900   **Fax:** 212 798-8185
Web: www.glbsm.com

2011 Sales

	$ mil.	% of total
US	625.7	89
Argentina	57.2	8
Poland	14.1	2
Canada	5.4	1
China	3.1	-
Total	**705.5**	**100**

PRODUCTS/OPERATIONS

2011 Sales

	$ mil.	% of total
Silicon metal	360.7	51
Silicon-based alloys	269.9	38
Other	74.9	11
Total	**705.5**	**100**

Selected Subsidiaries

Globe Metais Industria e Comercio S.A. (Brazil)
Globe Metales S.A. (Argentina)
Globe Metallurgical Inc. (US)
Ningxia Yongvey Coal Industrial Co. Ltd. (China)
Solsil Inc. (US)

COMPETITORS

Dow Corning   Simcala
Elkem AS   Timminco
Orkla   Wacker Chemie

HISTORICAL FINANCIALS

Company Type: Public

Income Statement

FYE: June 30

	REVENUE ($ mil.)	NET INCOME ($ mil.)	NET PROFIT MARGIN	EMPLOYEES
06/14	752.8	14.4	1.9%	1,569
06/13	757.5	(21.0)	—	1,353
06/12	705.5	54.5	7.7%	1,493
06/11	641.8	52.8	8.2%	1,213
06/10	472.6	34.1	7.2%	1,136
Annual Growth	**12.3%**	**(19.4%)**	**—**	**8.4%**

2014 Year-End Financials

Debt ratio: 15.9%
Return on equity: 3.2%
Cash ($ mil.): 97
Current ratio: 3.29
Long-term debt ($ mil.): 132
No. of shares (mil.): 73
Dividends
  Yield: 1.3%
  Payout: 151.3%
Market value ($ mil.): 1,533

	STOCK PRICE ($) FY Close	P/E High/Low	PER SHARE ($) Earnings	Dividends	Book Value
06/14	20.78	115 57	0.19	0.29	5.80
06/13	10.87	— —	(0.28)	0.38	6.17
06/12	13.43	34 16	0.71	0.20	6.91
06/11	22.42	35 14	0.69	0.15	6.36
06/10	10.33	28 15	0.46	0.00	5.71
Annual Growth	**19.1%**	**— —**	**(19.8%)**	**—**	**0.4%**

Gorman-Rupp Co.

Gorman-Rupp keeps pumping out pumps. The company founded in 1933 by engineers J. C. Gorman and H. E. Rupp makes a myriad of pumps and fluid controls used in construction sewage treatment petroleum refining agriculture and fire fighting as well as for HVAC and military applications. Gorman-Rupp's pumps range in size from 1/4-inch (one gallon per minute) to 180-inch and ranging in rated capacity from less than one gallon per minute to nearly one million gallons per minute. Smaller pumps are used for dispensing soft drinks and making ice cubes while large pumps are central to refueling aircraft and boosting low water pressure in municipal fresh-water markets.

Geographic Reach

Gorman-Rupp owns facilities training centers and warehouses in in Sparks Nevada; Dallas; and Bangkok. In addition the company leases warehouse facilities in Jebal Ali Dubai; and Culemborg The Netherlands. Production operations reside in US (Ohio Arizona Texas Georgia Mississippi and Pennsylvania) Canada Ireland The Netherlands and South Africa. The US accounts for nearly 65% of sales.

Sales and Marketing

Gorman-Rupp sells its products through 1000 distributors OEM representatives distributor catalogs and direct sales.

Financial Performance

Gorman-Rupp has achieved unprecedented growth over the last few years with revenues rising 4% from $376 million in 2012 to $392 million in 2013 a company milestone. Profits climbed 7% from $28 million in 2012 to peak at a record-breaking $30 million in 2013.

The historic growth for 2013 was primarily due to the improving US economy and the inclusion of 2012 acquisitions sales for the entire year in 2013. Sales for its pumps and pumps systems jumped 6% in 2013 due to additional shipments for the fire and agricultural markets and for Gulf Coast flood control projects. Increased shipments for the petroleum and industrial markets were also the major contributors to a surge in non-water market sales.

The profit growth for 2013 was fueled by the higher revenue other income and gains made on the sale of machinery and equipment. From 2011 to 2013 Gorman-Rupp's cash flow from operations has steadily climbed to match its rising revenue trend.

Strategy

Over the last decade Gorman-Rupp has continued to pursue new routes to market its products. The company has reached outside North America by building distributor alliances and establishing plants and warehouses in Ireland and the Nether-

---

lands to serve customers in Europe and in Thailand to reach those in Asia.

Mergers and Acquisitions

In 2014 Gorman-Rupp purchased Bayou City Pump (BCP) based in Houston. BCP is a manufacturer of and service provider for highly-reliable and energy-efficient vertical turbine pumping systems primarily for the inland and coastal marine liquid petroleum and chemical transportation market.

EXECUTIVES

President and CEO, Jeffrey S. Gorman, age 62, $368,333 total compensation
CFO, Wayne L. Knabel, age 67, $231,250 total compensation
Vice President Finance, Kenneth Dudley
Vice President, Mark Kreinbihl
Vice-president, Tom Nelson
Vice President Sales And Marketing, Darrell Snyder
Vice President Technical Services, Mike Barnett
Vice President And General Manager Gorman Rupp Of, Gary Warren
Chairman, James C. Gorman, age 90
Auditors: Ernst&YoungLLP

LOCATIONS

HQ: Gorman-Rupp Co.
600 South Airport Road, Mansfield, OH 44903
Phone: 419 755-1011   **Fax:** 419 755-1233
Web: www.gormanrupp.com

2013 Sales

	$ mil.	% of total
US	257.1	64
Other countries	134.6	36
Total	**391.7**	**100**

PRODUCTS/OPERATIONS

2013 Sales

	$ mil.	% of total
Pumps & pump systems	336.8	86
Repairs & other	54.9	14
Total	**391.7**	**100**

Selected Operations

American Machine & Tool Co. Inc. (self-priming centrifugal standard centrifugal diaphragm engine-driven priming assist rotary drum and piston drum pumps)
Gorman-Rupp Europe B.V. (self-priming centrifugal standard centrifugal submersible rotary gear diaphragm and utility pumps and packaged pump stations)
Gorman-Rupp Industries (bellows metering centrifugal magnetic drive piston peristaltic gear and oscillating pumps and valves)
The Gorman-Rupp International Company (distribution facilities in Thailand and the Netherlands)
Gorman-Rupp Mansfield Division (self-priming centrifugal standard centrifugal submersible rotary gear diaphragm and utility pumps and packaged pump stations)
Gorman-Rupp of Canada Limited (self-priming centrifugal standard centrifugal submersible rotary gear diaphragm and utility pumps and packaged pump stations)
National Pump Company (vertical turbine line shaft and submersible pumps centrifugal pumps high-pressure booster pumps and packaged pump station systems)
Patterson Pump Company (horizontal split case vertical in-line end suction centrifugal vertical turbine sewage multipurpose vertical turbine axial and mixed flow pumps)

COMPETITORS

Ampco-Pittsburgh   Pentair
Colfax   Roper Industries

Flowserve
Goulds Pumps
Graco
Haskel
IDEX

SPX Flow Technology
Weir Group
Wilden Pump &
Engineering
Xylem

HISTORICAL FINANCIALS

Company Type: Public

Income Statement

FYE: December 31

	REVENUE ($ mil.)	NET INCOME ($ mil.)	NET PROFIT MARGIN	EMPLOYEES
12/13	391.6	30.1	7.7%	1,247
12/12	375.6	28.2	7.5%	1,247
12/11	359.4	28.8	8.0%	1,123
12/10	296.8	25.9	8.7%	1,082
12/09	266.2	18.2	6.9%	957
Annual Growth	10.1%	13.3%		6.8%

2013 Year-End Financials

Debt ratio: 2.5%	No. of shares (mil.): 26
Return on equity: 12.0%	Dividends
Cash ($ mil.): 31	Yield: 1.1%
Current ratio: 3.12	Payout: 38.6%
Long-term debt ($ mil.): —	Market value ($ mil.): 878

	STOCK PRICE ($) FY Close	P/E High/Low		PER SHARE ($)		
			Earnings	Dividends	Book Value
12/13	33.43	37 23	1.15	0.39	10.06
12/12	29.83	32 24	1.07	0.39	8.94
12/11	27.15	40 21	1.10	0.28	8.19
12/10	32.32	38 24	0.99	0.34	7.62
12/09	27.64	47 21	0.70	0.32	6.78
Annual Growth	4.9%		—	13.3% 4.7% 10.4%

Government Properties Income Trust

If Government Properties Income Trust had one request of Uncle Sam it would be this: "I want you to lease our properties." As a real estate investment trust (REIT) Government Properties Income Trust invests in properties that are leased to government tenants. It owns 10 million sq. ft. of leasing space at some 80 properties. The company leases mostly to federal agencies (such as the FBI IRS and FDA) but it does lease to some state-run agencies as well. Government Properties Income Trust went public in 2009. Former majority owner HRPT Properties Trust owns about 30% of the company following the IPO.

Geographic Reach

Although the company has It does have properties in 31 states many of its properties are located in the Washington DC area.

Financial Performance

Government Properties Income Trust's revenue has been steadily increasing year-over-year. It reported $211.1 million in revenue for fiscal 2012 after claiming $179 million in fiscal 2011 and $116.8 million in fiscal 2010.

EXECUTIVES

Treasurer Chief Financial Officer, Mark L. Kleifges, age 53

President and COO, David M. Blackman, age 52
Board Member, Barbara D Gilmore, age 64
Board Member, Jeffrey P Somers
Auditors: Ernst&YoungLLP

LOCATIONS

HQ: Government Properties Income Trust
Two Newton Place, 255 Washington Street, Suite 300,
Newton, MA 02458-1634
Phone: 617 219-1440 **Fax:** 617 219-1441
Web: www.govreit.com

COMPETITORS

Boston Properties
CapLease
Corporate Office
Properties Trust

First Potomac Realty
Piedmont Office Realty
Trust
USFP Trust

HISTORICAL FINANCIALS

Company Type: Public

Income Statement

FYE: December 31

	REVENUE ($ mil.)	NET INCOME ($ mil.)	NET PROFIT MARGIN	EMPLOYEES
12/13	226.9	54.6	24.1%	0
12/12	211.0	49.9	23.7%	0
12/11	178.9	46.0	25.7%	0
12/10	116.7	27.8	23.8%	0
12/09	78.9	25.9	32.9%	0
Annual Growth	30.2%	20.4%	—	—

2013 Year-End Financials

Debt ratio: 36.6%	No. of shares (mil.): 54
Return on equity: 5.4%	Dividends
Cash ($ mil.): 7	Yield: 6.9%
Current ratio: 0.37	Payout: 168.6%
Long-term debt ($ mil.): 507	Market value ($ mil.): 1,360

	STOCK PRICE ($) FY Close	P/E High/Low		PER SHARE ($)		
			Earnings	Dividends	Book Value
12/13	24.85	27 23	1.00	1.72	18.09
12/12	23.97	24 20	1.03	1.69	18.80
12/11	22.55	26 19	1.06	1.67	18.95
12/10	26.79	35 27	0.81	1.62	18.70
12/09	22.98	15 11	1.72	0.90	16.39
Annual Growth	2.0%		—	— (12.7%) 17.6% 2.5%

Graco Inc.

Graco has fluid management skills. The company which was founded in 1926 as Gray Company manufactures fluid-handling equipment designed to move measure control dispense and apply fluid materials. Products include pumps applicators spray guns pressure washers filters valves and accessories; these goods are used in industrial and commercial applications to handle paints adhesives sealants and lubricants. In addition to painting contractors Graco's customers include automotive construction equipment and vehicle lubrication companies. Graco sells its products through independent distributors worldwide.

Geographic Reach

Graco has subsidiaries located in Australia Belgium China Japan Korea Mexico and Switzerland which distribute products in their local areas. The

majority of manufacturing occurs in the US but some products are assembled in China and Belgium.

Operations

Graco's largest segment is industrial; its products account for 60% of company sales. The business which includes the Applied Fluid Technologies division manufactures and distributes equipment to apply paint and other coatings (liquid finishing) to move and dispense chemicals and liquefied foods (process pumps) and to refinish and repair automobiles (Sharpe brand by Graco) to customers who make assemble maintain repair and refinish products such as appliances vehicles airplanes electronics cabinets furniture and other articles. The alternative energy market utilizes the company's sealant and adhesive application equipment for solar panel seals and wind power components such as turbine blades.

The contractor segment generates about 30% of Graco's total sales. This segment markets a complete line of airless paint and texture sprayers hoses and filters and spare parts to painters in the construction and maintenance industries. Contractor products are also sold through general equipment distributors and retail home centers. The equipment is used to mark roads parking lots fields and floors; to paint and texture walls ceilings and structures; and to apply coatings to roofs. The lubrication segment represents approximately 10% of company sales. Graco makes pumps and applicators used by the vehicle services and industrial markets including oil-change outlets service garages fleet service centers automobile dealerships and auto parts stores.

Financial Performance

Revenues rose 13% and profits jumped 5% in 2012 compared with 2011. By segment industrial enjoyed an uptick of 20% thanks mainly to healthy sales in all regions where the segment operates and a key acquisition made in 2012. Contractor headed up 3% thanks to strong demand in the Americas and the Asia/Pacific. Lubrication increased by 7% once again as a result of a favorable economic climate in the Americas and Europe.

By region the Americas increased 13% on the back of demand from industrial end-markets as well as growth in the housing and construction markets. Europe was up 28% following investments in commercial resources of Eastern Europe Middle East and Africa. The region also benefited from more demand from the industrial and lubrication end markets. Asia/Pacific sales jumped 5% as a result of higher demand for powder finishing equipment and a spike in sales in the contractor segment.

Strategy

With a long-term financial growth target of 10% for revenue and 12% for net earnings the company focuses on strategies that include product development and geographic expansion. Graco's brass ring is to make at least 30% of its annual sales from new products introduced only as far back as three years; it achieved 17% sales in 2012 from such products. Geographically the company is focused on expanding distribution and sales outside the US especially in China.

A main strategy of the industrial segment is to develop standard products using a modular product structure in order to support a number of configurations and applications. In 2011 the company launched an entry-level Reactor plural component pump used to apply foam for insulation to the Chinese market. Again one of the main strategies of the contractor segment is to offer new technologies as well as re-engineer its existing products better. Geographically the segment is trying to transition contractors in Europe and Asia/Pacific from manual application of paint and other coatings to spray technology. The lubrication segment keeps competitive by developing products possessing unique features that cater to a particular industry.

Acquisitions are another important component of Graco's strategy. In spring 2012 Graco made a significant acquisition when it purchased the finishing businesses of Illinois Tool Works (ITW) for $650 million. The deal gave Graco access to an assortment of complementary powder and liquid finishing equipment operations brands and equipment. New primary brands include Gema (powder coating/finishing technology) and Binks (spray finishing equipment). The company also obtained spray guns and accessories marketed under the DeVilbiss name as well as Ransburg electrostatic equipment and accessories.

HISTORY

Graco is the successor to Gray Company founded by Russell and Leil Gray from a downtown Minneapolis garage in 1926 to make airpowered grease guns for car lubrication. Their devices proved more effective than hand-operated grease guns and by the 1930s were marketed nationally to car dealerships and service stations. The company expanded during the Depression and made battlefield lubrication equipment during WWII; afterward it moved into other industrial markets with sprayers finishers and dispensers.

Leil Gray's son-in-law David Koch helped lead the company for three decades starting in the 1960s as airless spray technology primed its pump. The company went public in 1969 and changed its name to Graco. Acquisitions in the 1970s built its global presence but market fragility in 1974 caused a two-year earnings slide. Unsuccessful forays into consumer painting (late 1970s sold 1984) and robotics (1981 sold 1991) convinced Graco to focus on its core markets.

Recessions early in the 1980s and 1990s reduced business. Graco responded during those times by consolidating operations to slash costs. Koch stepped down as CEO in 1996. In 1998 Graco bought back about 22% of its outstanding shares. The next year Graco acquired Bollhoff Verfahrenstechnik a German maker of industrial/automotive fluid-application equipment.

In 2001 Graco bought California-based ASM Company (spray tips guns poles and other accessories for professional painters) through the stock purchase of its holding company parent Panatech Research and Development Corporation from the St. Louis-based Harbour Group. Also that year David Roberts became CEO. (Roberts added the position of chairman in 2006 but left the company in 2007.)

The company closed its Bielefeld Germany manufacturing facility in 2002 and transferred a portion of its manufacturing lines to Minneapolis Minnesota. In early 2003 Graco repurchased 2.2 million shares of its common stock from its outgoing chairman emeritus David Koch. That year it acquired Sharpe Manufacturing giving it entry into the automotive component making business.

Late in 2004 Graco purchased resin-dispensing equipment maker Liquid Control Corp. for an undisclosed sum. It continued its acquisition efforts into 2005 when it bought New Jersey-based component maker Gusmer Corporation and its European operations Gusmer Europe. Over the next two years Graco expanded its fluid-handling product scope with the acquisitions of PBL Industries (2005) and Lubriquip from IDEX (2006).

In 2007 six-year CEO David Roberts left Graco to become the top executive at Carlisle Companies; VP Patrick McHale took on the title of president and CEO of Graco while board member Lee Mitau became chairman.

The industrial segment entered the composites market in 2008 with the acquisition of GlasCraft. The company agreed to acquire Cohesant Technologies for about $35 million but the real target of the purchase was Cohesant's GlasCraft unit a leading maker of metering mixing and dispensing equipment. That same year Graco acquired Airlessco's spray-painting assets of Durotech for approximately $15 million cash to enhance its contractor segment. Also in 2008 the company's Lubrication segment acquired certain assets of Lubrication Scientifics (LubeSci) for approximately $5 million cash.

Responding to the harsh economic conditions of 2009 Graco laid off about 330 employees or around 14% of its workforce in two rounds of job cuts. It also reduced capital expenditures and discretionary spending in the cost-cutting initiative.

In 2010 Graco formed commercial enterprise Graco Trading (Suzhou) to distribute its products in China.

EXECUTIVES

Vice President Engineering, Joseph H Keller, age 69
Vice President, Dale D Johnson, age 60
Vp And General Manager Industrial Products, David M Lowe, age 59
Vice President Distribution Operations, Charles L (Chuck) Rescorla, age 63
Vice President And General Manager; Emea, Jeffrey P Johnson, age 55
President CEO and Director, Patrick J. McHale, age 53, $641,700 total compensation
Chief Financial Officer, James A. Graner, age 70, $344,500 total compensation
Vp And Treasurer, Christian E Rothe
Vice President And General Manager South And Central America, Bernard Moreau
Vice President Sales, Dennis Bruce
Vice President Of Sales, Max Baumgartner
Vice President Of Sales, Jerry Powaser
Vice President Sales, Magee Mike
Vice President Sales, Jim Boren
National Accounts Manager, Mike Ivkovich
National Account Manager, Dan McDougal
Vice President Manufacturing, Charles Behrens
Senior Vice President International, George Bauers
Vice President Of Iaed Engineering, Bill Scherer
Vice President Supply Chain, Nancy Breitenstein
Vice President Supply Chain, James Toomey
Chairman, Lee R. Mitau, age 66
President CEO and Director, Patrick J. McHale, age 53
Board Of Directors, William G (Bill) Van Dyke, age 69
Advisory Board Member, Mike Butler
Board Of Directors, Pablo Luvinoff
Auditors: Deloitte&ToucheLLP

LOCATIONS

HQ: Graco Inc.
88 ?11th Avenue Northeast, Minneapolis, MN 55413
Phone: 612 623-6000   **Fax:** 612 623-6777
Web: www.graco.com

2012 Sales

	$ mil.	% of total
Americas	536	53
Europe	257	25
Asia/Pacific	219	22
Total	**1012**	**100**

PRODUCTS/OPERATIONS

2012 Sales

	$ mil.	% of total
Industrial	603.4	60
Contractor	298.8	29
Lubrication	110.3	11
Total	**1012.5**	**100**

Selected Products

Contractor Equipment
  Contractor accessories
  Field marking equipment
  Fine finish equipment
  Line stripping equipment
  Paint spraying equipment
  Pressure wash equipment
  Roof coating equipment
  Spray guns
  Texture spray equipment
Industrial Lubrication Equipment
  Centralized equipment controllers
  Centralized equipment monitors
  Centralized equipment metering devices
  Centralized equipment pump packages
  Centralized equipment pumps
  Compressor lubrication
  Industrial lubrication accessories
  Mobile off-road equipment
  Mobile on-road equipment
  Single series single point lubricators

COMPETITORS

Arroyo Process Equipment	Illinois Tool Works
Briggs & Stratton	Meggitt (North Hollywood)
Colfax	Nordson
Cross Co.	Raven Industries
Dürr	United Air Specialists
EXEL Industries	Valcor Engineering Corporation
IDEX	Weir Group
IMI plc	

HISTORICAL FINANCIALS

Company Type: Public

Income Statement

FYE: December 27

	REVENUE ($ mil.)	NET INCOME ($ mil.)	NET PROFIT MARGIN	EMPLOYEES
12/13	1,104.0	210.8	19.1%	2,700
12/12	1,012.4	149.1	14.7%	2,600
12/11	895.2	142.3	15.9%	2,300
12/10	744.0	102.8	13.8%	2,200
12/09	579.2	48.9	8.5%	2,050
Annual Growth	**17.5%**	**44.0%**	**—**	**7.1%**

2013 Year-End Financials

Debt ratio: 31.4%	No. of shares (mil.): 61
Return on equity: 38.8%	Dividends
Cash ($ mil.): 19	Yield: 1.2%
Current ratio: 4.69	Payout: 29.9%
Long-term debt ($ mil.): 408	Market value ($ mil.): 4,747

	STOCK PRICE ($) FY Close	P/E High/Low		PER SHARE ($) Earnings	Dividends	Book Value
12/13	77.82	23	15	3.36	1.00	10.40
12/12	50.85	23	16	2.42	0.90	7.47
12/11	40.89	23	14	2.32	0.84	5.40
12/10	39.45	24	15	1.69	0.80	4.40
12/09	29.96	37	18	0.81	0.76	3.49
Annual Growth	**27.0%**	—	—	**42.7%**	**7.1%**	**31.3%**

Graham Corp.

Graham Corporation knows how to take the heat and not crack under pressure. The company through its two subsidiaries manufactures mainly heat-transfer equipment including helical coil heat exchangers plate and frame heat exchangers and vacuums such as pumps and compressors and steam jet ejector vacuum systems. The lineup is used in myriad industrial and energy applications from petroleum refining to chemical and petrochemical processing power generation propulsion systems for nuclear-powered defense vessels and even food and soap making. The company sells its products directly and through independent sales representatives worldwide. Some 40% to 55% of Graham's sales are generated outside of the US.

Thanks to a slow recovery in the global economy demand for energy including petroleum-based products and nuclear power is increasing. Graham's sales climbed nearly 20% in 2011 following a more than 35% decrease the prior year due to stalled investment in major capital projects.

The rise in revenue in 2011 was tied to both the improving business climate and the acquisition of Energy Steel & Supply Co. (Energy Steel). Graham's earnings which had taken roughly a 60% nose dive in 2010 declined modestly eroded in part by costs associated with its Energy Steel acquisition in late 2010.

Energy Steel provides custom fabrication and specialty machining of products used in nuclear power plants primarily in the US. The $18 million deal diversifies Graham's offerings to the energy industry as well as reduces its dependence on the oil and petrochemical market. It also positions Graham to score a share of the US Navy's nuclear propulsion projects.

Concurrently Graham continues to expand its global presence particularly in developing regions where the surge in refining and chemical processing is appreciable. Its Chinese subsidiary Graham Vacuum and Heat Transfer Technology (Suzhou) supports regional sales engineering services and subcontracted fabrication in Asia.

Graham Corporation was founded in 1983 as the successor company to Graham Manufacturing Co. Inc. The legacy business incorporated in 1936 took its name from its founder Harold Graham.

EXECUTIVES

President and CEO, James R. Lines, age 54, $350,200 total compensation
VP Operations, Alan E. Smith, age 48, $211,150 total compensation
VP Finance and Administration; CFO, Jeffrey F. Glajch, $247,200 total compensation
Vice President Operations, Avinash Smith
Vice President, Graham Kilvert
Chairman, Jerald D. Bidlack, age 79
Board Member, James Baraber
Auditors: Deloitte&ToucheLLP

LOCATIONS

HQ: Graham Corp.
20 Florence Avenue, Batavia, NY 14020
Phone: 585 343-2216
Web: www.graham-mfg.com

2011 Sales

	$ mil.	% of total
North America		
US	33.4	45
Canada	3.1	4

	$ mil.	% of total
Mexico	0.9	1
Asia	16.1	22
Middle East	11.8	16
South America	6.0	8
Africa	1.7	2
Western Europe	1.0	2
Australia & New Zealand	0.1	-
Other	0.1	-
Total	**74.2**	**100**

PRODUCTS/OPERATIONS

2011 Sales

	$ mil.	% of total
Heat transfer equipment	28.9	39
Vacuum equipment	26.2	35
All other	19.1	26
Total	**74.2**	**100**

2011 Sales

	% of total
Refining industry	35
Chemical & petrochemical industries	22
Other industrial applications	43
Total	**100**

Selected Products

Heat transfer equipment
  Desuperheaters
  Heliflow spiral tube heat exchangers
  MicroMix II and MicroMax water heaters
  Plate heat exchangers
  Surface condensers
Vacuum equipment
  Liquid ring vacuum pumps and compressors
  Process condensers
  Steam jet ejector vacuum systems

COMPETITORS

Alfa Laval	Kemco Systems
Dover Corp.	Parker Hannifin HPD
Gardner Denver	Pfeiffer Vacuum
Haskel	SPX
IDEX	Weatherford
ITT Corp.	International
Ingersoll-Rand	

HISTORICAL FINANCIALS

Company Type: Public

Income Statement

FYE: March 31

	REVENUE ($ mil.)	NET INCOME ($ mil.)	NET PROFIT MARGIN	EMPLOYEES
03/14	102.2	10.1	9.9%	395
03/13	104.9	11.1	10.6%	378
03/12	103.1	10.5	10.2%	349
03/11	74.2	5.8	7.9%	329
03/10	62.1	6.3	10.2%	237
Annual Growth	**13.2%**	**12.4%**	**—**	**13.6%**

2014 Year-End Financials

Debt ratio: 0.1%	No. of shares (mil.): 10
Return on equity: 10.2%	Dividends
Cash ($ mil.): 32	Yield: 0.4%
Current ratio: 3.73	Payout: 10.9%
Long-term debt ($ mil.): 0	Market value ($ mil.): 322

	STOCK PRICE ($) FY Close	P/E High/Low		PER SHARE ($) Earnings	Dividends	Book Value
03/14	31.85	39	23	1.00	0.13	10.49
03/13	24.74	22	15	1.11	0.11	9.30
03/12	21.89	24	14	1.06	0.06	8.20
03/11	23.94	41	23	0.59	0.08	7.47
03/10	17.99	34	14	0.64	0.08	7.01
Annual Growth	**15.4%**			**11.8%**	**12.9%**	**10.6%**

Gran Tierra Energy Inc

Gran Tierra Energy hopes the earth still holds a wealth of oil and gas to be tapped especially in South America. Headquartered in Canada and incorporated and trading in the US this oil and gas exploration and production company holds interests in producing and prospective properties primarily in Argentina Brazil Colombia and Peru and is moving into the next phase which is focused on production growth through drilling. It has estimated proved reserves of about 24 million barrels of oil equivalent thanks in large part to increasing production at Costayaco in the Putumayo Basin in Colombia. Colombian oil and gas sales generate a lion's share of Gran Tierra Energy's revenues.

Colombian state-owned oil company Ecopetrol is a major customer and currently buys most of Gran Tierra Energy's crude oil. With a small and not very diverse customer base the company has been embarking on a strategy to expand into other South American regions through acquisition. It marked a major milestone in 2011 when it purchased Petrolifera Petroleum which added substantially to its asset base in Colombia Peru and Argentina. The deal added undeveloped oil and gas reserve potential in Colombia exploration opportunities in Colombia and Peru and additional oil production and reserves in Argentina where oil prices are rising.

Subsequent to the acquisition Gran Tierra Energy announced a capital program to use more than $355 million from existing cash reserves and cash flow to fund the development of these acquired assets. Approximately $14 million will be spent on drilling in Colombia for the purpose of evaluating a potential production platform in the Lower Magdalena Basin. Another $14 million will be focused on reversing production declines in the Neuquen Basin in Argentina while $13 million will be spent on preparation for drilling in Peru in 2012. With combined assets Gran Tierra Energy expects average production in 2011 to range between 17500 and 19000 barrels of oil equivalent per day.

EXECUTIVES

President Gran Tierra Energy Peru, Carlos Monges
President Gran Tierra Energy Argentina, Rafael Orunesu
President Gran Tierra Energy Brasil, J Álio C. Moreira, $303,797 total compensation
Interim President and CEO; COO, Duncan Nightingale, $300,865 total compensation
CFO, James Rozon, $305,566 total compensation
President Gran Tierra Energy Colombia, Adrian Coral
Executive Chairman, Jeffrey Scott, age 51
Auditors: Deloitte&ToucheLLP

LOCATIONS

HQ: Gran Tierra Energy Inc
300, 625 11th Avenue S.W., Calgary, Alberta T2R 0E1
Phone: 403 265-3221   **Fax:** 403 265-3242
Web: www.grantierra.com

2010 Sales

	$ mil.	% of total
Colombia	359.30	96
Argentina	13.98	4
Total	**374.46**	**100**

COMPETITORS

Emerald Energy	Pacific Rubiales
Global Energy	Petrobras Argentina
Development	Woburn Energy
HKN	YPF
Houston American	
Energy	

HISTORICAL FINANCIALS

Company Type: Public

Income Statement

FYE: December 31

	REVENUE ($ mil.)	NET INCOME ($ mil.)	NET PROFIT MARGIN	EMPLOYEES
12/13	723.6	126.2	17.5%	520
12/12	585.1	99.6	17.0%	485
12/11	597.4	126.9	21.2%	446
12/10	374.4	37.1	9.9%	307
12/09	263.7	13.9	5.3%	269
Annual Growth	**28.7%**	**73.5%**	**—**	**17.9%**

2013 Year-End Financials

Debt ratio: —
Return on equity: 9.2%
Cash ($ mil.): 428
Current ratio: 1.92
Long-term debt ($ mil.): —

No. of shares (mil.): 283
Dividends
  Yield: —
  Payout: —
Market value ($ mil.): 2,070

	STOCK PRICE ($) FY Close	P/E High/Low	PER SHARE ($) Earnings	Dividends	Book Value
12/13	7.31	18 11	0.44	0.00	5.05
12/12	5.51	19 12	0.35	0.00	4.58
12/11	4.80	21 10	0.45	0.00	4.21
12/10	8.05	56 31	0.14	0.00	3.44
12/09	5.73	100 34	0.05	0.00	3.34
Annual Growth	**6.3%**	**—**	**— 72.2%**	**—**	**10.8%**

Grand Canyon Education Inc

Grand Canyon Education (dba Grand Canyon University) spans a broad educational horizon. The regionally accredited educator offers graduate and undergraduate degrees online at its campus in Phoenix and onsite at corporate facilities. Grand Canyon University offers career-oriented degree programs focused on the core disciplines of business education health care and liberal arts. Working adults make up most of the school's student body. Grand Canyon University enrolls almost 60000 students annually; about 83% are in online programs and about 45% of those pursue advanced degrees. Most classes have a student-teacher ratio of about 20:1. The company was formed in 1949 as a not-for-profit college and in 2004.

Operations

Grand Canyon University keeps its enrollment numbers up by marketing itself to working adults (whom the company defines as 25 years and older) seeking to complete their education switch careers or earn a higher degree in the field in which they already work. Grand Canyon University attracts adult students with the flexibility and convenience of online classes and conversely adult students are attractive to Grand Canyon University because they are generally more stable able to finance their education and have higher completion rates than younger students. The school offers more than 100 degrees and concentrations.

Grand Canyon University derives about 80% of its income from tuition that is financed under Title IV programs (federal grants and loans to students awarded on the basis of their financial need). Other sources of income come from self-funding private loans other financial aid programs and employer tuition reimbursements.

Geographic Reach

Grand Canyon University has a traditional campus in Phoenix and it enrolls students from all 50 states and the District of Columbia in its online and corporate classes.

Sales and Marketing

Grand Canyon University markets the flexibility and convenience of online classes to working adults ad traditional students.

Financial Performance

After several years of rising revenue the trend continued in 2013 as the company made $598 million a 17% increase over the previous year. Most of that growth came from a 36% jump in enrollment. Net income increased 28% from $69 million to $89 million. Cash from operations however dropped about 18% due to provisions for bad debt and depreciation and amortization.

Strategy

To enhance its brand and continue to attract students Grand Canyon University invests in technology to update its infrastructure and expanding its physical campus. In 2012 it built its first parking garage. Other improvements have included constructing a basketball and entertainment arena a new dorm an activity center and an Arts and Sciences classroom building. The university also keeps tabs on industry trends and adjusts its course offerings accordingly. For example increased demand for nursing programs led the school to establish satellite locations at multiple hospitals where nursing students can complete their clinical education while also completing other course work online. It has similar onsite arrangements with certain employers such as schools and school districts through which students can pursue a profession in teaching. Also in 2012 it began transitioning from the NCAA's Division II to Division I a four-year process.

In 2015 it will open its second campus in Mesa Arizona. The Eastmark campus will house many of its science technology engineering and math programs.

Company Background

Originally founded as Grand Canyon College a private not-for-profit college in 1949 the university moved to its existing campus in Phoenix in 1951. In 2004 several of its stockholders acquired Grand Canyon University and converted it to a for-profit institution. The company then raised about $126 million through a public offering which was completed in 2008 after a four-month-long IPO drought in the US.

EXECUTIVES

CFO, Daniel E. (Dan) Bachus, age 43, $362,250 total compensation
President and CEO, Brian E. Mueller, age 60, $621,000 total compensation
COO, W. Stan Meyer, age 53, $362,250 total compensation
Provost, Hank Radda
Chairman, Brent D. Richardson, age 52

Board Member, Bradley Casper
Auditors: Ernst&YoungLLP

LOCATIONS

HQ: Grand Canyon Education Inc
  3300 W. Camelback Road, Phoenix, AZ 85017
Phone: 602 639-7500
Web: www.gcu.edu

PRODUCTS/OPERATIONS

2013 Student Enrollment by Degree Type

	No. of students	% of total
Undergraduate degree	37182	62
Graduate degree	22476	38
Total	**59658**	**100**

2013 Enrollment by Instructional Delivery Method

	# of students	% of total
Online	49580	83
Ground (Phoenix campus corporate studies)	10078	17
Total	**59658**	**100**

Selected Colleges

College of Arts and Science
College of Theology
College of Education
College of Doctoral Studies
College of Fine Arts and Production
College of Nursing and Health Care Professions
College of Business

Selected Degree Programs

Athletic Training & Exercise Science
Business & Leadership
Computer Science & Information Technology
Health Care
Health Sciences & Pre-Med
Liberal Arts
MBA & EMBA
Nursing
Performing Arts & Digital Design
Psychology & Counseling
Teaching & Education Administration
Theology & Youth Ministry

COMPETITORS

American Public	Career Education
Education	Corinthian Colleges
Apollo Education	DeVry Education Group
Arizona State	Education Management
University	ITT Educational
Azusa Pacific	Northern Arizona
University	University
Baylor University	Strayer Education
Bridgepoint Education	UTI
Capella Education	University of Arizona

HISTORICAL FINANCIALS

Company Type: Public

Income Statement

FYE: December 31

	REVENUE ($ mil.)	NET INCOME ($ mil.)	NET PROFIT MARGIN	EMPLOYEES
12/13	598.3	88.7	14.8%	3,100
12/12	511.2	69.4	13.6%	2,655
12/11	426.7	50.5	11.8%	2,550
12/10	385.8	44.3	11.5%	2,600
12/09	261.9	27.3	10.4%	1,899
Annual Growth	**22.9%**	**34.3%**	**—**	**13.0%**

2013 Year-End Financials

Debt ratio: 15.2%
Return on equity: 30.6%
Cash ($ mil.): 55
Current ratio: 1.59
Long-term debt ($ mil.): 86

No. of shares (mil.): 46
Dividends
  Yield: —
  Payout: —
Market value ($ mil.): 2,008

STOCK PRICE ($) FY Close	P/E High/Low	PER SHARE ($) Earnings	Dividends	Book Value
12/13 43.60	24 11	1.92	0.00	7.49
12/12 23.47	16 10	1.53	0.00	5.23
12/11 15.96	18 11	1.12	0.00	3.69
12/10 19.59	28 16	0.96	0.00	2.99
12/09 19.01	34 22	0.60	0.00	1.88
Annual Growth 23.1%	— —	33.7%	—	41.2%

Green Dot Corp

If you've got the green but not the plastic Green Dot would like to help. The company offers pre-paid debit cards through more than 90000 retail locations in the US. The MasterCard- and Visa-branded reloadable cards function like credit cards for purchases and cash withdrawals. Green Dot which has about 4.5 million cards in circulation partners with Wal-Mart Kmart Walgreens Home Depot and other retailers to enable its customers to add funds to their accounts. The company's products are designed for people who aren't able or choose not to utilize traditional credit card and banking services. Green Dot makes most of its money from new card monthly maintenance and ATM fees.

Geographic Reach

California-based Green Dot has sales and support offices in Tampa Florida; and in Bentonville Arkansas; and in Pasadena Palo Alto and Westlake Village California.

Sales and Marketing

Green Dot has been the exclusive distributor of Walmart-branded GPR (short for general purpose reloadable) cards sold at Walmart stores since 2007. Indeed Wal-Mart Stores is the company's largest retail distributor representing 64% of its total operating revenue in 2013. Green Dot's cards are sold by mass merchants including Walmart and Kmart discount retailers (including dollar stores) drugstores convenience stores supermarkets and by financial service centers.

Financial Performance

Green Dot reported a 5% gain in sales in 2013 versus 2012 to $573.6 million due primarily to higher cash transfer and interchange revenues and a more modest uptick in card revenues and other fees. Indeed the company's sales have risen steadily over the past six years up more than 500% since 2007. Net income fell 28% in 2013 versus 2012 to $34 million on higher operating expenses related mainly to compensation and benefits higher processing expenses and higher usage of fee-free ATM networks. Cash flow from operations increased by $20.5 million year over year to $122.5 million due to an increase in accounts payable and accrued liabilities. 2013 marked the second consecutive year of declining profitability for Green Dot. However cash flow from operations continued its steady rise to $122.5 million.

Strategy

In February 2014 Green Dot completed the transition of its card issuing program with GE Capital Retail Bank to Green Dot Bank. As a result all Walmart MoneyCards are now issued by Green Dot Bank. In 2013 the firm launched its GoBank mobile checking account developed for smartphones and other mobile devices.

Unlike its nearest competitors which focus on check cashing and payday loans Green Dot has partnered with three of the top five retailers and other mainstream companies such as Radio Shack Kmart and Rite Aid. It also offers co-branded cards. The company's growth has stemmed by an increase in both its network and customer usage by offering improved services.

In addition to serving the underbanked community electronic payments companies have also attracted fully banked consumers seeking to safely shop online using separate accounts. Using prepaid cards as a companion to their primary accounts also allows users to control spending and prevent overdrafts. As the electronics payments industry evolves and competitors continue to introduce new products such as contactless cards Green Dot is exploring its various technological options. In addition to technological innovations card companies like Green Dot are also focusing on maintaining a stable and secure technology infrastructure.

In a move to become more vertically integrated the company in 2012 acquired certain processing and hardware assets of eCommLink for some $2.5 million. The move allows Green Dot to bring its transaction processing in house rather than rely on third-parties such as TSYS with whom the company has an outsourced processing agreement that expired in 2013. In another deal Green Dot acquired mobile app start-up Loopt for some $43 million. The deal will help Green Dot attract and retain customers and help advance the company's technology capabilities.

IPO

The company's July 2010 initial public offering exceeded its own expectations raising nearly $165 million. Although the IPO of secondary shares raised a significant amount Green Dot did not keep any of the money for itself. Instead the money was distributed to existing shareholders the most prominent being Wal-Mart. Prior to the IPO the retail giant took a minority stake in Green Dot —a move that cemented the pair's partnership.

EXECUTIVES

Chairman President CEO and Acting CFO, Steven W. Streit, $538,845 total compensation
Evp & Chief Product Officer-no, Kostas Sgoutas
Vice President Financial Planning, Paul Farina
Vice President Regulatory Compliance, Julie Linn
Vice President Of Investor Relations, Christopher Mammone
Vice President Technology Operations, Wayne Christian
Vice President Product Marketing Interactive, Sarah Howell
Sr Vice President Info Tech Governance, Christopher Strader
Svp Chief Audit Executive, Dawn Noble
Vice President Business Development, Ryan Rossow
Vp It, James Vanvelthuyzen
Senior Vice President Corporate Development Mergers And Acquisitions, Mark Shifke
Chairman President CEO and Acting CFO, Steven W. Streit
Auditors: Ernst&YoungLLP

LOCATIONS

HQ: Green Dot Corp
3465 E. Foothill Blvd., Pasadena, CA 91107
Phone: 626 765-2000
Web: www.greendot.com

PRODUCTS/OPERATIONS

2011 Sales

	$ mil.	% of total
Card revenues & other fees	209.5	43
Interchange revenues	141.1	29
Cash transfer revenues	134.1	28
Adjustments	(17.3)	-
Total	**467.4**	**100**

COMPETITORS

American Express	NetSpend
Blackhawk Network	PreCash
DFC Global	Western Union
FSV Payment Systems	nFinanSe
First Data	
MoneyGram International	

HISTORICAL FINANCIALS

Company Type: Public

Income Statement — FYE: December 31

	REVENUE ($ mil.)	NET INCOME ($ mil.)	NET PROFIT MARGIN	EMPLOYEES
12/13	573.6	34.0	5.9%	562
12/12	546.2	47.2	8.6%	596
12/11	467.4	52.0	11.1%	464
12/10	363.8	42.2	11.6%	352
12/09	112.7	13.6	12.1%	0
Annual Growth	50.2%	25.6%	—	—

2013 Year-End Financials

Debt ratio: —	No. of shares (mil.): 37
Return on equity: 9.3%	Dividends
Cash ($ mil.): 423	Yield: —
Current ratio: 1.52	Payout: —
Long-term debt ($ mil.): —	Market value ($ mil.): 949

STOCK PRICE ($) FY Close	P/E High/Low	PER SHARE ($) Earnings	Dividends	Book Value
12/13 25.15	34 16	0.76	0.00	10.66
12/12 12.20	29 8	1.07	0.00	9.11
12/11 31.22	52 21	1.19	0.00	7.14
12/10 56.74	61 41	0.98	0.00	3.95
Annual Growth (23.8%)	— —	(8.1%)	—	39.3%

Greenbrier Companies Inc (The)

On land and by sea: Greenbrier Companies' recipe for growth involves the manufacturing of freight cars and marine barges. Through its primary Manufacturing segment Greenbrier produces 100-ton-capacity boxcars; intermodal and conventional railcars; center-partition flat and tank cars; and marine vessels. Its Refurbishment & Parts segment repairs and services wheels and offers railcar refurbishment and parts in nearly 40 locations. Its Leasing & Services unit manages a fleet of about 11000 railcars. Alan James and William Furman founded The Greenbrier Companies in 1981.

Geographic Reach

Greenbrier is represented in North America and Europe through its manufacturing facilities based in the US Canada Mexico and Poland. It supplies railcar refurbishment and parts in nearly 40 locations in North America.

Operations

Greenbrier's Manufacturing segment makes insulated and non-insulated tank cars used to transport ethanol methanol caustic soda vegetable oils bio-diesel and more than 60 other commodities. Its European railcar line includes pressurized tank cars for liquid petroleum gas ammonia and non-pressurized railcars for light oil chemicals and other products.

In addition to providing repair refurbishment maintenance and wheel conditioning at more than 35 locations in North America Greenbrier's Railcar Refurbishment & Parts business produces doors and roofs and other related boxcar parts. Its Leasing & Services segment offers full service leasing. Additionally Greenbrier offers management services such as billing and collection and fleet management.

Sales and Marketing

The company's three biggest customers —TTX Company BNSF Railway (BNSF) and Union Pacific Railroad —accounted for 53% of total revenue in 2012. Collectively they also accounted for 57% of Manufacturing revenue 48% of Refurbishment & Parts revenue and 15% of Leasing & Services revenue for the year.

Financial Performance

Greenbrier has enjoyed significant growth over the last three years. Helped by a growing global demand for the manufacturing of freight cars and marine barges the company saw its revenues skyrocket by 45% from 2011 to 2012. Its profits also surged by over 800% from $6.5 million to $58.7 million.

Throughout 2012 Greenbrier's Manufacturing segment revenue soared by 74% due to higher railcar deliveries and a higher per unit average selling price attributed to a change in product mix. Railcar deliveries were up by 15000 units in 2012 compared to 9400 units for 2011. US sales increased 49% and accounted for 91% of the company's total sales in 2012.

Ownership

Investing giant Carl Icahn and related entities own 10% of the company.

HISTORY

Alan James and William Furman already owned a transportation-leasing equipment company when they founded The Greenbrier Companies in 1981. That year they bought Greenbrier Leasing Corporation which owned and leased railroad flatcars. Greenbrier entered the railcar-manufacturing business with its 1985 acquisition of Gunderson a unit of FMC Corporation. That year Greenbrier expanded its leasing business by buying subsidiaries of investment firm BRAE Corporation.

In 1993 Greenbrier formed a partnership with Mitsui to sell Greenbrier's Autostack container systems (for transporting cars by rail) in Japan. Greenbrier went public in 1994 and entered the marine vessel industry. The firm made a push into logistics operations by acquiring Standard Transportation Services and Interamerican Logistics in 1995. However Greenbrier recorded a loss in fiscal 1997 and abandoned its logistics and trailer- and container-leasing businesses that year to return to its railcar roots.

The company expanded internationally in 1998 by forming joint venture Gunderson-Concarril with Bombardier Transportation to operate a railcar manufacturing facility in Sahagun Mexico. It also bought 60% of WagonySwidnica (increased to

84% in 1999) a railcar repair and refurbishment facility in Poland. In 1999 Greenbrier boosted production of replacement railcars to serve North America's booming auto market. The following year the company gained a stronger foothold in the European railcar market when it purchased the Germany-based Freight Wagon division of Daimler Rail Systems.

As the economy slowed in 2001 and demand for railcars waned Greenbrier trimmed capacity at its three North American factories and cut about 40% of its workforce. In 2004 Greenbrier acquired the remaining interest in Greenbrier-Concarril a Mexico-based railroad freight car manufacturer.

Co-founder Alan James who served as Greenbrier's chairman and as a director died in 2005.

To reduce costs Greenbrier in 2005 cut railcar production at its Canadian manufacturing facility and moved to increase capacity at its plants in the US and Mexico. In 2007 after conditions at the Canada-based TrentonWorks failed to improve and as the Canadian dollar crept up in value against the US dollar Greenbrier shuttered Canadian facility.

In 2006 Greenbrier acquired Rail Car America Inc. (RCA) for about $34 million in cash. RCA was a provider of conventional and intermodal railcar repair services that operates through four locations in the US. The deal included RCA subsidiaries American Hydraulics (end-of-railcar cushioning parts) and Brandon Corp. (switching railroad operations in Nebraska).

Later in 2006 Greenbrier acquired Meridian Rail (now Greenbrier Rail Services) for about $227 million. Meridian was a leading provider of wheel maintenance products and services for the North American freight car industry. The deal created North America's largest wheel services network. Greenbrier and Meridian's combined operations boasted 10 wheelshops and 20 repair refurbishment and replacement part facilities.

In 2008 Greenbrier purchased the assets of American Allied Railway Equipment Company a maker of new and reconditioned wheelsets and other rail parts for around $83 million in cash. American Allied became part of Greenbrier's rail services business offering an expanded capacity to handle US demand as well as extending Greenbrier's geographic presence in the southeastern part of the country.

Also in 2008 investor Carl Icahn spent $27.8 million to buy an almost 10% stake in Greenbrier. Icahn was reportedly interested in exploring synergies between Greenbrier and fellow railcar maker American Railcar in which Icahn has a 53% stake. By mid-2008 Icahn Associates reported it was no longer interested in combining American Railcar and Greenbrier and the investment firm later reduced its equity stake in Greenbrier to less than 5%.

Greenbrier recorded its lowest revenue levels in 2010 primarily due to the catastrophic explosion of the Deepwater Horizon oil drilling platform and the related oil spill in the US Gulf of Mexico coupled with weak economic conditions leading to reduction in demand for marine barges.

By 2012 Carl Icahn and related entities upped their stake in the company to 10%.

EXECUTIVES

EVP and CFO, Mark J. Rittenbaum, age 58, $408,000 total compensation
Chairman; President and CEO, William A. (Bill) Furman, age 70, $829,333 total compensation
President Greenbrier Leasing Company LLC, James T. Sharp, age 61, $296,000 total compensation

President North American Manufacturing Operations, Alejandro Centurion, age 59, $421,333 total compensation
SVP Wheels and Strategic Execution, Rick M. Turner
Vice President Sales Midwest Region, Edwin Kindig
Senior Vice President General Counsel Chief Compli, Martin Stockdell
Vice President Sales Midwest, Brad Gornall
Vice President, Dionizy Studzinski
Executive Vice President Materials, Martin Graham
Vice President Information Technology, Zara Horn
Chairman; President and CEO, William A. (Bill) Furman, age 70
Auditors: KPMGLLP

LOCATIONS

HQ: Greenbrier Companies Inc (The)
One Centerpointe Drive, Suite 200, Lake Oswego, OR 97035
Phone: 503 684-7000   **Fax:** 503 684-7553
Web: www.gbrx.com

2012 Sales

	$ mil.	% of total
US	1642.3	91
Other countries	165.4	9
Total	**1807.7**	**100**

PRODUCTS/OPERATIONS

2012 Sales

	$ mil.	% of total
Manufacturing	1253.9	69
Wheel Services Refurbishment & Parts	481.9	27
Leasing & services	71.9	4
Total	**1807.7**	**100**

Selected Companies

European Freight Car Manufacturing & Refurbishment
Greenbrier Europe
Manufacturing of ocean-going barges
Gunderson Marine - Portland Oregon
North American Freight Car Leasing and Services
Greenbrier Leasing Company - Lake Oswego Oregon
Greenbrier Management Services - Lake Oswego Oregon
North American Freight Car Manufacturing
Greenbrier-Concarril - Concarril Mexico
Gunderson-Concarril
Gunderson-GIMSA - Monclova Mexico
Gunderson - Portland Oregon
North American Freight Car Repair and Refurbishment (freight cars components and wheels)
Greenbrier Rail Inc.
Shipping
Autostack Company

Selected Products

Freight cars (North American and European)
Marine barges
Railcar management services
Railcar parts
Repair and refurbishment
Shipping
Wheels

COMPETITORS

ACF Industries
ALSTOM
American Railcar Industries
Bombardier
Construcciones y Auxiliar de Ferrocarriles
Excel Railcar
FreightCar America
GATX
Pioneer Railcorp
Progress Rail Services
TTX
Trinity Industries

Union Tank Car
Wabash National

HISTORICAL FINANCIALS

Company Type: Public

Income Statement

FYE: August 31

	REVENUE ($ mil.)	NET INCOME ($ mil.)	NET PROFIT MARGIN	EMPLOYEES
08/14	2,203.9	111.9	5.1%	9,244
08/13	1,756.4	(11.0)	—	7,959
08/12	1,807.7	58.7	3.2%	7,396
08/11	1,243.2	6.4	0.5%	6,032
08/10	764.4	4.2	0.6%	4,194
Annual Growth	30.3%	126.2%	—	21.8%

2014 Year-End Financials

Debt ratio: 30.2%	No. of shares (mil.): 27
Return on equity: 23.8%	Dividends
Cash ($ mil.): 184	Yield: 0.0%
Current ratio: 1.79	Payout: 4.3%
Long-term debt ($ mil.): 445	Market value ($ mil.): 1,957

	STOCK PRICE ($) FY Close	P/E High/Low		PER SHARE ($) Earnings	Dividends	Book Value
08/14	71.52	18	6	3.44	0.15	18.69
08/13	22.57	—	—	(0.41)	0.00	15.25
08/12	14.45	12	5	1.91	0.00	15.91
08/11	17.38	111	43	0.24	0.00	14.36
08/10	11.67	76	33	0.21	0.00	13.07
Annual Growth	57.3%	—	—	—101.2%	—	9.3%

Guidewire Software Inc

Guidewire Software has staked its claim on providing software to the insurance industry. The company's InsuranceSuite offers applications to the property and casualty insurance industry for underwriting policy administration (PolicyCenter) claims management (ClaimsCenter) and billing (BillingCenter). Its software is intended to replace paper-based processes and legacy systems built around outdated programming languages. Guidewire counts about 100 customers in a dozen countries. It customers include Tokio Marine Nationwide Mutual and Zurich Financial Services.

Geographic Reach

Guidewire's corporate headquarters is in Foster City California. It also leases facilities for distributed sales and international operations in Dublin Ireland; Edina Minnesota; London United Kingdom; Mississauga Ontario Canada; Munich Germany; Paris France; Sydney Australia; and Tokyo Japan.

In 2012 the US accounted for 55% of Guidewire's revenues.

Sales and Marketing

The company has more than 120 employees in a sales and marketing capacity including 23 direct sales representatives organized by geographic region across Australia Canada France Germany Hong Kong Japan the UK and the US.

Operations

The company generates revenue through licensing its software providing professional services and maintenance. Its software is generally licensed over a five-year contract and is priced according to the number of the insurance provider's written premiums. Guidewire charges customers in advance for both term license and maintenance fees.

Financial Performance

Guidewire's revenues increased by 35% in 2012 driven by continued adoption of the company's Claim Center software increasing adoption of itsPolicy Center and Suite software and increased sales and marketing efforts in North America and Europe. The rise in maintenance revenues was primarily driven by new orders. Service revenues increased due to increase use of the company's software.

Net income decreased by 57% in 2012 due to an increase in operating expenses such as an increase in research and development expenses and Sales and Marketing and General Administrative expenses primarily due to an increase in personnel-related expenses (as a result of adding 45 employees). Other factors included an increase in administrative and other professional services expenses and an increase in stock-based compensation.

Strategy

The company has extensive relationships with system integration consulting and industry partners. It encourages partners to co-market pursue joint sales initiatives and drive broader adoption of their technology. Its leading system integrator partners include Capgemini Ernst & Young IBM Global Services and PricewaterhouseCoopers.

In 2012 Guidwire's customer base in Europe increased by 20%. Guidewire has 19 customers in seven countries across Europe. Ten insurers across the region are using a Guidewire system. These include Beazley Direct Line UK LV= NFU Mutual Towergate Rosgosstrakh QBE Europe and a top three French insurer.

Ownership

Funds affiliated with Bay Partners own 10.9% of the company.

Company Background

Guidewire was founded in 2001 by CEO Marcus Ryu Product Strategy Director Kenneth Branson and four others who are no longer with the company. Its ClaimCenter product launched in 2003 PolicyCenter in 2004 and BillingCenter in 2006.

Guidewire filed a $100 million initial public offering in September 2011 and began trading on the NYSE in 2012.

EXECUTIVES

SVP Marketing, Brian Desmond
President and CEO, Marcus S. Ryu, age 40, $387,500 total compensation
SVP Corporate Development and Chief Administrative Officer, Priscilla Hung, $243,400 total compensation
CTO, Ben Brantley
CFO, Richard Hart
Chief Delivery Officer, Mike Polelle, $80,827 total compensation
Vice President International, Ian Tavener
Vice President Product Development, Jeremy Henrickson, age 40
Senior Vice President Worldwide Sales, Scott Roza
Vice President Of Product Development, Ken Branson
Vice President Information Technology And Information Services Atguidewiresoftware, Sunny Azadeh
Vice President Finance And Administration, Justin Wiesman
Broker First Vice President, Lei Ding
Senior Vice President Operations, Michelle Foster
Vice President Finance, Dave Barter

Vice President Of Sales And Marketing, Rick Wong
Chairman, Craig A. Conway, age 59
Auditors: KPMGLLP

LOCATIONS

HQ: Guidewire Software Inc
1001 E. Hillsdale Blvd., Suite 800, Foster City, CA 94404
Phone: 650 357-9100   **Fax:** 650 357-9101
Web: www.guidewire.com

2012 Sales

	% of total
US	55
Canada	15
Australia	8
UK	7
Other	15
Total	**100**

PRODUCTS/OPERATIONS

2012 Sales

	$ mil.	% of total
Services	105.4	45
Licenses	97.1	42
Maintenance	29.6	13
Total	**232.1**	**100**

COMPETITORS

Accenture	Pegasystems
Applied Systems	SAP
CCC Information	Sapiens
Computer Sciences Corp.	StoneRiver
	SunGard Financial Systems
Cover-All	Tata Consultancy
Duck Creek	Vertafore
Ebix	
Oracle	

HISTORICAL FINANCIALS

Company Type: Public

Income Statement

FYE: July 31

	REVENUE ($ mil.)	NET INCOME ($ mil.)	NET PROFIT MARGIN	EMPLOYEES
07/14	350.2	14.7	4.2%	1,183
07/13	300.6	15.3	5.1%	1,149
07/12	232.0	15.2	6.6%	837
07/11	172.4	35.5	20.6%	684
07/10	144.6	15.5	10.7%	0
Annual Growth	24.7%	(1.3%)	—	—

2014 Year-End Financials

Debt ratio: —	No. of shares (mil.): 69
Return on equity: 3.3%	Dividends
Cash ($ mil.): 148	Yield: —
Current ratio: 5.41	Payout: —
Long-term debt ($ mil.): —	Market value ($ mil.): 2,798

	STOCK PRICE ($) FY Close	P/E High/Low		PER SHARE ($) Earnings	Dividends	Book Value
07/14	40.50	261	158	0.21	0.00	9.42
07/13	43.76	168	91	0.25	0.00	3.94
07/12	25.66	122	59	0.25	0.00	3.41
Annual Growth	25.6%	—	—	(8.3%)	—	66.2%

Gulf Island Fabrication, Inc.

Through its subsidiaries holding company Gulf Island Fabrication makes islands in the stream — the Gulf Stream that is. Its subsidiaries which operate under Gulf Island and Gulf Marine monikers make offshore drilling and production platforms for use mainly in the Gulf of Mexico. Products include jackets and deck sections of fixed production platforms hull and deck sections of floating production platforms piles subsea templates wellhead protectors and various production compressor and utility modules. Gulf Island also produces and repairs pressure vessels and refurbishes existing platforms. Reliant on a few key customers in 2013 94% of its backlog was accounted for by nine customers.

Geographic Reach

Through its subsidiaries Gulf Island provides customers with a complete range of design construction and maintenance services from four adjacent fabrication yards located in Houma Louisiana and from two yards in Ingleside Texas.

Gulf Island has more than 212 acres devoted to fabrication activities a large assembly capacity allowing it to work on both shallow water units and complex deepwater structures. Its Louisiana unit resides on 140 acres and has a water frontage along the Houma Navigational Canal only 30 miles from the central Gulf of Mexico.

Operations

Gulf Island serves as a holding company and conducts all of its operations through subsidiaries which include Gulf Island L.L.C. and Gulf Marine (fabrication of offshore drilling and production platforms and other specialized structures); Gulf Island Marine Fabricators L.L.C. (marine fabrication and construction services); Dolphin Services L.L.C. (offshore and onshore fabrication and construction services); Dolphin Steel Sales L.L.C. (steel plate and other steel products); and Gulf Island Resources L.L.C. (which hires laborers with similar rates and terms as those provided by contract labor service companies).The company's primary activity is the fabrication of offshore drilling and production platforms and other specialized structures including jackets and deck sections of fixed production platforms and/or deck sections of floating production platforms (such as TLPs SPARs FPSOs and MinDOCs) piles and utility modules. Gulf Island also produces and repairs pressure vessels used in the oil and gas industry refurbish existing platforms fabricate various other types of steel structures fabricate living quarters for installation on such platforms ranging in size from 4 to 250 beds and provides onshore and offshore scaffolding and piping insulation services. In addition the company fabricates towboats barges lift boats dry docks offshore support vessels other marine vessels and mid-body sections for offshore supply vessels. Its dry dock has the capacity to lift 9000 tons and is used to maintain and repair third party marine vessels as well as to launch vessels fabricated at its facilities.

Financial Performance

Gulf Island's revenues increased by 17% in 2013 thanks to an increase in pass-through costs related to sub-contracted service costs on its major deepwater projects as well as to and higher revenues associated with work on a Spar Hull for a large deepwater customer (after renegotiations con-

verted the contract from a unit rate basis to an alliance/partnering basis). The rise in revenues was partially offset by contract losses from a separate large deep-water project.The company's net income increased by more than 250% in 2013 thanks to higher revenues the absence of a provision for losses on contract receivables (compared to a provision for losses on contract receivables of $15 million in 2012. The increase was partially offset by contract losses during 2013 related to its inability to recover certain costs and the de-scoping of one of its major deepwater projects.

Strategy

The company's primary focus is to manage contract costs particularly labor force costs) as it and its customers face increasing challenges associated with developing and fabricating complex projects. To that end in 2013 it began implementing new tracking and reporting procedures to more effectively monitor and control the progress efficiency and safety on its projects. That year it transferred the project deliverables on a major project to the integration contractor's site and removed from backlog revenues of $25.5 million and labor hours of 271000 hours representing its previous estimate of remaining work to complete the project. It subsequently continued negotiations with this large deepwater customer to resolve outstanding claims and payments.

In 2013 Gulf Island's subsidiary Gulf Marine Fabricators won a contract from Walter Oil & Gas for the fabrication of topsides totaling about 4500 short tons.

Company Background

Historically the company has grown through acquisitions and internal expansion. In 2006 it grew its fabrication business by acquiring Technip subsidiary Gulf Marine Fabricators for $40 million. In 2007 Gulf Island formed Gulf Island Resources to employ laborers in Louisiana and Texas and in 2008 it formed Dolphin Steel Sales to boost the firm's marketing of its steel products.

EXECUTIVES

President CEO and Director, Kirk J. Meche, age 52, $285,000 total compensation
VP Finance CFO Treasurer and Chief Accounting Officer, Robin A. Seibert, age 58, $200,000 total compensation
President and Chief Executive Officer of Gulf Island; L.L.C, William G. (Bill) Blanchard, age 56, $175,000 total compensation
VP Marketing, Roy P. Francis
President and Chief Executive Officer of Gulf Marine Fabricators; L.P, Francis A. Smith, age 64, $150,000 total compensation
Vice President - Operations; General Manager, William J (Bill) Fromenthal
VP Finance CFO Treasurer and Chief Accounting Officer, Robin A. Seibert, age 58
Auditors: Ernst&YoungLLP

LOCATIONS

HQ: Gulf Island Fabrication, Inc.
16225 Park Ten Place, Suite 280, Houston, TX 77084
Phone: 713 714-6100   **Fax:** 985 876-5414
Web: www.gulfisland.com

2013 Sales

	$ mil.	% of total
US	570.7	94
Other countries	37.6	6
Total	**608.3**	**100**

PRODUCTS/OPERATIONS

2013 Sales

	% of total
Williams Field Services-Gulf Coast Company L.P.	36
Chevron	24
Other customers	40
Total	**100**

Selected Subsidiaries

Dolphin Services L.L.C. (offshore construction fabrication inshore construction steel sales and sand blasting and coating)
Dolphin Steel Sales L.L.C.(steel products marketing)
Gulf Island L.L.C. (offshore construction)
Gulf Island Resources L.L.C. (offshore construction)
Gulf Marine Fabricators (offshore construction and fabrication)
Southport L.L.C.(fabrication of living quarters for offshore platforms)

COMPETITORS

Babcock & Wilcox	Oceaneering
Hyundai Heavy	International
Industries	Technip
Kiewit Offshore	Tidewater Inc.
McDermott	

HISTORICAL FINANCIALS

Company Type: Public

Income Statement

FYE: December 31

	REVENUE ($ mil.)	NET INCOME ($ mil.)	NET PROFIT MARGIN	EMPLOYEES
12/13	608.3	7.2	1.2%	1,900
12/12	521.3	(4.0)	—	2,200
12/11	307.8	(1.8)	—	1,950
12/10	248.2	13.0	5.3%	1,250
12/09	311.5	20.8	6.7%	1,400
Annual Growth	18.2%	(23.2%)	—	7.9%

2013 Year-End Financials

Debt ratio: —	No. of shares (mil.): 14	
Return on equity: 2.6%	Dividends	
Cash ($ mil.): 36	Yield: 1.7%	
Current ratio: 1.80	Payout: 266.6%	
Long-term debt ($ mil.): —	Market value ($ mil.): 337	

	STOCK PRICE ($) FY Close	P/E High/Low		Earnings	Dividends	Book Value
12/13	23.22	53	38	0.50	0.40	19.01
12/12	24.03	—	—	(0.29)	0.40	18.92
12/11	29.21	—	—	(0.13)	0.24	19.67
12/10	28.18	34	16	0.90	0.04	20.03
12/09	21.03	16	4	1.44	0.13	19.14
Annual Growth	2.5%		—	(23.2%)	32.4%	(0.2%)

Gulfport Energy Corp.

Gulfport Energy put its energy into exploring for hydrocarbons near the Gulf of Mexico and elsewhere. The oil and gas exploration and production company' main producing properties are located along the Louisiana Gulf Coast in the Permian basin in West Texas in the Niobrara Shale Formation in western Colorado and in the Utica Shale in eastern Ohio. Additionally Gulfport Energy holds a sizeable acreage position in the Alberta oil sands in Canada through its interest in Grizzly Oil Sands ULC and it has interests in entities that operate in the Phu Horm gas field in northern Thailand. In 2012 the company reported proved reserves of 8.3 million barrels of oil and 33.8 trillion cu. ft. of natural gas.

Geographic Reach

The company's principal operating area includes Louisiana's West Cote Blanche Bay field East Hackberry field (in the Permian Basin) Utica shale in Ohio the Niobrara Shale in Colorado Canadian oil sands in Alberta and the Phu Horm gas field in Thailand.

Operations

In January 2013 Gulfport Energy's average daily net production from its Utica Shale was 792 barrels of oil equivalent 59% of which was from natural gas.In 2012 the company drilled 94 gross (71 net) wells in the Permian Basin the Niobrara Formation and the Bakken Formation and 12 gross (one net) wells in the Utica Shale play.At its West Cote Blanche Bay field it recompleted 61 wells and drilled 31 wells out of which 27 were completed as producing wells. The East Hackberry saw 32 wells recompleted and 23 wells drilled.

Sales and Marketing

In 2012 the company sold 92% of its oil production to Shell Trading Company and 91% of its natural gas liquids production to Diamondback O&G.

Financial Performance

Gulfport Energy's revenues grew by 9% in 2012 primarily due to a 10% increase in net production partially offset by a 2% decline in oil prices and a drop in natural gas liquid sales.However the company's net income decreased by 37% in 2012 as the result of higher income tax expenses caused by deferred tax expenses stemming form prior net operating losses from the Diamondback Energy contribution gain; and higher costs and expenses related to the depreciation depletion and amortization charges. (These declines were partially offset by increased income from equity method investments and gains on sale of assets).

Strategy

The company sells some assets to pay down debt. It is also focused on building up its lucrative Utica shale assets.

In 2014 Gulfport Energy sold Blackhawk Midstream's (50% owned by Gulfport) equity interest in two entities Ohio Gathering Company LLC and Ohio Condensate Company LLC to Summit Midstream Partners for $190 million. In 2012 the company completed its contribution of its oil and gas interests in the Permian Basin to Diamondback prior to the closing of the Diamondback IPO. In 2013 the company received an additional payment from Diamondback of $19 million.

Mergers and Acquisitions

In 2013 Gulfport Energy acquired 22000 net acres in the Utica Shale from Windsor Ohio LLC an affiliate of Wexford Capital for $220 million; with an expectation of net production to be about 22200 barrels of oil equivalent per day.

In 2012 the company purchased 37000 net acres in the Utica Shale for about $372 million boosting its leasehold interests in the shale play to 137000 gross (106000 net) acres.

EXECUTIVES

CEO; Director, Michael G. (Mike) Moore, age 57, $300,000 total compensation
Vice President Geological & Geophysical, Stuart Maier
Vice President Reservoir Engineering, Steve Baldwin
COO, J. Ross Kirtley

CFO, Aaron Gaydosik
Vice President Operations, Robert Luker
Chairman, David L. Houston, age 61
CEO; Director, Michael G. (Mike) Moore, age 57
Auditors: GrantThorntonLLP

LOCATIONS

HQ: Gulfport Energy Corp.
14313 North May Avenue, Suite 100, Oklahoma City, OK 73134
Phone: 405 848-8807
Web: www.gulfportenergy.com

PRODUCTS/OPERATIONS

2012 Sales

	$ mil.	% of total
Oil & condensate	242.7	98
Gas	3.2	1
Natural gas liquids	2.7	1
Other	0.3	-
Total	**248.9**	**100**

COMPETITORS

Abraxas Petroleum	EOG
Apache	Exxon Mobil
Bill Barrett	FieldPoint Petroleum
BreitBurn	MarkWest Energy
Cabot Oil & Gas	Partners
Chesapeake Energy	XTO Energy
Devon Energy	

HISTORICAL FINANCIALS

Company Type: Public

Income Statement				FYE: December 31
	REVENUE ($ mil.)	NET INCOME ($ mil.)	NET PROFIT MARGIN	EMPLOYEES
12/13	262.7	153.1	58.3%	118
12/12	248.9	68.3	27.5%	128
12/11	229.2	108.4	47.3%	50
12/10	126.9	47.3	37.3%	45
12/09	85.2	23.6	27.7%	40
Annual Growth	**32.5%**	**59.6%**	**—**	**31.1%**

2013 Year-End Financials

Debt ratio: 11.1%	No. of shares (mil.): 85
Return on equity: 9.6%	Dividends
Cash ($ mil.): 458	Yield: —
Current ratio: 2.60	Payout: —
Long-term debt ($ mil.): 299	Market value ($ mil.): 5,377

	STOCK PRICE ($) FY Close	P/E High/Low		PER SHARE ($) Earnings	Dividends	Book Value
12/13	63.13	35	18	1.97	0.00	24.07
12/12	38.22	32	13	1.21	0.00	16.68
12/11	29.45	17	9	2.20	0.00	11.37
12/10	21.68	21	8	1.07	0.00	4.73
12/09	11.45	21	3	0.55	0.00	2.93
Annual Growth	**53.2%**	**—**	**—**	**37.6%**	**—**	**69.3%**

Hackett Group Inc

The Hackett Group wants to make sure its clients can hack it in the business world. The business and technology consultancy provides corpo-

rations with advisory programs benchmarking business transformation services and working capital management. It specializes in such areas as IT human resources accounting and customer service. The Hackett Group also offers services related to best practice research with a focus on sales general and administrative functions and supply chain services. The company's business applications consulting is performed by its Hackett Technology Solutions (HTS) unit which specializes in software from Oracle and SAP. Its clients have included ABIOMED Exelon and Waste Management.

After a fiscal loss for 2009 that The Hackett Group attributed to expenses related to the purchase of Archstone Consulting that year and diminished revenues caused by the global economic downturn the company boosted its revenue by more than 40% in 2010 returning to profitability despite higher operating costs. The Hackett Group cited strong domestic demand for consulting and other services as driving sales growth for the year. Its expenses rose again in 2010 due to the Archstone purchase.

The company generated less than one quarter of its revenues outside the US in 2010. While its international sales are made primarily in Western Europe the company has plans to expand beyond its traditional markets by increasing its presence in the Asia/Pacific region in particular. The Hackett Group has specifically targeted Australia New Zealand Singapore and South Korea as areas for growth.

The Hackett Group has sales and service partnerships with other IT vendors including Accenture.

The company in 2008 changed its name from Answerthink to The Hackett Group. Answerthink acquired The Hackett Group —a specialist in best practices for sales administrative and supply chain functions —in 1991 and operated it as a subsidiary until the rebranding.

EXECUTIVES

Chairman and CEO, Ted A. Fernandez, age 57, $750,000 total compensation
EVP Finance and CFO, Robert A. Ramirez, age 47, $300,000 total compensation
Global Procurement Advisory Practice Leader, Christopher (Chris) Sawchuk
COO, George Chappelle
CFO, Richard Kelson
Vice Chairman and COO, David Dungan, $525,000 total compensation
Practice Leader Advisory and Executive Global Information Technology, Scott Holland
Practice Leader Global Finance, Richard Cardillo
Vice President Marketing, Christina Perkins
Vice President, Mark Wirth
Chairman and CEO, Ted A. Fernandez, age 57
Vice Chairman and COO, David Dungan
Board Member, Gilles Bonelli
Auditors: BDOSeidmanLLP

LOCATIONS

HQ: Hackett Group Inc
1001 Brickell Bay Drive, Suite 3000, Miami, FL 33131
Phone: 305 375-8005
Web: www.thehackettgroup.com

2011 Sales

	$ mil.	% of total
North America	158.2	79
Other regions	43.1	21
Total	**201.3**	**100**

PRODUCTS/OPERATIONS

2010 Sales

	$ mil.	% of total
The Hackett Group	144.9	72
Hackett Technology Solutions	56.4	28
Total	**201.3**	**100**

COMPETITORS

Accenture	Deloitte Consulting
Bain & Company	Edgewater Technology
Booz Allen	HP Enterprise Services
Boston Consulting	IBM Global Services
CIBER	McKinsey & Company
Capgemini North	NTT Data
America	Perficient
Computer Sciences	Zanett
Corp.	

HISTORICAL FINANCIALS

Company Type: Public

Income Statement

FYE: December 27

	REVENUE ($ mil.)	NET INCOME ($ mil.)	NET PROFIT MARGIN	EMPLOYEES
12/13	223.8	8.7	3.9%	848
12/12	234.0	16.7	7.1%	947
12/11	225.1	21.7	9.7%	914
12/10*	201.3	14.2	7.1%	854
01/10	142.7	(6.8)	—	810
Annual Growth	**11.9%**	**—**		**1.2%**

*Fiscal year change

2013 Year-End Financials

Debt ratio: 12.6%	No. of shares (mil.): 29
Return on equity: 9.3%	Dividends
Cash ($ mil.): 18	Yield: 1.6%
Current ratio: 1.77	Payout: 22.7%
Long-term debt ($ mil.): 19	Market value ($ mil.): 186

	STOCK PRICE ($) FY Close	P/E High/Low		Earnings	PER SHARE ($) Dividends	Book Value
12/13	6.21	25	13	0.27	0.10	3.11
12/12	4.00	12	6	0.50	0.10	3.05
12/11	3.74	9	6	0.52	0.00	3.24
12/10*	3.51	12	7	0.34	0.00	2.74
01/10	2.78	—	—	(0.18)	0.00	2.42
Annual Growth	**22.3%**			**—**	**—**	**6.5%**

*Fiscal year change

Hain Celestial Group Inc

The Hain Celestial Group serves up guiltless eating and grooming. The company manufactures and distributes natural and organic food snacks beverages and personal care and cleaning products in North America and Europe. Its vast pantry of "better-for-you" brands includes Celestial Seasonings (specialty teas) Terra and Garden of Eatin' (snacks) and Earth's Best (organic baby food). Hain's products are mainstays in natural foods stores and are increasingly available in mainstream supermarkets; club mass-market and drug stores; and grocery wholesalers. Fast-growing Hain is also

a supplier of TenderCare disposable diapers; its J S – N Natural Products makes grooming products.

HISTORY

Irwin Simon a former marketer at Slim-Fast and H ¤agen-Dazs founded Kineret Acquisition Corp. in 1993 to acquire Kineret Food a maker of kosher foods. Before closing the deal in late 1993 Simon acquired the product line of Pizsoy (soy-based pizza) and two small companies: California Slim (dietary foods) and Barricini Foods (frozen desserts and organic bread). He took the company public that year. In 1994 Kineret quadrupled its size by adding Hain Pure Food (natural foods and cooking oils); the company changed its name later that year to The Hain Food Group to take advantage of the well-known Hain label.

Hain expanded in 1995 with its purchase of diabetic foods maker Estee Corp. Sales dropped during fiscal 1997 in part because of decreasing demand for rice cakes which had accounted for nearly three-quarters of Hain Pure Food's sales. To invigorate its stable of brands in 1997 Hain bought Boston Better Snacks (chips and popcorn); a Weight Watchers line and Alba Foods (dietary drinks) from Heinz; and Westbrae Natural (including Westsoy nondairy drinks). The company added more brands in 1998 when it bought four business lines from Shansby Group: Arrowhead Mills (grains) DeBoles Nutritional Foods (pasta) Terra Chips and Garden of Eatin' (snack foods). It then added Quaker Oats' Nile Spice (soups and meal cups) to the mix.

The company added Natural Nutrition Group a natural and organic foods maker in 1999. Hain enriched its alliance with Heinz when the giant bought nearly 20% of Hain in exchange for access to the rapidly growing natural foods market. In 2000 Hain bought leading specialty tea-maker Celestial Seasonings for about $330 million and subsequently changed the company name to The Hain Celestial Group.

In 2001 Hain Celestial bought Netherlands-based chip maker Fruit Chips (Gaston's fruit vegetable and potato chips) and later changed its name to Terra Chips to reflect the expansion of the Terra Chips brand in Europe. It followed that purchase with the acquisition of Yves Veggie Cuisine a Canadian maker of soy protein meat and cheese alternatives. Also that year the company formed a joint venture with Grupo Siro of Spain to market snack foods in southern Europe and it acquired Belgian natural and organic foods marketer Lima.

The company expanded into the Asia/Pacific region in 2002 by agreeing to distribute and sell some of its products (including its Yves Veggie Cuisine line) though Japanese food manufacturer and distributor Shin-shin. That year Hain agreed to supply veggie burgers to all Canadian McDonald's restaurants. It also formed a joint venture with pasta maker Barilla to manufacture market and distribute Terra brand products in Europe. That June Hain discontinued its supplements business and terminated its licensing agreement with Weight Watchers.

Later in 2002 Hain purchased Imagine Foods for $52 million in cash and stock. The acquisition added such well-known milk-substitute brands as Rice Dream Power Dream and Soy Dream as well as Imagine's frozen dessert and organic soup and broth business to the Hain stable.

The company created a soy-based patty called the McVeggie Burger for McDonald's in 2003. Hain's subsidiary Yves Veggie Cuisine manufactures the patties for and supplies them to McDon-

ald's. Later that year Hain acquired Acirca maker of Walnut Acres brand foods. It also introduced a line of low-carbohydrate food called Carb Fit. Also in 2003 the company announced a joint venture with Cargill to develop healthy functional foods and beverages using Cargill's isoflavones inulin and chondroitin products.

In 2004 Hain bought Natumi AG a German maker of non-dairy beverages and desserts. Later that year it acquired frozen food brands Ethnic Gourmet and Rosetto from Heinz. The company also announced a relationship with Sesame Workshop to promote children's healthy eating habits. Later that year Hain began making a soy burger called the McVeggie Burger for McDonald's Manhattan New York locations.

And perhaps in its biggest move in 2004 Hain expanded into a new but complementary natural product market with the acquisition of J S – N Natural Products a maker of health and body care products. At the same time Hain introduced a selection of its own body care products called Earth's Best for babies and children. In 2005 Hain purchased another personal care company Zia Natural Skincare. Also on Hain's shopping list was Pennsylvania-based College Hill Poultry a joint venture with Pegasus Capital. Not forgetting its food lineup in 2005 Hain acquired Spectrum Organic Products. In addition Hain sold its Kineret and Kosherific frozen food brands to Kedem Food Products International for an undisclosed amount.

In 2006 the company introduced its Estee brand –a product line of Low-G (glycemic) nutrition bars. It also acquired personal care product company Para Laboratories whose brands include Batherapy Footherapy and Queen Helene. That year it acquired Spectrum Organic Products as well as a 51% interest in organic chicken producer Hain Pure Protein.

Expanding its European operations in 2006 Hain acquired the England-based fresh prepared foods business of H. J. Heinz as well as Heinz's frozen meat-free business (including the Linda McCartney brand) both located in England. It also bought the 100-year-old UK firm Haldane Foods (including its meat-free and non-dairy beverages businesses) from Archer Daniels Midland. The Haldane acquisition brought the Realeat (frozen foods and dry mixes) Granose and WhiteWave's non-dairy beverages brands to the Hain roster.

The company also acquired Avalon Natural Products that year from private equity firm North Castle Partners for $120 million. The deal added such organic personal care brands as Avalon Organic Botanicals and Alba Botanica to Hain's portfolio.

Hain Pure Protein (HPP) a joint venture between Hain Celestial and private equity firm Pegasus Capital Advisors acquired Plainville Turkey Farm in 2007. The enterprise renamed Plainville Farms joined FreeBird organic chicken producer also owned by Hain Pure Protein. In 2008 HPP acquired the turkey operations (New Oxford Foods) of Pilgrim's Pride. New Oxford's operations were switched to antibiotic-free and joined Plainville and FreeBird in furthering Hain's strategy of offering organic branded food products.

In 2009 HPP introduced a line of kosher chicken and turkey products under the Kosher Valley name which is available at Whole Foods and specialty retailers. The brand serves two customer bases: those of the Jewish faith and those preferring more healthful proteins. In mid-2010 Hain Pure Protein sold the Kosher Valley brand to Empire Kosher Poultry an established Pennsylvania-based processor. In exchange Hain Pure Protein received shares in Empire.

EXECUTIVES

Vice President Of Human Resources, Roxanne Parmele

Senior Vice President Special Projects, Benjamin Brecher

Svp Finance And Chief Accounting Officer, Michael J Speiller, age 61

Chairman President and CEO, Irwin D. Simon, age 56, $1,400,000 total compensation

SVP Global Technical Services and Chief Sustainability Officer, Ellen B. Deutsch, $160,000 total compensation

COO, Jay Lieberman

CEO Hain Celestial Europe, Philippe Woitrin

President Grocery and Frozen, John Carroll, age 55, $525,000 total compensation

President Celestial Seasonings and Chief Sales Officer Grocery Snacks and Personal Care, Peter J. Burns, age 53

President Hain Celestial Personal Care and Chief Supply Chain Officer Grocery Snacks and Personal Care, James R. (Jim) Meiers

President Hain Celestial Canada, Beena G. Goldenberg

EVP General Counsel and Chief Compliance Officer, Denise M. Faltischek, age 41

VP Finance, Ross Weiner

National Account Manager, Paul Miller

Vice President, Ray Mauro

Vice President Of Manufacturing, Stephen Powhida

Vice President Of Marketing, Donna Iannucci

Vice President Asian Business Development Corporate Services, Geoffrey Goldberg

Vp Or Senior Vp, Pat Conte

Vice President Personal Care, Emma Froelich

Vice President Of Finance, Rose Eng

Vice President, Paul Rudkin

Vice President Logistics, Anthony Leis

Vice President Marketing, Joe Beauprez

Vice President, Steven Siwinski

Vice President Se Asia, Ron Boser

Vp Technical Services Sensible Portions, Robert King

National Vp Personal Care Division, Tom Brown

Vice President Of Marketing At The Hain Celestial Group Inc, Heather Taylor

Chairman President and CEO, Irwin D. Simon, age 56

Auditors: Ernst&YoungLLP

LOCATIONS

HQ: Hain Celestial Group Inc
1111 Marcus Avenue, Lake Success, NY 11042
Phone: 516 587-5000
Web: www.hain-celestial.com

2013 Sales

	$ mil.	% of total
US	1095.9	63
UK	420.4	24
Rest of world	218.4	13
Total	**1734.7**	**100**

PRODUCTS/OPERATIONS

2013 Sales

	$ mil.	% of total
Grocery	1286.4	74
Snacks	220.5	13
Personal care	117.0	7
Tea	110.8	6
Total	**1734.7**	**100**

Selected Subsidiaries

Arrowhead Mills Inc.
Celestial Seasonings Inc.
Daily Bread Ltd. (UK)
Ella' s Kitchen Group Ltd. (UK)
Health Valley Company
Histon Sweet Spread Ltd. (UK)
Jason Natural Products
Lima S.A.R.L. (France)
Spectrum Organic Products LLC
Terra Chisp B.V. (Netherlands)
Zia Cosmetics Inc.

Selected Brands and Products

Fresh and Frozen Foods
Daily Bread (fresh prepared foods UK only)
    Ethnic Gourmet (frozen meals)
    Linda McCartney (frozen vegetarian meals)
    Rice Dream (frozen desserts)
    Rosetto (frozen Italian foods)
    Soy Dream (frozen desserts)
Milk-free Beverages
    BluePrint (raw juice)
    Natumi (non-dairy beverages and desserts Europe only)
    Rice Dream (rice-based non-dairy milk and ice cream)
    Soy Dream (soy-based non-dairy milk and ice cream)
Natural Foods
    Arrowhead Mills (natural and organic whole grain products)
    Bearitos (canned chilies and sauce mixes)
    Breadshop (cereal)
    Casbah (prepared vegetarian mixes and side dishes)
    Danival (organic fruits vegetables and deli products)
    DeBoles (dried pasta)
    Earth' s Best (organic baby and toddler food licensed)
    Europe' s Best (frozen fruits and vegetables)
    FreeBird (organic chicken)
    GG UniqueFiber (whole grain crackers)
    Hain Pure Foods (condiments cookies cooking oils rice cakes sea salt snacks and soups)
    Health Valley (fat-free soups cereals and baked products)
    Hollywood (edible oils US only)
    Imagine Foods (soups and broths)
    Little Bear (organic snacks)
    MaraNatha (nut butters)
    Mountain Sun (juice)
    Nile Spice (soups and meal cups)
    Plainville Farms (antibiotic-free chicken and turkey)
    Spectrum (edible oil vinegar condiments and butter substitutes)
    SunSpire (nut butters)
    Walnut Acres (juice pasta sauce salsa and soup)
    Westbrae Natural (canned vegetables)
    Westsoy (soy-based beverages)
    Yves (soy protein meat alternatives)
Snack Foods
    Boston' s (popcorn)
    Garden of Eatin' (snack foods)
    Harry' s Premium Snacks
    Terra Chips (gourmet vegetable chips)
Specialties
    ALBA (dry milk mixes and shakes)
    Celestial Seasonings (teas)
    Estee (sugar-free products)
    Hollywood (carrot juice condiments and cooking oils)
    Mountain Sun (juice)
    TenderCare (disposable diapers and baby wipes)
    Tushies (disposable diapers and baby wipes)
Natural Body Care and Home Care
    Alba Botanica (personal care products)
    Avalon Organics (Personal care products)
    JÃSÖN (shampoo soap and shaving products)
    Orjene Organics (beauty and personal care products)
    Queen Helene (body care products)
    Zia Natural Skincare (therapeutic skin care products)

COMPETITORS

Amy' s Kitchen	Inventure foods
Annie' s Inc.	Jennie-O
Armanino Foods	Johnson & Johnson
Associated British Foods	Kellogg
Beech-Nut	Kerry Group
Boca Foods	Kimberly-Clark
Burt' s Bees	Kiss My Face
Butterball	Kraft Foods Group Inc.
	Monterey Gourmet Foods

Campbell Soup	Nature' s Path
Cargill	Nestlé
Clif Bar	Newman' s Own
Colgate-Palmolive	Pilgrim' s Pride
ConAgra	Procter & Gamble
Danone	R.C. Bigelow
Dean Foods	Small Planet Foods
Dr. Bronner' s	Smucker
Eden Foods	Spectrum Foods
Empire Kosher Poultry	Stash Tea
Estée Lauder	Stonyfield Farm
Frito-Lay	Tofutti Brands
Galaxy Nutritional Foods	Tom' s of Maine
	TreeHouse
General Mills	Tyson Foods
Gerber Products	Unilever
Hormel	Vita Food Products

HISTORICAL FINANCIALS

Company Type: Public

Income Statement

FYE: June 30

	REVENUE ($ mil.)	NET INCOME ($ mil.)	NET PROFIT MARGIN	EMPLOYEES
06/14	2,153.6	139.8	6.5%	4,400
06/13	1,734.6	114.6	6.6%	3,665
06/12	1,378.2	79.2	5.7%	3,720
06/11	1,130.2	54.9	4.9%	2,031
06/10	917.3	28.6	3.1%	2,059
Annual Growth	23.8%	48.7%	—	20.9%

2014 Year-End Financials

Debt ratio: 29.2%
Return on equity: 9.9%
Cash ($ mil.): 123
Current ratio: 1.89
Long-term debt ($ mil.): 767

No. of shares (mil.): 100
Dividends
Yield: —
Payout: —
Market value ($ mil.): 8,896

	STOCK PRICE ($) FY Close	P/E High/Low		PER SHARE ($) Earnings	Dividends	Book Value
06/14	88.74	68	46	1.40	0.00	16.16
06/13	65.01	59	42	1.21	0.00	12.60
06/12	55.04	63	30	0.87	0.00	10.73
06/11	33.36	57	31	0.62	0.00	9.87
06/10	20.17	65	41	0.35	0.00	8.99
Annual Growth	44.8%	—	—	41.9%	—	15.8%

Hancock Holding Co.

Hancock Holding holds its own as a Gulf Coast financial force. It is the holding company of Mississippi-based Hancock Bank and Louisiana-based Whitney Bank. Together the banks have about 250 branches and 300 ATMs throughout the Gulf South from Florida to Texas. The community-oriented banks offer traditional products and services such as deposit accounts trust services and consumer and business lending. Hancock Holding also has subsidiaries or business units that offer insurance discount brokerage services mutual funds and consumer financing.

EXECUTIVES

President CEO and Director, John M. Hairston, age 51, $707,000 total compensation

Chief Retail Banking Officer, Richard T. Hill, $375,000 total compensation

Chief Wealth Management Officer, Clifton J. Saik, $384,961 total compensation
Chief Commercial Banking Officer, Edward G. Francis
COO, D. Shane Loper
CFO, Michael M. Achary, $400,000 total compensation
President Whitney Bank, Joseph S. Exnicios
Chief Credit Officer Whitney Bank, Suzanne C. Thomas
Chief Credit Officer, Samuel B. Kendricks
Chief Risk Officer, Michael K. Dickerson
Vice President, Sandy Porter
Vp, Beth Elrod
Vice President Information Technology, Ron Milliet
Retail Area Manager Vice President, Julie Burke
Vice President, Andrea J Hood
Vice President And Private Banker, Larry Cuervo
Senior Vice President And Director, Scott Erlichman
Vice President, Jennifer Busby
Vice President Consumer Credit Risk Analytics, Alan Eads
Senior Vice President Enterprise Performance Measurement Fpanda And Decision Support, Jeffry Barno
Vice President Commercial Banker, Christopher Papp
Vice President, Brad Schild
Chairman, James B. Estabrook, age 70
President CEO and Director, John M. Hairston, age 51
Auditors: PricewaterhouseCoopersLLP

LOCATIONS

HQ: Hancock Holding Co.
One Hancock Plaza, P.O. Box 4019, Gulfport, MS 39502
Phone: 228 868-4000
Web: www.hancockbank.com

2013 Sales

	$ mil.	% of total
Whitney	571.8	59
Hancock	337.4	35
Other	63.8	6
Adjustment	(4.6)	-
Total	**968.4**	**100**

PRODUCTS/OPERATIONS

2013 Sales

	$ mil.	% of total
Interest		
Loans including fees	630.8	65
Securities	90.0	10
Other	1.4	-
Noninterest		
Service charges on deposit accounts	79.0	8
Bank card and ATM fees	45.9	5
Trust fees	38.2	4
Investment and annutiy fees	19.7	2
Insurance commissions and fees	15.8	1
Secoudary mortgage market operations	12.5	1
Other	35.1	4
Total	**968.4**	**100**

Subsidiaries
Berwick LLC
Community First Inc.
Dudley Ventures Hancock Fund LLC
Gulf South Technology Center LLC
The Gulfport Building Inc.
Hancock Bank
Hancock Bank of Alabama
Hancock Bank Securities Corporation II
Hancock Community Investment Corporation
Hancock Enterprise Investment Fund LLC
Hancock Insurance Agency
Hancock Insurance Agency of Alabama
Hancock Insurance Agency of Florida
Hancock Investment Services of Alabama Inc.

Hancock Investment Services of Florida Inc.
Hancock Investment Services of Louisiana Inc.
Hancock Investment Services of Mississippi Inc.
Hancock Investment Services Inc.
Harrison Finance Company
Harrison Loan Company
HBSC LLC
HMC LLC
Invest-Sure Inc.
J Everett Eaves Inc.
Lighthouse Services Corporation
Peoples First Transportation Inc.
Town Properties Inc.
Whitney Bank

COMPETITORS

BancorpSouth	Investar
Capital One	MidSouth Bancorp
First Horizon	Regions Financial
First NBC Bank	Renasant
IBERIABANK	Trustmark

HISTORICAL FINANCIALS
Company Type: Public

Income Statement

FYE: December 31

	ASSETS ($ mil.)	NET INCOME ($ mil.)	INCOME AS % OF ASSETS	EMPLOYEES
12/13	19,009.2	163.3	0.9%	3,978
12/12	19,464.4	151.7	0.8%	4,235
12/11	19,774.1	76.7	0.4%	4,745
12/10	8,138.3	52.2	0.6%	2,271
12/09	8,697.0	74.7	0.9%	5,837
Annual Growth	**21.6%**	**21.6%**	**—**	**(9.1%)**

2013 Year-End Financials

Return on assets: 0.8%	Dividends
Return on equity: 6.7%	Yield: 2.6%
Long-term debt ($ mil.): —	Payout: 47.0%
No. of shares (mil.): 82	Market value ($ mil.): 3,016
Sales ($ mil): 968	

	STOCK PRICE ($) FY Close	P/E High/Low		Earnings	PER SHARE ($) Dividends	Book Value
12/13	36.68	19	14	1.93	0.96	29.49
12/12	31.73	21	16	1.75	0.96	28.91
12/11	31.97	31	22	1.15	0.96	27.95
12/10	34.86	32	19	1.40	0.96	23.22
12/09	43.81	20	10	2.26	0.96	22.74
Annual Growth	**(4.3%)**	**—**	**—**	**(3.9%)**	**(0.0%)**	**6.7%**

Hardinge Inc.

Hardinge keeps on turning. The company manufactures precision turning milling and grinding machine tools that shape metals composites and plastics. It makes industrial machine tools for small and midsized shops that create machined parts for the aerospace automotive construction medical equipment and farm equipment industries. Its computer-controlled machines cut horizontally or vertically and can be connected to automatic material feeders for unattended machining. Hardinge also offers a line of work- and tool-holding devices. It gets about 70% of its sales outside of North America predominantly in China and Western Europe.
Geographic Reach

Hardinge has manufacturing facilities in China Switzerland Taiwan the UK and the US. It has sales operations in China France Germany the Netherlands North America and the UK.
Operations

The company operates through two segments: metalcutting machine solutions (MMS; 85% of sales) which includes operations related to grinding turning and milling; and aftermarket tooling and accessories (ATA; 15%) which includes products that are purchased by manufacturers throughout the lives of their machines.
Sales and Marketing

The company sells products under brand names that include Bridgeport Hauser Jones & Shipman Kellenberger and Tschudin. Products are sold through a direct sales force but about 69% of sales are made through distributors and agents. Machine sales account for about 77% of sales. Non-machine products and services include workholding repair parts and accessories.
Financial Performance

Hardinge's revenues have marginally decreased the last few years. Revenues dipped 1% from $334 million in 2012 to $329 million in 2013. Profits also fell 44% from $18 million in 2012 to $10 million in 2013.

The lower revenue for 2013 was driven by a 9% decrease in MMS sales fueled by softer demand for machine tool consumption in Europe and North America. Europe sales dipped by 26% due to continued economic uncertainty throughout most of Europe especially for high end machine tools. Asia sales also decreased due to a decelerating Chinese economy in addition to the absence of several large specialty multi-machine orders to the consumer electronics industry over the course of the year.

Its erosion of profits for 2013 was due to an increase in an impairment charge as part of the company's review of goodwill and other intangible assets. It also paid higher interest expenses in 2013. After experiencing negative operating cash flow in 2011 Hardinge saw its cash flow steadily rise in 2012 and 2013.
Strategy

To create new products Hardinge goes beyond internal product development to expand its offerings through acquisitions joint ventures license agreements and partnerships. To extend its international reach in late 2014 Hardinge announced it was acquiring Germany-based Voumard Internal Diameter Grinding an expert in the internal diameter grinding market with an installed base of over 9000 machine products serving more than 2500 customers around the world.

To strengthen its core offerings Hardinge in 2012 bought Usach Technologies an Illinois-based manufacturer of custom built high precision internal and external grinding machines and systems. The acquisition complemented and enhanced its grinding product portfolio.

EXECUTIVES

Chairman President and CEO, Richard L. Simons, age 58, $293,313 total compensation
Senior Vice President - Asia Operations, James P (Jim) Langa, age 56
Chairman President and CEO, Richard L. Simons, age 58
Auditors: Ernst&YoungLLP

LOCATIONS

HQ: Hardinge Inc.
One Hardinge Drive, Elmira, NY 14902-1507
Phone: 607 734-2281
Web: www.hardinge.com

2013 Sales

	$ mil.	% of total
North America		
US	105.8	32
Other North America	5.7	1
Europe		
Germany	40.3	13
England	21.1	6
Switzerland	6.1	2
Other Europe	32.7	10
Asia		
China	96.5	29
Taiwan	4.5	1
Other Asia	18.8	6
Total	**329.5**	**100**

PRODUCTS/OPERATIONS

2013 Sales

	$ mil.	% of total
Metalcutting machine solutions	278.4	84
Aftermarket tooling and accessories	51.6	16
Elimination	(0.5)	-
Total	**329.5**	**100**

Selected Products

CNC lathes
Grinders
Knee-mills
Vertical machining centers
Workholding
  Spindle tooling
  Tool holders

Selected Subsidiaries

Canadian Hardinge Machine Tools Ltd
Hardinge China Limited
Hardinge GmbH (Germany)
Hardinge Holdings B.V. (Netherlands)
Hardinge Holdings GmbH (Switzerland)
Hardinge Machine (Shanghai) Co. Ltd.
Hardinge Machine Tools B.V. (Netherlands)
Hardinge Machine Tools B.V. Taiwan Branch
  ("Hardinge Taiwan")
Hardinge Machine Tools Ltd. (UK)
Hardinge Taiwan Precision Machinery Limited
Hardinge Technology Systems Inc. (US)
L. Kellenberger & Co. AG (Switzerland)

COMPETITORS

Actuant	Indústrias Romi
DMG Mori Seiki	Kennametal
Doosan Infracore	KÄTber
Flow International	MAG Giddings & Lewis
Gleason Corp.	Mazak
Haas Automation	Okuma
Hurco	Thermwood
Hyundai Motor	Toyoda Machinery USA
IMTA	

HISTORICAL FINANCIALS

Company Type: Public

Income Statement

FYE: December 31

	REVENUE ($ mil.)	NET INCOME ($ mil.)	NET PROFIT MARGIN	EMPLOYEES
12/13	329.4	9.9	3.0%	1,445
12/12	334.4	17.8	5.3%	1,417
12/11	341.5	11.9	3.5%	1,332
12/10	257.0	(5.2)	—	1,189
12/09	214.0	(33.3)	—	1,138
Annual Growth	**11.4%**	**—**	**—**	**6.2%**

2013 Year-End Financials

Debt ratio: 7.7%	No. of shares (mil.): 12
Return on equity: 5.4%	Dividends
Cash ($ mil.): 34	Yield: 0.5%
Current ratio: 2.62	Payout: 9.6%
Long-term debt ($ mil.): 18	Market value ($ mil.): 179

	STOCK PRICE ($) FY Close	P/E High/Low		PER SHARE ($) Earnings	Dividends	Book Value
12/13	14.47	20	12	0.83	0.08	16.42
12/12	9.94	8	5	1.53	0.08	13.74
12/11	8.05	13	7	1.02	0.05	12.61
12/10	9.74	—	—	(0.46)	0.02	13.60
12/09	5.50	—	—	(2.93)	0.03	14.00
Annual Growth	**27.4%**	—	—	**—**	**33.7%**	**4.1%**

Hawaiian Holdings Inc

Luaus leis and laying in the sun —Hawaiian Holdings knows how to get you there. The company's main subsidiary Hawaiian Airlines transports passengers and cargo between Honolulu and about a dozen major cities in the western US. Transpacific routes account for most of the carrier's revenue. Hawaiian Airlines also serves four of the six main Hawaiian Islands and destinations in the South Pacific such as American Samoa Australia the Philippines and Tahiti. It operates a fleet of about 45 aircraft (most are Boeing 717s for flights between the Hawaiian Islands and Boeing 767s for transpacific flights). In addition to its scheduled passenger and cargo operations Hawaiian Airlines provides charter services.

Operations

To supplement its own inter-island offerings Hawaiian Airlines serves other destinations within Hawaii via a code-sharing deal with Island Air. In addition Hawaiian Airlines maintains code-sharing arrangements with carriers such as American Airlines Continental Airlines Delta Air Lines United and US Airways. Code-sharing allows airlines to extend their networks by selling tickets on other carriers' flights.

Sales and Marketing

Hawaiian Airlines uses various distribution channels including its website (mostly for North America and regional island routes) and travel agencies and wholesale distributors for international flights.

Financial Performance

Hawaiian Airlines has enjoyed four straight years of steady growth. Revenues spiked 10% from $1.96 billion in 2012 to reach a historical milestone of $2.2 billion in 2013. After suffering a net loss of nearly $3 million in 2011 the airline posted $53 million in net income for 2012 and $52 million in 2013.

The growth in 2013 was driven by an increase in passenger revenue due to an uptick in capacity across its network. It was also attributed to a $16 million increase in cargo revenue due to the additional cargo capacity provided by the Airbus A330-200 aircraft; this was the result of the expansion of its network and improved production on its existing routes.

The positive net income for 2012 and 2013 was primarily due to the absence of a $70 million litigation charge it incurred in 2011 related to the purchase of aircraft. The company's cash flow decreased by $84 million in 2013 due to more cash it was forced to use for its operating activities as it experienced a smaller increase in air traffic liability due to fewer new routes introduced in 2013 compared to 2012.

Strategy

Hawaiian Airlines is counting on continued growth in its transpacific and South Pacific operations through expanded service to Tahiti Australia Japan and the Philippines. It has instituted a code-sharing agreement with Korean Air Lines and now offers nonstop flights to that country. Hawaiian Airlines is currently the only airline to offer nonstop service from Honolulu to Pago Pago and American Samoa. To support its expansion plans the company has ordered 16 wide-body and extra-wide-body aircraft from Airbus for delivery between 2017 and 2020.

In mid-2013 the airline announced plans to launch a non-stop service between Honolulu and Beijing beginning in April 2014. This flight represents the airlines' tenth international destination and makes China one of Hawaiian Airlines' most important visitor destinations. Shortly after it also signed a code-share agreement with Air China China's exclusive national flag carrier.

HISTORY

In 1929 former Navy pilot Stanley Kennedy general manager of the Inter-Island Steam Navigation Company persuaded the Inter-Island board to fund a passenger line linking Honolulu (Oahu) with the other Hawaiian Islands. The new airline which started out with amphibian aircraft began inter-island airmail service in 1934.

The company became Hawaiian Airlines in 1941. TWA bought control in 1944 but sold out four years later after the new Trans-Pacific Airlines (later Aloha Airlines) ended Hawaiian's 17-year monopoly in Hawaii in 1946. The two competed intensely for the same routes. Investor John Magoon bought control of Hawaiian in 1964. The rival airlines agreed to merge in 1970 but negotiations failed a year later.

Airline deregulation in 1978 gave Hawaiian access to new markets. It adopted the name HAL in 1982 and by 1985 had added service to the US West Coast (where it was hammered by United and Continental) and to the South Pacific. HAL built the $8.5 million West Maui Airport in 1987. Rising costs forced Magoon to sell 47% of HAL to an investor group that included Magoon's friend former baseball commissioner Peter Ueberroth. The group led by Jet America Airlines founder Thomas Talbot bought control of HAL in 1989 and Talbot took over as chairman and CEO.

Rival Aloha surpassed HAL at home capturing 61% of the interisland market in 1991. HAL had also gained a nickname "Hawaiian Always Late" from complaining passengers. To raise $20 million HAL sold Northwest a 25% stake (which Northwest later disposed of) along with some international routes. HAL's president John Ueberroth (Peter's brother) replaced Talbot as chairman. In 1992 as HAL was narrowing its losses Hurricane Iniki cost it some $7 million in sales. HAL filed for bankruptcy in 1993 and Ueberroth resigned.

Airline veteran Bruce Nobles became CEO that year. He guided HAL through reorganization and in 1994 the slimmed-down airline took the name Hawaiian Airlines once again.

John Adams of Smith Management formed a partnership to invest in the airline in 1996 and was subsequently named Hawaiian's chairman. Before CEO Nobles made way for Paul Casey in 1997 he won a union wage concession and an agreement from American to defer aircraft lease payments. In 1998 Hawaiian partnered with American in a code-sharing deal and launched another in 1999 this time with Continental. Also in 1999 Hawaiian began negotiations with the pilots union and in 2000 the airline requested a federal mediator to assist in the negotiations.

The airline came to an agreement with the pilots in 2001 and reached another agreement with the union representing its flight attendants later that year. Also in late 2001 Hawaiian and Aloha Airlines both suffering from the industry downturn that followed the September 11 terrorist attacks agreed to merge and form a new company Aloha Holdings but the plans were abandoned in 2002 because of heavy opposition to the merger by employees and shareholders of Hawaiian. The company formed a holding company later that year called Hawaiian Holdings.

As the effects of September 11 on the air travel market lingered Hawaiian Airlines filed for Chapter 11 bankruptcy protection in March 2003. (Hawaiian Holdings was not included in the filing.) During the carrier's reorganization San Diego-based investment firm Ranch Capital's RC Aviation bought Adams' stake in Hawaiian Holdings. (RC Aviation dissolved in 2008 and distributed the shares among the investors in the group.)

Hawaiian Airlines completed its reorganization and emerged from bankruptcy in June 2005. The carrier established its dominance in Hawaii once again when Aloha Airlines filed for bankruptcy and liquidated its inventory in March 2008.

EXECUTIVES

Vp Sales And Marketing Hawaiian Airlines, Richard J (Rick) Peterson

Vp Finance Hawaiian Airlines, Karen A Berry, age 58

Vp Inflight Services Hawaiian Airlines, Louis D Saint-cyr

Vp Flight Operations Hawaiian Airlines, Kenneth E Rewick

Secretary; Senior Vice President; General Counsel And Corporate Secretary Of Hawaiian, Hoyt H Zia, age 61

President and CEO Hawaiian Holdings and Hawaiian Airlines, Mark B. Dunkerley, age 50, $625,000 total compensation

EVP and Chief Commercial Officer Hawaiian Airlines, Peter R. Ingram, age 47, $413,125 total compensation

EVP and CFO, Scott Topping, $330,000 total compensation

EVP and Chief Administrative Officer Hawaiian Airlines, Ron Anderson-Lehman, age 50

EVP and COO Hawaiian Airlines, Sean Menke

Senior Vice President Marketing, Avi A Mannis

Vice President Of Flight Operations, Ken Rewick

President and CEO, Lawrence Hershfield

Auditors: Ernst&YoungLLP

LOCATIONS

HQ: Hawaiian Holdings Inc
3375 Koapaka Street, Suite G-350, Honolulu, HI 96819
Phone: 808 835-3700
Web: www.hawaiianairlines.com

PRODUCTS/OPERATIONS

2013 Sales

	$ mil.	% of total
Passenger	1942.8	90
Other	213.1	10
Total	**2155.9**	**100**

Selected Transpacific Destinations
Las Vegas
Los Angeles
Oakland CA
Phoenix
Portland OR
Sacramento CA
San Diego
San Francisco
San Jose CA
Seattle

COMPETITORS

ANA Holdings	Hawaii Island Air
Air Canada	Japan Airlines
Alaska Air	Mesa Air
American Airlines Group	Qantas
	US Airways
Delta Air Lines	United Continental

HISTORICAL FINANCIALS
Company Type: Public

Income Statement
FYE: December 31

	REVENUE ($ mil.)	NET INCOME ($ mil.)	NET PROFIT MARGIN	EMPLOYEES
12/13	2,155.8	51.8	2.4%	5,249
12/12	1,962.3	53.2	2.7%	4,906
12/11	1,650.4	(2.6)	—	4,314
12/10	1,310.0	110.2	8.4%	4,023
12/09	1,183.3	116.7	9.9%	3,844
Annual Growth	**16.2%**	**(18.4%)**		**8.1%**

2013 Year-End Financials

Debt ratio: 37.2%	No. of shares (mil.): 52
Return on equity: 15.5%	Dividends
Cash ($ mil.): 423	Yield: —
Current ratio: 0.92	Payout: —
Long-term debt ($ mil.): 744	Market value ($ mil.): 505

	STOCK PRICE ($) FY Close	P/E High/Low		Earnings	PER SHARE ($) Dividends	Book Value
12/13	9.63	10	5	0.98	0.00	7.57
12/12	6.57	7	5	1.01	0.00	5.22
12/11	5.80	—	—	(0.05)	0.00	4.39
12/10	7.84	4	2	2.10	0.00	5.53
12/09	7.00	4	1	2.22	0.00	3.42
Annual Growth	**8.3%**	—	—	**(18.5%)**	—	**22.0%**

HCP, Inc.

Old age isn't for sissies but as far as HCP is concerned it's for making money. HCP is a self-administered real estate investment trust (REIT) that invests in develops and manages real estate that it leases to health care facilities. Its diversified real estate portfolio consists of senior living and skilled nursing facilities hospitals medical office buildings and biotech and pharmaceutical laboratories. HCP has interests in more than 1050 properties in 40-plus states and Mexico. California and Texas are its largest markets. The REIT which has nearly $22 billion in assets under management invests in properties through direct ownership mortgage loans and joint ventures.

Geographic Reach

Based in Irvine California HCP operates in 41 US states and in Mexico. The REIT which main-

tains offices in both Nashville and San Francisco generates 41% of its revenue from properties located in California (20%) Texas (10%) and Florida (9%).

Operations

The company operates its business through five segments: senior housing post-acute/skilled nursing life science medical office and hospital.

HCP's five investment products include properties under lease debt investments developments and redevelopments investment management and investments in senior housing operations. Besides its investments in properties under lease and debt investments HCP at the beginning of 2013 had an aggregate investment of $540 million in assets under development including redevelopment and land held for future development primarily in its life science and medical office segments.

Sales and Marketing

HCR ManorCare was HCP's biggest tenant in 2013 accounting for 28% of the REIT's total revenue. Other major tenants include Brookdale Senior Living which recently acquired another of the REIT's tenants Emeritus Corp. as well as Sunrise Senior Living.

Financial Performance

HCP's revenues have increased every year for about a decade while profits have risen sharply for four consecutive years following two years of decline (2008 2009) during the financial crisis.

Revenue increased 10% in 2013 versus 2012 to $2.1 billion while net income rose 17% to $970.8 million. Driving the increase was the acquisition of 133 senior housing communities in late 2012 and the first quarter of 2013. Net income rose on higher revenue and increased income from the sale of real estate.

Strategy

With the population of Americans 65 and older growing rapidly and living longer HCP expects increased demand for senior housing and health care services in general. The REIT has built its business by leasing health care properties under long-term leases with fixed and/or inflation indexed escalators. Most of the company's rents and other earned income from leases are received under triple-net leases or leases that provide for substantial recovery of operating expenses. Some of its medical office and life science leases however are structured as gross or modified gross leases.To meet growing demand the company regularly invests in its business. Indeed in 2013 it invested nearly $600 million. Deals included the four remaining senior housing facilities from the Blackstone JV acquisition among other deals.

Mergers and Acquisitions

The REIT's go-to strategy is to grow by acquisitions —often major ones —rather than through development.

HCP acquired 129 senior housing facilities from a joint venture between Emeritus and Blackstone Real Estate Partners in late 2012 for $1.7 billion followed by four more in March 2013 for $38 million. The acquired properties are located in 29 states and the portfolio encompasses 10077 units representing a diversified care mix of 61% assisted living 25% independent living 13% memory care and 1% skilled nursing. The purchase bolstered HCP's senior housing portfolio its largest business.

HCP in 2012 bought eight on-campus medical office buildings for $80 million from Scottsdale Healthcare as well as 12 medical office buildings from The Boyer Company valued at $188 million primarily located on the campuses of HCA Iasis Healthcare and Community Health Systems. Previously the health care REIT bought 334 post-acute skilled nursing and assisted living facilities of HCR ManorCare in 2011 for $6 billion. As part of the purchase HCP entered into a long-term triple-net master lease under which HCR ManorCare will continue to operate the facilities.

EXECUTIVES

Evp, Edward J (Ed) Henning, age 62
Senior Vice President And Associate General Counsel, Brian Maas
Vp Medical Office Properties, Thomas W Hulme
President and CEO, Lauralee E. Martin, $196,970 total compensation
EVP Acquisitions and Valuations, Thomas D. (Tom) Kirby
EVP and Chief Investment Officer, Paul F. Gallagher, $500,000 total compensation
EVP Medical Office Properties, Thomas M. (Tom) Klaritch, $350,000 total compensation
EVP, Susan M. Tate
EVP and CFO, Timothy M. (Tim) Schoen, $500,000 total compensation
Sr V Pres-asset Management, Sharon Yester
EVP Life Science Estates, Jonathan M. Bergschneider
EVP Chief Administrative Officer General Counsel and Secretary, James W. (Jim) Mercer, $500,000 total compensation
EVP Senior Housing, Kendall K. Young
Vice President, Reid L Babin
Vice President Corporate And Securities Counsel, Troy McHenry
Assistant To Executive Vice President, Claudia Adair
Chairman, Michael D. McKee
Auditors: Deloitte&ToucheLLP

LOCATIONS

HQ: HCP, Inc.
1920 Main Street, Suite 1200, Irvine, CA 92614
Phone: 949 407-0700   **Fax:** 562 733-5200
Web: www.hcpi.com

PRODUCTS/OPERATIONS

2013 Sales

	$mil.	% of total
Rental and related revenue	1128.1	54
Income from direct financing leases	636.9	30
Resident fees and services	146.3	7
Tenant recoveries	100.6	5
Interest income	86.2	4
Investment management fee income	1.8	-
Total	**2099.9**	**100**

2013 Sales

	$mil.	% of total
Senior housing	760.4	37
Post-acute/skilled nursing	615.4	29
Medical office	354.2	17
Life science	296.9	14
Hospital	73.0	3
Total	**2099.9**	**100**

Selected Subsidiaries

HCP Atrium MOB LLC (95.30%)
HCP DR California LLC
HCP CTE L.P. (99.9%)
HCP Pleasant LLC
HCP DR MCD LLC (69.34%)
HCP MCD TRS LLC
HCP EGP Inc.
HCP ETE L.P. (99.9%)
HCP Life Science REIT Inc. (99.99%)

COMPETITORS

Cousins Properties   Omega Healthcare

Extendicare
Health Care REIT
Healthcare Realty Trust
LTC Properties
National Health Investors
Investors
Sabra Health Care
Senior Housing Properties
Ventas

HISTORICAL FINANCIALS

Company Type: Public

Income Statement

FYE: December 31

	REVENUE ($ mil.)	NET INCOME ($ mil.)	NET PROFIT MARGIN	EMPLOYEES
12/14	2,266.2	922.2	40.7%	170
12/13	2,099.8	970.8	46.2%	154
12/12	1,900.7	832.5	43.8%	149
12/11	1,725.3	538.8	31.2%	147
12/10	1,255.1	330.7	26.3%	148
Annual Growth	**15.9%**	**29.2%**		**3.5%**

2014 Year-End Financials

Debt ratio: 45.6%
Return on equity: 8.6%
Cash ($ mil.): 183
Current ratio: 0.52
Long-term debt ($ mil.): 9,759

No. of shares (mil.): 459
Dividends
Yield: 4.9%
Payout: 98.2%
Market value ($ mil.): 20,243

	STOCK PRICE ($) FY Close	P/E High/Low	PER SHARE ($) Earnings	Dividends	Book Value
12/14	44.03	23 18	2.00	2.18	23.35
12/13	36.32	26 17	2.13	2.10	23.47
12/12	45.16	25 20	1.90	2.00	23.28
12/11	41.43	32 22	1.29	1.92	22.11
12/10	36.79	38 27	1.00	1.86	21.45
Annual Growth	**4.6%**	**— —**	**18.9%**	**4.0%**	**2.1%**

Healthcare Services Group, Inc.

Healthcare Services Group gets swept up in its work every day. The company provides housekeeping laundry and linen food and maintenance services to hospitals nursing homes rehabilitation centers and retirement facilities. It tidies up around 3000 long-term care facilities in Canada and almost every state in the US. Housekeeping and laundry and linen services are the company's top revenue generators. The company's dietary division prepares food for residents and monitors nutritional needs in more than 600 facilities. Healthcare Services Group was established in 1977.

Geographic Reach
The company operates in 48 states and Canada.
Operations
The company's operations are divided in two segments: Housekeeping and Dietary.
Housekeeping consists of the managing of the client's housekeeping department which is principally responsible for the cleaning disinfecting and sanitizing of patient rooms and common areas of a client's facility as well as the laundering and processing of the personal clothing belonging to the facility's patients. Dietary consists of managing the client's dietary department which is principally responsible for food purchasing meal preparation

and providing dietitian consulting professional services which includes the development of a menu that meets the patient's dietary needs.
Dietary services represented 32% of consolidated revenues in fiscal 2012 while Housekeeping services represented about 68%.
Sales and Marketing
The company markets its services primarily through referrals and in-person solicitation of target facilities. They also utilize direct mail campaigns and participate in industry trade shows health care trade associations and healthcare support service seminars.
Financial Performance
The company has seen its revenues and net income steadily increase year over year for a long time.
Healthcare Services Group revenues increased 21% and net income increased 16% in fiscal 2012 compared with 2011. Net cash inflow increased by $31 billion in 2012 compared with the prior year.
The increase in revenues was attributed to the increase in revenue from the company's reportable segments. Housekeeping revenues increased 13% driven by an increase in revenues attributable to service agreements entered into with new clients. Dietary segment revenues increased 45% primarily as a result of providing this service to a greater number of existing Housekeeping clients.
Mergers and Acquisitions
In 2013 Healthcare Services Group agreed with Platinum Health Services to acquire substantially all of its operating assets for approximately $380 million. Platinum is a privately-held provider of professional housekeeping laundry and maintenance services to long-term and post-acute care facilities.

EXECUTIVES

Executive Vice President, Joseph F McCartney, age 60
Chairman and CEO, Daniel P. McCartney, age 62, $1,005,108 total compensation
EVP, Michael E. McBryan, $102,492 total compensation
EVP, Bryan D. McCartney, $102,492 total compensation
President and COO, Theodore Wahl, age 41, $996,255 total compensation
CFO, John Shea, $389,039 total compensation
Vice President, Jim Keeley
Senior Vice President Underwriting, Helen Winge
Vice President Western Division, David Smigel
Vice President Midwest Division, James Schreck
Vice President Midwest Division, David Hurlock
Regional Vice President, Jim Bleming
Vice President Southeast Division, Nicholas Rucker
Vice President, Steven Rothman
Regional Vice President, Brian Mejia
Regional Vice President, Ryan Viets
Vice President Northeast Division, Kevin McCartney
Divisional Vice President, Stephen Foresman
Divisional Vice President, James Pliego
Chairman and CEO, Daniel P. McCartney, age 62
Auditors: GrantThorntonLLP

LOCATIONS

HQ: Healthcare Services Group, Inc.
3220 Tillman Drive, Suite 300, Bensalem, PA 19020
Phone: 215 639-4274   **Fax:** 215 639-2152
Web: www.hcsgcorp.com

PRODUCTS/OPERATIONS

2014 Sales

	% of total
Housekeeping services	65
Dietary services	35
Total	**100**

COMPETITORS

ABM Industries	Ecolab
ARAMARK	G&K Services
Alsco	Sodexo USA
Angelica Corporation	SureQuest Systems
Crothall Healthcare	

HISTORICAL FINANCIALS

Company Type: Public

Income Statement
FYE: December 31

	REVENUE ($ mil.)	NET INCOME ($ mil.)	NET PROFIT MARGIN	EMPLOYEES
12/13	1,149.8	47.1	4.1%	7,600
12/12	1,077.4	44.2	4.1%	7,000
12/11	889.0	38.1	4.3%	6,850
12/10	773.9	34.4	4.5%	5,400
12/09	692.7	30.3	4.4%	4,900
Annual Growth	13.5%	11.6%	—	11.6%

2013 Year-End Financials

Debt ratio: —	No. of shares (mil.): 69
Return on equity: 18.3%	Dividends
Cash ($ mil.): 64	Yield: 2.3%
Current ratio: 3.12	Payout: 84.0%
Long-term debt ($ mil.): —	Market value ($ mil.): 1,985

	STOCK PRICE ($) FY Close	P/E High/Low		PER SHARE ($) Earnings	Dividends	Book Value
12/13	28.37	43	32	0.67	0.67	4.07
12/12	23.23	37	27	0.65	0.65	3.37
12/11	17.69	33	22	0.56	0.63	3.26
12/10	16.27	48	30	0.51	0.60	3.22
12/09	21.46	47	30	0.46	0.49	3.19
Annual Growth	7.2%	—	—	9.9%	8.1%	6.3%

Healthstream Inc

HealthStream replenishes the well of knowledge for medical workers. The company supplies Internet-based learning and research content to health care organizations throughout the US to meet their training certification and development needs. HealthStream's core learning product is HealthStream Learning Center (HLC) which offers educational and training courseware to about 3.5 million subscribers (representing some 4000 hospitals) via a software-as-a-service (SaaS) model. The company's research offerings include quality and satisfaction surveys data analysis and other research-based management tools; the Patient Insights survey generates most of the research business' revenues.

Operations

The company operates through two segments — HealthStream Workforce Development (employee training and development) and HealtStream Research/Patient Experience (surveys and other re-

search). It generates about three-fourths of sales through the Workforce Development unit.

Geographic Reach

HealthStream serves customers in all US states from its corporate headquarters in Nashville and its satellite offices in Laurel Maryland; Brentwood Tennessee; and Pensacola Florida.

Sales and Marketing

HealthStream generates sales from subscription fees based on the number of users and type of content provided. Clients include US health care organizations –primarily acute care hospitals such as HCA Tenet and LifePoint –and pharmaceutical and medical device companies.

HealthStream markets its products primarily through direct sales teams consultants and account relationship managers. Its marketing programs include catalogs trade shows online promotions telemarketing campaigns public relations direct mail and advertising.

Financial Analysis

HealthStream's revenues have climbed steadily over the last decade. For instance in 2013 the company reported a more than 25% sales increase to some $132 million due to growth in both the learning and research segments. The learning division saw a 32% increase in sales due to its growing subscriber base and expanded courseware offerings (including the SimVentures program) while research revenues rose 13% from increased patient survey volumes and the acquisition of Baptist Leadership Group. HealthStream's revenue growth also prompted a 10% increase in profits to some $8.4 million that year.

Strategy

While many of its competitors are offering course material in a range of formats (print online instructor-led) HealthStream focuses on its Internet-based offerings. In order to remain competitive HealthStream tailors its HLC course delivery methods to provide clients with access to the specific educational resources they need. While HealthStream is focused on adding subscribers to the HLC platform it also aims to have existing subscribers order additional courses and new software applications. To take advantage of the increasing use of simulation technology to educate students and medical professionals HealthStream partnered with Laerdal Medical to form a joint venture called SimVentures in 2011. The venture sells patient simulation scenarios through a simulation management platform called SimCenter.

Partnerships are a key to HealthStream's growth. In 2014 the company began providing content from some 900 courses from The Institute for Professional Care Education QueTech and Mather LifeWays Institute on Aging via the HealthStream Learning Center.

HealthStream's Research division only brings in about 20% of its income but it could start seeing more demand since the government is increasingly tying reimbursements to improved patient safety and performance results. The company's research services are meant to complement its learning segment. Its HealthStream Improvement Center is an online system designed to help hospital leaders accelerate the execution of the improvement plans they come up with thanks to the research services. Plans are generally based on results from patient employee physician and community surveys.

Mergers and Acquisitions

In 2012 the company added competency management products when it acquired Decision Critical a private firm that provides software-as-a-service (SaaS) solutions that allow hospitals to manage and develop their workforce. The purchase expanded HealthStream's talent management offerings through the addition of the Critical Portfolio SaaS platform; it also adds other learning management and skill evaluation tools. Also that year it bought Sy.Med Development which produces credentialing software.

In 2013 and 2014 HealthStream added Baptist Leadership Group the consulting practice of Baptist Health Care for about $8.5 million and Health Care Compliance Strategies a compliance training firm for about $13 million.

EXECUTIVES

Sr Vp, Thomas Hutchinson
EVP, Arthur E. Newman, $241,800 total compensation
Chairman President and CEO, Robert A. Frist, $265,567 total compensation
SVP and CFO, Gerard M. (Gerry) Hayden, $237,667 total compensation
SVP and COO, J. Edward Pearson, $252,133 total compensation
SVP and CTO, Jeffrey S. Doster, $128,077 total compensation
SVP, Michael J. Sousa, $198,917 total compensation
Associate Vice President, Tom Noser
Associate Vice President Management, Kimberly Clark
Vice President Of Marketing, Kerry Cicero
Chairman President and CEO, Robert A. Frist
Board Member, Frank Gordon, age 52
Auditors: Ernst&YoungLLP

LOCATIONS

HQ: Healthstream Inc
209 10th Avenue South, Suite 450, Nashville, TN 37203
Phone: 615 301-3100
Web: www.healthstream.com

PRODUCTS/OPERATIONS

2013 Sales

	$ mil.	% of total
Workforce development	103.8	78
Research/Patient experience	28.5	22
Total	**132.3**	**100**

Selected Solutions

ICD-10 Education
CAHPS Surveys
Nurse Orientation
Healthcare Compliance
Resuscitation Training
Post-Acute Care Solutions

COMPETITORS

AMA	Medscape llc
Cengage Learning	NRC
Cornerstone OnDemand	Press Ganey
EBSCO	Reed Elsevier Group
Foresight Group	Saba Software
Gallup	SuccessFactors
Kenexa	SumTotal

HISTORICAL FINANCIALS

Company Type: Public

Income Statement

FYE: December 31

	REVENUE ($ mil.)	NET INCOME ($ mil.)	NET PROFIT MARGIN	EMPLOYEES
12/13	132.2	8.4	6.4%	686
12/12	103.7	7.6	7.4%	587
12/11	82.0	6.9	8.5%	504
12/10	65.7	4.1	6.3%	432
12/09	57.4	13.9	24.3%	397
Annual Growth	23.2%	(11.9%)	—	14.7%

2013 Year-End Financials

Debt ratio: —	No. of shares (mil.): 27
Return on equity: 5.9%	Dividends
Cash ($ mil.): 59	Yield: —
Current ratio: 2.62	Payout: —
Long-term debt ($ mil.): —	Market value ($ mil.): 892

	STOCK PRICE ($) FY Close	P/E High/Low		PER SHARE ($) Earnings	Dividends	Book Value
12/13	32.63	127	65	0.30	0.00	5.47
12/12	24.31	105	57	0.28	0.00	5.04
12/11	18.45	61	22	0.29	0.00	4.67
12/10	8.04	38	18	0.18	0.00	2.60
12/09	3.95	8	3	0.64	0.00	2.40
Annual Growth	69.5%	—	—	(17.3%)	—	22.9%

Heico Corp.

Here's a HEICO haiku: HEICO companies/ Providing for jet engines/ In flight or on land. Its Flight Support Group consisting of HEICO Aerospace and its subsidiaries makes FAA-approved replacement parts for jet engines that can be substituted for original parts including airfoils bearings and fuel pump gears. Flight Support also repairs overhauls and distributes jet engine parts as well as avionics and instruments for commercial air carriers. HEICO's second segment Electronic Technologies Group makes a variety of electronic equipment for the aerospace/defense electronic medical and telecommunications industries. The company has facilities in the US Canada India Singapore and the UK.

Operations

HEICO's Flight Support Group competes with industry leading OEMs and to a lesser extent with smaller independent parts distributors. Historically the three main jet engine OEMs General Electric Pratt & Whitney and Rolls Royce have been the source of substantially all jet engine replacement parts for their own jet engines. HEICO is seeking to capture some of that market by adding new products at a rate of 400 manufacturer-approved parts (also called PMAs) per year.

Strategy

The company uses acquisitions to build out a diverse product and service portfolio in order to reduce exposure to cyclical swings in any single market. Its current set of offerings have broad-range applications in aircraft missiles ships surveillance systems computer and networking devices telecom equipment surgical equipment CT scanners and X-ray systems.

In mid-2013 HEICO announced it was acquiring Reinhold Industries a leading producer of components in the solid rocket propulsion industry. Reinhold will be folded into HEICO's Flight Support Group.

HISTORY

Founded in 1957 as Heinicke Instruments to make laboratory products the company moved into jet engine parts in 1974 with the acquisition of Jet Avion. The company changed its name to HEICO (a shortened version of its previous name) in 1985. After a faulty combustion chamber erupted in flames that year the FAA ordered all combustion chambers on US jets to be inspected and if necessary replaced. HEICO's sales skyrocketed but descended back to earth after airlines found they had overstocked.

By the early 1990s defense cutbacks and declining aircraft orders reduced business and HEICO began to diversify. In 1991 it formed MediTek to acquire medical imaging facilities but then sold the company to U.S. Diagnostic for $24 million five years later. Lufthansa Technik AG the service subsidiary of Deutsche Lufthansa paid HEICO $26 million for a 20% stake in HEICO's flight support operations in 1997.

HEICO acquired jet engine parts companies McClain International and Rogers-Dierks in 1998. The next year the company added Radiant Power (back-up power supplies and battery packs for aerospace applications) Turbine Kinetics and Aero-Kinetics (replacement parts for aircraft engines) Santa Barbara Infrared (infrared and ground support equipment) and Thermal Structures (insulation products).

HEICO sold its Trilectron Industries ground support equipment subsidiary to Illinois Tool Works in 2000 in a deal worth about $64 million. The following year the company formed a joint venture with AMR (parent of American Airlines) to accelerate development of FAA-approved replacement parts. Also in 2001 HEICO bought Inertial Airline Services Avitech Engineering Corp. and Aviation Facilities Inc. In 2003 HEICO acquired Niacc Technology an aircraft component repair and overhaul company.

The company added to its aerospace electronics operations with the acquisition of Connectronics a maker of high-voltage wire and interconnection devices in 2004.

In 2005 HEICO moved to expand its flight support business by buying a 51% stake in Seal Dynamics a designer and distributor of hydraulic pneumatic mechanical and electromechanical components for the commercial regional and general aviation markets.

HEICO's Flight Support Group acquired Arger Enterprises a subsidiary of Melrose PLC in 2006. Arger made and distributed aircraft parts mainly for the commercial aviation market. That year HEICO bought a controlling stake in Prime Air Parts which dealt in spare parts for aircraft.

In 2007 HEICO's Electronic Technologies Group acquired EMD Technologies a maker of high-voltage energy generators used in medical industrial imaging and baggage scanning systems.

A few years of careful acquisitions complemented by organic growth contributed to record sales and profits for HEICO in fiscal 2007. The company's Flight Support Group led the charge with a 38% increase in sales; Electronic Technologies was no slouch with an 8% increase.

In 2009 the Electronic Technologies Group acquired VPT a maker of DC-DC power converters and other electronics which complemented HEICO's customer base in electronics and telecommunications and to a lesser extent in the industrial and medical sectors.

Later that year Electronic Technologies bought the Seacom division of Dukane Corp. a maker of acoustic beacons. Officially known as an Underwater Locator Beacon (ULB) pingers are attached to flight data and cockpit voice recorders as well as marine voyage recorders and are required to be installed on aircraft by the FAA and European Aviation Safety Agency.

In 2011 HEICO acquired France-based 3D Plus a leading designer and manufacturer of three-dimensional microelectronic and stacked memory products which are used primarily in satellites. The acquisition expanded HEICO's presence in the space products business as well as the medical sector. Earlier in the year HEICO's Flight Support Group enhanced its parts and repair operations and competitive position by acquiring an 80% interest in Blue Aerospace. Since 2002 Blue Aerospace has supplied military aircraft parts and support services for the C-130 P-3 and F-16 aircraft largely to foreign military allies of the US. It also manages aircraft parts repair. The deal is expected to boost earnings within the year.

Later in the year HEICO through its Electronics Technologies group acquired Chicago-based Switchcraft. Switchcraft founded in 1946 is the manufacturer of electronic connectors for use in harsh environments as well as cables jacks and plugs patch panels and other products requiring high performance and reliability. The terms of the deal were not disclosed but adds a product line and customer base not presently served by HEICO.

EXECUTIVES

Vice President Finance Administration, Luis J Morell, age 69
Vice President Corporate Development, William S Harlow, age 67
Chairman of the Board; Chief Executive Officer, Victor H. Mendelson, age 46, $519,178 total compensation
Evp Heico Aerospace, James L Reum, age 83
EVP CFO and Treasurer, Carlos Macau
Vice President Sales, Brandi Dague
Vice President And General Manager, Jeff Perkins
Senior Vice President Business Dev, Jim O'Sullivan
Vice President And General Manager, Vladimir Cervera
Vice President, Thomas S Irwin, age 69
Auditors: Deloitte&ToucheLLP

LOCATIONS

HQ: Heico Corp.
3000 Taft Street, Hollywood, FL 33021
Phone: 954 987-4000   **Fax:** 954 987-8228
Web: www.heico.com

2013 Sales

	$ mil.	% of total
US	654.1	65
Other countries	354.7	35
Total	**1008.8**	**100**

PRODUCTS/OPERATIONS

2013 Sales

	$ mil.	% of total
Flight Support Group	665.2	66
Electronic Technologies Group	350.0	34
Adjustments	(6.4)	-
Total	**1008.8**	**100**

Selected Products

Flight Support Group

Cockpit/avionics parts
Electro-mechanical components
Engine parts
Fuselage/interior parts
Wing parts
Electronic Technologies Group
Aircraft power supplies and batteries
Circuit board shielding
Electro-optical infrared simulation and test equipment
Electro-optical laser products
High-voltage interconnect and cable assembly devices
Medical power supplies and power generators

COMPETITORS

AAR Corp.	Kellstrom Industries
ATI Ladish	LMI Aerospace
BBA Aviation	Pratt & Whitney
Barnes Group	Rolls-Royce
CIC International	SAFRAN
Doncasters	SIFCO
GE Aviation	TIMCO Aviation
Honeywell Aerospace	Triumph Group

HISTORICAL FINANCIALS
Company Type: Public

Income Statement
FYE: October 31

	REVENUE ($ mil.)	NET INCOME ($ mil.)	NET PROFIT MARGIN	EMPLOYEES
10/14	1,132.3	121.2	10.7%	3,500
10/13	1,008.7	102.4	10.2%	3,500
10/12	897.3	85.1	9.5%	3,100
10/11	764.8	72.8	9.5%	2,500
10/10	617.0	54.9	8.9%	2,300
Annual Growth	16.4%	21.9%	—	11.1%

2014 Year-End Financials

Debt ratio: 22.1%
Return on equity: 18.5%
Cash ($ mil.): 20
Current ratio: 2.83
Long-term debt ($ mil.): 328

No. of shares (mil.): 66
Dividends
  Yield: 0.8%
  Payout: 26.7%
Market value ($ mil.): 3,609

	STOCK PRICE ($) FY Close	P/E High/Low		PER SHARE ($) Earnings	Dividends	Book Value
10/14	54.24	35	26	1.80	0.47	10.51
10/13	53.58	45	25	1.53	2.27	9.14
10/12	38.63	47	26	1.28	0.11	9.33
10/11	57.02	57	37	1.09	0.09	8.05
10/10	49.78	65	41	0.83	0.06	7.28
Annual Growth	2.2%			— 21.4%	70.7%	9.6%

Hennessy Advisors Inc

EXECUTIVES

Chb-pres-ceo; Chief Information Officer, Neil J Hennessy
Exec V Pres-chief Compliance O, Daniel B Steadman
Vice President Marketing, Tania Kelley

LOCATIONS

HQ: Hennessy Advisors Inc
  7250 Redwood Blvd., Suite 200, Novato, CA 94945
Phone: 415 899-1555   **Fax:** 415 899-1559
Web: www.hennessyadvisors.com

HISTORICAL FINANCIALS
Company Type: Public

Income Statement
FYE: September 30

	REVENUE ($ mil.)	NET INCOME ($ mil.)	NET PROFIT MARGIN	EMPLOYEES
09/14	34.5	7.6	22.2%	19
09/13	24.3	4.8	19.8%	18
09/12	7.0	0.9	13.7%	11
09/11	7.6	1.2	15.9%	11
09/10	7.7	0.9	11.8%	11
Annual Growth	45.4%	70.2%	—	14.6%

2014 Year-End Financials

Debt ratio: 35.4%
Return on equity: 22.8%
Cash ($ mil.): 7
Current ratio: 1.64
Long-term debt ($ mil.): 22

No. of shares (mil.): 6
Dividends
  Yield: 0.7%
  Payout: 12.9%
Market value ($ mil.): 120

	STOCK PRICE ($) FY Close	P/E High/Low		PER SHARE ($) Earnings	Dividends	Book Value
09/14	19.88	14	9	1.30	0.15	6.22
09/13	7.65	9	3	0.83	0.13	5.05
09/12	2.85	19	12	0.17	0.12	4.38
09/11	3.00	17	11	0.21	0.17	4.33
09/10	2.35	22	14	0.16	0.09	4.29
Annual Growth	70.5%			— — 68.8%	13.9%	9.7%

Heritage Financial Group Inc.

Established in the 1950s as a credit union to serve its hometown Marine base HeritageBank of the South (HBOS) has remained always faithful to its local customers. The flagship subsidiary of Heritage Financial Group operates more than 25 branches that provide traditional deposit and loan products and services to individuals and small to midsized businesses in southwestern Georgia Florida and Alabama. Nonresidential commercial real estate loans make up nearly a third of the bank's loan portfolio. HBOS also operates 15 mortgage offices and five investment offices. In late 2014 Heritage Financial Group was acquired by Renasant in a merger agreement totaling $258 million.

Change In Company TypeIn late 2014 Renasant Corporation purchased Heritage Financial Group in an all stock merger deal that amounted to $258 million which significantly expanded Renasant's geographic reach into the Southeast region of the United States. Combined the two merged companies carried $7.5 billion in total assets $5.2 billion in gross loans and $6.1 billion in deposits with 171 banking insurance mortgage insurance wealth management and investment offices in Mississippi Alabama Tennessee Georgia and Florida. All told the deal made Renasant one of the largest community banks in the Southeast region of the United States. Financial Performance

In 2013 Heritage Financial Group reported net income of $11.3 million compared to $6.8 million in 2012. The improvement in operating results was primarily driven by growth in net interest in-

come (up 24%) and non-interest income (up 47%) coupled with a decline in provision for loan losses expense partially offset by an increase in non-interest expense. Total assets increased by $283.4 million or 26% to $1.381 billion in 2013 up from $1.1 billion in 2012.

Strategy

The community-oriented bank is expanding in its key markets of Georgia Florida and Alabama through acquisitions. To this end in March 2013 HBOS completed an FDIC-assisted whole-bank purchase of a bank based in LaGrange Georgia with $98 million in loans and $211.6 million in deposits which were primarily located in Alabama. In June 2012 the bank entered the Alabama market through the purchase of a single branch in Auburn with $10.9 million in loans and $18.7 million in deposits.

EXECUTIVES

President CEO and Director, O. Leonard (Len) Dorminey, age 61, $285,533 total compensation
SVP and CFO, T. Heath Fountain, age 39
CEO Atlanta and Director Mergers and Acquisitions, Brian D. Schmitt, age 53
Executive Vice President; Chief Banking Officer, David Durland
Assistant Vice President Secondary, Marla Millar
Senior Vice President, Mark Imes
Auditors: Mauldin&JenkinsLLC

LOCATIONS

HQ: Heritage Financial Group Inc.
  721 N. Westover Blvd., Albany, GA 31707
Phone: 229 420-0000
Web: www.eheritagebank.com

COMPETITORS

BB&T	Regions Financial
Bank of America	SunTrust
Citigroup	Synovus
First Horizon	

HISTORICAL FINANCIALS
Company Type: Public

Income Statement
FYE: December 31

	REVENUE ($ mil.)	NET INCOME ($ mil.)	NET PROFIT MARGIN	EMPLOYEES
12/13	84.0	11.3	13.5%	426
12/12	68.4	6.7	9.9%	321
12/11	56.9	3.8	6.7%	327
12/10	40.9	1.4	3.4%	217
12/09	31.1	(1.6)	—	194
Annual Growth	28.1%	—	—	21.7%

2013 Year-End Financials

Debt ratio: 12.2%
Return on equity: 9.2%
Cash ($ mil.): 38
Current ratio: 0.32
Long-term debt ($ mil.): 169

No. of shares (mil.): 7
Dividends
  Yield: —
  Payout: —
Market value ($ mil.): 151

	STOCK PRICE ($) FY Close	P/E High/Low		PER SHARE ($) Earnings	Dividends	Book Value
12/13	19.25	13	9	1.50	0.00	15.96
12/12	13.79	16	13	0.85	0.36	14.76
12/11	11.80	29	21	0.47	0.12	14.25
12/10	12.42	74	60	0.17	0.36	13.70
Annual Growth	15.7%			— —106.6%	—	5.2%

Hersha Hospitality Trust

Hersha Hospitality Trust's fortune is in hotels not chocolate. The self-advised real estate investment trust (REIT) invests in hotel properties primarily midscale upscale and extended stay properties in metropolitan markets. It owns or co-owns about 70 hotels containing more than 9600 rooms most of them in Boston New York and Washington DC as well as in Miami and Los Angeles. The properties are operated under such brand names as Marriott International Hilton Hotels Starwood Hotels and Hyatt. Hersha Hospitality Trust owns a minority stake in Hersha Hospitality Management which manages the REIT's properties. Starwood Capital Group owns the remainder of Hersha Hospitality Management

Hersha Hospitality Trust leases its wholly owned hotels to subsidiary 44 New England Management Company. In the past the company has provided on a limited basis financing for hotel property development loans though it stopped pursuing new investments during the economic downturn. It maintains first right of purchase or refusal on these newly developed properties. Hersha Hospitality doesn't expect to make any new property joint ventures development loans or land leases.

The hotel REIT sector along with Hersha is recovering from the economic downturn which drove down demand in 2008 and 2009. The lack of demand sent hotel occupancy rates and revenues down. By 2010 the economy began to improve and profits and revenues rebounded at Hersha. However the sector remained volatile. While revenues remained steady in 2011 the company reported a 25% drop in net income. The net loss in 2011 was attributed mainly to impairment charges recorded on its noncore properties.

Hersha Hospitality has repositioned itself to accommodate the unstable and fluid market. It raised capital and revamped its portfolio to focus on urban high-demand gateway markets such as New York and Washington DC. In 2010 and 2011 Hersha Hospitality acquired 12 properties (many at discount prices). The company also acquired its first hotels in Los Angeles and Miami.

Hersha also is disposing of properties in less-appealing markets. Towards that end the REIT sold a portfolio of 18 noncore properties to Starwood Capital Group for about $155 million in 2012. (It will use the proceeds to repay debt among other purposes.)

In addition to acquisitions in urban areas the REIT is focused on property renovations designed to boost occupancy rates and enhance hotel value. In 2011 the company undertook a $26 million renovation project at several of its hotels.

EXECUTIVES

President and COO, Neil H. Shah, age 40, $400,000 total compensation
President and COO, Jay H. Shah, age 45, $425,000 total compensation
VP Finance, Bennett Thomas
Vice President Of Group Marketing, Stephanie Esposito
Sales Vice President, Erik McDonald
Vice President Of Revenue Management, Kimberly Furlong

Vice President Information Technology, Michael Sokorai
Chairman, Hasu P. Shah, age 69
Auditors: KPMGLLP

LOCATIONS

HQ: Hersha Hospitality Trust
44 Hersha Drive, Harrisburg, PA 17102
Phone: 717 236-4400 **Fax:** 717 774-7383
Web: www.hersha.com

PRODUCTS/OPERATIONS

2011 Sales

	$ mil.	% of total
Hotel operating revenues	282.7	99
Interest from development loans	3.4	1
Other	0.3	-
Total	**286.4**	**100**

COMPETITORS

Ashford Hospitality Trust	Innkeepers USA
DiamondRock Hospitality	LaSalle Hotel Properties
FelCor	Shaner Hotel Group
Hospitality Properties Trust	Strategic Hotels
Host Hotels & Resorts	Sunstone Hotel Investors
	Supertel Hospitality

HISTORICAL FINANCIALS

Company Type: Public

Income Statement

FYE: December 31

	REVENUE ($ mil.)	NET INCOME ($ mil.)	NET PROFIT MARGIN	EMPLOYEES
12/13	338.4	49.9	14.8%	49
12/12	358.2	22.2	6.2%	46
12/11	286.4	(26.9)	—	36
12/10	282.7	(17.2)	—	28
12/09	220.4	(58.4)	—	24
Annual Growth	**11.3%**	**—**		**19.5%**

2013 Year-End Financials

Debt ratio: 44.2%	No. of shares (mil.): 202
Return on equity: 5.9%	Dividends
Cash ($ mil.): 36	Yield: 4.3%
Current ratio: 0.89	Payout: 1,200.0%
Long-term debt ($ mil.): 773	Market value ($ mil.): 1,129

	STOCK PRICE ($) FY Close	P/E High/Low	Earnings	PER SHARE ($) Dividends	Book Value
12/13	5.57	39 31	0.16	0.24	4.13
12/12	5.00	145 107	0.04	0.24	4.18
12/11	4.88	— —	(0.21)	0.23	4.30
12/10	6.60	— —	(0.16)	0.20	4.04
12/09	3.14	— —	(1.08)	0.33	5.24
Annual Growth	**15.4%**	— —	—	**(7.7%)**	**(5.8%)**

Hexcel Corp.

The first footprints on the moon didn't come from Neil Armstrong but from Hexcel a maker of composite materials. Back then Hexcel made the footpads on the Apollo 11 lunar module; today the company makes advanced structural materials used in everything from aircraft components to wind turbine blades. Its composite materials include structural adhesives and honeycomb panels used in products like satellites auto parts golf clubs and even window blinds. Commercial aerospace companies account for nearly 60% of Hexcel's sales; governmental space and defense sales and industrial sales account for the rest. Markets for Hexcel industrial products include wind energy recreational equipment and transportation.

Geographic Reach

Hexcel operates domestic manufacturing facilities in Alabama Arizona Colorado Pennsylvania Texas Washington. International locations reside in Belgium China France Germany Spain and the UK. It also holds an interest in a manufacturing joint venture in Malaysia that makes composite structures for the company's Commercial Aerospace segment.

The US represents 50% of its total sales while France and Spain account for 18% and 10% respectively.

Operations

The company's advanced composites are divided into two main segments: Composite Materials (78% of total sales) and Engineered Products (22%). Composite Materials include carbon fiber resins specialty reinforcements prepegs (resins impregnated with fibers) and other fiber-reinforced materials and honeycomb core products.

Engineered Products include lightweight high-strength composite structures molded components and specialty machined honeycomb products. The end markets for Hexcel's products make up its three main sales segments: Commercial Aerospace (60% of total sales) Space and Defense (23%) and Industrial (17%).

Sales and Marketing

Hexcel gets about 30% of its total sales from contracts from Boeing and related contractors (25% for its Commercial Aerospace segment and 5% for its Space and Defense segment). Airbus including its subcontractors account for another quarter of the company's total sales. The Space and Defense segment has worked on a number of military projects including Blackhawk helicopters the F/A-18 Hornet the F-35 Joint Strike Fighter and the Airbus A400M military transport.

Financial Performance

Hexcel has enjoyed three straight years of growth. From 2011 to 2012 its net revenues increased by 13% to reach $1.58 billion and its profits surged by 21% to reach $164 million. Both of these totals were record highs for the company.

The growth was due to higher sales and volumes in all its segments but especially in its Commercial Aerospace unit. This unit was helped by new aircraft programs and increased build rates. In 2012 sales for Airbus and Boeing programs increased by 16%. Total sales for Space and Defense surged by 12% while Industrial increased by 11%. Within the Industrial segment wind energy sales jumped by 30% for 2012.

Hexcel attributes the 2012 profit growth to the strong performance of its segments coupled with a tight control on costs over the last few years.

Strategy

Hexcel has cut down on spending but it continues to add production capacity in key areas and to develop new products. It seeks new opportunities for both its Composite Materials and Engineered Products segments to compensate for weakened demand from defense markets. Among trends it hopes to capitalize on is the use by helicopter manufacturers of new rotor blades based on composite materials for better lift and durability. Hexcel also focuses on growth markets where it believes it can achieve a competitive advantage over the long term.

The company's strategy has succeeded with demand for Hexcel composites —used to build both Airbus and Boeing aircraft —soaring. Production rates for the super jumbo A380 of Airbus and the ramp up of Boeing's new B787 and B747-8 jets have helped grow Hexcel's sales each year for the last four years. The company's involvement in major product development with both Boeing and Airbus have driven its sales increases. Hexcel has been a major parts supplier for Boeing's 787 Dreamliner and 747-8 Series as well as the Airbus A360 and A380 —all aircraft that have a large amount of advanced composite parts.

HISTORY

Hexcel was founded in 1946 and incorporated in California in 1948. The company's businesses formerly included polymer technology for medical devices chemicals electromagnetic materials and a European resins unit. These were all sold as part of Hexcel's restructuring following Chapter 11 bankruptcy in 1993.

In 1996 Hexcel purchased the composite divisions of specialty chemicals maker Hercules and Swiss drugmaker Ciba-Geigy; it then combined the operations with similar businesses of Arizona's Fiberite in 1997 thus positioning itself for leadership in the manufacture of preimpregnated reinforcing materials and honeycomb products used to make aircraft wings flaps and elevators.

In 1998 Hexcel bought Clark-Schwebel's glass fiber business to broaden its printed circuit board offerings to the electronics and telecommunications industries and reduce its reliance on the aerospace industry. To establish a presence in Asia the company formed China-based BHA Aero Composite Parts a joint venture with Boeing and Aviation Industries of China and Asian Composite Manufacturing a Malaysian joint venture with Boeing Sime Darby Berhad and Malaysia Helicopter Services.

The US Department of Justice began an antitrust investigation of Hexcel in 1999 as the market leader in the production and sale of carbon fiber and preimpregnated materials (ongoing in 2002). Hexcel sold its aircraft interiors unit to Britax International for $117 million in 2000. The same year Ciba Specialty Chemicals sold the bulk of its 49% stake in Hexcel to a Goldman Sachs investor group.

In another effort to decrease its reliance on the aerospace market in 2001 the company announced production of an energy-absorbing honeycomb made of spun-bond nylon and polyester for the automotive market. Responding to the downturn in the aerospace market after September 11 Hexcel began a restructuring plan that cut fixed overhead costs capital spending and about 25% of its workforce.

In 2008 investment group OSS Capital initiated a proxy fight to place three new independent directors on Hexcel's Board. OSS said that it believed Hexcel's management hadn't done enough to improve its margins and lagged behind competitors like Cytec and Toray Industries. In the end the company-backed slate of directors won out.

EXECUTIVES

Chairman and CEO, David E. Berges, age 65, $950,000 total compensation
Vice President And General Manager, Mike Canario
President, Nick L. Stanage, age 56, $545,700 total compensation

SVP and CRO, Wayne C. Pensky, age 59, $390,958 total compensation
Vice President Of Tax, Mark Seymour
Vice President Media Relations, Rachel Woolerton
Vice President Gen Mgr, Thierry Merlot
Vice President Technology, Alex Koletsos
Chairman and CEO, David E. Berges, age 65
Senior Treasury Analyst, Michele Mazabras
Auditors: PricewaterhouseCoopersLLP

LOCATIONS

HQ: Hexcel Corp.
Two Stamford Plaza, 281 Tresser Boulevard, Stamford, CT 06901-3238
Phone: 203 969-0666
Web: www.hexcel.com

2012 Sales

	$ mil.	% of total
US	801.4	51
France	302.9	18
Spain	150.6	10
UK	114.7	7
Austria	105.0	7
Other	103.6	7
Total	**1578.2**	**100**

PRODUCTS/OPERATIONS

2012 Sales

	$ mil.	% of total
Composite Materials	1230.9	78
Engineered Products	347.3	22
Total	**1578.2**	**100**

2012 Sales

	% of total
Commercial Aerospace	60
Space & Defense	23
Industrial	17
Total	**100**

Selected Products

Carbon fibers
Composite structures
Honeycomb
Honeycomb composite panels
Honeycomb parts
Preimpregnated materials (prepegs)
Structural adhesives

COMPETITORS

Alcoa	PRC-DeSoto
BP	Park Electrochemical
Baltek	SGL CARBON
Cytec	Teijin
Dow Corning	Toho Tenax
Honeywell	Toray Industries
International	Zoltek

HISTORICAL FINANCIALS

Company Type: Public

Income Statement

FYE: December 31

	REVENUE ($ mil.)	NET INCOME ($ mil.)	NET PROFIT MARGIN	EMPLOYEES
12/13	1,678.2	187.9	11.2%	5,274
12/12	1,578.2	164.3	10.4%	4,973
12/11	1,392.4	135.5	9.7%	4,508
12/10	1,173.6	77.4	6.6%	4,043
12/09	1,108.3	56.3	5.1%	3,734
Annual Growth	**10.9%**	**35.2%**	**—**	**9.0%**

2013 Year-End Financials

Debt ratio: 16.0%
Return on equity: 17.4%
Cash ($ mil.): 65
Current ratio: 2.44
Long-term debt ($ mil.): 292
No. of shares (mil.): 98
Dividends
Yield: —
Payout: —
Market value ($ mil.): 4,420

	STOCK PRICE ($) FY Close	P/E High/Low	PER SHARE ($) Earnings	Dividends	Book Value
12/13	44.69	24 14	1.84	0.00	11.73
12/12	26.96	17 14	1.61	0.00	9.95
12/11	24.21	19 13	1.35	0.00	8.12
12/10	18.09	24 13	0.77	0.00	6.78
12/09	12.98	23 8	0.57	0.00	5.96
Annual Growth	**36.2%**		**34.0%**	**—**	**18.5%**

HFF Inc

Don't huff and puff —HFF will help you finance that high-rise. The company's Holliday Fenoglio Fowler subsidiary is a large commercial real estate capital intermediary. The firm provides capital markets services including structured financing commercial loan servicing investment sales loan sales and debt placement. Real estate investment banking subsidiary HFF Securities provides advisory services seeks private and joint venture equity capital places private listings and provides institutional marketing for property investments. Unlike most commercial property brokerage firms HFF does not provide leasing or property management services. The company operates about 20 offices throughout the US.

Geographic Reach

The company operates more than 20 offices throughout the US. HFF offers capital markets services throughout Canada Mexico Puerto Rico and the US.

Financial Performance

The company has seen its revenues rebound after they plummeted during the global financial downturn when frozen credit markets reduced liquidity and severely impacted commercial real estate activity. From 2011 to 2012 the firm's revenues jumped 12% from $255 million to $285 million. This was driven by an 11% surge in capital markets services revenue as a result of production volumes and related revenues in a majority of its capital markets services platforms. The company also enjoyed an 85% increase in interest on mortgage notes due to a higher average loan value and a higher number of loans originated.

Strategy

The company continues to seek to improve its market share by penetrating national and regional markets. The company's biggest capital services market is Texas accounting for about 20% of total revenues. Other key markets include Florida Massachusetts and the DC area. HFF hopes to grow by opening additional offices in key US markets and it is also looking at expanding in foreign markets.

EXECUTIVES

Executive Managing Director Washington D.C., Stephen C. Conley
Executive Managing Director, Gerard Sansosti
Vice Chairman, Mark D. Gibson, age 55

Vice Chairman, John P. Fowler, age 68
Auditors: Ernst&YoungLLP

LOCATIONS

HQ: HFF Inc
One Oxford Centre, 301 Grant Street, Suite 600,
Pittsburgh, PA 15219
Phone: 412 281-8714
Web: www.hfflp.com

PRODUCTS/OPERATIONS

2012 Sales

	$ mil.	% of total
Capital markets services	276.9	97
Interest on mortgage notes receivable	6.0	2
Other	2.1	1
Total	**285.0**	**100**

COMPETITORS

Arbor Commercial	Cushman & Wakefield
BGC Partners	Eastdil Secured
Boston Capital	Jones Lang LaSalle
CBRE Group	NorthMarq Capital
Capmark	Trammell Crow Company

HISTORICAL FINANCIALS

Company Type: Public

Income Statement

FYE: December 31

	REVENUE ($ mil.)	NET INCOME ($ mil.)	NET PROFIT MARGIN	EMPLOYEES
12/13	355.6	51.4	14.5%	637
12/12	284.9	43.8	15.4%	574
12/11	254.6	40.0	15.7%	498
12/10	139.9	10.8	7.8%	427
12/09	77.4	(0.7)	—	376
Annual Growth	46.4%	—	—	14.1%

2013 Year-End Financials

Debt ratio: 19.2%	No. of shares (mil.): 37
Return on equity: 34.6%	Dividends
Cash ($ mil.): 201	Yield: —
Current ratio: 1.79	Payout: —
Long-term debt ($ mil.): 0	Market value ($ mil.): 1,000

	STOCK PRICE ($) FY Close	P/E High/Low		PER SHARE ($) Earnings	Dividends	Book Value
12/13	26.85	20	11	1.36	0.00	4.71
12/12	14.90	14	9	1.18	1.52	3.27
12/11	10.33	15	7	1.11	0.00	3.52
12/10	9.66	25	15	0.40	0.00	2.45
12/09	6.25	—	—	(0.05)	0.00	2.36
Annual Growth	44.0%	—	—	—	—	18.9%

Higher One Holdings Inc.

The higher ambition at Higher One Holdings is to facilitate higher education payments. The company provides payment processing and disbursement services to colleges and universities and their students. Designed to make financial transactions in higher education settings more efficient the company's suite of offerings includes OneDisburse which more than 500 US schools use to electronically distribute financial aid and other funds to students. For students it offers the OneAccount banking service a deposit account and debit card. The company also provides online billing and payment services to make tuition payments convenient. Higher One Holdings went public in June 2010 after several years of steady growth.

The company raised some $171 million in the offering which it used to pay down debts and other obligations. By taking itself public Higher One expects to further expand its market position as a service provider in the higher education industry targeting schools whose in-house disbursement and payment systems may be outdated or inefficient. It has also been pursuing cross-selling opportunities presented by its 2009 acquisition of CASHNet a provider of cashiering and payment services for higher education.

Since its 2000 inception the company has experienced overall growth in revenue cash flow and net income. The majority of its revenues comes from ATM interchange and other service fees charged through its OneAccount service for students. Other revenues are generated from convenience fees charged to parents and students who make online tuition payments and annual subscription fees charged to schools. Recent federal legislation has passed limiting bank overdraft and related fees which translates to lower fee-per-account revenues. However Higher One has continued to land new schools expanding the number of accounts it services so those revenues are still growing.

Higher One sells itself as a "one-stop shop" of technology and payment services to keep a leg up on such competitors as Nelnet Sallie Mae and TouchNet which offer similar payment software and services. In addition to serving student banking needs it addresses the needs of its educational institution clients by helping them to streamline administrative processes reduce paper and other expenses and remain compliant with federal regulations governing financial aid transactions. Higher One's strategic attention to customer service and brand development has helped it grow a diverse base of clients.

The company partners with banks to provide depository and other services for its OneAccounts. Previously it worked solely with The Bancorp Bank but in 2012 Higher One established new agreements with savings bank Urban Trust Bank and Wright Express Financial Services (an industrial banking subsidiary of Wright Express Corporation) to provide the same functions. The company plans to secure more bank partners in its shift away from using a single provider.

Private equity firm Lightyear Capital invested in Higher One in 2008 and helped take the company public. It owns 26% of the company and has board representation through director Stewart Gross.

EXECUTIVES

Chief Executive Officer; Director, Mark Volchek, age 37, $275,000 total compensation
COO and Director, Miles Lasater, age 37, $275,000 total compensation
Vice President Marketing, Sean Glass, age 36
Vice President General Counsel, Thomas Kavanaugh
Vice President Atm Operations, Kristen Krop
Vice President Software Development, Sean Townsend
Senior Vice President Client Operations, Andrew Crawford
Vice President, Michele Kirkby
Vice President Software Engineering, Coz Wilson
Vice President Campus Marketing, Edward Worrilow
COO and Director, Miles Lasater, age 37
Board Member, Paul A Biddelman, age 69
Board Member, Shamez Kanji
Auditors: PricewaterhouseCoopersLLP

LOCATIONS

HQ: Higher One Holdings Inc.
115 Munson Street, New Haven, CT 06511
Phone: 203 776-7776
Web: www.higherone.com

PRODUCTS/OPERATIONS

2011 Sales

	$ mil.	% of total
Account revenue	142.6	79
Payment transaction revenue	18.7	10
Higher education institution revenue	16.6	9
Other	3.1	2
Total	**181.0**	**100**

COMPETITORS

American Student Assistance	Mohela
Bank of America	Nelnet
CampusLogic	PNC Financial
First Marblehead	Sallie Mae
Great Lakes Higher Education	U.S. Bancorp
	Wells Fargo

HISTORICAL FINANCIALS

Company Type: Public

Income Statement

FYE: December 31

	REVENUE ($ mil.)	NET INCOME ($ mil.)	NET PROFIT MARGIN	EMPLOYEES
12/13	211.1	14.1	6.7%	1,000
12/12	197.7	36.8	18.6%	880
12/11	176.3	31.8	18.1%	700
12/10	144.9	25.0	17.3%	450
12/09	75.5	14.2	18.8%	380
Annual Growth	29.3%	(0.2%)	—	27.4%

2013 Year-End Financials

Debt ratio: 38.3%	No. of shares (mil.): 47
Return on equity: 21.6%	Dividends
Cash ($ mil.): 6	Yield: —
Current ratio: 0.69	Payout: —
Long-term debt ($ mil.): 89	Market value ($ mil.): 460

	STOCK PRICE ($) FY Close	P/E High/Low		PER SHARE ($) Earnings	Dividends	Book Value
12/13	9.76	40	23	0.29	0.00	1.55
12/12	10.54	27	13	0.65	0.00	1.24
12/11	18.44	36	24	0.54	0.00	2.18
12/10	20.23	46	24	0.44	0.00	1.49
Annual Growth	(21.6%)	—	—	(13.0%)	—	1.4%

Hillenbrand Inc

Hillenbrand knows a thing or two about life and death. Through its largest subsidiary BatesvilleHillenbrand is a top supplier to the death care industry providing nearly half the caskets used in the US. Batesville makes a variety of caskets in materials ranging from wood to stainless steel. Increasingly it also produces urns and other cremation products to satisfy increasing demand for lower-cost cremation. The company's Process Equipment Group (PEG) designs and makes equipment and systems used by industrial manufacturers. The PEG includes subsidiaries K-Tron Rotex and Coperion and was formed by a trio of acquisitions made in the past several years. Hillenbrand was spun off from Hillenbrand Industries.

Geographic Reach

Historically a US-centric business Hillenbrand has worked to lessen its reliance on US customers by extending its reach abroad. To this end the company has concentrated on developing its presence in Switzerland and Canada. In fiscal 2012 (ended September) the US accounted for 83% of Hillenbrand's sales (versus 93% in 2009) while Switzerland and Canada accounted for 8% and 5% respectively. Batesville makes most of its caskets in the US but also operates production facilities in Mexico.

Operations

Hillenbrand has two primary businesses. The largest Batesville accounting for about 60% of Hillenbrand's sales is an established company founded in 1884 that sells its burial products through a direct sales force to more than 12000 licensed funeral homes in the US Puerto Rico Canada Mexico the UK and Australia. Batesville manufactures both metal and solid and veneer hardwood caskets cremation urns and burial vaults. It also makes caskets suitable for "green" burials.

The company's Process Equipment Group (PEG) was formed by the purchases of Coperion Rotex and K-Tron. It accounts for about 40% of sales. New Jersey-based K-Tron produces feeders crushers conveying systems and other equipment used in the industrial manufacturing processes. Under the Rotex brand the PEG designs makes sells and services dry material separation machines that sort particles based on their size. Rotex brand equipment is used in a variety of industries including frac sand potash urea phosphates plastics and food processing.

Sales and Marketing

Batesville branded burial and cremation caskets and other funeral supplies are marketed by a direct sales force to licensed funeral professionals. The PEG also sells its material handling equipment through independent sales representatives.

Financial Performance

Hillenbrand's sales topped $983 million in fiscal 2012 (ended September) an increase of 11% versus the prior year. Net income declined by 1% over the same period. Driving the double-digit increase was the PEG which posted a 53% increase in annual sales due primarily to the Rotex acquisition in 2011. Batesville's sales declined 5% over the same period. 2012 marked the third year of increasing sales for the company. The small decline in net income was attributed to increased operating expenses and the amortization expense related to the Rotex purchase.

Strategy

Hillenbrand has moved to diversify its revenue stream in recent years as consumer preferences are shifting and as the total number of deaths in North America where most of Batesville's products are sold has been flat. More consumers are choosing cremation and other alternatives to traditional burials. Cremations as a percentage of total deaths now represent more than one-third in the US and more than one-half in Canada.

Mergers and Acquisitions

Aiming to build a "family of companies" revolving around manufacturing distribution and customer service Hillenbrand acquired Stuttgart Germany-based Coperion Capital GmbH for $545 million in December 2012. The purchase expanded the company's global footprint bolstered its PEG and leveraged replacement parts and service capabilities. It's anticipated that the group with Coperion under its umbrella will generate more than $1 billion in revenue and represent two-thirds of Hillenbrand's overall sales in fiscal 2013.

Previously the firm expanded its manufacturing equipment division through the purchase of ROTEX Global from Windjammer Capital Investors for $240 million in cash in September 2011. ROTEX makes machines (along with replacement parts and accessories) that separate dry materials for various industrial applications a complementary addition to Hillenbrand's existing equipment line. Although its products are sold throughout the US and abroad ROTEX boasts a significant customer base in Europe and Asia — two regions in which Hillenbrand has been looking to strengthen its presence.

In 2010 the company acquired New Jersey-based K-Tron International which produces feeders crushers conveying systems and other equipment used in the industrial manufacturing processes. The $435-million purchase gave Hillenbrand access to a much more diverse customer base that comprises chemical food pharmaceutical and plastics companies.

EXECUTIVES

President Coperion K-Tron, Kevin C. Bowen, age 63
President Chief Executive Officer and Director, Joseph A. (Joe) Raver, age 49, $450,697 total compensation
Vice President Enterprise Information Systems, Darryl M. Maslar
Senior Vice President and Chief Financial Officer, Cynthia L. (Cindy) Lucchese, age 54, $348,205 total compensation
President Rotex, Anthony S. Casablanca
Senior Vice President President Batesville, Kimberly K. Ryan
President Coperion, Thomas Kehl
President TerraSource Global, Mark L. Kohler
Sr V Pres-chief Admin Officer, Paul D Wilson
Member Board Of Directors, William J Cernugel
Chairperson, F. Joseph (Joe) Loughrey, age 64
President Chief Executive Officer and Director, Joseph A. (Joe) Raver, age 49
Auditors: PricewaterhouseCoopersLLP

LOCATIONS

HQ: Hillenbrand Inc
One Batesville Boulevard, Batesville, IN 47006
Phone: 812 934-7500
Web: www.hillenbrand.com

2012 Sales

	$ mil.	% of total
US	817.5	83
Switzerland	76.6	8
Canada	46.0	5
Other foreign business units	43.1	4
Total	**983.2**	**100**

PRODUCTS/OPERATIONS

2012 Sales

	$ mil.	% of total
Batesville caskets	606.8	62
Other	376.4	38
Total	**983.2**	**100**

Selected Subsidiaries

Batesville (Batesville Indiana)
Coperion (Germany)
K-Tron International (Pitman New Jersey)
Rotex Global (Cincinnati Ohio)

COMPETITORS

Aurora Casket	Key Technology
Badger Meter	Matthews International
Costco Wholesale	Wal-Mart
Goliath Casket	Wilbert
Heat and Control	York Group

HISTORICAL FINANCIALS

Company Type: Public

Income Statement

FYE: September 30

	REVENUE ($ mil.)	NET INCOME ($ mil.)	NET PROFIT MARGIN	EMPLOYEES
09/14	1,667.2	109.7	6.6%	5,900
09/13	1,553.4	63.4	4.1%	6,000
09/12	983.2	104.8	10.7%	3,900
09/11	883.4	106.1	12.0%	4,200
09/10	749.2	92.3	12.3%	3,850
Annual Growth	**22.1%**	**4.4%**	**—**	**11.3%**

2014 Year-End Financials

Debt ratio: 29.1%	No. of shares (mil.): 62
Return on equity: 19.0%	Dividends
Cash ($ mil.): 58	Yield: 2.5%
Current ratio: 1.30	Payout: 46.2%
Long-term debt ($ mil.): 543	Market value ($ mil.): 1,943

	STOCK PRICE ($) FY Close	P/E High/Low	PER SHARE ($) Earnings	Dividends	Book Value
09/14	30.89	19 15	1.72	0.79	9.27
09/13	27.37	28 18	1.01	0.78	9.03
09/12	18.19	14 10	1.68	0.77	8.09
09/11	18.40	14 10	1.71	0.76	7.09
09/10	21.51	17 12	1.49	0.75	5.97
Annual Growth	**9.5%**	**— —**	**3.7%**	**1.3%**	**11.6%**

Hilltop Holdings, Inc.

Hilltop Holdings sits on top of a mound of money-related businesses. The company's PlainsCapital subsidiary operates more than 80 branches in Texas and an offshore branch in the Caymans offers residential mortgages through 200 PrimeLending offices in 40-plus and provides public finance advisory services through First Southwest. Subsidiary National Lloyds Corporation (NLC) offers fire and homeowners' coverage for low-value and manufactured homes and insurance through independent agents in Texas and more than 25 other (mostly) southern states. NLC operates as National Lloyds Insurance and American Summit Insurance. Hilltop which acquired Plains

Capital in 2012 has about $9 billion in assets under management.

Operations

The purchase of PlainsCapital in a transaction valued at about $700 million moved Hilltop from insurance as its primary revenue generator to banking. It now operates in banking mortgage origination insurance and financial advisory services.

The PlainsCapital entities serve niche markets such as midsized businesses investors and high-net worth individuals. NLC's operating subsidiaries primarily write the kind of lower-cost homeowners' policies that only pay out cash value instead of replacement costs and most of its policies exclude coverage for water or mold damage. Texas accounts for over 70% of the company's premiums. While personal lines account for more than 90% of its premiums the company does write a small amount of commercial insurance covering builders' risk sports liability and transportation insurance which is known as "inland marine" policies.

Geographic Reach

PlainsCapital's banking operations are in Texas and its mortgages are secured by property in Texas mostly in or around major cities. NLC is licensed in 42 states and sells in 27 but primarily does business in Texas Oklahoma Arizona Tennessee Georgia and Louisiana with Texas accounting for more than 60% of sales. PrimeLending concentrates on nine states and does most of its business in Texas California and North Carolina.

Financial Performance

The PlainsCapital acquisition did what it was meant to do - gave the company a shot in the arm. For 2013 revenue rose nearly 350% to $1.3 billion. Net loss in 2012 became a net income of $125 million and cash from operations grew 71%.

Strategy

After the 2012 purchase of PlainsCapital Hilltop began to focus on being a Texas-based bank and financial services company. It plans to continue expanding its empire through organic growth and acquisitions. To that end in 2013 PlainsCapital purchased First National Bank a Texas-based company and its 51 branches. The same year Hilltop subsidiary NLASCO changed its name to National Lloyds Corporation or NLC as part of an overall re-branding effort.

Mergers and Acquisitions

In 2013 the company purchased Texas-based First National Bank with about 50 branches mostly in South Texas. It followed that up in early 2015 with the acquisition of Dallas-based securities brokerage SWS Group. SWS and its Southwest Securities unit continue to operate as subsidiaries of Hilltop.

Company Background

The company began life as Affordable Residential Communities (ARC) and spent its early days as a real estate investment trust (REIT). It went public in 2004 dropped its REIT status in 2006 and built up its collection of manufactured housing communities through acquisitions.

After several years of losses in the housing business the company chose to transition into another industry. It acquired NLASCO a niche provider of fire and homeowners insurance for manufactured homes and other low-value properties at the start of 2007. The company then renamed itself Hilltop Holdings.

EXECUTIVES

President CEO and Director, Jeremy B. Ford, age 39, $303,077 total compensation

Senior Vice President - Finance; Chief Operating fficer at NLASCO; Inc., Darren Parmenter, age 51, $275,000 total compensation
Board Member, William Hill
Chairman, Gerald J. Ford, age 70
Board Member, Rhodes Bobbitt
Board Member, Robert Nichol
Board Member, Kenneth D Russell
Board Member, Carl B Webb
Board Member, Charles R Cummings
Board Member, Joris W Brinkerhoff
Board Member, Markham J Green
Board Member, Clifton C Robinson
Auditors: PricewaterhouseCoopersLLP

LOCATIONS

HQ: Hilltop Holdings, Inc.
200 Crescent Court, Suite 1330, Dallas, TX 75201
Phone: 214 855-2177
Web: www.hilltop-holdings.com

PRODUCTS/OPERATIONS

2013 Sales

	% of total
Mortgage Origination	43
Banking	32
Insurance	15
Financial Advisory	10
Total	**100**

COMPETITORS

American Modern Insurance	International Bancshares
Bank of America	JPMorgan Chase
Comerica	Morgan Keegan
Compass Bancshares	Raymond James
Costco Wholesale	Financial
Cullen/Frost Bankers	Republic Group
Fannie Mae	Texas Capital
Foremost Insurance	Bancshares
Freddie Mac	Travelers Companies
ING	Wells Fargo

HISTORICAL FINANCIALS

Company Type: Public

Income Statement

FYE: December 31

	REVENUE ($ mil.)	NET INCOME ($ mil.)	NET PROFIT MARGIN	EMPLOYEES
12/13	1,179.1	125.3	10.6%	4,550
12/12	263.2	(5.5)	—	3,950
12/11	152.1	(6.5)	—	135
12/10	131.7	(0.5)	—	133
12/09	128.8	(2.1)	—	134
Annual Growth	**73.9%**	—	—	**141.4%**

2013 Year-End Financials

Debt ratio: 2.4%
Return on equity: 10.2%
Cash ($ mil.): 746
Current ratio: 0.12
Long-term debt ($ mil.): 123

No. of shares (mil.): 90
Dividends
Yield: —
Payout: —
Market value ($ mil.): 2,086

	STOCK PRICE ($) FY Close	P/E High/Low		Earnings	Dividends	Book Value
12/13	23.13	17	9	1.40	0.00	14.54
12/12	13.54	—	—	(0.10)	0.00	13.71
12/11	8.45	—	—	(0.12)	0.00	11.60
12/10	9.92	—	—	(0.24)	0.00	11.56
12/09	11.64	—	—	(0.22)	0.00	13.88
Annual Growth	**18.7%**			—	—	**1.2%**

HMS Holdings Corp

HMS Holdings makes sure health benefits providers are paying only as much as they have to. Through its Health Management Systems subsidiary the company specializes in helping providers determine participant eligibility coordinate benefits and identify and recover claims that were paid in error or should have been paid by another party. It serves state Medicaid agencies and Children's Health Insurance Programs in some 40 states as well as federal agencies including Centers for Medicare & Medicaid Services and Veterans Health Administration. The company also provides services to commercial insurers employer groups and pharmacy benefits managers.

Sales and Marketing

HMS Holdings largest customer is the Centers for Medicare & Medicaid Services (CMS) which accounts for about 22% of its annual revenue.

Financial Performance

HMS's revenue has been trending upward due in part to acquisitive and organic growth measures that have widened its customer base and its service offerings. Indeed revenue has grown by 166% over the last five years to $491.8 million in 2013. In the latest annual comparison the rate of increase slowed to about 4%. Growth was primarily due to the addition of new clients and doing more business with existing ones.

Net income declined 21% in 2013 versus 2012 to $40 million on higher compensation expenses.

Strategy

HMS regularly seeks to add new government and private clients to its customer base as well as to provide a wider breadth of services to existing clients. Towards that end the company has added new service offerings to its lineup over the years partly through acquisitions of niche providers in areas such as dependent eligibility audits and employer sponsored benefits.

HMS has benefited in recent years from US government agencies placing increasing pressure on medical providers to cut health care costs and drive out process inefficiencies. It first received a boost from federal mandates under the 2006 Deficit Reduction Act and then again with the Patient Protection and Affordable Care Act in 2010.

Mergers and Acquisitions

In December 2012 HMS Holdings acquired MedRecovery Management LLC a provider of Workers' Compensation recovery services for commercial health plans for $11.7 million. In late 2011 it purchased HealthDataInsights for some $400 million to expand its recovery audit contractor services for government and commercial health plans. The previous year the company built up its employer-sponsored benefits division with the 2010 acquisition of Chapman Kelly which provides dependent eligibility audits and claims audits to large self-insured employers and expanded its fraud detection services through the purchase of Allied Management Group's Special Investigation Unit.

EXECUTIVES

President CEO and Director, William C. (Bill) Lucia, age 56, $650,000 total compensation
EVP CFO and Treasurer, Jeffrey S. (Jeff) Sherman, age 48
Chief Security Officer, Scott Pettigrew
EVP General Counsel and Corporate Secretary, Gene DeFelice
EVP and Chief Information Officer, Cynthia Nustad

EVP Operations, Semone Wagner, $337,500 total compensation

Division President Commercial Solutions, Douglas M. (Doug) Williams

Division President Government Solutions and Corporate Strategy, Joel Portice

Division President Commercial Solutions, Doug Williams

Vice President Information Technology, Ramin Rastin

Chairman, Robert M. Holster, age 68

President CEO and Director, William C. (Bill) Lucia, age 56

EVP CFO and Treasurer, Jeffrey S. (Jeff) Sherman, age 48

EVP General Counsel and Corporate Secretary, Gene DeFelice

Auditors: KPMGLLP

LOCATIONS

HQ: HMS Holdings Corp
5615 High Point Drive, Irving, TX 75038
Phone: 214 453-3000
Web: www.hms.com

PRODUCTS/OPERATIONS

Selected Services

Coordination of Benefits
Customer Service Operations
Eligibility and Enrollment
Healthstone Data Analytics
Pharmacy Services
Program Integrity

COMPETITORS

Accretive Health	MAXIMUS
ActiveHealth	Magellan Medicaid
Management	Administration
Allscripts	McKesson
Argus	MedAssets
Catamaran	OptumnInsight
CorVel	PRGX
Emdeon	Performant
Expert Global	Quality Systems
Solutions	Verisk Health
HP Enterprise Services	athenahealth

HISTORICAL FINANCIALS

Company Type: Public

Income Statement

FYE: December 31

	REVENUE ($ mil.)	NET INCOME ($ mil.)	NET PROFIT MARGIN	EMPLOYEES
12/13	491.7	40.0	8.1%	2,657
12/12	473.7	50.5	10.7%	2,702
12/11	363.8	47.7	13.1%	2,249
12/10	302.8	40.0	13.2%	1,736
12/09	229.2	30.0	13.1%	1,306
Annual Growth	21.0%	7.4%	—	19.4%

2013 Year-End Financials

Debt ratio: 26.5%	No. of shares (mil.): 87
Return on equity: 8.2%	Dividends
Cash ($ mil.): 93	Yield: —
Current ratio: 3.31	Payout: —
Long-term debt ($ mil.): 232	Market value ($ mil.): 1,982

	STOCK PRICE ($) FY Close	P/E High/Low		PER SHARE ($) Earnings	Dividends	Book Value
12/13	22.70	68	41	0.45	0.00	5.76
12/12	25.92	62	35	0.57	0.00	5.32
12/11	31.98	150	40	0.55	0.00	4.57
12/10	64.77	136	89	0.47	0.00	3.69
12/09	48.69	130	76	0.36	0.00	2.96
Annual Growth	(17.4%)	—	—	5.5%	—	18.1%

Holly Energy Partners LP

Holly Energy Partners is having a jolly good time piping petroleum products and crude oil from refineries. It operates petroleum product and crude gathering pipelines (in New Mexico Oklahoma Texas and Utah) distribution terminals (in Arizona Idaho New Mexico Oklahoma Texas Utah and Washington) and refinery tankage in New Mexico and Utah. It operates 1330 miles of refined petroleum pipelines (340 miles leased) 960 miles of crude oil trunk lines 10 refined product terminals one jet fuel terminal and two truck-loading facilities. It also has three 65-mile pipelines that ship feedstocks and crude oil. HollyFrontier holds a 41% stake in Holly Energy Partners.

Holly Energy Partners' strategy is to make acquisitions that complement its existing portfolio both in tandem with HollyFrontier and independently.

Holly Energy Partners is integral to HollyFrontier's business growth by developing and extending that company's assets. In 2009 it picked up the Roadrunner pipeline a 65-mile pipeline connecting HollyFrontier's refining facilities in Lovington New Mexico to the terminus of a Centurion pipeline linking West Texas and Cushing Oklahoma. In 2010 it acquired petroleum storage tanks at HollyFrontier's Tulsa refinery (2 million barrels of capacity) and other assets from HollyFrontier for $93 million.

Building the largest refinery complex in the area in 2009 HollyFrontier acquired refineries and related assets in Tulsa from Sunoco and Sinclair. In 2011 HollyFrontier's acquisition of Frontier Oil (with refineries in Kansas and Wyoming) boosted its total refining capacity to 443.000 barrels per day.

Building its portfolio in 2011 Holly Energy Partners acquired pipeline tankage loading rack and crude receiving assets from HollyFrontier's El Dorado and Cheyenne refineries for $340 million. In 2012 it also acquired HollyFrontier's 75% stake in UNEV Pipeline for $315 million. The UNEV refined products pipeline runs from Woods Cross Utah to Las Vegas Nevada.

Increased pipeline shipments and higher operating margins (thanks to the 2011 asset expansion and higher oil prices) helped to lift Holly Energy Partners' revenues and net income in 2011 by 17% and 32 % respectively.

EXECUTIVES

Vp And Treasurer, Stephen D Wise
Svp And General Counsel Secretary, Denise C McWatters, age 55

EVP and CFO, Douglas Aron
Principal Accounting Officer Vice President Controller Of Holly Logistic Services Llc, Kenneth Norwood
Vice President Environmental Affairs, Phillip L Youngblood
Vp Pipeline Operations, James G Townsend, age 61
Board Member, Buford P Berry, age 79
Board Member, Robert G McKenzie, age 77
Board Member, Herman Janes
Board Member, Douglas Bech
Board Member, Franklin Myers
Board Member, James Lee
Auditors: Ernst&YoungLLP

LOCATIONS

HQ: Holly Energy Partners LP
2828 N. Harwood, Suite 1300, Dallas, TX 75201-1507
Phone: 214 871-3555
Web: www.hollyenergy.com

PRODUCTS/OPERATIONS

2011 Sales

	$ mil.	% of total
Pipelines		
Refined products	86.2	40
Crude oil	46.5	22
Intermediates	21.9	10
Terminals & truck loading racks	58.9	28
Total	**213.5**	**100**

COMPETITORS

ExxonMobil Pipeline	Shell Pipeline
Magellan Midstream	Wolverine Pipe Line
NuStar Energy	Company

HISTORICAL FINANCIALS

Company Type: Public

Income Statement

FYE: December 31

	REVENUE ($ mil.)	NET INCOME ($ mil.)	NET PROFIT MARGIN	EMPLOYEES
12/13	305.1	86.0	28.2%	257
12/12	292.5	91.1	31.1%	232
12/11	213.5	78.0	36.5%	216
12/10	182.1	58.8	32.3%	148
12/09	146.5	66.0	45.0%	140
Annual Growth	20.1%	6.9%	—	16.4%

2013 Year-End Financials

Debt ratio: 58.4%	No. of shares (mil.): 58
Return on equity: —	Dividends
Cash ($ mil.): 6	Yield: 5.9%
Current ratio: 0.87	Payout: 186.8%
Long-term debt ($ mil.): 807	Market value ($ mil.): 1,896

	STOCK PRICE ($) FY Close	P/E High/Low		PER SHARE ($) Earnings	Dividends	Book Value
12/13	32.33	82	34	0.88	1.93	6.30
12/12	65.78	57	41	1.29	1.81	6.21
12/11	53.78	45	35	1.34	1.72	6.02
12/10	50.91	50	37	1.06	1.64	2.48
12/09	39.84	26	13	1.59	1.56	4.39
Annual Growth	(5.1%)	—	—	(13.7%)	5.4%	9.4%

Home Bancorp Inc

Making its home in Cajun Country Home Bancorp is the holding company for Home Bank a community bank which offers deposit and loan services to consumers and small to midsized businesses in southern Louisiana. Through about two dozen branches the bank offers standard savings and checking accounts as well as lending services such as mortgages consumer loans and credit cards. Its loan portfolio includes commercial real estate commercial and industrial loans as well as construction and land loans. Home Bancorp also operates about half a dozen bank branches in west Mississippi which were formerly part of Britton & Koontz Bank.

Geographic Reach

Home Bancorp serves the Louisiana areas of Greater Lafayette Baton Rouge Greater New Orleans and Northshore (of Lake Pontchartrain). Its markets in Mississippi include Vicksburg and Natchez.

Financial Performance

Although the company saw assets and loans grow in 2013 net income fell 20% that year to $7.3 million on lower operating income.

Mergers and Acquisitions

In early 2014 Home Bancorp spent about $35 million on Britton & Koontz Capital Corporation the holding company of Britton & Koontz Bank; the deal added five branches in west Mississippi to Home Bancorp's operations.

EXECUTIVES

President CEO and Director, John W. Bordelon, age 58, $215,000 total compensation
Chief Operations Officers And Executive Vice President Of The Bank, Scott T Sutton, age 62
Executive Vice President And Chief, Scott Ridley
Auditors: PorterKeadleMooreLLP

LOCATIONS

HQ: Home Bancorp Inc
503 Kaliste Saloom Road, Lafayette, LA 70508
Phone: 337 237-1960   **Fax:** 337 264-9280
Web: www.home24bank.com

COMPETITORS

Capital One	MidSouth Bancorp
IBERIABANK	Regions Financial
JPMorgan Chase	Teche Holding
Louisiana Bancorp	

HISTORICAL FINANCIALS

Company Type: Public

Income Statement

FYE: December 31

	ASSETS ($ mil.)	NET INCOME ($ mil.)	INCOME AS % OF ASSETS	EMPLOYEES
12/13	984.2	7.2	0.7%	0
12/12	962.9	9.1	1.0%	0
12/11	963.7	5.1	0.5%	0
12/10	700.4	4.6	0.7%	0
12/09	524.6	4.6	0.9%	0
Annual Growth	17.0%	11.7%	—	—

2013 Year-End Financials

Return on assets: 0.7%	Dividends
Return on equity: 5.1%	Yield: —
Long-term debt ($ mil.): —	Payout: —
No. of shares (mil.): 7	Market value ($ mil.): 134
Sales ($ mil): 51	

	STOCK PRICE ($) FY Close	P/E High/Low		PER SHARE ($) Earnings	Dividends	Book Value
12/13	18.85	17	15	1.06	0.00	19.99
12/12	18.25	14	12	1.28	0.00	19.03
12/11	15.50	22	18	0.71	0.00	17.30
12/10	13.82	23	19	0.62	0.00	16.18
12/09	12.19	22	16	0.58	0.00	15.13
Annual Growth	11.5%	—	—	16.3%	—	7.2%

Home BancShares, Inc.

At this Home you don't have to stash your cash under the mattress. Home BancShares is the holding company for Centennial Bank which operates about 150 branches in Arkansas Alabama and Florida. The bank offers traditional services such as checking savings and money market accounts; IRAs; and CDs. It focuses on commercial real estate lending including construction land development and agricultural loans which make up more than 55% of its lending portfolio. The bank also writes residential mortgage business and consumer loans. Nonbank subsidiaries offer trust and insurance services. Investments are available to customers through an agreement with third-party provider LPL Financial.

Geographic Reach

The Arkansas-based bank holding company's Centennial Bank operates 149 branches in Arkansas the Florida Keys southwestern Florida Central Florida the Florida Panhandle and south Alabama.

Financial Performance

Home BancShares reported $257.5 million in revenue in 2013 up 14% versus 2012. The rise in revenue was due primarily to increased interest income from a higher level of earning assets combined with higher yields on their covered loans.

Net income rose 6% over the same period to $66.5 million. The increase was primarily due to additional net income and other non-interest income resulting from acquisitions completed in 2012.

Strategy

The acquisitive bank holding company is expanding in its core Florida and Arkansas markets through the purchase of local managed community banks. Home continues to look for additional acquisitions including institutions seized by regulators in and contiguous to its geographical markets.

Mergers and Acquisitions

In July 2014 Home BancShares completed the acquisition of Florida Traditions Bank (FTB) in a $43 million deal. FTB operated eight branches in central Florida. Post purchase Home had approximately $7 billion in total assets $5.5 billion in depositions $4.7 billion in loans and 149 branches.

In October 2013 the firm acquired the $2.8 billion holding company Liberty Bancshares Inc. parent company of 46-branch Liberty Bank of Arkansas. The Liberty purchase significantly increased Home's deposit market share in Arkansas making it the second largest bank holding company headquartered in Arkansas.

Home BancShares entered another new market with the 2012 acquisition of Vision Bank from Park National. The deal included 17 branches along the Florida panhandle and Gulf Coast and gave Home BancShares its first locations in Alabama. Also in 2012 it bought Florida-based Premier Bank from Premier Bank Holding Company and Heritage Bank of Florida with offices in Tampa Lutz and Wesley Chapel.

EXECUTIVES

Chief Financial Officer; Treasurer; Director, Randy E. Mayor, age 49, $203,000 total compensation
Chief Executive Officer; Director, C. Randall (Randy) Sims, age 59, $279,125 total compensation
Regional President Centennial Bank, Robert F. Birch, age 64, $213,150 total compensation
Regional President Centennial Bank, Tracy M. French, age 52, $213,150 total compensation
Senior Vice President Director Loan Rvw, Tish Cartwright
Chairman, John W. Allison, age 67
Vice Chairman, Robert H. Adcock, age 65
Auditors: BKDLLP

LOCATIONS

HQ: Home BancShares, Inc.
719 Harkrider, Suite 100, Conway, AR 72032
Phone: 501 328-4770
Web: www.homebancshares.com

PRODUCTS/OPERATIONS

2013 Sales

	$ mil.	% of total
Interest		
Loans	198.5	74
Investment securities	18.6	7
Noninterest		
Service charges on deposit accounts	17.9	7
Other service charges & fees	16.0	6
Other income	6.8	2
Mortgage lending income	6.0	2
Insurance commission	2.4	1
Gain on OREO	1.7	1
FDIC indemnification accretion	(10.4)	-
Total	**257.5**	**100**

Selected Services

Personal Banking
Business Banking
ebanking
Investment & insurance
Trust Services

COMPETITORS

Arvest Bank	Bear State Financial
BB&T	Regions Financial
BBX Capital	Simmons First
Bank of America	TIB Financial
Bank of the Ozarks	Woodforest Financial

HISTORICAL FINANCIALS

Company Type: Public

Income Statement

FYE: December 31

	ASSETS ($ mil.)	NET INCOME ($ mil.)	INCOME AS % OF ASSETS	EMPLOYEES
12/13	6,811.8	66.5	1.0%	1,497
12/12	4,242.1	63.0	1.5%	926
12/11	3,604.1	54.7	1.5%	774
12/10	3,762.6	17.5	0.5%	698
12/09	2,684.8	26.8	1.0%	605
Annual Growth	26.2%	25.5%	—	25.4%

2013 Year-End Financials

Return on assets: 1.2%
Return on equity: 9.8%
Long-term debt ($ mil.): —
No. of shares (mil.): 65
Sales ($ mil): 257

Dividends
Yield: 0.9%
Payout: 28.4%
Market value ($ mil.): 2,431

	STOCK PRICE ($) FY Close	P/E High/Low	PER SHARE ($) Earnings	Dividends	Book Value
12/13	37.35	38 18	1.14	0.36	12.92
12/12	33.02	32 22	1.12	0.29	9.17
12/11	25.91	28 22	0.93	0.13	8.38
12/10	22.03	111 76	0.26	0.11	8.38
12/09	24.07	52 29	0.51	0.11	8.23
Annual Growth	11.6%	— —	22.3%	34.3%	11.9%

HomeAway, Inc.

There's no place like a home away from home for fun or functionality. HomeAway boasts nearly 1 million paid listings for vacation rental properties across 190 countries worldwide and helps property owners rent out their shack condo or ch teau. Its HomeAway.com website is free to travelers who are typically affluent and is searchable by destination. Its listings include information on weekly rates availability and amenities as well as photographs descriptions and contact information. HomeAway also maintains 30 other travel-related websites. Founded in 2005 as WVR Group the company changed its name in 2006 to HomeAway launched its flagship website that year and went public in mid-2011.

IPO

Raising $216 million through its initial public offering HomeAway used the proceeds to not only pay off investors but to continue its strategy of buying businesses expanding into new global markets adding more product lines and increasing the functionality and relevance of its websites. The company has grown organically and by acquiring several US-centric vacation rental websites.

Operations

While HomeAway doesn't quite have the vacation rental market cornered it's coming close. In addition to its flagship HomeAway.com site the company also operates VRBO.com and Vacation-Rentals.com in the US and HomeAway-branded sites in the UK Germany Spain and Australia it also holds OwnersDirect (UK) Abritel and Homelidays (France) Toprural (Spain) Aluque Temporada (Brazil) Stavz (Australia) Bookabach (New Zealand) and Asia Pacific's travelmob.com. It also owns BedAndBreakfast.com for those who just want the B&B experience.

Listing revenue accounts for about 85% of sales while services and products for property owners including property and trip insurance booking software and partner revenue made up the rest.

Geographic Reach

HomeAway is headquartered in Austin Texas and has offices in Denver and Seattle in the US as well as in Paris Marseilles Geneva Madrid and London. The US generates about 60% of the company's revenues while France accounts for about 15% followed by the UK with 12%

Sales and Marketing

With property owners and managers paying for online marketing HomeAway looks to attract tech-savvy travelers who regularly book vacation rentals. Its websites also showcase temporary housing for those who are having a home remodeled and need another place to hang their hat. Compared to the average leisure traveler the firm cites that vacation rental bookers spend more and travel more frequently and for longer periods of time.

Financial Performance

In 2013 HomeAway's revenue rose 24% to $346.5 million up from $280.4 million due to the acquisition of Toprural along with new listing growth of $56.2 million. Other revenue also increased by nearly $10 million. Higher revenue lead to a 16% increase in net income from $16.9 million to $17.3 million and a $9 million bump in cash from operations.

Strategy

The company grows through acquisitions and to a lesser extent by extending the services and products it offers vacation home owners. HomeAway owns vacation rentals sites throughout Europe and is working on entering the Chinese market.

Mergers and Acquisitions

Since its inception HomeAway has acquired more than 20 companies and booking site operators. Its most recent purchases include travelmob in Singapore Bookabach in New Zealand and Stayz in Australia.

EXECUTIVES

Chief Strategy and Development Officer and Director, Carl G. Shepherd, age 62, $316,275 total compensation

CFO, Lynn Atchison, age 54, $316,275 total compensation

President CEO and Director, Brian H. Sharples, age 53, $487,500 total compensation

CTO, Ross A. Buhrdorf, age 49, $276,250 total compensation

President Europe, Petra Friedmann

COO, Brent Bellm, age 42, $354,975 total compensation

Vice President Business Intelligence, William Bowles

Global Vice President Sales Mkt Ops, Anand Srinivasan

Senior Vice President Global Marketing Sales Opera, Michael Osborne

Vice President Software Engineering, Alex Victoria

Vice President Product Development, Venu Venugopal

Senior Vice President Technology, Steve Vanderbilt

Vice President Software Development, Chas Erickson

Vice President And General Counsel, Melissa Frug

V Pres Emea, Marcello Mastioni

Vice President Brand And Regional, Jason Morros

National Sales Manager, Davasha Bacon

Chief Strategy and Development Officer and Director, Carl G. Shepherd, age 62

President CEO and Director, Brian H. Sharples, age 53

Board Member, Jeffrey D (Jeff) Brody, age 55

Board Member, Charles Baker

Board Member, Todd C Chaffee

Board Member, Philip Siegel

Board Member, Susan D Wojcicki

Board Member, Christopher P (Woody) Marshall, age 47

Secretary, Roxana Monroe

Auditors: PricewaterhouseCoopersLLP

LOCATIONS

HQ: HomeAway, Inc.
1011 W. Fifth Street, Suite 300, Austin, TX 78703
Phone: 512 684-1100
Web: www.HomeAway.com

2013 Sales

	$ mil.	% of total
US	211.5	61
France	52.2	15
UK	41.2	12
Germany	20.7	6
Other international	20.9	6
Total	**346.5**	**100**

PRODUCTS/OPERATIONS

2013 Sales

	$ mil.	% of total
Listings	294.7	85
Other	51.8	15
Total	**346.5**	**100**

Company Trademarks
Abritel.fr
Aluguetemporada BedandBreakfast.com
Clearstay
CyberRentals.com
Entech
Escapia
FeWo-Direkt
First Resorts
Holiday-Rentals
HomeAway
Homelidays
InstantSoftware
OwnersDirect
PropertyPlus
Rezovation
V12
VacationRentals.com
Villanao.fr
VRBO
Webervations

Selected Websites
Abritel.fr (France)
AlugueTemporada.com.br (Brazil)
BedandBreakfast.com
HomeAway.co.uk (UK)
HomeAway.com (US)
HomeAway.de (Germany)
HomeAway.es (Spain)
HomeAwayRealEstate.com
Homelidays.com (France)
OwnersDirect.co.uk (UK)
VacationRentals.com (US)
VRBO.com (US)

COMPETITORS

Century 21 Real Estate	Orbitz Worldwide
Coldwell Banker	Priceline
Expedia	Prudential
Fairfax Media	RE/MAX
Google	Telecom Italia
Hotels.com	Teletext
Hotwire Inc.	Travelocity
Internet Brands	Wyndham Worldwide
Interval Leisure Group	Yahoo!
Kayak Software	craigslist
MSN	eBay

HISTORICAL FINANCIALS

Company Type: Public

Income Statement

FYE: December 31

	REVENUE ($ mil.)	NET INCOME ($ mil.)	NET PROFIT MARGIN	EMPLOYEES
12/13	346.4	17.6	5.1%	1,542
12/12	280.4	14.9	5.3%	1,228
12/11	230.2	6.1	2.7%	935
12/10	167.8	16.9	10.1%	842
12/09	120.2	7.6	6.4%	0
Annual Growth	30.3%	23.2%	—	—

2013 Year-End Financials

Debt ratio: —
Return on equity: 2.6%
Cash ($ mil.): 324
Current ratio: 2.04
Long-term debt ($ mil.): —

No. of shares (mil.): 92
Dividends
  Yield: —
  Payout: —
Market value ($ mil.): 3,776

	STOCK PRICE ($) FY Close	P/E High/Low	PER SHARE ($) Earnings	Dividends	Book Value
12/13	40.88	195 105	0.20	0.00	9.03
12/12	22.00	151 110	0.18	0.00	6.20
12/11	23.25	— —	(0.31)	0.00	5.47
Annual Growth	32.6%		—	—	28.5%

Homefed Corp.

HomeFed won't provide you with room and board but it can help you get a home. The company earns its keep by investing in and developing residential real estate in California. Through subsidiaries HomeFed is developing a master-planned community in San Diego County called San Elijo Hills which contains approximately 3500 residences as well as commercial space and a town center. The company is responsible for design engineering; infrastructure such as streets utilities and public facilities; and the completion of individual lots. It owns a 68% stake in the development.

Like many real estate developers in California HomeFed has been affected by the battered housing market. San Elijo Hills is more than 80% sold but the company completed only one residential lot sale between 2006 and 2009. HomeFed also owns a portion of another community under development Otay Ranch in addition to some 1500 acres of a grape vineyard in California that is not zoned for residential or commercial use. It did not any real estate at Otay Ranch from 2007 to 2009.

Leucadia from which the company acquired the San Elijo Hills and Otay Ranch projects controls more than 30% of HomeFed's stock. Jospeh Steinberg president of Leucadia and chairman of HomeFed owns almost 10%. Ian Cumming who is chairman of Leucadia and a director of HomeFed holds more than 7%.

EXECUTIVES

V Pres, John K Aden
V Pres, Christian E Foulger
Vice President And Senior Development Manager, Kent Aden
Vp Treasurer And Controller, Erin Ruhe
Auditors: PricewaterhouseCoopersLLP

LOCATIONS

HQ: Homefed Corp.
1903 Wright Place, Suite 220, Carlsbad, CA 92008
Phone: 760 918-8200
Web: www.homefedcorporation.com

PRODUCTS/OPERATIONS

2009 Sales

	$ mil.	% of total
Sales of real estate	14.7	99
Co-op marketing & advertising fees	0.2	1
Total	14.9	100

COMPETITORS

Brookfield Homes
Corky McMillin
Irvine Company
Newhall Land
Tejon Ranch

HISTORICAL FINANCIALS

Company Type: Public

Income Statement

FYE: December 31

	REVENUE ($ mil.)	NET INCOME ($ mil.)	NET PROFIT MARGIN	EMPLOYEES
12/13	56.6	11.2	19.9%	16
12/12	35.6	6.0	16.9%	14
12/11	34.1	4.4	13.2%	13
12/10	35.9	3.5	9.8%	13
12/09	14.8	2.8	18.9%	13
Annual Growth	39.7%	41.5%	—	5.3%

2013 Year-End Financials

Debt ratio: —
Return on equity: 6.4%
Cash ($ mil.): 57
Current ratio: 6.60
Long-term debt ($ mil.): —

No. of shares (mil.): 7
Dividends
  Yield: —
  Payout: —
Market value ($ mil.): 288

	STOCK PRICE ($) FY Close	P/E High/Low	PER SHARE ($) Earnings	Dividends	Book Value
12/13	36.60	27 19	1.43	0.00	22.82
12/12	26.50	38 24	0.76	0.00	21.37
12/11	19.40	53 32	0.57	0.00	20.01
12/10	21.80	73 45	0.45	0.00	19.42
12/09	24.50	71 36	0.36	0.00	18.95
Annual Growth	10.6%		41.2%	—	4.8%

Hospitality Properties Trust

Hospitality Properties Trust (HPT) rolls out the welcome mat for the road-weary. The real estate investment trust (REIT) owns nearly 300 hotels throughout the US and in Canada and Puerto Rico as well as 185 full-service truck stops operating as TravelCenters of America and Petro Stopping Centers. Unlike some hospitality REITs HPT is not affiliated with any one hotel company. Its properties target different markets from upscale (Crowne Plaza Hotels & Resorts) to business and family travelers on long-term trips (Residence Inn by Marriott). HPT maintains a geographically diverse portfolio with hotels or travel centers (usually both) in nearly 45 states as well as Canada and Puerto Rico.

HPT's portfolio is also fairly stable with a minimal number of property dispositions. Though the company has made few new acquisitions in recent years it prefers to purchase new hotels in bulk from owners and operators that wish to divest their properties in order to raise capital but want to stay in the hospitality business. While the company manages some of its properties the vast majority are leased. Its leases typically have terms of 15 or more years and include agreements in which property managers or tenants must pay minimum rent or returns to the company.

The REIT's revenue rose in 2010 and 2011 amid increasing occupancy rates. However the company suffered a loss in 2010 as its tenants reported higher operating costs and lower rates per room. It returned to profitability in 2011 when those metrics improved. As a REIT HPT is usually not subject to federal income tax but is required to distribute up to 95% of its net income to shareholders.

HPT made a bold move beyond hotels when it acquired truck stop chain TravelCenters of America (TA) in 2007 for almost $2 billion signifying the REIT's first foray into the travel convenience industry. While the hotel industry is cyclical HPT wanted to capitalize on the fact that travel centers which are located along most major US interstate highways perform well even in recession. TA was spun off not long after the acquisition and now operates as a separate company leasing all travel center properties from owner HPT.

The company is managed by Reit Management & Research (RMR). The real estate management company oversees one of the largest portfolios in the US with more than 1300 properties under its supervision.

HISTORY

Lawyer Barry Portnoy founded Health and Retirement Properties Trust (now HRPT Properties Trust) in 1986 to finance New MediCo a chain of nursing homes and head injury centers owned by one of his law clients and the client's cousin Gerard Martin. When New MediCo ran into financial trouble in 1992 HRPT privately restructured the debt and took over eight of the facilities.

In 1995 HRPT established and spun off Hospitality Properties Trust (HPT) as a separate public company with an initial portfolio of 21 Marriott International mid-market hotels. Over the next several years HPT bought hundreds of hotel properties often in large blocks; an example was its 1997 acquisition of 45 Marriott-branded hotels.

The company continued to add properties as REIT stock prices soared in the 1990s. But in 1999 REITs (particularly hospitality REITs) fell out of favor because of a perceived oversupply of rooms. Nevertheless the company succeeded in raising capital in 1999 to continue enlarging its portfolio. In early 2005 it acquired a portfolio of about a dozen properties from hotel management company InterContinental Hotels Group. The package included one hotel in San Juan Puerto Rico and two in Toronto that represent HPT's first non-US properties.

EXECUTIVES

Vice President Investor Relations, Timothy A (Tim) Bonang
President; Chief Operating Officer; Assistant Secretary, John G. Murray, age 53
CFO and Treasurer, Mark L. Kleifges, age 53

Vice President Systems, Aaron Chamberland
Senior Vice President, Ethan S Bornstein, age 41
Secretary, Jennifer B Clark, age 54
Auditors: Ernst&YoungLLP

LOCATIONS

HQ: Hospitality Properties Trust
Two Newton Place, 255 Washington Street, Suite 300,
Newton, MA 02458-1634
Phone: 617 964-8389
Web: www.hptreit.com

PRODUCTS/OPERATIONS

2011 Sales

	$ mil.	% of total
Hotel operating revenues	889.1	74
Rental income	304.6	25
FF&E reserve income	16.6	1
Total	**1210.3**	**100**

Selected Hotel Tenants

Candlewood Suites
Crowne Plaza Hotels & Resorts
Country Inns & Suites by Carlson
Courtyard by Marriott
Holiday Inn Hotels & Resorts
Hyatt Place
InterContinental Hotels & Resorts
Marriott Hotels and Resorts
Park Plaza Hotels & Resorts
Radisson Hotels & Resorts
Residence Inn by Marriott
SpringHill Suites by Marriott
Staybridge Suites
TownePlace Suites by Marriott

COMPETITORS

Ashford Hospitality
Trust
FelCor
Hersha Hospitality
Host Hotels & Resorts
Innkeepers USA
LaSalle Hotel
Properties

Shaner Hotel Group
Starwood Hotels &
Resorts
Strategic Hotels
Sunstone Hotel
Investors

HISTORICAL FINANCIALS

Company Type: Public

Income Statement

FYE: December 31

	REVENUE ($ mil.)	NET INCOME ($ mil.)	NET PROFIT MARGIN	EMPLOYEES
12/13	1,563.8	133.1	8.5%	0
12/12	1,296.9	151.9	11.7%	0
12/11	1,210.3	190.4	15.7%	0
12/10	1,085.4	21.3	2.0%	0
12/09	1,037.2	193.3	18.6%	0
Annual Growth	**10.8%**	**(8.9%)**	**—**	**—**

2013 Year-End Financials

Debt ratio: 45.3%
Return on equity: 4.5%
Cash ($ mil.): 22
Current ratio: 0.30
Long-term debt ($ mil.): 2,704

No. of shares (mil.): 149
Dividends
Yield: 6.9%
Payout: 273.9%
Market value ($ mil.): 4,044

	STOCK PRICE ($) FY Close	P/E High/Low	PER SHARE ($) Earnings	Dividends	Book Value
12/13	27.03	44 32	0.73	1.89	20.63
12/12	23.42	33 26	0.84	1.82	22.11
12/11	22.98	20 15	1.30	1.80	22.66
12/10	23.04	— —	(0.07)	1.80	23.17
12/09	23.71	16 6	1.51	2.31	25.06
Annual Growth	**3.3%**	**— —**	**(16.6%)**	**(4.9%)**	**(4.7%)**

Houston Wire & Cable Co

Houston Wire & Cable (HWC) may have a Texas name but it can keep customers wired from Seattle to Tampa. The company is a conduit between cable manufacturers and electrical distributors and their customers. It distributes specialty (electrical and electronic) wire and cable products such as cable terminators fiber-optic cables and bare copper and building wire as well as voice data and premise wire. It also owns the brand Life-Guard a low-smoke zero-halogen cable. HWC operates a network of multiple distribution centers across the US and sells primarily to electrical distributors.

Geographic Reach

Headquartered in Houston the company has sales and distribution facilities in 25 locations in about 20 states.

Operations

Founded in 1975 HWC has grown to serve approximately 6200 customers. It annually sells about 44000-plus SKUs (stock-keeping units) made by leading manufacturers of electrical wire and cable such as Lake Cable Belden General Cable Nexans and Southwire.

The company is adding inventory with lower copper content along with its high copper content products to self-correct for fluctuations in commodity prices. Concurrently HWC is marketing an array of new private-label products. It has developed a cable product branded Lifeguard which is manufactured using zero halogens. Halogens contain reactive elements that can create smoke and toxic fumes if burned. LifeGuard provides a zero-halogen polymer jacket that is flame resistant and safer to use in extreme environments.

The company sells LifeGuard cables to the utilities petrochemical and wastewater treatment industries where cables are often exposed to more extreme environments. Already commonplace in parts of Europe and Asia HWC looks to leverage the typically higher margins zero halogen cables command over standard cables.

Financial Performance

HWC's revenues dipped 2% from $393 million in 2012 to $383 million in 2013. The declines in 2013 were driven by the fluctuation in metal prices and a decline in project business primarily due to delays in project starts and market uncertainty.

Its profits plunged 54% from $17 million in 2012 to $8 million in 2013 due to a $7.6 million goodwill impairment charge coupled with higher operating expenses. After experiencing negative operating cash flow of $3 million in 2012 HWC posted about $21 million in positive cash flow during 2013.

Strategy

HWC's current growth strategy is to concentrate its purchases of wire and cable between a small number of suppliers. As a result in 2013 roughly 55% of its purchases derived from five suppliers. The company also added two new distribution centers in 2013 and a third in early 2014.

EXECUTIVES

CEO and Director, Charles A. Sorrentino, age 67, $475,000 total compensation

Chief Financial Officer Treasurer Secretary, Nicol G. (Nic) Graham, age 62, $191,394 total compensation
VP Southern Region, Eric S. Blankenship, age 63
VP Eastern Region, Marcus L. Jones, age 58
President, James L. Pokluda, age 49
Regional Vice President, John Marchiando
National Account Manager, Kevin Kelly
Vice President Marketing, Douglas Brady
Vice President Of Technical Services, Armando Gonzales
CEO and Director, Charles A. Sorrentino, age 67
Chairman, Scott L. Thompson, age 56
Board Member, Joe Ezekiel
Auditors: Ernst&YoungLLP

LOCATIONS

HQ: Houston Wire & Cable Co
10201 North Loop East, Houston, TX 77029
Phone: 713 609-2100
Web: www.houwire.com
Anchorage AK
Atlanta GA
Baton Rouge LA
Charlotte NC
Chicago IL
Denver CO
Houma LA
Houston TX
Kansas City MO
Los Angeles CA
Memphis TN
Minneapolis MN
New Iberia LA
Odessa TX
Philadelphia PA
San Francisco CA
Seattle WA
Sulphur LA
Tampa FL

PRODUCTS/OPERATIONS

Selected Products

Armored cable
Bare copper and building wire
Cable terminators
Chain and accessories
Fiber-optic cables
Flexible and portable cords
Instrumentation and thermocouple cable
Lead and high-temperature cable
Medium-voltage power cable
Mining cable
Mooring products
Outside plant communication cable
Sound security and fire alarm cable
Synthetic rope and slings
Tray cables 600 volt control and power
Variable frequency drive cable
Voice data and premise wire
Wire rope and hardware

Selected Services

Application engineering support
Asset management program
Cable management program
Cable selection system
Custom fabrication (cutting of wire and cable to specifications)
Service (24-hours/7-days)

Selected Markets

Environmental compliance
    Baghouse optimization
    Flue gas desulfurization (FGD)
    Mercury capture in FGD systems
    Selective catalytic reduction (SCR)
Industrial
    Ethanol
    Food processing
    Petrochemical
    Pharmaceutical

Pulp and paper
Steel
Infrastructure
  Government
  Mass transit
  Security
  Transportation
  Waste water
Power Generation
  Co-generation
  Fossil fuel
  Hydro
  Nuclear
  Wind
Wire and cable training programs

COMPETITORS

Accu-Tech	Graybar Electric
DXP Enterprises	Stuart C. Irby
Electro-Wire	WESCO International
Elliott Electric	Wholesale Electric
Supply	Supply

HISTORICAL FINANCIALS

Company Type: Public

Income Statement

FYE: December 31

	REVENUE ($ mil.)	NET INCOME ($ mil.)	NET PROFIT MARGIN	EMPLOYEES
12/13	383.2	7.9	2.1%	403
12/12	393.0	17.0	4.3%	427
12/11	396.4	19.6	5.0%	410
12/10	308.5	8.6	2.8%	380
12/09	254.8	8.0	3.2%	268
Annual Growth	10.7%	(0.4%)	—	10.7%

2013 Year-End Financials

Debt ratio: 24.4%	No. of shares (mil.): 17
Return on equity: 7.1%	Dividends
Cash ($ mil.): —	Yield: 3.1%
Current ratio: 4.33	Payout: 80.7%
Long-term debt ($ mil.): 47	Market value ($ mil.): 240

	STOCK PRICE ($) FY Close	P/E High/Low	PER SHARE ($) Earnings	Dividends	Book Value
12/13	13.38	34 25	0.44	0.42	6.17
12/12	12.27	16 11	0.96	0.36	6.09
12/11	13.82	15 9	1.11	0.36	5.46
12/10	13.44	29 18	0.49	0.34	4.83
12/09	11.90	31 10	0.45	0.34	4.56
Annual Growth	3.0%	— —	(0.6%)	5.4%	7.8%

Hovnanian Enterprises, Inc.

You don't have to live in a hovel if you buy a Hovnanian. Hovnanian Enterprises designs builds and markets single-family detached homes condominiums and townhomes for first-time move-up and luxury buyers as well as for empty-nesters and active adults. The company offers homes for sale under the K. Hovnanian Brighton Matzel and Mumford Oster Parkwood Builders and Town & Country names. Its average home price is about $280000. The company operates in about 200 communities in 16 states. Its K. Hovnanian Amer-

ican Mortgage unit offers mortgage financing and title services. Members of the Hovnanian family control about 90% of Hovnanian Enterprises.

Like its peers Hovnanian was hit hard by the housing downturn and credit crunch. Revenues have fallen sharply since 2006 as housing demand has declined. The company managed to achieve a profit in 2010 due to a favorable tax credit. However Hovnanian fell into the red again in 2011 as the housing industry struggled to make a strong comeback. Sales were down by 17% in 2011.

As a result of the weaker demand the company has built fewer homes and as a result sales have declined. Hovnanian delivered about 4200 homes (including joint ventures) in fiscal 2011 (down from more than 20000 in 2006).

In order to reduce costs the company cut its workforce some 75% between 2006 and 2010. Hovnanian also has reduced its general and administrative expenses. The company "mothballed" or stopped development on more than 50 communities (half of which were in California). However the firm did begin investing in the future in 2010 and reactivated more than a dozen previously mothballed communities. The following year Hovnanian invested some $400 million in new land purchaes and land development. But it continued to reconfigure its communities by mothballing eight selling three and re-activting four.

Anticipating a housing recovery Hovnanian is increasing its community count and has purchased land at discounted prices in the Southeast (Florida Georgia and the Carolinas) Southwest (Arizona and Texas) and West (California). The Southwest (in particular Texas) is a major contributor to Hovnanian's revenues (some 30% in 2010). Home prices in Texas have been relatively stable compared to the rest of the country.

The company in 2009 and 2010 also entered into joint ventures with GTIS Partners to design build and sell homes across communities in the greater Chicago; Palm Beach County Florida; California; and Virginia markets. Hovnanian owns about 20% stake in the ventures.

HISTORY

After fleeing revolution in his home of Iraq in the 1950s Kevork Hovnanian came to America and began building homes in New Jersey in 1959 with his three brothers (including brother Vahak later to become founder of Internet service provider SPEEDUS.COM). His firm incorporated as K. Hovnanian Enterprises in 1967 and Kevork's son Ara came on board in 1979. (Ara became president in 1988 and CEO in 1997.) The company's 1983 IPO helped Hovnanian take advantage of New Jersey's strong housing market which peaked in 1986. However the boom had declined dramatically by 1990 and Hovnanian landed in the red.

Responding to the setback Hovnanian expanded geographically in the 1990s. It moved into the Washington DC area in 1992 and into Southern California in 1994. But the new markets did not add much to the bottom line thanks to a slowdown in North Carolina and a recession in California.

Hovnanian crews traveled to Armenia in 1988 to help rebuild the country after devastating earthquakes had rumbled though wreaking havoc. The trip convinced Kevork an Armenian who grew up in Iraq to expand Hovnanian operations into the emerging economies of Eastern Europe. Because of its relatively more advanced real estate and mortgage laws Poland was chosen and Hovnanian began constructing townhouses there in 1996.

In 1997 Hovnanian began to divest itself of commercial holdings to focus on housing; by 1998 the

company had exited the investment properties business.

With cash to plow into homebuilding Hovnanian strengthened its Washington DC operations in 1998 by acquiring Virginia's P.C. Homes. The next year the builder purchased New Jersey luxury homebuilder Matzel & Mumford and entered Texas with the purchase of Dallas-based Goodman Family of Builders. In 2001 Hovnanian bought Washington Homes which operated primarily in North Carolina and the Washington DC metropolitan area.

In early 2002 Hovnanian acquired the homebuilding assets of The Forecast Group increasing Hovnanian's presence in California. The company was listed that year as one of the 100 fastest-growing companies in the US by "FORTUNE" magazine. Also that year Hovnanian expanded its presence in Texas entering the Houston homebuilding market with its purchase of Parkside Homes.

Hovnanian initiated plans in 2003 to stop selling homes in Poland and to liquidate some of its homebuilding operations in portions of the southern US. On the expansion side the company acquired Brighton Homes to strengthen its position in the Houston area. It also acquired Great Western Homes expanding its market into the Phoenix area and the Southwest and Tampa Florida-based Windward Homes expanding its southeastern US market into Florida. In 2004 Hovnanian expanded its metro DC presence by acquiring the homebuilding assets of McLean Virginia-based Rocky Gorge Homes for an undisclosed amount.

In 2005 Hovnanian entered the Chicago market by acquiring homebuilder Town and Country Homes. It also entered the Orlando market and expanded its operations in Florida and Minnesota by acquiring Cambridge Homes. Hovnanian also acquired Oster Homes (Ohio) and First Home Builders (Florida) in 2005.

EXECUTIVES

Senior Vice President Human Resources, Robyn Mingle
Vice President, Joseph Riggs
Chief Financial Officer; Executive Vice President; Director, J. Larry Sorsby, age 59, $600,000 total compensation
COO, Thomas J. Pellerito, age 67, $500,000 total compensation
President, Peter R. (Pete) Thompson
President Eastern Title Agency and affiliated title agencies, Michael P. Kehoe
President K. Hovnanian American Mortgage, Dan A. Klinger
Area Vp Monmouth County, R Hoffman
Vice President Organizational Development, Bill Moore
Region Vp Operations, William Cadigan
Area President, Steve Pittard
Senior Vice President, Paul W Buchanan, age 65
Vice President Customer Relationship Management Processes, Jim McConnell
Senior Vice President, Bill Carpitella
Vice President Marketing, Tullos Kim
Vice President Of Sales And Marketing At K Hovnanian Homes, Emilio Martinez
Vice President, Dean Potter
Vice President, George Economy
Vice President, Chris Moreno
Area President, Mark Brown
Vice President Corporate Operations, Andre Miesnieks
Vice President Marketing, Dawn Huffinks
Vice President Crm Envision, John Cummins
Area President, Steve Caporaso

Area President, Bob Cummings
Vice President Account Manager, Frances Knight
Iicf Western Division Board Chairman And
  Regional Vice President North Western Region,
  Ron Goetz
Vice President, David Friend
Vice President And Chief Legal Counsel, Stephen
  Dahl
Area Vice President, Ronald Morgan
Vice President Land Acquisition, Harry Lourimore
Vice President Of Sales And Marketing, Ceilie
  Holmes
Vice President Controller, Dave Damico
Vice President Corporate Marketing And Sales,
  Laura Vanvelthoven
Area President, Andrew Konovodoff
Vice President Of Sales And Marketing, Martinez
  Emilio
Vice President Safety And Risk Management,
  Michael Petros
Area President, David Vanderslice
Vice President Corporate Operations, Larry
  Miesnieks
Board Member, Robert Galano
Auditors: Deloitte&ToucheLLP

LOCATIONS

HQ: Hovnanian Enterprises, Inc.
  110 West Front Street, P.O. Box 500, Red Bank, NJ
  07701
Phone: 732 747-7800
Web: www.khov.com
Mid-Atlantic
  Delaware
  Maryland
  Virginia
  Washington DC
  West Virginia
Midwest
  Illinois
  Kentucky
  Minnesota
  Ohio
Northeast
  New Jersey
  New York
  Pennsylvania
Southeast
  Florida
  Georgia
  North Carolina
  South Carolina
Southwest
  Arizona
  Texas
West
  California

2014 Home Building Sales

	% of total
Southwest	37
Mid-Atlantic	16
Northeast	13
Midwest	11
Southeast	10
West	11
Others	2
Total	100

PRODUCTS/OPERATIONS

2014 Sales

	$ mil.	% of total
Homebuilding		
Sale of homes	2013.0	98
Land sales & other	8.0	-
Financial services	42.4	2
Total	2063.4	100

Selected Trade Names

Brighton Homes

K. Hovnanian Homes
K. Hovnanian Homes Built On Your Lot
K. Hovnanian Homes Metro Living
K. Hovnanian' s Four Seasons (active-adult
  communities)
Matzel and Mumford
Oster Homes
Parkwood Builders
Town & Country Homes

COMPETITORS

Beazer Homes	PulteGroup
D.R. Horton	Rottlund
KB Home	The Ryland Group
Lennar	Toll Brothers
M/I Homes	Weyerhaeuser Real
NVR	Estate
Orleans Homebuilders	

HISTORICAL FINANCIALS

Company Type: Public

Income Statement

FYE: October 31

	REVENUE ($ mil.)	NET INCOME ($ mil.)	NET PROFIT MARGIN	EMPLOYEES
10/14	2,063.3	307.1	14.9%	2,006
10/13	1,851.2	31.3	1.7%	1,749
10/12	1,485.3	(66.2)	—	1,565
10/11	1,134.9	(286.0)	—	1,500
10/10	1,371.8	2.5	0.2%	1,629
Annual Growth	10.7%	230.1%	—	5.3%

2014 Year-End Financials

Debt ratio: 81.0%
Return on equity: ***,***.*%
Cash ($ mil.): 291
Current ratio: 3.76
Long-term debt ($ mil.): 1,855
No. of shares (mil.): 145
Dividends
Yield: —
Payout: —
Market value ($ mil.): 549

	STOCK PRICE ($) FY Close	P/E High/Low		PER SHARE ($) Earnings	Dividends	Book Value
10/14	3.76	3	2	1.87	0.00	(0.81)
10/13	5.06	32	20	0.22	0.00	(3.11)
10/12	4.30	—	—	(0.52)	0.00	(3.65)
10/11	1.44	—	—	(2.85)	0.00	(5.23)
10/10	3.56	266	114	0.03	0.00	(4.36)
Annual Growth	1.4%	—	—	—181.0%	—	—

Hurco Companies, Inc.

When it comes to improving automation and productivity Hurco happily helps. The company designs and makes computerized metal cutting and forming machine tools such as vertical machining (mills) and turning (lathes) centers as well as the software that automates the machinery. Its machines are manufactured and assembled by Taiwan subsidiary Hurco Manufacturing using components produced by neighboring contract suppliers. Hurco markets its five-axis machines through its TM/TMM TMX and VMX series and other specialty product lines. It sells to customers in the aerospace/military automotive computers/electronics energy medical equipment and transportation industries spanning about 50 countries.
Geographic Reach
Hurco subsidiaries are located in Canada China France Germany India Italy Poland Singapore

South Africa the UK and the US. Its manufacturing and distribution facilities reside in the Netherlands Taiwan China and the US.
  The company derives about 60% of its revenues from Europe. Around 10% of its sales come from the Asia/Pacific region due largely to its expansion into the markets of China and India where entry-level lower-priced machines are popular.
  Sales and Marketing
  Hurco sells its products through more than 100 independent agents and distributors targeting the aerospace defense medical equipment energy automotive/transportation electronics and computer equipment sectors. The end-users of its products include precision tool die and mold manufacturers independent metal parts manufacturers and specialized production application or prototype departments within large manufacturing companies.
Financial Performance
  Hurco has hit a setback after it managed to increase its revenue and finally get out of the red. After two straight years of growth the company saw its revenues drop 5% from $203 million in 2012 to $193 million in 2013. The declines for 2013 were attributed to the adverse impact of weak market conditions in Europe and the primary market for its high-performance machine tools and continuing weakness throughout the Asia/Pacific region.
  The company's profits also plunged 48% from $16 million in 2012 to $8 million in 2013 due to the decline in revenue coupled with a rise in other expenses as a result of foreign currency losses. Hurco's cash flows have fluctuated over the years showing peaks in 2010 and 2013 and drops in 2011 and 2012. The growth in cash flow for 2013 was due to a decrease in capital expenditures and an increase in inventories.
  Strategy
  Going forward Hurco continues to invest in research and development enabling introduction of new products touting productivity features. Also on the lookout for acquisitions Hurco in 2013 obtained the machine tool component business of LCM S.r.l an Italian designer and manufacturer of high-end electro-mechanical components and accessories for machine tools. LCM's products develop advanced machine tool technologies to support Hurco's customers who need a more versatile spectrum of CNC machine tools.

EXECUTIVES

Chairman and CEO, Michael Doar, $408,077 total
  compensation
VP Secretary Treasurer and CFO, Sonja K.
  McClelland, $168,077 total compensation
EVP Worldwide Sales and Service, John P. Donlon,
  $214,846 total compensation
President, Gregory S. Volovic, $248,077 total
  compensation
Senior Vice President Software Engineer, Darrel
  May
Vice President Of Engineer, Himat Patel
Vice-president, Lyn Hudson
Vice President Customer Service, Mike Garlick
Vice-president, Alex Shkiler
Chairman and CEO, Michael Doar
Board Of Directors, Janaki Sivanesan, age 44
Auditors: Ernst&YoungLLP

LOCATIONS

HQ: Hurco Companies, Inc.
  One Technology Way, Indianapolis, IN 46268
Phone: 317 293-5309   Fax: 317 328-2811
Web: www.hurco.com

2013 Sales

	$ mil.	% of total
Europe		
Germany	43.6	22
UK	27.4	14
France	10.9	6
Italy	8.7	5
Other countries	22.7	12
North America	60.7	31
Asia	17.4	9
Other regions	1.4	1
Total	**192.8**	**100**

PRODUCTS/OPERATIONS

2013 Sales

	$ mil.	% of total
Computerized machine tools	166.9	86
Service parts	16.5	9
Service fees	6.4	3
Computer control systems & software	3.0	2
Total	**192.8**	**100**

Selected Products

Computerized machine tools
  5-axis vertical machining centers
  Autobend/back gauges
  Controls
  Machining centers (vertical and horizontal)
  Metal-forming systems
  Milling machines
  Rotary tables
  Turning centers
Other
  Control upgrades
  Hardware accessories
  Replacement parts
  Retrofit systems for metal-cutting and metal-forming machine applications
  Software

COMPETITORS

DMG Mori Seiki	MAG Giddings & Lewis
Doosan Corp	Mazak
FANUC	NicolÂs Correa
Genesis Worldwide	Okuma
Gleason Corp.	Siemens AG
Haas Automation	TRUMPF
Hardinge	Thermwood
IMTA	Toyoda Machinery USA

HISTORICAL FINANCIALS

Company Type: Public

Income Statement

FYE: October 31

	REVENUE ($ mil.)	NET INCOME ($ mil.)	NET PROFIT MARGIN	EMPLOYEES
10/14	222.3	15.1	6.8%	617
10/13	192.8	8.1	4.2%	625
10/12	203.1	15.6	7.7%	560
10/11	180.4	11.1	6.2%	520
10/10	105.8	(5.7)	—	440
Annual Growth	**20.4%**	**—**	**—**	**8.8%**

2014 Year-End Financials

Debt ratio: 1.3%
Return on equity: 9.5%
Cash ($ mil.): 53
Current ratio: 3.15
Long-term debt ($ mil.): —
No. of shares (mil.): 6
Dividends
  Yield: 0.6%
  Payout: 14.0%
Market value ($ mil.): 251

	STOCK PRICE ($) FY Close	P/E High/Low		PER SHARE ($) Earnings	Dividends	Book Value
10/14	38.53	17	10	2.30	0.26	25.30
10/13	24.49	25	17	1.25	0.10	23.43
10/12	22.98	12	8	2.40	0.00	22.30
10/11	26.12	20	11	1.71	0.00	19.60
10/10	18.40			(0.89)	0.00	17.81
Annual Growth	**20.3%**	**—**	**—**	**—**	**—**	**9.2%**

Iconix Brand Group Inc

Once a shoemaker Iconix Brand Group has stepped it up as a licensing and brand management company. Its company-owned consumer and home brands are licensed to third parties that make and sell apparel footwear and a variety of other fashion and home products. Consumer brands in the Iconix stable include Badgley Mischka Danskin Ocean Pacific Mossimo London Fog Mudd and Rocawear; among the company's home brands are Cannon Fieldcrest and Waverly. The firm diversified through its high-profile purchase of the Peanuts cartoon brand from E. W. Scripps in 2010. Along with licensing the brands Iconix markets and promotes them through its in-house advertising and public relations services.

Iconix uses acquisitions to broaden its revenue stream and stretch its brand portfolio. The company owns about 20 brands and hopes to one day own a collection of 25-30 brands. To that end it acquired the Umbro football brand from shoe giant NIKE for $225 million in 2012.

In late 2011 Iconix acquired The Sharper Image brand from Sharper Image Acquisition LLC for about $66 million in cash. It projects the deal will add between $12 million and $13 million in annual royalty revenue. The Sharper Image brand name also blankets a wide variety of categories in the consumer electronics sector including audio and video electronics personal home products kitchen and bath accessories and travel gear among others.

Iconix previously made industry news in 2010 when it acquired a majority stake in United Media Licensing the owner of Charles M. Schulz's world-famous Peanuts brand and its cast of characters including Charlie Brown and Snoopy. Iconix and the Schulz family teamed up to buy the business for $175 million. (Iconix owns 80% of the company and the Schulz family owns the rest.) In addition the deal included properties such as disgruntled office worker Dilbert and children's book heroine Fancy Nancy. The deal was a strong play by Iconix to expand its business beyond fashion brands. Iconix also hopes the worldwide Peanuts presence will open up new international markets for its existing fashion business. (E. W. Scripps' United Media Syndicate subsidiary continues to syndicate the Peanuts comic strip.)

In May 2013 Iconix purchased the remaining 49% of urban fashion firm Marc Ecko Enterprises that it didn't already own for $45 million. The company had taken a controlling interest in the brand in 2009. The firm manages such brands as Ecko Unlimited Marc Ecko the Rhino logo and Zoo York.

Collectively the acquisitions of the Peanuts and Ecko assets generated around $90 million in ad-

ditional revenue for the company in 2010. Iconix also enjoyed a 31% increase in net income ($75 million to almost $99 million) from 2009 to 2010.

As another means for growth Iconix expects to grow through its licensing agreements with Wal-Mart to sell Ocean Pacific Danskin Now and Starter apparel and accessories. The company also is looking to international markets to boost revenues as the US economy weakens; it has joint ventures in China Europe and Latin America to advance its brands.

Iconix formerly a footwear company known as Candie's Inc. changed its name in 2005 to reflect a shift in focus from manufacturing to brand management. The company continues to keep a toe in the footwear business with the Candie's brand and through its subsidiary Bright Star which oversees the design and arranges for the manufacturing and distribution of men's shoes sold under private labels primarily by Wal-Mart.

EXECUTIVES

Svp Brand Management, Lanie Pilnock
Chairman President and CEO, Neil Cole, age 57, $1,500,000 total compensation
CFO, Jeff Lupinacci
EVP and CFO, Warren Clamen, age 50, $450,000 total compensation
EVP and General Counsel, Andrew Tarshis, age 48, $450,000 total compensation
EVP and Head Strategic Development, David Blumberg, age 55, $400,000 total compensation
COO, Seth Horowitz
Vp Finance, Gary Klein
Evp Men's Division, Rodney Hutton
Vice President Marketing, Jennifer Wexler
Vice President Men's Division, Bill Hackett
Executive Vice President Marketing Men's Division, Spencer Jameel
Chairman President and CEO, Neil Cole, age 57
Auditors: BDOSeidmanLLP

LOCATIONS

HQ: Iconix Brand Group Inc
  1450 Broadway, New York, NY 10018
Phone: 212 730-0030   **Fax:** 212 391-2057
Web: www.iconixbrand.com

2013 Sales

	$ mil.	% of total
US	292.6	68
Japan	29.7	7
Other countries	110.3	25
Total	**432.6**	**100**

PRODUCTS/OPERATIONS

2013 Sales

	$ mil.	% of total
Wholesale license	225.2	52
Direct-to-retail license	147.8	34
Entertainment & other (commissions sales of trademarks etc.)	59.6	14
Total	**432.6**	**100**

Selected Brands

Consumer
  Badgley Mischka
  Bongo
  Buffalo David Bitton (51%)
  Candie' s
  Danskin
  Dilbert
  Fancy Nancy
  Joe Boxer
  London Fog
  Material Girl
  Mossimo

Mudd
Ocean Pacific
Peanuts
Rampage
Rocawear
Starter
Home
Cannon
Charisma
Fieldcrest
Royal Velvet

COMPETITORS

Ann Taylor	L' OrÂ©al
Billabong	Levi Strauss
Calvin Klein	NIKE
Cherokee Inc.	Nine West
Collective Licensing	Pacific Sunwear
Diesel SpA	Pentland Group
Guess?	Quiksilver
H&M	R. Griggs
Hanesbrands	Ralph Lauren
J. C. Penney	The Gap
Jaclyn	VF Corporation
Jordache Enterprises	Vera Wang
Kate Spade	Williamson-Dickie
Kellwood	Manufacturing
L Brands	

HISTORICAL FINANCIALS

Company Type: Public

Income Statement

FYE: December 31

	REVENUE ($ mil.)	NET INCOME ($ mil.)	NET PROFIT MARGIN	EMPLOYEES
12/13	432.6	128.0	29.6%	151
12/12	353.8	109.4	30.9%	148
12/11	369.8	126.1	34.1%	129
12/10	332.5	98.8	29.7%	133
12/09	232.0	75.1	32.4%	66
Annual Growth	16.9%	14.3%	—	23.0%

2013 Year-End Financials

Debt ratio: 49.9%
Return on equity: 11.8%
Cash ($ mil.): 278
Current ratio: 3.73
Long-term debt ($ mil.): 1,366

No. of shares (mil.): 51
Dividends
  Yield: —
  Payout: —
Market value ($ mil.): 2,030

	STOCK PRICE ($) FY Close	P/E High/Low		PER SHARE ($) Earnings	Dividends	Book Value
12/13	39.70	18	10	2.11	0.00	19.26
12/12	22.32	14	9	1.52	0.00	17.81
12/11	16.29	15	8	1.67	0.00	16.36
12/10	19.31	15	9	1.32	0.00	14.29
12/09	12.67	16	6	1.10	0.00	12.71
Annual Growth	33.0%	—	—	17.7%	—	11.0%

IDEX Corporation

The idea at IDEX is to dispense with inefficiencies and pump up profits. The company organized into three business segments that consist of various operating units is a diversified manufacturer of pumps and other engineered products geared at different niche markets around the world. Its largest segment Fluid & Metering Technologies makes pumps flow meters and injectors used to handle or monitor water chemicals and fuels. Health & Science Technologies produces fluidics and pumps used in medical devices analytical instrumentation and photonics. The Fire & Safety/Diversified Products segment manufactures firefighting pumps and rescue tools including the branded Hurst Jaws of Life.

Geographic Reach

IDEX has production facilities in China and India that support multiple business units. Personnel in various locations in Europe Asia South America and the Middle East provide sales and marketing support to IDEX business units in those regions. The US accounts for nearly 50% of sales; Europe 25%.

Operations

The Fluid & Metering Technologies segment (43% of total sales) is made up of such business units as Banjo (special-purpose severe-duty pumps valves and fittings); Energy & Fuels (including Liquid Controls); Chemical Food & Process Diaphragm & Dosing Pump Technology; and Water Services & Technology. This segment serves a range of markets including agriculture chemical processing food and beverage industrial infrastructure (fossil and alternative fuels) plastics pulp and paper transportation and water and wastewater.

The Health & Science Technologies segment (35%) consists of IDEX Health & Science; IDEX Optics & Photonics; Containment; Gast; Micropump; and Materials Process Technologies (including Microfluidics and Quadro Engineering). Meanwhile the Fire & Safety/Diversified Products segment (22%) is comprised of the Fire Suppression Rescue Band-It and Dispensing Equipment units.

Financial Performance

IDEX saw its revenues reach a record-setting high in 2013 spiking 4% to $2.02 billion. The historic growth for 2013 was driven by a 5% increase in Fluid & Metering Technologies due to organic growth of 2%. In addition Health & Science Technologies and Fire & Safety/Diversified Products each increased by 2% for the year.

After experiencing a massive 81% drop in profits during 2012 the company saw its profits significantly soar by more than 500% to peak at a record-setting $255 million in 2013. This was primarily due to the absence of asset impairments charges of $199 million and $33 million of restructuring expenses throughout 2013 that were present the previous year.

Strategy

IDEX's strategy is to grow through organic investments and acquisitions. In 2014 it purchased Aegis Flow Technologies for $26 million. Aegis makes valve products and will be integrated into IDEX's Fluid & Metering Technologies segment. In 2013 IDEX swallowed up FTL Seals Technology a maker of rotary seals specialty bearings and other custom products for the oil and gas mining power generation and marine markets. The deal fortified IDEX's Precision Polymer Engineering subsidiary within its Health & Science Technologies segment.

The company also boosted its Health & Science Technologies' optics and photonics capabilities by acquiring Colorado-based Precision Photonics Corporation (PPC) for $20.6 million in 2012 and purchasing New Mexico-based CVI Melles Griot (CVI MG) for about $395 million in mid-2011. PPC makes optical components and coatings for applications for such markets as scientific research aerospace and telecommunications. CVI makes lasers and light sources and other electro-optical and opto-mechanical components and assemblies.

HISTORY

IDEX is the successor of Houdaille (pronounced "WHO-dye") Industries which took its name from Maurice Houdaille the French inventor of recoilless artillery used in World War I. After that war a US firm bought the name and the rights to Houdaille's patented rotary shock absorber. By the 1930s Houdaille was the #1 maker of shock absorbers in the US. During WWII it was involved in building the atomic bomb. With the trend toward in-house manufacture by the auto giants in the 1950s the company diversified into industrial and construction products pumps and machine tools. Facing difficult economic conditions Phil Reilly (Houdaille's then CEO-nominee) and investors Kohlberg Kravis Roberts took the company private in 1979 in the first leveraged buyout of any company worth more than $100 million.

In 1987 IDEX (an acronym for "innovation diversity and excellence") was formed to buy back six units Houdaille had sold to the British TI Group earlier that year. In 1989 IDEX went public. Following the IPO the company pursued an aggressive acquisition strategy. Purchases included Corken (1991) Devjo's Pump Group (now Viking Pump 1992) and Hale Products (1994).

The company acquired Micropump (small magnetically driven pumps) for $33 million in 1995. The following year it paid $135 million for Fluid Management a top maker of color-formulation equipment for paints coatings inks and dyes.

In 1998 IDEX acquired Gast Manufacturing which makes vacuum pumps air motors and compressors for about $118 million. The following year it gained a foothold in Italy when it paid $62 million for FAST (refinishing and color-formulation equipment). In 2000 IDEX acquired Trebor International maker of high purity fluid handling products for the microelectronics industry.

In 2001 IDEX acquired displacement flow meter and process control systems maker Liquid Controls LLC. Acquisitions in 2003 included Sponsler Co. (turbine meters) and Classic Engineering (industrial pumps). In early 2004 Idex acquired Manfred Vetter a Germany-based rescue equipment (pneumatic lifting and sealing bags) manufacturer as well as Systec a vacuum degassing product manufacturer. Later in the year IDEX purchased Scivex a pump and valve manufacturer that serves medical companies.

In 2006 it acquired Banjo Corporation which makes specialized pumps and related hardware for handling fluids in agricultural and industrial applications. The following year the company expanded its sanitary control operations with the purchase of Quadro Engineering which provides particle handling products to the pharmaceutical laboratory market. Quadro operates as a unit of IDEX's FMT segment. That same year it picked up Isolation Technologies which makes analytical chemistry instruments. IDEX paid about $30 million for the company.

Acquisitions in 2008 (Richter Integrated Environmental Technology Group and iPEK) gave IDEX additional water distribution and sewer management products and services as well as wastewater infrastructure inspection capabilities. These deals followed IDEX's move to pick up ADS a provider of metering technology and flow monitoring services. Later in 2008 IDEX's HST segment snagged Semrock a supplier of optical filters was acquired. The deal widened IDEX's access to health and life science OEMs specializing in biotechnology and analytical instrumentation.

In 2010 IDEX purchased Seals Ltd. (now called PPE) a manufacturer of advanced sealing systems for about $54 million. The company now operating within the HST segment opened the door to new markets including clean room food processing and pharmaceutical research.

The next year IDEX scooped up Colorado-based Advanced Thin Films for $34.5 million. Advanced Thin Films added optics design technology as well as an impressive list of customers to the Health & Science Technologies segment. Boosting its Fluid & Metering Technologies segment IDEX in spring 2011 acquired Microfluidics in a $18.5 million cash deal that added pharmaceutical and chemical equipment for making micro particles.

EXECUTIVES

Vice President Accounting, Michael J Yates, age 49
SVP and CFO, Heath A. Mitts, age 42, $455,289 total compensation
Chairman and CEO, Andrew K. Silvernail, age 42, $856,808 total compensation
SVP and Group Executive Industrial Markets, Brett Finley, age 43
SVP and CIO, James MacLennan, age 50
SVP and Group Executive Health and Science Technologies, Eric D. Ashleman
SVP and Group Executive, Matthew J. Stillings
Vice President Sales Emea Mpt Group, Xavier Leroy
Vice President Of Marketing And Business Development, Turan Erdogan
National Accounts Manager, Michael Hurley
Vice President Human Resources And Corporate, Dan Goitein
Vice President Strategy And Business Development Fluid And Metering, John Boland
Executive Vice President Human Resources Health And Science Technologies, Jeff Krautkramer
Vice President Of Operations, Bob Hallock
Vice President Of Global Sales, Kevin Marzano
Vice President Of Engineering, Del Thomas
Vice President Corporate Strategy And Strategic Planning, Peter Johansson
Vice President Human Resources Energy And Fuels, Andrea Davey
Vice President Acquisition Integration, Art Laszlo
Business Line Vice President Mame, Krishna Ranganathan
Chairman and CEO, Andrew K. Silvernail, age 42
Auditors: Deloitte&ToucheLLP

LOCATIONS

HQ: IDEX Corporation
1925 West Field Court, Lake Forest, IL 60045
Phone: 847 498-7070
Web: www.idexcorp.com

2013 Sales

	$ mil.	% of total
US	983.8	49
Europe	521.5	26
Asia	306.5	15
Other countries	212.3	10
Total	**2024.1**	**100**

PRODUCTS/OPERATIONS

2013 Sales

	$ mil.	% of total
Fluid & Metering Technologies	870.7	43
Health & Science Technologies	708.9	35
Fire & Safety/Diversified Products	444.5	22
Total	**2024.1**	**100**

Selected Business Units Products and Brands

Fire & Safety/Diversified Products
BAND-IT (stainless-steel bands buckles and clamping systems)
Hale-Fire Suppression and Hale-Hydraulic Equipment (fire pumps and rescue tool systems)
HURST Jaws of Life/LUKAS/Dinglee/Vetter (hydraulic rescue tools re-railing equipment lifting and position devices)
Fluid & Metering Technologies
ADS (metering and flow monitoring equipment)
Air operated double diaphragm pumps (air-operated and motor-driven double diaphragm pumps)
Banjo (severe-duty pumps valves fittings and systems)
iPEK (remote-controlled infrastructure inspection equipment)
Liquid controls (flow meters and electronic controls)
Pulsafeeder (rotary pumps metering pumps peristaltic pumps electronic controls and dispensing equipment)
Richter (corrosion-resistant lined pumps valves and controls)
Viking Pump (gear pumps strainers and reducers and controls)
Health & Science Technologies
Gast Manufacturing (air motors blowers compressors vacuum generators and vacuum pumps)
HST Core (valves fitting injectors medical tubing assemblies optical filters filter sensors nano-fluidic components and engineered plastics)
Micropump (rotary gear piston and centrifugal pumps)
Seals Ltd. (seals for analytical instrumentation clean room environments food processing hazardous applications and pharmaceutical research)

Selected Markets

Agriculture
Analytical instrumentation
Chemical processing
Clinical diagnostics
Custom precision dispensing
Fire and rescue
Fuels and energy
Medical
Sanitary
Semiconductor
Water

COMPETITORS

American Cast Iron Pipe	Parker-Hannifin
Dover Corp.	Pentair
Flowserve	Robbins & Myers
Gardner Denver	Roper Industries
Gorman-Rupp	Thermo Fisher Scientific
Graco	Tuthill
Graham Corp.	United Technologies
ITT Corp.	Weir Group
Illinois Tool Works	Wilden Pump & Engineering
Oilgear	
Panduit	

HISTORICAL FINANCIALS

Company Type: Public

Income Statement

FYE: December 31

	REVENUE ($ mil.)	NET INCOME ($ mil.)	NET PROFIT MARGIN	EMPLOYEES
12/13	2,024.1	255.2	12.6%	6,787
12/12	1,954.2	37.6	1.9%	6,717
12/11	1,838.4	193.8	10.5%	6,814
12/10	1,513.0	157.1	10.4%	5,966
12/09	1,329.6	113.3	8.5%	5,300
Annual Growth	**11.1%**	**22.5%**	**—**	**6.4%**

2013 Year-End Financials

Debt ratio: 26.8%
Return on equity: 16.8%
Cash ($ mil.): 439
Current ratio: 3.25
Long-term debt ($ mil.): 772
No. of shares (mil.): 81
Dividends
  Yield: 1.2%
  Payout: 103.4%
Market value ($ mil.): 5,996

	STOCK PRICE ($) FY Close	P/E High/Low	PER SHARE ($)		
			Earnings	Dividends	Book Value
12/13	73.85	24 15	3.09	0.89	19.37
12/12	46.53	103 80	0.45	0.77	17.71
12/11	37.11	20 13	2.32	0.66	18.18
12/10	39.12	21 14	1.90	0.57	16.76
12/09	31.15	23 12	1.40	0.48	15.66
Annual Growth	**24.1%**	**— —**	**21.9%**	**16.7%**	**5.5%**

iGate Corp

iGate is open to all things IT. The company provides business process outsourcing (BPO) and offshore development services including software development and maintenance outsourcing. In addition to IT-related services iGate handles such tasks as mortgage and claims processing and call center operations. The company targets midsized and large corporations in the banking financial services and insurance industries. Its more than 300 active customers include General Electric IBM Royal Bank of Canada and TEKsystems. The majority of iGate's operations are in India but the company earns most of its sales from customers in North America.

Operations
iGate separates itself from the pack by offering both IT and business services in what it calls the iTOPS (integrated technology and operations) model. Other companies including rival Infosys manage their IT and business operations separately which iGate claims can lead to competing interests and redundancy. The company specializes in BPO applications by Oracle (PeopleSoft and Siebel) and SAP.

Geographic Reach
While headquartered in the US most of its employees are based in India which has lower wages than the US and Europe for skilled technical professionals. iGate maintains more than 3 million sq. ft. of office space in India compared to its 12000-sq.-ft. corporate headquarters in the US.

iGate also has offices in Australia Canada China Japan Malaysia Mauritius Mexico Singapore South Africa Switzerland the UAE and the UK.

Sales and Marketing
The company's customer base fell to about 300 in 2012 down from 380 in 2011 as iGate ended relationships with some of its smaller clients in order to focus on larger accounts. Its top two customers General Electric and the Royal Bank of Canada together account for about a quarter of overall sales.

Financial Performance
iGate became a billion-dollar company in 2012 after acquiring India-based Patni. In 2013 overall sales grew 7% to $1.15 billion while profits climbed 35% to $129 million.

Mergers and Acquisitions
In 2011 iGate bought a majority stake in Patni Computer in a transaction valued at around $1 billion. Patni Computer the sixth- largest Indian software exporter was considered a pioneer of the outsourcing industry in India. By 2012 iGate acquired the remainder of Patni which has since been absorbed into iGate.

HISTORY

Sunil Wadhwani and Ashok Trivedi Indian emigrants who met at a party in the late 1970s formed Mastech in 1986. Started in Carnegie Mellon graduate Wadhwani's home the company offered systems integration and networked computer software development consultants to IT departments. Demand blossomed with the increased pace of technological change that left in-house IT departments struggling and sales leapt from $200000 in 1987 to $50 million by 1993.

Mastech fed its expansion by making overseas recruiting a top priority. The company attracted a broad base of technical talent interested in traveling the US on different jobs rather than working full-time at a single company. In the mid-1990s Mastech established an offshore software development facility in India to take advantage of that country's lower employment costs and its large pool of qualified job candidates.

The company opened offices in Canada and Singapore in 1995 and went public a year later. It continued growth in 1999 through acquisitions buying UK financial services firm Direct Resources among others.

In 2000 Mastech restructured as a holding company changing its name to iGate Capital and forming independent e-commerce consulting-focused units. Also that year it formed a venture fund to invest in e-services companies. The restructuring helped cause losses for 2000. In response iGate stopped funding the investment arm in 2001 and shuttered or sold its interests in several operating companies.

In 2002 it further divested and changed its name to iGATE Corporation. It formed iGATE Clinical Research International (formerly iGATE Clinical Management) in 2003 through the acquisition of 90% of Pennsylvania clinical trial manager PCRN a group created by the University of Pittsburgh Medical Center. iGate also acquired DiagnoSearch a clinical research outsourcer based in India in 2003.

The company sold its recruiting and placement firm jobcurry in 2007.

EXECUTIVES

Senior Vice President Legal, Mukund Srinath
CEO and Director, Ashok Vemuri, age 47, $379,167 total compensation
EVP and Chief People Officer, Srinivas Kandula, age 50, $150,121 total compensation
EVP and CFO, Sujit Sircar, age 46, $157,045 total compensation
EVP and Head of Banking and Financial Services North America, Sanjay Tugnait, $499,229 total compensation
EVP and Global Head of Strategic Deals Team, Derek Kemp, $568,900 total compensation
SVP and Head of Europe and Australia, Srikanth Iyengar
Associate Vice President Sales, Anil Patel
Vice President, Navin Gupta
Assistant Vice President Organizational, Taranjit Rekhi
Vice President Healthcare Life, Vivek Sondhi
Co-Chairman, Ashok Trivedi, age 64
Co-Chairman, Sunil Wadhwani, age 61
CEO and Director, Ashok Vemuri, age 47
Auditors: Ernst&Young

LOCATIONS

HQ: iGate Corp
100 Somerset Corporate Blvd, Bridgewater, NJ 08807
Phone: 908 219-8050
Web: www.igate.com

2012 Sales

	% of total
North America	81
Europe	13
Asia-Pacific	6
Total	**100**

PRODUCTS/OPERATIONS

Selected Services

Application Development
Application Management
BI and DW
Business Process Management
CIS and BPO
Customized Learning Solutions
Embedded Systems
Engineering Services
Enterprise Application Solutions
Enterprise Integration
Enterprise Mobility
Infrastructure Management
IT Consulting
IT Governance
IT Services
Open Source Software Services
User Experience Management
Verification and Validation
Web Technology Solutions

COMPETITORS

ADP	Getronics
Accenture	HCL Technologies
Boston Consulting	HP Enterprise Group
CGI Group	HP Enterprise Services
Capgemini	Hexaware Technologies
Cognizant Tech Solutions	IBM Global Services
	Infosys
Computer Enterprises	MindTree
Computer Sciences Corp.	Tata Consultancy
	Tech Mahindra
Deloitte Consulting	Wipro Technologies
Genpact	

HISTORICAL FINANCIALS

Company Type: Public

Income Statement

FYE: December 31

	REVENUE ($ mil.)	NET INCOME ($ mil.)	NET PROFIT MARGIN	EMPLOYEES
12/13	1,150.9	129.7	11.3%	29,733
12/12	1,073.9	95.8	8.9%	27,616
12/11	779.6	51.4	6.6%	26,889
12/10	280.6	51.7	18.4%	8,338
12/09	193.1	28.5	14.8%	6,910
Annual Growth	**56.2%**	**46.0%**	—	**44.0%**

2013 Year-End Financials

Debt ratio: 62.2%	No. of shares (mil.): 58
Return on equity: 27.0%	Dividends
Cash ($ mil.): 204	Yield: —
Current ratio: 1.53	Payout: —
Long-term debt ($ mil.): 680	Market value ($ mil.): 2,347

	STOCK PRICE ($) FY Close	P/E High/Low		PER SHARE ($) Earnings	Dividends	Book Value
12/13	40.16	32	11	1.21	0.00	8.25
12/12	15.77	22	17	0.85	0.00	8.31
12/11	15.73	51	24	0.38	0.00	7.51
12/10	19.71	27	10	0.90	0.26	4.41
12/09	10.00	19	4	0.51	0.11	3.47
Annual Growth	**41.6%**		— —	**24.1%**	—	**24.2%**

IHS Inc

IHS Inc. (Information Handling Services Inc.) handles the hottest commodity around: information. A publisher of technical documents for clients in industries such as energy defense aerospace electronics and automotive the company distributes its data in several electronic formats (Internet intranet extranet CD-ROM). Products such as collections of technical specifications and standards regulations parts data and design guides are sold through its four areas of information: Energy Product Lifecycle Security and Environment. The company also offers economic-focused information and analysis through its IHS Global Insight subsidiary. IHS primarily earns revenue through subscription sales.

The company specializes in delivering information to engineers designers technical professionals senior managers compliance officers marketing executives and strategic planners at both small and large businesses as well as goverment agencies. Topics range from detailed technical specifications to industry trends and geopolitical analysis.

IHS's Energy segment is focused on information related to all aspects of oil and gas exploration development production and transportation while its Product Lifecycle segment provides information on all areas of a product's development including conception research production maintenance and disposal. The Security segment focuses on topics such as defense aerospace and weapon systems and the Environment segment provides data to help customers comply with environmental regulations and related issues.

Subscription sales account for more than 75% of business. In 2011 the company achieved higher revenues compared to the previous year due to an increase in subscription sales. (It also reported a dip in net income due to pension-related costs without which net income would have increased.) Much of this increase in subscription sales is due to its acquisition activity a key component of the company's growth strategy. IHS has completed more than 40 purchases since its IPO in 2005. The acquisitions reflect the firm's growth strategy of selecting information-intensive companies in industries in which it already has a significant presence such as energy defense manufacturing and technology.

In 2012 the company made a string of strategic acquisitions to enhance its capabilities in technology media and telecommunications electronic components and energy. That year it acquired GlobalSpec provider of a searchable online database of supplier catalogs for engineers from Warburg Pincus for $135 million. IHS also purchased Displaybank a provider of market research and consulting for the display industry; the Computer Assisted Product Selection electronic components database and tools business; and the digital oil and gas pipeline and infrastructure information business from Hild Technology Services. The combined purchase price of those three acquisitions was approximately $45 million.

IHS made its largest acquisition to date in 2011 when it purchased Seismic Micro-Technology a provider of geoscience software for $500 million in cash. The deal enabled IHS to provide information browsing and analysis tools for the oil and gas industry. Prior key acquisitions gave the company subsidiaries such as IHS Jane's (a provider of information and analysis on global defense and security) and IHS Global Insight (economic-focused research). And in 2011 the company formed IHS Chemical in part from assets it acquired from Access Intelligence (business-to-business periodicals in the energy and chemical sectors including Chemical Week and The Energy Daily).

All total IHS operates in some 180 countries; nearly 50% of its sales are conducted outside of the US. The company's sales teams are organized to support three geographic segments: Americas; Europe Middle East and Africa; and the Asia/Pacific region.

The Thyssen-Bornemisza family controls about 25% of IHS.

HISTORY

IHS Group traces its roots to Rogers Publishing a company formed by Thomas Rogers in the 1940s to publish engineering magazine "Design News." In the 1950s Rogers Publishing branched into automated information retrieval systems choosing microfilm as a publishing medium for reference information.

In 1959 Richard O'Brien an executive with Rogers Publishing developed a product catalog database for aerospace engineers. The flagship product Vendor Specs Microfilm File (VSMF) was indexed to locate information quickly and was produced on microfilm to conserve space that was generally occupied by libraries of hardcopy documents. When Cahners Publishing bought Rogers in 1961 the technical services division which included catalog operations was spun off as a separate company and named Information Handling Services (IHS).

An extended series of acquisitions helped to shape the company and bring it to the forefront of technical publishing. By the 1980s global giant TBG had become Information Handling Services' parent company and established the foundation for further growth. IHS Group was formed in 1989 as the holding company for new subsidiaries as the company expanded into other markets including regulatory information and entered the international arena through a series of acquisitions.

Among the company's 1990s acquisitions were Beilstein Informationssysteme (Germany 1994) Global Info Center Hong Kong (1994) Media Library (Japan 1995) and Petroconsultants (Switzerland 1996). The company branched into cyberspace in 1997 with the debut of its first Web-based products. Focusing on Web-based and electronic products IHS Group ceased production of microfilm products the following year.

As IHS Group expanded into energy information. it acquired Petroleum Information/Dwights PI (ERICO) IEDS MAI Consultants and QC Data Petroleum Services Division and its AccuMap Enerdata Division forming IHS Energy in 1998 as a separate division of IHS Group to streamline energy information operations and services.

In 2000 IHS Group formed a joint venture with standards and quality service organization British Standards Institution (BSI) to distribute BSI's content. Additional acquisitions included the 2004 purchase of USA Information Systems and Intermat the 2004 purchase of Cambridge Energy Research Associates (CERA) and the 2005 acquisition of American Technical Publishers.

IHS underwent a reorganization in 2005 which included 100 job cuts and two office closings in its Engineering segment; also that year the company filed an initial public offering and began using the name IHS Inc. In 2006 IHS further reduced its headcount by 40 and sold certain IHS Energy assets.

Also in 2006 the company bought geoPLUS Corporation (software used by oil and gas companies to analyze data from oil and gas wells); Construction Research Communications Limited (products relating to the construction industry ranging from environmental issues to fire safety); and Canadian Hydrodynamics Ltd (drillstem test information for the Western Canadian Sedimentary Basin).

Purchases in 2007 included Jane's Information Group a provider of information and analysis on global defense and security (now IHS Jane's) and John S. Herold Inc. a research firm specializing in the oil and gas sector (now IHS Herold). Also in 2007 it acquired EnvironMax a provider of environmental management information systems; and McCloskey Group a coal research firm.

In 2008 the company added economic-focused research offerings to its portfolio with the purchase of consulting firm Global Insight which became IHS Global Insight after the deal closed. IHS paid about $165 million in cash and stock for Global Insight. In 2009 IHS acquired Environmental Support Solutions (ESS) for approximately $59 million. ESS provides software to help companies comply with environmental health and safety regulations.

Acquisitions in 2010 included Atrion International (hazardous materials document management) and Syntex Management Systems (operational risk management software and services) for a combined purchase price of about $80 million. IHS bought those two companies in order to beef up its Environment practice. Later in 2010 IHS acquired iSuppli for approximately $94 million. The iSuppli deal included Screen Digest Limited a digital media and technology research company. iSuppli and Screen Digest boosts IHS's technology value chain research and advisory services.

Also in 2010 the company added a few key business-to-business periodicals to its holdings with the acquisition of the energy and chemical portfolio of information publisher Access Intelligence for approximately $79 million. Included in the deal were key brands such as Chemical Week and The Energy Daily. In 2011 IHS made its largest acquisition yet when it obtained Seismic Micro-Technology for $500 million.

EXECUTIVES

Senior Vice President Finance, Gil Hamilton
Executive Vice President Legal, Stephen Green, age 63
Vice President Investor Relations, Andy Schulz
Vice President, Graham W Howard
Chairman and CEO, Jerre L. Stead, age 71, $602,154 total compensation
EVP Global Finance, Richard G. (Rich) Walker, age 51, $382,321 total compensation
SVP and CIO, Mark F. Settle, age 61
VP Finance Engineering Segment, Todd Hyatt
President and COO, Scott Key, age 55, $527,061 total compensation
EVP; Chairman CERA, Daniel Yergin, age 67, $600,000 total compensation
EVP of Information and Insight Operations and Research and Analysis, Arshad Matin
Executive Vice President Products and OperationsAnurag, Anurag Gupta
Vice President Commodities, Mark Ulmer
Vp Ihs Canada, Carl Garrison
Vice President Standards Business, Richards David
Vice President Inside Sales, John Lysinger
Vice President Sales, Charles Dunn
Vp International, Brian Sweeney

Vice President Aerospace And Defence, Blake Bartlett
Vice President Chief Legal Counsel, Jaspal Chahal
Senior Vice President Research, Atul Arya
Vice President Of Information, Chris Doig
Vice President Of Technology Systems, Tatyana Lavrova
Vice President Sales Logtech, Darin Brazel
Vice President Of Technology, Lynn Danielson
Vice President Big Data And Analytics, Michael Dejesus
Senior Vice President Financial Planning And Analysis, Michael Easton
Senior Vice President Worldwide Product Development, Randy Harvey
Senior Vice President Senior Financial Editor, Tom Biracree
Vice President It, Andrzej Dostatni
Vice President Business Development, Anthony Armando
Vice President Energy Sales, Philip Salisbury
Vice President Of Information Systems, Jay Meyerson
Vice President Supply Chain Global, Glenn Bassett
Vice President Human Resources Apac, Paul McAvoy
Vice President Sr Eqty Analyst Ihs, Matti Teittinen
Vice President Sales Emea, Jim Osbourne
Clinical Director, Charles Knifechief
Vice President Of Information Systems, Matt Robertson
Vice President, Mark Eramo
Vice President Energy Research Upstream And Downstream, Andrew Slaughter
Vice President And Chief Analyst, Dale Ford
Vice President Of Information Systems, Kumar Guhan
Vice President Of Information Systems, Anandhi Chandran
Vice President Of Technology Systems, Kath Watkins
Vice President, Stewart Johnston
Senior Vice President Energy Technical, Slavo Pastor
Vice President Research Upstream, Peter Jackson
Vice President Sales, Andrew Vasko
Vice President Of Information, David Mansel
Vice President Tax, Steve McGuar
Senior Vice President Information Services, Michael Thorne
Vice President Syndicated Research, Peter Augustini
Vice President Of Information Systems, Jessica Michael
Vice President Ihs Canada, Russ Sagert
Vice President Americas, Ken Aubrey
Senior Vice President Of Information Technology, Jayalakshmi Srinivas
Senior Vice President Legal Reg Cmpl, Yelena Shliomenzon
Vice President Of Information Systems, Sara Morgan
Vice President Sales, Johannes Lapre
Vice President Commercial Information Technology, Frank Wade
Vice President Manufacturing, Art Salmons
Vice President Energy Content Delivery, Franz Deimbacher
Vice President Customer Care Emea Coe, Mary Burke
Vice President Of Information Systems, Celeste Penney
Vp Marketing, Tim Hopkins
Vice President Of Global Sales Strategy, Brad Turner
Vice President Chemical Strategy Consulting, John Mulholland

Vice President Of Information Technology, Jim Croteau
Vice President, Tony Nash
Vice President Business Groups Chemical, Don Bari
Vice President Asia Pacific, Tony Potter
Vice President Of Technology Systems, Eric Knight
Vice President Consulting, Nick Lowes
Vice President Engineering, Ryan Saunders
Vice President Product Development Ehs, Ted Williams
Vice President Of Software Engineering, Hugo Kohmann
Senior Vice President Worldwide Product, Randy Martin
Vice President Chief Counsel Apac, Paul Wu
Senior Vice President Human Resources, James Yost
Vice President Global Gas Consulting, Ron Kapavik
Clinical Director, Ann Vaughn
Vice President Downstream Research, Bill Sanderson
Vice President, Justin Pettit
Senior Vice President Publications, Tom Whitman
Vice President Solution Marketing, Jon Ekoniak
Executive Vice President Of Information Technology, Cyrus Chinoy
Clinical Director, Harry Goldenberg
Medical Director, Francis Torres
Director Of Nursing, Sherry Killingsworth
Vice President, Susan Farrell
Vice President E&m Research, Ian Weightman
Vice President Of Information Technology, Mike Orendorf
Vice President Of Information Technology, John Kiefer
Vice President, John Lorson
Clinical Director, Ira Salom
Vice President Senior Equity Analyst, Dan Pratt
Vice President, Gil Nebeker
Vice President, David Brown
Vice President, Bill Harradence
Vice President Digital Media Sales Global Specialist, Katherine Rizzuto
Chairman and CEO, Jerre L. Stead, age 71
Vice President Corporate Treasurer, Grant Nicholson
Board Member, Cyndi Tamayo
Board Vice Chair, Chris Allen
Secretary, Jannie Nelson
Board Member, Balakrishna Iyer
Auditors: Ernst&YoungLLP

LOCATIONS

HQ: IHS Inc
15 Inverness Way East, Englewood, CO 80112
Phone: 303 790-0600
Web: www.ihs.com

2014 Sales

	$ mil.	% of total
Americas	1470.3	66
Europe Middle East & Africa	549.0	25
Asia/Pacific	211.5	9
Total	**2230.8**	**100**

PRODUCTS/OPERATIONS

2014 sales

	$ mil.	% of total
Subscription	1719.6	77
Non-Subscription	511.2	23
Total	**2230.8**	**100**

2014 Sales

	$ mil.	% of total
Resources	927.2	42
Industrials	736.4	33
Horizontal Products	567.2	25
Total	**2230.8**	**100**

Selected Information Offerings

Energy
  Exploration analysis
  Oil and gas well data
  Production data
  Reservoir data
Product Lifecycle
  Catalog information
  Electronic components parts information
  Government parts information
  Regulatory data
  Specifications and standards
Security
  Defense forecasting
  Ports and terminals data
  Public safety handbooks and guides
  Terrorism and insurgency monitoring
Environment
  Climate change greenhouse gas and sustainability information
  Hazardous materials compliance

Selected Acquisitions

Canadian Hydrodynamics Ltd (2006 drillstem test information for the Western Canadian Sedimentary Basin $3.5 million)
CDS (2005 electronic component parts data $33 million)
CERA (2004 research service $31 million)
Chemical Market Associates (2011 chemical information and analysis $73 million)
Construction Research Communications Limited (2006 construction industry data $5.8 million)
Documental Solutions (2008 market intelligence and analysis tools for the defense and aerospace industry $22.2 million)
Dolphin Software (2008 chemical data information and software $23.7 million)
Emerging Energy Research (2010 advisory for technological and regulatory trends in emerging energy $18 million)
Environmental Support Solutions (2009; environmental health and safety and crisis management software; $59 million)
geoPLUS Corporation (2006 software used by oil and gas companies to analyze data $42.1 million)
Global Insight (2008; global economic information analysis and consulting; $165 million)
Intermat (2004 decision support $5 million)
International Petrodata Limited (2004 geological information provider $16 million)
iSuppli (2010 technology value chain research and advisory services $94 million)
McCloskey Group (2007 coal research firm $28 million)
ODS-Petrodata (2011 information and market intelligence to the offshore energy industry $75 million)
Seismic Micro-Technology (2011 geoscience software $500 million)
USA Information Systems (2004 decision support $20 million)

COMPETITORS

Advanstar	John Wiley
Bureau of National Affairs	MSDSonline
Crain Communications	McGraw Hill Financial
Divestco	Nielsen
GlobalSpec	Pearson plc
Hearst Corporation	Penton Media
Informa	Reed Elsevier Group
International Data Group	Thomson Reuters
	Wolters Kluwer
	ubm

HISTORICAL FINANCIALS

Company Type: Public

Income Statement

FYE: November 30

	REVENUE ($ mil.)	NET INCOME ($ mil.)	NET PROFIT MARGIN	EMPLOYEES
11/14	2,230.7	194.5	8.7%	8,800
11/13	1,840.6	131.7	7.2%	8,000
11/12	1,529.8	158.1	10.3%	6,000
11/11	1,325.6	135.4	10.2%	5,500
11/10	1,075.4	141.3	13.1%	4,400
Annual Growth	**20.0%**	**8.3%**	**—**	**18.9%**

2014 Year-End Financials

Debt ratio: 34.4%	No. of shares (mil.): 68
Return on equity: 9.5%	Dividends
Cash ($ mil.): 153	Yield: —
Current ratio: 0.81	Payout: —
Long-term debt ($ mil.): 1,806	Market value ($ mil.): 8,373

	STOCK PRICE ($) FY Close	P/E High/Low		PER SHARE ($) Earnings	Dividends	Book Value
11/14	122.46	50	39	2.81	0.00	31.59
11/13	114.43	59	45	1.95	0.00	28.30
11/12	92.14	49	34	2.37	0.00	24.16
11/11	88.38	43	33	2.06	0.00	21.26
11/10	72.32	34	22	2.18	0.00	18.31
Annual Growth	**14.1%**	**—**		**6.6%**	**—**	**14.6%**

II-VI Inc.

II-VI sees the world through amber-colored lenses. The company (pronounced "two-six") makes lenses mirrors prisms and other optical components and materials. It also produces selenium and tellurium metals and silicon carbide substrates. II-VI's clients —drawn from the aerospace health care industrial military and telecom equipment sectors —use these components in lasers and other systems used in precision manufacturing communications networks military targeting and navigation systems and other applications. The company has manufacturing operations throughout the US as well as in Asia and Germany. Customers have included Caterpillar Volkswagen Raytheon and the US government.

Geographic Reach

The US is II-VI's largest market accounting for 45% of its total sales. China is next representing more than 20% of annual sale while Germany represents about 10%. The company has production facilities in nine US states including its home state of Pennsylvania and half a dozen foreign countries such as China and Vietnam.

Operations

Vertically integrated II-VI operates four primary business segments. The largest is infrared optics which accounts for more than a third of its sales. II-VI Infrared manufactures optical and opto-electronic components for industrial laser and thermal imaging systems and subsidiary HIGHYAG Lasertechnologie GmbH ((YAG stands for yttrium aluminum garnet) manufactures fiber-delivered beam delivery systems and processing tools for industrial lasers.

The near-infrared optics business (nearly 30% of sales) Photop Technologies manufactures crystal materials optics microchip lasers and opto-electronic modules for use in optical communication networks and other diverse consumer and commercial applications. Photop Aegis makes tunable optical devices required for high speed optical networks that provide the bandwidth expansion necessary for increasing Internet traffic.

II-VI's military & materials business (20% of sales) LightWorks Optical Systems manufactures infrared products for military applications precision optical systems and components for defense aerospace industrial and life science applications. Lastly the advanced products group the Wide Bandgap Materials unit manufactures and markets single crystal silicon carbide substrates for use in the solid-state lighting wireless infrastructure RF electronics and power switching industries; Marlow Industries Inc. (Marlow) designs and manufactures thermoelectric cooling and power generation solutions for use in defense space photonics telecommunications medical consumer and industrial markets.

Financial Performance

The company reported sales of about $558 million in fiscal 2013 (ended June) a 4% increase versus the prior year. Net income declined by 16% over the same period. Driving the revenue gain in fiscal 2013 was a 28% jump in sales by the company's Advance Products Group buoyed by the acquisition of M Cubed Technologies in November 2012. The infrared optics business posted a modest 1% increase in sales while near-infrared optics saw sales climb 11%. The Military & Materials business saw its sales fall 12% on lower product demand and pricing for both tellurium and selenium at Pacific Rare Specialty Metals & Chemicals (PRM) which more than offset the additional revenue resulting from the purchase of LightWorks Optics in December 2012.

On a geographic basis sales in the US (II-VI's largest market) increased 23% in fiscal 2013 compared to the prior year while international sales declined 1% over the same period. Germany and the UK both posted double-digit annual sales increases while sales in China were flat and declined in most other foreign markets.

Strategy

Research and development is vital to the company's success. Indeed II-VI aims to invest between 5% and 7% of its revenues each year in R&D. Its recent focus has been in silicon carbide substrates chemical vapor deposition (CVD) synthetic diamond materials photonics and thermoelectric materials and devices. II-VI uses a mix of internal and external funding for most areas but devotes only internal funds to CVD diamond and photonics.

II-VI's Pacific Rare Specialty Metals & Chemicals (PRM) subsidiary in 2013 discontinued its tellurium line and downsized its selenium production line to focus on providing selenium metal to the company's Infrared Optics business while distancing the business from volatile metal index price fluctuations.

The company uses acquisitions to build its business around core strengths in engineered materials and components.

Mergers and Acquisitions

In September 2013 the company acquired the Switzerland-based semiconductor laser business of Oclaro Inc. for $115 million. II-VI will operate the newly acquired business as II-VI Laser Enterprise GmbH.

In 2012 it bought Connecticut-based M Cubed Technologies for about $71 million and California-based LightWorks Optics for about half that amount. M Cubed manufactures advanced ceramic materials and precision motion control products and LightWorks supplies advanced optical systems used in defense aerospace and commercial operations. The prior year brought the acquisition of Massachusetts-based Aegis Lightwave for $52 million. Aegis' tunable optical devices are used to expand bandwidth in high speed optical networks and will contribute to II-VI's near-infrared optics business.

In early 2010 the company purchased China-based crystal materials and optical components maker Photop Technologies in a deal valued at about $83 million. The acquisition reinforced II-VI's focus on materials and components for the optical communications and display markets strengthened its photonics portfolio and expanded its presence in China. In a move to expand its product line late that year the company acquired Max Levy Autograph a manufacturer of microfine conductive mesh patterns for optical mechanical and ceramic components used in electronic circuitry target calibration and the suppression of electromagnetic interference.

Ownership

Columbia Wanger Asset Management owns about 12% of II-VI's shares.

HISTORY

Electrical engineer Carl Johnson who had worked at Bell Labs (now part of Alcatel-Lucent) among other companies founded II-VI in 1971 to produce infrared optical materials for the emerging laser market. These materials —including cadmium zinc telluride zinc selenide and zinc sulfide —gave the company its name; they are from the "two-six" family of materials. (Cadmium and zinc are from column two on the periodic table; tellurium and selenium are from column six.)

By the 1980s II-VI was the leading maker of optical components for carbon dioxide lasers. The company went public in 1987 and the next year added a factory in Singapore.

Decreased military spending during the early 1990s stifled II-VI's growth. To compensate the company invested: it acquired eV Products in 1992 (divested in 2009) and Sandoz Chemicals' Virgo Optics Division (now VLOC) in 1994. The company opened a factory in China in 1996.

In 1999 II-VI formed a new division Electronic & Photonic Materials to develop uses for silicon carbide and sapphire materials. That year II-VI acquired 15% of rival Laser Power.

II-VI completed its acquisition of Laser Power in 2001. That year it also purchased Silicon Carbide (SiC) Group from Litton Systems (now part of Northrop Grumman). In 2003 II-VI consolidated Laser Power's operations into other branches of the company.

In 2004 the company bought Dallas-based Marlow Industries for around $31 million in cash. Marlow became an operating unit of II-VI's Compound Semiconductor Group.

In 2005 the company set plans to establish a silicon carbide semiconductor substrate manufacturing facility in Mississippi in cooperation with Mississippi State University and SemiSouth Laboratories. II-VI also made an equity investment in SemiSouth.

Also that year the company acquired the 25% equity interest in II-VI Deutschland GmbH it didn't already own buying the minority equity stake from L.O.T.-Oriel Laser Optik GmbH & Co. KG.

Carl Johnson chairman and CEO of II-VI since 1985 gave up the CEO's post in 2007 while remaining executive chairman. Francis Kramer the company's president and COO since 1985 succeeded Johnson as CEO retaining the president's title.

Also in 2007 II-VI acquired Pacific Rare Specialty Metals & Chemicals adding a long-term supply of selenium and tellurium raw materials essential to the company's operations. The following year II-VI sold its 36% stake in 5NPlus for about $30 million. 5NPlus was a supplier of high-purity antimony cadmium selenium tellurium and zinc — all materials that went into II-VI products.

The company's 2008 purchase of HIGHYAG Lasertechnologie brought expertise in high-power lasers for welding drilling and cutting. In 2009 II-VI sold eV Products (X-ray and gamma-ray sensors for nuclear radiation detection) to Endicott Interconnect Technologies. Also that year it entered into a joint venture with Beijing Supower Science and Technology Developing Co. in mid-2009; II-VI holds a minority share in the venture which makes diamond and laser cutting machines.

EXECUTIVES

VP Military and Materials Businesses, James Martinelli, age 56, $309,375 total compensation

Chairman and CEO, Francis J. Kramer, age 65, $628,000 total compensation

President and COO, Vincent D. (Chuck) Mattera, age 58, $380,000 total compensation

CFO and Treasurer, Mary Jane Raymond, age 55

Vice President And General Manager, Chuck Mattera

Vice President Worldwide Materials, Elgin Eissler

National Sales Manager, Tom Neff

Vice President Information Technology, Chris Shigley

Chairman and CEO, Francis J. Kramer, age 65

CFO and Treasurer, Mary Jane Raymond, age 55

Board Of Directors, Thomas Mistler

Secretary, Robert German

Board Of Directors, Joseph Corasanti

Board Of Directors, Peter Sognefest

Auditors: Ernst&YoungLLP

LOCATIONS

HQ: II-VI Inc.
375 Saxonburg Boulevard, Saxonburg, PA 16056
Phone: 724 352-4455
Web: www.ii-vi.com

2013 Sales

	$ mil.	% of total
US	251.7	45
Asia/Pacific		
China	123.3	22
Vietnam	29.4	5
Philippines	24.7	4
Japan	29.5	5
Singapore	6.3	1
Europe		
Germany	59.6	11
Switzerland	10.3	2
Italy	7.6	1
UK	6.9	2
Belgium	5.8	1
Australia	3.3	1
Total	**558.4**	**100**

Selected Production Operations

US
California
Connecticut
Delaware
Florida
Massachusetts
Mississippi
New Jersey
Pennsylvania
Texas
International
Australia
China

Germany
Philippines
Singapore
Vietnam

PRODUCTS/OPERATIONS

2013 Sales

	$ mil.	% of total
Infrared Optics	203.3	36
Near-Infrared Optics	154.9	28
Military & Materials	104.4	19
Advanced Products Group	95.8	17
Total	**558.4**	**100**

Selected Business Segments

dvanced Materials Development Center (AMDC)
AOFR
Aegis Lightwave
HIGHYAG Lasertechnologie
LightWorks Optical Systems
M Cubed
Marlow Industries
Max Levy Autograph
Photop Technologies
Pacific Rare Specialty Metals & Chemicals (PRM)
Wide Bandgap Materials Group

Selected Products

Beam expanders
Beam splitters
Detectors
Etalons
Infrared and near-infrared optics
Laser crystals
 Clear yttrium aluminum garnet (YAG) laser crystals
 Custom crystals and fluorides
 Machined and polished laser rods
 Monolithic crystal assemblies (MCA)
 Neodymium doped YAG
 Non-linear crystals
 Oxide laser crystal products
 Ruby laser crystals
Laser gain materials
Lenses
Military infrared optics
Mirrors
Modulators
One micron laser
Optical assemblies
Optical coatings
Output windows
Partial reflectors
Phase retarders
Polarization devices
Prisms
Rhombs
Selenium metal (material processing and refinement)
Silicon carbide substrates (SiC)
Solid-state laser optics and optical cavities
Substrates
Tellurium metal (material processing and refinement)
Thermo-electric coolers
Wave plates

COMPETITORS

AXSUN Technologies
Coherent Inc.
CoorsTek
Cree
Cymer
DRS Technologies
Dow Corning
Ferrotec
Jenoptik
Komatsu
Laird Technologies
LightPath
Newport Corp.
Nippon Steel & Sumitomo Metal Corporation
Northrop Grumman
Oplink Communications
Orbotech

ROFIN-SINAR
Raytheon
Saint-Gobain
Spectra-Physics
Sumitomo Electric
Umicore
Zygo

HISTORICAL FINANCIALS

Company Type: Public

Income Statement

FYE: June 30

	REVENUE ($ mil.)	NET INCOME ($ mil.)	NET PROFIT MARGIN	EMPLOYEES
06/14	683.2	38.4	5.6%	6,796
06/13	558.4	50.8	9.1%	6,185
06/12	534.6	60.3	11.3%	6,030
06/11	502.8	82.6	16.4%	6,195
06/10	345.0	38.5	11.2%	6,869
Annual Growth	**18.6%**	**(0.1%)**	**—**	**(0.3%)**

2014 Year-End Financials

Debt ratio: 22.5%	No. of shares (mil.): 61
Return on equity: 5.8%	Dividends
Cash ($ mil.): 174	Yield: —
Current ratio: 3.74	Payout: —
Long-term debt ($ mil.): 221	Market value ($ mil.): 889

	STOCK PRICE ($) FY Close	P/E High/Low		PER SHARE ($) Earnings	Dividends	Book Value
06/14	14.46	33	21	0.60	0.00	10.98
06/13	16.26	25	18	0.80	0.00	10.22
06/12	16.67	29	17	0.94	0.00	9.39
06/11	25.60	44	19	1.30	0.00	8.33
06/10	29.63	59	30	0.63	0.00	6.64
Annual Growth	**(16.4%)**	**—**	**—**	**(1.0%)**	**—**	**13.4%**

Illumina Inc

Illumina elucidates the human genome. The firm makes tools used by life sciences and drug researchers to isolate and analyze genes. Its systems include the machinery and the software used to sequence pieces of DNA and RNA and the means to put them through large-scale testing of genetic variation and biological function. Its proprietary BeadArray technology uses microscopic glass beads which can carry samples through the genotyping process. The tests allow medical researchers to determine what genetic combinations are associated with various diseases enabling faster diagnosis better drugs and individualized treatment. Customers include pharma and biotech companies research centers and academic institutions.

Operations

Though Illumina's expensive analysis systems are its primary focus sales of such systems account for only about one-quarter of revenues while the related consumables (chemical reagents flow cells and BeadChip microarrays) account for more than 60% of annual sales. Products are marketed directly and through independent distributors to life science researchers in medical forensics agriculture and animal health industries around the globe.

For customers who choose not to buy its systems and consumables Illumina offers outsourced life science research services such as genome sequencing and genotyping array services. Customers for such services include schools agricultural and energy biotech research firms and drug development companies. In addition the company has a consumer genomics unit (launched in 2009) to meet the growing demand for personal genome sequencing through physician intermediaries. And while most of the company's revenues come from providing life sciences equipment and services Illumina has also established a small business in the field of molecular diagnostics which uses genetic biomarkers to diagnose clinical health conditions.

Geographic Reach

Illumina gets about half of its annual revenues from sales in the US market. Other key regions include Europe (25% of sales) and Asia/Pacific (20%). The company has increased revenues across all geographic markets in recent years with sales in the Asia/Pacific region in the lead.

Financial Analysis

Illumina has steadily augmented its life sciences product lines and has experienced rapidly climbing revenues in recent years as a result. The company reported a 24% increase in sales in 2013 to some $1.4 billion due to increased instrument sales (due to new product launches) and consumable sales (driven by a higher base of installed equipment) as well as a rise in its sequencing services segment. However profits dropped by more than 15% to some $125 million that year due to increased operating expenses from sales and marketing efforts and R&D programs as Illumina continues to invest in the growth of the business.

Strategy

Illumina makes significant investments in research and development to make its systems faster more advanced and more affordable. In early 2014 it upgraded its HiSeq X Ten and NextSeq 500 platforms with improved technology. In 2013 the company introduced a simpler gene sequencing panel and a new genome sequencing technology to help doctors identify genetic causes for rare or undiagnosed diseases among other products.

Illumina is also focused on expanding use of its genomics products into reproductive health oncology and other clinical and research markets. It has several products in the pipeline for 2014 to address these markets.

In 2012 Illumina's board of directors rejected two hostile takeover bids from Swiss drugmaker Roche one for $5.7 billion and the second for $6.7 billion. After shareholders further rejected Roche's attempt to elect members to Illumina's board Roche —which is looking to expand in the life science research and molecular diagnostics industries —stated that it would not extend or raise its offer.

Mergers and Acquisitions

Acquisitions that have enhanced Illumina's offerings include the 2013 purchases of NextBio (clinical and genomic informatics) Advanced Liquid Logic (digital microfluidics and liquid handling) and Varinata Health (which markets the verifi prenatal test for high-risk pregnancies). In 2012 Illumina also purchased UK-based BlueGnome to expand its reproductive health screening offerings.

Illumina bought Epicentre Biotechnologies in early 2011 adding the Nextera line of nucleic acid sample preparation reagents and enzymes used in sequencing and microarrays.

EXECUTIVES

President & Chief Executive Officer; Director, Jay T. Flatley, age 62, $749,615 total compensation

Senior Vice President & Chief Commercial
Officer, Tristan B. Orpin, age 48, $379,403 total
compensation
Senior Vice President & General Manager
Genomic Solutions, Christian O. Henry, age 46,
$410,139 total compensation
Senior Vice President & General Manager
Diagnostics, Gregory F. (Greg) Heath, age 57,
$398,865 total compensation
Chief Technology Officer; Senior Vice President,
Mostafa Ronaghi, age 46, $337,800 total
compensation
Senior Vice President & Chief Financial Officer,
Marc Stapley, age 44
Senior Vice President and General Manager
Molecular Biology & PCR, Mark L. Lewis, age 61
Vp-global Supply Chain, Elizabeth Brady
Sr Vice President Human Resrcs, Paul L Bianchi
Senior Vice President General Manager, Kirk D
Malloy
Vice President Diagnostic Development, Karen
Gutekunst
Vice President Engineering At Illumina, Susan
Tousi
Vice President Emea Commercial Operations, Tim
Orpin
Chairman of the Board, William H. Rastetter
President & Chief Executive Officer; Director, Jay
T. Flatley, age 62
Auditors: Ernst&YoungLLP

LOCATIONS

HQ: Illumina Inc
5200 Illumina Way, San Diego, CA 92122
Phone: 858 202-4500   Fax: 858 587-4297
Web: www.illumina.com

2013 Sales

	$ mil.	% of total
US	714.7	50
Europe	354.7	25
Asia/Pacific	276.4	20
Other regions	75.4	5
Total	1421.2	100

PRODUCTS/OPERATIONS

Selected Systems

BaseSpace
HiScan
HiSeq 2500
HiSeq X Ten
iScan
MiSeq
NextSeq 500
Software

Selected Applications

Agrigenomics
Cancer Genomics
Cytogenomics
Forensic Genomics
Gene Expression Analysis
Gene Regulation & Epigenetic Analysis
Genetic Disease
Genotyping
Microbial Genomics
Sequencing
SNP Genotyping & CNV Analysis

COMPETITORS

Affymetrix	Life Technologies
Agilent Technologies	Corporation
Beckman Coulter	Luminex
Complete Genomics	Pacific Biosciences
Fluidigm	QIAGEN
GE Healthcare Medical	Roche Diagnostics
Diagnostics	Sequenom
Helicos	

HISTORICAL FINANCIALS

Company Type: Public

Income Statement

FYE: December 29

	REVENUE ($ mil.)	NET INCOME ($ mil.)	NET PROFIT MARGIN	EMPLOYEES
12/13	1,421.1	125.3	8.8%	3,000
12/12*	1,148.5	151.2	13.2%	2,400
01/12	1,055.5	86.6	8.2%	2,200
01/11	902.7	124.8	13.8%	2,100
01/10	666.3	72.2	10.8%	1,781
Annual Growth	20.8%	14.7%	—	13.9%

*Fiscal year change

2013 Year-End Financials

Debt ratio: 28.7%	No. of shares (mil.): 127
Return on equity: 8.8%	Dividends
Cash ($ mil.): 711	Yield: —
Current ratio: 5.02	Payout: —
Long-term debt ($ mil.): 839	Market value ($ mil.): 14,098

	STOCK PRICE ($) FY Close	P/E High/Low	PER SHARE ($) Earnings	Dividends	Book Value
12/13	110.38	110 48	0.90	0.00	12.00
12/12*	54.75	46 25	1.13	0.00	10.64
01/12	30.48	111 37	0.62	0.00	8.81
01/11	63.34	65 30	0.87	0.00	9.46
01/10	30.68	74 40	0.53	0.00	7.23
Annual Growth	37.7%	— —	14.2%	—	13.5%

*Fiscal year change

Immersion Corp

Immersion isn't afraid to get touchy-feely when
doing business. The company develops haptics
(touch feedback) technology that simulates tactile
experiences —such as the feel of an object or the
jolt of an explosion during a video game —in order
to improve how people interact with digital devices. Immersion licenses its TouchSense technology to companies such as Motorola and Samsung
for use in mobile phones and to Logitech and Microsoft which use TouchSense in joysticks mice
steering wheels and other peripherals. Its technology backed by more than 1200 patents is also
used in automotive consumer electronics and medical products.

Geographic Reach

Headquartered in California the company operates from international offices in Canada China
Japan South Korea and Taiwan. In 2013 South
Korea (home to its largest customer Samsung) accounted for almost 60% of sales followed by the
US with 25%. The remainder came from Japan and
other countries.

Sales and Marketing

Immersion uses a direct sales force in Asia Europe and the US to license its software and patents
as well as partnerships and licensing agreements
with component suppliers and system integrators.
Samsung is its largest customer accounting for almost half of all sales in 2013.

Financial Performance

Overall sales were up 48% in 2013 to $47.5
million driven by increases in royalty and licensing
revenues for mobile device technology especially as
the company renewed a multi-year license agreement with Samsung and won new customer con-

tracts in China Japan and the US. In addition after
five straight years of losses the company recorded
profits of $40 million thanks to a $36 million benefit for income taxes. The tax benefit also affected
the company cash flow for the year - a record
$21.2 million from operating activities.

Strategy

Immersion doesn't face a lot of competition in
the market for licensing haptics IP except from the
customers themselves who may choose to develop
their own haptics technology. Still it owns so many
of the patents for the technology that Immersion
has had to take some users to court.

EXECUTIVES

President CEO and Director, Victor (Vic) Viegas,
age 58, $346,710 total compensation
VP Engineering, Rob Lacroix
SVP Sales & Marketing, Dennis Sheehan
CFO, Paul Norris
VP and General Manager Content and Media
Business, Jason Patton
Vp Of Market Strategy, Mark Belinsky
Senior Vice President General Counsel, Craig
Vachon
Vp And Chief Technology Officer, Bruce Schena
Vp General Manager Gaming & Design, Leslie
Mulligan
Medical Director, Kevin Kunkler
Vice President Of User Experience, Chris Ulevitch
Vice President And General Manager, Michael Levin
Vice President And General Manager, Bhartendu
Parekh
Vice President, Dexter Tight
Vice President, Ciro Granato
Vice President Of Product Planning And
Management, John Fanelli
Vpres Worldwide Oem Sales, Mahesh Sundaram
Vice President Asia Pacific, Daniel Cho
President CEO and Director, Victor (Vic) Viegas,
age 58
Chairman, Carl P. Schlachte, age 51
Board Member, Rob Van
Secretary, James Koshland
Board Member, Jack Saltich
Auditors: Deloitte&ToucheLLP

LOCATIONS

HQ: Immersion Corp
30 Rio Robles, San Jose, CA 95134
Phone: 408 467-1900
Web: www.immersion.com

2013 Sales

	% of total
Far East	68
North America	28
Europe	4
Total	100

PRODUCTS/OPERATIONS

2013 Sales

	$ mil.	% of total
Royalty & license	46.2	97
Development contracts & other	1.2	3
Product sales	0.1	-
Total	47.5	100

2013 Sales by Market

	% of total
Mobile communications	66
Gaming	21
Medical	8
Automotive	5
Total	100

COMPETITORS

Interlink Electronics	Nokia
LG Electronics	Panasonic Corp
Logitech	Philips Electronics
Microsoft	Samsung Group
Moog	Sony

HISTORICAL FINANCIALS

Company Type: Public

Income Statement

FYE: December 31

	REVENUE ($ mil.)	NET INCOME ($ mil.)	NET PROFIT MARGIN	EMPLOYEES
12/13	47.4	40.1	84.6%	105
12/12	32.1	(5.5)	—	94
12/11	30.6	(1.6)	—	85
12/10	31.1	(5.9)	—	82
12/09	27.7	(28.2)	—	124
Annual Growth	14.4%	—	—	(4.1%)

2013 Year-End Financials

Debt ratio: —
Return on equity: 64.0%
Cash ($ mil.): 14
Current ratio: 5.03
Long-term debt ($ mil.): —

No. of shares (mil.): 28
Dividends
 Yield: —
 Payout: —
Market value ($ mil.): 297

	STOCK PRICE ($) FY Close	P/E High/Low		PER SHARE ($) Earnings	Dividends	Book Value
12/13	10.38	11	4	1.37	0.00	2.82
12/12	6.87	—	—	(0.20)	0.00	1.64
12/11	5.18	—	—	(0.06)	0.00	1.85
12/10	6.71	—	—	(0.21)	0.00	1.90
12/09	4.58	—	—	(1.01)	0.00	1.99
Annual Growth	22.7%			—	—	9.1%

Independence Holding Co.

Independence Holding (IHC) wants to hold insurance policies in the US. Through its wholly-owned subsidiaries Madison National Life Insurance and Standard Security Life Insurance Company of New York it sells and reinsures health and life insurance to groups and individuals. Though it does offer some major medical plans the company prefers to offer niche coverage such as medical stop-loss insurance (which allows employers to limit their exposure to high health insurance claims) short-term medical coverage critical illness small-group major medical and pet insurance. IHC's majority-owned subisidiary American Independence also writes medical stop-loss insurance.

IHC distributes its products through a variety of methods including independent and affiliated agents and brokers as well as managing general underwriters. In an unusual twist in its distribution IHC has introduced a program that rewards its distributors with company stock.

The company has been widening its offering of health insurance products which now account for more than 85% of the company's premiums. Its health products also include dental and vision Medicare supplement and travel medical insurance. IHC is also focusing on selling medical stop-loss

products to employers who have fewer than 100 employees. These smaller businesses are predictably trying to rein in medical insurance costs.

In addition the firm's growth strategy involves buying up blocks of insurance policies and sometimes the companies that issued them. Independence Holding is also growing in the administration marketing and managing general underwriting segments to expand its direct sales organization.

IHC also owns a controlling interest in American Independence (AMIC) the owner of Independence American Insurance which despite its confusing rearrangement of names specializes in employer medical stop-loss and managed care insurance. AMIC became a majority owned subsidiary of IHC in 2010 after the company bought more than half of AMIC's stock. After securing the controlling interest in 2010 the company enjoyed an income bounce from a bargain purchase gain that came from AMIC's shares being undervalued in the market.

Private holding company Geneve Holdings owns slightly more than 50% of IHC's stock.

EXECUTIVES

SVP and COO, David T. Kettig, age 55, $309,000 total compensation
CFO and SVP, Teresa A. Herbert, age 52, $256,134 total compensation
Chief Life and Annuity Actuary and SVP Independence Holding Company, Larry R. Graber, age 64, $200,000 total compensation
CEO; President and Chairman, Roy T.K. Thung, $421,601 total compensation
Chief Underwriting Officer and SVP, Michael A. Kemp
Vice President, Dave Keller
Corporate Vice President Accounting And Finance Of Independence Holding Company Nyse:ihc And Its Affiliate, Gary J Balzofiore
Vp Internal Audit, Paul R Janerico, age 48
Vice President Finance, Colleen Maggi
Regional Vice President Of Sales, Peter Doran
Executive Vice President Of Business Development, Gumbiner Ken
Auditors: KPMGLLP

LOCATIONS

HQ: Independence Holding Co.
 96 Cummings Point Road, Stamford, CT 06902
Phone: 203 358-8000 **Fax:** 203 348-3103
Web: www.ihcgroup.com

PRODUCTS/OPERATIONS

2011 Sales

	$ mil.	% of total
Fully insured health	167.9	40
Medical stop-loss	123.5	30
Group disability life annuities & DBL	60.4	14
Individual life annuities & other	58.1	14
Corporate & investment gains	8.1	2
Total	418	100

Selected Operating Subsidiaries

Actuarial Management Corporation Inc.
American Independence Corp (78% ownership)
 healthinsurance.org LLC
 IHC Risk Solutions
 Independence American Insurance Company
 Independent Producers of America LLC
Hospital Bill Analysis LLC
IHC Health Solutions
Madison National Life Insurance Company
Managing General Underwriters
MedWatch LLC
Standard Security Life Insurance Company of New York

COMPETITORS

Aetna	Health Net
BEST Life	MetLife
CIGNA	Prudential
Great-West Life & Annuity	Regence Life and Health Insurance
HM Insurance Group	

HISTORICAL FINANCIALS

Company Type: Public

Income Statement

FYE: December 31

	ASSETS ($ mil.)	NET INCOME ($ mil.)	INCOME AS % OF ASSETS	EMPLOYEES
12/13	1,269.0	13.7	1.1%	600
12/12	1,262.3	19.6	1.6%	580
12/11	1,358.8	13.0	1.0%	580
12/10	1,361.7	21.7	1.6%	650
12/09	1,304.4	(7.1)	—	600
Annual Growth	(0.7%)	—	—	0.0%

2013 Year-End Financials

Return on assets: 1.0%
Return on equity: 4.9%
Long-term debt ($ mil.): —
No. of shares (mil.): 17
Sales ($ mil): 575

Dividends
 Yield: 0.5%
 Payout: 6.1%
Market value ($ mil.): 238

	STOCK PRICE ($) FY Close	P/E High/Low		PER SHARE ($) Earnings	Dividends	Book Value
12/13	13.49	19	12	0.77	0.07	15.22
12/12	9.52	10	7	1.09	0.09	15.93
12/11	8.13	15	9	0.74	0.05	14.46
12/10	8.12	8	4	1.29	0.05	13.76
12/09	5.80	—	—	(0.42)	0.05	11.96
Annual Growth	23.5%			—	11.4%	6.2%

Infinity Property & Casualty Corp

Infinity Property and Casualty does have its limits but it goes farther than most to cover high-risk drivers. The insurer primarily provides personal nonstandard auto policies —Infinity is a leading writer of policies for high-risk drivers in the US. The company also offers standard and preferred personal auto commercial small fleet and classic collector auto insurance. Licensed in all 50 states the company currently focuses its business on targeted urban areas of a handful of states. Personal non-standard auto insurance accounts for more than 90% of its premiums; California accounts for about half of that business. Infinity distributes its products through more than 12900 independent agents.

Infinity has its sights set on expanding its business in the urban areas of large states (specifically California Florida Texas Georgia Pennsylvania Arizona Nevada and Illinois). The company has increased advertising spending and agency incentives including commissions to stimulate growth in these areas. It is however also happily maintaining its presence in less densely populated states with plenty of bad drivers such as Colorado Alabama South Carolina Tennessee and Connecticut.

Infinity is pursuing a strategy for growth that it hopes will help it to overcome the soft insurance market of the past several years and deliver shareholder value. It is depending on meeting customers' lifestyle and budget needs by providing flexible product offerings and pricing options. For example the company offers products with buy-up/buydown options and introduced its new DriverClub service with free membership for roadside assistance. The company is also committed to building relations with its agents and brokers by investing in agency productivity lead generation and training.

Factors that contributed to strong premium growth (11%) for Infinity in fiscal 2011 included improvements in agency incentives the addition of policies with broader coverage into its business mix decreases in rates in some states and competitor rate increases in some states. As a result revenues for the year increased by about 10%. Net income however decreased by 54%. The decline in net earnings was mainly due to unfavorable development related to accident year 2010 resulting from increases in severities on personal injury protection in Florida.

By the end of fiscal 2011 Infinity had repurchased $403 million or about 46% of the shares issued since its 2003 IPO. The company had also increased dividends by 309% for a total compound annual return to shareholders (dividends and capital appreciation) of 16% for that same time period.

Before its IPO Infinity was owned by property/casualty giant American Financial Group (AFG). AFG transferred the personal insurance business of its property/casualty subsidiary Great American Financial Resources to Infinity but that business is now in runoff with no new policies being written.

EXECUTIVES

Assistant Vice President Of Office, Bo Cupps
Executive Vice President; General Counsel; Assistant Secretary; Director, Samuel J Simon, age 58
Senior Vice President - Product Management, Scott C Pitrone, age 52
Vice President Investor Relations, Amy Jordan
Chairman President and CEO, James R. Gober, age 62, $558,800 total compensation
Chief Financial Officer; Executive Vice President; Treasurer; Director, Roger Smith, age 53, $304,800 total compensation
Senior Vice President And Cio, Ralph Gravelle
Vice President Tax, Troy P Ballard
Assistant Vice President, Pam Jenkins
Asst Vice President Mgmt, Gena Woodfield
Assistant Vice President Data Management, Barry Ralston
Assistant Vice President Corporate Litigation, Larry Levine
Vice President Claims, Greg Schnee
Assistant Vice President Benefits, Robin Adams
Treasurer, Mary L Clark
Auditors: Ernst&YoungLLP

LOCATIONS

HQ: Infinity Property & Casualty Corp
3700 Colonnade Parkway, Suite 600, Birmingham, AL 35243
Phone: 205 870-4000
Web: www.infinityauto.com

PRODUCTS/OPERATIONS

2011 Revenues

	$ mil.	% of total
Earned premiums	1019.1	95
Net investment income	40.5	4
Realized investment gains	8.6	1
Gain on sale of subsidiaries	4.1	-
Other income	0.3	-
Total	**1072.6**	**100**

2011 Gross Written Premiums

	% of total
Personal automobile	93
Commercial vehicle	6
Classic collector and other	1
Total	**100**

COMPETITORS

Affirmative Insurance
Direct General
First Acceptance Corporation
GMAC Insurance
Hagerty Insurance
Kingsway America
Permanent General
Progressive Corporation
Safe Auto

HISTORICAL FINANCIALS

Company Type: Public

Income Statement

FYE: December 31

	ASSETS ($ mil.)	NET INCOME ($ mil.)	INCOME AS % OF ASSETS	EMPLOYEES
12/13	2,317.2	32.6	1.4%	2,400
12/12	2,303.5	24.3	1.1%	2,200
12/11	1,936.7	42.0	2.2%	2,100
12/10	1,852.3	91.5	4.9%	1,900
12/09	1,803.6	70.5	3.9%	1,780
Annual Growth	**6.5%**	**(17.5%)**	**—**	**7.8%**

2013 Year-End Financials

Return on assets: 1.4%
Return on equity: 4.9%
Long-term debt ($ mil.): —
No. of shares (mil.): 11
Sales ($ mil): 1,344
Dividends
Yield: 1.6%
Payout: 44.9%
Market value ($ mil.): 825

	STOCK PRICE ($) FY Close	P/E High/Low		PER SHARE ($) Earnings	Dividends	Book Value
12/13	71.75	25	19	2.80	1.20	57.09
12/12	58.24	30	24	2.04	0.90	56.55
12/11	56.74	18	13	3.39	0.72	56.59
12/10	61.80	9	5	6.95	0.56	53.03
12/09	40.64	9	6	5.09	0.48	45.80
Annual Growth	**15.3%**			**—(13.9%)**	**25.7%**	**5.7%**

Informatica Corp.

Big data is a big opportunity for Informatica. The company provides enterprise data integration software that enables companies to access integrate and consolidate their data across a variety of systems and users. Its PowerCenter platform consolidates codes and moves large data warehouses and its PowerExchange software enables access to bulk or changed data. Other products include Master Data Management (MDM) and the Informatica B2B Data Exchange as well as Fast Clone (data replication) Data Explorer (data quality) and a range of software-as-a-service (SaaS) offerings which integrate data from other business applications into a single hosted platform.

Geographic Reach

Informatica has offices in about 45 countries. North America is its largest market accounting for about two-thirds of sales. Customers in Europe account for about a quarter of sales.

Sales and Marketing

The company's products are sold directly in 20 countries and also through systems integrators resellers and distributors and strategic partners in 80 other countries. Informatica targets chief information officers and other departmental heads in marketing sales service finance human resources manufacturing distribution and procurement as well as other IT professionals focused on data integration. Altogether it counts more than 5000 corporate customers.

Financial Performance

Informatica's sales continued along a decade-long upward trajectory in 2013. Overall revenues increased 17% in 2013 to $948 million. Software revenues were up 18% license revenues were up 14% and subscription revenues were up 60%. The company cited continuing strong demand for its data integration applications data warehousing offerings and compliance program. It attributed increased sales of services to a growing customer base that is opting for more consulting and training as well as requiring more maintenance. Profits fell 7% to $86 million.

Strategy

Informatica continues to shift its focus from data warehousing to a broader enterprise data integration platform which encompasses data migration consolidation management and synchronization capabilities. The company has targeted the financial services industry by tailoring versions of its software for customers in banking and insurance. It also develops tools specifically for the retail health care and telecommunications industries among others.

Mergers and Acquisitions

The company supplements its organic growth with acquisitions. In 2012 it bought DataScout Solutions Group Limited and TierData combined for $12 million. It also bought a 98% stake in Germany-based Heiler Software AG for $82.1 million. Heiler Software AG provides enterprise product information management and master data management that allows retailers distributors and manufacturers to manage product information across channels and data sources.

EXECUTIVES

Chairman President and CEO, Sohaib Abbasi, age 58, $700,000 total compensation
EVP and Chief Product Officer, Girish Pancha, age 50, $390,000 total compensation
EVP and CFO, Michael J. (Mike) Berry, age 50
SVP and CTO, James Markarian, age 47, $315,000 total compensation
Executive Vice President and General Manager Data Quality Product Division, Ivan Chong, age 47, $315,000 total compensation
Executive Vice President and Chief Product Officer, Anil S. Chakravarthy
EVP of Worldwide Field Operations, John McGee, $175,641 total compensation
EVP and Chief Marketing Officer, Margaret Breya, $19,952 total compensation
EVP Operations, Charles Race
Vp Product Strategy Office Of The Cto, David Lyle

Vice President Product Development, Vaikom
Krishnan
Senior Vice President Global Human Resources,
Jo Stoner
Senior Vice President And Cio, Tony Young
Vice President Pre Sales Ilm, Josh Alpern
Vice President General Manager Pub Sctr, William
Sullivan
Senior Vice President, John Nolan
Vice President And General Manager, Ronen
Schwartz
Vice President And General Manager Enterprise
Data Integration, Todd Goldman
Senior Vice President Of Worldwide, Brad Kern
Vice President Americas Ilm Sales, Steve Jensen
Sales Marketing Customer Service Vice President
Director Manager, Debbie Walery
Executive Vice President Evp, Mohan Sankaran
Vice President Product Strategy, Robert Karel
Vice President Research And Development,
Richard Spencer
Senior Vice President And General, Dennis Moore
Senior Vice President Global Manufacturing And
Supply Chain Management, Steven Ford
Vice President Healthcare, Corby Marshall
Global Vice President Of Talent Acquisition, Brad
Cook
Senior Vice President World Wide, Brian Hodges
Vice President, Narayan Sivaramakrishnan
Vice President Of Marketing, Laura Wang
Vice President Global Sales Operations, Yasser
Said
Vice President Product Development, Scott Corbin
Sr Vice President Worldwide Sales, Ford Goodman
Vice President Product Marketing, Julie Lockner
Senior Vice President Sales Asia Pacific Sales
Operations, Graham Sowden
Executive Vice President Evp, David Silvey
Vice President Product Marketing, Piet Loubser
Vice President West And Central Sales, Eric Salava
Vice President Regional Marketing North
America, Kim Salem
Vice President Strategy Pln Mst Data, Dmitri
Korablev
Vice President Product Development, Sridhar Ganti
Vice President Sales Healthcare, Scott Harper
Vice President Financial Services And Emerging
Vertical Market, Timothy Sutter
Vice President Global Sales And Marketing
Operations, Richard Steinhart
Vice President Global Mdm Services, Randy Mickey
Vice President Corporate Communications, Debbie
Obrien
Senior Vice President And General, Amit Walia
Senior Vice President And General Manager Data
Integration, Sachin Chawla
Senior Vice President And General, Richard Cramer
Vice President Latin America, Andr Petroucic
Vice President Of Research, Meir Zelzer
Vice President Informatica Cloud Marketing, Ajay
Gandhi
Vice President Product Marketing, Ravi Devaraj
Executive Assistant Svp Gm Of Ilm, Cindy
Vanwassenhove
Vice President Global Information Technology
Operations And Infrastructure, Tarakam Peddada
Vice President Of Research And Development
Ilm, Bala Kumaresan
Regional Vice President, Bryan Finnegan
Senior Vice President Marketing, Franz Aman
Vice President Finance, Bob Pape
Senior Vice President Sales Usa Territory, Bob
Markese
Vice President Ww Channels, Wayne Monk
Senior Vice President Alliances Marketing, George
Paolini

Vice President Sales Central Europe, Dirk
Haeussermann
Regional Sales Vice President Addressdoctor,
Kimo Kong
Chairman President and CEO, Sohaib Abbasi, age
58
Auditors: Ernst&YoungLLP

LOCATIONS

HQ: Informatica Corp.
2100 Seaport Boulevard, Redwood City, CA 94063
Phone: 650 385-5000
Web: www.informatica.com

2014 Sales

	$ mil.	% of total
North America	688.2	66
Europe the Middle East and Africa	241.8	23
Other regions	118.0	11
Total	**1048.0**	**100**

Selected Products

Informatica PowerCenter
  Standard Edition
  Real Time Edition
  Advanced Edition
  Big Data Edition
  Data Virtualization Edition
Informatica PowerExchange
Informatica Data Services
Informatica Data Quality
  Informatica Data Explorer
  AddressDoctor
Informatica Master Data Management (MDM)
  Informatica Cloud MDM
  Informatica Identity Resolution
Informatica B2B Data Exchange
  Informatica B2B Data Transformation
  Informatica HParser
Informatica Application Information Lifecycle
  Management (ILM)
  Informatica Data Archive
  Informatica Data Subset
  Informatica Persistent Data Masking
  Informatica Dynamic Data Masking
  ILM Nearline
Informatica Data Replication
  Informatica Fast Clone
Informatica Complex Event Processing (CEP)
  Informatica RulePoint
  Informatica Proactive Monitoring
Informatica Ultra Messaging
  Informatica Ultra Messaging Streaming Edition
  Informatica Ultra Messaging Queuing Edition
Informatica Cloud Data Integration
  Informatica Cloud Integration Applications
  Informatica Cloud Connectors

PRODUCTS/OPERATIONS

2014 Sales

	$ mil.	% of total
Service		
Maintenance	456.7	43
Consulting education & other	133.9	13
Software		
License	387.7	37
Subscription	69.7	7
Total	**1048.0**	**100**

Selected Acquisitions

FY2012
  DataScout Solutions Group Limited
  Heiler Software AG ($82 million)
  TierData Inc.
FY2011
  ActiveBase Ltd.
  WisdomForce Technologies Inc.
FY2010
  Siperian Inc. ($171 million)

COMPETITORS

Embarcadero	Oracle
Technologies	SAP
IBM	SAS Institute
MicroStrategy	Trillium
Microsoft	

HISTORICAL FINANCIALS

Company Type: Public

Income Statement

FYE: December 31

	REVENUE ($ mil.)	NET INCOME ($ mil.)	NET PROFIT MARGIN	EMPLOYEES
12/13	948.1	86.4	9.1%	3,234
12/12	811.5	93.1	11.5%	2,814
12/11	783.7	117.5	15.0%	2,554
12/10	650.0	86.3	13.3%	2,126
12/09	500.6	64.2	12.8%	1,755
Annual Growth	**17.3%**	**7.7%**	**—**	**16.5%**

2013 Year-End Financials

Debt ratio: —
Return on equity: 7.3%
Cash ($ mil.): 297
Current ratio: 2.14
Long-term debt ($ mil.): —

No. of shares (mil.): 108
Dividends
  Yield: —
  Payout: —
Market value ($ mil.): 4,509

	STOCK PRICE ($) FY Close	P/E High/Low		PER SHARE ($) Earnings	Dividends	Book Value
12/13	41.50	52	38	0.78	0.00	11.37
12/12	30.32	63	29	0.83	0.00	10.28
12/11	36.93	54	32	1.05	0.00	9.28
12/10	44.03	49	25	0.83	0.00	6.83
12/09	25.88	37	16	0.66	0.00	5.36
Annual Growth	**12.5%**	**—**	**—**	**4.3%**	**—**	**20.7%**

InSite Vision Inc.

InSite Vision provides insight into the murky realm of eye disease. The company develops ophthalmic products using its DuraSite eyedrop-based drug delivery system. Its topical anti-infective product AzaSite is marketed in the US by licensing partner Inspire Pharmaceuticals as a treatment for conjunctivitis (pink eye). Various other AzaSite products are in development to treat eyelid inflammation and other infections. InSite Vision has licensed rights to use azithromycin (the active ingredient in AzaSite) from Pfizer. Inspire markets AzaSite in the US and Canada while international units are supplied by Catalent Pharma Solutions.

InSite Vision and partner Inspire are directing their marketing efforts of AzaSite towards ophthalmologists optometrists and pediatricians since the bacterial form of pink eye is more common in children than adults.

In line with its strategy to begin commercializing AzaSite outside of North America the company granted international licensing and distribution rights to Shin Poong Pharma to sell the product in South Korea. It has also established distribution partners in Turkey China and several South American countries.

In response to expenses incurred during the proxy context in late 2008 the ompany launched a restructuring and cut its workforce by 35%. Those cuts were not quite enough and in early

2009 the company restructured again to focus more fully on commercializing AzaSite. The second restructuring eliminated 50% of the company's remaining employees.

EXECUTIVES

Vp Clinical Affairs And Chief Medical Officer, Kamran Hosseini, age 50
Auditors: BurrPilger&MayerLLP

LOCATIONS

HQ: InSite Vision Inc.
965 Atlantic Avenue, Alameda, CA 94501
Phone: 510 865-8800   **Fax:** 510 865-5700
Web: www.insitevision.com

PRODUCTS/OPERATIONS

2007 Sales

	$ mil.	% of total
Licensing fees & milestones	22.1	93
Royalties	0.7	3
Other products & services	1.0	4
Total	**23.8**	**100**

Selected Products

Marketed
  AzaSite (bacterial conjunctivitis or pink eye)
In Development
  AzaSite Plus (blepharoconjunctivitis)
  AzaSite Xtra (eye infections)

COMPETITORS

Alcon	Johnson & Johnson
Allergan	Novartis
Bausch & Lomb	Pfizer
Daiichi Sankyo	

HISTORICAL FINANCIALS

Company Type: Public

Income Statement

FYE: December 31

	REVENUE ($ mil.)	NET INCOME ($ mil.)	NET PROFIT MARGIN	EMPLOYEES
12/13	30.8	5.7	18.8%	33
12/12	21.6	(8.2)	—	30
12/11	15.9	(6.9)	—	25
12/10	11.8	(9.5)	—	12
12/09	9.8	(14.1)	—	10
Annual Growth	**33.2%**	**—**		**34.8%**

2013 Year-End Financials

Debt ratio: 291.4%
Return on equity: ***,***.*%
Cash ($ mil.): 3
Current ratio: 0.26
Long-term debt ($ mil.): —

No. of shares (mil.): 131
Dividends
  Yield: —
  Payout: —
Market value ($ mil.): 40

	STOCK PRICE ($) FY Close	P/E High/Low		Earnings	PER SHARE ($) Dividends	Book Value
12/13	0.30	9	4	0.04	0.00	(0.27)
12/12	0.31	—	—	(0.06)	0.00	(0.32)
12/11	0.44	—	—	(0.06)	0.00	(0.26)
12/10	0.34	—	—	(0.10)	0.00	(0.45)
12/09	0.38	—	—	(0.15)	0.00	(0.35)
Annual Growth	**(6.0%)**			**—**	**—**	**—**

Insteel Industries, Inc.

Insteel Industries is part of many concrete victories. The company manufactures steel welded wire reinforcement (WWR) used primarily in concrete construction materials such as pipe (pipe mesh building mesh engineered structural mesh and precast manholes) driveways and slabs. Its prestressed concrete (PC) strand products are the spine for concrete structures from bridges to parking garages. Insteel's customers include concrete pipe and precast and prestressed producers distributors and rebar fabricators. A majority of its sales come from manufacturers of non-residential concrete construction products.

Geographic Reach Insteel Industries operates about 10 manufacturing facilities in the US the company's core market. Operations Insteel Industries' products consist of welded wire reinforcement and prestressed concrete strand. Welded wire reinforcement product sales accounted for 63% and prestressed concrete strand accounted for 37% of the company's revenue in fiscal 2013. Sales and Marketing The company sells its products nationwide as well as into Canada Mexico and Central and South America delivering its products primarily by truck using common or contract carriers. Products are sold primarily to manufacturers of concrete products that are used in nonresidential construction; and to a lesser extent distributors rebar fabricators and contractors. In 2013 about 70% of the company's net sales were to manufacturers of concrete products and 30% were to distributors rebar fabricators and contractors Financial Performance Revenues have remained consistent for Insteel Industries hovering around the $363 million mark for both 2912 and 2012. Profits also skyrocketed from $1.8 million in 2013 to $11.7 million in 2013 due to wider spreads between average selling prices and raw material costs relative to fiscal 2012 together with higher shipments. Shipments for 2013 increased while average selling prices decreased from previous levels in 2012. The increase in shipments was driven by modest improvement in market conditions and demand for its products. The dip in average selling prices was driven by competitive pricing pressures. Strategy As a part of growth strategy in 2013 Insteel Industries purchased the entire concrete pipe and box culvert reinforcement production equipment and certain related assets of Tatano Wire and Steel a Pennsylvania-based producer of welded wire reinforcement and wire products.

HISTORY

Howard Woltz Sr. bought a premixed concrete and concrete-block plant and formed Exposaic Industries Inc. in 1953. Son Howard Woltz Jr. took over as chairman and president in 1958 adding welded-wire production equipment to the plant in 1975 during a shortage of wire reinforcing for its precast-concrete operations. Exposaic diversified again into industrial wire products in 1981 and went public in 1985.

The company sold its precast concrete unit in 1988 and changed its name to Insteel Industries. The next year it formed a joint venture with EVG (Austria) to make Insteel 3-D Panels (used in building construction) in Mexico.

Earnings fluctuated during the 1990s as Insteel tinkered with product lines and facilities under Howard Woltz III who became CEO in 1991. Wan-

ing sales in its industrial wire and bulk nail segments caused it to seek increased market share in higher margin businesses —PC strand (used to strengthen concrete) collated fasteners and tire bead wire. Insteel reorganized and consolidated its wire products subsidiaries in 1993. The company then opened a PC-strand facility in 1994. It bought the rest of the Insteel 3-D Panel joint venture in 1995 only to sell it to management two years later.

Insteel added welding wire and tire bead wire but start-up costs and slow sales of the new lines contributed to losses in fiscal 1997 and 1998. The company sold its agricultural fencing product line in 1998 and in 1999 agreed to buy the Florida Wire and Cable unit (prestressed concrete strand) of GS Industries for $68.5 million. The deal closed in 2000. The following year Insteel sold its galvanized strand business to Bekaert Corporation for approximately $9 million. In 2002 the company sold its South Carolina industrial wire unit to Leggett & Platt for approximately $10.2 million.

EXECUTIVES

Vice President Secretary, James F (Jim) Petelle, age 64
VP CFO and Treasurer, Michael C. Gazmarian, age 55, $280,000 total compensation
VP and General Manager Concrete Reinforcing Products Business Unit, Richard T. Wagner, age 55, $260,000 total compensation
Chairman President and CEO, H. O. Woltz, $477,000 total compensation
Vice-president, Richard Burgess
Chairman President and CEO, H. O. Woltz
Board Member, Charles B Newsome, age 77
Auditors: GrantThorntonLLP

LOCATIONS

HQ: Insteel Industries, Inc.
1373 Boggs Drive, Mount Airy, NC 27030
Phone: 336 786-2141
Web: www.insteel.com

2013 Sales

	$ mil.	% of total
US	358.9	99
Other countries	5.0	1
Total	**363.9**	**100**

PRODUCTS/OPERATIONS

2013 Sales

	$ mil.	% of total
Welded wire reinforcement	228.0	63
Prestressed concrete strand	135.9	37
Total	**363.9**	**100**

Selected Products

Prestressed concrete (PC) strand (seven-wire strand used to strengthen concrete)
Welded wire reinforcement (used to reinforce concrete structures)
  Concrete pipe reinforcement
  Engineered structural mesh
  Standard welded wire reinforcement

Selected Subsidiaries

Insteel Wire Products Company
Intercontinental Metals Corporation (an inactive subsidiary)

COMPETITORS

Dayton Superior	Oklahoma Steel and
Gerdau Ameristeel	Wire
Keystone Consolidated	SteelFab

MMI Products
MNP Corp.
Nucor

Sumitomo Electric
U.S. Concrete

HISTORICAL FINANCIALS
Company Type: Public

Income Statement
FYE: September 27

	REVENUE ($ mil.)	NET INCOME ($ mil.)	NET PROFIT MARGIN	EMPLOYEES
09/14	408.9	16.6	4.1%	847
09/13	363.9	11.7	3.2%	687
09/12*	363.3	1.8	0.5%	682
10/11	336.9	(0.3)	—	725
10/10	211.5	0.4	0.2%	421
Annual Growth	17.9%	143.5%	—	19.1%

*Fiscal year change

2014 Year-End Financials

Debt ratio: —
Return on equity: 9.8%
Cash ($ mil.): 3
Current ratio: 2.26
Long-term debt ($ mil.): —

No. of shares (mil.): 18
Dividends
  Yield: 0.0%
  Payout: 13.4%
Market value ($ mil.): 385

	STOCK PRICE ($) FY Close	P/E High/Low		PER SHARE ($) Earnings	Dividends	Book Value
09/14	20.97	26	17	0.89	0.12	9.73
09/13	16.00	30	16	0.64	0.37	8.86
09/12*	11.73	137	91	0.10	0.12	8.44
10/11	10.07	—	—	(0.02)	0.12	8.43
10/10	8.93	451	260	0.03	0.12	7.98
Annual Growth	23.8%	—	—	133.4%	(0.0%)	5.1%

*Fiscal year change

Interactive Intelligence Group Inc.

Interactive Intelligence knows legacy PBX telephone systems are going the way of the telegraph. The company's software manages call center operations for both inbound and outbound applications. Its Customer Interaction Center software can process thousands of interactions per hour across various media channels: telephone calls emails faxes voice mail Internet chat sessions IP telephony calls text messages and social media. Products are available in two dozen languages and have been installed in more than 100 different countries. The company's technology handles the automated call center operations for more than 6000 customers including CarMax IKEA and Walgreens.

Geographic Reach

Interactive Intelligence operates from a half dozen offices in the US. International offices are located in Australia Brazil Canada Colombia France Germany India Japan Malaysia Poland Sweden the Netherlands and the UK.

Sales and Marketing

The company sells its products and services directly (40% of sales) and through a channel of some 360 partners (60% of sales).

Customers come various industries including insurance banking utilities health care retail technology government and business services.

Interactive Intelligence's products are available as both hosted applications and premise-based. Customers pay a monthly subscription fee to access all the business communications offerings the company provides.

Strategy

The company markets its software-based products as a cost-efficient alternative to traditional business communication systems (which include PBX phone systems automated call distributors voice mail systems and interactive voice response systems) which require significant working capital to purchase and maintain.

Financial Performance

Interactive Intelligence has enjoyed steady revenue growth for the past decade and while profits have fluctuated it's never had a bad year. In 2013 overall sales grew 34% to $318 million and in 2014 the company expects to grow another 15% to $370 million.

Mergers and Acquisitions

The company steadily makes acquisitions to bolster its business. In 2014 it bought OrgSpan whose software connects customer service agents with colleagues in other departments. In 2013 came Amtel Communications of New Zealand and its 24 customers. In 2012 it bought two resellers for gain more control in international markets –Brightware B.V. based in the Netherlands (rebranded it as ININ Netherlands B.V.) and South African reseller ATIO (rebranded as Interactive Intelligence South Africa Pty Ltd.)

Also that year it paid $13 million for Bay Bridge Decisions Technologies which helped businesses with contact center capacity planning. Previous acquisitions include Agori Communications (2011) Latitude Software (2010) and AcroSoft (2009).

Company Background

Chairman and CEO Donald Brown founded Interactive Intelligence in 1994.

EXECUTIVES

VP Finance and Administration CFO Secretary and Treasurer, Stephen R. (Steve) Head, age 61, $290,000 total compensation
Chairman President and CEO, Donald E. Brown, age 59, $450,000 total compensation
Chief Scientist, Michael D. Gagle
SVP International Sales and Chief International Officer, Gary R. Blough, age 59, $240,000 total compensation
Vice President Of Operations Europe, Michael E Ford
Sr V Pres, Thomas J Fisher
Vice President Global Infrastructure, Jose Martinez
Vice President Of Business Development, Brian Smith
Senior Vice President Information Tech, Rebecca Ruselink
Chairman President and CEO, Donald E. Brown, age 59

LOCATIONS

HQ: Interactive Intelligence Group Inc.
  7601 Interactive Way, Indianapolis, IN 46278
Phone: 317 872-3000
Web: www.inin.com

2013 Sales

	% of total
US	63
Other	37
Total	100

PRODUCTS/OPERATIONS

2013 Sales

	$ mil.	% of total
Recurring revenues	147.9	46
Product sales	117.7	37
Services	52.6	17
Total	318.2	100

Selected Software
Automatic frequently asked question processing (e-FAQ)
Call center automation (Customer Interaction Center)
Call routing software (Interaction Director)
Call recording storage and management (Interaction Recorder)
Outbound call management (Interaction Dialer)
Proxy server (Interaction SIP Proxy)

Selected Services
Education and certification
Project management
Systems engineering and customization
Technical support
Training

COMPETITORS

Alcatel-Lucent	Mitel Networks
AltiGen Communications	Nokia Siemens Networks
Aspect Software	ShoreTel
Avaya	Siemens AG
Cisco Systems	Vertical
Five9	Communications
Genesys	eOn
Telecommunications	inContact

HISTORICAL FINANCIALS
Company Type: Public

Income Statement
FYE: December 31

	REVENUE ($ mil.)	NET INCOME ($ mil.)	NET PROFIT MARGIN	EMPLOYEES
12/13	318.2	9.5	3.0%	1,848
12/12	237.3	0.9	0.4%	1,437
12/11	209.5	14.8	7.1%	1,106
12/10	166.3	14.9	9.0%	849
12/09	131.4	8.6	6.6%	654
Annual Growth	24.7%	2.4%	—	29.7%

2013 Year-End Financials

Debt ratio: —
Return on equity: 5.7%
Cash ($ mil.): 65
Current ratio: 1.78
Long-term debt ($ mil.): —

No. of shares (mil.): 20
Dividends
  Yield: —
  Payout: —
Market value ($ mil.): 1,381

	STOCK PRICE ($) FY Close	P/E High/Low		PER SHARE ($) Earnings	Dividends	Book Value
12/13	67.36	145	69	0.45	0.00	9.23
12/12	33.54	682	455	0.04	0.00	7.41
12/11	22.92	53	26	0.74	0.00	6.85
12/10	26.16	33	17	0.79	0.00	5.47
12/09	18.45	45	12	0.47	0.00	3.91
Annual Growth	38.2%	—	—	(1.1%)	—	23.9%

Intuitive Surgical Inc

Intuitive Surgical gives an artistic flair to advanced surgical equipment. Employing haptics (the science of computer-aided touch sensitivity) the firm developed the da Vinci Surgical System a combination of software hardware and optics that allows doctors to perform robotically aided surgery from a remote console. The da Vinci system reproduces the doctor's hand movements in real time during minimally invasive surgery performed by tiny electromechanical arms and instruments. The company manufactures its systems and relies upon contract manufacturers to supply the instruments and accessories used with the systems.

Operations

The da Vinci system's oldest applications —gynecological and urological procedures —still account for more than 90% of da Vinci-assisted surgeries. (About 450000 procedures are performed each year.) Over time the company has widened the system's applications to include cardiothoracic transoral (head and neck) and general surgical procedures.

Along with reducing trauma to the patient related to large incisions Intuitive Surgical promotes its minimally invasive robotic systems as a means of increasing a surgeon's precision intuitive control range of motion and vision during procedures.

Initial sales of the da Vinci systems make up about 40% of revenues while follow-up sales of instruments and accessories account for another 45% of sales. Intuitive Surgical also maintains relationships with (and earns additional revenues from) customers by providing system support and physician training services.

Geographic Reach

Though Intuitive Surgical sells its products in North America Asia and Europe about 70% of sales come from the US.

Sales and Marketing

Intuitive Surgical sells its products through a direct sales force in the US Korea and most European countries. It uses independent distributors in other global markets.

Hospitals can take several routes to obtain the big-ticket da Vinci systems. Some can plunk down the $1 million plus in cash while others work with third-party leasing companies to spread the payments out over time. Once the system is in place a hospital must continue to purchase replacement instruments and accessories from the company.

Financial Performance

The leading maker of surgical robots Intuitive Surgical has seen strong growth in recent years as demand for less traumatic minimally invasive surgical procedures has increased. But revenues were flat in 2013 only a 4% increase to nearly $2.3 billion due to slowed growth in all US surgical categories and a decline in prostate-related procedures. As revenue growth slowed so did net income - it increased a modest 2% to $671 million as expenses kept climbing. Cash flow from operations naturally followed suit and grew from $814.2 million to $880 million.

Strategy

Part of Intuitive Surgical's growth strategy is to introduce next generation versions of the original da Vinci system. Newer models build on the robot's core technology adding enhancements that include increased visual acuity and ease of use. The da Vinci Single-Site instruments and accessories were introduced in 2011 to allow the systems to work through a single incision reducing trauma to the patient. Additional uses were approved in 2013 along with the Firefly fluorescent imaging product for use during gallbladder surgery. While previous system were all surgical or anatomical system specific in 2014 the FDA approved the da Vinci XI for use in a wide variety of surgeries. To increase adoption of newer systems Intuitive discontinued its standard system in 2013.

The company is also expanding its organization as use of the da Vinci system increases. Intuitive Surgical is growing its direct sales organization as well as its manufacturing and R&D workforces. It also occasionally forms strategic alliances with other medical device firms in areas including product development training and marketing

Mergers and Acquisitions

Intuitive Surgical grows through occasional acquisitions as well. In 2012 it expanded its direct sales operations by purchasing its Korean distributor for an undisclosed price.

EXECUTIVES

Vp Product Quality, William C Nowlin
President and CEO, Gary S. Guthart, age 49, $560,000 total compensation
EVP Worldwide Sales and Marketing, Jerome J. (Jerry) McNamara, age 56, $400,000 total compensation
SVP and CFO, Marshall L. Mohr, age 59, $391,400 total compensation
VP Product Development, David J. (Dave) Rosa, $350,000 total compensation
SVP and Chief Medical Officer, Myriam Curet
Vice President Marketing And Sales And Marketing, Frank P Grillo
V Pres-cao-corp Controller, Jamie E Samath
Vice President Product Engineering, Henry Hazebrouck
Clinical Vice President, Marc Bland
Vice President Quality Clinical, Louis Mazzarese
Area Vice President, Glenn Vavoso
Da Vinci Area Sales Vice President, Dan Karl
Area Vice President North Central United States, David Castiglioni
Chairman, Lonnie M. Smith, age 70
Board Member, Keith Garossman
Auditors: Ernst&YoungLLP

LOCATIONS

HQ: Intuitive Surgical Inc
1020 Kifer Road, Sunnyvale, CA 94086
Phone: 408 523-2100
Web: www.intuitivesurgical.com

2013 Sales

	$ mil.	% of total
US	1625.9	72
Other countries	639.2	28
Total	**2265.1**	**100**

Selected Locations

Sunnyvale CA: U.S. Headquarters
Switzerland
Shanghai China
Seoul Korea
Tokyo Japan

PRODUCTS/OPERATIONS

2013 Sales

	$ mil.	% of total
Products	1867.8	82
Services	397.3	18
Total	**2265.1**	**100**

Selected Products

da Vinci Xi
da Vinci Surgical System
da Vinci Si System
da Vinci Single-Site

COMPETITORS

Accuray	Johnson & Johnson
Bard	Medical
Boston Scientific	Medtronic
Curexo Technology	Medtronic Sofamor
Ethicon Endo-Surgery	Danek
Freehand 2010	Stereotaxis
Hansen Medical	Toshiba

HISTORICAL FINANCIALS

Company Type: Public

Income Statement

FYE: December 31

	REVENUE ($ mil.)	NET INCOME ($ mil.)	NET PROFIT MARGIN	EMPLOYEES
12/14	2,131.7	418.8	19.6%	2,978
12/13	2,265.1	671.0	29.6%	2,792
12/12	2,178.8	656.6	30.1%	2,362
12/11	1,757.3	495.1	28.2%	1,924
12/10	1,413.0	381.8	27.0%	1,660
Annual Growth	**10.8%**	**2.3%**	**—**	**15.7%**

2014 Year-End Financials

Debt ratio: —
Return on equity: 12.1%
Cash ($ mil.): 600
Current ratio: 3.69
Long-term debt ($ mil.): —

No. of shares (mil.): 36
Dividends
　Yield: —
　Payout: —
Market value ($ mil.): 19,359

	STOCK PRICE ($) FY Close	P/E High/Low	PER SHARE ($) Earnings	Dividends	Book Value
12/14	528.94	48 31	11.11	0.00	92.33
12/13	384.08	34 21	16.73	0.00	91.66
12/12	490.37	36 27	15.98	0.00	89.06
12/11	463.01	37 20	12.32	0.00	67.32
12/10	257.75	40 25	9.47	0.00	52.38
Annual Growth	**19.7%**	**— —**	**4.1%**	**—**	**15.2%**

Inventure Foods Inc.

Inventure Foods caters to avid snackers and the more health conscious alike. The company's Rader Farms business grows and processes berries and produces frozen fruits vegetables and beverages for sale primarily to grocery and club stores and mass merchandisers. The snack business makes potato and other snack chips pretzels and more under Bob's Texas Style Braids Poore Brothers Boulder Canyon Natural Foods to name a few. Inventure Foods also makes salted snacks branded with the T.G.I. Friday's and Nathan's Famous names and manufactures private label snacks for food stores in the US. Costco is the company's #1 customer. With roots in salty snacks Inventure is now focused on healthier fare.

Geographic Reach

Phoenix-based Inventure Foods operates manufacturing facilities in Arizona Georgia Indiana Oregon and Washington. While the company sells its products in both the US and Canada the US accounts for essentially all of its sales.

Operations

Inventure Foods operates two segments: frozen products and snack foods. The frozen products business produces frozen fruits vegetables and beverages which are sold primarily to grocery stores club stores and mass merchandisers. Brands include Rader Farms Boulder Canyon Natural Foods and Willamette Valley Fruit Co. (Products in the company's healthy/natural category account for about two-thirds of Inventure's annual sales.) The snack segment makes potato and kettle chips potato crisps pellet snacks sheeted dough products and extruded products for sale primarily to snack food distributors and retailers. Products in Inventure's indulgent specialty snack food category include T.G.I. Friday's and Nathan's Famous brand snacks (both under license) and Poore Brothers kettle cooked potato chips Tato Skins and other brands.

Sales and Marketing

Costco Wholesale is the company's biggest customer accounting for 35% of net sales in 2013. Indeed 27% of 2013 net revenue was attributable to Rader Farms/Kirkland co-branded frozen berry product sales to Costco. The remainder comes from sales to grocery chains club stores regional distributors and other manufacturers.

Financial Performance

Inventure Foods reported sales of $215.6 million in 2013 an increase of 16% versus 2012. The double-digit gain was driven primarily by an increase in sales by the frozen products segment and to a lesser extent snack products. ((Products in the company's healthy/natural category accounted for 67% of Inventure's total 2013 sales an increase of 6% versus 21012.) Indeed 2013 marked the seventh consecutive year of growing sales for the company which have tripled from just shy of $70 million in 2006.

Despite rising sales net income declined by 11% in 2013 versus 2012 to $6.6 million on higher operating and interest expenses.

Strategy

While Inventure Foods is growing its healthy/natural foods business it's reluctant to leave salty snacks behind —although its focus of late is on healthier snack foods including the Boulder Canyon brand. The $20.9-million purchase of Rader Farms (in 2007) launched Inventure's effort to move beyond its core business as a salty snack-food manufacturer. (Rader grows processes freezes and markets raspberries blueberries rhubarb and berry blends. It also purchases marionberries cherries cranberries and strawberries from fruit growers for processing and sale.) In 2013 the company continued to build its portfolio of higher-margin healthy/natural foods with a pair of acquisitions. Also to fund future purchases in 2014 the company filed a shelf registration that allows it to increase the number of shares outstanding up to $100 million worth.

On the salty side of the business Inventure in 20143 signed a long-term licensing agreement (ending 2024) which included international distribution and expended product line rights with T.G.I. Friday's. That deal followed another signed in 2013 with Vidalia Brands that resulted in a new line of snacks.

Mergers Acquisitions and Divestments

In November 2013 Inventure Foods acquired Fresh Frozen Foods a processor and packager of vegetables breads and other items sold under the Fresh Frozen brands for $38.4 million. In May 2013 the company bought Willamette Valley Fruit Co. which packages marionberries other blackberries blueberries strawberries and other types of berries fruits and vegetables at two plants in Oregon for $9.5 million in cash.

In 2012 the company sold its direct-store-delivery (DSD) business for $1.2 million.

Company Background

The company changed its name from The Inventure Group to Inventure Foods in 2010.

HISTORY

The Company was formed in 1995 as a holding company to acquire a potato chip manufacturing and distribution business which had been founded by Donald and James Poore in 1986.

In 1996 the company went public.

In 1998 it acquired Bob's Style Potato Chips.

A Bluffton Indiana facility - the location where T.G.I. Friday's snack foods are produced - was acquired in 1999 and the Boulder Canyon brand was purchased in 2000.

In 2005 the company proposed changing its name from Poore Brothers Inc. to The Inventure Group Inc. in order to reflect its array of holdings which includes many well-known national snack brands. The change was approved by the shareholders in 2006.

In May 2007 Inventure acquired Rader Farms Inc. a farm and berry processing facility in Lynden Washington.

In May 2010 the company changed its name from The Inventure Group to Inventure Foods to better reflect its changing strategy in recent years.

EXECUTIVES

CEO, Terry McDaniel, age 57, $458,205 total compensation
SVP and CFO, Steve Weinberger, age 62, $301,428 total compensation
General Manager Frozen Division, Dan Hammer
Vice President Operations, Brian Foster
Vice President Manufacturing, Jay Poore
Vice President Purchasing, Matt Simonian
Vice President Sales, Russell Law
Senior Vice President Marketing, Steve Sklar
Director, Larry R. Polhill, age 62
Auditors: MossAdamsLLP

LOCATIONS

HQ: Inventure Foods Inc.
5415 East High Street, Suite #350, Phoenix, AZ 85054
Phone: 623 932-6200
Web: www.inventurefoods.com

PRODUCTS/OPERATIONS

2013 Sales

	$ mil.	% of total
Frozen products	117.15	54
Snack products	98.5	46
Total	**215.6**	**100**

Selected Brands

Bob's Texas Style
Boulder Canyon Natural Foods
Braids
BURGER KING (licensed)
Jamba All Natural Smoothies
Knots
O' Boisies
Pizzarias
Poore Brothers
Rader Farms
T.G.I. Friday's (licensed)
Tato Skins

Selected Subsidiaries

BN Foods Inc.
Boulder Natural Foods Inc.
La Cometa Properties Inc.
Poore Brothers - Bluffton LLC
Rader Farms Inc.
Tejas PB Distributing Inc.
Willamette Valley Fruit Company

COMPETITORS

American Pop Corn	Kellogg U.S. Snacks
Auntie Anne's	King Nut Companies
Beer Nuts	Legacy Bakehouse
Bridgford Foods	Mondelez International
C.J. Vitner	Monster Beverage
Campbell Soup	Mrs. Fields
ConAgra	Nestlé©
Diamond Foods	Pepperidge Farm
Dole Food	Pictsweet
Encore Software	Pinnacle Foods
Frito-Lay	Pretzels Inc.
General Mills	Shoreline Fruit
Global Trading	Silver Lake Cookie
Goya	Small Planet Foods
Graceland Fruit	Snappy Popcorn
Grupo Bimbo	Snyder's-Lance
Hain Celestial	SunOpta
Hanover Foods	Texoma Peanut
Herr Foods	Weaver Popcorn Company
Idaho Fresh-Pak	Wetzel's Pretzels
J & J Snack Foods	Wise Foods

HISTORICAL FINANCIALS

Company Type: Public

Income Statement

FYE: December 28

	REVENUE ($ mil.)	NET INCOME ($ mil.)	NET PROFIT MARGIN	EMPLOYEES
12/13	215.5	6.6	3.1%	785
12/12	185.1	7.4	4.0%	497
12/11	162.2	2.8	1.7%	448
12/10	133.9	4.4	3.3%	389
12/09	121.0	3.7	3.1%	372
Annual Growth	15.5%	15.0%	—	20.5%

2013 Year-End Financials

Debt ratio: 41.8%	No. of shares (mil.): 19
Return on equity: 12.0%	Dividends
Cash ($ mil.): 0	Yield: —
Current ratio: 1.95	Payout: —
Long-term debt ($ mil.): 65	Market value ($ mil.): 262

	STOCK PRICE ($) FY Close	P/E High/Low		PER SHARE ($) Earnings	Dividends	Book Value
12/13	13.47	40	19	0.33	0.00	3.04
12/12	6.31	19	9	0.38	0.00	2.66
12/11	3.74	30	21	0.15	0.00	2.28
12/10	4.32	18	9	0.24	0.00	2.10
12/09	2.32	14	6	0.21	0.00	1.84
Annual Growth	55.2%	—	—	12.0%	—	13.4%

Investors Bancorp Inc (New)

Investors Bancorp is the holding company for Investors Savings Bank which serves New Jersey and New York from more than 85 branch offices. Founded in 1926 the bank offers such standard deposit products as savings and checking accounts CDs money market accounts and IRAs. Over the past few years Investors Savings Bank has increasingly focused on commercial lending; its residential mortgages have gone from more than 90% to around 60% of the bank's total loan portfolio.

Other offerings include commercial mortgages multifamily loans and construction loans.

Investors Bancorp has been growing through acquisitions and by opening new branches. In 2012 it announced plans to acquire Marathon Banking Corporation (a subsidiary of Greece-based Piraeus Bank) for $135 million. The deal will add 13 branches in the New York metro area —more than doubling its branches in New York. The deal also will mark Investors Bancorp's entry into Manhattan and Staten Island.

In 2011 Investors acquired Brooklyn Federal Bancorp a deal that added five branches in Brooklyn and Long Island New York. The company has focused on expanding its geographic footprint since it entered New York in 2010 through its purchase of Millennium Bank which had 17 branches in New Jersey New York and Massachusetts. (It sold the four Massachusetts locations to Rhode Island-based Domestic Bank after the deal closed.)

The company's growth has helped it improve income and grow deposits. Sales grew by 10% in 2011 pushing that figure to half a billion. Net income also improved that year by more than 27%. Investors Bancorp's level of nonperforming loans has remained low as it sticks to conservative lending standards. The company's funding costs also have been low thanks to favorable interest rates.

Mutual holding company Investors Bancorp MHC owns a majority of Investors Bancorp's stock.

EXECUTIVES

SEVP and COO, Domenick A. Cama, age 58, $621,000 total compensation
President and CEO, Kevin Cummings, age 59, $935,000 total compensation
EVP and Chief Lending Officer, Richard S. Spengler, age 52, $400,000 total compensation
EVP and Chief Retail Banking Officer, Paul Kalamaras, $375,000 total compensation
SVP and CFO, Sean Burke
Vice President, Mary Rose Genovese
Second Vice President, Cathy Murray
Assistant Vice President Information Technology, Benny Cuppini
Senior Vice President Information Technology, Sergio Alonso
Vice President Client Care Manager, Deborah Leonard
Senior Vice President, Sharon Lingswiler
Assistant Vice President And Manager, Edward Nejman
Senior Vice President, Robert Zajac
Senior Vice President, Dominick Petramale
Vice President Team Leader, Anthony Silva
Vice President Business Banking, Deena Sattaur
Senior Vice President, Ana Oliveira
Vice President, Betty Spiropoulos
Vice President Payroll Manager, Mary Ward
Senior Vice President Commercial, John Nietzel
Vice President Business Development, Peter Provenzale
Vice President, Robert Spitzer
Assistant Vice President, Margaret Munch
Vice President Senior Portfolio Manager, Kim Ickovic
Assistant Vice President Senior Const, Jose Jurado
Vice President Business Banking, Lynsey Ward
Assistant Vice President, Gayle Galenas
Mortgage Underwriter Assistant Vp, Silvia Merino Topley
Assistant Vice President, Calvin Pascall
Position In Vice President Team Leader, Biagio Madaio
Chairman, Robert M. Cashill, age 71
Auditors: KPMGLLP

LOCATIONS

HQ: Investors Bancorp Inc (New)
101 JFK Parkway, Short Hills, NJ 07078
Phone: 973 924-5100
Web: www.myinvestorsbank.com

PRODUCTS/OPERATIONS

2013 Sales

	$ mil.	% of total
Interest		
Loans receivable and held-for-sale	504.6	87
Mortgage-backed securities	28.1	5
Federal Home Loan Bank stock	6.4	1
Municipal bonds & other debt	5.9	1
Other	0.1	—
Noninterest		
Fees & service charges	18.8	3
Gain on loan transaction	8.7	2
Others	10.0	1
Adjustments	(1.0)	-
Total	**581.6**	**100**

COMPETITORS

Bank of America	M&T Bank
Bank of New York Mellon	New York Community Bancorp
Center Bancorp	OceanFirst Financial
Citigroup	PNC Financial
Fulton Financial	Susquehanna Bancshares

HISTORICAL FINANCIALS

Company Type: Public

Income Statement

FYE: December 31

	ASSETS ($ mil.)	NET INCOME ($ mil.)	INCOME AS % OF ASSETS	EMPLOYEES
12/13	15,623.0	112.0	0.7%	1,597
12/12	12,722.5	88.7	0.7%	1,219
12/11	10,701.5	78.8	0.7%	982
12/10	9,602.1	62.0	0.6%	892
12/09	8,357.8	22.5	0.3%	731
Annual Growth	**16.9%**	**49.3%**	**—**	**21.6%**

2013 Year-End Financials

Return on assets: 0.7%
Return on equity: 9.3%
Long-term debt ($ mil.): —
No. of shares (mil.): 138
Sales ($ mil): 582
Dividends
Yield: —
Payout: 20.0%
Market value ($ mil.): 3,542

	STOCK PRICE ($) FY Close	P/E High/Low	PER SHARE ($) Earnings	Dividends	Book Value
12/13	25.58	25 17	1.01	0.00	9.64
12/12	17.78	23 16	0.82	0.00	9.53
12/11	13.48	21 17	0.73	0.00	8.72
12/10	13.12	25 19	0.56	0.00	7.99
12/09	10.94	64 33	0.21	0.00	7.43
Annual Growth	**23.7%**	**— —**	**48.1%**	**—**	**6.7%**

Investors Title Co.

Investors Title insures you in case your land is well not completely yours. It's the holding company for Investors Title Insurance and Northeast Investors Title Insurance which underwrite land title insurance and sell reinsurance to other title companies. (Title insurance protects those who invest in real property against loss resulting from defective titles.) Investors Title Insurance serves customers from about 30 offices in North Carolina South Carolina Michigan and Nebraska and through branches or agents in 20 additional states. Northeast Investors Title operates through an agency office in New York. Founder and CEO J. Allen Fine and his family own more than 20% of Investors Title.

While the company does business throughout the eastern and midwestern US North Carolina accounts for 50% of its title insurance premiums.

Investors Title also provides tax-deferred exchange services through its Investors Title Exchange and Investors Title Accommodation subsidiaries. Its Investors Capital Management Company subsidiary offers investment advisory and management services.

EXECUTIVES

Evp National Marketing, George A Snead
Vice President, Beth Lewter
Vice President Sales And Marketing, Kim Dean
Vice President Finance, Todd Murphy
Vice President Human Resources, Mitchell Ward
Vice President, Jane Turner
Vice President Of Services, Carol Hayden
Svp Agency And Branch Operations, Joanna Biliouris
Vice President Southeast Region Marketing And Information Technology Director, Kim Wells
Assistant Vice President Corporate Marketing And Communications, Lee Brown
Vice President Multi State Marketing, Norma Carroll
Vice President Human Resources, Mitchell Warren
Vice President, Peter Walther
Svp National Markets, Patricia B Wolak
Vice President Compliance Officer And Title Attorney, Michael Aiken
Vice President Sales Manager La County, Robert Gomez
Senior Vice President, James Hicks
Vice President Of Information Systems, Peter Cole
Senior Vice President Operations, Joanna Tillottson
Auditors: DixonHughesGoodmanLLP

LOCATIONS

HQ: Investors Title Co.
121 North Columbia Street, Chapel Hill, NC 27514
Phone: 919 968-2200
Fax: 919 968-2227
Web: www.invtitle.com

PRODUCTS/OPERATIONS

2007 Revenues

	$ mil.	% of total
Net premiums written	70.0	83
Investment income	5.2	6
Exchange services	4.3	5
Net realized gain on sale of investments	0.9	1
Other	4.5	5
Total	**84.9**	**100**

Selected Subsidiaries

Investors Title Accommodation Corporation
Investors Title Exchange Corporation
Investors Title Insurance Company
Investors Title Management Services Inc.
Northeast Investors Title Insurance Company

COMPETITORS

Fidelity National Financial	Ticor Title Co.
	Title Resource Group

First American
Old Republic
Stewart Information
Services

United General Title
Insurance

HISTORICAL FINANCIALS
Company Type: Public

Income Statement
FYE: December 31

	ASSETS ($ mil.)	NET INCOME ($ mil.)	INCOME AS % OF ASSETS	EMPLOYEES
12/13	188.3	14.7	7.8%	233
12/12	171.9	11.1	6.5%	212
12/11	157.9	6.9	4.4%	199
12/10	153.4	6.3	4.2%	196
12/09	146.4	4.8	3.3%	216
Annual Growth	6.5%	32.1%	—	1.9%

2013 Year-End Financials

Return on assets: 8.1%
Return on equity: 12.1%
Long-term debt ($ mil.): —
No. of shares (mil.): 2
Sales ($ mil): 126

Dividends
Yield: 0.4%
Payout: 4.5%
Market value ($ mil.): 165

	STOCK PRICE ($) FY Close	P/E High	P/E Low	PER SHARE ($) Earnings	PER SHARE ($) Dividends	PER SHARE ($) Book Value
12/13	80.98	12	8	7.08	0.32	62.86
12/12	60.00	13	7	5.24	0.29	56.10
12/11	35.77	13	9	3.20	0.28	50.54
12/10	30.50	13	10	2.78	0.28	45.53
12/09	30.90	18	9	2.11	0.28	42.56
Annual Growth	27.2%	—	—	35.3%	3.4%	10.2%

IPC Healthcare, Inc.

IPC The Hospitalist Company (IPC) is on the leading edge of a growing US trend toward hospitalist specialization. The staffing firm provides 1800 hospitalists to more than 400 hospitals and 1200 post-acute care facilities facilities in about 30 states. Hospitalists are health care providers (physicians nurses and physicians assistants) who oversee all of a patient's treatment from the beginning to the end of their stay. They answer questions and coordinate treatment programs to improve the quality of care and reduce the length of a patient's hospital stay. In addition to providing staff IPC offers training data management billing and risk management services for its medical professionals and clients.

Geographic Reach
The company offers its services in 27 US states. In 2013 about 59% of its net revenues were generated by operations in Arizona Florida Michigan Missouri and Texas.

Operations
In addition to its staff of affiliated hospitalists IPC also uses another 730 physician and non-physician providers as needed; the doctors are contracted through about 100 independent physician groups. Altogether the company's hospitalists have handled about 16.5 million patient encounters since 2011. Private-pay patients make up only 5% of the company's revenues; the remainder is attributed to Medicare (48%) Medicaid (5%) and other third-party payers (42%).

Through its affiliated hospitalists IPC coordinates the care of hospitalized patients and serves as the inpatient partner of primary care physicians and specialists. It also provides its affiliated hospitalists with the infrastructure information management systems specialized training programs and administrative support necessary to perform these services. The company generates 93% of its net revenues through its affiliated hospitalists' patient encounters at hospitals and other inpatient and post-acute care facilities.

Financial Performance
As IPC has expanded its operations the company has seen steadily rising revenues over the last decade (and profits since 2008). In 2013 IPC reported a 16% growth in revenues due to an increase in patient encounters in new and existing markets. Of this increase 77% was attributable to same-market area growth (including tuck-in acquisitions and new hires) and 23% to operations in new markets. It also got a 1.8% increase from a combination of Medicare fee schedule rate increases and Medicaid parity offset by the automatic cut in Medicare payments triggered by sequestration in April 2013.IPC's net income increased by 27% in 2013 due to an increase in revenues and a net change in fair value of contingent consideration.In 2013 the company's operating cash flow increased by $3 million thanks to a growth in accounts receivable of $24 million (due to higher revenues a buildup of receivables resulting from acquired practices and delayed Medicaid parity payments a growth in prepaid expenses and other current assets of $2.1 million an increase in accounts payable and accrued liabilities of $1.2 million a net increase in medical malpractice and self-insurance reserves of $2.5 million and an growth in accrued compensation of $6.5 million (primarily related to timing of payrolls and physician bonus payments).

Strategy
In addition to its main growth strategy of acquiring existing practice groups in new markets IPC strives to offer its services to new institutions in areas where it already operates.
In 2011 2012 and 2013 the company has acquired a total of 47 practice groups.

Mergers and Acquisitions
Continuing its investment in the Mid-Atlantic region in 2014 IPC acquired Comprehensive Health Solutions based in Newtown Square PA. That year it also bought Midland Hospitalists PLC in Midland. Michigan and added two practices to its established presence in Florida including Eddin Medical Services a post-acute practice in the Daytona Beach area and TriCounty Hospitalists an acute care practice in the Orlando area.In 2014 the company also acquired GeriCare LLC based in Connecticut; Eastside Medical Consultants LLC (EMC) based in Wichita Kansas; RG Psychological Services P.C headquartered in Lynbrook New York; Total Inpatient Services P.A. (TIPS) based in Sugar Land Texas; Preferred Hospitalists of Michigan PLLC (PHM) based in Warren Michigan; and CAP Medical Group PLLC headquartered in New Hartford New York.
During 2013 IPC acquired 19 hospitalist physician practices for $125 million.That year it expanded its presence in Florida with Cape Coral Hospitalists Inc. in Ft. Myers; Steward Health Care System LLC in Massachusetts (for $45 million) and the hospitalist operations and related assets in White Plains New York acquired from four affiliated entities: Park Avenue Health Care Management LLC; Park Avenue Medical Associates PC; Park Avenue Medical Associates LLC; and Geriatric Services PC for $39.7 million.

Company Background
IPC made acquisitions in 2011 of about 15 additional practices adding approximately 240000 annual patient encounters. These included practices in new areas of operation such as Idaho Washington State Southern California and Orlando Florida. Other acquisitions expanded operations in established practice areas in Arizona Florida Michigan and Nevada. The company continued its practice of buying up small regional hospitalist groups in 2012 expanding its operations in the greater St. Louis area southern Florida northwestern Ohio southern Texas Massachusetts and Rhode Island.

Also in 2012 IPC entered a new service market behavioral health through the acquisition of Asana Integrated Medical Group which provides coordination of mental health services through a team of psychologists psychiatrists and nurse practitioners in Arizona and California.

In 2012 it signed contracts to provide hospitalist services to four Methodist Healthcare System hospitals in San Antonio. The company also sees room for growth by recruiting and training additional hospitalists. Targeted regions for expansion include New England the Northwest the Southwest and the Southeast. IPC is also looking to expand into specialist areas such as behavioral health.

IPC completed an IPO in 2008 using funds to help pay off debt and acquire smaller regional hospitalist practice groups.

EXECUTIVES

Vice President Marketing Development, Todd Kislak
Chairman and CEO, Adam D. Singer, age 54, $543,000 total compensation
President and COO, R. Jeffrey Taylor, age 65, $435,000 total compensation
EVP and Chief Development Officer, Richard G. Russell, age 54, $360,000 total compensation
CFO, Richard H. (Rick) Kline, $360,000 total compensation
VP Technology, Patrick Holmes
VP Health Services, Kathleen Loya
Chief Medical Officer, Kerry Weiner, $370,000 total compensation
SVP Sales and Marketing, Jeffrey L. Winter
Vice President Information Systems, Mark C Citron
Executive Vice President, John Fretz
Vice President Commercial Lending, Melody Rassouli
Chairman and CEO, Adam D. Singer, age 54
Auditors: Ernst&YoungLLP

LOCATIONS

HQ: IPC Healthcare, Inc.
4605 Lankershim Boulevard, Suite 617, North Hollywood, CA 91602
Phone: 888 447-2362

PRODUCTS/OPERATIONS

2013 Employees

	No.	% of total
Clinical		
Employed physicians	1257	45
Nurse practitioners & phycician assistants	508	18
Independent contracted physicians	97	4
Non-clinical employees	907	33
Total	**2769**	**100**

Selected Acquisitions
2013
Cape Coral Hospitalists Inc (Ft.Myers Florida)

Selected Administrative and Professional Services

Billing and collections
Compliance
Financial reporting
Information management system
Recruiting
Regional management
Risk management
Training
Transition management

COMPETITORS

Cogent HMG	MEDNAX
EmCare	Schumacher Group
Envision Healthcare	Sheridan Healthcare
Hospital Physician	Team Health
Partners	

HISTORICAL FINANCIALS

Company Type: Public

Income Statement

FYE: December 31

	REVENUE ($ mil.)	NET INCOME ($ mil.)	NET PROFIT MARGIN	EMPLOYEES
12/13	609.5	41.4	6.8%	2,769
12/12	523.4	32.5	6.2%	2,381
12/11	457.4	29.2	6.4%	2,030
12/10	363.4	24.2	6.7%	1,792
12/09	310.5	18.6	6.0%	1,451
Annual Growth	18.4%	22.1%	—	17.5%

2013 Year-End Financials

Debt ratio: 16.3%
Return on equity: 14.4%
Cash ($ mil.): 25
Current ratio: 1.84
Long-term debt ($ mil.): 90
No. of shares (mil.): 17
Dividends
  Yield: —
  Payout: —
Market value ($ mil.): 1,011

	STOCK PRICE ($) FY Close	P/E High/Low	PER SHARE ($) Earnings	Dividends	Book Value
12/13	59.39	26 16	2.39	0.00	18.51
12/12	39.71	24 16	1.92	0.00	15.36
12/11	45.72	29 20	1.74	0.00	12.91
12/10	39.01	27 15	1.46	0.00	10.71
12/09	33.25	29 13	1.14	0.00	8.98
Annual Growth	15.6%	— —	20.3%	—	19.8%

IPG Photonics Corp

IPG Photonics has a laser focus. The company makes fiber lasers and amplifiers and diode lasers which are primarily used in materials processing applications (nearly 90% of sales) such as welding cutting marking and engraving. Its fiber lasers also have applications in medicine and in telecommunications networks from enabling data signal transmission to surgical cosmetic urological and dental procedures. The company's customers have included BAE SYSTEMS Mitsubishi Heavy Industries and Nippon Steel. Deriving more than 80% of its sales outside North America IPG Photonics operates sales offices in about a dozen countries in Asia and Europe.

Operations

The vertically integrated manufacturer design and makes most of the components used in its finished products from semiconductor diodes to optical fiber preforms finished fiber lasers and amplifiers. It also manufactures other products used in its lasers including optical delivery cables fiber couplers beam switches optical heads and chillers. By not outsourcing its manufacturing to third-party companies IPG Photonics is able to better control its proprietary processes and technologies as well as the supply of its materials.

Geographic Reach

The company conducts R&D in the same city as its headquarters as well as in New Hampshire and overseas in the German city of Burbach (near Frankfurt) and in Fryazino Russia (outside Moscow).

It has four manufacturing facilities for lasers amplifiers and components one in each of its R&D cities and the fourth one in Cerro Maggiore Italy outside Milan. Manufacturing facilities for optical components are in India and China.

Sales and Marketing

IPG Photonics primarily uses a direct sales force. It has a diverse customer base - its five-largest customers only account for about 15% of sales. In 2012 it shipped more than 25000 units to some 1900 customers worldwide.

It has sales offices at each of its manufacturing facilities as well as in Michigan and California in the US. International sales offices are located in China France India Spain Singapore Turkey and the UK.

Financial Performance

Overall sales were up 19% in 2012 to $562 million. Its core business materials processing applications sold more high-power and medium-power lasers used in cutting and welding applications and pulsed lasers used in marking and engraving applications. The advanced applications segment which makes and sells high-power high-brightness lasers saw sales shoot up 66%. The company has relatively low operating expenses and profits were up 23% in 2012 to $145 million.

Mergers and Acquisitions

Increasing demand has led IPG to pursue operational expansion in Russia Germany and the US. In 2012 the company paid $55.4 million to acquire the 22.5% of Russia-based subsidiary NTO IRE-Polus that it did not already own to extend its control over R&D sales and manufacturing infrastructure in the country.

Also in 2012 IPG bought privately held J.P. Sercel Associates (JPSA) a New Hampshire-based supplier of UV excimer and diode-pumped solid-state industrial laser micromachining systems used in high-volume biomedical industrial automation LED microelectromechanical systems (MEMS) microfluidics thin-film solar panel and semiconductor manufacturing applications. The purchase expands IPG's custom laser system offerings to include fine processing precision cutting drilling and micromachining of ceramics glass and semiconductors. The company further enhanced its UV laser development with the purchase the following year of California-based Mobius Photonics.

Strategy

IPG remains focused on fiber lasers as an alternative to conventional lasers such as gas or crystal. Its strategy is to exploit the advantages that fiber lasers offer such as superiority in electrical efficiency beam quality and control maintenance costs longevity flexibility and usability. Traditional laser technologies have advantages that make them more suitable for some applications but fiber lasers continue to gain ground. Crystal lasers generate higher peak power pulses fiber lasers don't achieve the deep ultraviolet light needed for some semiconductor applications and carbon dioxide lasers are better for non-metallic applications such has plastics. Fiber lasers however have made improvements in power output that has opened them up to new markets and IPG believes the technology can reach additional nascent applications such as natural resource extraction.

HISTORY

IPG Photonics raised about $100 million in private equity funding with its investors including Apax Partners Merrill Lynch TA Associates and Winston Partners. The company filed for an IPO in 2000 and withdrew the registration statement six months later. It filed for another IPO in 2006 and completed the offering by the end of the year.

The company used proceeds of its public offering to repurchase warrants pay off debts and for general corporate purposes including working capital expansion of manufacturing facilities purchases of equipment and expansion of applications development and services.

In 2007 IPG Photonics acquired its Chinese distributor HM Laser and established a subsidiary IPG China with an office in Beijing. China is one of IPG's principal markets along with Germany Japan Russia and the US.

The company stepped forward with its purchase of laser material manufacturer Photonics Innovations (PII) in January 2010. The acquisition expanded IPG's products and services portfolio for optical and laser materials fabrication tunable laser design and optical and sensing systems. Transaction details were not divulged.

EXECUTIVES

Vice President, Paolo Sinni
General Counsel Secretary Vice President, Angelo P Lopresti, age 52
Vice President Of Industrial Markets, William Shiner
CEO and Chairman, Valentin P. Gapontsev, age 76, $542,800 total compensation
Managing Director IPG Laser GmbH; SVP Europe and Director, Eugene Scherbakov, age 66, $432,777 total compensation
SVP and CFO, Timothy P. V. Mammen, age 45, $391,834 total compensation
Director of Research and Development IPG Laser, Igor Samartsev, age 52
SVP Components, Alexander (Alex) Ovtchinnikov, age 53, $363,600 total compensation
SVP U.S. Operations, Felix Stukalin
Vice President Strategic Marketing, Yuri Erokhin

Vice President, Denis Gapontsev
Senior Vice President World Wide Sales, Trevor D Ness
CEO and Chairman, Valentin P. Gapontsev, age 76
Board Of Directors, Michael Kampfe
Auditors: Deloitte&ToucheLLP

LOCATIONS

HQ: IPG Photonics Corp
  50 Old Webster Road, Oxford, MA 01540
Phone: 508 373-1100
Web: www.ipgphotonics.com

2012 Sales

	$ mil.	% of total
Asia-Pacific	251.8	45
Europe	200.7	36
US	108.3	19
Other	1.7	-
Total	**562.5**	**100**

PRODUCTS/OPERATIONS

2012 Sales by Market

	$ mil.	% of total
Materials processing	492.0	87
Advanced applications	43.1	8
Communications	21.7	4
Medical	5.7	1
Total	**562.5**	**100**

Selected Products

Broadband light sources
Continuous wave lasers
Diode laser systems
Diode-pumped solid-state laser systems
Erbium lasers
Fiber amplifiers
Fiber lasers
Fiber-coupled direct diode laser systems
Pulsed fiber lasers
Raman pump lasers
Thulium lasers
UV excimer laser systems
Ytterbium lasers

COMPETITORS

Cisco Systems	Mitsubishi Materials
Coherent Inc.	Newport Corp.
EMCORE	Oclaro
FANUC	Presstek
Furukawa Electric	ROFIN-SINAR
GSI Group	Swatch
Huawei Technologies	TRUMPF
JDS Uniphase	

HISTORICAL FINANCIALS

Company Type: Public

Income Statement

FYE: December 31

	REVENUE ($ mil.)	NET INCOME ($ mil.)	NET PROFIT MARGIN	EMPLOYEES
12/13	648.0	155.7	24.0%	2,800
12/12	562.5	145.0	25.8%	2,400
12/11	474.4	117.7	24.8%	2,137
12/10	299.2	53.9	18.0%	1,760
12/09	185.8	5.4	2.9%	1,430
Annual Growth	**36.6%**	**131.6%**	**—**	**18.3%**

2013 Year-End Financials

Debt ratio: 1.5%
Return on equity: 18.6%
Cash ($ mil.): 448
Current ratio: 7.86
Long-term debt ($ mil.): 11

No. of shares (mil.): 51
Dividends
  Yield: —
  Payout: —
Market value ($ mil.): 4,030

	STOCK PRICE ($) FY Close	P/E High/Low		PER SHARE ($) Earnings	Dividends	Book Value
12/13	77.61	26	18	2.97	0.00	17.87
12/12	66.65	23	12	2.81	0.65	14.47
12/11	33.87	31	12	2.41	0.00	9.31
12/10	31.62	28	12	1.13	0.00	6.74
12/09	16.73	145	57	0.12	0.00	5.57
Annual Growth	**46.8%**	**—**		**—123.0%**	**—**	**33.9%**

Iridium Communications Inc

If you want to make a phone call from the North Pole you want Iridium Communications (formerly Iridium Satellite). The company offers mobile voice data and Internet services worldwide targeting companies that operate in remote areas. While Iridium focuses on such commercial industries as energy defense maritime and mining its main customer is the US Department of Defense. Boeing primarily operates and maintains the Iridium satellite system which consists of 66 low-earth-orbit satellites linked to ground stations (the world's largest commercial satellite operation). The mobile satellite communications company has operations centers in the US Canada and Europe.

Geographic Reach

Virginia-based Iridium Communications operates telemetry tracking and control stations and satellite earth station facilities in Alaska Arizona Maryland Virginia as well as in northern Canada and Norway. The company generates about 60% of its sales in North America. The UK represents about 10% of sales.

Operations

Iridium has three principal lines of business: land0based handset machine-to-machines (M2M) maritime aviation and government solutions.

Sales and Marketing

The US government is the company's largest single customer generating $76.7 million in revenue or 20% of Iridium Communications' total in 2012. The company has 611000 billable subscribers worldwide in 2012 a 17% increase compared with 2011.

Financial Performance

Iridium's total revenue declined from $384.3 million in 2011 to $383.5 million in 2012. Sales in the US and Canada were up about 1% year over year while sales in the UK declined by 13%. Net income rose 63% over the same period to $64.6 million.

Strategy

Iridium has slated the launch of new satellites for 2014 in order to replace aging equipment and boost its transmission capacity so that it can offer more and better services. The company's next generation system will be known as Iridium NEXT which will also be operated and maintained by Boeing. In 2013 the company received a $400 million five-year contract from the Defense Information Systems Agency (DISA) to provide satellite airtime services to meet the communications needs of the US Department of Defense and its federal partners.

In 2012 the satellite communications company began commercial operations in Russia.

Ownership

The company's largest shareholder is Khalid bin Abdullah bin Abdulrahman through Baralonco Ltd. with about 17% of the stock.

EXECUTIVES

Chief Executive Officer, Matthew J. (Matt) Desch, age 56, $734,474 total compensation
President and Chief Executive Officer Aireon LLC, Don L. Thoma, age 52, $313,500 total compensation
Chief Financial Officer, Thomas J. Fitzpatrick, age 56, $434,360 total compensation
Vice President and General Manager Iridium PRIME℠, David A. Anhalt
COO, S. Scott Smith, age 55, $334,400 total compensation
EVP Government Programs, Scott T. Scheimreif
Executive Vice President Sales & Marketing, Bryan J. Hartin
Vice President Controller, Richard P Nyren
Vice President And Deputy General, Christian O'Connor
Vice President Satellite And Amp Launch, Ramona Jackson
Vice President Tax, John Dellavecchia
Chairman, Robert H. (Bob) Niehaus, age 58
Board Member, Parker Rush
Board Member, Alvin B Krongard
Board Member, Darrel J Barros

LOCATIONS

HQ: Iridium Communications Inc
  1750 Tysons Boulevard, Suite 1400, McLean, VA 22102
Phone: 703 287-7400
Web: www.iridium.com

2012 Sales

	$ mil.	% of total
US	178.1	46
Canada	53.3	14
UK	42.7	11
Other countries	109.4	29
Total	**383.5**	**100**

PRODUCTS/OPERATIONS

Selected Services

Aviation
  Flight communications
  Flight training
  Helicopter systems
Land Mobile
  Prepaid phone services
Maritime
  Crew calling (ship to shore calls for crew members)
  Fax
  In network (calls between ships via Iridium's network)
  Long range identification and tracking
  Ship safety and alert system
  Vessel monitoring

COMPETITORS

Globalstar	ORBCOMM
Inmarsat	TerreStar
LightSquared	

HISTORICAL FINANCIALS
Company Type: Public

Income Statement
FYE: December 31

	REVENUE ($ mil.)	NET INCOME ($ mil.)	NET PROFIT MARGIN	EMPLOYEES
12/13	382.6	62.5	16.3%	224
12/12	383.5	64.6	16.9%	211
12/11	384.3	39.6	10.3%	197
12/10	348.1	22.6	6.5%	174
12/09	75.9	(44.1)	—	166
Annual Growth	49.8%			7.8%

2013 Year-End Financials

Debt ratio: 44.9%	No. of shares (mil.): 76
Return on equity: 6.8%	Dividends
Cash ($ mil.): 186	Yield: —
Current ratio: 3.64	Payout: —
Long-term debt ($ mil.): 1,039	Market value ($ mil.): 479

	STOCK PRICE ($) FY Close	P/E High/Low		PER SHARE ($) Earnings	Dividends	Book Value
12/13	6.25	13	8	0.71	0.00	12.25
12/12	6.72	11	7	0.83	0.00	11.46
12/11	7.71	17	10	0.54	0.00	9.58
12/10	8.25	34	20	0.31	0.00	9.33
12/09	8.03	—	—	(0.82)	0.00	8.94
Annual Growth	(6.1%)			—	—	8.2%

iRobot Corp

Fans of The Jetsons appreciate iRobot. The company makes robots for all sorts of applications — from defense and security to industrial use and home appliances. Its Roomba FloorVac and Scooba are the first of their kind to automatically clean floors. The company's defense and security robots perform tasks such as battlefield reconnaissance and bomb disposal. iRobot has sold more than 4500 robots to military and civil defense forces including PackBots to the US Army. The firm has offices in the US and Hong Kong and sells its home products worldwide through retailers. iRobot was founded in 1990 by robot engineers from the Massachusetts Institute of Technology.

Geographic Reach

Massachusetts-based iRobot has offices in the US and Hong Kong. Sales to customers outside the US accounted for about 57% of the company's revenue in 2012 (up from 42% in 2011).

Operations

iRobot operates two primary business segments. Home Robots account for more than 80% of sales while Defense & Security Robots represent the remainder. In 2012 the company sent four robots to Japan to explore reactor buildings at the Fukushima Daiichi nuclear plant.

Sales and Marketing

The US federal government accounted for about 15% of the company's total revenue in 2012 down from 36% and 38% in 2011 and 2010 respectively. Boeing as a subcontractor for the government is another significant customer contributing 4.5% of 2012 sales. Sales to Japan's Sales on Demand Corp. and a network of affiliated European distributors accounted for about 30% of home robot sales in 2012.

Financial Performance

iRobot's sales declined by 6% in 2012 compared with 2011 while net income fell 57% over the same period. The decrease was caused by a 57% decline in sales of defense and security robots as the wars in Iraq and Afghanistan wound down and demand for the company's PackBot and small unmanned ground vehicle (SUGV) robots wanes. Away from the battlefield sales of home robots jumped 28% to nearly $357 million in 2012 due to more items shipped and a 7% increase in average selling price.

The decline in sales and profits in 2012 reversed two years of significant sales gains for the company and three consecutive years of increasing profitability.

Strategy

Amid falling sales of its tactical military robots the company is focusing on its home care robots. In 2012 iRobot reorganized into three newly formed business units focused on home robots military robots and emerging technologies in a bid to advance its long-term strategy to be the technology leader in remote presence and automated home maintenance. With its foothold in the robotic appliances niche iRobot has boosted its consumer business by developing new products such as the new Roomba 700 series built on popular brand names. It has introduced several products including the Roomba for Pets Roomba Discovery for Pets and the Dirt Dog Workshop Robot which is designed to keep work spaces free of sawdust small nails and debris. To keep its product pipeline full iRobot invested $37.2 million in research and development in 2012 up from $36.5 million and $24.8 million in 2011 and 2010 respectively.

Mergers and Acquisitions

iRobot acquired privately-held Evolution Robotics the maker of Mint brand automatic floor cleaning robots for $74 million in October 2012. The purchase expanded iRobot's technology leadership through a combination of intellectual property engineering talent and new products that broadened its robot offering.

EXECUTIVES

Vp Marketing Communications, Nancy Dussault Smith
Chairman and CEO, Colin M. Angle, age 46, $463,897 total compensation
EVP and Chief Legal Counsel, Glen D. Weinstein, age 43, $290,353 total compensation
EVP and CFO, Alison Dean, age 49, $228,654 total compensation
Chief Technology Officer, Paolo Pirjanian
Vice President Of Strategy, Tom Frost
Vice President, M Adler
Vice President, Pat Haegele
Svp Human Resources, Russell J (Russ) Campanello, age 59
Vice President Investor Relations, Elise P Caffrey
Partner Vice President Of Private, Gianluca Pandullo
Senior Vice President Engineering, Carl Calabria
Vice President Programs Government And Industrial Division, Tim Burroughs
Vice President Americas Home Robots, Richard Campbell
Vice President Business Development Home Robots, Debra Rider
Evp Of Finance, Dave Adler
Svp Sales, Steven Rogers
Vice President For Strategy And Business Development, Tom Gramaglia
Senior Vice President Research And De, Indraji Purkayastha
Senior Vice President, Elizabeth Pratt

Chairman and CEO, Colin M. Angle, age 46
Board Member, Joseph Endris
Auditors: PricewaterhouseCoopersLLP

LOCATIONS

HQ: iRobot Corp
 8 Crosby Drive, Bedford, MA 01730
Phone: 781 430-3000
Web: www.irobot.com

PRODUCTS/OPERATIONS

2012 Sales

	$ mil.	% of total
Product	418.5	96
Contract	17.7	4
Total	**436.2**	**100**

2012 Sales

	$ mil.	% of total
Home robots	356.8	82
Defense & security	79.4	18
Total	**436.2**	**100**

COMPETITORS

AM General	General Dynamics
Allen-Vanguard Corporation	LG Electronics
BAE SYSTEMS	Lockheed Martin
BISSELL	QinetiQ
Electrolux	Samsung Electronics
GE Appliances & Lighting	

HISTORICAL FINANCIALS
Company Type: Public

Income Statement
FYE: December 28

	REVENUE ($ mil.)	NET INCOME ($ mil.)	NET PROFIT MARGIN	EMPLOYEES
12/13	487.4	27.6	5.7%	528
12/12	436.2	17.3	4.0%	534
12/11*	465.5	40.1	8.6%	619
01/11	400.9	25.5	6.4%	657
01/10	298.6	3.3	1.1%	538
Annual Growth	13.0%	69.7%	—	(0.5%)

*Fiscal year change

2013 Year-End Financials

Debt ratio: —	No. of shares (mil.): 28
Return on equity: 9.1%	Dividends
Cash ($ mil.): 165	Yield: —
Current ratio: 3.72	Payout: —
Long-term debt ($ mil.): —	Market value ($ mil.): 1,025

	STOCK PRICE ($) FY Close	P/E High/Low		PER SHARE ($) Earnings	Dividends	Book Value
12/13	35.41	42	19	0.94	0.00	11.43
12/12	18.59	61	26	0.61	0.00	9.93
12/11*	29.85	26	15	1.44	0.00	8.93
01/11	24.88	25	15	0.96	0.00	6.77
01/10	17.60	136	55	0.13	0.00	5.31
Annual Growth	19.1%			—	—	—

*Fiscal year change

ITC Holdings Corp

ITC Holdings (ITC) owns and operates 15000 circuit miles of power transmission lines. Through its subsidiaries ITC Transmission Michigan Electric Transmission Company (METC) ITC Great Plains and ITC Midwest ITC operates regulated high-voltage transmission systems in Michigan's Lower Peninsula and portions of Illinois Iowa Kansas Minnesota Missouri and Oklahoma serving a combined peak load of more than 26000 MW. ITC is a member of the Midwest ISO (MISO) a regional transmission organization. The company also operates as ITC Grid Development which invests in transmission infrastructure development.

Geographic Reach

ITC's regulated operating subsidiaries' transmission facilities are located in Michigan's Lower Peninsula and portions of Illinois Iowa Kansas Minnesota Missouri and Oklahoma.

Operations

Through subsidiaries ITC Transmission Michigan Electric Transmission Company (METC) ITC Great Plains and ITC Midwest ITC operates regulated high-voltage transmission systems incuding 15000 miles of.

Sales and Marketing

Detroit Edison Consumers Energy and Interstate Power and Light accounted for 26.7% 25.6%. and 27.0% respectively of ITC's total operating revenues in 2012.

Financial Performance

ITC's 2012 revenues increased by 10% (to $831 million) reflecting growth across all of its segments. Network revenues grew by 5% due due to a higher rate base partially offset by a short term ITC Transmission rate freeze revenue deferral. Regional cost sharing revenues increased by 40% thanks to additional capital projects that were placed into service. Point-to-point revenues grew by 10% thanks to an increase in the number of point-to-point reservations. Scheduling control and dispatch revenues jumped by 30% as the result of a change in MISO's revenue distribution methodology (implemented by MISO in 2012 to better align billing rates with projected expenses).The company's net income increased by 9% in 2012 thanks to higher revenues and lower operational and maintenance expenses.

ITC has seen a steady growth in revenues and net income since 2008.

Strategy

ITC's strategy is to operate maintain and invest in transmission infrastructure while pursuing development projects to improve overall grid reliability.

ITC is working on building a robust regional power infrastructure using both renewable and traditional power resources. Through its Green Power Express unit ITC is looking to integrate wind and other renewable sources into ITC's future energy mix as the company strives to meet state and federal demands for power generators to use cleaner energy. It is developing a network of 765 kV transmission facilities that will move up to 12000 MW of renewable energy (primarily windpowered) to major load centers in the Midwest.

The company has a capital investment plan aimed at investing $1.7 billion from 2012 through 2016 to construct its portions of various development projects in the South Central and North Central regions of the US.

In a major move to grow its business in 2012 the company agreed to acquire the electric transmission business of Entergy to create a leading transmission enterprise with more than 30000 miles of lines.

EXECUTIVES

Vice President Information Technology, Denis Y Desrosiers

Vp Itc Holdings Corp And President Itc Michigan, Gregory (Greg) Ioanidis

Chairman President and CEO, Joseph L. Welch, age 66, $977,686 total compensation

EVP and Chief Business Officer; Business Unit Head ITCTransmission and METC, Linda H. Blair, age 45, $570,808 total compensation

EVP and General Counsel, Daniel J. Oginsky, age 41, $365,808 total compensation

EVP and COO, Jon E. Jipping, age 49, $479,700 total compensation

VP ITC Holdings Corp and President ITC Midwest, Doug Collins

SVP CFO and Treasurer, Rejji P. Hayes

VP Information Technology and CIO, Ron Hinsley

VP ITC Holdings Corp and President ITC Great Plains, Kristine M. Schmidt

VP and President ITC Midwest, Krista Tanner

President ITC Great Plains, Brett Leopold

Chairman President and CEO, Joseph L. Welch, age 66

Auditors: Deloitte&ToucheLLP

LOCATIONS

HQ: ITC Holdings Corp
27175 Energy Way, Novi, MI 48377
Phone: 248 946-3000
Web: www.itc-holdings.com

PRODUCTS/OPERATIONS

2012 Sales

	$ mil.	% of total
Network revenues	669.1	80
Regional cost sharing revenues	122.6	15
Point-to-point	17.4	2
Scheduling control & dispatch	15.1	2
Other	6.3	1
Total	**830.5**	**100**

COMPETITORS

DTE Electric	SEMCO ENERGY
Indiana Michigan Power	We Energies
Integrys Energy Group	Wolverine Power Supply
Lansing Board of Water and Light	Xcel Energy
Midland Cogeneration Venture	

HISTORICAL FINANCIALS

Company Type: Public

Income Statement

FYE: December 31

	REVENUE ($ mil.)	NET INCOME ($ mil.)	NET PROFIT MARGIN	EMPLOYEES
12/13	941.2	233.5	24.8%	539
12/12	830.5	187.8	22.6%	503
12/11	757.4	171.6	22.7%	452
12/10	696.8	145.6	20.9%	433
12/09	621.0	130.9	21.1%	413
Annual Growth	**11.0%**	**15.6%**	**—**	**6.9%**

2013 Year-End Financials

Debt ratio: 57.5%	No. of shares (mil.): 157
Return on equity: 15.4%	Dividends
Cash ($ mil.): 34	Yield: 5.0%
Current ratio: 0.38	Payout: 123.7%
Long-term debt ($ mil.): 3,412	Market value ($ mil.): 15,092

	STOCK PRICE ($) FY Close	P/E High/Low	PER SHARE ($) Earnings	Dividends	Book Value
12/13	95.82	71 52	1.47	1.61	10.25
12/12	76.91	65 55	1.20	1.46	9.03
12/11	75.88	69 55	1.10	0.46	8.18
12/10	61.98	65 51	0.95	1.31	7.34
12/09	52.09	60 37	0.86	1.25	6.73
Annual Growth	**16.5%**	**— —**	**14.4%**	**6.4%**	**11.1%**

Ixia

Ixia nixes network glitches. The company designs network validation testing hardware and software that provides visibility into traffic performance and also addresses the network applications. Hardware consists of optical and electrical interface cards and the chassis to hold them. Its software tests the functionality of video voice conformance and security across ethernet wi-fi and 3G/LTE equipment and networks. Ixia primarily serves network equipment manufacturers (Cisco) service providers (AT&T) corporate customers (Bloomberg) the federal government (US Army) and its contractors (General Dynamics). Geographically sales are about evenly divided between the US and international customers.

Geographic Reach

Headquartered in the US Ixia has international offices in Australia Canada China France Germany India Ireland Japan South Korea Sweden the UAE and the UK.

It outsources the manufacturing of its hardware to third-party contract and assembly companies in Malaysia.

Sales and Marketing

For the most part Ixia uses a direct sales force except in certain foreign markets where it relies on distributors partners and other resellers.

Cisco is its largest customer accounting for about 10% of overall sales.

Financial Performance

Overall sales increased 34% in 2012 to $413 million a record in revenues for the company. The growth was mostly inorganic that is due to recent acquisitions. But Ixia did sell another $36.7 million in hardware spearheaded by its 10 Gigabit 40/100 Gigabit Ethernet cards and IxVeriwave products. It also enjoyed another $21 million in revenue for services such as customer support and maintenance-related warranty contracts. In addition the company took in $45 million in profits for an 11% profit margin.

Strategy

Ixia's goal of being a leader in network test and visibility capabilities involves expanding its product base through acquisitions and internal research and development. R&D is a big focus; the company spends about 25% of annual revenue on it and also operates Ixia Labs a technology development incubator.

Mergers and Acquisitions

Ixia frequently adds to its product portfolio through acquisitions. In late 2013 it bought Net Optics a provider of network visibility hardware and software for $190 million in cash. The year before it network optimization systems provider Anue Systems for $145 million to strengthen its capabilities in validating wirelessly-delivered next-generation networks and applications. Later that year it bought network security testing company BreakingPoint Systems for $160 million rounding out its network test and visibility product offerings. In 2011 Ixia paid more than $15 million for Veri-Wave a performance testing company for wireless LAN and Wi-Fi enabled smart devices.

HISTORY

Chairman Errol Ginsberg founded Ixia in 1997 "in rather humble digs above a Mexican restaurant" in Calabasas California about an hour north of Los Angeles. The company went public in 2000 in a $57.5 million IPO but sales failed to top $100 million for three more years.

In 2003 Ixia acquired G3 Nova Technology a developer of VoIP test tools for enterprise call centers communications networks and network devices for about $12 million in cash and stock. Two years later it bought Communication Machinery Corp. (CMC) a developer of Wi-Fi network testing tools for $4 million in cash.

In 2006 Ixia acquired the video telephony test products of Dilithium Networks for around $5 million in cash. With the acquisition the company introduced a product based on the Dilithium Network Analyzer (DNA). The IxMobile Video Telephony test tools are focused on mobile wireless conformance interoperability capacity and performance testing.

Atul Bhatnagar who came from Nortel succeeded Ginsberg as CEO in 2007.

The company made two acquisitions in 2009 that helped it reach record revenues in 2010. Ixia purchased the assets of Agilent Technologies' N2X Data Networks product line for about $44 million in cash. The purchase brought an intuitive and powerful user interface as well as a customer base to open further markets in the Middle East and Asia/Pacific regions. Earlier in 2009 Ixia bought Catapult Communications for about $105 million in cash. The company sees Catapult's 3G and 4G wireless networking test products as complementary to its Internet protocol performance test systems and service verification platforms.

EXECUTIVES

Vice President Business Development, Maik Lankau
Vice President, Christopher Willia
Vp Sales Nvg, Kevin Przybocki
SVP Corporate Affairs and General Counsel, Ronald W. (Ron) Buckly, age 62, $350,000 total compensation
President and CEO, Bethany J. Mayer, age 53
SVP Operations, Raymond de Graaf, age 48, $304,808 total compensation
Chief Product Officer, Dennis Cox
COO, Alex Pepe
CFO, Brent Novak
SVP Marketing, Bob Shaw
Vice President Sales & Marketing, Paul Mallinder
Vp Acquisitions And Strategy, Cliff Hannel, age 53
Vice President Human Resources, Tim Jones
Vp Marketing, Alan Amrod
Vice President Security Solutions Marketing, Fred Kost
Vp Sales, Joshua Goldstein

Vp Sales, Gary Stone
Vice President Nvs Sales, Jim Alnwick
Vice President Of Marketing Network, Roark Pollock
Vice President Of Sales Strategic, Rob Johnson
Vp Hardware Development, Keith Brewer
Vice President, Sunil Kalidindi
Senior Vice President And General, Arlan Harris
Vice President Patent Engineering, Peter Marsico
Vice President Market Development, Kevin Formby
Vice President Operations, Nitesh Jha
Chairman and Chief Innovation Officer, Errol Ginsberg, age 59
Member Board Of Directors, Gail Hamilton
Auditors: PricewaterhouseCoopersLLP

LOCATIONS

HQ: Ixia
26601 West Agoura Road, Calabasas, CA 91302
Phone: 818 871-1800 **Fax:** 818 871-1805
Web: www.ixiacom.com

2012 Sales

	$ mil.	% of total
US	198.4	48
International	215.0	52
Total	**413.4**	**100**

PRODUCTS/OPERATIONS

2012 Sales

	$ mil.	% of total
Products	330.3	80
Services	83.1	20
Total	**413.4**	**100**

COMPETITORS

Aeroflex	JDS Uniphase
Agilent Technologies	RADCOM
Anritsu	Rohde & Schwarz
Azimuth Systems	Spirent
Digital Lightwave	Sunrise Telecom
EXFO	Tektronix
Emrise	Tollgrade
Fluke Networks	Communications

HISTORICAL FINANCIALS
Company Type: Public

Income Statement
FYE: December 31

	REVENUE ($ mil.)	NET INCOME ($ mil.)	NET PROFIT MARGIN	EMPLOYEES
12/13	467.2	11.8	2.5%	1,846
12/12	413.4	45.4	11.0%	1,710
12/11	308.3	23.7	7.7%	1,300
12/10	276.8	11.2	4.0%	1,100
12/09	177.9	(44.2)	—	1,073
Annual Growth	**27.3%**	**—**		**14.5%**

2013 Year-End Financials

Debt ratio: 22.3%	No. of shares (mil.): 76
Return on equity: 2.5%	Dividends
Cash ($ mil.): 34	Yield: —
Current ratio: 1.76	Payout: —
Long-term debt ($ mil.): 200	Market value ($ mil.): 1,023

	STOCK PRICE ($) FY Close	P/E High/Low	PER SHARE ($) Earnings	Dividends	Book Value
12/13	13.31	139 75	0.15	0.00	6.49
12/12	16.98	27 16	0.59	0.00	6.04
12/11	10.51	56 21	0.33	0.00	4.90
12/10	16.78	107 41	0.17	0.00	4.31
12/09	7.45	— —	(0.70)	0.00	3.75
Annual Growth	**15.6%**	**— —**	**—**	**—**	**14.7%**

j2 Global, Inc. (New)

Checked your messages lately? j2 Global provides Web-based communications and other cloud services that allow customers to retrieve e-mail faxes and voicemail from a single phone line. Clients receive a private phone number that can handle unlimited incoming messages. The company operates primarily under the eFax eVoice FuseMail CampaignerCRM KeepItSafe and Onebox brands and claims more than 11 million phone numbers for customers located in nearly 50 countries. In 2012 the company expanded to digital media when it bought Ziff Davis the online publisher of PCMag.com and Toolbox.com among others. j2 Global generates more than 60% of its revenues in the US.

Geographic Reach
Outside the US the company has customers in Canada (20% of sales) and Ireland (10%). It also has offices there as well as in Hong Kong and Japan.

Financial Performance
j2 Global is profitable and revenues increase every year. In 2012 sales grew 12% to $371 million and profits increased 6% to $121 million. Its growth is primarily due to acquisitions.

Mergers and Acquisitions
Acquisitions are a large part of the company's growth strategy. It has bought more than 40 companies since 2000. In 2013 it bought Backup Connect BV an online backup provider based in The Netherlands. With this acquisition j2 now has customer bases and prospects serviced by local sales support and online backup infrastructures in Ireland New Zealand The Netherlands the US and the UK. Also that year it bought MetroFax a US provider of Internet faxing services.

Its most substantial acquisition however has been the 2012 purchase of online publisher Ziff Davis for $167 million. Ziff Davis publishes technology gaming and lifestyle content through its digital properties. Titles include PCMag.com IGN.com AskMen.com Toolbox.com and others. It also operates BuyerBase a digital ad targeting platform and Ziff Davis B2B which offers research to enterprise buyers and leads to IT vendors. j2 Global expects the new digital media division to add $60 million in sales every year.

Other 2012 acquisitions include Australia-Based Zintel Communications UK-based Zimo Communications and US-based Landslide Technologies and Offsite Backup Solutions.

HISTORY

What did rap music East Berlin and the dot-com crowds have in common? The answer was Jaye Muller. Born in the former East Germany Muller moved to Paris at 17 to pursue a rap music career. During a 1994 UK concert tour he became frustrated at missing too many faxes and phone messages. Conveniently enough Muller had attended tech school and invented a virtual fax machine. He moved to New York to work on music but it was the siren song of a universal inbox that haunted him. Finding software programmers in Australia to help develop a system he launched the company in 1995 as JFAX Communications.

JFAX began offering voice and fax messages via e-mail in 1996 in Atlanta London and New York. The service soon caught on and by the end of the year the company had phone numbers available in 15 cities. Muller snagged professional talent hiring Motorola's Hemi Zucker as COO.

In 1997 the company introduced its outbound faxing service and Muller brought in big investors including Richard Ressler who left his job at IT firm MAI Systems to become CEO. Shifting coasts JFAX left New York for Los Angeles. The company penned a deal with QUALCOMM to offer JFAX through its Eudora e-mail client and closed out the year serving 45 cities.

JFAX came of age in 1998 when it embarked on a three-year marketing agreement with America Online (now AOL) which promoted JFAX as its exclusive unified messaging service while e-mail provider Critical Path Internet portal Yahoo! and ISP Prodigy Communications became strategic partners. Anxious to get back to his music at least part time Muller hired former AT&T executive Gary Hickox as president.

The company went public in 1999 and changed its name to JFAX.COM and it launched free service in hopes of attracting customers that would upgrade to fee-based plans.

In 2000 JFAX.COM acquired Internet-based messaging provider SureTalk.Com for $9 million. SureTalk's Steven Hamerslag became president (Hickox left the company) and CEO (Ressler became chairman). Later the company changed its name again this time to j2 Global Communications and expanded by purchasing rival message services provider eFax.com. When Hamerslag resigned at year's end the board replaced him with a management team made up of the company's top executives.

The next year j2 Global was granted a US patent for its core technology. Also in 2001 the company announced an expansion of its network into Argentina Chile Colombia and Mexico.

Expansion remained a big part of j2 Global Communications' scheme. The company increased its customer base with the acquisitions of rival messaging services providers SureTalk.com and eFax.com and in 2004 it acquired British Columbia-based outsourced e-mail and messaging services provider The Electric Mail Company. That year the company also acquired the unified communications assets branded Onebox from Call Sciences.

Its expansion plans in Europe got a boost with the company's acquisition in 2005 of UK-based messaging services provider Puma United Communications. In 2007 j2 Global acquired messaging services firm YAC (as in "you're always connected") Limited. The company specialized in hosted messaging and communications services such as inbound call management fax to e-mail virtual numbers audio conferencing and personal numbers. j2 Global also bought the RapidFax business of EasyLink Services International.

In 2008 j2 Global bought San Diego-based Phone People Holdings Corporation (toll-free calling services); UK-based Mediaburst (digital faxing products and services); the assets of MailWise a provider of hosted e-mail security services; and the

fax and voice messaging assets of Mijanda which offers digital fax and voice messaging applications. The company made just one acquisition in 2009 buying the Internet fax technology business of CallWave.

J2 Global bought seven companies in 2010 including the voice assets of UK-based Realty Telecom LTD the email assets of Quexion and the fax assets of Comodo Communications which does business as TrustFax. It also acquired the messaging and communications business of Australia-based mBox in a move to build its Asia/Pacific client base particularly in Australia New Zealand and Singapore where mBox is most active. Additionally it purchased Miami-based Internet fax messaging specialist Venali for $17 million (following the dismissal of a patent dispute between j2 and Venali by the courts) online data backup specialist KeepItSafe and UK-based Alban Telecom.

j2 Global ended 2010 with the purchase of Canada-based Protus IP Solutions a provider of hosted Internet fax (MyFax) e-mail marketing (Campaigner) and voice communications (My1Voice) services for the enterprise market. j2 paid about $213 million for the company which boosted its number of paid subscribers to around 1.9 million.

EXECUTIVES

Vp Marketing Services And Support, Ken Ford
Vp Sales, Thomas (Tom) Dolan
Vice President Product Marketing, Mike Pugh
EVP Corporate Strategy, Zohar Loshitzer, age 56
CEO, Nehemia (Hemi) Zucker, age 57, $459,000 total compensation
CFO, Kathleen M. (Kathy) Griggs, age 60, $270,000 total compensation
President, R. Scott Turicchi, age 51, $375,000 total compensation
VP Products, Michael W. Harris, age 52
VP Network Operations, Alan Alters
VP International, Tim McLean
VP and General Manager Europe, Paul Kinsella
Vice President, Gary P Kapner
Senior Vice President, Dustin Finer
National Account Manager, Gigi Crowe
Vp Sales & Marketing, Steve Rosen
Vice President, Stephen Weisswasser
Vice President, Linda Silva
Hr Director & Vp, Christin Dennis
Vice President Of Call Centre, Bill Threlkeld
Vice President, Ajit Dalvi
Vice President, Michael Guadarrama
Vp, Paul Yee
Senior Vice President, Michael Benevento
Vice President Information Technology, Kamran Izadpanah
Vice President Engineering, Doug Chey
Vice President Communications, Laura Hinson
Vice President, Daniel Kwoh
Vice President Business Development, Tim Johnson
Vice President, Andrew Duncan
National Accounts Manager, John Luther
Vice President Business Development Web, Marco Sprenkels
Vice President, Joe Naylor
Vice President Engineering Netwk Operations, Vincent Niedielsky
Vice President General Counsel Secretary, Jeffrey D (Jeff) Adelman, age 48
Chairman, Richard S. Ressler, age 56
Auditors: SingerLewakLLP

LOCATIONS

HQ: j2 Global, Inc. (New)
6922 Hollywood Boulevard, Suite 500, Los Angeles, CA 90028
Phone: 323 860-9200
Web: www.j2global.com

2014 Sales

	% of total
US	67
Canada	12
Ireland	7
Other	14
Total	**100**

PRODUCTS/OPERATIONS

2014 Sales

	% of sales
Business cloud	72
Digital media	28
Total	**100**

Mergers & Acquisitions

2013
Backup Connect (The Netherlands online data backup)
MetroFax (US Internet faxing)

2012
Landslide Technologies (US CRM for small and midsized businesses)
Offsite Backup Solutions (US online data backup)
Zimo Communications (UK voice services)
Zintel Communications (Australia voice services)
Ziff Davis (US online publisher)

2011
Data Haven (Ireland online data backup)
C Infinity (Ireland online data backup)
Offsite Backup Solutions (US online data backup)

COMPETITORS

CommTouch Software	Notify Technology
Deltathree	Open Text
FuzeBox	Satellink

HISTORICAL FINANCIALS

Company Type: Public

Income Statement

FYE: December 31

	REVENUE ($ mil.)	NET INCOME ($ mil.)	NET PROFIT MARGIN	EMPLOYEES
12/13	520.8	107.5	20.6%	1,130
12/12	371.4	121.5	32.7%	680
12/11	330.1	114.7	34.8%	600
12/10	255.3	83.0	32.5%	600
12/09	245.5	66.8	27.2%	400
Annual Growth	20.7%	12.6%	—	29.6%

2013 Year-End Financials

Debt ratio: 21.2%	No. of shares (mil.): 46	
Return on equity: 16.5%	Dividends	
Cash ($ mil.): 207	Yield: 1.9%	
Current ratio: 3.39	Payout: 39.0%	
Long-term debt ($ mil.): 245	Market value ($ mil.): 2,306	

	STOCK PRICE ($) FY Close	P/E High/Low	PER SHARE ($) Earnings	Dividends	Book Value
12/13	50.01	24 13	2.28	0.98	15.32
12/12	30.60	13 9	2.61	0.87	13.19
12/11	28.14	13 10	2.43	0.41	11.87
12/10	28.95	16 10	1.81	0.00	9.59
12/09	20.35	16 11	1.48	0.00	7.60
Annual Growth	25.2%	— —	11.4%	—	19.2%

K12 Inc

K12 isn't a missing element from the periodic table but it could help kids learn about the periodic table. The company offers online educational programs to students in kindergarten through 12th grade through "virtual schools." It also offers online curriculum to public and private schools. It provides course material and product sales directly to parents and individualized supplemental programs offered through schools. K12 also manages and sells its products and services to blended schools (public schools that combine online and face-to-face instruction) and provides services to US school districts and to international partners. K12 was founded in 2000 by former CEO Ron Packard.

Geographic Reach

K12 serves students in some 100 countries around the world. K12 operates overseas through the K12 International Academy a private school that enables K12 to deliver its learning system to students in other countries. In the 2014-2015 school year K12 will manage virtual and blended public schools in 33 states and the District of Columbia.

Operations

The company operates in three segments: Managed Public Schools (virtual and blended); Institutional Business (school district partnerships focused on curriculum development and teacher training); and International and Private Pay Business (three online and one brick and mortar private school and international distribution partnerships).

K12's Managed Public School segment (its largest revenue generator) develops online programs that adhere to the policies of public entities such as public school districts independent nonprofit charter school boards and state education agencies. It offers the same coursework and curriculum as most school districts' "brick and mortar" campuses. However since virtual schools don't have the requirement of a physical classroom they can accommodate a large dispersed student population. They also allow for more capital resources to be directed toward teaching curriculum and technology rather than keeping up a physical infrastructure. Students who attend virtual public schools receive assignments complete lessons and obtain instruction from certified teachers with whom they interact online telephonically in virtual classroom environments and at times face-to-face.

K12 also has a contract with the Delaware Department of Education to manage the Moyer Charter School. The agreement (reached in2010) representes K12's first foray into bricks-and-mortar school management. Through the agreement K12 is authorized to serve up to 460 students in grades 6-12. K12 intends to expand its work with school districts and has established a dedicated sales team to further that effort. The services it provides to districts include teacher training programs administrator support and a student account management system.

Financial Performance

K12 reported revenue of $919.5 million in fiscal 2014 (ended June) an increase of 8% versus the prior year driven by increases of around 10% in both its Managed Public Schools and International and Private Pay businesses partially offset by a 9% decline in its Institutional division. The Managed Public Schools business which accounted for 87% of K12's total revenue in fiscal 2014 benefited from enrollment growth and increases in the per-pupil rate of funding in some states. The company credited strong growth in iCademy course enrollment for the uptick in its International and Private Pay operation. While revenue has risen steadily in recent years as online education gains acceptance profit growth has been more erratic. After two years of increasing profitability net income tumbled 30% in fiscal 2014 to $19.6 million on rising instructional costs and services and other charges.

Strategy

K12's growth strategy consists of leveraging the investments it has made in curriculum online learning and school management to serve adjacent markets and to diversify its risk profile. It plans to increase enrollment in its public school programs and expand into additional US states and cities while increasing its institutional and international footprint. It has grown in recent years via acquisitions.

Mergers and Acquisitions

In 2011 the company acquired IS Berne a traditional private school located in Berne Switzerland serving students in grades Pre-K through 12. That year K12 agreed to acquire the online high school business of Kaplan. The unit targets adults without high school diplomas and high school students who are looking to augment their brick-and-mortar education.

K12 started out offering programs for children in kindergarten through second grade. It gradually expanded and now instruction all the way up to a self-paced high school program. The company made a greater investment in its middle and high school products with its 2010 acquisition of KC Distance Learning (KCDL). The purchase brought in three brands targeting both public and private schools: Aventa Learning The Keystone School and iQ Academies. Also that year K12 formed a 60-40 joint venture with Middlebury College to create online foreign language classes.

In late 2010 K12 acquired AEC a provider of research-based core curriculum instructional software for kindergarten through adult learners. The acquisition added to K12's portfolio of instructional and curriculum offerings and assessment tools.

EXECUTIVES

SVP General Counsel and Secretary, Howard D. Polsky, age 62

Chairman and CEO, Nathaniel A. (Nate) Davis, age 60

EVP and CFO, James Rhyu

Executive Vice President and Chief Marketing & Enrollment Officer, Chuck Sullivan, age 56

President and COO, Timothy L. Murray, $94,871 total compensation

Chief Academic Officer, Margaret Jorgensen

SVP and CIO, James Donley

EVP School Management and Services, Allison Cleveland

Evp-curriculum Product & Mark, Tim McEwen

Vice President Information Technology, Todd McAnally

Vice President For Education, Tom Trautman

Chairman and CEO, Nathaniel A. (Nate) Davis, age 60

Auditors: BDOUSALLP

LOCATIONS

HQ: K12 Inc
2300 Corporate Park Drive, Herndon, VA 20171
Phone: 703 483-7000
Web: www.k12.com

PRODUCTS/OPERATIONS

2014 Sales

	$ in mil	% of total
Managed public schools	804.5	87
Institutional business	66.8	8
International and private pay business	48.3	5
Total	**919.6**	**100**

Selected Schools and Programs

Early Learning Programs
High School Program
K-8 Program
Online Privatre Schools
Online Public Schools

Selected Students Served/Services

Advanced and Enrichable Learners
Athletes and Performers
Credit Recovery (for missed classes make-up credits)
Expat Foreign Service Overseas
Homebound
Homeschoolers
Military Families
Reading Program
Struggling Students
Summer School
Supplemental Education
World Languages

COMPETITORS

Apollo Education	ITT Educational
Capella Education	Kaplan
DeVry Education Group	McGraw-Hill Education
Edison Learning	Nobel Learning
Edmentum	Communities
Florida Virtual School	Pearson plc
Houghton Mifflin	Renaissance Learning
Harcourt	Rosetta Stone

HISTORICAL FINANCIALS

Company Type: Public

Income Statement

FYE: June 30

	REVENUE ($ mil.)	NET INCOME ($ mil.)	NET PROFIT MARGIN	EMPLOYEES
06/14	919.5	19.6	2.1%	4,200
06/13	848.2	28.1	3.3%	3,500
06/12	708.4	17.5	2.5%	3,300
06/11	522.4	12.7	2.4%	2,500
06/10	384.4	21.5	5.6%	1,065
Annual Growth	24.4%	(2.3%)	—	40.9%

2014 Year-End Financials

Debt ratio: 5.1%	No. of shares (mil.): 38
Return on equity: 3.7%	Dividends
Cash ($ mil.): 196	Yield: —
Current ratio: 4.09	Payout: —
Long-term debt ($ mil.): 16	Market value ($ mil.): 937

	STOCK PRICE ($) FY Close	P/E High/Low		PER SHARE ($) Earnings	Dividends	Book Value
06/14	24.07	76	35	0.50	0.00	13.58
06/13	26.27	42	22	0.72	0.00	13.19
06/12	23.30	80	38	0.45	0.00	12.99
06/11	33.14	106	58	0.37	0.00	12.49
06/10	22.18	36	22	0.71	0.00	7.29
Annual Growth	2.1%	—	—	(8.4%)	—	16.8%

Kadant Inc

Kadant wants to hear the ka-ching of profits being made from its papermaking equipment. The company's papermaking machinery and components which Kadant develops and manufactures can be found in most of the world's pulp and paper mills. Its papermaking products include stock preparation (including pulping screening cleaning and de-inking) doctoring (cleaning of paper rolls) fluid handling (mainly drying) and water management (water cleaning draining and filtering) systems. It also recycles papermaking byproducts into biodegradable fiber-based granules for oil and grease absorption and other uses. Kadant has operations in North America South America Europe and Asia.

Geographic Reach

Kadant has 15 manufacturing facilities in nine countries in Europe North and South America and Asia and services 150 countries around the globe. During 2013 approximately 63% of its sales were to customers outside the US principally in Europe and China.

Operations

The company's papermaking equipment is sold to pulp and paper manufacturers worldwide while its byproduct granules are geared at agricultural and home and garden customers. A majority of its sales are made to customers in Europe and China. China with its growing economy is where Kadant has historically generated significant revenues. Already it operates manufacturing facilities in the lower-cost country and it expects to manufacture and source even more of its equipment and components there in the future.

Financial Performance

Revenues climbed 4% from $332 million in 2012 to nearly $345 million in 2013 its highest total in six years. The revenue growth for 2013 was fueled by an increase in its papermaking systems segment generated from acquisitions and an increase of $4 million from favorable currency translation effects.

Profits dropped 26% from $32 million in 2012 to $23 million in 2013 due to higher income taxes paid and the absence of a tax credit benefit that was present in 2012. The company's operating cash flow has fluctuated over the last five years. In 2013 cash flow increased by $11 million to $40 million due to a rise in customer deposits on stock-preparation contracts and an increase in accounts payable primarily due to the timing of payments.

Strategy

Kadant's strategic growth initiatives involves increasing its penetration into emerging markets expanding its parts and consumables revenue leveraging its low-cost manufacturing operations and acquiring well-positioned companies that offer differentiated products to process industries. The company completed three acquisitions in 2013 including its former Brazilian licensee Companhia Brasileira de Tecnologia Industrial Noss Group out of Sweden and Canada-based Carmanah Design and Manufacturing. These acquisitions resulted in the expansion of its presence in emerging markets and enhanced its aftermarket parts operations.

EXECUTIVES

President and CEO, Jonathan W. (Jon) Painter, age 55, $482,000 total compensation
EVP and CFO, Thomas M. O'Brien, age 62, $333,000 total compensation

EVP and COO, Eric T. Langevin, age 51, $318,000 total compensation
EVP, Jeffrey L. Powell, age 55, $300,000 total compensation
Vp, Edwin D Healy
Vp Sales & Marketing, Frederic Bontempelli
Vice President General Counsel Secretary, Sandra Lambert
Treasurer, Daniel Walsh
Chairman, William A. (Bill) Rainville, age 72
Secretary, Kathy Murphy
Auditors: Ernst&YoungLLP

LOCATIONS

HQ: Kadant Inc
One Technology Park Drive, Westford, MA 01886
Phone: 978 776-2000

2013 Sales

	$ mil.	% of total
US	129.1	37
China	50.7	15
Other	164.7	48
Total	**344.5**	**100**

PRODUCTS/OPERATIONS

2013 Sales

	$ mil.	% of total
Papermaking systems		
Stock preparation	122.7	36
Doctoring cleaning & filteration	112.6	33
Fluid handling	93.4	27
Wood processing system	4.6	1
Fiber-based products	11.2	3
Total	**344.5**	**100**

Selected Products

Doctoring
  Doctor systems (for cleaning papermaking rolls)
  Profiling systems (for controlling moisture web curl and gloss during paper converting)
Fluid handling
  Components
  Controls
  Mechanical rotary joints
  Precision unions
  Steam and condensate systems
  Syphons
  Tubulator bars
Stock preparation
  Recycling and approach flow systems (for removing contaminants to prepare them for the recycled paper production process)
  Virgin pulping process equipment (for removing lignin concentrate condensate gases and recycle process chemicals)
Wood processing products
  Stranders
  Rotary Debarkers
  Chippers

COMPETITORS

Andritz AG	GLV
AstenJohnson	Lorentzen & Wettre
Barco	Metso
Columbus McKinnon	Sandusky International
Deublin	Voith

HISTORICAL FINANCIALS

Company Type: Public

Income Statement

FYE: December 28

	REVENUE ($ mil.)	NET INCOME ($ mil.)	NET PROFIT MARGIN	EMPLOYEES
12/13	344.5	23.4	6.8%	1,800
12/12	331.7	31.6	9.5%	1,600
12/11*	335.4	33.5	10.0%	1,700
01/11	270.0	18.5	6.9%	1,600
01/10	225.5	(5.9)	—	1,600
Annual Growth 11.2%	—	—	3.0%

*Fiscal year change

2013 Year-End Financials

Debt ratio: 8.7%
Return on equity: 9.0%
Cash ($ mil.): 50
Current ratio: 2.07
Long-term debt ($ mil.): 38
No. of shares (mil.): 11
Dividends
  Yield: 0.0%
  Payout: 18.1%
Market value ($ mil.): 453

	STOCK PRICE ($) FY Close	P/E High/Low	PER SHARE ($) Earnings	Dividends	Book Value
12/13	40.79	20 12	2.07	0.38	24.28
12/12	26.26	10 8	2.73	0.00	22.33
12/11*	22.61	13 6	2.74	0.00	19.11
01/11	23.57	16 9	1.48	0.00	16.80
01/10	15.96	— —	(0.48)	0.00	15.53
Annual Growth 26.4%	—		—		11.8%

*Fiscal year change

Kaman Corp.

Kaman makes fixed and rotary wing aircraft but it's the distribution of four million industrial items that makes the company fly. The company operates through two segments. Industrial Distribution supplies power transmission/motion control industrial products while the Aerospace segment manufactures Kaman-branded aircraft bearings and components and metallic/composite aerostructures for commercial military and general aviation (fixed and rotary wing) aircraft. It also makes safety arming and fuzing devices for missile and bomb systems for the US and its allies. Customers include such notable names as Airbus BAE Systems Bell Boeing Lockheed Martin Raytheon and Sikorsky.

The company's Industrial Distribution business includes subsidiary Kaman Industrial Technologies (KIT) which commands almost two-thirds of the company's revenues and leads the company in distributing bearings; components for power transmission electrical and motion control applications; fluid power and material handling systems; as well as MRO supplies such as seals and sealants lubricants chemicals and adhesives. In addition to KIT other subsidiaries within this segment include Minarik Delamac de Mexico and Industrial Rubber and Mechanics. In 2012 KIT deepened its engineering expertise even further with the purchase of Zeller Corporation a provider of motion control machine vision and electrical control systems.

Kaman Aerospace Group operates through Kaman Aerospace Corporation's Aerostructures Helicopters and Precision Products divisions. Its Helicopters division produces SH-2G Super Seasprite maritime and K-MAX medium-to-heavy lift rotary aircraft. This division also designs tests certifies and delivers major assemblies components and parts to other aerospace manufacturers. Additionally it subcontracts for commercial and military aerospace and defense markets. Customers include the Egyptian Air Force and the naval forces of Australia New Zealand and Poland.

Almost 90% of Kaman's total sales derive from the US where it operates through 15 owned and leased offices. Internationally it operates out of two offices in Mexico two in the UK one in Germany and one in Puerto Rico.

Kaman's revenues reached a milestone of $1.5 billion in 2011 up by 14% over 2010 ($1.3 billion). Profits too increased by 33% from $38 million to a historic $51 million. The company credits this to growth in its base business the impact of cost reduction programs and the contribution of sales from previous acquisitions. Going forward Kaman plans to grow its Industrial distribution segment by as much as 8% to 11% in sales (by entrenching its reach in major industrial markets and expanding its product line) and Aerospace by as much as 11% to 14% (by penetrating further into the defense and commercial markets and keeping its manufacturing costs down).

During 2011 Kaman acquired Catching Fluidpower and Target Electronic Supply and both businesses were folded into its Industrial Distribution segment. Also that year the company obtained Vermont Composites and integrated it into Aerospace. For these three acquisitions Kaman paid a collective amount of almost $80 million.

Kaman in 2010 snatched up Minarik Corporation a distributor of motion control and automation products to manufacturers in the US for about $39 million. The purchase gave it a higher level of expertise in motion control and brought a better balance between products for the OEM (original equipment manufacturer) and MRO (maintenance repair and overhaul) markets. Kaman also that year purchased Global Aerosystems (Global) an engineering design analysis firm based in Washington State. The $15 million deal brought with it more than 120 of Global's aerospace engineers and a blue chip customer lineup including Boeing Kawasaki Heavy Industries Bombardier and the US Department of Defense among others.

HISTORY

The late Charles Kaman (1919-2011) grew up with two passions: aviation and guitars. In the 1930s he competed in model airplane contests and became an accomplished guitar player turning down an offer to join the Tommy Dorsey band. In 1940 Kaman went to work for the helicopter division of United Aircraft (later United Technologies) which was guided by helicopter pioneer Igor Sikorsky. When United rejected Kaman's revolutionary design ideas (especially the servo-flap controlled rotor which greatly reduced vibration) he raised $2000 and set up Kaman Aircraft in 1945.

For the next 10 years Kaman Aircraft operated as a pioneering designer and manufacturer of several helicopters that set world records. Its first helicopter the K-125 was launched in 1947. In 1951 Kaman built the world's first gas turbine helicopter the K-225 and in 1953 it launched the HOK the first helicopter designed for military applications. A year later a modified Kaman HTK-1 became the world's first twin-turbine helicopter.

Kaman diversified into aerospace subcontracting and began making parts for jet fighters in 1956. It founded Kaman Nuclear (which later became Kaman Sciences) in 1957.

Kaman founded Ovation Instruments in 1966. A marriage of his two passions its signature Ovation guitar used aerospace composite materials and a unique "roundback" acoustic design.

The company moved into the industrial products distribution business with the acquisition in 1971 of Reliable Bearing and Supply Co. and Western Bearings Inc. That year it also purchased C. Bruno and Son a national distributor of musical instruments.

In 1984 Kaman Sciences won a contract to work on the Strategic Defense Initiative (also called Star Wars). The next year the company acquired Electromagnetic Launch Research (later Kaman Electromagnetics) which develops electromagnetic launchers.

Kaman secured a contract to build wing structures for the Boeing 777 in 1991. Two years later Kaman's SH-2G Super Seasprite helicopter entered service with the US Navy although overall defense cutbacks hurt Kaman's sales in the early 1990s. In 1994 Kaman launched the K-MAX aerial truck the first commercial heavy-duty helicopter. Kaman delivered its first Magic Lantern laser-based mine-detection system to the US Navy Reserve in 1996. The next year the company sold Kaman Sciences (information technology and services) to ITT Industries.

In 1998 Kaman received orders for SH-2Gs for the armed forces of Australia New Zealand and Egypt. Also that year CEO and founder Charles Kaman suffered a mild stroke and announced that he would step down from that position but remain as chairman.

The following year Paul Kuhn formerly a senior VP with Coltec Industries took the CEO spot and restructured the company's industrial distribution business. In 2000 MD Helicopters awarded the company a multi-year contract worth an estimated $100 million to produce helicopter fuselages.

Kaman acquired Plastic Fabricating Company Inc. (composite parts and assemblies for aerospace applications Kansas) and A-C Supply (industrial distribution Wisconsin) in 2001. The company also gained exclusive distribution and sales licensing rights with Fred Gretsch Enterprises adding its Gretsch drum kit lines to its offerings in US and foreign markets. That same year Charles Kaman stepped down as chairman (due to health reasons) and CEO Kuhn took on the role.

In early 2002 the company opened up new markets for growth for its US customers operating in Mexico by acquiring majority ownership of Mexico City-based industrial distributor Delamac de Mexico S.A. de C.V. In that same year Kaman sold its microwave products line to Meggitt Safety Systems a subsidiary of the UK-based Meggitt PLC. It also acquired Latin Percussion a maker of hand percussion instruments; Dayron a maker of bomb fuzes; and RWG Frankenjura a maker of aerospace bearings. The following year Kaman purchased southeastern US distributor Industrial Supplies Inc.

Kaman used to run the lucrative Kaman Music Corporation (now KMC Music) which distributes Ovation Hamer and Takamine guitars as well as percussion instruments and accessories. In 2007 Kaman sold the music company to Fender Musical Instruments for $117 million and used the proceeds to focus more specifically on its aerospace and industrial distribution businesses.

In 2009 Kaman launched its branded ReliaMark family of bearings roller chains oil seals and shaft collars.

EXECUTIVES

Vp National Sales Manager, Michael J Kelly, age 50
Vice President Investor Relations, Eric B Remington, age 48
Vice President T, John Lockwood
SVP and CIO, Ronald M. Galla, age 63, $355,134 total compensation
Chairman President and CEO, Neal J. Keating, age 58, $875,000 total compensation
EVP and President Kaman Aerospace Group, Gregory L. (Greg) Steiner, age 57, $416,150 total compensation
Assistant VP Corporate Risk Safety and Environmental Management, Gary L. Tong
SVP and CFO, Robert D. Starr, age 46, $291,611 total compensation
EVP and President Kaman Industrial Technologies, Steven J. (Steve) Smidler, age 55, $350,175 total compensation
SVP and General Manager Fluid Power, Tribby Warfield
Division President Kaman Composite Structures, Alphonse J. Lariviere
President Kamatics Corporation, Robert G. Paterson
President Precision Products, Gerald C. Ricketts
VP and General Manager Kaman Engineering Services, Clifford A. Ward
VP and General Manager Kaman Integrated Structures & Metallics, William H. Zmyndak
General Manager Air Vehicles and MRO, Robert G. Manaskie
Managing Director RWG Frankenjura-Industrie Flugwerklager GmbH, Hermann Mannschatz
Managing Director Kaman Composites U.K. Holdings Limited, Guy Thomas
Vice President Contracts And Compliance, Richard C (Rick) Forsberg, age 60
Vice President Marketing At Kaman, Kristofer Kolstad
Chairman President and CEO, Neal J. Keating, age 58
Auditors: KPMGLLP

LOCATIONS

HQ: Kaman Corp.
1332 Blue Hills Avenue, Bloomfield, CT 06002
Phone: 860 243-7100
Web: www.kaman.com

2013 Sales

	$mil.	% of total
North America	1470.4	87
Europe	107.3	6
Oceania	28.9	3
Middle East	39.4	2
Asia	32.4	2
Others	3.4	-
Total	**1.681.8**	**100**

PRODUCTS/OPERATIONS

2013 Sales

	$ mil.	% of total
Industrial distribution	1067.8	63
Aerospace	614.0	37
Total	**1681.8**	**100**

2013 Sales

	$mil.	% of total
Bearings and Power Transmission	649.9	39
Military and Defence	384.1	22
Automation Control and Energy	271.5	16
Commercial Aerospace	229.9	14
Fluid Power	146.4	9
Total	**1681.8**	**100**

Selected Products and Services

Aerospace
- Aerostructures (US & JK)
- Bearings (KAron self-lubricating bearings)
- Electromagnetic motors
- Electro-optics (LIDAR - light detection and ranging targeting subsystem; SODAR - soft-landing parachute system technology)
- Flexible drive couplings
- Fuselage and wing structures
- Fuzing
- Generators and drives
- Helicopter components and parts
- KAflex Couplings (driveshafts and couplings for helicopters)
- Helicopters
- K-MAX "aerial truck" commercial helicopter (and unmanned helicopter)
- SH-2G Super Seasprite multi-mission naval helicopter
- Measuring equipment and systems (non-contact position sensors)
- Memory systems (data storage and retrieval systems)

Industrial Distribution
- Bearings
- Electronic drive items
- Fluid-power systems
- Linear-motion systems
- Materials-handling systems
- Power-transmission systems

Selected Subsidiaries

Industrial Supply Corporation
Kaman Aerospace Group Inc.
- Kaman Aerospace Corporation
- K-MAX Corporation (aerial truck helicopter)
- Kaman SH-2G (maritime helicopters)
- Kamatics Corp.
Kaman Industrial Technologies Corp. (KIT)
- Delamac de Mexico S.A. de C.V. (90% Mexico)
- Kaman Industrial Technologies Ltd. (Canada)
- Industrial Rubber and Mechanics Inc. (Puerto Rico)
- Minarik Corporation

COMPETITORS

AgustaWestland Philadelphia
Applied Industrial Technologies
GKN
Kaydon
Kellstrom Industries
MSC Industrial Direct
Motion Industries
Orbital ATK
Spirit AeroSystems
Textron
Triumph Aerostructures - Vought Aircraft Division
United Technologies
W.W. Grainger
WESCO International

HISTORICAL FINANCIALS

Company Type: Public

Income Statement

FYE: December 31

	REVENUE ($ mil.)	NET INCOME ($ mil.)	NET PROFIT MARGIN	EMPLOYEES
12/13	1,681.8	57.1	3.4%	4,743
12/12	1,592.8	55.0	3.5%	5,007
12/11	1,498.1	51.1	3.4%	4,614
12/10	1,318.5	38.3	2.9%	4,269
12/09	1,146.2	32.6	2.8%	4,032
Annual Growth	10.1%	15.0%	—	4.1%

2013 Year-End Financials

Debt ratio: 24.1%
Return on equity: 12.2%
Cash ($ mil.): 10
Current ratio: 2.92
Long-term debt ($ mil.): 264
No. of shares (mil.): 26
Dividends
  Yield: 1.6%
  Payout: 29.6%
Market value ($ mil.): 1,067

	STOCK PRICE ($) FY Close	P/E High/Low	PER SHARE ($) Earnings	Dividends	Book Value
12/13	39.73	19 15	2.10	0.64	19.04
12/12	36.80	18 13	2.07	0.64	15.79
12/11	27.32	20 13	1.93	0.60	14.22
12/10	29.07	20 14	1.47	0.56	13.93
12/09	23.09	19 8	1.27	0.56	12.14
Annual Growth	14.5%	— —	13.4%	3.4%	11.9%

KapStone Paper & Packaging Corp

Rock paper sissors? KapStone Paper and Packaging has the upper hand in the game of unbleached kraft. The company manufactures largely linerboard a type of paperboard that is converted into laminated tier sheets and wrapping material. It also produces kraft paper (industry-speak for strong wrapping paper) for multiwall bags; saturating kraft (sold under the Durasorb brand) to produce mainly high pressure laminates for furniture construction materials and electronics; and unbleached folding carton board (Kraftpak) which is converted into packaging for consumer goods. KapStone counts 3200-plus customers including Graphic Packaging Exopack and other major converters. The US represents about 80% of sales.

Geographic Reach

KapStone operates some 22 corrugated products manufacturing plants comprised of 12 box plants eight sheet plants and two sheet feeder plants. In addition it operates two warehouse locations in Las Vegas; and Logan Utah.

Financial Performance

KapStone has achieved extraordinary growth over the last few years with revenues rising 44% from $1.22 billion to peak at a historic $1.75 billion. Profits also more than doubled from $62 million in 2012 to a record-setting $127 million in 2013 due to the large uptick in revenue.

The historic growth for 2013 was primarily attributed to nearly $440 million in additional revenue from its Longview acquisition. It was also helped by an 8% spike in sales due to higher average selling prices.

KapStone's cash flow from operating activities has followed an upward trend over the course of the last four years climbing from $136 million in 2010 to almost $300 million in 2013.

Mergers and Acquisitions

Previous acquisitions have helped to fuel KapStone's earnings and set revenue milestones. In mid-2013 KapStone acquired Longview Fibre Paper and Packaging for nearly $1 billion. Longview is a manufacturer of high quality containerboard kraft papers and corrugated products. Longview's operations includes a paper mill located in Longview Washington equipped with five paper machines which has the capacity to produce 1.3 million tons of containerboard and kraft paper. The deal allowed KapStone to post historical annual revenues of $1.75 billion in 2013.

EXECUTIVES

President COO and Director, Matthew S. (Matt) Kaplan, age 57, $575,000 total compensation
Chairman and CEO, Roger W. Stone, age 79, $575,000 total compensation
VP and CFO, Andrea K. Tarbox, age 63, $367,000 total compensation
President Kapstone Kraft Paper Corporation, Randy J. Nebel, $176,580 total compensation
President Kapstone Container Corporation, Timothy P. Keneally, $373,000 total compensation
Vice President Corporate Controller, Mark Niehus
Vice President, Mark Favre
Mechanic Rescue Squad V Pres, Richard Puckett
Vpp Coordinator, Thomas Baker
Chairman and CEO, Roger W. Stone, age 79
Auditors: Ernst&YoungLLP

LOCATIONS

HQ: KapStone Paper & Packaging Corp
1101 Skokie Blvd., Suite 300, Northbrook, IL 60062
Phone: 847 239-8800
Web: www.kapstonepaper.com

2013 Sales

	$ mil.	% of total
US	1398.3	80
Other countries	349.9	20
Total	**1748.2**	**100**

PRODUCTS/OPERATIONS

2013 Sales

	$ mil.	% of total
Containerboard/corrugated products	1129.6	65
Speciality paper	530.9	30
others	87.7	5
Total	**1748.2**	**100**

COMPETITORS

Canfor	International Paper
Caraustar	Longview Fibre
Georgia-Pacific	Rock-Tenn
Graphic Packaging Holding	West Fraser Timber

HISTORICAL FINANCIALS

Company Type: Public

Income Statement

FYE: December 31

	REVENUE ($ mil.)	NET INCOME ($ mil.)	NET PROFIT MARGIN	EMPLOYEES
12/13	1,748.1	127.3	7.3%	4,601
12/12	1,216.6	62.5	5.1%	2,760
12/11	906.1	123.9	13.7%	2,715
12/10	782.6	65.0	8.3%	1,600
12/09	632.4	80.2	12.7%	1,600
Annual Growth	28.9%	12.2%	—	30.2%

2013 Year-End Financials

Debt ratio: 45.1%
Return on equity: 21.5%
Cash ($ mil.): 12
Current ratio: 1.78
Long-term debt ($ mil.): 1,192
No. of shares (mil.): 95
Dividends
  Yield: —
  Payout: —
Market value ($ mil.): 5,346

	STOCK PRICE ($)	P/E		PER SHARE ($)		
	FY Close	High/Low	Earnings	Dividends	Book Value
12/13	55.86	43 17	1.32	0.00	6.96
12/12	22.19	34 23	0.66	2.00	5.46
12/11	15.74	13 9	1.31	0.00	5.88
12/10	15.30	22 11	0.69	0.00	4.54
12/09	9.83	9 1	1.15	0.00	3.84
Annual Growth	54.4%	— —	3.6%	—	16.0%

KB HOME

For a dwelling done your way you might turn to KB Home. KB builds houses mainly for first-time move-up and active adult buyers primarily in California Colorado Texas and southeastern US. The company markets houses under its Built to Order brand which allows buyers to customize their homes by choosing a floor plan as well as exterior and interior features. The average selling price of a KB home is around $291700. KB offers attached and detached single-family homes in addition to townhomes and condos. It offers title and insurance through its KB Home Mortgage. KB has built more than a half a million homes since it was founded in 1957.

HISTORY

Kaufman and Broad Building Co. was founded in Detroit in 1957 by Eli Broad and Donald Kaufman. Broad an accountant parlayed an initial $25000 investment into sales of $250000 on the first weekend of business. By the end of its first year the company was posting revenues of $1.7 million.

The company expanded rapidly and went public in 1961. A year later it was the first homebuilder to be listed on the NYSE. Kaufman and Broad moved into California in 1963. Through acquisitions it rapidly became a top US homebuilder expanding into New York San Francisco and Chicago. In 1965 it formed a mortgage subsidiary to arrange loans for its customers.

In the early 1970s the firm entered Europe and Canada. Sales passed the $100 million mark in 1971 and the company diversified buying Sun Life Insurance. Housing operations were renamed Kaufman and Broad Development Group (KBDG).

In 1980 the flamboyant Bruce Karatz who had joined the firm in 1972 was appointed president. Karatz steered the company through the recession of the early 1980s focusing on California France and Canada. KBDG acquired Bati-Service a major French developer of affordable homes in 1985.

The company was renamed Kaufman and Broad Home Corporation in 1986. In 1989 it reorganized into two separate billion-dollar companies: Broad Inc. (now SunAmerica) an insurance firm with Eli Broad as its chairman and CEO. The Kaufman and Broad Home company had Karatz as CEO (and later chairman).

When the California real estate market crashed in 1990 earnings plummeted. Karatz diversified by buying up strong regional builders. Kaufman and Broad entered Arizona Colorado and Nevada in 1993 and Utah in 1994. Profits dropped in 1995-96 because of weakness in the California

and Paris markets and the company's winding down of Canadian operations. But expansion continued including the acquisition of Rayco a Texas builder in 1996.

Borrowing from the methods of Rayco Kaufman and Broad began surveying homebuyers for suggestions to incorporate into new designs. In 1998 the company began to build its New Home Showrooms. The corporation continued its expansion drive that year when it paid about $165 million for Dover/Ideal PrideMark and Estes privately held builders based in Houston Denver and Tucson respectively. In 1999 Kaufman and Broad bought Lewis Homes a major California builder and the #1 builder in Las Vegas for about $545 million.

The company raised $117 million in 2000 by taking half of its French subsidiary public but retained a controlling interest. Also the company formed a joint venture —American CityVista —with former Department of Housing and Urban Development secretary Henry Cisneros to develop homes in inner-city communities.

In 2001 the company changed its name again shortening it to KB Home. Later that year it expanded into the northern Florida market by buying Jacksonville-based Trademark Home Builders.

KB Home launched a division in Tampa and expanded operations into Central Florida in 2002 by acquiring Orlando-based American Heritage Homes for about $74 million. It also expanded in other markets which included Tucson (by acquiring assets of New World Homes gaining more than 1600 lots in 12 new home communities there) and the Rio Grande Valley of Texas (by opening a division in the fast-growing McAllen region about four miles from the Mexican border). For its fifth consecutive year KB Home reported record earnings in 2002.

KB Home continued to build its empire in 2003 by acquiring Atlanta-based Colony Homes one of the Southeast's largest privately owned homebuilders with principal operations in Atlanta Raleigh and Charlotte which are among the largest markets in the Southeast for new-home permits. The company also moved into the Midwest with the $33 million purchase of privately held homebuilder Zale Homes (Chicago). KB Home also added to its French holdings by acquiring Euro Immobilier.

In 2004 KB Home expanded its operations in the Southeast by acquiring South Carolina-based Palmetto Traditional Homes which builds in the state's three largest metropolitan areas: Charleston Columbia and Greenville-Spartanburg-Anderson. It also acquired Indianapolis builder Dura Builders and two French builders Groupe Avantis and Foncier Investissement.

KB Home sold its KB Home Mortgage subsidiary to Countrywide Home Loans in 2005 and then formed its Countrywide KB Home Loans joint venture to serve KB customers.

After nearly two decades as CEO Karatz retired from KB Home when charges of fraud surrounding company stock options were leveled against him. Former COO Jeff Mezger was then named president and CEO.

Hard hit by the economic downturn KB began looking for options to raise capital and downsize operations. In a measure to stem the bleeding in 2007 KB sold its 49% stake in its French subsidiary Kaufman & Broad to PAI Partners for about $800 million thus exiting all international operations. The sale enabled the company to reduce its outstanding debt by about $1 billion.

2013 Housebuilding Sales

	% of total
West Coast (CA)	49
Central (CO TX)	27
Southeast (FL MD NC VA)	16
Southwest (AZ NV NM)	8
Total	**100**

PRODUCTS/OPERATIONS

2013 Sales

	$ mil.	% of total
Homebuilding		
Housing	2084.1	99
Land	0.9	–
Financial services	12.1	1
Total	**2097.1**	**100**

COMPETITORS

Beazer Homes	Meritage Homes
Capital Pacific	NVR
D.R. Horton	PulteGroup
David Weekley Homes	Standard Pacific
Highland Homes	The Ryland Group
Hovnanian Enterprises	Toll Brothers
Lennar	Weyerhaeuser Real
M.D.C.	Estate
Mercedes Homes	William Lyon Homes

HISTORICAL FINANCIALS

Company Type: Public

Income Statement

FYE: November 30

	REVENUE ($ mil.)	NET INCOME ($ mil.)	NET PROFIT MARGIN	EMPLOYEES
11/14	2,400.9	918.3	38.2%	1,590
11/13	2,097.1	39.9	1.9%	1,430
11/12	1,560.1	(58.9)	—	1,200
11/11	1,315.8	(178.7)	—	1,200
11/10	1,590.0	(69.3)	—	1,300
Annual Growth	**10.9%**	**—**	**—**	**5.2%**

2014 Year-End Financials

Debt ratio: 54.1%	No. of shares (mil.): 102
Return on equity: 86.1%	Dividends
Cash ($ mil.): 358	Yield: 0.0%
Current ratio: 15.65	Payout: 1.0%
Long-term debt ($ mil.): 2,576	Market value ($ mil.): 1,797

	STOCK PRICE ($) FY Close	P/E High/Low		Earnings	PER SHARE ($) Dividends	Book Value
11/14	17.57	2	1	9.25	0.10	15.60
11/13	17.53	52	29	0.46	0.10	5.69
11/12	14.36	—	—	(0.76)	0.14	4.29
11/11	7.35	—	—	(2.32)	0.25	5.03
11/10	11.30	—	—	(0.90)	0.25	7.18
Annual Growth	**11.7%**	**—**	**—**		**—(20.5%)**	**21.4%**

Key Tronic Corp.

Contract electronics manufacturing is key for Key Tronic. The company which does business as KeyTronicEMS to highlight its focus on electronics manufacturing services provides printed circuit board assembly tooling and prototyping box build (completely built) systems and plastic injection molding. In addition Key Tronic offers such services as product design engineering materials management and in-house testing. The company also makes customized and standard keyboards for PCs terminals and workstations.

Geographic Reach

Though the company maintains facilities in the US most of its manufacturing takes place in Mexico and China. Customers located in the US account for two-thirds of Key Tronic's sales.

Sales and Marketing

A majority of Key Tronic's sales are to the communications consumer device and printer industries; its top five customers account for nearly 60% of sales.

Financial Performance

After posting milestone revenues of $361 million in 2013 Key Tronic saw its revenues fall 15% to $305 million in 2014. The declines for 2014 were driven by decreased demand from its current customer programs and a $5 million decrease in revenues related to program losses.

Key Tronic's profits fell 40% from $13 million in 2013 to $8 million in 2014. This was fueled by a dip in US sales and spike in research development and engineering expenses. The company's operating cash flow has fluctuated over the years peaking at $29 million in 2013 but dropping to nearly $1.5 million.

Strategy

To move beyond its single-product emphasis — keyboards once accounted for almost all of sales — and overcome years of spotty profitability Key Tronic rapidly expanded its contract manufacturing service offerings. As price erosion in the keyboard market made that segment less profitable the company continued its manufacturing push increasing the range of electronic products it can manufacture.

Mergers and Acquisitions

In 2014 Key Tronic paid $47 million to acquire CDR Manufacturing a provider of printed circuit board assembly and other EMS services. CDR caters to a diversified customer base including a number of large multi-national companies. In 2013 the company purchased Texas-based Sabre Assembly & Manufacturing a sheet metal fabrication company with facilities located in Juarez Mexico offering metal fabrication plastic molding PCB assembly complete product assembly design engineering and testing engineering services.

HISTORY

Lewis Zirkle who had worked for more than 20 years at General Electric in various engineering and manufacturing positions founded Key Tronic in 1969. In 1975 Key Tronic became the first independent supplier to develop and market keyboards for heavy-duty office use. By 1981 the company was a leader in manufacturing ergonomic keyboards. It went public two years later. In 1987 Key Tronic developed a membrane switch technology that integrated switching points into a custom-designed structure.

Hard times hit in 1991 and 1992 as overseas competition and a failed attempt to produce a computer notebook contributed to losses. Turnaround artist Stanley Hiller stepped in as CEO in 1992. Key Tronic acquired Honeywell's keyboard operations in 1993 and the following year it moved much of its production to Honeywell's former plant in Mexico to reduce expenses.

In 1995 more efficient operations and new products pushed Key Tronic's sales above the $200 million mark for the first time; net income also hit a 10-year high. Former Honeywell manager Jack Oehlke replaced Hiller as CEO in 1997 the year

Key Tronic launched a fingerprint scanning line that let a user's fingerprints function as a password. In 1998 the company intensified a push into contract manufacturing. To reduce costs Key Tronic cut about 200 jobs at its Washington plant and moved those operations to its facility in Mexico. It also closed its manufacturing plant in Taiwan. After a profitable fiscal 1997 a decline in keyboard sales caused a loss for fiscal 1998.

In 2000 Key Tronic agreed to manufacture circuits for glucose-monitoring devices made by Cygnus and make point-of-sale printers for Axiohm Transaction Solutions (now TPG IPB). During the first half of 2001 the company began doing business as KeyTronicEMS as part of a company-wide transition to firmly plant itself in the electronics manufacturing services (EMS) industry. Later that year the company was ordered to pay $16.5 million in damages when a jury found that it had misappropriated trade secrets and breached a confidentiality agreement with F&G Scrolling Mouse in 1993.

Key Tronic returned to profitability in fiscal 2003 although profits were typical of the razor-thin margins in the EMS industry. Lewis Zirkle who retired from Key Tronic in 1993 died in 2005 at the age of 90.

Keyboards continued to dwindle as a business in the early 21st century from one-quarter of sales in 2001 to about 4% in fiscal 2006 and around 3% in fiscal 2007 and fiscal 2008.

After closing its Las Cruces New Mexico plant in 2005 Key Tronic sold the facility in 2007 to Adevco Corp. for about $4 million including nearly $3 million in cash. Jack Oehlke retired as president and CEO in 2009. EVP/GM Craig Gates succeeded him.

EXECUTIVES

EVP Worldwide Operations, Douglas G. (Doug) Burkhardt, age 55, $256,692 total compensation
EVP Administration and CFO, Ronald F. (Ron) Klawitter, age 62, $306,000 total compensation
President and CEO, Craig D. Gates, age 55, $469,272 total compensation
VP Program Management, Duane D. Mackleit
VP Supply Chain, Frank Crispigna
EVP Business Development, Philip S. Hochberg, $245,850 total compensation
Director Engineering, Chad Orebaugh
Vice President Of Finance And Controller, Brett R Larsen, age 41
Officer Not Vice President, Dave Manky
Vp Operations Production Mfg, Efren Perez
Vice President, Ricardo Hernandez
Vice President Operations, Brian Johnson
Executive Vice President Materials, Robert Alford
Chairman, Dale F. Pilz
Auditors: BDOSeidmanLLP

LOCATIONS

HQ: Key Tronic Corp.
N. 4424 Sullivan Road, Spokane Valley, WA 99216
Phone: 509 928-8000
Web: www.keytronicems.com

2014 Sales

	$ mil.	% of total
US	197.7	65
Other countries	107.7	35
Total	**305.4**	**100**

PRODUCTS/OPERATIONS

2014 Sales by Industry

	% of total
Consumer	30
Communication	23
Industrial and Commercial printer	17
Gaming	15
Transaction printer	11
Computer & peripheral	4
Total	**100**

Services
Circuit board assembly
Contract design and manufacturing
Custom molding and tooling
Engineering services
Logistics
Materials management
Product design
Prototyping
Products
Computer keyboards

COMPETITORS

APEM	Hon Hai
Am-Mex	Jabil
Applied Technical	Mitsumi Electric
Services	Plexus
Celestica	Sanmina
DDi Corp.	Sparton
Flextronics	ZF Electronics

HISTORICAL FINANCIALS

Company Type: Public

Income Statement

FYE: June 28

	REVENUE ($ mil.)	NET INCOME ($ mil.)	NET PROFIT MARGIN	EMPLOYEES
06/14	305.3	7.6	2.5%	3,343
06/13	361.0	12.5	3.5%	2,584
06/12*	346.4	11.6	3.4%	2,700
07/11	253.8	5.7	2.3%	1,997
07/10	199.6	8.6	4.4%	2,036
Annual Growth	**11.2%**	**(3.3%)**	**—**	**13.2%**

*Fiscal year change

2014 Year-End Financials

Debt ratio: 5.0%
Return on equity: 7.7%
Cash ($ mil.): 5
Current ratio: 2.36
Long-term debt ($ mil.): —
No. of shares (mil.): 10
Dividends
  Yield: —
  Payout: —
Market value ($ mil.): 113

	STOCK PRICE ($) FY Close	P/E High/Low		PER SHARE ($) Earnings	Dividends	Book Value
06/14	10.73	16	13	0.67	0.00	9.83
06/13	10.35	10	6	1.15	0.00	8.97
06/12*	8.24	12	3	1.10	0.00	7.50
07/11	4.52	12	8	0.55	0.00	6.54
07/10	4.88	8	2	0.85	0.00	5.79
Annual Growth	**21.8%**	**—**	**—**	**(5.8%)**	**—**	**14.1%**

*Fiscal year change

Kilroy Realty Corp

Kilroy is still here especially if you're referring to the West Coast. A self-administered real estate investment trust (REIT) Kilroy Realty owns manages and develops Class A office space mostly in suburban Southern California's Orange County San Diego and Los Angeles but it has since expanded to the San Francisco Bay and greater Seattle area to woo technology companies as tenants. Its portfolio includes about 115 office properties encompassing more than 13 million square feet of leasable space. A majority of Kilroy Realty's 500-plus tenants are involved in technology media financial services and real estate.

Geographic Reach

Besides 10 office buildings in Washington all of the REIT's property is located in California.

Sales and Marketing

Its 15 largest tenants accounted for 34% of the REIT's base rental revenue in 2012; these include DIRECTV Intuit and Bridgepoint Education. Its properties are 92% occupied.

Financial Performance

Overall sales grew 10% to $405 million in 2012. Profits jumped more than 300% to $270 million after the trust recorded gains on properties it sold.

As a REIT Kilroy Realty is exempt from paying federal income tax as long as it distributes quarterly dividends to shareholders.

Strategy

Kilroy Realty has moved away from owning industrial properties in order to focus on office buildings which generally earn more in rental income. In late 2012 it sold its entire portfolio of 44 industrial properties in California to two unnamed buyers for $355 million. The industrial properties totaled almost 4 million-sq.-ft. of space.

At the same time the trust boosted its portfolio of office buildings in San Francisco and Seattle home to many of the nation's wealthy tech companies. In 2012 it paid $330 million for three properties totaling 837000 square feet in Seattle $162 million for a 374000-sq.-ft. office park in Silicon Valley and it paid $52 million for a building in downtown San Francisco that it will spend another $200 million redeveloping into a 27-story glass office tower for new tenant salesforce.com. In addition the trust is spending $315 million to develop a 587000-sq.-ft. office complex for LinkedIn in Sunnyvale California.

Not missing a beat in 2013 the trust boosted its Bay Area construction pipeline to more than 1.8 million square feet with new developments in Redwood City and downtown San Francisco (most of the space is pre-leased).

In addition Kilroy Realty has approximately 110 acres of undeveloped land in San Diego with the capacity for more than 2 million sq. ft. of rentable office space.

EXECUTIVES

Senior Vice President, Heidi Roth
Vice President Information Technology, S Low
EVP and CFO, Tyler H. Rose, age 54, $500,000 total compensation
EVP and COO, Jeffrey C. Hawken, age 56, $675,000 total compensation
Chairman President and CEO, John B. Kilroy, age 66, $1,225,000 total compensation
SVP San Diego, Steven R. Scott, age 58, $375,000 total compensation
EVP Development and Construction Services, Justin W. Smart, $400,000 total compensation
EVP and Chief Investment Officer, Eli Khouri, $500,000 total compensation
EVP Southern California, David Simon
EVP Business Development, A. Robert Paratte
Vp Northern Ca& Pacific Northw, Mike L Sanford
Vice President Commercial Development, Robert Little
Vice President Asset Management, David Weinstein
Executive Vice President Chief Financial Officer, Richard Moran
Vice President, Rick Buziak
Vice President, Chris Heimburger
Vice President Finance, Walter Baynes
Executive Vice President Human, Michael Thompson
Vice President Int Rpt Strat, Joe Bruna
Vice President Development And Government Affairs, Elizabeth Smagala
Vice President Financial Reporting, Merryl Werber Thompson
Chairman President and CEO, John B. Kilroy, age 66
Auditors: Deloitte&ToucheLLP

LOCATIONS

HQ: Kilroy Realty Corp
12200 W. Olympic Boulevard, Suite 200, Los Angeles, CA 90064
Phone: 310 481-8400
Web: www.kilroyrealty.com

PRODUCTS/OPERATIONS

2012 Sales

	% of total
Rental income	91
Tenant reimbursements	8
Other	1
Total	**100**

COMPETITORS

BioMed Realty	Irvine Company
Brandywine Realty	Majestic Realty
Digital Realty	PS Business Parks
Douglas Emmett	Prologis
Equity Commonwealth	Shorenstein
Equity Office	The Koll Company
Hudson Pacific	Trammell Crow Company

HISTORICAL FINANCIALS

Company Type: Public

Income Statement

FYE: December 31

	REVENUE ($ mil.)	NET INCOME ($ mil.)	NET PROFIT MARGIN	EMPLOYEES
12/13	465.1	43.8	9.4%	219
12/12	404.9	270.9	66.9%	201
12/11	367.1	66.0	18.0%	169
12/10	301.9	19.7	6.5%	141
12/09	279.4	36.9	13.2%	132
Annual Growth	**13.6%**	**4.4%**	**—**	**13.5%**

2013 Year-End Financials

Debt ratio: 43.1%
Return on equity: 1.8%
Cash ($ mil.): 35
Current ratio: 1.01
Long-term debt ($ mil.): 2,204
No. of shares (mil.): 82
Dividends
  Yield: 2.7%
  Payout: 79.1%
Market value ($ mil.): 4,122

	STOCK PRICE ($) FY Close	P/E High/Low		PER SHARE ($) Earnings	Dividends	Book Value
12/13	50.18	161	128	0.36	1.40	29.96
12/12	47.37	14	11	2.56	1.40	29.22
12/11	38.07	48	34	0.87	1.40	23.25
12/10	36.47	525	382	0.07	1.40	22.16
12/09	30.67	63	29	0.53	1.63	21.52
Annual Growth	**13.1%**	**—**	**—**	**(9.2%)**	**(3.7%)**	**8.6%**

Kirby Corp.

Where Kirby hauls cargo the only curbs are riverbanks –the company is the largest inland tank barge operator in the US. Its fleet operated by subsidiary Kirby Inland Marine consists of over 860 barges and about 250 inland towboats with a transportation capacity of 17.3 million barrels. The vessels are used to transport liquid bulk cargo: petrochemicals crude and refined petroleum products and agricultural chemicals. Its Marine Transportation segment (inland/offshore operations) is joined by its Diesel Engine Services segment which is a leading provider of diesel engine services and parts for marine rail and power generation customers.

Geographic Reach

Kirby provides marine transportation of refined petroleum products petrochemicals and black oil products in the coastal regions of the US. The coastal operations consist of the Mississippi River System the Gulf Intracoastal Waterway the Atlantic New York Pacific and Hawaii Divisions.

Operations

The Marine segment represents 76% of its total sales and manages its core tank barge transportation services for the inland and coastal markets. Diesel Engine Services (24%) offers services throughout the US and in parts of the Caribbean and the Pacific Rim. This division provides overhaul and repair of diesel engines and reduction gears line boring and block welding for its customers; it also sells and distributes parts for diesel engines as well as fuel lubrication and engine control systems to the nuclear industry.

Sales and Marketing

Kirby targets the marine power generation and land-based oil and gas operator and producer markets. Two marine transportation customers –Dow and SeaRiver Maritime –accounted for 13% of its 2013 revenue. The company has a contract with Dow through 2016 and with SeaRiver through 2017.

Financial Performance

Kirby has enjoyed unprecedented growth over the years. Revenues jumped 6% from $2.11 billion in 2012 to $2.24 billion in 2013. Profits also climbed 21% from $209 million in 2012 to $253 million in 2013. Both these totals for 2013 represented historic milestones for the company.

The growth was driven by a 22% jump in Marine transportation revenue for 2013 reflecting its expansion into the coastal transportation business from several acquisitions made in previous years. This growth was offset by a 25% drop in Diesel Engine Services sales due to lower demand for the manufacturing of oil service equipment and the sale and service of land-based diesel engines transmissions and parts.

Kirby's rise in profits was fueled by an increase in revenue and a gain on the disposition of assets from the sale or retirement of marine equipment and the sale of a diesel engine services facility in 2013. The company's operating cash flow has steadily climbed the last three years and increased by $275 million in 2013 due to a decrease in inventory and an increase in advance billings.

Strategy

Both segments have expanded via acquisitions and capital investments. In late 2012 Kirby acquired Allied Transportation in a transaction valued at $116 million. Kirby gained Allied's fleet of 13 offshore barges and seven tugboats serving petrochemical companies (some of which were current Kirby customers). The deal bolstered Kirby's hold in the petrochemical market. Kirby also in 2012 purchased Penn Maritime a coastal transportation provider with 18 coastal double hull tank barges and 16 tugboats for $300 million.

Kirby continued to reinvest in its marine transportation fleet during 2013 spending $253 million on capital expenditures including $148 million for new inland tank barges inland towboats and progress payments on the construction of two offshore dry-bulk barge and tugboat units completed in 2013. It also invested $105 million primarily for upgrades to its existing inland and coastal fleets and diesel engine services facilities.

HISTORY

Kirby Petroleum entered the marine transportation business in 1968 with the purchase of Dixie Carriers an inland barge business started in 1948 by the family of George Peterkin. In 1969 Kirby Exploration was set up as a subsidiary of Kirby Petroleum to operate Dixie Carriers. Kirby Petroleum went public in 1976 and in 1982 it entered the diesel-repair business by acquiring Marine Systems.

In 1988 Kirby exited the oil and gas industries to focus on marine transportation. Kirby Exploration was renamed Kirby Corporation in 1990. Because of overbuilding in the 1970s Kirby was able to snap up several shipping companies at bargain prices (including Brent Towing in 1989 and Sabine Towing in 1992); its fleet expanded from 71 vessels in 1988 to more than 400 by 1993. The next year the company created Rail Systems a diesel locomotive repair service and bought Dow Chemical's marine assets.

In 1995 J. H. Pyne was promoted to CEO replacing longtime leader Peterkin who became chairman. A company restructuring hurt sales the following year. Flooding on the Mississippi River disrupted barge traffic and slowed Kirby's performance in 1997.

To raise cash and focus on the inland market Kirby sold its offshore tanker and harbor service operations in 1998 to Hvide Marine (subsequently renamed Seabulk International) for $38.6 million. It exited the insurance market with the sale of its 45% stake in Universal Insurance Company a Puerto Rican property and insurance firm. Kirby also sold its remaining offshore tug and tank barge units.

In 1999 the company gained 256 inland tank barges and 104 tow boats when it bought rival Hollywood Marine in a $325 million deal. Hollywood's Berdon Lawrence took over as Kirby's chairman.

That year and into 2000 the company's diesel engine services unit faced difficulties as a result of depressed Gulf Coast drilling and offshore supply vessel markets. In 2001 with the oil market rebounding Kirby leased 94 inland tank barges from a subsidiary of Dow Chemical vessels that Dow had acquired as part of its merger with Union Carbide. Kirby bought the former Union Carbide barges for $23 million in December 2002.

In 2003 Kirby acquired 45 double-hull inland tank barges and seven inland towboats from SeaRiver Maritime an affiliate of Exxon Mobil for about $32 million. The next year Kirby bought a one-third interest in Osprey Line a provider of barge transportation of cargo containers along the Gulf Coast and on the Mississippi River. It bought another one-third stake in Osprey in January 2006.

In 2005 the company bought 10 inland tank barges configured for carrying black oil products from rival American Commercial Lines. The next year Kirby expanded its diesel engine services business by acquiring Houma Louisiana-based Global Power Holding owner of Global Power Systems. Kirby paid about $100 million for Global Power which posted sales of $63 million in 2005.

In 2008 Kirby acquired the assets of Lake Charles Diesel a high-speed diesel engine service provider for over $3.6 million in cash. Lake Charles Diesel brought with it the marine dealerships it operated for Cummins Detroit Diesel Volvo as well as Caterpillar engines (in Louisiana).

Buoying its Marine Transportation business in 2011 Kirby scooped up K-Sea Transportation Partners in a deal valued at approximately $604 million. K-Sea specialized in transporting gasoline and other fuel-related products with a particular presence on the East and West coasts –a geographic market that further diversified Kirby's business. Kirby has benefited from strong demand for petrochemicals which accounts for a large portion of the company's transportation revenue. In addition to its primary inland tank barge operations Kirby maintains a fleet of four offshore dry cargo barges and seven offshore tugboats which are operated by Kirby Ocean Transport.

The company signed another deal earlier in 2011 to bulk up its Marine Transportation business with the acquisition of Enterprise Marine Services bunker fuel transportation operations for a reported $53.2 million. Included in the deal were 21 tank barges and 15 towboats (used to deliver engine fuel to cruise ships) and container vessels and freighters at ports in South Florida Alabama and Kirby's home port of Houston.

EXECUTIVES

Executive Vice President Chief, Norman Nolen
Vice President Sales And Horsepower Management, Richard Northcutt
Vice President Kirby Logistics Management, Patrick Kelly
Vice President Sales, Toby Whitehead
President Kirby Engine Systems, Dorman L. Strahan, age 58, $261,000 total compensation
President Marine Transportation Group and Kirby Inland Marine, William G. (Bill) Ivey, $352,500 total compensation
President Kirby Offshore Marine, James F. (Jim) Farley, $337,500 total compensation
President and CEO, David W. Grzebinski, age 53, $440,000 total compensation
VP and CIO, David R. Mosley, age 52
EVP and CFO, C. Andrew (Andy) Smith, age 44
President Osprey Line, John T. Hallmark
President United Holdings, Michael W. Coulter
Vice President Sales, Christian G O'Neil
Vice President Supply Chain, Joseph Reiners
Executive Vice President Kirby Engine, Walter Berry
Senior Vice President Vessel Operations, Thomas Sullivan
Senior Vice President Vessel Operations, James Hollingsworth
Executive Vice President Operations, Jim Gregory
Vice President River Operations, Gene Daniels
Senior Vice President Sales, Mel Edwards
Senior Vice President Sales, William Thomson
Chairman, Joseph H. (Joe) Pyne, age 66
Auditors: KPMGLLP

LOCATIONS

HQ: Kirby Corp.
55 Waugh Drive, Suite 1000, Houston, TX 77007
Phone: 713 435-1000   **Fax:** 713 435-1010
Web: www.kirbycorp.com

PRODUCTS/OPERATIONS

2013 Sales

	$ mil.	% of total
Marine transportation	1713.2	76
Diesel engine services	529.0	24
Total	**2242.2**	**100**

COMPETITORS

Adams Resources	Ingram Industries
American Commercial Lines	International Shipholding
Burlington Northern Santa Fe	Kansas City Southern
CSX	Kenan Advantage Group
Canadian National Railway	Norfolk Southern
Crowley Maritime	Quality Distribution
Cummins	SEACOR
Illinois Auto Electric	Trimac
	Union Pacific

HISTORICAL FINANCIALS

Company Type: Public

Income Statement

FYE: December 31

	REVENUE ($ mil.)	NET INCOME ($ mil.)	NET PROFIT MARGIN	EMPLOYEES
12/13	2,242.2	253.0	11.3%	4,450
12/12	2,112.6	209.4	9.9%	4,575
12/11	1,850.4	183.0	9.9%	4,100
12/10	1,109.5	116.2	10.5%	2,520
12/09	1,082.1	125.9	11.6%	2,675
Annual Growth	**20.0%**	**19.1%**	**—**	**13.6%**

2013 Year-End Financials

Debt ratio: 20.3%
Return on equity: 13.6%
Cash ($ mil.): 4
Current ratio: 1.57
Long-term debt ($ mil.): 749

No. of shares (mil.): 56
Dividends
  Yield: —
  Payout: —
Market value ($ mil.): 5,642

	STOCK PRICE ($) FY Close	P/E High/Low		PER SHARE ($) Earnings	Dividends	Book Value
12/13	99.25	22	14	4.44	0.00	35.37
12/12	61.89	19	12	3.73	0.00	29.95
12/11	65.84	20	13	3.33	0.00	25.88
12/10	44.05	21	15	2.15	0.00	21.59
12/09	34.83	17	9	2.34	0.00	19.55
Annual Growth	**29.9%**	**—**	**—**	**17.4%**	**—**	**16.0%**

Knight Transportation Inc.

Knight Transportation drivers don't drive long hours into the night. The truckload carrier instead focuses on short- to medium-haul trips averaging about 500 miles. From some 35 regional operations centers mainly in the southern midwestern and western US Knight carries such cargo as consumer goods food and beverages and paper products. It has a fleet of more than 4000 tractors and 9500 trailers including nearly 900 refrigerated trailers. Besides for-hire hauling Knight provides dedicated contract carriage in which drivers and equipment are assigned to a customer long-term. It also offers freight brokerage services.

Geographic Reach

Knight is stationed in Phoenix and operates through nearly 30 locations in the US in about 25 states. Other operations reside in Canada and Mexico.

Operations

Knight has one reportable segment comprised of five operating segments including three asset-based operating segments (dry van truckload temperature-controlled truckload and port services) and two non-asset-based operating segments (brokerage and intermodal services). Its asset-based and non-asset-based operations provide transportation and arrange for the transportation of general commodities for customers throughout the US and parts of Canada and Mexico.

Sales and Marketing

Knight has a nationwide network of service centers through 500 independent contractors third-party carriers and its rail providers. Its top 5 customers accounted for 15% of its total revenue in 2012.

Financial Performance

Finally in the wake of the Great Recession Knight has enjoyed three straight years of unprecedented growth. Revenues jumped 8% from $866 million in 2011 to peak at $936 million in 2012 a historical milestone. Profits also spiked 6% from $60 million to reach a record high of $64 million due to the higher revenue and a decrease in operating expenses.

The growth for 2012 was driven by a 9% rise in fuel surcharge revenue due to rising fuel prices and improvements in freight mix and contract pricing. It also experienced growth from its asset-based operations due to an increase in average loaded miles and improved pricing.

Strategy

With 18 wheels of optimism the company is pushing ahead to expand into new geographic regions by opening new service centers. These regional service centers are linked to Knight's corporate computer system which provides detailed information regarding equipment shipment status and customer requirements. The company believes its regional structure helps the company control costs and not be as susceptible to regional economic downturns. The regional system also serves as an aid in recruiting drivers because it gives them more time at home.

In late 2013 Knight Transportation proposed a deal to acquire Arkansas-based dry van truckload carrier USA Truck for $242 million. However by November 2013 both parties were having disagreements surrounding the purchase price of the deal.

Ownership

Four members of the Knight family collectively own about 30% of the company. Investment manager Wasatch Advisors owns a 15% stake.

Company Background

Four Knight cousins —Kevin Gary Keith and Randy —started the company in 1990.

EXECUTIVES

Vice President Human Resources, Glen Palmer
Vice President Director Information, Bob Anderson
Vice President Of Operations, Paul Johnides
President and CEO, David A. (Dave) Jackson, age 39, $198,846 total compensation
Executive Vice President and Chief Operations Officers, Kevin Quast
Executive Vice President of Sales and Marketing, James E. Updike

CFO, Adam Miller
Senior Vice President Business Development, Ramsey Bill
Vice President Of Information Systems, Joseph Kauffman
Vice President Of Enterprise Services Division, Julie Leblanc
Vice President, William Sommerville
Vice President Sales, Glenn Macilroy
Executive Vice President, Mark Noga
Divison Vice President, Linley Holland
Vice President Of Sales, Jimmy Tunnell
Vice President Of Engineering, Chantal Picard
Vice President Operations, Paul Mei
Vice President Operations, Robert Dick
Vice President Operations, Miguel Denga
Vice President Of Maintenance, Steve Collins
Vice President Of Engineering, James Williams
Vice President Operations, Richard Benjee
Vice President Operations, Martin Stafford
Senior Vice President Of Finance, Reed Kiefer
National Accounts Manager, Nick Parish
National Accounts Manager, Richard Alber
National Accounts Manager, Karlene Ricks
Vice Chairman, Gary J. Knight, age 62
Chairman, Kevin P. Knight, age 57
President and CEO, David A. (Dave) Jackson, age 39
Auditors: GrantThorntonLLP

LOCATIONS

HQ: Knight Transportation Inc.
20002 North 19th Avenue, Phoenix, AZ 85027
Phone: 602 269-2000
Web: www.knighttrans.com

PRODUCTS/OPERATIONS

2012 Sales

	$ mil.	% of total
Revenues	752.1	80
Fuel surcharges	183.9	20
Total	**936.0**	**100**

Selected Services

Brokerage
Dedicated truckload service
Driver training
Dry van truckload
Refrigerated truckload
Sales

COMPETITORS

C.H. Robinson Worldwide	J.B. Hunt
C.R. England	Landstar System
Celadon	Prime Inc.
Covenant Transportation	Schneider National
Frozen Food Express	Swift Transportation
Heartland Express	U.S. Xpress
	USA Truck
	Werner Enterprises

HISTORICAL FINANCIALS

Company Type: Public

Income Statement

FYE: December 31

	REVENUE ($ mil.)	NET INCOME ($ mil.)	NET PROFIT MARGIN	EMPLOYEES
12/13	969.2	69.2	7.1%	5,177
12/12	936.0	64.1	6.8%	5,176
12/11	866.2	60.2	7.0%	4,682
12/10	730.7	59.0	8.1%	4,526
12/09	651.7	50.5	7.8%	4,414
Annual Growth	**10.4%**	**8.2%**	**—**	**4.1%**

2013 Year-End Financials

Debt ratio: 4.7%
Return on equity: 13.3%
Cash ($ mil.): 0
Current ratio: 2.62
Long-term debt ($ mil.): 38

No. of shares (mil.): 80
Dividends
  Yield: 1.3%
  Payout: 28.5%
Market value ($ mil.): 1,471

	STOCK PRICE ($) FY Close	P/E High/Low		PER SHARE ($) Earnings	Dividends	Book Value
12/13	18.34	21	17	0.86	0.24	6.88
12/12	14.63	23	18	0.80	0.74	6.15
12/11	15.64	27	17	0.74	0.24	6.00
12/10	19.00	31	25	0.70	0.98	6.06
12/09	19.29	33	20	0.60	0.19	6.24
Annual Growth	(1.3%)	—	—	9.4%	6.0%	2.4%

Korn/Ferry
International (DE)

High-level executives can jump ship via Korn/Ferry International. The world's largest executive recruitment firm Korn/Ferry has almost 75 offices in more than 35 countries. The company's more than 600 consultants help prominent public and private companies as well as government and not-for-profit organizations find qualified job applicants for openings in a variety of executive level positions (including CEOs CFOs and other senior-level jobs). Through Futurestep job seekers use the Internet and videotaped job interviews to find mid-level management positions. In addition the company provides management assessment as well as coaching and executive development services. Korn/Ferry was founded in 1969.

After an unprofitable 2009 Korn/Ferry seems to have bounced back on the heels of the recession. In addition to its net income skyrocketing from $5.3 million in 2010 to almost $59 million in 2011 the company saw its revenue levels increase almost 30% from $600 million to $776 million during that same time period.

The company works with more than 4700 global clients including about 47% of the Fortune 500. Throughout 2011 placements within the industrial consumer and financial services sectors collectively accounted for almost 64% of its total assignments. It relies heavily on customer loyalty with almost 75% of work coming from previous clients each year. Korn/Ferry is also focused on broadening its product and service offerings especially its mid-level recruitment operations. These operations accounted for 26% of its overall revenue in 2011.

Over the years the company has relied on acquisitions to expand its domestic and international footprints and beef up its executive search and coaching services operations. In 2013 Korn/Ferry acquired the Minneapolis-based management consulting firm PDI Ninth House for about $80 million plus up to $15 million more based on future results. Previously in early 2010 Korn/Ferry enhanced its position in a new market when it acquired Sensa Solutions a management consulting company providing executive coaching training and strategic planning services to the federal government.

In mid-2009 Korn/Ferry expanded its core business in Europe with the acquisition of rival executive search firm Whitehead Mann for undisclosed terms. UK-based Whitehead Mann also brought strengths in the Middle East Asia Africa Australia and North America.

HISTORY

Korn/Ferry was founded in 1969 by Lester Korn and Richard Ferry. A year later the firm debuted its first specialty division a unit serving the national real estate industry. Its specialization approach was a unique (and successful) slant on the practice of headhunting and the company soon added more specialties. Korn/Ferry went public in 1972; it also expanded overseas with offices in Brussels and London that year and in Tokyo a year later. Volatile stock prices became a distraction to the two founders so in 1974 they took the company private by repurchasing all its stock. Korn/Ferry moved into Latin America in 1977 by acquiring 49% of Hazzard & Associates.

By 1980 steady growth had made Korn/Ferry one of the top headhunting firms in the country. A decade later the firm established a foothold in central Europe by opening an office in Budapest Hungary; it further strengthened its old-country presence by acquiring European search firm Carre/Orban (at the time it was the largest merger in search firm history). Traditionally a search firm for high-level executives Korn/Ferry pushed into the middle management arena in 1998 with its Internet-based Futurestep service. Also that year former COO Windle Priem took over the company from Michael Boxberger who left after 19 months.

Korn/Ferry went public again in 1999. The following year it acquired online college recruitment service JobDirect. In 2001 Priem stepped down as president and CEO and was replaced by Paul Reilly former CEO of KPMG International. Also that year in an effort to strengthen its Web offerings the company cobranded its Futurestep site with online giant Yahoo! Later in 2001 Korn/Ferry cut 500 jobs or 20% of its workforce and reduced salaries. It also reorganized management and closed JobDirect. In 2002 and 2003 the company continued reducing its workforce and streamlining its operations.

Over the next few years Korn/Ferry expanded beyond its traditional executive recruitment services (by beefing up its management assessment business among others). In 2006 Korn/Ferry primarily focusing on its information technology products portfolio launched its K/F One software platform. The product aggregates Microsoft Outlook the Internet and proprietary Korn/Ferry software. Keeping this focus on technology the company acquired Lominger Limited a provider of leadership development software for $24 million later in the year.

Gary Burnison the company's former COO and CFO took over the reins as CEO in mid-2007 while Reilly remained chairman.

To further boost its leadership and talent consulting business Korn/Ferry in late 2008 acquired Lore International a provider of leadership development executive education and coaching services that has offices in the US and Europe.

EXECUTIVES

President Asia Pacific, Charles Tseng
Vice President General Counsel, Peter L Dunn, age 70
Senior Vice President Corporate Development, Brian Suh

EVP and CFO, Robert P. Rozek, age 53, $475,000 total compensation
President and CEO, Gary D. Burnison, age 53, $700,000 total compensation
CEO Futurestep, Byrne K. Mulrooney, age 53, $300,000 total compensation
Executive Chairman Americas, Robert A. Damon
Vice Chairman Board & CEO Services EMEA, Olof Pripp, age 56
EVP Global Human Resources, Linda Hyman
President Europe Middle East and Africa, Bernard S. Zen-Ruffinen
President Americas, Doug Charles
SVP and CIO, Bryan Ackermann
President Leadership and Talent Consulting, R. J. Heckman, $133,333 total compensation
Senior Vice President Of Finance And Corporate Controller, Mark Neal, age 55
Vice President, Didier Vuchot
Vice President Comp Benefits Human, Marat Fukson
Vice President Human Resources, Janet Clardy
Vice President Corporate Finance, Ronald Johnston
Vice President, Karen Wong
Vice President And General Manager, David Marzo
Vice President, Teruo Seno
Exec Vice President For Mkt Sales, David Pugh
Vice President, Ken Koyama
Vice President Of Sales Information Technology, Mike Carlin
Vice President Operations, Colleen Fullen
Senior Vice President Solution Management And Marketing, Sean Klunder
Senior Client Partner Chief Technology Officer
Vice President Development Searches Ppt 3 6, Robert McHale
Vice President Business Development Edu, Gregory Elkins
Vice President Internet Services, Jim Saltmar
Vice President Financial Applications, Daniel Fincher
Assistant Vice President Information Technology Services, Kurt Vaag
Vice President Human Resources, Lynn Mandle
Vp Finance, Bob Teh
Vice President Business Development, Darryl Smith
Vice President Global Operations, Bill King
Vice President Communications Solutions Lead, Anne Gunderson
Vice President Consulting Services, Jim Davidson
Chairman, George T. Shaheen, age 70
Vice Chairman Board & CEO Services EMEA, Olof Pripp, age 56
Secretary, Susan Long
Secretary, Rebecca Ng
Secretary, Cecily Mai
Secretary, Pearlyn Lim
Board Member, Debra Perry
Secretary, Lay-tin Koh
Auditors: Ernst&Young

LOCATIONS

HQ: Korn/Ferry International (DE)
1900 Avenue of the Stars, Suite 2600, Los Angeles, CA 90067
Phone: 310 552-1834
Web: www.kornferry.com

2011 Sales

	$ mil.	% of total
Executive recruitment		
North America	376.0	48
EMEA	155.8	20
Asia/Pacific	90.3	12
South America	32.0	4
Futurestep	90.2	12
Other	32.0	4
Total	**776.3**	**100**

PRODUCTS/OPERATIONS

Selected Services

Executive coaching
Executive recruitment
Management assessment
Middle-management recruitment (Futurestep)

COMPETITORS

A.T. Kearney	Handler & Associates
CCL	Heidrick & Struggles
CTPartners	J.C. Wilson Associates
Development Dimensions	Michael Page
International	Russell Reynolds
Diversified Search	Solomon Page
Egon Zehnder	Spencer Stuart
Gap International	

HISTORICAL FINANCIALS

Company Type: Public

Income Statement

FYE: April 30

	REVENUE ($ mil.)	NET INCOME ($ mil.)	NET PROFIT MARGIN	EMPLOYEES
04/14	995.5	72.6	7.3%	3,396
04/13	849.7	33.2	3.9%	3,272
04/12	826.7	54.3	6.6%	2,654
04/11	776.2	58.8	7.6%	2,463
04/10	599.6	5.3	0.9%	1,664
Annual Growth	13.5%	92.5%		19.5%

2014 Year-End Financials

Debt ratio: —	No. of shares (mil.): 49
Return on equity: 10.2%	Dividends
Cash ($ mil.): 333	Yield: —
Current ratio: 1.96	Payout: —
Long-term debt ($ mil.): —	Market value ($ mil.): 1,447

	STOCK PRICE ($) FY Close	P/E High/Low		PER SHARE ($) Earnings	Dividends	Book Value
04/14	29.05	20	10	1.48	0.00	15.17
04/13	16.55	27	18	0.70	0.00	13.63
04/12	16.15	20	10	1.15	0.00	13.14
04/11	20.71	19	10	1.27	0.00	12.30
04/10	16.21	155	81	0.12	0.00	10.69
Annual Growth	15.7%	—	—	87.4%	—	9.2%

L&L Energy Inc

You'll excuse L & L Energy (formerly L & L International) if it's a bit jet lagged. Incorporated in Nevada with headquarters in Seattle the company mines coal in China. Granted a license by the government to extract a set amount of coal in exchange for up-front fees L & L owns mines in China's Yunnan and Guizhou provinces. The company currently extracts more than 630000 tons of coal per year from the mines. It also processes coal to produce coke used in steel production medium coal used for heating and coal slurries used as a lower quality fuel. L & L is swapping a stake in a coking mine with Singapore-based Union Energy to acquire a 50% stake in the LuoZhou coal mine.

On the heels of the Chinese government's mandate for coal industry consolidation L & L Energy plans to expand its existing coal mines and pur-

chase smaller operations that fail to meet the government's mandated production minimums. Inland China has begun to develop at a more rapid rate leading to an increased demand for energy which is 70% coal fueled in that country.

As part of its plan to focus on inland coal operations in 2009 L & L sold its 80% share in LEK air compressor operations back to the company for about $4.2 million. The following year it sold its 93% interest in Hon Shen Coal to Guangxi Liuzhou Lifu Machinery for $6 million. It had purchased the coal washing facility in late 2009 for $3.8 million. Also in 2010 the company purchased its Ping Yi mine Hong Xing Coal Washing and Zone Lin Coking.

President and CEO Dickson Lee holds about a quarter of the company's stock.

EXECUTIVES

Vice Chairman, Norman Y. (Norm) Mineta, age 82
VP Corporate Infrastructure, Edmund C. Moy
Chairman and CEO, Dickson V. Lee, age 65, $174,503 total compensation
EVP US Operations, Clayton Fong, $75,000 total compensation
CEO of a Hong Kong listed energy company, James Schaeffer
Controller, Keith So
Senior Sales Director, Zhi Xie
Director, Ian Robinson, age 74
Vice Chairman, Norman Y. (Norm) Mineta, age 82
Director, Shirley Kiang, age 62
Director, Dennis Bracy, age 64
Director, Joseph J. Borich, age 69
Independent Director, Jingcai Yang
Independent Director, Syd Peng
Auditors: Kabani&CompanyInc.

LOCATIONS

HQ: L&L Energy Inc
130 Andover Park East, Suite 200, Seattle, WA 98188
Phone: 206 264-8065   Fax: 206 838-0488
Web: www.llenergyinc.com

PRODUCTS/OPERATIONS

2010 Sales

	$ mil.	% of total
Mining	64.5	59
Washing	18.3	17
Wholesale	13.2	12
Coking	13.2	12
Total	**109.2**	**100**

COMPETITORS

Anglo American	Rio Tinto plc
BHP Billiton	Shenhua
BHP Billiton Plc	Yanzhou Coal
China Coal Energy	

HISTORICAL FINANCIALS

Company Type: Public

Income Statement

FYE: April 30

	REVENUE ($ mil.)	NET INCOME ($ mil.)	NET PROFIT MARGIN	EMPLOYEES
04/13	198.9	38.3	19.3%	1,364
04/12	143.5	14.2	9.9%	1,330
04/11	223.8	36.7	16.4%	1,600
04/10	109.2	32.9	30.1%	1,400
04/09	40.9	9.9	24.3%	1,200
Annual Growth	48.5%	40.1%	—	3.3%

2013 Year-End Financials

Debt ratio: 1.7%	No. of shares (mil.): 38
Return on equity: 19.8%	Dividends
Cash ($ mil.): 9	Yield: —
Current ratio: 1.66	Payout: —
Long-term debt ($ mil.): 0	Market value ($ mil.): 147

	STOCK PRICE ($) FY Close	P/E High/Low		PER SHARE ($) Earnings	Dividends	Book Value
04/13	3.87	4	1	0.98	0.00	5.61
04/12	2.25	17	5	0.42	0.00	4.70
04/11	6.95	11	4	1.21	0.00	4.40
04/10	10.80	11	1	1.28	0.00	2.76
04/09	1.80	5	1	0.46	0.00	1.06
Annual Growth	21.1%	—	—	20.8%	—	51.8%

Lakes Entertainment Inc

Even though Lakes Entertainment doesn't own a casino it still keeps its eye on the slots. The company manages Indian-owned casinos including the Four Winds Casino Resort in New Buffalo Township Michigan (approximately 75 miles east of Chicago) for the Pokagon Band of Potawatomi Indians; and the Red Hawk Casino in El Dorado County California (some 30 miles east of Sacramento) for the Shingle Springs Band of Miwok Indians. Nearly all of Lakes Entertainment's revenues come from management fees. The company is also exploring other development projects through agreements with tribes for additional casinos in Michigan and California and a possible non-Indian casino project in Mississippi.

The amount of management fees Lakes Entertainment earns is dependent on how much revenue its casinos generate. Not surprisingly its managed casinos have been feeling the negative effects of a down economy. At Red Hawk the casino is hurting from an especially challenging market in California and in 2009 the property cut 250 of its 1750 full-time staff positions. Lakes Entertainment is also hurting from new competition that entered the Four Winds Casino Resort market that year.

Then in 2010 the Iowa Tribe of Oklahoma terminated its contract with the company for the management of its Cimarron Casino in Perkins Oklahoma. Cimarron houses approximately 375 slot machines and a snack bar. The end of that agreement put a dent in one of Lakes Entertainment's main revenue streams —Lakes had been receiving an annual management fee that amounted to 30% of Cimarron's total revenues in excess of $4 million.

Chairman and CEO Lyle Berman owns more than 15% of Lakes Entertainment.

EXECUTIVES

Vp Gaming, Scott Just
Vp Of Human Resources, Diane Stone
Vice President Of Marketing, Mike Montross
Svp Operations, Rick Charles
Vice President, Dick Bienapfl
Vice President Marketing, Ed Reynolds
Vice President For Brand Integration And Strategic Development, Jack Malisow

Managing Director, Lisa Jolicoeur
Auditors: PiercyBowlerTaylor&Kern

LOCATIONS

HQ: Lakes Entertainment Inc
130 Cheshire Lane, Suite 101, Minnetonka, MN 55305
Phone: 952 449-9092
Web: www.lakesentertainment.com

COMPETITORS

Caesars Entertainment
Choctaw Resort Development Enterprise
Colville Tribal Enterprise Corporation
Hollywood Casino Bay St. Louis
Isle of Capri Casinos
Pinnacle Entertainment

HISTORICAL FINANCIALS

Company Type: Public

Income Statement

FYE: December 29

	REVENUE ($ mil.)	NET INCOME ($ mil.)	NET PROFIT MARGIN	EMPLOYEES
12/13	38.7	18.6	48.1%	536
12/12*	10.9	3.2	29.4%	134
01/12	35.5	(1.8)	—	19
01/11	24.6	(13.8)	—	22
01/10	26.2	3.7	14.1%	40
Annual Growth	10.3%	49.8%	—	91.3%

*Fiscal year change

2013 Year-End Financials

Debt ratio: 7.8%
Return on equity: 15.3%
Cash ($ mil.): 37
Current ratio: 18.71
Long-term debt ($ mil.): 10

No. of shares (mil.): 13
Dividends
  Yield: —
  Payout: —
Market value ($ mil.): 53

	STOCK PRICE ($) FY Close	P/E High/Low		PER SHARE ($) Earnings	Dividends	Book Value
12/13	3.97	3	2	1.40	0.00	9.89
12/12*	3.06	13	8	0.24	0.00	8.49
01/12	1.85	—	—	(0.14)	0.00	8.24
01/11	2.85	—	—	(1.04)	0.00	8.34
01/10	2.51	17	7	0.28	0.00	9.38
Annual Growth	12.1%	—	—	49.5%	—	1.3%

*Fiscal year change

Landec Corp.

Landec's products don't turn into pumpkins at midnight but the changes are nearly as sudden and much more practical. The company has developed a technology that allows polymers to change physical characteristics when exposed to temperature changes. Its BreatheWay permeable membrane packaging allows oxygen and carbon dioxide to enter and escape from sealed fresh-cut produce packages to keep produce fresh. It's used primarily by subsidiary Apio which grows and packages fresh vegetables. Landec's Lifecore Biomedical subsidiary is a leading supplier of premium hyaluronan-based biomaterials for the ophthalmic and orthopedic markets. Landec has licensing deals with Air Products and Chemicals and Monsanto.

Financial Analysis

Landec's revenues increased by 15% in fiscal year 2012 due to a 19% increase in Apio's value-added revenues thanks to an 11% increase in unit volume sales to existing customers resulting primarily from expanded product offerings $9.1 million of revenues from GreenLine (acquired in 2012) and a larger percentage of Apio's value-added revenues being generated from sales to club stores rather than retail grocery chains. Other factors included a 16% increase in Apio Export due to 11% increase in export unit volume sales due to a greater volume of fruit and vegetables being available to export and due to more favorable pricing for export products in fiscal year 2012.

Apio Packaging's revenues decreased by 32% due to lower sales of BreatheWay membranes to Chiquita for packaged avocados as a result of Chiquita placing large initial orders of membranes during the first half of fiscal year 2011.

The hyaluronic acid-based (HA) biomaterials segment revenue grew by 5% in fiscal year 2012 due to an increase in sales to existing customers. Technology licensing revenue decreased by 39% due to the termination of the Monsanto Agreement in fiscal year 2012.

Net income increased by 207% in fiscal year 2012 thanks to an increase in other income of $5.8 million in the fair market value of the Windset investment (made in 2010) and increase in dividend income due to the receipt of a full year of dividends from the $15 million preferred stock investment in Windset. (Windset is a Canada-based company that packages greenhouse grown cucumbers peppers and tomatoes.)

Strategy

In 2012 the company agreed to sell its seed coating business Landec Ag to INCOTEC Holding North America for $600000. It also agreed to partner with INCOTEC Coating and Seed Technology Companies which will give it access to global markets for its polymer technology used in seed treatment. Landec also signed a seven-year technology licensing and polymer supply agreement with IN-COTEC Field Crops North America to license its polymer seed coating technology for corn sold under the label Pollinator Plus. It also signed a five-year agreement with INCOTEC Holdings to partner on the development of new polymer and unique coatings for seed treatment. The agreements allow Landec to focus on its food products and biomedical materials businesses.

Through Apio a food subsidiary Landec acquired Ohio-based GreenLine Foods in 2012 which processes fresh-cut green beans in North America. The acquisition combined GreenLine's green beans brand with the Apio Eat Smart brand to cover about 80% of market presence in North American retail grocery stores.

Moving into the healthcare materials market in 2010 Landec acquired Lifecore Biomedical from Warburg Pincus in a $40 million cash and debt deal. Lifecore is a supplier of hyaluronic acid-based biomaterials for the medical and veterinary markets. Hyaluronan biopolymers are used in many therapeutic treatments including cataract surgery degenerative joint disease spinal defect filling and medical device coatings.

Ownership

Wynnefield Capital owns 10% of the company; Security Investors 9%.

Company Background

In 1999 Landec bought its largest customer Apio.

EXECUTIVES

Chairman President and CEO, Gary T. Steele, age 66, $450,000 total compensation
CFO, Gregory S. (Greg) Skinner, age 54, $310,000 total compensation
VP Corporate Technology, Steven P. Bitler, age 57, $190,000 total compensation
CEO Apio Inc., Ronald L. (Ron) Midyett, age 49, $330,000 total compensation
COO, Molly A. Hemmeter, $285,000 total compensation
President Lifecore Biomedical, Larry D. Hiebert, $259,231 total compensation
Senior Vp Mrktng, Brad Bartlett
Chairman President and CEO, Gary T. Steele, age 66
Auditors: Ernst&YoungLLP

LOCATIONS

HQ: Landec Corp.
3603 Haven Avenue, Menlo Park, CA 94025
Phone: 650 306-1650   **Fax:** 650 368-9818
Web: www.landec.com

PRODUCTS/OPERATIONS

2011 Sales

	$ mil.	% of total
Apio		
Value-added	205.6	65
Export	71.5	22
Packaging	2.0	1
HA	34.3	11
Technology licensing	4.2	1
Total	**317.6**	**100**

COMPETITORS

Dow Chemical	Pioneer Hi-Bred
DuPont Agriculture	Rexam
FreshPoint	Sealed Air Corp.
Packaging Dynamics	

HISTORICAL FINANCIALS

Company Type: Public

Income Statement

FYE: May 25

	REVENUE ($ mil.)	NET INCOME ($ mil.)	NET PROFIT MARGIN	EMPLOYEES
05/14	476.8	19.1	4.0%	531
05/13	441.7	22.8	5.2%	526
05/12	317.5	13.1	4.1%	532
05/11	276.7	4.2	1.5%	255
05/10	238.2	4.4	1.9%	229
Annual Growth	18.9%	43.9%	—	23.4%

2014 Year-End Financials

Debt ratio: 10.9%
Return on equity: 10.0%
Cash ($ mil.): 14
Current ratio: 1.88
Long-term debt ($ mil.): 28

No. of shares (mil.): 26
Dividends
  Yield: —
  Payout: —
Market value ($ mil.): 322

	STOCK PRICE ($) FY Close	P/E High/Low		PER SHARE ($) Earnings	Dividends	Book Value
05/14	12.01	22	14	0.71	0.00	7.57
05/13	13.88	17	8	0.85	0.00	6.77
05/12	7.07	14	10	0.49	0.00	5.84
05/11	5.83	47	36	0.15	0.00	5.15
05/10	6.19	50	38	0.15	0.00	4.94
Annual Growth	18.0%	—	—	47.5%	—	11.3%

Lannett Co., Inc.

Lannett banks on the designation of "bioequivalent" for its products. The firm markets generic prescription drugs in the US including thyroid treatment levothyroxine digoxin for congestive heart failure migraine drug butalbital and anticonvulsant primidone. Such medicines are pharmaceutical equivalents or bioequivalents of branded medicines made by other drug companies. While Lannett maintains two plants it also relies on manufacturer Jerome Stevens Pharmaceuticals for a significant portion of its inventories. The company produces medicines in oral solid (tablets liquids and capsules) and topical dosages forms. Chairman emeritus William Farber and his family own a controlling stake in the company.

Operations
Two of Lannett's product lines levothyroxine and digoxin collectively accounted for about 50% of the company's net sales in fiscal year 2012. Both of the top products as well as two other products are manufactured by Jerome Stevens Pharmaceuticals.

Sales and Marketing
Lannett's customers include the big wholesale US pharmaceutical distributors as well as group purchasing organizations chain drug stores and other pharmaceutical companies. Top customers include Walgreen (18%) Cardinal Health (12%) AmerisourceBergen (11%) and McKesson (9%). Lannett employs a direct sales force; it also promotes products through trade shows and publications.

Financial Analysis
Though its revenues and net income were on an upward trend between 2008 and 2010 Lannett experienced a drop in both sales and profits during 2011 largely due to competitive price reductions on certain products. The company was able to pull its net income back into the black in 2012 reporting some $4 million in profits as well as a 15% increase in revenues to some $123 million. Growth in 2012 was attributed to a change in the mix of products that the company sells with increases in sales of C-Topical and pain management products (including the launch of new morphine sulfate tablets but excluding sales of oxycodone products which declined).

Strategy
Like any drug developer Lannett maintains a steady stream of potential drugs in its pipeline. New product introductions are key to keeping ahead of its competitors and as such the firm focuses on developing products with few or no generic competitors. The company maintains its own research and development staff partners with third-party developers and sometimes simply purchases new products from other generic makers.

One of the company's focus areas of development is the market of narcotics and controlled substances as Lannett believes the demand for pain medicine will continue to increase as the Baby Boomer generation ages. Lannett is also looking to grow in new specialty fields of medicine as well as new dosage formulations (such as ophthalmic or nasal products) through strategic relationships or acquisitions.

Company Background
Formed in 1942 Lannett is one of the oldest generics manufacturers in the US. Chairman emeritus William Farber and his family (including chairman Jeffrey Farber) together own about 40% of the company.

EXECUTIVES
President, Michael J. (Mike) Bogda, age 53
CEO and Director, Arthur P. Bedrosian, age 69, $425,096 total compensation
VP Sales and Marketing, Kevin Smith, age 55, $212,755 total compensation
COO, William Schreck, age 66, $250,000 total compensation
VP Logistics and CIO, Robert Ehlinger, $170,000 total compensation
CFO, Martin P. Galvan, $235,577 total compensation
Vp Regulatory Affairs And Chief Compliance Officer, Ernest Sabo, age 68
CEO and Director, Arthur P. Bedrosian, age 69
Vice Chairman, Jeffrey K. Farber, age 55
Auditors: GrantThorntonLLP

LOCATIONS
HQ: Lannett Co., Inc.
9000 State Road, Philadelphia, PA 19136
Phone: 215 333-9000
Web: www.lannett.com

PRODUCTS/OPERATIONS

2012 Sales

	$ mil.	% of total
Wholesalers	68.1	55
Retail chains	45.6	37
Mail-order pharmacy	9.3	8
Total	**123.0**	**100**

Selected Products
Amantadine (generic Symmetrel Parkinson' s Disease)
Butalbital (generic Fiorinal migraine)
Clindamycin (generic Cleocin antibiotic)
C-Topical solution (anesthetic)
Danazol (generic Danocrine endometriosis)
Dicyclomine (generic Bentyl irritable bowel syndrome)
Diethylpropion (generic Tenuate obesity)
Digoxin (generic Lanoxin congestive heart failure)
Doxycycline (generic Adoxa antibiotic)
Fluphenazine (generic Proxlixin antipsychotic)
Hydromorphone (generic Dilaudid pain management)
Levothyroxine (generic Levoxyl thyroid deficiency)
Loxapine (generic Loxitane antipsychotic)
Morphine sulfate (pain)
Oxycodone (generic Roxicodone pain management)
Phentermine (generic Adipex obesity)
Pilocarpine (generic Salagen dry mouth)
Primidone (generic Mysoline epilepsy)
Probenecid (generic Benemid gout)
Rifampin (generic Rifadin antibiotic for meningitis)
Terbutaline (generic Brethine bronchospasms)
Triamterene with hydrochlorothiazide (generic Byazide hypertension)
Unithroid (thyroid deficiency)
Ursodiol (generic Actigall gallstone)

COMPETITORS

Abbott Labs	Mylan
Actavis	Obagi Medical
Akorn	Par Pharmaceutical
Chiesi USA	Companies
Cumberland	Pfizer
Pharmaceuticals	Purdue Pharma
Derma Sciences	Ranbaxy Laboratories
Forest Labs	Roxane Laboratories
GlaxoSmithKline	Salix Pharmaceuticals
Hi-Tech Pharmacal	Sandoz International
IMPAX Laboratories	GmbH
Jazz Pharmaceuticals	SciClone
Momenta	Teva
Pharmaceuticals	

HISTORICAL FINANCIALS
Company Type: Public

Income Statement
FYE: June 30

	REVENUE ($ mil.)	NET INCOME ($ mil.)	NET PROFIT MARGIN	EMPLOYEES
06/14	273.7	57.1	20.9%	399
06/13	151.0	13.3	8.8%	356
06/12	122.9	3.9	3.2%	324
06/11	106.8	(0.2)	—	310
06/10	125.1	7.8	6.2%	305
Annual Growth	**21.6%**	**64.4%**	**—**	**6.9%**

2014 Year-End Financials

Debt ratio: 0.3%	No. of shares (mil.): 35
Return on equity: 27.0%	Dividends
Cash ($ mil.): 105	Yield: —
Current ratio: 5.65	Payout: —
Long-term debt ($ mil.): 1	Market value ($ mil.): 1,765

	STOCK PRICE ($) FY Close	P/E High/Low		PER SHARE ($) Earnings	Dividends	Book Value
06/14	49.62	29	7	1.62	0.00	8.28
06/13	11.91	27	9	0.46	0.00	4.46
06/12	4.24	37	25	0.14	0.00	3.93
06/11	4.98	—	—	(0.01)	0.00	3.72
06/10	4.57	30	13	0.31	0.00	3.57
Annual Growth	**81.5%**			**51.2%**	**—**	**23.4%**

LaSalle Hotel Properties

LaSalle Hotel Properties is a self-administered and self-managed real estate investment trust (REIT) that invests in renovates and leases full-service luxury hotels in the US. It owns more than 45 properties in 10 states and the District of Columbia. LaSalle Hotel Properties' holdings which altogether boast about 11400 rooms are typically located in major urban markets near convention centers business districts and resorts. The properties are managed by outside hotel companies that operate under such names as Marriott Sheraton Hilton and Hyatt. LaSalle Hotel Properties became self-managing in 2001 after three years under the wing of Jones Lang LaSalle.

Geographic Reach
Headquartered in Maryland LaSalle Hotel Properties owns and leases luxury hotels and resorts nationwide. It has a presence in 10 US states and Washington DC.

Operations
LaSalle Hotel Properties targets the metropolitan markets of Boston Chicago Los Angeles New York City San Diego San Francisco Seattle and Washington DC. It invests in properties elsewhere if the investment aligns with its strategy of improving value through renovations.

Strategy
The company works to own redevelop and reposition upscale full-service hotels that are located in urban resort and convention markets. It partners with premier lodging companies through strategic relationships to grow its business. These partners include the likes of Westin Hilton Hotels Hyatt Ho-

tels Benchmark Hospitality Commune Hotels and Resorts and Viceroy Hotel Group among others.

Mergers and Acquisitions

The real estate investment trust regularly invests in new properties to add to its portfolio.

In 2013 the company purchased three properties in San Francisco: the Harbor Court Hotel and Hotel Triton (both for $47.8 million) as well as the Serrano Hotel ($71.5 million). In Key West Florida LaSalle Hotel Properties acquired the 260-room Southernmost Hotel Collection for $184.5 million.

Through a joint venture (in which the company holds a 99.99% controlling interest) LaSalle Hotel Properties in 2012 acquired a majority ownership interest in The Liberty Hotel for $170 million. Located in Boston the full-service luxury hotel has 298 rooms.

Financial Performance

Thanks to numerous new properties in its portfolio and an increase in occupancy rates LaSalle Hotel Properties is growing its revenue. In 2012 LaSalle Hotel Properties posted a 21% increase in revenue vs. 2011 to $871 million. Its net income rose by 63% to $71 million during the same reporting period due to boosts in revenue and interest income offset in part by increasing hotel operating expenses and depreciation and amortization expenses.

EXECUTIVES

President and CEO, Michael D. (Mike) Barnello, age 48, $780,000 total compensation
EVP; CFO and Secretary, Bruce A. Riggins, age 41, $406,000 total compensation
EVP and COO, Alfred L. Young, age 45, $470,000 total compensation
Senior Vice President Acquisitions, Ian Gaum
Vice President, Jennifer Collins
Senior Vice President Of Marketing, Nicole Rohloff
Vice Presidentasset Management, Sarah Gulla
Senior Vice President Asset Management, Larry Kaminsky
Chairman, Stuart L. Scott, age 76
Auditors: KPMGLLP

LOCATIONS

HQ: LaSalle Hotel Properties
7550 Wisconsin Avenue, 10th Floor, Bethesda, MD 20814
Phone: 301 941-1500   **Fax:** 301 941-1553
Web: www.lasallehotels.com
LaSalle Hotel Operating Partnership L.P.
LaSalle Washington One Lessee Inc.
LHO Hollywood Financing Inc. (QRS)
LHO New Orleans Financing Inc.
LHO Hollywood LM L.P.
LHO New Orleans LM L.P.
LHO Viking Hotel L.L.C.
LHO Harborside Hotel L.L.C.
LHO Mission Bay Hotel L.P.
LHO San Diego Financing L.L.C.
LHO Washington Hotel One L.L.C.
LHO Washington Hotel Two L.L.C.

PRODUCTS/OPERATIONS

2012 Sales

	% of total
Hotel operating revenues	
Room	68
Food & beverage	24
Other operating department	7
Other income	1
Total	**100**

Selected Portfolio Property Types

Convention hotels
Resorts
Urban hotels

COMPETITORS

Ashford Hospitality Trust	Host Hotels & Resorts
FelCor	Innkeepers USA
Hersha Hospitality	Starwood Hotels & Resorts
Hospitality Properties Trust	Sunstone Hotel Investors

HISTORICAL FINANCIALS

Company Type: Public

Income Statement

FYE: December 31

	REVENUE ($ mil.)	NET INCOME ($ mil.)	NET PROFIT MARGIN	EMPLOYEES
12/13	977.2	89.9	9.2%	36
12/12	867.0	71.3	8.2%	33
12/11	719.0	43.6	6.1%	31
12/10	600.3	1.9	0.3%	29
12/09	607.0	7.6	1.3%	26
Annual Growth	**12.6%**	**85.4%**	**—**	**8.5%**

2013 Year-End Financials

Debt ratio: 35.0%
Return on equity: 4.5%
Cash ($ mil.): 13
Current ratio: 0.29
Long-term debt ($ mil.): 1,255
No. of shares (mil.): 103
Dividends
Yield: 3.1%
Payout: 137.1%
Market value ($ mil.): 3,208

	STOCK PRICE ($) FY Close	P/E High/Low		Earnings	PER SHARE ($) Dividends	Book Value
12/13	30.86	44	32	0.73	0.96	20.23
12/12	25.39	58	43	0.52	0.71	19.42
12/11	24.21	184	98	0.16	0.44	21.07
12/10	26.40	—	—	(0.36)	0.24	19.76
12/09	21.23	—	—	(0.34)	0.04	20.38
Annual Growth	**9.8%**	**—**	**—**	**—121.3%**	**(0.2%)**	

Lattice Semiconductor Corp.

The garden that grows on this Lattice is made up of silicon. Lattice Semiconductor is a top developer of programmable logic devices (PLDs) including in-system programmable (ISP) devices that manufacturers configure and reconfigure once the chips are attached to a printed circuit board. Lattice also makes low-density logic devices and sells software used to customize its chips which are used in communications computing industrial military consumer and automotive applications. The fabless chipmaker has expanded into the market for field-programmable gate arrays (FPGAs) another type of programmable chip. The majority of sales come from Asia.

Operations

The fabless semiconductor company uses contract manufacturers to produce its wafers. Fujitsu Semiconductor makes most of the company's new products. Other chip makers that produce devices for Lattice on a contract basis include Taiwan Semiconductor Manufacturing Company and United Microelectronics.

Geographic Reach

Lattice Semiconductor continues to conduct most of its product development work in the US through facilities in California and Oregon. It also has development centers in China India and the Philippines and operational centers in the Philippines and Singapore.

Sales and Marketing

Lattice Semiconductor sells primarily through distributors: Arrow Electronics and its Nu Horizons Electronics subsidiary combined account for a third of sales. Taiwan-based wholesaler Weikeng accounts for another 14%. Lattice ended its relationship with Avnet in 2011 but signed on Future Electronics in 2013. It also sells directly through a network of sales representatives and uses direct sales management and a field applications engineering organization to provide end-user and indirect sales support.

Financial Performance

Year-over-year sales in 2012 were down 12% to $279 million primarily due to reduced demand for electronics and declines in its military business. (Logic circuits are used in digital electronic equipment such as communications computing industrial automotive medical and military systems.) Sales were down in all geographic areas as well in the Americas Asia and Europe. That year it also recorded a net loss of $29 million after earning $78 million in profit in 2011.

Strategy

The company addressed its 2012 results through restructuring and improvements in its distribution channels. A 2012 restructuring plan further reduced and refocused its workforce and closed its offices in Illinois and Pennsylvania. In 2011 it reduced headcount streamlined supply chain activities at its headquarters and moved certain development capabilities and logistics activities to the Philippines.

Mergers and Acquisitions

Lattice Semiconductor looks for growth through acquisitions that complement existing product lines expand market reach and increase technological capabilities. In 2012 it paid about $62 million for SiliconBlue Technologies which provides field-programmable gate arrays (FPGA) devices for the consumer handheld industry. SiliconBlue's devices let mobile designers quickly add features to their mobile platform primarily in the areas of connectivity memory storage sensors imaging and video.

In 2011 it bought Hong Kong-based Rise Technology Development Company and its Philippine-based subsidiary APAC IC Layout Consultants which provides engineering layout and design services. The purchase of Rise and APAC IC was part of an effort by Lattice to improve its research and development capabilities while reducing related costs. APAC IC added a development center in the Philippines where labor costs are lower.

HISTORY

Lattice Semiconductor was founded in 1983 by Rahul Sud who quit his job at Intel to start the company. In 1985 Lattice introduced programmable logic devices (PLDs) that employed its pioneering electronically erasable CMOS technology. Losses led Lattice to file for Chapter 11 in 1987. A year later the company brought in Cyrus Tsui who was then general manager of the programmable logic division of Monolithic Memories (now part of Advanced Micro Devices) as CEO to turn things around. Tsui became chairman in 1991.

In 1994 the company debuted its in-system programmable (ISP) technology. Lattice invested $60 million with Taiwan's United Microelectronics for a new chip plant in 1995. In 1997 the company teamed up with Seiko Epson another silicon foundry contractor to build a new wafer fabrication facility.

The company bought Vantis (created in 1996 from AMD's PLD operations) in 1999 for $500 million. The next year Lattice released its next-generation BFW (big fast wide) PLD line —part of a wave of a company-record 35 new products for the year.

Early in 2002 the company acquired the FPGA business of Agere Systems for $250 million in cash. Later that year Lattice acquired privately held Cerdelinx Technologies which designed high-speed input/output devices for about $25 million.

Lattice Semiconductor extended its distribution relationship with Eurodis Electron in 2004 to the Scandinavian countries the UK and Ireland. Also that year the company extended and expanded its OEM relationship with Mentor Graphics to supply software used in designing Lattice chips.

Cyrus Tsui was placed on paid leave in mid-2005 as the board's audit committee examined issues related to executive compensation and internal controls. Rodney Sloss the VP of finance was placed on paid leave as well. Both executives were fired in August 2005. The board forwarded the findings of its audit committee to the Securities and Exchange Commission which was conducting an informal inquiry into Lattice.

Under new management in late 2005 Lattice initiated a corporate restructuring that included a reduction in force of 12%-14% more than 100 employees. The company shuttered three R&D sites in the US and one in the UK.

Lattice reached a settlement in early 2007 with the SEC on the stock options and compensation issue with the company agreeing to a cease-and-desist order.

In 2008 as the global economic downturn hit a chip industry already in a down cycle Lattice restructured including layoff of about 125 employees a reduction in force of around 14%.

Faced with lower sales a weak global economy in 2009 Lattice Semiconductor again moved to reduce costs. The company moved its warehouse from Oregon to Singapore in order to lower shipping and fulfillment costs and reduce inventory on hand. It also laid off another 8% of its workforce. Late in the year the company announced yet another restructuring plan including another round of layoffs and establishment of an operations center in Singapore.

In 2010 CEO Bruno Guilmart resigned from all positions with Lattice Semiconductor. Darin Billerbeck —a technology industry veteran with 30 years of experience working for the likes of Intel AMD and ZiLOG —replaced Guilmart shortly after the resignation.

In 2011 Lattice Semiconductor restructured for the third time in four years. In the cost cutting effort the company reduced headcount and refocused its workforce at R&D facilities in Pennsylvania and China and streamlined supply chain activities at its corporate headquarters. It also extended certain silicon development capabilities along with planning and logistics activities to the Philippines.

Also in 2011 Lattice Semiconductor acquired Hong Kong-based Rise Technology Development Company and its Philippines-based subsidiary APAC IC Layout Consultants. The purchase of Rise and APAC IC added a development center in the Philippines and new engineering layout and design capabilities.

In 2012 Lattice Semiconductor acquired SiliconBlue Technologies which provides FPGA devices for the consumer handheld industry for about $62 million.

EXECUTIVES

Vp Manufacturing, Randy D Baker
Corporate Vp And General Manager Business Group, Sean P Riley, age 46
President CEO and Director, Darin G. Billerbeck, age 55, $450,000 total compensation
Corporate VP Marketing and Business Development, Mustafa Veziroglu
Corporate VP and CFO, Joe Bedewi, $272,500 total compensation
CTO, David L. Rutledge
Corporate VP Operations, Rick White
Vice President, Rodney F Sloss
Vp It, Kenneth K Yu, age 68
Vp It, Stanley J (Stan) Kopec
Vice President Sales, Ed Markiewicz
Vice President Of Sales, Paul Kollar
Vice President Technology Development, Stewart Logie
Vice President, Martin Baker
Vice President Operations Asia General, Fina Borda
Corporate Vice President Of World Wide, Stacy Michael
Vice President Packaging Solutions, Mike Orr
Vice President Business Development, Jonathan Yu
Vice President Software Development, Kwok Wu
Vice President Finance Controller, Max Downing
Hr Director & Vp, Terry Dols
Senior Vice President, Brian Schwarz
Vice President, Byron Brown
Vice President, Scott Wilken
Vice President Manufacturing, Willy Zarosinski
Vice President Product Operations, Tom Knudson
Corporate Vice President Product Development, David Sherwood
Corporate Vice President Product, Lisa Blevins
Senior Vice President Reliability Quality Assuranc, Michael Heth
Vice President, Al Hawtin
Vice President, Demetri Elias
Vice President Software Development, Kwok Eads
Vice President, Frank Wu
Vice President Technology Development, Stewart Dias
Vice President Mng Director Lattice Asia, Kenneth Crooks
Vice President Of Systems Development, Suresh Menon
Senior Vice President And Chief, Steve Laub
Vice President Corporate Marketing, Doug Hunter
Vice President Technology Development, Stewart Feil
President CEO and Director, Darin G. Billerbeck, age 55
Chairman, Patrick S. (Pat) Jones, age 69
Board Member, Robin Abrams
Auditors: KPMGLLLP

LOCATIONS

HQ: Lattice Semiconductor Corp.
5555 N.E. Moore Court, Hillsboro, OR 97124-6421
Phone: 503 268-8000   **Fax:** 503 268 8347
Web: www.latticesemi.com

2012 Sales

	$ mil.	% of total
Asia/Pacific		
China	113.6	40
Japan	35.7	13
Taiwan	8.3	3
Other countries	32.3	12
Americas		
US	34.2	12
Other countries	7.0	3
Europe	48.2	17
Total	**279.2**	**100**

PRODUCTS/OPERATIONS

2012 Sales

	$ mil.	% of total
Programmable logic devices	184.1	66
Field-programmable gate arrays	95.2	34
Total	**279.3**	**100**

2012 Sales by Market

	$ mil.	% of total
Communications	127.7	46
Computing	33.6	12
Consumer	41.5	15
Industrial & other	76.5	27
Total	**279.3**	**100**

Selected Products

Field-programmable gate arrays (FPGAs; ORCA family LatticeECP LatticeXP LatticeSC)
Programmable mixed-signal analog circuits (ispClock Platform Manager Power Manager)
Programmable logic devices (PLDs)
  High-density complex PLDs (ispLSI and ispMACH families)
  Low-density PLDs (GAL family)
  Non-volatile reconfigurable PLDs (MachXO MachXO2)
  Signal switching/interface devices (ispGDX family)
Software development tools

COMPETITORS

Altera	LSI Corp.
Atmel	Microsemi SoC
Cypress Semiconductor	QuickLogic
Fairchild Semiconductor	Texas Instruments
	Xilinx
Infineon Technologies	

HISTORICAL FINANCIALS

Company Type: Public

Income Statement

FYE: December 28

	REVENUE ($ mil.)	NET INCOME ($ mil.)	NET PROFIT MARGIN	EMPLOYEES
12/13	332.5	22.3	6.7%	783
12/12	279.2	(29.6)	—	739
12/11*	318.3	78.2	24.6%	852
01/11	297.7	57.0	19.2%	749
01/10	194.4	(6.9)	—	708
Annual Growth	**14.4%**	—		**2.5%**

*Fiscal year change

2013 Year-End Financials

Debt ratio: —
Return on equity: 6.0%
Cash ($ mil.): 114
Current ratio: 5.56
Long-term debt ($ mil.): —

No. of shares (mil.): 115
Dividends
  Yield: —
  Payout: —
Market value ($ mil.): 621

	STOCK PRICE ($) FY Close	P/E High/Low		PER SHARE ($) Earnings	Dividends	Book Value
12/13	5.37	30	20	0.19	0.00	3.33
12/12	3.83	—	—	(0.25)	0.00	3.10
12/11*	5.94	11	7	0.65	0.00	3.34
01/11	6.06	12	5	0.48	0.00	2.70
01/10	2.70	—	—	(0.06)	0.00	2.20
Annual Growth	**18.8%**	—	—	—	—	**11.0%**

*Fiscal year change

Liberator Medical Holdings, Inc.

Miscellaneous retail stores nec nsk

EXECUTIVES

Coo, John Leger
Vice President Operations, Jennifer Libratore

LOCATIONS

HQ: Liberator Medical Holdings, Inc.
2979 S.E. Gran Park Way, Stuart, FL 34997
Phone: 772 287-2414
Web: www.liberatormedical.com

HISTORICAL FINANCIALS

Company Type: Public

Income Statement

FYE: September 30

	REVENUE ($ mil.)	NET INCOME ($ mil.)	NET PROFIT MARGIN	EMPLOYEES
09/14	74.5	7.8	10.5%	319
09/13	69.1	7.0	10.2%	297
09/12	60.9	2.5	4.1%	326
09/11	52.7	0.2	0.5%	307
09/10	40.9	2.6	6.4%	214
Annual Growth	16.2%	31.6%	—	10.5%

2014 Year-End Financials

Debt ratio: 2.7%
Return on equity: 25.0%
Cash ($ mil.): 12
Current ratio: 2.58
Long-term debt ($ mil.): 1

No. of shares (mil.): 53
Dividends
Yield: 3.9%
Payout: 76.5%
Market value ($ mil.): 166

	STOCK PRICE ($) FY Close	P/E High/Low		PER SHARE ($) Earnings	Dividends	Book Value
09/14	3.13	40	13	0.15	0.12	0.61
09/13	2.04	17	4	0.14	0.08	0.57
09/12	0.79	24	14	0.05	0.00	0.56
09/11	0.85	154	77	0.01	0.00	0.50
09/10	1.26	35	16	0.05	0.00	0.41
Annual Growth	25.5%	—		31.6%	—	10.3%

Limoneira Co.

When life gives you lemons you name your company Limoneira. The agriculture and real estate development business grows you guessed it lemons in three counties in California's fertile San Joaquin Valley. It also grows avocados oranges and other crops on a total of 6.200 acres. The company one of the state's oldest citrus growers is a leading producer of both lemons and avocados. Limoneira packs its own lemons and those of other growers; its products are marketed through agreements with Sunkist (oranges) and Calavo (avocados). Real estate holdings include residential commercial and agricultural rental properties and land holdings in California and Arizona. Limoneira traces its roots to 1893.

Geographic Reach

The company owns about 4000 acres in Venture County California and another 2200 acres in Tulare Country in the San Joaquin Valley. Limoneira operates a packinghouse in Santa Paula California where it processes and packs its lemons and those grown by others.

Operations

Citrus is Limoneira's main squeeze accounting for more than 90% of total sales. The company grows and packs lemons avocados oranges and other fruits. Real estate rental and development accounts for the rest. The rental operation includes some 200 housing units in Ventura and Tulare counties. as well as several commercial office buildings and a combination convenience store/gas station. The firm also leases about 610 acres of land to agricultural tenants who grow other crops besides citrus. Also Limoneira with the help of a tenant runs an organic recycling operation in Oxnard California.

Financial Performance

The lemon grower reported sales of $65.8 million in fiscal 2012 (ended October) an increase of 25% versus the prior year. Net income rose 97% over the same period. Driving the double-digit increases in sales and profits was growth of the company's Agribusiness segment which posted a 33% rise in sales in 2012 versus 2011. Lemon sales were strongest (up 41%) followed by avocados (up 27%) and oranges (up 7%). Revenue from the company's rental business rose 2% year-to-year while its real estate development business posted a 90% decline. The solid sales performance in fiscal 2012 reversed a decline in fiscal 2011. Net income increased for the third consecutive year in 2012.

Strategy

To boost its capacity by 850000 cartons of lemons Limoneira in 2012 partnered with Associated Citrus Packers of Yuma Arizona to pack and market lemons. While lemons are its focus the Arizona company also harvests and packs Rio Red grapefruit Mineola tangelos Navel oranges Blood oranges and Valencia oranges.

Controlling as many factors that could affect its business as possible the company owns 90% of the land it farms owns the water rights on most of its land uses solar panels to power its packing and warehouse facilities and pump its water participates in recycling programs that earn it money and provide mulch material and leases housing to many of its employees. To cut marketing costs Limoneira in 2010 terminated its lemon marketing agreement with Sunkist and began selling its main crop directly to food service retail and wholesale customers in North America Asia and Australia. Sunkist continues to handle Limoneira's oranges and specialty citrus. Limoneira maintains its real estate operations because it believes the holdings and rentals help it retain workers and protect its revenue stream from the volatility of agricultural markets.

Going forward the company intends to grow both its agriculture business and its real estate holdings. To that end it's increasing its acreage by leasing and acquiring citrus orchards in the San Joaquin Valley and upgrading its packing capabilities to increase lemon exports. In real estate Limoneira will acquire develop and continue to lease out land to farmers; acquire and develop residential real estate holdings; and expand its industrial land holdings.

Ownership

Calavo Growers owns about 15% of Limoneira's shares. (Limoneira sells all of its avocados to Calavo.)

EXECUTIVES

President CEO and Director, Harold S. Edwards, age 49, $475,000 total compensation
SVP Agribusiness, Alex M. Teague, age 51, $324,039 total compensation
CFO Treasurer and Corporate Secretary, Joseph Rumley, age 55, $274,040 total compensation
President CEO and Director, Harold S. Edwards, age 49
Vice Chairman, John W. Blanchard, age 71
Chairman, Gordon E. Kimball, age 61
Vice Chairman, Robert M. Sawyer, age 65
CFO Treasurer and Corporate Secretary, Joseph Rumley, age 55
Director Board Of Directors, Stewart Lockwood
Auditors: Ernst&YoungLLP

LOCATIONS

HQ: Limoneira Co.
1141 Cummings Road, Santa Paula, CA 93060
Phone: 805 525-5541   **Fax:** 805 525-8211
Web: www.limoneira.com

PRODUCTS/OPERATIONS

2012 Sales

	$ mil.	% of total
Agribusiness	61.5	94
Rental operations	4.0	6
Real estate development	0.3	-
Total	65.8	100

2012 Agribusiness Sales

	$ mil.	% of total
Lemons	44.2	72
Avocados	9.5	15
Navel and Valenciaoranges	4.0	7
Specialty citrus & other	3.8	6
Total	61.5	100

Selected Products Brands and Varieties

Avocados
  Hass
  Zutano
Lemons
  Bridal Veil
  Fountain
  Golden Bowl
  Level
  Paula
  Santa
Oranges
  Navel
  Valencia
Specialty citrus & other
  Cara cara oranges
  Cherries
  Minneola tangelos
  Moro blood oranges
  Olives
  Peaches
  Pistachios
  Plums
  Pummelos
  Satsuma mandarin oranges
  Star Ruby grapefruit

COMPETITORS

American Realty Investors	Gables Residential Services
Apartment Investment and Management	Hardie's Fruit & Vegetable Company
Berkshire Property	Silver Springs
Brothers Produce	Southern Gardens Citrus
Camden Property	Stratus Properties
Chiquita Brands	Sunkist
Dole Food	Trammell Crow Residential
Edinburg Citrus	
Fresh Del Monte Produce	

HISTORICAL FINANCIALS

Company Type: Public

Income Statement

	REVENUE ($ mil.)	NET INCOME ($ mil.)	NET PROFIT MARGIN	EMPLOYEES
10/14	103.4	6.9	6.8%	331
10/13	84.8	4.9	5.8%	254
10/12	65.8	3.1	4.8%	226
10/11	52.5	1.6	3.0%	203
10/10	54.2	0.3	0.6%	206
Annual Growth	17.5%	115.7%	—	12.6%

2014 Year-End Financials

Debt ratio: 27.6%
Return on equity: 5.7%
Cash ($ mil.): 0
Current ratio: 0.76
Long-term debt ($ mil.): 67

No. of shares (mil.): 14
Dividends
Yield: 0.6%
Payout: 28.9%
Market value ($ mil.): 361

	STOCK PRICE ($) FY Close	P/E High/Low	PER SHARE ($) Earnings	Dividends	Book Value
10/14	25.66	60 45	0.46	0.17	9.28
10/13	26.34	75 49	0.36	0.15	7.89
10/12	22.47	90 55	0.26	0.13	4.70
10/11	17.35	243 117	0.12	0.13	4.65
10/10	20.24	1730 01500	0.01	0.13	4.65
Annual Growth	6.1%	—	—160.4%	7.2%	18.8%

Lindsay Corp

Liquid resources are big assets at Lindsay Corp. The company designs and manufactures irrigation systems primarily for farmers. The Zimmatic brand irrigation system a self-propelled center-pivot and lateral-move lineup is designed to use water energy and labor more efficiently than traditional flood or surface irrigation equipment. Touting better-to-bumper crop yields a dealer network sells to farmers in key markets worldwide. (The US represents more than 60% of sales.) Lindsay offers chemical injection systems water pumping stations (via subsidiary Watertronics) as well as replacement parts. An infrastructure division supplies movable barriers for traffic control and crash cushions for road safety.

Geographic Reach

With most of its operations residing in the US Lindsay has production and sales operations in Brazil China France Italy as well as distribution and sales operations in Australia New Zealand and South Africa.

Operations

Lindsay operates through two primary segments. Its largest irrigation is responsible for making its irrigation systems and water pumping stations. It also offers repair services and replacement parts. The company's infrastructure segment makes road safety equipment such as movable barriers for traffic control and crash cushions for road safety.

Financial Performance

Due to favorable economic conditions within key US agriculture markets Lindsay has seen historic growth over the years. From 2011 to 2012 its total sales increased by 15% leveling out at $551 million. During that same time period its net income increased by 18% to $43 million. Both to-

tals were the highest posted in the company's recent history.

The surge in revenue is attributed to healthy growth in the irrigation markets. For 2012 irrigation equipment revenues increased by 28% and international revenues for this segment jumped by 19% (mostly in the Middle East Latin America China Canada and Africa). In addition overall revenues in the US grew by 15%.

The bad news for Lindsay was that revenues for its infrastructure products segment declined by 30% from 2011 to 2012.

Strategy

Lindsay looks to drive growth through acquisitions. In 2011 it obtained IRZ Consulting an irrigation consulting and design firm that caters to large growers to help them design water delivery systems. IRZ helps its clients with soil moisture monitoring and energy usage monitoring to save on costs. Around that same time period Lindsay snapped up ez-Wireless a company that provides wireless communications solutions to power advanced applications such as sensor networks video surveillance and telemetry. It purchased Digitec an electronics R&D and manufacturing company specializing in irrigation products in 2010.

Simultaneously Lindsay invests in its own product portfolio. It spends around $3 million to more than $4 million a year in research and development of irrigation products. Its irrigation systems are made to work in harsh environments such as on steep grades. Among its recent introductions Lindsay launched a pivot control for smartphones. The application allows farmers to control and monitor their irrigation pivots whenever and wherever they are. Benefits include optimized growing conditions and lower labor costs. R&D expenses related to its roadway infrastructure products are also considerable averaging more than $3 million annually.

Ownership

Neuberger Berman Management LLC owns 10% of Lindsay Corporation.

HISTORY

Lindsay Manufacturing was founded in 1955 as a farm equipment repair firm. In 1969 the company introduced its first Zimmatic brand center-pivot irrigation system. Diversified agricultural firm DEKALB bought Lindsay in 1974. Gary Parker was appointed Lindsay's CEO in 1984 and in 1988 DEKALB spun off the company.

Lindsay's export revenues grew to a peak of $48 million (44% of total revenues) in 1992. The company began losing market share in Saudi Arabia (its major non-US market) when the Saudi government put an end to farm subsidies in 1994. That year investment firm Bass Management Trust led by Perry Sid and Lee Bass bought an initial 7% stake in the firm. In 1995 exports slumped to only 10% of total revenues.

Bass Management Trust increased its stake in Lindsay to about 18% in 1997 then upped it to 27% the following year. With the Asian financial crisis hurting foreign sales and US farmers unable to afford equipment outlays Lindsay's revenues dropped 25% in fiscal 1999. That year Bass Management Trust decreased its stake in the company to 15%.

Parker retired in 2000. He was replaced by Richard Parod who had been the VP of Toro's Irrigation Division. Also that year Lindsay acquired Colorado-based irrigation systems maker Oasis Enterprises.

Lindsay acquired a facility in La Chappelle d'Aligne France in 2001 in order to establish a European location for the manufacture of its irriga-

tion products. As part of its continuing global expansion Lindsay established Lindsay Manufacturing Africa to promote local manufacturing inventory and support for the long term in 2002.

In 2003 the company introduced its Growth Smart Micro Climate Station which enables farmers to monitor precise evapotranspiration readings and graphic modeling to predict potentially damaging situations in the fields.

The company changed its name from Lindsay Manufacturing to Lindsay Corporation late in 2006.

Lindsay Corporation entered a new market segment in 2006 when it acquired Barrier Systems Inc. of California for $35 million in cash. Barrier Systems was a maker of specialty roadway barriers and crash cushion products used to increase highway safety and reduce traffic congestion.

Later in 2006 Lindsay complemented its new infrastructure segment with the purchase of Italy's Snoline S.P.A. a maker of road marking and other roadway safety equipment.

In 2007 Lindsay further augmented its infrastructure division with the purchase of certain assets of Traffic Maintenance Attenuators Inc. and Albert W. Unrath Inc. (or U-Mad). U-Mad designed truck- and trailer-mounted crash attenuators that improved motorist safety and protected workers in roadway work zones. In 2008 Lindsay obtained Watertronics a maker of water pumping stations and controls used with irrigation systems in the golf landscaping and municipal markets. Lindsay's Infrastructure division in 2009 expanded its safety offerings swallowing up the business of GE Transportation Systems Global Signaling.

Lindsay enjoyed an 80% increase in year-over-year earnings in 2010. The result marked a rebound; earnings took a 65% hit in 2009 from 2008 largely attributed to flagging capital investments in farm equipment coupled with weak commodity prices as well as delayed or reduced public infrastructure activity. Lindsay responded by cutting 25% of its workforce in 2009 but with improving revenues increased headcount by more than 15% in 2010.

EXECUTIVES

Vice President Global Marketing, Dirk A Lenie
Vice President - Corporate Development & Treasurer, Mark A Roth, age 40
President CEO and Director, Richard W. (Rick) Parod, age 61, $532,439 total compensation
President Agricultural Irrigation, David B. Downing, age 59, $303,819 total compensation
President Technology Business, Douglas A. (Doug) Taylor, age 51
Chief Financial Officer, Jim Raabe
Vp Sales & Marketing, Randy Wood
Vice President Human Resources, Reuben Srinivasan
Vice President Engineering And Research, Dick Welch
Vice President International, Olivier Debart
Chairman, Michael N. Christodolou, age 53
Auditors: KPMGLLP

LOCATIONS

HQ: Lindsay Corp
2222 North. 111th Street, Omaha, NE 68164
Phone: 402 829-6800   Fax: 402 829-6834
Web: www.lindsay.com

2012 Sales

	$ mil.	% of total
US	354.7	64
International	196.6	36
Total	551.3	100

PRODUCTS/OPERATIONS

2012 Sales

	$ mil.	% of total
Irrigation	475.3	86
Infrastructure	76.0	14
Total	**551.3**	**100**

Selected Products

Infrastructure
  Crash cushions
  Large diameter steel tubing
  Movable barriers for traffic lane management
  Preformed reflective pavement tapes
  Railroad signals and structures
  Specialty barriers
Irrigation
  Aerators
  Center-pivot irrigation systems
  Chemical injection systems
  Fertilizer injectors
  Filters and screens
  Hose reel irrigation systems
  Irrigation controls
  Lateral-move irrigation systems
  Pond controls
  Pump systems
  Custom-built
  Horizontal centrifugal
  Self-contained enclosed
  Submerged sled
  Vertical centrifugal
  Vertical turbine
  Remote monitoring and control systems

Selected Mergers and Acquisitions

FY2011
  IRZ Consulting (Irrigation consulting and design firm)
  ez-Wireless (Wireless communications solutions)
FY2010
  Digitec (electronics R&D and manufacturing company specializing in irrigation products)

COMPETITORS

AK Steel Holding Corporation	Rain Bird Corporation
Habasit America	Toro Company
Quanex Building Products	Valmont Industries

HISTORICAL FINANCIALS

Company Type: Public

Income Statement

FYE: August 31

	REVENUE ($ mil.)	NET INCOME ($ mil.)	NET PROFIT MARGIN	EMPLOYEES
08/14	617.9	51.5	8.3%	1,202
08/13	690.8	70.5	10.2%	1,262
08/12	551.2	43.2	7.9%	1,082
08/11	478.8	36.8	7.7%	999
08/10	358.4	24.8	6.9%	891
Annual Growth	**14.6%**	**20.0%**	**—**	**7.8%**

2014 Year-End Financials

Debt ratio: —
Return on equity: 13.5%
Cash ($ mil.): 171
Current ratio: 3.21
Long-term debt ($ mil.): —

No. of shares (mil.): 12
Dividends
Yield: 0.0%
Payout: 23.0%
Market value ($ mil.): 968

	STOCK PRICE ($) FY Close	P/E High/Low		PER SHARE ($) Earnings	Dividends	Book Value
08/14	77.78	23	18	4.00	0.92	30.76
08/13	76.02	17	12	5.47	0.48	29.57
08/12	65.36	22	15	3.38	0.39	24.43
08/11	62.20	27	13	2.90	0.35	21.75
08/10	36.87	23	16	1.98	0.33	18.39
Annual Growth	**20.5%**	**—**	**—**	**19.2%**	**29.7%**	**13.7%**

LinkedIn Corp

Feeling a bit disconnected to the business world? LinkedIn wants to help. The firm operates an online professional network designed to help members find jobs connect with other professionals and locate business opportunities. The site has grown to reach more than 160 million users in some 200 countries since its launch in 2003. LinkedIn is free to join; it offers a paid premium membership with additional tools and sells advertising. It additionally earns revenue through its job listing service which allows companies to post job openings and search for candidates on LinkedIn. Former CEO and current chairman Reid Hoffman co-founded the company which filed to go public in 2011.

LinkedIn's public offering is significant in that as the precursor to Facebook's IPO it was the first major social networking company to file an IPO and was initially the biggest US Internet IPO since Google. Through the offering LinkedIn raised more than $352 million. That figure was at the high end of underwriters' expectations and valued LinkedIn at about $4.25 billion. The company is using the proceeds for more investment increasing its product development efforts and expanding its sales organization in the US and internationally.

The IPO came during a period of rapid growth via the addition of new users. Total members have jumped from about 55 million in 2009 to its current figure of some 160 million. While this increase in membership caused revenue growth over the last four consecutive fiscal years reaching revenues of more than $522 million in 2011 the company warned that it expects its growth rate to decline. It made only $11.9 million in 2011 down from about $15.4 million in 2010. The drop was due to higher income taxes and higher expenses (such as sales and marketing product development and general and administrative) associated with growing the business.

Continued growth efforts include acquisitions such as the 2012 purchase of SlideShare for some $119 million. SlideShare is an application that allows users to share slide show presentations and LinkedIn made the deal to strengthen its professional content offerings. In addition the company has launched its Talent Pipeline offering a new recruiter product. Mobile is another area of focus; in 2011 about 15% of member visits came from mobile and mobile page views were up more than 300% year-over-year.

LinkedIn is also ramping up its international expansion activities having experienced growth in India Brazil and China. About 60% of its member base comes from outside the US and its service is available in languages such as French German Italian Portuguese and Spanish. A reflection of its global focus LinkedIn recently opened international offices in London Mumbai and Sydney. These operations add to its presence in Canada Ireland and the Netherlands.

Hoffman and his wife Michelle Yee control more than 40% of LinkedIn's total votes.

EXECUTIVES

Vice President, Steve Patrizi
Svp Products And User Experience, Dipchand (Deep) Nishar, age 46
SVP and CFO, Steven J. (Steve) Sordello, age 45
CEO, Jeffrey (Jeff) Weiner, age 44
SVP Engineering and Operations, Kevin Scott
VP Corporate Communications, Shannon Stubo

Vice President People Operations, Steve Cadigan
Vice President, Larry Denny
Vice President Corporate Controller And Chief Accounting Office, Sue Taylor
Vice President Operations, Daniel Odell
Vice President Sales Marketing, Jaime Templeton
Vice President And Deputy General Counsel, J P Bennett
Vice President Communications, Cassandra Wilson
Vice President, Lucian Beebe
Vice President, Kasey Crete
Vice President, Sarah Imbach
Vice President, Lloyd Taylor
Vice President Sales, Simon Andrew
Vice President Of Marketing, Justin Bingham
Senior Vice President Astd Media And Event Sales, Sean Soth
Vice President, Ted Harvey
Vice President And Relationship Manager, Eric Baird
Vice President Recruitment, Michael O'Brien
Vice President Global Talent Organization, Pat Wadors
Vice President Business Development, Bob Rosin
Board Of Directors, Leslie J Kilgore, age 50
Chairman, Reid Hoffman, age 47
Board Of Directors, Mark Kvamme
Corporate Treasurer, Janice Phan
Assistant Treasurer, Albert Huang
Treasurer, Jun Li
Auditors: Deloitte&ToucheLLP

LOCATIONS

HQ: LinkedIn Corp
  2029 Stierlin Court, Mountain View, CA 94043
Phone: 650 687-3600
Web: www.linkedin.com

2013 Sales

	$ mil.	% of total
US	942.1	62
Europe the Middle East and Africa	358.2	23
Asia-Pacific	118.5	8
Canada Latin America and South America	109.7	7
Total	**1528.5**	**100**

International Locations
Australia
Canada
India
Ireland
The Netherlands
The UK

PRODUCTS/OPERATIONS

2013 Sales

	$ mil.	% of total
Talent solutions	859.7	56
Marketing solutions	362.3	24
Premium subscriptions	306.5	20
Total	**1528.5**	**100**

Selected Offerings

Premium Subscriptions
  Enhanced search results
  Enhanced communication capability
  Improved organizational functionality
  Priority customer support
Marketing Solutions
  Display ads
  Text ads
Hiring Solutions
  View candidates based on select criteria
  Industry
  Job function
  Geography
  Education

COMPETITORS

CareerBuilder	Socialtext
Classroom Connect	Spoke Software
Facebook	TheSquare
Gather Inc.	Tribe Networks
Harris Connect	Twitter
Jigsaw Data	Vault.com
Monster Worldwide	ZoomInfo
Plaxo	

HISTORICAL FINANCIALS

Company Type: Public

Income Statement

FYE: December 31

	REVENUE ($ mil.)	NET INCOME ($ mil.)	NET PROFIT MARGIN	EMPLOYEES
12/13	1,528.5	26.7	1.8%	5,045
12/12	972.3	21.6	2.2%	3,458
12/11	522.1	11.9	2.3%	2,116
12/10	243.1	15.3	6.3%	1,288
12/09	120.1	(3.9)	—	0
Annual Growth 88.9%				

2013 Year-End Financials

Debt ratio: —	No. of shares (mil.): 120
Return on equity: 1.5%	Dividends
Cash ($ mil.): 803	Yield: —
Current ratio: 4.29	Payout: —
Long-term debt ($ mil.): —	Market value ($ mil.): 26,096

	STOCK PRICE ($) FY Close	P/E High/Low	PER SHARE ($) Earnings	Dividends	Book Value
12/13	216.83	1067463	0.23	0.00	21.85
12/12	114.82	587294	0.19	0.00	8.36
12/11	63.01	733394	0.11	0.00	6.16
Annual Growth 85.5%		— —	44.6%	—	88.3%

Liquidity Services Inc

Hey bidder bidder. Take a swing at Liquidity Services (LSI). The online auction firm provides manufacturers retailers corporations and governments with an electronic marketplace to dispose of liquidate and track goods in the reverse supply chain. More than one million professional buyers are registered on the firm's online marketplaces through which they can bid for wholesale surplus and salvage items like retail customer returns overstock products and end-of-life goods. LSI founded in 1999 also offers valuation appraisal inventory marketing sale and logistical management of assets; warehousing and inspection of inventory; and transaction support such as collections and dispute mediation.

Geographic Reach

Liquidity Services (LSI) operates in more than 25 countries around the world. The company is growing by expanding into new markets and geographic areas.

Operations

LSI's online auction marketplaces include liquidation.com govliquidation.com and govdeals.com. Subsidiary Government Liquidation provides a marketplace for US military surplus assets. One of the company's largest sellers is the US Department of Defense which sells scrap and surplus assets. The government's surplus contract with LSI

accounts for some 30% of the company's yearly revenues. Liquidity Services Limited (liquibiz.com) manages the sale and disposal of surplus assets in Europe. Clients there include corporations and government agencies such as the Ministry of Defence in the UK. The company's goWholesale.com portal connects advertisers with buyers seeking products for sale and business services.

LSI operates about 10 warehouses which house surplus products and act as distribution centers once items are sold.

Sales and Marketing

LSI utilizes a direct sales and marketing force to acquire and manage its seller and buyer accounts. The company currently has about 160 sales and more than 55 marketing personnel. Its sales activities are focused primarily on acquiring new sellers and improving the value to existing sellers. Its marketing activities are focused primarily on acquiring new buyers and increasing existing buyer participation.

Products sold on LSI's sites are organized within more than 500 categories and are sold by the truckload pallet or individual package. Most of the products fall within categories such as consumer electronics apparel scientific equipment aerospace parts and equipment technology hardware specialty equipment store fixtures and general merchandise.

Financial Performance

The company has enjoyed a dramatic upward trend in revenue during recent fiscal years. After claiming about $286.8 million in fiscal 2010 LSI brought in around $327.4 million in fiscal 2011. Fiscal year 2012 was even better as LSI reported more than $475 million in revenue.

The nearly 45% increase in revenue during 2012 compared to 2011 was attributed to increases in LSI's commercial business as a result of its acquisitions in 2011 and early 2012 along with several new programs for large retailers and manufacturers.

Mergers and Acquisitions

LSI enhanced its ability to deliver large retailers and OEMs across Canada and the US through its acquisition of National Electronics Service Association (NESA) for $18.3 million in 2012.

In early 2012 LSI expanded through the acquisition of GoIndustry-DoveBid a provider of surplus asset management auction and valuation services for $31 million. The deal added big names to its client roster (including Pfizer and Honeywell) and added some 458000 professional buyers and 1000 annual online sales events to its holdings.

In late 2011 LSI swallowed up Jacobs Trading Co. for $140 million in cash and stock. The purchase enhanced LSI's ability to resell retail merchandise and it expanded its relationship with important companies like Wal-Mart.

EXECUTIVES

Chairman and CEO, William P. (Bill) Angrick, age 47, $600,000 total compensation
EVP Federal Sector, Thomas B. Burton, age 56, $306,300 total compensation
EVP and President Asset Recovery division, G. Cayce (Cayce) Roy, age 49, $300,900 total compensation
EVP EMEA and APAC, Holger Schwarz, age 48
CFO and Treasurer; President Retail Supply Chain, James M. (Jim) Rallo, age 49, $320,800 total compensation
CIO, Leoncio (Leo) Casusol, $271,233 total compensation
President Capital Assets Group, Gardner Dudley
President GovDeals, Roger Gravley

Vice President Marketing, Rob Caskey
Vice President And General Manager Canada, John Lee
Vice President Of Strategic Business Development, Chad Farrell
Vice President Marketing Capital Assets Group Network Inter, Bob Francis
Vice President, Thomas Stoerck
Vice President Finance, Owen Powell
Vice President Client Services, Michael Livatino
Vice President Sales, Darron Hanner
Sales Vice President, Chuck Rueger
Vice President Of Strategic Business Development, Mike Besecker
Vice President Of Finance And Buyer, Kevin Smith
Vice President Product Management, Pradheep Sampath
Chairman and CEO, William P. (Bill) Angrick, age 47
Auditors: Ernst&YoungLLP

LOCATIONS

HQ: Liquidity Services Inc
1920 L Street, N.W., 6th Floor, Washington, DC 20036
Phone: 202 467-6868
Web: www.liquidation.com

PRODUCTS/OPERATIONS

Selected Mergers and Acquisitions

FY2012
National Electronics Service Association ($18.3 million; Toronto Canada; distribution and logistics service)
GoIndustry-DoveBid ($31 million; Owings Mills MD; provider of surplus asset management auction and valuation services)
FY2011
Jacobs Trading Co. ($140 million; Des Moines IA; merchandise reseller)

Selected Subsidiaries

DOD Surplus LLC
GovDeals Inc.
Government Liquidation.com LLC
Liquidity Services Limited
Surplus Acquisition Venture LLC

COMPETITORS

Argent Trading	Overstock.com
Buxbaum Group	Taylor & Martin Group
ICON International	eBay
ITEX	
International Monetary Systems	

HISTORICAL FINANCIALS

Company Type: Public

Income Statement

FYE: September 30

	REVENUE ($ mil.)	NET INCOME ($ mil.)	NET PROFIT MARGIN	EMPLOYEES
09/14	495.6	30.3	6.1%	1,049
09/13	505.8	41.1	8.1%	1,302
09/12	475.3	48.3	10.2%	965
09/11	327.3	8.5	2.6%	694
09/10	286.7	12.0	4.2%	704
Annual Growth 14.7%		26.1%	—	10.5%

2014 Year-End Financials

Debt ratio: —	No. of shares (mil.): 29
Return on equity: 9.6%	Dividends
Cash ($ mil.): 62	Yield: —
Current ratio: 1.73	Payout: —
Long-term debt ($ mil.): —	Market value ($ mil.): 408

STOCK PRICE ($)		P/E		PER SHARE ($)		
	FY Close	High/Low		Earnings	Dividends	Book Value
09/14	13.75	35	13	0.97	0.00	10.68
09/13	33.50	38	22	1.26	0.00	9.90
09/12	50.21	42	18	1.47	0.00	8.03
09/11	32.07	112	41	0.29	0.00	5.56
09/10	16.01	37	18	0.44	0.00	4.18
Annual Growth	(3.7%)	—		21.9%	—	26.5%

Littelfuse, Inc.

Littelfuse is big on circuit protection. The company is one of the world's largest fuse makers. In addition to its fuses Littelfuse's other circuit protection devices include positive temperature coefficient devices that limit current when too much is being supplied and electrostatic discharge suppressors that redirect transient high voltage. The company's thyristors protect telecommunications circuits from transient voltage caused by lightning strikes. Littelfuse's 5000-plus customers include electronics manufacturers (Hewlett-Packard and Samsung) automakers (Ford and GM) and the automotive aftermarket (O'Reilly Automotive and Pep Boys).

Geographic Reach

The company operates in three geographic territories –the Americas Europe and Asia/Pacific — and has 35 manufacturing and distribution facilities in about 20 countries. The company gets about two-thirds of its sales outside the US. China is another large market representing 20% of sales.

Operations

The company operates through three business unit segments. Electronics includes circuit protection products for wireless telephones consumer electronics computers modems and telecommunications equipment and markets the products under brand names PICO and NANO. Considering the average car contains 30 to 100 fuses the automotive segment stays busy making fuses for gas and electric automobiles trucks and buses and to protect electrical power to operate lights heating air conditioning radios windows and other controls.

Some automotive brand names include ATO MasterFuse JCASE and CablePro. In addition to fuses electrical makes ground-fault and protection relays to safeguard personnel and equipment from electrical shock hazards in industrial environments and underground mining or water treatment applications. Brand names include POWR-GARD.

Sales and Marketing

Littelfuse markets its products indirectly through a worldwide organization of 60 manufacturers' representatives and distributes through a network of electronics automotive and electrical distributors. Its domestic sales and marketing staff of over 35 people maintains relationships with major OEMs and distributors.

Financial Performance

Littelfuse enjoyed unprecedented growth in 2013 as sales surged 13% to peak at a record-setting $758 million. Profits also climbed 18% to nearly $89 million another milestone due to the increased revenue and gains on foreign exchange rates.

The growth for 2013 was due to an incremental $66 million from business acquisitions and growth in electronic and automotive products due to incremental sales from Hamlin (2013 acquisition) of $24.1 million. Littelfuse was also helped by improved demand across all geographies and a slightly more favorable macroeconomic outlook.

Littelfuse's operating cash flow has been consistent over the last four years. It increased by a marginal $1 million in 2013 due to cash generated from deferred income taxes and impairment and equity in the net loss of a unconsolidated affiliate.

Strategy

Littelfuse operates in a highly competitive industry matching up against much larger manufacturers by focusing on brand name price quality and service. The automotive industry witnessed a rash of bankruptcies before and during the recession and the electronics industry reeled from the economic downturn as well. The company's dependence on customers in the automotive communications and consumer electronics industries leaves Littelfuse vulnerable to cyclicality in those industries.

One important element of Littelfuse's strategy is product development which has resulted in about 200 patents in North America some 85 in the European Union and more than 60 in other foreign countries. After consulting with customers sales and marketing staff often suggest new products which then undergo a development process that can last from a few months to up to 18 months.

Mergers and Acquisitions

InIn 2014 the company picked up SymCom a South Dakota-based provider of overload relays and pump controllers serving the industrial market. The acquisition allowed Littelfuse to diversify and grow its protection relay platform.

In 2013 Littelfuse acquired Hamlin a provider of sensor technology for the automotive industry as well as the electronics and industrial markets for $145 million. Hamlin has facilities are in Lake Mills Wisconsin; Norwich UK; Suzhou China; and Matamoros Mexico. The deal extended Littelfuse's sensing technology product portfolio outside the automotive market with products that can be sold through its electronics distribution partners.

HISTORY

Littelfuse was formed in 1927 to make the first small fast-acting fuse able to protect test meters. In 1968 military electronics firm Tracor (later part of the UK's General Electric Company now telent) bought the company. Littelfuse entered the power (industrial) fuse market in 1983. Tracor ran into financial troubles with the end of the Cold War and filed for bankruptcy protection in 1991. As a result of Tracor's reorganization Littelfuse became an independent company in 1992. In 1994 it started marketing its protectors.

Expansion of its product lines and geographic markets sparked growth. It bought South Korea-based Sam Hwa Fuse in 1995 and opened a support facility in Japan in 1996. That year Littelfuse entered the market for resettable devices with its line of PTCs. The company formed its first South American operation a sales and distribution facility in Brazil in 1997. Also that year Littelfuse acquired Samjoo Electrical Industrial Co. South Korea's largest fuse maker and consolidated its holdings there into a subsidiary called Littelfuse Triad.

The soft Asian economy wholesaler inventory tightening and the General Motors strike drove down Littelfuse's sales and profits in 1998. Littelfuse bought a unit from Harris that made voltage suppressors in 1999. In 2000 the firm cut its workforce by 9% amid a slowdown in sales from the automotive industry. A patent infringement dispute between Littelfuse and Polytronics Technology that resulted in an injunction against Littelfuse doing business in Taiwan was settled in 2001.

In 2003 the company acquired Teccor Electronics a subsidiary of Invensys and a manufacturer of transient voltage suppression devices and power switching devices. Gordon Hunter an Intel executive joined Littelfuse as COO in 2003. A director of the company since 2002 he became chairman president and CEO of Littelfuse in 2005.

Littelfuse acquired an 82% stake in Germany-based fuse maker Heinrich Industrie AG for about $47 million in 2004 and later boosted its ownership to around 97%. In 2005 the company sold the Efen product line of fuse-switches for electrical power distribution equipment which it acquired through its ownership of Heinrich Industrie to Weber AG of Switzerland. Also that year the company reduced staff in sales administration and other functions citing a slowdown in sales.

In 2006 Littelfuse acquired SurgX Corp. a developer of surge protection technology for overvoltage circuit protection for $2.5 million in cash. It also bought Concord Semiconductor a manufacturer of diodes and other over-voltage circuit protection products for the automotive computer consumer electronics industrial and telecommunications markets. Concord Semi had facilities in China and Taiwan. Littelfuse paid $25 million in cash for Concord while assuming $1.4 million in debt.

The following year the company acquired the assets of Song Long Electronics a Taiwanese firm that made metal oxide varistors at a plant in Dongguan China. Littelfuse paid $5.5 million in cash for the assets. Song Long was a supplier to Littelfuse for five previous years.

EXECUTIVES

Executive Senior Vice President, Don McFeggan
Vp Human Resources And General Counsel, Ryan K Stafford, age 47
SVP and CFO, Philip G. (Phil) Franklin, age 63, $384,307 total compensation
Chairman President and CEO, Gordon B. Hunter, age 63, $709,431 total compensation
VP and General Manager Electrical Business Unit, Dal Ferbert, age 60, $232,662 total compensation
COO, David W. Heinzmann, age 50, $307,178 total compensation
VP and General Manager Automotive Business Unit, Dieter Roeder, age 57
VP and General Manager Electronics Business Unit, Deepak Nayar
VP and General Manager Semiconductor Business Products, Ian Highley
VP and General Manager Protection Relays and Custom Electrical Products, Daniel Stanek
VP Supply Chain and Operational Excellence, Michael P. Rutz
Vice President, Charles Cary
National Account Manager, Al Schuler
National Sales Manager, Ron Olson
Chairman President and CEO, Gordon B. Hunter, age 63
Auditors: Ernst&YoungLLP

LOCATIONS

HQ: Littelfuse, Inc.
8755 West Higgins Road, Suite 500, Chicago, IL 60631
Phone: 773 628-1000
Web: www.littelfuse.com

2013 Sales

	$ mil.	% of total
Americas	274.7	36
China	158.5	21
Other countries	324.7	4.3
Total	**757.9**	**100**

PRODUCTS/OPERATIONS

2013 Sales

	$ mil.	% of total
Electronics	367.1	48
Automotive	267.2	36
Electrical	123.6	16
Total	**757.9**	**100**

Selected Brands

ATO
JCASE Fuse
MAXI
MEGA
MIDI
MINI
NANO2
OMNI-BLOK
PICO II
POWR-GARD
PulseGuard

Selected Products

Discrete diodes
Electrostatic discharge suppressors
Fuses
Gas discharge tubes
Positive temperature coefficient (PTC) resettable fuses
Thyristors
Varistors

COMPETITORS

AVX	ON Semiconductor
Bel Fuse	S&C Electric
Bourns	STMicroelectronics
EPCOS	TE Connectivity
Mersen Group	

HISTORICAL FINANCIALS

Company Type: Public

Income Statement

FYE: December 28

	REVENUE ($ mil.)	NET INCOME ($ mil.)	NET PROFIT MARGIN	EMPLOYEES
12/13	757.8	88.7	11.7%	7,400
12/12	667.9	75.3	11.3%	6,000
12/11*	664.9	87.0	13.1%	6,000
01/11	608.0	78.6	12.9%	6,000
01/10	430.1	9.4	2.2%	5,500
Annual Growth	**15.2%**	**75.3%**	**—**	**7.7%**

*Fiscal year change

2013 Year-End Financials

Debt ratio: 21.4%
Return on equity: 13.9%
Cash ($ mil.): 305
Current ratio: 2.71
Long-term debt ($ mil.): 93

No. of shares (mil.): 22
Dividends
Yield: 0.0%
Payout: 21.3%
Market value ($ mil.): 2,082

	STOCK PRICE ($) FY Close	P/E High/Low		PER SHARE ($) Earnings	Dividends	Book Value
12/13	92.67	24	15	3.94	0.84	30.57
12/12	59.97	19	12	3.40	0.76	26.66
12/11*	42.98	16	10	3.90	0.66	23.24
01/11	47.06	14	8	3.52	0.15	20.80
01/10	32.15	77	21	0.43	0.00	17.37
Annual Growth	**30.3%**	**—**	**—**	**74.0%**	**—**	**15.2%**

*Fiscal year change

Louisiana-Pacific Corp.

Louisiana-Pacific (LP) has you surrounded. The building materials company specializes in manufacturing products for floors walls and roofs. LP produces oriented strand board (OSB) siding products and engineered wood products. It also makes decorative molding and cellulose insulation. Products are used in new home and manufactured housing construction and for repair and remodeling. The company sells its products to distributors dealers professional lumberyards and retail home centers including The Home Depot. It has production facilities throughout North and South America. After a difficult period during the recession and housing crisis LP is poised to capitalize on the uptick in housing starts.

Geographic Reach

Nashville Tennessee-based LP operates about 20 production facilities in the US and Canada. It also owns two facilities in Chile and one in Brazil. The US is LP's largest market accounting for nearly three-quarters of its sales. Canada is second with 18% of sales.

Operations

LP operates four business segments. The largest oriented strand board (OSB) makes and distributes OSB panels and accounts for about 45% of sales. Siding products and related accessories represents about 30% while engineered wood products (laminated veneer lumber) accounts for more than 10%. The company's South America business which manufactures and distributes OSB and siding products in South America and certain export markets account for the rest. Other products include decorative moulding and a joint venture that makes cellulose insulation.

Sales and Marketing

LP's sales and marketing efforts are focused on traditional two-step distribution professional building products dealers home centers third-party wholesale buying groups and other retailers. The company's wholesale distribution channel includes a variety of specialized and broadline wholesale distributors and dealers focused primarily on supplying products used by professional builders and contractors. LP also supplies large retail chains and smaller independent retailers. The company's top 10 customers accounted for 46% of sales in 2012. The Home Depot was the company's single largest customer representing 10% of sales.

Financial Performance

Buoyed by improvement in the housing industry LP's 2012 sales increased 26% versus 2011 to $1.72 billion. Net income swung from a loss in 2011 to $28.8 million in 2012. Indeed 2012 was the company's first profitable year since 2006. All of the company's product categories posted sales gains with oriented strand board posting a 50% increase year over year on higher pricing and volume. Siding sales rose nearly 17%. Sales in Chile jumped 26%.

Strategy

LP is dusting itself off after enduring the tough market conditions that plagued operations during the economic downturn. Declining new home construction created low demand for LP's products from 2008 through 2010 and sales suffered and profits suffered. The company moved to cut costs refinance debt and improve operations. In order to reduce costs and adjust to lower demand for its products LP shut down plants in Alabama Georgia Maine North Carolina Tennessee Texas and other locations in the US and Canada. Production was curtailed at other plants.

Housing starts are slowly improving but demand is still not at pre-recession rates. In light of the challenges the company remains focused on cash management while at the same time preparing for the future.

Still the recent rebound in sales and profits has LP looking to grow again.

Mergers and Acquisitions

In September 2013 the company agreed to acquire Canada's Ainsworth Lumber Company a maker and marketer of oriented strand board (OSB) with a focus on value-added specialty products for sale in North America and Asia. Ainsworth operates four OSB manufacturing plants in Alberta British Columbia and Ontario with a combined annual capacity of 2.5 billion square feet. The pending deal is valued at $1.1 billion including debt.

Ownership

Investment firm BlackRock Inc. owns 10% of the company's shares.

HISTORY

Louisiana-Pacific (LP) was spun off in 1972 from Georgia-Pacific after the Federal Trade Commission contended that Georgia-Pacific had created a monopoly in the softwood plywood industry. Harry Merlo the company's first CEO became chairman in 1974.

In 1978 the company acquired Fibreboard Corporation a maker of asbestos and other products used in furniture and cabinets. (Despite spinning off Fibreboard in 1988 LP has been a co-defendant in hundreds of asbestos-related lawsuits.) Also in 1978 the US government acquired some of LP's timberlands as part of the expansion of the Redwood National Park in California.

Facing a shortage of Douglas fir and southern pine trees LP experimented with making wood products from fast-growing less-expensive trees including aspen and cottonwood. Oriented strand board (OSB) —pieces of logs mixed with resin and pressed into sheets —was developed in the late 1970s and was touted as a cheaper stronger alternative to plywood.

LP profited from a housing boom and a strong pulp market in the 1980s. It began marketing OSB as an exterior siding alternative in 1985. Between 1990 and 1994 however thousands of property owners in Florida complained that its OSB siding deteriorated in the humid climate. Three class-action suits were filed. The attorney general of Minnesota sued the company over defective siding in 1991. LP settled that case in 1992 and by the end of that year LP had paid $22 million to settle OSB claims throughout the US. But consumers armed with the siding's 25-year warranty continued to complain about rotting and cracking boards. The company paid out another $15 million in 1993 and 1994.

After a 1995 grand jury indicted LP for environmental violations and product misrepresentation Merlo and other top executives were dismissed. International Paper EVP Mark Suwyn was named chairman and CEO in 1996 and immediately became the subject of a non-compete lawsuit filed by his former employer. (In 1997 a federal judge ruled in Suwyn's favor.)

In 1996 the company agreed to pay at least $275 million to 800000 homeowners who had used its wood siding. LP also started growing its complementary building-products business by purchasing companies such as wood-coating and chemical producer Associated Chemists (sold in

1999) and cellulose insulation maker GreenStone Industries. Meanwhile a weak OSB market prompted LP to close several of its OSB plants. LP chopped operations and some 25% of its workforce in 1997 to focus on its core building products.

LP sold its Northern California lumber operations in 1998 and closed down its fiber-cement roofing operations. In 1999 LP acquired ABT Building Products (paneling and siding) as well as Canadian companies Le Groupe Forex (OSB) for $510 million and Evans Forest Products (laminated veneer and plywood). The following year it added Hoff Companies' composite decking assets and the Sawyer Lumber Company (low-cost lumber for residential construction). In 2001 the company sold a controlling interest in its Samoa California pulp mill to LaPointe Partners.

It continued to trim operations in 2002 by selling a controlling interest in an OSB plant in Ireland; the company recorded a $2 million gain on the sale and reduced its debt by $6.5 million. LP bought out its joint venture in Chile for $3 million that year. Also in 2002 due to low paper demand and falling profits LP announced a radical restructuring plan in which the company would cut 45% of its workforce (or 4400 jobs) and close unprofitable businesses to focus on its core structural products business.

The company in 2003 sold more than 600000 acres of timberland in a series of deals. Also that year LP sold six lumber facilities an industrial panel facility and a veneer facility in part because of an industry wide oversupply of lumber and historically low prices for lumber.

In 2004 LP sold a hardboard plant in Michigan a decorative panel facility in Ohio and a Washington sawmill. The following year the selling continued with several operations siphoned off.

At the helm since 2004 Rick Frost retired as CEO in 2012 replaced by Curt Stevens who'd joined the company in 1997.

EXECUTIVES

Chief Executive Officer; Director, Curtis M. (Curt) Stevens, age 62, $471,912 total compensation
Vice President, Brian Luoma
Vice President Procurement Logistics And Supply Management, Neil Sherman
EVP and CFO, Sallie B. Bailey, age 54
VP Corporate Engineering; Director Technology, David (Dave) Crowe
VP Specialty Operations, Brad Southern
EVP Oriented Strand Board (OSB), Jeffrey N. (Jeff) Wagner, age 60, $330,750 total compensation
EVP Sales and Marketing and South America, Richard S. (Rick) Olszewski, age 58, $374,000 total compensation
Chairman, E. Gary Cook, age 70
Secretary Treasurer, Barbara Hamilton
Auditors: Deloitte&ToucheLLP

LOCATIONS

HQ: Louisiana-Pacific Corp.
414 Union Street, Nashville, TN 37219
Phone: 615 986-5600   **Fax:** 615 986-5666
Web: www.lpcorp.com

2012 Sales

	% of total
US	73
Canada	18
South America	9
Total	**100**

PRODUCTS/OPERATIONS

2012 Sales

	$ mil.	% of total
Oriented Strand Board	814.1	47
Siding	500.9	29
Engineered wood products	213.4	12
Other	187.4	12
Total	**1715.8**	**100**

COMPETITORS

Amos-Hill Associates	Pratt Industries USA
Associated Materials	Rayonier
Georgia-Pacific	RockTenn CP
Hanafee Bros.	Roseburg Forest
International Paper	Products
J.D. Irving	Royal Group
James Hardie	Simpson Investment
Industries	South Coast Lumber Co.
Norbord	USG
Potlatch	Weyerhaeuser

HISTORICAL FINANCIALS

Company Type: Public

Income Statement

FYE: December 31

	REVENUE ($ mil.)	NET INCOME ($ mil.)	NET PROFIT MARGIN	EMPLOYEES
12/13	2,085.2	177.1	8.5%	4,200
12/12	1,715.8	28.8	1.7%	3,900
12/11	1,356.9	(181.3)	—	3,900
12/10	1,383.6	(39.0)	—	3,800
12/09	1,054.7	(121.4)	—	4,000
Annual Growth	**18.6%**	—	—	**1.2%**

2013 Year-End Financials

Debt ratio: 30.6%
Return on equity: 15.6%
Cash ($ mil.): 656
Current ratio: 6.22
Long-term debt ($ mil.): 762

No. of shares (mil.): 141
Dividends
  Yield: —
  Payout: —
Market value ($ mil.): 2,612

	STOCK PRICE ($) FY Close	P/E High/Low		PER SHARE ($) Earnings	Dividends	Book Value
12/13	18.51	17	12	1.23	0.00	8.69
12/12	19.32	90	37	0.20	0.00	7.46
12/11	8.07	—	—	(1.36)	0.00	7.30
12/10	9.46	—	—	(0.30)	0.00	9.23
12/09	6.98	—	—	(1.12)	0.00	9.87
Annual Growth	**27.6%**	—	—	—	—	**(3.1%)**

LTC Properties, Inc.

Specializing in TLC LTC Properties sees real estate as a healthy investment. The self-administered real estate investment trust (REIT) primarily invests in health care and long-term care facilities. Its portfolio includes about 90 assisted living centers (homes for elderly residents not requiring constant supervision) more than 100 skilled nursing facilities (which provide rehabilitative and restorative nursing care) a dozen other health care properties (such as independent living or memory care) and even a couple of schools. It owns properties in more than 25 states. Top tenants include Brookdale Senior Living Extendicare and Prestige Care.

Operations

The REIT also invests in mortgage loans secured by long-term health care properties and participates in joint ventures that invest in health care properties and loans.

Geographic Reach

LTC's properties are located in 26 states. Texas Ohio Colorado and Florida are its largest markets.

Financial Performance

As a REIT the company is exempt from paying federal income tax as long as it distributes quarterly dividends to shareholders.

The trust makes money from rent and interest earned on outstanding loans. Rental income accounts for almost 95% of revenue; interest income contributes the other 5%.

EXECUTIVES

Chairman CEO and President, Wendy L. Simpson, age 64, $568,750 total compensation
EVP CFO and Secretary, Pamela (Pam) Shelley-Kessler, $335,000 total compensation
EVP and Chief Investment Officer, Clint B. Malin, $335,000 total compensation
EVP and CFO, Pam Kessler
Chief Operating Officer, Nick Cafferillo
SVP Investment and Portfolio Management, Brent P. Chappell
Vice President, Laura Coon
Senior Vice President, Christophe Ishihawa
Group Vice President, Pamela Shelley
Senior Vice President Chief Financial, Pamela Shelley Kessler
Chairman CEO and President, Wendy L. Simpson, age 64
Auditors: Ernst&YoungLLP

LOCATIONS

HQ: LTC Properties, Inc.
2829 Townsgate Road, Suite 350, Westlake Village, CA 91361
Phone: 805 981-8655
Web: www.LTCProperties.com

2012 Properties

	No.
Texas	41
Ohio	19
Colorado	13
Florida	13
Washington	9
Iowa	8
Kansas	8
Arizona	7
New Mexico	7
Oklahoma	6
North Carolina	5
Alabama	4
Idaho	4
Nebraska	4
Oregon	4
California	4
Georgia	3
Indiana	3
Pennsylvania	3
South Carolina	4
Virginia	4
New Jersey	5
Tennessee	2
Total	**184**

PRODUCTS/OPERATIONS

2012 Sales

	$ mil.	% of total
Rental income	87.6	93
Interest income from mortgage loans	5.5	6
Interest & other income	0.9	1
Total	**94.0**	**100**

COMPETITORS

Aviv REIT	NorthStar Healthcare
Chartwell Seniors	Investors
Housing	Omega Healthcare
HCP	Investors
Health Care REIT	Sabra Health Care
Healthcare Realty	Senior Housing
Trust	Properties
Legacy Healthcare	Tiptree
NHC	Ventas
National Health	
Investors	

HISTORICAL FINANCIALS

Company Type: Public

Income Statement

FYE: December 31

	REVENUE ($ mil.)	NET INCOME ($ mil.)	NET PROFIT MARGIN	EMPLOYEES
12/13	104.9	57.8	55.1%	18
12/12	94.0	51.2	54.5%	18
12/11	85.1	49.2	57.8%	17
12/10	74.3	45.8	61.7%	13
12/09	69.8	44.0	63.0%	13
Annual Growth	10.7%	7.0%	—	8.5%

2013 Year-End Financials

Debt ratio: 29.9%	No. of shares (mil.): 34
Return on equity: 10.5%	Dividends
Cash ($ mil.): 6	Yield: 5.3%
Current ratio: 1.52	Payout: 117.5%
Long-term debt ($ mil.): 257	Market value ($ mil.): 1,230

	STOCK PRICE ($) FY Close	P/E High/Low		PER SHARE ($) Earnings	Dividends	Book Value
12/13	35.39	29	21	1.63	1.91	18.20
12/12	35.19	24	19	1.57	1.79	15.16
12/11	30.86	23	16	1.36	1.68	15.38
12/10	28.08	24	19	1.21	1.58	17.29
12/09	26.75	22	13	1.27	1.56	19.40
Annual Growth	7.2%	—	—	6.4%	5.1%	(1.6%)

lululemon athletica inc

lululemon athletica designs and sells yoga-inspired apparel under the lululemon athletica and ivivva athletica brands to the limber and athletically hip. It operates some 250 company-owned stores primarily located in North America. The rest are in Australia and New Zealand where lululemon operates through a joint venture. While it specializes in making women's clothing for yoga dance and running the company also offers men's apparel. Third-party mostly Taiwanese vendors make its clothing which is distributed from facilities in Canada the US and Australia. The fast-growing company was founded in 1998 by Chairman Dennis "Chip" Wilson.

Geographic Reach

Vancouver Canada-based lululemon athletica rings up about 60% of its sales in the US with stores in some 35 states and the District of Columbia. California is the company's largest market home to nearly 20% of its US stores. Canada accounts for about a third of the company's sales with other countries (including Australia and New Zealand) bringing in the rest.

Operations

Lululemon's growing network of company-owned stores accounts for 80% of its sales. Online sales account for nearly 15% of the total while wholesale sales (to select yoga studios health clubs and fitness centers) brings in the rest. The company's chain of eight ivivva athletica stores specialize in dance-inspired apparel for girls.

Sales and Marketing

Lululemon's target customer is an sophisticated educated physically-active woman who can afford to spend upwards of $80 on a pair of yoga pants.

Financial Performance

Lululemon's sales have soared along with the growing popularity of yoga and its growing brand awareness —from about $40 million in fiscal 2004 to more than $1.3 billion in fiscal 2013 (ended January) —despite an economic downturn that conspired against the company. The apparel retailer logged its most recent revenue leap from about $1 billion in fiscal 2012 to $1.37 billion in fiscal 2013 and increase of 37%. Growth drivers included a 33% sales gain at its corporate-owned stores due to more than 35 new store openings and a 16% gain in same-store sales. Online sales increased 86% year over year while wholesale sales fell.

Strategy

Fiscal 2014 proved to be a tough year for lululemon during which quality control problems (too-shear pants) in its core yoga pant line plagued the company and lead to changes in the management and organization of the product organization the resignation of its CEO and the pending departure of its founder and chairman in June 2014. The company's new CEO is the former president of TOMS Shoes. Nevertheless the company continued to grow its store network and online business in the US and abroad. Beyond North America lululemon is looking to the Asia/Pacific region and eventually Europe for expansion. (The company has a showroom in Hong Kong.)

Granted most of lululemon's sales are to women but the retailer is working to attract men as well as more males are participating in yoga to stay fit. It's enticing men by marketing the "technical rigor" of its products. Aging Baby Boomers looking to adopt a lifestyle focused on longevity is another gain for lululemon. The apparel maker also concentrates on developing its ivivva dance-inspired line targeted to dancers and gymnasts age 6 to 12 years. Part of this strategy includes adding company-owned stores under the ivivva banner.

EXECUTIVES

CFO, John E. Currie, age 58, $332,780 total compensation
CEO; Director, Laurent Potdevin
EVP Retail Operations North America, Delaney Schweitzer
CIO, Kathryn Henry
CFO, Stuart C Haselden
Chairman, Michael Casey, age 68
CEO; Director, Laurent Potdevin
Auditors: PricewaterhouseCoopersLLP

LOCATIONS

HQ: lululemon athletica inc
1818 Cornwall Avenue, Vancouver, British Columbia V6J 1C7
Phone: 604 732-6124 **Fax:** 604 874-6124
Web: www.lululemon.com

2013 Stores

	No.
US	135
Canada	51
Australia	23
New Zealand	2
Total	**211**

2013 Sales

	$ mil.	% of total
US	839.9	61
Canada	461.6	34
Outside North America	68.9	5
Total	**1370.4**	**100**

PRODUCTS/OPERATIONS

2013 Sales

	$ mil.	% of total
Corporate-owned stores	1090.2	80
Direct to consumer	197.3	14
Other	82.9	6
Total	**1370.4**	**100**

COMPETITORS

Capezio	NIKE
Finish Line	The Gap
Gildan Activewear	Triumph Apparel
Jacques Moret	Under Armour
Jockey International	adidas
Lucy Activewear	bebe stores

HISTORICAL FINANCIALS

Company Type: Public

Income Statement

FYE: February 2

	REVENUE ($ mil.)	NET INCOME ($ mil.)	NET PROFIT MARGIN	EMPLOYEES
02/14	1,591.1	279.5	17.6%	7,622
02/13*	1,370.3	270.5	19.7%	6,383
01/12	1,000.8	184.0	18.4%	5,807
01/11	711.7	121.8	17.1%	4,572
01/10	452.9	58.2	12.9%	3,219
Annual Growth	36.9%	48.0%	—	24.0%

*Fiscal year change

2014 Year-End Financials

Debt ratio: —	No. of shares (mil.): 145
Return on equity: 28.2%	Dividends
Cash ($ mil.): 698	Yield: —
Current ratio: 8.31	Payout: —
Long-term debt ($ mil.): —	Market value ($ mil.): 6,639

	STOCK PRICE ($) FY Close	P/E High/Low		PER SHARE ($) Earnings	Dividends	Book Value
02/14	45.69	43	24	1.91	0.00	7.55
02/13*	67.86	43	28	1.85	0.00	6.14
01/12	64.12	94	34	1.27	0.00	4.19
01/11	68.61	85	31	0.85	0.00	2.74
01/10	28.24	78	11	0.41	0.00	1.65
Annual Growth	12.8%	—	—	46.9%	—	46.2%

*Fiscal year change

Lumber Liquidators Holdings Inc

Customers can find their floors at Lumber Liquidators Holdings. Known for its low prices Lumber Liquidators is one of the nation's largest retailers of hardwood flooring. It sells more than 25 domestic and exotic species of hardwoods from more than 300 Lumber Liquidators stores in about 45 states and Canada online by catalog and from its Virginia call center. The company also offers antique and reclaimed boards laminate flooring moldings and installation products. Its brands include Bellawood Builder's Pride Sch fh Morning Star and Virginia Mill Works. Homeowners represent about 90% of Lumber Liquidators' customer base. The company was founded in 1994 by chairman Tom Sullivan.

Geographic Reach

Virginia-based Lumber Liquidators operates more than 300 stores in 46 US states and nine retail stores in Ontario Canada. The company's largest markets are California Texas Florida New York and Pennsylvania which combined are home to about a third of its stores.

Sales and Marketing

The flooring company makes use of celebrity endorsements and product placement opportunities to tout its brands. Lumber Liquidators has a long-standing relationship with home improvement celebrities Bob Vila and Ty Pennington Vila in particular has been associated specifically with the company's Bellawood brand for several years. It also uses targeted television advertising on cable networks such as Discovery Channel HGTV TLC and DIY Network.

Financial Performance

Lumber Liquidators sales increased 19% in 2012 versus 2011 to about $813 million. Net income rose 79% over the same period to $47 million. The double-digit increases in sales and profits were driven by higher sales at existing Lumber Liquidator stores (up 11% year over year) and the addition of 25 new locations in 2012. Higher average retail price per unit sold has also contributed to sales gains. Also customers' preferences for premium flooring products has increased particularly within certain product categories including laminates engineered hardwood bamboo cork and resilient. Indeed Lumber Liquidators has enjoyed about a decade of steadily increasing sales despite the deep recession and crisis in the housing market.

Strategy

Lumber Liquidators markets itself as a supplier of premium hardwoods and flooring products with a cost-effective retail format. Typically situated in low-rent commercial and industrial districts its stores average about 6500 sq. ft. They allot up to 1000 sq. ft. for the showroom area which spotlights flooring samples on racks and as part of the showroom floor. The warehouse area takes up the remaining space stocking a combination of high-volume products with the most popular items at that particular location.

The company has rapidly expanded its retail footprint in recent years. In 2012 the fast-growing chain added 25 stores. It plans to continue adding 40 to 50 locations annually in new and existing markets for the next several years as part of its growth strategy. It is also remodeling select older stores. During 2011 Lumber Liquidators extended its network north of the US border opening its first Canadian locations in Ontario.

Because of its size Lumber Liquidators believes it can obtain better prices from its suppliers which helps to keep costs under control and ensures a competitive edge. The company purchases its products from about 90 vendors (mostly mills and trading companies) in the US and abroad however the Sequoia Floorings trading company handles more than a third of Lumber Liquidators' purchases. About 40% of Lumber Liquidators' prod-

ucts come from North America and some 45% are sourced from the Asia/Pacific region.

The company has been investing in its infrastructure to support continued expansion in recent years including refining its product selection improving logistics and providing training to store managers. In 2010 it launched an integrated software system that offers enhancements for its existing point-of-sale merchandising store operations and inventory control systems. (Lumber Liquidators said it faced decreased productivity while the integrated system was rolled out however and could not adequately serve customers during the second half of the year.)

Ownership

The investment firms T. Rowe Price and FMR LLC each own about 12% of the company's shares while BlackRock holds about 11%.

EXECUTIVES

CFO, Daniel E. Terrell, age 49, $332,587 total compensation
President and CEO, Robert M. Lynch, age 48, $655,769 total compensation
Chief Merchandising Officer, William K. Schlegel, $358,728 total compensation
SVP Supply Chain, Carl Daniels, $300,092 total compensation
Svp Sales, James Davis
Chairman, Thomas D. (Tom) Sullivan, age 54
Auditors: Ernst&YoungLLP

LOCATIONS

HQ: Lumber Liquidators Holdings Inc
3000 John Deere Road, Toano, VA 23168
Phone: 757 259-4280
Web: www.lumberliquidators.com

2012 Stores

	No.
US	
California	27
Texas	22
Florida	19
New York	15
Pennsylvania	13
Illinois	11
Virginia	11
North Carolina	10
Ohio	10
Georgia	9
Michigan	8
New Jersey	8
Massachusetts	7
Washington	7
Colorado	6
Indiana	6
Tennessee	6
Alabama	5
Arizona	5
Connecticut	5
Louisiana	5
Maryland	5
Minnesota	5
Missouri	5
Other states	52
Canada	9
Total	**291**

PRODUCTS/OPERATIONS

2012 Sales

	% of total
Hardwood (solid & engineered)	47
Laminates	22
Moldings & accessories	16
Bamboo cork and Resilient	14
Other	1
Total	**100**

COMPETITORS

CCA Global	Lowe's
Floor and DÂ©cor	MasterTile
Outlets	Menard
Home Depot	Sears

HISTORICAL FINANCIALS

Company Type: Public

Income Statement

FYE: December 31

	REVENUE ($ mil.)	NET INCOME ($ mil.)	NET PROFIT MARGIN	EMPLOYEES
12/13	1,000.2	77.4	7.7%	1,750
12/12	813.3	47.0	5.8%	1,420
12/11	681.5	26.2	3.9%	1,302
12/10	620.2	26.2	4.2%	1,191
12/09	544.5	26.9	4.9%	934
Annual Growth	**16.4%**	**30.2%**	**—**	**17.0%**

2013 Year-End Financials

Debt ratio: —	No. of shares (mil.): 27
Return on equity: 28.4%	Dividends
Cash ($ mil.): 80	Yield: —
Current ratio: 3.29	Payout: —
Long-term debt ($ mil.): —	Market value ($ mil.): 2,835

	STOCK PRICE ($) FY Close	P/E High/Low		PER SHARE ($) Earnings	Dividends	Book Value
12/13	102.89	42	19	2.77	0.00	11.22
12/12	52.83	34	10	1.68	0.00	8.62
12/11	17.66	30	15	0.93	0.00	7.71
12/10	24.91	33	21	0.93	0.00	6.57
12/09	26.80	28	7	0.97	0.00	5.45
Annual Growth	**40.0%**			**30.0%**	**—**	**19.8%**

Luminex Corp

William Blake could "see a world in a grain of sand" and Luminex Corporation can reveal 100s of secrets in a drop of fluid. Its xMAP (Multi-Analyte Profiling) technology allows simultaneous analysis of up to 500 bioassays or tests from a single drop of fluid. xMAP consists of instruments software and disposable microspheres (microscopic polystyrene beads on which tests are performed). Luminex's systems are used by clinical and research laboratories and are distributed through strategic partnerships with other life sciences firms. Luminex also develops testing assays and disposable testing supplies for the clinical diagnostics market.

Geographic Reach

More than 80% of Luminex's sales are made in the US. It also sells to customers in other countries in North America Europe and the Asia/Pacific region. Luminex has facilities in Australia Canada China Japan the Netherlands and the US.

Operations

The company's TSP (technology and strategic partners) segment accounts for 60% of annual revenues and makes Luminex's instrumentation systems used by clinical labs as well as the research labs of pharmaceutical biotech diagnostic medical and life science entities. The division primarily sells systems through licensing or distribution relationships with more than 55 strategic partners. The partners distribute Luminex systems (or their own systems that incorporate the xMAP technology) to end users or use Luminex systems to perform testing services for their customers. About 40 partners have commercialized their own reagent-based tests using the xMAP technology. Altogether the strategic partners have sold some 9700 Luminex instrumentation sets to laboratories around the world.

Luminex earns royalties from the sales of xMAP-based assays and services developed by partners. In addition the TSP segment sells of the disposable microspheres and fluids used with the systems and it earns fees through maintenance services through contracts with laboratories.

Sales from the ARP (assays and related products) segment have grown in recent years accounting for 40% of revenues in 2012 as the firm works to increase direct sales of testing assays in core fields including human genetics infectious disease and personalized medicine testing.

Sales and Marketing

About 55% of the company's TSP segment revenues in 2012 were generated by its top three strategic partner customers: Thermo Fisher Scientific Bio-Rad Laboratories and EMD Millipore. The ARP segment also has three customers that account for a majority (more than 70%) of sales: LabCorp Thermo Fisher Scientific and Abbott Laboratories. Luminex shifted its ARP distribution model to focus on direct sales in 2013 (as opposed to sales through distribution partners) and as a result it expects to see less customer concentration in the ARP segment in future years.

Advertising expenses including trade show and convention activities were some $2.4 million in 2012 down from $3.1 million in 2011.

Financial Performance

Revenues increased 10% to some $202.6 million in 2012 due to 44% growth in the ARP segment on higher assay sales primarily in the infectious disease category. Growth in the ARP segment was offset by declined sales of systems and consumables in the TSP segment. Net income fell 14% due to higher R&D sales administrative and general expenses including costs related to recent acquisitions.

Strategy

The technology-based company has implemented a strategy to transform itself into a market-driven customer-focused company. To achieve this goal Luminex is focusing on key markets including life sciences research molecular infectious disease genetic disease pharmacogenetic testing bio-defense testing and immunodiagnostics. In addition it aims to develop next-generation systems to bring efficient portable testing solutions to market as well as market-leading assays in the human molecular diagnostic testing market. It is also working to develop strategic partnerships in its key markets and to pursue acquisitions that could hasten its goals.

To increase product demand and build on direct end-user relationships in the ARP segment the company assumed responsibility from major distributors of proprietary molecular diagnostic products in 2013.

Mergers and Acquisitions

Luminex has made careful acquisitions to build up its product and geographic range. For example to further its goal of delivering a market leading molecular diagnostics system the company in 2012 paid some $50 million (along with potential milestone and performance payments) to acquire GenturaDx a private molecular diagnostics firm that is developing an automated real-time testing system that extracts and analyzes molecular samples using patented single-use cartridges. Luminex hopes to integrate its MultiCode-RTx chemistry with GenturaDx's instrument to make better and faster molecular testing tools available to health providers throughout the world.

Ownership

New Orleans-based investment advisor St. Denis J. Villere & Company is Luminex's largest stockholder owning about 11% of the company.

Company Background

Luminex takes its name from the special laser beams that each microsphere passes through during the bioassay screening process. The lasers excite dyes inside and on the surface of the microspheres and the resulting fluorescence is measured in real time and analyzed by the system's software.

EXECUTIVES

Sr V Pres Assay Group, Jeremy B Cook
Vice President Operations, Darin Leigh
V Pres Scientific Affairs, Ralph L McDade
Chief Financial Officer Senior Vice President Finance and Treasurer, Harriss T. Currie, age 53, $324,422 total compensation
President and Chief Executive Officer; Director, Patrick J. Balthrop, age 58, $513,674 total compensation
Senior Vice President Research and Development, Jeremy Bridge-Cook, age 45, $355,048 total compensation
Senior Vice President Corporate Development and Global Marketing, Russell W. Bradley, age 51, $282,705 total compensation
Vice President Manufacturing and Quality Surveillance, Steve Back
Senior Vice President Operations, Michael F. Pintek, age 45, $325,297 total compensation
Vice President Luminex Molecular Diagnostics, Nancy Krunic
Vice President Biodefense, Amy L. Altman
Vice President Human Resources, Nancy Capezzuti
Vice President Business Development, Jeremy Bridgecook
Vice President Sales And Marketing, Darrin Lee
Vice President Product Development, Scott Johnson
Vice President Research And Development, Tim Denney
Vice President Quality Assurance And Regulatory Affairs, Oliver H Meek, age 64
Executive Vice President Chief, Gail Page
Vice President Systems R&d, Charles Collins
Vice President Emerging Markets And Technologyluminex Molecular Diagnostics, Richard Janeczko
Vice President Of Product Development, Vecheslav Parker
Vice President Quality Assurance, Oliver H Koptchak
Executive Vice President, Michael Bengtson
Vice President Product Development, Slava Tidwell
Vice President Manufacturing, Steven Back
Chairman, G. Walter Loewenbaum, age 69
Chief Financial Officer Senior Vice President Finance and Treasurer, Harriss T. Currie, age 53
President and Chief Executive Officer; Director, Patrick J. Balthrop, age 58
Auditors: Ernst&YoungLLP

LOCATIONS

HQ: Luminex Corp
12212 Technology Blvd., Austin, TX 78727
Phone: 512 219-8020
Web: www.luminexcorp.com

2012 Sales

	$ mil.	% of total
US	167.9	83
Europe	17.4	9
Asia	10.9	5
Canada	3.8	2
Australia	1.0	-
Other regions	1.7	1
Total	**202.6**	**100**

PRODUCTS/OPERATIONS

2012 Revenues

	$ mil.	% of total
TSP segment	121.0	60
ARP segment	81.6	40
Total	**202.6**	**100**

2012 Revenues

	$ mil.	% of total
Assay revenue	75.0	37
Consumable sales	48.0	24
Royalty revenue	31.2	15
System sales	31.1	15
Service revenue	8.1	4
Other	9.2	5
Total	**202.6**	**100**

Selected Products

Assay Development Tools
Calibration and Control Microspheres
Clinical Diagnostic Assays
FLEXMAP 3D
Life Science Research Assays
Luminex LX 100/200 (LX Systems)
MagPlex Microspheres
MicroPlex Microspheres
SeroMAP Microspheres
xPONENT
xTAG Microspheres

Selected Acquisitions

2012
GenturaDx ($50 million molecular diagnostics testing system)
2011
EraGen Biosciences (renamed Luminex Madison; $34 million; diagnostic assay technologies based on its proprietary MultiCode platform and marketed diagnostic products for such conditions as herpes simplex virus and organ transplant infections)
2010
Bizpac (dry sample preparation newborn screening forensics and molecular diagnostics; Australia)

COMPETITORS

Abbott Labs	Illumina
Affymetrix	Johnson & Johnson
Beckman Coulter	Life Technologies
Becton Dickinson	Corporation
Celera	Orchid Cellmark
Cepheid	QIAGEN
GE Healthcare	Roche Diagnostics
Gen-Probe	Sequenom
GenMark	Siemens Healthcare
Hologic	

HISTORICAL FINANCIALS

Company Type: Public

Income Statement

FYE: December 31

	REVENUE ($ mil.)	NET INCOME ($ mil.)	NET PROFIT MARGIN	EMPLOYEES
12/13	213.4	7.1	3.3%	731
12/12	202.5	12.4	6.1%	687
12/11	184.3	14.4	7.9%	614
12/10	141.5	5.2	3.7%	525
12/09	120.6	17.7	14.7%	437
Annual Growth	15.3%	(20.5%)	—	13.7%

2013 Year-End Financials

Debt ratio: 0.5%
Return on equity: 2.6%
Cash ($ mil.): 67
Current ratio: 5.14
Long-term debt ($ mil.): 0

No. of shares (mil.): 41
Dividends
Yield: —
Payout: —
Market value ($ mil.): 798

	STOCK PRICE ($) FY Close	P/E High/Low	PER SHARE ($) Earnings	Dividends	Book Value
12/13	19.40	140 91	0.17	0.00	6.55
12/12	16.80	85 54	0.30	0.00	6.36
12/11	21.23	70 48	0.34	0.00	6.12
12/10	18.28	152104	0.12	0.00	5.69
12/09	14.93	50 30	0.43	0.00	5.37
Annual Growth	6.8%	— —	(20.7%)	—	5.1%

Lumos Networks Corp.

Lumos Networks hopes your every telephone conversation is illuminating. The company spun off from wireless operator NTELOS in 2011 comprises NTELOS' wireline business. Lumos Networks provides data voice and IP service to carrier business government and residential customers over a 7400-mile fiber network in the Mid-Atlantic region (Virginia West Virginia and portions of Kentucky Maryland Ohio and Pennsylvania). Its network allows it to offer bundled cable Internet and phone service. It also operates as a rural local-exchange carrier (RLEC) in the rural Virginia cities of Waynesboro and Covington and portions of Alleghany Augusta and Botetourt counties.

Operations

The company operates in two segments: strategic data services (60% of sales) and its legacy voice services (40% of sales). Strategic data services include Multiprotocol Label Switching-based Ethernet Metro Ethernet Fiber to the Cell site wireless backhaul and data transport services wavelength transport services and IP services. Lumos Networks expects its legacy phone businesses to decline 10% to 15% every year due to technological advances as fewer households use landlines.

Geographic Reach

Lumos has offices in Virginia and West Virginia. It serves customers in four additional states: Kentucky Maryland Ohio and Pennsylvania.

Sales and Marketing

While NTELOS caters to individuals with cell phone plans Lumos Networks' 1400 customers are mostly regional enterprise business government and carrier customers. In fact Verizon accounted for 12% of sales in 2013.

Financial Performance

The company's revenues have remained flat over the past three years at $207 million. While its data business enjoys growth —it experienced 12% growth in 2013 —the legacy voice business continues to decline. It fell 12% in 2013 due to line loss access rate reductions resulting from regulatory actions access reconfigurations and network grooming by carriers. Profits however did receive a slight boost growing 9% to $17 million.

Mergers and Acquisitions

Lumos Networks has grown its fiber network to 7400 miles primarily through acquisitions beginning in late 2009 with Allegheny Energy's 2200-mile network for $27 million. A year later it bought the FiberNet business of One Communications

Corp. for $163 million which expanded its footprint to Kentucky Maryland Ohio and Pennsylvania and brought 30000 business customers.

EXECUTIVES

Chief Technology Officer, Craig M. Drinkhall
SVP and General Manager Residential and Small Business Segment, Diego B. Anderson, age 46
President and CEO, Timothy G. Biltz, $425,000 total compensation
EVP and CFO, Johan G. Broekhuysen
EVP and Chief Revenue Officer, Joseph E. McCourt, $210,000 total compensation
VP Information Technology, John Lewis
Auditors: KPMGLLP

LOCATIONS

HQ: Lumos Networks Corp.
One Lumos Plaza, Waynesboro, VA 22980
Phone: 540 946-2000
Web: www.lumosnetworks.com

PRODUCTS/OPERATIONS

2013 Sales

	$ mil.	% of total
Data services	121.3	59
Legacy voice services	56.5	27
Access services	29.7	14
Total	**207.5**	**100**

COMPETITORS

AT&T
CenturyLink
Comcast
Cox Communications
EarthLink
Frontier Communications
Level 3 Communications
Shenandoah Telecommunications
Suddenlink Communications
Time Warner Cable
Verizon
Windstream
Zayo Group

HISTORICAL FINANCIALS

Company Type: Public

Income Statement

FYE: December 31

	REVENUE ($ mil.)	NET INCOME ($ mil.)	NET PROFIT MARGIN	EMPLOYEES
12/13	207.4	17.7	8.6%	579
12/12	206.8	16.3	7.9%	602
12/11	207.4	(43.9)	—	524
12/10	145.9	20.8	14.3%	0
12/09	130.6	23.3	17.9%	0
Annual Growth	12.3%	(6.6%)	—	—

2013 Year-End Financials

Debt ratio: 62.6%
Return on equity: 23.6%
Cash ($ mil.): 52
Current ratio: 2.00
Long-term debt ($ mil.): 373

No. of shares (mil.): 22
Dividends
Yield: 2.6%
Payout: 77.7%
Market value ($ mil.): 464

	STOCK PRICE ($) FY Close	P/E High/Low	PER SHARE ($) Earnings	Dividends	Book Value
12/13	21.00	31 11	0.80	0.56	3.90
12/12	10.02	23 10	0.76	0.56	2.98
12/11	15.34	— —	(2.11)	0.14	2.47
Annual Growth	17.0%	— —	—100.0%	25.6%

Lydall, Inc.

Lydall's products help to beat the heat nix the noise and filter the rest. The company makes thermal and acoustical barriers automotive heat shields and insulation products that offer protection in extreme temperatures. Lydall's thermal and acoustical products are used by the appliance and automotive industries and in industrial kilns and furnaces. The company rounds out its offerings with industrial and commercial air and liquid filtration products and –through its subsidiary Charter Medical —fluid management systems for the medical and biopharmaceutical markets. Export sales represent about 45% of the company's annual net sales.

Geographic Reach

The company has operations in Europe Asia and the US which accounted for about 70% of its revenue in 2013.

Operations

Lydall's segments include Thermal/Acoustical Metals and Fibers (nearly 70% of sales) which produces noise and heat abatement products for automotive applications and Performance Materials which encompasses its filtration and industrial thermal insulation businesses. Its Other Products and Services (OPS) division comprises primarily Lydall's vital fluids businesses and offers products to the life science industry.

Sales and Marketing

Lydall's products are primarily sold directly to customers through an internal sales force and external sales representatives and distributed via common carrier. The majority of products are sold to original equipment manufacturers and tier-one suppliers. Sales to Ford Motor Company accounted for 20% of net sales in 2013.

Financial Performance

Lydall's revenues peaked at a record-setting $398 million in 2013 while its profits reached $19 million another company milestone. After experiencing a large surge in operating cash flow during 2012 Lydall saw its cash flow decrease by $4 million due to an increase in cash used in accounts receivable driven by increased sales and inventories.

The growth for 2013 was driven by higher sales within its Thermal/Acoustical Fibers segment attributed to increased production of vehicles on Lydall's platforms in North America. The company also experienced a 13% surge in parts sales as well as increased tooling revenues to support the launch of new vehicle platforms.

Strategy

For its growth strategy Lydall focuses on new product development geographic expansion into Asia and Europe acquisitions and the application of Lean Six Sigma initiatives. A major focus for the company in 2014 is the integration of its acquired companies and the introduction of Lean Six Sigma principles to the acquired businesses.In early 2014 the company acquired the industrial filtration business from Andrew Industries Limited for $83 million. The acquisition enhanced Lydall's already strong position in the filtration and engineered materials markets.

EXECUTIVES

Vp Human Resources, Mona G Estey, age 60
President and CEO, Dale G. Barnhart, age 61, $522,000 total compensation

EVP and CFO, Robert K. Julian, $351,427 total compensation
President Performance Materials business, David H. Williams, $276,121 total compensation
CIO, Joseph (Joe) Tait
Vp-human Resources, William M Lachenmeyer
Vice-president Business Develo, David Glenn
Chairman, W. Leslie Duffy, age 75
Auditors: PricewaterhouseCoopersLLP

LOCATIONS

HQ: Lydall, Inc.
One Colonial Road, Manchester, CT 06042
Phone: 860 646-1233   **Fax:** 860 646-8847
Web: www.lydall.com

2013 Sales

	$ mil.	% of total
US	270.0	68
Germany	77.2	19
France	47.9	12
Other countries	2.9	1
Total	**398.0**	**100**

PRODUCTS/OPERATIONS

2013 Sales

	$ mil.	% of total
Thermal/Acoustical		
Metal parts	135.8	34
Tooling	22.6	6
Thermal/Acoustical		
Fiber parts	105.9	26
Tooling	8.5	2
Performance Materials		
Filtration	64.7	16
Industrial thermal insulation	36.9	9
Life science filtration	10.3	3
Other products and services		
Life sciences virtual fluids	17.2	4
Adjustments	(3.9)	-
Total	**398.0**	**100**

Selected ProductsThermal/Acoustical

Automotive components (thermal/acoustical barrier and heat-shielding components)
Industrial components (heat or thermal barriers)
Performance Materials
Air filtration media
Consumer air/liquid filtration products (including HEPA/ULPA filters)
Fuel cells
Liquid filtration media
Other Products
Vital fluids management products (Charter Medical)
  Bio process containers
  Blood and cell therapy products
  Fluid sampling devices

COMPETITORS

CTA Acoustics	Morgan Advanced
Dana Holding	Materials
Donaldson Company	Pall Corporation
FiberMark North	Specialty Products &
America	Insulation
Johns Manville	Tower International
Kaydon	Unifrax
Magna International	

HISTORICAL FINANCIALS
Company Type: Public

Income Statement

FYE: December 31

	REVENUE ($ mil.)	NET INCOME ($ mil.)	NET PROFIT MARGIN	EMPLOYEES
12/13	397.9	19.1	4.8%	1,600
12/12	378.9	16.8	4.4%	1,600
12/11	383.5	13.7	3.6%	1,600
12/10	338.0	2.7	0.8%	1,600
12/09	248.9	(14.1)	—	1,200
Annual Growth	**12.4%**	**—**	**—**	**7.5%**

2013 Year-End Financials

Debt ratio: 0.6%
Return on equity: 10.2%
Cash ($ mil.): 75
Current ratio: 3.54
Long-term debt ($ mil.): 1

No. of shares (mil.): 16
Dividends
  Yield: —
  Payout: —
Market value ($ mil.): 296

	STOCK PRICE ($) FY Close	P/E High/Low		PER SHARE ($) Earnings	Dividends	Book Value
12/13	17.62	17	12	1.14	0.00	11.90
12/12	14.34	14	9	0.99	0.00	10.29
12/11	9.49	15	9	0.82	0.00	9.38
12/10	8.05	58	33	0.16	0.00	9.06
12/09	5.21	—	—	(0.85)	0.00	9.17
Annual Growth	**35.6%**	**—**	**—**	**—**	**—**	**6.7%**

Lyon (William) Homes

William Lyon's compass is pointed due west. That's where the homebuilder and its joint venture partners design and build single-family detached and attached houses. California accounts for about 80% of the company's home closings; William Lyon also builds and sells homes in Arizona and Nevada. The company targets entry-level and move-up buyers; its homes range from $110000 to $700000 averaging some $350000. William Lyon owns about 10000 development lots and holds options to buy more than 400 additional lots. The company assists with financing through William Lyon Mortgage. Chairman William Lyon and his family control the company which went public in 2013.

The company filed for Chapter 11 bankruptcy in 2011 but emerged the following year. The filing which listed some $600 million in liabilities included a pre-approved restructuring plan to raise some $85 million and reduce its debt by 37%. The Lyon family invested $25 million as part of the recapitalization plan in exchange for additional equity.

Lyon Homes already is planning the development of two new projects in South Orange County that will include more than 190 single-family attached units. The company also acquired a 27-acre parcel of land in Palo Alto and Mountain View California. The development will include about 300 units.

Like other homebuilders William Lyon has been dealing with declining sales in the economic downturn. Because of decreased home orders and high cancellation rates in all but its California market the company in 2008 slashed its workforce by about 25% and sold properties in 10 communities for about $90 million to raise cash. The company fared a bit better in 2009 as cancellations decreased and new home orders began picking up. William Lyon also cut the base prices of its homes and offered new incentives to keep sales up.

In 2010 sales continued to slump and new home orders slacked off at the end of the year after a federal tax credit for new homebuyers expired. Lyon Homes temporarily suspended development sales and marketing on certain projects. The company shifted its acquisitions on finished lots in stable markets.

EXECUTIVES

EVP, Matthew R. Zaist
Chief Executive Officer, William H. (Bill) Lyon, age 41, $350,000 total compensation
Senior Vice President and Colorado Division President, Eric Eckberg
Chief Financial Officer, Colin T. Severn, age 43
Regional Vice President Of Sales, Lesley Pennington
Regional Vice President Marketing, Janet Kemmerer
Vice President President Orange, Carl Morabito
Regional Vice President Of Operation California Division, Gary Haddy
Vice President Operations, Santiago Ibarra
Vice President Tax And Internal Audit, Cynthia Hardgrove
Secretary, Kathy Sampson
Auditors:
Windes&McClaughryAccountancyCorporation

LOCATIONS

HQ: Lyon (William) Homes
4695 MacArthur Court, 8th Floor, Newport Beach, CA 92660
Phone: 949 833-3600

2010 Sales

	$ mil.	% of total
California		
Southern California	206.2	70
Northern California	56.1	19
Arizona	16.6	6
Nevada	15.8	5
Total	**294.7**	**100**

2009 Sales

	$ mil.	% of total
California		
Southern California	179.3	58
Northern California	43.2	14
Arizona	51.2	17
Nevada	35.5	11
Total	**309.2**	**100**

PRODUCTS/OPERATIONS

2010 Sales

	$ mil.	% of total
Home sales		**266.9**
91		
Lots land & other sales	17.2	6
Construction services	10.6	4
Total	**294.7**	**100**

COMPETITORS

Beazer Homes	M.D.C.
Capital Pacific	Meritage Homes
Corky McMillin	Standard Pacific
D.R. Horton	The Ryland Group
KB Home	Toll Brothers
Lennar	

HISTORICAL FINANCIALS

Company Type: Public

Income Statement

FYE: December 31

	REVENUE ($ mil.)	NET INCOME ($ mil.)	NET PROFIT MARGIN	EMPLOYEES
12/13	572.5	129.1	22.6%	350
12/12*	372.7	(8.8)	—	259
02/12	25.5	228.3	893.2%	0
12/11	226.8	(193.3)	—	0
12/10	294.7	(136.7)	—	219
Annual Growth	18.1%	—	—	12.4%

*Fiscal year change

2013 Year-End Financials

Debt ratio: 46.4%
Return on equity: 45.9%
Cash ($ mil.): 171
Current ratio: 11.36
Long-term debt ($ mil.): 469

No. of shares (mil.): 31
Dividends
Yield: —
Payout: —
Market value ($ mil.): 687

	STOCK PRICE ($) FY Close	P/E High/Low	PER SHARE ($) Earnings	Dividends	Book Value
12/13	22.14	5 0	4.95	0.00	13.80
Annual Growth	—	— —	—	—	—

M.D.C. Holdings, Inc.

Being king of the mountain isn't enough for M.D.C. Holdings (MDC). Operating through its Richmond American Homes subsidiary and several other units the company is one of the largest homebuilders in Colorado and is active in about a dozen other states in the West and East. The homebuilder targets first-time and move-up buyers and annually builds about 4700 single-family detached homes that sell for an average price of $345000. The company also constructs a limited number of luxury homes. Subsidiary HomeAmerican Mortgage provides loans to buyers of MDC's homes. MDC also has subsidiaries that offer homeowners and title insurance.

Geographic Reach

MDC's largest market is the West (Arizona California Nevada Washington) which contributes more than 40% of its total home sales. The Mountain states of Colorado and Utah contribute about a third while three eastern states (Maryland Virginia and Florida) represent the balance.

Operations

The company is engaged in home and land sales and to a much lesser extent financial services. Its Richmond American Homes subsidiary builds and sells primarily single-family detached homes. MDC is the general contractor for its projects and hires subcontractors for land development and home construction. It targets first-time and first-time move-up home buyers. Its HomeAmerican Mortgage arm is a full-service mortgage lender and the principal originator of mortgage loans for its home buyers.

Financial Performance

MDC's 2013 sales increased 41% versus 2012 to more than $1.6 billion. Net income was up 401% over the same period to $314.4 million. 2013 marked the second year of steeply increasing sales and profits for the homebuilder after a decline in

2011. Driving the double-digit increase in 2013 sales was an 26% jump (from 3740 in 2012 to 4710 in 2013) in the number of homes delivered and a 12% increase in average selling price year over year. However the temporary spike in mortgage interest rates from historically low levels significant year-over-year home price increases, and the economic uncertainty created by the government shutdown debt ceiling debates and the discussion surrounding tapering of federal stimulus slowed housing demand during the second half of 2013.

The company's West and Mountain segments outperformed the East.

Strategy

The company focuses its homebuilding efforts on high-growth areas including metropolitcan Denver Colorado Springs Salt Lake City Las Vegas Phoenix Tucson Riverside-San Bernardino Los Angeles San Francisco Bay Area Washington D.C. Baltimore Philadelphia Jacksonville Orlando South Florida and Seattle. Buoyed by an improving housing market MDC is acquiring land on which to build more homes. The company made several land buys in Florida in early 2014.

EXECUTIVES

President and COO, David D. Mandarich, age 66, $830,000 total compensation
Chairman and CEO, Larry A. Mizel, age 72, $1,000,000 total compensation
SVP and CFO, John M. Stephens, age 46
Senior Vice President, Liesel W Cooper
Senior Vice President; General Counsel, Michael Touff, age 70
Exec Vp Phoenix West Div, Harry Lourimore
National Vice President Acquisitions, Jeff Handlin
Vp Financial Reporting And Corporate, Christine Laplaca
Vice President Of Construction, Andrew Harris
Vice President Purchasing And Product Development National, David Lemnah
Vice President Training And Organizational Development, Paul Forsythe
Vice President Operations, Chris Schofield
Vice President, Johanne Sigbornsen
Vice President Operations, Fred Peck
Vice President Operations, Patricia Vitola
Vice President Operations, Arlene Davis
Vice President Operations, Liz Chavez
Vice President Training And Development, Susan Sorensen
Vp Corporate Communications, Alex Delanghe
Vp Human Resources, Colleen Gangl
Svp Business Development, Ryan Linder
Vp Strategic Planning & Partnerships, Frann Gray
Vp Integrated Customer Engagements, Mary Schaub
Chairman and CEO, Larry A. Mizel, age 72
Manager Treasury Operations, Ramon Pena
Auditors: Ernst&YoungLLP

LOCATIONS

HQ: M.D.C. Holdings, Inc.
   4350 South Monaco Street, Suite 500, Denver, CO 80237
Phone: 303 773-1100
Web: www.richmondamerican.com

2013 Home and Land Sales

	$ mil.	% of total
West	671.3	41
Mountain	546.8	34
East	411.1	25
Total	1629.2	100

Selected Markets

Arizona
California
Colorado
Delaware
Florida
Illinois
Maryland
Nevada
New Jersey
Pennsylvania
Utah
Virginia
Washington

PRODUCTS/OPERATIONS

2013 Sales

	$ mil.	% of total
Home sale	1626.7	100
Land sale	2.5	-
Total	1629.2	100

Selected Subsidiaries

Allegiant Insurance Company Inc. A Risk Retention Group
American Home Insurance Agency Inc.
American Home Title and Escrow Company
HomeAmerican Mortgage Corporation
Richmond American Construction Inc.
Richmond American Homes Corporation
StarAmerican Insurance Ltd.

COMPETITORS

Beazer Homes	Meritage Homes
D.R. Horton	NVR
Hovnanian Enterprises	PulteGroup
J.F. Shea	Ryan Building
KB Home	Standard Pacific
Lennar	The Ryland Group
M/I Homes	Toll Brothers

HISTORICAL FINANCIALS

Company Type: Public

Income Statement

FYE: December 31

	REVENUE ($ mil.)	NET INCOME ($ mil.)	NET PROFIT MARGIN	EMPLOYEES
12/13	1,680.4	314.3	18.7%	1,111
12/12	1,203.0	62.7	5.2%	920
12/11	844.1	(98.3)	—	854
12/10	958.6	(64.7)	—	1,119
12/09	898.3	24.6	2.7%	1,089
Annual Growth	16.9%	88.9%	—	0.5%

2013 Year-End Financials

Debt ratio: 2.4%
Return on equity: 30.0%
Cash ($ mil.): 199
Current ratio: 1.61
Long-term debt ($ mil.): —

No. of shares (mil.): 48
Dividends
Yield: —
Payout: —
Market value ($ mil.): 1,573

	STOCK PRICE ($) FY Close	P/E High/Low	PER SHARE ($) Earnings	Dividends	Book Value
12/13	32.24	7 4	6.34	0.00	24.87
12/12	36.76	31 14	1.28	2.00	18.09
12/11	17.63	— —	(2.12)	1.00	18.11
12/10	28.77	— —	(1.40)	1.00	20.87
12/09	31.04	74 45	0.52	1.00	22.82
Annual Growth	1.0%	— —	86.9%	—	2.2%

M/I Homes Inc

M/I has its eye on the homebuilding prize in nearly a dozen markets throughout the Midwest Mid-Atlantic and South. M/I Homes sells single-family detached homes to first-time move-up empty-nest and luxury buyers under the M/I Homes Showcase Homes and TriStone Homes names. It delivers more than 2200 homes a year at prices ranging from about $107000 to $1 million (averaging $242000) and sizes ranging from 1200 to 4200 sq. ft. M/I Homes also builds attached townhomes and condominiums in select markets. Its M/I Financial mortgage banking subsidiary provides title and mortgage services. M/I Homes was founded in 1976 by Melvin and Irving Schottenstein.

Geographic Reach

M/I Homes's biggest market is the Midwest (40% of sales) followed by the Mid-Atlantic region (35%). The South including Texas accounts for more than 20% of sales.

Operations

Complementing its homebuilding activities (97% of sales) the company provides financing through its wholly-owned subsidiary M/I Financial Corp.

Financial Analysis

New home sales across most housing markets in the US remained at historically low levels in 2011 and the company's financial results reflected the continued malaise. The homebuilder's sales fell 8% in 2011 vs. 2010 and the company once again failed to turn a profit. Indeed the company's sales have dropped more than 50% since 2006 the last year in which it turned a profit. M/I Homes blamed the decline in sales in 2011 on a 6% drop in the number of homes delivered and a decrease in average sales price from $247000 in 2010 to $242000 in 2011. The decline in homebuilding sales was partially offset by an increase in revenue from the company's financial services unit. While the fallout from the deep recession and housing crisis continues to plague the firm's operations in the Midwest and Mid-Atlantic states the South performed better with sales up by more than a third last year.

Strategy

Since the beginning of the downturn in the housing market in 2006 the company has attempted to better align its operations with the unpleasant new reality. M/I Homes has reduced its land purchasing activities and home inventory. It has also exited particularly ugly markets including West Palm Beach Florida and entered more promising ones such as San Antonio in 2011 Houston in 2010 and Chicago in 2007.

Despite the lack of recovery in the housing market the company opened another 40 new communities in 2011. However M/I has made a few changes to the new homes it builds. The company is designing the homes and the communities to reap higher profit margins. Its homes are all eco-friendly slightly smaller and in line with consumer demands.

Ownership

Investment firm BlackRock Inc. owns more than 12% of the company's shares.

HISTORY

To provide a framework for future growth and increase its operational and administrative efficiency the company restructured and became a holding company in 2003. It transferred the com-

pany's homebuilding assets for its markets in Charlotte and Raleigh North Carolina; Washington DC; and Cincinnati and Columbus Ohio to five limited liability companies. In 2004 the company changed its name to M/I Homes marking the completion of its holding company restructuring.

In 2005 M/I Homes acquired Tavares Florida-based Shamrock Homes a privately held homebuilder and land developer for an undisclosed amount.

Cofounder and chairman Irving Schottenstein died in February 2004. Son Robert continues to manage the company as CEO; son Steven resigned as COO in 2006.

EXECUTIVES

EVP and CFO, Phillip G. Creek, age 61, $594,231 total compensation

Chairman President and CEO, Robert H. Schottenstein, age 61, $891,346 total compensation

EVP Chief Legal Officer and Secretary, J. Thomas (Tom) Mason, age 56, $450,000 total compensation

Senior Vice President Land, Tom Simpson

Vice President Land And Assistant General Counsel, Rick Stevens

Vice President Operations North, Rodney Howerton

Vice President Human Resources, Mark Pringle

Vice President Operations, Jerry Whelan

Area President, Greg Williams

Vice President Of Information Technology And Supply Chain, Peter Batchelder

Vice President Of Land Acquisition, Jimmy Gaskins

Vice President Of Sales, Hayes Kelly

Vice President Of Sales, Greg Jones

Area President, Mickey Pizzitola

Vice President Of Sales, Kelly Scattergood

Vp Of Sales & Marketing, David Balcerzak

Vice President Of Operations, Ray Phillips

Region Manager Vice President Mifc, Todd Miller

Vice President Sales And Marketing, Kreg Conner

Vice President Of Construction, Larry Krippendorf

Vice President Of Operations, Greg Svajian

Vice President Of Land, Royce Rippy

Vice President National Sales Training, Barbara Connelly

Vice President Finance, Angie Alexander

Vice President Land Acquisition, Matt Pagoria

Vice President Of Land Acquisition, George Young

Chairman President and CEO, Robert H. Schottenstein, age 61

City Treasurer, Randy Schoen

Auditors: Deloitte&ToucheLLP

LOCATIONS

HQ: M/I Homes Inc
3 Easton Oval, Suite 500, Columbus, OH 43219
Phone: 614 418-8000   **Fax:** 614 418-8080
Web: www.mihomes.com

2011 Sales

	$ mil.	% of total
Midwest homebuilding	228.2	40
Mid-Atlantic homebuilding	200.7	35
Southern homebuilding	123.0	22
Financial services	14.5	3
Total	**566.4**	**100**

PRODUCTS/OPERATIONS

2011 Sales

	$ mil.	% of total
Homebuilding	551.9	97
Financial services	14.5	3
Total	**566.4**	**100**

Selected Markets

Charlotte NC
Chicago IL
Cincinnati OH
Columbus OH
Dayton OH
Houston TX
Indianapolis IN
Maryland
Orlando FL
Raleigh NC
San Antonio TX
Tampa FL
Virginia

COMPETITORS

Beazer Homes	M.D.C.
Comstock Holding	NVR
D.R. Horton	Orleans Homebuilders
David Weekley Homes	PulteGroup
Dominion Homes	Rottlund
Drees Homes	Standard Pacific
Hovnanian Enterprises	The Ryland Group
John Wieland Homes	Toll Brothers
KB Home	WCI Communities
Lennar	Woodbridge Holdings

HISTORICAL FINANCIALS

Company Type: Public

Income Statement

FYE: December 31

	REVENUE ($ mil.)	NET INCOME ($ mil.)	NET PROFIT MARGIN	EMPLOYEES
12/13	1,036.7	151.4	14.6%	827
12/12	761.9	13.3	1.8%	651
12/11	566.4	(33.8)	—	583
12/10	616.3	(26.2)	—	522
12/09	569.9	(62.1)	—	535
Annual Growth	**16.1%**	**—**	**—**	**11.5%**

2013 Year-End Financials

Debt ratio: 41.4%
Return on equity: 36.5%
Cash ($ mil.): 128
Current ratio: 10.23
Long-term debt ($ mil.): 459

No. of shares (mil.): 24
Dividends
  Yield: —
  Payout: —
Market value ($ mil.): 620

	STOCK PRICE ($) FY Close	P/E High/Low		Earnings	PER SHARE ($) Dividends	Book Value
12/13	25.45	5	3	5.24	0.00	20.23
12/12	26.50	38	14	0.67	0.00	15.47
12/11	9.60	—	—	(1.81)	0.00	14.59
12/10	15.38	—	—	(1.42)	0.00	16.38
12/09	10.39	—	—	(3.71)	0.00	17.64
Annual Growth	**25.1%**			**—**	**—**	**3.5%**

Madden (Steven) Ltd.

Steven Madden elevates chunky heels to new heights. It operates through five business segments: wholesale footwear wholesale accessories retail first cost and licensing. Its wholesale business boasts seven divisions such as Madden Girl Steven Steve Madden Men's and Stevies as well as its Daisy Fuentes Betsey Johnson and Olsenboye accessories business through licenses. Its retail operations include about 120 Steve Madden Steven and Report stores along with several websites. Its

First Cost segment designs and sources private-label footwear such as Candie's for mass merchants. Steven Madden shoes are sold in the US and Canada through its own shops and such stores as Nordstrom and Dillard's.

Geographic Reach

New York-based Steven Madden rings up 92% of its sales in the US. The company's shoes and accessories are also sold in Asia Europe the Middle East Mexico Australia South Africa South America and India through special distribution arrangements. More than 120 Steven Madden-owned stores are located across the US with noteworthy penetration in New York California and Florida.

Operations

The company's wholesale operation accounts for 85% of its revenue with footwear contributing 65% of that. Subsidiary Steven Madden Retail owns and operates about 120 stores including about 90 Steve Madden full price stores a dozen Steve Madden outlet stores a pair of Steven stores a single Report shop and Superga store and thee e-commerce sites. The retail business accounted for 15% of sales in 2012. The company's First Cost business earns commissions as a buying agent for footwear products under private labels and licensed brands such as Candies for many large mass merchants shoe chains and other retailers.

Sales and Marketing

Steven Madden looks to department stores specialty stores and independent boutiques for the majority of its revenue. The company's sells its footwear and accessories through 15 department store chains throughout North America. Major accounts include Macy's Nordstrom Bloomingdale's Dillard's and Lord & Taylor. Major specialty store accounts include DSW Famous Footwear and Journeys.

To promote itself as a leading designer of fashion footwear for style-conscious young women and men the company's marketing activities include placements in lifestyle and fashion magazines personal appearances by founder and design chief Steve Madden and in-store promotions. The company's website and social media forums including Facebook and Twitter are other sales and marketing tools.

Financial Performance

Steven Madden's sales jumped 24% in 2012 versus 2011 to $.123 billion after rising more than 50% in the previous annual comparison. Indeed 2012 marked the fourth consecutive year of rapidly rising sales and profits for the firm with growth accelerating in 2011 and 2012. The strong sales performance in 2012 was broadly supported by double-digit growth across all of the company's business segments. Gains by the wholesale business have been the primary sales driver in recent years. Net income increased 23% in 2012 versus 2011 to nearly $120 million driven by rising sales.

Strategy

Steven Madden's recent success is a result of its focus on its wholesale operation. The company is also gaining a foothold in areas beyond shoes and it continues to invest in its accessories business. (The footwear maker's accessories business has eclipsed its men's business.) While small compared to the wholesale business retail is an important avenue for growth at Steve Madden. The company has added more than 30 stores over the past two years and is looking to enter new markets.

Mergers and Acquisitions

In August 2014 Steve Madden acquired Dolce Vita Holdings a designer and wholesaler of branded and private-label footwear for $60.3 million.

In February 2012 the company acquired its licensee Steve Madden Canada (SMC) for about $29 million. Privately-held SMC markets Steven Madden products in Canada on a wholesale basis and well as in Steve Madden-branded retail stores.

Looking to increase its private-label footprint Steven Madden bought Topline Corp. for $55 million in May 2011. Topline which rang up sales of about $189 million in 2010 sells private-label and branded footwear (Report Report Signature R2 by Report) primarily to specialty retailers and department stores. Also in May Steven Madden acquired the Cejon group of design and marketing companies for about $30 million. The purchase included Cejon Inc. Cejon Accessories and New East Designs. The companies design scarves wraps winter accessories and other items and expanded Steven Madden's accessories business beyond handbags and belts.

EXECUTIVES

Vice President, Alan Novich
COO, Awadhesh K. Sinha, age 69, $575,000 total compensation
Chief Financial Officer; Secretary, Arvind Dharia, age 64, $528,304 total compensation
Brand Director, Robert (Rob) Schmertz, age 50, $660,000 total compensation
EVP Wholesale, Amelia Newton Varela, age 43, $450,000 total compensation
EVP Strategic Planning and Finance, Edward R. (Ed) Rosenfeld, age 39, $52,500 total compensation
Senior Vice President Retail, Karla Frieders
Vice President Sales And Operations For Retail Division, Mike Willhite
Senior Vice President Sales, Amelia Newton
Vice President Sales Madden Girl, Teri Cashel
Senior Vice President Planning And Allocation, Caryn Coleman
Senior Vice President Logistics, Sanjeev Sahni
Vice President Of Finance And Operations, Dante Gioia
EVP Strategic Planning and Finance, Edward R. (Ed) Rosenfeld, age 39

LOCATIONS

HQ: Madden (Steven) Ltd.
52-16 Barnett Avenue, Long Island City, NY 11104
Phone: 718 446-1800
Web: www.stevemadden.com

2012 Sales

	$ mil.	% of total
Domestic	1133.1	92
International	94.0	8
Total	**1227.1**	**100**

PRODUCTS/OPERATIONS

2012 Sales

	$ mil.	% of total
Wholesale		
Footwear	794.5	65
Accessories	241.3	20
Retail	191.3	15
Total	**1227.1**	**100**

Selected Segments

Wholesale Footwear
 Betsey Johnson shoes
 Big Buddha Shoes
 Elizabeth and James (licensed)
 l.e.i. (licensed)
 Madden
 Madden Girl
 Olsenboye (licensed)
 Report

Steve Madden Men' s
Steve Madden Women' s
Steven
Stevies
Superga (licensed)
Wholesale Accessories
 Betsey Johnson
 Betseyville
 Big Buddha
 Cejon
 Daisy Fuentes (licensed)
 Olsenboye (licensed)
 Steve Madden
 Steven by Steve Madden
Steven Madden Retail
 Steve Madden retail stores
 Steven retail stores
 www.stevemadden.com
First Cost
 Buying agent for footwear products under private labels
Licensing
 Betsey Johnson trademark
 Betseyville trademark
 Steve Madden trademark
 Steven by Steve Madden trademark
Licensed Products
Belts
Hair accessories
Handbags
Hosiery
Jewelry
Outerwear
Socks
Sportswear
Sunglasses

COMPETITORS

Brown Shoe	Kenneth Cole
Diesel SpA	NIKE
Donna Karan	R. Griggs
Guess?	Reebok
Iconix Brand Group	Skechers U.S.A.
Jimlar	

HISTORICAL FINANCIALS

Company Type: Public

Income Statement

FYE: December 31

	REVENUE ($ mil.)	NET INCOME ($ mil.)	NET PROFIT MARGIN	EMPLOYEES
12/13	1,314.2	132.0	10.0%	2,864
12/12	1,227.0	119.6	9.7%	2,650
12/11	968.5	97.3	10.0%	2,370
12/10	635.4	75.7	11.9%	1,440
12/09	503.5	50.1	10.0%	1,370
Annual Growth	27.1%	27.4%	—	20.2%

2013 Year-End Financials

Debt ratio: —	No. of shares (mil.): 67
Return on equity: 20.2%	Dividends
Cash ($ mil.): 180	Yield: —
Current ratio: 3.21	Payout: —
Long-term debt ($ mil.): —	Market value ($ mil.): 2,464

	STOCK PRICE ($) FY Close	P/E High/Low		PER SHARE ($) Earnings	Dividends	Book Value
12/13	36.59	27	17	1.98	0.00	10.08
12/12	42.27	24	17	1.81	0.00	9.06
12/11	34.50	37	18	1.50	0.00	7.36
12/10	41.72	48	25	1.19	0.00	5.67
12/09	41.24	52	16	0.81	0.00	4.34
Annual Growth	(2.9%)	—	—	25.1%	—	23.4%

Magellan Midstream Partners LP

Having circumnavigated the world of midstream energy assets Magellan Midstream Partners is looking to discover even more profits. The energy infrastructure enterprise has ammonia and petroleum products storage transportation and distribution assets. Magellan Midstream Partners' portfolio includes 27 inland terminals and 1100 miles of ammonia pipeline 9600 miles of refined petroleum pipeline and 49 distribution terminals (with a combined usable storage capacity of 37 million barrels) in the US Midwest. The partnership also owns seven marine terminal facilities on the US East and Gulf coasts.

Geographic Reach
The company's petroleum products pipelines provide transportation storage and distribution services for liquefied petroleum gases and refined petroleum products in 14 US states extending from refineries on the Gulf Coast across Texas and through the Midwest to Colorado North Dakota Minnesota Wisconsin and Illinois. The company's major refineries are in Kansas Minnesota Oklahoma Texas and Wisconsin. Magellan Midstream Partners' ammonia pipeline and storage system delivers ammonia from Texas and Oklahoma to the Midwest primarily for use as fertilizer by the agricultural industry.

Sales and Marketing
The company ships petroleum products for a range of customers including oil companies wholesalers retailers railroads regional farm cooperatives and airlines. End markets for Magellan Midstream Partners' refined products deliveries retail gasoline stations truck stops farm cooperatives railroad fueling depots and airports (both military and commercial).In 2012 the company's petroleum pipeline system had 60 transportation customers primarily independent refining companies integrated oil companies and farm cooperatives. Its top 10 shippers in 2012 accounted for 46% of total revenues.

Operations
Magellan Midstream Partners manages a portfolio of ammonia petroleum products storage transportation and distribution assets. It owns the longest refined petroleum products pipeline system in the US with access to more than 40% of the country' refining capacity and can store over 80 million barrels of petroleum products (including gasoline diesel fuel and crude oil).

Financial Performance
Magellan Midstream Partners' revenues grew by 1% in 2012 primarily due to a 9% rise in transportation and terminals revenues. This increase was due to higher petroleum pipeline system sales and a rise in petroleum terminals revenues as a result of leasing tanks that came on line in 2011 (including new crude oil storage tanks in Cushing Oklahoma) and higher rates at the company's marine terminals. Other factors included stronger ammonia pipeline system sales thanks to a rate increase and higher product sales volumes. Also affiliate management fee revenues increased by 153% in 2012.Net income grew by 5% in 2012 as higher net sales outpaced an increase in operating expenses.With the exception of a revenue slump in 2009 (the result of the global recession dampening both demand and prices) the company saw an upward trend in revenues between 2008 to 2012.

Strategy
Magellan Midstream Partners has grown through acquisitions and has spent more than $2 billion in buying complementary assets since going public in 2001. It focuses on growth through organic growth projects joint ventures and acquisitions that expand or upgrade its existing facilities.

Expanding its existing refined products distribution system and moving into new markets in 2013 the company bought 800 miles of refined petroleum products pipeline in the Rockies and New Mexico from Plains All American Pipeline for $190 million.In 2012 it formed joint venture BridgeTex Pipeline Company LLC with an affiliate of Occidental Petroleum. BridgeTex was formed to build and operate the BridgeTex pipeline a 400-mile pipeline that will move 300000 barrels per day of Permian Basin crude oil from Colorado City Texas to an East Houston Texas terminal. The project also includes a 50-mile pipeline between East Houston and Texas City and 2.6 million barrels of crude oil storage. Magellan Midstream Partners expects to spend a $600 million in connection with its 50% stake in BridgeTex.Further growing its infrastructure assets in 2011 the company bough the remaining 50% stake it did not own in a Southlake Texas terminal a 38-mile petroleum products pipeline segment connected to its petroleum pipeline system at Reagan Texas petroleum products storage tanks in Riverside Missouri and a private investment group's interest in Magellan Crude Oil LLC (for $40.5 million). That year Magellan Midstream Partners also teamed up with Copano Energy forming a joint venture to deliver Eagle Ford Shale condensate to Corpus Christi Texas. The Double Eagle Pipeline JV will build 140 miles of new pipeline to connect an existing 50-mile pipeline segment owned by Copano enabling delivery of condensate to Magellan's terminal in Corpus Christi.

Boosting its oil storage assets in 2011 the company bought the remaining stake it did not own in a joint venture to build a 4.25 million barrels oil storage terminal in Cushing. The project has a price tag of about $110 million including the price of the acquisition. To better serve Gulf Coast refineries that year the company announced plans to reverse the flow and purpose of its Longhorn Houston-El Paso pipeline (formerly a petroleum products carrier) to deliver oil from West Texas fields.

EXECUTIVES

Vp Business Development, Brett C Riley, age 46
Chairman President and CEO, Michael N. (Mike) Mears, age 51, $441,932 total compensation
SVP and CFO, John D. Chandler, age 45, $334,842 total compensation
SVP Operations and Technical Services, Larry J. Davied
Vice President Of Technical Services, Michael Pearson
Vice President, Bob Hiser
Vice President Transportation, Jeff Selvidge
Chairman President and CEO, Michael N. (Mike) Mears, age 51
Auditors: Ernst&YoungLLP

LOCATIONS
HQ: Magellan Midstream Partners LP
One Williams Center, P.O. Box 22186, Tulsa, OK 74121-2186
Phone: 918 574-7000
Web: www.magellanlp.com

PRODUCTS/OPERATIONS

2012 Sales

	$ mil.	% of total
Transportation & terminals	970.7	55
Products	799.4	45
Affiliate management fees	2.0	-
Total	**1772.1**	**100**

COMPETITORS

Dynegy	Sunoco Logistics
Enterprise Products	Trammo
Gateway Energy	TransMontaigne
Kinder Morgan Energy Partners	

HISTORICAL FINANCIALS
Company Type: Public

Income Statement

FYE: December 31

	REVENUE ($ mil.)	NET INCOME ($ mil.)	NET PROFIT MARGIN	EMPLOYEES
12/13	1,897.6	582.2	30.7%	1,459
12/12	1,772.0	435.6	24.6%	1,339
12/11	1,748.6	413.5	23.7%	1,297
12/10	1,557.4	311.5	20.0%	1,271
12/09	1,014.1	226.4	22.3%	1,217
Annual Growth	**17.0%**	**26.6%**	**—**	**4.6%**

2013 Year-End Financials

Debt ratio: 55.7%	No. of shares (mil.): 226
Return on equity: —	Dividends
Cash ($ mil.): 25	Yield: 3.3%
Current ratio: 0.62	Payout: 87.4%
Long-term debt ($ mil.): 2,435	Market value ($ mil.): 14,342

	STOCK PRICE ($) FY Close	P/E High/Low		Earnings	Dividends	Book Value
12/13	63.27	24	17	2.56	2.10	7.27
12/12	43.19	47	21	1.92	1.78	6.70
12/11	68.88	38	29	1.83	1.56	6.49
12/10	56.50	40	29	1.43	1.45	6.47
12/09	43.33	39	23	1.11	1.42	5.61
Annual Growth	**9.9%**		**— —**	**23.2%**	**10.2%**	**6.7%**

Main Street Capital Corp

Main Street Capital doesn't care if its investments are on Main St. Manufacturing Blvd or Professional Services Pkwy. just as long as they are not too big and are (preferably) located in the southwestern US. As an investment firm Main Street provides long-term debt and equity capital to lower middle-market companies with annual revenues between $10 million and $100 million. Its portfolio includes more than 40 active investments in traditional and niche companies in the manufacturing technology restaurant business services and other sectors. Main Street tends to partner with business owners and management and provides capital to support buyouts recapitalizations growth financings and acquisitions.

The firm typically offers debt capital in the form of single tranche debt and mezzanine loans; it often makes its equity investments in connection to its debt investments. Single tranche debt is a type of hybrid asset-backed security that combines low-risk secured debt and higher-risk subordinated debt into a single instrument. Main Street believes this type of debt capital is ideal for investments in lower middle-market companies primarily because it lessens the risk associated with such companies generates a somewhat predictable return on its investments and is structured in way that reduces complexity and benefits creditors.

While 75% of the firm's investments are located in the western and southwestern US Main Street does maintain some investments in the southeastern and central US.

EXECUTIVES

SVP, Dwayne L Hyzak, age 41, $223,229 total compensation
CFO and Treasurer, Brent D. Smith
Managing Director, Sam Humphreys
Senior Vice President, Dwayne Mitchell
Vice President Business Development, Jessica Whitman
CFO and Treasurer, Brent D. Smith
Senior Vice President General Counsel Chief Compliance Officer Secretary, Jason B Beauvais, age 38
Assistant Treasurer, Kate Chandler
Board Member, Michael Appling, age 47
Assistant Treasurer, Jasmine Ali
Assistant Treasurer, Katherine Silva

LOCATIONS

HQ: Main Street Capital Corp
1300 Post Oak Boulevard, Suite 800, Houston, TX 77056
Phone: 713 350-6000
Web: www.mainstcapital.com

COMPETITORS

American Capital	MCG Capital
Apollo Investment	Sentinel Capital
Ares Capital	Partners
Capital Southwest	WestView Capital
Castle Harlan	Partners

HISTORICAL FINANCIALS

Company Type: Public

Income Statement

FYE: December 31

	REVENUE ($ mil.)	NET INCOME ($ mil.)	NET PROFIT MARGIN	EMPLOYEES
12/13	116.5	75.4	64.7%	37
12/12	90.5	59.3	65.5%	30
12/11	66.2	39.2	59.3%	22
12/10	36.5	19.2	52.8%	18
12/09	16.0	9.2	57.6%	16
Annual Growth	**64.3%**	**69.1%**	**—**	**23.3%**

2013 Year-End Financials

Debt ratio: 37.8%	No. of shares (mil.): 39
Return on equity: 10.5%	Dividends
Cash ($ mil.): 34	Yield: 6.6%
Current ratio: 1.03	Payout: 105.5%
Long-term debt ($ mil.): 514	Market value ($ mil.): 1,303

	STOCK PRICE ($) FY Close	P/E High/Low	PER SHARE ($) Earnings	Dividends	Book Value
12/13	32.69	17 13	2.06	2.18	19.89
12/12	30.51	15 11	2.01	1.73	18.59
12/11	21.24	13 9	1.69	1.70	15.19
12/10	18.19	16 12	1.16	1.50	13.06
12/09	16.12	18 10	0.92	1.50	11.96
Annual Growth	**19.3%**	**— —**	**22.3%**	**9.7%**	**13.6%**

Manhattan Associates, Inc.

Manhattan Associates serves up a cocktail of supply chain management software and systems sans cherry. It provides customers in the retail distribution transportation and manufacturing industries with supply chain management software and related services. The company's line of supply chain execution software includes warehouse transportation trading partner distributed order and reverse logistics management applications. Manhattan also offers performance management and radio-frequency identification tools designed to enhance the functionality of its other products and sells third-party hardware such as bar code scanners.

Geographic Reach In addition to the US the company has offices in Australia China France India Japan the Netherlands Singapore and the UK. It has reseller agreements or third-party representatives in a host of other markets throughout Latin America Eastern Europe the Middle East South Africa and Asia. Manhattan generates about 80% of sales from customers in North and Latin America; Europe the Middle East and Asia (EMEA) and the Asia-Pacific region contribute about 15% and 5% respectively. The company saw growth across all regions in 2012.

Sales and Marketing Manhattan primarily sells through its direct sales force but it has made efforts to broaden its approach through programs such as Manhattan Value Partner and Manhattan GeoPartner that enable joint sales and marketing with organizations such as Accenture Deloitte IBM and Microsoft. A sizable portion of the company's sales come from apparel and consumer products manufacturers and retailers including Abercrombie & Fitch PETCO American Eagle Restoration Hardware and The Container Store.

Financial Performance The company has been on a growth trajectory since seeing its sales decline more than 25% in 2009 amid the economic recession. In 2012 Manhattan reported revenue of $376 million up 14% from the prior year. Net income was also up that year jumping 15% to nearly $52 million. The company's growth was driven largely by its core services segment which rose 16% on the strength of professional services (consulting and customer training) related to upgrades and other customer-specific activity. In addition the company signed a dozen deals worth more than $1 million each in 2012.

Strategy Looking ahead Manhattan's growth strategy includes international expansion and it plans to target the overseas operations of its existing client base. It is also pursuing partnerships with international systems integrators as international sales have been steadily growing as a percent of overall revenue in recent years.

EXECUTIVES

SVP Sales Americas, Jeffrey S. (Jeff) Mitchell, age 46, $360,000 total compensation
EVP and CFO, Dennis B. Story, age 50, $335,000 total compensation
President CEO and Director, Eddie Capel, age 52, $400,000 total compensation
CIO, Michael Barrett
Vice President Sales, Anthony Arona
Senior Vice President Chief Lgl, Bruce S Richards, age 60
Vice President Development Project, Deepak Rao
Vice President Warehouse Management For Open Syste, Neal Castaldi
Senior Vice President And Chief Information Officer, Eric Wilson
Vice President Finance, Gary Luoma
Senior Vice President Strategic Planning And Development, Linda Penne
Vice President Of Mid Marketing, Bobby Collins
Vice President, Chris Hine
Vice President Planning Forecasting, Jim Schwender
Senior Vice President, Rama Tetali
Vice President It Software Engineering, Naresh Holla
Vice President And Chief Scientist, Amit Garg
Senior Vice President New Media, Molly Lee
Vice President Retail, Bob McFarlane
Senior Vice President Chief Legal, David Dabbiere
National Accounts Manager, Tony Cianci
Senior Vice President International, Jeffry W (Jeff) Baum, age 52
Chairman, John J. Huntz, age 63
President CEO and Director, Eddie Capel, age 52
Auditors: Ernst&YoungLLP

LOCATIONS

HQ: Manhattan Associates, Inc.
2300 Windy Ridge Parkway, Tenth Floor, Atlanta, GA 30339
Phone: 770 955-7070   **Fax:** 770 995-0302
Web: www.manh.com

2014 Sales

	$ mil.	% of total
Americas	402.0	82
Europe Middle East & Africa	60.8	12
Asia/Pacific	29.3	6
Total	**492.1**	**100**

PRODUCTS/OPERATIONS

2014 Sales

	$ mil.	% of total
Services	376.0	76
Licenses	71.6	15
Hardware & other	44.5	9
Total	**492.1**	**100**

Selected Services

Carrier Management
Distribution Management
Inventory Optimization
Mobile Supply Chain
Order Lifecycle Management
Planning and Forecasting
Supply Chain Event Management
Supply Chain Intelligence
Supply Chain Visibility
Total Cost to Serve
Transportation Lifecycle Management

HISTORICAL FINANCIALS

Company Type: Public

Income Statement

FYE: December 31

	REVENUE ($ mil.)	NET INCOME ($ mil.)	NET PROFIT MARGIN	EMPLOYEES
12/13	414.5	67.3	16.2%	2,530
12/12	376.2	51.8	13.8%	2,400
12/11	329.2	44.9	13.6%	2,135
12/10	297.1	28.0	9.4%	1,925
12/09	246.6	16.5	6.7%	1,819
Annual Growth	13.9%	42.0%	—	8.6%

2013 Year-End Financials

Debt ratio: —
Return on equity: 39.2%
Cash ($ mil.): 124
Current ratio: 2.10
Long-term debt ($ mil.): —

No. of shares (mil.): 76
Dividends
Yield: —
Payout: —
Market value ($ mil.): 8,972

	STOCK PRICE ($) FY Close	P/E High/Low		PER SHARE ($) Earnings	Dividends	Book Value
12/13	117.48	139	69	0.86	0.00	2.38
12/12	60.34	95	60	0.64	0.00	2.06
12/11	40.48	85	53	0.52	0.00	1.98
12/10	30.54	98	64	0.31	0.00	2.11
12/09	24.04	134	76	0.18	0.00	2.04
Annual Growth	48.7%	—	—	47.3%	—	3.9%

Manitex International Inc

Manitex International makes products that are uplifting –literally. One of the largest manufacturers of lifting equipment in North America Manitex makes and sells boom trucks and sign cranes used in industrial jobs as well as energy exploration construction and commercial building. Through Liftking the company makes rough terrain forklifts heavy handling transports and military specialty vehicles. The Manitex family includes Badger Equipment (cranes and material handling) and Load King (trailers). A Crane & Machinery unit distributes Manitex Terex and Fuchs equipment.

Geographic Reach

Headquartered at Bridgeview Illinois the company has six main operating plants in North America and Italy. It has operations throughout the Americas Autralia and the EMEA regions including Russia Korea Switzerland and other countries. The US accounts for nearly 55% of the company's total revenue; Canada contributes nearly 25%.

Operations

The company divides its operations across two segments: lifting equipment (92% of sales) and equipment distribution (8%). Sales for boom trucks contributed 44% of its total revenue in 2012

while part sales and container handling equipment represented 16% and 12% respectively.

Sales and Marketing

Manitex sells its products through a network of about 50 full service dealers in Canada Mexico South America the US and the Middle East. It uses direct sales to sell its Sign Cranes. The company's exported military products are sold through Canadian Commercial Corporation to various foreign countries (outside of Canada). Major customers include Cropac Equipment (about 11% of its total revenue) the US Department of Defense and other government agencies (both domestic and foreign).

Financial Performance

Manitex has enjoyed unprecedented growth over the last few years. Revenues surged 44% from $142 million in 2011 to $205 million in 2012. Profits more than doubled from $2.8 million to $8.1 million. Both these totals represented historic milestones for the company.

The growth for 2012 was attributed to a 45% spike in lifting equipment sales and a 43% rise in equipment distribution sales. The company saw explosive growth in both Canada (80%) and the US (52%). Sales in both Germany and Venezuela skyrocketed by more than 100% during 2012.

The surge in profits for 2012 was attributed to the higher revenue and the favorable impact of non-recurring expenses related to legal settlements of two product liability cases.

Mergers and Acquisitions

Manitex grows through the use of acquisitions. In 2013 it bought Indiana-based Sabre Manufacturing a manufacturer of specialized tanks for liquid storage and containment services for a purchase price of $14 million. The acquisition expanded its specialized product portfolio in its target markets.

EXECUTIVES

CFO, David H. Gransee, age 62, $182,188 total compensation
President and COO, Andrew M. Rooke, age 56, $250,508 total compensation
Chairman of our Board of Directors and our Chief Executive Officer, David J. Langevin, age 63, $310,625 total compensation
President - Manufacturing Operations, Lubomir Litchev
Senior Vice President Of Sales And Marketing, Bruce Peterson
Board Of Director, Marvin B Rosenberg, age 74
Board Of Director, Stephen J Tober, age 50
Board Member, Ronald M Clark, age 67
Auditors: UHYLLP

LOCATIONS

HQ: Manitex International Inc
9725 Industrial Drive, Bridgeview, IL 60455
Phone: 708 430-7500
Web: www.manitexinternational.com

2012 Sales

	$ mil.	% of total
US	114.6	56
Canada	55.5	27
Italy	11.7	6
Other Countries	23.4	11
Total	205.2	100

PRODUCTS/OPERATIONS

2012 Sales

	$ mil.	% of total
Lifting equipment	188.5	92
Equipment distribution	16.7	8
Total	205.2	100

2012 Sales

		% of total
Boom trucks		44
Part sales		**16**
Container handling equipment	12	
Specialized trainers	8	
Military forklifts	6	
Rough terrain forklifts	6	
Rough terrain & truck cranes	4	
Used construction equipment	4	
Total		100

Selected Products

Boom trucks
Container handling equipment (ports and inter-modal customers)
Empty container handlers
Equipment distribution segment (infrastructure development and commercial construction)
Forklifts
Fuchs material handlers
Hydroscopic Truck Mounted Excavators
Lattice Boom Cranes
Lift Trucks
Lifting equipment segment
Manitex boom trucks and sky cranes
Military forklifts (national militaries)
Mission oriented vehicles and specialized carriers (utility ship building steel mill industries)
Reach stackers
Repair and replacement parts
Repair parts
Rough terrain cranes
Rough terrain forklifts
Sign cranes
Specialized tanks
Straddle carriers
Terex rough terrain and truck cranes
Trailers (low-bed heavy-haul bottom-dump and platform trailers and hauling systems)
Used Equipment
Wheeled Excavators

COMPETITORS

Altec Industries
Linamar Corp.
MANITOU BF

Manitowoc Crane Group
Terex
Trail King Industries

HISTORICAL FINANCIALS

Company Type: Public

Income Statement

FYE: December 31

	REVENUE ($ mil.)	NET INCOME ($ mil.)	NET PROFIT MARGIN	EMPLOYEES
12/13	245.0	10.1	4.2%	501
12/12	205.2	8.0	3.9%	386
12/11	142.2	2.7	2.0%	344
12/10	95.8	2.1	2.2%	229
12/09	55.8	3.6	6.5%	172
Annual Growth	44.7%	29.3%	—	30.6%

2013 Year-End Financials

Debt ratio: 29.6%
Return on equity: 14.0%
Cash ($ mil.): 6
Current ratio: 2.54
Long-term debt ($ mil.): 42

No. of shares (mil.): 13
Dividends
Yield: —
Payout: —
Market value ($ mil.): 219

	STOCK PRICE ($) FY Close	P/E High/Low		PER SHARE ($) Earnings	Dividends	Book Value
12/13	15.88	19	9	0.80	0.00	6.16
12/12	7.14	15	6	0.68	0.00	4.85
12/11	4.24	27	14	0.24	0.00	4.01
12/10	3.85	20	9	0.19	0.00	3.80
12/09	1.92	9	1	0.33	0.00	3.62
Annual Growth	69.6%	—	—	24.8%	—	14.2%

Marine Products Corp.

A day on the water for you is a day at the office for Marine Products. The company builds recreational powerboats mainly though its Chaparral subsidiary. Its lineup includes fiberglass sterndrive and inboard deckboats cruisers and sport yachts ranging from 18 feet to 42 feet. Marine Products also makes a line of freshwater/saltwater sport fishing boats known for their "unsinkable hull" through subsidiary Robalo. Boats are sold to a network of about 200 independent dealers who then sell the lines to retail customers. The US generates the majority of the company's sales.

Geographic Reach

Headquartered at Atlanta the company sells its products to clients in Europe South America Asia Russia the Middle East and the US. Sales outside of the US accounted for 20% of its sales in 2012.

Sales and Marketing

Marine Products leverages a network of roughly 75 Chaparral dealers 16 Robalo dealers and 45 dealers selling both brands throughout the US. Oversees its boats are sold through some 70 international dealers.

Financial Performance

As the economy has gradually recovered Marine Products' total sales increased 13% from $149 million in 2012 to $168 million in 2013. Profits also surged 12% from $7 million in 2012 to $7.8 million in 2013.

The growth was fueled by a surge in the number of boats sold primarily due to sales of its recently introduced Chaparral H20 Sport and Fish & Ski Boats in addition to its Roobalo 180 and 200 models. Marine Products has also been helped by higher sales in Canada due to its efforts to expand its dealer network in the region.

Strategy

With a health level of cash from operations and increasing production the company anticipates replenishing dealer inventories now normalizing from their historic low levels. Simultaneously it aims to enhance dealer offerings and spur retail purchases by manufacturing more models with standard features and fewer options.

Marine Products has recently launched new Chaparral and Robalo models: the Chaparral H2O Sport and Fish & Ski Boats and the Robalo R180 and R200. The new models are more affordable with a small number of standard features. They adhere to the company's strategy to produce lower-priced entry level models appealing to a value-conscious consumer.

In 2013 Marine Products entered the jet boat market. It has partnered with Bombardier Recreational Products (BRP) to supply engines for a planned new line of jet boats. Chaparral's new product line will be powered by BRP's Rotax 4-TEC in-board jet propulsion system a reliable power source and a strong complement to Chaparral's new model line.

EXECUTIVES

President CEO and Director, Richard A. Hubbell, age 70, $350,000 total compensation
EVP and President Chaparral Boats, James A. Lane, age 71, $250,000 total compensation
VP CFO and Treasurer, Ben M. Palmer, age 53, $175,000 total compensation
Vice President Corporate Finance, James C Landers
Chairman, R. Randall Rollins, age 83
Treasurer, John Burt
Auditors: GrantThorntonLLP

LOCATIONS

HQ: Marine Products Corp.
2801 Buford Highway, Suite 520, Atlanta, GA 30329
Phone: 404 321-7910
Web: www.marineproductscorp.com

PRODUCTS/OPERATIONS

Selected Products

Chaparral (family recreational cruiser and sport yachts)
  Premiere sport yachts (fiberglass sport yachts)
  Signature cruisers (fiberglass cruisers)
  SSi sportboats (fiberglass closed deck runabouts)
  SSX sportdecks (fiberglass bowrider crossover sportboats)
  Sunesta Xtreme tow boats (fiberglass pleasure boats)
Robalo (outboard sport fishing boats)

COMPETITORS

Bombardier	Rodriguez Group
Brunswick Corp.	Sea Fox Boats
BÂOnÂ©teau	Sea Ray Boats
Cigarette Racing Team	Sunseeker
Correct Craft	Taylor Made Group
Duckworth Boat Works	Viking Yacht
Fountain Powerboat	Yamaha Motor

HISTORICAL FINANCIALS

Company Type: Public

Income Statement

FYE: December 31

	REVENUE ($ mil.)	NET INCOME ($ mil.)	NET PROFIT MARGIN	EMPLOYEES
12/13	168.2	7.5	4.5%	651
12/12	148.9	6.9	4.7%	587
12/11	106.4	6.7	6.3%	450
12/10	101.0	3.8	3.8%	360
12/09	39.4	(10.6)	—	300
Annual Growth	43.7%	—	—	21.4%

2013 Year-End Financials

Debt ratio: —	No. of shares (mil.): 38
Return on equity: 9.4%	Dividends
Cash ($ mil.): 5	Yield: 1.4%
Current ratio: 3.11	Payout: 88.2%
Long-term debt ($ mil.): —	Market value ($ mil.): 383

	STOCK PRICE ($) FY Close	P/E High/Low	PER SHARE ($) Earnings	Dividends	Book Value
12/13	10.05	51 29	0.20	0.15	2.14
12/12	5.72	35 26	0.19	0.63	2.06
12/11	4.96	42 18	0.18	0.00	2.50
12/10	6.66	73 42	0.11	0.00	2.33
12/09	4.93	— —	(0.30)	0.14	2.21
Annual Growth	19.5%		—	1.7%	(0.8%)

MarketAxess Holdings Inc.

A little creative spelling never got in the way of a good bond trade. MarketAxess offers an electronic multi-dealer platform for institutional traders buying and selling US corporate high-yield and emerging market bonds as well as Eurobonds. Participating broker-dealers include some of the world's largest such as BNP Paribas Citigroup Deutsche Bank Goldman Sachs and Merrill Lynch. In all MarketAxess serves more than 800 investment firms mutual funds insurance companies pension funds and other institutional investors. The company also provides real-time corporate bond price information through its Corporate BondTicker service.

Geographic Reach

The company is focused on countries it classifies as emerging markets such as Argentina Brazil Colombia Mexico Peru the Philippines Russia Turkey and Venezuela.

In late 2010 MarketAxess began offering services to institutions based in the Asia/Pacific region. The company is targeting sovereign wealth funds pension funds asset managers and central banks in the region.

Operations

The majority of the company's revenues come from monthly distribution fees and commissions for transactions executed on its platform between institutional investor and broker-dealer clients.

Financial Performance

MarketAxess has enjoyed an upward trend in revenue during recent fiscal years. The company's revenue increased to about $198.2 million in fiscal 2012 up from the roughly $181.1 million the company brought in during fiscal 2011 and the $146.2 million it claimed in revenue for fiscal 2010. The spikes came from increases in commission revenue and increased revenue from technology products and services.

Strategy

MarketAxess is focusing on technology investments to expand its connectivity offerings for electronic transactions. In 2012 the company expanded its suite of electronic trading protocols to help investors and broker-dealers more effectively source liquidity in the credit markets.

Mergers and Acquisitions

In 2012 MarketAxess expanded its capacity when it acquired Xtrakter Limited a leading provider of regulatory transaction reporting financial market data and trade matching services to the European securities markets.

EXECUTIVES

Chairman and CEO, Richard M. (Rick) McVey, age 55, $400,000 total compensation
CFO, Antonio L. (Tony) DeLise, age 52, $200,000 total compensation
CIO, Nicholas Themelis, age 51, $250,000 total compensation
Chief Credit and Risk Officer, James N.B. (Jim) Rucker, $200,000 total compensation
Head of Marketing and Communications, Florencia Panizza
Head of US Sales, Kevin McPherson
Head Europe and Asia, Robert H. Urtheil
Vice President, Jim Dulin
Corporate Level Senior Management Vp, Robert Hoog
Senior Vice President, Armand Palatucci
Chairman and CEO, Richard M. (Rick) McVey, age 55
Auditors: PricewaterhouseCoopersLLP

LOCATIONS

HQ: MarketAxess Holdings Inc.
299 Park Avenue, 10th Floor, New York, NY 10171
Phone: 212 813-6000　　**Fax:** 212 813-6390
Web: www.marketaxess.com

PRODUCTS/OPERATIONS

Selected Mergers and Acquisitions
FY2012
Xtrakter Limited (undisclosed price; London UK; provider of regulatory transaction reporting)

COMPETITORS

BGC Partners
BondsOnline
Cantor Fitzgerald
GFI Group
ICAP
Interactive Brokers

Intercontinental
  Exchange
TRADEBOOK
Tradeweb
Weeden

HISTORICAL FINANCIALS

Company Type: Public

Income Statement

FYE: December 31

	REVENUE ($ mil.)	NET INCOME ($ mil.)	NET PROFIT MARGIN	EMPLOYEES
12/13	238.7	76.0	31.8%	293
12/12	198.2	60.0	30.3%	240
12/11	181.1	47.7	26.3%	232
12/10	146.2	31.4	21.5%	229
12/09	114.4	16.1	14.1%	212
Annual Growth	20.2%	47.4%	—	8.4%

2013 Year-End Financials

Debt ratio: —
Return on equity: 27.4%
Cash ($ mil.): 132
Current ratio: 4.05
Long-term debt ($ mil.): —

No. of shares (mil.): 37
Dividends
  Yield: 2.7%
  Payout: 93.8%
Market value ($ mil.): 2,525

	STOCK PRICE ($) FY Close	P/E High/Low		PER SHARE ($) Earnings	Dividends	Book Value
12/13	66.93	34	17	2.01	1.82	8.23
12/12	35.30	23	16	1.59	1.74	6.49
12/11	30.11	24	15	1.20	0.36	8.06
12/10	20.81	24	14	0.80	0.28	7.85
12/09	13.90	31	14	0.42	0.07	7.18
Annual Growth	48.1%	—	—	47.9%	125.8%	3.5%

Markwest Energy Partners L.P.

MarkWest Energy Partners marks its territory as an alpha dog in the US midstream markets. It has oil natural gas natural gas liquids and gathering and processing pipelines as well as storage terminals and fractionation plants. Its Northeast (Appalachia and Michigan) segment includes processing and storing plants and Southwest (Texas and Oklahoma) has port pipeline processing and treating facilities. MarkWest's Liberty segment operates natural gas processing fractionating storage and marketing facilities in the Marcellus Shale play while its Utica segment consists of a joint venture with The Energy & Minerals Group to develop natural gas infrastructure in the Utica Shale play in Ohio.

Geographic Reach

MarkWest has facilities in nine US states: Texas Oklahoma Pennsylvania Ohio Kentucky Michigan New Mexico Louisiana and West Virginia.

Financial Performance

While falling natural gas prices have thrilled many consumers MarkWest reported a 4% dip in revenue due to lower natural gas prices and a drop in volumes. Net income increased strongly due to debt retired in 2011.

Strategy

MarkWest's strategy includes expanding both organically and via acquisitions increasing the use of its facilities and shielding itself from oil and gas price fluctuations by using long-term contracts for more than half its business revenue.

Mergers and Acquisitions

Growing its midstream portfolio in 2012 MarkWest Energy Partners bought Keystone Midstream Services for $512 million. Keystone's assets include two cryogenic gas processing plants (90 million cu. ft. per day) a gas gathering system and associated field compression all located in Butler County Pennsylvania.

Company Background

A spinoff from oil and gas company MarkWest Hydrocarbon MarkWest Energy Partners was created in 2002 to hold the natural gas gathering and processing assets of its parent. To streamline its business and deepen its financial resources in 2008 the company acquired MarkWest Hydrocarbon and merged it into its operations.

EXECUTIVES

Evp And Chief Commercial Officer Markwest Energy Gp Llc (General Partner), Randy S Nickerson, age 53
Vice President Business Development, Bert Dillman
Vice President Of Information Technology, Dan Cory
Vice President Oh, Dave Ladonne
Senior Vice President Chief Operating, William Janacek
Vice President Of Northeast Business, Jim Crews
Information Technology Vice President, Ron Spingler
Treasurer, Stephen C Newman
Auditors: Deloitte&ToucheLLP

LOCATIONS

HQ: Markwest Energy Partners L.P.
  1515 Arapahoe Street, Tower 1, Suite 1600, Denver, CO 80202-2137
Phone: 303 925-9200

PRODUCTS/OPERATIONS

2012 Sales

	$ mil.	% of total
Southwest	856.4	61
Liberty	319.9	23
Northeast	225.8	16
Utica	0.6	-
Total	**1402.7**	**100**

COMPETITORS

DCP Midstream Partners
Dynegy
Enterprise Products

Kinder Morgan Energy
  Partners
Williams Companies

HISTORICAL FINANCIALS

Company Type: Public

Income Statement

FYE: December 31

	REVENUE ($ mil.)	NET INCOME ($ mil.)	NET PROFIT MARGIN	EMPLOYEES
12/13	1,662.4	38.0	2.3%	1,139
12/12	1,451.7	220.4	15.2%	881
12/11	1,505.4	60.7	4.0%	683
12/10	1,187.6	0.4	0.0%	590
12/09	738.2	(118.6)	—	520
Annual Growth	22.5%	—	—	21.7%

2013 Year-End Financials

Debt ratio: 32.1%
Return on equity: —
Cash ($ mil.): 85
Current ratio: 0.59
Long-term debt ($ mil.): 3,023

No. of shares (mil.): 173
Dividends
  Yield: 5.0%
  Payout: 726.0%
Market value ($ mil.): 11,489

	STOCK PRICE ($) FY Close	P/E High/Low		PER SHARE ($) Earnings	Dividends	Book Value
12/13	66.13	290	196	0.24	3.34	27.62
12/12	51.01	31	23	1.69	3.16	19.58
12/11	55.06	75	55	0.75	2.75	12.46
12/10	43.31	—	—	(0.01)	2.56	14.98
12/09	29.27	—	—	(1.97)	2.56	16.55
Annual Growth	22.6%	—	—	—	6.9%	13.7%

Masimo Corp.

As important as the blood running through your veins is the oxygen it carries. Masimo knows that and makes tools that monitor arterial blood-oxygen saturation levels and pulse rates in patients. The company's product range which is based on Signal Extraction Technology (SET) offers pulse oximeters in both handheld and stand-alone (bedside) form. Product benefits include the provision of real-time information and elimination of signal interference such as patient movements. In addition to general product sales Masimo licenses SET-based products to dozens of medical equipment manufacturers including CareFusion Covidien Medtronic and Welch Allyn.

Geographic Reach

While the Americas account for about three-fourths of its product sales Masimo is working to grow its operations in Africa Asia Australia Europe and the Middle East. It has operations in about 25 countries.

Sales and Marketing

The company markets its products globally through direct sales representatives and distributors. Customers include hospitals alternative care entities OEMs and wholesalers. Two distributors Owens & Minor and Cardinal Health each account for more than 10% of annual sales.

Advertising costs for fiscal 2012 was about $9.5 million compared to $5.6 million in 2011. Masimo is expanding marketing programs to build consumer brand awareness through means including print and digital advertising trade show participation and direct mail campaigns. It also distributes publications and sponsors seminars to educate medical professionals about its products.

In 2012 the company entered partnerships with several group purchasing organizations (GPOs) to facilitate increased direct sales of pulse oximetry products to hospitals.

Financial Performance

Masimo increased revenues in 2012 by 12% to $493 million due to higher product sales especially of consumable items (related to its rising number of installed equipment locations) and increased sales of new Rainbow SET products. It also experienced growth from acquisitions increased marketing efforts and through partnerships with OEMs and GPOs. Increased product sales were offset by lower royalties (caused by a decrease in the royalty rate of its partnership with Covidien).

Net income decreased 2% to $62 million in 2012 due to higher costs for goods sold and increased operating expenses (related to increased staffing levels in the administrative and research divisions) and non-operating expenses (from currency exchange recognitions).

Masimo has reported steadily rising revenues over the last five years from organic growth measures. However net income has declined over the past three years due to the increased costs of a growing business.

Strategy

Expansion is key to Masimo's strategy for growth. Its research and development efforts (with expenses of around $40 to $50 million per year) focus on novel products as well as improvements to existing products. Product enhancements have included a new monitoring capability that can detect methemoglobin (a form of hemoglobin that can cause a lack of oxygen in the blood) and the addition of total hemoglobin (oxygen in red blood cells) measurement. It is expanding the applications of its Rainbow SET products which measure multiple blood components at once; it is also adding products that reduce the invasiveness of testing and that provide remote monitoring and alarm capabilities.

To branch out beyond its traditionally targeted emergency and critical care setting markets Masimo is promoting existing products (and adding new products) to meet the general treatment needs of hospitals and non-hospital environments. For example the company is promoting its SET technology as ideal for use by home care agencies post-acute care hospitals and sleep diagnostic centers. It is also introducing new handheld products that allow for fast and simple measurement of perimeters in a variety of care settings. The company expects moves such as these to greatly expand its presence in non-critical care markets.

Masimo also expands by entering new OEM licensing agreements (such as a long-term agreement for the use of its Rainbow SET products in GE Healthcare's patient monitors in 2012); by widening agreements with wholesale distributors; and by making occasional acquisitions.

Mergers and Acquisitions

To bring manufacturing of some key components in-house Masimo acquired Spire Semiconductor for $7 million in early 2012. Masimo had been one of Spire's largest customers and having the LED manufacturer under its wing promises to speed development of new products.

Also in 2012 Masimo acquired Phasein AB which manufactures and sells ultra-compact capnography and gas analyzers for some $30 million. The added products complement the company's existing portfolio of OEM solutions.

Ownership

Chairman and CEO Joe Kiani who founded Masimo in 1989 holds roughly 10% of the company's stock. The company went public in 2007 and used proceeds from the IPO towards capital and equipment expenses and product development efforts.

EXECUTIVES

Chairman and CEO, Joe E. Kiani, age 50, $712,545 total compensation
EVP and CIO, Yongsam Lee, age 50, $329,244 total compensation
President Worldwide OEM Business and Corporate Development, Rick Fishel, age 56, $335,669 total compensation
EVP Business Development, Paul R. Jansen, age 43
COO, Anand Sampath, age 48
EVP and CFO, Mark P. de Raad, age 53, $334,442 total compensation
EVP and General Counsel, Tom McClenahan, age 40
President Masimo Worldwide Sales Professional Servicesand Medical Affairs, Jon Coleman, age 49, $332,410 total compensation
Vice President Program Management, Tony Roberts
Vice President Finance, Andy Wilsack
Vice President Business Development, Eli Kammerman
Executive Vice President North America, Haruki Fukushima
Vice President, Tom Layne
Vice President Of Education, Jeff Whippo
Vice President Of Engineering, Ron Coverston
Vice President Regulatory Affairs, Gordon Richman
Rocky Mountain Region Vice President, Scott Rasband
Vice President Regulatory Affairs, Patricia Milbank
Vice President Marketing Communications, Mark Scott
Regional Vice President, Amy Brown
Regional Vice President Sales, Jim Learned
Senior Vice President Corporate, Max Safai
Senior Vice President Global Services, Josiane Margueron
Vice President Information Systems, Mark Brinton
Global Vice President Of Sales, Brad Snow
Regional Vice President, Jerry Fronzaglio
Chairman and CEO, Joe E. Kiani, age 50
Board Member, Julie Bradley
Auditors: GrantThorntonLLP

LOCATIONS

HQ: Masimo Corp.
40 Parker, Irvine, CA 92618
Phone: 949 297-7000
Web: www.masimo.com

2012 Product Sales

	% of total
The Americas	73
Europe Middle East & Africa (EMEA)	15
Asia & Australia	12
Total	**100**

PRODUCTS/OPERATIONS

2012 Sales

	$ mil.	% of total
Product	464.0	94
Royalty	28.3	6
Total	**493.2**	**100**

Selected Products

Capnography and Multigas Monitoring
Patient SafetyNet Remote Monitoring
Rainbow Acoustic Monitoring
Rainbow Pulse CO-Oximetry
SedLine Brain Function Monitoring
Signal Extraction Pulse Oximetry

Selected OEM Customers

3F Medical Co. Ltd (China)
Atom Medical Corporation
Biolight Meditech Co. Ltd. (China)
Bitmos GmbH (Germany)
BMEYE (The Netherlands)
CareFusion
CAS Medical Systems Inc.
Comen Medical Instruments Co. Ltd. (China)
Corpuls
Digicare
Dräger Medical AG & Co. KG (Germany)
Excel-Tech Ltd (XLTEK a Canadian division of Natus Medical Incorporated)
Fritz Stephan GmbH (Germany)
Fukuda Denshi Co. LTD. (Japan)
GE Healthcare
GETEMED Medizin- und Informationstechnik AG (Germany)
Imagenes y Medicina S.A. de C.V. (Mexico)
Impact Instrumentation Inc.
International Biomedical
IRadimed Corporation
Ivy Biomedical Systems Inc.
Medtronic Inc.
Mennen Medical Corp. (Israel)
Mindray
Newtech Inc. (China)
Nihon Kohden
Norwood Scientific
Oridion Capnography Inc.
Osypka Medical Inc.
Philips Healthcare/Respironics Inc. (The Netherlands and US)
Phoenix Medical Systems Pvt. Ltd. (India)
Physio-Control
Pooyandegan Rah Saadat Co. Ltd. (Iran)
Radiometer Medical ApS (Denmark)
RDECON
Schiller AG (Switzerland)
ShenZhen HeXin ZONDAN Medical Equipment CO. LTD (China)
Spacelabs Healthcare
Toitu Co. Ltd. (Japan)
Welch Allyn Inc.
ZOLL Medical Corporation

Selected Acquisitions

2012
Phasein AB ($30 million Sweden ultra-compact capnography and gas analyzer manufacturing)
Spire Semiconductor ($7 million New Hampshire LED manufacturing)
2010
SEDLine (brain function monitoring equipment for hospital patients under anesthesia and sedation)

COMPETITORS

Bio-logic	Mindray
CAS Medical	Philips Healthcare
Criticare	Siemens Healthcare
GE Healthcare	Thoratec Corp
Instrumentation	
Laboratory Company	

HISTORICAL FINANCIALS

Company Type: Public

Income Statement

FYE: December 28

	REVENUE ($ mil.)	NET INCOME ($ mil.)	NET PROFIT MARGIN	EMPLOYEES
12/13	547.2	58.3	10.7%	3,139
12/12	493.2	62.2	12.6%	2,866
12/11*	438.9	63.7	14.5%	2,548
01/11	405.4	73.5	18.1%	2,397
01/10	349.1	53.2	15.2%	2,199
Annual Growth	11.9%	2.3%	—	9.3%

*Fiscal year change

Debt ratio: 0.0%
Return on equity: 19.5%
Cash ($ mil.): 95
Current ratio: 2.62
Long-term debt ($ mil.): 0

No. of shares (mil.): 56
Dividends
Yield: —
Payout: —
Market value ($ mil.): 1,634

	STOCK PRICE ($) FY Close	P/E High/Low		PER SHARE ($) Earnings	Dividends	Book Value
12/13	28.86	29	18	1.02	0.00	5.77
12/12	20.58	23	17	1.07	1.00	4.77
12/11*	18.69	33	17	1.05	0.00	4.75
01/11	29.07	26	17	1.21	2.75	3.83
01/10	30.42	34	24	0.88	0.00	5.00
Annual Growth	(1.3%)	—	—	3.8%	—	3.6%

*Fiscal year change

Materion Corp

Materion (formerly Brush Engineered Materials) provides advanced engineered materials and services worldwide. It sells products to a number of markets including consumer electronics aerospace and defense industrial components telecommunications infrastructure automotive electronics and medical and appliance. It manufactures a variety of precious and specialty metal products including frame lid assemblies and clad and plated metal systems. Other products include precision optics and thin film coatings; inorganic chemicals and powders; specialty coatings; beryllium (which it mines in Utah) beryllium composites and beryllium alloys.

Geographic Reach
Materion serves customers in 50 countries. It has manufacturing plants in the US (Arizona California Connecticut Massachusetts New York Ohio Pennsylvania Rhode Island Utah and Wisconsin) and in China Ireland the Philippines Singapore Taiwan and the UK.

In 2012 the US accounted for 69% of Materion's sales.

Operations
The company operates in four segments: Advanced Material Technologies; Beryllium and Composites; Performance Alloys; and Technical Materials.

Each of Materion's divisions serves specialized markets but its Advanced Materials Technologies group is the company's primary breadwinner accounting for two-thirds of annual sales. The Advanced Materials Technologies group manufactures precious non-precious and specialty metal products such as clad and precious metal preforms high temperature brazing materials ultrafine wire optics performance coatings and electronic packages.

Other groups have a different mission. For example the Beryllium and Composites group is focused on the defense industry. The company extracts beryllium from its bertrandite mine in Utah where it also produces beryllium hydroxide at its milling facilities. In addition to using the beryllium hydroxide as a raw material for its strip and bulk products it sells the material to NGK INSULATORS.

Performance Alloys makes high precision strip and bulk products from copper and nickel-based alloys while Technical Materials makes clad inlay

and overlay metals precious and base metal electroplated systems and other related items.

Sales and Marketing
Materion has service and distribution centers in Germany Japan Singapore the UK and the US. The company sells its products both directly and through independent sales representatives throughout the world.

It serves customers in range of industries including aerospace automotive electronics consumer electronics defense energy industrial components medical and telecommunications infrastructure. In 2012 Materion's major customer NGK INSULATORS which is accounted for 4% of the Performance Alloys segment's total sales.

Financial Performance
Materion's revenues dropped by 17% in 2012 due to lower metal commodity prices an increase in the use of customer-supplied metal and the loss of a non-strategic product line. Advanced Material Technologies' revenues slumped by 19% due to lower revenues. Performance Alloys' sales were down by 13% as the result of weaker demand for strip products from consumer electronics and appliance customers.Net income decreased by 38% in 2012 primarily due lower revenues and higher selling general and administrative expenses and higher research and development expenses stemming from its acquisition of Aerospace Metal Composites and EIS Optics.

Strategy
Materion's key strategy for growth has been to pursue niche acquisitions primarily for its advanced material business.

Mergers and Acquisitions
In 2012 the company acquired UK-based Aerospace Metal Composites (AMC). AMC makes a product line that fits in with Materion's beryllium metal-based product lines (including AlBeMet) and is derived from powder metals. AMC also produces reinforced metal matrix composites made mainly from aluminum and it sells to the aerospace and defense automotive and precision machinery markets.

In keeping with Materion's overall strategy for growth subsidiary Materion Advanced Materials Technologies and Services acquired EIS Optics in 2011 to bolster its precision thin film optical filters and coatings operations. The acquisition also widens Materion's footprint in Asia and gives it access to the fast-growing Chinese market where EIS Optics operates a manufacturing site in Shanghai. The buy complements a number of recent acquisitions Materion has made to bolster its precision thin film optical filters and coatings operations.

Ownership
Heartland Advisors Inc. owns 9.3% of Materion.

Company Background
The company was founded in 1931. The company consolidated all divisions under the Materion name in 2011.

EXECUTIVES

Vp Sales And Marketing Beryllium Products, Larry Ryczek
Vice President Controller, James Marrotte
Chairman President and CEO, Richard J. (Dick) Hipple, age 62, $704,634 total compensation
VP Finance and CFO, Joseph P. Kelley, age 42
Vice President Information Services, Mark Jasany
Vice President Finance, Hugh Hanes
Vice President Alloy Technology, Fritz Grensing
Vice President Human Resources, Joe Szafraniec
Vice President, Tom Hornacky

Vice President Environmental Health And Safety, Marc Kolanz
Human Resources Director Vice President, Richard Chesnick
Vice President Product And Market Development, Kaiser Joe
Strategic Business Unit Vice President, Robert Naranjo
Vice President Taxes, Christopher Eberhardt
Secretary, Michael C Hasychak
Chairman President and CEO, Richard J. (Dick) Hipple, age 62
Treasurer, Mike Hasychak
Auditors: Ernst&YoungLLP

LOCATIONS

HQ: Materion Corp
6070 Parkland Boulevard, Mayfield Heights, OH 44124
Phone: 216 486-4200   **Fax:** 216 383-4091
Web: www.materion.com

2012 Sales

	$ mil.	% of total
US	882.0	69
Other countries	391.1	31
Total	**1273.1**	**100**

Archive This ChartArchive This Chart

PRODUCTS/OPERATIONS

2012 Sales

	$ mil.	% of total
Advanced Material Technologies	847.8	66
Performance Alloys	292.5	23
Technical Materials	72.7	6
Beryllium & Composites	60.0	4
Other	0.1	-
Total	**1273.1**	**100**

Selected Mergers and Acquisitions

2012
Aerospace Metal Composites (UK; beryllium metal-based products and reinforced metal matrix composites)
2011
EIS Optics (precision thin film optical filters and coatings)

COMPETITORS

Aeroflex	Honeywell
American Technical	International
Ceramics	Kyocera
Anaren	NGK INSULATORS
BASF Catalysts	Olin
Carpenter Technology	Praxair
Heraeus Holding	Vesuvius

HISTORICAL FINANCIALS

Company Type: Public

Income Statement

FYE: December 31

	REVENUE ($ mil.)	NET INCOME ($ mil.)	NET PROFIT MARGIN	EMPLOYEES
12/13	1,166.8	19.7	1.7%	2,671
12/12	1,273.0	24.6	1.9%	2,833
12/11	1,526.7	39.9	2.6%	3,015
12/10	1,302.3	46.4	3.6%	2,484
12/09	715.1	(12.3)	—	2,196
Annual Growth	**13.0%**	—	—	**5.0%**

2013 Year-End Financials

Debt ratio: 8.3%
Return on equity: 4.4%
Cash ($ mil.): 22
Current ratio: 3.06
Long-term debt ($ mil.): 29

No. of shares (mil.): 20
Dividends
Yield: 1.0%
Payout: 33.5%
Market value ($ mil.): 644

Matrix Service Co.

Matrix Service Company makes sure that oil and water don't mix. The company provides a variety of construction repair and maintenance services mainly to the petroleum and power industries. Its Storage Solutions business which accounts for about 45% of sales specializes in above-ground storage tanks to hold oil gas and specialty materials. It also designs and builds plants refineries and other installations. Through its Oil Gas & Chemical segment Matrix provides preventive routine and emergency repair services focusing on turnarounds outages and shutdowns when time is of the essence. Founded in 1984 the firm has around a dozen locations in the US and Canada.

Geographic Reach

Tulsa Oklahoma-based Matrix Service Company generates about 90% of its revenue in the US. The firm is licensed to operates in all 50 US states and four Canadian provinces.

Operations

Matrix's other operations include its Electrical Infrastructure segment which builds and repairs substations and power generation facilities while its Industrial segment provides services for the mining and minerals sector as well as other industrial and manufacturing markets.

Sales and Marketing

The specialty contractor services about 500 customers including petroleum companies refiners pipeline operators and oil and gas marketing firms. Enbridge is its single largest client accounting for about 11% of sales of fiscal 2013 (ended June) sales.

Financial Performance

After a whopping 70% decline in revenue between fiscal 2007 and 2010 Matrix's sales are on the road to recovery. In fiscal 2013 (ended June) sales increased 21% versus the prior year to $892.6 million. Net income increased by 40% over the same period to $24 million. (2013 marked the third consecutive year of rising sales and profits for the firm.) The double-digit increase in annual sales was broadly supported across all four of the firm's operating segments with Industrial (the firm's smallest unit) up 172% while Oil Gas & Chemical posted a 33% year over year gain followed by Electrical Infrastructure up 27%. The Electrical Infrastructure business got a boost from increased demand for high voltage work primarily related to storm restoration services and higher transmission and distribution work in the Northeastern US. Still the $892 million in fiscal 2013 revenue was below 2007's nearly $940 million. Cash flow from operations was up sharply.

Strategy

The company hopes that environmental regulations will lead customers to seek out Matrix's services to help them meet compliance standards. One of the largest above-ground storage tank builders in North America Matrix also expects that business to grow over the long term as infrastructure ages and demand for storage capacity increases.

In an effort to diversify Matrix has been focused on expanding its customer base and geographic presence. The company is making inroads in the alternative energy sector by adding products and services related to wind farms geothermal projects and solar panel installation.

Mergers and Acquisitions

In December 2013 Matrix acquired Kvaerner North American Construction a provider of capital construction and maintenance services to power generation integrated iron and steel and industrial process facilities in North America for about $80.3 million in cash. Post sale the business was renamed Matrix North American Construction. In January 2013 the company acquired Pelichem Industrial Cleaning Services LLC a privately-owned industrial cleaning business based in Louisiana. The Pelichem purchase expanded Matrix's industrial cleaning business and extended its geographic reach along the Gulf Coast.

HISTORY

Doyl West and William Lee both former officers with Tank Service founded Matrix in 1984 in Oklahoma. After buying Petrotank Equipment in 1989 they reincorporated as Matrix Environmental Co. which became Matrix Service Co. in 1990. Matrix grew rapidly through acquisitions including Midwest Industrial Contractors (1990) San Luis Tank Piping Construction (1991) and Brown Steel Contractors (1994). Its innovations included a "tank jacking" process to elevate and support water tanks during renovation and a safety nozzle that revolutionized the cleaning and desludging of crude oil tanks.

In 1993 Matrix's sales dropped from increased competition but rebounded in late 1994 as US petroleum companies rescheduled work they had postponed while the EPA finalized rules for the Clean Air Act.

To broaden its reach Matrix acquired General Service Corp. in 1997. That year ITEQ which provides liquid and gas storage systems and services agreed to buy Matrix but the deal was called off in early 1998 amid perceived integration problems. Founders West (who had served as CEO) and Lee (who had been CFO) retired in 1998. Longtime executive Martin Rinehart took over as CEO that year but left in 1999 during the company's second year of losses. Bradley Vetal (formerly COO of Matrix's industrial services unit) succeeded him.

Matrix recovered after disposing of its troubled municipal water services subsidiaries: It sold one Brown Steel Contractors to Caldwell Tanks in 1999 and closed the other San Luis Tank Piping in 2000. Once it disposed of its municipal water services Matrix was able to focus on aboveground storage tank (AST) operations and grow its construction services operations in 2001.

The next year Matrix experienced a healthy hike in sales with the growth in new tank construction (many of the industry's tanks were 20 years old or older) and an increase in the company's services to power plants.

To strengthen its presence in the mid-Atlantic region the company in 2003 acquired Pennsylvania-based Hake Group an industrial contractor for the power generation petroleum chemical and manufacturing industries.

Vetal resigned as CEO in 2005; director Michael Hall stepped in as interim CEO (Michael Bradley ultimately took over the position) and director Ed Hendrix was elected chairman. That year two employees who worked at subsidiary Matrix Service Industrial Contractors lost their lives after being exposed to nitrogen fumes while working at a Valero Energy Corporation refinery in Delaware City Delaware.

The company also expanded its capabilities when it purchased oilfield construction equipment and cryogenic tank technology use from Chicago Bridge & Iron Co. in 2008. The deal which helped grow the company's liquefied natural gas business also included $20 million in contract work.

In 2009 Matrix enhanced its electrical and instrumentation capabilities with the acquisition of S.M. Electric Company in New Jersey. The addition helps Matrix grow its business in the Mid-Atlantic and southern New England.

Michael Bradley resigned as CEO and president in 2010 along with CFO and VP Thomas Long. Both men left the firm to join the same midstream petroleum business that they had worked for before Matrix. The following year John Hewitt of Aker Solutions was named CEO of Matrix Service Company.

EXECUTIVES

Vice President Business Development, Kevin A Durkin, age 53

President Matrix Service Inc., James P. (Jim) Ryan, age 60, $309,074 total compensation

President and CEO, John R. Hewitt, $527,307 total compensation

CFO, Kevin S. Cavanah, age 50, $249,823 total compensation

President Matrix SME, Matthew J. Petrizzo, age 52, $295,705 total compensation

COO, Joseph F. Montalbano, age 65, $381,570 total compensation

Chairman, Michael J. Hall, age 70

Auditors: Deloitte&ToucheLLP

LOCATIONS

HQ: Matrix Service Co.
5100 East Skelly Drive, Suite 700, Tulsa, OK 74135
Phone: 918 838-8822   **Fax:** 918 838-8810
Web: www.matrixservice.com

2013 Sales

	$ mil.	% of total
US	814.9	91
International	77.7	9
Total	**892.6**	**100**

PRODUCTS/OPERATIONS

2013 Sales By Segment

	$ mil.	% of total
Storage solutions	393.2	44
Oil gas & chemical	273.9	31
Electrical infrastructure	171.2	19
Industrial	54.3	6
Total	**892.6**	**100**

COMPETITORS

Arizona Instrument
Brown and Caldwell
Chart Industries
Chicago Bridge & Iron
Denali
ENGlobal
Halliburton
OP-TECH Environmental
Veolia Environmental Services North America
ZCL Composites

HISTORICAL FINANCIALS

Company Type: Public

Income Statement

FYE: June 30

	REVENUE ($ mil.)	NET INCOME ($ mil.)	NET PROFIT MARGIN	EMPLOYEES
06/14	1,263.0	35.8	2.8%	4,491
06/13	892.5	24.0	2.7%	3,587
06/12	739.0	17.1	2.3%	2,692
06/11	627.0	18.9	3.0%	2,623
06/10	550.8	4.8	0.9%	2,477
Annual Growth	23.1%	64.6%	—	16.0%

2014 Year-End Financials

Debt ratio: 2.0%
Return on equity: 13.8%
Cash ($ mil.): 77
Current ratio: 1.39
Long-term debt ($ mil.): 11

No. of shares (mil.): 26
Dividends
Yield: —
Payout: —
Market value ($ mil.): 867

	STOCK PRICE ($) FY Close	P/E High/Low	PER SHARE ($) Earnings	Dividends	Book Value
06/14	32.79	27 11	1.33	0.00	10.61
06/13	15.58	19 11	0.91	0.00	9.12
06/12	11.33	23 12	0.65	0.00	8.20
06/11	13.38	20 12	0.71	0.00	7.54
06/10	9.31	65 45	0.18	0.00	6.74
Annual Growth	37.0%	—	64.9%	—	12.0%

Mattress Firm Holding Corp

Mattress Firm Holding is soft on comfort. The bedding retailer owns and operates or franchises more than 2000 stores primarily under the Mattress Firm name in some 40 states. It sells conventional (Simmons) and specialty (Tempur Sealy) mattresses which together account for most of its sales in addition to other brands. The company also sells bed frames and bedding accessories. From its humble beginnings in 1986 when three friends pooled their resources to purchase a downtrodden spot in a Houston strip center the chain has grown into the top US bedding retailer. Since its 2011 IPO Mattress Firm has made multiple acquisitions to solidify its position as the nation's top mattress seller.

Geographic Reach

Houston-based Mattress Firm boasts more than 2000 stores in 40 states. Its largest markets include Florida home to about 280 stores Illinois and North Carolina both with more than 100 locations. The company operates 70 distribution centers the largest of which are located in Texas Florida and Georgia.

Operations

Nearly half of the mattress chain's revenue comes from sales of conventional mattresses while specialty mattresses contribute about 45% of annual sales. Delivery service represents 2%.

Sales and Marketing

The company reported advertising and media production expenses of $105.3 million in fiscal 2014 (ended January) up from $87.2 million and $60.2 million in fiscal years 2013 and 2012 respectively.

Financial Performance

Mattress Firm reported $1.2 billion in sales in fiscal 2014 (ended January) an increase of 21% versus the prior year. Net income rose 33% over the same period to $52.9 million. The addition of new stores at the fast-growing chain and a 1% increase in same-store sales fueled the rise. Sales of conventional mattresses rose 36% year over year while furniture and accessories sales increased by 30%. The double-digit increase in sales contributed to the gain in profits as did the absence of an impairment charge booked in fiscal 2013. Other expenses including operating and sales and marketing costs rose in fiscal 2014.

Fueled by acquisitions including West Coast mattress retailer The Sleep Train in fall 2014 the company is forecasting pro forma annual sales of some $2 billion.

Strategy

Fast-growing Mattress Firm is doing its bit to further the consolidation of the mattress business through an active acquisition schedule both of independent chains and its own franchisees. The retailer has extended its reach into new markets including Hawaii and consolidated its hold on existing ones by snapping up other bedding companies. Indeed in fiscal 2015 (ends January) alone the company added about 800 locations.

Mergers and Acquisitions

In October 2014 the company acquired The Sleep Train a West Coast specialty bedding retail chain with some 310 stores in California Oregon Washington Idaho Nevada and Hawaii. The purchase strengthened Mattress Firm's position on the West Coast and its status as a national multi-brand bedding retailer. Other acquisitions in fiscal 2014 including Yotes a franchisee of the company with 34 mattress retail stores in Colorado and Kansas were made for an aggregate price of $80.5 million.

In fiscal 2013 Mattress Firm acquired Olejo a growing online retailer focused primarily on mattresses and related accessories. Other purchases that year included NE Mattress People operator of Mattress People stores and Perfect Mattress of Wisconsin (another franchisee). It also bought two mattress-related stores in the Houston market. Together the acquisitions increased Mattress Firm's presence in Iowa Wisconsin Texas and Nebraska (a new market for the company).

Mattress Firm acquired Mattress Giant in 2012. The acquisition valued at about $47 million gave Mattress Firm an additional 180 stores in seven markets across Texas and Florida where the company has already built a strong foundation. The move made Mattress Firm the nation's largest specialty bedding retailer. The Mattress Giant stores were later re-branded under the Mattress Firm banner.

IPO

Mattress Firm Holding raised $105.6 million in its initial public offering in November 2011. (It initially sought to raise about $115 million.) The IPO allowed the company's primary investor J.W. Childs Associates to cash out. Most of the proceeds from the offering were used to repay more than $84 million in debt and fees to JWC. The IPO came as the industry benefited from economic improvements and pent-up demand for mattresses and related bedding products in the aftermath of the deep recession and housing crisis.

EXECUTIVES

Evp New Business Development, Daniel J (Dan) McGuire, age 54
CEO, R. Stephen (Steve) Stagner, age 45, $500,000 total compensation
EVP and Chief Marketing Officer, Karrie D. Forbes, age 38, $275,000 total compensation
EVP and CFO, Alexander S. (Alex) Weiss
SVP Merchandising, Brian Baxter
EVP and General Counsel, Kindel L. Elam
EVP Real Estate and Construction, Bruce Levy, $275,000 total compensation
Co-COO, Kenneth E. Murphy
Co-COO, Rob Kilgore
President and Chief Strategy Officer, Dale Carlsen
Vice President Human Resources, Christine Brinkley, age 46
Chief Accounting Officer And Senior Vice President, Michael Galvan
Chief Accounting Officer And Senior Vice President, Cathy Hauslein
Regional Vice President, Kevin Etheridge
Vice President Of Merchandising, Chris Marsh
Regional Operations Vice President, Mike Cannizzaro
Chairman, William E. Watts, age 61
Auditors: GrantThorntonLLP

LOCATIONS

HQ: Mattress Firm Holding Corp
5815 Gulf Freeway, Houston, TX 77023
Phone: 713 923-1090
Web: www.mattressfirm.com

2014 Stores

	No.
Florida	281
Illinois	116
North Carolina	105
Georgia	98
Arizona	86
Ohio	62
Colorado	60
South Carolina	52
Tennessee	51
Missouri	50
Indiana	42
Wisconsin	40
Virginia	36
Pennsylvania	29
Louisiana	26
Minnesota	26
Nevada	23
Oklahoma	23
Alabama	21
Kansas	19
Utah	19
New Mexico	18
Iowa	15
Kentucky	14
Mississippi	12
Michigan	11
Arkansas	10
Idaho	8
Nebraska	7
New York	6
Maine	4
South Dakota	4
Washington	4
West Virginia	3
New Hampshire	1
Total	**1382**

PRODUCTS/OPERATIONS

2014 Sales

	$ mil.	% of total
Conventional mattresses	569	47
Speciality mattresses	540	44
Furniture and accessories	85	7
Delivery services	22	2

| Total | 1217 | 680 |

Selected Brands
Hampton & Rhodes
Sealy Posturpedic
Simmons Beautyrest
Sleep to Live
Stearns & Foster
Tempur-Pedic
YuMe

COMPETITORS

1800Mattress.com	Macy's
Ashley Furniture	Rooms To Go
Costco Wholesale	Sears
Dillard's	Sleepy's
Gallery Furniture	The RoomStore
Havertys	Wal-Mart
J. C. Penney Company	

HISTORICAL FINANCIALS

Company Type: Public

Income Statement

FYE: January 28

	REVENUE ($ mil.)	NET INCOME ($ mil.)	NET PROFIT MARGIN	EMPLOYEES
01/14	1,222.4	52.9	4.3%	3,861
01/13	1,012.7	39.8	3.9%	3,340
01/12*	708.6	34.3	4.8%	2,230
02/11	497.3	0.3	0.1%	2,040
02/10	434.3	(4.6)	—	0
Annual Growth 29.5%		—	—	—

*Fiscal year change

2014 Year-End Financials

Debt ratio: 28.1%
Return on equity: 17.8%
Cash ($ mil.): 22
Current ratio: 1.15
Long-term debt ($ mil.): 217

No. of shares (mil.): 33
Dividends
  Yield: —
  Payout: —
Market value ($ mil.): 1,426

	STOCK PRICE ($) FY Close	P/E High/Low	PER SHARE ($) Earnings	Dividends	Book Value
01/14	41.95	30 17	1.55	0.00	9.66
01/13	27.75	39 19	1.18	0.00	7.92
01/12*	33.03	23 15	1.40	0.00	6.64
Annual Growth 12.7%		— —	5.2%	—	20.6%

*Fiscal year change

MAXIMUS Inc.

Efforts by government agencies to maximize efficiency mean money for MAXIMUS. The company gets about two-thirds of its sales from its health services segment which offers outsourced program management and administrative services mainly to government agencies responsible for health and human services programs. Its human services segment provides administrative and consulting support to welfare-to-work programs child support enforcement and higher education and K-12 special education schools. MAXIMUS conducts consulting and programs management services for government-sponsored programs such as Medicaid Medicare the Children's Health Insurance Program (CHIP) and Welfare-to-Work.

Geographic Reach

Operating through more than 220 offices MAXIMUS gets more than 70% of its revenue from the US where the company has drawn clients from all 50 states. It also has won contracts in Australia Canada Israel Saudi Arabia and the UK.

Operations

The company operates through two segments: Health Services and Human Services. The Health Services Segment generated 64% of total revenue in fiscal 2012 while the Human Services segment accounted for the other 36%.

Financial Performance

MAXIMUS has enjoyed an upward trend in revenue over the course of recent fiscal years. The company reported $1.05 billion in revenue for fiscal 2012 up from the $929.6 million it claimed for fiscal 2011. MAXIMUS brought in $831.7 million back in fiscal 2010.

Strategy

The company hopes to continue to benefit from the trend toward outsourcing of administrative functions by government agencies. However MAXIMUS faces the risk of losing business when economic downturns lead to spending cuts by state and local governments.

In fiscal 2012 more than 60% of the company's total revenue came from state and local government agencies whose programs received significant federal funding.

HISTORY

David Mastran who worked for the Department of Health Education and Welfare during the Nixon administration founded MAXIMUS in 1975. The company's name comes from its goal of maximizing US government efficiency.

Most of MAXIMUS' growth has come in the past decade. In 1989 it won a contract to help California welfare recipients get job training and education and in 1995 it helped Nebraska find $50 million in federal funds. However it has not been easy sailing. In 1994 Mississippi froze a child-support collection contract with MAXIMUS when costs nearly doubled the state's expectations. MAXIMUS was disqualified from bidding on a West Virginia contract in 1995 after a state employee was convicted of bribery (MAXIMUS was not charged).

In 1996 California chose MAXIMUS to create a benefits information program for Medi-Cal applicants and beneficiaries. But late that year the federal government eliminated a Social Security Administration program that had been a major income source for MAXIMUS (55% in 1996).

MAXIMUS went public in 1997. Also that year the company added some 2500 new clients to its roster with four acquisitions which included government services providers David M. Griffith & Associates and Spectrum Consulting.

In 1999 MAXIMUS moved to bolster its human services and fleet management software capabilities respectively with acquisitions of Public Systems and Control Software. The company also landed large contracts to manage Medicaid enrollment for the state of Massachusetts child support enforcement for Maryland and Wisconsin's nationally recognized welfare-to-work program.

In 2000 MAXIMUS made acquisitions across the board in such areas as Web-enabled information systems child support collection services and infrastructure management systems. MAXIMUS only made one acquisition in 2001 preferring to integrate its previous purchases into a new business structure.

The company branched out internationally in 2004 when it signed a 10-year agreement with the Ministry of Health Services in British Columbia Canada.

Mastran retired in 2004 and company veteran Lynn Davenport replaced him as CEO. Davenport was dismissed in April 2006 however because of "conduct towards a female MAXIMUS employee" the company said. Richard Montoni a former EVP and CFO of the company was named president and CEO.

To concentrate on its core operations MAXIMUS discontinued its student loan collections business and sold its corrections services business in 2006. The next year MAXIMUS engaged advisers to help evaluate a wide range of options —including a sale of the company —in an effort to improve shareholder value. After the review the company's board decided in November 2007 to sharpen its focus on its core health and human services-related operations and to buy back up to $150 million worth of stock.

EXECUTIVES

CEO and Director, Richard A. (Rich) Montoni, age 63, $700,000 total compensation
Chief of Human Capital, Mark S. Andrekovich, age 53, $389,000 total compensation
Chairman MAXIMUS Foundation, John F. Boyer, age 67, $412,000 total compensation
CFO and Treasurer, Richard J. Nadeau
President and President & General Manager Health Services, Bruce L. Caswell, age 48, $431,000 total compensation
CFO, David N. Walker, age 56, $410,000 total compensation
President and General Manager Human Services, Akbar Piloti, age 57, $400,000 total compensation
CIO, Kelly L. Clark
Vice President Office Of Information Services, Barbara Bartell
Vice President Business Development, Christa Ballew
Senior Vice President, Richard Sankey
Senior Vice President, Relich Peter
Vice President Maximus Health Management Services, Melinda Metteauer
Vice President Business Development, John Kirby
Vice President Human Resources, Pamela Fauntroy
Vice President Health Systems East And Product Management, Gary Deluca
Senior Vice President Consulting Segment, Philip Geiger
Vice President Human Capital And Controller, Dave Timmons
Vice President Integrated Services, Pam Tomlinson
Director Of Clinical Services, Lynda Ferrell
Vice President, Anna Sever
Vice President Federal Operations, Terry Parham
Vice President, Viann Hardy
Vice President Health West, Barbara Selter
Vice President In The Financial, Mark Elvin
Vice President, Kinte Ibbott Maximus
Program Executive And Vice President, Helene Fisher
Vice President Health Systems West, Daniel Goodwin
Vice President Software Development, Viraf Bankwalla
Vice President, Rick Sankey
CEO and Director, Richard A. (Rich) Montoni, age 63
Chairman, Peter B. Pond, age 69
Director Board Of Directors, Ellen Simon
Board Member, Russell Beliveau
Auditors: Ernst&YoungLLP

LOCATIONS

HQ: MAXIMUS Inc.
1891 Metro Center Drive, Reston, VA 20190
Phone: 703 251-8500
Web: www.maximus.com

COMPETITORS

Accenture	Goodwill Industries
Bain & Company	HP Enterprise Services
Booz Allen	IBM
Boston Consulting	McKinsey & Company
CACI International	Oracle
Catholic Charities USA	SAP
Computer Sciences	Unisys
Corp.	United Way
Deloitte Consulting	Xerox

HISTORICAL FINANCIALS

Company Type: Public

Income Statement

FYE: September 30

	REVENUE ($ mil.)	NET INCOME ($ mil.)	NET PROFIT MARGIN	EMPLOYEES
09/14	1,700.9	145.4	8.6%	13,000
09/13	1,331.2	116.7	8.8%	12,000
09/12	1,050.1	76.1	7.2%	8,657
09/11	929.6	81.1	8.7%	7,102
09/10	831.7	70.4	8.5%	6,834
Annual Growth	19.6%	19.9%	—	17.4%

2014 Year-End Financials

Debt ratio: —
Return on equity: 26.8%
Cash ($ mil.): 158
Current ratio: 2.01
Long-term debt ($ mil.): —
No. of shares (mil.): 66
Dividends
  Yield: 0.4%
  Payout: 8.6%
Market value ($ mil.): 2,673

	STOCK PRICE ($) FY Close	P/E High/Low		PER SHARE ($) Earnings	Dividends	Book Value
09/14	40.13	23	18	2.11	0.18	8.35
09/13	45.04	47	21	1.67	0.18	7.73
09/12	59.72	53	30	1.10	0.18	6.64
09/11	34.90	72	27	1.14	0.15	5.54
09/10	61.58	64	44	0.98	0.12	4.93
Annual Growth	(10.2%)	—	—	21.1%	10.7%	14.1%

Maxwell Technologies, Inc.

Maxwell Technologies is more than capable of making products that store energy and deliver power you might even say ultracapable. The company makes ultracapacitors postage stamp-sized cells that are able to provide quick bursts of energy to meet power demands then recharge by capturing excess power that would otherwise be lost. Its ultracapacitors are used to provide additional power for hybrid cars electric trains and semi-trucks as well as in energy grid solid-state memory and other applications that need fast reliable power. Maxwell also makes high-voltage capacitors that protect power grid systems and radiation-shielded microelectronics for satellites and spacecraft.

Geographic Reach

Customers outside the US account for more than 80% of sales. Nearly half of its sales come from China and Germany. Maxwell has significant operations in Switzerland and the US (in San Diego); it also opened another larger US production facility in Arizona. The company has sales offices in China Germany and the UK.

Sales and Marketing

In addition to direct sales Maxwell sells through distributors that include Digi-Key TTI (and its Mouser Electronics unit) Tecate Group RUTRONIK and Bainacap.

Maxwell's ultracapacitors are used in wind turbine blade-pitch systems to regulate voltage to the power grid. In data centers the products provide the energy between power failures and the initiation of backup power systems such as diesel generators and fuel cells. In another application the company announced that ShinMaywa Industries a Japanese maker of special purpose trucks designed Maxwell's ultracapacitors into the all-electric loading mechanism for garbage trucks to reduce noise and emissions during loading and unloading.

Strategy

Maxwell continues to seek opportunities in China its largest market where it has a contract manufacturing arrangements with Belton Technology Group and Tianjin Lishen Battery. Maxwell collaborates with Chinese companies to expand its presence in that burgeoning market supplying ultracapacitor electrode materials to Shanghai Sanjui Electric Equipment and Yeong-Long Technologies. In China the company must carefully guard its intellectual property rights since some contract manufacturers will illegally copy a company's product and then sell it for less in export markets.

EXECUTIVES

Marketing Vice President, Michael J Liedtke, age 54
SVP CFO Treasurer and Secretary, Kevin S. Royal, age 50, $332,900 total compensation
President and CEO, Franz J. Fink
VP Advanced Power/Energy Development and CTO, Michael A. (Mike) Everett
VP and General Manager Microelectronics Products, Larry Longden
VP Marketing and Engineering, Chris Humphrey
VP High Tension and General Manager Maxwell SA, Sacha Jenny, age 45
VP and General Manager Engine Starting Group, Jeremy Cowperthwaite
Vp Corp & Business Dev't, Andrew McLean
Vp Sales-americas, David Wojciechowski
Vice-president Engineering, Curt Alexander
Vice President Sales For Maxwells, Piera Iori
Vice President Engineering, Clancy Sloan
Chairman, Mark Rossi, age 57
Treasurer, Victor Smolensky
Auditors: McGladreyLLP

LOCATIONS

HQ: Maxwell Technologies, Inc.
3888 Calle Fortunada, San Diego, CA 92123
Phone: 858 503-3200
Web: www.maxwell.com

PRODUCTS/OPERATIONS

COMPETITORS

Analog Devices	Murata Manufacturing
BAE SYSTEMS	Panasonic Corp
EPCOS	Silicon Valley Analog
Honeywell	Teledyne Technologies
International	Vishay Intertechnology

KEMET	W.L. Gore
Lockheed Martin	

HISTORICAL FINANCIALS

Company Type: Public

Income Statement

FYE: December 31

	REVENUE ($ mil.)	NET INCOME ($ mil.)	NET PROFIT MARGIN	EMPLOYEES
12/13	193.5	6.3	3.3%	448
12/12	159.2	7.1	4.5%	408
12/11	157.3	0.8	0.5%	435
12/10	121.8	(6.0)	—	368
12/09	101.3	(22.9)	—	361
Annual Growth	17.6%	—		5.5%

2013 Year-End Financials

Debt ratio: 4.2%
Return on equity: 4.7%
Cash ($ mil.): 30
Current ratio: 2.43
Long-term debt ($ mil.): 0
No. of shares (mil.): 29
Dividends
  Yield: —
  Payout: —
Market value ($ mil.): 230

	STOCK PRICE ($) FY Close	P/E High/Low		PER SHARE ($) Earnings	Dividends	Book Value
12/13	7.77	50	22	0.22	0.00	4.74
12/12	8.30	84	24	0.25	0.00	4.28
12/11	16.24	707	463	0.03	0.00	3.67
12/10	18.89	—	—	(0.23)	0.00	3.24
12/09	17.84	—	—	(0.94)	0.00	2.96
Annual Growth	(18.8%)	—	—	—	—	12.5%

McRae Industries, Inc.

McRae Industries has interests ranging from bar codes to boots. The company's footwear segment consisting of subsidiaries McRae Footwear and Dan Post Boot Co. makes combat boots for the US and foreign militaries Western boots and work boots. Dan Post Boot markets and distributes boot brands Laredo Dingo John Deere and Dan Post. A third subsidiary Compsee makes bar code readers printers and optical data-collection equipment. Compsee also licenses and sells computer software worldwide. McRae Industries makes most of its money from the Western and work boot segment. The McRae family controls more than 50% of the company's voting power.

EXECUTIVES

Vice President Product Development Dan, David Mitchell
Auditors: GrantThorntonLLP

LOCATIONS

HQ: McRae Industries, Inc.
400 North Main Street, Mount Gilead, NC 27306
Phone: 910 439-6147   **Fax:** 910 439-4190
Web: www.mcraeindustries.com

COMPETITORS

Ariat	Ricoh USA
Datalogic Scanning	Rocky Brands
Intermec	ScanSource
Justin Brands	TPG IPB

Office Depot
PEAK Technologies
Printronix
R. Griggs
Red Wing Shoe

Timberland
Wellco Enterprises
Wolverine World Wide
Xerox
Zebra Technologies

HISTORICAL FINANCIALS

Company Type: Public

Income Statement
FYE: August 2

	REVENUE ($ mil.)	NET INCOME ($ mil.)	NET PROFIT MARGIN	EMPLOYEES
08/14	103.6	7.5	7.3%	0
08/13*	97.0	7.5	7.7%	0
07/12	75.6	4.8	6.4%	0
07/11	74.7	3.8	5.1%	0
07/10	62.5	2.9	4.7%	0
Annual Growth	13.4%	26.5%	—	—

*Fiscal year change

2014 Year-End Financials

Debt ratio: —
Return on equity: 12.7%
Cash ($ mil.): 18
Current ratio: 8.11
Long-term debt ($ mil.): —

No. of shares (mil.): 2
Dividends
Yield: 0.0%
Payout: 13.6%
Market value ($ mil.): 73

	STOCK PRICE ($) FY Close	P/E High/Low		PER SHARE ($) Earnings	Dividends	Book Value
08/14	30.00	9	6	3.51	0.48	25.69
08/13*	24.50	5	3	3.79	0.86	23.07
07/12	14.80	6	5	2.27	0.36	20.82
07/11	13.63	7	6	1.84	0.36	19.06
07/10	13.25	8	4	1.47	0.36	17.78
Annual Growth	22.7%	—	—	24.3%	7.5%	9.6%

*Fiscal year change

MedAssets Inc

MedAssets helps hospitals widen their profit margins —or at least not lose quite as much. The company's Spend and Clinical Resource Management (SCM) segment is its largest with almost 60% of sales. It operates a group purchasing organization (GPO) that negotiates lower prices on medical supplies and devices for hospitals and health systems. The company's Revenue Cycle Management (RCM) segment provides software and consulting services that help track and analyze a hospital's revenue stream. Such services aim to increase collections and reduce account balances. MedAssets' customers include more than 4200 hospitals and about 122000 non-acute health providers mainly in the US but also in Canada to a lesser extent.

Geographic Reach

The company is headquartered in Georgia with offices in Massachusetts Colorado Missouri Washington Florida California New Jersey Texas and Tennessee.

Sales and Marketing

MedAssets sells its products and services through an in-house sales team. It also maintains a software development group which accounts for most of its R&D expenditures for creating new software products. In some cases rather than simply competing against other large group purchas-

ing organizations the company will actually contract with them as affiliates to extend its product range and share marketing efforts. Vendors including more than 1150 contracted manufacturers and distributors pay administrative fees to MedAssets based on the volume purchased by its health care-providing clients.

Financial Performance

The company posted an 11% increase in revenue with improved sales across all segments. It's still in the red however due to debt dragging down net income resulting in negative cash flow. Net income while still in the negative did begin to improve in 2013.

Strategy

As US health care policies shift and sway MedAssets aims to remain a steady partner to its customers who have been scrambling to not only upgrade to electronic health record systems adding more reimbursement codes but also keep abreast of changes to managed care reimbursement plans and track consumer out-of-pocket payments. These expensive pressures help Med Asset's solutions look quite attractive to hospitals and health systems.

MedAssets is expanding its product offerings to better serve customers. To improve its revenue cycle management solutions the company expanded its partnership with Cerner to provide interoperable solutions. The companies aim to combine Cerner's patient accounting offering with MedAssets' claims management program to enhance the claims handling process. It also formed a partnership with SAP subsidiary Ariba to expand its supply chain management and outsourced procurement capabilities.

Mergers and Acquisitions

While its overall strategy is focused on securing more new customers and selling those customers more products the company has grown significantly through acquisitions. In 2010 MedAssets acquired Broadlane a leading GPO provider for the US health care industry for some $850 million. The larger-than-usual transaction not only brought MedAssets to the forefront of the GPO market but also added complementary operations in areas such as supply chain process consulting and workforce optimization and allowed MedAssets to provide a full range of cost management services to its clients. Broadlane's operations were merged into the MedAssets organization with the core GPO operations combined with MedAssets' Spend Management division. Earlier acquisitions such as its $227-million purchase of revenue management provider Accuro Healthcare Solutions (2008) also helped to build up MedAssets' services.

EXECUTIVES

Executive Vice President Scm Operations, Scott E Gresset
Vice President, Richard Morrow
Chairman and CEO, R. Halsey Wise, age 49
EVP and CFO, Anthony Colaluca
EVP and Chief Strategy and Transformation Officer, Charles O. (Chuck) Garner, $350,000 total compensation
EVP and Chief Legal and Administrative Officer, Jonathan H. (Jon) Glenn, age 64, $240,000 total compensation
President Revenue Cycle Management Segment, Amy D. Amick
President Spend and Clinical Resource Management Segment, Keith Thurgood
President and COO, Michael P. (Mike) Nolte, $342,981 total compensation
VP Information Technology, Richard Momberger

Sr Vp Ne Zone, Brian Kelly
Senior Vice President, Becky Maclin
Vice President, Tim Murray
Senior Vice President, Beth Graefe
Vice President Software, Irina Vaserfirer
Vice President Clinical Pharmacy East, Christopher D Kohl
Sr Vp Client Management, Ann Pentz
Vice President Oncology Solutions, David McKeehan
Senior Vice President Sm West Zone, John Cunningham
Vice President Strat Clnt Mgmt Rct West, Leslie Flowers
Vice President Maintenance, Stephanie Adams
Vice President Finance, Jim McManus
Regional Vice President Sm, Chris Spain
Vice President Revenue Cycle Solutions, Kathy Willis
Vice President, Aaron Groves
Vice President Corporate Accounts, Kara Haugland
Vice President Of Specialty Centers, Larry Lane
Vice President Content Operations, Angela Applegeet
Senior Vice President Supl Chn, Jerry Rayburn
Regional Vice President Spend Management, Michael O'Gull
Vice President Client Management, Evan Cooper
Vice President Client Executive, Elizabeth Gass
Senior Vice President Product, Chris Harding
Vice President Procurement Services, Bejan Shamsy
Vice President Human Resources Legal, Anne Lang
Senior Vice President Spend Management, Madonna Pruett
Vice President Client Executive, Mary Hamner
Vice President Client Executive, Juleus Sullivan
Vice President, Rishabh Parmar
Vice President Client Strategy, Angela Brown
Senior Vice President Rcs, David Hammer
Vice President Human Resources Operations And Talent Management, Mary Simmons
Senior Vice President Management Rcm, Christopher Moreira
Vice President Financial Planning And Analysis, Thaddeus Kwiatkowski
Vice President Information Technology, Scott Grubenhoff
Vice President Laboratory Division, Mary Ellen
Vice President Customer Improvement, Russell Vantyle
Vice President, Rodney Shifflette
Vice President Financial Planning, Rob Decarlo
Vice President Supply Chain Services, Terry Cox
Vice President Of Operations, Sandra Hayter
Sr Vp Sourcing Operations, Les Popiolek
Regional Vice President Rcm Tech, Bruce Pulver
Vice President Cardiology Radiology, Scott Lawson
Vice President Product Management, William Knox
Vice President Client Executive, Anne Morgan
Vice President Account Management, Brenda Laforge
Vice President, Colleen Vetere
Regional Vice President Spend, Al Wiseman
Senior Vice President Enterprise Solutions Sales, Jennifer Holmes
Vice President Revenue Cycle Services West, Nicole Guido
Vice President Client Executive, Kevin Scott
Senior Vice President Chief Accounting Officer, Lance M Culbreth, age 45
Senior Vice President Revenue Cycle Services Operations, Caitlin Zulla
Vice President Strategic Operations Management, Tammi Smith
Vice President Operations, Fabrienne Wade

Executive Vice President Chief, Joe Miles
Vice President Rcm Strategic Client Management, Sam Thrower
Senior Vice President Enterprise Solutions, Paula Dipaolo
Executive Vice President Chief, Duy Tran
Vice President Technology, Michael Muessle
Vice President Technology, Jim Smith
Vice President Of Operations, Gretchen Ryan
Vice President Information Technology, Pedro Tomcsanyi
Regional Vice President Health Systems, John Lopez
Vice President Of Operations, Kim Lemmons
Vice President Operations, Joe Gomes
Vice President Finance, John Rupinski
Executive Vice President Strategic, Michael Lancaster
Vice President Support Operations, Bill Mohon
Vice President Finance, Jeffrey Hostler
Vice President Information Technology, Jenny Kwan
Vice President Western Region, Charles Kirkpatrick
Vice President Executive Services, Terrilynn Cunningham
Vice President Supply Chain Serivces, Scott Rue
Vice President Information Systems, Irene Mann
Vice President Of Product Development, Gary McQueen
Vice President Technology, Jim Grey
Vice President, Mehdi Khaleghi
Vice President Product Management, Ruchi Prasad
Senior Vice President General Manager Spend Management Sales, Costa Alvanos
Vice President Associate General, Julie A Taggart
Vice President Technology Dev Delvr, Robb Bartz
Senior Vice President Strategic, Kerry Tucker
Vice President Marketing, Marcia Shields
Vice President President, Fran Maddox
Vice President President, Keith Gregory
Vice President President Manager, Patrick Burton
Vice President President Enterprise, Bill Barber
Vice President Sourcing Analytics, Matthew Peterson
Vice President Corporate Technology, Dena Castellon
Senior Vice President Of Contracting, Deanna Herrin
Senior Vice President Enterprise Operations, Bharat Sundaram
Vice President Of Solution Strategy, Patricia Bounds
Vice President Marketing, Pam Glusing
Senior Vice President, William Howell
Vice President Professional Services, Jon Woodruff
Vice President Software Development, Robert Goldstein
Vice President Enterprise Solutions, Shaun Cleary
Vice President Market Management, Barbara Anspach
Vice President Client Executive, Frank Longo
Vice President Supply Chain Services, Anis Sabeti
Regional Vice President, John Wilkens
Chairman and CEO, R. Halsey Wise, age 49
Vice Chairman, Bruce F. (Toby) Wesson, age 71
Vice Chairman, Terrence J. Mulligan, age 68
President and COO, Michael P. (Mike) Nolte
Auditors: KPMGLLP

LOCATIONS

HQ: MedAssets Inc
100 North Point Center East, Suite 200, Alpharetta, GA 30022
Phone: 678 323-2500
Web: www.medassets.com
Alpharetta GA
Bedford MA

Bellevue WA
Bridgeton MO
Cape Girardeau MO
Centennial CO
El Segundo CA
Franklin TN
Nashville TN
Oakland CA
Plano TX
Saddle River NJ
Southborough MA
Yakima WA

PRODUCTS/OPERATIONS

2012 Revenues

	$ mil.	% of total
Spend & clinical resource management	393.6	61
Revenue cycle management	246.5	39
Total	640.1	100

Selected Affiliates

Advantage Practice Partners
Associated Purchasing Service (APS)
Carolina Healthcare Solutions
CHA Shared Services Program
Comprehensive Pharmacy Services
CostCor LLC
Crandall & Associates
Dallas Fort Worth Hospital Council
Esurg.com
Excel Rx GSO
Financial Resource Group
Greater Cincinnati Health Council
Group Purchasing Advantage
Group Purchasing Services Inc
GroupSource
Hawaii LTC Association
Healthcare Purchasing Resources
Homeplate Group Inc.
Hospital Purchasing Services (HPS)
Hunter Pharmacy Services Inc.
Kentucky Hospital Association
Maine Health Care Association
Maryland PRIME
Medical Consulting Solutions
MediGroup Physicians Services
Metro Chicago Health Council
MGMA
MHA Ventures Inc
National Cooperative of Health Networks
Nevada Health Cooperative
Northwest Ohio Shared Services
NovaMed Alliance Inc.
Pharmacy Management Services
Pharmacy Systems Inc.
Principle Pharmacy Group
Procure Health LLC
Provider Services of America
Rural Health Alliance
South Carolina Healthcare Resources
St. Joseph Health System
Stratum
Tennessee Hospital Association
Value First Inc.
Veira Medical Group

Selected Subsidiaries

Aspen Healthcare Metrics LLC
The Broadlane Group Inc.
Broadlane Intermediate Holdings Inc.
Broadlane NY Inc.
Dominic & Irvine LLC
Health Equipment Logistics and Planning Inc.
Healthcare Performance Partners Inc.
KP Select Inc.
MedAssets Analytical Systems LLC
MedAssets Insurance Solutions LLC
MedAssets Net Revenue Systems LLC
MedAssets Services LLC
MedAssets Supply Chain Systems LLC
MedAssets Ventures LLC

COMPETITORS

Accenture
Accretive Health
Advisory Board
Allscripts
CRANEWARE PLC
Deloitte & Touche
Emdeon
Epic Systems
Ernst & Young LLP
HealthTrust

Huron Consulting
McKesson
Navigant Consulting
Novation
Premier Inc.
PricewaterhouseCoopers US
SSI Group
Siemens Healthcare
UnitedHealth Group

HISTORICAL FINANCIALS

Company Type: Public

Income Statement

FYE: December 31

	REVENUE ($ mil.)	NET INCOME ($ mil.)	NET PROFIT MARGIN	EMPLOYEES
12/13	680.4	27.4	4.0%	3,200
12/12	640.1	(6.8)	—	3,100
12/11	578.2	(15.4)	—	3,040
12/10	391.3	(32.1)	—	3,100
12/09	341.2	19.9	5.8%	2,200
Annual Growth	18.8%	8.3%	—	9.8%

2013 Year-End Financials

Debt ratio: 47.9%
Return on equity: 5.9%
Cash ($ mil.): 2
Current ratio: 0.55
Long-term debt ($ mil.): 757

No. of shares (mil.): 61
Dividends
　Yield: —
　Payout: —
Market value ($ mil.): 1,224

	STOCK PRICE ($) FY Close	P/E High/Low		PER SHARE ($) Earnings	Dividends	Book Value
12/13	19.83	57	36	0.45	0.00	7.93
12/12	16.77	—	—	(0.12)	0.00	7.31
12/11	9.25	—	—	(0.27)	0.00	7.24
12/10	20.19	—	—	(0.57)	0.00	7.46
12/09	21.21	68	33	0.34	0.00	7.71
Annual Growth	(1.7%)	—	—	7.3%	—	0.7%

Medical Properties Trust Inc

Hospitals trust Medical Properties to provide the leases under which their facilities operate. The self-advised real estate investment trust (REIT) invests in and owns more than 110 health care facilities including acute care hospitals inpatient rehabilitation hospitals and wellness centers in 25 US states and Germany. California and Texas combined account for nearly 50% of the REIT's annual revenue. It leases the facilities to more than 25 hospital operating companies under long-term triple-net leases where the tenant bears most of the operating costs. Prime Healthcare Services and Ernest Health are among the REIT's largest clients. Medical Properties Trust entered the European health care market in 2013.

Geographic Reach

Alabama-based Medical Properties Trust (MPT) has properties in 25 US states and Germany. The REIT has 32 properties in Texas and 14 in California representing about 24% and 26% of its revenue respectively. New Jersey is another important market for the firm accounting for about 7% of annual revenue.

Financial Performance

MPT reported $242.5 million in revenue in 2013 an increase of 20% versus 2012. Net income increased by 8% over the same period to $97 million. The REIT has experienced rapid revenue and profit growth in recent years as it portfolio of properties has grown and rents and other income increased. Annual escalation provisions in its leases have contributed to the growth of rental revenue. Cash flow increased by $73 million in 2013 over 2013 due to an increase in cash from financing activities. MPT has more than $3 billion in assets.

Strategy

The REIT is focused on expanding and diversifying its tenant roster both in terms of the types of hospitals it owns and location. To that end Medical Properties Trust entered the European market in late 2013 with the purchase of 11 rehabilitation facilities in Germany from RHM Klinik-und Altenheimbetriebe GmbH & Co. for Â184 million ($254.3 million) The REIT which is looking to expand in other markets beyond the US was attracted by Germany's strong economic position and the health care environment. Back home in the US the REIT has been investing heavily in acquisitions and other related investments in 2013 and 2012 amounting to about $655 million and $621.5 million respectively. Purchases included three general acute-care hospitals from IASIS Healthcare LLC as well as two acute-care hospitals in Kansas.

The firm owns a variety of health care related properties including acute care hospitals inpatient rehabilitation hospitals long-term acute care hospitals wellness centers medical office buildings and surgical facilities.

EXECUTIVES

EVP CFO and Director, R. Steven Hamner, age 58, $400,000 total compensation
Chairman President and CEO, Edward K. Aldag, age 50, $600,000 total compensation
EVP COO Treasurer and Secretary, Emmett E. McLean, age 59, $395,000 total compensation
EVP CFO and Director, R. Steven Hamner, age 58
Chairman President and CEO, Edward K. Aldag, age 50
Vice Chairman, William G. McKenzie, age 56
Auditors: KPMGLLP

LOCATIONS

HQ: Medical Properties Trust Inc
1000 Urban Center Drive, Suite 501, Birmingham, AL 35242
Phone: 205 969-3755   **Fax:** 205 969-3756
Web: www.medicalpropertiestrust.com

2013 Sales

	% of total
$ mil	
Domestic	
California	62.2
26	
Texas	57.3
24	
New Jersey	17.0
7	
Idaho	10.5
4	
Arizona	10.1
4	
Louisiana	9.9
4	
Nevada	9.6
4	
South Carolina	9.5
4	
Utah	8.5
3	

Kansas	6.7
3	
New Mexico	5.6
2	
Pennsylvania	5.5
2	
Missouri	4.8
2	
Colorado	4.6
2	
Oregon	3.1
1	
Indiana	3.0
1	
Wyoming	2.6
1	
Montana	2.4
1	
Florida	2.3
1	
Massachusetts	1.8
1	
Michigan	1.4
1	
Others	2.3
1	
International	
Germany	1.8
1	
Total	**242.5**
100	

PRODUCTS/OPERATIONS

2013 Sales

	$ mil.	% of total
Rent billed	132.6	55
Interest & fee income	58.4	24
Income from direct financing leases	40.8	17
Straight-line rent	10.7	4
Total	**242.5**	**100**

2013 Sales by Property Type

	$ mil	% of total
General acute care hospitals	144.3	59
Long-term acute care hospitals	53.1	22
Rehabilitation hospitals	43.4	18
Wellness centers	1.7	1
Total	**242.5**	**100**

COMPETITORS

Extendicare	Omega Healthcare
HCP	Investors
Health Care REIT	Physicians Realty
Healthcare Realty	Universal Health
Trust	Realty
LTC Properties	Ventas
National Health	
Investors	

HISTORICAL FINANCIALS

Company Type: Public

Income Statement

FYE: December 31

	REVENUE ($ mil.)	NET INCOME ($ mil.)	NET PROFIT MARGIN	EMPLOYEES
12/13	242.5	96.9	40.0%	38
12/12	201.4	89.9	44.6%	33
12/11	143.3	26.5	18.5%	29
12/10	121.8	22.9	18.8%	29
12/09	129.7	36.3	28.0%	29
Annual Growth	**16.9%**	**27.8%**	**—**	**7.0%**

2013 Year-End Financials

Debt ratio: 48.9%
Return on equity: 8.1%
Cash ($ mil.): 45
Current ratio: 1.27
Long-term debt ($ mil.): 1,421

No. of shares (mil.): 161
Dividends
  Yield: 6.6%
  Payout: 110.9%
Market value ($ mil.): 1,971

	STOCK PRICE ($) FY Close	P/E High/Low		PER SHARE ($) Earnings	Dividends	Book Value
12/13	12.22	27	18	0.63	0.81	8.33
12/12	11.96	18	13	0.67	0.80	7.70
12/11	9.87	54	36	0.23	0.80	7.48
12/10	10.83	52	39	0.22	0.80	8.16
12/09	10.00	23	6	0.45	0.80	8.53
Annual Growth	**5.1%**	**—**	**—**	**8.8%**	**0.3%**	**(0.6%)**

Medicines Co (The)

The Medicines Company will meet you at the hospital. The drug developer focuses on treatments used in acute ER care settings including the ER the surgical suite and the cardiac catheterization lab. Its marketed products are Angiomax an anticoagulant used during coronary angioplasties and Cleviprex an IV drug used to control blood pressure spikes. It also sells Argatroban Recothrom Thrombin and Brilinta. The Medicines Company has other compounds in various stages of development including cangrelor an anti-platelet agent with possible use during cardiac catheterization and antibiotic oritavancin.

Geographic Reach

The US accounts for more than 90% of The Medicine Company's annual revenues. Its products are sold in more than 25 countries.

Operations

A majority of the company's income (98%) comes from sales of Angiomax in the US; the drug is also available internationally and is known in some regions as Angiox. The company depends on third parties (including Lonza) for manufacturing of its drugs. Sales of Cleviprex and other products accounted for about 2% of annual revenues in 2012. It also sells acute care generics.

Sales and Marketing

Angiomax Cleviprex and Argatroban are sold in US through sole-source distributor ICS (Integrated Commercialization Solutions); ICS markets and sells the products to hospitals and wholesalers. For Angiomax its sales force targets hospitals with cardiac catheterization laboratories that perform 200 or more coronary angioplasties annually.

In Europe Angiomax is sold as Angiox through an inside sales force consisting of 30 representatives; the company also directly sells Angiomax in Australia and New Zealand. In other international markets Angiomax/Angiox is sold through distributors including Sunovion in Canada and Grupo Ferrer Internacional in Greece Portugal Spain and some Central and South American countries.

Financial Performance

The Medicines Company reported increased revenues over the past five years as its product offerings have grown including a 15% increase to $558.6 million in 2012. The rise in earnings was driven by a price increase on Angiomax in the US as well as increased global Angiomax sales and higher sales of Cleviprex and Argatroban. Net income fell 60% to $51 million in 2012 however due to income tax provisions and higher operating expenses.

Strategy

The company has been working to expand the number of approved indications for Angiomax as well as to expand the drug into new markets. The

Medicines Company is also moving Cleviprex into new markets. Development candidates include products aiming to reduce blood loss during surgery and to reduce the risk of coronary events in patients who have heart problems including angina and coronary thrombosis.

Without a drug discovery operation of its own The Medicines Company licenses or acquires clinical-stage compounds from others and shepherds them through clinical trials and (hopefully) onto the market. It licensed Angiomax for example from Biogen Idec and Cleviprex and another compound from AstraZeneca. It is on the lookout for additional candidates (or approved drugs) that would fit easily into its portfolio of products aimed at the hospital market. In 2012 it licensed Recothrom marketing rights from Bristol-Myers Squibb.

The company implemented a workforce reduction program to reduce costs and increase efficiencies. The program reduced The Medicines Company's workforce by some 12%.

Mergers and Acquisitions
The company has made selected acquisitions of development candidates over the years to expand its pipeline in fields including cardiovascular care. It also occasionally purchases small stakes in drug technology firms. In 2013 it purchased Incline Therapeutics for $185 million to add a pain management candidate. The Medicines Company acquired ProFibrix for biologic surgery candidates that year.

EXECUTIVES

Chairman of the Board; Chief Executive Officer, Clive A. Meanwell, age 56, $702,000 total compensation
President; Chief Financial Officer; Director, Glenn P. Sblendorio, age 58, $486,675 total compensation
Vice President Global Product, Nitin Joshi
Vice President & Head Global, Garineh Dovletian
Vice President Eu Qppv, Barbara Dawson
Vice President Global Chest Pain, Raymond Russo
Vice President Business Development, Christopher Visioli
Vice President Controller, David Carroll
Vp, Tanya Quinn
Vice President Global Health Science Center, Jill Massey
Senior Vice President Global Launch Leader, Alan Levy
Vice President Human Strategy, Juliet Agranoff
Vice President Infectious Disease Pathway, Mike McGuire
Manufacturing Operations Vp, Anthony Flammia
Vice President Engagement Partner, Shane Judge
Vice President Human Resources, Amit Mohindra
Vice President Innovation Leader, Peter Wijngaard
Vice President Medical Affairs, John Pribble
Senior Vice President Global Launch Leader, Loretta Itri
Vice President Us Customer Engagement, William Knopf
Medical Director, Norman Huang
Vice President Global Medical Cangrelor, Jonathan Day
Vice President Manufacturing, Bill Doheny
Vice President Global Medical Strategy, Marco Navetta
Vice President Head Of Global Research And Development, Dimitrios Goundis
Board Member, Hiroaki Shigeta, age 71
Auditors: Ernst&YoungLLP

LOCATIONS

HQ: Medicines Co (The)
8 Sylvan Way, Parsippany, NJ 07054
Phone: 973 290-6000
Web: www.themedicinescompany.com

2012 Sales

	$ mil.	% of total
US	512.1	92
Europe	38.5	7
Other	8.0	1
Total	**558.6**	**100**

PRODUCTS/OPERATIONS

2012 Sales

	$ mil.	% of total
Angiomax	548.2	98
Cleviprex/Argatroban	10.4	2
Total	**558.6**	**100**

COMPETITORS

Baxter International	Medicure
Bayer HealthCare	Merck
Pharmaceuticals Inc.	Mitsubishi Chemical
Bristol-Myers Squibb	Pfizer
Eisai	Sandoz International
Eli Lilly	GmbH
GlaxoSmithKline	Sanofi
Janssen Biotech	

HISTORICAL FINANCIALS

Company Type: Public

Income Statement

FYE: December 31

	REVENUE ($ mil.)	NET INCOME ($ mil.)	NET PROFIT MARGIN	EMPLOYEES
12/13	687.8	15.5	2.3%	571
12/12	558.5	51.2	9.2%	538
12/11	484.7	127.8	26.4%	421
12/10	437.6	104.6	23.9%	420
12/09	404.2	(76.2)	—	462
Annual Growth	**14.2%**	**—**	**—**	**5.4%**

2013 Year-End Financials

Debt ratio: 13.5%
Return on equity: 2.1%
Cash ($ mil.): 376
Current ratio: 3.39
Long-term debt ($ mil.): 236
No. of shares (mil.): 64
Dividends
  Yield: —
  Payout: —
Market value ($ mil.): 2,487

	STOCK PRICE ($) FY Close	P/E High/Low		PER SHARE ($) Earnings	Dividends	Book Value
12/13	38.62	144	89	0.25	0.00	13.86
12/12	23.97	28	19	0.93	0.00	10.87
12/11	18.64	8	5	2.35	0.00	9.42
12/10	14.13	8	4	1.97	0.00	6.69
12/09	8.34	—	—	(1.46)	0.00	4.55
Annual Growth	**46.7%**	**—**	**—**	**—**	**—**	**32.1%**

Medidata Solutions, Inc.

Medidata Solutions has electronic remedies to help clinical trials run smoothly. Founded in 1999

the company offers cloud-based applications that help biotechnology pharmaceutical and other life sciences companies conduct clinical trials and related research. Its products include hosted software for administering and managing clinical trials electronic data capture applications study management applications and patient diaries. The company also offers a variety of professional services such as consulting implementation integration and maintenance. Medidata operates in more than 115 countries but most of its sales come from the US.

Geographic Reach
Metidata does most of its business in the US which accounted for 67% of the company's sales in 2012. Japan is the company's second-largest geographic market accounting for 14% of sales during the same period. Other key markets include the UK and Switzerland.

Sales and Marketing The company markets its products primarily through a direct sales force across North America Europe and Asia; however it does leverage relationships with contract research organizations such as PAREXEL and Quintiles Transnational to make its software the foundation for outsourced services they provide. Medidata's top five customers including Johnson & Johnson Roche and AstraZeneca account for more than 30% of sales.

Financial Analysis Medidata continued its strong upward revenue trajectory in 2012 with sales increasing 18% year-over-year. The application services segment (its core business) was up 18% with revenue from new customers (including those brought in via the 2011 Clinical Force acquisition) driving that growth. Higher revenues from the professional services segment also contributed to the overall revenue increase. Higher operating expenses particularly research and development and sales and marketing costs drove the company's profits down 54% in 2012 from 2011 levels.

Strategy Expanding its customer base is a key element of Medidata's strategy. It has grown from less than 100 customers in 2008 to some 350 by the end of 2012. Among the segments the company is targeting are midsized companies non-US geographies the medical device industry and academic research centers and government organizations. Medidata is also focused on expanding its product line including through acquisitions.

Mergers and Acquisitions In 2011 the company acquired UK-based Clinical Force which added clinical trial management software to its offerings for $7 million.

Ownership Investment management firm Brown Capital Management owns about 14% of Medidata.

EXECUTIVES

Vice President Of Engineering, Keith Howells
Vice President Sales Operations, Joseph A (Joe) Tyers
Vp Global Quality Assurance, Frances (Fran) Nolan
Vice President Operations, Lori Shields
Vp New Products, Richard J Piazza, age 56
SVP Sales, Steven I. (Steve) Hirschfeld, age 52, $300,000 total compensation
Executive Vice President Chief Financial Officer, Cory Douglas, age 48, $246,719 total compensation
Chairman and CEO, Tarek Sherif, age 52, $423,000 total compensation
EVP Product and Marketing, Lineene N. Krasnow, age 63, $300,000 total compensation
COO, Michael L. (Mike) Capone, age 47
Executive Vice President Strategy & Corporate Development, Bryan Spielman

Executive Vice President Human Resources,
Eileen Schloss
President, Glen Vries
Executive Vice President Chief Marketing Officer,
Steve Wilhite
Vice President Application Strategy, Daniel Mudgett
**Senior Vice President Business Development
Inside Press,** Mitchell Bayer
Vice President Implementation Services, Daniel
Shannon
Senior Vice President Chief Data Officer, Adindu
Uzoma
Vp It, Glenn Glen
Vice President Product Marketing, Pease Jeffrey
Vice President, Bob Wharam
Vice President Technology Solutions, Ross
Rothmeier
Senior Vice President Learning, Dan Klein
Vice President Global Talent, Susan Hailey
Vice President Alliances, Anne Zielinski
Senior Vice President And Chief Data Officer,
David Lee
Vice President Professional Services, Jeffrey
Handen
**Senior Vice President And Chief Accounting
Officer,** David Colistra
Vice President Implementation Services, Nick
Lucas
Chairman and CEO, Tarek Sherif, age 52
Auditors: Deloitte&ToucheLLP

LOCATIONS

HQ: Medidata Solutions, Inc.
350 Hudson Street, 9th Floor, New York, NY 10014
Phone: 212 918-1800
Web: www.mdsol.com

2011 Sales

	$ mil.	% of total
US	118.0	64
Japan	25.2	14
UK	11.6	6
Switzerland	10.6	6
Other countries	19.1	10
Total	**184.5**	**100**

PRODUCTS/OPERATIONS

2012 Sales

	$ mil.	% of total
Application services	171.6	79
Professional services	46.7	21
Total	**218.3**	**100**

Selected Customers

Pharmaceutical
 Abbott Laboratories
 Astellas Pharma
 AstraZeneca
 Baxter International
 Bayer HealthCare
 Daiichi Sankyo
 F. Hoffmann-La Roche
 Johnson & Johnson
 H. Lundbeck
 Orion Corporation
 Pfizer
 Roche Holding
 Shionogi & Co.
 Takeda Pharmaceutical
Biotechnology
 Amgen
 Array BioPharma
 Elan Pharmaceuticals
 Genzyme Corporation
 Gilead Sciences
 Infinity Pharmaceuticals
 Seattle Genetics
Medical Devices and Diagnostics
 bioMérieux

 Boston Scientific
 DePuy International
 Edwards Lifesciences
Contract Research Organizations
 CMIC
 EPS
 ICON Clinical Research
 INC Research
 Kendle International
 PRA International
 Quintiles Transnational
 Sumisho Computer Systems
Institutions
 Ludwig Institute for Cancer Research
 Northwestern University

COMPETITORS

Aptuit	MedNet Solutions
BioClinica	Merge Healthcare
DATATRAK International	Microsoft
DRS Data & Research	OmniComm
DrugLogic	Oracle
Liquent	Perceptive Informatics
M2S	eResearchTechnology

HISTORICAL FINANCIALS

Company Type: Public

Income Statement

Income Statement   FYE: December 31

	REVENUE ($ mil.)	NET INCOME ($ mil.)	NET PROFIT MARGIN	EMPLOYEES
12/13	276.8	16.6	6.0%	923
12/12	218.3	18.0	8.3%	796
12/11	184.4	39.4	21.4%	690
12/10	166.4	22.8	13.7%	598
12/09	140.4	5.1	3.7%	574
Annual Growth	**18.5%**	**33.9%**	**—**	**12.6%**

2013 Year-End Financials

Debt ratio: 40.0%
Return on equity: 9.0%
Cash ($ mil.): 241
Current ratio: 3.04
Long-term debt ($ mil.): 229

No. of shares (mil.): 53
Dividends
 Yield: —
 Payout: —
Market value ($ mil.): 3,245

	STOCK PRICE ($) FY Close	P/E High/Low	PER SHARE ($) Earnings	Dividends	Book Value
12/13	60.50	374 119	0.31	0.00	4.21
12/12	39.18	117 51	0.36	0.00	2.73
12/11	21.75	32 17	0.80	0.00	2.09
12/10	23.88	49 28	0.48	0.00	1.06
12/09	15.62	116 90	0.13	0.00	0.44
Annual Growth	**40.3%**	**— —**	**25.5%**	**—**	**75.7%**

Medifast Inc

Medifast tries to help people slim down and shape up... fast. The company develops and sells Medifast brand health and diet products including food and beverages (meal replacement shakes bars) as well as disease management products for diabetics. Subsidiary Jason Pharmaceuticals makes some of the company's products. Medifast operates through two segments Medifast and MWCC and Wholesale. Medifast includes Direct (customers order Medifast products online) and Take Shape for Life (personal coaching division with independent contractor "health coaches"). MWCC and

Wholesale covers Medifast Weight Control Centers' (MWCC) bricks-and-mortar walk-in clinics while Wholesale includes doctor's offices that sell the products.

Operations

Medifast the direct and coaching part of the business makes up 85% of revenue. MWCC and Wholesale the weight control centers and wholesale division makes up the rest. The company has about 50 company-owned weight loss centers and 70 franchised locations though it's transitioning many company-owned shops to franchisees. Medifast has about 20 weight loss centers outside the US.

Geographic Reach

Currently the company has about 50 company-owned weight loss centers in about half a dozen states including Florida New Jersey and Texas; it is transitioning many locations to franchisees. About 70 weight loss centers in six other states including Arizona and California are run by franchisees. Medifast has about 20 weight loss centers in South America (mostly Mexico).

Sales and Marketing

Medifast uses multiple marketing strategies to reach its target audiences. It runs ads in national and regional magazines on television radio and the Web. It also uses direct mail and social media channels. Advertising costs (excluding direct-response advertising) totaled $24 million in 2013 compared with $31 million in 2012.

Financial Analysis

Medifast's sales and profits were growing with the rise in obesity rates and the diabetic population. Indeed its sales increased 255% between 2007 and 2013 while profits and cash flow also climbed steeply. However in 2013 the company reported flat revenue of $257 million as sales fell in all areas except the Take Shape for Life coaching segment. Net income on the other hand rose 50% after declining for several years. The turnaround is attributed to a decline in expenses including an FTC lawsuit settlement and other one-time expenses that were on the books for 2012. Cash flow has been growing steadily for several years and in 2013 it grew $2 million to $42 million.

Strategy

While the ranks of the overweight are growing the company is also working to tailor its products to the rapidly growing population of diabetics. It maintains an in-house call center and support staff with registered dieticians on hand to assist customers.

Medifast's promotion and distribution model has changed over time. When it was founded in 1993 the company primarily sold its products through doctor's offices. Customers received supervision from their family physician who in turn received commissions on any products sold. However as physicians had increasingly less time to spend with patients the method grew less effective. While some doctors still stock an inventory and resell the company's products most of Medifast's sales are made through the its website thus reducing the complexity of its product distribution. Even its Take Shape For Life coaches simply direct customers to the website or call centers and receive commissions for orders placed there. New doctors who wish to promote the products are signed on as coaches.

In 2012 the company moved into international territory by partnering with Productos Medix a leader in pharmaceutical obesity products in Mexico to exclusively distribute its Medifast meal replacement products and programs through physicians and Weight Control Centers in Mexico under its Medifast brand. By the end of the year the two companies had three locations in Mexico. The following year they opened a center in Colombia. In 2014 Medifast bought 21 centers in Mexico and opened its first Canadian center.

EXECUTIVES

EVP Human Resources, Jeanne M. Uphouse, age 54
Chairman and CEO, Michael C. MacDonald, age 61, $344,231 total compensation
EVP and General Counsel, Jason L. Groves, age 43
EVP and Chief Marketing Officer, Brian Kagen
President and COO, Margaret Sheetz, $247,115 total compensation
CFO, Timothy Robinson
EVP Information Technology, Donald Gould, $220,000 total compensation
EVP Company Strategy International and Business Development, Brian Lloyd
EVP Take Shape for Life, Jeannette Mills
EVP Supply Chain, Guy Sheetz
EVP Medifast Weight Control Centers, Dominick Vietri
Vp Corporate Communications, Jamie Elwood
Vice President Marketing, Michael Decker
Vp Operations Production Mfg, Joe Dibartolomeo
Chairman and CEO, Michael C. MacDonald, age 61
Board Member, John P Mc Daniel
Auditors: BagellJosephsLevine&CompanyLLC

LOCATIONS

HQ: Medifast Inc
3600 Crondall Lane, Owings Mills, MD 21117
Phone: 410 581-8042
Web: www.medifastnow.com

PRODUCTS/OPERATIONS

2013 Sales

	$ mil	% of total
Medifast	304.3	85
Medifast Weight control centers and wholesale	52.6	15
Total	**356.9**	**100**

Selected Subsidiaries

Jason Enterprises Inc.
Jason Pharmaceuticals Inc.
Jason Properties LLC
Medifast Franchise Systems Inc.
Medifast Nutrition Inc.
Seven Crondall Associates LLC
Take Shape For Life Inc.

COMPETITORS

Atkins Nutritionals	Slim-Fast
Herbalife Ltd.	True Drinks
Jenny Craig	USANA Health Sciences
NBTY	Weight Watchers
Nu Skin	International
Nutrisystem	eDiets.com
Reliv' International	

HISTORICAL FINANCIALS

Company Type: Public

Income Statement

FYE: December 31

	REVENUE ($ mil.)	NET INCOME ($ mil.)	NET PROFIT MARGIN	EMPLOYEES
12/13	356.8	23.9	6.7%	808
12/12	356.7	15.8	4.5%	947
12/11	298.1	18.5	6.2%	860
12/10	257.5	19.6	7.6%	507
12/09	165.6	11.9	7.2%	365
Annual Growth	**21.2%**	**19.0%**	**—**	**22.0%**

Mednax, Inc.

MEDNAX is a multi-specialty medical group with a national focus. Through its Pediatrix Medical Group American Anesthesiology and Mednax Services units the holding company operates a medical network comprised of more than 2500 affiliated physicians specialty practitioners and sub-specialists who focus on women's and children's health. It provides neonatal obstetric and pediatric care primarily in hospitals; it also operates a growing number of anesthesia practices. In addition MEDNAX conducts clinical research and offers practice administration services to physician members and hospital customers in the areas of billing compliance managed care contracting recruiting risk management and staffing.

Operations

Pediatrix Medical Group's affiliated physicians include about 1000 doctors who provide neonatal care for premature or ill newborns primarily in hospital-based neonatal intensive care units; others specialize in fields including pediatric cardiology (120 physicians) and pediatric intensive care (100 doctors). Altogether neonatal and pediatric subspecialty services account for about 60% of annual patient service revenues. The company's maternal-fetal unit (10% of sales) employs some 200 physicians specializing in the care of pregnant women (including general obstetrics and pregnancy complications). The Pediatrix unit also conducts multi-center clinical trials and research studies and it provides educational opportunities to its physicians.

The American Anesthesiology division —accounting for about a quarter of patient service revenues —includes some 775 affiliates who provide medication and pain management services at hospitals (including birthing wings) physician practices and outpatient health and surgery centers.

Geographic Reach

The company operates in about 35 states and Puerto Rico. MEDNAX's five largest markets are Texas (with more than 20% of patient service revenues) North Carolina Florida Georgia and Tennessee.

Sales and Marketing

Some two-thirds of the company's net patient service revenue comes from managed care reimbursements from contracted services provided to hospitals. Another significant portion is received from government-sponsored plans principally state Medicaid programs.

Financial Performance

The company's revenues and profits have continued to climb alongside its business expansion efforts over the last several years. Acquisitive growth as well as higher income from existing practices (from patient volume and reimbursement contract increases) led to a 19% increase in revenue from $1.82 million to $2.15 million in 2013. Net income has followed suit all along and in 2013 it increased $40 million or 16% to $280 million from $240 million the previous year. Cash from operations grew $80 million from $325 million to $405 million due to higher revenue and improved efficiency.

Strategy

Today the company's business strategy is to become a leading provider of physician services by acquiring smaller physician practice groups across the US and continuing to develop administrative expertise. MEDNAX added 11 physician groups during 2013 through transactions totaling more than $250 million in value. Purchases included six anesthesiology practices and five neonatal practices.

The company also works to retain and strengthen existing physician practice relations and win new contracts by offering services and management information systems that improve operational efficiencies. In addition MEDNAX has established a Patient Safety Organization tasked with improving the quality and safety of care by collecting and analyzing data related to patients.

Mergers and Acquisitions

In 2013 the company acquired Neonatology Associates based in Arizona Gwinnett Anesthesia Service of Georgia Anesthesia Specialists of Houston Anesthesia Group of Onondaga New York and Neonatal Intensive Care Associates in Texas for a total of $250 million.

Company Background

Hoping to reproduce its pediatric business model for its anesthesiology business MEDNAX expanded its acquisitions beyond maternal-fetal newborn and pediatric care to include anesthesiology practices in 2007. To reflect its broadening operations the company —formerly named Pediatrix Medical Group —undertook a name and business structure change in late 2008 with MEDNAX established as a holding company.

EXECUTIVES

Vp Human Resources, Claire Fair, age 47
Senior Vice President Research Education And Development, Alan R Spitzer
Senior Vice President Business, John F Rizzo
Senior Vice President Operations Anest, William C Hawk
President American Anesthesiology, Karl B. Wagner, age 48, $500,000 total compensation
CEO, Roger J. Medel, age 68, $1,000,000 total compensation
Regional President Central Region, Robert J. Balcom
President and COO, Joseph M. Calabro, age 53, $600,000 total compensation
Regional President Mountain Region, Eric H. Kurzweil
Regional President Caribbean Region, Carlos A. P Aez
Medical Director, Jose Colindren
SVP and CIO, Robert C. Bryant
President Pediatrix Medical Group, Michael D. Stanley, $450,000 total compensation
Regional President Pacific Region, Gary A. Twiggs
Regional President Atlantic Region, Alan Oliver
Regional President South Central Region, Tony M. Lacaze

CFO and Treasurer, Vivian Lopez-Blanco, age 56, $400,000 total compensation
Vp Advanced Practitioner Program, Margaret Steinbach
Regional Vp Operations Central Region, Arnold (Dick) Poole
Vp Patient Accounts, Christine Lewandowski
Vp Budget And Financial Analysis, John Pepia
Vp Newborn Screening Program, Beverly (Gail) Lim
Vice President And Chief Compliance, James Evans
Vice President Applications At Mednax, Jennifer Arriza
Vice President Operations, David Mintz
Vice President Business Development, Harris Thompson
Vice President Business Development, Mathew Devine
Medical Records Director, Michael B Fernandez
Vp-strategy & Investor Relatio, Charles Lynch
Vice President, William Peoples
Vice President Of Business Developmnt, Mike Bell
Executive Vice President, Joyce Cashman
Medical Director, Manuel Peregrino
Medical Director, Jack Hirsch
Medical Director, Salvatore Lombardi
Vice President, Darren Patz
Vice President Business Development, Robert Manning
Operations Vice President, Jennifer Granberry
Assoc Vice President, Raji White
Medical Director, William Caplan
Vice President Operations Mountain Reg, Darin Crowell
Vice President Practice Integration, Deborah Medel-guerrero
Vice President Sales And Marketing, Rita Hernandez
Vice President Information Systems, Dennis Rhoads
Vice President Operations Central, James Askew
Medical Director, John P McCloskey
Vice President, David Parker
Senior Vice President For Med Affairs, Pascal Goldschmidt
Vice President Program Development, Lim Gail
Vice President Information Technology, Lisa Finch
Medical Director, Manuel Manny
Medical Director, Mitch Rodriguez
Vice President, Michele Luna
Vice President H, Jennifer Schultz
Executive Vice President, Stephen Shapiro
Vice President Operations Pacific, John Bradley
Vice President Human Resources, Dan Porter
Regional Vice President, Lee Wood
Executive Vice President, Brian Gillon
Vice President International Operations, Francisco Paez
Vice President Of Tax, Lee Steinberg
Senior Vice President Operations, James Clark
Vice President Operations Central, Arnold Moore
Vice President Of Operations Central, Dick Sawyer
Vice President Information Technology, Steven Humphries
Vice President Of Marketing, Joseph Harris
Vice President Of Operations Pacific, David Jorgensen
Vice President Budget And Financial, Anita Butler
Vice President Accounting And Finance, Mike Moody
Director Of Nursing, Paula Delmore
Director Of Nursing, Frances Molina
Vice President Operations Central, James Spence
Vice President Human Resources, John Schultz
Vice President Technology Services, James Vernie
Senior Vice President Education, Alan Starnes
Vice President Operations Pacific, John Crowell
Senior Vice President And Chief, Robert Nicholson

Senior Vice President Operations, Neil Hawk
Medical Director, Steven L Goldman
Vice President Operations Mountain, Darin Hunt
Vice President, Hoffman David
Vice President Operations, William Silmak
Vice President H, Sandra Wyant
Vice President Operations, Ted Carlson
Board Of Directors, Dany Garcia
Chairman, Cesar L. Alvarez, age 67
CFO and Treasurer, Vivian Lopez-Blanco, age 56
Board Member, Donna E Shalala
Secretary, Jan Bodin
Treasurer, David King
Treasurer, Ronald Long
Secretary, Mindy Lewaklski
Secretary, Heather Stewart
Treasurer, Melvin Goldberger
Vice Chairman, Candy Ergen
Secretary, Nicole Pinsky
Board Member, Kevin Clark
Board Member, Stephanie Foster
Auditors: PricewaterhouseCoopersLLP

LOCATIONS

HQ: Mednax, Inc.
  1301 Concord Terrace, Sunrise, FL 33323
Phone: 954 384-0175
Web: www.mednax.com
Alaska
Arizona
Arkansas
California
Colorado
Florida
Georgia
Idaho
Indiana
Illinois
Iowa
Kansas
Kentucky
Louisiana
Maryland
Michigan
Missouri
Montana
Nevada
New Jersey
New Mexico
New York
North Carolina
Ohio
Oklahoma
Oregon
Pennsylvania
South Carolina
Tennessee
Texas
Utah
Virginia
Washington
West Virginia
Puerto Rico

PRODUCTS/OPERATIONS

2013 Net Patient Service Revenue

	% of total
Neonatal & other pediatric subspecialties	52
Anesthesia	32
Maternal-fetal	11
Pediatric cardiology	5
Total	**100**

2013 Payer Mix

	% of total
Contracted managed care	69
Government	24
Other third parties	5
Private-pay patients	2
Total	**100**

Selected Physician Specialties

Anesthesia care (inpatient pain relief care before during and after surgery)
Anesthesia subspecialty care (obstetrical critical care cardiac and pediatric anesthesia subspecialties)
Maternal-fetal care (inpatient and outpatient clinical care of high-risk expectant mothers and fetuses)
Neonatal care (clinical care of premature newborns or babies with complications)
Pain management (acute and chronic pain management services; postoperative acute pain management; outpatient chronic pain services at clinics and medical offices)
Pediatric cardiology care (inpatient and outpatient care of fetuses infants children and adolescents with congenital heart defects or acquired heart diseases; through affiliations care of adults with congenital heart defects)
Other pediatric subspecialty care (inpatient care for critically ill or injured children and adolescents)

COMPETITORS

ApolloMD	IPC The Hospitalist
CEP America	Company
Cogent HMG	Orion HealthCorp
EmCare	Physician Staffing
Hospital Physician	Sheridan Healthcare
Partners	Team Health

HISTORICAL FINANCIALS

Company Type: Public

Income Statement

FYE: December 31

	REVENUE ($ mil.)	NET INCOME ($ mil.)	NET PROFIT MARGIN	EMPLOYEES
12/14	2,438.9	317.2	13.0%	10,175
12/13	2,154.0	280.5	13.0%	8,800
12/12	1,816.6	240.9	13.3%	7,900
12/11	1,588.2	218.0	13.7%	6,967
12/10	1,401.5	202.6	14.5%	6,270
Annual Growth	**14.9%**	**11.9%**	**—**	**12.9%**

2014 Year-End Financials

Debt ratio: 15.7%	No. of shares (mil.): 96
Return on equity: 13.7%	Dividends
Cash ($ mil.): 47	Yield: —
Current ratio: 1.12	Payout: —
Long-term debt ($ mil.): 558	Market value ($ mil.): 6,349

	STOCK PRICE ($) FY Close	P/E High/Low		PER SHARE ($) Earnings	Dividends	Book Value
12/14	66.11	21	16	3.18	0.00	23.58
12/13	53.38	40	19	2.78	0.00	23.15
12/12	79.52	33	24	2.43	0.00	20.35
12/11	72.01	33	26	2.24	0.00	17.69
12/10	67.29	31	21	2.13	0.00	15.10
Annual Growth	**(0.4%)**	**—**	**—**	**10.5%**	**—**	**11.8%**

Medytox Solutions Inc.

Fabricated rubber products nec nsk

EXECUTIVES

Ceo, Bill Forhan

LOCATIONS

HQ: Medytox Solutions Inc.
400 South Australian Ave., 8th Floor, West Palm
Beach, FL 33401
Phone: 561 855-1626
Web: www.medytoxsolutionsinc.com

HISTORICAL FINANCIALS

Company Type: Public

Income Statement

FYE: December 31

	REVENUE ($ mil.)	NET INCOME ($ mil.)	NET PROFIT MARGIN	EMPLOYEES
12/13	52.5	8.2	15.7%	115
12/12	21.0	2.3	11.1%	68
12/11	3.9	0.0	2.3%	33
12/10	0.0	(0.3)	—	0
12/09	0.0	(0.0)	—	0
Annual Growth	729.7%	—	—	—

2013 Year-End Financials

Debt ratio: 17.1%
Return on equity: 159.4%
Cash ($ mil.): 4
Current ratio: 1.15
Long-term debt ($ mil.): 0

No. of shares (mil.): 30
Dividends
  Yield: —
  Payout: —
Market value ($ mil.): 219

	STOCK PRICE ($) FY Close	P/E High/Low	PER SHARE ($) Earnings	Dividends	Book Value
12/13	7.30	38 27	0.19	0.00	0.29
Annual Growth	—	— —	—	—	—

MercadoLibre Inc

Mercadolibre greases the wheels of commerce in Latin America. Its online trading service enables individuals and businesses to electronically arrange the sale and purchase of items in more than 2000 categories. In addition to its auction and classified listing services Mercadolibre offers an online payment service (MercadoPago) to further facilitate electronic transactions. The company serves some 550 million users in about a dozen countries in Latin America; the majority of its sales come from Brazil. Sales come from listing fees fees based on the value of goods sold and ancillary services. Online auction giant eBay owns about 18% of Mercadolibre.

Geographic Reach

Mercadolibre's reporting segments include its operations in Brazil Argentina Mexico Venezuela and other countries (Chile Colombia Costa Rica Dominican Republic Ecuador Panama Peru Portugal and Uruguay).

Financial Performance

The company's annual revenue has been trending upward year-over-year. In fiscal 2012 it claimed revenue of $373.6 million up from the $298.9 million it brought in during fiscal 2011 and the $216.7 million the company reported for revenue during fiscal 2010.

EXECUTIVES

EVP and COO, Hern Ân Kazah, age 44, $206,840 total compensation
Chairman President and CEO, Marcos Galperin
Auditors: PriceWaterhouse&Co.SRL

LOCATIONS

HQ: MercadoLibre Inc
Arias 3751, 7th Floor, Buenos Aires C1430CRG
Phone: (54) 11 4640 8000
Web: www.mercadolibre.com

COMPETITORS

Amazon.com	Yahoo!
Google	eBay
PayPal	

HISTORICAL FINANCIALS

Company Type: Public

Income Statement

FYE: December 31

	REVENUE ($ mil.)	NET INCOME ($ mil.)	NET PROFIT MARGIN	EMPLOYEES
12/13	472.5	117.5	24.9%	2,171
12/12	373.6	101.2	27.1%	1,892
12/11	298.9	76.7	25.7%	1,633
12/10	216.7	56.0	25.9%	1,567
12/09	172.8	33.2	19.2%	1,466
Annual Growth	28.6%	37.2%	—	10.3%

2013 Year-End Financials

Debt ratio: —
Return on equity: 37.1%
Cash ($ mil.): 140
Current ratio: 1.46
Long-term debt ($ mil.): —

No. of shares (mil.): 44
Dividends
  Yield: 0.5%
  Payout: 23.7%
Market value ($ mil.): 4,759

	STOCK PRICE ($) FY Close	P/E High/Low	PER SHARE ($) Earnings	Dividends	Book Value
12/13	107.79	54 30	2.66	0.57	7.78
12/12	78.55	45 28	2.30	0.44	6.56
12/11	79.54	55 29	1.73	0.32	4.97
12/10	66.65	59 29	1.27	0.00	3.89
12/09	51.87	73 17	0.75	0.00	2.59
Annual Growth	20.1%	— —	37.2%	—	31.7%

Meridian Bancorp Inc

Contrary to its name Meridian Interstate Bancorp pretty much keeps it to a single state. It is the holding company of East Boston Savings Bank which provides standard deposit and lending services to individuals and businesses in the greater Boston area. The bank writes single-family commercial and multifamily mortgages as well as construction and business loans and consumer loans. East Boston Savings operates about 30 branches in eastern Massachusetts. Mutual holding company Meridian Financial Services owns 59% of Meridian Interstate Bancorp.

Geographic Reach

Meridian Interstate operates across the greater Boston metropolitan area in Essex Middlesex and Suffolk.

Operations

The bank has about $2.7 billion in assets; commercial real estate loans comprise 45% of its loan portfolio.

Meridian Interstate owns a 40% stake in Hampshire First Bank a New Hampshire-chartered bank established in 2006.

Sales and Marketing

Meridian Interstate has devoted more dollars to advertising in recent years. It spent $2.95 million in fiscal 2013 on advertising up from $2.54 million in 2012 and $2.45 million in 2011.

Financial Performance

Like many small banks that survived the Great Recession Meridian Interstate has grown steadily the last few years. In 2013 it reported an 8% increase in revenue from $106 million to $115 million due to increased loan payments as interest rates recovered. Net income grew 24% from $12 million to $15 million on the strength of higher revenue and changes in the company's bookkeeping. Cash from operations jumped to $28 million after the company sold some of its loans.

Strategy

As part of its growth strategy the bank has bolstered its commercial real estate and business loans as well as its construction loans. Previously residential mortgages represent the company's largest loan segment.

The bank also intends to grow through the opening of new branches and pursuing branch acquisitions. It has opened 14 new branches in upscale Boston neighborhoods in the last two years and acquired another six.

To further enable growth Meridian Interstate in 2014 announced that it will convert from a mutual company to a public corporation.

EXECUTIVES

Senior Vice President Human Resources, Eric M Heath
Senior Vice President Consumer & Business Banking, Keith D Armstrong
CFO, Mark L. Abbate, age 59
Chairman and CEO, Richard J. Gavegnano, age 66, $311,400 total compensation
Executive Vice President Corporate Banking, Frank Romano
President and COO, Deborah J. Jackson
Executive Vice President Lending, John Migliozzi
Chairman and CEO, Richard J. Gavegnano, age 66
Board Member, Carl Lagreca
Auditors: Wolf&CompanyP.C.

LOCATIONS

HQ: Meridian Bancorp Inc
67 Prospect Street, Peabody, MA 01960
Phone: 617 567-1500
Web: www.ebsb.com
Allpoint Locator
Allston
Belmont
Cambridge
Danvers
Dorchester
East Boston
Everett
Jamaica Plain
Lynn
Medford
Melrose
Peabody
Revere
Saugus
Somerville
South Boston
South End
Wakefield
West Roxbury

PRODUCTS/OPERATIONS

2013 Sales

	$ mil.	% of total
Interest & dividend income		
Interest & fees on loans	89.4	78
Interest & debt securities	4.1	4
Dividends on equity securities	1.7	1
Non-interest income		
Gain on sale of securities	9.6	8
Customer service fees	7.1	6
Income from bank-owned life insurance	1.2	1
Mortgage banking gains	0.6	1
Loan fees & other income	0.9	1
Total	**114.6**	**100**

Selected Products & Services

Personal
Deposit Rates
Investments
Personal Checking
Personal Lending
Personal Online Banking
Retirement Services
Savings & CDs
Business
Business Checking
Business Lending
Business Online Banking
Business Retirement Services
Business Savings
Deposit Rates
Institutional Banking
Merchant Services
Commercial
Cash Management
Commercial Lending
Corporate Banking
Deposit Rates

COMPETITORS

Bank of America	Middlesex Savings
Cambridge Financial	Peoples Federal
Citizens Financial	Bancshares Inc.
Group	Sovereign Bank
Eastern Bank	TD Bank USA

HISTORICAL FINANCIALS

Company Type: Public

Income Statement

FYE: December 31

	ASSETS ($ mil.)	NET INCOME ($ mil.)	INCOME AS % OF ASSETS	EMPLOYEES
12/13	2,682.1	15.4	0.6%	455
12/12	2,278.7	12.4	0.5%	433
12/11	1,974.3	11.9	0.6%	392
12/10	1,835.8	13.3	0.7%	360
12/09	1,211.3	3.7	0.3%	197
Annual Growth	**22.0%**	**42.3%**	**—**	**23.3%**

2013 Year-End Financials

Return on assets: 0.6%
Return on equity: 6.3%
Long-term debt ($ mil.): —
No. of shares (mil.): 22
Sales ($ mil): 114

Dividends
Yield: —
Payout: —
Market value ($ mil.): —

Merit Medical Systems, Inc.

When it comes to medical devices this company believes its merits speak for themselves. Merit Medical Systems makes disposable medical products used during interventional and diagnostic cardiology radiology gastroenterology and pulmonary procedures. The company's products include catheters guide wires needles and tubing used in heart stent procedures pacemaker placement and angioplasties as well as products for endoscopy dialysis and other procedures. Merit Medical sells its products as stand-alone items or in custom-made kits to hospitals and other health care providers as well as to custom packagers and equipment makers worldwide.

Geographic Reach

Though the US accounts for more than 60% of sales the company is focused on growth in overseas markets. It experienced a 37% increase in international sales during 2012.

Headquartered in South Jordan Utah Merit Medical has a major manufacturing and distribution center in Ireland. It also has manufacturing centers in Texas and Virginia in the US as well as in the Netherlands and France.

Operations

The company's largest operating segment —accounting for more than 95% of sales —is its cardiovascular division which makes cardiology and radiology devices for the diagnosis of arterial and vascular disease among other conditions. Offerings include stand-alone devices custom procedure trays and kits inflation devices and catheters. It also includes embolotherapy products which use bioengineered microspheres to create targeted vascular occlusion (the blockage of blood vessels) and drug delivery.

Merit Medical's much smaller endoscopy segment makes devices for gastroenterology and pulmonary treatments including minimally-invasive treatment of throat and biliary constriction from malignant tumors. The endoscopy operations are conducted through Merit Medical's Endotek subsidiary.

The company also conducts selected manufacturing of custom medical kits and components for third parties through its OEM division.

Sales and Marketing

Marketing and sales efforts in the US and abroad are conducted through a direct sales force of about 200 representatives as well as through independent distributors and manufacturers. Products are marketed to hospital and clinic-based medical professionals in fields including cardiology radiology gastroenterology pulmonary medicine vascular surgery pain management and thoracic surgery.

Financial Performance

Continuing on its growth trajectory over the last five years Merit Medical's revenues grew by 10% in 2012 thanks to increased sales from its cardiovascular and endoscopy segments. The increase in sales of guidewires hemostasis valves catheters and custom kits and trays attributed to growth in the Cardiovascular segment and a rise in sales of the EndoMAXX esophageal stent helped to grow revenue in the Endoscopy segment.

Net income has fluctuated however as Merit Medical has worked to balance costs with earnings. The company's net income decreased by 14% due to higher operating expenses primarily from the expansion of its sales and marketing force as well as higher R&D costs. In 2011 jumped by 85% in 2011 due to increased sales volumes higher gross margins and a lower effective income tax rates.

Strategy

Though a sizable part of Merit Medical's strategy is growth by acquisition the company also invests about 5% of its annual income in research and development efforts. In 2012 the company got FDA clearance to market the Merit Laureate hydrophilic guide wire as well as its 30-60um QuadraSphere Microspheres and its ONE Snare endovascular system. Also in 2012 the company made several investments to expand its international sales and distribution network especially in emerging markets such as Brazil India and Russia.

Mergers and Acquisitions

In 2012 Merit Medical acquired Ostial Solutions LLC a privately-held company based in Kalamazoo Michigan which makes a tool that improves the accuracy of stent placement. Also that year it purchased catheter-based vascular access device maker Thomas Medical Products for some $167 million and peritoneal dialysis catheter manufacturer Medigroup for $4 million.

Ownership

Investors in Merit Medical include Edgepoint Investment Group and Blackrock each of which hold a 10% stake.

EXECUTIVES

Vp Marketing Department, Larry R Tolman
Vice President Regulatory Medical Affairs And Quality, Melodie Domurad
Chairman President and CEO, Fred P. Lampropoulos, age 65, $860,000 total compensation
EVP Sales and Marketing, Martin R. (Marty) Stephens, age 61, $400,000 total compensation
President Merit Endotek, Darla R. Gill
President Merit Technology Group, Joseph (Joe) Wright
COO, Arlin D. Nelson, age 74, $325,000 total compensation
EVP Global OEM and Europe the Middle East and Africa, Justin Lampropoulos
Chief Information Officer, Joseph Pierce
Chief Accounting Officer, Greg Barnett
Vice President Personnel, Brent Bowen
Vice President Advanced Products, Rich Snider
National Sales Manager, Matt Lyons
Vice Presidaent Of Molding, Mazhar Shah
Vice President Manufacturing, Neil Peterson
Vice President Regulatory Affairs Europe, Tony Keaveney
Vice President Randd At Merit Med Sys, Jim Mottola
Vice President European Sales, Robert Jenkins
Vice President Research And Innovation, Niall Behan
Vice President Manufacturing, Gearoid Quinn
Vice President Regulatory Affairs, Glenn Norton
Assistant To Executive Vice President, Karen Smyth
Vice President, Kent Bachman
Vice President Advanced Products Group, Zeke Eller
Vice President Sales And Business Development, Michael Blackham
Chairman President and CEO, Fred P. Lampropoulos, age 65
Auditors: Deloitte&ToucheLLP

LOCATIONS

HQ: Merit Medical Systems, Inc.
1600 West Merit Parkway, South Jordan, UT 84095
Phone: 801 253-1600
Web: www.merit.com

2012 Sales

	$ mil.	% of total
US	248.0	63
Other countries	146.3	37
Total	**394.3**	**100**

PRODUCTS/OPERATIONS

2012 Sales

	$ mil.	% of total
Cardiovascular	378.5	96
Endoscopy	15.8	4
Total	**394.3**	**100**

Selected Products

Backstop (waste handling system)
BasixCOMPAK (inflation devices)
Blue Diamond (inflation devices)
Captiva Blood Containment Device (safety and waste management)
DialEase (sheath introducers)
En Snare (retrieval device)
Fountain (thrombolytic infusion catheters)
Inqwire (diagnostic guide wire)
Intellisystem (inflation devices)
Majestik (angiography needles)
Medallion (specialty syringes)
Merit Disposal Depot (waste handling system)
Meritrans (disposable blood pressure transducer)
Monarch (inflation devices)
Prelude (sheath introducers)
ProGuide (chronic dialysis catheter)
Smart Tip (coronary control syringes)

COMPETITORS

Abbott Labs	ICU Medical
AngioDynamics	Johnson & Johnson
B. Braun Medical	Medtronic
Bard	St. Jude Medical
Baxter International	Teleflex
Boston Scientific	Terumo
Cook Incorporated	Vascular Solutions
Cordis	

HISTORICAL FINANCIALS

Company Type: Public

Income Statement

FYE: December 31

	REVENUE ($ mil.)	NET INCOME ($ mil.)	NET PROFIT MARGIN	EMPLOYEES
12/13	449.0	16.5	3.7%	2,888
12/12	394.2	19.7	5.0%	2,760
12/11	359.4	23.0	6.4%	2,400
12/10	296.7	12.4	4.2%	2,178
12/09	257.4	22.5	8.8%	1,875
Annual Growth	**14.9%**	**(7.4%)**	**—**	**11.4%**

2013 Year-End Financials

Debt ratio: 34.1%	No. of shares (mil.): 42
Return on equity: 4.2%	Dividends
Cash ($ mil.): 7	Yield: —
Current ratio: 2.53	Payout: —
Long-term debt ($ mil.): 238	Market value ($ mil.): 674

	STOCK PRICE ($) FY Close	P/E High/Low		PER SHARE ($) Earnings	Dividends	Book Value
12/13	15.74	42	25	0.39	0.00	9.47
12/12	13.90	32	25	0.46	0.00	8.98
12/11	13.38	41	21	0.58	0.00	8.50
12/10	15.83	56	40	0.34	0.00	6.64
12/09	19.24	31	15	0.63	0.00	6.21
Annual Growth	**(4.9%)**	**—**	**—**	**(11.4%)**	**—**	**11.1%**

Meritage Homes Corp

Meritage Homes sees merit in building houses in high-growth areas of the western and southern US. The company typically constructs single-family homes targeted at first- and second-time homebuyers as well as the luxury and older adult market. Home prices range from about $130000 to $1 million and average about $339000. Meritage Homes controls roughly 15500 lots and most often builds in nearly 190 communities in Arizona California Colorado Florida North Carolina Texas and Tennessee. Homes are sold under the Meritage Homes brand as well as Monterey Homes (in Arizona and Texas) and Phillips Builders (in Tennessee). The company which was founded in 1985 also develops active-adult communities.

Geographic Reach

Arizona-based Meritage is actively selling homes in 188 communities across eight US states. In 2013 communities in Arizona California Colorado and Nevada —the West region —account for just over 50% of the homebuilder's sales. (The company exited Nevada during 2013.) The Central region which includes operations in Texas brings in about 28% of sales while in the East North Carolina Florida and Tennessee contribute about 20%.

Operations

Meritage boasts eight operating segments representing the eight states in which the company operates. The segments acquire and develop land build homes market and sell the homes and provide warranties and customer service.

Sales and Marketing

Meritage serves several markets including Dallas/Fort Worth Austin Houston and San Antonio in Texas; Phoenix and Tucson in Arizona; East Bay/Central Valley Sacramento and Inland Empire in California; Las Vegas Denver Colorado; Orlando and Tampa in Florida; Raleigh and Charlotte in North Carolina; and (since late 2013) Nashville Tennessee.

It caters to first-time move-up luxury and active adult buyers and sells its home under three brand names: Meritage Homes Monterery Homes and Phillips Builders. Through an agreement appliance behemoth Whirlpool supplies Meritage with its appliances in the company's Southern and Western states.

It boasts some 350 sales and marketing employees across its business. In fiscal 2013 Meritage spent about $6.3 million on advertising up from $5.5 million the year before.

Financial Performance

After years of struggling through the economic downturn the homebuilder's sales have soared as of late. In 2013 sales increased 54% versus 2012 to $1.83 billion after posting a 39% gain in the previous annual comparison. Indeed sales have about doubled since 2010 and profits have soared. Cash flow from operations increased after three years of steep decline. Meritage's net income meanwhile increased 18% in 2013 versus 2012 to $124.5 million.

Texas was the company's largest volume market in 2013 generating about $493 million in revenue.

Strategy

One of the nation's top homebuilders Meritage has largely focused on the southern and western regions. However the housing downturn which has been especially severe in California and Florida changed Meritage's game plan. The homebuilder is getting more choosey about where it builds focusing on high-growth areas with low foreclosure rates. It entered Raleigh North Carolina in 2011 exited Nevada in 2013 and entered Tennessee in 2013 by buying Phillips Builders.

Indeed Meritage is now increasing its lot supply and looking for well-priced deals on land in growing markets.

Meritage also increased its sales and marketing efforts to sell its backlog of existing homes and has added a line of lower-cost homes under the Simply Smart brand aimed at first-time buyers. Meritage plans to continue offering new homes at lower price points to attract first-time buyers. It's also building more energy efficient homes to lure buyers. In 2011 Meritage unveiled its first "Net-Zero" home which produces as much energy as it consumes. Still Meritage faces intense competition from other builders and from the excess supply of re-sale and foreclosure homes.

Mergers and Acquisitions

As Meritage was hanging up its hat in Nevada and exiting the market the company bought Phillips Builders a three-generation residential developer in Nashville Tennessee. Since 1952 the company has built more than 20000 homes there that range in price from $175000 to $425000. The acquisition included about 500 lots.

EXECUTIVES

Chairman and CEO, Steven J. (Steve) Hilton, age 53, $1,017,500 total compensation
EVP and CFO, Larry W. Seay, age 58, $500,000 total compensation
Vice President Taxation, Peter Hebert
EVP and COO, Steven M. (Steve) Davis, age 55, $500,000 total compensation
EVP General Counsel and Secretary, C. Timothy White, age 53, $525,000 total compensation
Regional President Southwest Region Acting Division President Tucson Active Adult, Jeffrey Grobstein
Vice President Sales, John Bargnesi
Vice President Of Land Acquisitions, Micheal Ilescremieux
Vice President I Division, Kevin Kimball
Vice President I Region Purchasing, Rob Smith
Vice President, Jimmy Gaskins
Vice President I Strategic Operations, Wayne Yamano
Vice President Finance, Rick Roberson
Vice President I Division Land, Ben Wilson
Vice President Sales And Marketing, Andrew Hall
Vice President Of Sales, Michelle Shepherd
Vice President Operations, Don Hatcher
Vice President Client Services, Amy Etzkorn
Vice President Regional Counsel, Austin Woffinden
Vice President And Associate General, Melvin Faraoni
Regional Vice President Purchasing, Tom Kelley
Vice President Of Sales, Staci Belew
Vice President Of Operations, Vince Hunter

Vice President Sales, Steve Hextel
Vice President Division Operations, Ramon
  Gonzalez
Vice President, James Hindmarsh
Vice President Operations, Owen Brandli
Vice President Marketing, Keri Couples
Vice President, Lynn Collins
Vice President Operations, Randall Gamino
Vice President, Bryan Robertson
Senior Vice President Of Land, Ed Depinto
Vice President I Division Finance, James Saunders
Regional Vice President Of Finance, Lawrence
  Lane
Vice President I Division Finance, Bryan Beil
Chairman and CEO, Steven J. (Steve) Hilton, age 53
EVP General Counsel and Secretary, C. Timothy
  White, age 53
Treasurer, Darin Rowe
Board Member, Kenneth Nault
Auditors: Deloitte&ToucheLLP

LOCATIONS

HQ: Meritage Homes Corp
  8800 East Raintree Drive, Suite 300, Scottsdale, AZ
  85260
Phone: 480 515-8100
Web: www.meritagehomes.com

2013 Sales

	$ mil.	% of total
West	937.1	52
Central	509.0	28
East	368.5	20
Total	1814.6	100

Selected Markets

Phoenix AZ
Dallas/Ft. Worth TX
Austin TX
Tucson AZ
Houston TX
East Bay/Central Valley CA
Sacramento CA
Las Vegas NV
San Antonio TX
Inland Empire CA
Denver CO
Orlando FL
Raleigh NC
Tampa FL
Charlotte NC

COMPETITORS

Beazer Homes	NVR
D.R. Horton	PulteGroup
David Weekley Homes	Shea Homes
Hovnanian Enterprises	Standard Pacific
KB Home	The Ryland Group
Lennar	Toll Brothers
M.D.C.	Warmington Group
Maracay Homes	William Lyon Homes

HISTORICAL FINANCIALS

Company Type: Public

Income Statement

FYE: December 31

	REVENUE ($ mil.)	NET INCOME ($ mil.)	NET PROFIT MARGIN	EMPLOYEES
12/13	1,820.7	124.4	6.8%	1,050
12/12	1,193.6	105.1	8.8%	830
12/11	861.2	(21.1)	—	660
12/10	941.6	7.1	0.8%	650
12/09	970.3	(66.4)	—	700
Annual Growth	17.0%	—		10.7%

2013 Year-End Financials

Debt ratio: 45.1%
Return on equity: 16.2%
Cash ($ mil.): 325
Current ratio: 1.27
Long-term debt ($ mil.): 905

No. of shares (mil.): 36
Dividends
  Yield: —
  Payout: —
Market value ($ mil.): 1,739

	STOCK PRICE ($) FY Close	P/E High/Low		PER SHARE ($) Earnings	Dividends	Book Value
12/13	47.99	15	11	3.25	0.00	23.21
12/12	37.35	14	8	3.00	0.00	19.49
12/11	23.19	—	—	(0.65)	0.00	15.05
12/10	22.20	114	71	0.22	0.00	15.56
12/09	19.33	—	—	(2.12)	0.00	15.26
Annual Growth	25.5%	—	—	—	—	11.1%

Mesa Laboratories, Inc.

Mesa Laboratories is reaching a plateau in the field of measurements. The company makes niche-market electronic measurement testing and recording instruments for medical food processing electronics and aerospace applications. Mesa's products include sensors that record temperature humidity and pressure levels; flow meters for water treatment polymerization and chemical processing applications; and sonic concentration analyzers. The company also makes kidney hemodialysis treatment products including metering equipment and machines that clean dialyzers (or filters) for reuse. It also provides repair recalibration and certification services.

Operations

The company is organized into two segments - biological indicators and instruments - each accounting for about half of sales. Biological indicators sold under the Mesa and Apex brands are used by dental offices hospitals and manufacturers of medical devices and pharmaceuticals for quality control testing in sterilization processes. The instruments division includes the DataTrace (data loggers) Bios Torqo (bottle cap test systems) and Nusonics (ultrasonic fluid measurement systems) brands.

A third division continuous monitoring was created in 2013 through the acquisition of two businesses. Continuous monitoring systems provide temperature control to laboratories that require stable environments such as hospitals blood banks pharmacies and medical device manufacturers.

Geographic Reach

Mesa Laboratories has manufacturing plants in Lakewood Colorado; Butler New Jersey; Bozeman Montana; and Omaha Nebraska. The new continuous monitoring division operates from Marlton New Jersey; and Emeryville California.

Sales and Marketing

The company uses a direct sales force as well as distributors for international sales. Customers in the US account for about 60% of revenue.

Financial Performance

Overall sales grew 17% in fiscal 2013 (year-end March) to $46 million. Both product segments - biological indicators and instruments - enjoyed increased sales from both organic (new customers) and inorganic (acquisitions) growth. Profits grew 6% to $8 million. While the company has always been small (less than $50 million in sales) it also

---

keeps low operating expenses and thus has always been profitable.

Mergers and Acquisitions

Inorganic growth is a key strategy of Mesa Laboratories. In November 2013 it bought two companies to create the continuous monitoring systems segment which is expected to add about $10 million a year to its top line. The company paid almost $22 million for New Jersey-based Amega Scientific Corporation and California-based TempSys Inc. Continuous monitoring systems provide temperature control to laboratories that require stable environments such as hospitals blood banks pharmacies and medical device manufacturers.

Earlier that year it bought the SureTorque line of bottle cap torque testing instruments from ST Acquisitions LLC for $2 million. SureTorque instruments can be configured for a variety of industries including pharmaceutical biotechnology and food and beverage.

In 2012 Mesa bought the flow calibrator business of Bios International for more than $15 million. Bios flow calibration instrumentation is used in applications such as industrial hygiene and process control environmental monitoring and meteorology in sectors such as automotive biotech food processing semiconductors and more. The purchase followed Mesa's acquisition strategy of finding successful products in regulated industries.

HISTORY

In 2009 president John Sullivan took the reins as CEO replacing Luke Schmieder who had been CEO since founding the company in 1982. Still chairman of the board Schmieder owns about 9% of Mesa Laboratories.

EXECUTIVES

CEO President Treasurer and Director, John J.
  Sullivan, age 62, $302,495 total compensation
Chief Sales and Marketing Officer, Glenn E.
  Adriance, age 60, $194,999 total compensation
Chief Financial and Chief Accounting Officer and
  Secretary, John Sakys, age 44, $204,997 total
  compensation
SVP Operations, Bryan T Leo, $145,000 total
  compensation
SVP Operations, Garrett Krushefski, $150,000 total
  compensation
National Sales Manager, James O'Malley
Chairman, Luke R. Schmieder, age 72
Auditors: EhrhardtKeefeSteiner&HottmanPC

LOCATIONS

HQ: Mesa Laboratories, Inc.
  12100 West Sixth Avenue, Lakewood, CO 80228
Phone: 303 987-8000
Web: www.mesalabs.com
FY2013
  Amega Scientific Corporation
  TempSys Inc.
FY2012
  Bios International
FY 2010
  SGM Biotech
  Apex Laboratories

2013 Sales

	$ mil.	% of total
US	28.6	62
Other countries	17.8	38
Total	46.4	100

PRODUCTS/OPERATIONS

2013 Sales

	$ mil.	% of total
Product	35.3	76
Other	11.1	24
Total	**46.4**	**100**

2013 Sales

	$ mil.	% of total
Instruments	25.0	53
Biological indicators	21.4	47
Total	**46.4**	**100**

Selected Products

Biological and chemical indicators (Raven Biological
  Laboratories)
Electronic thermal sensors
  DATATRACE
  DATATRACE Micropack Tracers
  ELOGG
  Flatpack Tracers
  FRB Tracers
Hemodialysis products (Automata)
  Database management software (Reuse Data
  Management System)
  Dialyzer reprocessors (ECHO MM-1000)
  Meters (Western Meters)
Sonic fluid measurement products (NuSonics)
  Sonic concentration analyzers
  Sonic flowmeters

COMPETITORS

3M Health Care	Mikron Infrared
Badger Meter	Rockwell Medical
Cantel Medical	STERIS
Danaher	Siemens Corp.
Emerson Electric	Siemens Water
Euro Tech	Technologies
GE	Teledyne Isco
Gambro AB	Thermo Fisher
K-Tron	Scientific
MEDIVATORS	Velocys

HISTORICAL FINANCIALS

Company Type: Public

Income Statement

FYE: March 31

	REVENUE ($ mil.)	NET INCOME ($ mil.)	NET PROFIT MARGIN	EMPLOYEES
03/14	52.7	9.0	17.1%	273
03/13	46.4	8.4	18.2%	215
03/12	39.6	7.9	20.0%	186
03/11	32.8	6.1	18.8%	177
03/10	21.9	4.7	21.7%	112
Annual Growth	**24.5%**	**17.2%**	**—**	**25.0%**

2014 Year-End Financials

Debt ratio: 16.9%
Return on equity: —
Cash ($ mil.): 5
Current ratio: 2.60
Long-term debt ($ mil.): 16

No. of shares (mil.): 3
Dividends
  Yield: 0.6%
  Payout: 26.6%
Market value ($ mil.): 315

	STOCK PRICE ($) FY Close	P/E High/Low		PER SHARE ($) Earnings	Dividends	Book Value
03/14	90.25	36	18	2.49	0.58	18.43
03/13	52.78	22	17	2.35	0.54	15.57
03/12	49.32	24	12	2.29	0.50	13.22
03/11	28.80	16	11	1.86	0.46	11.20
03/10	25.96	19	11	1.45	0.42	9.74
Annual Growth	**36.5%**	**—**	**—**	**14.5%**	**8.4%**	**17.3%**

Mesabi Trust

In the Iron Range of Mesabi the stockholders trust. Mesabi Trust collects royalties and bonuses from the sale of minerals that are shipped from Northshore Mining's Silver Bay Minnesota facility. The mining company is a wholly owned subsidiary of Cliffs a supplier of iron ore products to the steel industry. Northshore Mining pays royalties to Mesabi Trust based on production and sales of crude ore pulled from the trust's property; it has curtailed its extraction efforts citing lack of demand. Independent consultants track production and sales for Mesabi Trust. Deutsche Bank Trust Company Americas is the corporate trustee of Mesabi Trust.

The company was formed in 1961 to hold the interests formerly owned by Mesabi Iron Company. Mesabi Trust's revenues are generated solely in the form of leasehold royalty income.

EXECUTIVES

Individual Trustee, Norman F. Sprague III, age 65
Individual Trustee, Richard G. Lareau, age 84
Individual Trustee, Robert C Berglund, age 66
Individual Trustee, James A. Ehrenberg, age 70
VP; Deutsche Bank Trust Company Americas,
  Kenneth R. Ring
Auditors: WipfliLLP

LOCATIONS

HQ: Mesabi Trust
c/o Deutsche Bank Trust Company Americas, Trust &
Agency Services, 60 Wall Street, 16th Floor, New York,
NY 10005
Phone: 615 271-2520
Web: www.mesabi-trust.com

PRODUCTS/OPERATIONS

2009 Sales

	$ mil.	% of total
Royalties under amended lease agreements	35.0	99
Royalties under Peters Lease fee & interest	0.5	1
Total	**35.5**	**100**

COMPETITORS

BHP Billiton	Rio Tinto Limited
Great Northern Iron	
Ore	

HISTORICAL FINANCIALS

Company Type: Public

Income Statement

FYE: January 31

	REVENUE ($ mil.)	NET INCOME ($ mil.)	NET PROFIT MARGIN	EMPLOYEES
01/14	22.0	21.0	95.5%	0
01/13	31.5	30.6	97.1%	0
01/12	34.1	33.2	97.3%	0
01/11	33.3	32.4	97.4%	0
01/10	13.2	12.4	93.8%	0
Annual Growth	**13.6%**	**14.1%**	**—**	**—**

2014 Year-End Financials

Debt ratio: —
Return on equity: 1,943.9%
Cash ($ mil.): 7
Current ratio: 1.06
Long-term debt ($ mil.): —

No. of shares (mil.): 13
Dividends
  Yield: 8.0%
  Payout: 102.5%
Market value ($ mil.): 264

	STOCK PRICE ($) FY Close	P/E High/Low		PER SHARE ($) Earnings	Dividends	Book Value
01/14	20.09	15	11	1.61	1.62	0.08
01/13	24.67	14	9	2.34	2.33	0.09
01/12	32.06	17	8	2.53	2.53	0.08
01/11	33.33	23	5	2.47	2.49	0.08
01/10	13.82	16	6	0.95	1.15	0.09
Annual Growth	**9.8%**	**—**	**—**	**14.1%**	**8.9%**	**(3.4%)**

Methode Electronics, Inc.

When it comes to making gear for manufacturers there's no madness in Methode Electronics' methods. Methode produces a wide variety of components especially electronic connectors and controls that are used by automotive manufacturers (products made for Ford and GM together account for more than half of sales) and in computers communications equipment industrial systems aircraft and spacecraft and consumer electronics. It also makes electrical bus systems and radio remote controls among other products. Methode offers electrical environmental and other industrial testing services through its Trace Laboratories unit.

Operations

Methode Electronics divides its business into three segments: automotive (70% of ales) interconnect (20% of sales) and power products (10% of sales). Automotive devices include control switches for electrical power and signals connectors for electrical devices integrated control components and switches and sensors that monitor components or systems. The interconnect segment provides copper and fiber-optic interconnect and interface products such as connectors custom cable assemblies industrial safety radio remote controls and optical and copper transceivers. The power products segment manufactures braided flexible cables current-carrying laminated bus devices custom power-product assemblies high-current low voltage flexible power cabling systems and powder coated bus bars.

Geographic Reach

The company has manufacturing plants in China Malta Mexico the Philippines Switzerland and the US (in Illinois Oklahoma and Texas.) R&D centers are located in India Italy Lebanon the UK and the US. Due to its dependence on the US automotive industry more than half of sales come from the US.

Sales and Marketing

Methode Electronics uses a direct sales force that works with customers to design custom-engineered and application-specific products. For certain automotive products the company distributes products to suppliers of automotive OEMs.

Financial Performance

The company has experienced substantial revenue growth over the past four years. Overall sales in fiscal 2014 (year-end April) skyrocketed to $772 million up 48% from the $519 million it made in 2013. All three product segments (automotive interconnect and power products) enjoyed double-digit growth and the automotive segment began supplying electronics for GM's center consoles.

Profits grew alongside revenue increasing 135% to $96 million. Cash flow followed suit as well swelling to $72 million.

HISTORY

William McGinley started Methode in 1947 to produce vacuum tube sockets for portable radios. Methode began making printed circuits for radios in 1952. During the early 1960s it supplied circuits for color TVs made by RCA. The rising dominance of Asian electronics manufacturers during the 1970s inspired Methode to turn to the nascent computer market for customers; it made electronic connectors for mainframe and midrange computers. During the 1980s the company began developing network products and fiber-optic connectors.

In 1993 Methode sold its automotive test equipment subsidiary to focus on interconnect products. That year the company began a prolonged acquisition drive when it bought Mikon Ltd. a UK-based supplier of fiber-optic cable assemblies and components. In 1994 Methode acquired Rogers Corp.'s power distribution business. The next year it bought Duel Systems a maker of sonic-welded PC memory cards and two cable manufacturing operations from ETOS Fujikura.

The company's 1997 acquisitions included Merit Elektrik a Malta-based maker of automotive switches and Magneteolastic Devices a research company with a passive transducer patent. In 1998 Methode bought Stratos Ltd. a UK-based maker of fiber-optic connectors for harsh environments.

Methode sold its printed circuit board operations in 1999. The company acquired network component maker Polycore Technologies and the optoelectronics division of Spire Corporation that year. In 2000 Methode spun off most of its optical components business as Stratos Lightwave retaining an 84% stake. (Stratos Lightwave later became Stratos International and was acquired in 2007 by Emerson Electric.)

After more than 50 years at the helm of his company William McGinley died in 2001 at the age of 77. William Jensen a 45-year veteran of the company was named chairman while EVP Donald Duda became president. Also that year the company distributed its remaining stake in Stratos to shareholders.

With a stagnant economy in the early 21st century putting pressure on revenue growth Methode consolidated some of its manufacturing facilities to control costs and increase margins. In 2003 Methode acquired its longtime automotive products distributor Kill & Bolton Associates.

In 2004 Duda was named CEO. Later the same year Jensen retired as chairman and director Warren Batts (retired chairman and CEO of Tupperware Brands) was tapped to replace him. Also that year Methode acquired and then retired about two-thirds of the Class B shares owned by the estate and survivors of company founder William McGinley and agreed to buy the rest. Despite efforts by Dura Automotive Systems to purchase the remaining Class B shares in a hostile bid for control of Methode the merger of Class A and Class B shares was approved by Methode shareholders.

The company acquired Cableco Technologies a manufacturer of high-current flexible cabling systems for electronic and electrical power applications in 2005.

In 2007 Methode acquired TouchSensor Technologies from Gemtron Corporation for $65 million. TouchSensor supplied solid-state field-effect switches used in automobiles beverage dispensers and home appliances among other applications.

The acquisition helped the company diversify into a variety of consumer products.

In 2008 the company acquired the assets of radio remote control manufacturer Hetronic. The deal worth nearly $54 million in cash included operations in Germany Malta the Philippines and the US. Hetronic was incorporated into Methode's Interconnect segment. The deal expanded Methode's reach in the human/machine interface market. That year Methode also restructured operations at three of its US plants.

The global automotive industry had one of its worst years on record during Methode's fiscal 2009 due to the recession and credit crisis and that dramatic downturn was reflected in the company's results. Sales were off by nearly 23% from the year before. In fiscal 2010 sales in the auto market continued to drop by 18% over 2009 as the economy continued to slump.

Sales in North America where the auto industry was particularly hard hit led the decline. Sales to Ford were lower in 2010 due to Methode's decision to relocate business from its facility in Reynosa Mexico to other suppliers. Delphi once a significant customer terminated its supply agreement with Methode in 2009. Additionally the company decided to exit the Chrysler business which was completed during 2009. That year Methode restructured by consolidating manufacturing facilities in order to cut costs. Only its torque-sensing and testing businesses were spared.

EXECUTIVES

Vp Global Sales, Theodore P Kill
VP Corporate Finance, Douglas A. Koman, $331,250 total compensation
Vp Quality Assurance, Robert A Miller
President CEO and Director, Donald W. Duda, age 59, $664,538 total compensation
VP Europe, Joseph E. Khoury, $309,787 total compensation
COO, Thomas D. Reynolds, age 51, $433,173 total compensation
VP and General Manager North American Operations, Timothy R. Glandon, $275,192 total compensation
Vice President Of Business Development, Mark R Shermetaro
Chairman, Walter J. Aspatore, age 70
Auditors: Ernst&YoungLLP

LOCATIONS

HQ: Methode Electronics, Inc.
7401 West Wilson Avenue, Harwood Heights, IL 60706-4548
Phone: 708 867-6777   **Fax:** 708 867-6999
Web: www.methode.com

2014 Sales

	$ mil.	% of total
North America	456.6	59
Malta	186.4	24
China	97.4	13
Other	32.4	4
Total	**772.8**	**100**

PRODUCTS/OPERATIONS

2014 Sales

	$ mil.	% of total
Automotive	524.3	68
Interconnect	170.7	22
Power products	72.7	9
Other	10.4	1
Adjustments	(5.3)	-
Total	**772.8**	**100**

Selected Products

Automotive electronic controls
Bus bar and power distribution products
CompactFlash and PC memory card products
Connectors (electrical fiber-optic and radio-frequency)
Copper Fibre Channel products
Optical fiber products
Small Computer System Interface (SCSI) products
Specialty inks

Selected Testing Services (Trace Laboratories)

Electrical
Environmental
Failure analysis
Materials
Mechanical

COMPETITORS

AVX	Molex
Amphenol	Northrop Grumman
CTS Corp.	Parlex
Delphi Automotive	QualMark
Systems	Radiall
FCI	STRATTEC
Hirose Electric	Stoneridge
ITT Corp.	TE Connectivity
Japan Aviation	Thomas & Betts
Electronics Industry	Underwriters Labs
Lear Corp	

HISTORICAL FINANCIALS

Company Type: Public

Income Statement

FYE: May 3

	REVENUE ($ mil.)	NET INCOME ($ mil.)	NET PROFIT MARGIN	EMPLOYEES
05/14*	772.8	96.1	12.4%	4,566
04/13	519.8	40.7	7.8%	3,960
04/12	465.1	8.3	1.8%	3,143
04/11	428.2	19.5	4.6%	2,743
05/10	377.6	13.6	3.6%	2,315
Annual Growth	**19.6%**	**62.9%**	**—**	**18.5%**

*Fiscal year change

2014 Year-End Financials

Debt ratio: 8.3%	No. of shares (mil.): 37
Return on equity: 27.7%	Dividends
Cash ($ mil.): 116	Yield: 0.0%
Current ratio: 3.20	Payout: 11.9%
Long-term debt ($ mil.): 48	Market value ($ mil.): 1,107

	STOCK PRICE ($) FY Close	P/E High/Low		PER SHARE ($) Earnings	Dividends	Book Value
05/14*	29.20	15	6	2.51	0.30	10.33
04/13	14.05	13	6	1.08	0.28	7.80
04/12	8.63	56	32	0.22	0.28	6.89
04/11	12.36	26	15	0.52	0.28	7.01
05/10	11.10	38	15	0.37	0.28	6.43
Annual Growth	**27.4%**	**—**	**—**	**61.4%**	**1.7%**	**12.6%**

*Fiscal year change

Microchip Technology, Inc.

While bigger chip makers fight over your PC and mobile phone Microchip Technology has embedded itself in your car your copier and even your wallet. The semiconductor maker offers a variety of embedded devices including eight-bit microcontrollers (it's one of the top makers of them worldwide); specialty memory products such as electrically erasable programmable read-only memories (EEPROMs); and KEELOQ brand code-hopping devices used in keyless locks garage door openers and smart cards. Its chips are used by tens of thousands of customers in the automotive consumer industrial office automation and telecommunications markets. Microchip gets about 80% of sales from customers outside the US.

Operations

Microchip Technology's product line includes microcontrollers (about 65% of sales) which offers a broad family of proprietary general purpose microcontroller products marketed under the PIC brand; Analog Interface and Mixed Signal Products (20% of sales) which consists of several families with more than 1100 power management linear mixed-signal thermal management RF Linear drivers USB ethernet and wireless products; Memory Products (about 10% of sales) consists of serial electrically erasable programmable read-only memory (referred to as Serial EEPROMs) Serial Flash memories Parallel Flash memories and Serial SRAM memories; and Technology Licensing (5% of sales) includes license fees and royalties associated with technology licenses for the use of its SuperFlash embedded flash and Smartbits one time programmable NVM technologies.

Geographic Reach

The company has three manufacturing plants in the US (two in Arizona and one in Oregon) and one in Thailand. In addition it outsources a significant portion of its wafer needs from contract manufacturers or foundries.

Sales offices are located throughout the world. Sales operations in the Americas (the US Canada and Central and South America) and Europe support much of design for products shipped for Asia.

The percentage of sales attributable to Asia has increased as more customers have moved their manufacturing operations to the region generating 60% of sales. Customers in Europe and the Americas each account for 20% of sales.

Sales and Marketing

Microchip Technology uses both a direct sales force and distributors to sell its products worldwide. In fiscal 2014 (year-end March) 53% of is business was through distributors and 47% was sold directly.

Financial Performance

Net sales increased 22% to a record $1.93 billion in fiscal 2014 (year-end March) driven by general strength in the semiconductor industry and inorganic growth from its 2012 acquisition of SMSC. Microchip Technology is consistently profitable; in 2014 it enjoyed $395 million in profits a 210% jump from 2013's $127 million a direct result of topline growth. Along the same lines cash flow from operations increased almost 50% to $676 million.

Strategy

The company's stated goal is to provide specialized semiconductor products for a wide variety of embedded control applications such as consumer automotive industrial office automation and telecommunications. Its strategic focus is on the embedded control market which includes microcontrollers high-performance analog interface and mixed-signal devices power management and thermal management devices connectivity devices interface devices Serial EEPROMs SuperFlash memory products and its patented KeeLoq security devices and Flash IP solutions. Unlike many chip makers Microchip doesn't experience significant

fluctuations in average selling prices particularly in its microcontroller and analog and interface groups where a large proportion of products are considered proprietary.

Mergers and Acquisitions

Microchip Technology expands through acquisition making about one per year. In 2014 it paid almost $235 million for Supertex which makes mixed-signal ICs from its foundry in California. Supertex will operate as a wholly owned subsidiary of Microchip Technology. The prior year it bought EqcoLogic a Belgian fabless semiconductor company that designs equalizer and coaxial transceiver products and technologies for automotive and industrial applications.

In 2012 Microchip bought Standard Microsystems Corporation (SMSC) for about $940 million. SMSC's mixed-signal connectivity products for embedded applications complemented Microchip's embedded control products and further expanded its reach in the automotive computing consumer industrial and wireless audio markets. Earlier that year Microchip bought Roving Networks a fabless developer of low-power embedded Wi-Fi transceivers and Bluetooth modules. The purchase improved its ability to target new markets for embedded components especially for such products as smartphone accessories.

HISTORY

Investment firm Sequoia Capital acquired a washed-up semiconductor subsidiary from General Instrument in 1989. Sequoia executive Steve Sanghi a veteran of Intel was tapped to head the operation Microchip Technology. Sanghi instituted a bare-bones operating budget and broadened the company's focus beyond low-cost memory products to include more profitable embedded microcontrollers. By 1992 Microchip turned a small profit.

In 1995 Microchip acquired the rights to KEELOQ secure data transmission products developed by South Africa's Nanoteq Ltd. The following year the company introduced its own line of secure data transmission products and its first flash memory microcontrollers. In 1997 Microchip unveiled the world's smallest erasable read-only memory to be used in devices such as keyless entries dimmers and thermostats. In 1998 Microchip settled litigation with ROHM whose Exel Microelectronics unit was an original KEELOQ licensee; ROHM surrendered its licensing rights to the technology.

Streamlining around its more cost-effective manufacturing operations Microchip in 1999 closed a wafer fabrication plant (or fab) and a test facility. In 2001 the company beefed up its analog product line by acquiring TelCom Semiconductor a maker of chips for wireless phones.

In 2002 Microchip paid $54 million in cash for privately held PowerSmart a Duracell spinoff that made embedded controllers and battery sensors. Also that year the company acquired a large wafer fab in Oregon from Fujitsu for about $180 million in cash. Microchip launched a new e-commerce Web site in 2003.

CEO Steve Sanghi and former HR VP Michael Jones wrote a book about the company's early years and how Microchip survived and prospered. Published in 2006 by John Wiley & Sons Driving Excellence: How the Aggregate System Turned Microchip Technology from a Failing Company to a Market Leader recounted the hardscrabble measures taken in 1990 and following years to save the company from collapse leading to its successful IPO in 1993. The "aggregate system" referred to

in the title was a collection of 10 corporate precepts including clear company values and having employees share in the company's prosperity.

Also in 2006 Microchip created a Medical Products Group targeting the $100 billion medical devices market especially those devices used by consumers.

In 2008 Microchip made an unsolicited takeover offer for competitor Atmel a supplier of microcontrollers and other chips. The company privately approached Atmel about a potential merger before going public with a cash offer to buy the company valued at around $2.3 billion.

Microchip made the bid in concert with ON Semiconductor which wanted to buy Atmel's automotive nonvolatile memory and radio-frequency (RF) product lines if Microchip succeeded in acquiring Atmel. Microchip also planned to divest Atmel's application-specific integrated circuit business which provides customized chips to customers to a third party.

Atmel's board of directors rejected the Microchip/ON Semi bid. Microchip then said it intended to nominate a slate of directors at Atmel's next annual meeting. The company reported that it received clearance from US antitrust regulators on acquiring Atmel.

In late 2008 however ON Semi reported it was dropping out of the bid citing "the unforeseen deterioration in the semiconductor market since we announced our proposal as well as the unprecedented weakness in the financial markets." Microchip withdrew its proposal as a result while later nominating a dissident slate of nominees for Atmel's annual meeting. The company dropped the proxy battle in 2009 citing deteriorating conditions in Atmel's business the semiconductor industry in general and the global economy.

In 2009 the company purchased R&E International. R&E developed integrated circuits used in security and life safety equipment (smoke and carbon monoxide detectors). Also that year Microchip acquired Australia-based HI-TECH Software. The purchase added development tools for embedded systems and extended the company's market share in the compiler technology sector.

Microchip's 2010 acquisition of Silicon Storage Technology (SST) contributed to higher sales of memory products in 2011 and an increase in global memory market share. The company acquired flash memory maker SST for around $275 million in cash. The deal added SST's flash technology more than 360 patents and more microcontrollers to Microchip's portfolio. As part of the transaction Microchip sold SST's NAND drives NAND controllers smart card integrated circuits and other products to Greenliant Systems a company formed by Bing Yeh the former chairman and CEO of SST.

Also in 2010 Microchip picked up ZeroG Wireless. The acquisition of Wi-Fi technology which is being used more in embedded applications was the crux of the purchase enhancing the company's product line with Wi-Fi capability and related software.

EXECUTIVES

Vp Human Resources, Lauren A Carr
Vp Advanced Microcontroller Architecture Division, Mitchel Obolsky
Vp High-performance Microcontroller Division, Sumit K Mitra
Vp Global Sales Support And Electronic Manufacturing Systems, Paul R Breault
Vice President Finance, Eric Bjornholt
Vp European Sales, Gary P Marsh

Vp Worldwide Applications Engineering, Ken N
Pye
Chairman President and CEO, Steve Sanghi, age
59, $595,647 total compensation
EVP and COO, Ganesh Moorthy, age 54, $281,686
total compensation
VP Information Services, Robert H. Owen
VP and CFO, J. Eric Bjornholt, age 43, $198,861 total
compensation
Vp Pacific Rim Manufacturing Operations, Mathew
B Bunker
Vice President Europe Finance, Nawaz Sharif
Vice President Computing Products Group, Ian F
Harris
Vice President Of Marketing, Ron Cates
Executive Vice President Administration, Marcella
Soloway
Chairman President and CEO, Steve Sanghi, age 59
Auditors: Ernst&YoungLLP

LOCATIONS

HQ: Microchip Technology, Inc.
2355 West Chandler Boulevard, Chandler, AZ 85224-
6199
Phone: 480 792-7200   **Fax:** 480 792-7790
Web: www.microchip.com

2014 Sales

	$ mil.	% of total
Asia	1154.1	60
Europe	411.5	21
Americas	365.6	19
Total	**1931.2**	**100**

PRODUCTS/OPERATIONS

2014 Sales

	$ mil.	% of total
Microcontrollers	1261.0	65
Analog & interface products	428.1	22
Memory products	134.6	7
Technology licensing	94.6	5
Other	12.9	1
Total	**1932.2**	**100**

Selected Products

Analog and Interface Integrated Circuits (ICs)
Interface devices
Controllers
Infrared codecs
Linear devices
Audio amplifiers
Comparators
Operational amplifiers
Mixed-signal devices
Analog-to-digital (A/D) and digital-to-analog (D/A)
converters
Digital potentiometers
Power management devices
DC-to-DC converters
Linear regulators
Power MOSFET drivers
Switching regulators
System supervisors
Voltage detectors
Voltage references
Thermal management devices
Brushless DC fan controllers
Temperature sensors
KEELOQ Security Devices
Decoders
Encoders
Transcoders
Memory Chips
Serial and parallel erasable programmable read-only
memories (EPROMs)
Serial electrically erasable programmable read-only
memories (EEPROMs)
Microcontrollers
Eight-bit microcontrollers (PICmicro and rfPIC lines)
Mixed-signal controllers
Radio-frequency identification (RFID) ICs

COMPETITORS

Altera	Maxim Integrated
Analog Devices	Products
Atmel	Mitsubishi Electric
Cypress Semiconductor	ON Semiconductor
Dialog Semiconductor	Oki Semiconductor
Echelon Corporation	ROHM
Fairchild	RadiSys
Semiconductor	Ramtron International
Freescale	Renesas Electronics
Semiconductor	STMicroelectronics
Fujitsu Semiconductor	Silicon Labs
Intel	Texas Instruments
Intersil	Winbond Electronics
Linear Technology	ZiLOG
Macronix International	

HISTORICAL FINANCIALS

Company Type: Public

Income Statement

FYE: March 31

	REVENUE ($ mil.)	NET INCOME ($ mil.)	NET PROFIT MARGIN	EMPLOYEES
03/14	1,931.2	395.2	20.5%	8,604
03/13	1,581.6	127.3	8.1%	8,003
03/12	1,383.1	336.7	24.3%	6,923
03/11	1,487.2	418.9	28.2%	6,970
03/10	947.7	217.0	22.9%	5,418
Annual Growth	**19.5%**	**16.2%**	**—**	**12.3%**

2014 Year-End Financials

Debt ratio: 25.0%
Return on equity: 19.4%
Cash ($ mil.): 466
Current ratio: 5.86
Long-term debt ($ mil.): 1,003

No. of shares (mil.): 200
Dividends
Yield: 2.9%
Payout: 88.5%
Market value ($ mil.): 9,552

	STOCK PRICE ($) FY Close	P/E High/Low		PER SHARE ($) Earnings	Dividends	Book Value
03/14	47.76	24	17	1.82	1.42	10.68
03/13	36.77	57	45	0.62	1.41	9.84
03/12	37.20	23	17	1.65	1.39	10.31
03/11	38.01	17	12	2.15	1.72	9.56
03/10	28.16	25	17	1.16	1.36	8.27
Annual Growth	**14.1%**	**—**		**11.9%**	**1.1%**	**6.6%**

Microsemi Corp.

Microsemi is on a power trip. The company makes power management semiconductors that regulate and condition electricity to make it more usable by electrical and electronic systems. Its products include discrete components such as diodes and rectifiers along with integrated circuits such as amplifiers and voltage regulators. Microsemi also makes devices for pacemakers GPS products LCD TVs and wireless networks. The company's high-reliability semiconductors go into jet engines missile systems oilfield equipment and satellites. Top customers have included big names like Boeing Dell Honeywell Medtronic Boston Scientific and Lockheed Martin. More than 40% of sales come from outside the US.

HISTORY

Microsemiconductor Corporation started in 1960 as a maker of power conditioning equip-

ment. Early acquisitions included two lines of semiconductors from Globe Union. Philip Frey joined the company as CEO and president in 1971. It went public in 1981 and changed its name to Microsemi in 1982.

Throughout the mid-1980s and early 1990s military business accounted for up to 75% of sales. By means of acquisitions Microsemi consolidated its clout as a military contractor and diversified its customer base. In 1992 it bought a semiconductor manufacturing division of Unitrode —a purchase that also increased its presence in Europe and Asia. Other acquisitions included units from Raytheon (1995) SGS-Thomson (now STMicroelectronics) and National Semiconductor (1996) PPC Products (1997) and BKC Semiconductors and Semicon (1998).

Microsemi sold its low-growth contract circuit board assembly operations in 1998. It formed a development pact with Advanced Power Technology (APT) that year to expand in the medical market. In 1999 Microsemi acquired SymmetriCom's Linfinity Microelectronics subsidiary (power management products for consumer electronics) and Narda Microwave's semiconductor operations.

In 2000 former Linfinity president James Peterson replaced Frey as CEO (Frey remained chairman until 2002). The following year saw Microsemi acquire Compensated Devices and New England Semiconductor both makers of electronic components primarily for aerospace customers.

In 2002 Microsemi launched a restructuring effort that included closing plants and relocating operations. The company also sold its Carlsbad design center to AMI Semiconductor as well as its India-based Semcon Electronics subsidiary.

Nick Yocca who had served as the company's chairman since 2002 retired from the board in 2004. Dennis Leibel succeeded him as chairman. Later that year Microsemi sued rival Monolithic Power Systems alleging patent infringement involving certain products. (The litigation was settled in 2006.) Also that year the company licensed packaging technology from Diodes Inc.

Microsemi initiated further consolidation in 2005 planning to shutter its wafer fab in Broomfield Colorado and its plant in Ennis Ireland. Work done in those two facilities was to be reassigned to other Microsemi facilities.

The company later reversed its plant-closing moves due to customer demand. The reprieve for the Broomfield fab was temporary lasting into 2009 while increased demand for high-reliability defense and commercial air/satellite products kept the Ennis plant open.

In 2006 Microsemi acquired Advanced Power Technology (APT) for about $130 million in cash and stock. APT became a wholly owned subsidiary of Microsemi functioning as the company's Power Products Group.

In 2007 the company acquired PowerDsine for about $245 million in cash and stock. PowerDsine specialized in chips for transmitting electrical power over Ethernet local-area networks. The Israeli-American firm complemented Microsemi's analog and mixed-signal semiconductor design expertise.

In 2008 the company acquired the assets of Microwave Device Technology Corporation (MDT) for nearly $9 million. The purchase added microwave diodes made of gallium arsenide to Microsemi's portfolio of silicon-based microwave semiconductors as well as added sensor devices for intrusion alarms motion and speed detectors and other products.

In 2009 Microsemi acquired the defense electronics and security business of Endwave strengthening its existing RF operations. Earlier that year it bought the Space Level Power Products business of Spectrum Microwave Inc. a wholly owned subsidiary of Spectrum Control. The acquisition complements the company's offerings in radiation-hardened and radiation-tolerant transistors for the military/aerospace market as well as Microsemi's DC-DC power management devices.

In 2009 the company also bought Electro Module and subsidiary Babcock Inc. adding power supplies flat-panel displays and relays to its power management division. In its last purchase of the year Microsemi bought Nexsem which makes high-voltage DC-DC power conversion devices for LCD TV notebook netbook and set-top box applications.

In 2009 the company announced it would lay off about 300 employees (an 18% reduction in workforce) and that it would close its Scottsdale Arizona facility as part of consolidation efforts.

In 2010 the company acquired Actel a maker of field programmable gate arrays (FPGAs) in a transaction valued at around $430 million. Actel became Microsemi's SoC Division. Earlier the same year the company swallowed up White Electronic Designs (semiconductor design assembly and test integration for military/aerospace applications) for about $163 million in cash.

In a deal that bolstered its US Defense Department (DoD) business Microsemi bought the Arxan Defense Systems subsidiary of Arxan Technologies in 2010. Arxan Defense Systems made the EnforcIT software and firmware platform that defense contractors use to protect their systems against piracy reverse engineering tampering and other threats.

EXECUTIVES

Vp And Gm, John A Caruso
Vp Quality And Business Process Improvement, John J Petersen, age 70
Vice President Business Development Commercial Air And Space, Siobhan Dolan-clancy
Executive Vice President Chief Financial Officer Secretary and Treasurer, John W. Hohener, age 60, $397,100 total compensation
Chairman of the Board and Chief Executive Officer, James J. (Jim) Peterson, age 59, $700,000 total compensation
Executive Vice President, Ralph Brandi, age 68, $485,320 total compensation
President and Chief Operating Officer, Paul Pickle
EVP and Chief Strategy Officer, Steven G. Litchfield, age 45, $336,380 total compensation
EVP of Worldwide Marketing, Russell Garcia, age 53
Chief Technology Officer, Jim Aralis
Vp-marketing & Busi Devel, Manuel Lynch
Vice President Manufacturing, Charlie Susa
Vice President Engineering Research, Dah Tsang
V Pres-strategic Marketing, Amr El-ashmawi
Vp Human Resources, James M Thomas
Vp International Operations, Andy T Yuen
Vp; General Manager Microsemi Broomfield, Sven Nelson, age 58
Vice President Of Rf Integrated Systems, David H Hall
Vice President Business Development, Madhu Rayabhair
Vice President Engineering, Bjarne Heggli
Vice President And General Manager Soc, Esam Elashmawi
Vice President Operations, Greg Ellis
Executive Assistant To Evp, Mac Kenzie Meneades
Vice President Of Marketing, Jacques Issa
Vice President Of Product Management, Michael Mehlberg

Senior Vice President Bu Manager Ulp Bu, Stephen Swift
Vice President Sales, Fabian Battaglia
V P General Manager, Doug Milne
Vice President Research And Development, David Pincu
Vice President Silicon Engineering, Lyle Smith
Sr Vp Sls Worldwide, Rick Goerner
Vice President Of Engineering, Dick Battisti
Vice President And General Manager, Amir Asvadi
Senior Vice President Of Corporate, Kelly Jones
Vice President Global Operations, Asaf Silberstein
Vice President Information Technology, Sumana Achar
Vice President Operations And Quality, Scott Shah
Vice President Discrete Power Products, Jimmy Wright
Vice President Operations And Quality, Russ Ford
Vice President Of Product Marketing, Sunil Baliga
Vice President Of Marketing Amsg, Farshad Zarghami
Vice President Ww Product Marketing, Farhad Mafie
Vice President Of Engineering, Barry Lewis
Senior Vice President And General, Roger Holliday
Vice President Of Operations, Gerry Leo
Vice President Gov't Programs Business, Karl Pendergast
Vp, Al Simon
Executive Vice President Chief Strategy, Steve Litchfield
Vice President And General Manager Hi Rel Group, Simon Wainwright
Vice President Sales Emea And Russia, Eric Heijden
Vice President Sales And Business Development, Neal Austin
Executive Vice President Chief Financial Officer Secretary and Treasurer, John W. Hohener, age 60
Chairman of the Board and Chief Executive Officer, James J. (Jim) Peterson, age 59
Board Member, Lupe Gonzalez
Board Member, Mel Clark
Auditors: PricewaterhouseCoopersLLP

LOCATIONS

HQ: Microsemi Corp.
One Enterprise, Aliso Viejo, CA 92656
Phone: 949 380-6100
Web: www.microsemi.com

2013 Sales

	$ mil.	% of total
US	514.6	53
Asia	292.6	30
Europe	142.3	14
Other	26.4	3
Total	**975.9**	**100**

PRODUCTS/OPERATIONS

2013 Sales by Market

	$ mil.	% of total
Security & defense	306.3	31
Communications	278.1	29
Industrial	204.5	21
Aerospace	187.0	19
Total	**975.9**	**100**

Selected Products

Application-specific standard products (ASSPs)
  Audio amplification integrated circuits (ICs)
  Backlight inverters
  Small computer standard interface (SCSI) terminators
Discrete components
  Automatic surge protectors
  Computer switching diodes
  Low-leakage and high-voltage diodes

  Silicon rectifiers
  Transient suppressor diodes
  Transistors
  Zener diodes
EnforcIT software and firmware platform for securing defense-related projects
Standard linear ICs (SLICs)
  Low-dropout regulators (LDOs)
  Pulse width modulators (PWMs)

COMPETITORS

ANADIGICS	Micrel
Aeroflex	Monolithic Power
Altera	Systems
Analog Devices	NXP Semiconductors
Conexant Systems	O2Micro
Diodes	ON Semiconductor
Fairchild	RF Micro Devices
Semiconductor	Sanken Electric
Freescale	Semtech
Semiconductor	Shindengen Electric
IXYS	Manufacturing
Integrated Device	Silicon Labs
Technology	Skyworks
International	Supertex
Rectifier	Texas Instruments
Linear Technology	TriQuint
M/A-COM	Vishay Intertechnology
Maxim Integrated	Vitesse Semiconductor
Products	Xilinx

HISTORICAL FINANCIALS

Company Type: Public

Income Statement

FYE: September 28

	REVENUE ($ mil.)	NET INCOME ($ mil.)	NET PROFIT MARGIN	EMPLOYEES
09/14	1,138.2	23.1	2.0%	3,400
09/13	975.9	43.6	4.5%	3,100
09/12*	1,012.5	(29.6)	—	2,200
10/11	835.8	54.4	6.5%	2,700
10/10	518.2	59.0	11.4%	2,250
Annual Growth	**21.7%**	**(20.9%)**	**—**	**10.9%**

*Fiscal year change

2014 Year-End Financials

Debt ratio: 33.8%	No. of shares (mil.): 95
Return on equity: 2.1%	Dividends
Cash ($ mil.): 162	Yield: —
Current ratio: 3.84	Payout: —
Long-term debt ($ mil.): 698	Market value ($ mil.): 2,398

	STOCK PRICE ($) FY Close	P/E High/Low	PER SHARE ($) Earnings	Dividends	Book Value
09/14	25.08	110 90	0.24	0.00	11.67
09/13	23.92	54 36	0.48	0.00	11.00
09/12*	20.07	— —	(0.35)	0.00	10.28
10/11	15.98	38 23	0.63	0.00	10.26
10/10	17.11	25 18	0.72	0.00	9.21
Annual Growth	**10.0%**	**— —**	**(24.0%)**	**—**	**6.1%**

*Fiscal year change

MicroStrategy Inc.

MicroStrategy knows you need the details to make a good plan. The company's business intelligence software addresses functions such as building reports and dashboards managing mobile applications and capitalizing on social media. Specific analytics modules include human resources management Web traffic analysis and sales and distribution. Its Angel.com unit provides cloud-based customer experience management software. It sells to many of the world's largest companies such as Aetna and eBay as well as midsized companies and government agencies such as NASA and the US Army. MicroStrategy also offers consulting and support services. Founded in 1989 MicroStrategy has operations in about 25 countries.

Geographic Reach

North America is the Virginia-based company's largest market accounting for 60% of its revenue. Europe the Middle East and Africa accounts for about 30%.

Sales and Marketing

Marketing its products worldwide MicroStrategy targets a variety of user types. In addition to large and medium-sized enterprises and government customers the company also targets advertising agencies and systems integrators that cater to those clients as well targeting independent software vendors that want to incorporate MicroStrategy's tools. The company primarily uses a direct sales force but it also distributes through indirect channel partners that include value-added resellers system integrators and OEMs.

Financial Performance

The company's revenue increased 6% in 2012 versus 2011 to $595 million driven by a 16% jump in sales by its Angel.com subsidiary. Also revenue from product support and other services grew 9% year over year on an increase in the number of product support contracts and an overall increase in renewal pricing on existing support contracts. While MicroStrategy has added more than $200 million in revenue since 2009 the rate of increase slowed in 2012.

Net income grew 15% to $21 million in 2012 versus 2011 primarily due to the increase in sales. The increase in profitability in 2012 followed two years of steep decline as the firm invested heavily in research and development sales and marketing and consulting capabilities during 2011. While it continued to invest in R&D in 2012 the rate of increase of expenses related to such investments was lower in 2012 compared with 2011. Investments in R&D and related expenses are expected to be higher in 2013.

Strategy

Areas of investment focus for the company include software technologies designed to help clients capitalize on four technology trends: Big Data; Mobile applications; Cloud-based services: and Social Networking. Recent entries include mobile and cloud-based platforms. The company's MicroStrategy 9 is the software platform that contains its core products. Mobile apps based on MicroStrategy 9 include integrated mapping with Google Maps integration with on-device sensors such as bar-code readers and mobile alerts. Besides mobile Microstrategy sees three other disruptive trends that it will focus on: big data the cloud and social media. The company's Microstrategy Wisdom for example analyzes Facebook data.

MicroStrategy has faced increasing competition from large enterprise software companies such as Oracle SAP and IBM as those companies acquire smaller business intelligence software makers in deals similar to IBM's purchase of SPSS. Despite the competitive relationship with these companies MicroStrategy also works through partnerships with them and many others including Leidos Symantec and Adobe.

MicroStrategy serves such industries as communications (Sky plc Cox Communications) consumer goods (Chiquita Danone) financial services (ABN AMRO Credit Agricole) healthcare (Bayer HealthCare Novation) insurance (Pacific Life GEICO) manufacturing (Michelin Philips Electronics) retail (Starbucks Guess?) technology (eBay McAfee) and the government (US Postal Service US Department of Homeland Security).

Ownership

Chairman and CEO Michael Saylor control the company through ownership of 64% of the company's voting shares and an 18% stake in the common stock.

EXECUTIVES

Co-President and Chief Legal Officer, Jonathan F. Klein, age 48, $770,625 total compensation
Chairman and CEO, Michael J. Saylor, age 50, $875,000 total compensation
Co-President, Paul N. Zolfaghari, age 50, $800,000 total compensation
SEVP and CFO, Douglas K. Thede, age 46, $562,500 total compensation
SEVP and CTO, Timothy E Lang
Vice President Product Marketing, Sid Banerjee
Region Sales Vice President, Karthik Gopalakrishnan
Vice President Internal Audit, Rodney Larsen
Vice President Healthcare Solutions, Caleb Decker
Vice President Finance Billing Manager, Christina Ross
Vice President Technology Programs Web And User Experience, L Everhart
Vice President Worldwide Sales Enablement, Eric Franz
Vice President Australia And New Zealand, Mark Fazackerley
Vice President Finance And Worldwide Controller, Emmett Pepe
Vice President Technology Programs Web And User Experience, Doug Everhart
Vice President Sales Latin America, Flavio Bolieiro
Vice President Engineering, Ram Ramachandran
Senior Vice President Technology Programs, Guy Levy-yurista
Vice President Strategic Development, Dale Olson
Sevp And Chief Technology Officer, Minnie Sandhu
Vice President Finance Emea, Mark Gay
Area Vice President Country Manager Canada, Rob Nascimben
Executive Vice President North American Sales, Susan Cook
Vice President Product Marketing, Michael Hiskey
Senior Vice President Product Marketing Identity, Christian Campagnuolo
Chairman and CEO, Michael J. Saylor, age 50
Auditors: GrantThorntonLLP

LOCATIONS

HQ: MicroStrategy Inc.
1850 Towers Crescent Plaza, Tysons Corner, VA 22182
Phone: 703 848-8600 **Fax:** 703 848-8610
Web: www.microstrategy.com

2012 Sales

	$ mil.	% of total
US & Canada	355.2	60
Europe the Middle East & Africa	177.5	30
Other regions	61.9	10
Total	**594.6**	**100**

PRODUCTS/OPERATIONS

2012 Sales

	$ mil.	% of total
Product support &other services	418.4	70
Product licenses	147.3	25

Angel.com	28.9	5
Total	**594.6**	**100**

Selected Products

MicroStrategy 9
  Command Manager
  Desktop
  Distribution Services
  Intelligence Server
  Office
  Report Services
  SDK
  Transaction Services
MicroStrategy Cloud
MicroStrategy Mobile
MicroStrategy Social
  Emma
  Usher
  Wisdom

COMPETITORS

Actuate	Oracle
IBM	QlikTech
Infor Global	SAP
Informatica	SAS Institute
Information Builders	TIBCO Software
JasperSoft	Tableau Software
Microsoft	Teradata

HISTORICAL FINANCIALS

Company Type: Public

Income Statement

FYE: December 31

	REVENUE ($ mil.)	NET INCOME ($ mil.)	NET PROFIT MARGIN	EMPLOYEES
12/13	575.8	83.3	14.5%	3,158
12/12	594.6	20.5	3.5%	3,221
12/11	562.1	17.9	3.2%	3,088
12/10	454.5	43.7	9.6%	2,597
12/09	377.7	74.8	19.8%	1,816
Annual Growth	**11.1%**	**2.7%**	**—**	**14.8%**

2013 Year-End Financials

Debt ratio: —   No. of shares (mil.): 11
Return on equity: 32.6%   Dividends
Cash ($ mil.): 220   Yield: —
Current ratio: 2.06   Payout: —
Long-term debt ($ mil.): —   Market value ($ mil.): 1,404

	STOCK PRICE ($) FY Close	P/E High/Low		PER SHARE ($) Earnings	Dividends	Book Value
12/13	124.24	18	11	7.37	0.00	27.46
12/12	93.38	84	46	1.84	0.00	17.75
12/11	108.32	105	51	1.62	0.00	15.67
12/10	85.47	27	18	3.72	0.00	14.02
12/09	94.02	15	5	6.09	0.00	17.93
Annual Growth	**7.2%**	**—**	**—**	**4.9%**	**—**	**11.2%**

Mid-America Apartment Communities Inc

For Mid-America Apartment Communities the Sunbelt is where it's at. Operating as MAA the firm is a self-administered self-managed real estate investment trust (REIT) that focuses solely on buying multifamily residences. MAA owns or has interests in approximately 49500 apartment units in some 160 suburban communities primarily located in the Southeast and south-central US. Its largest markets are California Florida Tennessee and Texas where about 75% of its portfolio is located. The REIT's properties comprise some 49 million sq. ft. of rentable space. MAA which has an average property occupancy rate of 95% targets large and midsized markets. MAA has agreed to buy Colonial Properties.

Change in Company Type

MAA has offered to buy its smaller rival Colonial Properties Trust for about $2.1 billion in stock to create a Sunbelt-focused multifamily REIT with approximately 85000 apartments across 285 properties. Upon completion of the deal which has been approved by the boards of both companies and is expected to close in the third quarter of 2013 the combined company will retain the MAA name and be headquartered in Memphis.

Strategy

Rather than developing new properties MAA prefers to buy and upgrade existing complexes increasing curb appeal to attract middle-income residents. Although MAA generally considers property management and maintenance its focus and strength it does invest in new properties with joint venture partners from time to time and anticipates that that will be a growing part of its strategy.

The REIT has grown through acquisitions and development over the years. Although acquisition activity slowed a bit during the recession the company's purchasing has picked up speed as the country recovers from the economic downturn. Limited supply of new apartment communities being built and a decline in home ownership will drive up the demand for established apartment properties. Since the beginning of 2009 the REIT has invested in about two dozen new communities in its target markets; it acquired about a dozen new properties in 2011 alone. MAA also develops new properties but on a very limited scale. Occasionally the company sells properties that no longer fit in with its strategy; it sold two communities in 2011.

Multifamily investors have been leading the way in the slowly recovering property markets and MAA in particular has had strongly growing sales for at least a decade. Net income for the company rose 64% in 2011 largely due to an increase in revenues (which grew 11% to $499 million) and a gain on the sale of discontinued operations of about $12.8 million. The REIT's revenues grew as a result of the property acquisitions and rent increases at its existing holdings.

EXECUTIVES

Senior Vp & Director Hr, Cynthia Bowden
Senior Vice President Training, Ginny Doane
Senior Vice President Controller, Rick Barton
Svp And Director Of Physical Assets, Kevin Perkins
Vice President Corporate Support, James Maclin
Vp Marketing, Melintha Ogle
Vp And Director Of Risk Management, Doug Clark
Vp Central Region Operations, Beth Brock
Chairman President and CEO, H. Eric Bolton, age 57, $404,133 total compensation
Svp West Region Operations, Cynthia C McMillion
Executive VP Chief Operating Officer, Thomas L. (Tom) Grimes, $168,928 total compensation
SVP and Director Financial Planning, Albert M. (Al) Campbell, age 47, $158,223 total compensation

SVP Management Information Systems, Shelton Barron
Svp North Region Operations, Kim Banks
Senior Vice President Director Property Redevelopment, David Nischwitz
Vice President Of Human Resources, Melanie Carpenter
Vice President Business Development, Tim Argo
Vice President Director Property Accounting, Peg Wahl
Senior Vice President Controller, Micah Holton
Executive Vice President, James Taylor
Training Dev Dir Asst Vice President, Andreah Churchill
Vice President Operations, Kevin Suares
Vice President, Mark Aldy
Director Of Landscape Operations Vice President, Josh White
Vice President Finance, William B (Bill) Sansom, age 73
Senior Vice President Information Technology, Ray Day
Regional Vice President, Charles Llewellyn
Senior Vice President Of Information Technology, Ray Thornton
Chairman President and CEO, H. Eric Bolton, age 57
Board Member, W Sanders
Auditors: Ernst&YoungLLP

LOCATIONS

HQ: Mid-America Apartment Communities Inc
6584 Poplar Avenue, Memphis, TN 38138
Phone: 901 682-6600   **Fax:** 901 682-6667
Web: www.maac.com

2010 Wholly-Owned Properties

	No.
Texas	33
Georgia	26
Florida	25
Tennessee	22
South Carolina	14
Kentucky	7
North Carolina	7
Mississippi	6
Alabama	4
Arkansas	3
Arizona	3
Ohio	1
Virginia	1
Total	**152**

PRODUCTS/OPERATIONS

2011 Sales

	$ mil.	% of total
Rental income	410.6	92
Other property income	37.4	8
Management fees	1.0	-
Total	**449.0**	**100**

COMPETITORS

AMLI Residential	Colonial Properties
Apartment Investment and Management	Equity Residential
	Milestone Management
Berkshire Income Realty	Post Properties
	Southern Management
Camden Property	UDR

HISTORICAL FINANCIALS

Company Type: Public

Income Statement

FYE: December 31

	REVENUE ($ mil.)	NET INCOME ($ mil.)	NET PROFIT MARGIN	EMPLOYEES
12/13	634.7	119.2	18.8%	2,241
12/12	497.1	105.2	21.2%	1,446
12/11	448.9	48.8	10.9%	1,466
12/10	402.2	29.7	7.4%	1,389
12/09	378.5	37.2	9.8%	1,282
Annual Growth	**13.8%**	**33.8%**	**—**	**15.0%**

2013 Year-End Financials

Debt ratio: 50.7%
Return on equity: 6.1%
Cash ($ mil.): 89
Current ratio: 5.49
Long-term debt ($ mil.): 3,472

No. of shares (mil.): 74
Dividends
  Yield: 4.5%
  Payout: 80.8%
Market value ($ mil.): 4,545

	STOCK PRICE ($) FY Close	P/E High/Low	PER SHARE ($) Earnings	Dividends	Book Value
12/13	60.74	33 26	2.25	2.78	39.45
12/12	64.75	27 23	2.56	2.64	21.71
12/11	62.55	55 42	1.31	2.51	18.54
12/10	63.49	113 80	0.56	2.46	14.98
12/09	48.28	58 27	0.85	2.46	14.89
Annual Growth	**5.9%**	**—**	**27.6%**	**3.1%**	**27.6%**

Mid-Con Energy Partners LP

Mid-Con Energy Partners is a Delaware limited partnership that owns operates and develops producing oil and natural gas properties in North America. With a focus on the Mid-Continent region of the US in particular Oklahoma and Colorado the company's operations primarily consist of enhancing the development of mature producing oil properties through an oil recovery method called waterflooding. It has total estimated proved reserves of about 8 million barrels of oil equivalent a majority of which is oil. Managed by Mid-Con Energy GP Mid-Con Energy Partners was formed in July 2011 and went public in December 2011.

Following its $97 million offering Mid-Con Energy I and Mid-Con Energy II were merged into Mid-Con Energy Partners' wholly-owned subsidiary Mid-Con Energy Properties which holds the title to its parent's properties. A portion of the net proceeds from its IPO was used to pay the cash portion of the consideration in the merger.

Mid-Con Energy Partners filed its IPO on the strength of an asset portfolio that largely consists of properties that have relatively predictable production profiles modest capital requirements and good growth potential for waterflood development. More than 90% of its properties are already being waterflooded and have been producing since 1982 or earlier. Mid-Con Energy Partners' management team has actively operated most of its properties since 2005.

The company's primary business strategy is to generate stable cash flow by continuing to exploit its proved reserves to maximize production. It also plans to pursue acquisitions of onshore properties with long-lived reserves low production decline rates and low-risk development potential as well as properties within mature oil fields with opportunities for incremental improvements in oil recovery. In addition the company will seek to reduce the impact of commodity price volatility on its cash flow through a commodity hedging strategy.

EXECUTIVES

Executive Chairman, S. Craig George, age 62
CEO and Director, Charles R. (Randy) Olmstead, age 66
President CFO and Director, Jeffrey R. Olmstead, age 37
VP and Chief Accounting Officer, David A. Culbertson, age 49
VP and Chief Engineer, Robbin W. Jones, age 55
Director, Peter A. Leidel, age 58
CEO and Director, Charles R. (Randy) Olmstead, age 66
President CFO and Director, Jeffrey R. Olmstead, age 37
Director, Cameron O. Smith, age 64
Director, Robert W. Berry, age 90
Director, Peter Adamson III, age 73
Auditors: GrantThorntonLLP

LOCATIONS

HQ: Mid-Con Energy Partners LP
2501 North Harwood Street, Suite 2410, Dallas, TX 75201
Phone: 972 479-5980
Web: www.midconenergypartners.com

COMPETITORS

Abraxas Petroleum
Chaparral Energy
Chesapeake Energy
Denbury Resources
EXCO Resources

HISTORICAL FINANCIALS

Company Type: Public

Income Statement

FYE: December 31

	REVENUE ($ mil.)	NET INCOME ($ mil.)	NET PROFIT MARGIN	EMPLOYEES
12/13	80.0	28.1	35.2%	0
12/12	67.2	29.8	44.4%	0
12/11	39.3	18.9	48.3%	0
12/10	17.4	1.0	6.2%	0
12/09	5.9	(9.1)	—	0
Annual Growth 91.3%		—	—	—

2013 Year-End Financials

Debt ratio: 58.9%
Return on equity: —
Cash ($ mil.): 1
Current ratio: 1.20
Long-term debt ($ mil.): 112

No. of shares (mil.): 19
Dividends
Yield: 8.8%
Payout: 152.6%
Market value ($ mil.): 441

	STOCK PRICE ($) FY Close	P/E High/Low	PER SHARE ($) Earnings	Dividends	Book Value
12/13	22.85	19 13	1.44	2.03	3.46
12/12	18.70	15 11	1.62	1.49	3.80
12/11	18.35	18 17	1.05	0.00	2.46
Annual Growth 11.6%		— —	17.1%	—	18.6%

Middleby Corp.

Middleby Corp. has been cashing in on cooks for more than a century. Founded in 1888 the company makes a slew of commercial and institutional foodservice equipment for restaurants retailers and hotels worldwide. Middleby operates through two segments: Commercial Foodservice Equipment and Food Processing Equipment. The largest Foodservice makes machines for most types of cooking and warming activities. Products are sold under some two dozen blue chip brands —Anets Blodgett Southbend and TurboChef among them. The Food Processing arm makes cooking mixing slicing and packaging machines for global food processing giants notably precooked meat.

Geographic Reach
Middleby operates nearly 20 manufacturing facilities in the US and 12 internationally throughout the Americas Europe Asia and the Middle East. About 70% of its revenues come from the US and Canada. Europe and the Middle East account for 15%.

Operations
The company's mainstay Commercial Foodservice Equipment segment offers ovens ranges broilers fryers toasters coffee and tea brewers and other cooking equipment; it generates around 75% of total sales each year. Its Food Processing Equipment group (25% of sales) offers a slate of labor-saving products from batch ovens to mixing and slicing machines packaging and food safety equipment. The group's manufacturing facilities often neighbor major food processors.

Sales and Marketing
Middleby's Commercial Foodservice Equipment products are sold in 100 countries through a combination of sales and marketing personnel and an extensive network of independent dealers distributors consultants sales representatives and agents. International sales are primarily made through a network of independent local country stocking and servicing distributors and dealers and directly to major chains hotels and other large end-users.

For its Food Processing Equipment segment Middleby employs regional sales managers each with responsibility for a group of customers and a particular region. Internationally it has sales and distribution offices in Australia Brazil Denmark France Italy Germany and Mexico along with global sales managers supported by a network of independent sales representatives.

Financial Performance
Middleby has enjoyed unprecedented growth over the last three years. Revenues rose by 21% from $856 million in 2011 to more than $1 billion in 2012. Profits also surged by 26% from $95 million in 2011 to $121 million in 2012. (Both these totals represented historic milestones for the company.)

Sales from its Food Processing Equipment segment soared by almost 90% for 2012 and Latin America sales shot up by more than 50%. The company attributes its sizable growth to incremental sales generated from acquisitions as well as the proliferation of chain restaurants in developing regions coupled with a slow recovery by major chains at home. The uptick in sales also reflects growing demand by retailers and restaurants for processed foods.

Strategy
Acquisitions have added to Middleby's revenue stream and strengthened its competitive position as a one-stop-shop for such giants as Cracker Bar-

rel McDonald's Olive Garden and Panda Express. In 2013 it bought Spooner Vicars Bakery Systems a UK-based maker of baking machinery used in the cookie and cracker sector. The year before it purchased Nieco Corporation a maker of automatic broilers for $24 million. It also scooped up Viking Range Corporation a manufacturer of residential cooking ranges ovens and kitchen appliances for $380 million during 2012.

The company in 2011 obtained Denmark-based Danfotech a supplier of processing equipment (meat tenderizers presses and defrosting systems) for the meat industry. In a larger move Middleby purchased cooking equipment rival Lincat Group for almost $95 million. The acquisition not only expanded Middleby's international presence with brand names Lincat IMC and Brittania but secured manufacturing capacity in the UK.

EXECUTIVES

Chairman and CEO, Selim A. Bassoul, age 58, $1,000,000 total compensation
VP and CFO, Timothy J. (Tim) Fitzgerald, age 45, $575,000 total compensation
COO Commercial Foodservice, David Brewer, age 58, $400,000 total compensation
Vice President Of Engineering, William S Schjerven
Vice President New Business Development, Todd Olds
Vice President Operations Wells, Jeff Heck
Vice President Of Operations, Bruce Grau
Vice President Middleby Food Processing, Stephen Nunn
Sr Vice President Tech Solutions, Kelly Lee
Treasurer, Martin M Lindsay, age 51
Chairman and CEO, Selim A. Bassoul, age 58
Auditors: Deloitte&ToucheLLP

LOCATIONS

HQ: Middleby Corp.
1400 Toastmaster Drive, Elgin, IL 60120
Phone: 847 741-3300

2012 Sales

	$ mil.	% of total
US & Canada	711.2	68
Europe & Middle East	167.9	16
Asia	91.0	9
Latin America	68.1	7
Total	**1038.2**	**100**

PRODUCTS/OPERATIONS

2012 Sales

	$ mil.	% of total
Commercial foodservice	786.4	76
Food processing	251.8	24
Total	**1038.2**	**100**

Selected Mergers and Acquisitions

FY2013
Spooner Vicars Bakery Systems ($10 million; baking systems)
FY2012
Turkington USA LLC ($10 million; maker of baked ovens)
Stewart Systems Global LLC ($28 million; automated proofing and oven baking systems)
Nieco Corporation ($24 million; manufacturer of automatic broilers)
Viking Range Corporation ($280 million; cooking ranges ovens and kitchen appliances)
FY2011
Lincat Group PLC ($82 million; ranges ovens and counterline equipment)

Selected Products and Brands

Commercial Foodservice Equipment Group

Anets (griddles fryers dough rollers)
Blodgett (convection and combi-ovens)
Bloomfield (coffee and tea brewers beverage dispensing equipment)
Carter-Hoffmann (heated cabinets rethermalizing and foodservice equipment)
CookTek (induction cooking and warming systems)
CTX (conveyor oven equipment)
Doyon (baking ovens)
Frifri (fryers and frying systems)
GIGA Grandi Cucine (ranges steam cooking equipment and ovens)
Holman (high-speed conveyor toasting equipment)
Houno (combi-ovens and baking ovens)
Jade (specialty cooking equipment)
Lang (gas and electric solutions for commercial and marine applications)
MagiKitch' n (charbroiling products)
Middleby Marshall (conveyor oven equipment)
Nu-Vu (on-premise baking equipment)
Pito Frialator (fryers)
Perfect Fry (fryers)
Southbend (heavy-duty gas-fired equipment)
Star (equipment for fast food and concessions)
Toastmaster (conveyor toasters hot food servers griddles)
TurboChef (rapid-cook ovens)
Wells (countertop and drop-in warmers)
Food Processing Equipment Group
Alkar (batch and belt ovens conveyor cooking systems)
Cozzini (food processing equipment for grinding slicing emulsification mixing & blending)
MP Equipment (breading battering mixing forming and slicing machines)
RapidPak (packaging and food safety equipment)

COMPETITORS

AGA Rangemaster	Heat and Control
Ali SpA	Hobart Corp.
Alto-Shaam	Illinois Tool Works
Bally Refrigerated Boxes	Ingersoll-Rand
	Krack
Cleveland Range	Lincoln Foodservice
Dover Corp.	Manitowoc Foodservice
Electrolux	Standex
Franke Group	Strategic Equipment
Frymaster	and Supply
Gold Medal Products	Vulcan-Hart

HISTORICAL FINANCIALS

Company Type: Public

Income Statement

FYE: December 28

	REVENUE ($ mil.)	NET INCOME ($ mil.)	NET PROFIT MARGIN	EMPLOYEES
12/13	1,428.6	153.9	10.8%	4,491
12/12	1,038.1	120.7	11.6%	3,140
12/11*	855.9	95.4	11.2%	2,150
01/11	719.1	72.8	10.1%	2,060
01/10	646.6	61.1	9.5%	1,902
Annual Growth	21.9%	26.0%	—	24.0%

*Fiscal year change

2013 Year-End Financials

Debt ratio: 31.4%	No. of shares (mil.): 57
Return on equity: 20.7%	Dividends
Cash ($ mil.): 36	Yield: —
Current ratio: 1.75	Payout: —
Long-term debt ($ mil.): 570	Market value ($ mil.): 13,913

	STOCK PRICE ($) FY Close	P/E High/Low	PER SHARE ($) Earnings	Dividends	Book Value
12/13	242.50	89 46	2.74	0.00	14.61
12/12	125.47	60 42	2.16	0.00	11.52
12/11*	94.04	55 38	1.72	0.00	9.13
01/11	84.42	63 31	1.32	0.00	7.67
01/10	49.02	49 18	1.10	0.00	6.16
Annual Growth	49.1%	— —	25.7%	—	24.1%

*Fiscal year change

MidSouth Bancorp, Inc.

For banking in the Deep South try MidSouth. MidSouth Bancorp is the holding company for MidSouth Bank which operates some 40 branches in Louisiana and Texas. Targeting individuals and local business customers the bank offers such standard retail services as checking and savings accounts savings bonds investment accounts and credit card services. It also writes real estate mortgages (about 35% of its loan portfolio) and commercial (more than 30%) consumer and construction loans. MidSouth also offers lease-financing loans for business equipment.

The company is expanding its operations. To that end it bought five Jefferson Bank branches in the Dallas/Fort Worth area from First Bank and Trust in 2011. MidSouth also bought a branch in Tyler from Beacon Federal Bancorp which exited Texas. In late 2011 the bank acquired First Louisiana National Bank which operates three branches in St. Martin Parish. The next year it agreed to acquire PSB Financial which operates 16 branches in Louisiana under the Peoples State Bank banner.

EXECUTIVES

SEVP and CFO, James R. McLemore, age 55
President CEO and Director MidSouth Bancorp and MidSouth LA, C. R. (Rusty) Cloutier, age 66, $200,000 total compensation
Vice Chairman of the Board and Chief Operating Officer of the Company and MidSouth Bank; N.A., Gerald Reaux
Svp And Cio Midsouth La, Jennifer S Fontenot, age 60
Svp Credit Administration Midsouth La, Christopher J Levanti, age 48
Assistant Vice President Commercial, Maureen A Dunham
Executive Vice President Marketing, David Locke
President CEO and Director MidSouth Bancorp and MidSouth LA, C. R. (Rusty) Cloutier, age 66
Chairman MidSouth Bancorp and MidSouth LA, Will G. Charbonnet, age 66
Vice Chairman, J. B. Hargroder, age 83
Auditors: PorterKeadleMooreLLP

LOCATIONS

HQ: MidSouth Bancorp, Inc.
102 Versailles Boulevard, Lafayette, LA 70501
Phone: 337 237-8343
Web: www.midsouthbank.com

COMPETITORS

American Bancorp	Home Bank
Bank of America	IBERIABANK
Capital One	Regions Financial
Hancock Holding	Teche Holding
Henderson Citizens Bancshares	

HISTORICAL FINANCIALS

Company Type: Public

Income Statement

FYE: December 31

	ASSETS ($ mil.)	NET INCOME ($ mil.)	INCOME AS % OF ASSETS	EMPLOYEES
12/13	1,851.1	14.1	0.8%	604
12/12	1,851.7	9.6	0.5%	604
12/11	1,396.7	4.4	0.3%	444
12/10	1,002.3	5.7	0.6%	389
12/09	972.1	4.6	0.5%	416
Annual Growth	17.5%	32.5%	—	9.8%

2013 Year-End Financials

Return on assets: 0.7%	Dividends
Return on equity: 7.4%	Yield: 1.7%
Long-term debt ($ mil.): —	Payout: 32.6%
No. of shares (mil.): 11	Market value ($ mil.): 201
Sales ($ mil): 102	

	STOCK PRICE ($) FY Close	P/E High/Low	PER SHARE ($) Earnings	Dividends	Book Value
12/13	17.86	16 12	1.12	0.31	16.95
12/12	16.35	22 16	0.77	0.28	16.84
12/11	13.01	57 37	0.27	0.28	15.46
12/10	15.36	36 26	0.47	0.28	14.04
12/09	13.90	36 16	0.51	0.28	13.87
Annual Growth	6.5%	— —	21.7%	2.6%	5.1%

Miller Industries Inc. (TN)

This body builder wants to pump up your chassis. Miller Industries makes bodies for light- and heavy-duty wreckers along with car carriers and multi-vehicle trailers. It serves as the official recovery team at some of the NASCAR races (including Talladega) as well as the Indy 500 races. Miller makes its recovery and towing vehicles at plants in the US and Europe. Its multi-vehicle transport trailers can carry as many as eight vehicles and loads up to 75 tons. Miller Industries' US brand names include Century Challenger Champion Chevron Eagle Holmes Titan and Vulcan. The company's European brands are Jige (France) and Boniface (UK). Miller and rival Jerr-Dan dominate the US market for wrecker bodies.

Geographic Reach

The company has six manufacturing facilities in France the UK and the US. These facilities reside in Ooltewah (Chattanooga) Tennessee; Hermitage Pennsylvania; Mercer Pennsylvania; and Greeneville Tennessee. It also has manufacturing operations at two facilities located in the Lorraine region of France and manufacturing operations in Norfolk England. North America accounted for 80% of Miller's revenue in 2013.

Operations

Professional wrecker operators repossession and salvage companies comprise the light-duty wrecker market. Commercial vehicle operators and professional wreckers are served by the company's heavy-duty vehicles.

The company creates vehicles by bending steel and aluminum and welding the parts together to create a frame; hydraulic cylinders pumps winches and valves are attached to complete the carrier or wrecker body. The bodies are then attached to truck chassis made by third-party manufacturers such as Kenworth (a brand belonging to PAC-CAR) which is Miller's primary provider of truck chassis.

Miller has developed a wrecker that allows for damage-free towing of newer aerodynamic vehicles that are made of composite or lighter weight materials. The company boasts innovative technology which includes underlift parallel linkage and L-arms and the Vulcan "scoop" —these systems offer better lift-and-carry options that also protect cargo.

Sales and Marketing

Its products primarily are sold through independent distributors consisting of approximately 80 distributors in North America that serve all 50 states Canada and Mexico and other foreign markets.

Financial Performance

Miller has seen it balance sheet fluctuate the last few years. After experiencing steep drops in both revenue and net income during 2012 it posted revenue growth of 18% in 2013. Its profits remained static staying at the $9 million mark for 2012 and 2013 due to about $28 million it paid in selling general and administrative expenses for both those years.

The revenue growth for 2013 was attributed to increased demand from its commercial customers and corresponding increases in production levels based on recovering economic conditions. Sales from North America spiked by 19% as sales from other regions climbed by 13% during 2013.

Miller's cash flow from operations nosedived from $28 million in 2011 to $1 million in 2013. The steep fall was primarily due to $22 million it did not collect from customers from accounts receivable during 2013.

Strategy

The company's involvement with professional racing increases the exposure of Miller's products and supports sales and marketing efforts. Additionally the company focuses on domestic and international trade shows where it partners with its independent distributors in promotions. Miller plans to pursue more contract opportunities in export sales and government related orders; about 20% to 30% of its annual sales are generated by the US government.

HISTORY

Headed by William Miller the Miller Group (which owned Challenger Wrecker and Holmes International) acquired the wrecking operations of Century Holdings in 1990 and formed the basis for Miller Industries. However Miller Industries wasn't officially created until 1994 when the Miller Group placed all of its wrecking and towing businesses under that nameplate. The company went public in 1995.

With an established base in tow-truck manufacturing Miller Industries began to expand vertically in 1996. The company created a financial services unit that year to provide loans to towing-service and distribution companies. It started acquiring towing-equipment distributors of its own at that time. Also in 1996 the company moved overseas with the acquisition of European tow-truck makers S.A. Jige Lohr Wreckers (France) and Boniface Engineering Limited (UK).

In early 1997 Miller Industries made a massive push into towing-service companies creating Road-One with the intention of becoming a nationwide

entity. The company acquired 29 towing-service companies in fiscal 1997 47 in 1998 and 35 in 1999. Then its pace slowed —Miller Industries acquired only a handful of towing-service businesses in 2000.

Miller proposed a 1-for-5 stock split to shareholders in 2001 in hopes of avoiding being delisted from the New York Stock Exchange (NYSE). The company managed to keep its shares trading on the NYSE by trimming costs which it accomplished by moving to exit the distribution and towing services businesses beginning in 2002. By the end of 2004 Miller had disposed of the assets of RoadOne and nearly all of its distribution operations.

In 2008 the company renovated and expanded its manufacturing operations in Hermitage Pennsylvania and Ooltewah Tennessee. The Ooltewah plant produces light and heavy duty wreckers and trailers its 302000 square foot plant; the Hermitage plant is a 118000 square foot facility that manufacturers car carriers.

EXECUTIVES

EVP CFO and Treasurer, J. Vincent Mish, age 63, $225,009 total compensation

EVP Secretary and General Counsel, Frank Madonia, age 65, $225,009 total compensation

Co-CEO, Jeffrey I. (Jeff) Badgley, age 62, $450,017 total compensation

President and Co-CEO, William G. Miller, $175,007 total compensation

Vp-mktg, Randy Olson

Chairman, William G. Miller, age 67

Auditors: JosephDecosimoandCompanyLLP

LOCATIONS

HQ: Miller Industries Inc. (TN)
8503 Hilltop Drive, Ooltewah, TN 37363
Phone: 423 238-4171   **Fax:** 423 238-5371
Web: www.millerind.com

2013 Sales

	$ mil.	% of total
North America	336.0	83
Other regions	68.2	17
Total	**404.2**	**100**

PRODUCTS/OPERATIONS

Selected Products and Brands

Boniface (heavy-duty wreckers for the European market)
Century (wreckers car carriers)
Challenger (wreckers car carriers)
Champion (car carriers)
Chevron (wreckers car carriers towing and recovery equipment)
Eagle (light-duty wreckers)
Holmes (mid-priced wreckers and car carriers)
Jige (light- and heavy-duty wreckers and car carriers for the European market)
Miller (parts and accessories catalog)
SP Series (medium-duty wreckers & carriers)
Titan (multi-vehicle transport trailers)
Trailers (Titan T Series)
Vulcan (wreckers car carriers towing and recovery equipment)

COMPETITORS

Daimler Trucks North America	Penske Truck Leasing
Jerr-Dan	Peterbilt
Mitsubishi Fuso	United Rentals

HISTORICAL FINANCIALS

Company Type: Public

Income Statement

FYE: December 31

	REVENUE ($ mil.)	NET INCOME ($ mil.)	NET PROFIT MARGIN	EMPLOYEES
12/13	404.1	9.2	2.3%	820
12/12	342.6	9.1	2.7%	750
12/11	412.6	23.0	5.6%	760
12/10	306.9	11.7	3.8%	700
12/09	237.5	6.0	2.5%	680
Annual Growth	**14.2%**	**11.3%**	**—**	**4.8%**

2013 Year-End Financials

Debt ratio: —	No. of shares (mil.): 11
Return on equity: 5.7%	Dividends
Cash ($ mil.): 42	Yield: 3.0%
Current ratio: 2.91	Payout: 72.7%
Long-term debt ($ mil.): —	Market value ($ mil.): 210

	STOCK PRICE ($) FY Close	P/E High/Low		PER SHARE ($) Earnings	Dividends	Book Value
12/13	18.63	23	18	0.82	0.56	14.40
12/12	15.25	21	17	0.82	0.52	14.11
12/11	15.73	11	7	1.92	0.48	13.88
12/10	14.23	16	11	0.96	0.10	12.86
12/09	11.35	22	10	0.51	0.00	12.16
Annual Growth	**13.2%**	**—**	**—**	**12.6%**	**—**	**4.3%**

Mistras Group, Inc.

Mistras could be all that stands between you and a massive oil refinery explosion nuclear facility meltdown or big bridge collapse. The engineering services company conducts non-destructive testing on critical equipment and processes used by petroleum aerospace infrastructure power generation and chemical manufacturing companies worldwide. It checks plant infrastructure for defects and problems without interrupting production; inspections take place during facility design build maintenance and operation phases. Mistras works from about 75 offices in 15 nations to serve clients that include Alcan Honeywell Bechtel BP Dow Chemical Airbus and federal and state governments.

Operations

Mistras helps its customers beyond just avoiding catastrophic events. The company help clients comply with government safety standards minimize repair costs extend the useful life of assets and increase productivity.

In addition to its on-site testing services the company also offers testing equipment instruments and software through its Software and Products division. Testing services include mechanical integrity and visual testing along with digital radiography ground penetrating radar and infrared and ultrasonic sensor testing. Mistras' software offerings include databases and enterprise software to store and analyze testing data planning software and on-line monitoring systems.

Sales and Marketing

Asset heavy companies make up the bulk of Mistras' clients. Customers coming from the oil gas and chemical industries have historically comprised more than 50% of the company's international revenues stemming primarily from contracts with major oil refineries in Brazil and Russia. Smaller pieces of the revenue pie come from testing other safety-critical industrial sites infrastructure manufacturing facilities research centers and universities.

Financial Performance

The company's revenue has been growing steadily year-over-year. Its revenue was $623.4 million in fiscal 2014 up from $529.3 million in fiscal 2013 and $436.9 in fiscal 2012.

The company's net revenue increased from $11 million in fiscal 2013 up to $22 million in fiscal 2014. It cash flow decreased from $43 million in fiscal 2013 down to $36 million in fiscal 2014.

Strategy

In the past Mistras has grown through acquisitions. More recently though the company has grown organically. The company also wants to delve into newer markets seeing opportunities in alternative energy and public infrastructure. The company hopes to expand its services into such emerging markets as India and China. Mistras also wants to expand its services to existing clients which includes providing multinational companies services in many of the countries they operate.

EXECUTIVES

EVP CFO and Treasurer, Jonathan H. (Jon) Wolk, age 48

V Pres-sales, Nick Sowa

Chairman President and CEO, Sotirios J. Vahaviolos, age 68, $424,679 total compensation

Group EVP Services and Director, Michael J. Lange, age 54, $283,292 total compensation

Executive Vice President Products and Systems, Mark F. Carlos, age 63, $130,000 total compensation

EVP of International, Phillip T. Cole, age 61, $175,088 total compensation

President and COO, Dennis M. Bertolotti, $231,360 total compensation

Evp General Counsel And Secretary, Michael C Keefe, age 58

Vice President On Line Aset Integrity, Sam Ternowchek

Vice President Predictive Maintenance, Michael Burch

Vice President, Richard Hilyard

Senior Vice President Market Manager, David C Sinay

Vice President Of Services Gulf Region, Randy Sweet

Vice President Sales And Marketing Products And Systems Division, Robert Marino

EVP CFO and Treasurer, Jonathan H. (Jon) Wolk, age 48

Chairman President and CEO, Sotirios J. Vahaviolos, age 68

Group EVP Services and Director, Michael J. Lange, age 54

Auditors: PricewaterhouseCoopersLLP

LOCATIONS

HQ: Mistras Group, Inc.
195 Clarksville Road, Princeton Junction, NJ 08550
Phone: 609 716-4000
Web: www.mistrasgroup.com

COMPETITORS

GE Inspection Technologies	Siemens AG
Lloyd's Register	Team
SGS	The Carlyle Group

HISTORICAL FINANCIALS

Company Type: Public

Income Statement

FYE: May 31

	REVENUE ($ mil.)	NET INCOME ($ mil.)	NET PROFIT MARGIN	EMPLOYEES
05/14	623.4	22.5	3.6%	5,300
05/13	529.2	11.6	2.2%	4,400
05/12	436.8	21.3	4.9%	3,500
05/11	338.5	16.4	4.9%	2,700
05/10	272.1	10.4	3.8%	2,300
Annual Growth	**23.0%**	**21.2%**	**—**	**23.2%**

2014 Year-End Financials

Debt ratio: 21.9%
Return on equity: 9.9%
Cash ($ mil.): 10
Current ratio: 2.02
Long-term debt ($ mil.): 82

No. of shares (mil.): 28
Dividends
Yield: —
Payout: —
Market value ($ mil.): 648

	STOCK PRICE ($) FY Close	P/E High/Low	PER SHARE ($) Earnings	Dividends	Book Value
05/14	22.76	32 20	0.77	0.00	8.51
05/13	21.38	66 45	0.40	0.00	7.45
05/12	22.54	34 19	0.74	0.00	6.89
05/11	17.41	30 15	0.61	0.00	6.04
05/10	11.94	19 13	0.43	0.00	4.89
Annual Growth	**17.5%**	**— —**	**15.7%**	**—**	**14.9%**

MKS Instruments, Inc.

In case it's not clear from the name MKS Instruments makes instruments. In particular it makes systems that analyze and control gases during semiconductor manufacturing and other thin film industrial processes such as those used to make flat panel displays LEDs solar cells and data storage media. Top customers include chip equipment heavyweights Applied Materials Lam Research Novellus Systems and Tokyo Electron. Other applications include medical equipment pharmaceutical manufacturing energy generation and environmental monitoring. MKS Instruments generates about half its revenue from the US.

Operations

MKS groups its products into four categories: Instruments and Control Products Power and Reactive Gas Products Analytical Solutions and Vacuum Products. Instruments and Control Products and Power and Reactive Gas Products each account for about 40% of sales while Analytical Solutions and Vacuum Products each account for about 10% of sales.

Geographic Reach

The company has manufacturing plants in the US UK Germany China Israel and Mexico. It buys electronic mechanical and electrical components from other companies to assemble into its instruments.

Sales and Marketing

It uses a direct sales force operating in about a dozen countries. MKS generates about half its revenue from the US. Another 35% comes from Asia while Europe accounts for about 15% of sales.

Financial Performance

Overall sales fell 22% in 2012 to $643 million as its semiconductor customers experienced lower demand and rising chip inventories; they didn't

need to make as many chips using MKS's instruments. In addition its solar and LED customers are still using products made in 2010 and 2011 and haven't needed to buy new instruments. The drop in product revenue was countered by services (maintenance upgrades installation) revenue which picked up as a result of a larger base of installed equipment and a push by MKS to increase its services revenue. Profits were also affected by reduced sales. Despite keeping costs down profits sank more than 63% to $48 million.

Mergers and Acquisitions

The 2013 purchase of Italy's Alter Power Systems expands MKS's opportunities in the food and beverage market as well as the industrial heating market. The year before it paid $23 million for Korea-based Plasmart which designs and makes radio frequency (RF) plasma generation and monitoring systems for the semiconductor flat panel display AMOLED and solar photovoltaic industries. The Plasmart acquisition will help MKS grow in the Asian market.

In late 2011 the company bought GE's EO3 line of ozone generators used for water sterilization. Part of deal included MKS becoming a key supplier of ozone products to GE. The line expanded its existing ozone offering to pharmaceutical food and beverage and industrial manufacturing companies.

EXECUTIVES

President and COO, Gerald G. Colella, age 57, $411,200 total compensation

CEO and Director, Leo Berlinghieri, age 60, $600,000 total compensation

Chief Financial Officer; Vice President; Treasurer, Seth H. Bagshaw, age 54, $300,000 total compensation

SVP Analytical Solutions Group, John A. Smith, age 63, $295,467 total compensation

Senior Vice President - Controls; HPS and PFMC, John T. C. Lee, age 51, $320,002 total compensation

Vice President Global Applications Engineering, John Doherty

Sr V Pres Global Oprs, Brian C Quirk

Senior Vice President Of Operations, Bill Sullivan

Vice President And Corporate Controller, Derek D'Antilio

CEO and Director, Leo Berlinghieri, age 60

Chairman, John R. Bertucci, age 74

Auditors: PricewaterhouseCoopersLLP

LOCATIONS

HQ: MKS Instruments, Inc.
2 Tech Drive, Suite 201, Andover, MA 01810
Phone: 978 645-5500
Web: www.mksinst.com

2012 Sales

	% of total
US	51
Asia (excl. Japan)	23
Europe	13
Japan	13
Total	**100**

PRODUCTS/OPERATIONS

2012 Sales

	% of total
Instruments & Control Products	40
Power & Reactive Gas Products	39
Analytical Solutions	11
Vacuum Products	10
Total	**100**

Selected Products

Instruments and Control Systems
  Pressure Measurement and Control Products
  Baratron® Pressure Measurement Products
  Automatic Pressure and Vacuum Control Products
  Materials Delivery Products
  Flow Measurement and Control Products
  Gas Composition Analysis Products
  Mass Spectrometry-Based Gas Composition Analysis
  Instruments
  Fourier Transform Infra-Red (FTIR) Based Gas
  Composition Analysis Products
  Control and Information Technology Products
  Control Products
  Information Technology Products
Power and Reactive Gas Products
  Power Delivery Products
  Reactive Gas Generation Products
  Processing Thin Films
  Equipment Cleaning
Vacuum Products
  Vacuum Gauging Products
  Vacuum Valves Stainless Steel Components Process
  Solutions and Custom Stainless Steel Hardware
  Custom Manufactured Components

COMPETITORS

ATMI	INFICON
Advanced Energy	KLA-Tencor
Industries	L' Air Liquide
Arizona Instrument	Nova Measuring
BW Technologies	Pall Corporation
Brooks Automation	Veeco Instruments
CVD Equipment	WIKA
Ebara	Winton Products
Entegris	Company
HORIBA	
Hitachi	
High-Technologies	

HISTORICAL FINANCIALS

Company Type: Public

Income Statement
FYE: December 31

	REVENUE ($ mil.)	NET INCOME ($ mil.)	NET PROFIT MARGIN	EMPLOYEES
12/13	669.4	35.7	5.3%	2,394
12/12	643.5	48.0	7.5%	2,305
12/11	822.5	129.7	15.8%	2,429
12/10	853.1	142.5	16.7%	2,673
12/09	411.4	(212.6)	—	2,178
Annual Growth	12.9%	—	—	2.4%

2013 Year-End Financials

Debt ratio: —
Return on equity: 3.5%
Cash ($ mil.): 288
Current ratio: 6.85
Long-term debt ($ mil.): —

No. of shares (mil.): 53
Dividends
  Yield: 2.1%
  Payout: 168.4%
  Market value ($ mil.): 1,597

	STOCK PRICE ($) FY Close	P/E High/Low		PER SHARE ($) Earnings	Dividends	Book Value
12/13	29.92	46	37	0.67	0.64	19.14
12/12	25.78	35	25	0.90	0.62	19.19
12/11	27.82	14	8	2.45	0.60	18.86
12/10	24.50	9	6	2.80	0.60	16.72
12/09	17.40	—	—	(4.31)	0.00	13.83
Annual Growth	14.5%	—	—	—	—	8.5%

Monarch Financial Holdings Inc

Money rules at Monarch Financial Holdings. The holding company serves the South Hampton Roads area of southeastern Virginia through Monarch Bank Monarch Mortgage Monarch Capital Monarch Investment and OBXBank. With nearly a dozen branches Monarch Bank offers standard services including savings and checking accounts IRAs and CDS. Bank subsidiary Monarch Mortgage formed in 2007 has about a dozen offices. Other divisions sell insurance title and investment products. Single-family mortgages make up the largest portion of the company's loan portfolio which also includes commercial construction and land development loans. Monarch Bank division OBX Bank operates in North Carolina's Outer Banks area.

Strategy

Monarch Mortgage in 2013 entered into a marketing agreement to provide mortgage banking services to clients of Rose & Womble Realty Company with offices in Hampton Roads Virginia and North Carolina. The two firms are planning to form a joint venture to support a long-term mortgage partnership.

EXECUTIVES

Svp And Chief Credit Officer, Andrew N Lock, age 51
Evp And Senior Operations Officer, Barbara N Lane, age 65
Svp-cash Mgmnt Services, Terri Ruby
Auditors: Goodman&CompanyL.L.P.

LOCATIONS

HQ: Monarch Financial Holdings Inc
  1435 Crossways Blvd., Chesapeake, VA 23320
Phone: 757 389-5111
Web: www.monarchbank.com

COMPETITORS

BB&T	SunTrust
Bank of America	
Hampton Roads	
Bankshares	

HISTORICAL FINANCIALS

Company Type: Public

Income Statement
FYE: December 31

	ASSETS ($ mil.)	NET INCOME ($ mil.)	INCOME AS % OF ASSETS	EMPLOYEES
12/13	1,016.7	11.0	1.1%	634
12/12	1,215.5	12.8	1.1%	663
12/11	908.4	7.1	0.8%	579
12/10	825.5	5.9	0.7%	527
12/09	689.5	4.8	0.7%	432
Annual Growth	10.2%	22.9%	—	10.1%

2013 Year-End Financials

Return on assets: 0.9%
Return on equity: 12.0%
Long-term debt ($ mil.): —
No. of shares (mil.): 10
Sales ($ mil): 114

Dividends
  Yield: 1.9%
  Payout: 22.2%
  Market value ($ mil.): 129

	STOCK PRICE ($) FY Close	P/E High/Low		PER SHARE ($) Earnings	Dividends	Book Value
12/13	12.31	12	8	1.08	0.24	9.29
12/12	8.22	7	5	1.25	0.16	10.21
12/11	7.69	11	8	0.70	0.13	10.59
12/10	7.80	14	10	0.63	0.12	9.99
12/09	6.10	16	8	0.55	0.00	9.65
Annual Growth	19.2%	—	—	18.4%	—	(1.0%)

Monotype Imaging Holdings Inc

Monotype Imaging may be the one to thank if you're reading this whether it's on a portable electronic device or a printed page. With most sales going to device manufacturers (OEMs) the company's text imaging software is integrated into applications and embedded in electronics ranging from mobile phones to laser printers automotive displays and digital cameras. Its applications manage compression scaling color and layout. Providing customers access to thousands of typefaces OEM sales are complemented by about a quarter of revenue coming from licenses to creative professionals mostly commercial clients. Customers have included Nokia Sony and Microsoft.

Geographic Reach

Geographic recognition of revenue does not necessarily reflect the destination of Monotype Imaging's products as sales are attached to the subsidiary receiving the revenue. Sales by a US subsidiary to Korea-based customers for example are classified as US sales. The company's products are sold from offices in Germany Hong Kong Japan South Korea the UK and the US. Sales from Asia generally go to Asian customers while the other subsidiaries cover many different countries including the US.

The company's research and development operations are located in Woburn Massachusetts; San Mateo California; Boulder Colorado; Belfast Northern Ireland; Salford United Kingdom; Bad Homburg Germany; Noida India; Hong Kong China; and Tokyo Japan.

Operations

The US has grown as a percentage of total revenues contributing more than half of Monotype Imaging's revenues in 2013. The company does however expect international to continue to be a major percentage of total revenues. Since Asia is an underpenetrated region for Monotype Imaging it is a particularly attractive growth opportunity specifically in Chinese Japanese and Korean language markets for laser printers digital copiers and other devices.

Sales and Marketing

Although no customer accounts for more than 10% of sales Monotype Imaging's top ten clients account for about 40% of annual revenues. The company serves many of its target industries' leaders including four of the top five e-book reader makers including Amazon and Kobo top automotive brands such as Chrysler Ford Honda and Hyundai eight of the top 10 laser printer manufacturers and twelve of the top fifteen phone makers. Company's advertising expenses were $1.7 million $1.3 million and $3.8 million for the years 2013 2012 and 2011 respectively.

Financial Performance

Monotype Imaging has seen an upward trend in its revenues of the past few years. In 2013 it reported an 11% rise in revenues driven by a 23% increase in its Creative Professional revenues (thanks to an $11.9 million growth in web sales) together with an increase in its OEM revenues which grew by $4.8 million (or 4.9%) attributable to higher revenues from per unit royalty arrangements with printer and display imaging-based OEM customers.The company posted a 7% increase in net income in 2013 driven by higher sales offset by an increase its operating expenses (including marketing and selling expenses research and development expenses general and administrative expenses) and amortization of other intangible assets.Monotype Imaging's cash flow in operating activities in 2013 was $51.3 million (up $900000 on 2012) driven by increased net income after adjusting for depreciation and amortization amortization of deferred financing costs loss on retirement of fixed assets share based compensation provision for doubtful accounts deferred income taxes unrealized currency gain on foreign denominated intercompany and accreted interest.

Strategy

At the center of Monotype Imaging's growth strategy is a focus on serving high growth consumer electronic devices such as smartphones tablets navigation devices and consumer appliances to name a few. It will however also stay focused on the slower-growth laser printer market where it holds a leadership position and sees a demand for customized driver applications such as language interpretation. The company also continues to value its creative professionals and consumer users. It has several Websites including fonts.com and linotype.com.

In 2014 the company expanded its Fonts.com Web Fonts inventory to include typefaces from the famous FontFont library.

Company Background

In 2012 the company furthered its aspirations for both of its primary customer groups when it acquired major competitor Bitstream for $50 million. With that purchase Monotype Imaging gained the 62000 fonts on MyFonts.com font capabilities such as an identification service and font rendering and layout technologies fonts for embedded and mobile settings and 10 patents as well as 40 engineers and type designers at a facility in India. That year the company also acquired Design by Front Limited a privately held web strategy design and technology studio in Belfast Northern Ireland for $4.6 million.

In 2009 Monotype Imaging saw a chance to build on its strategy of expanding its offerings for OEM customers acquiring Planetweb for about $2 million. PlanetWeb provided user interface developer tools for consumer electronics manufacturers.

Monotype Imaging was formed when a group of investors including TA Associates acquired Agfa Monotype (then a subsidiary of Agfa) in 2004. The company does business as International Typeface Corporation or ITC in the US; Monotype Hong Kong and Monotype Japan in Asia; and Monotype UK and Linotype in Europe.

EXECUTIVES

Chief Executive Officer President, Douglas J. (Doug) Shaw, age 59, $390,000 total compensation
Executive Vice President, John L. Seguin, age 60, $315,315 total compensation
VP and General Manager E-Commerce, Christopher J. Roberts, age 48
Senior Vice President Chief Financial Officer Treasurer Secretary, Scott Landers, age 43, $298,116 total compensation
Vice President; General Manager - Display Imaging, Ira Mirochnick
President of the Lanston Monotype Machine Company, Harvey Best
Vice President Corporate Development, Daniel T (Dan) Gerron, age 49
Vice President Engineering, Al Ristow
Vice President Of Oem Sales And Traini, Don Macdonald
Senior Vice President Engineering, Steve Martin
General Counsel Secretary, Janet M Dunlap, age 50
Auditors: Ernst&YoungLLP

LOCATIONS

HQ: Monotype Imaging Holdings Inc
500 Unicorn Park Drive, Woburn, MA 01801
Phone: 781 970-6000
Web: www.monotypeimaging.com

2013 Sales

	$ mil.	% of total
US	91.0	55
Asia	50.2	30
Germany	18.4	11
UK	7.0	4
Total	**166.6**	**100**

PRODUCTS/OPERATIONS

2013 Sales

	$ mil.	% of total
OEM	102.9	62
Creative Professional	63.7	38
Total	**166.6**	**100**

Selected Customers

E-book readers
 Amazon
 Kobo
Digital TVs and set-top-boxes
 Sharp
 Toshiba
 TTE Technology
Mobile phones
 Motorola
 Nokia
 RIM
 Sony
 ZTE
Other
 Activision
 Gannett Company
 Google
 Microsoft
 Nintendo
 Ubisoft
 UBS
 TiVo
 Whirlpool

COMPETITORS

Adobe Systems Xara
Extensis

HISTORICAL FINANCIALS

Company Type: Public

Income Statement

FYE: December 31

	REVENUE ($ mil.)	NET INCOME ($ mil.)	NET PROFIT MARGIN	EMPLOYEES
12/13	166.6	31.0	18.7%	354
12/12	149.8	28.9	19.3%	335
12/11	123.2	22.6	18.4%	272
12/10	106.6	18.3	17.2%	251
12/09	94.0	13.4	14.3%	239
Annual Growth	**15.4%**	**23.4%**	**—**	**10.3%**

2013 Year-End Financials

Debt ratio: —
Return on equity: 11.9%
Cash ($ mil.): 78
Current ratio: 3.43
Long-term debt ($ mil.): —
No. of shares (mil.): 39
Dividends
 Yield: 0.7%
 Payout: 30.3%
Market value ($ mil.): 1,245

	STOCK PRICE ($) FY Close	P/E High/Low		PER SHARE ($) Earnings	Dividends	Book Value
12/13	31.86	40	20	0.78	0.24	7.34
12/12	15.98	22	16	0.76	0.08	6.32
12/11	15.59	27	16	0.61	0.00	5.47
12/10	11.10	22	14	0.51	0.00	4.66
12/09	9.03	24	5	0.38	0.00	4.06
Annual Growth	**37.1%**	**—**	**—**	**19.7%**	**—**	**15.9%**

Monro Muffler Brake, Inc.

If you can't stop point your car toward Monro Muffler Brake and coast on in. The company provides a full range of brake tire exhaust system suspension and steering and alignment services at more than 800 automotive repair shops. Its operations span nearly 20 states in the Northeast and Midwest and include Monro Muffler Brake & Service Mr. Tire Tread Quarters Autotire Car Care Center and Tire Warehouse. Along with under-car work the company offers air conditioning maintenance state inspections and scheduled maintenance services including fleet maintenance. Tire replacements and service account for more than 35% of sales. Monro Muffler Brake services more than 4.4 million vehicles annually.

Geographic Reach

Monro Muffler Brake operates company stores in 19 states including New York Pennsylvania Ohio Massachusetts New Jersey the Carolinas and Illinois.

Operations

Monro Muffler Brake operates about 535 service stores which specialize in repairing and replacing worn out auto parts as well as some 265 tire stores which sell install and align tires. In addition to Monro Muffler Brake's 800-plus company owned stores there are three franchised locations and 14 dealer-operated stores providing automotive under-car repair and tire services.

Sales and Marketing

Monro Muffler Brake advertises through direct mail coupon inserts and in-store promotional signage and displays. It also advertises through radio yellow pages newspapers service reminders and digital marketing. It cross markets its services promoting the Monro Muffler Brake & Service brand in its Tire Warehouse stores. During fiscal 2012 (ends March) the company launched mobile apps on the iPhone and Android platforms that allow customers to manage and maintain their vehicle maintenance records make appointments locate stores and search for promotions/coupons and tires.

Financial Performance

Monro Muffler Brake's $686.5 million in fiscal 2012 (ends March) sales was an all-time high for the fast-growing company. Indeed 2012 marked the fifth consecutive year of increasing sales and fourth year of steadily increasing profits. The company's sales climbed 8% in 2012 vs. the prior year while net income rose by 19% over the same period. Sales got a boost from the addition of new stores several acquisitions and rising comparable sales at existing shops (up 2%). Monro has widened its margins by controlling spending on operations amid increased sales.

Strategy

The company whose roots reach back to 1957 has seen its revenues steadily climb over the years as its footprint expanded. The business continues to grow through both acquisitions and organic growth. Unlike many of its competitors Monro owns almost all of its stores believing it can better manage repair shops and train employees through more centralized control. Independent dealers operate only about 15 locations. It also operates nearly 35 full-service Monro stores onsite at BJ's Wholesale Clubs.

In recent years Monro's sales have also been helped by the economic downturn which has resulted in tightened credit markets and decreased consumer spending prompting Americans to drive and maintain their vehicles instead of trade them in for new models.

Mergers and Acquisitions

With earnings on a roll Monro in fiscal 2012 spent approximately $50 million to buy 18 retail tire and automotive repair stores in North Carolina from Colony Tire Corp. as well as 20 other tire and repair stores in Virginia from Kramer Tire Co. The Kramer purchase included two heavy-truck tire and truck repair stores two wholesale operations and a retread facility in Virginia. The acquired stores operate primarily under the Tread Quarters name. In 2011 the firm purchased Vespia Tire Centers which operated two dozen locations throughout New Jersey and Pennsylvania. During 2010 Monro acquired Import Export Tire a five-store tire chain in Pittsburgh and three Courthouse Tire auto repair and tire shops in Fredericksburg Virginia.

Ownership

T. Rowe Price owns about 12% of Monro Muffler Brakes' shares.

HISTORY

Charles August founded Monro Muffler Brake in 1957 as a franchise of Midas Muffler (later Midas Inc.). August hoped to expand his services under the Midas name but was refused so in 1966 he broke with Midas and began his own full line of undercar services. The company name was derived from Monroe County New York where it is headquartered; August decided to drop the "e" to save money on his sign. Monro Muffler Brake had 59 shops by 1984 when an investor group led by Peter Solomon and Donald Glickman purchased a controlling interest. In 1987 despite Solomon's objections August retired and was replaced by Jack

Gallagher a 20-year veteran of the automotive industry. The firm went public in 1991.

Gallagher stepped down in March 1995. New CEO Lawrence Day wasted little time in expanding Monro Muffler Brake's customer base. In July 1995 the company acquired Durham North Carolina-based Muffler Xpress establishing Monro Muffler Brake in the Carolinas. The company also opened its first store in Maine that year.

In 1997 Monro Muffler Brake agreed to sell Bridgestone/Firestone tires in its stores and entered a joint venture with Q-Lube (a subsidiary of Pennzoil-Quaker State which was acquired by Royal Dutch Shell in 2002) to develop co-branded stores offering fast oil changes and undercar services. (The company abandoned the concept the following year.)

Monro Muffler Brake bought about 205 repair shops mostly in the Northeast in 1998 from Speedy Muffler King for $52 million. Store expansions hurt earnings that year and Day stepped down. Robert Gross was named president and CEO later in 1998. Monro Muffler Brake began opening shops in BJ's Wholesale Club outlets in 1999. In 2000 the company which previously had carried only Firestone tires announced it would sign with another tire supplier in order to assuage customers alarmed by the Firestone recall.

Monro Muffler Brake purchased Kimmel Automotive Inc. in 2002 and 10 Frasier Tire Service stores in 2003.

In March 2004 Monro Muffler Brake acquired more than 35 Mr. Tire locations in Maryland and Virginia from Atlantic Automotive. The next year Monro Muffler Brake added Donald B. Rice Tire and Henderson Holdings gaining a total of 15 tire and auto repair shops. The company also opened additional shops inside BJ's Wholesale Clubs.

In November 2005 Monro acquired a minority stake in Strauss Discount Auto and an option to take full ownership but the company said it would not exercise the option after Strauss filed for bankruptcy protection in August 2006. (Monro wrote-off its $2.8 million investment in Strauss in fiscal 2008.)

In 2006 the company bought key operations of bankrupt ProCare Automotive Service Solutions. The $15 million deal gave Monro an additional 75 stores in Ohio and Pennsylvania. Monro went on to acquire Valley Forge Tire & Auto Centers and Craven Tire & Auto in mid-2007 adding about 20 locations and expanding Monro's tire business to Philadelphia and Northern Virginia.

Peter Solomon stepped down as chairman in August 2007. He was succeeded by Robert Gross.

In early 2008 the firm acquired seven retail tire and automotive repair stores in Buffalo New York from the Broad Elm Group. In 2009 the company acquired privately owned Tire Warehouse Central with 40-plus locations throughout New England; Midwest Tire & Auto Repair a small chain in northwest Indiana; and Autotire Car Care Centers of St. Louis from American Tire Distributors.

EXECUTIVES

Chief Financial Officer; Executive Vice President - Finance; Treasurer; Secretary, Catherine D'Amico, age 58, $230,000 total compensation
Divisional VP Western Operations, Christopher R. Hoornbeck, age 63, $168,100 total compensation
Divisional Vice President - Southern Operations, Craig L. Hoyle, age 60, $145,000 total compensation
EVP of Store Operations, Joseph Tomarchio, age 58, $380,000 total compensation

President and CEO, John W. Van Heel, age 48, $308,000 total compensation
Auditors: PricewaterhouseCoopersLLP

LOCATIONS

HQ: Monro Muffler Brake, Inc.
200 Holleder Parkway, Rochester, NY 14615
Phone: 585 647-6400   **Fax:** 585 647-0945
Web: www.monro.com
Connecticut
Delaware
Illinois
Indiana
Maine
Maryland
Massachusetts
Missouri
New Hampshire
New Jersey
New York
North Carolina
Ohio
Pennsylvania
Rhode Island
South Carolina
Vermont
Virginia
West Virginia

PRODUCTS/OPERATIONS

2012 Sales

	% of total
Tires	39
Maintenance	28
Brakes	18
Steering	10
Exhaust	5
Total	**100**

2012 Company-owned Stores

	No.
Service (including BJ's)	536
Tire	267
Total	**803**

COMPETITORS

AAMCO	Pep Boys
Bridgestone Retail Operations	Precision Auto
Discount Tire	Sears
Goodyear Tire & Rubber	TBC
Jiffy Lube	TCI Tire Centers
Meineke	Valvoline
Midas	Wal-Mart

HISTORICAL FINANCIALS

Company Type: Public

Income Statement

FYE: March 29

	REVENUE ($ mil.)	NET INCOME ($ mil.)	NET PROFIT MARGIN	EMPLOYEES
03/14	831.4	54.4	6.6%	6,139
03/13	732.0	42.5	5.8%	5,850
03/12	686.5	54.6	8.0%	5,113
03/11	636.6	45.8	7.2%	5,005
03/10	564.6	33.1	5.9%	4,926
Annual Growth	**10.2%**	**13.2%**	**—**	**5.7%**

2014 Year-End Financials

Debt ratio: 25.6%	No. of shares (mil.): 31
Return on equity: 13.9%	Dividends
Cash ($ mil.): 1	Yield: 0.0%
Current ratio: 1.23	Payout: 26.3%
Long-term debt ($ mil.): 187	Market value ($ mil.): 1,780

STOCK PRICE ($)		P/E		PER SHARE ($)		
	FY Close	High/Low		Earnings	Dividends	Book Value
03/14	56.51	36	22	1.67	0.44	13.21
03/13	39.71	31	23	1.32	0.40	11.68
03/12	41.49	27	17	1.69	0.35	10.60
03/11	31.78	35	20	1.44	0.33	9.20
03/10	35.99	33	21	1.07	0.18	7.77
Annual Growth	11.9%	—	—	11.7%	25.0%	14.2%

Monster Beverage Corp

Monster Beverage certainly has the energy to reach beyond the blue sky. Along with its Blue Sky beverages the company serves up a variety of "alternative" sodas juices and teas. Its most popular and now namesake brand Monster is the #2 energy drink behind Red Bull and has spawned the Java Monster coffee drink. Other products include fruit juice smoothies and dry juice mixes. The company sells most of its products in the US and Canada through a distribution network but also directly to retailers such as grocery chains and wholesale clubs. Monster has agreed to form a long-term strategic partnership with The Coca-Cola Company which will acquire a minority stake in the business for $2.1 billion.

Operations

California-based Monster Beverage is organized into two separate business segments. The company's Direct Store Delivery (DSD) segment generated 96% of 2013 revenues up from 90% in 2008. Because Monster is the top brand in this segment the company works aggressively to pique the interest of trendy consumers in the niche market by regularly rolling out new products. In recent years the beverage maker has been focused on launching new products as extensions of the Monster brand. Monster Beverage's other business segment Warehouse comprises juice-based beverages and sodas. The business has stalled in recent years bringing in just 4% of 2013 sales compared with 10% in 2008 as customers have bypassed pricier sodas and functional drinks for more mainstream options.

Sales and Marketing

A multi-channel marketer Monster Beverage serves a variety of customers. Customers include full service distributors (63% of 2013 sales); those outside the US (23%); club stores drug chains and mass merchants (9%); retail grocery specialty chains and wholesalers (3%); and other (2%).

Looking to increase brand awareness and spur sales Monster Beverage spent more on advertising and promotional activities in 2013 shelling out $181.8 million up from $165 million in 2012 and $149 million in 2011.

Financial Performance

Monster Beverage has a long record of steady sales gains. Indeed 2013 capped a decade of growth with record sales of $2.25 billion a 9% gain versus 2012. Driving the rise was an increase in sales of the company's namesake brand Monster Energy which added about $177 million in sales representing about 96% of the overall increase for the year. Increased domestic and international demand —in new and established foreign markets —led to volume increases for its Monster

Energy drinks. Hubert's Lemonades posted a 4% gain in sales on rising domestic demand.

Despite the increase in 2013 sales net income for the same reporting period declined by $1.4 million to $338.7 million. The dip was attributed primarily to increased interest and other expenses in 2013.

Strategy

In a deal that appears to hold promise for both Monster and its new long-term strategic partner The Coca-Cola Company (TCCC) TCCC in August 2014 agreed to purchase a 16.7% equity stake in Monster for $2.15 billion. Under the terms of the deal TCCC will transfer ownership of its worldwide energy drink business including NOS Full Throttle Burn Mother Play and Power Play and Relentless to Monster; and Monster will transfer its non-energy beverages including Hansen's Natural Sodas Peace Tea Hubert's Lemonade and Hansen's Juice Products to TCCC. The deal is expected to close in late 2014 or early 2015.

The "alternative beverage" industry has grown increasingly crowded as it includes bottled water and juices from beverage giants such as Coca-Cola and PepsiCo. To compete Monster Beverage's product line includes "functional" drinks made by adding Echinacea ginseng guarana and other supplements to the beverages. The company also benefits from consumers who thrive on caffeine consumption whether it's Boomers needing more energy to retain their youthful pace or Gen Y's use of the drink to stay awake to study and party.

Like Big Red Monster Beverage does not make its own products. It outsources the manufacturing and packaging to third-party bottlers and contract packers. Instead the company purchases the concentrates juices flavors supplements and other ingredients along with packaging materials (cans bottles aseptic boxes aseptic pouches caps labels) and has them delivered to the bottlers and co-packers.

Monster Beverage also relies on distributors such as Anheuser-Busch to sell the Monster Energy Lost Energy Rumba Samba and Tango brands in markets determined by the company. Monster Beverage also has agreements with The Coca-Cola Company and Coca-Cola Enterprises for distribution of its products in selected parts of the US and Canada. Its agreement with Jumex calls for distribution in Mexico. Although most of Monster Beverage's sales are generated in the US it continues to expand its international footprint; its products are now available in some 70 countries worldwide.

EXECUTIVES

Vp Finance, Thomas J Kelly, age 60
Chief Brand Officer, Mark J. Hall, age 58, $425,000 total compensation
Vice Chairman COO CFO President and Secretary, Hilton H. Schlosberg, age 61, $550,000 total compensation
Chairman and CEO, Rodney C. Sacks, age 64, $550,000 total compensation
Vice President Controller, Pam Sciarra
Vice President General Mgr Cen Bus Unit, Ray Larue
Vice President Digital Marketing Brand Lifestyle And Licensing, Neil Calvesbert
National Accounts Manager, Trusha Patel
National Account Manager, Brent Larson
Vice President Category Management, Rich Frediani
Vice President Business Development, Dan Lamb
Senior Vice President Sales, Emelie Tirre
First Vice President, Michael Cucchiara
Vice President Trade Channels, David Van Winkle

Vice President And Senior Legal Counsel, Paul Dechary
Vice President New Product Development, Eva Lilja
Monster Manager Vice President Of Marketing, Sam Pontrelli
Senior Vice President International, Don Blaustein
National Account Manager, Matt Angarone
Vice President Sales C Store, John Kenneally
Vice President Coca Cola Systems, Steve McCown
Vice Chairman COO CFO President and Secretary, Hilton H. Schlosberg, age 61
Chairman and CEO, Rodney C. Sacks, age 64
Auditors: Deloitte&ToucheLLP

LOCATIONS

HQ: Monster Beverage Corp
1 Monster Way, Corona, CA 92879
Phone: 951 739-6200   **Fax:** 909 739-6210
Web: www.monsterbevcorp.com

2013 Sales

	% of total
US	74
Other countries	26
Total	**100**

PRODUCTS/OPERATIONS

2013 Sales

	$ mil.	% of total
Energy drinks	2082.2	93
Non-carbonated beverages	120.2	5
Carbonated beverages	29.2	1
Other	14.8	1
Total	**2246.4**	**100**

2013 Sales

	$ mil.	% of total
DSD	2147.3	96
Warehouse	99.1	4
Total	**2246.4**	**100**

2013 Sales

	% of total
Full service distributors	63
Outside the US	23
Club stores drug chains & mass merchandisers	9
Retail grocery specialty chains & wholesalers	3
Other	2
Total	**100**

Selected Products and Brands

Bottled water
  Blue Sky Seltzer Water
  Hansen's Junior Organic Water
  Vidration
Energy drinks
  Blue Sky
  Diet Red Energy
  Hansen Energy
  Java Monster
  Lost Energy
  Monster Energy
  Monster Hitman Energy Shooter
  Nitrous Monster Energy
  X-Presso Monster
Energy juices
  Rumba
  Samba
  Tango
Juice products and smoothies
  Hansen
  Hubert's Lemonades
Juices for children
  Juice Blast
Soda
  Blue Sky
  Hansen's Diet
  Hansen's Natural
Tea
  Hansen's Iced Tea
  Peace Tea

COMPETITORS

5-hour ENERGY	Naked Juice
Big Heart Pet Brands	National Beverage
Campbell Soup	National Grape
Caribou Coffee	Cooperative
Celsius Holdings	Nestlé©
Chiquita Brands	Ocean Spray
Cinnabon	Odwalla
Clearly Canadian	PepsiCo
Coca-Cola	Red Bull
Cott	Reed's
Dole Food	Smucker
Dr Pepper Snapple	South Beach Beverage
Group	Starbucks
Energy Brands	Sunny Delight
Gatorade	Suntory Holdings
Godiva Chocolatier	Tree Top
Goya	Tropicana
Hornell Brewing	True Drinks
IZZE	Unilever
Impulse Energy USA	Welch's
Jones Soda	Wet Planet Beverages
Kraft Foods Group Inc.	illy
Mott's	

HISTORICAL FINANCIALS

Company Type: Public

Income Statement

FYE: December 31

	REVENUE ($ mil.)	NET INCOME ($ mil.)	NET PROFIT MARGIN	EMPLOYEES
12/13	2,246.4	338.6	15.1%	2,013
12/12	2,060.7	340.0	16.5%	2,180
12/11	1,703.2	286.2	16.8%	1,900
12/10	1,303.9	212.0	16.3%	1,497
12/09	1,143.3	208.7	18.3%	1,430
Annual Growth	18.4%	12.9%	—	8.9%

2013 Year-End Financials

Debt ratio: —
Return on equity: 41.3%
Cash ($ mil.): 211
Current ratio: 3.74
Long-term debt ($ mil.): —

No. of shares (mil.): 166
Dividends
Yield: —
Payout: —
Market value ($ mil.): 11,306

	STOCK PRICE ($) FY Close	P/E High/Low		PER SHARE ($) Earnings	Dividends	Book Value
12/13	67.77	33	23	1.95	0.00	5.95
12/12	52.84	56	21	1.86	0.00	3.89
12/11	92.14	60	32	1.53	0.00	5.62
12/10	52.28	45	31	1.14	0.00	4.65
12/09	38.40	38	24	1.11	0.00	3.32
Annual Growth	15.3%	—	—	15.3%	—	15.7%

Motorcar Parts of America Inc

Motorcar Parts of America (MPA) is always ready for a fresh start. The company manufactures remanufactures and distributes alternators and starters for cars and all-weight trucks. MPA sells the remanufactured products to retailers and warehouse distributors which sell to do-it-yourself (DIY) consumers and to repair shops (DIFM or do-it-for-me) primarily in the US and Canada. Some of its top customers include retail chains AutoZone

(more than 50% of sales) Advance Genuine Parts Pep Boys and O'Reilly Automotive. Although most of MPA's products are sold under its customers' private labels (about 90%) the company does market alternators and starters with its Quality-Built Reliance and Xtreme brands.

Financial Performance

The auto parts maker reported sales of $258.7 million in fiscal 2014 (ended March) a 36% decline versus the prior year. The steep decline reflected the company's liquidation of its Fenwick Automotive Products (Fenco) business (acquired in 2011). When adjusted for discontinued operations Motorcar Parts of America's sales increased by $45.5 million (21%) year over year driven by its new wheel hub products and the growth in sales of its rotating electrical products primarily to existing customers. The company began selling wheel hubs in mid-2013 and they quickly grew to account for approximately 11% of net sales during fiscal 2014. Motorcar Parts of America's profit swung from a loss of $91.5 million in fiscal 2013 to a profit of more than $100 million in 2014 on a $118 million gain on the deconsolidation of Fenco a tax benefit and other factors.

Strategy

With its disastrous acquisition of Fenwick Automotive Products in its rearview mirror –the unit filed for bankruptcy in June 2013 –things are looking up for MAP. Its new wheel hub business and rotating electrical products businesses which contributed to growth in fiscal 2014 are poised for strong organic growth in the future. Also the company recently added brake master cylinders to its product line.

While MPA has historically served the DIY market –which is popular in times of recession –it is also pursuing the DIFM market which it views as a growth opportunity. MPA is especially looking to sell to major automotive manufacturers for their aftermarket and warranty replacement programs. In order to serve the large producers MPA generally must enter into longer-term agreements which requires expending more working capital and building inventory through increased production. To counteract costs associated with this strategy the company has relocated the vast majority of its US remanufacturing operations to offshore facilities. Approximately 99% of MPA's manufacturing now takes place in Malaysia and Mexico. It also operates a warehousing testing and distribution facility in Singapore.

Mergers and Acquisitions

In May 2011 MAP acquired Canada-based Fenwick Automotive Products (Fenco) —a manufacturer of private label and branded products such as steering components brakes and clutches which are marketed to OE replacement customers —for about 360000 shares of MPA's common stock. (Fenco filed for bankruptcy in June 2013 amid recurring operating losses.)

HISTORY

A former executive with auto parts maker Echlin (now part of Dana) Mel Marks founded Motorcar Parts & Accessories (MPA) in 1968. Initially MPA only distributed imported auto parts but in 1986 it expanded into remanufacturing through foreign affiliates. The next year the company began remanufacturing in the US. As the number of imported cars in the US grew so did MPA. The company went public in 1994.

MPA signed up major retail chains AutoZone and Pep Boys in 1995 and expanded eastward from its stronghold in the West by opening a distribution center in Nashville Tennessee to serve

eastern and southern markets. A 1997 secondary public offering helped MPA fund factory upgrades and acquisitions in the consolidating automotive aftermarket. The same year MPA bought the outstanding stock of its two overseas subsidiaries which maintained remanufacturing operations in Singapore and Malaysia.

In 1998 MPA opened an automated factory in California. The next year the company restated its earnings for prior fiscal years nearly halving income reported for 1997 and reducing by $600000 income for 1998. Mel Marks stepped down as CEO that year but remained chairman and the company was hit with shareholder lawsuits claiming the income misstatements artificially inflated MPA's stock price. Early in 2000 the SEC began an investigation into the accuracy of MPA's SEC filings.

In 2001 Mel Marks stepped down as chairman but remained a director. Also in 2001 the company settled the class action shareholder lawsuit for $7.5 million. Actions were eventually brought against Richard Marks the company's former president and COO in late 2003 by the SEC and the US attorney's office. In addition the company's former CFO Peter Bromberg was sentenced in 2004 to five months in prison and five months of home detention for making false and misleading claims in the company's 1997 and 1998 10-K forms.

Selwyn Joffe was named chairman president and CEO of MPA in early 2003. The next year the company changed its name from Motorcar Parts & Accessories Inc. to Motorcar Parts of America Inc.

EXECUTIVES

Vp Heavy Duty Alternator And Starter Division, Larry Fedoruk
COO, Steven Kratz, age 57, $282,800 total compensation
Chairman President and CEO, Selwyn Joffe, age 56, $500,000 total compensation
CFO, David Lee, age 45, $178,500 total compensation
Vice President Traditional Sales, Rick Mochulsky
National Sales Manager, Gary Delgreco
Vice President, Kevin Keenan
Vice President, Kori Bernards
Vice President Strategic Planning, Alex Alvarez
Vice President Sales Aftermarket, Bill Laughlin
Chairman President and CEO, Selwyn Joffe, age 56
Board Member, Philip Gay
Auditors: Ernst&YoungLLP

LOCATIONS

HQ: Motorcar Parts of America Inc
2929 California Street, Torrance, CA 90503
Phone: 310 212-7910
Web: www.motorcarparts.com

PRODUCTS/OPERATIONS

Selected Subsidiaries

Motorcar Parts de Mexico S.A. de C.V.
Motorcar Parts of Canada
MVR Products Pte. Limited (Singapore)
Unijoh Sdn. Bhd. (Malaysia)

Selected Products

Alternators
Bearings
Brake Master Cylinders
Hub Assemblies
Starters

BERU
Cardone Industries
DENSO
Federal-Mogul
Fred Jones Enterprises
Jasper Engines
Keystone Automotive Operations
Prestolite Electric

Remy International
Robert Bosch LLC
Standard Motor Products
Steel City Products Inc.
Universal Manufacturing

HISTORICAL FINANCIALS

Company Type: Public

Income Statement

FYE: March 31

	REVENUE ($ mil.)	NET INCOME ($ mil.)	NET PROFIT MARGIN	EMPLOYEES
03/14	258.6	107.3	41.5%	2,270
03/13	406.2	(91.5)	—	2,756
03/12	363.6	(48.5)	—	3,340
03/11	161.2	12.2	7.6%	1,689
03/10	147.2	9.6	6.6%	1,762
Annual Growth	15.1%	82.7%	—	6.5%

2014 Year-End Financials

Debt ratio: 30.5%
Return on equity: 202.3%
Cash ($ mil.): 24
Current ratio: 1.21
Long-term debt ($ mil.): 79

No. of shares (mil.): 15
Dividends
Yield: —
Payout: —
Market value ($ mil.): 400

	STOCK PRICE ($) FY Close	P/E High/Low		PER SHARE ($) Earnings	Dividends	Book Value
03/14	26.57	4	1	7.01	0.00	7.28
03/13	6.13	—	—	(6.39)	0.00	(0.24)
03/12	9.62	—	—	(3.90)	0.00	5.88
03/11	13.98	15	6	0.99	0.00	9.71
03/10	6.50	8	5	0.80	0.00	8.62
Annual Growth	42.2%	—	—	72.1%	—	(4.1%)

Movado Group, Inc.

Movado Group knows that time is of the essence. Its watch brands —including namesake Movado Concord and Ebel as well as the licensed Coach Tommy Hilfiger Hugo Boss Lacoste and Juicy Couture lines —are sold worldwide. While its watches range in price from about $75 to $10000 for luxury designs the watch maker is focused on the middle market. Movado sells its watches to major jewelry store and department store chains (including Nordstrom and Macy's) as well as to independent jewelers (such as Zale Corp.). The company operates a growing chain of more than 35 outlet stores across the US. The family of the late Gerry Grinberg who founded Movado controls about 70% of the company's voting power.

Geographic Reach

New Jersey-based Movado Group rings up more than half of its sales in the US. Beyond the US Movado's timepieces are sold throughout North and South America Europe Asia and the Far East.

Operations

Movado operates its business through two reportable segments. Wholesale which focuses on watch design through distribution generates some 90% of the company's sales. Movado's retail seg-

ment accounting for 10% of sales comprises its outlet stores. The jewelry company divides its attention equally between the US and international segments which each bring in 50%. Based on the customer's location Movado conducts its business globally in Europe Asia Canada the Middle East South America and the Caribbean. Switzerland is the company's primary hub for its international activities.

Movado makes its Movado Concord and Ebel watches primarily in Switzerland; Swiss suppliers provide the Coach lines. Substantially all of Movado's international assets are located in Switzerland and Asia.

Financial Performance

Movado Group reported sales of $570.3 million in fiscal 2014 (ended January) an increase of 13% versus the prior year. Driving the double-digit gain was the wholesale business where sales were driven by increases in licensed brand watches particularly Coach brand watches as a result of their repositioning into the fashion watch category. Accessible luxury brand watches including the Movado BOLD and Museum watch collections also posted higher sales. The introduction of Movado TC and the SE Pilot watch and Scuderia Ferrari watches also helped boost sales in fiscal 2014. On the retail side of the business sales rose nearly 6% year over year due to the opening of new stores. Same-store sales at the company's outlet stores rose 1.5%.

Despite the sales gain net income fell 11% to $50.9 million on higher marketing and trade show expenses primarily related to the Baselworld Watch and Jewelry Show and an increase in the effective tax rate to 25% in fiscal 2014 versus 18% in 2013.

Strategy

After a rough patch during the recession when sales of pricey luxury watches plummeted —and Movado's profits evaporated —the company revised its marketing strategy to focus more on accessible luxury and moderate and fashion brands. Movado's repositioning of Coach brand watches from the fine watch department to the fashion watch category is a case in point. The move is luring a broader audience to watches with price points between $75 and $2500. This price segment is generating revenue and allowing Movado to gain market share. Fueling sales further are new product launches such as the company's $495 Museum Classic strap and $695 Museum Classic bracelet.

After shutting down its money-losing US retail division in 2010 and its flagship shop in New York's Rockefeller Center in 2012 Movado has returned to retail with an outlet store model. Indeed the company has plans to open two additional outlets stores in fiscal 2015 (ends January). Most of the outlet stores are located near vacation destinations.

HISTORY

Cuban-born Gedalio "Gerry" Grinberg arrived in Miami in 1960. He had been the exclusive distributor of Piaget and Omega watches in Cuba before Castro took over. Grinberg began distributing Piaget watches in the US in 1961 and his company took the name North American Watch in 1967 when it acquired US distribution rights to Corum another line of gold Swiss-made watches. The firm bought the Concord brand four years later.

In 1983 North American Watch acquired Movado a company that had begun in 1881 in the Swiss workshop of 19-year-old Achille Ditesheim. Movado ("always in motion" in Esperanto) was

chosen as a brand name in 1903. The company helped usher in the era of wristwatches early in the century. In 1962 it introduced its Museum watch (a plain ebony face with a gold dot replacing the 12) the first watch chosen for the Museum of Modern Art's permanent collection.

Grinberg's son Efraim became North American Watch's president and COO in 1992. The company went public in 1993 and in 1996 took the Movado Group name. That year it launched the Vizio brand (part of its Movado line) and signed a deal to develop and distribute Coach watches.

Movado's second public offering in 1997 raised money for the opening of boutiques and other marketing efforts. The company sold its Piaget line —its original business line —to a subsidiary of Vendome Luxury Group in 1999 for about $30 million. In early 2000 Movado sold its second-oldest business its Corum line to the brand's Swiss owner Corum Ries Bannwart & Co. Later that year Movado licensed its name to Lantis Eyewear for several optical and sunglass styles ranging in price from $195 to $345. Movado launched its licensed Tommy Hilfiger line of fashion watches —and its lowest-priced watches —in March 2001. Efraim was named CEO in May with Gerry remaining as chairman.

In March 2004 Movado paid LVMH $48.9 million for premier luxury watch brand Ebel. In December of the same year Movado entered into a long-term worldwide licensing agreement with Hugo Boss to design and manufacture a collection of fashion watches under the Boss and Hugo brand names. Movado entered a similar licensing agreement with Juicy Couture in 2005.

Founder Gerry Grinberg died in January 2009. Efraim became chairman soon thereafter.

In 2013 Movado increased its ownership stake in MGS Distribution to 90% from 51% thereby taking greater ownership of its UK subsidiary.

EXECUTIVES

Chairman and CEO, Efraim Grinberg, age 57, $1,028,843 total compensation
CFO, Sallie A. DeMarsilis, age 49, $486,154 total compensation
SVP IT, Frank A. Morelli, age 63, $475,769 total compensation
President, Ricardo Quintero
Vice Chairman and COO, Richard J. Cot ÀC $717,309 total compensation
President Movado Group Asia Pacific, Julian Addison
Vp Controller Of The Americas, Steven Friedman
Senior Vice President Product Development, Harvey Driansky
Senior Vice President Human Resources, Vivian Delia
Vice President Treasurer And Assistant Secretary, Joe Bosch
Senior Vice President Field Sales Us, Keith Boughton
Vice President Product Development, Diane Fox
Senior Vice President Strategy And Co, Rob Cherrington
Vice President Creative Director, Richard Tassone
Vp Product Developement, Patti Horn
Senior Vice President, Joe Zanone
Vice President Business Controls, Joseph Nici
Vice President Of Marketing, Marcie Davidson
Vice President Of Product Development, Ann Kantra
Vice President Field Operations, Veronica Martin
Vice President National Accounts, Allyson Doherty
National Sales Manager, Kevin Dougherty
Sr Vice President Value Chain, Isaac Read

Vp Of Design, Kristen Cavagnuolo
Vice President Of Tax, Scott Gregory
Vice President Of Marketing, Marcie Foster
Vice President Latin America, Luis Conde
Vice President Sales, Kristin Starry
Vice President, Cathy James
Chairman and CEO, Efraim Grinberg, age 57
Vice Chairman and COO, Richard J. Cot A©
Board Of Directors, Alan Howard
Auditors: PricewaterhouseCoopersLLP

LOCATIONS

HQ: Movado Group, Inc.
 650 From Road, Suite 375, Paramus, NJ 07652-3556
Phone: 201 267-8000
Web: www.movadogroup.com

2014 Sales

	$ mil.	% of total
US	303.1	53
International	267.2	47
Total	**570.3**	**100**

PRODUCTS/OPERATIONS

2014 Sales

	$ mil.	% of total
Wholesale		
United States	243.8	43
International	267.2	47
Retail	59.3	10
Total	**570.3**	**100**

Selected Market Categories

Luxury ($2000 to $9999)
 Concord
 Ebel
Premium ($500 to $1999)
 Movado
Moderate ($100 to $499)
 Coach
 ESQ
 Hugo Boss
 Juicy Couture
 Lacoste
Fashion ($59 to $145)
 Tommy Hilfiger

COMPETITORS

Armitron	Richemont
Bulova	Rolex
CASIO COMPUTER	Seiko
Cartier	Seiko USA
Citizen	Swatch
Fossil Inc.	Swiss Watch
Gucci	International
Guess?	TAG Heuer
HermÄ s	Tiffany & Co.
LVMH	Timex
Patek Philippe	Victorinox Swiss Army

HISTORICAL FINANCIALS

Company Type: Public

Income Statement

FYE: January 31

	REVENUE ($ mil.)	NET INCOME ($ mil.)	NET PROFIT MARGIN	EMPLOYEES
01/14	570.2	50.8	8.9%	1,100
01/13	505.4	57.0	11.3%	1,100
01/12	468.1	32.0	6.8%	1,000
01/11	382.1	(44.9)	—	1,000
01/10	378.4	(54.6)	—	1,200
Annual Growth	**10.8%**	**—**	**—**	**(2.2%)**

2014 Year-End Financials

Debt ratio: —	No. of shares (mil.): 25
Return on equity: 11.4%	Dividends
Cash ($ mil.): 157	Yield: 0.6%
Current ratio: 5.81	Payout: 13.2%
Long-term debt ($ mil.): —	Market value ($ mil.): 956

	STOCK PRICE ($) FY Close	P/E High/Low		PER SHARE ($) Earnings	Dividends	Book Value
01/14	37.75	24	15	1.97	0.26	18.29
01/13	36.56	16	8	2.22	1.45	16.65
01/12	18.41	16	9	1.27	0.12	15.67
01/11	14.41	—	—	(1.81)	0.00	14.21
01/10	10.93	—	—	(2.23)	0.00	15.02
Annual Growth	**36.3%**			**—**	**—**	**5.0%**

MSCI Inc

You ask your asset manager how your portfolio is doing but who does he ask? Probably MSCI. The company formerly Morgan Stanley Capital International manages more than 145000 daily equity fixed income and hedge fund indices for use by large asset management firms. MSCI is organized through two business segments. Its Performance and Risk business provides equity indices portfolio risk and performance analytics credit analytics and environmental social and governance (ESG) products under brands such as MSCI RiskMetrics and Barra. Its Governance business provides corporate governance and specialized financial research and analysis. MSCI has about 7500 clients across more than 80 countries.

Geographic Reach

Nearly half of the company's revenues come from outside the Americas. MSCI has more than 38 offices in 22 countries worldwide including headquarters in New York and offices in San Francisco Chicago and S o Paulo Brazil. As part of its global expansion efforts in the last few years MSCI has opened international offices in Budapest Dubai Monterrey Mumbai and Shanghai.

Operations

The company's indices act as benchmarks that measure the performance of global funds. Institutional investors use the indices as research tools and as the basis for their various investment vehicles. MSCI's Performance and Risk segment is by far its largest accounting for 87% of the company's revenue in 2012 while the company's Governance segment brought in the remaining 13%. MSCI makes the majority of its revenues (more than 75%) from annual recurring subscriptions to its products.

Strategy

The company has consistently achieved revenue growth and positive earnings by continually expanding its relationships with investment institutions and regularly developing and enhancing its products. It has also made key acquisitions in order to complement or expand its client base and offerings.

Mergers and Acquisitions

In early 2013 the company acquired Investor Force Holdings a provider of asset performance reporting for $23.5 million in cash. The previous year 2012 the company acquired IPD Group a global real estate information business for approximately $125 million. The purchase expanded its

portfolio of investment tools for the equities fixed income hedge fund energy and commodities markets.

MSCI made a significant purchase in 2010 with the acquisition of rival RiskMetrics Group through a cash and stock transaction valued at approximately $1.5 billion. The deal united two risk management market leaders. The purchase enhanced MSCI's ability to provide investment decision support tools and widened its geographical reach. It also strengthened its customer base adding RiskMetrics' 3500 clients including several of the largest asset managers mutual funds and hedge funds.

Company Background

MSCI was formerly owned by financial services powerhouse Morgan Stanley which began spinning off the business in 2007. MSCI became an independent stand-alone public company 2009. Morgan Staley maintains an 8% share in the firm.

EXECUTIVES

Chairman President and CEO, Henry A. Fernandez, age 56, $900,000 total compensation
Head of Index Business Unit, C. D. Baer Pettit, $504,812 total compensation
CFO, Robert Qutub, $500,000 total compensation
Chief Information Officer, Chris Corrado
Vice President, Gerald Wilson
Vice President Of Product Management Us, Josh Gray
Vice President, Matt Kelso
Vice President Hedge Fund Transparency, Austin Wheeler Caia
Vice President, Rachel Reisman
Vice President, Tom Jenkins
Vice President Institutional, Caroline Tyburczy
Vp Team Lead Implementations Americas, Patrick Schmutte
Vice President, Francesco Daglio
Vice President, Judy Kim
Vice President, Michael Andeberhan
Vice President Portfolio Analytics, Yohsuke Miki
Vice President, Christopher Shepler
Senior Vice President And Chief, Hanifah Crawley
Vice President At Cfra An Msci Brand, Josh Mayer
Vice President Project Management, Stella Kondonijakos
Vice President Information Technology Internal Audit And Sox, Edwil Fontanilla
Vice President Application Development, Christopher Ingram
Vice President, Troy Daley
Vice President And Product Manager, James Wiegert
Vice President Sales (Ipd), Elizabeth Francis
Vice President, Cedric Tang
Vice President, David Young
Vice President, Marc Dorfman
Vice President Product Management, Susan Quintin
Consultant Vice President, Philippe Durand
Hungary Vice President Info Tech Ops, Gabor Kiss
Vice President Public Relations, Meza Kristin
Vice President, Nicole Lebow
Vice President Finance, Yilin Lee
Vice President, Juli Mosier
Vice President, Altaf Mubaraki
Vice President Product Management, Max Arkey
Vice President Portfolio Management, Ting Fang
Vp Dmx, Henry Sharr
Vp Sales Specialist, Ronald Dipietro
Senior Vice President Vice President, Edward Allen
Vice President Risk Management Analytics, Barton Haneberg
Vice President Finance, Kinga Demartis

Managing Director Executive Vice President, Baer Pettit

Vice President Talent Management, Russ Maile

Vice President, Alex Meller

Vice President Recruitment Team Lead Asia Pacific, Michelle Loong

Vice President, Jean Creidi

Vice President Of Analytics Client Service, Emilio Olivares

Vice President, Beth Byington

Assistant Vice President, Hiral Desai

Vice President Marketing, Rick Bogden

Vice President Client Coverage, Brian Robinson

Vice President Americas Recruitment At Msci, Seth Corwin

Vice President, Thomas Reynolds

Vice President Human Resources At Msci, Susi Damilano

Vice President Product Development, Harsh Deshpande

Vice President, Mark Brown

Vice President Marketing, Susan Hunt

Executive Vice President Of Information Technology, Susan Gledhill

Vice President And Manager Wealth Management Client Services, Michael McGourty

Vice President Global Learning And Development, John Rogener

Vice President, Bryan Murphy

Vice President, Aaron Young

Vice President, Matthew Holm

Vice President, Marc Buon

Vice President, Michael Falag-ey

Vice President Product Management, Jean-michel Huet

Vice President Application Development, Aleksandr Meller

Vice President, John Fickle

Vice President, Rakesh Chandhok

Vice President Market Data, Lindsey Robbins

Vice President Business Development, Rob Bilse

Vice President Hedge Funds Transparency Manager, Laurasusana Boren

Vice President Human Resources Generalist, Michelle Davidson

Vice President, Yiqing Du

Vice President Finance Senior Payroll Manager, Jose Blanco

Chairman President and CEO, Henry A. Fernandez, age 56

Auditors: Deloitte&ToucheLLP

LOCATIONS

HQ: MSCI Inc
7 World Trade Center, 250 Greenwich Street, 49th Floor, New York, NY 10007
Phone: 212 804-3900
Web: www.msci.com

2012 Sales

	$ mil.	% of total
Americas	517.5	55
Europe Middle East & Africa	308.3	32
Asia & Australia	124.3	13
Total	**950.1**	**100**

PRODUCTS/OPERATIONS

2012 Sales

	$ mil.	% of total
Index and ESG	441.5	47
Risk management analytics	260.3	27
Portfolio management analytics	116.1	12
Governance	123.1	13
Energy & commodity analytics	9.1	1
Total	**950.1**	**100**

Selected Offerings

Barra (equity and multi-asset class portfolio analytics product)

CFRA (forensic accounting risk research legal/regulatory risk assessment due-diligence and educational services)

FEA (entergy and commodity asset valuation analytics)

ISS (governance research and outsourced proxy voting and reporting services)

MSCI Indices (flagship global equity indices)

RiskMetrics (risk and wealth management products)

COMPETITORS

Algorithmics	Liquid Holdings
Deutsche Bôrse	Nomura Securities
Dow Jones	Russell
FTSE Group	S&P
FactSet	

HISTORICAL FINANCIALS

Company Type: Public

Income Statement

FYE: December 31

	REVENUE ($ mil.)	NET INCOME ($ mil.)	NET PROFIT MARGIN	EMPLOYEES
12/13	1,035.6	222.5	21.5%	3,261
12/12	950.1	184.2	19.4%	2,759
12/11	900.9	173.4	19.3%	2,429
12/10*	72.5	13.8	19.1%	0
11/10	662.9	92.1	13.9%	2,077
Annual Growth	**11.8%**	**24.7%**	**—**	**11.9%**

*Fiscal year change

2013 Year-End Financials

Debt ratio: 25.7%
Return on equity: 14.8%
Cash ($ mil.): 358
Current ratio: 1.27
Long-term debt ($ mil.): 788

No. of shares (mil.): 118
Dividends
  Yield: —
  Payout: —
Market value ($ mil.): 5,163

	STOCK PRICE ($) FY Close	P/E High/Low		PER SHARE ($) Earnings	Dividends	Book Value
12/13	43.72	24	17	1.83	0.00	13.35
12/12	30.99	25	17	1.48	0.00	11.87
12/11	32.93	28	20	1.41	0.00	10.77
12/10*	38.96	364248		0.11	0.00	9.22
11/10	34.06	46	33	0.81	0.00	9.04
Annual Growth	**6.4%**			**22.6%**	**—**	**10.2%**

*Fiscal year change

MTS Systems Corp.

In this world nothing is certain but death and taxes —and those things tested by MTS Systems. The company produces testing systems that simulate repeated or harsh conditions to determine mechanical behavior of materials products and structures. Its systems are used worldwide in infrastructure markets from inspecting steel to locomotive rail testing. MTS caters to auto makers with road simulators. In aerospace MTS tests aircraft fatigue. Services include maintenance and training. MTS also supplies industrial sensors (Temposonics) to increase machine efficiency and safety. About three-quarters of the company's customers operate outside the US.

Operations

MTS's test segment primarily comprises products for the testing of ground vehicles (accounting for 50% of the segment's revenue) and products for testing materials in industries that include power generation aerospace vehicles and bio-medicine (30% of the segment's revenue). Structure-testing products for aerospace wind energy structural engineering petroleum and other industries account for the remainder of the test segment's revenue. Product orders range in value from a few hundred dollars to $11 million but the average order is about $115000.

The company's sensors which account for 20% of sales automate machinery to increase safety and productivity. They're used in such industries as the manufacturing of plastic injection molding machines steel mills fluid power oil and gas and alternative energy. Sensor product orders are sold at unit prices ranging from $25 to $10000 with an average price of $500.

Geographic Reach

MTS has manufacturing plants in China Germany and the US (in Minnesota and North Carolina). Other offices are located across Asia Central and South America Europe and North America. Asia generated about 40% of overall sales in 2013 while Europe accounted for a third and the US a quarter.

Sales and Marketing

The test segment has sales staff in the US and China and sales and service subsidiaries in Canada China France Germany Italy Japan South Korea Sweden the UK. Sold through a direct sales force and independent distributors MTS's sensors are engineered and assembled in North Carolina Germany and Japan.

Financial Performance

Behind both a high backlog (some $300 million) and new orders within its test segment revenue was up 5% in fiscal 2013 (year-end September) to $570 million. The company's test segment grew 7%. Sales for the sensors segment however decreased 5%. MTS' profits increased 12% due to the higher revenue levels.

Strategy

The company's long-term goal is to reach $1 billion in sales. It plans through both organic growth and strategic acquisitions as well as aggressively building out its infrastructure expanding its product offerings and pursuing more opportunities with key customers around the world. To that end it opened an engineering test lab in China with Chery Automobile in 2014. It's the company's first vehicle testing lab in China. It also launched a new line of sensors called the T-Series for the energy market.

HISTORY

MTS Systems a spinoff of Research Incorporated was started in 1966 to make software so automakers could replicate test track conditions in the laboratory. MTS's first products measured auto body endurance. Donald Sullivan who became president in 1982 and CEO in 1987 pulled the company through a market slump in the early 1990s by steering it into the factory automation business. The move was initiated by the 1992 acquisition of small startup Custom Servo Motors a maker of compact powerful motors used to control fabrication and packaging motions in factory applications. Sullivan was named chairman in 1994 replacing company co-founder George Butzow.

To feed revenue momentum the company made some of its systems compatible with Microsoft's Windows NT environments and it tailored tools to specific customers. In 1996 the Japanese government bought a $23 million seismic simulator in the wake of the 1995 Hanshin earthquake. The company moved into the aerospace products market in 1997 creating titanium-based component subsidiary AeroMet. (MTS shut down AeroMet in late 2005 saying the unit could not achieve a sustainable business model.)

Sullivan stepped down as CEO in 1998 and was replaced by longtime Honeywell executive Sidney (Chip) Emery. MTS in 1999 bought engine design testing specialist DSP Technology. A drop in profits for the fiscal year partly the result of the purchase prompted MTS to restructure and lay off nearly 10% of its workforce.

In 2000 the company won a $37 million contract from the US Army to design manufacture and install an advanced roadway simulator. The next year MTS sold its electronic assembly operations to PEMSTAR and expanded its line of software products for the auto industry.

MTS sold its automation division in 2003 to Parker Hannifin.

The company signed an agreement with National Instruments in 2004 to cooperate on research and development of a low-cost framework for noise and vibration testing.

In 2005 MTS sold its Powertrain Technology (engine testing) division to A&D Co. Ltd. of Japan.

Chip Emery left the CEO's post in early 2008 and was succeeded by president/COO Laura Hamilton. Emery remained chairman until the end of fiscal 2008.

In mid 2008 the company sold off its Nano Instruments business to Agilent Technologies. The deal marked MTS's exit from supplying nanoindentation systems and related equipment used in verifying structural integrity of semiconductor devices and coatings and thin films.

In late 2008 the company widened its pipeline to China. MTS acquired the assets of SANS Group a Chinese supplier of materials testing systems for nearly $44 million. The Shenzhen-based firm makes electromechanical and static-hydraulic testing machines among other products. The deal builds upon MTS' move to establish a wholly foreign-owned enterprise in Shanghai in 2007. A sales office was first opened in China in 1985.

EXECUTIVES

SVP and CFO, Susan E. (Sue) Knight, age 60, $346,930 total compensation
President and CEO, Jeffrey A. (Jeff) Graves, age 53, $612,467 total compensation
SVP Sensors, William E. Bachrach, age 55, $161,538 total compensation
SVP MTS Test, Michael B. Jost
SVP and CIO, Mark D. Losee
SVP and CTO, Rich Baker, $295,998 total compensation
Svp Test, Alfred Richter, age 46
Vice President Finance, Jeff Oldenkamp
Vice President Purchasing, Steven G Mahon
Vice President Human Resources, Kristin Trecker
Vice President National Accounts, Elena M Larosa
Svp, Donn Wiese
Vice President Of Engineering, Pat Morton
Vice President Service At Mts Systems, Ellen White
Vice President Vehicle Dynamics And Powertrain Technology Div, Larry Moulton
Vice President Operations, J Howell Owens
Vice President And Treasurer, Brenda McInnes
Vice President Operations, Rob Bisaillon
Vice President Division Research, Grant Novackk
Vice President Sales And Marketing, Hanoch Magid

Vice President Customer Care Consumer, Patricia Solman
Vice President Asia Pacific, Ryoji Yamaguchi
Sr Vice President And General Manager, Mike Jost
Chairman, David J. (Dave) Anderson, age 67
Treasurer Vice President Finance, Jim Bain
Auditors: KPMGLLP

LOCATIONS

HQ: MTS Systems Corp.
14000 Technology Drive, Eden Prairie, MN 55344
Phone: 952 937-4000
Web: www.mts.com

2013 Sales

	$ mil.	% of total
Asia		
China	127.3	22
Other Asian countries	96.7	17
Europe	178.6	32
US	137.8	24
Other	29.0	5
Total	**569.4**	**100**

PRODUCTS/OPERATIONS

2013 Sales

	$ mil.	% of total
Test	474.1	83
Sensors	95.3	17
Total	**569.4**	**100**

2013 Sales

	$ mil.	% of total
Product	497.6	87
Service	71.8	13
Total	**569.4**	**100**

COMPETITORS

ACS Motion Control	Mechanical Technology
AMETEK	Moog
Aero Systems	OYO
Engineering	Pepperl+Fuchs
GE	PerkinElmer
HORIBA	Pure Technologies
Illinois Tool Works	Schmitt Industries
Instron	Tech/Ops Sevcon
JT3	

HISTORICAL FINANCIALS

Company Type: Public

Income Statement

FYE: September 27

	REVENUE ($ mil.)	NET INCOME ($ mil.)	NET PROFIT MARGIN	EMPLOYEES
09/14	564.3	42.0	7.4%	2,180
09/13	569.4	57.8	10.2%	2,299
09/12*	542.2	51.5	9.5%	2,147
10/11	467.3	50.9	10.9%	2,003
10/10	374.0	18.5	5.0%	1,948
Annual Growth	**10.8%**	**22.6%**	**—**	**2.9%**

*Fiscal year change

2014 Year-End Financials

Debt ratio: 12.3%	No. of shares (mil.): 15
Return on equity: 16.3%	Dividends
Cash ($ mil.): 60	Yield: 0.0%
Current ratio: 1.73	Payout: 43.9%
Long-term debt ($ mil.): —	Market value ($ mil.): 1,043

	STOCK PRICE ($) FY Close	P/E High/Low		PER SHARE ($) Earnings	Dividends	Book Value
09/14	68.74	27	23	2.73	1.20	17.00
09/13	63.65	18	12	3.64	1.20	16.65
09/12*	53.55	17	9	3.21	1.05	14.50
10/11	30.64	15	9	3.24	0.85	13.49
10/10	31.50	28	22	1.14	0.60	10.88
Annual Growth	**21.5%**		**—**	**24.4%**	**18.9%**	**11.8%**

*Fiscal year change

Multi-Color Corp.

Multi-Color Corporation's labels aren't just black and white and red all over. The company produces printed labels for product makers in markets such as home and personal care wine and spirit food and beverage and specialty consumer goods. Multi-Color serves customers in North and South America Europe the Asia/Pacific region and South Africa. The company prints and affixes heat transfer re-sealable shrink wrap pressure sensitive and other label types to glass and plastic containers. Multi-Color also offers gravure printing and injection in-mold labels. Over the years the company has counted Procter & Gamble and Miller Brewing among its biggest customers. Multi-Color traces its roots to 1916.

The company has been working to alleviate its dependency on a concentrated set of customers. Major consumer product and beverage manufacturers Procter & Gamble and Miller Lite collectively accounted for 28% of the company's total sales in fiscal year 2011 down from 38% in 2010 45% in 2011 and 50% in 2008. Multi-Color attributes the decline to the addition of international customers and products it gained through prior acquisitions such as Collotype (a maker of pressure-sensitive labels for wine and spirits that has operations in Australia South Africa and California); Guidotti CentroStampa (a European wine spirit and olive oil label printer based in Italy); and Monroe Etiquette (a French wine label specialist based in Montagny France).

In fiscal year 2011 the company reported an increase in revenues and net income. Positive earnings were primarily due to the acquisitions of Guidotti CentroStampa and Monroe Etiquette. The remaining gains were due to growth in sales volume a favorable foreign exchange rate and the increase of operating efficiencies through cutting costs.

Multi-Color continued its international expansion strategy in 2011. That year it purchased La Cromografica an Italian wine label specialist in Florence Italy. Later that year it entered the growing Latin American wine and spirit markets when it acquired 70% of two label operations one in Santiago Chile and the other in Mendoza Argentina. It acquired rival LabelCorp Holdings doing business as York Label Group for about $356 million to expand in North America and Chile. It also entered the Chinese market establishing operations in the major southern city of Guangzhou in 2011.

EXECUTIVES

Vice President Sales And Marketing, Dirk Edwards

Vice President Information Technology, Gregory Myers
President and CEO, Nigel A. Vinecombe, age 50, $706,250 total compensation
VP Finance International, Sharon E. Birkett, age 48, $337,500 total compensation
COO Wine and Spirit Markets, Vadis A. Rodato
COO Consumer Product Goods, Floyd E. Needham
Vp Operations, Philip Cody
Vice President Information Technology, Greg Myers
Vice President Operations Controller, Steve Walker
Chairman, Robert R. Buck, age 66
Assistant Treasurer, Nancy Thomas
Board Member, Lee A Wright
Auditors: GrantThorntonLLP

LOCATIONS

HQ: Multi-Color Corp.
4053 Clough Woods Dr., Batavia, OH 45103
Phone: 513 381-1480
Web: www.mcclabel.com

2013 Sales

	$ mil.	% of total
US	445.0	64
Australia	66.6	9
Italy	59.0	8
Other International	135.8	19
Total	**706.4**	**100**

PRODUCTS/OPERATIONS

Selected Products and Services

Labels
  Heat transfer
  In-mold
  Neck bands
  Peel-away
  Pressure sensitive
  Re-sealable
  Shrink sleeve

COMPETITORS

Convergent Label Technology	H. S. Crocker
Fort Dearborn	Outlook Group
	WS Packaging Group

HISTORICAL FINANCIALS

Company Type: Public

Income Statement

FYE: March 31

	REVENUE ($ mil.)	NET INCOME ($ mil.)	NET PROFIT MARGIN	EMPLOYEES
03/14	706.4	28.2	4.0%	3,250
03/13	659.8	30.3	4.6%	2,800
03/12	510.2	19.7	3.9%	2,749
03/11	338.2	18.4	5.4%	1,430
03/10	276.8	14.2	5.2%	1,186
Annual Growth	**26.4%**	**18.6%**	**—**	**28.7%**

2014 Year-End Financials

Debt ratio: 49.5%
Return on equity: 9.8%
Cash ($ mil.): 10
Current ratio: 1.36
Long-term debt ($ mil.): 435
No. of shares (mil.): 16
Dividends
  Yield: 0.5%
  Payout: 9.6%
Market value ($ mil.): 574

STOCK PRICE ($) FY Close	P/E High/Low		PER SHARE ($) Earnings	Dividends	Book Value
03/14 35.00	22	14	1.70	0.20	18.14
03/13 25.79	14	10	1.86	0.20	17.02
03/12 22.51	21	14	1.32	0.20	15.68
03/11 20.21	14	7	1.40	0.20	14.40
03/10 11.98	15	9	1.16	0.20	11.86
Annual Growth 30.7%	—	—	10.0%	(0.0%)	11.2%

MV Oil Trust

Call it what you will black gold Texas tea or the black blood of the earth MV Oil Trust is wringing out the value from each drop and distributing it to shareholders. MV Oil Trust receives royalty interests from the mature oil and gas properties of MV Partners located in Kansas and Colorado. The properties have proved reserves of 9.5 million barrels of oil from 922 net wells. The trust receives royalties based on the amount of oil (and gas) produced and sold and then distributes virtually all of the proceeds to shareholders on a regular basis. MV Partners a private company engaged in the exploration production gathering aggregation and sale of oil and natural gas has the rights to 80% of net proceeds.

MV Partners has an agreement by which Vess Oil and Murfin Drilling operate the underlying properties on behalf of MV Partners for which MV Partners is designated as the operator.

The trust has 43 882 net acres of undeveloped acreage.

Auditors: GrantThorntonLLP

LOCATIONS

HQ: MV Oil Trust
The Bank of New York Mellon Trust Company, N.A., Trustee, Global Corporate Trust, 919 Congress Avenue, Austin, TX 78701
Phone: 855 802-1094

COMPETITORS

Cross Timbers Royalty Trust	Mesa Royalty Trust
Hugoton Royalty Trust	Panhandle Oil and Gas
LL&E Royalty Trust	Sabine Royalty Trust
	San Juan Basin

HISTORICAL FINANCIALS

Company Type: Public

Income Statement

FYE: December 31

	REVENUE ($ mil.)	NET INCOME ($ mil.)	NET PROFIT MARGIN	EMPLOYEES
12/13	37.8	37.0	97.8%	0
12/12	41.5	40.8	98.3%	0
12/11	40.5	39.6	97.8%	0
12/10	32.5	31.6	97.4%	0
12/09	18.7	17.9	95.6%	0
Annual Growth	**19.2%**	**19.9%**	**—**	**—**

2013 Year-End Financials

Debt ratio: —
Return on equity: 129.1%
Cash ($ mil.): 0
Current ratio: —
Long-term debt ($ mil.): —
No. of shares (mil.): 11
Dividends
  Yield: 13.5%
  Payout: 94.7%
Market value ($ mil.): 273

STOCK PRICE ($) FY Close	P/E High/Low		PER SHARE ($) Earnings	Dividends	Book Value
12/13 23.76	10	7	3.22	3.22	(0.00)
12/12 23.76	12	6	3.55	3.55	(0.00)
12/11 39.64	13	10	3.45	3.45	(0.00)
12/10 39.87	14	7	2.76	2.76	(0.00)
12/09 20.20	13	5	1.56	1.56	(0.00)
Annual Growth 4.1%	—	—	19.9%	19.9%	—

Myriad Genetics, Inc.

There are a myriad of diseases out there and Myriad Genetics is working to detect which ones you might develop based on your genes. The company develops and sells molecular diagnostic tests in three main areas: predictive medicine (to assess a patient's risk for developing disease) personalized medicine (to identify likelihood of drug response to therapies) and prognostic medicine (to assess risk of disease progression or recurrence). Its biggest revenue maker BRACAnalysis helps determine risk for breast or ovarian cancer. Myriad Genetics markets its products in the US through its own sales force and uses collaborations to sell them elsewhere.

Operations

The company operates in three segments: research molecular diagnostics and companion diagnostics. The research segment is focused on the discovery of genes related to major common diseases and includes corporate services such as finance human resources legal and information technology. The molecular diagnostics segment provides testing that is designed to assess an individual's risk for developing disease later in life identify a patient'slikelihood of responding to drug therapy and guide a patient's dosing to ensure optimal treatment or assess a patient's risk of disease progression and disease recurrence. The companion diagnostics segment provides testing products and services to the pharmaceutical biotechnology and medical research industries.

Myriad Genetics' primary line of molecular diagnostic testing products includes BRACAnalysis COLARIS and MELARIS. The company markets these to physicians engaged in preventive rather than reactive treatments. These tests are designed to assess whether a patient's genetic makeup makes the patient more likely to develop certain cancers such as breast colorectal and skin. Myriad is ramping up its sales marketing and education efforts aimed at OB/Gyn doctors in the US a market that targets women.

The company's personalized medicine line of products gauges a patient's response to certain drugs and dosages which then helps physicians tailor treatments to the individual. The THERAGUIDE 5-FU product shows oncologists whether a cancer patient through a small blood sample is likely to have adverse reactions to a common chemotherapy.

A third set of tests includes prognostic medicine diagnostics that assess disease progression or recurrence rates. Its PROLARIS product helps physicians predict the aggressiveness of prostate cancer in men.

Geographic Reach

Based in the US the company serves major markets in Asia Europe and Latin America. In the US Myriad Genetics operates from offices and labs in Austin Texas; Salt Lake City; and Lake Placid New York. In Europe it has sales offices in Munich Paris Madrid and Milan laboratory operations in Munich and an international headquarters in Zurich.

Financial Analysis

Myriad Genetics reported a 23% increase in revenues in 2011 thanks to increased molecular diagnostic testing volume (18% of revenue growth) thanks to increased demand for its BRACAnalysis COLARIS & COLARIS AP and other products and higher companion diagnostic service revenues (5% of growth) thanks to the acquisition of the Rules-Based Medicine company.

The 11% increase in net income in 2011 was primarily due to higher revenues offset by higher research and development expenses.

Strategy

In order to develop the next generation of molecular diagnostic products Myriad Genetics continues to develop its own proprietary technologies including bioinformatics and robotics to better understand genes and proteins and their role in human disease. It also seeks to license or acquire biomarkers or genes from third-party organizations to augment its own in-house product development programs. For instance in 2012 Myriad Genetics obtained an exclusive worldwide license (excepting co-exclusivity in Germany) to commercially test the RAD51C gene for hereditary breast and ovarian cancer risk. That year it also signed a deal with Cephalon to conduct BRCA1 and BRCA2 mutation testing on patients to be enrolled in a Phase I/II clinical study.

In 2011 the company moved to expand its offerings by acquiring Austin Texas-based diagnostics firm Rules-Based Medicine for some $80 million. The purchase added biomarker products that aid in the diagnoses of neurological disorders and inflammatory and infectious diseases as well as companion diagnostic offerings and additional products under development. Renamed Myriad RBM it operates as an R&D subsidiary in Austin.

In 2010 a federal court revoked two of Myriad Genetics' patents related to the BRACAnalysis test on the premise that isolated DNA strains are not patentable since they are products of nature. The ruling could affect future research projects and have a lasting impact on the entire biopharmaceutical development market.

Mergers and Acquisitions

In early 2014 the company announced it would pay $270 million for autoimmune diagnostics company Crescendo Bioscience. The move gives Myriad entree into the autoimmune market and provides product diversification. Crescendo will benefit from Myriad's superior development and sales and marketing infrastructure.

Ownership

In 2012 Royce and Associates LLC owned 12.4% of the company.

Company Background

Myriad Genetics spun off its drug development operations in mid-2009. The spin-off of its drug development arm Myriad Pharmaceuticals into a separate publicly traded company (called Myrexis) has allowed Myriad Genetics to dedicate substantial focus on molecular diagnostics. Previously the company had used revenue from its profitable diagnostics business to fund its drug development efforts. But with the company reaching profitability overall for the first time in 2008 it revisited the dual business structure and decided to split itself into two.

EXECUTIVES

President CEO and Director, Peter D. Meldrum, age 67, $915,812 total compensation
EVP General Counsel and Secretary, Richard M. Marsh, age 56, $425,811 total compensation
EVP International Operations, Gary A. King, age 58
Chief Scientific Officer, Jerry S. Lanchbury, age 55, $420,812 total compensation
President and CEO, Mark C. Capone, age 52, $501,191 total compensation
CIO, Robert G. Harrison, age 48
EVP Corporate Communications, Ronald Rogers
President Myriad RBM, T. Craig Benson
EVP Human Resources, Jayne B. Hart
Chief Operating Officer, Ralph L. McDade
EVP CFO and Treasurer, R. Bryan Riggsbee
Vice President Sales, Alexander Ford
Vice President Quality And Compl, Eric Pratts
National Accounts Manager, Amisha Shah
Senior Vice President Of Information Technology, Alexander Gutin
Executive Vice President And Cio, Michael Brawer
Vice President Pharmacogenomics, Susanne Wagner
Vice President Medical Affairs, Loren Clarke
President CEO and Director, Peter D. Meldrum, age 67
Vice Chairman, Walter Gilbert
EVP General Counsel and Secretary, Richard M. Marsh, age 56
Chairman, John T. Henderson, age 70
EVP CFO and Treasurer, R. Bryan Riggsbee
Auditors: Ernst&YoungLLP

LOCATIONS

HQ: Myriad Genetics, Inc.
320 Wakara Way, Salt Lake City, UT 84108
Phone: 801 584-3600   **Fax:** 801 584-3640
Web: www.myriad.com

PRODUCTS/OPERATIONS

2014 Sales

	$ mil.	% of total
Molecular Diagnostics	748.2	96
Companion Diagnostics	30.0	4
Total	**778.2**	**100**

2014 Molecular Diagnostics Sales

	$ mil.	% of total
BRACAnalysis	517.9	69
BART	89.4	12
COLARIS & COLARIS AP	59.1	8
Myriad myRisk	53.7	7
VectraDA	14.0	2
Other	14.1	2
Total	**748.2**	**100**

Selected Molecular Diagnostic Tests

BRACAnalysis (breast and ovarian cancer predictive test)
COLARIS (colorectal and uterine cancer predictive test)
COLARIS AP (colon cancer predictive test)
MELARIS (melanoma predictive test)
Myraid myRisk (hereditary cencer test)
OnDose (chemotherapy dosing level personalized diagnostic test)
PREZEON (cancer drug responsivity personalized diagnostic test)
PROLARIS (prostate cancer prognostic test)
THERAGUIDE 5-FU (chemotherapy toxicity personalized diagnostic test)
Vectra DA (rheumatoid arthritis test)

Selected Companion Diagnostic Services

Multi-Analyte Profile (MAP): library contains more than 550 individual human and rodent immunoassays for use in MAP testing

Multiplexed Immunoassay Kits: enable customers to leverage Myriad's technology services with their in-house capabilities
TruCulture: a self-contained whole blood culture that can be deployed worldwide to clinical sites for acquiring cell culture data without specialized facilities or training
p>d

COMPETITORS

Abbott Labs	Innogenetics
Beckman Coulter	Interleukin Genetics
Becton Dickinson	NeoGenomics
Bio-Rad Labs	Oncolab
Celera	Pathwork Diagnostics
Clarient	QIAGEN
CombiMatrix	Roche Diagnostics
DiagnoCure	Sequenom
Epigenomics	Siemens Healthcare
EraGen Biosciences	Diagnostics
Foundation Medicine	Third Wave
Genzyme	Technologies
Hologic	Transgenomic
Illumina	

HISTORICAL FINANCIALS

Company Type: Public

Income Statement

FYE: June 30

	REVENUE ($ mil.)	NET INCOME ($ mil.)	NET PROFIT MARGIN	EMPLOYEES
06/14	778.2	176.2	22.6%	1,649
06/13	613.1	147.1	24.0%	1,325
06/12	496.0	112.1	22.6%	1,169
06/11	402.0	100.7	25.0%	1,057
06/10	362.6	152.3	42.0%	870
Annual Growth	**21.0%**	**3.7%**	**—**	**17.3%**

2014 Year-End Financials

Debt ratio: —	No. of shares (mil.): 73
Return on equity: 24.3%	Dividends
Cash ($ mil.): 64	Yield: —
Current ratio: 4.00	Payout: —
Long-term debt ($ mil.): —	Market value ($ mil.): 2,861

	STOCK PRICE ($) FY Close	P/E High/Low		Earnings	PER SHARE ($) Dividends	Book Value
06/14	38.92	18	9	2.25	0.00	9.78
06/13	26.87	19	13	1.77	0.00	9.04
06/12	23.77	20	13	1.30	0.00	7.70
06/11	22.71	23	13	1.10	0.00	6.57
06/10	14.95	23	10	1.54	0.00	5.93
Annual Growth	**27.0%**			**9.9%**	**—**	**13.3%**

Nathan's Famous, Inc.

Patrons of this restaurateur are in the dog house. Nathan's Famous is a leading franchisor of quick-service restaurants with a chain of about 300 Nathan's outlets known for all-beef frankfurters served with a variety of toppings. The eateries located in about 25 states and a half dozen other countries also serve hamburgers crinkle-cut fries and breakfast sandwiches. More than 50 Nathan's units also feature fish and chips under the Arthur Treacher's brand. In addition to restaurants the company sells Nathan's branded products through vending machines Subway units at

Wal-Mart stores and Auntie Anne's pretzel shops. Specialty Foods Group makes Nathan's hot dogs for retail sale under a licensing deal.

Geographic Reach

Nathan's has been expanding internationally in recent years. The company opened several locations in Beijing China and Nathan's first franchised location in Canada.

Operations

While its restaurant chain still forms the core identity of Nathan's the company has been focused on expanding the sale of branded products through third-party foodservice operators. It branded products segment accounts for more than 50% of sales. Meanwhile Nathan's has launched a limited-menu concept designed to allow other quick-service restaurants such as Brusters Real Ice Cream shops to offer its branded hot dogs.

Sales and Marketing

With its flagship store still operating in Coney Island New York Nathan's is the official "nonkosher" hot dog of both the New York Yankees and the New York Mets. The company also holds a competitive eating contest held at Coney Island every July Fourth.

Financial Performance

The company's revenue has increased year-over-year. It reported revenue of $82.9 million for fiscal 2014 up from $71.5 million in fiscal 2013 and $66.2 million in fiscal 2012.

Net income also went up in fiscal 2014 compared to the prior period. Nathan's reported net income of $8.3 million for fiscal 2014 up from $7.4 million in fiscal 2013. However despite the increased revenue and net income the company's cash flow decreased by more than $7 million in fiscal 2014 compared to fiscal 2013 levels.

HISTORY

Company Background

Ida Handwerker and her husband Nathan opened the first Nathan's Famous food stand in Coney Island in 1916. Ida's special blend of herbs and spices helped popularize the hot dogs and Nathan's went on to become a Coney Island institution. In 1957 the Handwerker family opened a second restaurant and by 1969 the year Nathan's went public the company operated four stores.

In 1987 investment group Equicor bought Nathan's. The next three years the company suffered through multiple changes in leadership and posted a record loss in 1990. A turnaround led by Wayne Norbitz who took over as president in 1989 helped restore the company's stability.

Nathan's went public again in 1993. Also that year Howard Lorber (who came on board as part of Equicor) was named CEO. Two years later the company opened its first outlets inside Home Depot stores. In 1996 Nathan's implemented a co-branding strategy and by the following year it participated in nearly 60 co-branded operations.

In 1998 the company introduced a new product line (chicken strips creamed spinach salads) available in grocery stores and the next year it acquired the Miami Subs sandwich shop chain (sold in 2007) and the Kenny Rogers Roasters chain of rotisserie chicken outlets (disposed of in 2008). Later in 1999 the company's traditional Fourth of July hot dog eating contest was marred by controversy when a videotape showed the winner biting into his wiener before the gun went off.

The following year Nathan's Famous became the official hotdog of the New York Yankees. The 16 new restaurants opened by the company during 2001 included locations in Israel and Egypt. Hard economic times led the company to close several stores in 2002 and Home Depot later terminated its agreements to sell Nathan's Famous in its stores. In 2003 locations in Israel and Brunei were closed and a new location in Japan was opened.

Nathan's Famous acquired the Arthur Treacher's brand and franchising system from TruFoods in 2006. The following year Eric Gatoff was named CEO; Lorber remained as chairman.

Nathan's sold Kenny Rogers Roasters to an affiliate of Malaysia's Berjaya Corporation in 2008. The company disposed of its Miami Subs sandwich chain the previous year selling the business for $3.2 million.

The company expanded into China in 2011 and plans to open locations in Canada during 2012.

EXECUTIVES

Vp Franchise Operations, Randy K Watts, age 59
Executive Vice President; Director, Donald L. (Don) Perlyn, age 72, $210,000 total compensation
Chief Financial Officer; Vice President - Finance; Secretary, Ronald G. DeVos, age 59, $162,750 total compensation
President; Chief Operating Officer; Director, Wayne Norbitz, age 66, $288,750 total compensation
Chief Executive Officer; Director, Eric Gatoff, age 45, $225,000 total compensation
Vice President Franchise Operations, Susan McCann
Chairman, Howard M. Lorber, age 65
Auditors: GrantThorntonLLP

LOCATIONS

HQ: Nathan' s Famous, Inc.
One Jericho Plaza, Second Floor - Wing A, Jericho, NY 11753
Phone: 516 338-8500
Web: www.nathansfamous.com

COMPETITORS

Burger King	Kahala
CKE Restaurants	McDonald' s
Captain D' s	Popeyes
Chick-fil-A	Potbelly Sandwich Shop
Church' s Chicken	Quiznos
Dairy Queen	Sbarro
Galardi Group	Subway
Golden Krust	Wendy' s
HDOS Enterprises	YUM!
Jack in the Box	

HISTORICAL FINANCIALS

Company Type: Public

Income Statement

FYE: March 30

	REVENUE ($ mil.)	NET INCOME ($ mil.)	NET PROFIT MARGIN	EMPLOYEES
03/14	82.9	8.3	10.0%	210
03/13	71.5	7.4	10.4%	161
03/12	66.2	6.1	9.3%	219
03/11	57.2	2.2	3.9%	219
03/10	50.8	5.5	10.9%	215
Annual Growth	13.0%	10.6%	—	(0.6%)

2014 Year-End Financials

Debt ratio: —	No. of shares (mil.): 4
Return on equity: 21.4%	Dividends
Cash ($ mil.): 22	Yield: —
Current ratio: 4.61	Payout: —
Long-term debt ($ mil.): —	Market value ($ mil.): 219

	STOCK PRICE ($)	P/E		PER SHARE ($)		
	FY Close	High/Low	Earnings	Dividends	Book Value
03/14	48.78	33 23	1.81	0.00	9.79
03/13	42.25	25 12	1.63	0.00	7.80
03/12	21.01	17 14	1.22	0.00	6.61
03/11	17.10	47 36	0.40	0.00	7.49
03/10	15.25	16 12	0.97	0.00	7.92
Annual Growth	33.7%	— —	16.9%	—	5.4%

National Health Investors, Inc.

National Health Investors has a financial investment in the nation's health. The real estate investment trust (REIT) owns or makes mortgage investments in health care properties primarily long-term care facilities. With about 120 facilities in some 17 states holdings also include residences for people with developmental disabilities assisted-living complexes medical office buildings retirement centers and an acute care hospital. About one-third of National Health Investors' properties are leased to its largest tenant National HealthCare Corporation; half are leased to regional health care providers. A majority of the REIT's facilities are located in Florida Texas and Tennessee.

Strategy

National Health Investors (NHI) typically takes a purchase-leaseback approach in which it acquires properties and leases them back to their previous operators. It provides mortgage and construction loans to operators who agree to lease the property once built. In 2012 the company teamed with Bickford Senior Living to build up to eight new assisted living and memory care centers; once completed the facilities will be leased to Bickford. Also in 2012 NHI acquired a 181-unit senior living campus in Loma Linda California for $12 million from Chancellor Health Care (CHC) thereby establishing a presence in Southern California. CHC will lease and continue to operate the facility.

More recently NHI in April 2013 acquired a pair of skilled nursing facilities in Canton and Corinth Texas for $26.3 million. The purchase added a total of 254 beds to the REIT's portfolio.

NHI in late 2013 has also agreed to buy 25 independent-living properties which boast 2841 units from Holiday Acquisition Holdings for $491 million.

Ownership

Chairman and CEO Andy Adams owns about 10% of National Health Investors. He previously made three management buyout offers to acquire the REIT all of which were rejected in 2007. The company subsequently announced that it was taking the possible sale of the company off the table.

EXECUTIVES

SVP Investments, Kevin Pascoe
Chief Accounting Officer, Roger R. Hopkins, age 53, $200,000 total compensation
President and CEO, Justin Hutchens, age 40
Chairman, W. Andrew (Andy) Adams, age 69
Auditors: BDOSeidmanLLP

LOCATIONS

HQ: National Health Investors, Inc.
222 Robert Rose Drive, Murfreesboro, TN 37129
Phone: 615 890-9100
Web: www.nhireit.com

COMPETITORS

Cousins Properties
HCP
Health Care REIT
Healthcare Realty
  Trust
LTC Properties
Medical Properties
  Trust
Omega Healthcare
  Investors
Senior Housing
  Properties
Ventas

HISTORICAL FINANCIALS

Company Type: Public

Income Statement

FYE: December 31

	REVENUE ($ mil.)	NET INCOME ($ mil.)	NET PROFIT MARGIN	EMPLOYEES
12/13	117.8	107.1	91.0%	11
12/12	96.9	90.9	93.8%	10
12/11	82.7	81.1	98.1%	0
12/10	78.4	69.4	88.6%	0
12/09	64.2	64.2	100.0%	0
Annual Growth	**16.4%**	**13.7%**	**—**	**—**

2013 Year-End Financials

Debt ratio: 42.3%
Return on equity: 17.5%
Cash ($ mil.): 11
Current ratio: 0.86
Long-term debt ($ mil.): 617
No. of shares (mil.): 33
Dividends
  Yield: 5.1%
  Payout: 67.7%
Market value ($ mil.): 1,854

	STOCK PRICE ($) FY Close	P/E High/Low	PER SHARE ($) Earnings	Dividends	Book Value
12/13	56.10	19 14	3.74	2.90	23.19
12/12	56.53	18 13	3.26	2.64	16.41
12/11	43.98	17 13	2.92	2.72	15.98
12/10	45.02	19 13	2.50	2.36	15.98
12/09	36.99	16 9	2.32	2.30	15.73
Annual Growth	**11.0%**	**— —**	**12.7%**	**6.0%**	**10.2%**

National Holdings Corp

National Holdings helps investors manage their holdings. Through subsidiaries National Securities Corporation vFinance and EquityStation the company provides brokerage services to retail clients wealthy individuals and institutional investors in the US. Products include stocks options bonds mutual funds and annuities. The subsidiaries also provide investment banking services to growth companies. The group employs more than 800 advisors and brokers most of whom are independent contractors responsible for their office expenses. National Holdings provides its representatives with research materials order execution trade processing and compliance support as well as higher-than-average commissions.

Another subsidiary of the company National Asset Management offers investment advisory services. National Insurance Corporation offers annuities and other fixed insurance products.

The financial services industry was hit especially hard by the recession and National Holdings was no exception. The 2008 acquisition of vFinance boosted the company's commissions and clearing fees but National Holdings remained in the red into 2010 as revenues stagnated. The company has said it may look for additional acquisitions as a means of growth.

In 2010 an investment group led by OpusPoint Partners completed a $3 million recapitalization of National Holdings; Michael Weiss a principal of OpusPoint was named chairman of National Holdings the following year. The two firms also formed a boutique investment banking joint venture called OPN Capital Markets.

Executive officers and directors of National Holdings own a majority of the company's stock. Institutional investor Bedford Oak Advisors holds around 17%.

EXECUTIVES

Vice Chairman and President; CEO National Securities, Mark A. Goldwasser, age 56, $440,000 total compensation
Chairman and CEO, Robert B. Fagenson, age 66
EVP Investment Banking, Jonathan C. Rich, age 45, $286,908 total compensation
President vFinance, William (Billy) Groeneveld
CFO, Alan B. Levin, age 51, $193,500 total compensation
Vice President Investment Banking, Brad Lane
Senior Vice President And Investments, Philip Diperna
Senior Vice President Of Investments, Michael Kaplan
Vice Chairman and President; CEO National Securities, Mark A. Goldwasser, age 56
Chairman and CEO, Robert B. Fagenson, age 66
Board Member, Paul Coviello
Board Member, Frank Plimpton
Board Member, Norman J Kurlan
Board Member, Gary A Rosenberg
Board Member, Robert J Rosan
Board Member, Marshall S Geller
Auditors: Sherb&Co.LLP

LOCATIONS

HQ: National Holdings Corp
410 Park Ave., 14th Floor, New York, NY 10022
Phone: 212 417-8000
Web: www.nhldcorp.com

PRODUCTS/OPERATIONS

2010 Sales

	$ mil.	% of total
Commissions	73.3	66
Net dealer inventory gains	14.1	13
Transfer fees & clearing services	8.3	7
Investment banking	6.5	6
Interest & dividends	2.6	2
Other	6.2	6
Total	**111.0**	**100**

COMPETITORS

Charles Schwab
Diamond Hill
  Investment
Edward Jones
LPL Financial
Merrill Lynch
Morgan Stanley
Paulson Capital
RBC Wealth Management
Ragen MacKenzie
Raymond James
  Financial

HISTORICAL FINANCIALS

Company Type: Public

Income Statement

FYE: September 30

	REVENUE ($ mil.)	NET INCOME ($ mil.)	NET PROFIT MARGIN	EMPLOYEES
09/14	184.2	18.6	10.1%	1,187
09/13	127.5	1.5	1.2%	900
09/12	118.6	(1.9)	—	948
09/11	126.5	(4.7)	—	1,011
09/10	110.9	(6.6)	—	917
Annual Growth	**13.5%**			**6.7%**

2014 Year-End Financials

Debt ratio: —
Return on equity: 61.8%
Cash ($ mil.): 26
Current ratio: 1.94
Long-term debt ($ mil.): —
No. of shares (mil.): 124
Dividends
  Yield: —
  Payout: —
Market value ($ mil.): 59

	STOCK PRICE ($) FY Close	P/E High/Low	PER SHARE ($) Earnings	Dividends	Book Value
09/14	0.48	4 2	0.15	0.00	0.36
09/13	0.37	20 7	0.02	0.00	0.16
09/12	0.20	— —	(0.08)	0.00	(0.11)
09/11	0.30	— —	(0.18)	0.00	(0.07)
09/10	0.40	— —	(0.41)	0.00	(0.36)
Annual Growth	**4.4%**		**— —**	**—**	**—**

National Instruments Corp.

National Instruments (NI) knows you like to take tests. The company's instrumentation hardware and graphical software convert standard PCs into industrial automation and test and measurement systems. These "virtual instruments" can observe measure and control electrical signals and physical attributes such as voltage and pressure. The company also offers programming environments (LabVIEW and Measurement Studio) for creating customizable graphical interfaces controlling instruments and capturing and analyzing data. In addition NI provides test management software for running automated factory test systems. Customers outside the Americas account for around 60% of sales.

Geographic Reach

NI has offices in more than 40 countries. Its manufacturing plants are located in the US (Texas) as well as in Hungary and Malaysia.

Customers located in North and South America account for 40% of sales. Asia accounts for another 35% of sales while customers in Europe round out the remaining 25%.

Sales and Marketing

NI relies on a direct sales force to sell hardware and software to its customer base of 35000 companies. Less than 10% of sales are made through alternative channels such as distributors original equipment manufacturers (OEMs) value-added resellers (VARs) system integrators and consultants.

The company targets the automotive aerospace computer and electronics automated test equipment consumer electronics education government and defense medical research energy pharmaceutical semiconductor and telecommunications industries among others.

Throughout its history NI has relied on relentless promotion and publicity to get its name out in front of engineers and researchers. It advertises heavily in trade publications from Reed Business Information US CMP MediaPenton Media and other publishers while unleashing barrages of product press releases on trade editors on an almost daily basis.

The company also promotes itself through technical seminars and conferences presented around the world and over the Internet. Its biggest event is the annual NIWeek conference staged each summer at the Austin Convention Center near NI's headquarters. Held every year since 1995 NIWeek attracts thousands of attendees from all over the world.

Financial Performance

Sales were up 12% in 2012 to a record $1.14 billion. (NI hit the $1 billion mark for the first time in 2011.) The company enjoyed robust sales in both product and software maintenance around the world. Large orders (valued at more than $100000) were also on the rise - in 2012 NI sold $59 million in graphical system design application products to one customer. That year the company also took in $90 million in profits.

Mergers and Acquisitions

NI is not heavily acquisitive but it did buy two companies in 2011 beginning with development partner Phase Matrix for $40 million. Phase Matrix makes radio-frequency (RF) and microwave test and measurement instruments subsystems and components. The acquisition drove growth in RF and microwave test instrumentation by adding high-frequency technology and manufacturing capabilities. Phase Matrix will operate as a subsidiary of NI and continue to sell products directly to customers and OEMs.

A couple months later it bought AWR Corporation a developer of software used to design RF and high-frequency components and systems for the aerospace and defense communications test equipment and semiconductor industries. NI paid around $66 million for the company which strengthened its LabVIEW software and RF testing hardware platforms.

HISTORY

In the 1970s James Truchard working at the University of Texas Applied Research Laboratory was frustrated by the lack of connectivity between the lab's computers and testing equipment. Truchard who as a kid built homemade radios founded National Instruments in 1976 with fellow lab employees Jeffrey Kodosky and William Nowlin. The trio raised $13000 which included part of Truchard's teacher retirement fund savings and set up camp in a room behind Truchard's garage.

Using Hewlett-Packard's technology for collecting test and measurement data from its own machines the trio created the general-purpose interface bus (GPIB) a device that links computers to scientific instruments. The devices eliminated the practice of using paper pencils and rulers to track instruments. The colleagues' vigor kept the company small but busy. Truchard designed hardware and wrote press releases. Kodosky developed programs and handled customer support.

National Instruments thrived as PCs became popular. LabVIEW introduced in 1986 used graphics to simulate the dials of an engineering instrument's control panel. Users worked the controls

simply by moving the mouse. The company expanded internationally in 1987 opening an office in Tokyo. It suffered a loss for 1989 after expanding into Europe.

In 1990 NASA used one of the company's programs to trace fuel system leaks affecting Space Shuttle launches. National Instruments went public in 1995 and intensified product development. It also began acquiring small businesses to expand its technology base buying industrial automation specialist Georgetown Systems (1996) and motion control equipment maker nuLogic (1997).

In 1998 National Instruments bought two German makers of data acquisition tools DATALOG and DASYtec. The next year the company and computer maker Dell joined forces to market a scientific measuring and testing workstation. National Instruments also launched an online store then followed that in 2000 with the NI Developer Zone a resource for information on automation and measurement systems.

In 2001 NI established a subsidiary in Russia. The following year it opened a manufacturing facility in Hungary. The company acquired Hyperception a provider of graphical development tools for digital signal processing in 2003.

NI expanded its product offerings with its 2005 purchases of data acquisition instrumentation makers Measurement Computing and IOtech. In 2007 chairman president and CEO James Truchard was elected to the National Academy of Engineering. The following year the company purchased microLEX Systems A/S a Danish instrumentation firm for about $18 million in cash.

EXECUTIVES

Vice President Manufacturing, Robert R Porterfield
EVP COO CFO and Treasurer, Alexander M. (Alex) Davern, age 47, $426,250 total compensation
Chairman President and CEO, James J. Truchard, age 70, $1 total compensation
SVP Research and Development, Phillip D. (Phil) Hester, $342,500 total compensation
VP Global Information Technology, Arleene Porterfield
SVP Marketing, Eric Starkloff
Vice President Regional Sales, Denver Dsouza
Vice President Of International Sales, Kurt Veggeburg
Sr V Pres Global R&d, Scott A Rust
Vice President Applications Engineering, Mark Linares
Vice President, John Hanks
Vice President Solutions Marketing, George Zafiropoulos
Vice President Research And Development, Robert Dcanik
EVP COO CFO and Treasurer, Alexander M. (Alex) Davern, age 47
Chairman President and CEO, James J. Truchard, age 70
Secretary, Tia Garnett
Auditors: Ernst&YoungLLP

LOCATIONS

HQ: National Instruments Corp.
  11500 North MoPac Expressway, Austin, TX 78759
Phone: 512 338-9119   **Fax:** 512 683-9300
Web: www.ni.com

2012 Sales

	% of total
Americas	40
Asia/Pacific	34
Europe	26
Total	**100**

PRODUCTS/OPERATIONS

2012 Sales

	% of total
Product	92
Software maintenance	8
Total	**100**

Selected Products

Measurement and Automation Software
  LabVIEW
  Measurement Studio
  LabWindows/CVI
  Switch Executive
  TestStand
  VI Logger
Measurement Hardware
  Counters and timers
  Data acquisition (DAQ) hardware
  Digital input and output devices
  Digital multimeters
  Dynamic signal acquisition devices
  Dynamic signal analyzers
  High-speed digitizers
  Radio-frequency measurement devices
  Signal sources

COMPETITORS

Advantest	Teradyne
Agilent Technologies	Thermo Fisher
MathWorks	Scientific
Tektronix	Wolfram Research

HISTORICAL FINANCIALS

Company Type: Public

Income Statement

FYE: December 31

	REVENUE ($ mil.)	NET INCOME ($ mil.)	NET PROFIT MARGIN	EMPLOYEES
12/13	1,172.5	80.5	6.9%	7,114
12/12	1,143.6	90.1	7.9%	6,869
12/11	1,024.1	94.0	9.2%	6,235
12/10	873.2	109.1	12.5%	5,280
12/09	676.5	17.0	2.5%	5,120
Annual Growth	**14.7%**	**47.3%**	**—**	**8.6%**

2013 Year-End Financials

Debt ratio: —	No. of shares (mil.): 125
Return on equity: 8.2%	Dividends
Cash ($ mil.): 230	Yield: 1.7%
Current ratio: 3.68	Payout: 100.0%
Long-term debt ($ mil.): —	Market value ($ mil.): 4,025

	STOCK PRICE ($) FY Close	P/E High/Low	Earnings	PER SHARE ($) Dividends	Book Value
12/13	32.02	50 40	0.64	0.56	8.14
12/12	25.81	39 32	0.73	0.56	7.64
12/11	25.95	61 27	0.78	0.40	7.06
12/10	37.64	41 30	0.92	0.35	6.31
12/09	29.45	203 109	0.15	0.32	5.64
Annual Growth	**2.1%**	**— —**	**44.5%**	**15.0%**	**9.6%**

National Interstate Corp

National Interstate stands behind you when you get on the bus! The specialty property/casualty insurer concentrates on the transportation market. One of the nation's largest insurers of truck and passenger transportation fleets the company also provides insurance to moving companies and personal lines of coverage for recreational vehicles. Additionally National Interstate offers general commercial insurance for small businesses in Alaska and Hawaii. The company distributes its products throughout the US. American Financial Group spun off National Interstate in 2005 but continues to control the company through a 52% stake held by its Great American Insurance Company.

National Interstate distributes its more than 35 product lines through affiliated agencies independent agents and brokers and agents' online initiatives. Its largest markets are California (with about 15% of gross premiums written) and Texas (with less than 10%). Other significant markets include New York Florida Pennsylvania North Carolina New Jersey Massachusetts and Missouri.

National Interstate insures charter bus companies school bus fleets limousine companies and public transportation operations as well as other passenger transportation and cargo truck fleets. In 2011 the company entered the ambulance insurance market by partnering with McNeil & Company. Together National Interstate and McNeil provide insurance coverage and claims services for emergency and non-emergency medical transportation operators through the Ambulance Services Insurance Program. McNeil administers the program and also provides risk management and loss control services.

National Interstate offers services to its commercial transportation customers under two models: alternative risk transfer and traditional coverage. Under the alternative risk transfer model (which accounts for the majority of the company's commercial transportation policies) the company provides underwriting and other services for captive insurance programs that are owned or rented by its customers; in such an arrangement the client participates in assuming risks and sharing in underwriting profits.

National Interstate operates primarily through five subsidiaries: Hudson Indemnity (reinsurance) National Interstate Insurance Company National Interstate Insurance Company of Hawaii Triumphe Casualty and Vanliner Insurance Company. It bought Vanliner Insurance Company for $128 million in 2010 to complement its existing transportation insurance offerings. Vanliner was previously a subsidiary of UniGroup.

National Interstate's strategic plans for growth include organic growth through the development of new products expansion into new product lines and expansion of its insurance distribution network. Additionally the company explores opportunities to acquire other companies or selected books of business.

In fiscal 2011 National Interstate achieved revenue of $468.5 million representing a 15% increase over 2010. Contributing to its growth were increases in gross premiums written and earned premiums income from investments (which were concentrated in commercial and residential mortgage-backed securities and municipal bonds) and realized gains on its investments. Although the company's net income from operations increased by 12% its total net income for 2011 dropped by nearly 10% due to the after-tax impact from the operating results of Vanliner's guaranteed runoff business.

Founder and chairman Alan Spachman controls 7.5% of the company.

EXECUTIVES

VP and CFO, Julie A. McGraw, age 50, $190,424 total compensation
Senior Vice President, Terry E Phillips, age 65
EVP and COO, Anthony J. (Tony) Mercurio
President CEO and Director, David W. Michelson, age 56, $350,000 total compensation
Assistant Vice President, Michelle Silvestro
Vice President Of Customer Service And Implementation, Terri Johnson
Vice President Transportation, James Parks
Assistant Vice President Truck Transportation Group, George Skuggen
Assistant Vice President National Marketing Manager, Michelle Wiltgen
Vice President Claims, Brad Scofield
Chairman, Joseph E. (Jeff) Consolino, age 47
Auditors: Ernst&YoungLLP

LOCATIONS

HQ: National Interstate Corp
3250 Interstate Drive, Richfield, OH 44286-9000
Phone: 330 659-8900
Web: www.natl.com

PRODUCTS/OPERATIONS

2011 Revenues

	$ mil.	% of total
Premiums earned		
Alternative risk transfer	204.6	44
Transportation	151.5	32
Specialty personal lines	53.3	11
Hawaii & Alaska	14.2	3
Other	6.3	1
Net investment income	30.6	7
Net realized gains on investments	4.5	1
Other	3.5	1
Total	**468.5**	**100**

2011 Premiums Earned

	% of total
Alternative risk transfer	48
Transportation	35
Specialty personal lines	12
Hawaii & Alaska	3
Other	2
Total	**100**

COMPETITORS

American Modern Insurance	Lancer Insurance
Canal Insurance	McM Corporation
Dongbu	Progressive Corporation
First Insurance Company of Hawaii	RLI
GMAC Insurance	Sentry Insurance
Great West Casualty	Travelers Companies
Island Insurance	Zurich American

HISTORICAL FINANCIALS

Company Type: Public

Income Statement

FYE: December 31

	ASSETS ($ mil.)	NET INCOME ($ mil.)	INCOME AS % OF ASSETS	EMPLOYEES
12/13	1,623.8	17.5	1.1%	580
12/12	1,570.2	34.2	2.2%	546
12/11	1,525.0	35.6	2.3%	532
12/10	1,488.6	39.5	2.7%	494
12/09	955.7	46.4	4.9%	351
Annual Growth	**14.2%**	**(21.6%)**	**—**	**13.4%**

2013 Year-End Financials

Return on assets: 1.1%	Dividends
Return on equity: 4.9%	Yield: 1.9%
Long-term debt ($ mil.): —	Payout: 50.0%
No. of shares (mil.): 19	Market value ($ mil.): 452
Sales ($ mil): 568	

	STOCK PRICE ($) FY Close	P/E High/Low		PER SHARE ($) Earnings	Dividends	Book Value
12/13	23.00	40	27	0.89	0.44	17.92
12/12	28.82	16	13	1.75	2.40	18.07
12/11	24.67	15	11	1.83	0.36	18.07
12/10	21.41	11	8	2.03	0.32	15.99
12/09	16.96	9	6	2.40	0.28	14.06
Annual Growth	**7.9%**	**—**		**(22.0%)**	**12.0%**	**6.3%**

National Research Corp

The ultimate father figure National Research Corporation (NRC) is there to let you know when you're not measuring up. Founded in 1981 NRC offers performance measurement and analysis services to clients within the health care industry including hospitals HMOs home care hospice and regulatory groups. The company's performance tracking system uses individualized questionnaires to better determine an organization's satisfaction rating and the NRC Healthcare Market Guide provides industry statistics allowing clients to compare their services to those of competitors. Founder and CEO Michael Hays owns more than 65% of the company.

Geographic Reach
During fiscal 2013 the US contributed 93% of sales while 7% of sales came from Canada.

Sales and Marketing
The company's uses a direct sales organization.

Financial Performance
Revenue increased 7% in fiscal 2013 compared to fiscal 2012. The company brought in about $92.59 million in fiscal 2013 after claiming roughly $86.4 million in fiscal 2013. The increase was caused by a combination of market share gain and vertical growth in the company's client base.

Net income increased to $15.484 million in fiscal 2013 up 3% from $15.06 million in fiscal 2012. The difference was the result of lower expenses. The company's cash flow has remained strong along with revenue in recent fiscal years.

Strategy
NRC works to grow its business through increasing sales of its existing solutions to its existing clients (or cross-selling) winning additional new clients through market share growth in existing market segments developing and introducing new solutions to new and existing clients and pursuing acquisitions.

EXECUTIVES

Vice President Partnership And Channel Development, Mary Oakes
Founder and Chief Executive Officer, Michael D. Hays, age 59, $127,400 total compensation
CFO, Kevin Karas
National Accounts Manager, Stephanie Kolbo
National Account Manager, Leah Luther
National Account Manager, Andrew Carlson
Vice President, Kendall Frantz

Vice President Product Development, Jennifer Volland
Vice President Systems Engineering Ops, Joe Morales
National Account Manager, Steph Denbeste
Vice President Software Engineering, Paul Cooper
National Account Manager, Adam Benash
National Account Manager, Katie Taff
Supervisor Vps, Zach Braxton
National Account Manager, Cassandra Styers
National Account Manager, Sean Swanson
Vice President, Sarah Wirth
National Account Manager, Jennifer Kimmons
Vp, Pat Connell
Chairman, Gail L. Warden
Auditors: KPMGLLP

LOCATIONS

HQ: National Research Corp
1245 Q Street, Lincoln, NE 68508
Phone: 402 475-2525
Web: www.nationalresearch.com

2013 Sales

	$ mil.	% of total
US	85.9	93
Canada	6.7	7
Total	**92.6**	**100**

PRODUCTS/OPERATIONS

Selected Solutions
Engagement Solutions
Growth Solutions
Retention Solutions
Thought Leadership Solutions

COMPETITORS

Abt Associates	Maritz Research
Abt SRBI	Nielsen
Brand Pharm	ORC International
Gallup	Press Ganey
GfK	ReGen Biologics
IMS Health	SDI Health
Ipsos	TNS Custom
Kantar Group	Walker Information
MSI	

HISTORICAL FINANCIALS
Company Type: Public

Income Statement
FYE: December 31

	REVENUE ($ mil.)	NET INCOME ($ mil.)	NET PROFIT MARGIN	EMPLOYEES
12/13	92.5	15.4	16.7%	388
12/12	86.4	15.0	17.4%	383
12/11	75.7	11.5	15.3%	376
12/10	63.4	8.5	13.4%	305
12/09	57.6	8.4	14.7%	302
Annual Growth	**12.6%**	**16.2%**	**—**	**6.5%**

2013 Year-End Financials
Debt ratio: 9.5%
Return on equity: 24.1%
Cash ($ mil.): 22
Current ratio: 1.54
Long-term debt ($ mil.): 8
No. of shares (mil.): 24
Dividends
Yield: 0.0%
Payout: 97.3%
Market value ($ mil.): 456

	STOCK PRICE ($) FY Close	P/E High/Low	Earnings	PER SHARE ($) Dividends	Book Value
12/13	18.82	54 34	0.37	0.36	2.96
Annual Growth	**—**	**—**	**—**	**—**	**—**

National Retail Properties Inc

For National Retail Properties good things come in big boxes. The self-administered real estate investment trust (REIT) acquires develops and manages freestanding retail properties in heavily traveled commercial and residential areas. Its portfolio includes about 1800 properties totaling more than 20 million sq. ft. of leasable space in nearly all 50 states concentrated in the Southeast the Midwest and Texas. National Retail Properties also invests in mortgages operates the retail businesses on some of its sites and develops properties with the intention of selling them for a profit. Convenience stores make up around 20% of its portfolio.

Operations

While some retail REITs own entire strip malls or shopping malls National Retail Properties keeps it simple with freestanding retail properties. The trust's retail tenants are made up of convenience store and gas stations such as Stripes (Susser Holdings) The Pantry and 7-Eleven. It also owns many buildings that house restaurants such as Applebee's Chili's Denny's and Logan's Roadhouse. Fast food tenants include Taco Bell and Wendys. Best Buy CarQuest and Pep Boys are also major tenants.

National Retail Properties typically signs triple-net leases with initial terms of 15 to 20 years in which tenants are responsible for expenses such as taxes utilities repairs and maintenance.

Financial Performance

Overall revenues increased 13% in 2012 to $350 million. That year the trust added another 400 properties to its portfolio. Profits also increased more than 50% to $142 million.

Strategy

National Retail Properties maintains a diverse portfolio in order to minimize risk. It often sells older properties and uses the proceeds to buy newer locations. For the past three years it's had an occupancy rate of at least 97%.

EXECUTIVES

EVP CFO and Treasurer, Kevin B. Habicht, age 54, $397,000 total compensation
Chairman and CEO, Craig Macnab, age 58, $716,000 total compensation
President and COO, Julian E. (Jay) Whitehurst, age 56, $479,000 total compensation
EVP and Chief Investment Officer, Paul E. Bayer, age 62, $319,000 total compensation
EVP and Chief Acquisition Officer, Stephen A. Horn
Vice President Of Leasing, David J Reif
Vice President Of Acquisitions, Josh Lewis
Vice President Underwriting, Matthew Sunderland
Senior Vice President Tax, Mike Iannone
Chairman and CEO, Craig Macnab, age 58
Auditors: Ernst&YoungLLP

LOCATIONS

HQ: National Retail Properties Inc
450 South Orange Avenue, Suite 900, Orlando, FL 32801
Phone: 407 265-7348   **Fax:** 407 423-2894
Web: www.nnnreit.com

2012 Properties

	No.
Texas	357
Florida	113
Pennsylvania	95
North Carolina	77
Georgia	77
Indiana	70
Illinois	60
Ohio	52
Virginia	52
California	40
Other	566
Total	**1622**

COMPETITORS

Acadia Realty Trust	Glimcher Realty
Brixmor	Kimco Realty
DDR	One Liberty Properties
Federal Realty	Realty Income
Investment	Regency Centers

HISTORICAL FINANCIALS
Company Type: Public

Income Statement
FYE: December 31

	REVENUE ($ mil.)	NET INCOME ($ mil.)	NET PROFIT MARGIN	EMPLOYEES
12/13	392.3	160.1	40.8%	62
12/12	331.7	142.0	42.8%	60
12/11	265.7	92.3	34.7%	59
12/10	229.0	73.0	31.9%	58
12/09	231.8	54.8	23.6%	57
Annual Growth	**14.1%**	**30.7%**	**—**	**2.1%**

2013 Year-End Financials
Debt ratio: 35.2%
Return on equity: 6.3%
Cash ($ mil.): 1
Current ratio: 0.75
Long-term debt ($ mil.): 1,523
No. of shares (mil.): 121
Dividends
Yield: 5.2%
Payout: 141.5%
Market value ($ mil.): 3,700

	STOCK PRICE ($) FY Close	P/E High/Low	Earnings	PER SHARE ($) Dividends	Book Value
12/13	30.33	38 27	1.10	1.60	22.76
12/12	31.20	29 23	1.11	1.56	20.58
12/11	26.38	28 24	0.96	1.53	19.12
12/10	26.50	35 24	0.80	1.51	18.27
12/09	21.22	37 22	0.60	1.50	18.98
Annual Growth	**9.3%**	**—**	**16.4%**	**1.6%**	**4.7%**

National Western Life Insurance Co. (Austin, TX)

National Western Life Insurance sells life insurance and annuity products including individual universal whole and term plans. The company operates throughout the US except in New York and internationally in Central and South America the Caribbean Eastern Europe Asia and the Pacific Rim. Annuities sold by independent agents make up most of its US sales. Some two-thirds of its life insurance premiums come from outside the US where the company targets wealthy individuals. Investments mainly in fixed debt securities account for some 70% of revenues.

Operations The company has more than 60000 US life insurance policies and some 140000 annuity contracts representing $7 billion. Internationally it claims nearly 75000 life insurance policies. National Western also operates two nursing homes (in Nevada and Texas) which account for less than 5% of sales.

Financial Analysis National Western's revenue was flat in 2011 down less than 1% to $573 million. The company experienced growth in its life and annuity product segments but investment income (its largest revenue contributor) was hit by derivative losses. Net income fell in 2011 declining nearly 25% to $56 million because of increased amortization costs.

Ownership CEO Robert Moody a member of the powerful Moody family of Galveston Texas owns one-third of the company and effectively controls its board of directors.

EXECUTIVES

Senior Vice President And Chief, Patricia L Scheuer, age 63
Chairman and CEO, Robert L. Moody, age 78, $1,768,475 total compensation
President COO and Director, Ross R. Moody, age 52, $703,141 total compensation
Vice President Marketing Of The Company, Gary Fischer
SVP CFO and Treasurer, Brian M. Pribyl, age 56, $279,071 total compensation
SVP and Chief Marketing Officer, S. Christopher Johnson, age 46, $164,187 total compensation
Vice President And Associate Actuary, Mark Gulas
Vice President Marketing, John Huber
Upper Management Vice President, Doris Kruse
Assistant Vice President Corporate, Rey Perez
Marketing Vice President, Tony Zager
Assistant Vice President Annuity, Karen Johnston
Vice President Valuation Actuary, Kitty Kennedy
Assistant Vice President International Life Underwriting, Fabiola Best
Vice President Human Resources, Jim Egan
Asst Vice President At Nat West Life, Robin Hulsey
Vice President Project Controller, John Bower
Senior Vice President And Chief Marketing Officer, Chris Johnson
Chairman and CEO, Robert L. Moody, age 78
President COO and Director, Ross R. Moody, age 52
SVP CFO and Treasurer, Brian M. Pribyl, age 56
Treasurer, Wil Ross
Assistant Secretary, Jessie Skrhak
Auditors: KPMGLLP

LOCATIONS

HQ: National Western Life Insurance Co. (Austin, TX)
850 East Anderson Lane, Austin, TX 78752-1602
Phone: 512 836-1010   **Fax:** 512 836-6980
Web: www.nationalwesternlife.com

PRODUCTS/OPERATIONS

2011 Revenues

	$ mil.	% of total
Investment income	391.0	68
Universal life & annuity contract revenues	132.1	23
Life & annuity premiums	18.1	3
Other income	25.4	5
Gains on investments	6.1	1
Total	**572.7**	**100**

COMPETITORS

Allstate	Lincoln Benefit Life
American Equity Life	Lincoln Life
American Fidelity	Old Mutual (US)
Assurance Company	Pan-American Life
Aviva	Presidential Life
BMI Financial Group	Sammons Financial
Citizens Inc.	Securian Financial
FBL Financial	

HISTORICAL FINANCIALS

Company Type: Public

Income Statement

FYE: December 31

	ASSETS ($ mil.)	NET INCOME ($ mil.)	INCOME AS % OF ASSETS	EMPLOYEES
12/13	10,830.4	96.2	0.9%	279
12/12	10,263.8	92.5	0.9%	280
12/11	9,728.0	55.6	0.6%	278
12/10	8,773.9	72.9	0.8%	292
12/09	7,518.7	45.4	0.6%	294
Annual Growth	**9.6%**	**20.6%**	**—**	**(1.3%)**

2013 Year-End Financials

Return on assets: 0.9%	Dividends
Return on equity: 6.7%	Yield: 0.1%
Long-term debt ($ mil.): —	Payout: 1.3%
No. of shares (mil.): 3	Market value ($ mil.): 813
Sales ($ mil): 860	

	STOCK PRICE ($) FY Close	P/E High/Low		PER SHARE ($) Earnings	Dividends	Book Value
12/13	223.55	8	6	27.19	0.36	398.36
12/12	157.74	6	5	26.19	0.36	382.88
12/11	136.16	11	8	15.73	0.36	351.27
12/10	166.72	9	6	20.61	0.36	335.83
12/09	173.62	15	5	12.87	0.36	307.24
Annual Growth	**6.5%**	**—**	**—**	**20.6%**	**(0.0%)**	**6.7%**

Nationstar Mortgage Holdings Inc

Nationstar Mortgage helps turn home ownership into more than just a wish upon a star. The company services residential mortgage loans throughout the US. Its servicing portfolio comprises more than 2.3 million loans that total in excess of $425 billion in unpaid principal balances. Nationstar also originates loans primarily government- and agency-backed mortgages which it typically sells or securitizes within one month of origination. The company serves consumers directly through its Texas-based call center; it also offers its products through wholesalers. The firm has seen rapid growth as a result of its expanding servicing portfolio.

Operations
Nationstar's services include servicing origination and real estate services. Its integrated loan origination business mitigates servicing portfolio runoff and improves credit performance for investors. Additionally the company's suite of ancillary businesses (Solutionstar) offers asset management processing title settlement valuation and appraisal services. The company services mortgage loans in all 50 US states and it is licensed as a residential mortgage loan servicer/originator and debt collector in all states that require such licensing.

Financial Performance
In 2013 Nationstar's revenues increased by 117% due to higher fee income (driven by an increase in average UPB for loans serviced) and a gain on mortgage loans held for sale (the result of a 204% increase in the amount of loans originated and an rise in the value of servicing capitalized due to the larger volume of loan sales and subsequent retention of mortgage servicing rights) partially offset by the lower margins on loans sold.After enjoying two straight years of profits in 2013 the company's net income grew by a further 6% due to interest income and gain on interest rate swaps and caps.That year the company posted cash outflow of $1.83 billion (compared to $1.96 billion in 2012) primarily due to a growth in mortgage loan origination and a change in current assets and liabilities as a result of a drop in accounts receivables and other assets.

Strategy
Nationstar sees opportunity in the weakened credit markets as it has been successful managing portfolios of higher-risk loans. Its high-touch approach an area in which the big banks tends to lack is well-suited to handling riskier loans. The firm has seen rapid growth as a result of its expanding servicing portfolio; it has added about a dozen new servicing clients in the past three years. Also by originating loans in-house Nationstar is further able to boost its servicing portfolio largely by offering borrowers refinancing options.

In 2013 major home builder KB Home and Nationstar agreed to form Home Community Mortgage to offer an array of mortgage banking services to KB Home's customers.

Since its 2102 IPO Nationstar has also been on a buying spree.

Mergers and Acquisitions
In 2013 the company acquired $97 billion in residential mortgage serving rights and certain other assets from Bank of America and agreed to acquire the mortgage origination business of Greenlight Financial Services for up to $75 million.

That year it also acquired Equifax Settlement Services Holding LLC (ESS) from Equifax. ESS is a leading provider of appraisal title insurance and settlement services in the US and serves a broad array of blue chip clients including the largest financial institutions in the country. Nationstar combined ESS with its Solutionstar platform and rebranded ESS as Solutionstar Settlement Services.

Company Background
In March 2012 the company raised $247 million through the initial public offering which coincided with the economy's modest recovery. Nationstar plans to use the money to grow its mortgage servicing portfolio.

Shortly after its public offering it purchased the servicing assets of Aurora Loan Services a subsidiary of Aurora Bank for $268 million. The deal included $63 billion in residential mortgages. As part of the transaction affiliate Newcastle Investment paid $170 million to receive a portion of the servicing rights to the Aurora portfolio.

Once a subsidiary of homebuilder Centex Nationstar Mortgage was acquired by Fortress Investment Group in 2006. At the time of the transaction which was valued at some $575 million Nationstar Mortgage (then named Centex Home Equity) was a subprime lender. Like many of its peers Nationstar Mortgage exited the subprime lending business in late 2007 thereby focusing on its servicing activities.

Fortress Investment Group owns about 80% of Nationstar.

EXECUTIVES

EVP Portfolio Investments, Amar R. Patel, $275,000 total compensation

Assistant Vice President Customer, Mark Wilson, age 60

President and COO, Harold Lewis, $380,192 total compensation

CEO, Jay Bray, $450,000 total compensation

EVP and CFO, David C. Hisey, $316,828 total compensation

EVP Corporate Development and Investor Relations, Marshall Murphy

EVP and General Counsel, Anthony W. Villani

EVP and Chief Risk Officer, Ramesh Lakshminarayanan, $190,001 total compensation

Interim Senior Vice President Info Tech, Brian Tutt

Vice President Finance, Daniel Brown

Senior Vice President, Chris Scheetz

Assistant Vice President Servicing, Caroline Cranz

Vice President Underwriting, Teresa Reber

Senior Vice President Investor Acct, Scott Clark

Vice President Operations Planning Perf, Brian Brown

Assistant Vice President Secondary Mkt, Greg Neal

Vice President Tactical Initiatives, Dee Ann Cox

Vice President Of Human Resources, Beth Davis

Sr Vice President Comp Benefits Human, John Lee

Senior Vice President, Brian Stock

Vice President Vendor Pcmt Governance, Ron Ausemus

Senior Vice President, Steve Lichti

Vice President Loss Mitigation, Michael McCollum

Assistant Vice President Spcl Projects, Alan Brodie

Vice President Human Resources, Brett Gerber

Claims Vice President Default Claims, Erin Landry

Assistant Vice President, Thomas Leflore

Assistant Vice President Advance Mgmt, Michael Jansson

Vice President, Parkson Young

Vice President Human Resources, Jennifer Winters

Assistant Vice President Txn Mgmt, Shelly Epp

Senior Vice President Structured, Pedro Alvarez

Vice President Instructional Dsgn Lms, Mike Schellen

Vice President Default Operations, Jorge Valadez

Vice President Of Portfolio Management, Kenneth Hill

Executive Vice President, Stacy Hodges

Assistant Vice President Investor Rpt, Justin Henry

Sr Vice President Prop Preservation, Dawn Campos

Assistant Vice President, Jonathan Hrubetz

Assistant Vice President Foreclosure, Jill Cruz

Assistant Vice President Repurchase, Carol Harms

Sr Vice President Originations Chief, Juan Gonzalez

Senior Vice President Cash Management, Shannon Clay

Vice President Change Of Law Manager, Tiffany Chinchurreta

Vice President Human Resources, Nichole Moseley

Vice President Sales, Jeff Puckett

Assistant Vice President Acquisitions, Nina Barron

Senior Vice President, Patrick Couture

Assistant Vice President Talent Acq, Tony Benware

Vice President, Steve Safavi

Assistant Vice President Customer Rel, Phillip Montes

Senior Vice President Operations, Shelli Pannell

Senior Vice President Strategy, Kent Lemon

Vice President Quality Assurance, Jason Devoney

Assistant Vice President, Thomas Brown

Performance Enhancement Vice President, Latrice Collins

Assistant Vice President, Manasseh Kamau

Vice President Secondary Marketing, Les Blotsky

Assistant Vice President Internal Audit, Larissa Turner

Vice President And General Counsel, Jason Wiley

Assistant Vice President, Tatiana Vakidis

Assistant Vice President Quality, Thu Nguyen

Asst Vice President Investor Rel Corp, Megan Portacci

Assistant Vice President Claims, Ryan White

Vice President Originations Training, Michael Reilly

Assistant Vice President Cpa, Adam Rice

Vice President Strategic Sourcing, Kent Knox

Senior Vice President Corporate Comm, John Hoffmann

Vice President Tax, John Vincze

Senior Vice President Marketing, John Milligan

Assistant Vice President Customer Rel, Josh Taylor

Assistant Vice President, Michael Stubbe

Asst Vice President Ops Mgr Dir Ops, Eric Field

Assistant Vice President Dflt Ops Rpt, Tommy Sunny

Assistant Vice President Revrs, Tanna Vazquez

Assistant Vice President Marketing, Ryan Larson

Assistant Vice President, Samantha Shiller

Assistant Vice President Acquisitions, Tonia Conner

Assistant Vice President Discharged, Kirk Ensign

Senior Vice President Training Emp Dev, Jon Briggs

Assistant Vice President General, Maria Belfield

Asst Vice President Revrs Mort Investor, Theresa Chase

Vice President Finance, Ken Archer

Assistant Vice President Info Tech Pmo, Kris Kinard

Corp Vice President Real Est Facilities, Doug Gordon

Vice President And Associate General, Beth Gormley

Vice President Human Resources, Humera Kassem

Vice President And Associate General, Ella Namaksy

Vice President Servicing, Noah Heldt

Vice President Loss Mitigation, Charles Nutter

Senior Vice President Financial, Bill Wilson

Assistant Vice President Accounting, Elizabeth Truong

Assistant Vice President Due Diligence, Julia Longsworth

Assistant Vice President Associate, Adrienne Kvello

Assistant Vice President Vendor, Paul Boone

Assistant Vice President Of Finance, Diana Ahmeti

Senior Vice President Core Servicing, Courtney Ehinger

Vice President Compensation, Dave Alderton

Senior Vice President Human Resources, Eric Austin

Assistant Vice President Finance, Santhi Gullapalli

Assistant Vice President Leadership, Curtis Brooks

Assistant Vice President Origination, Billy Allen

Senior Vice President Process, Craig Mundhenk

Assistant Vice President Government, David Perez

Assistant Vice President Servicing, Matt Drottz

Assistant Vice President Training, Lynley Vansingel

Vice President Finance, Brandonn Dukes

Assistant Vice President Customer, Jody Windhorst

Assistant Vice President Fnma Investor, Craig Gonzales

E Vice President Of Capital Planning, John Draghi

Assistant Vice President Customer, Ashley Ragan

Assistant Vice President Risk, Chris Joles

Assistant Vice President Compliance, Cherise Hubbard

Assistant Vice President Marketing, Fan Chen

Assistant Vice President Compliance, Renae Cobb

Assistant Vice President Litigated, Alan Flanagan

Assistant Vice President Credit Risk, Jason Swann

Executive Vice President, Chad Patton

Assistant Vice President, David Eastin

Vice President, Adam Wood

Vice President, Greg Self

Vice President, Ron Thomas

Assistant Vice President, Brenna Diffey

Assistant Vice President, Danielle Lally

Vice President, Scott Moss

Assistant Vice President, Bryan Minassian

Vice President, Joel Gendron

Assistant Vice President, Brent Gillen

Executive Vice President Chief, Caitlin Deyoung

Assistant Vice President, John Spurgin

Vice President, Alexander Baren

Assistant Vice President, Erin Johnson

Auditors: Ernst&YoungLLP

LOCATIONS

HQ: Nationstar Mortgage Holdings Inc
350 Highland Drive, Lewisville, TX 75067
Phone: 469 549-2000
Web: www.nationstarholdings.com

PRODUCTS/OPERATIONS

2013 Sales

	$ mil.	% of total
Servicing fees	1084.2	47
Gain on mortgages held for sale	702.8	31
Other fees	300.0	13
Interest income	197.2	9
Gain on interest rate swaps and caps	3.1	-
Total	**2287.3**	**100**

COMPETITORS

Bank of America	Stonegate Mortgage
CitiMortgage	Synovus Mortgage
DHI Mortgage	UAMC
GMAC Mortgage	Wells Fargo Home
JPMorgan Chase	Mortgage
PHH Mortgage	

HISTORICAL FINANCIALS

Company Type: Public

Income Statement

FYE: December 31

	REVENUE ($ mil.)	NET INCOME ($ mil.)	NET PROFIT MARGIN	EMPLOYEES
12/13	2,086.9	217.0	10.4%	6,984
12/12	984.3	205.2	20.9%	4,672
12/11	377.7	20.8	5.5%	2,599
12/10	261.4	(9.9)	—	0
12/09	78.8	(80.8)	—	0
Annual Growth	**126.8%**	—	—	—

2013 Year-End Financials

Debt ratio: 82.9%	No. of shares (mil.): 90
Return on equity: 24.9%	Dividends
Cash ($ mil.): 441	Yield: —
Current ratio: 5.10	Payout: —
Long-term debt ($ mil.): 11,637	Market value ($ mil.): 3,332

	STOCK PRICE ($) FY Close	P/E High/Low		PER SHARE ($) Earnings	Dividends	Book Value
12/13	36.96	24	13	2.40	0.00	10.92
12/12	30.98	15	6	2.40	0.00	8.38
Annual Growth	**19.3%**	—	—	**(0.0%)**	—	**30.4%**

Natus Medical Inc.

Natus Medical designs and manufactures audiological and neurological diagnostic and screening products. While the company's focus has historically been on infants (newborn hearing screening neonatal monitoring) it has expanded its product line to include an array of screening and diagnostic systems for use with children and adults. Its systems detect such neurological conditions as epilepsy and balance and sleep disorders. Natus also manufactures newborn and infant care products to diagnose and treat brain injury and jaundice. The company sells its wares worldwide through a direct sales force and distributors.

Operations

Natus Medical technically operates in one reportable segment —health care products for the screening detection treatment and monitoring of medical ailments in newborn care hearing impairment neurological dysfunction epilepsy sleep disorders and balance and mobility disorders. Within that segment Natus sells devices which generally generate non-recurring revenue and supplies and services which generally generate recurring revenue.

Geographic Reach

The company sells its products in more than 100 countries worldwide. The US contributes about 60% of Natus' revenues.

Sales and Marketing

Natus Medical sells in the US primarily through a direct sales force though certain products are sold under private-label and distribution arrangements. Internationally the company sells some products through direct sales channels in Canada French and German speaking parts of Europe Denmark and parts of Latin America. Other products are sold in those markets and other international markets through distributors who purchase products from Natus and resell them to end users or sub-distributors. End users include hospitals clinics labs physicians nurses audiologists and government agencies.

Strategy

Natus Medical has been an acquisitive company since 2003 and on average makes one to two strategic acquisitions per year. More recent acquisitions include the 2013 purchase of the Grass Technologies Product Group from Astro-Med for $18.6 million in cash which builds upon Natus' 2011 acquisition of Denver-based Embla Systems for $16.6 million in cash; both deals broaden Natus' existing diagnostic sleep analysis (polysomnography or PSG) product portfolio.

The company made a slightly larger acquisition in 2012 when it bought neurodiagnostic and monitoring products maker Nicolet from CareFusion for $58 million. The purchase added Nicolet's portfolio of electroencephalography (EEG) and electromyography (EMG) systems and related accessories as well as vascular and obstetric Doppler sensors and connectivity products.

Prior to that Natus bought Argentina-based Medix for $14.1 million in cash to add infant incubators to its newborn product lineup.

Financial Performance

The company's acquisitions of Embla and Nicolet helped boost revenue by 25% in 2012. Sales of other products dropped partly due to a change in sales emphasis. Natus continues to struggle with a number of challenges that are affecting its operating results including macro factors like the slow post-recession recovery in the US and the unprece-dented sovereign debt crisis that has impacted health care spending within the European Union. Natus is heavily dependent on both of these markets and saw declines in its business in these regions.

EXECUTIVES

President and CEO, James B. Hawkins, age 58, $500,000 total compensation

Vice President - Medical Affairs; Quality & Regulatory, Christopher Chung

VP and General Manager Newborn Care, Kenneth M. Traverso, age 53, $302,875 total compensation

VP Medical Affairs Quality and Regulatory, D. Christopher Chung, age 50, $257,000 total compensation

SVP and CFO, Jonathan A. Kennedy, age 43, $350,000 total compensation

VP and General Manager Neurology, Austin Noll, $265,000 total compensation

VP Global Engineering, Ajay A. Bhave

Vice President Of Sales, Marybeth Smith

Senior Vice President Sales, Stephanie Parenti

Vice President Opeartions, Robert Moss

Vice President International Sales, Thomas Dilworth

Chairman, Robert A. (Bob) Gunst, age 65

Board Member, Franco Avolio

Auditors: Deloitte&ToucheLLP

LOCATIONS

HQ: Natus Medical Inc.
6701 Koll Center Parkway, Suite 120, Pleasanton, CA 94566
Phone: 925 223-6700
Web: www.natus.com

2012 Sales

	$ mil.	% of total
US	163.0	56
Other countries	129.3	44
Total	**292.3**	**100**

PRODUCTS/OPERATIONS

2012 Sales

	% of total
Devices & systems	60
Supplies & services	39
Other	1
Total	**100**

2012 Sales by Product

	% of total
Neurology	56
Newborn care & other	44
Total	**100**

Selected Acquisitions

2012
Nicolet ($58 million; Middleton WI; neurodiagnostic and monitoring products)
2011
Embla Systems ($16.6 million; Denver; diagnostic sleep analysis and home testing devices)
2010
Medix ($14.1 million; Argentina; newborn incubators for hospitals and ambulances)

Selected Products

ALGO (newborn hearing screeners)
ABaer (newborn hearing screener)
Ceegraph VISION (neurodiagnostic monitor)
Echo-Screen (hearing screener)
EquiTest (balance disorder devices)
Navigator (diagnostic hearing system)
neoBLUE (treatment for newborn jaundice)
Oxydome (newborn oxygen tent)
Sleepscan (diagnostic sleep analysis system)

Selected Subsidiaries

Alpine ApS (Denmark)
Deltamed S.A. (France)
Embla Systems LLC (US)
Excel Tech Ltd. (aka Xltek Canada)
Medix I.C.S.A. (Argentina)
Natus Europe Gmbh (dba Fischer-Zoth Diagnosesysteme & Schwarzer Neurology. Germany)
Natus Medical Incorporated (US)
Natus Nicolet Ireland Ltd.

COMPETITORS

Astro-Med	Electrical Geodesics
Bio-logic	GE Healthcare
CAS Medical	Johnson & Johnson
CareFusion	Medela
Cleveland Medical	Starkey Laboratories
Deroyal Industries	Welch Allyn
Drägerwerk	

HISTORICAL FINANCIALS

Company Type: Public

Income Statement

FYE: December 31

	REVENUE ($ mil.)	NET INCOME ($ mil.)	NET PROFIT MARGIN	EMPLOYEES
12/13	344.1	22.8	6.6%	943
12/12	292.2	3.8	1.3%	1,028
12/11	232.6	(11.7)	—	835
12/10	218.6	11.9	5.5%	750
12/09	166.5	11.0	6.7%	635
Annual Growth	**19.9%**	**19.9%**	**—**	**10.4%**

2013 Year-End Financials

Debt ratio: 8.9%
Return on equity: 7.9%
Cash ($ mil.): 56
Current ratio: 2.46
Long-term debt ($ mil.): 27

No. of shares (mil.): 31
Dividends
Yield: —
Payout: —
Market value ($ mil.): 707

	STOCK PRICE ($) FY Close	P/E High/Low		PER SHARE ($) Earnings	Dividends	Book Value
12/13	22.50	30	15	0.74	0.00	9.75
12/12	11.16	103	76	0.13	0.00	8.93
12/11	9.43	—	—	(0.41)	0.00	8.75
12/10	14.18	43	28	0.41	0.00	9.10
12/09	14.79	42	17	0.39	0.00	8.57
Annual Growth	**11.1%**			**17.4%**	**—**	**3.3%**

NCI Building Systems, Inc.

NCI's buildings are quite a "steel." NCI Building Systems also known as NCI Group engineers designs manufactures and distributes metal buildings and components (doors roofs walls and trim) for nonresidential construction markets in North America. It sells its products to contractors developers and builders. The group also provides steel coil coating which is used by manufacturers of HVAC systems lighting fixtures and appliances. NCI has about 30 manufacturing facilities in the US and Mexico; it also operates distribution and sales offices in the US and Canada. Investment firm Clayton Dubilier & Rice owns NCI Group.

After a few turbulent years brought on by the economic downturn NCI is begining to recover despite continued declines in the nonresidential construction sector. NCI has restructured itself financially and organizationally in order to cope with significantly lower sales (as compared to prerecession figures).

To grow its metal buildings and components operations –the heaviest hit in the economic downturn —NCI is expanding into new markets. The company has converted one plant to an insulated panel systems manufacturing facility and is converting others. The company also is broadening its reach in its coatings group by diversifying its customer base to include the lighting appliance and HVAC sectors.

NCI is also weighing cost-saving opportunities including acquisitions and automation. In 2012 the company bought insulated panel supplier Metl-Span from BlueScope Steel for $145 million.

Revenues increased by 10% in 2011. NCI's returned to profitability that year and gross profit margin expanded by more than 20%. The improved results were attributed to an uptick in demand from manufacturing energy and mining customers. The company's components group posted good results in 2011. Strong demand for insulated metal panels rollup doors and agricultural products helped increase sales in that segment. NCI's buildings segment also experienced improved results in 2011. The company made several upgrades to its buildings operations that helped lower costs and improve delivery times. There also were more design/build projects up for bid in 2011. The coil coatings segment also experienced an increase in sales.

HISTORY

NCI Building Systems' founder Johnie Schulte Jr. began his career in the mid-1950s when he landed a job punching and shearing metal building pieces in Houston. In 1984 he founded NCI. The enterprise made only metal building components until 1987 when it began making metal buildings. That year NCI had sales of about $2 million. The company went public in 1992 and a year later its sales had reached more than $130 million. While competitors were shuttering plants in the soft market of the early 1990s NCI was buying companies —including its 1992 purchase of A&S Building Systems a metal building maker based in Caryville Tennessee. NCI later expanded its product line to include self-storage buildings. It entered the market for roll-up steel overhead doors in 1995 when it bought Doors & Building Components (also a maker of interior steel parts) and started its own line of steel-frame homes.

The company continued to make acquisitions in 1996 picking up a metal stud plant in Texas from Alabama Metal Industries the equipment of Carlisle Engineered Metals and Mesco Metal Buildings. The next year it bought the rest of Carlisle including a manufacturing plant in Alabama and began a 51%-owned joint venture in Mexico to manufacture framing systems. NCI bought the US metal building components business of UK-based BTR in 1998 for $593 million doubling its size and adding painting and coating capabilities. The company spent 1999 integrating the large business.

NCI bought out Consolidated System's share in their DOUBLECOTE metal coil-coating joint venture for $26 million in 2000. Later that year NCI bought Midland Metals a maker of metal building components. The move strengthened NCI's presence in the Midwest.

In 2001 NCI sold its 50% interest in Midwest Metal Coatings to its joint venture partner. The company closed five manufacturing facilities during the first quarter of fiscal 2002. NCI launched into direct selling to the public by opening a series of NCI Metal Depot retail factory stores that offer commercial and residential metal components (metal roof and wall panels light structural and tubing shapes and accessories) and a variety of small metal building packages (carports storage sheds and other metal buildings).

The company opened two retail stores in Texas in fiscal 2003. Also that year NCI entered the residential garage door market by acquiring Texas-based Able Manufacturing and Wholesale Garage Door Company for about $3.3 million. NCI shortened the company's name to Able Door Manufacturing. Able operates distribution centers in the Dallas Atlanta and Oklahoma City areas and Ontario California.

Founder president and CEO Johnie Schulte Jr. retired as an executive in November 2003 and retired as a director the next year; he was succeeded by A. R. Ginn. The following year NCI filed a suit against Schulte alleging he had violated non-competitive agreements. Schulte filed a countersuit; an undisclosed settlement was reached in 2005.

To expand its retail and builder distribution channels for its small engineered buildings NCI bought North Little Rock Arkansas-based Heritage Building Systems and Steelbuilding.com for approximately $30 million in 2004. NCI also acquired the 49% minority stake held by its partners in its manufacturing plant in Monterrey Mexico.

The next year NCI bought the intellectual property rights of metal building and components maker STEELOX Systems of Ohio gaining the patents and trademarks copyrights common law rights names logos websites and customer lists of the established (by more than 70 years) company.

In 2006 NCI paid $370 million in cash for metal buildings maker Robertson-Ceco Corporation and its Robertson Building Systems Ceco Building Systems Star Building Systems and Steelspec divisions. Late that year Ginn stepped down as CEO with president and COO Norm Chambers becoming president and CEO. The next year Chambers assumed the chairmanship. NCI also bought Garco Building Systems in 2007.

EXECUTIVES

Vp Corporate Development, Mark T Golladay, age 52
Vice President Of Human Resources, Rick Morrow
Vice President - Finance; Chief Accounting Officer, Richard W Allen, age 40
Vice President Of Sales, Dan Happel
President Metal Components Division, Mark W. Dobbins, age 55, $320,000 total compensation
Chairman President and CEO, Norman C. (Norm) Chambers, age 65, $750,000 total compensation
EVP General Counsel and Corporate Secretary, Todd R. Moore, age 55, $300,250 total compensation
EVP and CIO, Eric J. Brown, age 57
President NCI Buildings and Robertson-Ceco Divisions, Bradley D. (Brad) Robeson, age 52, $300,250 total compensation
EVP CFO and Treasurer, Mark E. Johnson, age 48, $346,000 total compensation
President Metal Coil Coatings, John L. Kuzdal, age 49
President Group Business Segments, Don Riley
Vice President Internal Audit, Lisa Santiago
Vice President Of Corporate Marketing, Brooke Yep
Vice President Treasury, Mimi Siracusa

Vice President, Fred Schubert
Vice President Environmental Affairs, Todd Harbour
Vice President Supply Chain Management, Dan Ronchetto
Vice President Controller, Mark Greer
Vice President Technical Services, Jerry Williams
Vice President Engineering, Stephen Heil
Vice President Internal Audit Services, Laura Santiago
Vice President, Brad Johnson
Vice President Finance, Chico Doughtie
Chairman President and CEO, Norman C. (Norm) Chambers, age 65
EVP General Counsel and Corporate Secretary, Todd R. Moore, age 55
EVP CFO and Treasurer, Mark E. Johnson, age 48
Auditors: Ernst&YoungLLP

LOCATIONS

HQ: NCI Building Systems, Inc.
10943 N. Sam Houston Parkway W., Houston, TX 77064
Phone: 281 897-7788
Web: www.ncilp.com

PRODUCTS/OPERATIONS

2011 Sales by Segment

	$ mil.	% of total
Engineered building systems	548.6	46
Metal components	437.7	37
Metal coil coating	201.1	17
Adjustments	(227.8)	-
Total	**959.6**	**100**

Selected Brands

A&S
All American
American Building Components (ABC)
Ceco
Doors and Buildings Components (DBCI)
Garco
Heritage
IPS
MBCI
Metallic
Metal Coaters
Metal Depots
Metal Prep
Mesco
Mid-West Steel
Star
SteelBuilding.com
Steel Systems

Selected Subsidiaries

Building Systems de México S.A. de C.V.
NCI Group Inc.
Robertson Building Systems Limited (Canada)
Robertson-Ceco II Corporation
Steelbuilding.com Inc.

Selected Products and Services

Metal building components and complete buildings (carports utility buildings etc.)
Metal cladding and accessories
Mini-storage buildings
Modular offices
Roll-up doors partitions and panels

COMPETITORS

American Buildings	Gibraltar Industries
Berger Building Products	Horton Homes
Berlin Steel	Johns Manville
Butler Manufacturing	Nucor
Design Components	Overhead Door
G-I Holdings	Varco Pruden Buildings
	Williams Scotsman

HISTORICAL FINANCIALS

Company Type: Public

Income Statement

FYE: November 2

	REVENUE ($ mil.)	NET INCOME ($ mil.)	NET PROFIT MARGIN	EMPLOYEES
11/14	1,371.8	11.1	0.8%	4,556
11/13*	1,309.4	(12.8)	—	4,484
10/12	1,154.0	4.9	0.4%	4,293
10/11	959.5	(9.9)	—	3,590
10/10	870.5	(26.8)	—	3,606
Annual Growth	12.0%	—	—	6.0%

*Fiscal year change

2014 Year-End Financials

Debt ratio: 31.0%	No. of shares (mil.): 73
Return on equity: 4.4%	Dividends
Cash ($ mil.): 66	Yield: —
Current ratio: 1.59	Payout: —
Long-term debt ($ mil.): 233	Market value ($ mil.): 1,461

	STOCK PRICE ($) FY Close	P/E High/Low	PER SHARE ($) Earnings	Dividends	Book Value
11/14	19.87	141 97	0.15	0.00	3.35
11/13*	14.45	— —	(0.29)	0.00	3.38
10/12	11.24	— —	(3.81)	0.00	12.25
10/11	9.47	— —	(2.58)	0.00	12.05
10/10	9.91	— —	(17.07)	0.00	13.17
Annual Growth	19.0% (29.0%)	— —	—	—	—

*Fiscal year change

Neenah Paper Inc

Neenah Paper regularly attends US Presidential Inaugurations —as the official invitation that is. Neenah's lineup includes technical products (durable saturated coated-base papers and wall coverings) as well as fine paper (premium writing specialty cover digital finish and stationery). The company operates through Neenah Paper and five subsidiaries; each handles select activities such as mills real estate and manufacturing assets and trademarks. Neenah products are sold under several brand names such as CAPITOL BOND NEUTECH and ENVIRONMENT (fine paper) as well as KIMDURA and SoftStretch (technical) among others. Customers are global paper distributors converters and specialty companies.

Geographic Reach

Headquartered in Georgia Neenah sells its products in more than 70 countries.

Operations

The paper producer boasts manufacturing operations in the US and in Germany. The US accounted for some 70% of its 2013 revenue.

Sales and Marketing

Neenah sells its products worldwide primarily to authorized paper distributors converters major national retailers and specialty companies the likes of Staples Office Depot OfficeMax and Wal-Mart. Indeed more than 400 wholesale distributors and retail paper stores are authorized to sell Neenah's premium uncoated printing papers.

The company's premium writing text and cover papers and specialty papers are used in both commercial printing and imaging applications for corporate identity packages invitations personal sta-

tionery and upscale advertising as well as for premium labels and luxury packaging.

Strategy

Neenah is looking for new customers by expanding its portfolio of products and by extending its reach into new geographic regions. To this end the company's working to enter adjacent markets that are growing and profitable. In 2013 for example Neenah rolled out the Design Collection which comprises 11 paper brands that blend half a dozen paper lines from North America and five from Italy.

The company also makes strategic acquisitions. In 2014 Neenah bought Crane Technical Materials from upscale paper firm Crane & Co. for $72 million renaming the Crane entity Neenah Technical Materials. Technical lines which are manufactured in Michigan and Germany include filtration component materials tape graphics and identification and wall covering. The segment is anticipated to continue to grow at a faster and more profitable rate as demand in niche technical markets evolves and sales volume and operating scale efficiencies improve.

EXECUTIVES

VP Sales and Marketing Fine Paper, Julie Schertell, age 45, $264,000 total compensation
VP Sales and Marketing, James H. Caudill, age 50
President CEO and Director, John ODonnell
Vice President Customer And Market Services, Cindy Hanson
Vp Human Resources, Richard F Read
Vice President Marketing Technical Products, Steve Rosenberg
Vice President Operations, Robert McDonald
Chairman, Sean T. Erwin, age 63
Board Member, O Everbach
Auditors: Deloitte&ToucheLLP

LOCATIONS

HQ: Neenah Paper Inc
3460 Preston Ridge Road, Alpharetta, GA 30005
Phone: 678 566-6500
Web: www.neenah.com

2013 Sales

	$ mil.	% of total
US	564.4	67
Europe	280.1	33
Total	844.5	100

PRODUCTS/OPERATIONS

2013 Sales

	$ mil.	% of total
Technical Products	416.1	49
Fine Paper	401.8	48
Other	26.6	3
Total	844.5	100

Selected Products & Brands

Technical products
Gessner
JET-PRO
KIMDURA
MUNISING LP
NEENAH
PREVAIL
SofStretch
varitess
Fine paper
CAPITOL BOND
CLASSIC
CLASSIC CREST
ENVIRONMENT
ESSE
NEENAH
NEUTECH

STARWHITE
SUNDANCE
UV/ULTRA II

COMPETITORS

Ahlstrom	International Paper
Appleton Coated	MeadWestvaco
ArjoWiggins	Mohawk Fine Papers
Arkwright	NewPage
Cascades Inc.	Resolute Forest
Central Lewmar	Products
Domtar	Tembec
FiberMark North	Wausau Paper
America	West Linn Paper
Hollingsworth and Vose	

HISTORICAL FINANCIALS

Company Type: Public

Income Statement

FYE: December 31

	REVENUE ($ mil.)	NET INCOME ($ mil.)	NET PROFIT MARGIN	EMPLOYEES
12/13	844.5	52.0	6.2%	1,875
12/12	808.8	44.3	5.5%	1,870
12/11	696.0	29.1	4.2%	1,635
12/10	657.7	159.1	24.2%	1,660
12/09	573.9	(1.2)	—	1,700
Annual Growth	10.1%	—	—	2.5%

2013 Year-End Financials

Debt ratio: 31.3%	No. of shares (mil.): 16
Return on equity: 22.3%	Dividends
Cash ($ mil.): 73	Yield: 1.6%
Current ratio: 2.95	Payout: 22.2%
Long-term debt ($ mil.): 190	Market value ($ mil.): 700

	STOCK PRICE ($) FY Close	P/E High/Low	PER SHARE ($) Earnings	Dividends	Book Value
12/13	42.77	14 9	3.12	0.70	16.35
12/12	28.47	11 8	2.68	0.48	12.43
12/11	22.32	12 7	1.81	0.44	11.01
12/10	19.68	2 1	10.21	0.40	10.75
12/09	13.95	— —	(0.08)	0.40	7.34
Annual Growth	32.3%		—	15.0%	22.2%

Neogen Corp.

Bacteriophobes have a friend in Neogen a maker of products for the food safety and animal health markets. Its food safety testing products are used by the food industry to make sure our edibles are clean unspoiled and free of toxins pathogens and allergens. In core markets in the Americas and Europe Neogen reaches end users (including dairies meat processors and animal feed producers) through a direct sales force; it uses distributors elsewhere. On the animal health front Neogen produces drugs vaccines diagnostics and instruments for the veterinary market; it also makes rat poisons and disinfectants used in animal production plants and diagnostic products for research laboratories.

Operations

Some of the company's best-selling food-safety testing products include its Reveal and Alert tests used by meat poultry and seafood processors to detect food-borne bacteria. Others include its Veratox Agre-Screen and Reveal tests which are used by grain producers to detect mycotoxins (toxins produced by fungi).

When it comes to animals lead products include PanaKare a digestive aid; RenaKare a supplement for potassium deficiency in cats and dogs; and the NeogenVet brand including Vita-15 and Liver 7 which are used for the treatment and prevention of nutritional deficiencies in horses. Sales in its Animal Safety unit accounted for more than half of Neogen's revenue in 2014.

Geographic Reach

The firm's animal products are sold to distributors around the world as well as through farm supply retailers in North America. International sales of all of its products account for about 40% of Neogen's sales.

The company has manufacturing plants in Michigan Kentucky Wisconsin Colorado North Carolina and Iowa as well as in Scotland.

Financial Analysis

Neogen continued its growth trend by reporting a 19% increase in revenues from $184 million to $247 million in 2014 due to strong product sales in both the food safety and animal safety segments. Part of the growth was from two acquisitions in the Animal Health segment. Net income also rose from $27 million to $28 million a 4% uptick on the strength of the strong revenue growth. Cash flow which has fluctuated in the past few years dropped $5 million from $27 million in 2014.

Strategy

Though the company has primarily used acquisitions to achieve relatively rapid growth Neogen is also looking for organic growth over the longer term through new product introductions higher sales of existing products and international expansion efforts. Neogen has ongoing development projects for new diagnostic tests and other complementary products for both the food safety and animal safety markets. The company also sees its over-the-counter animal health products as being particularly ripe for growth and because of that it seeks to increase its line of rodenticides disinfectants instruments and horse care products.

Mergers and Acquisitions

Neogen strengthened its diagnostic test development operations in 2012 by acquiring the assets of the Igenity animal genomics business from Merial Limited. Igenity had previously operated as a lab partner with GeneSeek to identify cattle traits. The company also widened its equine antibiotic offerings through the acquisition of Macleod Pharmaceuticals later that year. In 2013 it purchased the assets of veterinary instruments firm SyrVet and of Prima Tech.

The following year it picked up pest control manufacturing firm Chem-Tech for $17 million.

EXECUTIVES

Chairman of the Board; Chief Executive Officer, James L. Herbert, age 74, $310,000 total compensation
Chief Financial Officer; Vice President, Steven J. (Steve) Quinlan, age 51
President and COO, Richard E. (Rick) Calk
Director Industry Affairs and Hacco Operations, Keith Creagh
Vice President, Terri Juricic
Vice President - Animal Safety Operations, Terri A Morrical, age 50
National Accounts Manager, Lisa Peterson
Senior Vice President, Anna Quain

Chairman of the Board; Chief Executive Officer, James L. Herbert, age 74
Auditors: Ernst&YoungLLP

LOCATIONS

HQ: Neogen Corp.
620 Lesher Place, Lansing, MI 48912
Phone: 517 372-9200 **Fax:** 517 372-0108
Web: www.neogen.com

2014 Sales

	% of total
US	61
Other countries	39
Total	**100**

PRODUCTS/OPERATIONS

2014 Sales

	$ mil.	% of total
Animal safety	131.1	53
Food safety	116.3	47
Total	**247.4**	**100**

2014 Sales

	$ mil.	% of total
Food safety		
Natural toxins allergans drug residues	60.3	24
Dry culture media and other	31.1	14
Bacterial and general sanitation	24.9	10
Animal safety		
Rodenticides and disinfectants	36.7	15
Animal care & other	35.6	14
Veterinary instruments	28.4	11
DNA testing	22.9	9
Life sciences & other	7.5	3
Total	**247.4**	**100**

Selected Products

Food safety
AccuClean (detects proteins and sugars)
AccuPoint (rapid sanitation test)
AgriScreen (detects mycotoxins)
Alert (detects food-borne bacteria food allergens)
Beta Star (detects antibiotics in milk)
BioKits (detects allergens in food; also used for species identification)
GeneQuence (detects food-borne bacteria)
Reveal (detects food-borne bacteria food allergens ruminant by-products)
Soleris (detects spoilage organisms)
Veratox (detects mycotoxins food allergens)
Animal safety
AgTek (Kane) products (apparel accessories etc.)
BioSentry (chemicals)
CyKill (rodent control)
Di-Kill (rodent control)
ElectroJac (automated semen collection)
Havoc (rodenticide)
Ideal (animal health products and instruments)
NeogenVet (animal health products)
Prozap (rodenticide)
Ramik (rodenticide)
Rodex (rodenticide)
Squire (animal health products)

COMPETITORS

American Animal Health	Merck
Bayer Animal Health	Merck Animal Health
Bioniche Life Sciences	Merial
Celldex Therapeutics	Novartis
Ecolab	Orchid Cellmark
Eurofins Scientific	Pfizer
Hartz Mountain	Phibro Animal Health
Heska	Silliker
IDEXX Labs	Strategic Diagnostics
Life Technologies Corporation	Virbac Corporation

HISTORICAL FINANCIALS

Company Type: Public

Income Statement

FYE: May 31

	REVENUE ($ mil.)	NET INCOME ($ mil.)	NET PROFIT MARGIN	EMPLOYEES
05/14	247.4	28.1	11.4%	926
05/13	207.5	27.1	13.1%	781
05/12	184.0	22.5	12.2%	746
05/11	172.6	22.8	13.2%	654
05/10	140.5	17.5	12.5%	585
Annual Growth	**15.2%**	**12.6%**	**—**	**12.2%**

2014 Year-End Financials

Debt ratio: — No. of shares (mil.): 36
Return on equity: 9.9% Dividends
Cash ($ mil.): 40 Yield: —
Current ratio: 7.56 Payout: —
Long-term debt ($ mil.): — Market value ($ mil.): 1,388

	STOCK PRICE ($) FY Close	P/E High/Low	PER SHARE ($) Earnings	Dividends	Book Value
05/14	37.79	93 47	0.76	0.00	8.34
05/13	54.47	75 50	0.75	0.00	7.16
05/12	38.94	75 47	0.63	0.00	6.18
05/11	44.84	65 38	0.64	0.00	5.40
05/10	25.71	67 40	0.51	0.00	4.50
Annual Growth	**10.1%**	**— —**	**10.7%**	**—**	**16.7%**

Netgear, Inc.

NETGEAR keeps consumers and small businesses wired and wireless. The company designs a range of networking equipment —adapters hubs routers switches media servers and interfaces —for connecting PCs in home and small business settings to each other and the Internet. (Manufacturing is outsourced to contractors in Asia.) NETGEAR also supplies network-attached storage (NAS) systems VPN firewalls and digital media receivers. It sells through distributors including Ingram Micro and Tech Data and to retailers such as Best Buy Fry's Electronics and RadioShack. The company generates about half of its sales from international markets.

OperationsNETGEAR's products for homes include networking storage and digital media products that connect the Internet with computers and communication and entertainment devices such as smartphones and tablets. Known as its retail segment it accounts for 40% of sales. Broadband service providers which account for about 35% of sales look to NETGEAR for whole home networking products. The company serves the commercial market's networking storage and security needs with products that are less expensive than those traditionally used by large businesses. This segment makes up about 25% of sales.

Geographic Reach

The US is NETGEAR's largest market accounting for more than half of sales. The UK and the rest of the EMEA region contribute 35%. Customers in Asia account for about 10% of sales. Every region except the EMEA (outside the UK) experienced growth in 2012.

NETGEAR has a sales presence in 25 countries. Research and development facilities are located in

China Taiwan and the US (in Atlanta Chicago and San Diego).

Sales and Marketing

NETGEAR's products are sold in some 45000 retail locations around the world and through about 39000 resellers.

It spent $19 million on advertising and promotional expenses in 2012.

Financial Performance

NETGEAR became a billion-dollar company in 2011 and overall revenue grew another 7% in 2012 to $1.2 billion. While sales of home wireless products rose in its retail segment sales of its powerline and home storage products decreased slightly. Broadband service providers however bought plenty of broadband gateway products primarily driven by demand for the Docsis 3.0 line of products.

Profits for 2012 decreased 5% to $86 million primarily due to increased spending on R&D and income taxes. NETGEAR upped its R&D spend by 25% in 2012 to add employees and invest in new software development projects.

StrategyCommitted to expanding internationally the company uses third-party manufacturing services contractors in China Taiwan and Vietnam to produce its equipment. Cameo Communications Delta Networks Hon Hai Precision and Pegatron are currently contracted as manufacturers and NETGEAR also outsources its warehousing and distribution logistics to APL Logistics Americas Kerry Logistics (in the Asia Pacific region) DSV Solutions and ModusLink (in EMEA) and Agility Logistics (in Australia and New Zealand).

NETGEAR has also been focusing product development on connectivity NAS with enhanced user interfaces security DOCSIS 3.0 gateways and 4G/LTE related repeaters and routers.Mergers and Acquisitions

In early 2013 it acquired the AirCard unit of Sierra Wireless for $138 million. AirCard provides mobile broadband service to any computer through a USB port and the deal helps NETGEAR expand into LTE access devices.

In 2012 it paid $24 million for AVAAK which makes wire-free video networking products. NETGEAR believes the acquisition will bolster its retail business products and expand its presence into the smart home market. Also that year it paid $7 million for some intellectual property assets from Firetide to boost its wireless product offerings in its commercial segment and strengthen its market position in the campus wireless LAN market.

In 2011 NETGEAR bought the Customer Networking Solutions (CNS) division of Westell Technologies for about $34 million in cash. The division makes high-speed Internet networking products that allow telephone companies to offer voice data video and other streaming services over existing copper and fiber-optic wires. The acquisition expands NETGEAR's broadband networking product portfolio and its telecom provider customer base in the US.

HISTORY

Originally spun off from communications equipment giant Nortel Networks in 2000 NETGEAR bought out Nortel's remaining stake in 2002.

In 2008 NETGEAR acquired assets from security appliance developer CP Secure and hired engineers from the firm. The purchase of CP Secure's assets expanded its security offerings for small and midsized businesses.

EXECUTIVES

Vice President And General Manager, Paul Tien
Vice President Engineering, Charles Olson
Vice President And General Manager Home, Vivek Pathela
Chairman and CEO, Patrick C.S. Lo, age 57, $697,500 total compensation
Senior Vice President Advanced Engineering, Mark G. Merrill, age 59, $205,961 total compensation
SVP Operations and Support, Michael F. Falcon, age 57, $320,000 total compensation
CFO, Christine M. Gorjanc, age 57, $432,500 total compensation
SVP; General Manager Retail Business Unit, David S. Soares, age 47, $322,500 total compensation
SVP; General Manager Service Provider Business Unit, Michael P. Clegg, age 53, $285,000 total compensation
Chief Information Officer, Patrick Collins
Vice President Of Engineering, Derek Lam
Svp & Gm Commercial Business Unit, John McHugh
Vice President Interal Audit, Lisa Ferrigno
National Account Manager, Peggy Soo
Vice President, Marco Chiappetta
Executive Vice President And Sla, Paul Mah
Senior Vice President Of Corporate Development, Andrew Kim
Vice President Operations And Finance, Joe Burke
Vice President Retailsales, Tom Babula
Vice President, Jeff Shoffeitt
Vice President Engineering, Lily Chang
Vice President Direct Marketing Services, Kevin Casey
Vp Asia Pacific Sales, Ian McLean
Vice President Of Ip And Litigation, Brian Busse
Vice President Legal, Alex Phillips
Vice President Of Engineering, Wei Gao
Vice President Engineering, Steve Burrington
Vice President Of Legal And Corporate, Andrew Thomas
Vice President Sales Spbu, Mark Skurla
Vice President Sales, Mike O'Brien
Vice President, Lan McLean
Vice President, Lee Anthony
Sr Vice President And Cto Service, Jim Kirkpatrick
Vice President Sales Emea, Jean Michel Bielli
Senior Vice President, Deanna Lund
Vice President Rbu Europe, Natale Lavorato
Chairman and CEO, Patrick C.S. Lo, age 57
Auditors: PricewaterhouseCoopersLLP

LOCATIONS

HQ: Netgear, Inc.
350 East Plumeria Drive, San Jose, CA 95134
Phone: 408 907-8000
Web: www.netgear.com

2012 Sales

	$ mil.	% of total
North America		
US	661.0	53
Other	18.4	1
EMEA		
UK	184.4	14
Other	273.3	21
Asia-Pacific	134.8	11
Total	**1271.9**	**100**

PRODUCTS/OPERATIONS

2012 Sales

	$ mil.	% of total
Retail	504.8	40
Service provider	459.2	36
Commercial	307.9	24
Total	**1271.9**	**100**

Selected Products

Broadband access
- Gateways (routers with integrated modems wireless)
- Internet protocol (IP) telephony
- Routers

Ethernet networking
- Adapters
- Bridges
- Network interface cards (NICs)
- Peripheral servers
- Switches
- VPN firewalls

Network connectivity
- Media adapters
- Network-attached storage (NAS)
- Powerline adapters and bridges
- Wireless access points
- Wireless NICs and adapters

COMPETITORS

ARRIS	NetApp
Actiontec	Nokia Siemens Networks
Allied Telesis	Nortel Networks
Apple Inc.	Roku
Aruba Networks	SAFRAN
Barracuda Networks	SMC Corp.
Belkin	Seagate Technology
Buffalo Technology	SonicWALL
Cisco Systems	Technicolor
D-Link	WatchGuard
Dell	Technologies
Fortinet	Western Digital
Hewlett-Packard	ZTE
Huawei Technologies	ZyXEL Communications
Motorola Solutions	

HISTORICAL FINANCIALS

Company Type: Public

Income Statement

FYE: December 31

	REVENUE ($ mil.)	NET INCOME ($ mil.)	NET PROFIT MARGIN	EMPLOYEES
12/13	1,369.6	55.2	4.0%	1,029
12/12	1,271.9	86.5	6.8%	850
12/11	1,181.0	91.3	7.7%	791
12/10	902.0	50.9	5.6%	654
12/09	686.6	9.3	1.4%	586
Annual Growth	**18.8%**	**56.0%**	**—**	**15.1%**

2013 Year-End Financials

Debt ratio: —	No. of shares (mil.): 36
Return on equity: 7.2%	Dividends
Cash ($ mil.): 143	Yield: —
Current ratio: 2.67	Payout: —
Long-term debt ($ mil.): —	Market value ($ mil.): 1,213

	STOCK PRICE ($) FY Close	P/E High/Low		PER SHARE ($) Earnings	Dividends	Book Value
12/13	32.94	28	19	1.42	0.00	21.00
12/12	39.43	19	13	2.27	0.00	19.68
12/11	33.57	18	10	2.41	0.00	16.97
12/10	33.68	25	12	1.41	0.00	13.83
12/09	21.69	83	32	0.27	0.00	11.92
Annual Growth	**11.0%**	**—**	**—**	**51.4%**	**—**	**15.2%**

NetScout Systems Inc

NetScout Systems helps network administrators stay prepared. The company provides systems that monitor and report on the performance of software applications and the networks on which they run. Its probes —monitoring appliances that can be placed throughout a network —allow administrators to collect information about traffic flow and to optimize application and network performance. Its nGenius Service Assurance Solution monitors systems ranging from VoIP communications to customer relationship management applications. NetScout sells directly and through resellers and distributors to corporate and government customers. Founded in 1984 NetScout's technology is used by more than 90% of Fortune 100 companies.

Geographic Reach

Massachusetts-based NetScout Systems rings up about three-quarters of its sales in the US. Europe accounts for more than 10% of sales while countries in Asia represent most of the rest.

Sales and Marketing

Generating about 50% of its revenue through indirect sales channels the network monitoring technology company primarily markets to midsized and large corporate customers including more than 90 FORTUNE 100 companies and about 40 from the FORTUNE Global 200 list. Target industries include financial services health care Internet manufacturing retail technology telecommunications and utilities. Advertising expenses totaled $2.4 million $1.1 million and $273000 in fiscal 2014 2013 and 2012 respectively.

In the public sector NetScout provides professional services for its federal government customers to help them meet the Security Technical Implementation Guides and Trusted Internet Connection specifications.

Financial Performance

NetScout's revenue increased 13% in fiscal 2014 (ended March) versus the prior year to $396.6 million. Net income rose 21% over the same period to $49.1 million. The double-digit uptick in sales was primarily driven by higher product revenue (up 18% year over year) in the US. Sales in Asia and Europe also rose but not as dramatically. Profits rose on higher sales of products and services and the absence of restructuring charges in fiscal 2014. Fiscal 2014 marked the fourth consecutive year of increasing sales and the continued steady rise in profits (with the exception of fiscal 2012) as the firm gains market share amid strong demand from the enterprise and wireless service provider markets.

Cash flow from operations rose for the second consecutive year in fiscal 2014 on a substantial increase in accounts receivable.

Mergers and Acquisitions

In 2014 NetScout agreed to buy portions of Danaher's communications unit for $2.6 billion. NetScout will acquire Tektronix Fluke Networks and Arbor Networks. The deal is to improve NetScout's capability to compete with bigger competitors who offer a wider array of products especially in cyber security and communications services. Not part of the deal are Fluke's data cabling tools and carrier service provider tools businesses.

In late 2012 NetScout acquired privately held New Jersey-based ONPATH Technologies for about $41 million in a strategic move to aggressively expand its leadership position in the network monitoring switch market. (The ONPATH deal built upon NetScout's acquisition and integration of Virginia-based monitoring and switching technology company Simena LLC in late 2011.) In July 2012 NetScout bought voice services and technology assets from Italy's Accanto Systems S.r.l. for $15 million in cash. The technology acquired from Accanto includes all of the Pantera

hardware probes and middleware and session analysis applications to help identify poorly performing devices network quality issues by cell site and service outages.

Previously NetScout acquired IP voice video and telepresence technology provider Psytechnics in 2011 to boost its unified service delivery management operations which includes NGenius.

HISTORY

The company acquired the assets and business of Quantiva a supplier of automated analytics software for application performance management for about $9 million in cash in 2006. The acquisition added technology that automates the process of detecting and diagnosing application performance problems before they impact critical business services.

In 2007 NetScout purchased competitor Network General developer of the Sniffer line of performance and security analysis tools for $206 million. NetScout which developed products based on Sniffer technology prior to the acquisition more than doubled its revenue with the purchase.

EXECUTIVES

V Pres Sales Operations, John W Downing, age 57
Vp Business Development, Bruce Sweet
Vice President Human Resources, Victor P (Vic) Becker, age 62
SVP Services and CIO, Ken Boyd
VP Engineering and Product Development, Ashwani Singhal, $199,000 total compensation
SVP Product Operations, Michael Szabados, age 62, $275,000 total compensation
Chairman President and CEO, Anil K. Singhal, age 60, $325,000 total compensation
VP and CTO, Bruce Kelley
VP and General Manager Packet Flow Switch Business, Brian P. McCann, age 48
SVP and CFO, Jean A. Bua, age 55, $109,102 total compensation
VP Marketing, Steven Shalita
Vice President Of Manufacturing, Joe Wilson
Vice President Sales, Mike Hensley
Vice President Of Operations, Jim Ficaro
National Account Manager, Marc Graziano
Executive Assistance To The Senior Vice President Of Worldwide Sales, Hampson Kim
Vice President World Wide Marketing, Lesley Blume
Chairman President and CEO, Anil K. Singhal, age 60
Auditors: PricewaterhouseCoopersLLP

LOCATIONS

HQ: NetScout Systems Inc
310 Littleton Road, Westford, MA 01886
Phone: 978 614-4000
Web: www.netscout.com

2014 Sales

	$ mil.	% of total
US	303.4	76
Europe	45.8	12
Asia	20.6	5
Rest of world	26.8	7
Total	**396.6**	**100**

PRODUCTS/OPERATIONS

2014 Sales

	$ mil.	% of total
Product	234.2	59
Service	162.4	41
Total	**396.6**	**100**

2014 Sales by Channel

	$ mil.	% of total
Direct	201.1	51
Indirect	195.5	49
Total	**396.6**	**100**

COMPETITORS

Agilent Technologies	JDS Uniphase
Blue Coat	MedTel Services
CA Inc.	NIKSUN
EMC	Resonate Inc.
Fluke Networks	Riverbed Technology
Hewlett-Packard	SolarWinds
IBM	TTI Team Telecom
InfoVista	Tektronix

HISTORICAL FINANCIALS

Company Type: Public

Income Statement

FYE: March 31

	REVENUE ($ mil.)	NET INCOME ($ mil.)	NET PROFIT MARGIN	EMPLOYEES
03/14	396.6	49.1	12.4%	1,021
03/13	350.5	40.6	11.6%	983
03/12	308.6	32.4	10.5%	887
03/11	290.5	37.2	12.8%	845
03/10	260.3	27.9	10.7%	791
Annual Growth	**11.1%**	**15.2%**	**—**	**6.6%**

2014 Year-End Financials

Debt ratio: —
Return on equity: 12.5%
Cash ($ mil.): 102
Current ratio: 1.71
Long-term debt ($ mil.): —

No. of shares (mil.): 41
Dividends
  Yield: —
  Payout: —
Market value ($ mil.): 1,547

	STOCK PRICE ($) FY Close	P/E High/Low	Earnings	PER SHARE ($) Dividends	Book Value
03/14	37.58	33 18	1.17	0.00	9.94
03/13	24.57	28 19	0.96	0.00	8.97
03/12	20.34	35 14	0.76	0.00	8.19
03/11	27.32	31 14	0.87	0.00	7.51
03/10	14.79	23 10	0.67	0.00	6.39
Annual Growth	**26.3%**	**— —**	**15.0%**	**—**	**11.7%**

NeuStar, Inc.

NeuStar shines as a key provider of registry and clearinghouse services used in telecommunications and Internet networks. The company manages the registry of North American area codes and telephone numbers and the database used by telecom carriers (Verizon AT&T) and cable companies (Comcast Cox Communications) to route phone calls. It is also a leading provider of operations support systems (OSS) clearinghouse services that provide ordering service provisioning billing and customer service functions. In addition NeuStar operates an Internet registry supporting domain addresses and provides a host of other registry domain name system and IP services. The company makes most of its sales in North America.

Operations NeuStar offers such services as database services (telephone number databases domain names short-codes and fixed IP addresses) analytics platforms used for Internet security caller

ID web performance monitoring services and real-time information and analytics services.

Geographic Reach The company has a half-dozen locations in the US that support its three business segments - carrier services enterprise services and information services. An office in Costa Rica supports the information services segments and a small office in the UK supports the carrier and enterprise services segments.

Sales and Marketing In addition to major telecom and cable firms the company counts among its 14000 customers emerging telecom and VoIP service providers e-commerce companies information services providers media and advertising groups and domain name registrars such as Go Daddy.

Although no single customer accounts for more than 10% of sales NeuStar generates some 50% of revenue under contracts with North American Portability Management an industry group representing all US telecommunications services providers.

Financial Performance The company's revenue grew 34% in 2012 hitting $831 million as it saw double-digit growth in both of its traditional segments (carrier services and enterprise services) and the addition of a third segment information services that came about when NeuStar bought Targus Information in 2011. The information services segment contributed more than $158 million to NeuStar's top line in 2012.

Profits were down slightly (3%) to $156 million. In 2011 the company enjoyed a spike in profits after recording a one-time income tax benefit of more than $40 million after ceasing operations of its converged messaging services business.

Mergers and Acquisitions NeuStar uses periodic acquisitions to expand its business. In 2011 it bought Targus Information for about $650 million in cash. The Vienna Virginia-based company provided caller identification and other services that became the basis for a new operating segment - information services. NeuStar also paid $39 million in cash to buy the Numbering Solutions business of Evolving Systems that year to increase the number management and inventory capabilities of its carrier services business segment.

HISTORY

In 2006 the company bought UltraDNS a Reston Virginia-based provider of Domain Name System (DNS) and directory services in a cash deal valued at $61.8 million. It additionally purchased Followap a mobile instant messaging services provider for $139 million that year.

NeuStar acquired Webmetrics a provider of Web and network performance testing services in 2008 for $12.5 million in cash.

EXECUTIVES

President and CEO, Lisa A. Hook, age 55, $697,988 total compensation
SVP Data Solutions, Steven J. (Steve) Edwards, age 55, $364,304 total compensation
SVP and CFO, Paul S. Lalljie, age 41, $449,457 total compensation
Senior Vice President And Senior Technologist, Rodney Joffe
SVP Information Services, Ted Prince, $324,189 total compensation
Vice President Numbering Services, Greg Roberts
Vice President Product Engineering, Andrew Jackson
Svp-human Resources, Christine Brennan
Senior Vice President - Mrktng, Steven Johnson

Vice President Of Marketing Of And Customer Intel Content Strategy, Jim Rogers
Vice President Of Sales, Jayne Babine
Vice President Of Strategic Technical Initiatives, Tom McGarry
Vice President Business Operations, Randy Buffenbarger
Vice President, Melanie Shook
Vice President Finance Cost Management, Duane Deason
Vice President Operations, Marguerite Tsou
Vice President Marketing, David Dague
Vice President West Coast Sales, Matthew Weil
Vice President Technical Strategy, John Kelly
Senior Vice President And General Manager Carrier And Mobile Markets, Clayton Liabraaten
Senior Vice President Enterprise Sales, Kurt Gastrock
Regional Vice President Strategic Accounts, Vince Petrecca
National Sales Manager, Scott Heimbrodt
Chief Operating Officer Executive Vp, Robert Nascenzi
Vice President Product Management, Andrew Onufer
Sr V Pres Sls, Alex L Berry
Vice President Product Management, Paul McLenaghan
Chairman, James G. Cullen, age 72
Auditors: Ernst&YoungLLP

LOCATIONS

HQ: NeuStar, Inc.
21575 Ridgetop Circle, Sterling, VA 20166
Phone: 571 434-5400
Web: www.neustar.biz

2012 Sales

	$ mil.	% of total
North America	787.5	95
Europe & Middle East	27.5	3
Other Regions	16.4	2
Total	**831.4**	**100**

PRODUCTS/OPERATIONS

2012 Sales

	$ mil.	% of total
Carrier services	502.1	60
Enterprise services	170.4	21
Information services	158.9	19
Total	**831.4**	**100**

COMPETITORS

Accenture	Infogroup
Acxiom	Keynote Systems
Akamai	NetCracker Technology
Amdocs	Nielsen
BSG Clearing Solutions	Nokia
Billing Services Group	Oracle
CGI Group	PTGi International
Computer Sciences Corp.	Carrier Services
	Register.com
Evolving Systems	Sodalia North America
F5 Networks	Synchronoss
HP Enterprise Services	Syniverse
Hewlett-Packard	TNS Custom
IBM	Tucows
ICANN	VeriSign
Infoblox	XIUS-bcgi

HISTORICAL FINANCIALS

Company Type: Public

Income Statement

FYE: December 31

	REVENUE ($ mil.)	NET INCOME ($ mil.)	NET PROFIT MARGIN	EMPLOYEES
12/13	902.0	162.7	18.0%	1,623
12/12	831.3	156.0	18.8%	1,543
12/11	620.4	160.8	25.9%	1,488
12/10	526.8	106.2	20.2%	1,022
12/09	480.3	101.1	21.1%	896
Annual Growth	**17.1%**	**12.6%**	**—**	**16.0%**

2013 Year-End Financials

Debt ratio: 41.1%
Return on equity: 26.3%
Cash ($ mil.): 223
Current ratio: 2.55
Long-term debt ($ mil.): 610
No. of shares (mil.): 61
Dividends
  Yield: —
  Payout: —
Market value ($ mil.): 3,062

	STOCK PRICE ($) FY Close	P/E High/Low	PER SHARE ($) Earnings	PER SHARE ($) Dividends	PER SHARE ($) Book Value
12/13	49.86	22 17	2.46	0.00	9.60
12/12	41.93	18 13	2.30	0.00	9.77
12/11	34.17	16 10	2.16	0.00	7.60
12/10	26.05	19 14	1.40	0.00	8.10
12/09	23.04	18 10	1.34	0.00	6.77
Annual Growth	**21.3%**	**— —**	**16.4%**	**—**	**9.1%**

New York Mortgage Trust Inc

New York Mortgage Trust is ready to invest in real estate now that the credit crisis has passed. A self-advised real estate investment trust (REIT) the company invests in real estate assets including high-quality adjustable rate residential mortgages and mortgage-backed securities. It primarily buys agency-rated securities which carry less risk but the REIT is also building up its non-agency assets (which bring higher returns). Its owned assets include non-agency mortgage-backed securities prime adjustable rate mortgage loans held in trusts commercial mortgage-backed securities and other commercial real estate-related investments. New York Mortgage Trust was formed in 2003.

Operations

New York Mortgage Trust has expertise in acquiring investing in financing and managing primarily mortgage-related assets (and to a lesser extent financial assets). Its portfolio includes credit sensitive assets and investments sourced from distressed markets in recent years that have created the potential for capital gains as well as more traditional types of mortgage-related investments that generate interest income. Its current portfolio includes distressed residential mortgage loans and prime adjustable rate mortgage (ARM) loans held in securitization trusts.

Financial Performance

After years of stagnation New York Mortgage Trust saw its revenues absolutely skyrocket by 560% from $23 million in 2011 to $147 million in 2012. Profits also shot up nearly 500% from $5 million in 2011 to $28 million in 2012.

The impressive growth for 2012 was due to a nearly 450% spike in interest income fueled by an increase in investment securities and revenue generated from multi-family loans held in securitization trusts and distressed residential mortgage loans held in securitization trusts.

Strategy

New York Mortgage Trust's strategy for growth involves building a residential portfolio that includes elements of both interest rate and credit risk by focusing its investments on credit residential assets and leveraged residential mortgage-backed securities. During 2012 it focused most of its investments in credit residential assets intent on expanding its portfolio of multi-family commercial mortgage-backed securities comprised of first loss fixed rate PO securities a first loss floating-rate security and certain IO securities issued by multi-family K-series securitizations sponsored by Freddie Mac.

EXECUTIVES

President and CEO, Steven R. Mumma, age 55, $161,834 total compensation
CFO, Fredric S. Starker
President and CEO, Steven R. Mumma, age 55
Auditors: Deloitte&ToucheLLP

LOCATIONS

HQ: New York Mortgage Trust Inc
275 Madison Avenue, New York, NY 10016
Phone: 212 792-0107
Web: www.nymtrust.com

PRODUCTS/OPERATIONS

2012 Sales

	$ mil.	% of total
Interest income	137.5	93
Other income	9.7	7
Total	**147.2**	**100**

Selected Subsidiaries and Operations

Hypotheca Capital LLC
New York Mortgage Funding LLC
New York Mortgage Ownership Corporation
New York Mortgage Securities Corporation
New York Mortgage Securitization Trust 2012-1
New York Mortgage Servicing Corporation
New York Mortgage Trust 2005-1
New York Mortgage Trust 2005-2
New York Mortgage Trust 2005-3
NYM Preferred Trust I
NYM Preferred Trust II
NYMT Commercial LLC
NYMT Residential 2012-RP1 LLC
NYMT Residential Tax LLC
NYMT Residential LLC
NYMT-Midway LLC
RB Commercial Mortgage LLC
RB Commercial Trust Series 2012-RS1

COMPETITORS

Annaly Capital Management
Anworth Mortgage Asset
CIFC
Capstead Mortgage
Dynex Capital
Impac Mortgage Holdings
Institutional Financial Markets
MFA Financial
Newcastle Investment
Putnam Mortgage
Two Harbors
iStar Financial Inc

HISTORICAL FINANCIALS

Company Type: Public

Income Statement

FYE: December 31

	REVENUE ($ mil.)	NET INCOME ($ mil.)	NET PROFIT MARGIN	EMPLOYEES
12/13	322.0	68.9	21.4%	6
12/12	147.2	28.1	19.1%	4
12/11	22.2	4.8	21.9%	3
12/10	25.4	6.8	26.7%	3
12/09	34.2	11.6	34.1%	4
Annual Growth	**75.1%**	**55.9%**	**—**	**10.7%**

2013 Year-End Financials

Debt ratio: 92.6%
Return on equity: 17.1%
Cash ($ mil.): 31
Current ratio: 0.03
Long-term debt ($ mil.): 8,379

No. of shares (mil.): 64
Dividends
Yield: 15.4%
Payout: 128.5%
Market value ($ mil.): 448

	STOCK PRICE ($) FY Close	P/E High/Low		PER SHARE ($) Earnings	Dividends	Book Value
12/13	6.99	7	5	1.11	1.08	7.50
12/12	6.32	7	5	1.08	1.06	6.50
12/11	7.21	17	14	0.46	1.00	6.12
12/10	6.96	11	8	0.72	0.79	7.27
12/09	7.19	7	2	1.19	0.76	6.69
Annual Growth	**(0.7%)**	**—**	**—**	**(1.7%)**	**9.2%**	**2.9%**

NewMarket Corp

Some people think petroleum is just fine the way it is; NewMarket thinks it needs a little something extra added to it to improve engine performance. The company is a holding entity for two petroleum additive subsidiaries: Afton Chemical and Ethyl Corporation. Afton Chemical manufactures petroleum additives used to improve the performance of gasoline diesel and other fuels and as a lubricant in motor oil fluids and grease. Ethyl's main product is the antiknock additive tetraethyl lead though TEL has lost substantial ground in markets where unleaded gas is preferred.

Geographic Reach

The company has operations in Asia Australia Europe Latin America the Middle East and North America. It operates six Research Development and Testing facilities in Ashland and Richmond Virginia (US); Bracknell and Manchester (UK); Tsukuba Japan; and Suzhou China. It has about 10 Manufacturing and Distribution facilities in the US Belgium India the UK Brazil and China.The US accounted for 36% of total sales in 2013; Europe Middle East Africa India (EMEAI) 33%.

Operations

The company is engaged in one business segment —petroleum additives used in lubricating oils and fuels to enhance their performance in machinery vehicles and other equipment. The petroleum additives market is an international marketplace with customers ranging from oil companies and refineries to OEMs and other specialty chemical companies.

Its Afton Chemical unit is among the world leaders in producing lubricant additives. The company joins with Infineum Lubrizol and Chevron Oronite to produce more than 80% of the world market.

Though its Ethyl Corporation subsidiary still markets its primary product tetraethyl lead in the US and abroad sales have dwindled to less than 1% of NewMarket's overall business. The company plans to eliminate the Ethyl segment at some point in the future as the global market for leaded gasoline is phased out.

Another subsidiary NewMarket Services provides various administrative services to NewMarket Afton and Ethyl.

Sales and Marketing

Lubricants are widely used in operating machinery from heavy industrial equipment to vehicles. Sales to Royal Dutch Shell accounted for 11% of NewMarket's total revenues in 2013.

Financial Performance

Revenues increased by 3% in 2013 due higher lubricant additives sales partially offset by lower sales of fuel additives. The petroleum additives segment's net sales for 2013 were 3.2% higher than 2012. Regionally EMEAI and Asia/Pacific experienced increased revenues and shipments while revenues and shipments in North America and Latin America were lower. The increase reflects higher shipments of lubricant additives products overall mainly in EMEAI and Asia/Pacific. This was partially offset by a decrease in fuel additives product shipments mainly in EMEAI. Overall product shipments for 2013 increased by 3.7%.NewMarket's net income increased due to higher revenues as well as having no loss on early extinguishment of debt increased other income and higher gain related to the sale of its real estate assetsCash flow from operations increased in 2013 thanks to higher net income increased gain on sale of real estate business no loss on early extinguishment of debt and an increase in unrealized gain on derivative instruments.

Except for a recession-related revenue slump in 2009 NewMarket has seen an upward trend in revenues from 2008 to 2013. The slump in 2009 was due to lower total product shipments as well as a significant unfavorable foreign currency impact.

Strategy

The company pursues a strategy of organic growth with an emphasis on product innovation. In 2013 it launched new technologies across all of its lubricant additive and fuel additive product areas including new engine oil products including gasoline performance additives and diesel performance additives as well as specification and distribution fuel additives.That year NewMarket expanded its laboratory and mechanical testing capabilities in five of its principal technical centers around the world: Richmond Ashland Bracknell Suzhou and Tsukuba. This increased its capacity for providing differentiated solutions and additional process development capability to enhance its speed-to-market for new products and technologies.

To raise cash and streamline its operations in 2013 the company sold its real estate assets for $144 million. The real estate development segment (NewMarket Development) represented the operations of Foundry Park I. In 2007 Foundry Park I entered into a Deed of Lease Agreement with MeadWestvaco under which it is leasing an office building which NewMarket built on three acres in Richmond Virginia. The lease expires in 2023 subject to certain extension options.

Company Background

Bruce C. Gottwald owns 10% of the company.

In 2010 Afton completed its acquisition of Polartech for $43 million. Polartech is a global company specializing in the supply of metalworking additives. The company acquired all physical assets of the Polartech business including its headquarters R&D and manufacturing facilities in the UK as well as manufacturing sites in India China and the US.

NewMarket was founded in 1887 as the Albemarle Paper Manufacturing Company.

EXECUTIVES

Chairman President and CEO, Thomas E. (Teddy) Gottwald, age 54, $915,000 total compensation
President Afton Chemical Corporation, Robert A. (Rob) Shama, age 53, $433,333 total compensation
VP and CFO, Brian D. Paliotti, age 38
Vp Sales, Jeff Hiscox
Vice President Corporate Resources, Bruce Hazelgrove
Vice President Product Marketing, Bob Bennett
Chairman President and CEO, Thomas E. (Teddy) Gottwald, age 54
Auditors: PricewaterhouseCoopersLLP

LOCATIONS

HQ: NewMarket Corp
330 South Fourth Street, Richmond, VA 23219-4350
Phone: 804 788-5000
Web: www.newmarket.com

2013 Sales

	$ mil.	% of total
US	806.5	36
Europe Middle East Africa & India	759.9	33
Asia/Pacific	462.1	20
Other regions	251.9	11
Total	**2280.4**	**100**

PRODUCTS/OPERATIONS

2013 Sales

	$ mil.	% of total
Petroleum additives		
Lubricant additives	1829.7	80
Fuel additives	441.6	19
All other	9.1	1
Total	**2280.4**	**100**

COMPETITORS

BASF SE	Infineum
Balchem	Innospec
Chevron Oronite	Lubrizol
Clariant	Methanex
EPC United Kingdom	SNPE
Fuel Tech	

HISTORICAL FINANCIALS

Company Type: Public

Income Statement

FYE: December 31

	REVENUE ($ mil.)	NET INCOME ($ mil.)	NET PROFIT MARGIN	EMPLOYEES
12/13	2,280.3	264.7	11.6%	1,789
12/12	2,223.3	239.5	10.8%	1,710
12/11	2,149.5	206.9	9.6%	1,625
12/10	1,797.3	177.1	9.9%	1,527
12/09	1,530.1	162.2	10.6%	1,308
Annual Growth	**10.5%**	**13.0%**	**—**	**8.1%**

2013 Year-End Financials

Debt ratio: 26.3%
Return on equity: 54.3%
Cash ($ mil.): 238
Current ratio: 3.62
Long-term debt ($ mil.): 349
No. of shares (mil.): 13
Dividends
  Yield: 1.1%
  Payout: 19.2%
Market value ($ mil.): 4,377

STOCK PRICE ($) FY Close	P/E High/Low		PER SHARE ($) Earnings	Dividends	Book Value
12/13	334.15	17	12	19.90	3.80	43.70
12/12	262.20	16	10	17.85	28.00	29.98
12/11	198.11	13	8	15.09	2.39	41.00
12/10	123.37	11	7	12.09	1.57	35.03
12/09	114.77	11	3	10.65	1.08	30.12
Annual Growth	**30.6%**	—	—	**16.9%**	**37.1%**	**9.7%**

Newpark Resources, Inc.

Oil and gas activity means money for oil field support services company Newpark Resources. The company provides drilling fluid and engineering services to oil and gas drillers. Newpark Resources also supplies prefab work platforms and provides DuraBase brand composite mats used to make temporary access roads (through its Newpark Mats & Integrated Services unit) processes and disposes of oil field waste (injecting it underground or recycling it into drilling fluids) and performs fluid processing and recycling on site at rigs. It also processes and disposes of nonhazardous industrial waste.

Geographic Reach

The company serves oil and gas customers in North and South America Europe the Middle East Africa and the Asia/Pacific region. It has major offices in the US (Colorado Louisiana and Texas) Calgary Rome and Rio de Janeiro. The US accounted for 71% of Newpark Resources' revenues in 2013.

Operations

Newpark Resources operates in three segments: Fluids Systems and Engineering Mats and Integrated Services and Environmental Services. The Fluids Systems and Engineering business offers customized solutions including highly technical drilling projects such as horizontal directional geologically deep or deep water drilling.

The Mats and Integrated Services segment provides mat rentals location construction and related well site services to exploration and production customers providing environmental protection and ensuring all-weather access to sites with unstable soil conditions.

The Environmental Services segment processes and disposes of waste (generated by its oil and gas customers) that is treated as exempt under the Resource Conservation and Recovery Act. Waste is collected at the transfer facilities from drilling and production operations located offshore onshore and within inland waters primarily in the US.

Sales and Marketing

The company's customers include major integrated and independent oil and gas exploration and production companies.

Financial Performance

Newpark Resources' revenues increased by 8% in 2012 thanks to higher revenues in North America driven by improved drilling efficiency and strong demand for composite mat products from customers outside of the exploration and production segment. Non-US revenues increased thanks to the acquisition of the Asia Pacific business unit in 2011.

Environmental Services sales jumped by 11% due to higher offshore drilling activity along the US Gulf Coast. Mats and Integrated Services revenues also went up by 11% due to higher demand for the DuraBase composite mat products from utilities and the US military. The company reported net income of $60 million in 2012 (25% down on 2011) as the result of higher selling general and administrative expenses related to enterprise resource planning system conversion of its US-based businesses. It also posted a foreign currency exchange loss that year and higher interest expense stemming from increased borrowings.

Newpark Resources has seen a steady growth in revenues with the exception of 2009 when the global recession sapped demand for oil and gas activities.

Strategy

Newpark Resources is seeking to grow its international operations and innovative product lines as part of its strategy to focus on faster growing markets.

In 2013 the company announced plans to sell its Environmental Services division in order to focus on expanding its markets and developing leading technologies within the company's core drilling fluids and mats businesses.

That year Newpark Resources launched an innovative mat cleaning system. The DURA-BASE® T-REXA™Mat Cleaning System complements Newpark's widely used DURA-BASE® Advanced-Composite Mats to reduce the time exploration and production companies need to clean rig matting and redeploy equipment.

Mergers and Acquisitions

In the US the company is growing its drilling fluids portfolio to support the current shale oil and gas drilling boom. In 2012 Newpark Resources acquired Texas-based Alliance Drilling Fluids LLC a provider of drilling fluids proppants and related services for $53 million.

In 2011 Newpark Resources gained a foothold in the Asia/Pacific market acquiring Australia-based Rheochem PLC's drilling fluids and engineering services business for about $25 million.

Ownership

Wells Fargo & Company owns 13% of the company.

EXECUTIVES

President CEO and Director, Paul L. Howes, age 59, $521,850 total compensation
Vice President and Chief Financial Officer, Gregg Piontek, age 43
Executive Vice President and President - Fluids Systems and Engineering, Bruce C. Smith, age 62, $328,623 total compensation
VP; President Mats & Integrated Services and Environmental Services, Jeffery L. Juergens, age 58
Vice President Finance And Planning, Joseph L (Joe) Gocke
Vice President Sales, Steve Pierson
Vice President Operations, Darryl Arndt
Vice President Sales And Marketing, Keith Pearson
Vice President Global Procurement And Supply Chain, Pravin Tampi
Senior Vice President; Chief Administrative Officer; General Counsel; Secretary, Mark Airola
Vice President Finance, Tony Freitas
Chairman, Jerry W. Box, age 76
Auditors: Ernst&YoungLLP

LOCATIONS

HQ: Newpark Resources, Inc.
9320 Lakeside Blvd., Suite 100, The Woodlands, TX 77381
Phone: 281 362-6800
Web: www.newpark.com

2012 Sales

	$ mil.	% of total
North America		
US	738.2	71
Canada	48.6	5
Europe Middle East & Africa	121.2	12
Latin America & Mexico	88.2	8
Asia/Pacific	41.9	4
Total	**1038.1**	**100**

PRODUCTS/OPERATIONS

2012 Sales

	$ mil.	% of total
Fluids sales & engineering	861.7	83
Mats & integrated services	122.3	12
Environmental services	54.1	5
Total	**1038.1**	**100**

COMPETITORS

Baker Hughes	Philip Services
Halliburton	Schlumberger
Lufkin Industries	Willbros
M-I SWACO	

HISTORICAL FINANCIALS

Company Type: Public

Income Statement

FYE: December 31

	REVENUE ($ mil.)	NET INCOME ($ mil.)	NET PROFIT MARGIN	EMPLOYEES
12/13	1,042.3	65.3	6.3%	2,214
12/12	1,038.0	60.0	5.8%	2,248
12/11	958.1	80.0	8.4%	2,118
12/10	715.9	41.6	5.8%	1,001
12/09	490.2	(20.5)	—	1,664
Annual Growth	20.8%	—	—	7.4%

2013 Year-End Financials

Debt ratio: 19.1%	No. of shares (mil.): 87
Return on equity: 11.9%	Dividends
Cash ($ mil.): 65	Yield: —
Current ratio: 3.64	Payout: —
Long-term debt ($ mil.): 172	Market value ($ mil.): 1,072

	STOCK PRICE ($) FY Close	P/E High/Low	PER SHARE ($) Earnings	Dividends	Book Value
12/13	12.29	18 10	0.69	0.00	6.66
12/12	7.85	15 8	0.62	0.00	6.00
12/11	9.50	11 6	0.80	0.00	5.43
12/10	6.16	20 8	0.46	0.00	4.62
12/09	4.23	— —	(0.23)	0.00	4.14
Annual Growth	30.6%		—	—	12.7%

Newport Corp.

Newport helps all sorts of customers take a measured approach. The company makes lasers precision components and automated assembly measurement and test equipment. It makes prod-

ucts that are used around the world in such fields as fiber-optic communications health care life sciences military/aerospace scientific research and semiconductor manufacturing. Industrial and scientific components include lenses and other devices for vibration and motion control. Newport also offers automated systems used to make fiber-optic components and photonics. More than half of sales come from outside the US.

Geographic Reach

Newport operates manufacturing plants stateside and abroad. US plants are located in California Connecticut Massachusetts Montana New York and Utah. Internationally its plants are located in developed and emerging markets in Austria China France Germany Israel and Romania.

The US is its largest single market accounting for about 40% of sales. Europe and Asia each account for about a quarter of sales.

Sales and Marketing

Newport uses a direct sales force as well as an international network of independent distributors and sales representatives. It also uses e-commerce and has a product catalog The Newport Resource. Customers include OEMs and capital equipment makers.

Financial Performance

Overall sales for 2012 increased nearly 10% to $595 million due to inorganic growth from a couple of acquisitions in 2011. Sales for its Photonics and Precision Technologies (PPT) division and its Lasers division both decreased by 5%. In particular the Lasers division discontinued some products which affected sales.

Despite the increase in revenue Newport posted a net loss of -$89.4 million in 2012 against a profit of $79.7 million in 2011. The loss was due to a $130 million impairment charge relating to the 2011 acquisition of Ophir.

Strategy

Newport has made several acquisitions to help it shift from a provider of research instruments to one that manufactures both components and integrated systems for research and commercial applications. The company's brands now consist of ILX Lightwave New Focus Newport Ophir Optimet Oriel Instruments Richardson Gratings Spiricon and Spectra-Physics.

The company also divests businesses that are not considered part of its core operations. In late 2013 it announced plans to sell its Micro Robotics Systems advanced packaging business (MRSI) to a private investment group. MRSI makes turn-key die bonding and dispensing systems while Newport is focused on lasers optics and photonics technologies.

Mergers and Acquisitions

Several key acquisitions over the years helped spark sales in the life sciences and photonics research market. In 2012 it paid $9.3 million for ILX Lightwave which makes high-performance test and measurement products for laser diodes and other photonics components. It also bought Advanced Vibration Technologies Inc. (doing business as Vistek) for $2.5 million. Vistek makes vibration control and isolation products and became part of Newport's Photonics and Precision Technologies division.

In 2011 Newport paid $242 million for Israel-based Ophir Optronics a maker of precision infrared optics and photonics instrumentation to expand its product line and tap the market for thermal imaging equipment. Ophir became a new division.

That year it also bought High Q Technologies for $18.5 million a maker of ultrafast lasers used in surgical procedures based in Austria to bolster

its laser division with the addition of products for the health care industry. In addition it paid $3 million for Opticoat SRL which expanded its capabilities in making precision optical components and coatings.

EXECUTIVES

VP Sales Marketing and Business Development, Gary J. Spiegel, age 63, $278,462 total compensation
President CEO and Director, Robert J. Phillippy, age 54, $477,692 total compensation
Senior Vice President Marketing, William Takanabe
Chief Financial Officer; Senior Vice President; Treasurer, Charles F. (Chuck) Cargile, age 49, $336,923 total compensation
VP Precision Components and Systems Business Photonics and Precision Technologies Division, Dennis L. Werth
Executive Vice President General Counsel Corporate Secretary, Andrew Powell
Vice President And Chief Information Officer, Greg R Reischlein
Information Technology Vice President, Bernard Molinie
Vice President, Howard Loree
Senior Vice President Of Customer Services, Kerry Diaz
Vice President Nasso Sales, Jeff Parker
Information Technology Vice President, Maria Flansburg
Assistant Vice-president, Joe Mastromarino
Vp Of Finance, Michael Blajwas
Vice President Of Photonics Marketing And Technology, Christopher Palmer
President CEO and Director, Robert J. Phillippy, age 54
Chairman, Kenneth F. Potashner, age 56
Auditors: Deloitte&ToucheLLP

LOCATIONS

HQ: Newport Corp.
1791 Deere Avenue, Irvine, CA 92606
Phone: 949 863-3144
Web: www.newport.com

2012 Sales

	$ mil.	% of total
US	243.7	41
Asia	157.2	26
Europe	151.8	25
Other regions	42.6	7
Total	**595.3**	**100**

PRODUCTS/OPERATIONS

2012 Sales

	$ mil.	% of total
Photonics & precision technologies	311.3	53
Lasers	181.4	30
Ophir	102.6	17
Total	**595.3**	**100**

COMPETITORS

Adept Technology	Manz
Agilent Technologies	Nikon
Allied Motion Technologies	Nordson
	Oclaro
Anritsu	Palomar Technologies
Carl Zeiss	Parker-Hannifin
Coherent Inc.	ROFIN-SINAR
Corning	Renishaw
Danaher	Rockwell Automation
EXFO	Roper Industries
HORIBA	Spectris
II-VI	TRUMPF
IPG Photonics	Thermo Fisher

JDS Uniphase Scientific
Jenoptik Zygo
Kinetic Systems

HISTORICAL FINANCIALS
Company Type: Public

Income Statement
FYE: December 28

	REVENUE ($ mil.)	NET INCOME ($ mil.)	NET PROFIT MARGIN	EMPLOYEES
12/13	560.0	15.6	2.8%	2,400
12/12	595.3	(89.4)	—	2,440
12/11*	545.0	79.7	14.6%	2,550
01/11	479.7	41.1	8.6%	1,745
01/10	366.9	(17.4)	—	1,625
Annual Growth	11.1%	—	—	10.2%

*Fiscal year change

2013 Year-End Financials
Debt ratio: 15.6%
Return on equity: 5.0%
Cash ($ mil.): 53
Current ratio: 2.93
Long-term debt ($ mil.): 83
No. of shares (mil.): 39
Dividends
　Yield: —
　Payout: —
Market value ($ mil.): 718

	STOCK PRICE ($) FY Close	P/E High/Low		PER SHARE ($) Earnings	Dividends	Book Value
12/13	18.22	46	32	0.39	0.00	8.30
12/12	13.05	—	—	(2.35)	0.00	7.54
12/11*	13.61	9	5	2.06	0.00	9.84
01/11	17.43	16	7	1.09	0.00	8.01
01/10	9.19			(0.48)	0.00	7.01
Annual Growth	18.7%			—	—	4.3%

*Fiscal year change

NIC Inc.

So people can do business with government agencies NIC helps government agencies plug in to the Internet. The company is a leading provider of outsourced Web portal services for federal state and local governments. It designs implements and operates websites under contracts with more than 3500 government agencies. NIC generates much of its revenue from transaction fees for such services as online license renewals and for providing data on motor vehicle titles and business licenses to insurance companies lenders and other authorized organizations.

Geographic Reach

The company operates in about 30 states. NIC has offices in more than 40 of the top 50 major metropolitan areas in the US. It has international offices in Asia.

Operations

During fiscal 2012 Motor Vehicle Driver History Record retrieval service accounted for about 25% of NIC's total revenue. Motor Vehicle Registrations service accounted for about 10% of the company's revenue during fiscal 2012.

Sales and Marketing

The company has a national sales force and a marketing department dedicated to its outsourced portal businesses. NIC's largest client LexisNexis Risk Solutions (formerly ChoicePoint) accounted for about 26% of its total revenue during fiscal 2012.

Financial Performance

NIC's revenue has been steady and trending upwards over the course of recent fiscal years. Its revenue increased by 17% in fiscal 2012 ($211.1 million) compared to fiscal 2011 ($180.9 million). The spike was powered by double digit growth in the company's portal revenues which increased by 17% in fiscal 2012 compared to the previous fiscal period. NIC's software and services revenues increased by 11% in 2012 compared to fiscal 2011 largely because of higher revenues from its contract with the FMCSA.

NIC's net profit increased from $22.94 million in fiscal 2011 to $26.34 million in fiscal 2012.

Strategy

To grow NIC is striving to renew its existing contracts which typically run for three- to five-year terms and to win new portal contracts. In addition the company has been developing new applications for government websites from which it can generate transaction fees especially outside the realm of motor vehicle records.

EXECUTIVES

Chairman of the Board; Chief Executive Officer, Harry H. Herington, age 54, $390,450 total compensation
Executive Vice President; Chief Administrative Officer; General Counsel; Secretary, William F. (Brad) Bradley, age 59, $267,150 total compensation
CFO, Stephen M. (Steve) Kovzan, age 45, $267,150 total compensation
COO, Robert Knapp, age 46, $267,150 total compensation
Vice President Of Egovernment Innovation, Nolan Jones
Vice President Portal Operations, Scott Somerhalder
Vice President, Ron Thornburgh
Vice President Operations, Jennifer Rasmussen
Executive Vice President, Joseph Nemelka
Chairman of the Board; Chief Executive Officer, Harry H. Herington, age 54
Auditors: PricewaterhouseCoopersLLP

LOCATIONS

HQ: NIC Inc.
25501 West Valley Parkway, Suite 300, Olathe, KS 66061
Phone: 877 234-3468
Web: www.egov.com

PRODUCTS/OPERATIONS

2012 Sales

	$ mil.	% of total
Outsourced portals	199.4	94
Software & services	11.7	6
Total	211.1	100

COMPETITORS

Accenture	Manatron
Agency.com	Microsoft
CGI Group	Official Payments
Computer Sciences Corp.	Official Payments Holdings
HP Enterprise Services	Oracle
IBM Global Services	Tyler Technologies
Idea Integration	USTI
Leidos	Unisys
MAXIMUS	

HISTORICAL FINANCIALS
Company Type: Public

Income Statement
FYE: December 31

	REVENUE ($ mil.)	NET INCOME ($ mil.)	NET PROFIT MARGIN	EMPLOYEES
12/13	249.2	32.0	12.9%	773
12/12	211.1	26.3	12.5%	714
12/11	180.9	22.9	12.7%	653
12/10	161.5	18.3	11.4%	596
12/09	132.8	13.9	10.5%	606
Annual Growth	17.0%	23.1%		6.3%

2013 Year-End Financials
Debt ratio: —
Return on equity: 37.5%
Cash ($ mil.): 97
Current ratio: 1.95
Long-term debt ($ mil.): —
No. of shares (mil.): 64
Dividends
　Yield: 1.4%
　Payout: 67.3%
Market value ($ mil.): 1,616

	STOCK PRICE ($) FY Close	P/E High/Low		PER SHARE ($) Earnings	Dividends	Book Value
12/13	24.87	51	32	0.49	0.35	1.41
12/12	16.34	41	26	0.40	0.50	1.22
12/11	13.31	41	27	0.35	0.25	1.01
12/10	9.71	35	23	0.28	0.55	0.84
12/09	9.14	43	19	0.22	0.30	1.05
Annual Growth	28.4%			22.2%	3.9%	7.7%

Nordson Corp.

When it comes to adhesion coating and spraying Nordson dispenses with admirable stick-to-itiveness. Its adhesive dispensing systems are used on a range of packaging paperboard and nonwoven products. A line of sealant systems bond and seal plastic metal and wood products. Nordson's spray systems apply powder paints and coatings to appliances and auto parts. The company also produces inspection systems for high-tech manufacturing. Nordson sells to the appliance automotive medical solar energy and semiconductor markets among others. About 75% of sales come from outside the US.

Adhesive dispensing systems 50% of revenue are used to decrease consumption create more production efficiency and to make products stronger and more durable as well optimize their brand presence and appearance. The segment's products are divided between four families: nonwovens (equipment for such products as diapers feminine hygiene products surgical gowns shoe covers and face masks); packaging (systems for food packages wrappers and beverage containers); product assembly (for building and construction materials electronics bags sacks books and envelopes); web coating & extruding (for continuous-roll goods such as carpet labels tapes textiles wraps).

Advanced technology systems 36% of revenue serves the electronics medical and high-tech markets with technologies that help accomplish surface preparation (contact lenses electronics medical instruments printed circuit boards); dispensing materials on surfaces (piezoelectric and motionless two-component mixing dispensing systems for cell phones liquid crystal displays micro hard drives among other products); bond testing and X-ray inspection (for the semiconductor and printed circuit board industries' manufacturing related to desktop computers digital music players mobile phones and other products).

Industrial coating systems 14% of revenue provides equipment for applying coatings paint finishes sealants and for curing and drying applied material. The segment is divided between automotive (powertrain components body assembly final trim); container coating (beverage containers and food cans); liquid finishing (automotive components construction metal shelving drums); and powder coating (agriculture and construction equipment appliances automotive components metal shelving). Its curing and drying systems are used for electronics containers and durable goods.

The company has production facilities in seven US states and in Belgium China Germany India the Netherlands and the UK.

Nordson's revenue rose 18% in 2011 compared with 2010 as a result mainly of larger volume and favorable currency exchange rates. By segment adhesive dispensing systems increased 16% thanks in part to strong sales in the Americas and in the consumer end markets. Advanced technology systems headed up about 19% in 2011 vs. 2010 to meet strong demand in all regions but especially in the US and from the consumer electronics market. In the same period revenue for the industrial coating systems surged 24% partly as a result of strong sales in all regions but particularly in Asia/Pacific and the Americas. Along with healthier sales the company has also enjoyed a positive trend for net income. After weathering a net loss of more than $160 million in 2009 Nordson posted a net income of more than $168 million in 2010 and one of more than $222.3 million in 2011.

Nordson's strategy includes expanding its international footprint which already covers more than 30 countries through direct operations. The company focuses on its existing products nurturing them along with engineering and research and development while also seeking growth markets through such methods as the acquisition of companies active in the multinational market. A more specific strategy is the restructuring of adhesive dispensing systems' operations in Georgia which includes expanding a facility in Duluth and building a new plant to replace an old one in Swainsboro where operations in Norcross and Dawsonville are being transferred. The former Swainsboro plant and the Norcross and Dawsonville facilities are being sold.

Meanwhile Nordson has expanded both its offerings and network of direct operations through a series of acquisitions. In mid-2012 it acquired Wisconsin-based EDI Holdings (which stands for Extrusion Die Industries) a provider of slot coating and flat polymer extrusion dies serving plastic processors and web converters for around $200 million from private equity investment firm Bertram Capital. With overseas operations in Germany and China EDI will be integrated into Nordson's adhesive dispensing systems segment. Also in mid-2012 Nordson acquired Pennsylvania-based Xaloy Superior Holdings which makes melt delivery components for injection and extrusion machinery used in plastic processing. With overseas operations in Germany and Thailand Xaloy will also be integrated into Nordson's adhesive dispensing systems segment.

In 2011 Nordson paid $250 million for Colorado-based Value Plastics which manufactures plastic molded single-use fluid connection components used primarily in flow control applications. The acquisition helped Nordson build its medical and life sciences business. Also in 2011 the company acquired Constructiewerkhuizen G. Verbruggen a Belgium-based manufacturer of flexible packaging including bags wraps and pouches. It now operates as a part of the adhesive dispensing systems division.

HISTORY

Nordson was founded in 1909 as the U.S. Automatic Company a maker of low-cost screw machine parts for the auto industry. After the company went bankrupt in 1929 Walter Nord bought the company and reorganized it in 1935 as U.S. Automatic Corp. Following WWII Walter and sons Eric and Evan developed high-pressure paint-spraying equipment. In 1954 Evan formed the Nordson Division to make airless spray equipment; the division moved into thermoplastic adhesion in the 1960s. The division absorbed the parent company in 1966. In 1979 Nordson went public. Eric who became president and chairman brought in 20-year Standard Oil veteran William Madar as CEO in 1986. During Madar's tenure Nordson's sales quadrupled to $600 million annually.

Nordson grew by expanding its business geographically and by developing technology to open new industrial markets. In 1995 the company bought Walcom Benelux a Dutch maker of liquid adhesive-dispensing systems and it introduced the Versa-Spray II powder spray system which automatically adjusts electrostatic output to improve coating uniformity and operating efficiency. Nordson opened a subsidiary in India in 1996 and in 1997 Madar replaced Eric (who retired) as chairman. Edward Campbell the company's president and COO succeeded Madar as CEO that year.

In 1998 Nordson purchased competitor J&M Laboratories' parent company BDL Holdings. Nordson continued to focus on new technology by acquiring Advanced Plasma Systems and March Instruments (both made gas plasma systems used to clean components) as well as Horizon Lamps (ultraviolet lamps) in 1999. That year under its "Action 2000" plan Nordson began trimming its workforce. Late the next year Nordson agreed to acquire EFD Inc. a privately held maker of low-pressure industrial dispensing valves and components. The EFD deal was completed in mid-2001.

To expand the efficiencies of its high-tech technologies Nordson launched a companywide life sciences venture in 2002 to develop products for the pharmaceuticals and medical and genetic research industries and for manufacturers of medical instruments and medical supplies.

Edward Campbell who had joined the board in 1996 became chairman in March 2004 while remaining CEO. Eric Nord retired in November 2004 and was named to the honorary position of chairman emeritus.

Also in 2004 Nordson expanded its international operations through the acquisition of German-based dispensing systems manufacturer W. Puffe Technologie. In 2005 the company planned to buy Germany-based hhs Leimauftrags-Systeme GmbH a provider of cold glue and hot-melt adhesive dispensing technologies from the Baumer Group but the companies mutually terminated the agreement in July.

In 2006 Nordson acquired Dage Holdings a UK-based manufacturer of inspection and testing equipment for printed circuit boards and semiconductors. The purchase price was Â117 million (about $228 million). Dage's equipment tests the integrity of electronic connections in semiconductor packages and electronics assemblies a feature that grows more critical as electronics products continue to shrink in size. Dage employed more than 200 people and had sales of about $59 million for the 12 months ended October 31 2006.

In late 2006 Nordson sold its Fiber Systems Group which had come to the company through the acquisition of J&M Laboratories eight years earlier to the Neumag unit of Saurer a Swiss manufacturer of textile machinery and transmission systems. Nordson acquired the Fiber Systems business as part of its purchase of J&M Laboratories in 1998. The group manufactures systems used in the production of non-woven fibers. Neumag/Saurer paid nearly $6 million in cash for Fiber Systems. Nordson divested the business because it was not meeting financial performance objectives.

Eric Nord died in mid-2008 at the age of 90. Among other accomplishments he received 25 US patents.

Reaching into South Africa Nordson obtained MLT Systems along with its MLT Application Systems subsidiary in mid-2008. A familiar face MLT had been supplying Nordson products to South African markets since 1989.

In 2010 Nordson sold subsidiary Nordson UV Ltd. a supplier of graphic arts and lamps product lines (part of its advanced technology systems) to Baldwin Technology. The deal freed up Nordson's resources for use in markets more material to its bottom line.

Also in 2010 Nordson purchased Micromedics a St. Paul Minnesota-based company specialized in dispensing biomaterials for wound care and similar medical procedures. Earlier in the year Nordson acquired GLT a German distributor of the Nordson EFD (electron fusion devices) line since 1977. In 2011 GLT was rebranded as Nordson EFD Deutschland.

EXECUTIVES

Vp Advanced Tech Systems Asia, Greg Wood
Vp Global Continuous Improvement, James E (Jim) Devries
Vp General Counsel And Secretary, Robert E Veillette, age 63
Chairman and CEO, Edward P. (Ed) Campbell, age 64, $767,884 total compensation
General Manager Micromedics, Lise W. Duran, age 59
President CEO and Director, Michael F. Hilton, age 60, $700,000 total compensation
VP Human Resources and CIO, Shelly M. Peet, age 49
SVP and CRO, Gregory A. Thaxton, age 53, $330,000 total compensation
SVP, Gregory P. (Greg) Merk, age 43
President Nordson MARCH, Peter F. Bierhuis
President Nordson ASYMTEK, John Byers
Chief Executive Nordson DAGE, Steven Kew
President Nordson YESTECH, Donald Miller
President of Nordson DAGE, Phil Vere
President of Nordson, James Getty
Vp Adhesive Dispensing Europe, Axel Wenz
Vp Engineering And Operations Industrial Coating And Automotive Systems, Herman E Turner
Administrative Asst To Vice President, Lisa Ballard
Vice President Business Unit Nordson Asymtek, Greg Hartmeier
Vice President Finance Full Line Stores, Robert Campbell
Vice President, Doug Bloomfield
Chairman and CEO, Edward P. (Ed) Campbell, age 64
Assistant Treasurer And Corporate Cash, Raymond Cushing
Board Of Directors, Victor L Richey, age 58
Auditors: Ernst&YoungLLP

LOCATIONS

HQ: Nordson Corp.
28601 Clemens Road, Westlake, OH 44145
Phone: 440 892-1580
Web: www.nordson.com

2014 Sales

	$ mil.	% of total
Asia/Pacific		
Japan	127.1	7
Other Asia/Pacific	457.7	27
Americas		
US	503.8	30
Other Americas	121.0	7
Europe	494.4	29
Total	**1704**	**100**

PRODUCTS/OPERATIONS

2014 Sales

	$ mil.	% of total
Adhesive dispensing systems	8997	53
Advanced technology systems	561.8	33
Industrial coating systems	242.5	14
Total	**1704**	**100**

Selected Products

Adhesive Dispensing Systems
  Nonwovens (equipment for applying adhesives lotions liquids and fibers to disposable products)
  Packaging (automated adhesive dispensing systems used in the food and beverage and packaged goods industries)
  Product assembly (adhesive and sealant dispensing systems for bonding or sealing plastic metal and wood products)
  Web coating & extruding (laminating and coating systems used to manufacture continuous-roll goods in the nonwovens textile paper and flexible-packaging industries)
Advanced Technology Systems
  Bond testing & inspection systems (bond testing and automated optical and x-ray inspection systems used in the semiconductor and printed circuit board industries)
  Dispensing systems (controlled manual and automated systems for applying materials in customer processes typically requiring extreme precision and material conservation)
  Surface preparation (automated gas plasma treatment systems used to clean and condition surfaces for the semiconductor medical and printed circuit board industries)
Industrial Coatings Systems
  Automated & manual dispensing systems
  Automotive (used to apply materials in the automotive heavy truck and recreational vehicle manufacturing industries)
  Container coating (automated and manual dispensing and curing systems used to coat and cure containers)
  Liquid finishing (used to apply liquid paints and coatings to consumer and industrial products)
  Powder coating (used to apply powder paints and coatings to a variety of metal plastic and wood products)
  Curing & drying systems (ultraviolet equipment used primarily in curing and drying operations for specialty coatings semiconductor materials and paints)

Selected Divisions

Adhesive Dispensing Systems
Industrial Coating Systems
Nordson ASYMTEK
Nordson DAGE
Nordson EFD
Nordson MARCH
Nordson MICROMEDICS
Nordson YESTECH
UV Curing
Value Plastics

COMPETITORS

3M
Graco
BASF SE
Brady Corporation
Cohesant
Curran Group
DÄrr
EMS-CHEMIE
EXEL Industries
Illinois Tool Works
PPG Industries
Paper Converting Machine
Sono-Tek
Spraying Systems
W. R. Grace

HISTORICAL FINANCIALS

Company Type: Public

Income Statement

FYE: October 31

	REVENUE ($ mil.)	NET INCOME ($ mil.)	NET PROFIT MARGIN	EMPLOYEES
10/14	1,704.0	246.7	14.5%	5,966
10/13	1,542.9	221.8	14.4%	5,801
10/12	1,409.5	224.8	16.0%	5,361
10/11	1,233.1	222.3	18.0%	4,094
10/10	1,041.5	168.0	16.1%	3,680
Annual Growth	**13.1%**	**10.1%**	**—**	**12.8%**

2014 Year-End Financials

Debt ratio: 35.7%
Return on equity: 27.5%
Cash ($ mil.): 42
Current ratio: 1.81
Long-term debt ($ mil.): 693

No. of shares (mil.): 62
Dividends
  Yield: 0.9%
  Payout: 20.9%
Market value ($ mil.): 4,779

	STOCK PRICE ($) FY Close	P/E High/Low	PER SHARE ($) Earnings	Dividends	Book Value
10/14	76.55	22 17	3.84	0.76	14.49
10/13	72.09	22 17	3.42	0.63	13.83
10/12	59.03	18 11	3.45	0.53	10.42
10/11	46.37	36 11	3.25	0.44	8.71
10/10	78.02	32 21	2.46	0.39	7.44
Annual Growth	**(0.5%)**	**— —**	**11.8%**	**18.2%**	**18.1%**

Northern Oil & Gas Inc (NV)

The hydrocarbon-rich shale plays of the northern tier of US states are the main attraction for Northern Oil and Gas which explores for and produces oil and natural gas on properties in the northern US. The company keeps overhead and risk down by purchasing minority or non-operating interests in producing oil and gas projects. With leaseholds on more than 171130 acres in the Williston Basin (the Bakken and Three Forks oil and gas fields in North Dakota and Montana) the company in 2012 reported proved reserves of 67.6 million barrels of oil equivalent.

Geographic Reach

Northern Oil and Gas has operations in North Dakota (Mountrail Dunn McKenzie Divide and Williams counties) and Montana.

Operations

In 2012 the company participated in the drilling and completion of 563 gross (48.3 net) wells in the Williston Basin. It owned working stakes in 1227 gross (106.2 net) producing wells (1222 wells in the Bakken and Three Forks formations and five exploratory wells in other formations). It acquired leasehold interests in 17590 net acres in its core prospect areas.

Sales and Marketing

Northern Oil and Gas does not internally manage its commodities marketing activities. Instead its operating partners market and sell oil and gas produced from wells in which the company owns a stake. They also coordinate the transportation of oil production from its wells to pipelines or rail transport facilities as part of their contractual arrangements with the company.

Financial Performance

The company's revenues increased 109% in 2012 due to higher production and a $15.1 million non-cash gain from mark-to-market of derivative instruments (thanks to realized prices rising 4%). During 2012 production increased 95% to 3.8 million barrels of oil equivalent driven by an 83% growth in producing net wells (to 106).Net income rose to $72.3 million in 2012 from $40.6 million in 2011. This increase in net income was driven by higher production levels and higher sales prices partially offset by increased production expense production taxes general and administrative expenses depletion expenses and interest expenses.

The company has seen its revenues grow over the last several years thanks to its ability to ramp up production. Its revenues have grown from $3.5 million in 2008 to $311.6 million in 2012.

Strategy

Northern Oil and Gas looks for projects that are in the early stages of drilling or are about to start drilling.

In 2012 the company upped its proved reserves by 44% as a result of increased drilling activity and the acquisition of producing (or potentially productive) acreage. Its 2012 performance reflects another year of successfully executing its strategy of developing its acreage position and building a long-life reserve base in the Williston Basin. This success enabled it to increase proved reserves by 20.8 million barrels of oil equivalent (5.5 times its 2012 production).

The key elements of its business strategies include developing existing properties in the Williston Basin as a non-operator; diversifying its risk through non-operated participation in a larger number of Bakken and Three Forks Wells; making strategic acquisitions in the Williston Basin at Attractive Prices; maintaining a strong balance sheet; and managing commodity price risk.Its 2013 budget targeted the drilling and completing of 44 net wells in the Bakken and Three Forks formations.

Company Background

In 2012 the company drilled 170 exploratory wells and had a 100% success rate increasing its proved reserves by nearly 160%. It also acquired nearly 57000 acres across a handful of properties.

Northern Oil and Gas was formed in 2007.

EXECUTIVES

Chairman and CEO, Michael L. Reger, age 38, $285,000 total compensation
CFO, Thomas Stoelk
EVP Corporate Development and Strategy, Brandon Elliott
EVP General Counsel and Secretary, Erik Romslo
EVP Land, Darrell Finneman
Chairman and CEO, Michael L. Reger, age 38
Auditors: MantylaMcReynoldsLLC

LOCATIONS

HQ: Northern Oil & Gas Inc (NV)
315 Manitoba Avenue - Suite 200, Wayzata, MN 55391
Phone: 952 476-9800
Web: www.northernoil.com

PRODUCTS/OPERATIONS

2012 Sales

	$ mil.	% of total
Oil & sales	296.6	95
Unrealized gains on derivatives	15.2	5
Loss on Derivatives	(0.4)	—
Other revenues	0.2	—
Total	**311.6**	**100**

COMPETITORS

Adams Resources	EOG
American Oil & Gas	Exxon Mobil
Anadarko Petroleum	Hunt Consolidated
Apache	Jones Energy
BP	Key Energy
Cabot Oil & Gas	National Fuel Gas
Chesapeake Energy	Noble Energy
Chevron	Pioneer Natural
Cimarex	Resources
ConocoPhillips	Royal Dutch Shell
Devon Energy	

HISTORICAL FINANCIALS
Company Type: Public

Income Statement
FYE: December 31

	REVENUE ($ mil.)	NET INCOME ($ mil.)	NET PROFIT MARGIN	EMPLOYEES
12/13	335.7	53.0	15.8%	20
12/12	311.5	72.2	23.2%	19
12/11	149.3	40.6	27.2%	19
12/10	44.5	6.9	15.5%	11
12/09	14.2	2.8	19.7%	8
Annual Growth	**120.4%**	**108.7%**	**—**	**25.7%**

2013 Year-End Financials

Debt ratio: 38.4%	No. of shares (mil.): 61
Return on equity: 8.8%	Dividends
Cash ($ mil.): 5	Yield: —
Current ratio: 0.54	Payout: —
Long-term debt ($ mil.): 584	Market value ($ mil.): 932

	STOCK PRICE ($) FY Close	P/E High/Low		PER SHARE ($) Earnings	Dividends	Book Value
12/13	15.07	21	14	0.85	0.00	10.02
12/12	16.82	23	12	1.15	0.00	9.23
12/11	23.98	50	20	0.65	0.00	7.84
12/10	27.21	199	78	0.14	0.00	7.01
12/09	11.84	155	27	0.08	0.00	2.81
Annual Growth	**6.2%**	**—**	**—**	**80.5%**	**—**	**37.4%**

Nuvasive Inc

When a back is seriously out of whack NuVasive has some options. The company makes and markets medical devices for the surgical treatment of spinal disorders. NuVasive's products are primarily used in spinal restoration and fusion surgeries. Its minimally disruptive Maximum Access Surgery (MAS) platform enables surgeons to access the spine from the side of the body instead of from the front or back and helps them avoid hitting nerves. NuVasive also features a line of biologic bone grafting materials —both allograft and synthetic —and has a cervical disc replacement system in development. The company sells its FDA-ap-

proved products through a network of exclusive sales agents supported by an in-house sales team.

Geographic Reach

NuVasive maintains a facility in California where it trains doctors in the use of its products. It ships its products directly to doctors overnight from a distribution facility in Tennessee; other US facilities are located in New Jersey Ohio and Maryland. International offices are located in Australia Germany Italy Japan Malaysia Singapore and the UK.

The US accounts for the majority of NuVasive's sales but it is working to establish its products in Europe and Asia. The first hurdle is obtaining regulatory approval for all of the components in its platform for each country it seeks to enter.

Operations

The company offers more than 80 products for procedures in the lumbar thoracic and cervical regions includes the mesh plates screws and biological implants used with its MAS system. Its Osteocel product is an adult stem-cell bone graft used for bone regeneration in orthopedic procedures and at one point was the only commercially available stem-cell product in the US.

NuVasive's revenues primarily come from the sale of disposable materials and implants. The full system of software and instruments are loaned to hospitals for free as long as they keep ordering disposables and implants though a small portion of the company's revenues are from the sale of instruments and systems. Revenues from its monitoring services come from hospitals and are also billed through various payers.

Financial Performance

NuVasive's revenues have steadily increased as it has grown through increased product sales new product additions and acquisitions including a 15% jump to some $620 million in 2012.

Net income has fluctuated in recent years coming in at $3.1 million in 2012 after a dip into the red in 2011 after NuVasive lost a legal fight with another device maker.

Strategy

NuVasive's goal is to make its products and services part of the standard procedure for minimally invasive surgery up and down the entire spine. The firm is focused on expanding the reach of its MAS platform through marketing and sales force efforts to increase market penetration. It also conducts research and development efforts to improve existing offerings to make them more adaptable for surgeons and hospitals.

R&D efforts create new products as well; its MAS system for posterior lumbar interbody fusion (MAS PLIF) procedures was launched in the US and select international markets during 2012. As cervical disc replacement technology —the holy grail for spinal device makers —is advancing rapidly NuVasive has several cervical disc replacement devices in late-stage development.

Mergers and Acquisitions

To further diversify in 2011 the company acquired Impulse Monitoring which provides outsourcing of intraoperative monitoring services. Surgeons in the operating room can receive additional guidance and supervision from Impulse Monitoring's team of neurophysiologists during spine cardio ENT brain and orthopedic procedures.

In 2013 NuVasive added a spine implant manufacturing center in Dayton Ohio through the acquisition of ANC. The $4.5 million purchase allows the company to expand its manufacturing capacity to meet future market demand.

EXECUTIVES

Chairman and CEO, Alexis V. Lukianov, age 58, $900,000 total compensation
EVP Corporate Development and General Counsel, Jason M. Hannon, age 42, $400,000 total compensation
EVP Asia Pacific, Takaaki Tanaka
EVP Global Operations, Tyler P. Lipschultz
VP Accounting, Quentin Blackford
EVP International, Russell Powers
EVP Strategic Sales and Operations, Scott Durall
SVP IOS, Albert Pothier
President and COO, Patrick (Pat) Miles, $520,000 total compensation
President U.S. Sales and Services, Matthew W. (Matt) Link, $375,000 total compensation
EVP Corporate Affairs and Human Resources, Carol Cox
SVP EMEA, Paul Kosters
Evp Global Human Resources, Mike Paolucci
Vice President Research Clinical Resources, Bryan Cornwall
Vice President Of Research And Development, Greg Fisch
Exec Asst To Vice President Acct Cntrlr, Tina Frye Flores
Vice President Of Corporate Development, Rogan Fry
Vice President Human Resources, Campbell Fitch
Vice President Comp Benefits Hris, Karen Osgood
Vice President Sales And Marketing, Edward Bird
Executive Assistant To Vice President, April Ashton
Vice President And Chief Patent Counsel, Jonathan Spangler
Vice President, Bill Schabel
Chairman and CEO, Alexis V. Lukianov, age 58
Board Member, Peter Leddy
Abm, Greg Smith
Secretary, Melissa Previzo
Auditors: Ernst&YoungLLP

LOCATIONS

HQ: Nuvasive Inc
7475 Lusk Boulevard, San Diego, CA 92121
Phone: 858 909-1800   **Fax:** 858 909-2000
Web: www.nuvasive.com

PRODUCTS/OPERATIONS

2012 Sales

	$ mil.	% of total
Spine surgery products	471.2	76
Biologics	110.2	18
Monitoring services	38.9	6
Total	**620.3**	**100**

Selected Acquisitions
2013
ANC LLC ($4.5 million; Dayton Ohio; spinal implant manufacturing)
2011
Impulse Monitoring Inc. ($80 million; Maryland;outsourced monitoring services)
2009
Cervitech Inc. ($47 million; New Jersey; cervical disc replacement system)
Progentix Orthobiology B.V. (40%; Netherlands; synthetic bone)
2008
Osteocel ($35-$85 million; adult stem cell bone graft)

Selected Products
Maximum Access Surgery (MAS) Platform
Armada (pedicle screw system)
CoRoent (implants fixation systems)
MaXcess (retraction system for spine access)
NeuroVision (software to avoid nerves)

Osteocel (biologic grafting material)
Biologic products
    AttraX (synthetic bome graft material)
    FormaGraft (synthetic collagen product)
    Osteocel (allograft material with stem cells)

COMPETITORS

Alphatec Spine	Medtronic Sofamor
Biomet	Danek
CareFusion	Natus Medical
DePuy Spine	Orthofix
Globus Medical	Stryker
Integra LifeSciences	Synthes
Interpore	Zimmer Holdings

HISTORICAL FINANCIALS
Company Type: Public

Income Statement
FYE: December 31

	REVENUE ($ mil.)	NET INCOME ($ mil.)	NET PROFIT MARGIN	EMPLOYEES
12/13	685.1	7.9	1.2%	1,358
12/12	620.2	3.1	0.5%	1,173
12/11	540.5	(69.8)	—	1,093
12/10	478.2	78.2	16.4%	789
12/09	370.3	5.8	1.6%	665
Annual Growth	16.6%	8.0%		19.5%

2013 Year-End Financials

Debt ratio: 29.3%	No. of shares (mil.): 44
Return on equity: 1.3%	Dividends
Cash ($ mil.): 102	Yield: —
Current ratio: 4.58	Payout: —
Long-term debt ($ mil.): 346	Market value ($ mil.): 1,453

	STOCK PRICE ($) FY Close	P/E High/Low	PER SHARE ($) Earnings	Dividends	Book Value
12/13	32.33	186 86	0.17	0.00	13.26
12/12	15.46	368 162	0.07	0.00	12.31
12/11	12.59	— —	(1.73)	0.00	11.64
12/10	25.65	23 11	1.85	0.00	10.99
12/09	31.98	279 155	0.15	0.00	7.64
Annual Growth	0.3%	— —	3.2%	—	14.8%

Och-Ziff Capital Management Group LLC

In the marvelous land of OZ good investments are king. Och-Ziff Capital Management Group provides a variety of alternative asset management services for more than 600 fund investors through offices in New York and overseas in Mumbai Beijing Hong Kong and London. Och-Ziff Capital Management Group's investment strategies include private equity merger arbitrage and equity restructuring among others. With some $46.2 billion in assets under management the majority of its equity holdings are invested in Europe and Asia. The hedge fund firm which boasts about 148 investment professionals including two dozen partners began operations in 1994.

Geographic Reach

New York-headquartered Och-Ziff maintains global operations in London Hong Kong Beijing Mumbai and Dubai.

Operations

The company manages four main funds: its OZ Master Fund; OZ Europe Master Fund; OZ Asia Master Fund; and OZ Global Special Investments Master Fund. The OZ Global Special Investments fund invests in structured and distressed credit.

In 2014 the OZ Master Fund's geographic allocation was 65% in North Central and South America followed by 19% in Europe Africa and the Middle East. Asia Australia and New Zealand made up 16%.

Strategy

Och-Ziff attributes its economic resiliency to its diverse multi-strategy model which allows the firm to take advantage of a variety of opportunities in the market. Indeed the company's hedge fund industry assets under management grew some 17% in 2013 driven by performance-related appreciation and capital net inflows.

Och-Ziff is preparing for more growth spurred mostly by institutional investors. The firm is gaining new business from such investors who are attracted to its long-held policy of openness and transparency (it's the only US public hedge fund that reports fund performance and assets under management to the SEC every month). Institutional investors also are looking to hedge funds to further diversify their investments.

Company Background

Daniel Och (a former Goldman Sachs trader) and the Ziff family founded the company.

The marketplace was not kind to Och-Ziff during the global financial crisis. Overall US hedge funds lost massive amounts during the downturn. While Och-Ziff fared somewhat better than average it still saw significant losses primarily from negative investment performance and customer redemptions. Assets under management fell from $33 billion to $22 billion in 2008 and continued downward hitting $20 billion in April 2009.

EXECUTIVES

CEO, Daniel S. Och, age 53
Vice President Hedge Fund Market, Frances Orabona
CEO, Daniel S. Och, age 53
Auditors: Ernst&YoungLLP

LOCATIONS

HQ: Och-Ziff Capital Management Group LLC
9 West 57th Street, New York, NY 10019
Phone: 212 790-0041
Web: www.ozcap.com

2013 Assets Under Management by Geographic

	% of total
North America	62
Europe	23
Asia	15
Total	**100**

PRODUCTS/OPERATIONS

2013 Sales

	$ mil.	% of total
Incentive income	1076.5	58
Management fees	556.4	29
Och-Ziff funds income	260.8	13
Other	2.2	-
Total	**1895.9**	**100**

2013 Assets Under Management

	% of total
OZ Master Fund	63
Credit funds	11
CLOs	6
OZ Europe Master Fund	4

OZ Asia Master Fund	3
Real estate fund	2
Other multi-strategy fund	9
Other	2
Total	**100**

COMPETITORS

AXA Financial	Greenlight Capital
AllianceBernstein	Renaissance
Charles Schwab	Technologies LLC
Citigroup	UBS Financial Services
Elliott Management	

HISTORICAL FINANCIALS
Company Type: Public

Income Statement
FYE: December 31

	REVENUE ($ mil.)	NET INCOME ($ mil.)	NET PROFIT MARGIN	EMPLOYEES
12/13	1,895.9	261.7	13.8%	546
12/12	1,211.4	(315.8)	—	468
12/11	616.4	(418.9)	—	434
12/10	924.5	(294.4)	—	405
12/09	743.2	(297.4)	—	378
Annual Growth	26.4%	—		9.6%

2013 Year-End Financials

Debt ratio: 45.8%	No. of shares (mil.): 471
Return on equity: ***,***.*%	Dividends
Cash ($ mil.): 189	Yield: 9.5%
Current ratio: 1.51	Payout: 200.0%
Long-term debt ($ mil.): 3,148	Market value ($ mil.): 6,979

	STOCK PRICE ($) FY Close	P/E High/Low	PER SHARE ($) Earnings	Dividends	Book Value
12/13	14.80	9 5	1.62	1.42	(0.12)
12/12	9.50	— —	(2.21)	0.40	(0.58)
12/11	8.41	— —	(4.07)	1.07	(0.86)
12/10	15.58	— —	(3.35)	0.88	(0.95)
12/09	13.74	— —	(3.79)	0.19	(1.04)
Annual Growth	1.9%	— —	—	65.3%	

Old Dominion Freight Line, Inc.

Old Dominion Freight Line still makes its stand in Dixie but the trucking company serves the rest of the US as well. Less-than-truckload (LTL) shipments (freight from multiple shippers consolidated into a single truckload) accounts for the bulk of the company's revenues. Old Dominion operates a fleet of more than 6200 tractors and more than 25000 trailers from more than 220 service centers. In addition to its core LTL services the company offers its customers a broad range of logistics services including ground and air transportation supply chain consulting container delivery and warehousing and household moving.

Geographic Reach

Along with its standard LTL offerings Old Dominion provides expedited delivery and logistics services including warehousing and distribution. Old Dominion also offers drayage services such as direct point-to-point delivery and unloading from about 10 cities including Atlanta Chicago Dallas Los Angeles Memphis and Salt Lake City.

Though it operates throughout the US Old Dominion is a multiregional carrier rather than a national one. The company divides its US territory into six regions: Southeast Gulf Coast Northeast Midwest Central and West. It provides next-day and second-day service within regions.

Financial Performance

Old Dominion's revenues have grown steadily for four straight years to reach historical milestones. Revenues climbed 10% from $2.1 billion in 2012 to peak at $2.3 billion in 2013. The company increased its revenues and customer base in 2013 through organic growth fueled by increases in tonnage and pricing. Old Dominion's growth has also exceeded both the growth rate of the US economy as well as the growth rate for the LTL industry.

Profits surged 22% from $169 million in 2012 to a record-setting $209 million in 2013. This was the result of the higher revenue coupled with lower interest expenses. The company's operating cash flow has steadily increased over the last three years. Cash flow spiked by $23 million in 2013 due to improvement in profits and cash generated from depreciation and amortization deferred income taxes and prepaid expenses and other assets.

Strategy

Old Dominion grows primarily by gaining more customers in its current operating territory and by building out its network of service centers. The company added nearly 35 service centers between 2007 and 2012. It also expands by adding new services such as consumer household moving services added to the menu in 2012.

Throughout 2013 Old Dominion opened its Santa Maria Service Center to accommodate increased freight along US Route 101; launched a new service center in Tomah Wisconsin to serve as a vital transportation hub for the Midwestern US; and relocated its Cincinnati Service Center to a larger facility that will serve customers in Ohio Indiana and Kentucky. The company also opened new facilities in Salinas California; Chicago; and Birmingham Alabama.

Company Background

Old Dominion was founded in 1934 by Earl Congdon. Once a regional trucker the company has expanded beyond the southeastern US particularly since the mid-1990s.

EXECUTIVES

Vp Old Dominion Global, Gregory B Plemmons
President and CEO, David S. Congdon, $540,453 total compensation
SVP Finance and CFO, J. Wes Frye, $322,677 total compensation
EVP and COO, Gregory C. (Greg) Gantt, $397,392 total compensation
VP Technology, Chris Young
Vice President - Legal Affairs; General Counsel; Secretary, Ross Parr
Vice President Of Equipment, Jim Raynor
Vp Western Region, Robert H (Bob) Foote
Vp Midwest Region, Michael A (Mike) Wood
Vice President, Lemuel Clayton
Vice President Administrative Services, Eric Hastings
Executive Vice President, Charles Price
Chairman, Earl E. Congdon
Secretary, Eileen Duen
Auditors: Ernst&YoungLLP

LOCATIONS

HQ: Old Dominion Freight Line, Inc.
500 Old Dominion Way, Thomasville, NC 27360
Phone: 336 889-5000
Web: www.odfl.com

PRODUCTS/OPERATIONS

Domestic LTL Service
Continental US Coverage
Direct Points
Household Services
OD Domestic
Regional/Super-Regional Locations
Security Divider Service
Transit
OD Expedited Service
Expedited Transit Times
Expo Services
OD Expedited
Security Divider Service
Speed Service
Speed Service Air
Speed Service On Demand
Time-sensitive delivery
White Glove Service
Truckload and Special ServicesLTL/TruckloadGlobal Services
Global Assembly and Distribution
Nationwide Container Drayage
Pacific Promise
Worldwide LCL and FCL Service

COMPETITORS

AAA Cooper Transportation	Saia
ArcBest	Schneider National
Averitt Express	Southeastern Freight Lines
Central Freight Lines	Swift Transportation
Con-way Freight	UPS Freight
Estes Express	Vitran
FedEx Freight	YRC Worldwide
J.B. Hunt	

HISTORICAL FINANCIALS

Company Type: Public

Income Statement

FYE: December 31

	REVENUE ($ mil.)	NET INCOME ($ mil.)	NET PROFIT MARGIN	EMPLOYEES
12/13	2,337.6	206.1	8.8%	14,073
12/12	2,110.4	169.4	8.0%	13,016
12/11	1,882.5	139.4	7.4%	12,022
12/10	1,481.0	75.6	5.1%	11,179
12/09	1,245.0	34.8	2.8%	9,608
Annual Growth	17.1%	55.9%	—	10.0%

2013 Year-End Financials

Debt ratio: 9.9%
Return on equity: 18.2%
Cash ($ mil.): 30
Current ratio: 1.43
Long-term debt ($ mil.): 155
No. of shares (mil.): 86
Dividends
Yield: —
Payout: —
Market value ($ mil.): 4,568

	STOCK PRICE ($) FY Close	P/E High/Low	PER SHARE ($) Earnings	Dividends	Book Value
12/13	53.02	22 14	2.39	0.00	14.30
12/12	34.28	25 15	1.97	0.00	11.91
12/11	40.53	25 17	1.63	0.00	9.94
12/10	31.99	45 26	0.90	0.00	7.97
12/09	30.70	91 46	0.42	0.00	7.07
Annual Growth	14.6%	— —	54.7%	—	19.3%

Old Line Bancshares Inc

Old Line Bancshares is the holding company for Old Line Bank serving consumers businesses and wealthy individuals in the Old Line State and in the Washington DC area. With more than 20 branch offices and total assets in excess of $1.1 billion the bank offers standard retail products including deposit accounts CDs and credit cards. It uses funds from deposits to write business and consumer loans; commercial real estate loans make up about half of its portfolio. The bank also offers luxury boat financing. The company also owns 50% of real estate firm Pointer Ridge Office Investment. Old Line acquired Maryland Bankcorp in 2011 and WSB Holdings the parent company of The Washington Savings Bank in 2013.

Mergers and Acquisitions

Old Line Bancshares is pursuing growth via acquisitions. It $54.7-million purchase of WSB Holdings closed in May 2013. Previously Old Line acquired Maryland Bankcorp in 2011 in a move that doubled its branch network and asset portfolio.

EXECUTIVES

Svp Old Line Bank, William J Bush
EVP and Chief Lending Officer, Joseph E. Burnett, age 68, $215,180 total compensation
President and CEO, James W. Cornelsen, age 59, $400,000 total compensation
EVP and Chief Credit Officer, John Miller
CFO, Elise M. Hubbard
EVP and COO, Mark Semanie, $192,673 total compensation
Executive Vice President Marketing, Barbara Sellner
Executive Vice President, Keven B Zinn
Svp And Grp Leader For Montgo, Thomas Mee
Svp-director Of Cash Mgmt And, David Seyler
Svp For Calvert And St Mary's, Kevin M Frere
Svp Old Line Bank, Sandi F Burnett, age 57
Vice President, Rob Bowling
Vice President Commercial Lending, Margaret Sawyer
Assistant Vice President, Debbie Clemens
Vice President Commercial Lending, Katrice Simpson
Vice President Commercial Lender, Bill Gallagher
Assistant Vice President Lending, Nichole Paneck
Vice President Data Processing Manager, Roy Daugherty
Chairman, Craig E. Clark, age 72
Vice Chairman, Frank Lucente, age 72
Board Member, Jeffrey Rivest
Board Member, Frank Taylor
Board Member, Thomas G Daughtery
Auditors: Rowles&CompanyLLP

LOCATIONS

HQ: Old Line Bancshares Inc
1525 Pointer Ridge Place, Bowie, MD 20716
Phone: 301 430-2500
Web: www.oldlinebank.com

COMPETITORS

BB&T	M&T Bank
Bank of America	PNC Financial
First Mariner Bancorp	Tri-County Financial

Company Type: Public

Income Statement
FYE: December 31

	ASSETS ($ mil.)	NET INCOME ($ mil.)	INCOME AS % OF ASSETS	EMPLOYEES
12/13	1,167.2	7.8	0.7%	254
12/12	861.8	7.5	0.9%	182
12/11	811.0	5.3	0.7%	177
12/10	401.9	1.5	0.4%	81
12/09	357.2	2.0	0.6%	83
Annual Growth	34.4%	40.1%	—	32.3%

2013 Year-End Financials

Return on assets: 0.7%
Return on equity: 7.8%
Long-term debt ($ mil.): —
No. of shares (mil.): 10
Sales ($ mil): 53

Dividends
Yield: 1.1%
Payout: 24.6%
Market value ($ mil.): 156

	STOCK PRICE ($) FY Close	P/E High/Low		PER SHARE ($) Earnings	Dividends	Book Value
12/13	14.50	17	13	0.86	0.16	11.71
12/12	11.29	11	7	1.09	0.16	10.94
12/11	8.10	11	8	0.86	0.13	9.98
12/10	8.06	23	16	0.38	0.12	9.52
12/09	6.59	18	11	0.40	0.12	9.31
Annual Growth	21.8%	—	—	21.1%	7.5%	5.9%

Olympic Steel Inc.

Olympic Steel has bypassed gold silver and bronze in favor of carbon coated and stainless steel. A steel service center Olympic Steel provides flat-rolled sheet coil and plate steel products. Its processing services include cutting-to-length slitting and shearing along with blanking laser welding and precision machining. It also makes tubular and pipe products. Olympic Steel operates through subsidiaries including Olympic Steel Lafayette and Chicago Tube and Iron (CTI). It has processing and distribution facilities mainly in the eastern and midwestern US.

Geographic Reach

Olympic Steel operates 34 processing and sales facilities in the US in states including Connecticut Florida Georgia Illinois Indiana Iowa Kentucky Michigan Minnesota North Carolina Ohio Pennsylvania and Texas as well as in Mexico. International sales take place primarily in Canada and Mexico.

Operations

Olympic Steel which acts as an intermediary between metals producers and manufacturers that require processed metals for their operations has two operating segments. Accounting for more than 80% of annual sales the flat products includes processed carbon coated stainless and aluminum products including flat-rolled sheets coils and plates.

The tubular and pipe products segment consists of the Chicago Tube and Iron (CTI) business which distributes metal pipe tubing bars fittings and valves and provides fabrication of pressure parts for various industrial markets. The company use a number of internal management information systems to coordinate functions such as order fulfillment and inventory management.

Sales and Marketing

Olympic Steel uses a direct sales force to promote its products including field sales representatives. Its customers include manufacturers of cars material handling and transportation equipment farm and construction machinery energy equipment storage tanks and other products as well as fabrication and metal service entities. Other customers include makers of food service and electrical equipment military vehicles and equipment as well as general and plate fabricators and metals service centers.

Financial Performance

After experiencing three straight years revenue growth in 2013 the company's revenues dropped by 9% due to a 10% decline in Flat products revenues due to lower sales volume and a 5% decrease in selling prices. Tubular and pipe products revenues declined by 4% due to lower selling prices offset by higher sales volumes. After experiencing a large net income dip in 2012 due to higher debt interest and operating expenses related to the CTI acquisition in 2013 Olympic Steel's net income increased by 236% thanks to lower operating costs and interest and other expense on debt. The company's operating cash inflow increased to $54.68 million in 2013 (compared to $27.74 million in 2012) due to improved net income and a change in the working capital as a result of cash generated from inventories accounts payable and a change in outstanding checks.

Strategy

Olympic Steel hopes to grow by taking advantage of the trend toward outsourcing of manufacturing processes by OEMs. Toward that end the company continues to invest in processing and automation equipment in order to add more value to its products. It also invests in business and IT systems (including replacing data legacy systems) enhances safety awareness programs upgrades delivery and quality processes and keeps a keen eye on inventory turnover and cash turnover rates to maximize operational efficiencies.

In addition to adding to and updating its own operations Olympic has also expanded through targeted acquisitions.

Company Background

In 2012 the company spent some $23 million on capital growth initiatives including the completion of its new specialty metals facility in Ohio and new processing equipment additions at existing facilities. A new temper mill and cut-to-length line facility (Gary Works) was opened in Gary Indiana in 2011; the company also leased several new warehousing spaces in the US and Mexico that year.

Olympic significantly expanded its business in mid-2011 by acquiring CTI (which was founded in 1914) in a $150 million cash deal. The deal expanded Olympic's business by almost one-third allowing it to create the tubular and pipe products segment.

In 2010 Olympic Steel acquired a 100000-square-foot facility in Mount Sterling Kentucky. The facility performs plate burning machining forming and shot blasting and became operational in early 2011.

Chairman and CEO Michael Siegal a member of the family that founded Olympic Steel in 1954 owns a 11% stake in the company. Investment firm Royce & Associates owns a 13% stake.

EXECUTIVES

CFO, Richard T. Marabito, age 50, $450,000 total compensation
President and COO, David A. Wolfort, age 61, $700,000 total compensation
Chairman and CEO, Michael D. Siegal, age 61, $750,000 total compensation
VP Eastern Region, John Mooney
VP Central Region, Steve Mallory
VP Southern Region, John W. Brieck
President and COO Flat Rolled, Raymond Walker
CIO, Esther M. Potash, age 62, $182,022 total compensation
VP Purchasing, Frank Ruane
President Specialty Metals, Andrew S. Greiff
President and CEO Chicago Tube and Iron, Donald R. McNeeley, $575,000 total compensation
Vice President, Zachary Siegal
Chairman and CEO, Michael D. Siegal, age 61
Auditors: PricewaterhouseCoopersLLP

LOCATIONS

HQ: Olympic Steel Inc.
22901 Millcreek Boulevard, Suite 650, Highland Hills, OH 44122
Phone: 216 292-3800   Fax: 216 682-4065
Web: www.olysteel.com

PRODUCTS/OPERATIONS

2012 Sales

	$ mil.	% of total
Flat products	1138.1	82
Tubular & pipe products	245.6	18
Total	1383.7	100

Selected Products

Alloy
Coated
Cold Rolled Carbon
Hot Rolled Carbon
Specialty Metals

COMPETITORS

Allegheny Technologies	Reliance Steel
Feralloy	Ryerson
Friedman Industries	Shiloh Industries
Kenwal Steel	Steel Technologies
Metals USA	

HISTORICAL FINANCIALS

Company Type: Public

Income Statement
FYE: December 31

	REVENUE ($ mil.)	NET INCOME ($ mil.)	NET PROFIT MARGIN	EMPLOYEES
12/13	1,263.3	7.6	0.6%	1,790
12/12	1,383.7	2.2	0.2%	1,870
12/11	1,261.8	24.9	2.0%	1,700
12/10	805.0	2.1	0.3%	1,113
12/09	523.4	(61.2)	—	981
Annual Growth	24.6%	—	—	16.2%

2013 Year-End Financials

Debt ratio: 28.5%
Return on equity: 2.6%
Cash ($ mil.): 3
Current ratio: 2.52
Long-term debt ($ mil.): 186

No. of shares (mil.): 10
Dividends
Yield: 0.2%
Payout: 11.5%
Market value ($ mil.): 318

	STOCK PRICE ($) FY Close	P/E High/Low		PER SHARE ($) Earnings	Dividends	Book Value
12/13	28.98	45	28	0.69	0.08	27.24
12/12	22.14	131	72	0.21	0.08	26.49
12/11	23.32	15	7	2.28	0.08	26.28
12/10	28.68	183	103	0.20	0.08	24.04
12/09	32.58	—	—	(5.62)	0.11	23.85
Annual Growth	(2.9%)	—	—	—	(7.7%)	3.4%

Omega Flex Inc

Like a reed in a stream Grasshopper sometimes the flexible withstand pressure better than the rigid. That's certainly a concept that Omega Flex can get behind: The company makes corrugated metal and flexible tubular and braided metal (stainless steel bronze) hoses and reinforcements for liquid and gas transportation. Its products are designed to deal with high pressure motion extreme temperatures harsh liquids or gases and abrasion. Other applications include cryogenics and propane and natural gas installations. Chairman John Reed and his son Stewart together own a majority of Omega Flex which was spun off from Mestek in 2005.

Geographic Reach

Pennsylvania-based Omega Flex has manufacturing operations in Exton Pennsylvania. Some manufacturing is performed in the UK. The company rings up about 90% of its sales in North America. International sales are mainly in the UK and elsewhere in Europe.

Sales and Marketing

The company targets the commercial construction and general industrial sectors. Its typical customers include petrochemical plants steel mills transportation companies and pharmaceutical firms. Sales channels include independent sales representatives distributors OEMs direct sales and online sales via the company's website.

Omega Flex's brand names include OmegaFlex TracPipe and CounterStrike. Recently developed products include the DoubleTrac brand of piping used in gas stations and other underground petroleum piping applications and SolarTrac piping for solar-heated hot water systems.

Financial Performance

The flexible metallic hose maker reported sales of $77.1 million in 2013 an increase of 20% versus 2012. Net income rose 46% over the same period to $10 million. The company has posted steady revenue and profit growth in recent years and a sharp rebound in cash flow generated from operations since 2011. Omega Flex credited the double-digit increase in 2013 sales to improvements in the residential construction industry which supported higher volume sales and rising prices for its flexible piping.

EXECUTIVES

President CEO and Director, Kevin R. Hoben, age 67, $331,739 total compensation
Chief Operating Officer; Executive Vice President; Director, Mark F. Albino, age 61, $265,601 total compensation
VP Finance and CFO, Paul J. Kane, age 46
Vice President, Edwin Moran
President CEO and Director, Kevin R. Hoben, age 67
Vice Chairman, Edward J. (Ted) Trainor, age 74
Chief Operating Officer; Executive Vice President; Director, Mark F. Albino, age 61
Auditors: VitaleCaturanoandCompanyP.C.

LOCATIONS

HQ: Omega Flex Inc
451 Creamery Way, Exton, PA 19341
Phone: 610 524-7272
Web: www.omegaflex.com

PRODUCTS/OPERATIONS

Selected Brands
AutoFlare
CounterStrike
OmegaFlex
TracPipe

COMPETITORS

Dixon Valve	Kelly Pipe Co. LLC
Everett J. Prescott	Redlon & Johnson
Ferguson Enterprises	Tuthill
Gates Corp.	Ward Manufacturing

HISTORICAL FINANCIALS
Company Type: Public

Income Statement
FYE: December 31

	REVENUE ($ mil.)	NET INCOME ($ mil.)	NET PROFIT MARGIN	EMPLOYEES
12/13	77.1	10.0	13.0%	131
12/12	64.0	6.8	10.7%	129
12/11	54.1	4.6	8.6%	116
12/10	46.8	4.5	9.7%	107
12/09	44.1	4.3	9.9%	106
Annual Growth	15.0%	23.0%	—	5.4%

2013 Year-End Financials

Debt ratio: —	No. of shares (mil.): 10
Return on equity: 44.4%	Dividends
Cash ($ mil.): 8	Yield: 2.0%
Current ratio: 2.41	Payout: 55.9%
Long-term debt ($ mil.): —	Market value ($ mil.): 206

	STOCK PRICE ($) FY Close	P/E High/Low		PER SHARE ($) Earnings	Dividends	Book Value
12/13	20.46	21	12	0.99	0.43	2.53
12/12	12.36	25	15	0.68	1.00	1.95
12/11	14.13	36	23	0.46	0.00	2.26
12/10	16.54	39	22	0.45	0.00	1.80
12/09	14.00	52	26	0.43	2.00	1.35
Annual Growth	9.9%	—	—	23.2%	(32.1%)	16.9%

Omega Healthcare Investors, Inc.

Omega Healthcare Investors can put an end to the burdens of real-estate management. The self-administered real estate investment trust (REIT) invests in health care facilities throughout the US. It owns some 540 properties primarily long-term care facilities in nearly 40 states. The REIT specializes in sales/leaseback transactions in which it purchases properties owned by health care providers and leases them back to those companies (thereby freeing the health care companies from the responsibilities of real estate management). The REIT's properties are operated by third-party health care operating companies including Genesis HealthCare System and CommuniCare Health Services.

Geographic Reach

The Maryland-based REITs largest markets are Florida Indiana and Ohio which combined account for more than a third of its properties. Texas is an-other important market for the firm. Overall Omega Healthcare Investors has holdings in 38 states.

Sales and Marketing

The REIT's largest tenants include New Ark Investment Genesis Healthcare and CommuniCare Health Services which together represent about a third of its portfolio.

Financial Performance

Omega Healthcare Investors (OHI) reported revenue of $418.7 million in 2013 a 19% increase versus 2012. Driving the double-digit gain was rising rental income generated by investments made in 2013 and 2012. Net income grew 43% to $172.5 million on higher rental income. Both revenue and cash flow has increased steadily over the past four years and profitability has rebounded.

Strategy

The REIT is investing aggressively in the health care sector as demand for senior living facilities grows in tandem with the aging population and the real estate market makes a comeback. Indeed in 2013 the firm completed transactions totaling about $622 million in new investments. Its core portfolio consists of long-term lease and mortgage agreements. All of its leases are "triple-net" leases which require the tenants to pay all property related expenses. The REIT's mortgage revenue comes from fixed-rate loans. Omega Healthcare's geographically diverse portfolio comprises 476 skilled nursing facilities 18 assisted living locations and 11 specialty facilities such as rehabilitation hospitals. Its properties are operated by third parties.

EXECUTIVES

Chief Executive Officer; Director, C. Taylor Pickett, age 52, $600,000 total compensation
COO, Daniel J. Booth, age 50, $380,000 total compensation
CFO, Robert O. Stephenson, age 50, $305,000 total compensation
Chief Technology Officer, Galen Warren
Vice President Of Operations, Megan Krull
Chairman, Bernard J. (Bernie) Korman, age 82
Auditors: Ernst&YoungLLP

LOCATIONS

HQ: Omega Healthcare Investors, Inc.
200 International Circle, Suite 3500, Hunt Valley, MD 21030
Phone: 410 427-1700   **Fax:** 410 427-8800
Web: www.omegahealthcare.com

2013 Properties

	No.
Florida	86
Indiana	56
Ohio	50
Texas	40
Pennsylvania	25
Arkansas	23
California	22
Michigan	21
Mississippi	19
Tennessee	18
Maryland	16
South Carolina	16
Kentucky	15
Louisiana	14
Colorado	12
North Carolina	11
West Virginia	11
Arizona	10
Alabama	10
Massachusetts	8
Georgia	7
Idaho	6
Oklahoma	5

Virginia	4
Rhode Island	4
Wisconsin	4
Illinois	4
Iowa	3
Washington	3
Nevada	3
New Hampshire	3
Utah	3
New Mexico	2
Missouri	2
Vermont	2
Kansas	1
Oregon	1
Connecticut	1
Total	**541**

PRODUCTS/OPERATIONS

2013 Sales

	$ mil.	% of total
Rental income	375.1	90
Mortgage interest	29.4	7
Income from direct financing leases	5.2	1
Others	9.0	2
Total	**418.7**	**100**

COMPETITORS

G&L Realty Properties	National Health
HCP	Investors
Health Care REIT	Senior Housing
Healthcare Realty	Properties
Trust	Ventas
LTC Properties	

HISTORICAL FINANCIALS

Company Type: Public

Income Statement

FYE: December 31

	REVENUE ($ mil.)	NET INCOME ($ mil.)	NET PROFIT MARGIN	EMPLOYEES
12/13	418.7	172.5	41.2%	25
12/12	350.4	120.7	34.4%	25
12/11	292.2	52.6	18.0%	24
12/10	258.3	58.4	22.6%	24
12/09	197.4	82.1	41.6%	19
Annual Growth	**20.7%**	**20.4%**	**—**	**7.1%**

2013 Year-End Financials

Debt ratio: 58.4%	No. of shares (mil.): 123
Return on equity: 14.9%	Dividends
Cash ($ mil.): 2	Yield: 6.2%
Current ratio: —	Payout: 133.8%
Long-term debt ($ mil.): 2,024	Market value ($ mil.): 3,681

	STOCK PRICE ($) FY Close	P/E High/Low	PER SHARE ($) Earnings	Dividends	Book Value
12/13	29.80	26 16	1.46	1.86	10.52
12/12	23.85	22 17	1.12	1.69	9.00
12/11	19.35	53 31	0.46	1.55	8.50
12/10	22.44	46 34	0.52	1.37	10.12
12/09	19.45	23 14	0.87	1.20	9.80
Annual Growth	**11.3%**	**— —**	**13.8%**	**11.6%**	**1.8%**

Omega Protein Corp.

Omega Protein is the alpha dog of the fish-meal market. With a handful of US processing plants a fleet of some 40 fishing vessels and 30-plus spotter aircraft the company is the largest US producer of fish meal and fish oil derived from menhaden (an inedible fish found in the Gulf of Mexico and along the East Coast). Animal-feed makers and livestock ranchers use Omega Protein's fish meal for protein additives in feed; the fish oil is used in Europe in margarine and for industrial ends. Rich in Omega-3 fatty acids (linked to health benefits) fish oil is also used as a human food supplement. Through subsidiaries Omega Protein provides nutraceutical ingredients and compounds including Omega-3 fish oils.

Geographic Reach

The US is the Houston-based company's largest market accounting for 50% of its sales. Asia contributes nearly 30% while Europe represents more than 10%. Other markets include Canada South and Central America and Mexico.

Operations

Omega Protein's operations consist of four primary subsidiaries: Omega Protein processes and harvests menhaden fish; Omega Shipyards owns and manages the drydock facility for the company's fishing fleet and occasionally third parties; Cyvex Nutrition supplies ingredients to the nutraceutical market; and InCon Processing is a specialty toll processor that uses molecular distillation technology to create Omega-3 fish oils.

Omega Protein's fish oil brands include Virginia Prime OmegaPure and OmegaActiv; fish meal brands include Special Select and SeaLac. The company also makes fertilizer (OmegaGrow) and a fungicide/insecticide (SeaCide). Many customers are feed producers who use Omega Protein's products to manufacture feed for swine and dairy cattle as well as for domestic pets. An increasing percentage of the company's products are being used by the aquaculture industry as the practice of aquaculture increases worldwide.

Sales and Marketing

Omega Protein's largest customer in 2013 was Nestl @Purina PetCare which contributed approximately $22.7 million (or 9% of sales) to the company's coffers. The company's products are sold directly to some 200 domestic and foreign customers most of which are located in Canada Chile Norway Saudi Arabia China and Japan. Independent sales agents generate a small amount of sales.

Financial Performance

Omega Protein rang up $244.3 million in sales in 2013 an increase of nearly 4% versus 2012. Higher fish meal prices (up nearly 23%) and higher volume and prices for fish oil drove the increase. Sales of animal nutrition products were relatively flat in 2013 versus 2012 while sales of products for humans which includes dietary supplements and food ingredients rose 29%.

Net income soared 651% in 2013 versus the prior year to $30.5 million on higher sales and the absence of of charges related to an investigation by the US Attorney in 2012.

Strategy

Omega Protein's strategy going forward includes growth through acquisitions most recently of human nutrition businesses. In September 2014 the company acquired Bioriginal Food & Science Corp. to expand and diversify its human nutrition business. Canada-based Bioriginal Food & Science supplies plant- and marine-based specialty oils and essential fatty acids to the food and nutraceutical industries in North America Europe and Asia. Bioriginal Food & Science which has about $98 million in net revenues will operate as a wholly-owned subsidiary of Omega Protein. Omega Protein paid $70.5 million for the company.

In February 2013 the company purchased Wisconsin Specialty Protein (WSP) based in Madison to build on its human nutrition business with WSP's specialty whey protein products. In 2011 Omega Protein purchased Illinois-based InCon Processing L.L.C. The acquisition allowed Omega Protein to enhance its commercial fishery and human nutrition distribution channels. To extend its reach into the fish oil market and gain access to top supplement retailers Omega in 2010 acquired Cyvex which provides Omega protein and non-marine based products and boasts a vast Omega-3 distribution network.

The company is also acting to expand and trim select operations. In 2013 it announced plans to streamline operations in the Gulf of Mexico through the permanent closure of its menhaden fish processing plant in Cameron Louisiana and the redeployment of certain ships from that plant to reduce maintenance-related capital expenditures. Also in mid-2014 the company completed an expansion roughly doubling capacity its specialty dairy protein production facility in Reedsburg Wisconsin.

In June 2013 Omega Protein resolved investigations by the US Coast Guard and the US EPA by entering into a plea agreement with the US Attorney's Office. The company pleaded guilty to two Clean Water Act violations and paid a $5.5 million fine.

HISTORY

Omega Protein's predecessor dates back to a fish processing operation founded in Reedville Virginia by John and Thomas Haynie in 1878. (The site currently is home to the company's largest plant.) Almost a century later Zapata an oil and gas firm co-founded by George H.W. Bush acquired Haynie Products.

The division became known as Zapata Haynie. The company spent the late 1980s and 1990s fighting for FDA approval of refined menhaden oil for human consumption (the oil contains high levels of Omega-3 fatty acids touted as having health benefits); approval was finally granted in 1997.

Financier Malcolm Glazer first acquired a stake in Zapata in 1992. That year Zapata acquired 60% of Venture Milling a Delaware-based blender of animal protein products. Two years later the division was renamed Zapata Protein to reflect its expansion into animal feed. Zapata sold most of the assets of Venture Milling in 1997 and acquired two of its four US rivals: Chesapeake Bay area-based American Protein and Louisiana-based Gulf Protein. Also that year it renamed the division Marine Genetics.

In 1998 Zapata changed Marine Genetics' name to Omega Protein and spun off about 40% in that division to the public. Despite an active hurricane season that crimped the fishing season Omega Protein reported record profits in 1998. However dramatic price drops for fish meal and fish oil (caused by a global glut in those markets) squeezed the life out of sales and profits in 1999. Omega Protein responded by mothballing part of its fleet for the 2000 fishing season.

In 2003 Omega received two separate unsolicited takeover offers —the first at $45 per share by merger and acquisition firm Hollingsworth Rothwell & Roxford; the second at $9.50 per share from Australia-based Ferrari Investments and unidentified US partners.

Omega completed a processing facility in 2004 in Reedsville Virginia that tripled its existing refined fish-oil production capacity. The factory also expanded capacity for oils used in leather drilling fluid and animal food.

The company shut down its sales office in Mexico in 2005 and consolidated its functions with those at its Houston headquarters. The company's Moss Point processing facility and its shipyard in Mississippi were severely damaged due to Hurricane Katrina in August 2005. Its Cameron and Abbeville plants in Louisiana were shut down that September due to damage sustained from Hurricane Rita. Moss Point and Abbeville were reopened in mid-October. The Cameron facility was rebuilt and back in operation by 2006.

Omega Protein was 33% owned by investor and then Omega chairman Avram Glazer's family which maintained its shares through Zapata Corporation. However Zapata sold its holdings in Omega in 2006 at which time Glazer stepped down as chairman and president and CEO Joseph von Rosenberg replaced Glazer.

In 2007 the company opened a technical center in Houston (The OmegaPure Technology and Innovation Center) to research and develop new Omega-3 products.

EXECUTIVES

EVP General Counsel and Secretary, John D. Held, age 51, $300,000 total compensation
President and CEO, Bret Scholtes, age 44, $450,000 total compensation
President Animal Nutrition Division, Mark E. Griffin, age 47, $300,000 total compensation
EVP and CFO, Andrew C. Johannesen, $325,000 total compensation
President Bioriginal, Joseph R. Vidal
Senior Director Operations, Monty C. Deihl
Vice President, Vance Loiselle
Vice President Operations, Jonathan Specht
Vice President Refined Oils, Albert Riley
Chairman, Gary R. Goodwin
Auditors: PricewaterhouseCoopersLLP

LOCATIONS

HQ: Omega Protein Corp.
2105 City West Blvd., Suite 500, Houston, TX 77042-2838
Phone: 713 623-0060
Web: www.omegaproteininc.com

2013 Sales

	$ mil.	% of total
Asia	70.9	29
North America		
US	123.9	50
Canada	11.6	5
Mexico	1.3	1
Europe	31.5	13
Central & South America	4.8	2
Other	0.3	
Total	**244.3**	**100**

PRODUCTS/OPERATIONS

2013 Sales

	$ mil.	% of total
Fish meal	142.5	58
Fish oil	43.8	18
Refined fish oil	22.7	9
Dietary supplement ingredients	31.1	13
Fish solubles	4.2	2
Total	**244.3**	**100**

2013 Sales

$ mil		% of total
Animal nutrition	213.2	87
Human nutrition	31.1	13
Total	**244.3**	**100**

Selected Products

Fish meal
  Feed
  Animal
  Aquaculture
  Household pets
  Swine
Fish oil
  Feed
  Animal
  Aquaculture
  Dietary supplements
  Human foods
Fish solubles
  Aquaculture feed
  Bait
  Organic fertilizer

COMPETITORS

ADM	Ingredion
ADM Alliance Nutrition	Kodiak Fishmeal
Ag Processing Inc.	Land O' Lakes Purina
American Seafoods	Feed
Bayer CropScience	Marubeni
Blue Seal Feeds	Nippon Suisan
Bunge Limited	Nutreco
CHS	Scotts Miracle-Gro
Cargill	Scoular
Dow AgroSciences	Westward Seafoods
Griffin Industries	

HISTORICAL FINANCIALS

Company Type: Public

Income Statement

FYE: December 31

	REVENUE ($ mil.)	NET INCOME ($ mil.)	NET PROFIT MARGIN	EMPLOYEES
12/13	244.2	30.5	12.5%	450
12/12	235.6	4.0	1.7%	500
12/11	235.2	34.1	14.5%	495
12/10	167.7	18.2	10.9%	493
12/09	164.8	(6.2)	—	503
Annual Growth	**10.3%**	**—**	**—**	**(2.7%)**

2013 Year-End Financials

Debt ratio: 7.3%	No. of shares (mil.): 20
Return on equity: 13.4%	Dividends
Cash ($ mil.): 34	Yield: —
Current ratio: 4.11	Payout: —
Long-term debt ($ mil.): 21	Market value ($ mil.): 256

	STOCK PRICE ($) FY Close	P/E High/Low		PER SHARE ($) Earnings	Dividends	Book Value
12/13	12.29	10	4	1.45	0.00	11.88
12/12	6.12	43	29	0.20	0.00	10.34
12/11	7.13	8	4	1.71	0.00	10.04
12/10	8.10	8	4	0.97	0.00	8.37
12/09	4.36	—	—	(0.33)	0.00	7.32
Annual Growth	**29.6%**			**—**	**—**	**12.9%**

Omnicell Inc

Omnicell is all-knowing when it comes to dispensing drugs to patients. A developer of specialized software and hardware products Omnicell makes mobile cabinets and workstations that automatically dispense doses of medication and surgical supplies to help pharmacists and nurses reduce medical errors and increase patient safety.

More than 1600 hospitals use its OmniRx medication dispensing cabinets and complementary software such as SinglePointe and AnywhereRN a program that allows nurses to remotely operate the cabinets. Another top seller is WorkflowRx an automated pharmacy management software system that tracks inventory.

Geographic Reach

The company's products are used throughout the US and Canada. It also markets its products in Europe.

Operations

Omnicell is organized into two segments: Acute Care and Non-Acute Care. Acute Care products accounted for more than 80% of revenue in fiscal 2012.

The company has parlayed the technology behind its medication-dispensing cabinets into other hospital products that keep track of inventory and supplies. It makes a secure dispensing system for anesthesia supplies used in the operating room as well as a barcode inventory management system for controlled substances.

Omnicell's OptiFlex is an automated cabinet that dispenses surgical and medical supplies using barcodes to assign and bill products to patient accounts and its Tissue Center manages and documents tissue sample specimens taken from patients during biopsies and other procedures and used for medical research.

Sales and Marketing

Omnicell is only one of a handful of companies that make automated medication dispensing cabinets. Others include McKesson's AcuDose CareFusion's Pyxis and AmerisourceBergen's MedSelect. While its competitors manufacture a variety of products for the health care industry Omnicell is focused on providing its specialized hardware and software.

The company's sales force is organized by geographic region in the US and Canada. Omnicell uses a direct sales force for Non-Acute Care products in the UK and Germany. For other geographies the company's products are sold through distributors.

Financial Performance

The company has experienced mostly revenue growth in recent fiscal years. In fiscal 2012 it reported more than $314 million in revenue up from the $245.5 million it claimed in fiscal 2011 and the $222.4 million the company brought in during fiscal 2010.

Strategy

Omnicell's growth strategy centers on developing new products and enhancing existing products. Although it does not routinely pursue acquisitions as a means of bolstering its offerings Omnicell does make strategic acquisitions of product technologies and assets from time to time.

Mergers and Acquisitions

In 2012 Omnicell bought MTS Medication Technologies a maker of automated medication packaging systems and accessories for $156 million. The acquisition helped align Omnicell with the long term trends of the healthcare market. The combination of Omnicell and MTS created a comprehensive automated medication management offering across the acute and non-acute continuum of patient care.

Ownership

Omnicell was founded in 1992 by CEO Randall A. Lipps who owns less than 5% of the company's stock. Its largest shareholders are BlackRock with an 8% stake and Wellington Capital Management with 7.5%.

EXECUTIVES

Senior Vice President And General Council, Daniel Johnston, age 51

CFO and EVP Finance International and Manufacturing, Robin G. (Rob) Seim, age 54, $276,975 total compensation

Chairman President and CEO, Randall A. Lipps, age 56, $482,930 total compensation

EVP Sales and Marketing, J. Christopher (Chris) Drew, age 48, $304,440 total compensation

EVP Strategy and Business Development, Nhat H. Ngo, age 41

EVP Global Manufacturing, Michael Stevenson

EVP of Engineering, Jorge Taborga

Vice President International Sales, Gary Ervin

Vice President Human Resources, Susan Moriconi

Vice President Manager Director, Connie Ayala

Vice President Strategy Mkt Dev, Kimberly Howland

Vice President Strategic Accounts, James Taylor

Vice President Manager Director, Julie Varwig

Vice President Finance, Patrick Kelliher

Rvp, Bill Wingfield

Vice President Manager Director, Susan Dailey

Vice President Field Operations, Pat Diresta

Vice President General Manager West Division, Nick Reyes

Vice President Marketing, Marga Ortigas-wedekind

National Sales Manager, Bret Van Delden

Vice President And Gm, William Wingfield

Senior Vice President Field Operations, Chris Drew

Chairman President and CEO, Randall A. Lipps, age 56

Auditors: Ernst&YoungLLP

LOCATIONS

HQ: Omnicell Inc
590 East Middlefield Road, Mountain View, CA 94043
Phone: 650 251-6100
Web: www.omnicell.com

PRODUCTS/OPERATIONS

2012 Sales

	$ mil.	% of total
Acute care	260.1	83
Non-Acute care	53.9	17
Total	**314**	**100**

Selected Mergers and Acquisitions

FY2012

MTS Medication Technologies ($156 million; St. Petersburg FL; maker of automated medication packaging systems and accessories)

Selected Products

DecisionCenter (data analysis and decision support for inventory management)
Hospital inventory management systems (ScanREQ)
Pharmacy dispensing automation systems
Anesthesia Workstation (operating room anesthesia supply dispensing system)
OmniCenter (server for managing automated supply systems)
OmniLinkRx (physician order management system)
Patient Medication Profiling (software for patient-specific medication information)
SafetyMed (system for ensuring that patients get the correct medications on time)
SecureVault (dispensing and storage system for controlled substances)
SinglePointe (dispensing and storage system)
WorkflowRX (inventory management)
Supply dispensing automation systems
Omnicell Supply (automated supply dispensing systems)

COMPETITORS

Allscripts	Ergotron
AmerisourceBergen	McKesson
CareFusion	SciQuest
Cerner	Siemens Healthcare
Emerson Electric	

HISTORICAL FINANCIALS

Company Type: Public

Income Statement

FYE: December 31

	REVENUE ($ mil.)	NET INCOME ($ mil.)	NET PROFIT MARGIN	EMPLOYEES
12/13	380.5	23.9	6.3%	1,134
12/12	314.0	16.1	5.2%	1,089
12/11	245.5	10.3	4.2%	773
12/10	222.4	4.8	2.2%	753
12/09	213.4	0.4	0.2%	753
Annual Growth	**15.6%**	**171.1%**	**—**	**10.8%**

2013 Year-End Financials

Debt ratio: —
Return on equity: 7.3%
Cash ($ mil.): 104
Current ratio: 2.53
Long-term debt ($ mil.): —
No. of shares (mil.): 35
Dividends
Yield: —
Payout: —
Market value ($ mil.): 894

	STOCK PRICE ($) FY Close	P/E High/Low		PER SHARE ($) Earnings	Dividends	Book Value
12/13	25.53	37	22	0.67	0.00	9.97
12/12	14.87	36	26	0.47	0.00	9.17
12/11	16.52	55	42	0.30	0.00	8.53
12/10	14.45	100	74	0.15	0.00	8.03
12/09	11.69	1288	670	0.01	0.00	7.58
Annual Growth	**21.6%**	**—**	**—186.1%**			**7.1%**

OmniVision Technologies Inc

OmniVision Technologies gets the big picture with a single chip. The fabless semiconductor company designs semiconductor image sensors (CameraChips) that capture and convert images for cameras mobile phones notebooks webcams surveillance equipment and medical imaging systems among other applications. Its CameraCubeChip device combines the company's image sensors with wafer-level optics for a complete camera module. OmniVision outsources manufacturing chores to silicon foundries (contract semiconductor manufacturers) primarily Taiwan Semiconductor Manufacturing Company (TSMC). Most sales are from Asia predominantly China.

Geographic Reach Asia is OmniVision's largest market with China accounting for nearly 60% of sales; South Korea Malaysia and Japan together contribute nearly 30%. The US only accounted for 7% of sales in fiscal 2012 but that was up nearly 300% from the prior year. The company attributes the rise in US sales to a temporary change in purchasing preference for one customer that it does not expect to continue.

Sales and Marketing Manufacturers and value-added resellers account about three-fourths of OmniVision's sales while distributors make up the rest. Components manufacturer LG Innotek contributes about 15% of sales and distributor World Peace International (part of WPG Holdings) accounts for more than 10%.

Financial Performance After a banner year in fiscal 2011 in which revenue grew nearly 60% the company reported revenue for fiscal 2012 (ended April) of $898 million down about 6%. The decline was primarily the result of weakness in low-resolution sensors as competition intensified to serve the entry-level mobile phone and notebook markets.

Net income was also down that year falling nearly 50% to $66 million. In addition to lower sales net income was impacted by substantial growth in research and development expenses related to new product development and amortization of the patent portfolio OmniVision acquired in 2011.

Strategy OmniVision depends on sales to customers in many markets (automotive entertainment mobile phone notebook) that are particularly vulnerable to periods of economic turmoil. In addition much of OmniVision's business is in mobile phones a highly competitive market with a handful of leading manufacturers. The company must continually develop and introduce new products for the market to remain competitive with its industry rivals. OmniVision is looking to expand in the medical and surveillance markets which are less tied to consumer buying patterns. The company is making image sensors used in disposable medical ventilation tubes. Its automotive sensors are being used in driver assistance applications including lane departure warning systems and 360 degree viewers features that are growing in popularity on new cars. Mergers and Acquisitions In a move that showcases the company's commitment to new product growth in early 2011 it bought 850 patents related to sensor imaging from Eastman Kodak for $65 million in cash in 2011. The deal doubled the size of the company's intellectual property holdings. Also that year OmniVision moved to take more control of its CameraCube technology by reclaiming the CameraCubeChip production operations from VisEra its manufacturing joint venture with TSMC.

EXECUTIVES

Chief Executive Officer; Director, Shaw Hong, age 78, $633,750 total compensation

VP Finance and CFO, Anson H. Chan, age 46, $358,500 total compensation

Chief Operating Officer; Director, Henry Yang, $384,250 total compensation

Chief Technical Officer, Howard E. Rhodes, $350,833 total compensation

Vp-quality & Reliability, John T Yue, age 69

Vice President Ic Design Development, Chen David Datong

Vp Sales & Marketing, Christopher Peters

Administrative Assistant To The Vp, Stephanie Fish

Vice President Quality, Zille Baker

Vice President Of System Technology, Hongjun Li

Vice President Marketing And Sales, Victor Hsia

Vice President Of North America Sales, Michelle Milunovic

Vice President Of Worldwide Sales, Hank Ohara

Vice President Of Sales Worldwide, Aurelio Cisneros

Vice President Information Technology, Gary Chen

Vice President Asia Pacific Business, Jeanette Hong

Vice President, Li Hongjun

Chief Executive Officer; Director, Shaw Hong, age 78

Board Of Director, Max Lellouche
Auditors: PricewaterhouseCoopersLLP

LOCATIONS

HQ: OmniVision Technologies Inc
4275 Burton Drive, Santa Clara, CA 95054
Phone: 408 567-3000
Web: www.ovt.com

2012 Sales

	$ mil.	% of total
China	520.4	58
South Korea	147.4	16
US	61.8	7
Malaysia	50.9	6
Japan	46.1	5
Other countries	71.1	8
Total	**897.7**	**100**

PRODUCTS/OPERATIONS

2012 Sales

	% of total
OEMs and value-added resellers	78
Distributors	22
Total	**100**

Selected Products

CameraCube (combines image sensors chip scale
  packaging and wafer-level optics)
Single-chip image sensors (CameraChip OmniPixel)
Software drivers (for Linux Mac and Windows operating
  systems)

COMPETITORS

Aptina	Pixim
Avago Technologies	SANYO Semiconductor
Canon	SK Hynix
Eastman Kodak	STMicroelectronics
FUJIFILM	Samsung Electronics
Foveon	Sharp Corp.
Freescale	Sony
Semiconductor	Teledyne DALSA
Melexis	Tessera
Mitsubishi Electric	Texas Instruments
NXP Semiconductors	Toshiba Semiconductor
Panasonic Corp	& Storage Products
Pixelplus	

HISTORICAL FINANCIALS

Company Type: Public

Income Statement

FYE: April 30

	REVENUE ($ mil.)	NET INCOME ($ mil.)	NET PROFIT MARGIN	EMPLOYEES
04/14	1,453.9	95.0	6.5%	2,008
04/13	1,407.9	42.9	3.0%	2,057
04/12	897.7	65.8	7.3%	1,796
04/11	956.4	124.4	13.0%	1,465
04/10	602.9	6.7	1.1%	1,450
Annual Growth	**24.6%**	**93.9%**	**—**	**8.5%**

2014 Year-End Financials

Debt ratio: 2.7%
Return on equity: 10.3%
Cash ($ mil.): 297
Current ratio: 4.40
Long-term debt ($ mil.): 32

No. of shares (mil.): 56
Dividends
  Yield: —
  Payout: —
Market value ($ mil.): 1,095

	STOCK PRICE ($) FY Close	P/E High/Low		PER SHARE ($) Earnings	Dividends	Book Value
04/14	19.53	12	8	1.70	0.00	17.60
04/13	13.41	23	15	0.80	0.00	15.66
04/12	18.42	31	9	1.13	0.00	14.53
04/11	33.59	16	7	2.11	0.00	12.96
04/10	17.56	149	64	0.13	0.00	10.25
Annual Growth	**2.7%**	**—**	**—**	**90.2%**	**—**	**14.5%**

On Assignment, Inc.

Attention scientists: Tired of unreliable assistants? Try On Assignment. The specialist staffing agency places scientists and other professionals from lab assistants to nurses with clients in need of temporary help. The firm operates through several divisions: Apex (IT and engineering staffing for temporary temp-to-hire and permanent placements); Healthcare (nurse travel clinical lab diagnostic and imaging staffing services); Life Sciences (scientists chemists technicians); Oxford (engineering and specialized high-end IT consultants); and Physician (short- and long-term physician staffing). On Assignment provides staff to more than 6500 clients and was founded in 1985.

Geographic Reach

The company operates from about 130 branch offices in nearly 35 states and seven foreign countries including Belgium Canada China Ireland the Netherlands Spain and the UK. The US accounts for nearly 95% of its total sales.

Operations

On Assignment has changed its operating structure due to milestone acquisitions it has made over the last few years. Its chief operating segments include Apex (41% of total sales) Oxford (28%) Life Sciences (13%) Healthcare (10%) and Physician (8%).

Financial Performance

The company has enjoyed unprecedented growth over the last two years primarily due to acquisitions. Its revenues doubled from $598 million in 2011 to $1.2 billion in 2012. Profits also climbed 76% from $24 million in 2011 to nearly $43 million in 2012. Both these totals for 2012 represented historic milestones for the company.

Its 2012 purchase of Apex Systems was the main driver of growth in addition to 22% year-over-year growth from its other business segments. Its Oxford segment revenues jumped 30% due to an increase in the average number of contract professionals on assignment and a rise in the average bill rate and in conversion and permanent placement revenue.

Healthcare segment revenues in 2012 were up by 27% due to improved conditions within the healthcare sector resulting in a higher number of contract professionals on assignment and open orders and average bill rates. The 27% increase in Physician segment revenue was attributable to the inclusion of a full year's operating results from HCP an acquisition it made in 2011 and a nearly $8 million increase in its legacy physician business. Its Life Sciences segment revenues were also up by 5% during 2012.

Strategy

On Assignment's business strategy involves steady growth through targeted acquisitions. Since its founding it has purchased more than a dozen companies. In 2012 the company made its most meaningful acquisition to date with the purchase of Apex Systems the sixth largest staffing firm and one of the fastest growing IT staffing firms in the US for $600 million. The deal represented efforts to fortify its most lucrative segment the IT and engineering industry. The company sees the sector growing by 12% over the years while other industries shrink or remain stable.

On Assignment in 2011 obtained Valesta a provider of clinical research specialized staffing services with headquarters in Belgium and additional offices in Spain and The Netherlands. It also improved its Physician segment that year with the $19 million purchase of HealthCare Partners (HCP) a physician staffing firm based in Atlanta.

In early 2013 On Assignment sold its Nurse Travel business to focus on its five core business segments. It believes the nurse staffing market is a relatively small sector and is contracting at a much quicker pace than other specialized staffing spheres.

HISTORY

Chemists Bruce Culver and Raf Dahlquist concocted the company in 1985. Lab Support (its original name) got off to a good start but the founders were scientists not business strategists; by 1989 the company was losing steam. The firm's venture investors took over installing new management under Tom Buelter who had developed Kelly Services' home care division. He refocused operations to temporary scientific services and turned the company around. It went public in 1992 as On Assignment.

In 1994 On Assignment bought 1st Choice Personnel and Sklar Resource Group which specialized in temporary placement of financial professionals. The next year it started its Advanced Science Professionals unit to place temps in highly skilled scientific positions. With the 1996 purchase of Minneapolis-based EnviroStaff On Assignment also began providing temporary workers in environmental fields. On Assignment crossed the border and started operations in Canada in 1997. In 1999 it established Clinical Lab Staff as its fourth division. Also by 1999 the company had opened the first three of several planned European offices in the UK.

In 2001 Buelter relinquished the CEO position to Joe Peterson. (Buelter resigned as chairman early the following year.) Also in 2002 the company acquired Health Personnel Options Corporation a provider of temporary travel nurses and other health care professionals. The end of 2003 saw the appointment of Peter Dameris as the president and CEO of On Assignment.

In 2007 On Assignment reached new levels of growth with the key acquisitions of IT and engineering staffing provider Oxford Global Resources and physician staffing firm VISTA Staffing Solutions.

As with most players in the staffing sector On Assignment felt the painful effects of the global recession in 2008 and 2009 as it was hurt by high unemployment rates and shrinking demand for its staffing services.

As the economy began to pick up in 2010 On Assignment bought The Cambridge Group Ltd. a staffing services firm placing physicians clinical and scientific personnel and IT professionals. Also that year the company acquired Sharpstream a firm with expertise in search services for executive to middle managers residing in the life sciences sector. The deal added offices in the US the UK and Shanghai.

Continuing its string of acquisitions in 2011 On Assignment obtained Valesta a provider of clinical research specialized staffing services with headquarters in Belgium and additional offices in Spain and The Netherlands. The company next acquired Apex Systems the sixth largest staffing firm and one of the fastest growing IT staffing firms in the US in 2012.

EXECUTIVES

Vp, Eric Radke
President Apex, Randolph C. (Rand) Blazer, age 64, $650,000 total compensation
Chief Financial Officer and Executive Vice President, Edward L. Pierce, age 58, $455,885 total compensation
President CEO and Director, Peter T. Dameris, age 54, $799,615 total compensation
SVP Shared Services and CIO, Michael C. Payne, $216,000 total compensation
President Life Sciences and Allied Divisions, Emmett B. McGrath, age 52, $320,748 total compensation
Chief Operating Officer; President Oxford Global Resources, Michael J. McGowan, age 61, $570,917 total compensation
President VISTA Staffing Solutions, Christian Rutherford
V Pres Finance-corp Controller, Christina N Gibson
Senior Vice President International, Martyn Ward
Vice President, Tom Mc Kenna
Chief Financial Officer and Executive Vice President, Edward L. Pierce, age 58
Chairman, Jeremy M. Jones, age 72
President CEO and Director, Peter T. Dameris, age 54
Auditors: Deloitte&ToucheLLP

LOCATIONS

HQ: On Assignment, Inc.
26745 Malibu Hills Road, Calabasas, CA 91301
Phone: 818 878-7900
Web: www.onassignment.com

2014 Sales

	$ mil.	% of total
US	1778.6	94
Other countries	81.4	6
Total	**1860.0**	**100**

PRODUCTS/OPERATIONS

2014 Sales

	$ mil.	% of total
Apex	1190.1	64
Oxford	493.3	27
Physician	135.2	7
Life Sciences Europe	41.4	2
Total	**1860.0**	**100**

Selected Divisions and Operating Units

Apex (IT staffing)
On Assignment Allied Travel
On Assignment Clinical Research
On Assignment Engineering
On Assignment Healthcare Staffing
On Assignment Health Information Management
On Assignment Lab Support
Oxford Global Resources (IT and engineering staffing)
VISTA Staffing Solutions (physician staffing)

COMPETITORS

AMN Healthcare	IBM
ATC Healthcare	Insight Global
Accenture	Kelly Services
Adecco	Kforce
Aerotek	ManpowerGroup
Allegis Group	Professional Staff
CHG Healthcare	RehabCare
Cross Country Healthcare	Robert Half
	TEKsystems
Day & Zimmermann	The Everhart Group

HISTORICAL FINANCIALS

Company Type: Public

Income Statement

FYE: December 31

	REVENUE ($ mil.)	NET INCOME ($ mil.)	NET PROFIT MARGIN	EMPLOYEES
12/13	1,632.0	84.5	5.2%	33,870
12/12	1,239.7	42.6	3.4%	34,530
12/11	597.2	24.3	4.1%	15,511
12/10	438.0	(9.9)	—	12,530
12/09	416.6	4.7	1.1%	13,815
Annual Growth	**40.7%**	**105.8%**	**—**	**25.1%**

2013 Year-End Financials

Debt ratio: 31.7%
Return on equity: 14.4%
Cash ($ mil.): 37
Current ratio: 2.07
Long-term debt ($ mil.): 389
No. of shares (mil.): 53
Dividends
  Yield: —
  Payout: —
Market value ($ mil.): 1,883

	STOCK PRICE ($) FY Close	P/E High/Low	PER SHARE ($) Earnings	Dividends	Book Value
12/13	34.92	22 13	1.55	0.00	11.87
12/12	20.28	23 12	0.89	0.00	10.06
12/11	11.18	18 10	0.64	0.00	6.67
12/10	8.15	— —	(0.27)	0.00	6.03
12/09	7.15	57 11	0.13	0.00	6.25
Annual Growth	**48.7%**		**85.8%**	**—**	**17.4%**

OSI Systems, Inc. (DE)

OSI Systems is keeping a close scan on transportation security and health care worldwide. The company's security division manufactures specialized inspection equipment under the Rapiscan Systems name used to screen everything from baggage and people to cargo and vehicles at airports ports and borders. Its Spacelabs Healthcare subsidiary makes patient monitoring cardiac monitoring and clinical networking systems primarily for hospitals. A third division makes optoelectronic devices (OSI Optoelectronics) for aerospace/defense electronics industrial automation security medical diagnostics and other applications. That division also offers contract electronics manufacturing services (OSI Electronics).

Geographic Reach

The company maintains manufacturing research and development and sales operations in North America Europe Asia and Australia.

Operations

Security is OSI Systems' largest segment accounting for almost half of annual revenues. Offering a broad range of screening technologies Rapiscan Systems has built a solid reputation for its inspection systems having been installed in such security-tight locations as Buckingham Palace the Kremlin the Vatican and high-profile events such as the Olympic Games and the World Cup.

Meanwhile its health care division is focused on designing products that make critical patient information more readily accessible both within and outside of a hospital. Its optoelectronic products and manufacturing services are geared at OEM customers in need of specialized electronic components. They also serve OSI Systems' own security and health care divisions.

Sales and Marketing

There products are sold by direct sales and marketing representatives and by a network of independent distributors. Major customers within its security segment include the Transportation Security Administration the Bureau of Prisons and various international airports around the globe. Health care and optoelectronic customers include Eisenhower Medical Center and Honeywell respectively.

Financial Analysis

OSI Systems' revenues increased 21% to some $793 million due to increased sales in all of its operating segments primarily from new security contracts and a larger base of installed equipment in the health care and optoelectronics segments. Net income also increased by 36% to $46 million that year.

Strategy

In the security division OSI Systems depends on the growing needs of the international government security markets. It expands in this segment by forming new supply contracts with government agencies; for instance it entered new contracts with the US Army (for vehicle inspection and personal screening products) and the Mexican customs authority (for cargo and vehicle screening equipment) during 2011 and 2012.

OSI Systems believes demand for patient monitoring systems and other health solutions will continue to grow in the US market (and other developing countries) due to an aging population as well as in developing nations where health care infrastructures are being built and expanded. As such its research programs focus on new products such as the 2011 launch of the Cance critical care monitor.

EXECUTIVES

Executive Vice President; President - Security Division; Director, Ajay Mehra, age 53, $380,000 total compensation
Chairman President and CEO, Deepak Chopra, age 63, $1,000,000 total compensation
EVP and CFO, Alan I. Edrick, age 46, $355,000 total compensation
VP Global Marketing and Market Development Spacelabs Medical, Nicholas Ong, age 50
President Optoelectronics Division, Manoocher Mansouri, $250,000 total compensation
EVP OSI Systems and President, Ajay Merhra
Vice President Internal Audit, Felipe Velasquez
Vice President Sales And Marketing, Steven Cuffel
Vice President Business Development, Ajay Vashishat
Vp-corporate Marketing, Manoocher M Aliabadi
Senior Vice President, Allen Hobbs
Vice President Business Development And Medical Division, Lane Beard
Vice President Semiconductor Processing, Peter Bui
Vice President Global Strategic Sales And Marketing Spacelabs Medical, Jonathan Lauer
Vice President Sales, Eric Vanpoppelen
Vice President Manager, Michael Gaddy
Vice President Engineering, Felix Liu
Vp Sales & Marketing, Peter Modica

Vice President Of Finance And Operations, David Landwehr
Auditors: MossAdamsLLP

LOCATIONS

HQ: OSI Systems, Inc. (DE)
    12525 Chadron Avenue, Hawthorne, CA 90250
Phone: 310 978-0516
Web: www.osi-systems.com

2012 Sales

	$ mil.	% of total
North America	552.6	66
Europe	153.2	18
Asia	132.4	16
Adjustments	(45.2)	-
Total	**793.0**	**100**

PRODUCTS/OPERATIONS

2012 Sales

	$ mil.	% of total
Security	391.8	47
Healthcare	235.6	28
Optoelectronics & manufacturing	210.8	25
Adjustments	(45.2)	-
Total	**793.0**	**100**

Selected Products

Rapiscan Systems (Security segment)
  Gamma ray screeners (for detecting weapons explosives drugs & other hidden contraband)
  Metal detectors (for screening people)
  Neutron scanners (for detecting elemental ingredients in inspected objects)
  Passive millimeter wave scanners (for detecting concealed objects against wave energy emitted by the human body)
  Real-time tomography screeners (for detecting liquid explosives)
  X-ray screeners (for detecting weapons explosives drugs & other hidden contraband)
Spacelabs Healthcare (Healthcare segment)
  ARKON anesthesia delivery systems
  Blease anesthesia ventilators
  CardioDirect Stress Testing System
  CardioExpress ECG machines (cardiac monitors)
  XPREZZON patient monitors
  Sentinel Cardiology Data Management
  Vaporizers
OSI Optoelectronics (Optoelectronics segment)
  Blood pressure cuffs (medical devices and instrumentation)
  Bone densitometers (for measuring bone density in individuals with osteoporosis)
  Filters lenses mirrors prisms (passive components for copiers printers microscopes telescopes and other detection/vision equipment)
  Fluid delivery unifusors (medical devices and instrumentation)
  Laser-based remote sensing devices (for detecting vehicles in toll and traffic management systems)
  Oximetry sensors and accessories (medical devices and instrumentation)
  Photodetectors (active component for use in copiers laser printers microscopes telescopes and other detection and vision equipment)

COMPETITORS

American Science and Engineering	L-3 Communications
Analogic	Leidos
Benchmark Electronics	Maquet
CTS Corp.	Mindray
Cardiac Science Corporation	Optek Technology
Celestica	Orthometrix
Criticare	PerkinElmer
Dräegerwerk	Philips Healthcare
GE Healthcare	Plexus
Hamamatsu Photonics	Ranger Security Detectors
Jabil	Smiths Detection

HISTORICAL FINANCIALS

Company Type: Public

Income Statement

FYE: June 30

	REVENUE ($ mil.)	NET INCOME ($ mil.)	NET PROFIT MARGIN	EMPLOYEES
06/14	906.7	47.8	5.3%	5,607
06/13	802.0	44.1	5.5%	5,200
06/12	792.9	45.5	5.7%	3,900
06/11	656.1	33.4	5.1%	3,700
06/10	595.1	23.5	4.0%	3,183
Annual Growth	**11.1%**	**19.4%**		**15.2%**

2014 Year-End Financials

Debt ratio: 3.6%	No. of shares (mil.): 19
Return on equity: 9.4%	Dividends
Cash ($ mil.): 38	Yield: —
Current ratio: 1.87	Payout: —
Long-term debt ($ mil.): 10	Market value ($ mil.): 1,331

	STOCK PRICE ($) FY Close	P/E High/Low	Earnings	Dividends	Book Value
06/14	66.75	32 20	2.33	0.00	26.69
06/13	64.42	37 23	2.15	0.00	24.03
06/12	63.34	29 14	2.24	0.00	21.90
06/11	43.00	24 14	1.71	0.00	19.73
06/10	27.77	24 12	1.28	0.00	17.12
Annual Growth	**24.5%**	**— —**	**16.2%**	**—**	**11.7%**

Outerwall Inc

Outerwall (formerly Coinstar) takes its name from the previously underutilized "fourth wall" area between the cash registers and the front door in retail stores. The company began as an operator of coin-counting machines but underwent a major transformation when it acquired Redbox. Since then the DVD kiosk business which generates more than 85% of Outerwall's sales has eclipsed coin-counting. Redbox operates some 65800 DVD rental kiosks located at supermarkets big-box retailers drug and convenience stores and restaurants across North America. The fast-growing company changed its name to Outerwall in 2013 to reflect its evolution from coin counting to an operator of various automated retail businesses.

Geographic Reach
While the US accounts for 98% of Outerwall's sales its retail kiosks are also found inside and outside stores in Canada Puerto Rico the UK and Ireland.

Operations
Beyond DVD rentals and coin-counting machines Outerwall's other automated retail concepts include: ecoATM (acquired in 2013) an automated kiosk the pays cash for used electronic devices including mobile phones MP3 players and tablets.

Sales and Marketing
Walgreen and Wal-Mart Stores each account for about 15% of Outerwall's sales while grocery giant Kroger represents about 10% of sales.

Financial Performance
Outerwall's sales and profits have risen steadily in recent years. Indeed since acquiring Redbox in 2008 the company's sales have more than doubled from about $1.1 billion in 2009 to $2.3 billion in 2013.

In 2013 sales increased 5% versus 2012. Net income rose 16% over the same period to $174.8 million. Contributing to the gain in sales was a $65.8 million increase from the Redbox business due to new kiosk installations including the acquisition and replacement of NCR kiosks. Outerwall's acquisition of ecoATM added $31.5 million in new sales while growth at Coinstar added $9.5 million to the company's coffers. The higher sales and decline in income tax expenses partially offset by higher operating and R&D expenses drove the double-digit gain in net income.

Strategy
Since its purchase of Redbox in 2008 the company rapidly evolved from a one-product business —offering just coin-counting services —to one that offers a variety of products and services. Indeed its tiny New Ventures segment is a laboratory of sorts for the development and acquisition of new automated retail concepts. It has grown primarily through acquisitions including ecoATM in 2013 and is said to be exploring the sale of beauty products. Still its acquisitions have not been nearly as successful as Redbox which now accounts for more than 85% of the company's total revenue.

Focusing on its top-earning divisions the company has been exiting less profitable enterprises. In 2013 the company abandoned several concepts in its New Ventures segment including Rubi Coffe Crisp Market and Star Studio. After extending its Redbox Tickets pilot project from Philadelphia to Los Angeles the company shelved it as well.

Previously in 2011 Coinstar sold its money-transfer business which served the US and Latin America to California-based financial serves firm Sigue. The deal valued at about $40 million allowed Coinstar to concentrate on its automated retail strategy (i.e. coin counting and video rental). Indeed Coinstar also sold off some 900 DVDXpress kiosks (400 of which were active) in 2010 as well as DVD discs that were in the kiosks as it had deemed the business as unprofitable.

To speed new content to its kiosks in 2014 Redbox signed a multi-year distribution deal with Lions Gate Entertainment to bring Blu-ray and DVD titles to its kiosks on the day of their retail home entertainment release.

Mergers and Acquisitions
In July 2013 Outerwall acquired ecoATM an automated self-serve kiosk system to purchase used mobile phones tablets and MP3 players for cash for $350 million. Outerwall already owned 23% of ecoATM at the time of the purchase.

EXECUTIVES

Interim CEO, Nora M. Denzel, age 51
President Redbox, Mark Horak
President ecoATM, Maria D. Stipp, $167,500 total compensation
CTO, Carole McCluskey
CFO, Galen Smith, $371,044 total compensation
President Coinstar, James (Jim) Gaherity
Corporate Vice President Risk, Dave Hiatt
Vice President Sales, Randy Chilton
Vice President Human Resources, Pete Williams
Vice President North America, Rob Ayers
Vice President Of Talent Management, Megan Hansen
Vice President New Venture Growth And Portfolio Management, Andy Annacone
Regional Vice President, Ray Taddeo
Corporate Vice President Customer, Kathryn McGavick
Senior Vice President Technology New, Jeff Dirks
Vice President General Manager New, Ken Redding
Assistant To The Sr Vice President, Camille Pace

Vice President New Venture Growth, Andrew
  Annacone
Vice President Tax, Pat Harrell
Vice President Brand And Communications,
  Alejandro Cabrera
Vice President Legal, Sam Rosenthal
Vice President Planning Installation And Quality,
  Johnna Hobgood
Vice President Investor Relations, Angeline McCabe
Chairman, Nelson C. Chan, age 53
Interim CEO, Nora M. Denzel, age 51
Vice President Finance And Treasurer, Sonia Jain
Auditors: KPMGLLP

LOCATIONS

HQ: Outerwall Inc
  1800 114th Avenue SE, Bellevue, WA 98004
Phone: 425 943-8000
Web: www.outerwall.com

2013 Sales

	$ mil.	% of total
US	2254.8	98
All other	51.8	2
Total	**2306.6**	**100**

PRODUCTS/OPERATIONS

2013 Sales

	$ mil.	% of total
Redbox	1974.5	86
Coin	300.2	13
New ventures	31.9	1
Total	**2306.6**	**100**

COMPETITORS

Amazon.com	Hulu
Cash Technologies	Netflix
Cummins-Allison	Safeway
GameFly	
Global Payment	
Technologies	

HISTORICAL FINANCIALS

Company Type: Public

Income Statement   FYE: December 31

	REVENUE ($ mil.)	NET INCOME ($ mil.)	NET PROFIT MARGIN	EMPLOYEES
12/13	2,306.6	174.7	7.6%	2,900
12/12	2,202.0	150.2	6.8%	2,927
12/11	1,845.3	103.8	5.6%	2,676
12/10	1,436.4	51.0	3.6%	2,585
12/09	1,144.7	53.6	4.7%	2,600
Annual Growth	**19.1%**	**34.4%**	—	**2.8%**

2013 Year-End Financials

Debt ratio: 40.3%
Return on equity: 32.7%
Cash ($ mil.): 371
Current ratio: 1.12
Long-term debt ($ mil.): 661
No. of shares (mil.): 26
Dividends
  Yield: —
  Payout: —
Market value ($ mil.): 1,759

	STOCK PRICE ($) FY Close	P/E High/Low		PER SHARE ($) Earnings	Dividends	Book Value
12/13	67.27	11	7	6.16	0.00	19.83
12/12	52.01	14	8	4.67	0.00	19.18
12/11	45.64	17	11	3.26	0.00	17.20
12/10	56.44	41	16	1.57	0.00	13.93
12/09	27.78	21	11	1.76	0.00	13.27
Annual Growth	**24.7%**	—	—	**36.8%**	—	**10.6%**

Overstock.com Inc. (DE)

Overstock.com allows you to shop a Persian bazaar of clothes housewares music books and more. The online discount retailer hawks brand-name merchandise including furniture electronics jewelry travel and insurance. Most of its inventory comes from manufacturers stuck with overproduction older models or some color that wasn't as popular as the designer had envisioned. The company's products portfolio includes such brands as Bissell Hewlett-Packard Movado and Steve Madden among others. Besides its main website Overstock.com manages an online auction site and provides car and real estate listings. The retailer's Club O loyalty program offers discounts to members on selected items and shipping.

Operations

The online discount retailer boasts a pair of operating segments: Direct and Fulfillment. The direct business (12% of sales) sells merchandise to individual consumers and businesses. The larger Fulfillment partner business (88% of sales) sells merchandise for other retailers and manufacturers from the Overstock.com website. The company acts as a host for some 2400 third parties who supply about 488000 products.

Geographic Reach

While Overstock.com has no operations outside the US it sells products to customers in more than 100 countries outside the country from its website.

Sales and Marketing

For its customers Overstock.com serves as an alternative inventory liquidation service. Through its Supplier Oasis Fulfillment Services launched in 2014 the company offers multi-channel logistics.

The retailer has allocated more money to advertising in recent years spending $82.1 million in 2013 up from $55.6 million in 2012 and $52.5 million in 2011.

Financial Performance

Overstock.com logged $1.3 billion in sales in fiscal 2013 a 19% increase vs. 2012. The retailer attributes the gains to a 17% increase in average order size (from $135 to $158) a 2% boost in orders overall and a jump in direct revenue. Net income reached $88.5 million in 2013 representing a $73.8 million increase as compared to 2012 due to a 19% revenue boost offset by rising operating expenses most notably sales and marketing technology and general and administrative.

Strategy

In recent years Overstock.com has evolved from an online seller of discount merchandise to an operator of multiple websites that list cars and real estate for sale host online auctions and provides other specialized services.

Company Background

In 2010 the firm launched Eziba.com a private sale website where members shop for exclusive deals on home decor furniture jewelry and more. In 2009 its O.biz website began offering bulk and business related items. After selling its travel subsidiary at a loss to Castles Travel in 2009 —following the downturn in the travel industry —Overstock.com in 2011 began offering vacations.

Given Overstock.com's failure to turn a profit in eight of the past 10 years an ongoing investigation by the Securities and Exchange Commission following the discovery that the company violated various accounting rules and losses related to failed litigation by the company Overstock.com's shares have been battered.

EXECUTIVES

Svp Finance And Risk Management, Stephen J
  (Steve) Chesnut, age 55
CEO, Patrick M. Byrne, age 51
President, Stormy D. Simon, age 45, $300,000 total
  compensation
SVP Merchandising and Strategic Sourcing, Seth
  Marks
Senior Vice President - Technology, Bhargav Shah
Co-President, David Nielsen
SVP Finance and Risk Management, Robert
  Hughes
SVP Marketing, Saum Noursalehi
Senior Vice President Customer And Partner
  Care, Brian Popelka
Executive Vice President, Kevin Lane
Acting Vice President Of Development, Alec
  Wilkins
Vice President Of Technology Operations, Carter
  Rossi
Vice President Of Software Engineering, Dave
  Selinger
Chairman, Jonathan E. Johnson, age 48
President, Stormy D. Simon, age 45
Auditors: KPMGLLP

LOCATIONS

HQ: Overstock.com Inc. (DE)
  6350 South 3000 East, Salt Lake City, UT 84121
Phone: 801 947-3100
Web: www.overstock.com

PRODUCTS/OPERATIONS

2013 Sales

	% of total
Home & garden	72
Jewelry watches clothing & accessories	13
Books music movies games electronics & computers	4
Other	11
Total	**100**

2013 Sales

	$ mil.	% of total
Fulfillment partner	1148.2	88
Direct	156.0	12
Total	**1304.2**	**100**

Selected Suppliers

Anne Klein
Bissell
Blue Ridge Home Fashions
Broyhill
Canon
Charles David
Drexel Heritage
Dyson
Fuji
Hewlett-Packard
Hoover
Hunter Fan
Joseph Abboud
JVC
Kodak
Movado
Novica
Panasonic
Philips
Random House
RCA
Samsonite
Seiko
Simon & Schuster
Sony
Steve Madden
Thomasville
Toshiba
Wenger

Selected Products

At Home
Bedding
Books
Clothing and shoes
Electronics
Furniture
Jewelry
Sports
Watches
Worldstock

COMPETITORS

Amazon.com	OnlineAuction
American Express	Orbitz Worldwide
Barnes & Noble	Priceline
Best Buy	Ross Stores
Blue Nile Inc.	Sears Holdings
Bluefly	Sierra Trading Post
Buy.com	TJX Companies
Costco Wholesale	Target Corporation
Expedia	Travelocity
J. C. Penney	Wal-Mart
Kohl's	craigslist
Liberty Interactive	eBay

HISTORICAL FINANCIALS

Company Type: Public

Income Statement

FYE: December 31

	REVENUE ($ mil.)	NET INCOME ($ mil.)	NET PROFIT MARGIN	EMPLOYEES
12/13	1,304.2	88.5	6.8%	1,500
12/12	1,099.2	14.6	1.3%	1,300
12/11	1,054.2	(19.4)	—	1,300
12/10	1,089.8	13.8	1.3%	1,500
12/09	876.7	7.7	0.9%	1,300
Annual Growth	10.4%	83.8%	—	3.6%

2013 Year-End Financials

Debt ratio: —
Return on equity: 115.0%
Cash ($ mil.): 150
Current ratio: 1.13
Long-term debt ($ mil.): —

No. of shares (mil.): 23
Dividends
Yield: —
Payout: —
Market value ($ mil.): 732

	STOCK PRICE ($) FY Close	P/E High/Low		PER SHARE ($) Earnings	Dividends	Book Value
12/13	30.79	9	3	3.64	0.00	5.17
12/12	14.31	25	8	0.62	0.00	1.32
12/11	7.84	—	—	(0.84)	0.00	0.57
12/10	16.48	40	19	0.59	0.00	1.36
12/09	13.56	52	20	0.33	0.00	0.51
Annual Growth	22.8%		—	82.2%	—	78.7%

Pacific Premier Bancorp Inc

Pacific Premier Bancorp is the holding company of Pacific Premier Bank which has about 10 branches serving Southern California's Los Angeles Orange Riverside and San Bernardino counties. The bank offers standard deposit products and services including checking and savings accounts and cash management services. Multi-family residential mortgages account for about half of the company's loan portfolio. It also writes business and consumer loans such as Small Business Administration loans commercial and industrial loans and single-family residential mortgages.

After a stint during the 1990s in which the bank focused on subprime mortgages and nearly went under Pacific Premier reorganized as a commercial bank in 2007.

The company expanded into Riverside County in 2011 when it acquired the banking operations of the failed Canyon National Bank after that institution was seized by regulators. The transaction which included loss-sharing agreements with the FDIC brought in three branch locations. The following year Pacific Premier acquired the deposits and assets of the failed single-branch Palm Desert National Bank.

Los Angeles-based Security Pacific Bancorp owns some 25% of Pacific Premier Bancorp.

EXECUTIVES

Vice President Finance, John Shindler
Vice President Senior Relationship Officer, Douglas Wolfe
President CEO and Director Pacific Premier Bancorp and Pacific Premier Bank, Steven R. (Steve) Gardner, age 53, $415,000 total compensation
EVP CFO and Treasurer; EVP and CFO Pacific Premier Bank, Kent J. Smith, age 52, $195,000 total compensation
EVP and Chief Banking Officer Pacific Premier Bank, Edward (Eddie) Wilcox, age 47, $225,000 total compensation
Executive Vice President; Chief Credit Officer, Michael S Karr
Vice President Marketing, Frank Dick
Assistant Vice President Cash, James Gibson
Vice President, Jon Hagan
First Vice President, Josh Young
Vice President, Shane Pierson
Vice President Sales And Business Development, Ingmar Sterling
Assistant Vice President Underwriter, Candace Allahyari
Vice President Senior Portfolio Manager, Kent Newberry
First Vice President And Senior Credit Manager And Secondary Marketing Manager, Chris Porcelli
Assistant Vice President And Portfolio Manager, Susan Froboese
Assistant Vice President And Portfolio, Michelle Baeza
Assistant Vice President, Lynette Bartlomain
Assistant Vice President And Portfolio, Judy Winston
Vice President Business Banker, Cindy T Emnas
First Vice President Warehouse Lending Manager, Oscar Moran
Assistant Vice President And Deputy Bsa, Terri Benkey
First Vice President And Branch Manager, Eileen Eske
Vice President, Harman Malik
Assistant Vice President And Senior, Joey Ferrell
Assistant Vice President And Branch Manager, Chandra Olivas
Vice President Business Banker, Trisha Romero
Assistant Vice President Branch Manager, Rosita Juarez
Assistant Vice President Underwriter, Jaye Martin
First Vice President Mortgage, Ellen Schultz
Vice President Sba Business Develpoment Officer, Francine Connor
Vice President And Cash Management Banking, Patty Watkins-erp
Senior Vice President And Director, Cat Carmichael

Vice President And Sba Business Development Officer, Christopher Gavry
Vice President And Director, Rudy Ramirez
Senior Vice President And Director Of Hoa Operations, Greg Smith
Senior Vice President, Michael Kowalski
Vice President Construction Lending, Timothy Cody
Assistant Vice President Sba Business Development Officer, Laurie Peterson
Vice President And Marketing Manager, Diane Murico
Vice President, Chris Hilliard
Assistant Vice President And Senior Hoa Property Banker, Lauren Tedford
Assistant Vice President Portfolio, Alex Horst
Vice President Of Loans, Roy Painter
Senior Vice President And Director, Kathrine Duncan
Chief Credit Officer And Senior Vp, Bruce Larson
Assistant Vice President, Christopher Prorcelli
Assistant Vice President Portfolio Mgr, Michael Leavitt
Vice President Marketing, Melanie Gutzmer
Executive Vice President Director Of Franchise Lending, John Rinaldi
Vice President Marketing, Charles Fletcher
Board Member, Kenneth A (Ken) Boudreau, age 65
President CEO and Director Pacific Premier Bancorp and Pacific Premier Bank, Steven R. (Steve) Gardner, age 53
EVP CFO and Treasurer; EVP and CFO Pacific Premier Bank, Kent J. Smith, age 52
Chairman, Jeff C. Jones, age 59
Auditors: VavrinekTrineDay&Co.LLP

LOCATIONS

HQ: Pacific Premier Bancorp Inc
17901 Von Karman Avenue, Suite 1200, Irvine, CA 92614
Phone: 949 864-8000
Web: www.ppbi.com

PRODUCTS/OPERATIONS

2007 Sales

	$ mil.	% of total
Interest		
Loans	45.3	81
Other	4.1	7
Noninterest		
Net gain on sale of loans	3.7	7
Loan servicing fee income	1.1	2
Other	1.6	3
Total	**55.8**	**100**

COMPETITORS

Banc of California	Comerica
Bank of America	JPMorgan Chase
Citibank	U.S. Bancorp
City National	Zions Bancorporation

HISTORICAL FINANCIALS

Company Type: Public

Income Statement

FYE: December 31

	ASSETS ($ mil.)	NET INCOME ($ mil.)	INCOME AS % OF ASSETS	EMPLOYEES
12/13	1,714.1	8.9	0.5%	231
12/12	1,173.7	15.7	1.3%	183
12/11	961.1	10.5	1.1%	149
12/10	826.8	4.2	0.5%	105
12/09	807.3	(0.4)	—	91
Annual Growth	20.7%	—	—	26.2%

2013 Year-End Financials

Return on assets: 0.6%		Dividends		
Return on equity: 5.8%		Yield: —		
Long-term debt ($ mil.): —		Payout: —		
No. of shares (mil.): 16		Market value ($ mil.): 262		
Sales ($ mil): 72				

	STOCK PRICE ($) FY Close	P/E High/Low		PER SHARE ($) Earnings	Dividends	Book Value
12/13	15.74	28	18	0.54	0.00	10.52
12/12	10.24	8	4	1.44	0.00	9.85
12/11	6.34	7	5	0.99	0.00	8.39
12/10	6.48	15	8	0.38	0.00	7.83
12/09	3.38	—	—	(0.08)	0.00	7.33
Annual Growth 46.9%		—	—	—	—	9.5%

Pain Therapeutics Inc

Pain Therapeutics is providing opiates for the masses. The development-stage pharmaceutical company is working on abuse-resistant painkillers including Remoxy a version of the frequently abused Oxycontin. Pain Therapeutics is developing Remoxy in partnership with Pfizer which holds all of the commercialization rights to the drug except in Australia and New Zealand. In addition to its chronic pain candidates Pain Therapeutics has other development products in early stages. Because many of its drug candidates already contain FDA-approved components the firm hopes for a faster approval process for its lead candidate.

Operations

The company plans to use third-party manufacturers to formulate make and ship its products once they are approved. A key supplier is DURECT the company from which Pain Therapeutics originally licensed the rights to REMOXY.

Financial Performance

Pain Therapeutics hasn't seen any revenue except its payments from Pfizer; revenue was $41 million in 2013. The company however continues to spend heavily on R&D like any development-stage company. At the end of 2013 Pain Therapeutics had an accumulated deficit of $104.1 million.

Strategy

In order to begin making money Pain Therapeutics needs to get REMOXY or one of its other candidates approved for sale in the US or elsewhere. The company plans to retain the rights to its drugs other than REMOXY though it may seek marketing partners for niche products. It also plans to continue outsourcing it trials and manufacturing.

EXECUTIVES

Chairman President and CEO, Remi Barbier, age 54, $713,542 total compensation

COO and Chief Medical Officer, Nadav Friedmann, age 71, $263,542 total compensation

VP and CFO, Peter S. Roddy, age 54, $316,250 total compensation

Chief Scientific Officer, Grant L. Schoenhard, age 69, $263,542 total compensation

VP Technical Operations, Michael Zamloot

SVP Technology, George B. (Ben) Thornton

Chairman President and CEO, Remi Barbier, age 54

Auditors: Ernst&YoungLLP

LOCATIONS

HQ: Pain Therapeutics Inc
7801 N. Capital of Texas Highway, Suite 260, Austin, TX 78731

Phone: 512 501-2444

Web: www.paintrials.com

PRODUCTS/OPERATIONS

Selected Products

Remoxy (chronic pain candidate)
PTI-202 (chronic pain candidate)
PTI-721 (chronic pain candidate)

COMPETITORS

Abbott Labs	Johnson & Johnson
Actavis	Merck
Acura Pharmaceuticals	Novartis
Akela	Pfizer
Bayer AG	Purdue Pharma
Cephalon	Roxane Laboratories
Endo	Sanofi
Forest Labs	Teva
GlaxoSmithKline	Titan Pharmaceuticals

HISTORICAL FINANCIALS

Company Type: Public

Income Statement

FYE: December 31

	REVENUE ($ mil.)	NET INCOME ($ mil.)	NET PROFIT MARGIN	EMPLOYEES
12/13	41.1	31.5	76.7%	8
12/12	10.8	(3.4)	—	8
12/11	11.4	(2.6)	—	10
12/10	16.8	(12.0)	—	18
12/09	20.5	(3.4)	—	27
Annual Growth 18.9%		—	—	(26.2%)

2013 Year-End Financials

Debt ratio: —		No. of shares (mil.): 45		
Return on equity: 102.6%		Dividends		
Cash ($ mil.): 48		Yield: —		
Current ratio: 27.82		Payout: —		
Long-term debt ($ mil.): —		Market value ($ mil.): 221		

	STOCK PRICE ($) FY Close	P/E High/Low		PER SHARE ($) Earnings	Dividends	Book Value
12/13	4.86	8	3	0.70	0.00	1.06
12/12	2.71	—	—	(0.08)	0.75	0.29
12/11	3.80	—	—	(0.06)	0.00	0.99
12/10	6.75	—	—	(0.28)	2.00	0.77
12/09	5.36	—	—	(0.08)	0.00	2.56
Annual Growth (2.4%) (19.7%)		—	—	—	—	—

Panera Bread Co.

Panera Bread is ready for an epochal change in American eating habits. The company is a leader in the quick-casual restaurant business with more than 1800 bakery-cafes in about 45 states and Canada. Its locations which operate under the banners Panera Bread Saint Louis Bread Co. and Paradise Bakery & Caf ©offer made-to-order sandwiches using a variety of artisan breads including Asiago cheese bread focaccia and its classic sourdough bread. The chain's menu also features soups salads and gourmet coffees. In addition Panera sells its bread bagels and pastries to go. More than 850 of its locations are company-operated while the rest are run by franchisees.

Geographic Reach

Panera operates in 44 states in the US Washington D.C. and Ontario Canada. In 2010 Panera moved its corporate headquarters to spacious offices in a building previously occupied by Anheuser-Busch in St. Louis.

Operations

The company's three business segments consist of the Bakery-Cafe Operations segment the Franchise Operations segment and the Fresh Dough and Other Product Operations segment that provides fresh food supplies to company-owned and franchise-operated bakery-cafes through a contract manufacturing arrangement.

Sales and Marketing

The company's advertising spend was $55.6 million and $44.5 million for the fiscal years 2013 and 2012 respectively.

Panera sells its products directly to customers and also acts as its own distributor by supplying most of its company-owned and franchised locations with fresh product. The company was a pioneer in the quick-casual dining segment which offers quick counter service but boasts higher-quality ingredients.

The chain built significant brand loyalty by targeting suburban markets with its menu of European-inspired sandwich creations. It competes with other national fast-casual chains such as California Pizza Kitchen Chipotle Mexican Grill and Einstein Bros. Bagels (operated by Einstein Noah Restaurant Group) as well as #1 coffee house chain Starbucks.

Financial Performance

Panera's revenue has been trending up in recent fiscal years. The company reported $2.385 billion in revenue for fiscal 2013. That figure was an increase of 12% compared to the previous year's $2.130 billion. The spike in total revenues during fiscal 2013 was primarily due to the opening of 133 new bakery-cafes system-wide during the year.

Net income increased by 13% in fiscal 2013 compared to fiscal 2012. The increase was a result of increased revenue combined with lower tax expenses. The company's cash flow has also increased year-over-year in recent fiscal periods along with its revenue and net income.

Strategy

Like many other dining operators Panera (which is Latin for "time for bread") relies on a mix of corporate-run locations and franchising to expand and operate its restaurant chain. The company-owned stores give the chain a significant footprint from which to control the consistency of food and service quality.

Panera's franchising efforts allow the company to expand into new markets without the expense of construction and operation. Local franchisees pay the company royalties and other fees in order to use the Panera brand and other intellectual property.

HISTORY

Panera Bread traces its roots to a restaurant opened in Boston by French commercial oven manufacturer Pavailler. Au Bon Pain opened in 1976 was intended as a showcase for Pavailler's ovens. The scent of hot croissants (and money) caught the attention of Louis Kane who bought the business in 1978 and began expanding in Boston. Ron Shaich (pronounced "shake") joined Kane in 1981 and together they formed Au Bon Pain Co.

Inc. The chain grew rapidly until the early 1990s saturating the high-traffic areas in eastern US cities. After its IPO in 1991 Au Bon Pain began making acquisitions including Saint Louis Bread in 1993.

Saint Louis Bread was founded in 1987 when Ken Rosenthal spurred into the restaurant business by his brother opened his first cafe in Kirkwood Missouri. Based on sourdough bakeries in San Francisco the concept eventually spread to five stores by 1990 and nearly 20 units two years later. In 1993 the company made "Inc." magazine's list of the 500 fastest-growing companies. At the end of that year Au Bon Pain paid $24 million for the company franchising its new units outside of the St. Louis area as Panera Bread. Rosenthal stayed on with Au Bon Pain as chairman of its new chain before leaving to become a major franchisee.

By 1995 the company was facing new competition from coffee and bagel shops. Flat sales and sharp price increases for butter hurt the chain's bottom line. By 1997 the company had added bagels to its menu and was considering extensive renovations. It ultimately decided the chain had peaked in the US and it limited expansion to countries with dense urban areas and emerging middle classes such as Brazil and Indonesia.

During 1998 Au Bon Pain's Panera Bread unit perked up with new stores and growing sales. But that success was offset by the company's namesake chain where sales continued to struggle. The company eventually sold the Au Bon Pain chain in 1999 to investment firm Bruckmann Rosser Sherrill and Co. for $73 million. (Bruckmann Rosser later sold the chain to UK-based Compass Group which ran the eateries through its subsidiary ABP Corporation until it sold a majority stake to a management group.) Shaich remained with the company which was renamed Panera Bread as chairman and CEO. Panera Bread later moved its headquarters back to the St. Louis area.

In 2001 president and COO Rich Postle resigned to run a joint venture with Panera Bread to build and manage 40 bakery-cafes in the northern Virginia and central Pennsylvania regions.

The company introduced its new upscale takeout program Via Panera in 2004. With Via Panera the company simplified the to-go ordering process while upgrading its customization particularly for larger orders. Panera Bread also released its first cookbook that year The Panera Bread Cookbook: Breadmaking Essentials and Recipes from America's Favorite Bakery-Cafe.

In 2007 the company acquired a 51% stake in Paradise Bakery & Caf @the operator of a small bakery-cafe chain in the Southwest for about $20 million. (Panera acquired the remaining stake for about $22 million two years later.)

EXECUTIVES

EVP and Chief Concept and Innovation Officer, Scott G. Davis, age 50, $520,971 total compensation
Vice Chairman and Interim CFO, William W. (Bill) Moreton, age 54, $793,475 total compensation
Chairman and CEO, Ronald M. (Ron) Shaich, age 60, $793,475 total compensation
EVP Technology and Transformation, Blaine E. Hurst, age 56, $480,489 total compensation
EVP and COO, Charles J. (Chuck) Chapman, age 51, $419,923 total compensation
EVP and Chief Development Officer, Mark R. Wesley
SVP and CIO, John M. Meister
SVP Panera to You, Dan A. Wegiel
Vice President Purchasing, Paul Ray
V Pres Acctng-assoc Controller, Mark Wooldridge

Vice President Operations, Irene Cook
Vice President Finance, Jason Imlay
Vice President Brand Insight And Research, Shawn Utke
Vice President Of Opearations Pangenera, Phil Wood
Vice President Technical Operations And Services, Michael Wojcik
Senior Vice President Chief Legal, Scott Blair
Vice President Real Estate, Tim Ribant
Senior Vice President And Chief People Officer, Liz Dunlap
Vice President, John Clark
Vice President, Veronica Pacheco
Vice President Business Development, Stephanie Crimmins
Senior Vice President Strategic, Bryan Timko
Vice President Finance, David Sullivan
Vice President Of Design Panera Bread, Craig Grosinger
Vice President Of Operations, Tony Darden
Senior Vice President, Mark Bolan
Vice President Of Retail Operations, Patrick Mellor
Vice President Interactive Marketing, Thomas Howley
Vice President Ecommerce And Consumer Systems, Anita Klopfenstein
Vpc, S Salerno
Jvp, Doug Djordjevic
Vice President Retail Human Resources, Jaynanne Habeck
Vice President Of Operation Services, Bob Hynick
Vice President Of Franchise Operations, Todd Burns
Vpc, Anna Grant
Executive Vice President Chief Financial Officer, Roger Matthews
Vice President Construction, Ken Sisk
Vp Finance, Jon Lobell
Vice President, Michael Cortino
Executive Vice President Development, Chuck Chapman
Jvp, Tony Rolland
Vice President, Stefanie Jerry
Senior Vice President And Chief Company And Joint Venture Operations Officer, Hank Simpson
Vice Chairman and Interim CFO, William W. (Bill) Moreton, age 54
Chairman and CEO, Ronald M. (Ron) Shaich, age 60
Auditors: PricewaterhouseCoopersLLP

LOCATIONS

HQ: Panera Bread Co.
3630 South Geyer Road, Suite 100, St. Louis, MO 63127
Phone: 314 984-1000   **Fax:** 314 909-3300
Web: www.panerabread.com

PRODUCTS/OPERATIONS

2014 Sales

	$ mil.	% of total
Bakery-Cafe Sales	2230.4	88
Franchise royalties and fees	123.7	5
Fresh dough and other products sales to franchisees	175.1	7
Total	**2529.2**	**100**

COMPETITORS

ABP Corporation	Einstein Noah
Boston Market	Restaurant Group
Bruegger's	Fresh Enterprises
CBC Restaurant	Potbelly Sandwich Shop
California Pizza Kitchen	Qdoba Restaurants
	Quiznos
Caribou Coffee	Starbucks
Chipotle	Subway

HISTORICAL FINANCIALS
Company Type: Public

Income Statement
FYE: December 31

	REVENUE ($ mil.)	NET INCOME ($ mil.)	NET PROFIT MARGIN	EMPLOYEES
12/13	2,385.0	196.1	8.2%	40,100
12/12	2,130.0	173.4	8.1%	36,300
12/11	1,822.0	135.9	7.5%	32,600
12/10	1,542.4	111.8	7.3%	25,600
12/09	1,353.4	86.0	6.4%	25,300
Annual Growth	**15.2%**	**22.9%**		**12.2%**

2013 Year-End Financials

Debt ratio: —
Return on equity: 25.3%
Cash ($ mil.): 125
Current ratio: 1.00
Long-term debt ($ mil.): —

No. of shares (mil.): 27
Dividends
  Yield: —
  Payout: —
Market value ($ mil.): 4,890

	STOCK PRICE ($) FY Close	P/E High/Low		PER SHARE ($) Earnings	Dividends	Book Value
12/13	176.69	28	22	6.81	0.00	25.29
12/12	158.34	29	23	5.89	0.00	27.77
12/11	141.01	31	21	4.55	0.00	22.09
12/10	102.11	29	18	3.62	0.00	19.59
12/09	68.63	24	15	2.78	0.00	18.90
Annual Growth	**26.7%**			**25.1%**	—	**7.6%**

Panhandle Oil & Gas Inc

You won't find this Panhandle on a street corner but you will find it pocketing the oil and gas royalties from more than 6100 gross producing oil and gas wells. Panhandle Oil and Gas (formerly Panhandle Royalty) owns mineral interests both working and royalty in oil- and gas-producing properties in 10 states. The company does not operate any of its own wells but instead maintains them through partnerships with other oil and gas companies. Its major properties are located primarily in Oklahoma (44% of its net land holdings in fiscal 2013 of 255300 acres). In fiscal 2013 Panhandle Oil and Gas reported proved reserves of 151.8 billion cu. ft. of natural gas equivalent.

Geographic Reach

The company's primary assets are in Arkansas New Mexico North Dakota Oklahoma and Texas. Most of its oil NGL and natural gas production comes from wells in Arkansas and Oklahoma.

Financial Performance

In fiscal 2013 Panhandle Oil and Gas' revenues rose by 30% due to higher oil and natural gas sales volumes and prices partially offset by lower lease bonuses received.

Net income increased by 89% thanks to higher net sales and lower operating costs.

Strategy

Rather than operating any of the wells in which it has an interest the company relies on companies with more assets and experience to operate the wells during the drilling and production phases. It either elects to participate in drilling operations with these larger companies or to lease or farmout its mineral or leasehold acreage while retaining a royalty interest. This strategy allows Panhandle Oil and Gas to compete effectively in drilling operations while maintaining low overhead costs.

HISTORY

In 1926 Panhandle Cooperative Royalty was formed by ranchers and farmers in Range Oklahoma (located in that state's panhandle). At the time Oklahoma was a homesteader state in which hopeful landowners after cultivating a parcel of 160 acres would receive full title (including mineral rights) to the land. The cooperative got started by offering each prospective member one share for the undivided mineral rights to 40 acres. Royalties from any mineral production were divided 75% to the property owner and 25% to the cooperative. Earnings remaining at year-end were split among the shareholders. Because landowners with imminent drilling prospects were uninterested in joining the cooperative Panhandle often found itself striking deals in then-unexplored areas such as the Anadarko Basin.

In 1979 a period of rapidly rising oil prices Panhandle realized that as a cooperative its inability to retain any earnings severely limited its expansion potential. The cooperative was merged into the Panhandle Royalty Company and went public that year. In 1988 the company acquired New Mexico Osage Royalty Company itself a cooperative. In 1995 Panhandle acquired a half interest in more than 65000 acres from PetroCorp Inc.

Panhandle was primarily a passive owner until 1991 when it got a new CEO geologist H. W. Peace. The firm plans to continue expanding through acquisitions and to increase its participation in drilling projects. Peace retired in 2006. Company veteran Michael Coffman took over as CEO in 2007.

EXECUTIVES

President and CEO, Michael C. Coffman, age 61, $216,250 total compensation
Vice President-land, Wanda Tucker
VP; CFO and Secretary, Lonnie J. Lowry, age 62, $139,875 total compensation
SVP and COO, Paul F. Blanchard
Land Manager, Shelly S. Quimby
Board Member, Grant Swartzwelder
Auditors: Ernst&YoungLLP

LOCATIONS

HQ: Panhandle Oil & Gas Inc
Grand Centre, Suite 300, 5400 N Grand Blvd.,
Oklahoma City, OK 73112
Phone: 405 948-1560   **Fax:** 405 948-2038
Web: www.panhandleoilandgas.com

PRODUCTS/OPERATIONS

2013 Sales

	$ mil.	% of total
Oil & gas	60.6	96
Lease bonuses & rentals	0.8	2
Income from partnerships	0.8	1
Gains on derivatives	0.7	1
Total	**62.9**	**100**

COMPETITORS

Abraxas Petroleum	Hugoton Royalty Trust
Anadarko Petroleum	Matador Resources
Bill Barrett	Range Resources
Cabot Oil & Gas	SM Energy
Cross Timbers Royalty	Sabine Royalty Trust
Trust	Warren Resources
Gastar Exploration	

HISTORICAL FINANCIALS

Company Type: Public

Income Statement

FYE: September 30

	REVENUE ($ mil.)	NET INCOME ($ mil.)	NET PROFIT MARGIN	EMPLOYEES
09/14	84.4	25.0	29.6%	22
09/13	62.8	13.9	22.2%	21
09/12	48.5	7.3	15.2%	20
09/11	44.9	8.4	18.9%	19
09/10	51.9	11.4	22.0%	18
Annual Growth	**12.9%**	**21.6%**	**—**	**5.1%**

2014 Year-End Financials

Debt ratio: 31.6%
Return on equity: 23.2%
Cash ($ mil.): 0
Current ratio: 2.05
Long-term debt ($ mil.): 78

No. of shares (mil.): 16
Dividends
  Yield: 1.0%
  Payout: 25.0%
Market value ($ mil.): 984

	STOCK PRICE ($) FY Close	P/E High/Low		PER SHARE ($) Earnings	Dividends	Book Value
09/14	59.70	45	19	1.49	0.32	7.23
09/13	28.28	39	30	0.84	0.28	5.81
09/12	30.67	82	55	0.44	0.14	5.08
09/11	28.37	72	47	0.51	0.28	4.77
09/10	24.69	44	29	0.68	0.28	4.43
Annual Growth	**24.7%**			**21.7%**	**3.4%**	**13.0%**

PAREXEL International Corp.

PAREXEL International excels in pharmaceutical development services. A top contract research organization (CRO) the firm counts among its clients some of the world's largest drug biotech and medical device firms. Its Clinical Research Services segment provides clinical trial and data management study design patient recruitment biostatistical analysis clinical pharmacology and industry training and publishing. PAREXEL Consulting Services (PCS) handles the non-clinical aspects of drug development regulatory affairs and new product launches. Its Perceptive Informatics (PI) unit offers information technology systems and services that help manage clinical trials.

Operations

PAREXEL's largest segment Clinical Research Services (CRS) accounts for two-thirds of sales. Its core development business covers all phases of drug and device development from discovery research through clinical trials and post-marketing studies. The division has benefited from the market trend of increased R&D outsourcing by pharmaceutical and biotech drug companies.

Geographic Reach

The company has some 80 facilities in more than 50 countries in Europe the Asia/Pacific region the Middle East North America South America and Africa. About half of PAREXEL's sales are generated outside the US partly because of its core client base of large multinational corporations.

Sales and Marketing

PAREXEL's sales force directs custom marketing efforts towards niche market segments to match the appropriate services with each customer's needs. Its overall goal is to help clients reduce costs and risks related to product development and commercialization.

Financial Performance

The company's revenues have grown steadily over time including in fiscal 2014 when revenue grew 14% from $2 billion to $2.27 billion due to increased demand for its CRS services a 7% increase at PCS partially due to an acquisition and a 17% jump at PI also partially due to an acquisition.

Revenue growth lead to net income growth as PAREXEL declared a 35% increase from $96 million to $129 million. The rising tide also lifted cash from operations from $184 million to $287 million.

Strategy

The company seeks to widen its service offerings geographic presence and client base both through internal initiatives and via acquisitions. Purchases in 2012 through 2014 served to expand and enhance PAREXEL's offerings both across product lines and geographical regions while in-house development lead to new technology-based regulatory compliance tools units in China and Japan for navigating those countries' approvals processes and expansion of the company's facilities in Singapore and the US (Maine).

Mergers and Acquisitions

In late 2012 the company purchased Liquent for about $72 million which added regulatory software and technology to its PI unit. The following year it picked up biopharma commercialization services company Heron for $24 million to enhance its PCS unit. In 2014 PAREXEL acquired ATLAS Medical Services a CRO firm serving Turkey the Middle East and North Africa.

HISTORY

Founders Josef von Rickenbach a health care and international products specialist and Anne Sayigh a chemist and regulatory affairs specialist started PAREXEL in 1982 to provide regulatory consulting services to pharmaceutical firms. Its name referred to 16th-century Swiss physician Theophrastus Bombastus von Hohenheim –better known as Paracelsus the father of empirical chemistry.

In 1988 PAREXEL bought Consulting Statisticians and moved into the biostatistics and data management market. The next year it went international with the purchase of the biostatistics and data management division of McDonnell Douglas Information Systems. In 1991 PAREXEL augmented its European operations with the acquisition of German contract researcher AFB Arzneimittelforschung –a move that paid off in rising sales.

PAREXEL went public in 1995. In the following two years it bought six health consulting firms including State and Federal Associates and medical marketing firm Rescon with the intention of boosting its ability to get its clients' products on the market. The company continued its acquisition spree in 1998; this time European marketing and research companies were on the shopping list. Competitor Covance was set to buy PAREXEL in 1999 then called off the deal when investors balked.

The company announced in 2000 that it would lay off more than 400 workers after Novartis cancelled a major contract. That year the company formed new alliances with such companies as NeuroRecovery Research Phenome Sciences and Prevention Concepts. PAREXEL also bought a full-service clinical pharmacology unit in the UK from

GlaxoWellcome (now GlaxoSmithKline) as well as a majority stake in FARMOVS a clinical pharmacology research business and laboratory in South Africa.

In 2001 the company formed Perceptive Informatics a subsidiary focused on developing Internet-based information management systems. To strengthen its clinical trial management services PAREXEL bought software developer FW Pharma Systems in 2003. In 2006 it purchased US-based Behavioral and Medical Research LLC for $69 million to expand its research services.

EXECUTIVES

Senior Vice President Worldwide Regulatory Affairs, Alberto Grignolo
Senior Vice President - Clinical Research Services, Joseph C (Joe) Avellone, age 66
Vp Data Sciences Strategic Services, Imogene Grimes
Chairman and CEO, Josef H. von Rickenbach, age 59, $733,333 total compensation
COO and President, Mark A. Goldberg, age 54, $483,333 total compensation
President Perceptive Informatics, Xavier Flinois
VP and General Manager PAREXEL Consulting, Gadi Saarony
CFO, Ingo Bank
Vp-corp, Dieter Russmann
Vp Project Management Clinical Research Services, Niki Harrop
Svp General Counsel And Secretary, Douglas A Batt, age 50
Vice President Medical Imaging Consulting, George Q Mills
Medical Director, Richard P Jacobs
Vp And Worldwide Head Of Clinical Pharmacology, Herman Scholtz
Vp Clinical Pharmacology And Director Clinical Pharmacology Research Unit, Antoni A Piergies
Svp Clinical Research Services, Thomas Senderovitz
Vice President Clinical Science, Roland Andersson
Vice President Legal And Risk Management, Wolf Hillebrand
Medical Director, Spyros Triantos
Vice President Of Partnerships, Graham Bunn
Medical Director, Piotr Oblakowski
Technical Vice President, Terry Munson
Vice President Of Learning And Development, Albert Siu
Vice President Human Resources, Mark Williams
Vice President Strategic Account Leader, David Selkirk
Vice President Global Biostatistics, Martin Roessner
Vp Clinical Pharmacology Consulting, Matthias Grossmann
Associate Medical Director, Theodor Schulte
Vice President North American Medical Services, Paula Lutz
Vice President It, Holger Liebig
Vice President Client Services, Colette Andrea
Vice President, Rahul Kukreja
Vice President Quality, Bailey Bishop
Vice President, Dana Kroeze
Vice President, Martin Zuzulo
Medical Director, Bertrand Beau
Vice President North America Business Development Perceptive Informatics, David Kiger
Vice President Finance, Joanne Sullivan
Corporate Vice President Account Management, Angelika Riedl
Vice President Corporate Marketing, Susan Murphywarren

Vice President Compensation Benefits And Hris, Todd Cowgill
Vice President Na Project Management, Conal Burgess
Vice President Worldwide Head Of Medcom, Susan Kammerman
Vice President Global Data Management, Jeff Donovan
Associate Medical Director, Venkata Meka
Vice President Strategic Account Leader, Brian Thornton
Vice President Worldwide Head Bus Dev, Yves Grenon
Vice President Finance Phase Ii Iii Pace, Charlie Nicholson
Vice President Crs, Benedikt Egersdoerfer
Assistant To Senior Vice President, Joy Arsenault
Vice President Process Quality, Deborah Leander
Associate Medical Director, S Shi
Vice President Clinical Data Services, Dierk Schmidt
Vice President, Mario Papillon
Associate Medical Director, Sasaki Yukiya
Vice President Information Technology, Todd Kerstein
Vice President Of Training, John Snodgrass
Associate Medical Director, Janos Zambori
Vice President Accounts Payable, Sandra Stephenson
Vp, David Chesney
Vice President Worldwide Business, Jeffrey Yablon
Associate Medical Director, Monique Fano
Vice President Scientific Affairs, Stan Jhee
Vice President Global Procurement, Chad Trexler
Medical Director, Vivek Samnotra
Vice President Network Security, Christopher Rieder
Vp World Wide Technol, Clinton Gilliam
Vice President Worldwide Information Technology Operations, Todd Glendye
Vice President Information Technology, Frank Zaganjori
Vice President Global Talent, Thomas McGoldrick
Associate Medical Director, Hakop Gevorkyan
Medical Director, Eric Zafarana
Vice President Human Resources, Maureen Hanahoe
Associate Medical Director, David Bennett
Corporate Vice President, Janet Edwards
Medical Director, Wayne Dankner
Corp Vice President Finance, Kurt Norris
Vice President, Carmen Medina
Vice President Global Data Management, Hugh Donovan
Vice President Technical Strategic, Frank Harmon
Corporate Vice President And Worldwide, John Kerrigan
Vice President Human Resources, Michelle Parry
Vice President Customer Strategy, Elizabeth Thomae
Vice President Proc Qlty Mgmt Partn, Debbie Wade
Vice President Technical Strategic, Edwin Rivera Martinez
Vice President Account Management, Marsha Lund
Vp Technical, Edwin Rivera
Vice President Regulatory Information, Jeff Huntsman
Vice President Corporate Development, Frank Panaccio
Vice President Systems, Jim Ringwood
Vice President Of Information Technology Applicati, Donna Darwall-smith
Chairman and CEO, Josef H. von Rickenbach, age 59
Auditors: Ernst&YoungLLP

LOCATIONS

HQ: PAREXEL International Corp.
195 West Street, Waltham, MA 02451
Phone: 781 487-9900
Web: www.parexel.com

2014 Service Revenue

	% of total
Americas	50
Europe Middle East & Africa	37
Asia/Pacific	13
Total	**100**

PRODUCTS/OPERATIONS

2014 Sales

	$ mil.	% of total
Service revenue		
Clinical Research Services	1455.2	64
Perceptive Informatics	267.9	12
PAREXEL Consulting & Medical Communications Services	216.2	10
Reimbursement revenue	327.0	14
Total	**2266.3**	**100**

COMPETITORS

Albany Molecular Research
BioClinica
Charles River Laboratories
Covance
DATATRAK International
ICON
Life Sciences Research
PRA International
PharmaNet Development Group
Pharmaceutical Product Development
Quintiles Transnational
ReSearch Pharmaceutical Services
WuXi PharmaTech
eResearchTechnology

HISTORICAL FINANCIALS
Company Type: Public

Income Statement
FYE: June 30

	REVENUE ($ mil.)	NET INCOME ($ mil.)	NET PROFIT MARGIN	EMPLOYEES
06/14	2,266.3	129.0	5.7%	15,560
06/13	1,995.9	95.9	4.8%	14,700
06/12	1,618.2	63.1	3.9%	12,695
06/11	1,422.4	48.7	3.4%	10,550
06/10	1,335.8	41.5	3.1%	9,720
Annual Growth	**14.1%**	**32.8%**	**—**	**12.5%**

2014 Year-End Financials

Debt ratio: 18.9%	No. of shares (mil.): 54
Return on equity: 23.1%	Dividends
Cash ($ mil.): 188	Yield: —
Current ratio: 1.45	Payout: —
Long-term debt ($ mil.): 334	Market value ($ mil.): 2,888

	STOCK PRICE ($) FY Close	P/E High/Low	PER SHARE ($) Earnings	Dividends	Book Value
06/14	52.84	25 17	2.25	0.00	10.57
06/13	45.97	30 16	1.61	0.00	9.57
06/12	28.23	27 15	1.05	0.00	10.14
06/11	23.56	33 21	0.81	0.00	9.59
06/10	21.68	35 16	0.71	0.00	7.52
Annual Growth	**24.9%**	**— —**	**33.4%**	**—**	**8.9%**

Park Sterling Corp

Park Sterling Corporation owns Park Sterling Bank and CapitalBank community banks with about two dozen branches in North and South Carolina. The banks offer checking and savings accounts to individuals as well as small and mid-sized businesses such as real estate development and construction firms. With only a few locations the bank emphasizes its customer service. Commercial real estate and construction loans account for more than half of its loan portfolio. Residential mortgages and home equity loans make up another quarter and business loans account for about 10%. The first Park Sterling Bank opened in 2006. In 2012 the company agreed to merge with Citizens South Banking Corporation.

Citizens South Bank will be merged into Park Sterling after the merger. The deal falls in line with Park Sterling's ambitious growth aspirations. After Park Sterling Corporation formed in 2010 with plans to go public the company quickly expanded with its 2011 purchase of South Carolina's Community Capital Corporation. That purchase added 20 branches to the bank's network and doubled its asset holdings. Park Sterling is seeking other community banks to purchase particularly those in underserved markets. The company aims to become a regional presence with offices throughout the Carolinas and Virginia. It intends to grow its assets to some $10 billion by 2015 while still maintaining its identity as a community bank.

CEO James "Jim" Cherry a former Wachovia executive came out of retirement after the banking industry somewhat fell apart in late 2008. Together with CFO David Gaines and EVP Leonard Robinett also former Wachovia executives the three approached Park Sterling Bank's then-CEO (now president) Bryan Kennedy III about partnering with the bank to foster its growth. The three came on board as management assembled a board of directors and raised about $150 million in its initial stock offering.

EXECUTIVES

EVP and CFO, David L. Gaines
CEO, James C. Cherry
EVP and Chief Risk Offiecr, Nancy J. Foster, age 53
Senior Vice President Consumer And Commercial Lending, Barbara Jacks
Group Senior V Pres, Michael Williams
Group Sr V Pres, Steve Farbstein
Svp And Head Of Private Bankin, George Meyls
Senior Vice President Head Of Operations And Information Technology, Mark Ladnier

LOCATIONS

HQ: Park Sterling Corp
1043 E. Morehead Street, Suite 201, Charlotte, NC 28204
Phone: 704 716-2134
Web: www.parksterlingbank.com

COMPETITORS

BB&T	Four Oaks Fincorp
Bank of America	NewBridge Bancorp
Carolina Bank	North State Bancorp
CommunityOne Bancorp	Peoples Bancorp (NC)
ECB Bancorp	Select Bancorp
First BanCorp (Puerto Rico)	Southern Community Financial
First Citizens BancShares	Uwharrie Capital
First Trust Bank	Yadkin Financial

HISTORICAL FINANCIALS

Company Type: Public

Income Statement

FYE: December 31

	ASSETS ($ mil.)	NET INCOME ($ mil.)	INCOME AS % OF ASSETS	EMPLOYEES
12/13	1,960.7	15.3	0.8%	490
12/12	2,032.6	4.3	0.2%	482
12/11	1,113.2	(8.3)	—	270
12/10	616.1	(7.8)	—	65
12/09	473.8	0.5	0.1%	0
Annual Growth	42.6%	126.9%	—	—

2013 Year-End Financials

Return on assets: 0.7%	Dividends
Return on equity: 5.6%	Yield: 0.5%
Long-term debt ($ mil.): —	Payout: 11.7%
No. of shares (mil.): 44	Market value ($ mil.): 319
Sales ($ mil): 93	

	STOCK PRICE ($) FY Close	P/E High/Low		PER SHARE ($) Earnings	Dividends	Book Value
12/13	7.14	21	15	0.34	0.04	5.86
12/12	5.23	44	33	0.12	0.00	6.18
12/11	4.08	—	—	(0.29)	0.00	5.82
12/10	6.18	—	—	(0.58)	0.00	6.31
12/09	6.30	75	46	0.12	0.00	9.31
Annual Growth	3.2% (10.9%)	—	—	29.7%	—	—

Park-Ohio Holdings Corp.

Park-Ohio Holdings troubleshoots industrial supply chain logistics issues and makes a slew of fasteners and other industrial components. The company straddles three business segments: Supply Technologies sources and procures production components for OEMs in industries ranging from automotive to aerospace; Engineered Products produces specialized systems and parts used in such industrial applications as coatings forging oil and gas and rail; and the Assembly Components unit casts and machines metal parts —knuckles oil pans cylinders —used by auto agricultural construction and marine OEMs.

Geographic Reach

Park-Ohio operates more than 35 manufacturing sites and 52 supply chain logistics facilities in over 16 countries throughout North America South America Europe and Asia. The US generates nearly 75% of the company's net sales while Canada contributes 8%. Other major markets include Asia (6%) and Europe (5%).

Operations

Park-Ohio's business is divided across three main segments: Supply Technologies (39% of net sales) Assembly Components (34%) Engineered Products (27%).

Financial Performance

The company has achieved unprecedented growth over the last few years with revenues climbing around 7% from $1.13 billion in 2012 to peak at a record-setting $1.2 billion in 2013. The historic growth for 2013 was fueled by the addition of $82 million from acquisitions previously made.

Park-Ohio was also helped by stronger sales from its new automotive aluminum platform business within its Assembly Components segment.

Profits jumped 37% from $32 million in 2012 to $43 million in 2013 due to a decrease in litigation and settlement costs. After experiencing a steep decline in 2011 Park-Ohio's operating cash flow steadily increased during 2012 and 2013.

Strategy

To achieve growth Park-Ohio seeks out complementary businesses to acquire. In 2014 it bought Apollo Aerospace Group headquartered in the UK with operating locations in England France Poland and India. Apollo is a supply chain management services company providing Class C production components and supply chain products to aerospace customers worldwide.

Park-Ohio extended its European footprint further in 2013 with the purchases of other supply chain products and services providers: QEF Limited (locations in Ireland Scotland and England) and Henry Halstead (the UK and Ireland).

EXECUTIVES

President and COO, Matthew V. Crawford, age 44, $390,000 total compensation
Chairman and CEO, Edward F. Crawford, age 74, $731,250 total compensation
VP and CFO, Scott W Emerick
Vice President Operations, M L Justice
Chairman and CEO, Edward F. Crawford, age 74
Vice Chairman, James W. Wert, age 67
Assistant Treasurer, Carolina Schneider
Auditors: Ernst&YoungLLP

LOCATIONS

HQ: Park-Ohio Holdings Corp.
6065 Parkland Boulevard, Cleveland, OH 44124
Phone: 440 947-2000
Web: www.pkoh.com

2013 Sales

	% of total
North America	
US	74
Canada	8
Mexico	5
Asia	6
Europe	5
Other	2
Total	**100**

PRODUCTS/OPERATIONS

2013 Sales

	$ mil.	% of total
Supply technologies	471.9	39
Manufactured products	412.8	34
Aluminum products	318.5	27
Total	**1203.2**	**100**

Selected Products

Supply technologies —sourcing planning and procurement of:
  Clamps and fittings
  Fasteners
  Hoses
  Pins
  Rubber and plastic components
  Valves
  Wire harnesses
Manufactured products
  Forging presses
  Induction heating and melting systems
  Industrial oven systems
  Injection molded rubber components
  Pipe threading systems
Aluminum products

Clutch retainers/pistons
Control arms
Cooling modules
Flywheel spacers
Front engine covers
Knuckles
Master cylinders
Oil pans
Pump housings

COMPETITORS

Anixter Fasteners	MNP Corp.
Fastenal	MSC Industrial Direct
Federal Screw Works	Menlo Worldwide
GKN Sinter Metals	PennEngineering
Hillman Companies	Ryder System
Illinois Tool Works	Shiloh Industries
LISI	T3 Energy Services
Lawson Products	Textron
Logistics Plus	

HISTORICAL FINANCIALS

Company Type: Public

Income Statement

FYE: December 31

	REVENUE ($ mil.)	NET INCOME ($ mil.)	NET PROFIT MARGIN	EMPLOYEES
12/13	1,203.2	43.4	3.6%	5,000
12/12	1,134.0	31.7	2.8%	3,800
12/11	966.5	29.4	3.0%	3,200
12/10	813.5	15.1	1.9%	385
12/09	701.0	(5.2)	—	2,950
Annual Growth	14.5%			14.1%

2013 Year-End Financials

Debt ratio: 46.8%	No. of shares (mil.): 12
Return on equity: 33.2%	Dividends
Cash ($ mil.): 55	Yield: —
Current ratio: 2.51	Payout: —
Long-term debt ($ mil.): 379	Market value ($ mil.): 651

	STOCK PRICE ($) FY Close	P/E High/Low		PER SHARE ($) Earnings	Dividends	Book Value
12/13	52.40	14	6	3.56	0.00	12.79
12/12	21.31	9	6	2.62	0.00	8.32
12/11	17.84	10	4	2.45	0.00	5.39
12/10	20.91	17	4	1.29	0.00	3.92
12/09	5.65	—	—	(0.47)	0.00	1.93
Annual Growth	74.5%	—	—	—	—	60.4%

Patrick Industries, Inc.

A recreational vehicle is just an empty motor home until Patrick Industries adds the finishing interior touches. The company makes and distributes a range of building materials and prefinished products primarily for the manufactured home (MH) and RV industries. Patrick Industries manufactures decorative paper and vinyl panels moldings countertops doors and cabinet and slotwall components. In addition to these the firm distributes roofing siding flooring drywall ceiling and wall panels household electronics electrical and plumbing supplies and adhesives. Founded in 1959 the company operates about two dozen production facilities distribution centers and warehouses in a dozen states.

Operations

Patrick Industries operates seven manufacturing plants where it makes furniture shelving wall counter and cabinet products mouldings interior passage doors and slotwall panels and components among other products. Its manufacturing segment contributes about three-quarters of its annual revenue. The company also distributes prefinished wall and ceiling panels drywall and drywall finishing products. electronics. wiring electrical and plumbing products shower doors fireplaces and other miscellaneous products from five distribution facilities nationwide. Distribution accounts for about 25% of sales.

Sales and Marketing

Patrick Industries counts most of the major manufactured housing (MH) and RV manufacturers among its clientele but it also serves customers in the marine casegoods home furniture and the commercial furnishings and fixtures industries. The company has about 600 active customers of which five account for nearly two-thirds of its sales in 2012. The RV industry represented approximately 69% of the company's sales in 2012 while manufactured housing accounted for 19%. The industrial market represented the rest.

Financial Performance

The company's sales and profits have rebounded since the global economic downturn cut sales by more than a third. In 2012 Patrick's sales jumped 42% compared with 2011 to a record $437.4 million. Net income surged 232% over the same period to $28.1 million. Indeed 2012 marked the third consecutive year of rising sales and profits for the company. Increased wholesale shipments to the RV industry and contributions from recent acquisitions bolstered sales.

Strategy

The company took a beating as a result of the global economic downturn that began in late 2007. In response it disposed of non-core businesses streamlined administrative and support functions and reduced inventory levels. Now with the economy improving and RV business back on track Patrick Industries is looking to complement its existing product lines and has been expanding its operations through acquisitions.

Mergers and Acquisitions

In October 2012 the company bought Middlebury Hardwood Products a maker and distributor of hardwood cabinet doors as well as Indiana-based Creative Wood Designs which manufactures hardwood furniture including tables chairs and dinettes for the RV industry for $5.7 million. The purchase came on the heels of the July acquisition of another Indiana firm Gustafson Lighting a maker of lighting products ceiling fans and accessories also for RVs. It also acquired Oregon-based Decor Mfg. LLC which makes laminated and wrapped products specifically for the recreational vehicle market for about $4.4 million. Previously Patrick Industries purchased A.I.A. Countertops a fabricator of DuPont and Corian countertops backsplashes tables and more for about $5.7 million in 2011.

EXECUTIVES

EVP Finance CFO Secretary Treasurer and Director, Andy L. Nemeth, age 45, $211,347 total compensation
President CEO and Director, Todd M. Cleveland, age 46, $266,250 total compensation
COO, Jeffrey Rodino
Vice President Und, Thomas Baer
Vice President - Sales; South And West, James Ritchey
V Pres Hr, Courtney Blosser

Vice President Operations, R Brandon
Board Member, Joseph M (Joe) Cerulli, age 56
EVP Finance CFO Secretary Treasurer and Director, Andy L. Nemeth, age 45
Chairman, Paul E. Hassler, age 67
President CEO and Director, Todd M. Cleveland, age 46
Auditors: Ernst&YoungLLP

LOCATIONS

HQ: Patrick Industries, Inc.
107 West Franklin Street, P.O. Box 638, Elkhart, IN 46515
Phone: 574 294-7511
Web: www.patrickind.com

PRODUCTS/OPERATIONS

2012 Sales

	$ mil.	% of total
Manufacturing	331.0	76
Distribution	106.4	24
Total	**437.4**	**100**

2012 Sales by Customer Type

	% of total
RV industry	69
Manufactured housing	19
Industrial market	12
Total	**100**

COMPETITORS

Decorator Industries	Lowe's
Drew Industries	Quanex Building
Flexsteel	Products
HD Supply	Saint-Gobain
LaSalle Bristol	

HISTORICAL FINANCIALS

Company Type: Public

Income Statement

FYE: December 31

	REVENUE ($ mil.)	NET INCOME ($ mil.)	NET PROFIT MARGIN	EMPLOYEES
12/13	594.9	24.0	4.0%	2,387
12/12	437.3	28.1	6.4%	1,678
12/11	307.8	8.4	2.8%	900
12/10	278.2	1.2	0.4%	668
12/09	212.5	(4.5)	—	580
Annual Growth	29.3%	—	—	42.4%

2013 Year-End Financials

Debt ratio: 31.5%	No. of shares (mil.): 10
Return on equity: 33.4%	Dividends
Cash ($ mil.): 0	Yield: —
Current ratio: 2.71	Payout: —
Long-term debt ($ mil.): 55	Market value ($ mil.): 306

	STOCK PRICE ($) FY Close	P/E High/Low		PER SHARE ($) Earnings	Dividends	Book Value
12/13	28.93	15	5	2.23	0.00	7.79
12/12	15.56	8	2	2.64	0.00	5.66
12/11	4.10	5	2	0.83	0.00	2.89
12/10	1.90	28	13	0.12	0.00	1.95
12/09	2.43	—	—	(0.49)	0.00	1.78
Annual Growth	85.8%	—	—	—	—	44.6%

PDF Solutions Inc.

PDF Solutions can solve chip design and manufacturing inefficiencies. The company provides software and services that help integrated circuit makers get more working chips out of a production batch. PDF's products are used to simulate model and analyze the chip design and manufacturing processes. As part of the Design-to-Silicon-Yield program PDF also receives a portion of customers' cost savings called gain share. Three customers —GLOBALFOUNDRIES IBM and Samsung Electronics —collectively account for about 75% of sales. PDF Solutions generates about 60% of sales outside the US.

Geographic Reach

The company has offices in China France Germany Italy Japan South Korea Taiwan and the US (in California).

Sales and Marketing

PDF Solutions uses a direct sales force and strategic alliances to pursue targeted accounts. Its customers are foundries integrated device manufacturers (IDMs) and fabless semiconductor design companies who then go on to mke microprocessors memory graphics image sensor solutions and communications products.

Financial Performance

The company has enjoyed substantial revenue growth for the past four years. Overall sales increased 13% in 2013 to reach $101 million a record high. Revenues related to Design-to-Silicon-Yield software and services were up slightly due to fixed fee integrated solutions the result of more billable hours while revenues from its gainshare performance incentives rose 30% on increased production volumes at customer facilities.

PDF Solutions has struggled with profitability in the past decade but has been profitable for the past four years. Net income was $20 million in 2013 down 43% from $37 million in 2012. The decrease was due to a one-tax income tax provision.

Strategy

Yield improvement is the name of the game for PDF Solutions. It's not uncommon for an initial manufacturing run to yield only 20% leaving 80% of the ICs produced are wasted. The company has developed proprietary technologies for yield simulation analysis loss detection and improvement. Its products enable customers to electrically characterize the manufacturing process and establish failrate information needed to calibrate manufacturing yield models prioritize yield improvement activities and speed up process learning cycles.

EXECUTIVES

Vice President And General Manager Manufacturing Process Solutions, Cornelis (Cees) Hartgring, age 61

Vice President Marketing, Sharad Saxena

President and CEO, John K. Kibarian, age 49, $333,333 total compensation

VP Products and Solutions; Director, Kimon W. Michaels, age 48, $280,000 total compensation

Chief Technologist, Andrzej J. Strojwas

VP Finance and CFO, Gregory C. Walker, $315,000 total compensation

Vice President Sales, Leslie Krober

Vice President Of Ya Fdc Solution And Account General Manager, Yu Michael

Chairman, Lucio L. Lanza, age 70

Auditors: Deloitte&ToucheLLP

LOCATIONS

HQ: PDF Solutions Inc.
333 West San Carlos Street, Suite 1000, San Jose, CA 95110
Phone: 408 280-7900   **Fax:** 408 280-7915
Web: www.pdf.com

2013 Sales

	$ mil.	% of total
North America	39.2	39
Asia/Pacific	36.2	36
Europe	26.2	25
Total	**101.6**	**100**

PRODUCTS/OPERATIONS

2013 Sales

	$ mil.	% of total
Design-to-silicon-yield solutions	61.7	61
Gainshare performance incentives	39.8	39
Total	**101.5**	**100**

Selected Products and Services

Integration assessment
Manufacturing process simulation
Yield and performance monitoring modeling and prediction software and services (Design-to-Silicon-Yield program)

COMPETITORS

ARM Holdings	KLA-Tencor
AXIOM Design	MKS Instruments
Applied Materials	Mentor Graphics
Atrenta	Rudolph Technologies
Cadence Design	Silvaco
FEI	Synopsys
Intrinsix	

HISTORICAL FINANCIALS

Company Type: Public

Income Statement

FYE: December 31

	REVENUE ($ mil.)	NET INCOME ($ mil.)	NET PROFIT MARGIN	EMPLOYEES
12/13	101.4	20.9	20.6%	363
12/12	89.5	37.2	41.6%	345
12/11	66.7	1.8	2.8%	319
12/10	61.6	0.2	0.4%	292
12/09	48.4	(17.4)	—	306
Annual Growth	**20.3%**	—	—	**4.4%**

2013 Year-End Financials

Debt ratio: —
Return on equity: 17.7%
Cash ($ mil.): 89
Current ratio: 10.40
Long-term debt ($ mil.): —

No. of shares (mil.): 30
Dividends
  Yield: —
  Payout: —
Market value ($ mil.): 780

	STOCK PRICE ($) FY Close	P/E High/Low		PER SHARE ($) Earnings	Dividends	Book Value
12/13	25.62	36	20	0.67	0.00	4.43
12/12	13.78	11	5	1.25	0.00	3.46
12/11	6.97	102	52	0.07	0.00	2.01
12/10	4.82	511	346	0.01	0.00	1.84
12/09	3.85	—	—	(0.66)	0.00	1.72
Annual Growth	**60.6%**		—	—	—	**26.6%**

Pegasystems Inc.

Pegasystems helps companies soar through business changes without being tied down by their old processes. The company provides rules-driven business process management software PegaRules Process Commander designed to help large companies in the financial services insurance and health care industries update their operations and systems to reflect changes in business goals and strategies. Established in 1983 Pegasystems offers tools for analyzing and simulating processes integrating enterprise applications and portals managing content integration and managing processes for customer service claims resolution and transaction processing.

Geographic Reach

Pegasystems is headquartered in Massachusetts and has a half dozen other offices across the US. International locations are in Australia Canada China France Germany India India Poland Russia Spain Sweden Switzerland and the UK. The US accounts for 55% of sales; Europe makes up another 30%.

Sales and Marketing

The company sells its products through its direct sales force as well as through distributors resellers and trade shows (including its PegaWorld user conference). Financial services and health care companies are its primary markets but the company also sells to clients in the manufacturing government travel and hospitality retail consumer packaged goods and telecommunications industries.

Financial Performance

In 2013 Pegasystems' cash flow and net income again turned up to match its continuously improving revenue. Overall revenues grew 10% from $472 million in 2012 to $508 million in 2013 a historic milestone for the company. It attributed the growth for 2013 to a 17% surge in license revenue and an 18% increase in maintenance revenue due to the value of the installed base of its software coupled with higher renewal rates. Income from professional services however fell 3% as more clients became enabled and its partners led more implementation projects.

Profits skyrocketed almost 75% from $23 million in 2012 to $38 million in 2013 even as the company paid more in operating expenses and expanded its headcount by another 500 people. Cash flow also grew from $43 million in 2012 to $80 million in 2013 from the increased profits and deferred revenue from the difference in timing of billings and revenue recognition for annual maintenance.

Strategy

To extend its geographic reach and attract additional customers Pegasystems enters partnerships with major IT services and software providers. Its list of strategic partners includes Accenture Capgemini Cognizant Infosys Mahindra Tata Consultancy Services Virtusa and Wipro.

Mergers and Acquisitions

Pegasystems has made several recent acquisitions to further fuel growth. In 2014 it bought Profeatable Corporation the provider of Firefly cobrowsing technology and incorporated it into its Build for Change platform and customer service and sales applications. Earlier it bought MeshLabs a text analytics natural language and social engagement platform based in India. In 2013 it paid about $28 million for Antenna Software a leading provider of mobile application development platforms.

Ownership

Founder and CEO Alan Trefler owns more than 53% of Pegasystems.

EXECUTIVES

Chairman and CEO, Alan Trefler, age 58, $400,000 total compensation

SVP Engineering and Product Development, Michael R. (Mike) Pyle, age 59, $305,000 total compensation

SVP and Chief Marketing Officer, Robert Tas, age 35

SVP Global Customer Success, Douglas I. (Doug) Kra, age 51, $310,000 total compensation

SVP Business Unit Management, Louis Blatt

SVP CFO and Chief Administrative Officer, Rafael E. Brown, age 45, $80,000 total compensation

SVP Product Management and CRM Technologies, Kerim Akgonul

Vice President Marketing, Dave Donelan

Vice President Tax, Bruce Vaughan

Vice President Financial Solutions Frameworks, Richard Jefferson

Senior Vice President Client Services, Jon Rowlings

Vice President Business Process Management, Setrag Khoshafian

Vice President, Walter Heeger

Vice President Global Recruiting, Becky Smith

Vice President Global Solutions Engineering And Architecture, Tim Beachus

Chief Technology Officer And Vice President, Steven Benfield

Vice President Decisioning And Analytics, Rob Walker

Vice President Program And Finance Technology, Russell Lafond

Vice President, Phil Dekemper

Vice President Of World Wide Sales, Ron Visser

Senior Vice President Sales, William Hampton

Vice Presidet Sales And Product Opera, Dean Webster

Vice President Sales, Peter Morris

National Vice President, Michael Smaney

Vice President Product Management Technology Platform, Mark Replogle

Vice President Strategic Alliances, Robert Napolitano

Vice President Information Technology, John Parker

Vice President Of Engineering For Deci, Mike Ruggieri

Vice President Sales And Marketing, Simon Turowski

Vice President Of Appraisal Operations, Richard Neal

Vice President, Chris Sirna

Vice President Of Sales Enablement, Karen Beecher

Vice President, Ben Rice

Vice President Rules Engine Development, John Clinton

Senior Vice President Sales, Leon Trefler

Vice President Rules Engine Development, Clinton Bill

Vice President Sales And Marketing, John Barrone

Vice President Services, Rich Jackson

Vice President Marketing, David Donelan

Vice President Real Estate And Facilities, Dan Ryan

Vice President Corporate Communications, Lisa Pintchman

Chairman and CEO, Alan Trefler, age 58

Vice Chairman, Richard H. (Rick) Jones, age 63

Board Member, Par Industrie

Advisory Board Member, Bart Patrick

Board Member, Nach Branchen

Board Of Directors, Peter Gyenes

Auditors: Deloitte&ToucheLLP

LOCATIONS

HQ: Pegasystems Inc.
One Rogers Street, Cambridge, MA 02142-1209
Phone: 617 374-9600
Web: www.pega.com

2013 Sales

	$ mil.	% of total
US	278.9	55
UK	83.1	16
Rest of Europe	82.7	16
Asia	45.1	9
Other	18.9	4
Total	**508.9**	**100**

PRODUCTS/OPERATIONS

2013 Sales

	$ mil.	% of total
Software licenses	191.9	38
Professional services	159.8	31
Maintenance	157.3	31
Total	**508.9**	**100**

Selected Software

PegaCloud
PegaCRM
Pega Decision Management
PegaRULES Process Commander
Solutions Frameworks

COMPETITORS

Appian	SAP
EMC	Software AG
Fair Isaac	SunGard
Guidewire Software	TIBCO Software
IBM	TriZetto
Microsoft Dynamics	Trintech
Oracle	salesforce.com
Progress Software	

HISTORICAL FINANCIALS

Company Type: Public

Income Statement

FYE: December 31

	REVENUE ($ mil.)	NET INCOME ($ mil.)	NET PROFIT MARGIN	EMPLOYEES
12/13	508.9	38.0	7.5%	2,627
12/12	461.7	21.8	4.7%	2,160
12/11	416.6	10.1	2.4%	1,858
12/10	336.6	(5.8)	—	1,509
12/09	264.0	32.2	12.2%	1,076
Annual Growth	**17.8%**	**4.2%**	**—**	**25.0%**

2013 Year-End Financials

Debt ratio: —
Return on equity: 14.9%
Cash ($ mil.): 80
Current ratio: 1.85
Long-term debt ($ mil.): —

No. of shares (mil.): 76
Dividends
  Yield: 0.4%
  Payout: 24.4%
Market value ($ mil.): 3,754

	STOCK PRICE ($) FY Close	P/E High/Low		PER SHARE ($) Earnings	Dividends	Book Value
12/13	49.18	102	45	0.49	0.12	3.56
12/12	22.68	135	67	0.28	0.15	3.12
12/11	29.40	348	200	0.13	0.06	2.77
12/10	36.63	—	—	(0.08)	0.12	2.63
12/09	34.00	81	27	0.43	0.12	2.79
Annual Growth	**9.7%**	—	—	**3.6%**	**(0.0%)**	**6.3%**

Penford Corp.

Penford Corporation doesn't mind its reputation for being stiff and starchy –that's how it makes its money. The company makes carbohydrate-based specialty starches used by the paper packaging and food industries. Paper and packaging manufacturers use the specialty starches and film-forming ingredients from Penford's industrial ingredients segment to improve the strength and quality of containers and magazine and catalog paper. The division also produces and sells ethanol from corn. The company's food ingredients segment makes starches and dextrins that improve the crispness texture and shelf life of various food products (including pet food and treats). Penford generates most of its sales in the US.

Change in Company Type

Penford Corp. has agreed to be acquired by Ingredion Inc. for $19 per share in cash. The deal which could close by the end of 2014 values Penford at $340 million.

Geographic Reach Penford has offices and plants in Colorado Idaho Iowa Pennsylvania South Carolina Washington and Wisconsin. The US represents its largest market accounting for more than 90% of sales. North America as a whole contributes 97%.

Sales and Marketing As the company's sole customer for ethanol biofuels distributor Eco-Energy accounts for nearly 30% of overall revenue.

Financial Performance Penford's fiscal 2012 (ended August) revenue rose 15% to $361 million driven by the acquisition of Carolina Starches (which brought in about $15 million) and 25% growth in its smaller food ingredients business because of pricing improvements and substantial growth in pet chews and treats. The company reported a net loss of nearly $10 million double its 2011 loss because of a loss on redemption of preferred stock and an income tax expense.

Mergers and Acquisitions In a move to expand its specialty industrial products and food ingredients operations Penford acquired Carolina Starches and affiliate Keystone Starches in early 2012. Carolina Starches which generates about $25 million yearly sources domestic potato and corn starches as well as European potato starch and Asian tapioca starch for processing at its plants in South Carolina and Pennsylvania.

HISTORY

In 1984 giant chemical distributor Univar spun off subsidiaries Penick & Ford and Great Western Malting (a malt maker) as an independent company which became PENWEST. The next year Univar veteran Tod Hamachek became CEO.

PENWEST narrowed its focus in 1988 selling Great Western Malting to concentrate on specialty chemicals. In 1991 the company acquired Edward Mendell (pharmaceutical excipients) and diversified into the food industry by setting up Penwest Foods. PENWEST subsequently developed starch-based chemicals for cereal frozen fish low-fat hot dogs and tortillas. The company launched TIMERx Technologies a division focused on the development of controlled-release technology for pharmaceuticals in 1994. The next year it teamed up with the US's largest potato processor ConAgra's Lamb-Weston to supply potato-starch coatings for French fries to keep them crispy under heat lamps.

High corn prices and a slump in the paper industry in 1996 prompted PENWEST's decision to expand its pharmaceutical business. In 1997 the company changed its name to Penford Corporation. Penford began focusing on carbohydrate chemistry to create high-margin products. Penwest Pharmaceuticals was spun off and Hamachek left to head the new company.

One of Penford's first successes was the development of PenExcel a carbohydrate-based ink jet system for paper makers which the company developed in 1999 with help from Monsanto. In 2000 Penford acquired Starch Australasia Limited (corn starch products) from Goodman Fielder Limited for $54.5 million. Although paper product sales were down in 2001 the addition of Burger King as a french fry coatings product customer and Penford Australia's sales boosted Penford's overall sales by some 30%.

The acquisition of Starch Australasia (renamed Penford Australia) expanded Penford's geographic reach and given it Australia's only maker of corn starch products. From this new base the company began to target markets in Africa and Asia.

In 2002 Penford relocated its corporate headquarters from Bellevue Washington to Englewood Colorado. Related to the move the company took a charge of $1.4 million.

EXECUTIVES

Vice President; President - Food Ingredients, John R Randall, age 72
Chief Financial Officer; Senior Vice President; Assistant Secretary, Steven O Cordier, age 59
President CEO and Director, Thomas D. Malkoski, age 59, $550,000 total compensation
Medical Director, Ted Lengwin
Vp Industrial Ingredients, Greg Keenan
Vice President - Human Resources; General Counsel; Secretary, Christopher L Lawlor, age 65
Vice President Of Research, Nik Nikolic
Vice President Strategic Director Business Development, Kurt Moberg
Vice President Sales And Marketing, William Winetroub
Treasurer Executive Vice President, Andy Linajs
Auditors: Ernst&YoungLLP

LOCATIONS

HQ: Penford Corp.
7094 South Revere Parkway, Centennial, CO 80112-3932
Phone: 303 649-1900
Web: www.penx.com

PRODUCTS/OPERATIONS

Selected Products
Industrial
　Binders
　Cationic additive

Sizing agent
Starch series
Waterholding films
Food Ingredients
　Dextrins
　Dextrose
　Starches

COMPETITORS

ADM
Akzo Nobel
BASF Catalysts
Dow Corning

JR Simplot
MGP Ingredients
Tate & Lyle

HISTORICAL FINANCIALS

Company Type: Public

Income Statement
FYE: August 31

	REVENUE ($ mil.)	NET INCOME ($ mil.)	NET PROFIT MARGIN	EMPLOYEES
08/14	443.8	7.7	1.7%	443
08/13	467.2	4.0	0.9%	403
08/12	361.3	(9.5)	—	396
08/11	315.4	(5.1)	—	333
08/10	254.2	6.6	2.6%	330
Annual Growth	14.9%	3.8%	—	7.6%

2014 Year-End Financials

Debt ratio: 32.7%
Return on equity: 8.8%
Cash ($ mil.): 0
Current ratio: 2.52
Long-term debt ($ mil.): 76

No. of shares (mil.): 12
Dividends
　Yield: —
　Payout: —
Market value ($ mil.): 173

	STOCK PRICE ($) FY Close	P/E High/Low		PER SHARE ($) Earnings	Dividends	Book Value
08/14	13.62	24	18	0.60	0.00	7.23
08/13	13.55	49	22	0.32	0.00	6.63
08/12	7.31	—	—	(0.78)	0.00	5.57
08/11	5.50	—	—	(0.42)	0.00	7.53
08/10	4.90	20	9	0.57	0.00	7.35
Annual Growth	29.1%		— —	1.3%	—	(0.4%)

Peoples Financial Services Corp

Power to the Peoples Financial Services. The firm is the holding company for Peoples National Bank which operates about a dozen branches in northeastern Pennsylvania and neighboring Broome County in New York. With roots going back to 1905 the bank offers area businesses and individuals standard retail products and services including checking and savings accounts CDs and credit cards. Commercial loans including mortgages construction loans and operating loans make up the greatest portion of the company's loan book followed by residential mortgages and consumer loans. The company's Peoples Advisors subsidiary provides investment and brokerage services.

EXECUTIVES

Vp Peoples National Bank, Thomas (Tom) Bush
Assistant Vp Peoples National Bank, Paul Walsh

CEO and President, Alan W. Dakey, age 62
EVP and COO Peoples National Bank, Debra E. Dissinger, age 59, $110,000 total compensation
Director, Richard S. Lochen, age 50, $130,000 total compensation
Senior Vice President Chief Financial Officer, Scott Seasock
Executive Vice President Chief Lending Officer, Joseph M Ferretti, age 45
Chairman, William E. Aubrey, age 51

LOCATIONS

HQ: Peoples Financial Services Corp
82 Franklin Avenue, Hallstead, PA 18822
Phone: 570 879-2175
Web: www.peoplesnatbank.com

PRODUCTS/OPERATIONS

2007 Sales

	$ mil.	% of total
Interest		
Loans	19.5	70
Securities & other	5.1	18
Noninterest		
Customer service fees	1.9	7
Other	1.5	5
Total	**28.0**	**100**

COMPETITORS

Citizens & Northern
Citizens Financial Services
Fidelity D & D
First Keystone
First National Community Bancorp

HSBC USA
M&T Bank
NBT Bancorp
Penns Woods Bancorp
Penseco Financial Services

HISTORICAL FINANCIALS

Company Type: Public

Income Statement
FYE: December 31

	ASSETS ($ mil.)	NET INCOME ($ mil.)	INCOME AS % OF ASSETS	EMPLOYEES
12/13	1,688.2	5.7	0.3%	354
12/12	918.0	10.5	1.2%	0
12/11	621.4	7.8	1.3%	132
12/10	558.5	6.4	1.2%	124
12/09	516.4	5.0	1.0%	139
Annual Growth	34.5%	3.2%	—	26.3%

2013 Year-End Financials

Return on assets: 0.4%
Return on equity: 3.0%
Long-term debt ($ mil.): —
No. of shares (mil.): 7
Sales ($ mil.): 49

Dividends
　Yield: 2.4%
　Payout: 76.0%
Market value ($ mil.): 287

	STOCK PRICE ($) FY Close	P/E High/Low		PER SHARE ($) Earnings	Dividends	Book Value
12/13	38.00	33	25	1.21	0.92	31.62
12/12	30.50	13	12	2.37	0.86	29.65
12/11	28.25	11	10	2.49	0.80	19.11
12/10	26.60	14	9	2.06	0.79	16.08
12/09	18.05	12	10	1.61	0.76	14.34
Annual Growth	20.5%		— —	(6.9%)	4.9%	21.9%

Perficient Inc.

Perficient is proficient in helping its customers use technology to their advantage. The IT consultancy provides software development systems integration and technical support. It specializes in developing middleware applications used to integrate and modernize legacy computer hardware and software. Its expertise also encompasses content management systems ERP and CRM applications business process integration service oriented architectures business intelligence e-commerce and wireless communication. Perficient integrates and supports applications from vendors including IBM EMC Microsoft and Software AG. Customers have included Anheuser-Busch AT&T Mobility and Wachovia.

Geographic Reach

The company primarily serves customers in the US from about 20 locations. It has offshore software development facilities in China India and Macedonia.

Sales and Marketing

Perficient uses a direct sales force to target large enterprise customers that annually earn at least $500 million. Typically the company seeks to bill about $5 million for each account which it believes is below the target project range of most large systems integrators.

Financial Performance

Overall sales grew 25% in 2012 to $327 million primarily from acquisitions. (Perficient buys two or three companies every year.) The company makes most of its money by billing for services; less than 10% of sales come from licensing software and reselling hardware which have lower profit margins. Expenses grew because of increased headcount and higher employee-related expenses. Still Perficient is also consistently profitable earning $16 million in profit for 2012.

Mergers and Acquisitions

Perficient has traditionally been an aggressive buyer of complementary businesses. It expanded its operations in the northeastern US —adding offices in Boston New York City and Washington DC —with the $19 million purchase of TriTek Solutions in 2013. Also that year it added salesforce.com consulting expertise to its portfolio with two companies - New Jersey-based CoreMatrix Systems and San Francisco-based Clear Task.

In 2012 it expanded in the Chicago Milwaukee and Boston markets with the $22 purchase of PointBridge Solutions. The acquisition solidified its position as a Microsoft systems integrator consultant. It also acquired Dallas-based Nascent Systems a business and technology consultancy focused on ERP applications from Oracle such as its E-Business Suite. Later that year it bought Atlanta-based Northridge Systems a consulting firm that provides collaboration services primarily using the Microsoft SharePoint platform for about $14 million. The purchase bolstered its Microsoft practice and extended its presence in the southeastern US.

In 2011 Perficient bought Charlotte North Carolina-based management consultancy Exervio to extend its expertise in program and project management in particular and to establish its presence in the state. Perficient also bought IT consultancy JCB Partners that year to build the part of its services business that focuses on IBM's Cognos suite of enterprise applications. The deal was part of an effort to boost its business intelligence and performance management capabilities.

EXECUTIVES

VP Field Operations Western Region, Don Kasica
COO, Jeffrey S. (Jeff) Davis, age 50, $285,000 total compensation
Chief Financial Officer; Treasurer; Secretary, Paul E. Martin, age 54, $225,000 total compensation
COO, Kathryn J. (Kathy) Henely, age 49, $215,417 total compensation
VP Field Operations IBM Advanced Technology Services, John Jenkins
VP Field Operations Eastern Region, Chris Gianattasio
Chief Financial Officer; Treasurer; Secretary, Paul E. Martin, age 54
Auditors: KPMGLLP

LOCATIONS

HQ: Perficient Inc.
520 Maryville University Drive, Suite 400, Saint Louis, MO 63141
Phone: 314 529-3600
Web: www.perficient.com

PRODUCTS/OPERATIONS

2012 Sales

	% of total
Services	87
Software & hardware	8
Reimbursable expenses	5
Total	**100**

Mergers and Acquisitions

2013
TriTek Solutions
Clear Task

2012
Nascent Systems
Northridge Systems
PointBridge Solutions

2011
Exervio
JCB Partners

2010
Kerdock Consulting
speakTECH

COMPETITORS

Accenture	Edgewater Technology
Avanade	HP Enterprise Services
CIBER	Hackett Group
Cognizant Tech Solutions	Infosys
Deloitte Consulting	Sapient
Deloitte LLP	Wipro

HISTORICAL FINANCIALS

Company Type: Public

Income Statement

FYE: December 31

	REVENUE ($ mil.)	NET INCOME ($ mil.)	NET PROFIT MARGIN	EMPLOYEES
12/13	373.3	21.4	5.7%	1,874
12/12	327.1	16.1	4.9%	1,677
12/11	262.4	10.7	4.1%	1,484
12/10	214.9	6.4	3.0%	1,088
12/09	188.1	1.4	0.8%	1,015
Annual Growth	**18.7%**	**95.6%**	**—**	**16.6%**

2013 Year-End Financials

Debt ratio: 5.8%	No. of shares (mil.): 31
Return on equity: 8.6%	Dividends
Cash ($ mil.): 7	Yield: —
Current ratio: 2.51	Payout: —
Long-term debt ($ mil.): 19	Market value ($ mil.): 734

	STOCK PRICE ($) FY Close	P/E High/Low		PER SHARE ($) Earnings	Dividends	Book Value
12/13	23.42	34	14	0.67	0.00	8.28
12/12	11.78	25	19	0.52	0.00	7.60
12/11	10.01	34	17	0.37	0.00	6.92
12/10	12.50	54	34	0.23	0.00	6.50
12/09	8.43	186	68	0.05	0.00	6.22
Annual Growth	**29.1%**	**—**	**—**	**91.3%**	**—**	**7.4%**

Pharmacyclics, Inc.

Pharmacyclics wants to help cancer and other diseases cycle right out of your body. The clinical-stage company develops small-molecule drugs to fight cancer and auto-immune diseases. Its key product Imbruvica is approved in the US to treat mantle cell lymphoma a rare cancer and in testing for three other cancers. Pharmacyclis has two other cancer treatments and an autoimmune disease cure in its pipeline. The company has licensing and development agreements with Janssen Biotech Les Laboratories Servier and Novo Nordisk. It sells its products to specialty pharmacies whose customers are individuals and to specialty distributors whose customers are hospital pharmacies. Pharmacyclics was formed in 1991.

Operations

Pharmacyclics uses third-party manufacturers one for individual sales and one for bulk sales to produce Imbruvica.

Geographic Reach

Imbruvica is only approved in the US but development partner Janssen has submitted it for EU approval.

Financial Performance

Since its product was approved and began marketing in late 2013 the company hasn't had a full year of product revenues yet. Since it's formation Pharmacyclics has spent heavily on R&D and as of December 2013 had a total accumulated deficit of $216 million. The company expects to see increased spending as it markets existing products and continues R&D and trials on others.

Strategy

Key aspects of Pharmacyclics strategy include maintaining a large pipeline and continuing to outsource both clinical development and manufacturing so it can work on keeping the pipeline stocked.

EXECUTIVES

COO, Maky Zanganeh, $607,081 total compensation
CEO & Chairman of the Board of Directors, Robert W. Duggan, age 70
Executive Vice President of Toxicology, David J. Loury, age 58, $326,300 total compensation
Vice President Chemical Operations, Gregory Hemmi, age 48
Chief Medical Officer, Jesse McGreivy, age 45
Chief of Oncology Operations and Alliances, Maria Fardis, age 46

Executive Vice President Sales and Marketing,
 Paula Boultbee, age 55
Vice President Global Quality, Scott Shearer, age 49
Vice President of Clinical Medicine and Early
 Development, Darrin Beaupre
Vice President of Clinical Science, Thorsten Graef
Vice President of Research/Biology, Betty Y Chang
EVP Corporate Affairs, Ramses Erdtmann
Executive Vice President Global Manufacturing
 Technical Operations, Heow Tan
Vice President Regulatory Affairs, Urte Gayko
Vice President Information Technology, Christophe
 Suchet
Associate Medical Director, Danelle James
Vp Medical Affairs, Elizabeth Faust
Medical Director, Lori Styles
Rph, Steve Worthington
CEO & Chairman of the Board of Directors,
 Robert W. Duggan, age 70
Auditors: PricewaterhouseCoopersLLP

LOCATIONS

HQ: Pharmacyclics, Inc.
 995 E. Arques Avenue, Sunnyvale, CA 94085-4521
Phone: 408 774-0330   **Fax:** 408 774-0340
Web: www.pharmacyclics.com

PRODUCTS/OPERATIONS

2013 Sales

$ in mil		% of total
License and milestone revenue	235.0	91
Product revenue	13.6	5
Collaboration services revenue	11.6	4
Total	**260.2**	**100**

COMPETITORS

Accuray	Merck
Allos Therapeutics	OXiGENE
CTI BioPharma	Sanofi
Eli Lilly	

HISTORICAL FINANCIALS

Company Type: Public

Income Statement

FYE: December 31

	REVENUE ($ mil.)	NET INCOME ($ mil.)	NET PROFIT MARGIN	EMPLOYEES
12/13	260.1	67.0	25.8%	484
12/12*	160.6	117.5	73.2%	224
06/12	81.9	11.9	14.6%	150
06/11	8.2	(35.2)	—	77
06/10	9.3	(15.0)	—	58
Annual Growth	**129.9%**	**—**	**—**	**70.0%**

*Fiscal year change

2013 Year-End Financials

Debt ratio: —	No. of shares (mil.): 74
Return on equity: 15.0%	Dividends
Cash ($ mil.): 623	Yield: —
Current ratio: 8.45	Payout: —
Long-term debt ($ mil.): —	Market value ($ mil.): 7,845

	STOCK PRICE ($) FY Close	P/E High/Low		PER SHARE ($) Earnings	Dividends	Book Value
12/13	105.78	152	63	0.87	0.00	8.46
12/12*	57.78	41	9	1.58	0.00	3.74
06/12	54.61	321	53	0.17	0.00	1.91
06/11	10.44	—	—	(0.59)	0.00	1.50
06/10	6.66	—	—	(0.31)	0.00	1.13
Annual Growth	**99.6%**			**—**	**—**	**65.5%**

*Fiscal year change

PHI Inc

Whirlybird wizard PHI transports people and equipment mainly for oil and gas companies. One of the world's top commercial helicopter operators PHI maintains a fleet of about 280 aircraft and provides contract transportation services across the US and in Africa. Its fleet is primarily made up of helicopters but also includes fixed-wing aircraft. The company is a leading provider of helicopter transport services in the Gulf of Mexico.In addition to its energy-related operations PHI provides air transportation services to hospitals and other medical facilities and overhauls and maintains airframes engines and components.

Geographic Reach

In addition to the US PHI has operations in more than 40 countries. The US accounts for 82% of total sales.

Operations

PHI operates in three business segments: Oil and Gas (57% of sales) Air Medical (33%) and Technical Services (10%).

Sales and Marketing

PHI offers services to the offshore oil and gas onshore mining international air medical and technical services industries. Its customers include Shell Oil Company BP America Production Company ExxonMobil Production Co. and ConocoPhillips Company.

Financial Performance

PHI has experienced explosive growth over the last few years. Revenues jumped 32% from $647 million in 2012 to $857 million in 2013 a historical milestone. The strong growth for 2013 was fueled by an increase in its Oil and Gas segment revenues due to continuing improvement in the Gulf of Mexico deepwater drilling activity which drove higher utilization of its heavy aircraft.

The Air Medical segment increased primarily due to an expansion of its traditional provider programs as well as increased revenues from its independent provider programs driven by an improvement in its payor mix and rate increases. Technical Services segment revenues were up in 2013 primarily due to the sale of seven aircraft for use by a customer in one of its Air Medical's traditional provider programs.

Profits also skyrocketed over 200% from $18 million in 2012 to a record-setting $59 million in 2013 due to the higher revenue coupled with gains on the sale of two heavy aircraft during the year. In addition PHI's operating cash flow has climbed over the last two years. Cash flow increased by $55 million in 2013 due to the rise in profits and additional cash generated from deferred income taxes impairment of assets and cash from other assets.

Strategy

With oil- and gas-related revenues responsible for about two-thirds of sales oil production in the Gulf of Mexico is vital to PHI's business. With the 2010 BP oil spill disaster years behind the company believes the region is a stable and profitable source of revenue as deepwater operations tend to have longer lead times and consequently activity levels are less susceptible to short term volatility in commodity prices. The capital commitments are also substantially larger than shallow water operations and its client base is more heavily weighted to the major integrated and larger independent oil and gas companies as a result. PHI will also continue to seek to expand into international markets that its believes have attractive opportunities for growth.

HISTORY

Robert Suggs and M. M. Bayon formed Petroleum Bell Helicopters in 1949 with three small Bell helicopters. Pioneering the use of helicopters in oil and gas exploration the young firm served an oil exploration firm working in hard-to-reach areas of the Louisiana swamps. Previously a 15-man team had to wade through waist-high swamps for more than a day to perform one seismic test. PHI enabled several field tests to be conducted in one day with much less discomfort to the surveyors.

As its fleet expanded the company dropped the "Bell" from its name in the 1950s. In 1967 Petroleum Helicopters Inc. (PHI) stepped out internationally with operations in Angola and Saudi Arabia. It branched into aeromedical services in 1981 providing helicopter ambulance and other transport services for hospitals and medical units.

Suggs died in 1989 and his wife Carroll was appointed chairman president and CEO the next year. After an acrimonious and highly public family feud with her late husband's children from a previous marriage Carroll Suggs was awarded half the estate. She went on to control the company.

The downturn in the Gulf of Mexico oil and gas markets hurt revenues in the early 1990s prompting PHI to diversify. In 1994 the firm was chosen to patrol the Haiti-Dominican Republic border during the Haiti embargo; it was the first appointment of a civilian company for such a mission. The next year PHI added five new aircraft to its aeromedical services segment its fastest-growing unit. Also in 1995 it acquired a 49% interest in Irish Helicopters Limited of Dublin.

PHI's pilots voted against joining a union in 1997. Also that year the firm continued to diversify fighting forest fires for the US Forestry Service and creating Acadian Composites to repair and overhaul helicopter composite panels (for PHI aircraft and third parties). The company ramped up its medical transportation service with the 1997 acquisition of Arizona-based Samaritan AirEvac an aeromedical unit with six aircraft from Banner Health.

A depressed oil market and bad weather suppressed demand for PHI's helicopters in the Gulf in 1999 but the company looked forward to bouncing back with higher oil prices.

In 2000 Gulf Coast engineering and construction industry veteran Lance Bospflug became PHI president taking the reins from Suggs. Also that year the company's pilots unionized. PHI narrowly averted a pilot strike the following year and reached an agreement with pilots that would allow them to voluntarily pay union dues for a three-year period after which dues would become mandatory.

Also in 2001 one of the company's helicopters crashed off the Texas coast. Much of the aircraft was recovered but the pilot was not found. Bospflug was named CEO in 2001 replacing Suggs who remained chairman. Also that year Suggs sold her 52% stake in the company to oil industry veteran Al Gonsoulin. Suggs then retired from the company and Gonsoulin became chairman. PHI also moved its headquarters from Metairie Louisiana to Lafayette.

Gonsoulin took over as president and CEO in 2004 after Bospflug stepped down. Hurricanes Katrina and Rita damaged several of the company's facilities along the Gulf of Mexico in 2005. All but one of the PHI bases were back in service by the end of the year however.

The company officially changed its name from Petroleum Helicopters Inc. to PHI Inc. in 2006 in an effort to better align its corporate identity with its mix of business activities.

Hurricanes Gustav and Ike battered the Gulf of Mexico coast in September 2008 and cost PHI some $3.3 million in repair costs evacuation of aircraft at affected bases and relocation of operations. The hurricanes also caused flight hours and revenues to dip in PHI's oil and gas unit in Louisiana and Texas as well as its Air Medical segment in Texas.

EXECUTIVES

President and COO, Lance F. Bospflug, age 59, $554,246 total compensation
Chairman and CEO, Al A. Gonsoulin, age 71, $655,015 total compensation
Director PHI Air Medical Group, David Motzkin
Director Materials, Kenneth Highlander
CFO Secretary and Treasurer, Trudy P. McConnaughhay, $282,231 total compensation
Vice President, Robert Cummiskey
Chairman and CEO, Al A. Gonsoulin, age 71
Secretary, Ben Miller
Auditors: Deloitte&ToucheLLP

LOCATIONS

HQ: PHI Inc
  2001 SE Evangeline Thruway, Lafayette, LA 70508
Phone: 337 235-2452   **Fax:** 337 235-1357
Web: www.phihelico.com

2013 Sales

	$ mil.	% of total
US	699.3	82
International	157.2	18
Total	**856.5**	**100**

PRODUCTS/OPERATIONS

2013 Sales

	$ mil.	% of total
Oil & gas	489.0	57
Air medical	277.9	32
Technical services	89.6	11
Total	**856.5**	**100**

COMPETITORS

Air Methods	Erickson
Bristow Group Inc	Evergreen Holdings
CHC Group	SEACOR

HISTORICAL FINANCIALS

Company Type: Public

Income Statement

FYE: December 31

	REVENUE ($ mil.)	NET INCOME ($ mil.)	NET PROFIT MARGIN	EMPLOYEES
12/13	856.5	58.9	6.9%	2,791
12/12	646.6	18.0	2.8%	2,633
12/11	540.1	4.8	0.9%	2,362
12/10	517.3	7.1	1.4%	2,265
12/09	487.5	12.9	2.7%	2,299
Annual Growth	**15.1%**	**46.0%**	**—**	**5.0%**

2013 Year-End Financials

Debt ratio: 32.3%
Return on equity: 11.1%
Cash ($ mil.): 0
Current ratio: 3.88
Long-term debt ($ mil.): 379
No. of shares (mil.): 15
Dividends
  Yield: —
  Payout: —
Market value ($ mil.): 672

STOCK PRICE ($) FY Close	P/E High/Low		PER SHARE ($) Earnings	Dividends	Book Value
12/13	43.40	11	7	3.77	0.00	36.19
12/12	33.49	28	19	1.17	0.00	32.63
12/11	24.85	80	53	0.31	0.00	31.17
12/10	18.84	50	28	0.46	0.00	30.85
12/09	20.70	26	9	0.85	0.00	30.40
Annual Growth	**20.3%**	**—**		**45.1%**	**—**	**4.5%**

PhotoMedex, Inc.

For PhotoMedex beauty is skin deep. The company manufactures and markets dermatological treatments for skin disorders such as acne psoriasis and vitiligo (loss of skin pigmentation). Other products include gels and creams intended to promote skin rejuvenation and hair growth. PhotoMedex also develops lasers and fiber-optic equipment for dermatological and surgical applications. Its FDA-approved XTRAC Excimer laser system is used for the treatment of psoriasis and eczema and its VTRAC lamp system is sold outside the US to treat the same ailments. Customers in the US and overseas include consumers dermatologists cosmetic surgeons and spas.

Operations
PhotoMedex breaks its operations into three categories: consumer (no!no! branded products) physician recurring (XTRAC lasers and NEOVA topical skin care) and professional (VTRAC Velocity and other light therapy equipment).

PhotoMedex conducts R&D at three facilities; along with developing new products its R&D activities are focused on expanding uses of the XTRAC system to include the treatment of inflammatory skin disorders; the development of complementary devices to improve XTRAC and other light-based systems' performance; and developing additional surgical products.

Geographic Reach
With headquarters in the US PhotoMedex exports to about 30 countries around the world. Key markets include Japan the UK Argentina and Australia.

Sales and Marketing
The company uses a direct sales force along with a global distribution and retail network to spread its products globally. The no!no! branded consumer products are available in about 55 countries.

Financial Analysis
PhotoMedex saw its revenues increase by nearly 70% in 2012 thanks to an 33% jump in consumer products revenues as a result of a growth in direct-to-consumer revenues due to successful marketing programs and an increase in retailers and home shopping channels sales thanks to successful marketing programs to the various home shopping channel customers in the UK and the US. It also saw an 48% increase in professional segment revenues.

The company saw a huge 300% increase in net income in 2012 as it offset an increase in selling and marketing expenses as the result of a rise in its direct-to-consumer advertising and selling activities and higher engineering and product development expenses related to pre-merged PhotoMedex products.

Strategy
The company seeks to expand by providing dermatologists professional aestheticians and consumers with the equipment and skin care products they need to treat psoriasis vitiligo acne and UV damage among other skin conditions.

Growing its portfolio of offerings in 2011 PhotoMedex merged with private dermatology firm Radiancy. Radiancy makes home-use and professional dermatology devices for hair removal skin rejuvenation and acne treatment under the no!no! and Radiancy brands. PhotoMedex acquired Radiancy in an all-stock transaction. Although the combined operations retained the PhotoMedex name and publicly traded status former Radiancy shareholders obtained about 75% of the combined company.

As a result of its merger with Radiancy PhotoMedex added a range of home-use devices under the no!no! brand for various indications including hair removal acne treatment and skin rejuvenation.

PhotoMedex is working hard to expand outside the US. Its primary distributor GlobalMed sells the company's laser- and light-based devices in all PhotoMedex's markets outside the US. The company has even reformulated some of its clinical skincare products removing certain preservatives to better comply with international regulations.
  Ownership
CEO Dr. Dolev Rafaeli controls 10% of the company.

EXECUTIVES

Vice President Human Resources, Marge Dailey
Executive Vice President Of Sales And Marketing, Kevin Scanlon
President and CFO, Dennis M. McGrath, age 58, $337,500 total compensation
CEO, Dolev Rafaeli, $450,000 total compensation
Vice President Sales, Carol Lux
Vice President Engineer Research, Dean Irwin
Chairman, Lewis C. Pell
Executive Vice Chairman, Yoav Ben Dror
Board Member, Leonard L Mazur
Board Member, Paul J Denby
Auditors: FahnKanne&Co.GrantThorntonIsrael

LOCATIONS

HQ: PhotoMedex, Inc.
  100 Lakeside Drive, Suite 100, Horsham, PA 19044
Phone: 215 619-3600
Web: www.photomedex.com

2012 Sales

	$ mil.	% of total
North America	164.0	74
Asia/Pacific	28.0	13
Europe	25.6	12
South America	3.1	1
Total	**220.7**	**100**

PRODUCTS/OPERATIONS

2012 Sales

	$ mil.	% of total
Consumer	188.4	85
Physician Recurring	21.3	10
Professional	10.9	5
Total	**220.6**	**100**

COMPETITORS

Allergan Limited	Obagi Medical
Anacor	Osyris Medical
Boston Scientific	Palomar Medical
Candela Corporation	SkinMedica

Cutera
Cynosure
Lumenis
Murad Inc.

Solta Medical
Syneron
TRIA Beauty
Trimedyne

HISTORICAL FINANCIALS
Company Type: Public

Income Statement
FYE: December 31

	REVENUE ($ mil.)	NET INCOME ($ mil.)	NET PROFIT MARGIN	EMPLOYEES
12/13	224.6	18.3	8.2%	168
12/12	220.6	22.4	10.2%	177
12/11	132.0	(0.6)	—	183
12/10	34.8	(8.7)	—	144
12/09	32.6	(10.5)	—	131
Annual Growth	61.9%	—	—	6.4%

2013 Year-End Financials

Debt ratio: 4.9%	No. of shares (mil.): 18
Return on equity: 11.2%	Dividends
Cash ($ mil.): 45	Yield: —
Current ratio: 2.46	Payout: —
Long-term debt ($ mil.): 0	Market value ($ mil.): 245

	STOCK PRICE ($) FY Close	P/E High/Low		PER SHARE ($) Earnings	Dividends	Book Value
12/13	12.95	19	13	0.89	0.00	8.48
12/12	14.53	17	10	1.08	0.00	7.95
12/11	12.90	—	—	(0.06)	0.00	5.96
12/10	5.94	—	—	(3.37)	0.00	6.57
12/09	0.95	—	—	(6.42)	0.00	10.24
Annual Growth	92.1%	—	—	—	—	(4.6%)

Pope Resources

More earthly than divine Pope Resources owns or manages more than 150000 acres of timberland and development property in Washington. Its holdings include the 70000-acre Hood Canal and 44000-acre Columbia tree farms in Washington. It sells its Douglas fir and other timber products mainly in the US Japan China and Korea; Weyerhaeuser and Simpson Investment Company are major customers. Pope Resources also invests in and manages two timberland investment funds and provides investment management and consulting services to third-party timberland owners and managers in Washington Oregon and California. Its real estate unit acquires develops resells and rents residential and commercial real estate.

Pope Resources' fee timber segment also gains revenue by selling gravel and by leasing cellular communication towers.

The partnership's Olympic Property Group real estate operations relate to its nearly 3000-acre portfolio of higher-and-better-use properties that may be reforested developed for sale as improved property or sold in developed or undeveloped acreage tracts. The company's Rural Lifestyles projects allow it to resell fully logged plots that no longer have value for timber production. Its operations are focused on residential and commercial property in Port Gamble Kingston Bremerton and Gig Harbor.

In 2004 the company acquired 3300 acres of timberland in southwest Washington from Plum Creek Timber Company Inc. for $8.5 million; it also paid about $12 million to a private party for 1339 acres of timberland in western Washington. That year the company sold 426 acres in northern Kitsap County near Kingston Washington and agreed to extend to the county an option to acquire up to 360 additional acres of adjacent land (in one or two phases); the option will expire in July 2008.

In 2006 the company sold more than 200 acres of residential land for $12 million.

Pope Resources was spun off from Pope & Talbot in 1985 and the latter retains some control of the company through managing general partner Pope MGP Inc. Pope MGP is owned by Emily Andrews and Peter Pope (former chairman of Pope & Talbot) who own 12% and 7% respectively of Pope Resources.

EXECUTIVES

President CEO and Director, David L. (Dave) Nunes, age 52, $316,725 total compensation
VP and CFO, Thomas M. (Tom) Ringo, age 60, $205,872 total compensation
Director Real Estate and President Olympic Property Group, Jonathon P. (Jon) Rose, $123,257 total compensation
Director Business Development Olympic Resource Management, John T. Shea, $125,484 total compensation
Director Timberland Investment Management Olympic Resource Management, Kevin Bates
Director, John E. Conlin, age 54
Director, J. Thurston Roach, age 72
President CEO and Director, David L. (Dave) Nunes, age 52
Director, Peter T. Pope, age 79
Director, Douglas E. Norberg, age 73
Auditors: KPMGLLP

LOCATIONS

HQ: Pope Resources
  19950 7th Avenue NE, Suite 200, Poulsbo, WA 98370
Phone: 360 697-6626   Fax: 360 697-1156
Web: www.poperesources.com

PRODUCTS/OPERATIONS

Selected Subsidiaries
Olympic Property Group
Olympic Resource Management

COMPETITORS

Hampton Affiliates	Potlatch
International Paper	Rayonier
Plum Creek Timber	

HISTORICAL FINANCIALS
Company Type: Public

Income Statement
FYE: December 31

	REVENUE ($ mil.)	NET INCOME ($ mil.)	NET PROFIT MARGIN	EMPLOYEES
12/13	70.6	13.1	18.6%	58
12/12	54.0	(4.7)	—	55
12/11	57.2	8.7	15.3%	48
12/10	31.1	2.0	6.5%	45
12/09	20.4	(0.2)	—	45
Annual Growth	36.3%	—	—	6.6%

2013 Year-End Financials

Debt ratio: 24.3%	No. of shares (mil.): 4
Return on equity: —	Dividends
Cash ($ mil.): 6	Yield: 2.9%
Current ratio: 2.55	Payout: 100.5%
Long-term debt ($ mil.): 75	Market value ($ mil.): 293

	STOCK PRICE ($) FY Close	P/E High/Low		PER SHARE ($) Earnings	Dividends	Book Value
12/13	67.00	24	19	2.96	2.00	15.88
12/12	55.68	—	—	(1.11)	1.70	14.73
12/11	42.99	26	18	1.94	1.20	17.50
12/10	36.80	88	55	0.43	0.70	16.65
12/09	24.60	—	—	(0.07)	0.70	18.39
Annual Growth	28.5%	—	—	—	30.0%	(3.6%)

Power Integrations Inc.

Power Integrations develops high-voltage analog integrated circuits (ICs) that convert alternating current (AC) to lower-voltage direct current (DC). The fabless company's high-voltage analog semiconductors which account for virtually all of its sales are used in PCs cell phones cable boxes and other consumer and industrial electronics. The TOPSwitch line features products made with its environmentally friendly EcoSmart technology which reduces energy waste. Power Integrations sells its chips to electronics manufacturers and distributors such as Dell Nokia and Avnet. It earns nearly all of its sales overseas.

Operations The fabless manufacturing model allows Power Integrations to focus on engineering and design and still have access to high-volume manufacturing capacity while not having to maintain a silicon foundry. Power Integrations relies on four Japanese and German contract manufacturers to fabricate its chips: ROHM Lapis Semiconductor Seiko Epson X-FAB Dresden and Renesas Technology. Its products are then assembled and packaged by independent subcontractors in China Malaysia Thailand and the Philippines.

Geographic Reach Asia is Power Integrations' largest market representing nearly 85% of sales (China and Hong Kong the company's fastest-growing market contribute nearly 40% of overall revenue). Europe and North America account for about 10% and 5% of sales respectively.

Sales and Marketing About 70% of the company's sales are made to distributors such as Avnet and ATM Electronic (together accounting for more than 30%) while the rest come from original equipment manufacturers and merchant power supply manufacturers. Power Integrations has sales offices in 11 countries –China Germany India Italy Japan the Philippines Singapore South Korea Taiwan the UK and the US.

Financial Analysis After strong growth of nearly 40% in 2010 the company's revenue in 2011 remained flat at $299 million primarily because of general industry conditions. The semiconductor industry as a whole remains highly cyclical and high-voltage power supply is subject to intense competition and characterized by significant price sensitivity. Net income for 2011 fell just over 30% to $34 million as a result of higher input costs (including rising gold and copper prices).

Strategy Energy-efficiency is the driving factor in developing new power management chips and

Power Integrations has sold nearly 4 billion EcoSmart chips since they were introduced in 1998. The company has since introduced three more product lines that interrupt the power supply when electronics are turned off: CAPZero LinkZero and SENZero. In 2010 Power Integrations invested $30 million in SemiSouth Laboratories to accelerate the development of silicon-carbide energy-efficient power devices. SemiSouth Laboratories' silicon-carbide semiconductors used in solar and wind inverters and hybrid-electric vehicles are produced at its 10000-sq.-ft. clean room in Mississippi. Mergers and Acquisitions In 2012 Power Integrations paid about 105 million Swiss francs ($115 million) for CT-Concept Technologie a Swiss developer of energy-efficient drivers used in applications such as industrial motor drives electric trains and trams medical equipment and renewable energy generation. The acquisition complements Power Integrations' lower-power application focus with products used in high-power settings. The company is counting on Concept to provide a 10% bump to annual revenue.

HISTORY

At the end of 2007 Power Integrations acquired Potentia Semiconductor a Canadian developer of controller chips for high-power AC-DC power supplies. The company paid about $5.5 million in cash for Potentia.

In another example of the widening corporate scandals on options backdating where executives and board members have skirted US regulations on the timing and purchasing of stock-option grants Power Integrations reported in 2006 that its board of directors formed a special committee of independent directors to investigate company practices related to stock-option grants to executives and board members. Chairman Howard Earhart a former CEO of Power Integrations and CFO John Cobb resigned. The board soon after named Steven Sharp as non-executive chairman to succeed Earhart. Power Integrations later restated financial results for 2001 through 2004 and for the first three quarters of 2005.

The SEC's staff notified the company in 2007 that the commission's investigation into its past practices in granting stock options ended without any enforcement action recommended against Power Integrations. The company still faces a probe by the US Department of Justice regarding stock options. In addition Power Integrations is being audited by the Internal Revenue Service.

EXECUTIVES

Vice President Corporate Development, Clifford J Walker, age 63
Vice President Of Engineering, Derek Bell
Vice President Marketing, Douglas (Doug) Bailey, age 48
President CEO and Director, Balu Balakrishnan, age 60, $446,731 total compensation
VP Operations, John Tomlin, age 67, $298,654 total compensation
VP Finance and CFO, Sandeep Nayyar, age 54, $287,365 total compensation
Vice President Product Development, Mike Matthews
V Pres Technology Development, Vladimir Rumennik
Vp Marketing, Richard Faler
Vice President Engineering, Roger Colbeck
Hr Director & Vp, Ron Ketelsen
Vice President Divisional Business, Grace Zonio

Vice President Manufacturing Engineering, David Leblanc
Vice President High Power Products, Wolfgang Ademmer
President CEO and Director, Balu Balakrishnan, age 60
Director, E. Floyd Kvamme, age 76
Auditors: Deloitte&ToucheLLP

LOCATIONS

HQ: Power Integrations Inc.
5245 Hellyer Avenue, San Jose, CA 95138
Phone: 408 414-9200   **Fax:** 408 414-9201
Web: www.power.com

2011 Sales

	% of total
Asia/Pacific	
China & Hong Kong	39
Taiwan	21
South Korea	16
Japan	6
Singapore	2
Europe	
Germany	1
Other countries	10
Americas	4
Other regions	1
Total	**100**

PRODUCTS/OPERATIONS

2011 Sales

	% of total
LinkSwitch	42
TinySwitch	33
TOPSwitch	23
Other	2
Total	**100**

2011 Sales by Market

	% of total
Consumer	38
Communications	28
Industrial electronics	22
Computer	12
Total	**100**

Selected Products

AC-to-DC power conversion products (LinkSwitch)
DC-to-DC power conversion products (DPA-Switch)
Capacitor discharge ICs (CAPZero)
High-voltage analog ICs for power conversion (TOPSwitch TinySwitch Hiper SENZero)
Off-line switcher ICs (PeakSwitch)

COMPETITORS

Allegro MicroSystems
BCD Semiconductor
Fairchild Semiconductor
Infineon Technologies
Maxim Integrated Products
Micrel
Monolithic Power Systems

NXP Semiconductors
ON Semiconductor
STMicroelectronics
Samsung Electronics
Sanken Electric
Semtech
Vishay Intertechnology

HISTORICAL FINANCIALS

Company Type: Public

Income Statement

FYE: December 31

	REVENUE ($ mil.)	NET INCOME ($ mil.)	NET PROFIT MARGIN	EMPLOYEES
12/13	347.0	57.2	16.5%	562
12/12	305.3	(34.4)	—	526
12/11	298.7	34.2	11.5%	443
12/10	299.8	49.4	16.5%	444
12/09	215.7	23.2	10.8%	400
Annual Growth	**12.6%**	**25.3%**	**—**	**8.9%**

2013 Year-End Financials

Debt ratio: —
Return on equity: 14.7%
Cash ($ mil.): 92
Current ratio: 5.50
Long-term debt ($ mil.): —

No. of shares (mil.): 30
Dividends
  Yield: 0.5%
  Payout: 18.8%
Market value ($ mil.): 1,676

	STOCK PRICE ($) FY Close	P/E High/Low		PER SHARE ($) Earnings	Dividends	Book Value
12/13	55.82	29	17	1.88	0.32	14.55
12/12	33.61	—		(1.20)	0.20	11.95
12/11	33.16	36	24	1.14	0.20	13.04
12/10	40.16	26	15	1.67	0.20	12.48
12/09	36.36	43	20	0.82	0.10	10.44
Annual Growth	**11.3%**	**—**	**—**	**23.1%**	**33.7%**	**8.6%**

PRA Group Inc

When times are tough businesses find the going a little easier with Portfolio Recovery Associates (PRA). The firm collects on defaulted consumer debt. Its primary business is collections on behalf of clients (including banks credit unions consumer and auto finance companies and retail merchants) in the US and Scotland. PRA also buys charged-off and bankrupt consumer debt portfolios and then collects the debts on its own behalf. The company operates through its subsidiaries which specialize in location and skip tracing (PRA Location Services) class action claims monitoring (Claims Compensation Bureau or CCB) and government accounts receivable management (PRA Government Services).

Geographic Reach

PRA has locations in Alabama California Kansas Nevada Tennessee Texas and Virginia. Its Mackenzie Hall unit operates in Scotland. The majority of PRA's purchased accounts come from Florida Texas and California.

Operations

The company's Core Asset Collection segment is its largest representing more than half of sales. It's followed by the Bankruptcy Services segment which accounts for about 30% of sales; and the Fee-for-Services segment which makes up the rest of PRA's business.

Financial Performance

PRA has enjoyed several years of impressive growth. Revenues surged 29% from $459 million in 2011 to $593 million in 2012. PRA's profits jumped 26% in 2012 over 2011 due to the increase in revenue and a decrease in agent fees and interest expenses.

The 2012 growth was driven by an uptick in revenue from the income it recognized on finance receivables (up by 32%) and a 9% spike in revenue from fee income. The company attributes part of this growth to an acquisition it made in 2012.

Strategy

The company has focused on diversifying its business by expanding services through acquisitions of other companies and through the acquisition of debt portfolios. The company entered the UK market in early 2012 with its acquisition of Mackenzie Hall Holdings for some $51 million. In a much larger move PRA in 2014 announced it was acquiring Norway-based Aktiv Kapital AS for a total of $1.3 billion. The deal will give PRA an entry into new markets as Aktiv buys non-performing consumer loans through Europe and Canada.

EXECUTIVES

Chairman President and CEO, Steven D. (Steve) Fredrickson, age 55, $750,000 total compensation
EVP CFO Chief Administrative Officer Treasurer and Assistant Secretary, Kevin P. Stevenson, age 50, $400,000 total compensation
EVP General Counsel and Secretary, Judith S. (Judy) Scott, age 69, $245,000 total compensation
President Bankruptcy Services, Michael J. (Mike) Petit, $388,462 total compensation
EVP Core Asset Acquisitions, Chris Graves, $293,077 total compensation
EVP Operations, Neal Stern, $350,000 total compensation
EVP Strategy and Business Development, Peter K. (Kent) McCammon, $249,606 total compensation
President Business and Government Services, Steve Roberts
CEO Portfolio Recovery Associates UK, Owen James
President Claims Compensation Bureau, Brad Heffler
Chairman President and CEO, Steven D. (Steve) Fredrickson, age 55
Auditors: KPMGLLP

LOCATIONS

HQ: PRA Group Inc
120 Corporate Boulevard, Norfolk, VA 23502
Phone: 888 772-7326
Web: www.portfoliorecovery.com

PRODUCTS/OPERATIONS

2012 Sales

	$ mil.	% of total
Finance receivables net	560.6	90
Fee income	62.2	10
Total	**592.8**	**100**

2012 Portfolio Composition

	% of total
Major credit cards	57
Private-label credit cards	21
Consumer finance	20
Auto deficiency	2
Total	**100**

COMPETITORS

Asset Acceptance Capital	FTI Consulting
Asta Funding	FirstCity Financial
Encore Capital Group	GC Services
Epiq Systems	Nationwide Recovery Systems
Expert Global Solutions	Rampart Capital
	iQor

HISTORICAL FINANCIALS

Company Type: Public

Income Statement

FYE: December 31

	REVENUE ($ mil.)	NET INCOME ($ mil.)	NET PROFIT MARGIN	EMPLOYEES
12/13	735.1	175.3	23.8%	3,500
12/12	592.8	126.5	21.4%	3,200
12/11	458.9	100.7	22.0%	2,641
12/10	372.7	73.4	19.7%	2,473
12/09	281.0	44.3	15.8%	2,213
Annual Growth	**27.2%**	**41.0%**	**—**	**12.1%**

2013 Year-End Financials

Debt ratio: 28.2%
Return on equity: 22.2%
Cash ($ mil.): 162
Current ratio: 0.74
Long-term debt ($ mil.): 451

No. of shares (mil.): 49
Dividends
　Yield: —
　Payout: —
Market value ($ mil.): 2,634

	STOCK PRICE ($) FY Close	P/E High/Low		PER SHARE ($) Earnings	Dividends	Book Value
12/13	52.84	46	15	3.45	0.00	17.45
12/12	106.86	43	24	2.46	0.00	13.97
12/11	67.52	46	30	1.95	0.00	11.58
12/10	75.20	53	29	1.45	0.00	9.58
12/09	44.85	53	21	0.96	0.00	7.21
Annual Growth	**4.2%**			**37.8%**	**—**	**24.7%**

Preformed Line Products Co.

Masterful "preformances" are expected from Preformed Line Products (PLP) by its audience in the energy and communications industries. The company designs and manufactures components and systems used by utility crews and others to construct repair and maintain overhead and underground networks for energy communications and broadband network companies. It provides formed wire products (for maintenance and repair of aging plant infrastructures) protective fiber-optic closures and splice cases solar hardware and data communication interconnect devices and enclosures for data communications networks.

Geographic Reach

Headquartered in Cleveland Ohio PLP serves worldwide markets through international operations in Argentina Australia Brazil Canada China France Indonesia Malaysia Mexico New Zealand Poland Russia South Africa Spain the UK and Thailand.

Operations

PLP's operations are divided into four operating segments along geographic lines: PLP-USA (35% of total sales) The Americas (22%) EMEA (15%; Europe Middle East & Africa) and Asia/Pacific (27%). US operations adhere specifically to domestic energy and telecommunications products while the other three segments work across geographic regions.

Financial Performance

After achieving a revenue milestone of $439 million in 2012 PLP saw its revenues dip 7% to nearly $410 million in 2013. Profits fell 30% from

$29 million in 2012 to $21 million in 2013. PLP's operating cash flow has also been inconsistent the past three years: it jumped from 2011 to 2012 but fell by $32 million in 2013 due to the decline in net income among other factors.

The downward momentum for 2013 was driven by a 4% decrease within the the EMEA segment due to large energy transmission projects during 2012 that were not repeated in 2013. Asia/Pacific sales also dipped 2% due to lower transmission projects in the region and sales volume decreases in data communication.

Mergers and Acquisitions

Through the use of acquisitions PLP has been focusing its efforts to grow within the energy and communications markets both of which have been undergoing consolidation. Internationally however the company continues to concentrate specifically on the energy markets especially in developing nations.

In 2012 it acquired Australian Electricity Systems Pty Ltd. (AES) an Australian company. AES designs manufactures and markets hardware for the electrical utility industry. The acquisition strengthened the company's position in the power distribution transmission and substation hardware markets and enhanced its presence in the Asia-Pacific region. Also in 2012 PLP purchased all of the assets of Forma Line Industries CC in South Africa.In early 2014 PLP acquired Helix Uniformed Limited (Helix) located in Montreal Quebec Canada. The acquisition diversified its business in Canada expanding its manufacturing footprint and fortifying its local engineering capabilities.

EXECUTIVES

Chairman President and CEO, Robert G. Ruhlman, age 57, $675,000 total compensation
VP Finance and CFO, Eric R. Graef, age 62, $312,000 total compensation
Vice President - Marketing and Global Business Development, Dennis F. McKenna, age 47, $265,008 total compensation
National Account Manager, Luke Witgen
Auditors: Ernst&YoungLLP

LOCATIONS

HQ: Preformed Line Products Co.
660 Beta Drive, Mayfield Village, OH 44143
Phone: 440 461-5200　　**Fax:** 440 442-8816
Web: www.preformed.com

2013 Sales

	% mil.	% of total
Americas		
US	144.1	35
Other countries	91.5	22
Asia/Pacific	112.7	27
Europe Middle East & Africa (EMEA)	61.5	15
Total	**409.8**	**100**

PRODUCTS/OPERATIONS

2013 Sales

	% of total
Formed wire	68
Protective closures	16
Plastic products	4
Data communications cabinets	2
Other products	10
Total	**100**

Selected Products

Copper splice closures
Data communication cabinets
Fiber optic products (COYOTE brand)
Formed wire and related hardware products

High-speed cross-connect devices
Plastic products
Power transmission products (THERMOLIGN)
Protective closures (ARMADILLO stainless vault
    closures)
RAPTOR PROTECTOR (protects birds from power lines)

Selected Markets

Communication and cable
Data communication
Electric utilities and distribution
Electric utilities and transmission
Energy
Solar

COMPETITORS

3M	Maysteel
Corning Cable Systems	SWCC SHOWA
General Cable	Sumitomo Electric
Kyocera International	Tyco

HISTORICAL FINANCIALS

Company Type: Public

Income Statement

FYE: December 31

	REVENUE ($ mil.)	NET INCOME ($ mil.)	NET PROFIT MARGIN	EMPLOYEES
12/13	409.7	20.5	5.0%	2,794
12/12	439.1	29.2	6.7%	2,901
12/11	424.4	30.9	7.3%	2,854
12/10	338.3	23.1	6.8%	2,617
12/09	257.2	23.3	9.1%	2,304
Annual Growth	12.3%	(3.1%)	—	4.9%

2013 Year-End Financials

Debt ratio: 4.3%	No. of shares (mil.): 5
Return on equity: 8.3%	Dividends
Cash ($ mil.): 24	Yield: 0.8%
Current ratio: 3.56	Payout: 14.1%
Long-term debt ($ mil.): 13	Market value ($ mil.): 394

	STOCK PRICE ($) FY Close	P/E High/Low	PER SHARE ($) Earnings	Dividends	Book Value
12/13	73.16	24 15	3.77	0.60	46.81
12/12	59.42	13 9	5.45	1.00	44.83
12/11	59.66	13 7	5.78	0.80	39.91
12/10	58.53	14 6	4.33	0.80	37.21
12/09	43.80	11 6	4.35	0.80	32.58
Annual Growth	13.7%	— —	(3.5%)	(6.9%)	9.5%

Prestige Brands Holdings Inc

Prestige Brands is a lifesaver in the business of resuscitating offloaded consumer brands. The company acquires develops and markets over-the-counter (OTC) drugs and household cleaning products. Its portfolio includes Chloraseptic Clear Eyes Comet Compound W Dermoplast Doctor's Nightguard Little Remedies Pedia-Care Murine Monistat New-Skin and many other big-name brands. Prestige Brands contracts out manufacturing of its products which are sold through mass merchandisers and retail stores primarily in North America. The company was formed in 1996 to acquire and revitalize leading but neglected con-

sumer brands divested by major consumer companies such as Procter & Gamble.

Operations

Prestige operates two segments OTC healthcare and household cleaning. Its 14 core OTC brands which contribute about 85% of revenue include names that have stocked medicine cabinets for generations - Luden Efferdent Beano Debrox PediaCare Chloraseptic Compound W and Dramamine. Household cleaning brands Chore Boy Comet and Spic and Span have similar name recognition.

Instead of maintaining its own manufacturing facilities Prestige Brands contracts out product-making using third-party manufacturers and warehouse distribution partners to simplify its organizational structure.

Geographic Reach

Nearly all of Prestige Brands' sales come from North America but the company is working to increase international sales by licensing some brands to large multinational companies in desirable international markets. It has one such agreement for Comet in Eastern Europe. It also sells Clear Eyes Chloraseptic and Murine internationally. Prestige Brands which in 2014 generated 5% of sales outside North America has already designed and developed product packaging for specific international markets and it is focused now on growing its distribution network to help increase its international penetration. The US accounts for about 86% of sales.

Sales and Marketing

Prestige Brands generates revenue by leveraging several distribution channels to get its products on store shelves and in consumers' hands. Mass merchandisers represent the largest customer group it serves with a third of its 2014 sales coming from this retail channel. Drug stores (with 24%) and grocery stores (20%) also account for a huge percentage of sales. Other growing but smaller channels that Prestige Brands relies on include dollar stores (9%) club stores (3%) and other (8%). Uber worldwide retailer Wal-mart accounted for approximately 20% of the company's 2014 sales. Other notable customers include Walgreen CVS Target Dollar Tree Kmart Meijer Ahold and Kroger among others. Prestige Brands develops extensive marketing programs for new and existing products.

Financial Analysis

After several years of revenue growth Prestige in 2014 reported a 3% drop in revenue from $623 million to $602 million due to increased competition a weak cough and cold season and the impact of the divestiture of Phazyme. Household Cleaning revenue actually rose nearly 2%. Net income increased 11% from $66 million to $73 million as the company reduced costs in its Healthcare segment and lower promotional spending in the Household Cleaning segment. Cash from operations however fell 19% from $138 million to $111 million due to a $24 million drop in working capital related to a drop in accounts payable.

Strategy

The company's strategy lies in acquiring new brands and developing effective marketing programs for its existing products. Acquisitions are key to keeping its products portfolio fresh and it is constantly on the lookout for new additions to keep its two divisions competitive.

When Prestige Brands is evaluating a product for acquisition it takes a number of factors into consideration including the period of time the product has been in existence the product's market position (typically about three-quarters of the company's sales come from brands with a #1 or

#2 market position) its recent and projected sales growth and its potential for product extensions. Prestige Brands looks to acquire products that can be remarketed with additional enhancements such as its 2012 rollout of PediaCare 24 Hour Allergy Relief.

It uses a similar technique when marketing existing products introducing enhancements and line extensions. In 2013 it launched Luden's Moisture Drops BC Powder in cherry flavor and Chloraseptic Warming Spray followed by Goody's Headache Relief Shot Beano Plus Diary Defense and Efferdent Fresh Guard the next year.

After purchasing Phazyme gas relief treatment from GlaxoSmithKline in 2012 Prestige Brands divested it in 2013.

Mergers and Acquisitions

In 2012 Prestige Brands completed its largest asset acquisition to date spending $660 million to gain a portfolio of 17 North American OTC brands from GlaxoSmith Kline (GSK). The purchases added brands that included leading pain relief (BC Goody's and Ecotrin) gastrointestinal (Beano Fiber Choice Gaviscon Phazyme and Tagamet) sleep aid (Sominex) ear wax remover (Debrox) and oral rinse (Gly-Oxide) brands. Also in 2012 the company received an unsolicited acquisition proposal from Mexican health products firm Genomma Lab Internacional. The Prestige Brands board of directors rejected the proposal as inadequate and not in the best interest of the firm.

In 2013 Prestige Brands purchased Care Pharma and its Painstop Rectogesic Little Allergies and Fab line of products. The following year it picked up Hydralyte an oral rehydration product sold in Australia and New Zealand. It also bought Insight Pharmaceuticals which included yeast infection treatment Monistat along with e.p.t. home pregnancy tests Sucrets sore throat lozenges and about 25 other OTC brands.

Company Background

Prestige Brands was pieced together in 1996 from the parts of defunct manufacturer Medtech Labs (shampoos nail care products) The Spic & Span Company and Prestige Brands International (Comet cleaners and Clear Eyes eye drops).

EXECUTIVES

General Counsel Vice President Business Development, Samuel C (Sam) Cowley, age 53
President CEO and Director, Matthew M. (Matt) Mannelly, age 56, $556,154 total compensation
SVP Science and Technology, Jean A. Boyko, age 55, $250,000 total compensation
EVP Sales and Marketing, Timothy J. Connors, age 47, $350,000 total compensation
VP Operations, Paul A. Hennessey, age 47, $240,000 total compensation
CFO, Ronald M. Lombardi, age 50, $370,000 total compensation
Regional Vice President, Joe Bilello
Vice President Of Field Sales, Brian Fisher
President CEO and Director, Matthew M. (Matt) Mannelly, age 56
Auditors: PricewaterhouseCoopersLLP

LOCATIONS

HQ: Prestige Brands Holdings Inc
660 White Plains Road, Tarrytown, NY 10591
Phone: 914 524-6800
Web: www.prestigebrands.com

2014 Sales

	% of total
US & Canada	95
Other countries	5
Total	**100**

2014 Distribution Channels

	% of total
Mass	30
Drug	24
Food	19
Dollar	9
Convenience	7
Club	3
Other	8
Total	**100**

PRODUCTS/OPERATIONS

2014 Sales

	$ mil.	% of total
Over-the-counter healthcare	513.9	85
Household products	88.0	15
Total	**601.9**	**100**

2014 Sales

	$ mil.	% of total
Cough & Cold	115.2	22
Analgesics	110.6	22
Ear & Eye Care	86.4	17
Gastrointestinal	84.0	16
Dermatologists	52.4	10
Oral Care	48.8	9
Other OTC	16.5	4
Total	**513.9**	**100**

Selected Products

Over-the-counter
  Clear Eyes
  Chloraseptic
  Clear Eyes
  Compound W
  Dermoplast
  The Doctor's NightGuard
  The Doctor's Brushpicks
  Dramamine
  Ecotrin
  Efferdent
  Effergrip
  Fiber Choice
  Little Remedies
  Luden's
  Murine
  NasalCrom
  New-Skin
  PediaCare
  Phazyme
  Sominex
  Tagamet
  Wartner
Household cleaning
  Comet
  Chore Boy
  Spic and Span

COMPETITORS

3M	Hi-Tech Pharmacal
Airborne Inc.	Inter Parfums
Bayer Consumer Care	Johnson & Johnson
Boulder Brands	Lifetime Brands
Chattem	McNeil Consumer
Church & Dwight	Healthcare
Clorox	Merck
Colgate-Palmolive	Mondelez International
Combe	Novartis Corporation
Coty Inc.	Pfizer
GlaxoSmithKline	Procter & Gamble
Hain Celestial	Reckitt Benckiser
Helen of Troy	USANA Health Sciences
HemCon Medical	Unilever
Technologies	Zep Inc.
Henkel Corp.	

HISTORICAL FINANCIALS

Company Type: Public

Income Statement

FYE: March 31

	REVENUE ($ mil.)	NET INCOME ($ mil.)	NET PROFIT MARGIN	EMPLOYEES
03/14	601.8	72.6	12.1%	155
03/13	623.6	65.5	10.5%	117
03/12	441.0	37.2	8.4%	105
03/11	336.5	29.2	8.7%	100
03/10	302.0	32.1	10.6%	89
Annual Growth	**18.8%**	**22.6%**	**—**	**14.9%**

2014 Year-End Financials

Debt ratio: 52.0%	No. of shares (mil.): 51
Return on equity: 13.9%	Dividends
Cash ($ mil.): 28	Yield: —
Current ratio: 2.10	Payout: —
Long-term debt ($ mil.): 934	Market value ($ mil.): 1,412

	STOCK PRICE ($) FY Close	P/E High/Low		PER SHARE ($) Earnings	Dividends	Book Value
03/14	27.25	26	18	1.39	0.00	10.87
03/13	25.69	20	10	1.27	0.00	9.35
03/12	17.48	24	11	0.73	0.00	8.01
03/11	11.50	22	12	0.58	0.00	7.22
03/10	9.00	14	8	0.64	0.00	6.58
Annual Growth	**31.9%**	**—**	**—**	**21.4%**	**—**	**13.4%**

Primoris Services Corp

Since the beginning of time or at least since the 20th century Primoris has played a part in the evolution of the utility and infrastructure landscape. Through subsidiaries the firm provides construction engineering and maintenance services such as replacing and repairing underground pipelines upgrading and maintaining industrial plants designing and building concrete structures and managing the construction of water and wastewater facilities. It also engineers industrial machinery used in oil refineries petrochemical plants and other facilities. The firm primarily operates in the US. Primoris' clients have included Duke Energy Chevron Sempra and Kinder Morgan as well as public sector entities.

Geographic Reach

Dallas-based Primoris Services rings up 99% of its revenue in the US although its nationwide operations extend to Canada. The firm has regional offices in Eastern and Western US the Pacific Northwest Florida and along the Gulf Coast into Texas.

Operations

Primoris operates through three primary subsidiaries: West Construction Services accounts for more than 50% of annual revenue; East Construction Services accounts for nearly 45%; Engineering including Onquest Inc. and Born Heaters Canada represents the rest. The Engineering segment specializes in the design and installation of high-performance furnaces heaters burner management systems and related combustion and process technologies for clients in the oil refining petrochemical and power generation industries.

Sales and Marketing

Primoris counts among its customers major public utilities petrochemical firms energy compa-

nies and municipalities. The Louisiana Department of Transportation accounted for 11% of the firm's 2012 revenue.

Financial Peformance

The specialty contractor and infrastructure firm's revenue increased 6% in 2012 versus 2011 to more than $1.5 billion. Net income dipped 3% over the same period to $56.8 million. 2012 marked the third consecutive year of steeply rising sales for Primoris after a decline in 2009 due to the drop off in construction activity especially in California and Florida during the deep recession. Acquisitions are driving the year-over-year increases in revenue.

Mergers and Acquisitions

2012 was an busy year on the acquisition front for Primoris. In November it acquired Q3 Contracting Inc. a privately-held Minnesota corporation that specializes in small diameter pipeline and gas distribution construction. In September the firm purchased assets of The Saxon Group based outside of Atlanta. Saxon is a full-service industrial construction firm with expertise in the industrial gas processing and power plant industries. As part of the $3.2 million deal The Saxon Group operates as Saxon Construction Inc. under the East Construction Services segment of Primoris and serves power and process customers located primarily in the Southeastern US. In May it acquired Silva Contracting Co. of Houston a provider of transportation infrastructure maintenance asphalt paving and material sales in the Gulf Coast region. In March Primoris acquired Sprint Pipeline Services in Pearland Texas (near Houston). Sprint is engaged in pipeline construction maintenance upgrade fabrication and specialty services primarily in the southeastern US.

Previous purchases include Texas-based Cravens Partners which it merged into JCG in 2011 and the assets of Texas-based transportation infrastructure maintenance firm the Silva Companies which now operates as part of JCG's East Construction Services segment in 2012. Florida's James Construction Group (JCG) was purchased in 2009 and is one of the largest general contractors based in the Gulf Coast states engaging in highway industrial and environmental construction primarily in Louisiana Texas and Florida.

Strategy

Through acquisitions Primoris is able to deepen its presence in different markets and pick up niche industry operations. The firm is seeking more opportunities in the infrastructure and renewable energy sectors. It expects demand to rise as the need for electric power grows —a need that it could help deliver through solar power or other energy-efficient sources. To this end its Primoris Energy Services subsidiary in late 2012 acquired The Saxon Groupknown for its expertise in the industrial gas processing and power plant sectors.

With a focus on diversification Primoris is able to expand its service offerings and attract new clients. In 2009 the company created subsidiary Juniper Rock Corporation after buying the 88-acre Juniper Flats rock quarry in Southern California. The unit adds a new revenue source in the production and sale of aggregates and other construction materials.

In 2014 the firm announced it has secured new contracts worth about $200 million for construction work related to power pipeline and gas utility. Industrial highway infrastructure and water/wastewater are also part of the deal.

EXECUTIVES

Executive Vice President Chief Financial Officer, Peter J. Moerbeek, age 66

Executive Vice President General Counsel Secretary, John M. Perisich

Executive Vice President Director of Construction Services, Michael D. (Mike) Killgore

Executive Vice President Corporate Development, John P. Schauerman, age 57, $245,833 total compensation

President ARB Structures, Mark A. Thurman

Chief Executive Officer President Chairman of the Board, Brian Pratt, age 62, $500,000 total compensation

President ARB Underground, Scott E. Summers, $300,000 total compensation

President ARB Industrial, Timothy R. Healy

President Cardinal Contractors, William J. McDevitt

President James Construction Group?East Construction Services, Danny L. Hester

President Chief Executive Officer, Randy Kessler

COO, David King

Vice President Of Corporate Development, Chris Wolohan

Vice President Of Operations, Ed Hamud

Auditors: MossAdamsLLP

LOCATIONS

HQ: Primoris Services Corp
2100 McKinney Avenue, Suite 1500, Dallas, TX 75201
Phone: 214 740-5600
Web: www.prim.com

2012 Sales

$ in mil.		% of total
US		1531
99		
Other countries		11
1		
Total		**1542**
100		

PRODUCTS/OPERATIONS

2012 Sales by Segment

	$ mil.	% of total
West Construction Services	832.9	54
East Construction Services	662.2	43
Engineering	46.6	6
Total	**1541.7**	**100**

Selected Subsidiaries

ARB Inc.
Arb Chile Ltda
ARB Structures Inc.
Born Heaters Canada ULC
Cardinal Contractors Inc.
Cardinal Mechanical Inc.
Cravens Services Inc.
GML Coatings LLC
James Construction Group LLC
Juniper Rock Corporation
Onquest Inc.
Rockford Corporation
Stellaris LLC

COMPETITORS

Amec Foster Wheeler	KBR
Balfour Beatty	MasTec
Infrastructure	Parsons Corporation
Bechtel	Peter Kiewit Sons'
Boh Bros Construction	Quanta Services
EMS USA	Skanska
FCI Constructors	Sterling Construction
Fluor	Willbros
Jacobs Engineering	

Income Statement

FYE: December 31

	REVENUE ($ mil.)	NET INCOME ($ mil.)	NET PROFIT MARGIN	EMPLOYEES
12/13	1,944.2	69.6	3.6%	7,079
12/12	1,541.7	56.7	3.7%	6,911
12/11	1,460.1	58.5	4.0%	4,058
12/10	941.7	33.6	3.6%	4,034
12/09	467.0	25.9	5.5%	2,648
Annual Growth	**42.8%**	**28.0%**	**—**	**27.9%**

2013 Year-End Financials

Debt ratio: 21.4%	No. of shares (mil.): 51
Return on equity: 19.1%	Dividends
Cash ($ mil.): 196	Yield: 0.4%
Current ratio: 1.53	Payout: 10.8%
Long-term debt ($ mil.): 193	Market value ($ mil.): 1,605

	STOCK PRICE ($) FY Close	P/E High/Low		PER SHARE ($) Earnings	Dividends	Book Value
12/13	31.13	23	11	1.35	0.14	7.71
12/12	15.04	15	10	1.10	0.12	6.44
12/11	14.93	13	7	1.14	0.11	5.38
12/10	9.54	12	7	0.72	0.10	4.22
12/09	7.97	10	4	0.75	0.10	4.40
Annual Growth	**40.6%**	**—**	**—**	**15.8%**	**7.8%**	**15.0%**

Prologis Inc

Prologis is a pro when it comes to logistics. The industrial real estate investment trust (REIT) acquires and develops warehouses and distribution facilities for some 4700 clients including retailers and manufacturers such as The Home Depot Amazon.com and Hitachi. The company owns more than 1660 properties in North America Europe and Asia. Altogether Prologis owns has stakes in or is developing some 585 million sq. ft. of space. The company is selective about development and usually only develops pre-leased properties. Its fund management operations oversee long-term property investments. Prologis became the world's largest warehouse REIT when it joined forces with smaller rival AMB Property.

Mergers and Acquisitions

The all-stock deal dubbed a merger-of-equals created a new entity with an expanded global portfolio. Prior to the 2011 merger AMB and Prologis owned complementary international portfolios. AMB had a presence in China and Brazil while Prologis had a presence in Central and Eastern Europe and the UK. The merger allowed the two companies to better serve their multinational clients.

Geographic Reach

Prologis has properties in 21 countries. The US is the company's largest market home to about 1430 of its 1667 properties. Major US markets for the REIT include Southern California the San Francisco Bay Area and Chicago. The Americas (US Canada Mexico Brazil) account for more than 75% Of the REIT's revenue followed by Europe (with about 15%) and Asia (China Japan Singapore) nearly 10%.

Financial Performance

After a year of double-digit growth fueled by its merger with AMB and the acquisition of a controlling interest in its properties in Europe Prologis in 2013 saw its revenue decline 13% versus 2012 to $1.75 billion. However net income swung from a loss of $39.7 million in 2012 to $342.9 million primarily due to declining operating costs as a result of the absence of merger and acquisition and other integration-related expenses. Cash flow from operations also increased by $21.5 million to $485 million on higher net income and changes in assets and liabilities.

With rents increasing in the majority of its markets Prologis believes there's substantial room for revenue growth as current rents are below replacement-cost-adjusted rents.

Strategy

The merger with AMB marked a dramatic transformation for Prologis which was wounded by the global economic downturn. As with the real estate industry as a whole Prologis was hit hard by the credit crunch and global recession. Revenues fell sharply as occupancies were down and property values and rental rates decreased. In response the REIT pulled back on new development plans and began modifying its business to cut costs and reduce risk.

In the aftermath of its merger with AMB Prologis set about realigning its portfolio selling billions of dollars of assets that were in non-strategic markets. The money from the ongoing disposition program is being used for new development projects particularly in markets such as China Brazil and Mexico. In Japan the company took Nippon Prologis REIT (NPR) public in early 2013. Later in the year it extended it partnership in China forming Prologis China Venture 2 to acquire and manage properties there.

Prologis has also been concentrating on expanding its presence in Europe. In 2012 the company assumed full ownership of Prologis European Properties. (It had increased its stake in the European warehouse developer to some 60% in 2011.) The European market proved to be a resilient one as the rest of the world suffered through the economic recession. Demand for modern distribution warehouses in Europe remains high as booming exports in the region have helped drive growth. In the US the firm broke ground on a 1 million square foot facility in Tracy California.

Moving forward Prologis has a long-term strategy for conservative growth. It also plans to increase its building occupancy levels. The company will balance asset disposition with selected development of new industrial properties on its land in major markets. Another focus for Prologis post merger is its private capital business. The company is working to streamline the division which has about $25 billion of assets under management. It is ridding itself of unprofitable or otherwise undesirable funds.

Company Background

Founded in 1991 initially Prologis concentrated on acquiring properties in the southwestern US.

EXECUTIVES

CEO The Americas, Eugene F. (Gene) Reilly, age 53, $500,000 total compensation

Chairman and CEO, Hamid R. Moghadam, age 58, $800,000 total compensation

CEO Europe and Asia, Gary E. Anderson, age 48, $500,000 total compensation

President U.S. Northwest Region, W. Scott Lamson, age 48

CIO, Tom Sheraden

President Japan, Mike Yamada, age 61

Chief Investment Officer, Michael S. (Mike) Curless, age 50

CFO, Thomas S. (Tom) Olinger, age 48, $500,000 total compensation

SVP Southeast Region North America U.S., Jeremy Giles

President U.S. Southwest Region, Kim Snyder

President U.S. East Region, Nick Kittredge

Senior Vice President Head Operations, Steve Lueck

Vice President And Corporate Counsel, Bonnie Paz

Vice President Development And Leasing, Keisuke Kinugasa

Vice President Customer Service, Leah Dillon

Vice President, Richard Shleymovich

Vice President, Andrew Chew

Vice President Leasing And Marketing Director, Rick Kopla

Vice President Corporate Counsel, Jan Kneisel

Senior Vice President Development, Alan Sarjant

Vice President Capital Markets, Mike Brown

Vice President Financial Operations, Annette Fernandez

Vice President, Richard Malloy

Vice President Property Manager Benelux, Leonie Kooij

Vice President Market Officer Boston Operations, Skip Coppola

Senior Vice President Strategic, William O'Donnell

Vice President Project Management, Tim Fischer

Vice President Finance, Nando Pengel

Vice President Mexico Regional Property, Eduardo Garcia

Vice President Acquisitions Mexico, Mike Fangman

Vice President Business Development, John Morgan

Vice President Risk Management, Jeffrey Bray

Chairman and CEO, Hamid R. Moghadam, age 58

Senior Vice President Treasurer, Phillip Joseph

Treasury Manager, Jing Zhang

Advisory Board Member, Rene Hogenboom

Auditors: KPMGLLP

LOCATIONS

HQ: Prologis Inc
Pier 1, Bay 1, San Francisco, CA 94111
Phone: 415 394-9000   Fax: 415 394-9001
Web: www.prologis.com

2013 Operating Properties

	No.
North America	
US	1432
Mexico	124
Canada	16
Europe	
Germany	9
Poland	9
France	8
United Kingdom	8
Italy	4
Romania	4
Spain	4
Slovakia	3
Czech Republic	2
Sweden	2
Austria	1
Belgium	1
Hungary	1
Asia	
Japan	23
China	10
Singapore	6
Total	**1667**

2013 Sales

	$ mil.	% of total
Americas	1361.4	77
Europe	238.2	14
Asia	150.9	9
Total	**1750.5**	**100**

PRODUCTS/OPERATIONS

2013 Sales

	$ mil.	% of total
Rental income	1.228.0	70
Rental recoveries	331.5	19
Investment management income	179.5	10
Development management and other	11.5	1
Total	**1750.5**	**100**

COMPETITORS

AmeriCold Logistics	Liberty Property Trust
CenterPoint Properties	PS Business Parks
Duke Realty	Panattoni Development
First Industrial	Company
Realty	Vornado Realty
Kilroy Realty	

HISTORICAL FINANCIALS

Company Type: Public

Income Statement

FYE: December 31

	REVENUE ($ mil.)	NET INCOME ($ mil.)	NET PROFIT MARGIN	EMPLOYEES
12/13	1,750.4	342.9	19.6%	1,468
12/12	2,005.9	(39.7)	—	1,445
12/11	1,533.2	(153.4)	—	1,457
12/10	633.5	27.1	4.3%	0
12/09	633.8	(43.0)	—	521
Annual Growth	**28.9%**	**—**		**29.6%**

2013 Year-End Financials

Debt ratio: 36.6%
Return on equity: 2.5%
Cash ($ mil.): 491
Current ratio: 0.71
Long-term debt ($ mil.): 9,011

No. of shares (mil.): 498
Dividends
  Yield: 3.0%
  Payout: 2,240.0%
Market value ($ mil.): 18,431

	STOCK PRICE ($) FY Close	P/E High/Low		PER SHARE ($) Earnings	Dividends	Book Value
12/13	36.95	69	54	0.64	1.12	27.49
12/12	36.49	—	—	(0.18)	1.12	28.30
12/11	28.59	—	—	(0.51)	1.12	29.79
12/10	31.71	530	369	0.06	1.12	19.68
12/09	25.55	—	—	(0.37)	1.12	19.70
Annual Growth	**9.7%**	**—**	**—**	**—**	**(0.0%)**	**8.7%**

Prospect Capital Corporation

Prospect Capital is a closed-end investment fund with holdings in the consumer food health care and manufacturing sectors among others. The company targets privately held middle-market firms with annual revenues of less than $750 million; it also considers thinly traded public companies or turnaround situations. Prospect's portfolio includes interests in more than 100 companies mainly through senior loans and mezzanine debt. The company also makes equity and secured debt investments. Typically investing from $5 million to $250 million per transaction Prospect is a long-term investor that maintains regular contact with its portfolio company's management and participates in their board meetings.

Geographic Reach

New York-based Prospect Capital invests primarily in US companies but also in Canada the Cayman Islands and Ireland. About 80% of the firm's investment portfolio is in the US.

Operations

Prospect has elected to be regulated as a business development company (BDC) a status which affords the firm certain tax benefits. Although it initially targeted on industrial and energy investments the company has broadened its focus in the past few years and minimized its holdings in the energy sector.

Financial Performance

Prospect Capital reported revenue of $576.3 million in fiscal 2013 (ended June) an 80% increase over the year earlier period. Net income rose 16% over the same period to nearly $221 million. Prospect's financial prospects have brightened considerably in recent years with revenue up more than 500% since fiscal 2009 and steeply rising profits. The 80% increase in fiscal 2013 revenue was primarily due to 98% increase in interest income as a result of interest earned on the mezzanine loan. Dividend income rose as well.

Strategy

Prospect Capital pursues a diversified investment strategy investing in 124 long-term portfolio investments and CLOs (collateralized loan obligations) and to a lesser extent money market funds. In fiscal 2013 (ended June) the firm originated $3.1 million of new investments. Prospect's origination efforts are focused primarily on secured lending to reduce portfolio risk investing primarily in first lien loans and subordinated notes in CLOs though it also engages in select junior debt and equity investments. First lien loans represent about 55% of its investment portfolio with second lien loans representing about 25%. Diversified financial services is the firm's single largest industry sector for investment followed by consumer finance durable consumer products consumer services and software and computer services. Together these five industries constitute more than half of Prospect's investment portfolio.

In 2013 the firm invested $144.5 million in four new transactions encompassing 19 rent-producing multifamily residential properties totaling 5652 rental units. Combined with its prior investments Prospect has a invested a total of $288.3 million in 10 separate transactions encompassing 25 multifamily residential properties with more than 9100 rental units.

Mergers and Acquisitions

In 2013 Prospect acquired A 94% stake in Nationwide Acceptance LLC a Chicago based consumer finance company.

EXECUTIVES

Managing Director, Robert S Everett, age 51
Vice President, Sachin Sarnobat
Vice President, Frank V Saracino, age 49
Vice President Legal, Karl Huth
Vice President Capital Markets, Nishil Mehta
Vice President, John Kim
Vice President, Jason Wilson
Senior Vice President Of Finance, Eric Savino
Vice President, Seth Tutlis
Vice President Tax, David Wong
Vice President Investments And Portfolio Management And Vice President Legal, Ian Shainbrown
Treasurer, Brian H Oswald, age 54
Board Member, Andrew C Cooper, age 54
Auditors: BDOUSALLP

HQ: Prospect Capital Corporation
   10 East 40th Street, 44th Floor, New York, NY 10016
Phone: 212 448-0702
Web: www.prospectstreet.com

PRODUCTS/OPERATIONS

2013 Sales

	$ mil.	% of total
Interest	435.4	76
Dividends	82.7	14
Other	58.2	10
Total	**576.3**	**100**

Selected Current Investments

AIRMALL USA Inc. (property management)
Ajax Rolled Ring & Machine Inc. (manufacturing)
AWCNC (machinery)
Blue Coat Systems Inc. (software computer service)
Borga Inc. (manufacturing)
Boxercraft (textiles and leather)
Broder Bros. Co. (Textiles)
Crossman Corp. (manufacturing)
Focus Products (consumer products)
Grocery Outlet (supermarkets)
Harley Marine Services (transportation)
Injured Workers Pharmacy (health care)
Nationwide Acceptance Holdings LLC (consumer finance)
National Bankruptcy Services (financial services)
NMMB (advertising media buying)
NRG Manufacturing Inc. (drilling rig components)
R-V Industries Inc. (metal fabrication)
Wind River Resources (oil and gas production)

COMPETITORS

ACI Capital	NGPC
Apollo Investment	Stephens Group
First Reserve	TPG
GFI Energy Ventures	Venrock
Katalyst	

HISTORICAL FINANCIALS

Company Type: Public

Income Statement

FYE: June 30

	ASSETS ($ mil.)	NET INCOME ($ mil.)	INCOME AS % OF ASSETS	EMPLOYEES
06/14	6,477.2	357.2	5.5%	0
06/13	4,448.2	324.9	7.3%	0
06/12	2,255.2	186.6	8.3%	0
06/11	1,549.3	94.2	6.1%	0
06/10	832.7	66.4	8.0%	0
Annual Growth	**67.0%**	**52.3%**	**—**	**—**

	STOCK PRICE ($) FY Close	P/E High/Low		PER SHARE ($) Earnings	Dividends	Book Value
06/14	10.63	10	8	1.19	1.32	10.56
06/13	10.80	8	6	1.57	1.28	10.72
06/12	11.39	7	5	1.63	1.22	10.83
06/11	10.11	11	8	1.10	1.21	10.36
06/10	9.65	41	28	0.32	1.33	10.29
Annual Growth	**2.4%**	**—**	**—**	**38.9%**	**(0.0%)**	**0.7%**

Proto Labs Inc

Need a prototype pronto? Proto Labs can help with that. The industrial manufacturer creates custom parts in quick turnaround for prototype and short-run production. The company uses 3D CAD software to upload new parts designs and then its computer numerical control (CNC) process analyzes the design quotes a price and makes the parts. Proto Labs creates machined metal (Firstcut) and injection-molded plastic (Protomold) parts and can ship them the next business day. Its medical device electronics consumer products appliance and automotive manufacturing customers use the parts for prototyping market evaluation and functional testing. The company was established in 1999 and went public in 2012.

IPO

The company hoped to raise about $100 million in its IPO which it filed in July 2011 but ended up raising more than $70 million when it went public in February 2012. It used the proceeds for general corporate purposes but mostly it beefed up its sales and marketing teams.

Operations

Proto Labs makes the majority of its revenue (more than 70%) from its Protomold segment (also called ProtoQuote) which typically produces prototype quantities of 25-100 custom injection-molded plastic parts. It saves the designs and molds from these parts and benefits when the customer returns sometimes requesting up to 10000 additional parts for short-run production. The company's Firstcut segment (FirstQuote; nearly 30%) specializes in designing and cutting plastic and metal blocks but in smaller quantities.

Geographic Reach

Proto Labs has manufacturing facilities in Japan the UK and the US; sales offices also reside in Italy. The US accounts for around 75% of its revenue each year.

Sales and Marketing

Proto Labs sells its products through an internal sales team in more than 50 countries. Customers include Avox Systems BOSS Products PHT Aerospace Micro Engineering IFM Efector OEM controls Lombard Medical and Gamesman Limited.

Financial Performance

Proto Labs has grown significantly since it was founded as revenues and profits continue to climb to unprecedented heights. From 2012 to 2013 Pro Labs revenues surged by 29% from $126 million to $163 million and its net income increased by 47% from $24 million to $35 million. (Both these totals for 2013 represent historic milestones for the company.)

The growth for 2013 was driven by a 26% increase in US revenue a 39% rise in international revenue a 27% jump in Protomold revenue and a 35% increase in Firstcut revenue. Proto Labs enjoyed a 20% increase within its customer base from 2012 to 2013.

Proto Labs' operating cash flows has steadily climbed over the years. Cash flow from operations increased by $23 million in 2013 primarily due to the spike in net income additional tax benefits from stock-based compensation and a decrease in prepaid expenses.

Strategy

Its strategy includes increasing penetration within existing customer organization and in geographical markets it already operates (US Europe and Japan) moving into new geographic regions and expanding its parts range and manufacturing processes. Another important component of its strategy involves optimizing its 3D CAD and CNC technology in order to design parts faster and more efficiently.

Mergers and Acquisitions

Proto Labs added to its manufacturing services in 2014 through the $38 million acquisition of FineLine Prototyping a provider of stereolithography selective laser sintering and direct metal laser sintering services.

Company Background

Proto Labs began as The Protomold Company (molded plastic parts) but added CNC metal part machining its Firstcut business in 2007. In 2009 both branches began operating under the Proto Labs banner. It all started when founder and computer geek Lawrence Lukis started a desktop printer design business and was astounded at the long turnaround (weeks) and cost (thousands) for prototype parts. He turned his computer skills to solving the problem and found a way to completely automate the entire process and produce a part in a day for prices starting at $1500.

EXECUTIVES

Vice President Marketing, Bill Dietrick
COO, Donald G. Krantz, age 59, $265,000 total compensation
President and CEO, Victoria M. (Vicki) Holt, age 57
CFO, John R. Judd, age 57, $252,000 total compensation
Managing Director Proto Labs Limited, John B. Tumelty, age 43, $189,268 total compensation
CTO, Robert Bodor, age 41
National Account Manager, Aaron Windseth
National Account Manager, Stacey Kuhlman
National Account Manager, Shannon Gage
National Account Manager, Marc Makarem
Vice President Of Culture, Skip Bolton
National Account Manager, Grace Huber
National Account Manager, Lyndsay Pierson
National Account Manager, Dan Rasmussen
National Account Manager, Brian Slattery
National Account Manager, Chris Doyle
National Account Manager, Ben Masnado
Vice President Human Resources, Tim Bot
Vice President, Edward Bolton
Chairman, Lawrence J. Lukis, age 66
Auditors: Ernst&YoungLLP

LOCATIONS

HQ: Proto Labs Inc
5540 Pioneer Creek Drive, Maple Plain, MN 55359
Phone: 763 479-3680
Web: www.protolabs.com

2013 Sales

	% of total
US	73
International	27
Total	**100**

PRODUCTS/OPERATIONS

2013 Sales

	$ mil.	% of total
Protomold	115.1	71
Firstcut	48.0	29
Total	**163.1**	**100**

COMPETITORS

Ajax United Patterns and Molds	Materialise
Anchor Mfg. Group	Richco
Deswell	Total Plastics

HISTORICAL FINANCIALS

Company Type: Public

Income Statement

FYE: December 31

	REVENUE ($ mil.)	NET INCOME ($ mil.)	NET PROFIT MARGIN	EMPLOYEES
12/13	163.1	35.2	21.6%	749
12/12	125.9	24.0	19.1%	622
12/11	98.9	17.9	18.2%	511
12/10	64.9	10.9	16.9%	0
12/09	43.8	4.2	9.6%	0
Annual Growth	38.9%	70.0%	—	—

2013 Year-End Financials

Debt ratio: 0.1%
Return on equity: 19.1%
Cash ($ mil.): 43
Current ratio: 8.04
Long-term debt ($ mil.): 0

No. of shares (mil.): 25
Dividends
 Yield: —
 Payout: —
Market value ($ mil.): 1,818

	STOCK PRICE ($) FY Close	P/E High/Low	PER SHARE ($) Earnings	Dividends	Book Value
12/13	71.18	63 27	1.36	0.00	8.28
12/12	39.42	38 26	0.98	0.00	6.32
Annual Growth	80.6%	— —	38.8%	—	31.1%

Pzena Investment Management Inc

It takes money to make money and Pzena Investment Management has made plenty. The firm serves corporate institutional and high-net-worth individual clients in the US and abroad and has about $21 billion in assets under management. Through a dozen funds Pzena makes long-term investments in domestic and international companies —particularly financial services firms. Pzena also acts as a sub-investment adviser for about two dozen mutual funds and offshore funds. The firm is the sole managing member of its operating company Pzena Investment Management LLC. The employee-owned firm was founded by chairman and CEO Richard Pzena in 1995.

Financial Performance

A decline in management and performance fee revenue led to an 8% decline in the company's overall revenue between 2011 and 2012. The company's net income was up 14% in the same period due in large part to lower investment-related expenses.

Strategy

The company focuses on long-term investments made in US and global markets. It serves both US clients and non-US clients and has been expanding its non-US client base through targeted sales efforts.

EXECUTIVES

President International, A. Rama Krishna, age 51, $252,656 total compensation
Chairman CEO and Co-Chief Investment Officer, Richard S. Pzena, age 56, $300,000 total compensation
President and Co-Chief Investment Officer, John P. Goetz, age 57, $300,000 total compensation

President Marketing and Client Service, William L. Lipsey, age 56, $300,000 total compensation
Executive Vice President, Antonio DeSpirito
CFO, Gary Bachman
Executive Vice President, Michael Peterson
Chairman CEO and Co-Chief Investment Officer, Richard S. Pzena, age 56
Auditors: KPMGLLP

LOCATIONS

HQ: Pzena Investment Management Inc
 120 West 45th Street, New York, NY 10036
Phone: 212 355-1600
Web: www.pzena.com

COMPETITORS

AllianceBernstein
BlackRock
FMR
Morgan Stanley Investment Management
Principal Global
State Street

HISTORICAL FINANCIALS

Company Type: Public

Income Statement

FYE: December 31

	REVENUE ($ mil.)	NET INCOME ($ mil.)	NET PROFIT MARGIN	EMPLOYEES
12/13	95.7	6.6	7.0%	76
12/12	76.2	3.8	5.0%	70
12/11	83.0	3.3	4.1%	67
12/10	77.5	3.8	4.9%	70
12/09	63.0	3.3	5.3%	67
Annual Growth	11.0%	18.6%	—	3.2%

2013 Year-End Financials

Debt ratio: —
Return on equity: 43.1%
Cash ($ mil.): 33
Current ratio: 11.93
Long-term debt ($ mil.): —

No. of shares (mil.): 64
Dividends
 Yield: 2.1%
 Payout: 64.1%
Market value ($ mil.): 764

	STOCK PRICE ($) FY Close	P/E High/Low	PER SHARE ($) Earnings	Dividends	Book Value
12/13	11.76	21 9	0.45	0.25	0.25
12/12	5.40	20 10	0.32	0.28	0.23
12/11	4.33	24 9	0.32	0.12	0.22
12/10	7.35	20 14	0.34	0.24	0.16
12/09	8.14	22 4	0.28	0.00	0.13
Annual Growth	9.6%	— —	12.6%	—	18.3%

Q.E.P. Co., Inc.

Q.E.P. keeps getting underfoot. The company makes and distributes hardwood flooring and flooring installation tools (including adhesives trowels wet saws and carpet trimmers) for professionals and do-it-yourselfers. It sells more than 7000 flooring and flooring-related products mainly for installing marble carpet ceramic tile and drywall under the QEP Capitol ROBERTS Elastiment and RhinoGrip brands among others. Q.E.P. makes about 25% of its products and acquires the rest from about 200 suppliers. Its customers include retailers and distributors to the home improvement

hardware and construction trades primarily in the US. The family-run company was founded by chairman and CEO Lewis Gould in 1979.

Geographic Reach

Florida-based Q.E.P. Co. rings up more than 70% of its sales in North America. Europe and Australia/New Zealand roughly split the rest. The company has more than 1 million square feet of distribution and manufacturing space throughout the US Canada Australia/New Zealand the UK France and China.

Operations

The company operates four business segments: Domestic Canada Europe (UK France Holland) and Australia/New Zealand. Each segment markets and sells to home improvement retail centers and specialty distribution outlets in its region.

Sales and Marketing

The majority of Q.E.P's sales are generated by its two largest customers —The Home Depot and Lowe's. Abroad its products are sold in chain stores (Bunnings Wickes Topps Tiles Leroy Merlin and Sodimac).

Financial Performance

Q.E.P. reported record fiscal 2014 (ended February) sales of $302.7 million an increase of 7% versus the prior year. Sales in the US and Canada declined while sales in Europe increased 82% year over year driven by acquisitions there. The company's Australia/New Zealand business posted a 3% rise in sales. Operating income fell 14% over the same period from $11.6 million to $9.9 million. Q.E.P. blamed its declining profits on a concentration issue with a major customer.

Strategy

Since its founding Q.E.P. has grown though numerous acquisitions in the US and overseas. The company also grows by expanding its distribution network and market penetration. In June 2014 it added Ohio-based CDC Distributors to distribute its Harris Wood-branded engineered and Harris cork flooring products in Ohio Kentucky Michigan and four other states.

In May 2013 the company sold its manufacturing distribution and administrative facility in Canada and concurrently entered into a two year lease-back transaction for the facility.

Mergers and Acquisitions

Acquisitive Q.E.P. is busy building its business. Most recently in February 2014 it acquired the Georgia-based laminate maker Faus Group which makes and distributes laminate flooring under the Fausfloor brand. The $8.6 million purchase included a 380000-square-foot manufacturing and distribution facility in Calhoun Georgia and expanded Q.E.P.'s existing product lines and channels of distribution.

In 2013 the company purchased the Homelux and TileRite distribution businesses of UK-based Homelux Nenplas Ltd. a global supplier of tile accessories to the DIY and professional markets for $23 million. In late 2012 the company purchased Imperial Industries and Ludell brand striking tools. To keep hardwood floors spic and span Q.E.P. also acquired Harper Brush Works Inc. for about $2.2 million earlier that year. Based in Iowa Harper Brush Works makes and sells brushes brooms mops buckets dust pans and other household cleaning tools. Other acquisitions that expanded Q.E.P.'s product line include the addition of Porta-Nails a maker of hardwood installation equipment and fasteners in 2011.

EXECUTIVES

Chairman and CEO, Lewis Gould, age 71, $567,154 total compensation

President and Director, Leonard Gould, age 45, $280,385 total compensation
EVP and COO, James P. (Jim) Brower, age 49, $255,308 total compensation
Chief Financial Officer; Senior Vice President; Treasurer, Richard A. Brooke, age 66
Senior Vice President - Sales and Marketing, Jamie L. Clingan, age 52, $134,423 total compensation
Vp Retail Marketing, Brian Johnson
Vice President Of Marketing Flooring Division, Sarah Mozingo
Vice President National Accounts, Labanowitz Stan
Vice President Global Sourcing, Terry Hirschman
Senior Vice President, Darell Tweed
Vice President Store Operations, Joe Santinello
Vice President National Accounts, Kenneth Mosser
President and Director, Leonard Gould, age 45
Chief Financial Officer; Senior Vice President; Treasurer, Richard A. Brooke, age 66
Auditors: GrantThorntonLLP

LOCATIONS

HQ: Q.E.P. Co., Inc.
1001 Broken Sound Parkway N.W., Suite A, Boca Raton, FL 33487
Phone: 561 994-5550   **Fax:** 561 241-2830
Web: www.qep.com

2014 Sales

	$ mil.	% of total
Domestic	196.1	65
Europe	45.5	15
Australia & New Zealand	40.8	13
Canada	20.3	7
Total	**302.7**	**100**

PRODUCTS/OPERATIONS

Selected Brands

Capitol
Elastiment
Fausfloor
Harris Wood
HISCO
Homelux
Nupla
Porta-Nail
PRCI
QEP
Roberts
TileRite
Vitrex

Selected Products and Services

Adhesives
Carpet Installation
Grouts & Mortars
Hardwood Flooring
Laminate Installation
Plumbing Installation
Pneumatic Nailers
Stone & Tile Installation
Sundries
Surface Protection
Suspended Ceiling Tools
Underlayments

COMPETITORS

American Hardwood Industries
Armstrong World Industries
Brandywine International Hardwood
Danaher
Jore
Makita
Stanley Black and Decker

HISTORICAL FINANCIALS

Company Type: Public

Income Statement

FYE: February 28

	REVENUE ($ mil.)	NET INCOME ($ mil.)	NET PROFIT MARGIN	EMPLOYEES
02/14	302.7	16.0	5.3%	0
02/13	283.7	8.1	2.9%	0
02/12	261.4	10.2	3.9%	0
02/11	237.8	9.4	4.0%	0
02/09	203.6	(7.2)	—	381
Annual Growth	**10.4%**	—	—	

2014 Year-End Financials

Debt ratio: 28.4%
Return on equity: 27.1%
Cash ($ mil.): 2
Current ratio: 1.44
Long-term debt ($ mil.): 11

No. of shares (mil.): 3
Dividends
Yield: —
Payout: —
Market value ($ mil.): 62

	STOCK PRICE ($) FY Close	P/E High/Low		PER SHARE ($) Earnings	Dividends	Book Value
02/14	19.00	4	3	4.88	0.00	20.49
02/13	15.83	9	6	2.44	0.00	15.79
02/12	20.50	8	4	3.01	0.00	13.61
02/11	14.24	5	4	2.77	0.00	10.70
02/09	0.90	—	—	(2.13)	0.00	4.40
Annual Growth	**114.4%**	—	—	—	—	**46.9%**

Quality Systems, Inc.

Quality Systems can't help doctors' with the legibility of their signatures but it knows how to insure the integrity of their digital records. The company develops data management software for medical and dental practices and a variety of other health care businesses. Its NextGen subsidiary (more than 75% of sales) makes electronic records and practice management software tailored for patient data scheduling billing and claims handling. Its RCM unit focuses on electronic claims submission remittance and payments services. The company's QSI Dental division makes practice management software for dentists. Its Hospital Solutions unit focuses on clinical and financial software for rural hospitals.

Geographic Reach

California-based Quality Systems has offices in Georgia Maryland Missouri Pennsylvania and Texas.

Sales and Marketing

Quality Systems sells and markets its products via a direct sales force and resellers. Software license sales to resellers represent less than 10% of revenue. Its clients include medical and dental group practices and small hospitals.

Operations

Quality Systems is organized around four divisions: the largest is NextGen accounting for more than 75% of annual sales provides integrated clinical financial and connectivity products for ambulatory and dental providers; RCM Services (15% of annual sales) supplies technology products and consulting services spanning the full spectrum of health care providers revenue cycle management needs focused on billing and collection services; QSI Dental sells software to dental groups in the US; while Hospital Solutions caters to rural community and specialty hospitals with integrated clinical financial and connectivity products and services.

Sales and Marketing

While nearly all of Quality Systems' sales come from a traditional software licensing model the company has embraced the Software-as-a-Service (SaaS) delivery model which it offers as a way for smaller practices to quickly start using the select NextGen products. The company primarily makes sales directly with less than 10% of sales made through resellers.

Financial Performance

Quality Systems financial performance was subpar in fiscal 2014 (ended March). The health care management software provider's sales declined 3% versus the prior year to $444.7 million while net income sank 63% to $15.7 million. The slump in fiscal 2014 reversed nearly a decade of steadily increasing sales (over which revenue quintupled). The decline was broad based with three of the company's four business segments posting lower sales. Indeed Quality Systems' core NextGen unit and its QSI Dental division both posted about a 1% decline in sales while the Hospital Solution business saw its sales plunge 50% year over year. Only the RCM Services division posted a gain (up almost 6%). Revenue earned from company-wide sales of systems decreased 30% to $86.8 million in 2014 from $123.6 million in the prior year. The decline in systems sales was driven primarily by lower sales of software to both new and existing clients for both the NextGen and Hospital Solutions units.

While sales and profits fell cash flow from operations increased by $36.1 million to $104.1 million in fiscal 2014.

Strategy

Trends in the health care industry pose both threats and an opportunities for the health care management software provider. On the downside the consolidation of physician offices by hospitals and other large enterprises is reducing the number of potential sales opportunities. On a positive note the evolution of health care from a pay-for-services reimbursement model to a pay-for-performance model around the management of patient populations may create many new opportunities for the company.

To navigate the rapidly changing health care economy. Quality Systems is looking to acquisitions to expand in the small and specialty hospital market and to add new clients by taking advantage of cross selling opportunities between the ambulatory and hospital markets. Its strategy is to anticipate upcoming needs of accountable care organizations around interoperability patient engagements population health and data analytics.

Mergers and Acquisitions

In September 2013 Quality Systems acquired Mirth Corporation a health information technology company that enables interoperability across silo-structured data systems. The purchased enhanced Quality Systems' existing interoperability initiatives and broadened its accountable and collaborative care population health disease management and clinical data exchange offerings.

Expanding its inpatient services business in 2012 Quality Systems acquired The Poseidon Group which provides software and a Web-based system for managing emergency department documentation. The offerings complemented and were later integrated into the NextGen Healthcare portfolio.

EXECUTIVES

VP Operations and Software, Donn E. Neufeld, age 57, $296,667 total compensation

President and CEO, Steven T. Plochocki, age 62, $539,688 total compensation

EVP and CFO, Paul A. Holt, age 48, $323,750 total compensation

EVP and COO, Daniel J. Morefield

EVP NextGen Practice Solutions, Monte Sandler, $290,833 total compensation

EVP CTO, Steve Puckett

EVP General Counsel and Secretary, Jocelyn A Leavitt

CIO, Zachary Sherburne

Senior Vice President Global Operations, Robert Fosmire

Vice President, Jerry Sculz

National Sales Manager, Steve Noll

Vice President, Cathy Adams

Vice President Human Resources, Donna Cullen

Senior Vice President Hospital, Jonathan Isaacs

Chairman, Sheldon Razin, age 77

EVP General Counsel and Secretary, Jocelyn A Leavitt

Treasurer, Jeff Mergler

Auditors: PricewaterhouseCoopersLLP

LOCATIONS

HQ: Quality Systems, Inc.
18111 Von Karman Avenue, Suite 700, Irvine, CA 92612
Phone: 949 255-2600
Web: www.qsii.com

PRODUCTS/OPERATIONS

2014 Sales

	$ mil.	% of total
NextGen	341.2	77
RCM Services	68.1	15
QSI Dental	19.8	4
Hospital Solutions	15.6	4
Total	**444.7**	**100**

2014 Sales

	$ mil.	% of total
Software and hardware	60.8	14
Implementation and training services	25.9	6
Maintenance services	160.1	36
Electronic data interchange services	67.3	15
Revenue cycle management and related services	63	14
other services	67.6	15
Total	**444.7**	**100**

Selected Products

Clinical data management software
Dental charting software
Dental practice management systems
Internet-based consumer health portal
Medical records storage software
Medical practice management systems

Selected Subsidiaries

NextGen Healthcare Information Systems LLC
NextGen RCM Services LLC
QSI Management LLC
Opus Healthcare Solutions LLC
Quality Systems India Healthcare Pvt. Ltd.
ViaTrack Systems LLC
Matrix Management Solutions LLC
Mirth LLC
Mirth Limited

COMPETITORS

Allscripts	Healthland
CPSI	MEDITECH
CareCentric	McKesson
Cerner	QuadraMed
Epic Systems	athenahealth
GE Healthcare	eClinicalWorks
Global Med	
Greenway Medical Technologies	

HISTORICAL FINANCIALS

Company Type: Public

Income Statement

FYE: March 31

	REVENUE ($ mil.)	NET INCOME ($ mil.)	NET PROFIT MARGIN	EMPLOYEES
03/14	444.6	15.6	3.5%	2,697
03/13	460.2	42.7	9.3%	2,333
03/12	429.8	75.6	17.6%	1,938
03/11	353.3	61.6	17.4%	1,579
03/10	291.8	48.3	16.6%	1,502
Annual Growth	**11.1%**	**(24.5%)**	**—**	**15.8%**

2014 Year-End Financials

Debt ratio: —
Return on equity: 5.2%
Cash ($ mil.): 103
Current ratio: 2.10
Long-term debt ($ mil.): —

No. of shares (mil.): 60
Dividends
Yield: 4.1%
Payout: 636.3%
Market value ($ mil.): 1,016

	STOCK PRICE ($) FY Close	P/E High/Low	Earnings	PER SHARE ($) Dividends	Book Value
03/14	16.88	92 64	0.26	0.70	4.90
03/13	18.27	61 22	0.72	0.70	5.16
03/12	43.73	78 26	1.28	0.70	4.99
03/11	83.34	78 51	1.06	0.63	3.87
03/10	61.44	81 52	0.84	0.60	3.26
Annual Growth	**(27.6%)**	**—**	**—(25.4%)**	**3.9%**	**10.7%**

Rackspace Hosting Inc

Looking for server rack space to host your company's data network needs? Well look no further than Rackspace Hosting. The company provides a range of web hosting and managed network services for businesses. It offers traditional hosting services with dedicated servers but is expanding into cloud hosting which lets customers use pooled server resources on an on-demand basis. Its cloud computing services include public private and hybrid cloud hosting which provides a combination of dedicated hosting and cloud computing. Founded in 1998 Rackspace has more than 200000 business customers in 120 countries.

Operations

In the wake of big data Rackspace Hosting provides managed hosting and private and public cloud services. Public Cloud services accounts for more than 25% of revenue while the company's dedicated cloud segment contributes the rest. The firm relies on more than 90000 servers at its data centers worldwide.

Rackspace doesn't own the data center properties; it leases the space from real estate companies such as DuPont Fabros. It does however buy and manage its equipment such as servers routers switches firewalls load balancers cabinets software and wiring.

Geographic Reach

Texas-based Rackspace Hosting rings up about three-quarters of its sales in the US. The company has nine leased data centers in Texas Virginia and Illinois as well as Australia Hong Kong and the UK.

Sales and Marketing

Rackspace primarily uses a direct sales model to sell its data center space. Channel partners such as consultancies and software application providers also resell Rackspace's network capabilities to their clients. Certain other services are sold on the company's website.

Financial Performance

Rackspace Hosting's sales and profits are growing in tandem with the increased popularity of cloud computing. In 2013 sales increased 17% versus 2012 to $1.5 billion. (Indeed the company has added a billion dollars in sales over the past five years.) The double-digit increase in annual sales was driven by a 37% jump in the company's public cloud sales while dedicated cloud sales increased 11% thanks to an increase in new customers and incremental sales to existing ones. International sales increased 20% while US sales rose 16% year over year.

Profits fell 18% in 2013 versus 2012 to $86 million primarily due to increased spending on research and development sales and marketing and other expenses.

Strategy

Cloud computing is the company's growth engine and Rackspace Hosting continues to make significant investments in the emerging technology. Rackspace has invested in internal development and acquisitions to build its cloud hosting business. In 2013 it continued to transition data center space to the hybrid cloud platform which began with a strategic decision to adopt an open source architecture to power the public cloud. Its data centers in Australia and Hong Kong now offer hybrid cloud services. The company is also actively pursuing customers in Europe Asia and Latin America for international expansion.

Partnerships are another avenue for growth. In 2013 Rackspace partnered with Magento a division of X.commerce an eBay company to work collabortively to serve both dedicated and open hybrid cloud customers with one of the fastest growing e-commerce platforms on the market. In 2012 Rackspace partnered with Hortonworks to focus on pursuing an OpenStack-based Hadoop solution for the public and private cloud.

Mergers and Acquisitions

In 2013 Rackspace made three acquisitions for a combined $16.2 million. In February it bought ObjectRocket a MongoDB database-as-a-service provider and in March it picked up Exceptional Cloud Services a cloud computing service company with products geared toward developers. Later that year in October 2013 it acquired LiteStack a company that specializes in an open source hypervisor built to run cloud applications called ZeroVM.

In 2012 Rackspace acquired e-mail services company Mailgun looking to add functionality to its Rackspace Open Cloud platform. Mailgun let users integrate e-mail from within applications. Also that year it bought SharePoint911 a provider of consulting and training services for Microsoft's collaboration and document management software SharePoint. The purchase expanded its presence in SharePoint management market which it entered in 2008.

Previous purchases include San Francisco-based cloud data server management software startup Cloudkick in late 2010 to add tools for automating tasks for systems administrators. Previous purchases include cloud storage specialist Jungle Disk and cloud hosting service provider Slicehost.

EXECUTIVES

Senior Vice President Customer Care, John Lionato
Chief Technology Officer, John Engates
COO, Mark Roenigk, age 53, $350,000 total compensation
SVP CFO and Treasurer, Karl Pichler, age 42, $350,000 total compensation
SVP and General Manager Americas, Odus (Boogie) Wittenburg
SVP and General Manager Enterprise, Chris Cochran
President and CEO, Taylor Rhodes
President Safe Banking Systems, David Schiffer
Vp Customer Care, David Bryce
Vp Product, Paul Carmody
Vp Compliance And Risk Management, Rick Cavazos
Vice President Sales And Marketing, Frederick Mendler
Svp Sales Americas, Todd Cione
Vp Of Finance, Aaron Barfoot
Cio Chief Technology Officer Vice President Director, Olu Aluko
Brand Vice President, Debbie Serot
Vice President Architecture, Kannan Alagappan
Executive Assistant To Cmo & Vp, Monica Lawson
Senior Vice President Cloud Us, Pat Matthews
Vice President, Mark Collier
Vice President Support, Ken Skinner
Vice President Operations, Troy Toman
Vp Of Finance, Natalie Reynolds
Co-Chairman and CEO, Graham M. Weston, age 50
SVP CFO and Treasurer, Karl Pichler, age 42
Board Member, Sam Gilliland
Auditors: KPMGLLP

LOCATIONS

HQ: Rackspace Hosting Inc
1 Fanatical Place, City of Windcrest, San Antonio, TX 78218
Phone: 210 312-4000
Web: www.rackspace.com

2013 Sales

	$ mil.	% of total
US	1133.7	74
Other countries	401.1	26
Total	**1534.8**	**100**

PRODUCTS/OPERATIONS

2013 Sales

	$ mil.	% of total
Dedicated cloud	1119.6	73
Public cloud	415.2	27
Total	**1534.8**	**100**

COMPETITORS

AT&T	Microsoft
Amazon.com	NaviSite
BT	NetNation
Cable & Wireless	Communications
Computer Sciences	Red Hat
Corp.	SAVVIS
Critical Path	SoftLayer
DuPont Fabros	Terremark Worldwide
Equinix	Verio
Google	Verizon
HP Enterprise Services	XO Holdings
IBM	salesforce.com

HISTORICAL FINANCIALS

Company Type: Public

Income Statement

FYE: December 31

	REVENUE ($ mil.)	NET INCOME ($ mil.)	NET PROFIT MARGIN	EMPLOYEES
12/13	1,534.7	86.7	5.7%	5,651
12/12	1,309.2	105.4	8.1%	4,852
12/11	1,025.0	76.4	7.5%	4,040
12/10	780.5	46.3	5.9%	3,262
12/09	628.9	30.2	4.8%	2,774
Annual Growth	**25.0%**	**30.2%**	**—**	**19.5%**

2013 Year-End Financials

Debt ratio: 4.3%	No. of shares (mil.): 141
Return on equity: 9.1%	Dividends
Cash ($ mil.): 259	Yield: —
Current ratio: 1.70	Payout: —
Long-term debt ($ mil.): 25	Market value ($ mil.): 5,522

	STOCK PRICE ($) FY Close	P/E High/Low	PER SHARE ($) Earnings	Dividends	Book Value
12/13	39.13	126 53	0.61	0.00	7.48
12/12	74.27	94 53	0.75	0.00	6.12
12/11	43.01	78 50	0.55	0.00	4.54
12/10	31.41	86 42	0.35	0.00	3.46
12/09	20.85	92 18	0.24	0.00	2.82
Annual Growth	**17.0%**	**— —**	**26.3%**	**—**	**27.6%**

Range Resources Corp

Range Resources is riding the range as an independent acquirer and developer of US oil and gas resources. The company's long-term strategy involves acquiring long-lived established properties and it has major development areas in the Appalachian and Southwest (West Texas western Oklahoma and Texas Panhandle) regions. Natural gas accounted for about 80% of Range Resources' proved reserves of 4.7 trillion cu. ft. of natural gas equivalent in 2012. The company holds more than 2 million net acres of leasehold properties and an inventory of more than 9000 net drilling locations.

Geographic Reach

The company operates in two US regions: Appalachia (which includes Pennsylvania Virginia and West Virginia) and the Southwest (which includes the Permian Basin of West Texas the Texas Panhandle the Nemaha Uplift in Northern Oklahoma and Kansas and the Anadarko Basin of Western Oklahoma).

Financial Performance

The company's revenues grew by 18% in 2012 due to 2074% increase in gain on sale of assets as the result of the sale of Ardmore Woodford properties in Southern Oklahoma for $135 million (for a gain of $55.2 million). In addition in 2012 Range Resources recorded a $10.9 million pre-tax loss on the sale of 75% of an East Texas prospect for $8.6 million and an additional $6.8 million gain related to a 2011 unproved acreage transaction. The company also reported a 3% increase in derivative fair value income and an increase in brokered natural gas marketing and other revenues.

Net income decreased by 78% in 2012 due to an increase in General and administrative expense because of higher salaries and benefits; an increase in stock-based compensation and higher legal and

office expenses (including information technology); and an increase in interest expenses due to higher interest rates and outstanding debt balances.

Strategy

Range Resources has grown by concentrating on developing properties in its core areas and by making complementary acquisitions and strategic dispositions to manage cash flow. It pursues acquisition opportunities within its core operating areas in order to capitalize on regional expertise drive down unit operating costs and generate economies of scale.

In 2013 the company agreed to sell certain Permian Basin and Delaware properties in southeast New Mexico and West Texas $275 million.

During 2012 Range Resources spent $188.8 million to acquire unproved acreage. It continues selective acreage leasing to add to its acreage positions primarily in the Marcellus Shale play in Pennsylvania and the Mississippian play in Oklahoma and Kansas.

Ownership

Black Rock Inc. owns 10% of the company.

HISTORY

Lomak Petroleum was a small gas drilling company with assets in Ohio and West Virginia when Snyder Oil Company (later part of Santa Fe Snyder) bought a 75% stake in 1988. Though Snyder soon started divesting its stake Snyder VP John Pinkerton was appointed president of Lomak in 1990 (he became CEO in 1992). Pinkerton charted a 10-year mission: Acquire a critical mass of producing properties operate the properties to establish cash flow and then begin exploration where it had properties and operating experience.

In 1991 Lomak acquired properties in the Permian basin of West Texas. Acquisitions continued in 1993 and 1994 as the company beefed up its Appalachian business and established positions in the midcontinent and Gulf Coast areas.

Lomak launched exploration efforts in 1996. The next year the company acquired properties in Texas and the Gulf of Mexico from American Cometra. That year Lomak purchased natural gas properties in Appalachia and oil properties in West Texas. It sold $54 million in property in 1998 including all of its San Juan Basin New Mexico assets. Also that year the company changed its name to Range Resources after its purchase of Domain for $217 million.

The oil slump of the late-1990s led to heavy debts prompting Range Resources to sell some assets and cut back on exploration production and acquisitions.

Range Resources formed joint venture Great Lakes Energy Partners L.L.C. with Ohio-based utility FirstEnergy in 1999 to jointly develop their Appalachian oil and gas resources. As part of its ongoing plans to reduce debt Range Resources sold its Sterling gas processing plant the next year for about $20 million.

In 2004 Range Resources acquired the 50% of Great Lakes Energy Partners that it did not already own for $295 million.

In 2005 the company acquired Plantation Petroleum Holdings II LLC a company with Permian Basin oil and gas properties for $116.5 million.

Range Resources sold its Gulf of Mexico properties to a private entity for $155 million in 2007.

In 2008 turning its attention to lucrative shale opportunities (now available for exploitation thanks to modern drilling technology) it acquired producing and non-producing Barnett Shale properties for $284 million.

In 2009 the company sold its West Texas Fuhrman Mascho properties to Energen Resources for $182 million to pay down debt and to invest in its Huron and Marcellus Shale plays. Despite a down economy and lower commodity prices which dragged down the company's revenues and income in 2009 the company reported solid business growth adding 13% in production and 18% in proved reserves.

To raise cash in 2010 it sold its tight-sand assets in Ohio to EV Energy Partners for more than $300 million. Still needing to raise cash to pay down debt and to free up capital for its Marcellus Shale play in 2011 the company sold its Barnett Shale properties to a private company for about $900 million.

In 2010 Range Resources reported a 14% production growth and a 42% proved reserve growth which (with gains from the sale of assets and derivatives) lifted the company's revenues for the year. However increased expenses including a $469.7 million impairment of proved properties charge related to the company's Barnett shale properties led to a large loss for the year.

EXECUTIVES

Senior Vice President, Rodney L Waller, age 66
President and CEO, Jeffrey L. (Jeff) Ventura, age 56, $864,423 total compensation
EVP and CFO, Roger S. Manny, age 57, $453,654 total compensation
SVP Reservoir Engineering and Economics, Alan W. Farquharson, age 57
EVP and COO, Ray N. Walker, age 56, $446,039 total compensation
SVP Southern Marcellus Shale, John K. Applegath
Vice President And Controller, Dori A Ginn, age 57
Exec Asst To Sr Vice President Pbu Engr, Cindy Hendrix
Vice President, Will Clear
Vice President Geology, William A Zagorski
Vice President Of Operations North Texas, Mike Middlebrook
Vice President Engineering Technology, Joseph Frantz
Vice President Of Marketing, Greg Davis
Vice President Reservoir Engineering, Cory West
Vice President Legislative And Regulatory Affairs, Terry Bossert
Vice President Legal And Deputy General, David Goldberg
Chairman, John H. Pinkerton, age 61
Auditors: Ernst&YoungLLP

LOCATIONS

HQ: Range Resources Corp
100 Throckmorton Street, Suite 1200, Fort Worth, TX 76102
Phone: 817 870-2601   **Fax:** 817 870-2316
Web: www.rangeresources.com

PRODUCTS/OPERATIONS

2012 Sales

	$ mil.	% of total
Natural gas NGLs & oil sales	1351.7	93
Gain on the sale of assets	49.1	3
Derivative fair value income	41.5	3
Brokered natural gas marketing & other	15.4	1
Total	**1457.7**	**100**

COMPETITORS

Anadarko Petroleum	EQT Corporation
Apache	Exxon Mobil
BP	Forest Oil

Belden & Blake	Murphy Oil
Cabot Oil & Gas	Noble Energy
Chesapeake Energy	Pioneer Natural
Devon Energy	Resources
Dominion Resources	Royal Dutch Shell
EOG	XTO Energy

HISTORICAL FINANCIALS

Company Type: Public

Income Statement

FYE: December 31

	REVENUE ($ mil.)	NET INCOME ($ mil.)	NET PROFIT MARGIN	EMPLOYEES
12/13	1,862.7	115.7	6.2%	867
12/12	1,457.7	13.0	0.9%	841
12/11	1,218.6	58.0	4.8%	756
12/10	1,038.9	(239.2)	—	713
12/09	907.3	(53.8)	—	787
Annual Growth	**19.7%**	**—**	**—**	**2.4%**

2013 Year-End Financials

Debt ratio: 43.0%	No. of shares (mil.): 163
Return on equity: 4.8%	Dividends
Cash ($ mil.): 0	Yield: 0.1%
Current ratio: 0.50	Payout: 18.1%
Long-term debt ($ mil.): 3,140	Market value ($ mil.): 13,771

	STOCK PRICE ($) FY Close	P/E High/Low	PER SHARE ($) Earnings	Dividends	Book Value
12/13	84.31	118 87	0.70	0.16	14.78
12/12	62.83	916675	0.08	0.16	14.51
12/11	61.94	207124	0.36	0.16	14.85
12/10	44.98	— —	(1.53)	0.16	13.91
12/09	49.85	— —	(0.35)	0.16	15.04
Annual Growth	**14.0%**	**— —**	**—**	**(0.0%)**	**(0.4%)**

Raven Industries, Inc.

Quoth the Raven "Balloons (and more) evermore!" Raven Industries' Aerostar division does sell high-altitude research balloons as well as parachutes and protective wear used by US agencies. Its Engineered Films Division makes reinforced plastic sheeting for various applications. The Applied Technology Division manufactures high-tech agricultural aids from global positioning system (GPS)-based steering devices and chemical spray equipment to field computers. The Electronic Systems Division offers electronic manufacturing services and supports the other divisions. Goodrich is a major customer.

The rugged sheeting made by the Engineered Films Division 34% of sales are applied for industrial energy construction geomembrane and agricultural uses. "Geomembrane" refers to containment liners used for environmental projects and water conservation. Products are marketed through independent distributors. Because the segment extrudes a large part of its products it needs a significant amount of capital expenditures to stay operational. Extrusion is a process that includes pushing material through a circular or slot die.

Besides GPS-based products and computers the Applied Technology Division also 34% of sales markets a software platform called Slingshot that offers Real Time Kinematic (RTK) corrections of GPS signals for more accurate steering. Served by a globally based staff the division markets its prod-

ucts to OEMs and through the aftermarket. The Electronic Systems Division 19% of sales makes such assemblies as avionics secure communication and environmental controls. Sales are made through competitive bids.

Besides balloons Aerostar 13% of sales also sells tethered aerostats which are similar to blimps used for surveillance and aerial communication. Besides parachutes and protective gear the segment provides uniforms and also contracts to sew and seal products. Aerostar products are also marketed through competitive bids.

Net sales rose 21% in fiscal 2012 compared with 2011 a jump that was commensurate with upticks for all of the company's divisions. Thanks in part to more demand from a healthier agriculture market and international growth sales for Applied Technology Division increased 33%. The Engineered Films Division's sales were raised 26% on the back of high crude oil prices that caused more drilling and demand for pit liners. Electronic Systems headed up 9% thanks in part to demand for hand-held bed controls and secure communication electronics products. Aerostar gained 7% in 2012 compared with 2011. The slight uptick responded to demand for T-11 parachutes spare parts protective wear and tethered aerostats.

Operating income was up 26% in 2012 compared with year before. By division Engineered Films recorded a 10% uptick in operating income growth trailing sales growth mostly because of higher material costs. Operating income for Applied Technology soared 46% with higher sales and the better operating leverage that followed. A more favorable product mix as well as higher sales lifted Electronic Systems' operating income 14%. Higher sales and more efficient manufacturing boosted Aerostar's operating income by 22% in 2012 compared with 2011. Net income has been steadily rising from about $28.6 million in 2010 to more than $40.5 million in 2011 and then to more than $50.6 million in 2012.

Engineered Films touts its service in both extruding and converting films as a competitive advantage that provides more opportunity for customization to service its clients. One problem for Engineered Films is that no matter how well the economy may be operating adverse weather can limit construction and the division's sales of plastic sheeting as a result. Construction and energy are the segment's largest markets. While it can't predict the weather the company is optimistic about continued growth in oil and gas drilling that will increase demand for pit liners. Applied Technology has been innovating such improvements as Slingshot API though it too is subject to the same vagaries of the weather that challenge its agricultural clientele. The company is optimistic about the health of the agricultural economy in the immediate future however. Electronic Systems has struggled with lower avionics sales but division is expected to grow with demand for more support and service from its three sister divisions.

Raven's strategy for growth also includes acquisitions. In early 2012 Raven made a move to bolster the Aerostar division with the acquisition of Vista Research a provider of surveillance systems that use advanced algorithms to increase radar effectiveness. The company hopes to integrate Vista's technology with its marine navigation products and create better aerostat systems.

HISTORY

During 2009 Raven Industries purchased most the assets of Canadian-held Ranchview. Ranchview develops products that deliver real-time corrections to GPS equipment using cellular networks instead of radio systems. The same year Raven picked up a minority stake in SST Software a software development and information services provider for agricultural applications. The additions raised the efficiency and effectiveness of Raven's agricultural data transmission products.

EXECUTIVES

President and CEO, Daniel A. (Dan) Rykhus, age 50, $510,000 total compensation
Division VP and General Manager Applied Technology Division, Matthew T. (Matt) Burkhart, age 38, $270,000 total compensation
Division VP and General Manager Aerostar, Lon E. Stroschein, $235,000 total compensation
Division VP and General Manager Engineered Films Division, Anthony Schmidt
VP CFO and Treasurer, Steven Brazones
CIO, Brian Meyer
National Sales Manager, Daryl Mitzel
Vice President Of Human Resources, Jan Matthiesen
Vice President Materials, Brad Parker
Vice President Operations, David Hirsch
Vice President Secretary Chief Financial Officer, Thomas Mousa
Vice President Administration, Barbara Ledyard
Vp Of Sales, Larry McQuinn
Marketing Vice President, Steve Loge
Vice President Operations Aerostar International, Dick Funke
Board Member, Mark E Griffin, age 64
Chairman, Thomas S. Everist, age 64
Secretary & Travel Coordinator, Vance Brower
Auditors: PricewaterhouseCoopersLLP

LOCATIONS

HQ: Raven Industries, Inc.
205 East 6th Street, P.O. Box 5107, Sioux Falls, SD 57117-5107
Phone: 605 336-2750
Web: www.ravenind.com

PRODUCTS/OPERATIONS

2012 Sales By Segment

	$ mil.	% of total
Engineered Films Division	133.5	34
Applied Technology Division	132.6	34
Electronic Systems Division	71.7	19
Aerostar Division	52.4	13
Adjustments	(8.7)	-
Total	**381.5**	**100**

2012 Sales By Product Group

	$ mil.	% of total
Agricultural precision control devices & accessories Plastic films	131.2	34
Pit lining & geomembrane films	80.2	21
Other plastic films	53.3	14
Electronic manufacturing services	63.2	17
Parachutes & protective gear	26.1	7
Tethered aerostats	17.7	5
Other	9.8	2
Total	**381.5**	**100**

Selected Products and Divisions

Aerostar
  Aerostats
  Parachutes
  Protective outerware
  Research balloons
Applied Technology
  Data collection
  GPS steering devices
  Planting and spraying controls
Electronic Systems

Electronics manufacturing services
Secure communication devices
Engineered Films plastic sheeting
  Agricultural
  Construction
  Geomembrane
  Energy
  Industrial

COMPETITORS

Astronautics
Cohesant
Denali
Emerson Electric
Flowserve
Graco
Sigma Plastics
Williamson-Dickie Manufacturing

HISTORICAL FINANCIALS

Company Type: Public

Income Statement

FYE: January 31

	REVENUE ($ mil.)	NET INCOME ($ mil.)	NET PROFIT MARGIN	EMPLOYEES
01/14	394.6	42.9	10.9%	1,286
01/13	406.1	52.5	12.9%	1,379
01/12	381.5	50.5	13.3%	1,405
01/11	314.7	40.5	12.9%	1,112
01/10	237.7	28.5	12.0%	955
Annual Growth	**13.5%**	**10.7%**	**—**	**7.7%**

2014 Year-End Financials

Debt ratio: —
Return on equity: 18.1%
Cash ($ mil.): 52
Current ratio: 5.68
Long-term debt ($ mil.): —
No. of shares (mil.): 36
Dividends
  Yield: 1.2%
  Payout: 38.1%
Market value ($ mil.): 1,364

	STOCK PRICE ($) FY Close	P/E High/Low	PER SHARE ($) Earnings	Dividends	Book Value
01/14	37.45	36 22	1.17	0.48	6.90
01/13	26.93	51 17	1.44	0.42	6.09
01/12	64.89	48 32	1.39	0.36	4.98
01/11	47.24	44 24	1.12	0.95	3.91
01/10	28.58	42 20	0.79	0.28	3.70
Annual Growth	**7.0%**	**— —**	**10.3%**	**14.9%**	**16.9%**

RBC Bearings Inc

RBC Bearings keeps businesses on a roll. The company makes an array of plain roller and ball bearing products. It specializes in regulated bearings used by OEMs and their aftermarkets of commercial/military aircraft automobiles and commercial trucks industrial/agricultural machinery as well as air turbines. Targeting high-end markets its precision lineup satisfies thousands of applications from engine controls to radar systems mining tools and gear pumps. RBC's top customers include Boeing GE Lockheed Martin and the US Department of Defense. RBC Bearings has grown since 1919 to some 35 manufacturing facilities in Europe and North America.

Financial Performance

RBC has experienced unprecedented growth over the last few years. Its revenues climbed 4% from $403 million in 2013 to $419 million in 2014. Profits also jumped 7% from $56 million in 2013

to $60 million in 2014. Both these totals represented historic milestones for the company.

The growth for 2014 was driven by a 20% rise in sales from its roller bearings product line and a 3% bump from plain bearings. RBC also experienced growth in the aerospace and defense markets and a rise in sales due to previous acquisitions. From 2013 to 2014 the company's cash flow decreased from $66 million to $48 million as a result from a change made in operating assets higher inventory costs decreases in collections of accounts receivables and increased expenses and other liabilities.

Strategy

RBC has managed to increase its sales to the aftermarket. Bearings which are indispensable for a machine's operating efficiency periodically wear out which creates a second stream of replacement parts sales. During 2014 aftermarket sales of replacement parts for installed equipment accounted for nearly 50% of RBC's revenues. Aerospace and defense customers also promise a particularly reliable opportunity for replacement business.

Mergers and Acquisitions

The company makes acquisitions in order to further develop its offerings end-markets and geographic footprint. Throughout 2013 the company made several small acquisitions snapping up Turbine Components Climax Metal Products Company and Western Precision Aero LLC.

Company Background

RBC Bearings is an amalgamation of companies merged and acquired. The company got its start in 1919 making ball bearings; by the 1940s it became the sole supplier for landing gear bearings on military aircraft made by Ford Motor Company. In 2005 the company jetted onto the public investor market.

EXECUTIVES

Chairman President and CEO, Michael J. Hartnett, age 67, $814,174 total compensation
VP and General Manager RBC Division, Richard J. Edwards, age 57, $288,086 total compensation
CFO, Daniel A. (Dan) Bergeron, age 53, $313,212 total compensation
VP and General Manager Heim Bearings RBC Torrington CT Plant and Schaublin SA, Thomas C. Crainer, age 55, $306,803 total compensation
Vice President Of Sales, Michelle Dodson
Vice-president, Dieter Kuetemeier
Vice President Sales, Karen De Mestrio
Chairman President and CEO, Michael J. Hartnett, age 67
Corporate General Counsel Secretary, Thomas J Williams
Auditors: PricewaterhouseCoopersLLP

LOCATIONS

HQ: RBC Bearings Inc
One Tribology Center, Oxford, CT 06478
Phone: 203 267-7001
Web: www.rbcbearings.com

2014 Sales

	$ mil.	% of total
US	351.4	84
Other countries	67.5	16
Total	**418.9**	**100**

PRODUCTS/OPERATIONS

2014 Sales

	$ mil.	% of total
Plain bearings	223.1	53
Roller bearings	115.8	28

Ball bearings	49.6	12
Other	30.4	7
Total	**418.9**	**100**

2014 Sales by Market

	% of total
Aerospace and defense	58
Diversified industrial	42
Total	**100**

Selected Products

Aerospace (commercial and military)
 Airframe control ball bearings
 Airframe control needle track rollers
 Ball bearing rod ends
 Gear box and engine ball and roller bearings
 Journal bearings
 Links and assemblies
 Radial ball bearings
 Rod end plain bearings
 Spherical plain bearings
 Stud type track roller bearings
 Swage tubes and control rods
 Thin sections ball bearings
Industrial
 Ball bearings (Nice)
 Cam followers
 Collets and toolholders
 Heavy duty needle roller bearings
 Pins rollers shafts
 Rod ends
 Self-lubricating bearings (Fiberglide)
 Slewing ring bearings
 Spherical plain bearings
 Tapered roller/tapered thrust bearings
 Thin section ball bearings

COMPETITORS

Emerson Electric	Rexnord
General Bearing	SKF USA
Kaydon	Timken
Minebea	
NTN Bearing Corp. of America	

HISTORICAL FINANCIALS

Company Type: Public

Income Statement

FYE: March 29

	REVENUE ($ mil.)	NET INCOME ($ mil.)	NET PROFIT MARGIN	EMPLOYEES
03/14	418.8	60.2	14.4%	2,361
03/13	403.0	56.3	14.0%	2,145
03/12*	397.5	50.0	12.6%	2,137
04/11	335.6	34.8	10.4%	1,950
04/10	274.7	24.3	8.9%	1,791
Annual Growth	**11.1%**	**25.4%**	**—**	**7.2%**

*Fiscal year change

2014 Year-End Financials

Debt ratio: 1.6%	No. of shares (mil.): 23
Return on equity: 12.0%	Dividends
Cash ($ mil.): 121	Yield: —
Current ratio: 9.75	Payout: —
Long-term debt ($ mil.): 9	Market value ($ mil.): 1,461

	STOCK PRICE ($) FY Close	P/E High/Low		PER SHARE ($) Earnings	Dividends	Book Value
03/14	62.97	27	18	2.59	0.00	23.20
03/13	50.56	21	17	2.47	0.00	20.11
03/12*	46.13	21	13	2.23	0.00	17.44
04/11	38.86	24	17	1.58	0.00	15.07
04/10	31.73	28	15	1.12	0.00	13.05
Annual Growth	**18.7%**	**—**	**—**	**23.3%**	**—**	**15.5%**

*Fiscal year change

RCI Hospitality Holdings Inc

Far from Casablanca these night clubs offer topless entertainment as part of the floor show. Rick's Cabaret International operates more than 30 adult night clubs in Arizona Florida Minnesota New York North Carolina and Texas. Most of the gentlemen's clubs are run under the Rick's Cabaret name while others operate under such banners as Club Onyx and XTC. Rick's caters to highbrow patrons with dough to blow: It offers VIP memberships for individual and corporate clients that can cost hundreds of dollars annually. In addition to its night clubs Rick's operates adult websites and an auction site for adult entertainment products.

Rick's is focused on expanding its nightclub estate gradually by adding new locations organically and through acquisitions. In 2012 the company purchased 11 clubs in Texas and Arizona along with associated real estate through its acquisition of Jaguars Acquisitions. It made the deal —which included clubs in Phoenix Lubbock El Paso and Beaumont —for some $26 million.

Before the Jaguar deal a proposed deal to purchase rival strip club operator VCG Holding in 2010 fell through. The VCG deal valued at about $45 million in cash and stock would have expanded Rick's holdings to about 40 locations in about a dozen states.

Previous to its failed buyout of VCG Rick's added Dallas to its sphere of operations with the purchase of The Executive Club for $9.5 million in 2008. The company added another Dallas club with the purchase of Platinum Club II. Also in 2008 Rick's launched itself into print and online media when it acquired trade publisher ED Publications for a little more than $1 million. The deal included such adult industry titles as Adult Store Buyer and Exotic Dancer as well as trade shows and websites.

CEO Eric Langan owns about 14% of the company.

HISTORY

Dallas Fontenot and Salah Izzedin founded Trumps in 1982. The following year they bought a disco and turned it into a swank topless bar called Rick's Cabaret (the name came from an encounter with a drunk in a taxi who was looking for "Rick's"). Izzedin's attorney Robert Watters bought a 10% interest in Trumps in 1987 the same year that the company opened the first members-only VIP room in Houston. The partnership of Fontenot Izzedin and Watters soured in 1989 with allegations that Izzedin pocketed unreported money supplied narcotics to waitresses and dancers and forced some of them to have sex with him.

Watters took over as CEO in 1991 and became sole owner in 1993. He converted Trumps into Rick's Cabaret International the next year and made Rick's the first topless bar to go public in 1995. The company expanded to New Orleans the following year opening a club on Bourbon Street. Rick's opened a new club in Minneapolis in 1998 and bought a 93% stake in Taurus Entertainment. Watters resigned in 1999 sold his stock in the company to new CEO Eric Langan and his investment partner Ralph McElroy and acquired the firm's New Orleans location which operated as a Rick's Cabaret under a licensing agreement. (The

company sold it the same year.) Later in 1999 Rick's launched its adult Web sites.

In 2000 the company bought a third topless bar in Houston as well as another adult Web site xxxPasswords.com. It also began selling pre-paid debit cards that allow customers to anonymously buy access to adult entertainment Web sites. Rick's purchased the Chesapeake Bay Cabaret an upscale club in Houston in November. Later that year the company inked a deal with adult Web site operator Entertainment Network to offer its content through CandidCam.com.

Rick's launched NaughtyBids.com an auction site for adult products in 2001. It also began buying a number of porn auction sites including Pornauction.com and XXXbids.com in an effort to enhance the products available on NaughtyBids.com. Late that year it opened Encounters an upscale club for swinging couples in Houston.

During 2003 Rick's acquired a 51% stake in Houston's Wild Horse Cabaret and opened a sports bar called Hummers (later renamed under the Club Onyx brand). It also acquired the XTC clubs outright from Taurus Entertainment and reorganized some of its other holdings leaving it with a 51% stake in Encounters (sold 2004).

The company in 2004 converted its original Rick's Cabaret nightclub in Houston into Club Onyx an upscale venue that caters to urban professionals businessmen and professional athletes. It also bought a new location in Manhattan near Madison Square Garden. The following year the company closed on its acquisition of a three-in-one complex in North Carolina that included a men's club a male revue for women and a traditional night club. Also in 2005 it bought swingers-oriented dating Web site CouplesClick.net.

During 2006 Rick's purchased four new nightclubs in Texas. The following year it inked a licensing deal with a subsidiary of Argentina-based Latin Entertainment to open adult clubs in Buenos Aires and other Latin American cities under the Rick's Cabaret name.

EXECUTIVES

Executive Vice President; Director, Travis Reese, age 46
Auditors: WhitleyPenn

LOCATIONS

HQ: RCI Hospitality Holdings Inc
10959 Cutten Road, Houston, TX 77066
Phone: 281 397-6730
Web: www.rcihospitality.com

PRODUCTS/OPERATIONS

2011 Sales

	$ mil.	% of total
Nightclubs		
Services	38.1	46
Alcohol	32.5	39
Food & merchandise	7.7	9
Media	1.2	2
Internet	0.4	-
Other	3.6	4
Total	**83.5**	**100**

Selected Operations

Nightclubs
 Club Onyx (adult entertainment for urban professionals and professional athletes)
 Rick's Cabaret
 Rick's Sports Cabaret
 Tootsie's Cabaret
 XTC
Media

Club Bulletin (trade magazine for adult clubs)
Storerotica (trade magazine for adult stores and products)
VIP Guide (directory of clubs industry vendors entertainers)
Internet
CouplesClick.net (85% adult content and online dating)
CouplesTouch.com (85% adult content and online dating)
NaughtyBids.com (adult auction Web site)
xxxPassword.com (adult content)

Selected Subsidiaries

Adult Store Buyer Magazine LLC
Bobby's Novelty Inc.
Broadstreets Cabaret Inc.
ED Publications Inc.
Miami Gardens Square One Inc.
Playmates Gentlemen's Club LLC
RCI Dating Services Inc.
RCI Entertainment (Austin) Inc.
RCI Entertainment (Fort Worth) Inc.
RCI Entertainment (Las Vegas) Inc.
RCI Entertainment (Media Holdings) Inc.
RCI Entertainment (Minnesota) Inc.
RCI Entertainment (New York) Inc.
RCI Entertainment (North Carolina) Inc.
RCI Entertainment (Northwest Highway) Inc.
RCI Entertainment (Philadelphia) Inc.
RCI Entertainment (San Antonio) Inc.
RCI Entertainment (Texas) Inc.
Tantra Dance Inc.
Teeze International Inc.
TEZ Real Estate LP Philadelphia
Top Shelf Entertainment LLC
XTC Cabaret Inc.

COMPETITORS

FriendFinder Networks	Playboy.com
Galardi South	Private Media Group
LFP	Scores Holding
Million Dollar Saloon	Vivid Entertainment
New Frontier Media	

HISTORICAL FINANCIALS

Company Type: Public

Income Statement

FYE: September 30

	REVENUE ($ mil.)	NET INCOME ($ mil.)	NET PROFIT MARGIN	EMPLOYEES
09/14	129.1	11.2	8.7%	1,750
09/13	112.2	9.1	8.2%	1,750
09/12	95.2	7.5	8.0%	1,400
09/11	83.4	7.8	9.4%	1,200
09/10	82.9	(7.9)	—	1,200
Annual Growth	11.7%	—	—	9.9%

2014 Year-End Financials

Debt ratio: 29.4%
Return on equity: 11.0%
Cash ($ mil.): 9
Current ratio: 0.60
Long-term debt ($ mil.): 58

No. of shares (mil.): 10
Dividends
Yield: —
Payout: —
Market value ($ mil.): 111

	STOCK PRICE ($) FY Close	P/E High/Low		PER SHARE ($) Earnings	Dividends	Book Value
09/14	11.02	11	9	1.13	0.00	10.96
09/13	11.79	13	8	0.96	0.00	9.87
09/12	8.28	13	8	0.78	0.00	8.82
09/11	6.65	14	8	0.79	0.00	8.17
09/10	7.28	—	—	(0.82)	0.00	7.61
Annual Growth	10.9%	—	—	—	—	9.5%

RealPage Inc

RealPage touts its software as a real asset to real estate managers. The company's on-demand software platform is designed to make the property management process more efficient enabling owners and managers of single- and multifamily rental properties to oversee their accounting leasing marketing pricing and screening operations from a single shared database. The centralized system helps with managing incoming and outgoing residents and overseeing property functions from hiring plumbers to training staff. Its customers include all of the top 10 largest multifamily property management companies in the US.

IPO

RealPage went public in August 2010 with an offering valued at about $135 million. (The company sold 12.3 million shares at $11 each vs. a prior estimate of 13.5 million shares at $13 to $15 each.) The firm used the proceeds from its IPO to pay dividends repay debt and possibly to fund future acquisitions.

Operations

RealPage's on-demand software (95% of sales) is its primary revenue segment and consists of an integrated software platform that provides a single point of access containing data on residents prospects and properties. The software is generally licensed under one-year customer subscription agreements. A smaller portion of the company's revenue is generated from professional services which include consulting training and implementation services.

Sales and Marketing

RealPage sells its software and services through an in-house direct sales organization. The firm promotes its products via online marketing activities including email campaigns online advertising Web campaigns webinars and social media (blogging Facebook and Twitter). Advertising cost totaled $10.2 million in 2012 vs. $8.6 million in 2011.

In 2012 more than 8400 customers used one of more of the company's on-demand software products to help manage the operations of some 8.1 million rental housing units.

Financial Performance

The company's sales increased 25% in 2012 vs. 2011 driven by a 28% gain in sales of its on-demand software products. RealPage returned to profitability in 2012 with net income of $5.2 million vs. a loss of $1.2 million in 2011. Cash flow from operations continued its steep climb in 2012 exceeding $58 million.

Strategy

To fuel its expansion acquisitive RealPage has completed 21 acquisitions since mid-2002. The company's active acquisition schedule has allowed it to expand its platform enter new rental property markets and expand its customers base.

Mergers and Acquisitions

Recent purchases include Software-as-a-Service (SaaS) provider Vigilan which serves the assisted living industry in 2012. The company's products enable customers to manage care information labor costs billing and compliance boosting RealPage's on-demand software offerings in that market. Also that year the company paid $6 million to buy RentMineOnline which provides SaaS marketing driven by social sites such as Facebook and LinkedIn for the multifamily rental industry.

In 2011 Compliance Depot a provider of risk management and compliance services for the real estate industry in 2011. The deal continued the company's strategy of expanding its portfolio of products and services for the rental housing market. That year it also paid $4.5 million in cash for SeniorLiving.net a Web-based lead generation and placement service for the senior housing market. In a related move in 2011 RealPage acquired Multifamily Technology Solutions which operates the MyNewPlace website. Both the SeniorLiving.net and MyNewPlace acquisitions boost RealPage's origination and syndication operations.

Ownership

Chairman and CEO Stephen Winn owns about 37% of the company's shares. Apax Excelsior VI owns about 11%.

Company Background

RealPage was formed in 1998 to acquire Rent Roll Inc. which marketed and sold on-premise property management systems for certain multifamily housing markets. Three years later it released OneSite its first on-demand property management system.

EXECUTIVES

Senior Vice President Strategic Marketing, Ty Brewer
Chairman and CEO, Stephen T. (Steve) Winn, age 67, $470,833 total compensation
Chief Operations Officer, Jason D. Lindwall
SVP Marketing, Andrea Massey
EVP Enterprise Solutions, William Chaney, $273,808 total compensation
EVP Asset Optimization Solutions, Janine Steiner
President Velocity, John Lis
President LeasingDesk Insurance, Ed Wolff
EVP Marketing Solutions & Propertyware, Jamie Clymer
CFO, W. Bryan Hill
Svp Acquisition, Michael Britti
Vice President And Controller, Tony Howard
Vice President Marketing, Tracy Dean
Vp It, Adam Silverthorne
Vice President Business Development, Keith Dunkin
President Propertyware Svp Realpage, Jason Doyle
Vice President I, Catherine Parks
Senior Vice President I, Jason Russell
Vice President Of Research M Pf Yieldstar, Greg Willett
Vice President Consumer Marketing, Naeem Kayani
Svp, Dave Carner
Vice President I, Tracy Turner
Vice President Affordable, Gustavo Sapiurka
Vice President Market Development, Tiffany McNeil
Vice President Market Development, Daniel Ward
Vice President Ii, Sean Wheeler
Vice President Implementations And Account Management, Debi Cole
Senior Vice President Crossfire Operations, Anthony Pusateri
Vice President Product Management, Kimberly Lang
Vice President Assisted Living, Jim Wills
National Account Manager, Mike Brae
Vice President I, George Pickering
Vice President I Sales, Scott Bible
Vice President I, Ross Lewellyn
Vice President I Business Development, Don Coppersmith
Sr Vice President Onesite Entp, Ranjeev Teelock
Vice President, Richard Hughes
Senior Vice President Realpage President Of Sales And Marketing, Jon Tull
Vice President Of Training, Terresa Porizek
Vice President I, Tamika Davis

Vice President Leasingdesk Screening, Aaron
Durkee
Vice President Or Sales, Terri Nicholson
Vice President I Client Services, Robert Bishop
Vice President Professional Services, Jeremy
Batson
Vice President I, Doug Fullaway
Vice President Products, Deepak Bhasin
Vice President I, Ed Tonarelli
Vice President Market Development, Danny Boesch
Vice President Yieldstar Product Development At
Realpage, Kurt Johnson
Vice President Contact Center, Karl Hirschauer
Vice President Operations, Brian Balbinot
Vice President Product Management, Ed Thralls
Senior Vice President Ventures, Steve Small
Vice President Global Contact, Don Brooks
Vice President Activebuilding, Kobi Bensimon
Vice President Information Technology Security
And Operations, Bill Lines
Senior Vp Of Strategic & Institutional, Tamika
Davis McCuistion
Vp Institutional Business Development, Carl
Stockholm
Vp Social Products, Ed Spiegel
Vice President Mybuilding, Guy Blachman
Vice President Associate General, Sylvia Braddom
Vice President Enterprise Sales, Shani Podell
Vice President, Benjamin Strum
Vice President Business Development, Suellen
McFarling
Vice President Enterprise Sales, Wesley Taylor
Svp Secretary And General Counsel, Jim Harrison
Chairman and CEO, Stephen T. (Steve) Winn, age 67
Board Member, Maria Mireles
Auditors: Ernst&YoungLLP

LOCATIONS

HQ: RealPage Inc
4000 International Parkway, Carrollton, TX 75007-
1951
Phone: 972 820-3000
Web: www.realpage.com

PRODUCTS/OPERATIONS

2012 Sales

	$ mil.	% of total
On-demand	306.4	95
Professional & other	10.6	3
On-premise	5.2	2
Total	**322.2**	**100**

COMPETITORS

Archibus	Infor Global
Assurant	MoneyGram
Chase Paymentech	International
Solutions	PROS Holdings
Communities Group	SiteStuff
First Advantage	TransUnion
First Data	Who's Calling
Fiserv	Yardi Systems

HISTORICAL FINANCIALS

Company Type: Public

Income Statement

FYE: December 31

	REVENUE ($ mil.)	NET INCOME ($ mil.)	NET PROFIT MARGIN	EMPLOYEES
12/13	377.0	20.6	5.5%	3,337
12/12	322.1	5.1	1.6%	2,893
12/11	257.9	(1.2)	—	2,273
12/10	188.2	0.0	0.0%	1,759
12/09	140.9	28.4	20.2%	1,260
Annual Growth	**27.9%**	**(7.6%)**	**—**	**27.6%**

2013 Year-End Financials

Debt ratio: 1.8%	No. of shares (mil.): 78
Return on equity: 7.2%	Dividends
Cash ($ mil.): 34	Yield: —
Current ratio: 1.06	Payout: —
Long-term debt ($ mil.): 4	Market value ($ mil.): 1,834

	STOCK PRICE ($) FY Close	P/E High/Low	PER SHARE ($) Earnings	Dividends	Book Value
12/13	23.38	92 61	0.27	0.00	4.01
12/12	21.57	409242	0.07	0.00	3.36
12/11	25.27	— —	(0.02)	0.00	3.07
12/10	30.93	— —	(0.07)	0.00	2.52
Annual Growth	**(8.9%)**	**— —**	**—**	**—**	**16.7%**

Realty Income Corp.

Retail real estate is a reality for Realty Income
Corporation. The self-administered real estate investment trust (REIT) owns and manages primarily free-standing single-tenant properties which it
leases to regional and national consumer retail
and service chains. Realty Income owns more than
2600 properties containing some 27 million sq. ft.
of leasable space in every state except Hawaii.
Texas California Florida Minnesota Georgia Illinois and Virginia are its largest markets; combined they make up nearly half of the REIT's rental
revenue. Realty Income is buying fellow REIT
American Realty Capital Trust for nearly $3 billion.
The deal will add more than 480 commercial properties to its portfolio.

Realty Income's occupancy rate has been above
96% every year since its 1969 founding. Top tenants include restaurants convenience stores the-
aters child care providers automotive care centers
health and fitness facilities grocery stores and drug
stores.

The REIT focuses on long-term sale-leaseback
transactions in which the tenant is responsible for
taxes and maintenance. It targets established middle-market retail chains with more than 50 operating locations in at least two geographic areas. Realty Income has traditionally grown through
acquisitions and often sells properties with the intent to reinvest the proceeds in new real estate with
the potential for higher returns. Subsidiary Crest
Net owns properties which are held for sale rather
than for long-term investment.

After slowing its acquisition activity in 2008 and
2009 due to economic conditions Realty Income
resumed major dealmaking in 2010 when it
bought 186 properties in several different transactions. It diversified into the winery business when
it acquired nearly 1700 acres of vineyard property
and almost 400000 sq. ft. of associated production
retail and visitor center buildings of Sterling Vineyards and Beaulieu Vineyards. The company
bought the real estate for some from $270 million
in a sale-leaseback transaction with Diageo
Chateau & Estate Wines now one of the REIT's
largest tenants which will continue produce wine
on and manage the properties.

In 2011 Realty Income invested some $1 billion
to acquire more than 160 properties in 26 states
also through several separate transactions. It represented the largest increase in new property investments in the company's history. The additions
contributed to a 22% increase in rental income for
the year and a corresponding rise in net income.

Institutional shareholders own more than 40%
of Realty Income's stock.

EXECUTIVES

Svp And General Counsel, Laura S King, age 53
Associate Vice President Senior Legal Counsel,
Steve Burchett
Vice President, Lorena Duran
EVP and General Counsel Secretary, Michael R.
Pfeiffer, age 53, $300,000 total compensation
**Vice Chairman of the Board; Chief Executive
Officer,** Thomas A. (Tom) Lewis, age 61, $550,000
total compensation
President Crest Net Lease, Cary J. Wenthur
EVP CFO and Treasurer, Paul M. Meurer, age 48,
$325,000 total compensation
President Crest Net Lease, Richard G. Collins, age
65, $220,000 total compensation
President CEO and Director, John P. Case,
$205,769 total compensation
EVP COO and Chief Investment Officer, Sumit
Roy
Vice President Information Technologist, Theresa
M Casey
Associate Vice President Portfolio Management,
Kristin K Ferrell
**Associate Vice President Human Resources And
Operations,** Teresa Glenn
Associate Vice President Senior Legal Counsel,
Elizabeth Bonacci
Vp Asset Management, Benjamin Fox
Vice President Information Technology, Clint
Schmucker
Associate Vice President Senior Legal Counsel,
Shannon Jensen
Chairman, Donald R. Cameron, age 74
President CEO and Director, John P. Case
Auditors: KPMGLLP

LOCATIONS

HQ: Realty Income Corp.
600 La Terraza Boulevard, Escondido, CA 92025-3873
Phone: 760 741-2111   **Fax:** 760 741-2235
Web: www.realtyincome.com

PRODUCTS/OPERATIONS

2011 Sales

	$ mil.	% of total
Rents by property type		
Convenience stores	77.8	18
Casual dining restaurants	45.7	11
Theaters	36.8	9
Quick service restaurants	27.5	6
Health & fitness	26.8	6
Beverages	23.4	6
Automotive tire services	23.3	6
Child care	22.0	5
Drug stores	15.9	4
Automotive service	15.7	4
Transportation services	7.6	2

Grocery stores	6.9	2
Other	90.0	21
Other	1.7	-
Total	**421.1**	**100**

COMPETITORS

Acadia Realty Trust	National Retail
Capital Automotive	Properties
DDR	One Liberty Properties
EPR Properties	Regency Centers
Federal Realty	Simon Property Group
Investment	Weingarten Realty
Kimco Realty	

HISTORICAL FINANCIALS

Company Type: Public

Income Statement

FYE: December 31

	REVENUE ($ mil.)	NET INCOME ($ mil.)	NET PROFIT MARGIN	EMPLOYEES
12/13	778.3	245.5	31.5%	116
12/12	475.5	159.1	33.5%	97
12/11	421.0	157.0	37.3%	83
12/10	345.0	130.7	37.9%	79
12/09	327.5	131.1	40.0%	72
Annual Growth	**24.2%**	**17.0%**	**—**	**12.7%**

2013 Year-End Financials

Debt ratio: 41.9%	No. of shares (mil.): 207
Return on equity: 6.3%	Dividends
Cash ($ mil.): 10	Yield: 5.8%
Current ratio: 0.27	Payout: 205.4%
Long-term debt ($ mil.): 4,166	Market value ($ mil.): 7,745

	STOCK PRICE ($) FY Close	P/E High/Low		PER SHARE ($) Earnings	Dividends	Book Value
12/13	37.33	52	35	1.06	2.18	25.96
12/12	40.21	50	40	0.86	1.78	18.08
12/11	34.96	34	27	1.05	1.74	16.93
12/10	34.20	35	25	1.01	1.72	15.64
12/09	25.91	27	15	1.03	1.71	14.27
Annual Growth	**9.6%**	**—**	**—**	**0.7%**	**6.3%**	**16.1%**

Red Hat Inc

Red Hat doffs its cap to businesses that embrace open-source computing tools. The company dominates the market for Linux the open-source computer operating system (OS) that is the chief rival to Microsoft's Windows operating system. In addition to its Red Hat Enterprise Linux OS the company's product line includes database content and collaboration management applications; server and embedded operating systems; and software development tools. Red Hat also provides consulting custom application development support and training services. The company's business model is a mix of providing free open-source software paired with subscription-based support training and integration services.

Operations

Red Hat's JBoss unit specializes in open-source middleware software including application servers and messaging systems which are used to develop and deploy applications throughout an enterprise that are accessible via the Internet intranets extranets and virtual private networks.

Financial Analysis

Red Hat's revenue continued its upward march in 2012 cresting the $1 billion mark on growth of about 25% while net income rose 36% compared with 2010. Both subscription and training and services revenue rose by about one quarter for the year on strong global demand.

Strategy

Although Red Hat originally offered support for consumer-oriented Linux products the company shifted its focus entirely to the more lucrative business of supporting and servicing Linux technologies in enterprise environments. While Linux has failed to gain much traction against Microsoft's Windows operating system in the consumer space open-source platforms have been much more successful in corporate deployments especially for back-end tasks such as managing data center operations including virtualization server and data management and enterprise application integration.

With interest in open-source technologies growing in the Asia/Pacific region in 2012 Red Hat expanded two engineering centers in India. Located in Pune and Bangalore the company's software engineering teams in India work with local universities research organizations and agencies to develop standards for and support the adoption of open source in the region.

Mergers and Acquisitions

Red Hat acquired Massachusetts-based open-source integration and messaging provider FuseSource from Progress Software for an undisclosed sum in 2012 to enhance its ability to deliver application integration products to commercial customers. Later that year it agreed to purchase ManageIQ for some $104 million to enhance its hybrid cloud management services.

In 2011 Red Hat expanded into the storage market with the purchase of California-based Gluster for more than $136 million in cash. Gluster's open-source file system enables cloud-based storage of big data. Customers such as Brightcove and Pandora Media have used the GlusterFS open-source system to store large amounts of unstructured data (pictures audio video etc.) and minimize their investment in conventional hardware-based storage systems.

HISTORY

Finnish graduate student Linus Torvalds created the Linux operating system in 1991 as a hobby. When Torvalds released its programming code free over the Internet for anyone to revise Linux quickly attracted a core base of devoted programmers —including Marc Ewing. A programmer for IBM by day Ewing developed improvements to Linux in his spare bedroom. Soon he began selling the improved operating system as Red Hat — named after a red and white Cornell lacrosse cap Ewing's grandfather had given him.

In 1994 Ewing was contacted by Robert Young who after selling typewriters and running a computer leasing company had started a UNIX newsletter. But Young saw better profit margins in catalog sales. Young's ACC Corp. bought the rights to Ewing's creation and the two went into business together. ACC Corp. was renamed Red Hat Software Inc.

The company compiled Linux's most significant improvements and distributed them on a CD-ROM and through the budding Internet. Their revenues actually came from manuals and technical support sold to new users and businesses who were challenged by the software's ever-changing source code.

By 1997 Linux —and Red Hat's package —were known only among the most militant programmers who sought alternatives to Microsoft's Windows. Hundreds of developers had continually doctored Linux online to create an operating system known for its speed and reliability.

Red Hat exploded in popularity in 1998 after Intel and Netscape both made minor investments in the company. In 1999 Compaq IBM Novell Oracle and SAP invested in Red Hat. The company went public later that year.

In 2000 Red Hat used its soaring stock as currency to acquire embedded programming specialist Cygnus Solutions for $674 million and Hell's Kitchen Systems (HKS) a maker of payment processing software. President Matthew Szulik replaced Young as CEO and Ewing stepped down as CTO.

Red Hat expanded its software products in 2001 to include database applications and an e-commerce software suite designed for midsized businesses. The following year Szulik assumed the additional role of chairman.

In late 2003 Red Hat acquired Sistina Software a supplier of data storage infrastructure software for Linux operating systems for about $31 million in stock.

The company established a government business unit in 2005; Red Hat's US government customers have included the Department of Energy and the Federal Aviation Administration. In 2006 it acquired open-source middleware developer JBoss for about $350 million adding middleware applications to its product line.

Red Hat expanded its middleware offerings in 2007 through the acquisition of MetaMatrix. Jim Whitehurst took over as president and CEO that year. In 2008 the company purchased Qumranet an Israel-based virtualization software provider for $107 million.

In mid-2010 director Hugh Shelton a retired general replaced Szulik as chairman.

The company bought data services deployment and management software developer Makara in late 2010 to speed Red Hat's internal development of tools for moving and managing enterprise applications from the networks of corporate clients to hosted facilities enabling cloud computing.

EXECUTIVES

EVP and CFO, Charles E. (Charlie) Peters, age 62, $425,000 total compensation

Vice President Human Capital And Leadership And Management Development, Delisa Alexander

Vp Corporate Marketing, Michael Chen, age 42

Vice President Treasurer, Paul Argiry

President - Products and Technologies, Paul J. Cormier, age 57, $425,000 total compensation

VP Open Source Affairs, Michael (Mike) Tiemann, age 49

Vice President Corporate Development, Michael Evans

VP Middleware Business Unit, Craig Muzilla

President CEO and Director, James M. (Jim) Whitehurst, age 47, $700,000 total compensation

EVP and Chief Technology Officer, Brian Stevens

Executive Vice President; General Counsel, Michael R. Cunningham, age 53, $375,000 total compensation

EVP of Global Sales and Services, Arun Oberoi

Executive Vice President Strategy and Corporate Marketing, Jackie Yeaney

Vice President Cloud Computing, Tim Burke

Vice President Global Channel Sales, Mark Enzweiler

Vice President, James More

Executive Assistant To Vice President, Debra Kane
Vice President And Tax Counsel, Dennis Duquette
Vice President And Medical Doctor, Mark White
Vice President And General Manager Asia Pacific
  And Japan, Dirk-peter Van Leeuwen
Vice President Government Services, Jason Smith
Vice President Business Development Public
  Sector, Lynne O'Neill
Hr Director & Vp, Karen Clark
Vice President Virtualization, Moshe Bar
Vice President And General Manager, Werner
  Knoblich
National Account Manager, Steven Forage
Senior Software Engineer Systems Engineer Vice
  President Information System, Justin Ross
Vice President North America Channels, Kirk
  Jacobsen
National Sales Manager, Steve Grubb
Regional Vice President And General, Max McLaren
Senior Vice President Of Business, Bill Doyle
Vice President Platform Business Unit, Scott
  Crenshaw
Evp Worldwide Sales, Tom Zack
Vice President Engineering, Rami Tamir
Vice President Global Services, Lain Gray
Vice President, Katrinka McCallum
Vice President Ww Training Services, Ken Goetz
Vice President, Michel Isnard
Vice President Government Operations, Paul Smith
Vice President Global Support Services, Marco Bill-
  peter
Chairman, Henry H. (Hugh) Shelton, age 72
President CEO and Director, James M. (Jim)
  Whitehurst, age 47
Board Member, Benjamin Kosnik
Board Of Directors, Eugene McDonald
Board Member, Paul Frields
Auditors: PricewaterhouseCoopersLLP

LOCATIONS

HQ: Red Hat Inc
  100 East Davie Street, Raleigh, NC 27601
Phone: 919 754-3700
Web: www.redhat.com

2014 Sales

	% of total
US	55
Other countries	45
Total	**100**

PRODUCTS/OPERATIONS

2014 Sales

	$ mil.	% of total
Subscriptions	1336.8	87
Training & services	197.8	13
Total	**1534.6**	**100**

Selected Mergers and Acquisitions

2012
  FuseSource Corp. (undisclosed price; Bedford MA;
  provider of open-source integration and messaging
  products and services)
2011
  Gluster ($136 million; Sunnyvale CA; provider of
  open-source storage systems for big data)

COMPETITORS

Apple Inc.	Microsoft
BMC Software	Novell
CA Inc.	Oracle
Hewlett-Packard	Unisys
IBM	Xandros
Mandriva	

HISTORICAL FINANCIALS

Company Type: Public

Income Statement

FYE: February 28

	REVENUE ($ mil.)	NET INCOME ($ mil.)	NET PROFIT MARGIN	EMPLOYEES
02/14	1,534.6	178.2	11.6%	6,300
02/13	1,328.8	150.2	11.3%	5,600
02/12	1,133.1	146.6	12.9%	4,500
02/11	909.2	107.2	11.8%	3,700
02/10	748.2	87.2	11.7%	3,200
Annual Growth	**19.7%**	**19.6%**	**—**	**18.5%**

2014 Year-End Financials

Debt ratio: —	No. of shares (mil.): 189
Return on equity: 11.6%	Dividends
Cash ($ mil.): 646	Yield: —
Current ratio: 1.37	Payout: —
Long-term debt ($ mil.): —	Market value ($ mil.): 11,191

	STOCK PRICE ($) FY Close	P/E High/Low	PER SHARE ($) Earnings	Dividends	Book Value
02/14	58.99	64 45	0.93	0.00	8.18
02/13	50.81	79 61	0.77	0.00	7.88
02/12	49.46	69 42	0.75	0.00	7.26
02/11	41.28	87 49	0.55	0.00	6.69
02/10	28.05	68 29	0.45	0.00	5.93
Annual Growth	**20.4%**	**— —**	**19.9%**	**—**	**8.4%**

Renewable Energy Group, Inc.

Renewable Energy Group or REG wants alternative fuel to become a regular thing for its customers. The company sells SoyPOWER brand biodiesel throughout the US controlling about 40% of US sales. Biodiesel is a clean burning fuel made from waste including vegetable oil corn grain and soybeans. REG owns four and manages five plants that make about 260 million gallons of biofuel per year; that fuel is sold to fleet operators the military and mining agriculture and home-heating companies. In addition to its production and distribution activities REG also builds biodiesel production plants for other firms.

Geographic Reach

The company biodiesel segment has facilities in Ralston Iowa; Houston Texas; Danville Illinois; Newton Iowa; Seneca Illinois; Albert Lea Minnesota; Mason City Iowa; and New Boston Texas.

Operations

REG produces most of its biodiesel from a wide variety of lower cost feedstocks including inedible corn oil used cooking oil and inedible animal fat. It also produces a smaller portion from higher-cost virgin vegetable oils. In 2012 it sold 188 million gallons of biodiesel of which 25 million gallons were purchased from third parties and resold.The company biodiesel segment gets its revenues from the purchases and sales of biodiesel and raw material feedstocks acquired from third parties sales of biodiesel produced under toll manufacturing arrangements with third party facilities sales of processed biodiesel from company facilities related by-products and renewable energy gov-

ernment incentive payments.REG's services segment offers services for managing the construction of biodiesel production facilities and managing ongoing operations of third party plants. It collects fees related to the services provided.

Sales and Marketing

The company has a national distribution system. Each of its facilities is equipped with an on-site rail loading system a truck loading system or both and a logistics and supply chain management staff for facilitating the distribution of its products. It also leases more than 330 railcars and leases biodiesel storage tanks at 18 petroleum fuel terminals.In 2012 REG had 328 customers; Pilot Flying J accounted for 36% of the REG's revenues that year.

Financial Performance

The company's revenue grew by 23% in 2012 due to higher biodiesel sales reflecting increased production capacity at its Seneca facility and the Albert Lea facility. The company did not toll manufacture any gallons in 2012 for third parties (as it did in 2011 when it tolled 5.6 million gallons at the REG Houston facility) due to the absence of federal credits. Higher revenues were partially offset by lower prices in 2012.Net income dropped by 75% in 2012 as the result of higher biodiesel costs (due to higher volumes sold) partially offset by slightly lower feedstock prices. In addition a decrease in soybean oil prices and higher heating oil prices resulted in reduced market value of its derivative financial instruments related to biodiesel sales in the fourth quarter of 2012.

Strategy

REG's expertise in design build and upgrades experience has helped the company to improve and test new production technologies that enable lower operating costs improved yields and expand its ability to use lower cost feedstocks. This expertise has also allowed the company to quickly and cost effectively upgrade and integrate the acquired biodiesel plants. It is focused on improving its production process efficiency and quality and to deploy best practices throughout its network.In 2013 the company teamed up with Dutch Hill Terminals a leading heating oil terminal in New Jersey to market biodiesel and biodiesel blended heating oil at its Clifton New Jersey location. The deal gives REG additional capacity to serve markets in the Northeast.

Biodiesel government incentives expired in December 2011 but reinstated on January 2013 retroactively for 2012 through fiscal 2013.

Mergers and Acquisitions

As a part of its long term growth strategy in 2013 REG agreed to buy Oklahoma-based Syntroleum a leader in Fischer-Tropsch gas-to-liquids and renewable diesel fuel technologies and as well as its 50%-owned subsidiary Dynamic Fuels. The deal moves REG into renewable diesel and boost its advanced biofuel business enhances its intellectual property portfolio and grows its geographic footprint and customer base.

In 2013 REG purchased a 30-million gallon per year capacity biodiesel plant in Mason City Iowa (formerly owned by Soy Energy LLC) for $17 million.

In 2012 it also acquired BullDog Biodiesel LLC (an idled 15-million gallon per year nameplate capacity biodiesel facility near Atlanta) for $2.6 million and a biorefinery in New Boston Texas for $300000.

Company Background

Bunge North America and West Central Cooperative supply the company with biowaste; they are also investors. Affiliates of West Central own about 45%. Director Scott Chesnut controls more than half the company partially through his interest in the cooperative.

REG went public in 2011 with an IPO. It used the $60 million in proceeds of purchase the Danville Illinois manufacturing plant it formerly leased.

In 2010 REG leased commercialscale biodiesel plants in Newton Iowa and Danville Illinois making the company North America's largest wholly-owned biodiesel manufacturing and marketing source. Shareholders in Central Iowa Energy and Blackhawk Biofuels approve the sale. The facilities now named REG Newton and REG Danville added an additional 75 million gallons per year of production capacity to REG's operations. The company that same year acquired another biodiesel plant from ARES Corporation in Clovis New Mexico with a production capacity of 15 million gallons per year.

The company was formed in 2003 by West Central Cooperative.

EXECUTIVES

Chairman and CEO, Jeffrey (Jeff) Stroburg, age 64
President and COO, Daniel J. Oh, age 49, $260,926 total compensation
Vice President Sales and Marketing, Gary Haer, age 60
CIO, Patrick Hammen
CFO, Chad Stone, age 44, $186,252 total compensation
Vice President Corporate Business Development & Legal Affairs, Eric Bowen, age 43
Executive Vice-president, Harold Ahrenholtz
Chairman and CEO, Jeffrey (Jeff) Stroburg, age 64

LOCATIONS

HQ: Renewable Energy Group, Inc.
416 South Bell Avenue, Ames, IA 50010
Phone: 515 239-8000
Web: www.regi.com

PRODUCTS/OPERATIONS

Selected Products

Biodiesel
Bioheat
Co-Product Purchase Inquiries
Feedstock Supplier Inquiries
Glycerin
Other Products

Selected Services

Construction/Upgrades
Conversion to Fuel
Feedstock Development
Fuel Distribution
Fuel Marketing
Operations Management

COMPETITORS

ADM	Hawkeye Energy
Abengoa Bioenergy	Holdings
BP	Imperium
Cargill	Louis Dreyfus
Extreme Biodiesel	Commodities
GeoBio Energy	Owensboro Grain
Green Brick Partners	Valero Energy

HISTORICAL FINANCIALS

Company Type: Public

Income Statement

FYE: December 31

	REVENUE ($ mil.)	NET INCOME ($ mil.)	NET PROFIT MARGIN	EMPLOYEES
12/13	1,498.1	186.3	12.4%	368
12/12	1,015.0	22.2	2.2%	279
12/11	824.0	88.8	10.8%	245
12/10	216.4	(21.5)	—	234
12/09	131.5	(60.9)	—	0
Annual Growth 83.7%		—	—	—

2013 Year-End Financials

Debt ratio: 7.1%
Return on equity: 37.0%
Cash ($ mil.): 153
Current ratio: 3.54
Long-term debt ($ mil.): 35

No. of shares (mil.): 36
Dividends
Yield: —
Payout: —
Market value ($ mil.): 418

	STOCK PRICE ($) FY Close	P/E High/Low		PER SHARE ($) Earnings	Dividends	Book Value
12/13	11.46	3	1	5.00	0.00	16.38
12/12	5.86	7	3	0.27	0.00	13.34
Annual Growth 95.6%		—	—1751.9%		—	22.8%

Repligen Corp.

Repligen replies to the needs of the pharmaceutical industry by supplying bioengineered drug ingredients. Repligen's bioprocessing business develops and commercializes proteins and other agents used in the production of biopharmaceuticals. The firm also conducts drug research activities include development of a pancreatic imaging agent and potential therapies for bipolar disorder Friedreich's ataxia (a debilitating early adulthood disease) and spinal muscular atrophy. While all of Repligen's own drugs are in the clinical development stage it does receive royalty payments from Bristol-Myers Squibb (BMS) on sales of BMS' Orencia rheumatoid arthritis drug as well as by licensing out its technologies.

Operations

Repligen receives the majority of its revenues from its bioprocessing business which primarily sells Protein A a recombinant protein used in the production of monoclonal antibodies and other biopharmaceutical manufacturing applications. Its primary customer in this area is GE Healthcare with which it has a multi-year supply agreement.

Geographic Reach

Repligen's headquarters are in Massachusetts; it also has manufacturing facilities there and in Sweden.

The US accounts for about 50% of revenue with Sweden and the UK contributing 35% and 10% respectively.

Sales and Marketing

Repligen uses its own direct sales force and partners including GE Healthcare EMD Millipore and Sigma Aldrich to sell its products to life sciences and biopharma companies.

Financial Performance

The company has seen years of revenue growth including a huge 128% spike in 2012 that continued into 2013 when Repligen reported a 9% in-

crease from $62 million to $68 million. Royalties and payments related to settling a legal matter contributed to the growth. Increased manufacturing efficiency and a good product mix particularly in Sweden helped the company post a 14% improvement in net income. Cash from operations also trended up with a $12.5 million increase due to deferred tax expenses royalties and long-term liabilities.

Strategy

Repligen is developing RG1068 a synthetic human hormone designed to detect abnormalities in pancreatic duct function as part of a process to diagnose pancreatitis and other pancreatic diseases.

In 2014 it sold its histone deacetylase inhibitor (HDI) portfolio to BioMarin Pharmaceutical for $2 million plus potential future payments if the drug is developed. HDI are currently used to treat depression and other psychological conditions but they are also being investigated to treat cancers parasites and inflammatory diseases.

Mergers and Acquisitions

In 2014 Repligen paid $24.5 million for Refine Technology to strengthen its bioprocessing business and expand its direct sales force.

EXECUTIVES

Senior Vice President Research, James R Rusche, age 61
Vice President Business Development, Daniel P Witt
President and CEO, Walter C. Herlihy, age 63, $365,000 total compensation
VP Bioprocessing Sales and Marketing, Stephen Tingley
COO, Tony J. Hunt
CFO, Jon K. Snodgres
Vice President Business Development, Howard Benjamin
Vp Medical Research, Patrice Rioux
Vice President Regulatory Affairs, Karen Jauregui
Senior Vice President, James Hureau
Treasurer, Joseph Antebi
Chairman, Karen A. Dawes
Auditors: Ernst&YoungLLP

LOCATIONS

HQ: Repligen Corp.
41 Seyon Street, Bldg.1, Suite 100, Waltham, MA 02453
Phone: 781 250-0111   **Fax:** 781 250-0115
Web: www.repligen.com

2013 Sales

	% of total
US	51
Sweden	35
UK	12
Other countries	2
Total	**100**

PRODUCTS/OPERATIONS

2013 Sales

	$ mil.	% of total
Bioprocessing	47.5	70
Royalties and other	20.7	30
Total	**68.2**	**100**

Selected Pipeline Products

RG1068 (Phase III clinical trials to help with pancreatic imaging)
RG2417 (Phase II clinical trials for treatment of bipolar disorder)
RG2833 (Preclinical trials for treatment of Friedreich' s Ataxia)

RG3039 (Preclinical trials for treatment of spinal
  muscular atrophy)
Commercial Assets
Bioprocessing Business (biologics purification)
Orencia royalties (rheumatoid arthritis)

COMPETITORS

Abbott Labs	Life Technologies
Bio-Rad Labs	Corporation
Human Genome Sciences	NeuroNova
Incyte	PDL BioPharma

HISTORICAL FINANCIALS
Company Type: Public

Income Statement
FYE: December 31

	REVENUE ($ mil.)	NET INCOME ($ mil.)	NET PROFIT MARGIN	EMPLOYEES
12/13	68.1	16.0	23.6%	116
12/12	62.2	14.1	22.7%	120
12/11*	23.4	(1.6)	—	137
03/11	27.2	(0.0)	—	66
03/10	20.9	(4.0)	—	68
Annual Growth	34.3%	—	—	14.3%

*Fiscal year change

2013 Year-End Financials

Debt ratio: —	No. of shares (mil.): 31
Return on equity: 17.1%	Dividends
Cash ($ mil.): 39	Yield: —
Current ratio: 7.64	Payout: —
Long-term debt ($ mil.): —	Market value ($ mil.): 435

	STOCK PRICE ($) FY Close	P/E High/Low	PER SHARE ($) Earnings	Dividends	Book Value
12/13	13.64	27 12	0.50	0.00	3.25
12/12	6.28	16 7	0.45	0.00	2.70
12/11*	3.47	— —	(0.05)	0.00	2.15
03/11	3.74	— —	(0.00)	0.00	2.18
03/10	4.06	— —	(0.13)	0.00	2.15
Annual Growth	35.4%	— —	—	—	10.9%

*Fiscal year change

Reserve Petroleum Co.

The Reserve Petroleum Company has petroleum
reserves of about 266870 barrels of oil. It also has
1.6 billion cu. ft. of natural gas reserves. In 2008
the oil and gas exploration and production company owned non-producing properties of more
than 262000 gross acres (90330 net acres) located in nine states. About 64800 net acres of this
land asset are in Oklahoma South Dakota and
Texas. About 53% of Reserve Petroleum's oil production in 2008 was derived from royalty interests.
The company has royalty interests in 33 gross (1.1
net) wells that were drilled and completed as producing wells. President Mason McLain owns about
10% of Reserve Petroleum.

Its exploration strategy involves purchasing
stakes in prospects developed by third parties often
exploratory prospects with whom Reserve Petroleum management has conducted business in the
past. The company develops exploratory drilling
prospects by identifying an area of interest developing geophysical information and buying leaseholds in the area. Reserve Petroleum sometimes

sell a stake in the prospect to one or more companies in the petroleum industry with one of the
purchasing firms functioning as operator. In 2008
the company participated in the drilling of 17 exploration wells.

LOCATIONS

HQ: Reserve Petroleum Co.
  6801 Broadway Ext., Suite 300, Oklahoma City, OK
  73116-9037
Phone: 405 848-7551
Web: www.reserve-petro.com

PRODUCTS/OPERATIONS

2008 Sales

	$ mil.	% of total
Oil & gas	19.7	95
Lease bonuses & other	1.0	5
Total	20.7	100

2008 Sales

	% of total
Redland Resources	20
ConocoPhillips	19
EnCana Oil & Gas	13
Luff Exploration	12
Other customers	36
Total	100

COMPETITORS

Anadarko Petroleum	Range Resources
Cabot Oil & Gas	Samson Oil
PDC Energy	

HISTORICAL FINANCIALS
Company Type: Public

Income Statement
FYE: December 31

	REVENUE ($ mil.)	NET INCOME ($ mil.)	NET PROFIT MARGIN	EMPLOYEES
12/13	18.8	6.0	32.3%	8
12/12	15.1	4.5	30.1%	8
12/11	12.9	5.2	40.7%	8
12/10	13.8	5.2	38.0%	8
12/09	9.0	1.6	17.8%	8
Annual Growth	20.2%	39.4%	—	0.0%

2013 Year-End Financials

Debt ratio: —	No. of shares (mil.): 0
Return on equity: 19.4%	Dividends
Cash ($ mil.): 10	Yield: 4.7%
Current ratio: 29.49	Payout: 52.7%
Long-term debt ($ mil.): —	Market value ($ mil.): 68

	STOCK PRICE ($) FY Close	P/E High/Low	PER SHARE ($) Earnings	Dividends	Book Value
12/13	425.00	11 8	37.90	20.00	209.11
12/12	291.01	13 10	28.30	20.00	181.50
12/11	302.00	13 8	32.77	10.00	173.20
12/10	321.00	11 7	32.51	40.00	150.43
12/09	240.00	35 21	9.92	10.00	157.91
Annual Growth	15.4%	— —	39.8%	18.9%	7.3%

Resource Capital Corp

Resource Capital is looking to pump some capital into real estate resources. The real estate investment trust (REIT) was launched in 2005 and
invests in commercial real estate debt and other
real estate-related assets including first mortgage
loans mezzanine debt and commercial and residential mortgage-backed securities. To a lesser extent
the REIT invests in commercial finance assets such
as syndicated bank loans and equipment leases.
Bank loans account for about half of the REIT's
portfolio after it disposed of its risky residential
mortgage backed securities (RMBS) investments.
The firm's investments are managed by Resource
Capital Manager a subsidiary of Resource America.

Geographic Reach
The New York-based specialty finance com-
pany's portfolio is weighted toward California: split
between the Southern (29%) and Northern (10%)
parts of the state. Texas is home to 15% of the
REIT's holdings with Arizona representing 6%.
Other states represented in its portfolio include
Florida Minnesota Nevada Utah and Washington.

Operations
The REIT managed $2.2 billion in assets at the
end of 2013 including $2 billion of assets financed
and held in collateralized debt obligations (CDOs).
The firm's portfolio is about 90% focused on first
mortgage loans (aka whole loans) on four types of
properties: multifamily (38%) retail (19%) hotel
(18%) and office (16%).

Financial Performance
After three years of increasing profitability net
income fell 28% to $46.5 million in 2012. Revenue
declined by 8% over the same period to $168.6
million on decreasing interest income from loans
partially offset by an increase in interest income on
commercial real estate. The REIT's performance in
2013 suffered from faster than anticipated pay-
down of its corporate loan portfolio.

Strategy
Resource Capital is looking to reap the benefits
of the recovery in the real estate market in 2012
and 2013 and easier access to capital. The firm invests in higher risk commercial real estate and
mezzanine debt. The REIT is primarily focused on
originating holding and managing commercial
mortgage loans and other commercial real estate-
related debt and equity investments. The Company also makes other commercial finance investments.

Mergers and Acquisitions
Resource Capital acquired Churchill Pacific
Asset Management in February 2011 adding some
$1.9 billion in assets under management. It re-
named Churchill Resource Capital Asset Management.

EXECUTIVES

Senior Vice President Commercial Lending,
  Christopher D Allen, age 47
SVP Equipment Leasing, Crit S. DeMent, age 62
President and CEO, Jonathan Z. Cohen, age 44
SVP CFO Chief Accounting Officer and Treasurer,
  David J. (Dave) Bryant, age 57, $240,000 total
  compensation
SVP Real Estate Investments, David E. Bloom, age
  50
**SVP Real Estate Investments; CEO Resource
  Real Estate,** Alan F. Feldman, age 51

SVP; President and Managing Director Resource
Financial Fund Management Inc., Jeffrey D.
Blomstrom, age 45
SVP Loan Originations; Managing Director
Resource Real Estate Funding Inc., Kyle
Geoghegan, age 46
SVP CMBS, Joan M. Sapinsley, age 63
EVP, Jeffrey F. Brotman
Vp Real Estate Investments, Kevin M Finkel, age 43
Chairman, Steven J. Kessler, age 72
Auditors: GrantThorntonLLP

LOCATIONS

HQ: Resource Capital Corp
712 5th Avenue, 12th Floor, New York, NY 10019
Phone: 212 506-3870
Web: www.resourcecapitalcorp.com

PRODUCTS/OPERATIONS

2013 Sales

	$ mil.	% of total
Interest		
Loans	99.4	58
Securities	14.3	8
Other	4.2	2
Noninterest		
Rental income	19.9	12
Gain on sale of real estate	16.6	9
Net realized gain on sales of investment securities available-for sale and loans	11.0	6
Fee income	6.2	4
Equity in net earnings of unconsolidated subsidiaries and Dividend income	1.2	1
Others	(4.1)	-
Total	**168.6**	**100**

COMPETITORS

Annaly Capital
Management
Bimini Capital
Management
Capstead Mortgage
MFA Financial

Newcastle Investment
Redwood Trust
Walter Investment
Management
iStar Financial Inc

HISTORICAL FINANCIALS

Company Type: Public

Income Statement

FYE: December 31

	REVENUE ($ mil.)	NET INCOME ($ mil.)	NET PROFIT MARGIN	EMPLOYEES
12/13	152.0	46.4	30.6%	0
12/12	166.4	64.4	38.7%	0
12/11	124.5	37.7	30.3%	0
12/10	103.9	19.4	18.7%	0
12/09	97.5	6.3	6.5%	0
Annual Growth	**11.7%**	**64.5%**	—	—

2013 Year-End Financials

Debt ratio: 57.7%
Return on equity: 6.7%
Cash ($ mil.): 273
Current ratio: 2.88
Long-term debt ($ mil.): 1,242

No. of shares (mil.): 127
Dividends
Yield: 13.4%
Payout: 166.6%
Market value ($ mil.): 759

	STOCK PRICE ($) FY Close	P/E High/Low		PER SHARE ($) Earnings	Dividends	Book Value
12/13	5.93	21	16	0.33	0.80	6.05
12/12	5.60	9	7	0.71	0.80	5.83
12/11	5.61	14	8	0.53	1.00	5.38
12/10	7.38	19	12	0.41	1.00	5.99
12/09	4.92	25	6	0.25	1.15	6.26
Annual Growth	**4.8%**	—	—	**7.2%**	**(8.7%)**	**(0.9%)**

REX American Resources Corp

REX American Resources Corporation has gone from retail to renewables. The company formerly REX Stores closed its chain of retail appliance and electronics stores to move in a major way into the alternative energy —mainly ethanol —business. In 2013 the company has about $71 million investments in ethanol producers Big River Resources LLC and Patriot Holdings LLC; and invested about $105 million in its four ethanol entities. REX American's consolidated ethanol entities owned a combined 408 acres of land and two facilities had an annual nameplate capacity of 100 million gallons of ethanol each.

Operations
The company operates through two segments: alternative energy and real estate. REX American derives almost of all its revenues from the alternative energy segment.

REX American has interests in seven ethanol production facilities which shipped a total of 737 million gallons of ethanol in 2013. The company's effective ownership of the trailing twelve-month gallons shipped by the ethanol production facilities in which it has ownership interests was about 262 million gallons in 2013. On the real estate side of the ledger the company has lease agreements as landlord for four owned former retail stores (51000 square feet); and seven owned former retail stores (86000 square feet).

Financial Performance
REX American's revenues increased by 1% in 2013 thanks to higher sales in the alternative energy segment fueled by increased volume (partially offset by decreased average selling price) and higher food grade corn oil sales. Its modified distillers grains sales decreased due to declined volume produced as well as lower selling prices. Net income increased to $35 million in 2013 (compared to a loss of $2 million in 2012) due to lower cost of sales and higher Equity in Income from its equity investments in Big River and Patriot which were favorably impacted from the increased crush spread experienced in the ethanol market. This was partially offset by increased provision for income taxes which was impacted by the noncontrolling interests of the companies REX consolidates and by noncontrolling interests. Cash flow from operating activities increased by $47 million in 2013 primarily due to increased net income and higher accounts receivables. The company has seen growth in revenues since 2009 primarily the result of higher volumes due to increased investments made towards the improving affiliates' performance.

Strategy
REX American evaluates various investment opportunities including energy related agricultural or other ventures that fit its investment criteria It seeks to identify quality ethanol plant opportunities located near adequate feedstock supply with good transportation capabilities or other economically beneficial attributes and that use leading ethanol production technology.

In 2013 REX American invested in four ethanol production entities including One Earth Energy LLC (for a 74% ownership) NuGen Energy LLC (for an additional 50% ownership) Patriot Holdings LLC (for a 27% ownership) and Big River Resources LLC (for a 10% ownership).

Looking to diversify its operations in 2013 the company invested $1 million in eSteam a new technology utilizing steam to extract deep heavy oil. It continues to investigate investment opportunities in various companies and industries. Through wholly owned subsidiary REX I.P. LLC the company also entered into a joint venture with Hytken HPGP LLC to file and defend patents for eSteam technology relating to heavy oil and oil sands production methods and to commercially exploit the technology to generate license fees royalty income and development opportunities. It owns 60% and Hytken HPGP owns 40% of the entity named Future Energy LLC an Ohio limited liability company.

Company Background
In 2010 Rex American acquired a 48% stake in NuGen Energy for about $22 million. NuGen operates a 100 million gallon annual capacity ethanol plant in Marion South Dakota.

After fully divesting its retail holdings in 2009 the company focused on acquiring ethanol production facilities. By 2010 REX American had some $125 million invested in seven corn- or sorghum-based ethanol production plants controlling about 190 million gallons of production capacity per year.

The company began investing in ethanol production facilities in 2006 while it was still selling televisions and washing machines in small and medium-size markets across the US. REX actually began phasing out its retail operations in 2000 closing more than 100 of its underperforming units during the early part of that decade. In 2007 the company began planning in earnest to fully exit the retail business in favor of alternative fuels. It completed that process in mid-2009 selling almost all of its company-owned retail properties and terminating leases on the rest of its stores.

Chairman and CEO Stuart Rose owns about 20% of REX American with capital investment funds holding another 40%.

EXECUTIVES

VP Finance CFO and Treasurer, Douglas L. Bruggeman, age 53, $275,700 total compensation
Chairman and CEO, Stuart A. Rose, age 59, $154,500 total compensation
President and COO, Zafar A. Rizvi, $199,070 total compensation
Chairman and CEO, Stuart A. Rose, age 59
Board Member, Mervyn L Alphonso
Auditors: Deloitte&ToucheLLP

LOCATIONS

HQ: REX American Resources Corp
7720 Paragon Road, Dayton, OH 45459
Phone: 937 276-3931   Fax: 937 276-8643
Web: www.rexamerican.com

PRODUCTS/OPERATIONS

2013 Sales

	$ mil.	% of total
Alternative Energy	665.6	100
Real Estate	0.5	-
Total	**666.1**	**100**

COMPETITORS

ADM
Badger State Ethanol
Golden Grain

Green Brick Partners
Green Plains
Pacific Ethanol

HISTORICAL FINANCIALS

Company Type: Public

Income Statement

FYE: January 31

	REVENUE ($ mil.)	NET INCOME ($ mil.)	NET PROFIT MARGIN	EMPLOYEES
01/14	666.0	35.0	5.3%	105
01/13	657.7	(2.3)	—	102
01/12	409.9	28.2	6.9%	105
01/11	301.6	5.0	1.7%	58
01/10	170.2	8.6	5.1%	114
Annual Growth	40.6%	41.9%	—	(2.0%)

2014 Year-End Financials

Debt ratio: 17.7%
Return on equity: 13.3%
Cash ($ mil.): 105
Current ratio: 4.63
Long-term debt ($ mil.): 63

No. of shares (mil.): 8
Dividends
 Yield: —
 Payout: —
Market value ($ mil.): 332

	STOCK PRICE ($) FY Close	P/E High/Low		PER SHARE ($) Earnings	Dividends	Book Value
01/14	40.96	11	4	4.29	0.00	34.48
01/13	21.84	—	—	(0.28)	0.00	30.22
01/12	25.70	8	4	3.08	0.00	30.31
01/11	15.06	36	25	0.52	0.00	26.08
01/10	15.10	16	7	0.91	0.00	25.15
Annual Growth	28.3%	—	—	47.4%	—	8.2%

RigNet Inc

Because no one wants to be stranded on a desert island much less an offshore oil rig there's RigNet. A telecommunications company that caters mainly to the oil and gas drilling industry it provides Cisco-powered Internet protocol-based voice fax video and high-speed Internet to remote offshore and land-based locations. It serves drilling rigs and production platforms in the Gulf of Mexico South America West Africa the Middle East the North Sea and Asia. RigNet's 400 customers such as Noble Corporation (12% of sales) span 1000 remote sites in more than 30 countries. Customers outside the US make up the majority of sales.

Operations

RigNet estimates that it has about a third of the market share of the types of rigs it services (jackups semi-submersibles and drillships) and about a 17% market share in its onshore sites in the Continental US.

The company does not own any of the offsite infrastructure or equipment such as satellites opting instead to buy bandwidth from satellite operators such as Intelsat and other telecommunications providers. It focuses on providing the equipment and infrastructure deployed on the sites themselves. This strategy enables better quality control while keeping capital investments at a minimum. RigNet is one of a scant 1% of Cisco service providers in the world to hold the Cisco Powered Network designation which is granted based on meeting specific quality-of-service performance metrics.

It also provides a range of ancillary services in support of its core communications service. It manages equipment installation software configuration systems testing video conferencing Wi-Fi hotspots and Web access.

Geographic Reach

RigNet operates in the US from two offices in Houston and Lafayette Louisiana both hubs for the Gulf Coast offshore oil industry. Customers outside the US make up about 75% of sales. It has international offices in Australia Brazil Nigeria Norway Qatar Scotland and Singapore.

Financial Performance

Overall revenues rose almost 50% in 2012 to $162 million due to increased sales to new and existing customers with upgrades and value-added services. RigNet has been profitable since 2011.

Strategy

RigNet's strategy ticks all the boxes one might expect: it seeks to expand its take of offshore and onshore drilling rig clients cross-sell to similar customers on existing sites grow its products and services and explore related markets in the energy sector for its remote communications offerings using organic and inorganic growth.

Mergers and Acquisitions

In 2012 RigNet acquired Nessco a provider of telecommunications systems integration services for the oil and gas industry based in Scotland. The $46.4 million cash deal gives RigNet a broader range of communications offerings across the entire spectrum of oil and gas operations. Nessco's technologies include closed-circuit TV digital radio fiber-optic marine satellite and voice and data communications networks.

Ownership

Norwegian investment firm Cubera Private Equity owns almost 30% of RigNet's stock. Denver-based VC firm Altira Group owns anouth 15% and T. Rowe Price has a 12% stake.

EXECUTIVES

SVP and CFO, Martin L. (Marty) Jimmerson, age 51, $276,275 total compensation
President and CEO, Mark B. Slaughter, age 56, $365,393 total compensation
Group VP Eastern Hemisphere, Hector Maytorena, age 53, $204,500 total compensation
VP Energy Maritime, Pal Jensen
Group VP Western Hemisphere, James (Jim) Crenshaw, $191,026 total compensation
Group VP Telecommunications Systems Integration, Gerry Gutierrez
SVP Business Services and CTO, Morten Hagland Hansen
CIO, Sheldon Mundle
Vice President Corporate Development, Bradley Alexander
Vice President Of Sales And Business, Chad Winkle
Region Vice President Middle East, Ricky Begnaud
Vice President Of Finance And Billing, Jeff Zanardi
Vice President Engineering, Tony Ton
Vice President And Chief Accounting, Kevin Gerland
Vice President Of Tax, Tonya McDermott
Vice President, Leslile Babin
Vice President Of Production And Field, Brian Komasinski
Vice President Global Business Development, Michael Hall
Vice President Human Resources, Oscar German
Region Vice President Uk And Sub, Andrew Byers
Vice President Vice President Of Production And Field Development, Brian Keefover
Chairman, James H. Browning, age 64
Auditors: Deloitte&ToucheLLP

LOCATIONS

HQ: RigNet Inc
 1880 S. Dairy Ashford, Suite 300, Houston, TX 77077-4760
Phone: 281 674-0100
Web: www.rig.net

2012 Sales

	$ mil.	% of total
US	37.0	23
Other countries	124.7	77
Total	**161.7**	**100**

PRODUCTS/OPERATIONS

2012 Sales

	$ mil.	% of total
Europe/Africa	65.2	40
Americas	49.9	31
Middle East/Asia Pacific	46.6	29
Total	**161.7**	**100**

COMPETITORS

Blast Energy Services	Inmarsat
Harris CapRock	Schlumberger

HISTORICAL FINANCIALS

Company Type: Public

Income Statement

FYE: December 31

	REVENUE ($ mil.)	NET INCOME ($ mil.)	NET PROFIT MARGIN	EMPLOYEES
12/13	220.7	16.3	7.4%	481
12/12	161.6	11.8	7.3%	375
12/11	109.3	9.5	8.7%	243
12/10	92.9	(15.5)	—	204
12/09	80.9	(19.9)	—	197
Annual Growth	28.5%	—	—	25.0%

2013 Year-End Financials

Debt ratio: 24.9%
Return on equity: 14.4%
Cash ($ mil.): 59
Current ratio: 2.83
Long-term debt ($ mil.): 51

No. of shares (mil.): 17
Dividends
 Yield: —
 Payout: —
Market value ($ mil.): 826

	STOCK PRICE ($) FY Close	P/E High/Low		PER SHARE ($) Earnings	Dividends	Book Value
12/13	47.93	47	20	0.93	0.00	7.23
12/12	20.43	27	20	0.70	0.00	6.49
12/11	16.74	32	21	0.57	0.00	5.39
12/10	13.63	—	—	(3.38)	0.00	4.59
Annual Growth	52.1%	—	—	—	—	16.4%

Roadrunner Transportation Systems Inc

Running your cargo down the road is Roadrunner Transportation Systems (RRTS) business. The company offers less-than-truckload (LTL) freight transportation which combines freight from multiple shippers into a single truckload. In addition it arranges the transportation of truckload freight as well as provides logistics services. RRTS caters to small and mid-size shippers and some large national accounts throughout the US via a network of service centers. Rather than owning trucks and trailers the company relies on a network of independent contractors and on purchased transportation capacity.

Geographic Reach

RRTS operates through nearly 35 LTL service centers and nearly 30 TL service centers across the US. It also has 20 dispatch offices.

Operations

RRTS operates through three chief segments: Less-than-Truckload Truckload and Logistics and Transportation Management Solutions. The less-than-truckload (LTL) business manages the pickup consolidation linehaul deconsolidation and delivery of LTL shipments throughout the US and into Mexico Puerto Rico and Canada.

Within the truckload and logistics (TL) business it arranges for the pickup delivery and inventory management of TL freight. Transportation management solutions offers access to the most cost-effective and time-sensitive modes of transportation within the company's broad network.

Sales and Marketing

In addition to its 75 independent brokerage agents RRTS sells its transportation and logistics services through over 200 sales personnel located throughout the US and Canada. It is focused on expanding its sales force to new geographic markets where it lacks a strong presence.

Financial Performance

With the recession in its rear-view window RRTS has been enjoying unprecedented growth over the years. From 2012 to 2013 its revenues increased 27% from $1.07 billion to $1.36 billion its highest total in company history. RRTS saw its profits surge from nearly $37 million to peak at a record-setting $49 million from 2012 to 2013.

The sizable growth for 2012 and 2013 was attributed to increased TL and LTL revenues. The company has also been helped by previous acquisitions an uptick in the number of loads a year-over-year increase in revenue per load and the ongoing expansion of its TL agent network.

Strategy

RRTS' recent growth has largely been attributed to strategic acquisitions. In 2014 RRTS acquired Rich Logistics a provider of truckload and expedited services based in Little Rock Arkansas. In addition RRTS obtained Everett Transportation and certain assets of Keith Everett. The total enterprise value of the transaction was about $48 million.

In 2012 it obtained A&A Express a refrigerated truckload services provider in South Dakota for $24 million. Months later the company scooped up R&M Transportation and Sortino Transportation truckload services providers based in Nebraska for $24 million. Also in 2012 RRTS picked up Minnesota-based D&E Transport a flatbed carrier with expertise in transporting agriculture products and New Hampshire-based Capital Transportation Logistics for $6.25 million.

Looking ahead RRTS intends to maintain its asset-free approach to the transportation business. Under this strategy the company uses contractors and buys capacity from other carriers when needed as opposed to owning its own fleet thereby more efficiently deploying resources to meet demand and generating better returns.

Company Background

RRTS took its current shape in 2005 when investors led by Thayer | Hidden Creek bought

Dawes Transport and Roadrunner Freight Systems and combined them to form Roadrunner Dawes Freight Systems. The Roadrunner Transportation Systems name was adopted in mid-2008 as part of a comprehensive rebranding campaign.

EXECUTIVES

Vp Human Resources, Paul S Hoff
VP CFO Secretary and Treasurer, Peter R. Armbruster, $281,154 total compensation
President and CEO, Mark A. DiBlasi, $457,308 total compensation
President Truckload, Brian J. van Helden, $296,154 total compensation
EVP Sales, Mark T. Peterson
VP Information Technology and CIO, Ed Fares
President Less-than-Truckload (LTL), Grant Crawford
President Truckload Logistics (TL), Patrick McKay
President Transportation Management Solutions (TMS), Kevin Charlebois
Western Regional Vp, Roy Brace
Vice President Sales Marketing, Scott Dobak
Eastern Regional Account Vice President, Russell Williams
Vice President Flatbed Specialized Div, Jesse Kent
Vice President Integrated Solutions, David Floyd
Executive Vice President Of Strategy, Liliana Soto
Vice President Of Safety Compliance, Michael Humm
Regional Vice President, Steve Thebeau
Vice President Global Sales, Michael Venegoni
Vice President Sales And Marketing, Don Foust
VP CFO Secretary and Treasurer, Peter R. Armbruster
Chairman, Scott D. Rued
Auditors: Deloitte&ToucheLLP

LOCATIONS

HQ: Roadrunner Transportation Systems Inc
4900 S. Pennsylvania Ave., Cudahy, WI 53110
Phone: 414 615-1500   **Fax:** 414 615-1513
Web: www.rrts.com
Atlanta
Baltimore
Boston
Charlotte NC
Chicago
Cincinnati
Cleveland
Dallas
Detroit
Houston
Indianapolis
Los Angeles
Memphis
Milwaukee
Minneapolis/St. Paul
Nashville TN
Philadelphia
Pittsburgh
Portland OR
San Francisco
Seattle
St. Louis

PRODUCTS/OPERATIONS

2012 Sales

	$ mil.	% of total
Less-than-truckload (LTL)	511.0	47
Truckload (TL) & logistics	476.6	44
Transportation Management Solutions (TMS)	91.6	9
Adjustments	(5.8)	-
Total	**1073.4**	**100**

COMPETITORS

ArcBest	FedEx
C.H. Robinson	Landstar System
Worldwide	Menlo Worldwide
CRST International	Saia
Central Freight Lines	Schneider Logistics
Con-way Freight	Total Quality
Covenant	Logistics
Transportation	Transplace
Echo Global	UPS
Estes Express	YRC Worldwide

HISTORICAL FINANCIALS

Company Type: Public

Income Statement

FYE: December 31

	REVENUE ($ mil.)	NET INCOME ($ mil.)	NET PROFIT MARGIN	EMPLOYEES
12/13	1,361.4	49.0	3.6%	2,756
12/12	1,073.3	37.5	3.5%	2,395
12/11	843.6	25.8	3.1%	1,848
12/10	632.0	3.5	0.6%	1,054
12/09	450.3	0.1	0.0%	925
Annual Growth	**31.9%**	**313.9%**	**—**	**31.4%**

2013 Year-End Financials

Debt ratio: 22.0%
Return on equity: 10.9%
Cash ($ mil.): 5
Current ratio: 1.92
Long-term debt ($ mil.): 181

No. of shares (mil.): 37
Dividends
Yield: —
Payout: —
Market value ($ mil.): 1,012

	STOCK PRICE ($) FY Close	P/E High/Low	PER SHARE ($) Earnings	Dividends	Book Value
12/13	26.95	23 13	1.29	0.00	13.32
12/12	18.14	16 12	1.16	0.00	11.41
12/11	14.13	20 15	0.82	0.00	9.64
12/10	14.46	135 95	0.11	0.00	8.81
Annual Growth	**23.1%**	**—**	**—127.2%**	**—**	**14.8%**

Rogers Corp.

Rogers lives in a material world and it is a materials company. The company's specialty materials are used in a variety of electronic and consumer products. Its products include printed circuit board laminates and polyester-based industrial laminates which are used in wireless communications systems including hand-held devices GPS and direct broadcast TV. Rogers' high-performance foams include urethane and silicone foams used for making vehicle gaskets and seals communication devices computers and footwear insoles. It also makes high-performance elastomer components sold to OEMs in various markets including ground transportation office equipment and consumer industries.

Geographic Reach

A global player Rogers has operations in the US (Arizona Connecticut and Illinois) Europe (Belgium and Germany) and Asia (China Japan Singapore South Korea and Taiwan). In 2013 non-US based customers accounted for 78% of the company's total sales.

Operations

The company operates in three segments: High Performance Foams (polyurethane and silicone foam products sold to fabricators and OEMs); Printed Circuit Materials (circuit board laminate products for high frequency high performance applications to meet the demands of increasing speed complexity and power in analog digital and microwave equipment); and Power Electronics Solutions (Curamik Electronics Solutions and Power Distribution Systems). Curamik Electronics Solutions makes direct copper bonded ceramic substrate products used in the design of intelligent power management devices such as insulated gate bipolar transistor modules. Power Distribution Systems makes busbar power distribution products for manufacturers of high power electrical inverter and converter systems for use in mass transit and clean technology applications (such as electric vehicles solar farms and wind turbines).

Sales and Marketing

Rogers sells through direct channels. It sold its products to 3000 customers worldwide in 2013. The company's largest customer accounted for 4% of sales.

Financial Performance

After experiencing a revenue dip in 2012 due to a drop in Curamik Electronics Solutions and Power Distribution Systems' revenues in fiscal 2013 Rogers' revenues grew by 8% due to the significantly improved performance of the restructured Power Electronics Solutions operating segment (20% up on 2012 as the result of higher sales of technology applications across a number of markets including hybrid and electric vehicles solar and wind applications and industrial motor drives). The Printed Circuit Materials segment was up by 14%. These increases were partially offset by a 6% drop in High Performance Foams net sales.In 2013 the company's net income dropped by 45% due to higher operating expenses and higher income tax expenses.That year the company's operating cash inflow increased to $78.01 million (from $40.04 million in 2012) due to a change in working capital as a result of cash generated from accounts payable and other accrued expenses and inventories.

Strategy

The company focuses on offering advanced high-tech products at competitive prices in markets around the globe. It also seeks to be close to its customers marketing its products through direct sales channels in concentrated areas within its three major geographic regions. Rogers pursues growth organically by expanding its product line and market share as well as growth through acquisitions.

Its current strategy for growth focuses on developing high-tech products for industries involved in the Internet mass transit and clean technology. The growth of mobile devices for example has driven sales of one of the company's latest product brand lines its PORON molded components. In addition to being used in mobile devices such as iPADs and iPhones the shock-absorbing material is also used in sports apparel to protect athletes from crashes. The company's busbar products are used primarily in power distribution systems for mass transit and clean technology. It manufactures these components under the RO-LINX brand name.

In 2014 the Advanced Circuit Materials Division launched ROG Mobile a free mobile app for Apple and Android devices. The new app allows users to access Rogers' calculators literature technical papers and the ability to order samples. That unit launched COOLSPAN Thermally & Electrically Conductive Adhesive Film a thermosetting epoxy based silver filled adhesive film used to bond circuit boards to heavy metal backplanes heat sink coins and RF module housings.

As part of company's long-term strategy in 2014 Rogers and Northeastern University established the Rogers Innovation Center at Northeastern's George J. Kostas Research Institute for Homeland Security in Burlington Massachusetts. The center conducts complementary research and development initiatives in advanced materials with a focus on early stage technical and commercial development of new high-tech materials products.

To improve operational efficiency in 2013 the management of the Curamik Electronic Solutions and Power Distribution Systems operations were combined under one segment (Power Electronics Solutions) and the former operating segments became product lines.

Mergers and Acquisitions

In 2014 the company agreed to acquire Arlon LLC from Handy & Harman Ltd. for $157 million. The deal adds Arlon's complementary capabilities and technologies in circuit materials and engineered silicones.

Company Background

In Asia it formed a strategic alliance with Hitachi Chemical in 2011 to provide high-speed digital printed circuit materials. The materials produced help meet the growing demand for increased speed in Internet data and video transmission.

In 2011 Rogers acquired Curamik Electronics a manufacturer of power electronic substrate products in Eschenbach Germany for $153 million. Curamik Electronics is a global leader for the development of direct copper bonded ceramic substrate products which are used in industrial motor drives wind and solar energy converters and hybrid electric vehicle drive systems. The acquisition enhanced Rogers' existing power electronic products portfolio.

In late 2011 Rogers ceased operations at its underperforming Thermal Management Solutions segment after failing to gain traction in the market and having problems with the manufacturing process. With the acquisition of Curamik Electronics in 2011 Rogers restructured its business segments to add Power Electronics Solutions as one of its three core strategic units along with High Performance Foams and Printed Circuit Materials. Curamik Electronic Solutions and Power Distribution Systems comprise the Power Electronics Solutions business segment.

Rogers was founded in 1832 as a materials manufacturer for the textile industry by Peter Rogers.

HISTORY

In 2010 the company acquired South Korea-based high-performance polyurethane foam manufacturing firm SK Otis Co. Ltd. a unit of SK Chemicals. The deal extends Rogers specialty chemicals portfolio and gives the company access to a fast growing Korean market.

EXECUTIVES

Vp Logistics, Michael L Cooper, age 63
SVP and CTO, Robert C. (Bob) Daigle, age 51, $320,016 total compensation
VP Finance and CFO, David Mathieson, age 56
President and CEO, Bruce D. Hoechner, age 53, $490,773 total compensation
President Enterprise Business Unit, Nitin Kawale
VP Advanced Circuit Materials Division, Jeffrey M. Grudzien, age 52, $276,543 total compensation
VP High Performance Foams Division, John C. Quinn

VP Power Electronics Solutions; President Rogers Asia, Helen Zhang
National Accounts Manager, Elizabeth Simon
Vice President Information Technology, Scott Pifer
Vice President Information Technology, Scott Matherly
Vice President Of Research, Bob Truong
Vice President, John Ambrogi
Director Of Finance Nbd Treasurer, Paul B Middleton, age 48
Auditors: Ernst&YoungLLP

LOCATIONS

HQ: Rogers Corp.
P.O. Box 188, One Technology Drive, Rogers, CT 06263-0188
Phone: 860 774-9605
Web: www.rogerscorp.com

2013 Sales

	$ mil.	% of total
Asia	276.0	51
Europe	132.1	25
US	118.3	22
Other regions and countries	11.1	2
Total	**537.5**	**100**

PRODUCTS/OPERATIONS

2013 Sales

	$ mil.	% of total
Printed Circuit Materials	185.0	35
High Performance Foams	168.1	31
Power Electronic Solutions	160.7	30
Other Products	23.7	4
Total	**537.5**	**100**

Selected Products and Brands

High Performance Foams
  Plate backing and mounts for printing plates (R/bak)
  Silicon foams and sponges (BISCO)
  Urethane and silicon foams for high-impact cushioning gaskets and seals portable communications devices computers (PORON)
Printed Circuit Materials
  Flexible circuit materials (R/flex)
  Printed circuit board materials (DUROID ULTRALAM)
Power Electronics Solutions
  Curamik Electronics Solutions
  Direct copper bonded (DCB) ceramic substrate products
  Power distribution systems
  Busbar products used in mass transit and clean technology (RO-LINX)
Other Polymer Products
  Elastomer rollers and belts (ENDUR)
  Floats for fuel-level sensors (NITROPHYL)

Selected Mergers and Acquisitions

2011
Curamik Electronics GmbH ($153 million; Eschenbach Germany; power electronic substrate products manufacturer)

COMPETITORS

Hexcel	Kingboard
Honeywell Electronic Materials	Park Electrochemical
	Plexus
Insulectro	Vesuvius

HISTORICAL FINANCIALS
Company Type: Public

Income Statement

	REVENUE ($ mil.)	NET INCOME ($ mil.)	NET PROFIT MARGIN	EMPLOYEES
12/13	537.4	37.7	7.0%	2,500
12/12	498.7	68.6	13.8%	2,400
12/11	553.1	37.0	6.7%	2,600
12/10	379.1	34.5	9.1%	1,940
12/09	291.8	(62.8)	—	1,735
Annual Growth	16.5%	—	—	9.6%

2013 Year-End Financials

Debt ratio: 10.6%
Return on equity: 7.6%
Cash ($ mil.): 191
Current ratio: 4.19
Long-term debt ($ mil.): 67

No. of shares (mil.): 17
Dividends
  Yield: —
  Payout: —
Market value ($ mil.): 1,098

	STOCK PRICE ($) FY Close	P/E High/Low	PER SHARE ($) Earnings	Dividends	Book Value
12/13	61.50	29 18	2.13	0.00	31.11
12/12	49.66	12 8	4.04	0.00	25.68
12/11	36.86	22 16	2.21	0.00	20.85
12/10	38.25	17 11	2.16	0.00	20.87
12/09	30.31	— —	(4.01)	0.00	18.61
Annual Growth	19.4%	— —	—	—	13.7%

Rose Rock Midstream L P

A rose by any other name would smell as sweet or so says Rose Rock Midstream the new name for SemCrude L.P. Rose Rock Midstream was established in 2011 to take over the assets of Sem-Crude the storage and pipeline division of Sem-Group. Rose Rock Midstream's new assets include SemCrude's crude oil storage terminal in Cushing Oklahoma; its gathering and transportation system in Kansas and Oklahoma; its Bakken Shale operations and its Platteville Colorado crude oil unloading facility. The only midstream operation Rose Rock won't handle is the White Cliffs Pipeline which will continue to be 51%-owned by Sem-Crude Pipeline L.L.C. In 2014 Rose Rock Midstream acquired trucking assets from a unit of Chesapeake Energy.

Rose Rock Midstream used the net proceeds from its initial public offering to pay back Sem-Group for the partnership interests in SemCrude L.P. SemGroup also used the proceeds to pay down two loans totaling $275 million.

SemGroup filed for bankruptcy in 2008 and has been selling off and spinning off noncore assets beginning with SemGroup Energy Partners which was renamed Blueknight Energy Partners in 2009. Rose Rock Midstream was formed as a master limited partnership (MLP) a publicly traded legal entity exempt from paying corporate income taxes. MLPs are specific to the energy industry and enjoy tax-exempt status provided they pay taxable quarterly distributions to shareholders. As an MLP Rose Rock Midstream and its operating subsidiary Rose Rock Midstream Operating LLC don't have

any employees and are managed by a general partner SemGroup.

The company's crude oil terminal in Cushing Oklahoma has a storage capacity of 5 million barrels and is undergoing expansion to hold an additional 1.95 million barrels by 2013. About 95% of its storage is under long-term contracts with third parties none of which expire before 2015. It also owns a 640-mile crude oil gathering and transportation pipeline system across Kansas and Oklahoma that connects to the Cushing terminal and other third-party pipelines and refineries; a crude oil gathering storage transportation and marketing business in the Bakken Shale in North Dakota and Montana that handles about 5800 barrels of crude oil per day; and a 10-lane crude oil truck unloading facility in Platteville Colorado that connects to SemCrude Pipeline's White Cliffs Pipeline. The Platteville facility has a storage capacity of 120000 barrels and is also undergoing expansion to store an additional 100000 barrels and add six more truck unloading lanes by 2013. The whole company's operations depend on a small number of customers; three companies accounted for 69% of sales in 2010.

EXECUTIVES

President CEO and Director, Norman J. (Norm) Szydlowski, age 63
COO and Director, Peter L. Schwiering, age 70
Auditors: BDOUSALLP

LOCATIONS

HQ: Rose Rock Midstream L P
  Two Warren Place, 6120 South Yale Avenue, Suite 700, Tulsa, OK 74136-4216
Phone: 918 524-7700
Web: www.rrmidstream.com

PRODUCTS/OPERATIONS

2010 Sales

$ mil		% of total
Products	158.3	76
Services	49.4	34
Other	.4	-
Total	**208.1**	**100**

COMPETITORS

ConocoPhillips
Enbridge Energy
Enterprise Products
Magellan Midstream
National Cooperative
  Refinery Association
NuStar Energy
Plains All American
  Pipeline
Sunoco Logistics
Tesoro Logistics

HISTORICAL FINANCIALS
Company Type: Public

Income Statement

	REVENUE ($ mil.)	NET INCOME ($ mil.)	NET PROFIT MARGIN	EMPLOYEES
12/13	766.5	36.7	4.8%	230
12/12	620.4	23.9	3.9%	80
12/11	431.3	23.2	5.4%	80
12/10	208.0	23.4	11.3%	0
12/09	10.6	1.2	12.1%	0
Annual Growth	191.5%	131.3%	—	—

2013 Year-End Financials

Debt ratio: 27.3%
Return on equity: 12.4%
Cash ($ mil.): 15
Current ratio: 1.10
Long-term debt ($ mil.): 245

No. of shares (mil.): 29
Dividends
  Yield: 4.4%
  Payout: 98.4%
Market value ($ mil.): 1,124

	STOCK PRICE ($) FY Close	P/E High/Low	PER SHARE ($) Earnings	Dividends	Book Value
12/13	38.70	25 19	1.66	1.72	9.66
12/12	31.47	24 14	1.40	1.21	18.37
12/11	20.58	343319	0.06	0.00	17.80
Annual Growth	37.1% (26.3%)		——426.0%	—	—

Rosetta Resources, Inc.

Rosetta Resources is hoping that its hard work translates into oil and natural gas discoveries. The company which was built onCalpine Corporation's former domestic oil and natural gas exploration assets primarily focuses on developing acreage and production and Texas. In 2012 the company reported estimated proved reserves of 201 million barrels of which 37% was proved developed. Calpine (which spun off its US oil and gas business in 2005) accounted for 12% of Rosetta Resources' revenues in 2012. The company's management is largely made up of former Calpine employees.
Geographic Reach
The company's operations are in South Texas; its largest producing area is the Eagle Ford shale play.
Operations
In 2012 Rosetta Resources owned 72000 net acres in South Texas. Its production in South Texas comes primarily from the Eagle Ford area which averaged 35.9 million barrels of oil equivalent that day in 2012 an increase of 67% over 2011.
Financial Performance
The company's revenues grew by 37% in 2012 due to a large growth in oil sales NGL sales and derivative instruments offset by a drop in revenues from natural gas sales. Oil revenues grew due to higher oil and NGL production in the Eagle Ford and higher realized prices. The increase in oil production was primarily attributable to higher production from the Gates Ranch and Klotzman wells in the Eagle Ford.Natural gas revenues decreased in 2012 due to lower realized prices partially offset by higher natural gas production.
That year derivative instruments reported realized (cash settlements associated with commodity derivative contracts) and unrealized derivative gains (changes in fair value on commodity derivative contracts and the reclassification of commodity hedging gains) of $20.9 million and $19.6 million respectively.
Higher revenues helped Rosetta Resources' net income jump by about 59% in 2012 as increased sales outpaced higher operating costs and expenses.
Strategy
The company is focusing on the lucrative Eagle Ford Shale Play and divested certain gas-based assets that it believes did not offer the same investment opportunities or rates of return as its unconventional resources. For example in 2012 it sold

its Lobo assets and a portion of its Olmos assets in South Texas for $95 million.

Rosetta Resources added 65.6 million barrels of oil equivalent of proved reserves in the Eagle Ford in 2012 by drilling and completing 37 successful wells and by adding 54 proved undeveloped locations. The company completed 15 producing wells and added 47 proved undeveloped locations in the Gates Ranch area. It also added proved reserves in 2012 at Adele Dubose (two proved producing) Briscoe Ranch (three proved producing and five proved undeveloped) Klotzman (14 proved developed) Lasseter & Eppright (one proved developed) and Light Ranch (two proved developed and two proved undeveloped).

It is also using the cash generated from the Eagle Ford activities to help it target new drilling opportunities elsewhere.

Mergers and Acquisitions

In this regard in 2013 Rosetta Resources acquired Permian Basin assets from Comstock Resources for $811 million.

Company Background

Historically Rosetta Resources tapped into the conventional reserves previously drilled by Calpine while developing unconventional reserves (such as shale plays) to get a better return on investment. The company has developed holdings in the Sacramento Basin (California) the San Juan Basin (New Mexico) the Denver-Julesburg Basin (Colorado) the Lobo Field and the Eagle Ford play in (both in Texas) the Green River Basin (Wyoming) and the Bakken Play and Southern Alberta basin (Montana).

However in a major strategic shift in 2010 the company sold its assets in New Mexico and Wyoming in order to raise cash and to focus on developing the increasingly lucrative Eagle Ford shale South Texas (Lobos Field) and Southern Alberta Basin plays. As part of this refocus in 2011 Rosetta Resources also sold its Colorado and California assets.

EXECUTIVES

Vice President - Human Resources And Administration, Gerald L Maxwell, age 62

EVP and COO, John D. Clayton, age 51, $390,000 total compensation

Chairman CEO and President, James E. Craddock, age 55, $556,667 total compensation

EVP and CFO, John E. Hagale, $390,000 total compensation

VP South Texas, Dan Calnan

VP Permian, Larry Jernigan

VP Corporate Reserves and Technical Services, Mark Petrichuk

Vice President Business Development And Marketing, Chad Driskill

Chairman CEO and President, James E. Craddock, age 55

Auditors: PricewaterhouseCoopersLLP

LOCATIONS

HQ: Rosetta Resources, Inc.
1111 Bagby Street, Suite 1600, Houston, TX 77002
Phone: 713 335-4000
Web: www.rosettaresources.com

PRODUCTS/OPERATIONS

2012 Sales

	$ mil.	% of total
Oil	318.8	52
NGLs	160.5	26
Natural gas	93.7	15
Derivative instruments	40.5	7
Total	613.5	100

2012 Sales

	% of total
Enterprise Products Operating	21
Shell Trading (US) Company	21
Exxon Mobil	13
Calpine Energy Services	12
Other customers	33
Total	100

Selected Subsidiaries

Rosetta Resources Holdings LLC
Rosetta Resources Offshore LLC
Rosetta Resources Operating LP

COMPETITORS

Anadarko Petroleum	Newfield Exploration
Apache	Petrohawk Energy
Devon Energy	Range Resources
EOG	SM Energy
Lightstream Resources	

HISTORICAL FINANCIALS

Company Type: Public

Income Statement

FYE: December 31

	REVENUE ($ mil.)	NET INCOME ($ mil.)	NET PROFIT MARGIN	EMPLOYEES
12/13	814.0	199.3	24.5%	252
12/12	613.5	159.3	26.0%	183
12/11	446.2	100.5	22.5%	165
12/10	308.4	19.0	6.2%	168
12/09	293.9	(219.1)	—	203
Annual Growth	29.0%	—	—	5.6%

2013 Year-End Financials

Debt ratio: 45.7%
Return on equity: 18.5%
Cash ($ mil.): 193
Current ratio: 1.31
Long-term debt ($ mil.): 1,500
No. of shares (mil.): 61
Dividends
Yield: —
Payout: —
Market value ($ mil.): 2,945

	STOCK PRICE ($) FY Close	P/E High/Low	PER SHARE ($) Earnings	Dividends	Book Value
12/13	48.04	18 12	3.39	0.00	21.99
12/12	45.32	18 11	3.01	0.00	15.30
12/11	43.50	29 17	1.91	0.00	12.13
12/10	37.64	102 49	0.37	0.00	10.23
12/09	19.92	— —	(4.30)	0.00	9.66
Annual Growth	24.6%	— —	—	—	22.8%

Royal Gold, Inc.

Royal Gold deals only with royalty. Rather than operating gold mines the company buys the right to collect royalties from mine operators. This strategy allows Royal Gold to minimize its exposure to the costs of mineral exploration and development. The company also owns interests in exploration- and development-stage projects. Its operations in Chile accounted for 29% of the company's 2013 revenues; operations in Canada 24%. Royal Gold holds royalty stakes in other producing properties elsewhere in the Americas as well as in Africa and Australia.

Geographic Reach

The company owns interests on 204 properties on six continents including interests on 36 producing mines and 21 development-stage projects.

Operations

Royal Gold is a precious metals royalty and stream company engaged in the acquisition and management of precious metal royalties streams and similar production based interests. Its principal producing properties includes - Andacollo (Chile) Canadian Malartic (Canada) Cortez (US) Holt (Canada) Las Cruces (Spain) Mulatos and Pe ±asquito (Mexico).

Development-stage properties include Mt. Milligan (British Columbia Canada) and Pascua-Lama Project (Chile).

Financial Performance

Royal Gold's revenues increased by 10% in 2013 thanks to production increases at its Andacollo Holt Las Cruces Mulatos and Robinson properties and the continued ramp-up at Canadian Malartic and Wolverine. These increases were partially offset by lower gold silver copper and nickel prices and lower production at Voisey's Bay (copper) Cortez Leeville and Dolores. However the company's net income dropped by 25% in 2013 due to an increase in expenses including general and administrative; depreciation depletion and amortization; loss on available-for-sale securities; interest; and other expenses and income tax expenses.

Strategy

Royal Gold grows by acquiring and managing stakes in precious metal royalties and production streams.

To pay down debt raised $472.5 million in 2013 through a stock sale.

Mergers and Acquisitions

In 2013 it acquired the right to purchase an additional 12.25% of the payable gold produced from the Mt. Milligan copper-gold project located in British Columbia; it also obtained the right to increase the net smelter return royalty on all the gold and silver production from Seabridge Gold's Kerr-Sulphurets-Mitchell project in British Columbia by 0.75%.

That year it also acquired a 70% interest in a 2% NSR royalty on certain portions of the El Morro copper gold project in Chile from Xstrata Copper Chile for $35 million. Goldcorp holds 70% of the El Morro project and is the operator; New Gold the remaining 30%.

In 2012 Royal Gold bought a 3% smelter return royalty on the Ruby Hill gold mine from International Minerals for $38 million. The Ruby Hill mine is located in Nevada and operated by Barrick Gold Corporation. The mine managed by an experienced world-class operator enhances Royal Gold's portfolio in Nevada.

Company Background

In 2010 Royal Gold acquired the rights to 25% of the payable gold produced from the Mt. Milligan copper-gold project in British Columbia from Thompson Creek Metals Company. Royal Gold paid some $311 million for the rights.

It added another acquisition in 2009 when it paid Teck $100 million for a percentage of a Chilean gold mine's output. Early the next year it bought International Royalty for about $700 million. International Royalty owns percentage stakes in mines in Australia Canada and Chile.

EXECUTIVES

President and CEO, Tony Jensen, age 52, $540,000 total compensation

CFO and Treasurer, Stefan L. Wenger, age 41, $280,000 total compensation

Chairman, William M. (Bill) Hayes, age 69

President and CEO, Tony Jensen, age 52

CFO and Treasurer, Stefan L. Wenger, age 41

Auditors: Ernst&YoungLLP

LOCATIONS

HQ: Royal Gold, Inc.
1660 Wynkoop Street, Suite 1000, Denver, CO 80202
Phone: 303 573-1660
Web: www.royalgold.com

2013 Royalty Revenues

	% of total
Chile	29
Canada	24
Mexico	19
US	17
Australia	4
Africa	3
Other regions	4
Total	**100**

PRODUCTS/OPERATIONS

2013 Sales by Property

	% of total
Andacollo	28
Voisey's Bay	11
Pe Â Â¨asquito	10
Holt	7
Mulatos	6
Robinson	5
Cortez	3
Canadian Malartic	3
Las Cruces	2
Other	25
Total	**100**

COMPETITORS

Anglo American	Franco-Nevada
AngloGold Ashanti	Rio Tinto Limited
BHP Billiton	

HISTORICAL FINANCIALS

Company Type: Public

Income Statement

FYE: June 30

	REVENUE ($ mil.)	NET INCOME ($ mil.)	NET PROFIT MARGIN	EMPLOYEES
06/14	237.1	63.4	26.8%	20
06/13	289.2	73.4	25.4%	21
06/12	263.0	98.3	37.4%	19
06/11	216.4	77.3	35.7%	21
06/10	136.5	21.4	15.7%	20
Annual Growth	**14.8%**	**31.1%**	**—**	**0.0%**

2014 Year-End Financials

Debt ratio: 10.7%	No. of shares (mil.): 64
Return on equity: 2.7%	Dividends
Cash ($ mil.): 659	Yield: 1.0%
Current ratio: 32.70	Payout: 95.3%
Long-term debt ($ mil.): 311	Market value ($ mil.): 4,945

	STOCK PRICE ($) FY Close	P/E High/Low		PER SHARE ($) Earnings	Dividends	Book Value
06/14	76.13	78	42	0.96	0.82	36.25
06/13	42.08	92	36	1.09	0.70	36.22
06/12	78.40	51	36	1.61	0.41	30.94
06/11	58.57	48	33	1.29	0.42	26.48
06/10	48.00	114	79	0.49	0.35	26.32
Annual Growth	**12.2%**	**—**	**—**	**18.3%**	**23.7%**	**8.3%**

RPC, Inc.

RPC helps to grease the wheels of oil and gas production through a number of business units. Through its Cudd Energy Services division the company provides oil industry consulting and technical services including snubbing coiled tubing nitrogen services and well control. Another unit Patterson Services rents specialized tools and equipment such as drill pipe tubing and blowout preventers. RPC also provides maintenance emergency services and storage and inspection services for offshore and inland vessels. The company operates in most of the world's major oil producing regions.

Geographic Reach

The company has administrative offices in Texas and Louisiana. The headquarters location in Houston Texas also houses engineering and sales and marketing departments. The US market accounts for most of revenues though the company has limited international operations primarily in Africa Canada China Latin America the Middle East and New Zealand. In the US the company's operations are focused on gas producing regions such as the southwestern and midwestern regions the Gulf of Mexico the Rocky Mountains and the Appalachian Mountains.

In 2013 some 3% of RPC's consolidated revenues came from offshore operations in the US Gulf of Mexico and in the Gulf of Alaska.

Operations

RPC's operations are divided into two segments: Technical services (about 93% of revenues) and support services. Technical services include pressure pumping services snubbing services coiled tubing services nitrogen service firefighting and well control. Pressure pumping services account for more than half of the company's annual revenues and include the provision of fracturing and acidizing equipment and materials that stimulate the production of oil and gas. Meanwhile support services include the rental of drill pipe and other specialized oilfield equipment downhole tool rentals pipe inspection and storage services and oilfield training services.

About 64% of the company's 2013 revenues came from oil drilling and production activities; and 36% from natural gas drilling and production activities.

Sales and Marketing

RPC serves major oilfield companies –including multi-national national and independent firms — that are involved in oil and gas exploration production and development activities.

Financial Performance

Higher oil prices and increased customer activity (mostly in the US) lifted the company's revenues between 2009 and 2012. However in 2013 RPC's revenues decreased by 4% due to a 13% decrease in the Support Services segment revenue as a result of lower pricing in the rental tool service line (its largest) and a 4% drop in Technical Segment revenues due to lower pricing. This was partially offset by higher service intensity and activity in the pressure pumping service line. Operating profit in the both Technical Services and Support Services segments declined due to lower pricing. Although the company has seen positive net income since 2010 in 2012 it experienced a 7% dip in its net income due to increased selling general and administrative expenses depreciation and amortization and a loss on disposition of assets. The same trend continued in 2013 when RPC's net income dropped by 39% due to decreased revenues and higher operating costs. Selling general and administrative expenses increased due to higher total employment costs and bad debt expense and a loss on disposition of assets. The company had seen a steady growth in operating cash flow in the last few years. However in 2013 RPC's operating cash flow decreased to $365.6 million from $559.9 million in 2012 primarily due to a decrease in net income of $107.5 million an unfavorable change in deferred taxes of $17.9 million (due to a decrease in tax depreciation benefits from lower capital expenditures) coupled with an unfavorable change in working capital of $83.2 million.

Strategy

The company has built its portfolio of technical and support services through a series of acquisitions and strategic partnerships. It has also increased its service capacity in recent years by widening its equipment fleets in both the technical services and support services segments. RPC is looking to a rebounding world economy with its increased demand for oil and gas operations to open up further opportunities for acquisitions geographic expansion and market share growth.

The company continues to pursue strategic investments and opportunities designed to enhance its long-term value while improving market share product offerings and the profitability of existing businesses. Its growth strategies are focused on selected customers and markets in which it believes there exist opportunities for higher growth customer and market penetration or enhanced returns via consolidations or through providing proprietary value-added products and services.

Company Background

Chairman R. Randall Rollins and his brother Vice Chairman Gary Rollins (CEO of Rollins Inc.) own about two-thirds of RPC.

EXECUTIVES

President and CEO, Richard A. Hubbell, age 70, $900,000 total compensation
VP CFO and Treasurer, Ben M. Palmer, age 54, $375,000 total compensation
Vice President Patterson Services, Len Denson
Vice President Finance, Lewis Mazo
VP CFO and Treasurer, Ben M. Palmer, age 54
Chairman, R. Randall Rollins, age 83
Vp Secretary And Director, Linda H Graham, age 79
Auditors: GrantThorntonLLP

LOCATIONS

HQ: RPC, Inc.
2801 Buford Highway N.E., Suite 520, Atlanta, GA 30329
Phone: 404 321-2140   **Fax:** 404 321-5483
Web: www.rpc.net

2013 Sales

	$ mil.	% of total
US	1795.6	96
Other countries	65.9	4
Total	**1861.5**	**100**

PRODUCTS/OPERATIONS

2013 Sales

	$ mil.	% of total
Technical services	1729.7	93
Support services	131.8	7
Total	**1861.5**	**100**

Selected Services

Technical Services
Coiled Tubing

Nitrogen Units
Pressure Pumping
Snubbing
Thru Tubing Solution
Well Control
Wireline
Support Services
Energy Personnel International
Patterson Rental Tools
Patterson Tubular Services
Well Control School

COMPETITORS

Baker Hughes   Schlumberger
Ensign Energy Services   Transocean
Exterran   Weatherford
Halliburton   International
Precision Drilling

HISTORICAL FINANCIALS

Company Type: Public

Income Statement

FYE: December 31

	REVENUE ($ mil.)	NET INCOME ($ mil.)	NET PROFIT MARGIN	EMPLOYEES
12/13	1,861.4	166.9	9.0%	3,900
12/12	1,945.0	274.4	14.1%	3,600
12/11	1,809.8	296.3	16.4%	3,400
12/10	1,096.3	146.7	13.4%	2,500
12/09	587.8	(22.7)	—	1,980
Annual Growth	33.4%	—	—	18.5%

2013 Year-End Financials

Debt ratio: 3.8%
Return on equity: 17.8%
Cash ($ mil.): 8
Current ratio: 3.60
Long-term debt ($ mil.): 53

No. of shares (mil.): 218
Dividends
Yield: 3.3%
Payout: 69.7%
Market value ($ mil.): 3,909

	STOCK PRICE ($) FY Close	P/E High/Low		Earnings	PER SHARE ($) Dividends	Book Value
12/13	17.85	24	16	0.77	0.60	4.42
12/12	12.24	16	7	1.27	0.52	4.08
12/11	18.25	20	11	1.35	0.21	3.45
12/10	18.12	48	15	0.67	0.09	2.42
12/09	10.40	—	—	(0.11)	0.10	1.85
Annual Growth	14.5%		—	—	57.4%	24.3%

RPX Corp

In our litigious society RPX Corporation helps keep technology companies out of the courtroom. RPX owns a portfolio of more than 1500 intellectual property patents that it licenses to customers in order to prevent patent infringement lawsuits. (So one company can't sue another over a patent since it's RPX that owns the patent). Its patent portfolio spans six industries —consumer electronics software media content mobile communications and devices networking and semiconductors. RPX counts more than 70 customers including Cisco Google Nokia Sharp Sony and Verizon and earns one-third of its revenues from Asian firms. Founded in 2008 RPX launched an IPO in 2011.

Patent litigation is an emerging multi-billion dollar industry that even has its own insults - companies that make big business of suing others over alleged patent infringement are called non-practic-

ing entities (NPEs) but are known derogatively as patent trolls or patent pirates. Tech companies of all sizes have had their business operations disrupted by major verdicts and high settlement costs. Many patents can overlap; for example there are more than 6200 patents for the semiconductor technology known as DRAM (dynamic random access memory). Potential infringement can happen for any company that makes uses or sells a device with DRAM technology.

RPX operates as a legal middleman; so far it has spent about $250 million acquiring patents to help customers mitigate litigation risks. Its customers pay between $40000 to more than $5 million a year to license its intellectual property. RPX's separates itself from competitors (such as Acacia) by charging its subscription fees based on a company's revenues not the perceived value of the patent.

RPX is experiencing significant growth as its revenues doubled from 2009 its first full year of operations to the first nine months of 2010. Continuing this impressive trajectory the company saw its revenues increase from $32 million in 2009 to almost $95 million in 2010 —a staggering increase of 189%. In May 2011 the company raised almost $160 million by going public. It wants to use the proceeds to acquire additional patents in 2011 as well as hire more personnel for client relations patent research and analysis and to develop reporting systems. PRX also plans to offer complementary services such as facilitating joint defense agreements and cross-licensing arrangements for its clients. Finally it aims to recruit more clients that are consistently faced with IP-related lawsuits.

Several investment vehicles own major stakes in the company. Index Ventures Growth; Charles River Partnership; and Kleiner Perkins Caufield & Byers each own about 18%. They are represented on the company's board by Giuseppe Zocco Izhar Armony and Randy Komisar respectively.

EXECUTIVES

CEO and Co-Founder, John A. Amster, age 46, $500,000 total compensation
Executive Director and Co-founder, Geoffrey T. Barker, age 53, $300,000 total compensation
EVP, Mallun Yen, $50,000 total compensation
CFO, Robert Heath
Auditors: PricewaterhouseCoopersLLP

LOCATIONS

HQ: RPX Corp
One Market Plaza Suite 800, San Francisco, CA 94105
Phone: 866 779-7641
Web: www.rpxcorp.com

2013 Sales

	$ mil.	% of total
United States	145.3	61
Japan	39.5	17
Others	52.7	22
Total	**237.5**	**100**

PRODUCTS/OPERATIONS

Services
Services Defensive Patent Acquisitions
Market Intelligence and Advisory Services
Structured Acquisitions
Litigation Insurance
Sell Your Patent
RPX R&D

COMPETITORS

Acacia Research   Jones Day

Alston & Bird   Kirkland & Ellis
Baker & McKenzie   Walker Digital
Convex Group   White & Case
Duane Morris

HISTORICAL FINANCIALS

Company Type: Public

Income Statement

FYE: December 31

	REVENUE ($ mil.)	NET INCOME ($ mil.)	NET PROFIT MARGIN	EMPLOYEES
12/13	237.5	40.7	17.2%	137
12/12	197.6	38.9	19.7%	125
12/11	154.0	29.1	18.9%	110
12/10	94.8	13.8	14.6%	76
12/09	32.8	1.9	5.9%	0
Annual Growth	64.0%	114.3%	—	—

2013 Year-End Financials

Debt ratio: —
Return on equity: 10.3%
Cash ($ mil.): 100
Current ratio: 2.40
Long-term debt ($ mil.): —

No. of shares (mil.): 52
Dividends
Yield: —
Payout: —
Market value ($ mil.): 890

	STOCK PRICE ($) FY Close	P/E High/Low		Earnings	PER SHARE ($) Dividends	Book Value
12/13	16.90	24	12	0.76	0.00	8.06
12/12	9.04	26	11	0.74	0.00	7.05
12/11	12.65	51	20	0.57	0.00	6.09
Annual Growth	15.6%		—	15.5%	—	15.1%

RTI International Metals, Inc.

RTI International Metals has titanium on the cranium. Through its Titanium Group the company produces ingots bars plates sheets strips pipes wire and welded tubing used primarily by the aerospace industry to make bulkheads tail sections engine components and wing supports. Fabrication and Distribution groups operate through subsidiary RTI Energy Systems making pipe and tubing for offshore oil and gas exploration and production as well as geothermal energy production. RTI caters to commercial aerospace and defense industries which represent almost 80% of sales and a growing number of industrial and consumer customers.

Operations

The company operates through two segments: Titanium (45% of total revenue) and EP&S (55%). The Titanium segment melts forges processes and produces a complete range of titanium mill products which are further processed by its customers for use in a variety of commercial aerospace defense and industrial and consumer applications.The EP&S segment offers hard and soft-metal services that form extrude fabricate machine additively manufacture micro-machine and assemble titanium aluminum and other specialty metal parts and components.

Sales and Marketing

RTI markets its products to the international aerospace defense energy medical device and other consumer and industrial markets. Customers include prime aircraft manufacturers and their family of subcontractors including fabricators forge shops extruders castings producers fastener manufacturers machine shops and metal distribution companies.

Financial Performance

RTI achieved record-setting growth in 2013 with revenues peaking at $783 million. Profits however fell 40% from $24 million in 2012 to $14 million in 2013 due to increased expenses professional fees and a loss from discontinued operations. (Note: the company restated its annual financial report for 2012 due to discontinued operations.)

The historic revenue growth for 2013 was driven by a spike in EP&S segment sales due to higher Boeing 787 volumes and higher duty drawback recoveries. The company also earned additional revenues from previous acquisitions it made.

RTI's operating cash flow dropped significantly from $75 million in 2010 to $15 million in 2011. Its cash flow remained at $8 million in 2012 and $12 million in 2013.

Mergers and Acquisitions

RTI has been making acquisitions to add to its revenue stream. In 2014 the company acquired Directed Manufacturing for $23 million in cash. Directed Manufacturing provides additive manufacturing of titanium specialty metal and plastic components for both commercial production and engineering development applications in the commercial aerospace medical and oil and gas markets. RTI also in 2014 picked up Advanced Powder Materials for $19 million. Advanced Powder Materials has expertise in titanium powder metallurgy and is a supplier of near-net shape titanium and titanium alloy preforms and components to commercial aerospace defense biomedical and industrial customers. To extend its international reach in 2013 the company paid $16 million to acquire Extrusions Europe Limited (formerly the extrusions business of Osborn Metals Limited). Extrusions Europe manufactures extruded hot-or-cold stretched steel and titanium parts for a number of markets including the aerospace and oil and gas markets and its business complements RTI's existing titanium extrusion operations in Houston.

HISTORY

In 1964 Quantum Chemical (now a subsidiary of Millennium Chemical) and U.S. Steel (now United States Steel) formed Reactive Metals Inc. The company changed its name to RMI Titanium Company in 1971. It went public in 1990 with Quantum selling its shares and United States Steel retaining its interest.

The titanium industry is closely tied to the ups and downs of the aerospace industry and just after RMI's IPO the industry hit one of its cyclical slumps. RMI suffered years of losses even as it worked to cut costs and develop new markets. In 1992 it closed its titanium sponge (a porous metal used as raw material) facility and began buying lower-cost sponge from third parties. The next year it began providing seamless titanium pipe to California Energy Co. for use in that company's geothermal well. In 1995 RMI completed the world's first high-pressure titanium drilling riser for use in a Conoco North Sea oil rig.

In 1996 two events turned RMI's fortunes around. The aerospace industry took off once more and golfers discovered titanium club heads. RMI formed a joint venture with Earthline Technologies in 1997 to offer soil-remediation services (perhaps relying on its experience as an owner of a Superfund site). In 1997 RMI bought Galt Alloys a pro-

ducer of ferrotitanium. The next year the company signed long-term supply agreements with Boeing Northrop and Aerospatiale. The company changed its name to RTI International Metals in 1998. USX sold off its 27% stake in 1999.

In 2000 RTI International Metals received a $6 million settlement from Boeing after the aerospace giant failed to meet the conditions of a 1999 long-term supply agreement between the two companies. Later in the year the company purchased the remaining shares of Reamet S.A. a French-market distributor of titanium products. In 2001 RTI International Metals saw an increase in net income of over $12 million on sales of almost $286 million but noticed troubles ahead for its titanium group because of a weakening commercial aerospace industry.

In 2002 the company entered into agreements with Europe's largest aerospace group Airbus to supply titanium products and parts. The following year a work stoppage was held by the company's UAW employees at its Niles Ohio plant. Non-union employees operated the plant until union representatives and company management agreed on a contract settlement.

In mid-2008 RTI signed two long-term contracts to supply a wide range of structural and flight control component parts and complex electro-mechanical assemblies to Bombardier Aerospace and Bell Helicopter.

In 2009 the economic crisis grounded the aviation industry. RTI's commercial aerospace market which represented about 44% of company revenues sustained revenue losses of 6% over 2008 due to worldwide slowdown of travel.

EXECUTIVES

Vice Chairman President and CEO, Dawne S. Hickton, age 57, $646,538 total compensation
CTO, Kathryn J. (Kate) Jackson
Chief Risk Officer, William T. Hull, age 57, $336,500 total compensation
EVP Operations, James L. (Jim) McCarley, age 50, $468,077 total compensation
EVP Commercial, Patricia O'Connell, $396,923 total compensation
SVP CFO and Treasurer, Michael G. McAuley
Svp Commercial, William A Pallante
Vice President Titanium Production, Gary Urso
Executive Vice President Technology, Stephen Giangiordano
Vice Chairman President and CEO, Dawne S. Hickton, age 57
Chairman, Robert M. Hernandez, age 70
Auditors: PricewaterhouseCoopersLLP

LOCATIONS

HQ: RTI International Metals, Inc.
Westpointe Corporate Center One, 5th Floor, 1550 Coraopolis Heights Road, Pittsburgh, PA 15108-2973
Phone: 412 893-0026   **Fax:** 330 544-7876
Web: www.rtiintl.com

2013 Sales

	$ mil.	% of total
US	548.6	70
France	69.7	9
UK	56.7	7
Germany	31.0	4
Italy	14.3	2
Spain	12.7	2
Canada	11.5	1
Japan	10.7	1
Austria	10.0	1
Other countries	18.1	3
Total	**783.3**	**100**

PRODUCTS/OPERATIONS

2013 Sales

	$ mil.	% of total
Engineered products & services	436.7	55
Titanium	346.6	45
Total	**783.3**	**100**

2013 Sales by Market

	% of total
Commercial aerospace	55
Defense	22
Energy medical & other	23
Total	**100**

Selected Products and ServicesComponent Manufacture 3D PrintingExtrusionsFull Bore HoningHard Metal MachiningHigh Velocity MachiningHot Brake FormingHot FormingLong Bed LathesPrecision Robotic-Assisted MachiningSoft Metal MachiningSuperplastic FormingSur

Flat products (sheet and plate) precision grinding and surface etch
Hard metal extrusion
Heat treatment
Hot forming and superplastic forming
Lathe turning and bar peeling
Open die and GFM forging
Plasma hearth melting
Precision hot rolling
Revert recycling
Roller leveling
Vacuum arc re-melting
Vacuum creep flattening
Vacuum degassing

Selected Markets

Aerospace
Defense
Energy
Medical

COMPETITORS

Allegheny Technologies	Liquidmetal
Carpenter Technology	Metals USA
Ducommun	ThyssenKrupp Stainless
GKN Aerospace	Titanium Metals
Chem-tronics	Triumph Group
Hurlen Corporation	VSMPO-AVISMA

HISTORICAL FINANCIALS

Company Type: Public

Income Statement

FYE: December 31

	REVENUE ($ mil.)	NET INCOME ($ mil.)	NET PROFIT MARGIN	EMPLOYEES
12/13	783.2	14.0	1.8%	2,437
12/12	738.6	23.5	3.2%	2,362
12/11	529.6	6.5	1.2%	1,729
12/10	431.7	3.4	0.8%	1,534
12/09	407.9	(67.2)	—	1,478
Annual Growth	**17.7%**	**—**	**—**	**13.3%**

2013 Year-End Financials

Debt ratio: 28.5%	No. of shares (mil.): 30
Return on equity: 1.8%	Dividends
Cash ($ mil.): 343	Yield: —
Current ratio: 6.36	Payout: —
Long-term debt ($ mil.): 430	Market value ($ mil.): 1,047

	STOCK PRICE ($) FY Close	P/E High/Low	PER SHARE ($) Earnings	Dividends	Book Value
12/13	34.21	77 58	0.46	0.00	25.30
12/12	27.56	35 26	0.77	0.00	24.56
12/11	23.21	177 95	0.22	0.00	23.93
12/10	26.98	295 194	0.11	0.00	23.85
12/09	25.17	— —	(2.67)	0.00	22.63
Annual Growth	**8.0%**	**— —**	**—**	**—**	**2.8%**

Ryland Group, Inc.

Building the American dream is home sweet home for The Ryland Group. The homebuilder founded by James Ryan and Bob Gaw in 1967 constructs single-family detached homes as well as attached condominiums for entry-level first- and second-time move-up and retired buyers. Ryland has constructed more than 300000 homes in hundreds of communities around the US. The average price for a Ryland Home is around $260000. The company offers services that span the homeownership process. Homebuyers can select custom home finishes at a My Style Design Center. The group also provides mortgage financing title and escrow and insurance services.

Geographic Reach

Its homebuilding operations are divided into four major geographic regions: North Southeast Texas and West. Ryland focuses on diversification with no more than 10% of its capital resources allocated to any given geographic market. The strategy helps minimize vulnerability to economic and market fluctuations.

Operations

Ryland's homebuilding segment is its primary focus and biggest revenue generator (some 97% of sales). In addition Ryland also operates a financial services unit focused on retail mortgage loan originations including conventional Federal Housing Administration (FHA) and Veterans Administration (VA) mortgages. The unit primarily exists to support its homebuilding operations; more than 99% of the loans originated by the subsidiary are issued to Ryland homebuyers.

Financial Performance

A rise in average selling prices coupled with a rise in the number of homes sold contributed to a 47% increased in Ryland's revenue in 2012. Higher revenues also pulled Ryland into the black by $40 million the same year. The company's 2012 results follow years of declining revenues and operating losses as Ryland and other homebuilders weathered weak demand for new homes between 2006 and 2011. During that time homebuilders saw increases in foreclosures that created an oversaturated housing market as well as a tight credit market lagging consumer confidence and high unemployment rates that forced national housing demand and home prices down.

Strategy

Ryland's financial performance is heavily reliant on fluctuations in the US housing market and as such it tailors its growth strategy accordingly. It spreads its risk among numerous regional and community-level housing markets investing in growing and potentially lucrative markets while divesting its interests in slowing or flat housing markets. In 2012 it expanded its presence in growing markets like Austin Texas and acquired Timberstone Homes in the Charlotte and Raleigh North Carolina markets and Trend Homes in the Phoenix market.

Ryland has made several changes to its operations in response to turbulent market conditions of recent years. Over the course of the multi-year housing crisis that began in 2007 it cut its workforce by nearly 70% and reduced the number of communities in which it was active (exiting markets such as Northern California Cincinnati Dallas and Jacksonville). Ryland also cut back on its lot inventory and began building smaller more affordable homes that cater to demand.

HISTORY

The Ryland Group was founded in 1967 by entrepreneur James Ryan in the new planned community of Columbia Maryland. Ryan got the idea for the company name after seeing "Maryland" on a sign with the first two letters covered up so in 1970 the James P. Ryan Co. changed its name to The Ryland Group. Ryan took Ryland public in 1971 and the company expanded to a new planned community near Atlanta that year. In 1974 the company opened its first panel-building plant (Ryland Building Systems). By 1977 Ryland had moved into the Midwest and Philadelphia completing 10000 homes by year's end.

Ryland purchased Crest Communities (Cincinnati) in 1978. Crest's financial subsidiary became the basis for Ryland's mortgage operations (later known as Ryland Mortgage). Ryan retired in 1980 and Charles Peck became CEO. In 1981 the company entered the loan servicing business with the purchase of Guardian Mortgage. The following year Ryland formed Ryland Acceptance as an administrator and distributor of mortgage-backed securities. By 1985 the company had completed 50000 homes.

It formed Cornerstone Title in 1989 to conduct real estate closing services in Maryland. The following year Ryland teamed up with American Loyalty Insurance to offer homeowners' insurance. In the 1990s the firm entered the fast-growing California and Florida housing markets. It also dabbled in overseas markets building homes in Israel in 1991 and Russia in 1992.

A recession and overexpansion led to the company's loss in 1993. Chad Dreier a former Kaufman and Broad EVP was appointed as Ryland CEO in late 1993 and took the company in a new direction. He recognized that while Ryland's center-hall colonial-style house formed the foundation for the company's success that fixed image of a "Ryland Home" was also an impediment to its future growth. Under Dreier's leadership the company began enlisting the services of top architectural firms such as Bloodgood Sharp Buster and Kaufman Meeks to introduce new house designs and to offer Ryland's customers a greater degree of customization in house design. The company also placed a stronger emphasis on market research after securing plots of land to better determine the best house designs for any given area.

In 1995 as part of its plan to focus on its core homebuilding and retail mortgage finance operations the company sold its institutional mortgage-securities administration business (which included master servicing investor information services securities administration tax calculation and reporting). A year later it sold its wholesale mortgage operations.

The company purchased The Regency Organization a private Florida homebuilder in 1998 to expand into the growing retirement market and acquired Thomas Builders to expand operations in the Baltimore area. In 1999 Ryland relocated its mortgage subsidiary to California and the next year moved its corporate headquarters there.

Also in 2000 Ryland joined other major US homebuilders in an Internet-based marketing co-operative. The builder continued to surf the Net the next year as it invested $1 million in online sales company iBidCo after using iBidCo's system to sell 14 California homes for a total of nearly $11 million.

Company chairman and CEO Dreier scored in 2002 with a new employment agreement which gave him an annual base salary of $1 million through the year 2007. Ryland posted record revenue and closings results in 2003 a trend since 2000. Ryland opened 152 new communities (a 5% to 10% increase) in fiscal 2003. At the close of 2003 Ryland began operating in California's Inland Empire (Riverside and San Bernardino counties) and in 2004 the company opened communities in Las Vegas. In 2006 Ryland split its Northern California division and created two new divisions in Sacramento and the Central Valley.

EXECUTIVES

Svp; President Ryland Mortgage Company, Daniel G (Dan) Schreiner, age 57

Senior Vice President Marketing Group, Eric E Elder, age 57

Vice President Of Human Resources North, Karen Simons

Svp General Counsel And Secretary, Timothy J (Tim) Geckle, age 62

Vp Sales Training, Charles W (Charlie) Jenkins

Sr Vice President, Mark Beisswanger

Chief Financial Officer; Executive Vice President, Gordon A. Milne, age 63, $700,000 total compensation

COO, Peter G. (Pete) Skelly, age 51, $360,000 total compensation

President CEO and Director, Larry T. Nicholson, age 57, $900,000 total compensation

VP and CIO, Craig McSpadden

Area President - Ryland Homes, Alan Goldsticker

Vice President, Christopher Isherwood

Vice President Sales And Marketing, Jensen Craig

Executive Vp, Michael Oconnor

Sr Vice President, Ken L Trainer

Executive Vp, Rich Oconnor

Vice President Sales And Marketing, Carola Cherief

Vice President Construction, Brian Nelson

Vice President, Daune Bonabie

Vice President, Laurie Tarver

Vice President Operations, Marty Brunfield

Vp Sales And Marketing, Chris Contreras

Vice President Financial Operations Of Southeast Region, Robert Clark

Vice President Sales And Marketing, Pat Oflynn

Vice President Operations Southeast Reg, Joseph Sabella

Vice President Of Sales And Marketing, Melanie Sander

Vice President Sales And Marketing, Randy Char

Vice President Land, Royce Rippy

Vice President Of Sales And Marketing, Rick Perkins

Vice President Of Purchasing, Dave Desplinter

Vice President Of Financial Operations, Kevin Johnson

Senior Vice President, E Eric

Vice President Administration, Doug Strall

Vice President Information Systems, Kelley Riesing

Senior Vice President, Frank Scardina

Vice President Of Marketing, Drew McIntosh

Vice President Sales And Marketing, Rebecca Smith

Vice President, Maurice Sipkins

Vice President Of Operations, James Hostetler

Vp Sales And Marketing, Earl Robinson

Vice President Of Sales And Marketing, Bob Rademacher

Executive Vice President Sales, Douglas Holstein

Vice President Sales And Marketing, Diane L Morrison

Vice President Sales And Marketing, Heather Stevenson

Vice President Operations, Jeff Roberts

Vice President, Paul Gulbroson

Svp; President South Region Ryland Homes, Keith E Bass

Vice President, Anne Madison

Vice President, Viken Kasparian
Vice President Homebuilding, John Cappella
Vice President Of Investor Relations, Drew
  Mackintosh
Vp Operations, Joe Sabella
Vp Sales And Marketing, Bob Meyn
Board Member, Charlotte St Martin, age 69
Chairman, William L. (Bill) Jews, age 62
President CEO and Director, Larry T. Nicholson,
  age 57
Treasurer, Kimberly Nelson
Board Member, Robert G Van Schoonenbe
Auditors: Ernst&YoungLLP

LOCATIONS

HQ: Ryland Group, Inc.
  3011 Townsgate Road, Suite 200, Westlake Village, CA
  91361-3027
Phone: 805 367-3800
Web: www.ryland.com

2012 Sales

	$ mil.	% of total
Homebuilding		
North	393.3	30
Southeast	355.6	27
Texas	323.2	25
West	198.8	15
Financial services	37.6	3
Total	**1308.5**	**100**

Major Markets Served by Region
North
  Baltimore
  Chicago
  Indianapolis
  Minneapolis
  Northern Virginia
  Washington DC
Southeast
  Atlanta
  Charleston SC
  Charlotte NC
  Orlando FL
  Raleigh NC
  Tampa
Texas
  Austin
  Houston
  San Antonio
West
  Denver
  Las Vegas
  Southern California

PRODUCTS/OPERATIONS

2012 Sales

	$ mil.	% of total
Homebuilding	1270.9	97
Financial services	37.6	3
Total	**1308.5**	**100**

Selected Subsidiaries

Columbia National Risk Retention Group Inc.
Cornerstone Title Company (operates as Ryland Title
  Company)
LPS Holdings Corporation
RH Insurance Company Inc.
Ryland Homes Insurance Company
Ryland Homes of California Inc.
Ryland Homes of Texas Inc.
Ryland Mortgage Company (RMC)
Ryland Organization Company

COMPETITORS

Beazer Homes	M.D.C.
Champion Home Builders	M/I Homes
D.R. Horton	NVR
Hovnanian Enterprises	PulteGroup
J.F. Shea	Standard Pacific
KB Home	Toll Brothers
Lennar	

HISTORICAL FINANCIALS
Company Type: Public

Income Statement
FYE: December 31

	REVENUE ($ mil.)	NET INCOME ($ mil.)	NET PROFIT MARGIN	EMPLOYEES
12/13	2,140.7	379.2	17.7%	1,395
12/12	1,308.4	40.3	3.1%	1,100
12/11	890.7	(50.7)	—	922
12/10	1,063.8	(85.1)	—	991
12/09	1,283.6	(162.4)	—	1,019
Annual Growth	**13.6%**	—		**8.2%**

2013 Year-End Financials

Debt ratio: 52.8%	No. of shares (mil.): 46
Return on equity: 53.7%	Dividends
Cash ($ mil.): 227	Yield: 0.2%
Current ratio: 4.97	Payout: 1.9%
Long-term debt ($ mil.): 1,397	Market value ($ mil.): 2,007

	STOCK PRICE ($) FY Close	P/E High/Low		PER SHARE ($) Earnings	Dividends	Book Value
12/13	43.41	6	4	6.79	0.12	19.64
12/12	36.50	42	18	0.84	0.12	11.16
12/11	15.76	—	—	(1.14)	0.12	10.12
12/10	17.03	—	—	(1.93)	0.12	11.31
12/09	19.70	—	—	(3.74)	0.12	13.27
Annual Growth	**21.8%**	—	—	—	**(0.0%)**	**10.3%**

Sabine Royalty Trust

Sabine Royalty Trust owns royalty interests in
oil and gas properties located on about 2.1 million
gross acres (216551 net) in Florida Louisiana Mississippi New Mexico Oklahoma and Texas. The
trust which was formed in 1983 receives royalties
based on the amount of oil and gas produced and
sold and distributes them on a monthly basis to
shareholders. Although royalty trusts distribute essentially all royalties received to shareholders (at
substantial tax advantage) their profitability depends on the price of oil and gas and the continued productivity of the properties. Sabine Royalty
Trust's properties have proved reserves of about
5.3 million barrels of oil and 35.6 billion cu. ft. of
natural gas.

EXECUTIVES

**SVP and Administrator Bank of America N.A.
  Trustee,** Ron E. Hooper
Auditors: Deloitte&ToucheLLP

LOCATIONS

HQ: Sabine Royalty Trust
  Southwest Bank, Park Place, 2911 Turtle Creek Blvd,
  Suite 850, Dallas, TX 75219
Phone: 855 7839   **Fax:** 214 508-2431
Web: www.sbr-sabineroyalty.com

PRODUCTS/OPERATIONS

Trustee
Bank of America N.A.

COMPETITORS

Cross Timbers Royalty	San Juan Basin

Trust		Torch Energy
LL&E Royalty Trust		ZaZa Energy
Panhandle Oil and Gas		

HISTORICAL FINANCIALS
Company Type: Public

Income Statement
FYE: December 31

	REVENUE ($ mil.)	NET INCOME ($ mil.)	NET PROFIT MARGIN	EMPLOYEES
12/13	60.7	58.7	96.6%	0
12/12	54.6	52.3	95.7%	0
12/11	60.6	58.5	96.5%	0
12/10	56.0	53.9	96.2%	0
12/09	41.5	39.2	94.5%	0
Annual Growth	**10.0%**	**10.6%**	—	—

2013 Year-End Financials

Debt ratio: —	No. of shares (mil.): 14
Return on equity: 1,210.4%	Dividends
Cash ($ mil.): 6	Yield: 7.7%
Current ratio: 4.98	Payout: 101.2%
Long-term debt ($ mil.): —	Market value ($ mil.): 737

	STOCK PRICE ($) FY Close	P/E High/Low		PER SHARE ($) Earnings	Dividends	Book Value
12/13	50.56	14	10	4.03	3.92	0.39
12/12	39.79	18	11	3.59	3.70	0.28
12/11	63.05	17	13	4.02	3.97	0.39
12/10	59.55	16	11	3.70	3.70	0.35
12/09	40.99	17	11	2.69	2.79	0.36
Annual Growth	**5.4%**	—	—	**10.6%**	**8.8%**	**2.0%**

Sabra Health Care REIT Inc

Sabra Health Care REIT doesn't mind a little
healthy competition in the real estate sector. The
company invests in income-producing health care
facilities in the US. The REIT's investment portfolio includes about 120 properties most of which are
skilled nursing/post-acute centers. It also invests
in assisted living and independent living facilities
and hospitals. Sabra's facilities house more than
12300 beds and are located in more than 25 states.
Substantially all of the properties are leased to and
operated by subsidiaries of Sun Healthcare Group
which spun off its real estate assets to form Sabra
Health Care REIT in 2010.
  Geographic Reach
  The REIT has licensed beds in 27 US states including New Hampshire Kentucky and Connecticut its three largest markets.
  Financial Performance
  Sabra's revenue jumped 22% in 2012 versus
2011 due to an increase in rental income partially
offset by a decline in interest income. The lion's
share of the $21 million increase in rental income
is due to acquisitions made in 2011 and 2012. Net
income climbed 52% in 2012 compared with 2011
primarily on rising rental income.
  Strategy
  Sabra aims to profit from the aging of the US
population and increasing life expectancies both of
which are driving demand for long-term care serv-

ices. The REIT is focused on growing its geographically-diverse portfolio primarily through the purchase of senior housing and memory care facilities with a secondary emphasis on acquiring skilled nursing homes.

Mergers and Acquisitions

In 2012 the firm invested nearly $207 million to acquire 10 skilled nursing facilities and 13 senior living facilities. In 2011 the REIT acquired the Cadia portfolio Texas Regional Medical Center at Sunnyvale the Aurora portfolio the Encore portfolio Oak Brook Health Care Center and Creekside Senior Living for an aggregate cost of about $204.5 million.

Ownership

The Vanguard Group onws about 12% of the company's shares.

EXECUTIVES

Chairman and CEO, Richard K. Matros, age 60, $725,000 total compensation
Chief Investment Officer, Talya Nevo-Hacohen, $350,000 total compensation
EVP and CFO, Harold W. Andrews, age 50, $350,000 total compensation
Chief Technology Officer, Galen Warren
Chief Operating Officer, Nick Cafferillo
Svp Of Asset Management, Peter W Nyland
Chairman and CEO, Richard K. Matros, age 60
Auditors: Ernst&YoungLLP

LOCATIONS

HQ: Sabra Health Care REIT Inc
18500 Von Karman Avenue, Suite 550, Irvine, CA 92612
Phone: 888 393-8248
Web: www.sabrahealth.com

2012 Locations

	No.
Connecticut	13
New Hampshire	16
Kentucky	15
Ohio	8
Texas	8
Florida	5
Michigan	10
Montana	4
Delaware	4
Colorado	3
Other (17 states)	33
Total	**119**

PRODUCTS/OPERATIONS

2012 Locations

	No.
Skilled nursing/post-acute	96
Senior housing	22
Hospitals	1
Total	**119**

COMPETITORS

Extendicare
HCP
Health Care REIT
Healthcare Realty Trust
LTC Properties
National Health Investors
Omega Healthcare Investors
Senior Housing Properties
Ventas

HISTORICAL FINANCIALS

Company Type: Public

Income Statement

FYE: December 31

	REVENUE ($ mil.)	NET INCOME ($ mil.)	NET PROFIT MARGIN	EMPLOYEES
12/13	134.7	33.7	25.0%	9
12/12	103.1	19.5	18.9%	8
12/11	84.2	12.8	15.2%	7
12/10	8.8	0.0	0.1%	6
Annual Growth	148.4%	1588.8%	—	14.5%

2013 Year-End Financials

Debt ratio: 57.7%
Return on equity: 8.8%
Cash ($ mil.): 4
Current ratio: 0.21
Long-term debt ($ mil.): 691
No. of shares (mil.): 38
Dividends
Yield: 5.2%
Payout: 272.0%
Market value ($ mil.): 1,014

	STOCK PRICE ($) FY Close	P/E High/Low	PER SHARE ($) Earnings	Dividends	Book Value
12/13	26.14	46 31	0.68	1.36	11.86
12/12	21.72	42 23	0.52	1.32	8.23
12/11	12.09	45 20	0.43	0.96	8.85
12/10	18.40	— —	(0.00)	0.00	7.08
/0.00	—	—(0.00)	0.00	(0.00)	
Annual Growth	—	—	—	—	—

Sagent Pharmaceuticals Inc

Sagent Pharmaceuticals is imbued with a restorative spirit. Through its subsidiaries Sagent develops markets and sells a range of generic injectable products used by US hospitals and other health care organizations. Its products —which include anti-infection drugs chemotherapy drugs and critical care treatments used for anesthesia or to stabilize cardiac conditions like blood clotting and arrhythmia —consist of more than 30 ready-to-use pre-filled syringes single and multiple-dose vials and pre-mixed bags. Sagent develops its products using active pharmaceutical ingredients (APIs) and finished drugs supplied by partner pharmaceutical companies.

Founded in 2006 Sagent went public through an IPO in April 2011. The company changed its name from Sagent Holding to Sagent Pharmaceuticals and reincorporated from the Cayman Islands to the US shortly after its stock began trading. Sagent is using the IPO proceeds (about $92 million) for general corporate purposes such as funding its working capital product development and operating expenses as well as to potentially expand its collaborations and its commercial infrastructure.

Sagent's largest product segment is anti-infectives (about 40% of sales) followed by critical care (35%) and oncology (25%) treatments. Nearly all of Sagent's product revenues come from the US market. As it has expanded its product lines the company's revenues have become less dependent on any one product though blood thinner heparin and antibiotic cefepime still account for 25% and 10% of sales respectively. About 10 of Sagent's products are a result of a joint venture with manufacturer Strides Arcolab; other supply partners include Actavis Gland Pharma and Dobofar.

The company employs a direct sales force to market its products but it uses a third-party logistics manager (DDN) to administer the warehousing and shipping of its products from DDN's facility in Tennessee. Sales to wholesale drug distributors Cardinal Health AmerisourceBergen and McKesson account for about 85% of revenues; end-users who receive the Sagent products via wholesalers who include independent hospitals and group purchasing organizations (GPOs) such as Novation and HealthTrust.

Sagent's attempt to raise public funds through its 2011 IPO was at its core driven by the firm's ongoing effort to achieve profitability. The company has enjoyed a healthy rise in revenues since its inception including doubled sales of $152 million in 2011 (up from $74 million in 2010) due to new product launches and increased sales of existing products. However like many relatively young pharmaceutical companies the firm has also experienced recurring operating losses as supply commercialization and product development expenses outweigh revenues. High supply costs come from Sagent's business model of sourcing most of its product ingredients and finished products from partners which leaves the company with a small profit margin on product sales.

The company's growth strategy (and effort to obtain profitability) includes ramping up its revenues by growing its partner network and introducing more high-margin products. The company launched its leading heparin product line with drug partner Gland Pharma in 2010. Sagent launched about a dozen new products during 2011 and the firm has plans in the works to add 40 additional products in the near future (it hopes to launch about 20 during 2012).

Other aspects of its growth strategy include identifying new channels through which to generate income such as leveraging its sales staff to offer sales and marketing services to its pharmaceutical manufacturing partners (which it currently does for Actavis). Sagent also aims to improve its returns by entering new customer agreements with GPOs and negotiating more profitable agreements with its product suppliers.

To take some manufacturing operations into its own hands (and hopefully increase margins on sales) Sagent has a joint venture with Chinese pharmaceutical company CKT to construct and operate a manufacturing plant in China. The plant was completed in 2012 and is awaiting FDA inspection so that the joint venture can begin manufacturing products for the US market. Sagent also hopes to access the Chinese pharmaceutical market through the venture.

Prior to the 2011 IPO the company was owned by a group of institutional investors several of which still hold stakes in Sagent following the offering. For instance Vivo Ventures Funds holds a 32% stake (down from 42%) and Morgan Stanley & Affiliates owns 15% (down from 20%).

EXECUTIVES

Chairman and CEO, Jeffrey M. Yordon, age 66, $615,231 total compensation
EVP Chief Legal Officer and Corporate Secretary, Michael Logerfo, age 50, $312,711 total compensation
EVP National Accounts and Corporate Development, Albert Patterson, age 71, $287,415 total compensation

EVP and CFO, Jonathon Singer, $330,762 total compensation
President, James Hussey
Vice President Corporate Development, Anthony Gulczynski
Vice President, Ravi Malhotra
Vp Of Marketing & Bd, Joe Mase
Vice President Of Financial Planning And Analysis, Peter Jensen
Vice President Of Human Resources, John Matthei
Chairman and CEO, Jeffrey M. Yordon, age 66
Board Of Directors, Tony Krizman
Auditors: Ernst&YoungLLP

LOCATIONS

HQ: Sagent Pharmaceuticals Inc
1901 North Roselle Road, Suite 700, Schaumburg, IL 60195
Phone: 847 908-1600
Web: www.sagentpharma.com

PRODUCTS/OPERATIONS

2011 Sales

	$ mil.	% of total
Anti-infective	63.5	42
Critical care	54.5	36
Oncology	34.4	22
Total	**$152.4**	**100**

Selected Products

Adenosine
Ampicillin
Atracurium
Azithromycin
Bacitracin
Cefazolin
Cefepime
Cefoxitin
Ceftazidime
Ceftriaxone
Cefuroxime
Ciprofloxacin
Clindamycin
Epirubicin
Etomidate
Fluconazole
Fludarabine
Gemcitabine
Granisetron
Haloperidol
Heparin
Irinotecan
Labetalol
Levofloxacin
Mesna
Metoprolol
Midazolam
Orphenadrine
Oxacillin
Oxaliplatin
Paclitaxel
Pamidronate
Piperacillin
Polymyxin B
Rocuronium
Sumatriptan
Topotecan
Vecuronium bromide
Vinorelbine

COMPETITORS

AstraZeneca	Pfizer
Baxter International	Sandoz International
Boehringer Ingelheim	GmbH
DRAXIS	Spectrum
Fresenius	Pharmaceuticals
Hikma	Teva
Hospira	

HISTORICAL FINANCIALS

Company Type: Public

Income Statement

FYE: December 31

	REVENUE ($ mil.)	NET INCOME ($ mil.)	NET PROFIT MARGIN	EMPLOYEES
12/13	244.7	29.5	12.1%	269
12/12	183.6	(16.8)	—	98
12/11	152.4	(26.4)	—	99
12/10	74.0	(24.5)	—	85
12/09	29.2	(30.5)	—	0
Annual Growth	**70.1%**	**—**	**—**	**—**

2013 Year-End Financials

Debt ratio: 3.3%
Return on equity: 16.0%
Cash ($ mil.): 156
Current ratio: 3.71
Long-term debt ($ mil.): —

No. of shares (mil.): 31
Dividends
Yield: —
Payout: —
Market value ($ mil.): 807

	STOCK PRICE ($) FY Close	P/E High/Low	PER SHARE ($) Earnings	Dividends	Book Value
12/13	25.38	25 14	0.99	0.00	7.42
12/12	16.09	— —	(0.60)	0.00	4.69
12/11	21.00	— —	(1.31)	0.00	5.08
Annual Growth	**9.9%**	**— —**	**—**	**—**	**20.9%**

Salix Pharmaceuticals Ltd

Salix Pharmaceuticals is a finishing school for drugs. With a focus on treating gastrointestinal ailments the company prefers to acquire drug candidates nearing commercial viability. It then takes them through the final development stages and brings them to market. The company's marketed products include Xifaxan (an antibiotic for gastrointestinal troubles) Pepcid (gastric ulcers and acid reflux) and Apriso and Colazal (for ulcerative colitis). Other products include colonoscopy preparatory bowel purgatives MoviPrep OsmoPrep and Visicol. Its late-stage candidates include both new drugs and new uses for existing drugs.

Geographic Reach

Salix primarily conducts sales in the US market though it has limited commercial drug operations in Europe and about 20 countries in other global regions.

Operations

The company's biggest seller is Xifaxan (rifaximin) an antibiotic that has the ability to get into the gut but not into the bloodstream. The drug is approved as a treatment for travelers' diarrhea and other disorders and Salix is looking to expand its indications. Other medicines include fecal incontinence medication Solesta and Deflux a treatment for vesicoureteral reflux (a malformation of the bladder in children). The company launched a new proprietary product in 2012 after receiving FDA approval for Fulyzaq which treats diarrhea in HIV/AIDS patients.

Salix's Colazal Anusol Pepcid and Proctocort brands are mature with no patent protection but enjoy name brand recognition.

In the drug development realm Salix avoids the riskier capital intensive process of early-stage research by sticking strictly to late stage trials and commercialization activities. It holds the development and marketing rights to many of its products through long-standing licensing agreements with other drug companies. It also sidesteps the expense of maintaining manufacturing facilities by relying on third-party manufacturers to produce its materials.

Sales and Marketing

Salix's direct sales and marketing teams primarily targets US gastroenterologists as well as colorectal surgeons hepatologists and other medical professionals. The company has a small direct sales force in Europe and it uses independent distributors in Europe and other regions. Advertising expenses totaled about $21 million in 2012 up from $11 million the previous year.

Financial Performance

Salix has truly enjoyed the payoff of drug development and other growth efforts in recent years. Revenues increased 36% to $735 million in 2012 due to higher sales of Xifaxan Apriso Deflux and Relistor. Revenues jumped 60% in 2011 due in part to expanded indications for Xifaxan strong sales of purgatives and new products from acquisitions.

The revenue jump in 2011 also helped to give the company its first positive net income report since 2007; another profit of $36 million was reported in 2012 down 26% from the prior year due to increased expenses from sales force expansion and acquisition efforts.

Strategy

Salix is investing heavily in developing the Xifaxan antibiotic for additional uses including irritable bowel syndrome and Crohn's disease. It also aims to license or develop new late-stage pharmaceuticals and bring development-stage candidates to market.

Mergers and Acquisitions

To keep its operations nimble in the face of future additional patent expirations Salix depends on regular shopping trips to keep its pipeline well stocked. Sometimes it buys the rights to develop a candidate and sometimes it buys whole portfolios that include approved and marketed drugs.

In 2012 it paid $10 million for the licensing rights to an extended-release version of rifaximin with plans to use it as a treatment for Crohn's disease. Its 2011 purchase of US drugmaker Oceana Therapeutics added gastroenterology and urology therapeutics including Solesta and Deflux; the buy also added international operations as both drugs are sold overseas. The company also licensed rights to another drug Relistor which was launched in the US later that year.

Ownership

Wellington Management owns some 13% of the company.

EXECUTIVES

Vice President Human Resources, Jenifer Reynolds
President CEO and Director, Carolyn J. Logan, age 65, $867,450 total compensation
EVP Medical Research and Development and Chief Development Officer, William P. (Bill) Forbes, age 52, $466,395 total compensation
EVP Business Development, Rick D. Scruggs, $436,966 total compensation
SVP Finance and Administrative Services and Acting CFO, Timothy J. Creech
Senior Vice President Of Development Chief Security Officer, Lorin Johnson
Vice President Medical Affairs, Michael Steward

Vice President Sales, Stephen Casey
Chairman, Thomas W. (Tom) D'Alonzo, age 70
Auditors: PricewaterhouseCoopersLLP

LOCATIONS

HQ: Salix Pharmaceuticals Ltd
8510 Colonnade Center Drive, Raleigh, NC 27615
Phone: 919 862-1000
Web: www.salix.com

PRODUCTS/OPERATIONS

2012 Sales

	$ mil.	% of total
Xifaxan	514.5	70
Inflammatory bowel disease (Colazol Apriso Giazo)	85.5	12
Purgatives (OsmoPrep/MoviPrep)	64.9	10
Other	70.5	10
Total	735.4	100

Selected Products

Marketed
  Anusol (hydrocortisone suppositories)
  Apriso (ulcerative colitis)
  Azasan (rheumatoid arthritix kidney transplantation)
  Colazal (ulcerative colitis)
  Deflux (vesicoureteral reflux)
  Diuril (hypertension edema)
  Giazo (inflammatory bowel disease)
  Metozolv (gastroesophageal reflux)
  MoviPrep (purgative)
  OsmoPrep (purgative)
  Pepcid (ulcers)
  Proctocort (hydrocortisone suppositories)
  Relistor (treatment for opiod-induced constipation)
  Solesta (fecal incontinence)
  Visicol (purgative)
  Xifaxan (gastrointestinal antibiotic)

Selected Licensing Agreements

2012
  Extended-release rifaximin (Crohn's disease)
2011
  Relistor ($60 million upfront from Progenics
  Pharmaceuticals opiod-induced constipation)
2010
  Lumacan ($4 million from Photocure ASA
  colonoscopy fluorescent agent)

Selected Acquisitions

2011
  Oceana Therapeutics ($300 million gastroenterology &
  urology drugs)

COMPETITORS

Abbott Labs	Prometheus Labs
Aptalis Pharma	Ranbaxy
Bayer AG	Pharmaceuticals
Cubist Pharmaceuticals	Shire
Ferndale Pharma Group	Takeda Pharmaceutical
GlaxoSmithKline	Warner Chilcott
Pfizer	

HISTORICAL FINANCIALS

Company Type: Public

Income Statement

FYE: December 31

	REVENUE ($ mil.)	NET INCOME ($ mil.)	NET PROFIT MARGIN	EMPLOYEES
12/13	933.8	143.0	15.3%	552
12/12	735.4	64.2	8.7%	525
12/11	540.4	87.4	16.2%	490
12/10	336.9	(27.0)	—	390
12/09	232.8	(43.6)	—	395
Annual Growth	41.5%	—		8.7%

2013 Year-End Financials

Debt ratio: 55.7%
Return on equity: 21.9%
Cash ($ mil.): 1,157
Current ratio: 5.46
Long-term debt ($ mil.): 1,640
No. of shares (mil.): 62
Dividends
  Yield: —
  Payout: —
Market value ($ mil.): 5,661

	STOCK PRICE ($) FY Close	P/E High/Low		PER SHARE ($) Earnings	Dividends	Book Value
12/13	89.94	39	18	2.18	0.00	11.77
12/12	40.47	51	35	1.01	0.00	9.20
12/11	47.85	32	18	1.44	0.00	9.28
12/10	46.96	—	—	(0.47)	0.00	6.91
12/09	25.39	—	—	(0.88)	0.00	6.58
Annual Growth	37.2%	—	—	—	—	15.7%

Sanchez Energy Corp.

The Sanchez family has been around South Texas almost as long as the oil found in the Eagle Ford Shale. Sanchez Energy is a spin off from Sanchez Oil & Gas Corporation (SOG) a private firm owned by the Sanchez family who trace their family history back to the founding of Laredo in 1755. Sanchez Energy was formed in 2011 to take over almost 39000 acres (about 60 sq. mi.) of land in the oil-rich Eagle Ford Shale in South Texas. In 2013 it had 140000 net acres in the Eagle Ford play and 40000 net acres in the Tuscaloosa Marine Shale in Louisiana. It also has undeveloped acreage in Montana. The company reported estimated proved reserves of in 21.2 million barrels of oil equivalent in 2012.

Sales and Marketing

Three customers accounted for 97% of the company's revenues in 2012 (one for 66%).

Financial Performance

Sanchez Energy's revenue increased by 197% in 2012 primarily due to the higher oil and natural gas production and higher oil prices partially offset by lower natural gas prices. The company reported a net Loss of $16.2 million (compared to net income of $2 million in 2011) due to increased operating costs.

Strategy

Supported by strong oil prices the company is focused on developing oil shale plays in Texas and Louisiana.

Mergers and Acquisitions

In 2013 the company acquired 43000 net acres in the Eagle Ford Shale in South Texas from Hess for $265 million. The assets Dimmit Frio LaSalle and Zavala Counties included 50 gross wells producing 4500 barrels of oil equivalent per day. It completed another Eagle Ford purchase the Wycross acquisition for $230.1 million. That deal added production of 2000 barrels of barrels of oil equivalent per day. Moving into a new area in 2013 the company bought 40000 net undeveloped acres in the Tuscaloosa Marine Shale.

Company Background

Sanchez Energy went public in 2011 with a $203 million IPO.

Following the offering SOG subsidiary Sanchez Energy Partners I (SEPI) transferred the acreage assets to Sanchez Energy. SEP I began acquiring leases in the Eagle Ford Shale area in 2008 the same year Petrohawk Energy announced its discovery of the oil deposit. (Fortunately the Sanchez

businesses have a storied history with South Texas and wasted no time buying land leases).

EXECUTIVES

EVP and CFO, Michael G. Long, $240,000 total compensation
President and CEO, Antonio R. Sanchez, $325,000 total compensation
COO, Christopher Heinson
Vice President Global Marine And Energy, Jerri Jones
Vice President Engineering, William Satterfield
Vice President, Robert Ramsey
Senior Vice President Geoscience, Patrick Talamas
Chairman, A. R. Sanchez
Auditors: BDOUSALLP

LOCATIONS

HQ: Sanchez Energy Corp.
1111 Bagby Street, Suite 1800, Houston, TX 77002
Phone: 713 783-8000   Fax: 713 756-2784
Web: www.sanchezenergycorp.com

COMPETITORS

Abraxas Petroleum	Forest Oil
Alta Mesa Holdings	Freeport-McMoRan Oil &
Anadarko Petroleum	Gas LLC
Apache	Magnum Hunter
BP	Resources
Cabot Oil & Gas	Petrohawk Energy
Carrizo Oil & Gas	Rosetta Resources Inc.
Chesapeake Energy	SM Energy
Clayton Williams	Swift Energy
Energy	Talisman Energy
Comstock Resources	

HISTORICAL FINANCIALS

Company Type: Public

Income Statement

FYE: December 31

	REVENUE ($ mil.)	NET INCOME ($ mil.)	NET PROFIT MARGIN	EMPLOYEES
12/13	314.4	26.9	8.6%	0
12/12	43.1	(16.3)	—	0
12/11	14.5	1.9	13.6%	0
12/10	4.5	(2.7)	—	70
12/09	0.2	0.0	18.5%	0
Annual Growth	500.9%	395.2%	—	—

2013 Year-End Financials

Debt ratio: 36.4%
Return on equity: 4.3%
Cash ($ mil.): 153
Current ratio: 1.38
Long-term debt ($ mil.): 593
No. of shares (mil.): 46
Dividends
  Yield: —
  Payout: —
Market value ($ mil.): 1,136

	STOCK PRICE ($) FY Close	P/E High/Low		PER SHARE ($) Earnings	Dividends	Book Value
12/13	24.51	137	78	0.22	0.00	18.49
12/12	18.00	—	—	(0.56)	0.00	10.86
12/11	17.26	205	190	0.09	0.00	6.52
Annual Growth	19.2%	—	—	56.3%	—	68.4%

Schulman (A.), Inc.

A. Schulman might consider itself the master of all masterbatches. The company is a global leader in masterbatches color and additive concentrates that are combined with polymer resins by its customers to provide color to plastic products or enhance their performance in some way. A. Schulman also produces engineered plastics (compounded products used in making durable goods appliances and toys) and specialty powders (compounded resin powders used in rotationally molded products ranging from kayaks to gas tanks). It also serves as a distributor for polymer producers worldwide. Its high-performance plastic compounds and resins are used in packaging consumer products and automotive and industrial products.

Geographic Reach

The company organizes its core businesses — masterbatch engineered plastics specialty powders custom performance color and distribution services —into four main region-based segments: Europe Middle East and Africa (EMEA) the Americas and Asia/Pacific (APAC). The company operates 36 manufacturing facilities: 21 in the EMEA and APAC regions and 15 in the Americas.

Operations

Masterbatches are highly concentrated compounds combined with polymer resins by customers at the point-of-process to provide a material solution that meets needed performance criteria for a given product application. Its masterbatches are used as the key ingredient in a customer's product formula. Its additive compounds are used to provide a range of colors or to enhance performance properties including antibacterial heat-sensitive fluorescent and processing attributes. In fiscal year 2013 the masterbatch solutions product family accounted for 35% of the company's total sales. Engineered plastics combine high-performance polymer resins with various modifiers reinforcements additives and pigments which result in a compound tailored to meet stringent customer specifications for durable applications. A. Schulman has been formulating compounds since the early 1950s to meet the needs of the plastics industry. Its blends include polyolefins nylons polyesters elastomers and PVC (polyvinyl chloride).As a distributor A. Schulman works with leading global polymer producers to assist in servicing market segments that are not easily accessible to these producers or does not fit into these producers' core customer segment or supply chain. Specialty powders includes size reduction and resins for the injection blow molding and rotational molding markets. Specialty powders are used in applications such as powder coating cosmetics and the manufacture of additives. The rotational molding process is used to make plastic products including gas and water tanks and playground slides. The company provides other services such as grinding or size reduction of specialty powders for its customers. In fiscal year 2013 the specialty powders product family accounted for 15% of the A. Schulman's consolidated net sales. Custom Performance Colors offers powdered or pelletized color concentrates custom-designed to enhance thermoplastic resins.

A. Schulman offers tolling services to customers in all product families except for distribution services.

Sales and Marketing

The company's customers span a wide range of markets such as packaging mobility building and construction electronics and electrical agriculture personal care and hygiene sports leisure and home custom services and others. In fiscal year 2013 the company's five largest customers accounted for in the aggregate for less than 10% of total sales.

Financial Performance

A. Schulman's revenues have been restated due to divestiture of its rotational compounding business in Australia. In fiscal year 2013 its revenues grew by 1% due to incremental net sales and volume from the Elian and ECM Plastics Inc. acquisitions. Net sales also rose benefited from a $4.7 million favorable impact of foreign currency translation. In fiscal year 2013 the company's net income decreased by 49% due to higher foreign currency transaction losses as the result of increased import activity in Brazil and a growth in the loss from discontinued operations.A. Schulman's operating cash inflow decreased to $83.7 million in fiscal year 2013 (compared to $99.5 million in fiscal year 2012) was due to the decline in net income.

Strategy

Acquisitions are a key part of the company's strategy for growth as it continually seeks to expand its global footprint to maximize opportunities. It targets strategic acquisitions that will speed its entry into underserved markets. A. Schulman also looks to new product development to drive growth and is focusing on higher margin applications. In its engineered plastics business it seeks to reduce its North American auto capacity and focus on its most profitable lines of business. It also wants to continue development of sustainable "green" products. To counteract the global economic slump the company has been cutting back on capacity and using the assets of its global operations effectively.

Recent acquisitions have strengthened the company's core businesses serving its custom performance colors masterbatch solutions engineered plastics and specialty powders customers.

A. Schulman focuses its organic growth strategy on increasing the company's ability to leverage new and existing products into new geographic markets further explore adjacent markets and improve profitability. Creating new and collaborative innovation models is key to the growth strategy As part of this push therefore the company has introduced three new global innovation centers in Germany Mexico and the US (Akron Ohio) to help align the company's global technology and product development efforts with the current requirements and emerging needs of its customers and end-markets.

It also sells underperforming units. In 2013 it sold its Australia-based rotational compounding business and further restructured in its EMEA region due to the weak economic climate in Europe. This move will allow their APAC team to focus on their considerable opportunities in profitable growth markets and seek out further strategic acquisitions in the region including in Australia.

Mergers and Acquisitions

To complement its existing capabilities and expand its product offerings and geographic reach in target markets in 2014 the company acquired control of the Specialty Plastics business segment from US-based Ferro Corporation for $91 million and Australia-based marketbatch maker Compco for $6.7 million. The Perrite acquisition is expected to increase revenues in A. Schulman's APAC segment by 35% and will double the size of the company's existing engineered plastics business in the region.

Acquisitions in 2013 included Network Polymers Inc. a US-based niche engineered plastics compounding business for $49.5 million; Perrite Group a thermoplastics manufacturing business with operations in Malaysia the United Kingdom and France. for $51.3 million net of cash. Perrite has manufactured and distributed thermoplastic compounds for the electrical automotive and industrial markets for more than 35 years offering a broad portfolio of standard and custom compounded polymer products.

HISTORY

Alex Schulman founded A. Schulman in 1928 as a rubber brokerage. In 1937 he hired William Zekan as an office boy after meeting the 18-year-old caddie on a golf course. With rubber in short supply during WWII A. Schulman began using scrap plastic. Zekan was appointed head of the firm's New York sales office in 1947 and became #2 in the company in 1953.

A. Schulman abandoned the scrap market in the 1950s to focus on plastic compounds. Schulman died in 1962 and Zekan headed the company taking it public in 1972. A. Schulman set up a joint venture in 1988 with Mitsubishi to supply plastic compounds to Honda Nissan and Toyota.

Zekan died in 1991 and was replaced by company veteran Terry Haines. He expanded A. Schulman through acquisitions that included Diffusion Plastique from Atochem (subsidiary of Elf Aquitaine now called TOTAL) in 1991 and Exxon's ComAlloy International in 1994. The next year the company bought a polymer unit from J. M. Huber and polypropylene interests from Eastman Chemical.

A. Schulman opened its first plant in Asia in 1997. The next year it cut production to compensate for an industry slowdown. The company also bought an Italy-based distributor and agreed to supply all of the color concentrate for Procter & Gamble's molded white containers. In 1999 A. Schulman spent $35 million to renovate manufacturing facilities. It joined DuPont that year to make bumper fascias and other moldings for cars such as the Dodge Neon.

As pricing pressures continued in 2000 A. Schulman moved to cut its costs by closing a number of sales offices and its plant in Akron Ohio. The company's 2001 sales were hurt by the weakening economy especially in the US where capacity utilization was down by 5%. Although A. Schulman's sales remained flat in 2002 the company managed to boost profits mostly through a workforce reduction and the closing of more costly facilities.

Haines and other members of management came under fire with investors' criticism that began in 2007 and Haines stepped down early in 2008. He was replaced by director Joseph Gingo a former Goodyear executive. Barington Capital Group had demanded the right to name a director in 2007. Its success spurred another investor group Ramius Capital to offer up its own set of directors for A. Schulman's early-2008 elections. Ramius like Barington was eager to get Schulman to consider a sale or merger of the company or at the very least a change in company strategy that had led to continually disappointing results. Ultimately Ramius won the right to nominate candidates for the board.

Encouraged by the investors and their representative board members the company idled one manufacturing facility and sold another in 2008; it also brought in UBS to explore possibilities of selling part or all of the company. (An offer from an unidentified buyer was turned down in mid-2008.)

After failing to find a manufacturing partner for its Invision line of plastic sheet products it discontinued the line and shut down the operation in 2009. The next year it moved several of its operations from its Crumlin South Wales operation to larger facilities and eliminated 30 jobs in a move to improve efficiency.

In 2010 the company acquired McCann Color an Ohio-based producer of color concentrates. The deal for about $10 million in cash bolstered A. Schulman's existing master batch manufacturing and product development facilities in Akron Ohio and San Luis Potos Mexico.

That year the company also acquired Houston-based ICO in a deal that valued the plastics maker at $190 million. The deal expanded A. Schulman's global presence and its masterbatch and molding businesses.

The company completed its acquisition of Brazilian plastics maker Mash Compostos Pl˜sticos in 2011. Mash Compostos is a S o Paulo-based producer of additives and engineered plastics compounds. That year it extended its presence in South America by agreeing to acquire a 51% interest in a joint venture with Argentina-based Surplast. Surplast makes rotational molding products.

To broaden its stance as a global manfacturer of engineered plastics in niche markets the company agreed in 2012 to form a joint venture with Saudi Arabia-based National Petrochemical Industrial Company a subsidiary of Alujain Corp. The 50-50 joint venture is expected to be called NAT-PET-Schulman Engineering Plastic Compounds and will produce and market polypropylene compounds.

EXECUTIVES

VP and CFO, Joseph J. (Joe) Levanduski, age 51, $415,717 total compensation
General Manager ICO Australasia, Derek R. Bristow, age 54
General Manager and COO Americas, Gustavo P Áez, $350,000 total compensation
President CEO and Director, Bernard Rzepka, age 54, $555,000 total compensation
VP and CIO, Donald B. (Mickey) McMillan
VP and Chief Marketing Officer, Patricia M. Mishic
Senior Vice President Of Sales, Charlie Busceme
Vice President Global Supply Chain And Chief Procurement Officer, Gary Miller
Vp-gen Mngr Emea, Heinrich Lingnau
Senior Vice President Of Integrated Brand Development, Kay Schubert
Vice President Emea, Giovanna Rabolini
Vice President Chief Legal Officer, David Mi
Vice President North American, John Myles
Vice President General Counsel Secretary, David C Minc, age 66
President CEO and Director, Bernard Rzepka, age 54
Auditors: PricewaterhouseCoopersLLP

LOCATIONS

HQ: Schulman (A.), Inc.
3637 Ridgewood Road, Fairlawn, OH 44333
Phone: 330 666-3751   **Fax:** 330 668-7204
Web: www.aschulman.com

2013 Sales

	% of total
Germany	25
United States	18
France	10
Other international	47
Total	**100**

PRODUCTS/OPERATIONS

2013 Sales by Segment

	$ mil.	% of total
Europe Middle East & Africa (EMEA)	1405.9	66
Americas	600.8	28
Asia/Pacific (APAC)	126.7	6
Total	**2133.4**	**100**

2013 Sales by Product

	$ mil.	% of total
Plastics Products		
Masterbatch	745.2	35
Engineered Plastics	557.4	26
Specialty Powders	311.7	15
Distribution Services	359.4	17
Custom performance colors	159.7	7
Total	**2133.4**	**100**

Selected Brands

Masterbatch Products
Polybatch (additive compounds)
Polyblak (carbon black concentrates)
Polywhite (white concentrates)
Polypearl (additive compounds)
Polystat (antistatic Concentrates)
Papermatch (masterbatch for synthetic paper)
Engineered Plastics
Clarix (thermoplastic iconomer resins)
Invision (thermoplastic elastomers and vulcanizates)
Schuladur (PBT compounds)
Schulamid (nylon compounds)
Schulablend M/MK (nylon/ABS alloys)
Polyflam (flame-retardant thermoplastics)
Polyfort (polypropylene polyethylene EVA compounds)
Polyvin (flexible thermoplastic PVC compounds)
Specialty Powders
Ecorene (renewably sourced thermoplastic powders)
ICO-Fine (ultra-fine thermoplastic powders)
Icorene (compound powders for custom colors)
Polyaxis (compounds for rotational molding)
Schulink (cross-linkable resin used in rotational molding)
Superlinear (material offers high heat-distortion temperatures)

COMPETITORS

Albemarle	DuPont
Ampacet	Ferro
Axiall	Momentive
BASF SE	PolyOne
Clariant	RTP Company
Dow Chemical	

HISTORICAL FINANCIALS

Company Type: Public

Income Statement

FYE: August 31

	REVENUE ($ mil.)	NET INCOME ($ mil.)	NET PROFIT MARGIN	EMPLOYEES
08/14	2,447.0	56.1	2.3%	3,900
08/13	2,133.4	26.1	1.2%	3,200
08/12	2,106.7	50.8	2.4%	3,100
08/11	2,192.9	41.0	1.9%	3,000
08/10	1,590.4	43.9	2.8%	2,900
Annual Growth	**11.4%**	**6.4%**	**—**	**7.7%**

2014 Year-End Financials

Debt ratio: 24.5%	No. of shares (mil.): 29
Return on equity: 10.8%	Dividends
Cash ($ mil.): 135	Yield: 0.0%
Current ratio: 1.88	Payout: 41.8%
Long-term debt ($ mil.): 339	Market value ($ mil.): 1,134

	STOCK PRICE ($) FY Close	P/E High/Low	PER SHARE ($) Earnings	PER SHARE ($) Dividends	PER SHARE ($) Book Value
08/14	38.83	22 14	1.91	0.80	18.04
08/13	26.96	37 26	0.89	0.78	17.40
08/12	24.29	16 10	1.72	0.72	17.11
08/11	18.24	20 13	1.32	0.62	17.92
08/10	18.17	17 10	1.57	0.60	15.50
Annual Growth	**20.9%**		**5.0%**	**7.5%**	**3.9%**

SciClone Pharmaceuticals, Inc.

SciClone hopes its drug sales create a whirlwind in China. The drug firm's flagship product Zadaxin is approved for use in some 30 countries including China its primary market. Zadaxin treats hepatitis B as a vaccine adjuvant (to boost a vaccine's effectiveness) as well as certain cancers. The company also partners with other drug makers including Baxter International and Pfizer to market those companies' products in China. SciClone also maintains a pipeline of products that it is shepherding through the approval process in China. The company filed for bankruptcy in 2014

Operations

SciClone relies upon third parties in Europe and the US to manufacture Zadaxin. However the drug has yet to receive the regulatory green light in the world's two largest drug markets –the US and the European Union (EU). SciClone is working with development partner Sigma-Tau to gain marketing approval in the US and EU. In the meantime the company figures that China will be the second largest market in the world soon enough so it is focusing more of its efforts on development there. Its pipeline includes CDBead Neucardin Loramyc and ProFlow along with cardiovascular drug Aggrastat.

Geographic Reach

Zadaxin is sold in 30 countries across Asia/Pacific Latin American countries Eastern Europe and the Middle Ease. China accounts for about 97% of sales.

Sales and Marketing

SciClone's own sales force markets the drug to doctors and hospitals in China; distributors handle sales and marketing of the drug in other countries. In 2013 SinoPharm and Sanofi accounted for 75% and 20% of revenue respectively.

Financial Performance

In 2013 SciClone reported a 19% drop in revenue from $156 million to $127 million as demand dropped for Zadaxin and other products. About $5.5 million of the drop was due to the non-renewal of the company's agreements with Sanofi. Net income however recovered slightly after being down in 2012. In 2013 it was $11 million up $1 million a 14% increase as the company laid off about 300 sales people to cut expenses. Cash from operations also fell by $34 million to $9.5 million due to the absence of cash from intangible assets.

Strategy

SciClone makes no secret of its plans to expand in China particularly in the largest cities. It does this by launching new products from its pipeline and through acquisitions.

SciClone's purchase of China-based NovaMed Pharmaceuticals added a handful of products in development including cancer neurology and pain medicines and broadened SciClone's existing sales force in the country. While SciClone's Zadaxin commands higher prices due to its reputation and branding lower-priced generics from local manufacturers are a constant threat to its market share.

Distribution agreements include those with Biocompatibles Strakan International BIOALLIANCE PHARMA Applied Pharma Research Baxter International Pfizer Zensun Science & Technology and Taiwan Liposome Company.

As a research and development company SciClone has already gone through a couple of candidates that turned out to be duds. While such disappointments are expensive they are the nature of drug discovery and development.

EXECUTIVES

SVP Scientific Affairs and Chief Scientific Officer, Cynthia W. Tuthill
President and CEO, Friedhelm Blobel, $500,000 total compensation
SVP Finance and CFO, Wilson W. Cheung
Vice President - Finance; Chief Financial Officer - China Operations, Lan Xie
CEO China, Hong Zhao
Vice President, Eric Hoechstetter
Vice President Quality, Peter Shao
Executive Vice President Clinical Affairs, Willis Maddrey
Chairman, Jon S. Saxe
Board Member, Gregg A Lapointe, age 56
Board Member, Richard J (Rick) Hawkins, age 66
Director Board Of Directors, Ken Cheung
Board Member, Bo Shao
Board Member, Peter Barrett
Treasury Manager, Wayne Wang
Auditors: Ernst&YoungLLP

LOCATIONS

HQ: SciClone Pharmaceuticals, Inc.
950 Tower Lane, Suite 900, Foster City, CA 94404
Phone: 650 358-3456
Web: www.sciclone.com

2013 Revenues

	$ mil.	% of total
China	122.6	97
Rest of world	4.5	3
Total	**127.1**	**100**

PRODUCTS/OPERATIONS

2013 Revenues

	$ mil.	% of total
Product sales	99.4	78
Promotion sales	27.7	22
Total	**127.1**	**100**

Selected Acquisitions

NovaMed Pharmaceuticals (2011 $62 million)

COMPETITORS

Amgen	Hemispherx BioPharma
Biostar Pharmaceuticals	Idenix Pharmaceuticals
	Merck
Bristol-Myers Squibb	Roche Holding
Gilead Sciences	Sanofi

HISTORICAL FINANCIALS

Company Type: Public

Income Statement

FYE: December 31

	REVENUE ($ mil.)	NET INCOME ($ mil.)	NET PROFIT MARGIN	EMPLOYEES
12/13	127.0	10.9	8.6%	570
12/12	156.2	9.6	6.2%	870
12/11	133.6	28.4	21.3%	875
12/10	85.1	21.0	24.8%	261
12/09	72.4	11.9	16.5%	223
Annual Growth	**15.1%**	**(2.1%)**	**—**	**26.4%**

2013 Year-End Financials

Debt ratio: 0.9%
Return on equity: 7.5%
Cash ($ mil.): 85
Current ratio: 4.27
Long-term debt ($ mil.): —

No. of shares (mil.): 52
Dividends
Yield: —
Payout: —
Market value ($ mil.): 264

	STOCK PRICE ($) FY Close	P/E High/Low		PER SHARE ($) Earnings	Dividends	Book Value
12/13	5.04	31	22	0.20	0.00	2.80
12/12	4.31	44	25	0.16	0.00	2.63
12/11	4.29	13	7	0.50	0.00	2.60
12/10	4.18	10	5	0.43	0.00	1.71
12/09	2.33	19	3	0.25	0.00	1.22
Annual Growth	**21.3%**	**—**	**—**	**(5.4%)**	**—**	**23.2%**

Select Comfort Corp.

Select Comfort has got your number. The firm's line of Sleep Number beds which can carry hefty price tags use air-chamber technology to allow sleepers to adjust the firmness on each side of the mattress providing better sleep quality and addressing sleep-related problems such as lower back pain. Select Comfort also offers foundations frames pillows and a sofa bed. A leading bedding retailer in the US Select Comfort operates more than 425 company-owned stores. The air-bed maker also sells through a company-operated call center its own website and on the QVC shopping channel. Select Comfort was founded in 1987 has grown to become one of the nation's leading bed makers and retailers.

Geographic Reach
Minneapolis-based Select Comfort operates company-owned retail stores in 45 US states. Its two largest markets are California and Texas which combined account for 20% of its store base. The mattress giant distributes its products in the US and Canada and in Alaska Hawaii and Australia through retail partners.

Operations
The firm operates two manufacturing plants (South Carolina and Utah) which supply beds on a just-in-time basis to its retail stores.

Sales and Marketing
Select Comfort spent about $398 million on sales and marketing efforts in 2012 compared with $317.5 million in 2011 and about $270 million in 2010. The year-over-year increase was primarily due to a 39% increase in media spending. The company advertises on television radio and in print and is increasing its use of digital advertising.

Financial Performance

After a rough patch during the deep recession and housing crisis which decreased the demand for beds (especially expensive ones) Select Comfort's sales and profits have rebounded sharply posting record highs in 2012. Indeed the company's sales jumped 26% in 2012 compared with 2011 to $935 million after posting a 22% increase in the previous annual comparison. Driving sales was the addition of about 30 new retail stores as well as increasing direct online and wholesale sales. Net income increased 29% over the same period to $78.1 million.

Strategy
While Select Comfort began as a direct marketer of its unique air-filled mattresses over the years it has evolved into a multichannel retailer with company-owned stores in about 45 states. Retail store sales have grown to account for nearly 90% of Select Comfort's total sales.

With its mattresses starting at about $700 and approaching $4000 for its premium product it's not surprising the recession and housing crisis took the air out of the air-bed maker's sales. The steep sales decline put a halt to Select Comfort's aggressive expansion plans. While the company had hoped to grow to more than 600 company-owned stores throughout the US in coming years it is instead looking to end 2013 with between 435 and 445 company-owned locations having shuttered about 100 stores since 2007.

After entering the Canadian market in 2005 Select Comfort in 2007 partnered with two Australian companies to make and distribute Sleep Number beds and accessories in Australia and New Zealand. Additionally the company's air mattresses are found in luxury motor homes and in nearly all of Radisson's hotel rooms in the US Canada and the Caribbean.

Mergers and Acquisitions
In January 2013 Select Comfort acquired Greenville South Carolina-based Comfortaire Corp. a maker of adjustable air-supported sleep systems for $15.5 million.

EXECUTIVES

EVP and Chief Services and Fulfillment Officer, Kathryn V. Roedel, $368,713 total compensation
President and CEO, Shelly R. Ibach, $660,000 total compensation
SVP and CFO, David R. Callen
SVP and CTO, Hunter Saklad
SVP and Chief Legal and Risk Officer and Secretary, Mark A. Kimball
Sr V Pres Marketing, Noel F Schenker
Vice President Strategic Sourcing, Mark Sponsler
Vice President General Merchandise Manager, Annie Bloomquist
Sr Vp Strategic Planning, Tracey T Breazeale
Vice President, Peter Bils
Vice President Consumer Insight And Strategy, Melissa Barra
Vice President, Thomas Albani
Vice President, Christine Day
Vice President Wholesale Channels, Brooks Goldade
Human Resources Director And Vice President, Samantha Po
Vice President Of Product Development, Bill Leary
Vice President Architecture And Strategy, Todd Duran
Vice President Strategy And Architecture, Shailesh Bhor
Rvp, Keith Metting
Rvp South East Region, Kate Banse
Vice President Real Estate, Gary Cary
Rvp North Region, Julie Rude

Vice President Strategic Sourcing, Krista Robinson
Vice President Of Us Retail Sales, Andy P Carlin
Vice President, Jean Michel Valette
Chairman, Jean-Michel Valette
Senior Treasury Analyst, Brian Roth
Auditors: Deloitte&ToucheLLP

LOCATIONS

HQ: Select Comfort Corp.
9800 59th Avenue North, Minneapolis, MN 55442
Phone: 763 551-7000
Web: www.sleepnumber.com

2012 Company-Owned Stores

	No.
Alabama	4
Arizona	8
Arkansas	3
California	50
Colorado	11
Connecticut	6
Delaware	2
Florida	25
Georgia	13
Idaho	2
Illinois	19
Indiana	12
Iowa	6
Kansas	3
Kentucky	5
Louisiana	6
Maine	2
Maryland	11
Massachusetts	4
Michigan	12
Minnesota	13
Mississippi	3
Missouri	12
Montana	2
Nebraska	4
Nevada	4
New Hampshire	5
New Jersey	12
New Mexico	3
New York	9
North Carolina	13
North Dakota	2
Ohio	17
Oklahoma	4
Oregon	4
Pennsylvania	17
South Carolina	4
South Dakota	1
Tennessee	8
Texas	33
Utah	3
Vermont	1
Virginia	11
Washington	10
Wisconsin	11
Total	**410**

PRODUCTS/OPERATIONS

2012 Sales

	% of total
Retail	88
Direct & E-Commerce	9
Wholesale	3
Total	**100**

Selected Products

Bed frames
Foundations
Mattress pads
Mattresses
Pillows
Pillowtops
Sleep Number SofaBed

COMPETITORS

1800Mattress.com	Simmons
Mattress Firm	Spring Air
Serta	Tempur Sealy

HISTORICAL FINANCIALS

Company Type: Public

Income Statement

FYE: December 28

	REVENUE ($ mil.)	NET INCOME ($ mil.)	NET PROFIT MARGIN	EMPLOYEES
12/13	960.1	60.0	6.3%	2,858
12/12	934.9	78.0	8.4%	2,791
12/11*	743.2	60.4	8.1%	2,328
01/11	605.6	31.5	5.2%	2,165
01/10	544.2	35.5	6.5%	2,172
Annual Growth	**15.3%**	**14.0%**	—	**7.1%**

*Fiscal year change

2013 Year-End Financials

Debt ratio: —
Return on equity: 28.7%
Cash ($ mil.): 58
Current ratio: 1.38
Long-term debt ($ mil.): —

No. of shares (mil.): 54
Dividends
Yield: —
Payout: —
Market value ($ mil.): 1,165

	STOCK PRICE ($) FY Close	P/E High/Low		PER SHARE ($) Earnings	Dividends	Book Value
12/13	21.22	26	16	1.08	0.00	4.10
12/12	24.51	25	14	1.37	0.00	3.46
12/11*	21.69	20	8	1.07	0.00	2.29
01/11	9.13	20	9	0.57	0.00	1.05
01/10	6.52	9	0	0.77	0.00	0.41
Annual Growth	**34.3%**	—	—	**8.8%**	—	**77.5%**

*Fiscal year change

SemGroup Corp

Midstream energy player SemGroup moves oil and gas from the wellhead to the marketplace. Through its Crude unit it owns 58% of Rose Rock Midstream which has a 5 million-barrel storage terminal in Cushing Oklahoma and operates 640 miles of crude oil pipeline in Oklahoma and Kansas. Rose Rock Midstream owns 17% of the 530-mile White Cliffs Pipeline which links Midcontinent oil producers to the Cushing terminal. SemGas operates 1600 miles of natural gas and NGL transportation gathering and distribution pipelines. SemMexico makes asphalt products. The company also operates SemCAMS (Canadian natural gas) and SemLogistics (UK oil terminal).

Geographic Reach
The company has operations in Oklahoma City Oklahoma (US); Calgary Alberta (Canada); Puebla (Mexico); and Milford Haven (Wales).

Operations
the company's assets include1600 miles of natural gas and NGL transportation gathering and distribution pipelines in Kansas Oklahoma and Texas and Alberta Canada; 8.7 million barrels of storage capacity in the U.K.; 12 liquid asphalt cement terminals and two emulsion distribution terminals in Mexico; a controlling stake in four natural gas processing plants located in Alberta Canada with a combined capacity of 694 million cubic feet per day; three US-based natural gas processing plants (98 million cubic feet per day capacity).

Financial Performance
Revenues decreased by 16% primarily due to lower revenues from the SemLogistics segment as a result of a lower volume of storage leased and a drop in storage rates as well as a decline in Sem-

Stream results (it sold its last residential propane supply business in September 2012).

Net income increased by a whopping 830% in 2012 mainly due to the gain on disposal or impairment of long-lived assets (including the sale of a SemStream unit).

Strategy
In 2012 the company joined Gavilon Midstream Energy a subsidiary of The Gavilon Group and an affiliate of Chesapeake Energy Corporation to form a joint venture to build a 210-mile pipeline in Oklahoma to deliver crude oil to a 1 million barrel storage facility in Cushing Oklahoma. The pipeline and storage facility will serve the growing drilling industry in western Oklahoma including the Mississippi Lime play.

However despite expansion plans the company has been struggling to improve its financial position for several years. In 2013 it sold a 33% stake in SemCrude Pipeline L.L.C to Rose Rock Midstream for $274 million.

To raise further cash in 2011 the company sold most of its SemStream unit (which delivers natural gas liquids propane and feedstock supplies to customers in more than 40 US states) to NGL Energy Partners for about $282 million. It retained SemStream's residential Arizona propane business but sold that unit in 2012.

In 2011 Plains All-American Pipeline made an unsolicited $1.2 bid to acquire SemGroup which the SemGroup board rejected as substantially undervaluing the company. (The unsolicited bidder officially withdrew in 2012.)

Company Background
Facing a liquidity crisis (overextended by 64 acquisitions for $1.1 billion between 2000 and 2008) in 2008 SemGroup filed for bankruptcy protection from which it emerged in November 2009. Since then the company has been selling assets to pay down debt.

To raise cash as part of its reorganization in 2009 the company sold noncore assets. It sold its SemFuel refined petroleum terminals to Noble Americas (a subsidiary of a Chinese commodities conglomerate) for $65 million. It also sold its stake in SemGroup Energy Partners (now Blueknight Energy Partners) which provides gathering transporting terminalling and storage of crude oil in Oklahoma Kansas and Texas to Netherlands-based natural resources group Vitol for $614 million. In addition the company exited its US asphalt business (SemMaterials). It also sold SemCrude Canada (its Canadian crude oil operations) in 2010.

In 2010 the company realigned its SemGas and SemStream business under a common leadership team in a move to improve their operational efficiency.

EXECUTIVES

Vice President Commercial Development, Jerry Parsons
SVP and CFO, Robert N. (Bob) Fitzgerald, age 55, $371,767 total compensation
General Manager SemCAMS ,Â', David Williams
VP and General Manager SemCAMS, David Gosse
CEO, Carlin G. Conner
Vice President Business Development, Tom Soluri
Vice President, Charles Johnson
Vice President Of Marketing, Sarah Hordinski
Executive Vice President Strategic, James McCarthy
Board Member, Thomas R (Tom) McDaniel, age 65
Chairman, John F. Chlebowski, age 68
Board Member, Sarah M Barpoulis, age 50
Board Member, James Lytal
Auditors: BDOUSALLP

LOCATIONS

HQ: SemGroup Corp
Two Warren Place, 6120 S. Yale Avenue, Suite 700,
Tulsa, OK 74136-4216
Phone: 918 524-8100
Web: www.semgroupcorp.com

PRODUCTS/OPERATIONS

2012 Sales

	% of total
Crude	51
SemMexico	21
SemCAMS	18
SemGas	9
SemLogistics	1
Corporate & other	-
Total	**100**

COMPETITORS

Duke Energy	ONEOK
Dynegy	ProLiance Energy
Enable Oklahoma	Spectra Energy
Enbridge	Williams Companies
Enterprise Products	

HISTORICAL FINANCIALS

Company Type: Public

Income Statement

FYE: December 31

	REVENUE ($ mil.)	NET INCOME ($ mil.)	NET PROFIT MARGIN	EMPLOYEES
12/13	1,427.0	48.1	3.4%	890
12/12	1,237.5	22.1	1.8%	690
12/11	1,479.5	2.3	0.2%	710
12/10	1,630.3	(132.3)	—	800
12/09	157.3	(37.8)	—	0
Annual Growth	**73.5%**	—	—	—

2013 Year-End Financials

Debt ratio: 24.9%
Return on equity: 4.9%
Cash ($ mil.): 79
Current ratio: 1.07
Long-term debt ($ mil.): 615

No. of shares (mil.): 42
Dividends
Yield: 0.9%
Payout: 38.4%
Market value ($ mil.): 2,774

	STOCK PRICE ($) FY Close	P/E High/Low	PER SHARE ($) Earnings	Dividends	Book Value
12/13	65.23	57 34	1.13	0.60	24.78
12/12	39.08	75 50	0.52	0.00	21.25
12/11	26.06	562300	(0.60)	0.00	20.35
12/10	27.17	— —	(3.20)	0.00	20.61
Annual Growth	**33.9%**	— —	—	—	**6.3%**

Senior Housing Properties Trust

Senior Housing Properties Trust (SHPT) offers those in their golden years a place to rest their weary bones. The real estate investment trust (REIT) owns some 375 health care-related properties in about 40 states and Washington DC. Its portfolio includes senior apartments independent and assisted living facilities nursing homes medical

office buildings biotechnology laboratories rehabilitation hospitals and gymnasiums. Tenants such as Sunrise Senior Living and Brookdale Senior Living sign triple-net leases which require them not only to pay rent but to also pay operating expenses remove hazardous waste and carry insurance on their properties.

Geographic Reach

Massachusetts-based Senior Housing Properties Trust (SHPT) owns properties in 40 states and the District of Columbia. Major markets include Florida California and Texas although the REIT's property portfolio is geographically diverse.

Operations

The REIT's portfolio includes some 265 senior living communities 100 medical office buildings and 10 wellness centers. Its holdings are valued at about $5.3 billion. SHPT is managed by Reit Management & Research LLC (RMR) a real estate management company founded in 1986 to manage public investments in real estate.

Financial Performance

The health care REIT reported revenue of $761.4 million in 2013 an increase of 18% versus 2012. Net income rose 11% over the same period to $151.2 million. Driving the increase was the firm's managed senior living communities business which benefited from the acquisition of 12 communities since 2012. The REIT's medical office buildings (MOB) segment posted a gain due to increased rental income from 18 MOBs acquired partially offset by the sale of one MOB in 2012.

Cash generated from operations increased to $306.7 million in 2013 from $283.3 million in 2012 primarily due to a gain on the sale of a single senior living community and two rehabilitation hospitals over the course of the year.

Strategy

SHPT's business strategy is primarily focused on acquiring upscale senior living properties where the majority of residents pay rent through their own resources rather than through government programs. More recently the firm has diversified by purchasing medical office buildings (MOB). Indeed five years ago MOBs contributed just 5% of revenue with senior living communities contributing about 90%. In 2013 senior living accounted for about 70% of total revenue with MOBs contributing more than 25%. The REIT is continuing to grow its MOB holdings. SHPT's investment goals include acquiring additional properties for income and to a lesser extent their appreciation potential. The REIT is counting on the aging of the US population to increase demand for existing independent and assisted living communities nursing homes MOBs and other health care-related properties.

Mergers and Acquisitions

In May 2014 SHPT acquired the headquarters building of Vertex Pharmaceuticals in Boston for $1.1 billion. The purchase fit with the REIT's strategy of focusing on medical office buildings and private-pay (as opposed to government reimbursed) properties.

Company Background

SHPT was spun off from HRPT Properties Trust in 1999 when that REIT sold off its health facilities in order to focus on office and industrial properties.

EXECUTIVES

President and COO, David J. Hegarty, age 58, $217,170 total compensation
CFO and Treasurer, Richard A. (Rick) Doyle, age 46, $171,450 total compensation
Secretary, Jennifer B Clark, age 54
Auditors: Ernst&YoungLLP

LOCATIONS

HQ: Senior Housing Properties Trust
Two Newton Place, 255 Washington Street, Suite 300,
Newton, MA 02458-1634
Phone: 617 796-8350   **Fax:** 617 796-8349
Web: www.snhreit.com

2013 Properties

	No.
Florida	28
Texas	24
Georgia	23
Pennsylvania	21
South Carolina	21
California	20
Massachusetts	19
Wisconsin	19
Virginia	17
Maryland	15
Nebraska	13
North Carolina	13
Tennessee	13
Indiana	12
Colorado	11
Arizona	10
Kentucky	9
Minnesota	8
Alabama	6
Deleware	6
Illinois	6
Iowa	6
New Mexico	6
New York	6
Michigan	5
Kansas	4
New Jersey	4
Oklahoma	4
Washington	4
Mississippi	3
Ohio	3
South Dakota	3
Connecticut	2
District of Columbia	2
Idaho	2
Wyoming	2
Hawaii	1
Missouri	1
Nevada	1
New Hampshire	1
Rhode Island	1
Total	**375**

PRODUCTS/OPERATIONS

2013 Sales

	$ mil.	% of total
Managed Senior Living Communities	302.0	40
Triple Net Senior Living Communities	237.2	31
Medical Office Buildings	204.6	27
All Other Operations	17.6	2
Total	**761.4**	**100**

2013 Properties

	No.
Senior living facilities	265
Medical office buildings	96
Wellness centers	10
Total	**371**

COMPETITORS

Chartwell Seniors Housing	LTC Properties
Extendicare	Legacy Healthcare
G & K Industries	National Health Investors
HCP	Omega Healthcare Investors
Health Care REIT	Sabra Health Care Trust
Healthcare Realty Trust	Ventas

HISTORICAL FINANCIALS

Company Type: Public

Income Statement

FYE: December 31

	REVENUE ($ mil.)	NET INCOME ($ mil.)	NET PROFIT MARGIN	EMPLOYEES
12/13	761.4	151.1	19.9%	0
12/12	644.8	135.8	21.1%	0
12/11	450.0	151.4	33.6%	0
12/10	339.0	116.4	34.4%	0
12/09	297.7	109.7	36.8%	0
Annual Growth	26.5%	8.3%	—	—

2013 Year-End Financials

Debt ratio: 39.7%
Return on equity: 5.5%
Cash ($ mil.): 39
Current ratio: 1.87
Long-term debt ($ mil.): 1,892
No. of shares (mil.): 188
Dividends
  Yield: 7.0%
  Payout: 232.8%
Market value ($ mil.): 4,183

	STOCK PRICE ($) FY Close	P/E High/Low	PER SHARE ($) Earnings	Dividends	Book Value
12/13	22.23	37 27	0.81	1.56	14.76
12/12	23.64	30 25	0.80	1.53	14.99
12/11	22.44	24 19	1.01	1.49	15.20
12/10	21.94	28 21	0.91	1.45	15.00
12/09	21.87	25 13	0.90	1.42	14.92
Annual Growth	0.4%	— —	(2.6%)	2.4%	(0.3%)

Shenandoah Telecommunications Co.

If Virginia is for lovers Shenandoah Telecommunications must carry some interesting conversations. Through subsidiaries the company (which does business as Shentel) provides telecom services in the Shenandoah Valley and beyond. Shenandoah Telephone has more than 22000 access lines in service; (the population of Shenandoah County is 41000). As a Sprint Nextel affiliate subsidiary Shenandoah Personal Communications offers wireless services to more than 262000 customers. The company's cable TV unit serves about 115000 customers while about 13000 households subscribe to its dial-up and broadband Internet access.

Operations

Recognizing that the market for wireline service is shrinking from the rise of mobile phones as a primary phone and VoIP technology Shentel is now primarily a wireless provider. Some 60% of sales come from its being a Sprint affiliate. (It also offers prepaid wireless service from Sprint subsidiaries Virgin Mobile and Boost). Cable services account for about a quarter of sales and its wireline service (which includes Internet service) makes up the remaining 15%.

Geographic Reach

Shentel's wireless segment provides digital wireless service to a portion of a four-state area covering the region from Harrisburg York and Altoona Pennsylvania to Harrisonburg Virginia. Its wireline

cable and Internet services are offered throughout Shenandoah County and portions of northwestern Augusta County Virginia.

Financial Performance

Overall sales grew 15% in 2012 to $288 million due to increases in the number of wireless customers and fees specifically incremental data fees charged to smartphone owners. Its cable segment also enjoyed growth as customers switched to higher-priced digital TV and Internet packages and increased the price for video on-demand movies. Profits grew 25% to $16 million from the increase in revenue.

Strategy

In order to focus on its core communications offerings in 2013 the company sold off its Shentel Converged Services business that provided local and long distance voice video and Internet services to off-campus college student housing throughout the southeastern United States.

EXECUTIVES

Vice President Technology, Jeff Pompeo
Vice President - Wireless, William L. (Willy) Pirtle, age 55, $217,765 total compensation
Chairman President and CEO, Christopher E. (Chris) French, age 56, $422,958 total compensation
Executive Vice President and Chief Operating Officer, Earle A. MacKenzie, age 62, $324,304 total compensation
Vice President of Finance Chief Financial Officer and Treasurer, Adele M. Skolits, age 55, $242,115 total compensation
Vice President of Information Technology, Richard A. Baughman
Vice President of Wireline & Engineering, Edward McKay
Vice President - Cable, Thomas (Tom) Whitaker
Vice President, Pompeo Jeffrey
Human Resources Director Vice President, Ken Joyner
Vice President Legal General Counsel Secretary, Ann E Flowers
Chairman President and CEO, Christopher E. (Chris) French, age 56
Vice Chairman, Douglas C. Arthur, age 71
Auditors: KPMGLLP

LOCATIONS

HQ: Shenandoah Telecommunications Co.
500 Shentel Way, Edinburg, VA 22824
Phone: 540 984-4141
Web: www.shentel.com
Maryland
  Hagerstown
Virginia
  Ashburn
  Berryville
  Edinburg
  Front Royal
  Harrisonburg
  Herndon
  Leesburg
  Stephen City
  Warrenton
  Winchester
West Virginia
  Martinsburg

PRODUCTS/OPERATIONS

2012 Sales

	$ mil.	% of total
Wireless	179.6	57
Cable	76.3	25
Wireline	54.6	18
Adjustments	(22.5)	-
Total	**288.1**	**100**

Selected Services

Business telephone products
Cable TV
Cellular products and services
Centrex
Fiber-optic capacity
Internet access
ISDN
Local telephone access
Long-distance
Paging
Security systems

COMPETITORS

AT&T
Aquis Communications Group
Comcast
DISH Network
EarthLink
Lumos
NTELOS
Suddenlink Communications
T-Mobile USA
Time Warner Cable
U.S. Cellular
Verizon
Verizon Wireless Inc.

HISTORICAL FINANCIALS

Company Type: Public

Income Statement

FYE: December 31

	REVENUE ($ mil.)	NET INCOME ($ mil.)	NET PROFIT MARGIN	EMPLOYEES
12/13	308.9	29.5	9.6%	682
12/12	288.0	16.3	5.7%	693
12/11	251.1	12.9	5.2%	669
12/10	194.8	18.0	9.3%	636
12/09	160.6	15.0	9.4%	461
Annual Growth	17.8%	18.3%	—	10.3%

2013 Year-End Financials

Debt ratio: 38.5%
Return on equity: 13.3%
Cash ($ mil.): 38
Current ratio: 2.23
Long-term debt ($ mil.): 224
No. of shares (mil.): 24
Dividends
  Yield: 1.4%
  Payout: 30.7%
Market value ($ mil.): 617

	STOCK PRICE ($) FY Close	P/E High/Low	PER SHARE ($) Earnings	Dividends	Book Value
12/13	25.67	23 11	1.23	0.36	9.75
12/12	15.31	28 14	0.68	0.33	8.67
12/11	10.48	35 17	0.55	0.33	8.29
12/10	18.73	28 21	0.76	0.33	8.01
12/09	20.35	44 25	0.64	0.32	7.42
Annual Growth	6.0%	— —	17.7%	3.0%	7.1%

Shiloh Industries, Inc.

When Shiloh Industries draws a blank it's a good thing. The company produces stampings modular assemblies and steel and welded blanks for the automotive heating and air-conditioning and lawn and garden equipment industries. It also makes tools and assembly equipment for its own use and to sell to OEMs and other suppliers. Shiloh's largest customer is General Motors accounting for about 20% of sales. Other customers include Ford Chrysler (15% of sales) and Toyota as well as home appliance manufacturers construction companies and steel producers. The company traces its roots back to 1950 when it was founded as Shiloh Tool & Die Manufacturing.

Operations

In the stamping process steel is formed into three-dimensional parts as it passes through dies (patterns) in a stamping press. For the automotive and light and heavy truck markets the stampings made by Shiloh Industries are used in heat shields mufflers seat frames structural rails and other structural body components. Shiloh also makes engineered welded blanks (two or more steel sheets welded together) and steel blanks (flat steel cut into two-dimensional shapes). The blanks are used primarily for exterior steel panels such as doors frames and hoods.

Geographic Reach

The company operates 12 manufacturing plants in the US and one in Mexico. It also has sales and technical centers in Canton Michigan and Valley City Ohio; other offices are located in Alabama Georgia Indiana Kentucky Michigan Ohio Tennessee and Wisconsin.

Sales and Marketing

Its direct sales force targets four types of customers: OEM customers Tier I suppliers steel consumers and steel producers.

Financial Performance

The success of Shiloh Industries is linked to the success of North American auto manufacturers who realized an overall industry production increase of 5% in 2013. Shiloh's revenues followed suit and shot up 20% in 2013 to $700 million. Profits also grew 60% to $21 million. Cash provided from operating activities grew to $38 million in 2013 primarily due to the increased revenue base.

Strategy

In 2014 subsidiary Shiloh Die Cast Midwest planned to inject new capital and expand its two facilities in Indiana to support increased demand from automakers for advanced lightweighting technologies. As a part of the expansion it planned to invest about $8 million to renovate and add new equipment to two separate manufacturing sites in Indiana —a 120000 sq.-ft. plant in Auburn and a 106000 sq.-ft. plant in Pierceton. The renovations are scheduled to be complete by 2016.

Mergers and Acquisitions

In 2013 the company bought Contech Castings a provider of high-pressure aluminum die cast parts. The prior year it bought Albany-Chicago Company LLC which makes fully machined and complex aluminum die cast components.

In 2012 it also bought Atlantic Tool & Die's plant in Alabama but closed it the next year.

Company Ownership

Through MTD Holdings (owner of outdoor power equipment maker MTD Products) Shiloh chairman Curtis Moll controls more than half of the company.

HISTORY

Dominick Fanello founded the company in 1950 as Shiloh Tool & Die Manufacturing; in 1954 Fanello became chairman and CEO. In the early 1960s the business expanded into blanking and stamping operations. Shiloh formed a joint venture in 1977 with MTD Products (power equipment) to develop additional steel-processing capabilities.

Shiloh went public in 1993. Seeking to expand beyond northeastern Ohio it formed a joint venture with Shiloh of Michigan and Rouge Steel in 1995 to produce engineered steel blanks in Romulus Michigan. That year 32-year Shiloh veteran Robert Grissinger replaced Fanello as CEO.

In 1996 Shiloh expanded into the automotive tool and stamping business buying Michigan-based Greenfield Die & Manufacturing. Automakers

began to outsource more products and in 1997 Shiloh earmarked $60 million for improvements that included adding new equipment and expanding its welding capacity and warehouse space. It then formed a joint venture with Bing Steel to make steel blanks for cars. Also that year Shiloh bought Michigan steel processor C&H Design.

Fiscal 1998 brought a 23% dip in Shiloh's income in part from the GM strike increased tool and die competition falling prices for engineered scrap steel and the company's difficulty in assimilating acquisitions. Shiloh became more vertically integrated by buying the automotive unit of its majority stockholder MTD Products (later MTD Holdings) in 1999. The company also built a plant in Mexico to serve GM operations there. That year former GM executive John Falcon became CEO.

Shiloh sold its Canton Tool & Die Valley City Steel and Utica Tool & Die subsidiaries in 2000 to concentrate on its automotive operations. The next year the company penned a joint product development agreement with Pullman Industries to offer larger and stronger assemblies.

In early 2002 Theodore Zampetis replaced Jack Falcon as CEO. That year Valley City Steel LLC which was 49%-owned by Shiloh filed Chapter 11 bankruptcy protection through its controlling owner Viking Steel LLC. The following year Shiloh returned to profitability despite lower production in the North American automobile and light truck sectors.

The company was later charged with "constructive fraudulent conveyance" by the bankrupt estate of Valley City Steel which was subsequently awarded almost $5 million in damages. The case which was tried by the US District Court was based on Valley City Steel's claim that Shiloh's part of the transaction —to receive over $12 million plus 49% of Valley City Steel LLC —had not left Valley City Steel enough capital to continue operations. The verdict does not mean that Shiloh intended to defraud rather that the circumstances of the transaction were not fair. Shiloh appealed the verdict in 2007.

In late 2012 Ramzi Y. Hermiz was introduced as the company's newest CEO.

EXECUTIVES

Executive Vice President, David Frink
VP Finance and Treasurer, Thomas M. Dugan, age 50, $175,385 total compensation
President and CEO, Ramzi Y. Hermiz, $700,000 total compensation
VP Purchasing, Kimberly Buhl
VP Sales and Business Development and Managing Director Casting and Machining, David W. Jaeger
VP Information Systems, Tom Luttrell
VP Europe, Johan Westman
VP Operations, Eric McAlexander
Vice President Of Engineering, Bernhard Hoffmann
Svp Advanced Technology Sales, James Keys
Corporate Vice President Of Hmn Rsrcs, Nickolas Blauwiekel
Vice President Strategy And Market Development, Brad Tolley
Vice President Human Resources, Jesse Maurer
Vice President Sales And Business Development, Hal Gerber
Chairman, Curtis E. Moll, age 75
Auditors: GrantThorntonLLP

LOCATIONS

HQ: Shiloh Industries, Inc.
880 Steel Drive, Valley City, OH 44280
Phone: 330 558-2600　　**Fax:** 330 558-2666
Web: www.shiloh.com

PRODUCTS/OPERATIONS

2013 Sales

	$ mil.	% of total
Engineered welded blanks	280.2	41
Complex stampings & modular assemblies	215.9	31
Blanking	80.4	11
Highly engineered aluminum die casting and machining	71.7	10
Scrap & other	52.0	7
Total	**700.2**	**100**

Selected Products and Services

Body structures
Chassis systems
Cleaning and coating
Cut-to-length
Deep draw engine applications
Edge trimming
Engineered welded blanks
Exhaust & heat management
First operation blanking
Heavy gauge blanking and forming
Hot- and cold-rolled steel
Inspection
Interior metallics
Laminated products
Pickling
Slitting
Stamped components
Steel processing
Tool building
Warehousing

COMPETITORS

Cosma International
Flex-N-Gate
Gibbs Die Casting
Midway Products Group
Olympic Steel
Rose City Manufacturing
Thai Summit America
Tower International

HISTORICAL FINANCIALS

Company Type: Public

Income Statement

FYE: October 31

	REVENUE ($ mil.)	NET INCOME ($ mil.)	NET PROFIT MARGIN	EMPLOYEES
10/14	878.7	22.4	2.6%	3,200
10/13	700.1	21.5	3.1%	1,824
10/12	586.0	13.5	2.3%	1,430
10/11	517.7	7.8	1.5%	1,270
10/10	457.2	3.8	0.8%	1,250
Annual Growth	**17.7%**	**55.3%**	**—**	**26.5%**

2014 Year-End Financials

Debt ratio: 42.8%　　No. of shares (mil.): 17
Return on equity: 16.2%　　Dividends
Cash ($ mil.): 12　　　　Yield: —
Current ratio: 1.55　　　Payout: —
Long-term debt ($ mil.): 268　Market value ($ mil.): 293

	STOCK PRICE ($) FY Close	P/E High/Low	PER SHARE ($) Earnings	Dividends	Book Value
10/14	17.04	18　11	1.30	0.00	8.40
10/13	16.42	12　7	1.27	0.75	7.70
10/12	11.38	14　10	0.80	0.50	6.35
10/11	7.90	29　18	0.47	0.12	6.42
10/10	10.08	45　17	0.23	0.00	6.17
Annual Growth	**14.0%**	**—　—**	**54.2%**	**—**	**8.0%**

Shutterfly Inc

Whether or not you are the consummate shutterbug you can rely on Shutterfly for digital prints. An e-commerce company specializing in digital photo products and services for the consumer and professional photography markets the company offers customers the ability to upload share store and edit digital photos through its website. In addition to traditional 4-inch by 6-inch prints Shutterfly provides prints ranging from wallet-sized to jumbo enlargements. The company also offers personalized items including mugs photo books and calendars through its personalized products and services business segment. In 2012 Shutterfly acquired Kodak Imaging Network (doing business as KODAK Gallery).

The company purchased the online photo service of bankrupt photography company Eastman Kodak for nearly $24 million. Shutterfly made the deal to acquire Kodak's 75 million customers in the US and Canada. The purchase is helping it gain an even larger share of the online photo market which it shares with rivals such as Hewlett Packard's Snapfish and American Greetings' Photoworks and Webshots brands.

The deal comes after Shutterfly reported positive earnings in 2011. It earned revenue of $473.3 million and income of $35.4 million. These results were due to an increase in customers and orders combined with strong financial discipline. Customers for the year totaled more than 4.8 million (up from about 4 million in 2010) while orders equaled about 11.2 million (up from about 9.2 million in 2010). The average order in 2011 remained flat at about $33. The company also owes its success to investing in its personalized product line. In 2011 it reported an increase in sales of photo books and greeting and stationery cards.

The KODAK Gallery deal represents Shutterfly's efforts to grow all areas of the business through a steady stream of targeted acquisitions. It also acquired Penguin Digital in 2012. Penguin Digital is a mobile application developer that provides consumers with a way to create share and purchase photo merchandise directly from a mobile device.

In 2011 the company acquired personalized card and stationery seller Tiny Prints for $146.5 million in cash and about 4 million shares of common stock. Shutterfly made the deal to enhance efficiencies in product innovation merchandising manufacturing customer service and marketing. And in late 2010 Shutterfly enhanced its commercial printing services through the purchase of WSMG a digital direct marketing agency based in Dallas. Shutterfly is integrating WSMG's data management and marketing analytics capabilities with its own manufacturing and printing operations.

Shutterfly makes more than half its revenues during the fourth quarter of the year due to holiday sales. Sales of 4x6 prints account for about 7% of revenues. The company makes additional money through advertising —clients such as Sony ABC AT&T Universal Music and Proctor & Gamble have advertised on its website. Revenues from ads and sponsorship are included in the company's personalized products and services segment. Shutterfly also provides commercial printing services primarily to the direct marketing industry though that business accounts for only 3% of sales.

The company was founded in 1999 and was funded in part by Silicon Valley icon Jim Clark a co-founder of Netscape Communications. The company went public in a 2006 IPO.

EXECUTIVES

President and CEO, Jeffrey T. (Jeff) Housenbold, age 44, $555,000 total compensation
SVP and COO, Daniel C. (Dan) McCormick, age 48
SVP and CFO, Brian Regan, $400,000 total compensation
SVP and CTO, Satish Menon
Vice President Finance, John Kaelle
Vice President Strategic Finance, Kris Espiritu
Vice President Corporate Controller, Lisa Blackwood Kapral
Vice President Of Business Development, Meena Ravella
Vice President User Experience Design, Matthew Holloway
Vice President Enterprise Information Mangement, Sarang Kirpekar
Vice President Corporate Controller, Lisa Blackwood-kapral
Vice President Customer Acquisition And Internet Marketing, Jorie Waterman
Chairman, Philip A. (Phil) Marineau, age 67
Auditors: PricewaterhouseCoopersLLP

LOCATIONS

HQ: Shutterfly Inc
2800 Bridge Parkway, Redwood City, CA 94065
Phone: 650 610-5200
Web: www.shutterflyinc.com

PRODUCTS/OPERATIONS

2011 Sales

	$ mil.	% of total
Personalized products & services	374.7	79
Print	85.0	18
Commercial print	13.6	3
Total	**473.3**	**100**

Selected Products and Services

Online Services
  Edit and enhance
  Organize
  Print
  Share
  Upload
Photo-Based Products
  Greeting cards
  Personalized calendars
  Photo books
  Stationery

COMPETITORS

123Greetings	LifePics
AG Interactive	Rite Aid
Adobe Systems	Snapfish
CVS	Vistaprint
Costco Wholesale	Wal-Mart
Facebook	Walgreen
Google	Yahoo!

HISTORICAL FINANCIALS

Company Type: Public

Income Statement

FYE: December 31

	REVENUE ($ mil.)	NET INCOME ($ mil.)	NET PROFIT MARGIN	EMPLOYEES
12/13	783.6	9.2	1.2%	1,573
12/12	640.6	23.0	3.6%	1,107
12/11	473.2	14.0	3.0%	956
12/10	307.7	17.1	5.6%	611
12/09	246.4	5.8	2.4%	519
Annual Growth	**33.5%**	**12.2%**	**—**	**31.9%**

2013 Year-End Financials

Debt ratio: 19.2%
Return on equity: 1.2%
Cash ($ mil.): 499
Current ratio: 3.50
Long-term debt ($ mil.): 243

No. of shares (mil.): 38
Dividends
  Yield: —
  Payout: —
Market value ($ mil.): 1,945

	STOCK PRICE ($) FY Close	P/E High/Low		PER SHARE ($) Earnings	Dividends	Book Value
12/13	50.93	239	119	0.24	0.00	20.63
12/12	29.87	53	35	0.61	0.00	19.01
12/11	22.76	148	52	0.40	0.00	17.48
12/10	34.89	57	25	0.59	0.00	9.64
12/09	17.81	81	26	0.22	0.00	8.30
Annual Growth	**30.0%**	**—**	**—**	**2.2%**	**—**	**25.5%**

Signature Bank (New York, NY)

Signature Bank marks the spot where some professional New Yorkers bank. The institution provides customized banking and financial services to smaller private businesses their owners and their top executives through about two dozen locations throughout the metropolitan area including all five boroughs Long Island and affluent Westchester County. It attracts deposits by offering personal and business checking and money market accounts. The bank's lending activities mainly entail real estate and business loans. Subsidiary Signature Securities offers wealth management financial planning brokerage services and life and disability insurance.

Mortgage loans including commercial real estate loans multifamily residential mortgages home loans and lines of credit and construction and land loans comprise the bulk of Signature Bank's loan portfolio (and much of its asset base as well). The bank branched out into specialty lending in 2012 forming subsidiary Signature Financial to offer equipment finance and leasing transportation financing and funding for taxi medallions.

Founded in 2001 as an alternative to megabanks Signature Bank has grown into an institution with nearly $15 billion in assets a figure that has more than doubled since the bank was spun off from Bank Hapoalim in 2004. It plans to continue to fill a service void created by industry consolidation. The bank targets businesses that have fewer than 1000 employees and revenues of less than $50 million. Representative clients include real estate companies law firms entertainment agencies and foundations. Signature Bank has also been building its private client business by adding banking teams and opening offices throughout the New York metro area.

The bank's emphasis on personal service helped it to grow its deposit base and loan portfolio in 2011. During a time when many other banks struggled under the weight of bad loans in a bad economy Signature Bank achieved record earnings for the fourth consecutive year. Its 2011 revenue exceeded $622 million and its net income approached $150 million.

EXECUTIVES

Vice President, Michael Sharkey
Senior Vice President Group Director, Sandra Sapperstein
Senior Vice President Finance, Kenneth Baratto, age 71
President CEO and Director, Joseph J. DePaolo, $577,500 total compensation
SVP and CFO, Vito Susca
President CEO and Director, Michael G. O'Rourke
EVP, Kevin P. Bastuga
EVP, Bryan D. Duncan
VP Retail Operations Manager, Ella Riordan-Pacheco
Vice President, Dina Casella
Svp Private Client Bnkng Team, Richard Desousa
Svp Private Client Bnkng Team, Michael Doti
Svp-grp Dir Madison Ave Offce, Carl M Gambino
Grp Dir-svp, Andrew N McDonald
V Pres, John Buoniconti
Assoc Grp Dir & V Pres, Timothy F Collins
Assoc Grp Dir & V Pres, Robert S Derbabian
Assc Grp Dir-v Pres Jhn Myszk, Anna Garen
Executive Vice President, David S Bagatelle
Senior Vice President, Joseph Festa
Senior Vice President, Gabrielle Stern
Assoc Grp Dir-v Pres, John Millwood
Grp Dir-sr V Pres, George Taitt
Svp-group Dir Private Client, John Kourkoutis
Svp-group Dir Private Client, Joseph Alexander
Vp Assoc Grp Dir Pvt Client Ba, Patricia Modena
Svp Grp Dir Pvt Client Banking, Craig Anzalone
Svp-group Director, Gary Shulevich
Svp-group Director, Leon Kratsberg
Svp-jericho Ny, Lucy Mazany
Svp-melville Ny, Drew S Crowley
Svp-melville Ny, Andrew F Corrado
Vp-white Plains Ny, Richard Carr
Svp-white Plains Ny, Thomas P Mooney
Assistant Vice President And Security Officer, Randy Grigg
Assistant Vice President And Residential Mortgage Manager, Suzanne Bivens
Vice President, Gregory Woodin
Senior Vice President, Frank Sabalja
Senior Vice President, Gary Sarro
Executive Vice President, Mike Hill
Vice President, Cheryl Johnson
Grp Dir Sr Vice President Pvt Clnt, Norman Lowe
Vice President, Jeffrey P Schmitz
Vice President Portfolio Manager, Robert Wallace
Vice President, Johnadam Haridopolos
Vice President, Steven Deneff
Group Director Senior Vice President, James Raggi
Vice President, Melody Camacho
Vice President Information Systems, Traude Kump
Senior Vice President Group Director, Brian Hallinan
Vice President, Eugene Cartin
Vice President, Sal Trifiletti
Senior Vice President Group Director, James Buck
Vice Chairman, John Tamberlane
Treasurer, Peter Quinlan
Chairman and Director, Leonard S. Caronia
Board Member, George Cochran
Auditors: KPMGLLP

LOCATIONS

HQ: Signature Bank (New York, NY)
565 Fifth Avenue, New York, NY 10017
Phone: 646 822-1500
Web: www.signatureny.com

PRODUCTS/OPERATIONS

2013 Sales

	$ mil.	% of total
Interest		
Loans net	519.3	66
Securities available for sale	186.2	24
Securities held to maturity	46.2	6
Other	3.5	-
Noninterest		
Fees & service charges	17.2	2
Commissions	9.4	1
Net gains on sales of loans	6.3	1
Net gains on sales of securities	6.2	-
Other	1.7	-
Adjustments	(8.8)	-
Total	**787.2**	**100**

COMPETITORS

Apple Bank for Savings	Herald National Bank
Astoria Financial	JPMorgan Chase
Bank Leumi USA	New York Community
Capital One	Bancorp
Citigroup	Safra Bank
HSBC USA	TD Bank USA

HISTORICAL FINANCIALS

Company Type: Public

Income Statement

FYE: December 31

	ASSETS ($ mil.)	NET INCOME ($ mil.)	INCOME AS % OF ASSETS	EMPLOYEES
12/13	22,376.6	228.7	1.0%	945
12/12	17,456.0	185.4	1.1%	844
12/11	14,666.1	149.5	1.0%	720
12/10	11,673.0	102.0	0.9%	660
12/09	9,146.1	62.7	0.7%	614
Annual Growth	25.1%	38.2%	—	11.4%

2013 Year-End Financials

Return on assets: 1.1%
Return on equity: 13.2%
Long-term debt ($ mil.): —
No. of shares (mil.): 47
Sales ($ mil): 787

Dividends
Yield: —
Payout: —
Market value ($ mil.): 5,080

	STOCK PRICE ($) FY Close	P/E High/Low	Earnings	Dividends	Book Value
12/13	107.42	22 15	4.76	0.00	38.06
12/12	71.34	18 14	3.91	0.00	34.94
12/11	59.99	18 13	3.37	0.00	30.49
12/10	50.06	21 13	2.46	0.00	22.84
12/09	31.90	25 15	1.30	0.00	19.79
Annual Growth	35.5%	— —	38.3%	—	17.8%

Silicon Image Inc

It would be silly to imagine that Silicon Image's chips only produce pretty pictures. Silicon Image designs and sells a variety of integrated circuits including digital video controllers receivers transmitters and processors that are built into mobile devices digital TVs camera personal computers and DVD and Blu-ray players. The company helped create HDMI and DVI industry standards as well as MHL the standard for mobile devices and the 60GHz wireless HD video standard WirelessHD. Through subsidiary Simplay Labs it offers HDMI licensing and compliance testing services. Customers located outside the US account for about 60% of the company's sales.

Geographic Reach

As a fabless semiconductor company Silicon Image does not manufacture its own chips but outsources production to Taiwan Semiconductor Manufacturing. The company's only real estate is sales offices located in China Japan South Korea Taiwan and the US (in California) and an R&D centers in China and India.

Customers located in Asia account for about half of sales; those located in the US make up about 40% of sales.

Sales and Marketing

Silicon Image uses both a direct sales force and distributors to sell its products. About 40% of sales come from distributors such as Arrow Edom Technology Innotech TriStar and Weikeng Industrial. Its top customer is Samsung Electronics which accounts for 35% of sales.

Financial Performance

Overall sales rose 14% in 2012 to $252 million as sales for its mobile products almost doubled year over year. It products for the mobile market are based on Mobile High-Definition Link (MHL) a new standard used to directly connect HDTVs and mobile devices that also charges mobile device batteries all over a single cable. (Subsidiary MHL LLC is responsible for licensing and promoting the MHL specification —developed by Nokia Samsung Electronics Sony Toshiba and Silicon Image —as a standard for mobile wired connectivity.)

The company also recorded a net loss for 2012 as it invested in research and development initiatives and added 100 more people to its R&D center in India.

Strategy

Silicon Image is looking to MHL to boost its licensing revenues as HDMI did in the past. With a wide variety of consumer electronics manufacturers supporting the High Definition Multimedia Interface (HDMI) industry standard Silicon Image has had more than 500 companies license the technology from another subsidiary HDMI Licensing.

Mergers and Acquisitions

In a move to build out its product line the company bought assets from Anchor Bay Technologies in 2011 including its semiconductor intellectual property among DVDO systems for the digital television and home theater markets.

Also that year it paid $25.5 million for SiBEAM a designer of semiconductor products for wireless communications to expand its video connectivity product line. The deal added technology that enables wireless transmission of high-definition digital video to consumer electronics and personal computing devices.

EXECUTIVES

VP Worldwide Operations & Quality, Rashid Osmani, age 61
CEO, Camillo Martino, age 52, $420,170 total compensation
CFO, Raymond D. Cook, age 53
SVP and General Manager Connectivity Products Group, Timothy Vehling, age 47, $300,910 total compensation
CTO, Jeffrey M. Gilbert
President Human Resources, Nancy Hauge
Vice President Engineering, Badar Bagai
Vice President Worldwide Operations And Quality, Peter Rasmussen
Vice President Storage Products, Jimmy Garcia-meza

Vice President And Head Of Product, Eddie Sanford
Executive Vice President Legal Affairs, Paul Lippe
Vice President Engineering, John Shin
Vice President, Bruce Macdonald
Vice President Sales, Bob Rudy
Chairman, Peter G. Hanelt
Senior Director Global Tax, Jane Adamo
Auditors: Deloitte&ToucheLLP

LOCATIONS

HQ: Silicon Image Inc
   1140 East Arques Avenue, Sunnyvale, CA 94085
Phone: 408 616-4000
Web: www.siliconimage.com

2012 Sales

	% of total
US	42
Taiwan	22
Japan	15
China	8
Europe	6
Korea	6
Other	1
Total	**100**

PRODUCTS/OPERATIONS

2012 Sales

	% of total
Mobile	48
Consumer electronics	25
Licensing	19
Personal computers	8
Total	**100**

Selected Products

DVI (Digital Visual Interface)
   Receivers
   Transmitters
HDMI (High-Definition Multimedia Interface)
   Input processors
   Port processors (combine HDMI transmit and receive functions with active processing)
   Receivers
   Switches
   Transmitters
MHL (Mobile High-Definition Link)
   Bridge
   Port processor
   Transmitter
Storage
   Parallel ATA controllers
   RAID storage processors
   SATA (Serial ATA) controllers
   SteelVine bridges
   SteelVine SATA port multipliers
   SteelVine series core storage processors and port multipliers

COMPETITORS

Analog Devices	Philips Electronics
Analogix Semiconductor	Pixelworks
Atmel	Promise Technology
Broadcom	STMicroelectronics
Chrontel	Silicon Integrated
Hitachi	Systems
Intel	Sony
LSI Corp.	Technicolor
Marvell Technology	Texas Instruments
NVIDIA	Toshiba
NXP Semiconductors	VIA Technologies

HISTORICAL FINANCIALS

Company Type: Public

Income Statement

FYE: December 31

	REVENUE ($ mil.)	NET INCOME ($ mil.)	NET PROFIT MARGIN	EMPLOYEES
12/13	276.4	11.4	4.2%	640
12/12	252.3	(11.1)	—	623
12/11	221.0	(11.6)	—	521
12/10	191.3	8.1	4.3%	432
12/09	150.5	(129.1)	—	526
Annual Growth	**16.4%**	—		**5.0%**

2013 Year-End Financials

Debt ratio: —
Return on equity: 6.4%
Cash ($ mil.): 82
Current ratio: 4.20
Long-term debt ($ mil.): —

No. of shares (mil.): 77
Dividends
   Yield: —
   Payout: —
Market value ($ mil.): 476

	STOCK PRICE ($) FY Close	P/E High/Low		Earnings	PER SHARE ($) Dividends	Book Value
12/13	6.15	41	30	0.15	0.00	2.45
12/12	4.96	—	—	(0.14)	0.00	2.17
12/11	4.70	—	—	(0.14)	0.00	2.49
12/10	7.35	74	21	0.10	0.00	2.45
12/09	2.58	—	—	(1.72)	0.00	2.27
Annual Growth	**24.3%**	—	—	—	—	**1.9%**

Sinclair Broadcast Group, Inc.

To find out what's happening at Sinclair Broadcast Group (SBG) you could consult the TV Guide. The company is a leading television operator with more than 70 stations serving 45 midsized markets. Its portfolio reaches 26% of US households and includes affiliates of all four major broadcast networks as well as several affiliates of The CW Network and MyNetworkTV. (Most of the stations are affiliated with FOX.) More than 45 of SBG's stations are owned and operated while the rest are operated under local market agreements; the company has duopolies (more than one station) in about 20 of markets. The family of founder Julian Sinclair Smith led by CEO David Smith controls the company.
Geographic Reach
SBG serves midsized markets all around the US.
Sales and Marketing
The company spent about $12.2 million on advertising and marketing promotions in fiscal 2012.
Financial Performance
Revenue increased 39% net income decreased 91% in fiscal 2012 compared with 2011 while the company's net cash inflow increased by $189 million in 2012 compared with the prior year.
   The increase in revenues was attributed to stations acquired during fiscal 2012 and revenues earned from a LMA with the Freedom stations. In addition revenues increased increase in local broadcast revenues and an increase in advertising spending particularly in the automotive and direct response sectors.
   Strategy

Like most other commercial television broadcasters SBG relies on advertising for the bulk of its revenue with most of that coming from local advertisers. The company focuses on providing its stations with the best possible programming through both network affiliation agreements and syndication deals in order to attract and retain audiences. Within each market its stations compete for audiences against stations owned by other big broadcasting groups including Hearst Television Local TV and Media General.
   Mergers and Acquisitions

In 2013 SBG acquired Fisher Communications for approximately $373.3 million. In early 2012 SBG widened its broadcast reach when it bought Four Points Media and its seven TV stations for $200 million. The purchase helped the company to diversify its broadcast network with more non-FOX affiliates and added stations in four markets including Austin Texas; Providence Rhode Island; Salt Lake City; and West Palm Beach Florida. In addition to that deal SBG has an agreement in place to acquire eight TV stations owned by Freedom Communications for $385 million. Those stations reach 2.6% of US households across seven markets. In 2013 SBG agreed to acquire four TV stations from COX Media Group for some $95 million. Following the purchase the company's TV group will reach more than 27% of US households.

HISTORY

Julian Sinclair Smith founded the company in 1971 with TV station WBFF (one of the first UHF channels in the country) in Baltimore. Several years later came WPTT another UHF channel in Pittsburgh. A movement among the board's directors in 1985 to oust Smith (who controlled 40% of the company) was foiled when Smith and his son David allied with a director who held a 10.2% stake. Shortly after the family bought the dissidents out and hard-knuckled boss David took over management of the company renamed Sinclair Broadcasting Group (SBG) in 1986.
   The company bought Pittsburgh station WPGH in 1991 selling its WPTT station the same day. It expanded again with its 1994 purchase of four stations from ABRY Partners. SBG went public in 1995 using the $75 million raised to trim its debt. It also used the funds to back its growing appetite for acquisitions buying five stations in 1995 and buying River City Broadcasting in 1996.
   SBG came under fire in 1996 for pushing an FCC law barring duopolies (ownership of more than one UHF channel in a market) when a rival challenged its dealings with Glencairn a broadcasting company owned in part by Smith's mother Carolyn. The company's bad luck continued that year when David Smith was arrested (the charges were later dropped) after getting caught with a prostitute. Continuing Smith's philosophy to "get as many TV stations as we can" the company bought 14 TV stations from Sullivan Broadcast Holdings for $1 billion and seven TV stations from Guy Gannett Communications for $310 million in 1998. As its debt grew the company promised to sell some $500 million in noncore assets.
   SBG followed through on that claim in 1999 and 2000 by exiting the radio market when it sold its radio holdings to Entercom Communications for about $920 million. Amid a decline in ad sales the company cut nearly 200 jobs in 2001. SBG created News Central in 2002 which centralizes all of the

company's news operations so that it can more easily add coverage to all of its stations.

EXECUTIVES

Vp New Media, Rob Weisbord
Vp National Sales, Gregg L Siegel, age 54
EVP and COO, David B. Amy, age 61, $675,000 total compensation
SVP and CTO, Delbert R. Parks, age 61
Chairman President and CEO, David D. Smith, age 63, $1,000,000 total compensation
Executive Vice President; General Counsel, Barry M. Faber, age 52, $650,000 total compensation
President of Keyser Capital, W. Gary Dorsch, age 62
CFO, Christopher Ripley
General Manager WXLV-TV and WMYV-TV, Greg Conner
Vice President Digital Media, Lisa Bishop
Vp Secretary And Director, J Duncan Smith, age 61
Board Member, Delene Morgan
Auditors: Ernst&YoungLLP

LOCATIONS

HQ: Sinclair Broadcast Group, Inc.
10706 Beaver Dam Road, Hunt Valley, MD 21030
Phone: 410 568-1500   **Fax:** 410 568-1533
Web: www.sbgi.net

Asheville NC
Austin TX
Baltimore
Birmingham AL
Buffalo NY
Cape Girardeau MS
Cedar Rapids IA
Charleston SC
Charleston-Huntington WV
Cincinnati
Columbus OH
Dayton OH
Des Moines IA
Flint MI
Greensboro/Winston-Salem NC
Las Vegas
Lexington KY
Madison WI
Milwaukee
Minneapolis
Mobile AL
Nashville TN
Norfolk VA
Oklahoma City
Peoria-Bloomington IL
Pittsburgh
Portland ME
Providence RI
Raleigh-Durham NC
Richmond VA
Rochester NY
Salt Lake City
St. Louis
San Antonio
Springfield-Champaign IL
Syracuse NY
Tallahassee FL
Tampa
West Palm Beach FL

PRODUCTS/OPERATIONS

2012 Sales

	$ mil.	% of total
Broadcasting	1007.5	95
Other operating divisions	54.2	5
Total	**1061.7**	**100**

COMPETITORS

CBS	LIN Media
E. W. Scripps	Local TV
FOX Broadcasting	Media General
Gannett	Meredith Corporation

Granite Broadcasting
Gray Television
Hearst Television
Journal Broadcast Group

Newport Television
Nexstar Broadcasting
Raycom Media

HISTORICAL FINANCIALS

Company Type: Public

Income Statement

FYE: December 31

	REVENUE ($ mil.)	NET INCOME ($ mil.)	NET PROFIT MARGIN	EMPLOYEES
12/13	1,363.1	73.4	5.4%	6,400
12/12	1,061.6	144.6	13.6%	4,000
12/11	765.2	75.8	9.9%	3,130
12/10	767.1	76.1	9.9%	2,350
12/09	656.4	(135.6)	—	2,400
Annual Growth	**20.0%**	**—**		**27.8%**

2013 Year-End Financials

Debt ratio: 73.1%	No. of shares (mil.): 100
Return on equity: 52.5%	Dividends
Cash ($ mil.): 280	Yield: 1.6%
Current ratio: 2.03	Payout: 40.2%
Long-term debt ($ mil.): 2,985	Market value ($ mil.): 3,579

	STOCK PRICE ($) FY Close	P/E High/Low		PER SHARE ($) Earnings	Dividends	Book Value
12/13	35.73	45	16	0.78	0.60	3.96
12/12	12.62	7	4	1.78	1.54	(1.44)
12/11	11.33	14	7	0.94	0.48	(1.50)
12/10	8.18	9	4	0.94	0.43	(2.06)
12/09	4.03	—	—	(1.70)	0.60	(2.66)
Annual Growth	**72.6%**	**—**	**—**	**—**	**(0.0%)**	

Sirona Dental Systems Inc

Factoid for the day: The first electric dental drill was invented in 1882 and the company that made it is now known as Sirona Dental Systems. The company still makes handheld dental instruments as well as imaging systems dental CAD/CAM systems used in restorations and a full line of other products used by dentists and dental laboratories worldwide. Its CEREC system is a 3-D computer-aided contraption for making ceramic restorations (such as crowns and bridges) in the dentist's office rather than a lab. The firm's imaging systems include traditional X-ray equipment and digital radiography systems. Other products include dental chairs (known as "treatment centers") and instrument cleaning systems.

Geographic Reach

The company operates globally with the US and Germany as its largest markets. Its top distributors are Patterson and Henry Schein and it uses Patterson exclusively to distribute its CEREC products in North America. Sirona has production facilities in China Denmark Germany Italy and the US; it also outsources the manufacturing of some components.

Operations

Sirona operates through four main segments: Imaging systems dental CAD/CAM systems treat-

ment centers and instruments. Imaging systems contributed to 35% of the company's revenue in 2012 and produces diagnostic imaging equipment. Dental CAD/CAM systems products comprise CAD/CAM in-office systems for dentists and laboratories and a central manufacturing service for copings and bridge-frameworks. The dental CAD/CAM systems segment contributed 34% to Sirona's revenue.

Sirona's treatment centers (20% of revenue) make dentist chairs and centers with integrated diagnostic hygiene and ergonomic functionalities. Its instruments segment (around 11% of revenue) makes and supplies a range of handpiece products including handheld and power-operated devices used for cavity preparation endodontics period ontology and prophylaxis.

Financial Analysis

Sirona has enjoyed a steady rise in revenue profits and cash flow over the years. From 2011 to 2012 its revenue increased by 7% and its profits spiked by 7% to the highest amounts of total sales (almost $980 million) and net income ($135 million) in the company's history. The company is experiencing higher demand for its products on a global scales across all its segments. It also in 2012 benefited from a decrease in research and development expenses attributed to foreign currency exchange fluctuations.

Strategy

During the weakened global economy of the past few years dentists shied away from making non-crucial big-ticket equipment purchases which prompted the Sirona to restructure and reduce operating costs. However Sirona knows its customers still want cutting-edge technology and enjoy trading in their older Sirona systems for upgrades.

Growth has come from efforts to expand its distribution network both in the US and in international markets adding a number of sales and service centers in new regions of Asia/Pacific and Europe. The company also prides itself on a history of innovation and invests in research and development of new products —its area of fastest growth. Sirona keeps tabs on trends and has introduced more digital products as the industry has trended away from older non-digital equipment.

EXECUTIVES

Vp Management Information Systems, Ari Neugroschl
Vice President Of The Imaging Systems Division, Michael Geil
Vp Instruments, Jan Siefert
Vice President Dental Cad Cam Systems, Bart Doedens
President and CEO, Jeffrey T. Slovin, age 50, $12,815 total compensation
CEO of Sirona, Jost Fischer, age 60
EVP Sales, Walter Petersohn, $21,132 total compensation
Executive Vice President, Rainer Berthan
EVP and CFO, Ulrich Michel
Vice President Rsrch Dev Sirona Dental, Stanley Mandelkern
Vice President Investor Relations, Joshua Zable
Vice President Dental Cad Cam Systems, Kendall Doedens
Executive Vice President Human, Debbie Labelle
Senior Vice President Finance, Paul Murphy
Vice President Management Information, Madelyn Alfano
CEO of Sirona, Jost Fischer, age 60
Chairman, Thomas Jetter
Board Member, Nichilas Alexos

Board Member, Harry Jansen
Auditors: KPMGAGWirtschaftsprufungsgesellschaft

LOCATIONS

HQ: Sirona Dental Systems Inc
30-30 47th Avenue, Suite 500, Long Island City, NY
11101
Phone: 718 482-2011   **Fax:** 718 937-5962
Web: www.sirona.com

2012 Sales

	$ mil.	% of total
US	285.0	29
Germany	159.3	16
Other countries	535.1	55
Total	**979.4**	**100**

PRODUCTS/OPERATIONS

2012 Sales

	$ mil.	% of total
Imaging systems	343.5	35
Dental CAD/CAM systems	334.5	34
Treatment centers	197.2	20
Instruments	102.5	11
Other	1.7	-
Total	**979.4**	**100**

Selected Products

Imaging systems
  Computed digital radiography system (intra-oral
  digital imaging system)
  Galileos Compact
  Orthophos XG (digital panoramic X-ray system)
  Sidexis XG (imaging software)
Dental CAD/CAM systems
  CEREC (in-office dental restoration system)
  infiniDent (central production service)
  inLab (laboratory dental restoration system)
Treatment centers
  Basic dentists chairs
  Integrated treatment centers
  TENEO treatment center
  Kappler Dental Cabinetry
Instruments
  SIROair (airscaler)
  SIROEndo (root canal preparation unit)
  SIROLaser (diode laser used in endodontics period
  ontology and oral surgery)

COMPETITORS

American Medical Systems	Kinetic Concepts
American Medical Technologies	Midmark Corporation
Astra Tech (Sweden)	National Dentex
CONMED Corporation	Nobel Biocare
Carestream Health	NuVasive
Cooper Companies	Orthofix
DENTSPLY	Patterson Companies
Glidewell Laboratories	Philips Electronics
Henry Schein	ResMed
Hu-Friedy	STERIS
IDEXX Labs	Siemens Healthcare
ImageWorks	Straumann
Integra LifeSciences	Sybron Dental
	Thoratec Corp
	Young Innovations

HISTORICAL FINANCIALS

Company Type: Public

Income Statement

FYE: September 30

	REVENUE ($ mil.)	NET INCOME ($ mil.)	NET PROFIT MARGIN	EMPLOYEES
09/14	1,171.1	175.7	15.0%	3,327
09/13	1,101.4	146.7	13.3%	3,216
09/12	979.3	133.8	13.7%	2,979
09/11	913.8	121.7	13.3%	2,705
09/10	770.2	89.9	11.7%	2,345
Annual Growth	**11.0%**	**18.2%**	**—**	**9.1%**

2014 Year-End Financials

Debt ratio: 4.3%
Return on equity: 14.5%
Cash ($ mil.): 382
Current ratio: 2.90
Long-term debt ($ mil.): 78
No. of shares (mil.): 55
Dividends
  Yield: —
  Payout: —
Market value ($ mil.): 4,245

	STOCK PRICE ($) FY Close	P/E High/Low	PER SHARE ($) Earnings	Dividends	Book Value
09/14	76.68	27 21	3.13	0.00	22.74
09/13	66.93	28 21	2.61	0.00	21.01
09/12	56.96	24 16	2.36	0.00	17.97
09/11	42.41	26 16	2.13	0.00	16.70
09/10	36.04	26 16	1.59	0.00	14.56
Annual Growth	**20.8%**	**— —**	**18.5%**	**—**	**11.8%**

Six Flags Entertainment Corp

For millions of people Six Flags is the standard-bearer for theme park thrills. The company is the #2 amusement park operator in the world (behind Walt Disney) drawing about 25 million visitors to its nearly 20 parks in North America. Fancying itself a regional entertainment destination most of its parks operate under the Six Flags banner (including Six Flags Fiesta Texas and Six Flags Magic Mountain) offering roller coasters and other thrill rides water slides and additional family entertainment. Revenues come from gate receipts food and merchandise. Six Flags licenses characters from Warner Bros. and DC Entertainment such as Looney Tunes and Batman.

HISTORY

Today's Six Flags began life as The Tierco Group an Oklahoma City-based real estate development company that purchased a theme park on the outskirts of Oklahoma City called Frontier City (opened in 1958) in the early 1980s. By 1989 when Kieran Burke was appointed CEO Tierco had divested all of its real estate holdings to focus on the amusement park business. In 1994 it changed its name to Premier Parks and the next year acquired three properties from Funtime bringing its total to six. The company went public in 1996 and shifted its growth spree into overdrive acquiring four parks that year and three more in 1997 including Kentucky Kingdom (near Louisville) and Marine World (near San Francisco).

In 1998 the company bought Six Flags Theme Parks from Time Warner and investor group Boston Ventures for about $1.9 billion. Six Flags had been started by Dallas businessman Angus Wynne who opened Six Flags Over Texas in 1961. The Dallas-area park was followed by Six Flags Over Georgia (1967) and Six Flags Over Mid-America (1971 now called Six Flags St. Louis). In 1982 the company was bought by Bally Manufacturing (later Bally Entertainment) but was sold to New Jersey-based Wesray Capital Corp. five years later. Time Warner bought a stake in the business in 1991 and acquired the entire company in 1993. It sold a 51% stake in Six Flags to Boston Ventures in 1995. With the Six Flags acquisition Premier Parks gained eight theme parks three water attractions and a recognized national brand.

Premier Parks also began expanding globally in 1998 purchasing a 94% interest (now 98%) in Walibi Parks with six parks in Europe. In 1999 the company acquired Splashtown Water Park in Houston and went south of the border with the purchase of Mexico's largest theme park Reino Aventura (now Six Flags Mexico). In addition it acquired the White Water Atlanta park and Warner Bros. Movie World in Germany.

In 2000 the company changed its name to Six Flags. It bought Montreal's La Ronde amusement park in 2001 and opened Warner Bros. Movie World in Spain in 2002. Two years later the company rethought its Europe expansion strategy and sold those operations for $200 million. It also sold Six Flags Worlds of Adventure to rival Cedar Fair.

Washington Redskins owner Daniel Snyder (who later became Six Flags chairman) bought an 8% stake in the company in 2004; increasing it to about 12% in 2005. After a bitter proxy struggle Snyder and two business associates Mark Shapiro and Dwight Schar were voted onto the board of directors booting out then CEO Keirian Burke then CFO James Dannhauser and Stanley Schuman.

During the proxy fight the company announced that it was putting itself up for sale but plans for the sale were dropped when the board fired Burke at the end of 2005 and installed Shapiro as the company's new president and CEO. It also elected former presidential candidate Jack Kemp and Miramax co-founder Harvey Weinstein as new members of the company's board. Shapiro was brought in from ESPN to lead a reorganized focus on a family entertainment experience with more modest roller coasters and kiddie rides tied to movies and cartoon characters.

Six Flags sold its iconic AstroWorld park in Houston following the end of its 2005 season. The company's New Orleans property was located about a mile from Lake Pontchartrain and sat under 12 feet of water during the flooding that resulted from 2005's Hurricane Katrina. Extensively damaged by Katrina Six Flags New Orleans had remained closed since the storm and in 2008 the company finally decided that the park would not be re-opened.

On the international front the company sold most of its European operations to a private investment company for $200 million. Formerly part of StarParks most of the assets were sold to Compagnie des Alpes in 2006. Also that year Six Flags sold its water park in Columbus Ohio.

The company made further disposals in 2007 selling seven parks for about $310 million a Jacksonville Florida-based investment group. Later in 2007 Six Flags joined with Snyder's RedZone Capital to acquire dick clark productions for about $175 million. (The theme park operator ponied up $40 million for a 40% stake in the TV production company.) dick clark productions was eventually sold in 2012 for an undisclosed amount.

Efforts in 2008 included the launch of a new attraction program with "seven coasters for seven parks" and the addition of Wiggles Worlds and Thomas the Tank Engine attractions at certain parks. It also banned smoking in most areas.

In 2009 the company filed for bankruptcy. During bankruptcy proceedings Snyder lost his equity investment in the amusement park company. He and Schar left the Six Flags board in 2010 when the newly reorganized company exited Chater 11.

The company in 2010 posted its first annual profit since 1998. The turnaround was led by James Reid-Anderson who was hired in 2010. Reid-Anderson previously lead health care firm Dade Behring Holdings after it emerged from bankruptcy. He replaced Mark Shapiro who left the company after it emerged from bankruptcy.

EXECUTIVES

Chairman President and CEO, James W. P. (Jim) Reid-Anderson, age 55, $1,200,000 total compensation

SVP In-Park Services, John E. Bement, age 61, $250,000 total compensation

SVP U.S. Park Operations, Thomas (Tom) Iven, $285,980 total compensation

CFO, John M. Duffey, age 53, $578,846 total compensation

VP Central Region and General Manager Six Flags Over Georgia, John Odum, age 56

SVP and CIO, Michael S. Israel

V Pres-cao, Leonard A Russ

Vice President Design, Les Hudson

Vice President Treasurer, Stephen Purtell

Vice President Of In Park Services, Eugene Naughton

Chairman President and CEO, James W. P. (Jim) Reid-Anderson, age 55

Member Board Of Directors, John W Baker

Director Board Of Directors, Gene Wibbenmeyer

Auditors: KPMGLLP

LOCATIONS

HQ: Six Flags Entertainment Corp
924 Avenue J East, Grand Prairie, TX 75050
Phone: 972 595-5000
Web: www.sixflags.com

PRODUCTS/OPERATIONS

Selected Operations:

Theme parks
The Great Escape (Lake George NY)
Six Flags America (Largo MD)
Six Flags Discovery Kingdom (Vallejo CA)
Six Flags Fiesta Texas (San Antonio)
Six Flags Great Adventure (Jackson NJ)
Six Flags Great America (Gurnee IL)
Six Flags Magic Mountain (Valencia CA)
Six Flags Mexico (Mexico City)
Six Flags New England (near Springfield MA)
Six Flags Over Georgia (Atlanta)
Six Flags Over Texas (Arlington TX)
Six Flags St. Louis
Six Flags Wild Safari (Jackson NJ)
Water parks
Six Flags Hurricane Harbor (Arlington TX)
Six Flags Hurricane Harbor (Jackson NJ)
Six Flags Hurricane Harbor (Valencia CA)
Six Flags White Water (Atlanta)

COMPETITORS

Adventureland	LEGO
Cedar Fair	Ripley Entertainment

Disney Parks & Resorts	Santa Cruz Beach
Herschend	Boardwalk
Entertainment	SeaWorld
Hershey Entertainment	Universal Parks
Kennywood	Waterpark Management

HISTORICAL FINANCIALS

Company Type: Public

Income Statement

FYE: December 31

	REVENUE ($ mil.)	NET INCOME ($ mil.)	NET PROFIT MARGIN	EMPLOYEES
12/13	1,109.9	118.5	10.7%	40,900
12/12	1,070.3	354.0	33.1%	40,900
12/11	1,013.1	(22.6)	—	4,600
12/10*	847.8	50.0	5.9%	29,900
04/10	128.0	548.8	428.5%	0
Annual Growth	71.6%	(31.8%)	—	—

*Fiscal year change

2013 Year-End Financials

Debt ratio: 53.7%
Return on equity: 18.7%
Cash ($ mil.): 169
Current ratio: 1.63
Long-term debt ($ mil.): 1,394

No. of shares (mil.): 94
Dividends
Yield: 4.9%
Payout: 75.2%
Market value ($ mil.): 3,493

	STOCK PRICE ($) FY Close	P/E High/Low	Earnings	Dividends	Book Value
12/13	36.82	66 26	1.18	1.82	3.94
12/12	61.20	20 12	3.19	2.70	8.29
12/11	41.24	—	(0.21)	0.09	6.99
12/10*	54.40	125 71	0.45	0.03	7.75
Annual Growth	(12.2%) (20.2%)	—	—	37.6%	292.9%

*Fiscal year change

Skyworks Solutions, Inc.

The sky's the limit for Skyworks Solutions. The company makes integrated circuits (ICs) for wireless and other applications. Its flagship handset products include power amplifiers and front-end modules used by OEMs like Samsung Electronics Ericsson LG and Nokia in their mobile phones and communications infrastructure gear. Other analog devices include attenuators diodes couplers phase shifters receivers and switches used in a broad array of industries. Skyworks uses gallium arsenide (GaAs) a material that is faster and uses less energy than industry-standard silicon in many of its devices. The company gets more than 90% of its sales from customers in the Asia and Asia/Pacific regions.

Operations In addition to its handset business Skyworks sells its analog and mixed-signal (combines analog and digital circuits on a single chip) ICs to customers in the automotive energy management infrastructure medical and military markets. The company sells its portfolio of more than 2500 analog components to more than 2000 customers worldwide. It also licenses its intellectual property (IP) to encourage customers to incorporate its ICs into their products during the design phase.

Geographic Reach China leads the company's geographic segments accounting for more than half of sales; other Asian countries bring in an additional 33%. The Americas and the EMEA region contribute 6% of 2% of sales respectively. Skyworks saw year-over-year declines across nearly all regions (including China and South Korea) but that was offset by triple-digit growth in Taiwan and other countries in the Asia-Pacific region. Sales and Marketing Although Skyworks partners with some electronic components distributors it markets its products to OEMs primarily through its own global sales force. The company's largest customers include Foxconn and Samsung Electronics which each accounted for more than 10% of sales in 2012. Financial Analysis Revenue rose 11% in fiscal 2012 (ended September 30) to $1.6 billion as Skyworks brought new products to its customers through acquisitions. It also benefited from the ongoing wireless network upgrade to 3G and 4G as well as newly developed products for other markets. Acquisitions and high research and development costs led to an increase in expenses which contributed to an 11% drop in net income to $202 million.

Mergers and Acquisitions In 2012 Skyworks bought power management chip maker Advanced Analogic Technologies in a cash transaction valued at about $257 million. The deal added battery chargers DC/DC converters voltage regulators LED drivers and other devices for a wide range of electronic products and bolstered Skyworks' wireless communications portfolio by extending the company's reach into new vertical markets in the consumer and computing sectors. The analog power management market is expected to grow significantly over the next few years as manufacturers look to make their products more energy efficient and cost effective. In 2011 the company bought privately held wireless communications chip maker SiGe Semiconductor in a deal valued at around $275 million. Skyworks was looking to bolster its capabilities in wireless connectivity with a profitable and growing business. It was drawn to SiGe Semi which saw its business booming as its chips were increasingly included in home entertainment devices by Cisco Dell HP Microsoft Sony and other customers. SiGe filed an IPO in 2010 but never went public.

EXECUTIVES

Chairman and CEO, David J. Aldrich, age 58, $657,500 total compensation

VP Quality, Kenneth J. Huening, age 53

SVP Worldwide Operations, Bruce J. Freyman, age 54, $378,900 total compensation

EVP; General Manager Front End Solutions, Gregory L. (Greg) Waters, age 54, $378,846 total compensation

President, Liam K. Griffin, age 47, $397,800 total compensation

VP and CFO, Donald W. (Don) Palette, age 57, $373,300 total compensation

Vice President, Daniel Yannuzzi

Vice President Business Development, Sanjay Gokhale

Vice President For Business Development, Joe Adams

Sr Vpchief Financl Offcr, William Krein

Vice President Associate General, Robert John

Vice President Marketing, Carlos Bori

Vice President Plant Manager, J C Nam

Vice President Of Manufacturing, Bruce Framon

Vice President Of Supply Chain For World Wide Operations, Francisco Buitron

Vice President Of Sales, Yu Wu

Vice President, Robert Darveaux
Vice President Of Process Development, Ding Jagatheesan
Vice President General Manager Pld, Dipti Vachani
Vice President Sales And Marketing, Nicholas Aretakis
Vice President Marketing, Frank Mao
Senior Vice President Worldwide Sales, Brad Byk
Chairman and CEO, David J. Aldrich, age 58
Assistant Treasurer, Alice England
Treasurer, Roseann Colot
Assistant Treasurer, Lyn Picaro
Auditors: KPMGLLP

LOCATIONS

HQ: Skyworks Solutions, Inc.
20 Sylvan Road, Woburn, MA 01801
Phone: 781 376-3000
Web: www.skyworksinc.com

2012 Sales

	$ mil.	% of total
Asia/Pacific		
China	820.1	52
Taiwan	311.7	20
South Korea	103.2	7
Other Asia/Pacific	207.4	13
Americas		
US	70.3	5
Other Americas	18.4	1
Europe Middle East & Africa	37.5	2
Total	**1568.6**	**100**

PRODUCTS/OPERATIONS

Selected Products

Discrete semiconductors
  Gallium arsenide (GaAs) field-effect transistors (FETs)
  Receiving diodes
  Schottky diodes
  Varactor diodes
GaAs radio-frequency (RF) integrated circuits (ICs)
  Amplifiers
  Attenuators
  Control FETs
  Switches
Magnetic and dielectric materials
Microwave semiconductors
  Attenuators
  Schottky diodes
  Silicon pin diodes
  Step recovery diodes
  Switches
  Varactor diodes
Millimeter-wave semiconductors
  Attenuators
  Converters
  Driver low-noise multifunction and power amplifiers
  Mixers
  Schottky barrier mixer diodes
  Switches
Multifunction and passive components
  Directional couplers
  Mixers
  Power dividers
  Sampling phase directors
  Voltage variable attenuators
Phase shifters
Radio-frequency (RF) subsystems
Resonators
  Coaxial
  Dielectric
Technical ceramics
  Ceramic and technical powders
  Ceramic filters
Wireless infrastructure components

COMPETITORS

ANADIGICS	Microsemi
Analog Devices	Murata Manufacturing
Avago Technologies	Peregrine

Conexant Systems	Semiconductor
DSP Group	RF Micro Devices
Fairchild	Silicon Labs
Semiconductor	Sumitomo Electric
Filtronic	Device Innovations
Hittite Microwave	TDK
Linear Technology	TriQuint
Maxim Integrated	Vitesse Semiconductor
Products	

HISTORICAL FINANCIALS
Company Type: Public

Income Statement
FYE: October 3

	REVENUE ($ mil.)	NET INCOME ($ mil.)	NET PROFIT MARGIN	EMPLOYEES
10/14*	2,291.5	457.7	20.0%	5,550
09/13	1,792.0	278.1	15.5%	4,750
09/12	1,568.5	202.0	12.9%	4,700
09/11	1,418.9	226.5	16.0%	4,400
10/10	1,071.8	137.2	12.8%	3,700
Annual Growth	**20.9%**	**35.1%**	**—**	**10.7%**

*Fiscal year change

2014 Year-End Financials

Debt ratio: —	No. of shares (mil.): 189
Return on equity: 19.4%	Dividends
Cash ($ mil.): 805	Yield: 0.4%
Current ratio: 4.80	Payout: 11.5%
Long-term debt ($ mil.): —	Market value ($ mil.): 10,453

	STOCK PRICE ($) FY Close	P/E High/Low	PER SHARE ($) Earnings	Dividends	Book Value
10/14*	55.25	24 10	2.38	0.22	13.38
09/13	24.77	18 13	1.45	0.00	11.18
09/12	23.56	29 13	1.05	0.00	9.91
09/11	17.96	30 15	1.19	0.00	8.63
10/10	20.65	27 13	0.75	0.00	7.30
Annual Growth	**27.9%**	**— —**	**33.5%**	**—**	**16.4%**

*Fiscal year change

SM Energy Co.

SM Energy looks for energy (mainly natural gas) across the continental US. While the oil and gas exploration and production company spreads its operations across the US (the Midcontinent the Gulf Coast the Williston Basin in North Dakota and Montana and the Permian Basin in West Texas and New Mexico the Eagle Ford shale in South Texas and the Haynesville Shale play in East Texas) it gets most of its revenues from South Texas and the Gulf Coast. In 2013 the company posted estimated proved reserves of 428.7 million barrels of oil equivalent 46% up from 2012 reflecting increased activity in its shale plays.

Geographic Reach

SM Energy has properties in the Midcontinent the Williston Basin in North Dakota and Montana and the Permian Basin in West Texas and New Mexico the Gulf Coast and South and East Texas. Its Texas assets include the Eagle Ford Shale play and the Haynesville Shale play.

Operations

The company engaged in the acquisition exploration development and production of crude oil natural gas and natural gas liquids in onshore North America. In 2013 it had working interests

in 1061 gross (634 net) productive oil wells and 2293 gross (916 net) productive gas wells.

Sales and Marketing

In 2013 Regency Gas Services accounted for 26% of SM Energy's total production revenues; Anadarko Petroleum 16%; and Plains Marketing 12%.

Financial Performance

After experiencing a revenue dip in 2012 due to lower production in the Mid-Continent region and declining gas prices in 2013 SM Energy's revenues increased by 52% as a result of drilling activity increases in its Eagle Ford (South Texas) shale program. Thanks to higher oil and gas prices it also saw an increase in oil gas and NGL production revenues in the Mid-Continent region despite a decrease in production volumes. In 2013 the company reported net income of $170.94 million (compared to net loss of $54.25 million in 2012) thanks to higher revenues and increased income from continuing operations.Operating cash inflow increased to $1.34 billion in 2013 (compared to $921.97 million in 2012) as the result of higher net income and a change in current assets and liabilities.

Strategy

SM Energy primarily grows through developing its own properties. It is cashing in by using modern drilling technologies (fracking and horizontal drilling) that allow oil firms to exploit natural gas holdings in shale formations that were previously difficult to access. In particular the company is using such technologies to enhance its production in the Eagle Ford shale.

To raise cash to invest in its core activities in 2013 the company sold its assets in the Anadarko basin for $329 million.

Mergers and Acquisitions

In 2014 the company acquired North Dakota Gooseneck assets from Baytex Energy USA for $325 million.

Company Background

In 2011 it added 526.1 billion cu. ft. of natural gas equivalent from its drilling program the bulk of which was in the Eagle Ford Shale the Haynesville Shale as well as in North Dakota's Bakken/Three Forks shale play.

Aiming to raise $1 billion in cash in 2011 to pay down debt the company sold 15400 acres of non-producing land in the Eagle Ford shale play of Texas for $227.4 million. It also entered a $680 million acquisition and development deal with Mitsui & Co. to reduce its Eagle Ford acreage in the non-operated portion of the formation by nearly 50%. SM Energy also agreed to sell $110 million of Marcellus Shale assets to Endeavour International. However this deal fell through in late 2011 after the parties failed to agree to terms.

In 2010 the company changed its corporate name to SM Energy from St. Mary Land & Exploration to reflect the company's growth from a local oil company whose only properties were in St. Mary Parish Louisiana to a national player.

EXECUTIVES

EVP and CFO, A. Wade Pursell, age 50, $398,654 total compensation
Vice President Controller, Mark T Solomon, age 46
Exec Vpres, David W Copeland, age 59
SVP Business Development and Land, Kenneth Knott, age 49
President and CEO, Javan D. (Jay) Ottoson, age 56, $459,423 total compensation
SVP and Regional Manager Permian, Lehman E. (Newt) Newton, age 59

SVP and Regional Manager South Texas and Gulf Coast, Gregory T. (Greg) Leyendecker, age 57
SVP and Regional Manager Rocky Mountain, Mark D. Mueller, age 50
EVP Operations, Herbert S. Vogel, $335,423 total compensation
VP and Regional Manager Mid-Continent, Mary Ellen Lutey
VP IT, Dean Lutey
Vice President, Brenda Witthuhn
Executive Vice President And Chief Financial Officer, Wade Pucell
Senior Vice President Manager Of Energy, Bill Carignan
Vice President Geosciences Eastern, Craig Williams
Senior Vice President, Robert Nance
Vice President Land And Legal, Miliam Phare
Chairman, William D. (Bill) Sullivan, age 58
Board Member, Barbara Bauman
Auditors: Deloitte&ToucheLLP

LOCATIONS

HQ: SM Energy Co.
1775 Sherman Street, Suite 1200, Denver, CO 80203
Phone: 303 861-8140   **Fax:** 303 861-0934
Web: www.sm-energy.com

2013 Proved Reserves

	% of total
South Texas & Gulf Coast	73
Rocky mountain	18
Midcontinent	5
Permian	4
Total	**100**

PRODUCTS/OPERATIONS

2013 Sales

	$ mil.	% of total
Oil & gas	2199.6	95
Marketed gas system	60.0	3
Gain on divestitures	28.0	1
Other operating revenue	7.6	1
Adjustments	(1.8)	-
Total	**2293.4**	**100**

COMPETITORS

Abraxas Petroleum	Penn Virginia
Apache	Petrohawk Energy
BP	Pioneer Natural
Chesapeake Energy	Resources
Devon Energy	Range Resources
Exxon Mobil	Royal Dutch Shell

HISTORICAL FINANCIALS

Company Type: Public

Income Statement

FYE: December 31

	REVENUE ($ mil.)	NET INCOME ($ mil.)	NET PROFIT MARGIN	EMPLOYEES
12/13	2,293.3	170.9	7.5%	793
12/12	1,505.1	(54.2)	—	725
12/11	1,603.3	215.4	13.4%	639
12/10	1,092.8	196.8	18.0%	569
12/09	832.2	(99.3)	—	550
Annual Growth	**28.8%**	**—**	**—**	**9.6%**

2013 Year-End Financials

Debt ratio: 34.0%	No. of shares (mil.): 67
Return on equity: 11.3%	Dividends
Cash ($ mil.): 282	Yield: 0.1%
Current ratio: 1.01	Payout: 7.1%
Long-term debt ($ mil.): 1,600	Market value ($ mil.): 5,573

Stock Price ($) / P/E / Per Share ($)

	STOCK PRICE ($) FY Close	P/E High/Low	Earnings	Dividends	Book Value
12/13	83.11	36 20	2.51	0.10	23.96
12/12	52.21	— —	(0.83)	0.10	21.37
12/11	73.10	26 17	3.19	0.10	22.84
12/10	58.93	19 10	3.04	0.10	19.25
12/09	34.24	— —	(1.59)	0.10	15.51
Annual Growth	**24.8%**	**— —**	**—**	**(0.0%)**	**11.5%**

Smith & Wesson Holding Corp

Smith & Wesson has built a successful business shooting for the stars. Operating through subsidiary Smith & Wesson Corp. Smith & Wesson Holding Corporation makes and markets pistols revolvers tactical rifles and police accessories as well as gun-safety devices under the M&P Series name. The company founded in 1852 also sells handcuffs and hunting rifles and car boat and home alarm system packages. Smith & Wesson is the exclusive importer of Walther pistols with US production rights for the Walther PPK model. To diversify and add breadth to its brand the company licenses its name to makers of apparel watches sunglasses gift sets and more.

Geographic Reach

Smith & Wesson sells its products globally. Besides the US the company serves Europe Asia and Latin America. It maintains production facilities for its firearms in Springfield Massachusetts and in Houlton Maine.

Strategy

Smith & Wesson aims to diversify its products portfolio as the company evolves from being a gun maker to a top supplier of a variety of arms. As a result the company has traded sales of revolvers in favor of pistols. Smith & Wesson is also working to expand its products in the areas of tactical and long-gun lines as well as non-firearm products.

The company supports its firearms business through deals with other companies to make Smith & Wesson-branded products. A licensing agreement with BBC Imagewear inked in 2009 provides Smith & Wesson with branded T-shirts jackets and shirts. A similar deal with Kudzu/The Game offers branded hats and caps and hats T-shirts jackets gun pads license plates decals pins patches key chains glassware and mugs with the Thompson/Center Arms logo. Its licensing agreement with TruckVault calls for Smith & Wesson-brand lockable steel handgun safes for homes vehicles and public safety agencies including police government agencies fire departments and the military.

Financial Performance

Smith & Wesson has seen its net sales rise in recent years particularly following the November 2008 US presidential election as consumers began to stockpile arms for fear of losing some rights under new leadership. In 2011 however Smith & Wesson logged slightly fewer orders across the company's firearms businesses –returning to more normal levels temporarily as compared to the strong consumer demand it has experienced for years.

In fiscal 2012 net sales increased 20% and net income rose 119% as compared to 2011. Net cash outflow during the same reporting period was $1 million vs. $20 million in 2011. Net sales increases can be attributed to a 25% rise in handgun product sales and a 94% increase in sales of modern sporting rifles thanks to the late fiscal 2011 introduction of a new sport model that was competitively priced. International sales meanwhile accounted for 4% of Smith & Wesson's sales. The company's net income boost came from rising operating income due to increased sales volumes. Its net cash outflow in 2012 was primarily related to cash used in financing activities such as repurchasing Convertible Notes.

Sales and Marketing

Smith & Wesson taps several distribution channels to get its products in the hands of customers. Customers include distributors government and military agencies businesses retailers and consumers as well as federal state and municipal law enforcement agencies and officers. The company which spent $14.7 million on advertising and promotion expenses in 2012 leverages its websites to market products and services.

The company has increased its sales in recent years by forming and maintaining its own sales force instead of relying on the representatives of independent manufacturers to sell its products including its line of polymer pistols.

Company Background

Amid a shift in government spending the company exited the perimeter security systems business in 2011. It moved to divest its perimeter security division –Tennessee-based Universal Safety Response (later renamed Smith & Wesson Security Solutions) to Detroit Michigan-based FutureNet Group in mid-2012. Smith & Wesson Security Solutions has provided barriers and installation and other services used in approximately 110 military installations and more than a dozen federal agencies and commercial facilities. The operations generated about $130 million during the past three years accounting for some 10% of Smith & Wesson's sales.

EXECUTIVES

EVP CFO and Treasurer, Jeffrey D. Buchanan, age 59, $341,250 total compensation
President and CEO, P. James Debney, age 47, $537,500 total compensation
VP Manufacturing and Supply Chain Management, Mark P. Smith, $262,500 total compensation
SVP Sales and Marketing, Andrew S. Coccari
Vice President Marketing, Thomas Kelly
Vice President Information Tech Sys, Manuel Barragan
Assistant To Vice President Finance, Doreen Fildalgo
Vice President Human Resources, Anne Bruce
Vice Chairman Of The Board, Robert Scott
Board Member, John B Furman, age 70
Board Member, Robert H (Bob) Brust, age 72
Auditors: BDOUSALLP

LOCATIONS

HQ: Smith & Wesson Holding Corp
2100 Roosevelt Avenue, Springfield, MA 01104
Phone: 800 331-0852
Web: www.smith-wesson.com

PRODUCTS/OPERATIONS

2012 Sales

	$ mil.	% of total
Handguns	238.4	58
Modern sporting rifles	75.1	18
Walther	32.3	8
Hunting firearms	27.3	7
Parts & accessories	20.5	5
Non-firearms	18.3	4
Total	**412.0**	**100**

Selected Products

Accessories
  Cases
  Fiber optic sights
  Gloves
  Grips
  Holsters
  Locks
  Magazines
Apparel
Firearms
  Pistols
  Revolvers
  Rifles
Knives
Handcuffs and restraints
Personal security
  Racks
  Safes
  Vaults

COMPETITORS

American Derringer	Marlin Firearms
Browning Arms	Mossberg
Bushmaster Firearms	Para USA
Colt Defense	Remington Arms
Colt's	Ruger
Fabbrica D' Armi Pietro	Savage Arms
Beretta	Springfield Armory
Freedom Group	Taurus International
Glock	Tyco Fire & Security
Heckler & Koch	

HISTORICAL FINANCIALS

Company Type: Public

Income Statement

FYE: April 30

	REVENUE ($ mil.)	NET INCOME ($ mil.)	NET PROFIT MARGIN	EMPLOYEES
04/14	626.6	89.3	14.3%	1,758
04/13	587.5	78.7	13.4%	1,475
04/12	412.0	16.1	3.9%	1,346
04/11	392.3	(82.7)	—	1,520
04/10	406.1	32.5	8.0%	1,563
Annual Growth	**11.4%**	**28.7%**		**3.0%**

2014 Year-End Financials

Debt ratio: 26.2%	No. of shares (mil.): 55
Return on equity: 51.3%	Dividends
Cash ($ mil.): 68	Yield: —
Current ratio: 2.58	Payout: —
Long-term debt ($ mil.): 100	Market value ($ mil.): 850

	STOCK PRICE ($) FY Close	P/E High/Low		PER SHARE ($) Earnings	Dividends	Book Value
04/14	15.35	10	6	1.49	0.00	3.01
04/13	8.78	9	5	1.18	0.00	2.82
04/12	8.25	34	9	0.25	0.00	1.73
04/11	3.60	—	—	(1.37)	0.00	1.47
04/10	4.47	13	7	0.53	0.00	2.68
Annual Growth	**36.1%**	—	—	**29.5%**	—	**3.0%**

Snyder's-Lance Inc.

If you're familiar with the munchies named Toastchee Nipchee and Captain's Wafers Snyder's-Lance (formerly Lance) has undoubtedly helped you satisfy a snack attack. The company produces single-serve multi-pack and family-sized packages of bakery products and sweet and savory snack foods including cookies crackers nuts potato chips and pretzels. Its snacks are sold under the Lance Cape Cod Tom's Archway and Snyder's brands at food retailers mass merchants and convenience and club stores in the US. The company also makes private-label and branded snacks for food makers. The company changed its name to Snyder's-Lance in late 2010 after buying pretzel maker Snyder's of Hanover.

Geographic Reach

Based in North Carolina Snyder's-Lance operates manufacturing facilities in the US in North Carolina Pennsylvania Iowa Indiana Georgia Arizona Massachusetts Florida and Ohio as well as in Ontario Canada.

Sales and Marketing

Snyder's-Lance logged $23.1 million in advertising expenses in fiscal 2012. The snack food giant sells its products to mass merchandisers club stores discount stores convenience stores foodservice operators and other retailers the likes of drug stores the military schools and government facilities. Wal-Mart its largest customer represented about 18% of the company's revenues in both 2012 and 2011.

The company distributes snack food products nationwide using a large direct-store-delivery (DSD) network consisting of some 3000 distribution routes served mostly by Independent Business Owners (IBOs) and others that are company-owned.

Operations

Blending the Snyder's and Lance businesses has made Snyder's-Lance the No. 2 salty snack maker in the US. Snyder's-Lance boasts about a dozen owned brands as well as a vast collection of popular licensed names such as Bugles. Snyder's and Lance retained their corporate offices in North Carolina and Pennsylvania and knit together their executive suites to form a snack food powerhouse.

Financial Performance

During the past five years Snyder's-Lance logged its highest revenue in 2011 (the first full year it reported combined sales) thanks to the positive impact of the merger due to its incremental branded and non-branded revenue. The combined company's net sales decreased 1% in fiscal 2012 as compared to 2011 driven primarily by lower revenue per unit sold as a result of the IBO conversion and planned private brand volume declines. The company's net income saw a 54% boost during the same reporting period due in part to increased activity associated with the IBO conversion in 2012 as compared to 2011.

Strategy

As part of the company's effort to merge the two businesses Snyder's-Lance is paying particular attention to what it has deemed its core brands — Snyder's of Hanover pretzels Lance sandwich crackers and Cape Cod potato chips. It's fueling growth among these brands by developing them and expanding their distribution. Within Snyder's-Lance's allied brands defined as branded products that are outside its core brands the company's exploring pricing strategies product packaging and product configuration to improve profit margins.

The snack foods maker also is looking for add-on acquisitions to boost its core products portfolio. It added the popular Pretzel Crisps brand to its pretzel portfolio and entered the deli-bakery section of grocery stores —a retail area for snacks that's growing —through its $340-million purchase of Snack Factory in October 2012.

Following the merger Snyder's-Lance in early 2011 began to convert some 1300 company-owned direct-store-delivery (DSD) routes to independent operators to improve its distribution network's ability to serve customers. (At the time of the merger announcement Lance's DSD network was presented as a primary reason for Snyder's of Hanover's interest.) Snyder's-Lance is expanding its DSD network in the Southwestern US. Indeed it entered into a distribution agreement with Inventure Foods in fall 2012 to expand its route distribution system in Arizona.

Mergers and Acquisitions

The Snyder's deal attested to Lance's long-standing business strategy of growth through acquisitions. The company made it first purchase as a joint entity in mid-2012. Snyder's-Lance acquired O'Byrne Distributing a snack food distributor that serves the Augusta Georgia area. The deal marks the snack food company's continued push to expand and strengthen its national distribution network.

Previously Lance's takeovers included the Stella D'Oro brand of packaged cookies biscotti and breadsticks for which Lance paid $24 million. In 2008 Lance acquired the private-label gourmet cookie maker Brent & Sam's for $23 million as well as name brand cookie maker Archway for $31 million.

Snack food is a highly competitive sector in food manufacturing; there are many players from giants such as Frito-Lay (Lay's Potato Chips Doritos Cheetos Cracker Jack) to little guys like pork rinds maker Rudolph Foods that carve out a spot in either a regional or product niche. Whether large or small most snack food companies are bowing to customer demand to produce healthier products. The company has introduced 100-calorie snack packs and whole-grain snack crackers. (It had previously removed lard trans-fats and high-fructose corn syrup from its products.)

Company Ownership

Chairman Michael Warehime and his wife —director Patricia Warehime —own about 16% of the company's shares.

HISTORY

A business deal gone awry stuck coffee dealer Philip Lance with 500 pounds of peanuts in 1913. Selling nickel bags of roasted peanuts and then peanut butter Lance began packaging peanut-butter-and-cracker sandwiches. His son-in-law Salem Van Every joined him two years later to form Lance Packing. Lance introduced Toastchee in 1938 and by 1939 the year the firm became Lance sales reached $2 million. The company began serving the institutional market in 1953 and began selling through vending machines the next year. Lance went public in 1961.

The family continued to run the company until 1973 when Van Every's grandson retired as CEO. After decades of serving mom-and-pop retailers Lance found the snack market changing. Individual stores gave way to chains; Frito-Lay gobbled up grocery shelf space; and regional rival Austin Quality Foods nabbed sales in the new warehouse/club store market. Eventually the conservative company responded with an influx of new management restructuring and the advent of marketing.

Lance purchased Tamming Foods (sugar wafers) and Cape Cod Potato Chips (salty snacks) in 1999. Lance then signed an agreement with China Peregrine (now China Premium Food Corp) to export private-label snack foods to China. (Lance has since ceased distribution in China.)

In 2005 Lance's board of directors elected Bill Prezzano as chairman. David Singer formerly EVP and CFO of Coca-Cola Bottling Co. Consolidated was named president and CEO of the company. And in 2005 Lance purchased a Canadian sugar-wafer manufacturing plant from A&M Cookie Company Canada.

The $40 million acquisition of Tom's Foods in 2005 added four new bakery and potato chip manufacturing plants to the company's operations. Lance manufactures about 90% of its products; the remainder is purchased for resale.

While Frito-Lay dominates the snack-aisle grocery shelves Lance's stronghold has been its company-owned vending machines placed in 15000 locations such as break rooms and cafeterias. In order to concentrate on more profitable operations in 2006 Lance began phasing out its vending-machine sales and ceased vending operations altogether in 2007. In addition the company joined the ranks of munchies makers that offer healthier products in 2007 with the $2 million purchase of a minority interest in Late July Products a Massachusetts-based organic snack food maker (crackers and sandwich crackers and cookies).

In 2008 Lance acquired the private-label gourmet cookie maker Brent & Sam's for $23 million and name-brand cookie maker Archway for $31 million.

In 2009 Lance purchased the Stella D'Oro brand of packaged cookies biscotti and breadsticks for $24 million.

The company merged with pretzel maker Snyder's of Hanover in December 2010. As a result Snyder's became a wholly owned subsidiary of Lance and Lance changed its name to Snyder's-Lance.

In October 2012 Snyder's-Lance completed its acquisition of Snack Factory LLC from VMG Partners adding the Pretzel Crisps brand to its menu of snacks.

EXECUTIVES

EVP CFO and Secretary, Richard D. (Rick) Puckett, age 61, $455,000 total compensation

President and CEO, Carl E. Lee, $625,000 total compensation

Vice President Sales Human Resrcs Trng, Gregory Morris

Vice President Manufacturing, Patrick S McInerney

Vice President Financial Planning Accounting And Treasury, Troy W Bryce

Vice President Finance, Ron Trull

Vice President Marketing Private Brands, Todd Phillips

Vice President Operations, Tony Kennedy

Vice President Of Manufacturing And Corporate Engineering, Greg Flickinger

Vice President Midwest Region, Jim Tanking

Vice President Human Resources Supply Chain, Emily Berwager

Vice President Convenience And Military, Wade Batten

Vice President Sales, Eric Jordan

Vice President Sales And Marketing, Claude Oconnor

Vice President Sales, Scott Livingston

Vice President Marketing, Eric Van De Wal

Chairman, Michael A. (Mike) Warehime
President and CEO, Carl E. Lee
Auditors: KPMGLLP

LOCATIONS

HQ: Snyder's-Lance Inc.
13024 Ballantyne Corporate Place, Suite 900,
Charlotte, NC 28277
Phone: 704 554-1421
Web: www.snyderslance.com

2012 Revenue

	$ mil.	% of total
US	1564.3	97
Canada	54.3	3
Total	**1618.6**	**100**

PRODUCTS/OPERATIONS

2012 Revenue

	% of total
Branded products	59
Partner brands	17
Private brands	18
Other	5
Total	**100**

Selected Brands

Archway
Brent
Bugles
Cape Cod Potato Chips
Captain's Wafers
Choc-o-Lunch
Delicious
Don Pablo's
EatSmart
Grande
Jays
Krunchers!
Lance
Nekot
Nipchee
Pretzel Crisps
Sam's
Salerno
Snyder's of Hanover
Stella D'oro
Texas Pete
Thunder
Toastchee
Toasty
Tom's
Van-o-Lunch
Vista

COMPETITORS

American Pop Corn	Kellogg U.S. Snacks
Beer Nuts	Kettle Foods
Bridgford Foods	King Nut Companies
Campbell Soup	Legacy Bakehouse
Chattanooga Bakery	McKee Foods
ConAgra	Mondelez International
Diamond Foods	Old Dutch Foods
Evans Food Products	Otis Spunkmeyer
Flowers Foods	Pepperidge Farm
Frito-Lay	Poindexter Nut
General Mills	Pretzels Inc.
Golden Enterprises	Procter & Gamble
Inventure foods	Snappy Popcorn
John Sanfilippo & Son	Weaver Popcorn Company

HISTORICAL FINANCIALS

Company Type: Public

Income Statement

FYE: December 28

	REVENUE ($ mil.)	NET INCOME ($ mil.)	NET PROFIT MARGIN	EMPLOYEES
12/13	1,761.0	78.7	4.5%	5,700
12/12	1,618.6	59.0	3.7%	5,900
12/11*	1,635.0	38.2	2.3%	6,100
01/11	979.8	2.5	0.3%	7,000
12/09	918.1	35.7	3.9%	4,800
Annual Growth	**17.7%**	**21.8%**	**—**	**4.4%**

*Fiscal year change

2013 Year-End Financials

Debt ratio: 28.1%	No. of shares (mil.): 69
Return on equity: 8.8%	Dividends
Cash ($ mil.): 14	Yield: 0.0%
Current ratio: 2.30	Payout: 57.1%
Long-term debt ($ mil.): 480	Market value ($ mil.): 2,016

	STOCK PRICE ($) FY Close	P/E High/Low	PER SHARE ($) Earnings	Dividends	Book Value
12/13	28.85	28 21	1.12	0.64	13.15
12/12	23.68	31 25	0.85	0.64	12.63
12/11*	22.50	42 30	0.56	0.64	12.33
01/11	23.44	385229	0.07	4.39	12.55
12/09	26.42	24 17	1.11	0.64	8.56
Annual Growth	**2.2%**	**— —**	**0.2%**	**(0.0%)**	**11.3%**

*Fiscal year change

Sohu.com Inc

If you're hunting for something in China maybe a "search fox" can help. Sohu.com (Sohu means "search fox") operates China's leading Web portal and offers communication tools such as e-mail and instant messaging and more than 30 content channels covering news sports business and other topics. Sohu also operates Web sites devoted to alumni communities gaming and real estate. In addition the company provides Internet access through its Sohu Entertainment ISP and search services through Sogou ("search dog"). Chairman and CEO Charles Zhang founded Sohu in 1996 as Internet Technologies China. It launched Sohu.com in 1998 and changed its name the next year. Zhang owns more than 20% of the company.

Other Sohu offerings include Go2Map (a mapping service provider); ChinaRen (an online youth community); 17174.com (games information portal); GoodFeel.com.cn (wireless value-added services); and Focus.cn (real estate services).

In 2008 the company spun off its online games unit Changyou.com in an IPO allowing Sohu to focus on its core online media search and mobile services; Sohu remains Changyou's majority shareholder.

EXECUTIVES

Chairman and CEO, Charles Zhang, age 50, $280,000 total compensation

Co-President and COO, Xin Belinda Wang, age 42, $170,000 total compensation

COO, Yu Gong, age 46, $170,000 total compensation

Co-President and CFO, Carol Yu, age 52, $250,000 total compensation

VP, Luming Chen
CTO, Xiaochuan Wang, age 36
Secretary, Timothy B. Bancroft
VP Products, Gang Fang
VP Online Games Business, Tao Wang, age 38
**Director Investor Relations and Corporate
 Communications,** Helen Zhang
Vice President of Brand Advertising Sales, Lili Shi
Vice President of Technology, Lin Zhou
Director, Edward B. (Ed) Roberts, age 79
Director, Charles Huang, age 44
Director, Dave Qi, age 50
Director, Shi Wang, age 63
Director, John Z. H. Deng, age 46
Auditors:
PricewaterhouseCoopersZhongTianCPAsLimitedComp
any

LOCATIONS

HQ: Sohu.com Inc
Level 18, SOHU.com Media Plaza, Block 3, No. 2
Kexueyuan South Road, Haidian District, Beijing
100190
Phone: (86) 10 6272 6666
Web: www.corp.sohu.com

PRODUCTS/OPERATIONS

2007 Sales

	$ mil.	% of total
Advertising	119.2	63
Non-advertising	69.7	37
Total	**188.9**	**100**

Selected Operations

17173.com (games portal)
ChinaRen.com (online alumni club)
Focus.cn (real estate Web site)
Goodfeel.com (wireless services)
Sogou.com (search site)
Sohu.com (Web portal)

Selected Sohu.com Content Channels

Automobile
Business and finance
Career
Comics
Dating
Entertainment
Games
Going abroad
Health
Information technology
Learning
Lifestyle
Music
News
Real estate
Sports
Travel
Women

Selected Sohu.com Features and Offerings

Address book
Calendar
Chat rooms
Dating and friends matching
Directory
E-Commerce services
E-Mail
Greeting Cards
Internet access services
Instant messaging
Message boards
Online polling
Photo album
Search engine
Wireless services

COMPETITORS

AOL	NetEase
Baidu	SCMP
CRIC	SINA
China.com	SOFTBANK
Google	Shanda Games
KongZhong	SouFun
Lenovo	TOM Group
Linktone	The9
Microsoft	Yahoo!
Mtone Wireless	

HISTORICAL FINANCIALS

Company Type: Public

Income Statement

FYE: December 31

	REVENUE ($ mil.)	NET INCOME ($ mil.)	NET PROFIT MARGIN	EMPLOYEES
12/13	1,400.2	166.9	11.9%	13,000
12/12	1,067.2	87.1	8.2%	9,681
12/11	852.0	162.7	19.1%	8,035
12/10	612.7	148.6	24.3%	5,167
12/09	515.2	147.8	28.7%	3,997
Annual Growth	**28.4%**	**3.1%**	**—**	**34.3%**

2013 Year-End Financials

Debt ratio: 13.6%
Return on equity: 13.5%
Cash ($ mil.): 1,287
Current ratio: 1.84
Long-term debt ($ mil.): —

No. of shares (mil.): 38
Dividends
 Yield: —
 Payout: —
Market value ($ mil.): 2,795

	STOCK PRICE ($) FY Close	P/E High/Low		PER SHARE ($) Earnings	Dividends	Book Value
12/13	72.93	—	—	(0.47)	0.00	34.62
12/12	47.34	28	15	2.03	0.00	30.09
12/11	50.00	25	11	3.93	0.00	27.98
12/10	63.49	20	10	3.92	0.00	20.94
12/09	57.28	18	10	3.57	0.00	16.15
Annual Growth	**6.2%**	—	—	—	—	**21.0%**

SolarWinds Inc

SolarWinds helps IT professionals improve IT infrastructure management without burning holes in their wallets. The company provides fault and performance management configuration management and compliance and troubleshooting applications. Designed to work on single devices or networks with as many as 100000 machines its downloadable software can be installed and configured without professional implementation services. The company's customers range from small businesses to large enterprises and government agencies. Its clients have included Booz Allen Hamilton FedEx Lockheed Martin Microsoft Chevron and NASA. SolarWinds gets 70% of sales from customers in the US.

Geographic Reach

While the company generates most of its revenues in North America its expansion plans include increasing its presence globally. In addition to its Austin-Texas headquarters the company has offices in Salt Lake City and abroad in Australia the Czech Republic Ireland India Brazil and Singapore.

Sales and Marketing

While the company markets its products in all the typical ways it relies on word-of-mouth and free trials to really boost sales. Because its direct sales force (the biggest revenue generator) doesn't have to convince potential customers of the value of SolarWinds' products the sales cycle is shorter. The company also uses distributors to reach government agencies and enterprise customers who have deals with certain resellers.

Financial Performance

All lines continued to go up for SolarWinds. In 2012 sales were up 36% to $268 million. The record revenue was due to increased sales of new software licenses and new and renewal maintenance agreements related to an expanded customer base. Maintenance agreements continue to account for a little more than half of revenues. Net income increased 30% on higher sales and in spite of increased sales and administration expenses. Cash flow increased by $76 million due to the revenue growth and a lack of acquisitions.

Strategy

SolarWinds with a strategic focus on underselling its rivals with products that cost less to configure and maintain has experienced rapid revenue growth in recent years. It has a user base of more than 150000 customers that includes nearly all of the Fortune 500.

SolarWinds uses internal development and acquisitions to add new products (more than 80 in 2012) extend its reach into new markets and expand geographically. New products released during the year included localized products for Japan and Germany web-based help desks for IT pros to deploy within their networks and vendor firewall management software.

Mergers and Acquisitions

SolarWinds has also expanded through acquisitions. In 2013 it acquired for some $120 million privately held N-able Technologies which provides IT management and automation products for managed service providers. The deal expands SolarWinds' offerings to that customer segment as well as its cloud-based services. It also purchased database performance management software firm Confio for $103 million. The prior year it picked up companies that make web help desk firewall patch file transfer and mobile IT management software.

EXECUTIVES

Vice President Of Operations, David Owens
President CEO and Director, Kevin B. Thompson, age 49, $406,250 total compensation
EVP Strategic Operations, Douglas G. (Doug) Hibberd, age 49, $291,246 total compensation
EVP Worldwide Sales, Paul Strelzick, age 50, $271,250 total compensation
EVP and CFO, Jason Ream
SVP Marketing, Geeta Sachdev
EVP Chief Marketing Officer and Chief Customer Officer, John F. Rizzo, age 57
CIO, Jon Drake
EVP and Chief Accounting Officer, J. Barton Kalsu
Vice President Asia Pacific Sales, Gary Angel
Executive Vice President Products, Suaad Sait
Vice President Corporate Marketing, Tiffany Nels
National Account Manager, Tom Wiri
National Account Manager, Michael Scanio
Vice President Of Sales Emea, Dan Gamwell
Vice President Product Marketing And Product Management, Sanjay Castelino
National Sales Manager, Daniel Ochoa
Vice President North American Tech Sprt, Mindy Kerber
National Account Manager, Lavance Randle
Vice President Human Resources, Jen Rothfeld
Vice President North America Sales, Chad Savoy
Vice President, Joe Ciccarello

Vice President Ww Sales Engineering, Nikki Jennings
Vice President Of Product Development, Patrick Egan
National Account Manager, Alex Patterson
National Account Manager, Dana Woods
Vice President Market Development, David Stel
Vice President Of Finance, Sandy Ensminger
Vice President Products And Web Platforms, Denny Lecompte
Senior Vice President Human Resources, Jen Rothfield
Vice President Of Finance, David Owenns
Vice President International Channels, Joe Kushi
Auditors: PricewaterhouseCoopersLLP

LOCATIONS

HQ: SolarWinds Inc
7171 Southwest Parkway, Building 400, Austin, TX 78735
Phone: 512 682-9300
Web: www.solarwinds.com

2014 Sales

	$ mil.	% of total
US	287.0	67
Other countries	141.7	33
Total	**428.7**	**100**

PRODUCTS/OPERATIONS

2014 Sales

	$ mil.	% of total
License	161.8	38
Subscribers	28.0	6
Maintenance & other	238.9	56
Total	**428.7**	**100**

2014 Sales

	$mil.	% of total
Network management	252.2	59
Systems and application management	134.7	31
MSP and Cloud	41.8	10
Total	**428.7**	**100**

COMPETITORS

BMC Software	IBM
CA Inc.	Infoblox
Cisco Systems	NetApp
Dell Software	NetScout Systems
EMC	Tripwire
Hewlett-Packard	

HISTORICAL FINANCIALS

Company Type: Public

Income Statement

FYE: December 31

	REVENUE ($ mil.)	NET INCOME ($ mil.)	NET PROFIT MARGIN	EMPLOYEES
12/13	335.3	89.7	26.8%	1,312
12/12	268.9	81.3	30.2%	865
12/11	198.3	62.4	31.5%	628
12/10	152.3	44.7	29.4%	458
12/09	116.4	29.5	25.3%	354
Annual Growth	**30.3%**	**32.1%**	**—**	**38.7%**

2013 Year-End Financials

Debt ratio: 5.6%	No. of shares (mil.): 75
Return on equity: 20.7%	Dividends
Cash ($ mil.): 165	Yield: —
Current ratio: 1.25	Payout: —
Long-term debt ($ mil.): —	Market value ($ mil.): 2,838

	STOCK PRICE ($) FY Close	P/E High/Low	PER SHARE ($) Earnings	Dividends	Book Value
12/13	37.83	51 27	1.17	0.00	6.45
12/12	52.45	54 25	1.07	0.00	5.13
12/11	27.95	39 22	0.84	0.00	3.61
12/10	19.25	38 19	0.61	0.00	2.45
12/09	23.01	41 23	0.52	0.00	1.34
Annual Growth	**13.2%**	**— —**	**22.5%**	**—**	**48.1%**

Sotheby's

Sotheby's believes that one man's collection is another man's treasure —especially when that collection is a rare antique a unique collectible or a distinctive work of art. Along with rival Christie's International Sotheby's dominates the world's auction house market. It orchestrates hundreds of sales each year at its auction centers dealing mainly in fine art antiques and collectibles. Sotheby's receives commissions and fees from both the buyer and the seller on each sale. It also provides loans (secured against works of art) to clients as part of its finance services and acts as an art dealer through its Noortman Master Paintings business which specializes in Dutch Flemish and French paintings.

Geographic Reach

Sotheby's largest market is the US which accounts for 41% of its revenue. The UK contributes more than 25% while China represents 18%. The New York-headquartered auction house operates Agency operations across Continental Europe and Asia including sales centers in Zurich Milan Paris and Beijing. It also has salesrooms exhibition space and offices in Hong Kong.

Sales and Marketing

In 2013 Sotheby's claimed $5.1 billion or 47% of the total aggregate auction sales of the two major auction houses within the global auction market.

Operations

In addition to matching buyers and sellers of fine and decorative art and high-end jewelry through its Agency business (93% of sales) the company sells art and to a lesser extent wine that it has purchased itself known as its Principal business. The firm also provides financing to select collectors and dealers with loans secured by works of art.

Auction commission revenues account for about 80% of Sotheby's revenues. The company has overseen the sales of such items as Picasso's "Femme Assise dans un Jardin" Degas' "Petite Danseuse de Quatorze Ans" and the last baseball glove used by Lou Gehrig. Sotheby's has simultaneously used its expertise and high profile in art circles to offer secured financing and insurance and brokerage services for private sales. Additionally the company offers restoration and appraisal services and operates two art institutes in New York City and London.

Financial Performance

Sotheby's reported revenue of $853.7 million in 2013 an increase of 11% versus the prior year. Net income rose 20% over the same period to $130 million. After a strong rebound in 2012 the auction house's sales have fluctuated from year to year.

Strategy

Sotheby's has particularly benefited from buyers and sellers in developing regions notably China along with an increase in consigned Asian art collections. To cater to buyers and sellers in developing regions —notably China —the company publishes sales catalogs in Chinese and has launched a Chinese language website. Concurrently Sotheby's has set its sights on Russia the Middle East and South America for growth opening offices in Moscow and Doha Qatar.

Wine is matured into a growing area of business for the auction house. Indeed in October 2014 an auction in Hong Kong broke the world record for the most expensive lot of wine ever sold with 114 bottles of Burgundy selling for $1.6 million —the equivalent of $1700 per glass. The previous record for a single lot of wine —also held by Sotheby's — was $1.05 million for 50 cases of Bordeaux Chateau Mouton Rothschild sold in New York in 2006. China is a force in the wine market —as well as fine art and collectibles —overtaking France as the world's largest consumer of red wine.

HISTORY

Sotheby's Holdings traces its roots to Samuel Baker a London bookseller who held his first auction in 1744 to dispose of an English nobleman's library. After Baker died in 1778 his nephew John Sotheby took over placing his name over the door of the business. During the 19th century Sotheby's expanded into antiquities paintings jewelry and furniture. Business boomed as newly wealthy Americans swarmed across the Atlantic seeking the status symbols of the Old World.

By the end of WWI Sotheby's had become fully entrenched in the art market and in 1917 the company moved to New Bond Street (where its London office still stands). Following WWII Sotheby's expanded into the US opening its first office in New York City in 1955. It later acquired Parke-Bernet a leading US art auction house in 1964. The company prospered and expanded during the 1970s as rising interest rates and inflation fueled an art market boom and in 1977 Sotheby's went public.

A collapse of the art market left Sotheby's a target for corporate raiders in the early 1980s. The company's board asked US shopping center magnate Alfred Taubman to lead a buyout group in 1983. After weathering the storm the company was well positioned when the art market rebounded a turnaround driven in part by the desire of newly wealthy Japanese to confirm their status —just as Americans had done a century before. In 1988 the company went public again with Taubman as chairman.

After the boom peaked in 1990 (Christie's International sold van Gogh's "Portrait of Dr. Gachet" that year for a record $82.5 million) Sotheby's earnings plummeted and its share price tanked. In 1994 Diana Brooks became president and CEO. The company posted solid results in 1995 but the company slipped to the #2 auctioneer in the world for the first time in more than 20 years.

In 1997 Sotheby's acquired Chicago-based Leslie Hindman Auctioneers and Chicago wine auctioneers Davis & Co. in 1998. The next year Sotheby's created a co-branded auction website with Amazon.com. The site never turned a profit and was scaled back in 2000 and the partnership terminated in 2001. In 2002 Sotheby's partnered with eBay to sell high-end merchandise online within the eBay website.

In 2000 the US Justice Department reopened a 1997 investigation of an alleged price fixing scheme involving Sotheby's and Christie's. After the allegations became public Taubman and

Brooks resigned replaced by Michael Sovern (chairman) and William Ruprecht (CEO). The probe sparked additional lawsuits and investigations. Both companies agreed to pay $256 million each to settle the civil claims. Brooks pleaded guilty to violating antitrust laws but testified against Taubman in exchange for leniency. Taubman pleaded innocent and was convicted and sentenced to one year in prison after a vicious trial.

In 2001 Sotheby's laid off about 8% of its staff and raised fees in 2002 in its efforts to offset losses. The bleeding continued into 2002 as the company sold its Upper East Side headquarters in New York for $175 million and laid off 7% of its staff. In 2004 Sotheby's sold its International Realty operations to Cendant for about $100 million. (Cendant spun off its real estate businesses as Realogy in 2006.) Sotheby's dropped "Holdings" from its official name in mid-2006.

The auction house's legal woes continued in 2007 when a Canadian antitrust entity obtained a restrictive order against Sotheby's claiming that the company had agreed with competitors to fix the prices it charged to customers (between the years of 1993 to 2000).

EXECUTIVES

EVP of Global Auction Transactions, Mitchell Zuckerman, age 68, $490,073 total compensation
Vice President Controller, Matthew Hook
Vice President A, Karen Kettering
President and CEO, Thomas S. (Tad) Smith, age 48
EVP and COO, Bruno Vinciguerra, age 52, $540,833 total compensation
EVP and CFO, Patrick S. McClymont
Assistant Vice President, Catharine Becket
Vice President, Beverly Sonnenborn
Vice President, Malcolm Beadling
Vice President Sales Director, Frank Everett
Vice President Business Development, George Sirignano
Vice President Information Technology, Priyanka Mathew
Vice President, Thomas Denzler
Assistant Vice President, Courtney Booth
Senior Vice President Associate General, Stacy Chervin
Assistant Vice President Human, Mara Shulman
Vice President Digital Media Services, Josh Pullan
Senior Vice President Worldwide, Benjamin Doller
Vice President Technical Services, Andrew Tusa
Senior Vice President, Nancy Bialler
Vice President Worldwide Director Media, Anthony Calnek
Senior Vice President, Selby Kiffer
Board Of Directors, John M Angelo, age 74
Chairman, Domenico De Sole, age 71
Auditors: Deloitte&ToucheLLP

LOCATIONS

HQ: Sotheby' s
1334 York Avenue, New York, NY 10021
Phone: 212 606-7000
Web: www.sothebys.com

2013 Sales

	$ mil.	% of total
US	352.4	41
UK	230.3	27
China	153.9	18
France	46.9	5
Other countries	39.5	4
Adjustments	(10.5)	-
Total	**853.7**	**100**

PRODUCTS/OPERATIONS

2013 Sales

	$ mil.	% of total
Agency	793.6	93
Principal	30.6	4
Finance	21.3	2
License fees	6.9	1
Other	1.3	-
Total	**853.7**	**100**

COMPETITORS

Bonhams	Phillips de Pury &
Christie' s	Company
Collectors Universe	SinoCoking
Finarte-Semenzato	Spectrum Group
GoIndustry-DoveBid	Tiffany & Co.
Heritage Auction	eBay
Galleries	

HISTORICAL FINANCIALS

Company Type: Public

Income Statement

FYE: December 31

	REVENUE ($ mil.)	NET INCOME ($ mil.)	NET PROFIT MARGIN	EMPLOYEES
12/13	853.6	130.0	15.2%	1,577
12/12	768.4	108.2	14.1%	1,501
12/11	831.8	171.4	20.6%	1,446
12/10	774.3	160.9	20.8%	1,380
12/09	484.9	(6.5)	—	1,323
Annual Growth	**15.2%**	**—**	**—**	**4.5%**

2013 Year-End Financials

Debt ratio: 17.9%
Return on equity: 12.1%
Cash ($ mil.): 721
Current ratio: 1.73
Long-term debt ($ mil.): 515

No. of shares (mil.): 69
Dividends
 Yield: 0.7%
 Payout: 26.3%
Market value ($ mil.): 3,678

	STOCK PRICE ($) FY Close	P/E High/Low		PER SHARE ($) Earnings	Dividends	Book Value
12/13	53.20	28	17	1.88	0.40	16.48
12/12	33.62	25	17	1.57	0.52	14.65
12/11	28.53	22	10	2.46	0.23	13.41
12/10	45.00	20	9	2.34	0.20	11.46
12/09	22.48	—	—	(0.10)	0.30	8.59
Annual Growth	**24.0%**	**—**	**—**	**—**	**7.5%**	**17.7%**

South State Corp

South State Corporation (formerly First Financial Holdings) is the holding company for South State Bank (formerly South Carolina Bank and Trust and South Carolina Bank and Trust of the Piedmont both known as SCBT). The bank operates branches throughout the Palmetto state as well as in select counties in Georgia and North Carolina. Serving retail and business customers the banks provide deposit accounts loans and mortgages as well as trust and investment planning services. More than half of the company's loan portfolio is devoted to commercial mortgages; consumer real estate loans are more than a quarter. South State has assets of about $8 billion.

EXECUTIVES

Executive Vice President Treasurer, Richard Mathis
Evp Support Division, Allen M Hay
CEO, Robert R. Hill, age 47, $645,000 total compensation
Evp And Cio, Rodney W Overby
Senior Vice President, Dane Murray
Vice President And Community, Nathaniel A Barber
Vp And Public Relations And Special Projects Director, Donna Pullen
Svp And Assistant Controller, Keith S Rainwater
Executive Vice President, Renee Brooks
Senior Vice President And Director, Chrissie Casas
Vice President, Michael Coggin
CFO and COO, John C. Pollok, age 48, $442,000 total compensation
Chief Banking Officer, John F. Windley, age 62, $315,000 total compensation
Chief Credit Officer and Chief Risk Officer, Joseph Burns, $295,000 total compensation
President, R. Wayne Hall, $203,405 total compensation
EVP and Corporate Secretary, William C. Bochette
Senior Vice President, Kathy Revels
Vice President, Christine Thompson
Vice President Of Human Resources, Debbie Gable
Svp South Carolina Bank And Trust, Michael C King
Senior Vice President And Commercial Consumer Lender, Jimmy Lindsey
Vice President Network, Bruce Harrison
Vice President, James A Shuford
Vice President Sales Finance, Tracy Franklin
Vice President, David Drummond
Senior Vice President Private Banking, Scott Ferguson
Assistant Vice President Training, Pamme Eades
Senior Vice President And Investment, Doug Smith
Vice President And Investment, Michael Tollison
Senior Vice President Private Banker, Shields Cochran
Vice President, Kirby Tucker
Senior Vice President And Regional, David Charpia
Vp, R Laffitte
Assistant Vice President And Branch Manager, Matt Richardson
Vice President, Kelly Klaiber
Senior Vice President Corporate Counsel, V Nicole Comer
Vice President, Montague Laffitte
Assistant Vice President, John A Reagan
Vice President, Michelle Smoak
Vice President Of Human Resources, Rennie Roberts
Senior Vice President, John Hanna
Vice President, Al Matheny
Senior Vice President And Senior Relationship Manager, Bill Coker
Vice President, Donna Murray
Senior Vice President Portfolio Manager, Brian Ngo
Senior Vice President, Lee Cavell
Senior Vice President Corporate Counsel, V Comer
Vice President, Stacy Cannon
Senior Vice President, Michelle Porta
Vice President, Tena McKay
Senior Vice President, Shields Guerrero
Vice President Of Human Resources, Roger Mosby
Vice President, Carl Kilpatrick
Vice President, R Hayes
Vice President, Reid Davis
Senior Vice President Technology, Ross Bagley
Chairman, Robert R. Horger, age 63
Vice Chairman, Paula Harper Bethea
Board Member, A Waters
Auditors: DixonHughesGoodmanLLP

HQ: South State Corp
520 Gervais Street, Columbia, SC 29201
Phone: 800 277-2175
Web: www.scbtonline.com

PRODUCTS/OPERATIONS

2011 Sales

	$ mil.	% of total
Interest		
Loans including fees	162.2	68
Investment securities	8.5	4
Other	1.0	-
Noninterest		
Service charges on deposit accounts	22.6	10
Gain on acquisitions	16.5	7
Bankcard services	11.7	5
Mortgage banking	6.3	3
Securities gains net	5.5	2
Amortization of FDIC indemnification asset	(10.1)	-
Other	2.6	1
Total	**293.1**	**100**

COMPETITORS

BB&T	Regions Financial
Bank of America	Security Federal
Bank of South Carolina	
First Citizens Bancorporation	

HISTORICAL FINANCIALS

Company Type: Public

Income Statement

FYE: December 31

	ASSETS ($ mil.)	NET INCOME ($ mil.)	INCOME AS % OF ASSETS	EMPLOYEES
12/13	7,931.5	49.2	0.6%	2,106
12/12	5,136.4	30.0	0.6%	1,324
12/11	3,896.5	22.6	0.6%	1,071
12/10	3,594.7	51.8	1.4%	1,015
12/09	2,702.1	13.6	0.5%	700
Annual Growth	**30.9%**	**37.9%**	**—**	**31.7%**

2013 Year-End Financials

Return on assets: 0.7%
Return on equity: 6.6%
Long-term debt ($ mil.): —
No. of shares (mil.): 24
Sales ($ mil): 340

Dividends
Yield: 1.1%
Payout: 31.0%
Market value ($ mil.): 1,603

	STOCK PRICE ($) FY Close	P/E High/Low	PER SHARE ($) Earnings	Dividends	Book Value
12/13	66.51	28 17	2.38	0.74	40.72
12/12	40.18	20 14	2.03	0.69	29.97
12/11	29.01	22 15	1.63	0.68	27.19
12/10	32.75	10 7	4.08	0.68	25.79
12/09	27.69	47 23	0.74	0.68	22.20
Annual Growth	**24.5%**	**— —**	**33.9%**	**2.1%**	**16.4%**

Southern Missouri Bancorp, Inc.

Southern Missouri Bancorp is the holding company for Southern Bank (formerly Southern Missouri Bank and Trust) which serves local residents and businesses in southeastern Missouri and northeastern Arkansas through more than 10 branches. Residential mortgages account for the largest percentage of the bank's loan portfolio followed by commercial mortgages and business loans. Construction and consumer loans round out its lending activities. Deposit products include checking savings and money market accounts CDs and IRAs. The bank also offers financial planning and investment services. Originally chartered in 1887 Southern Bank acquired Arkansas-based Southern Bank of Commerce in 2009.

Jeffrey Gendell of Tontine Financial Partners owns more than 9% of Southern Missouri Bancorp; independent investor Donald Crandell owns more than 8%; employees own around 6%; and president CEO and director Greg Steffens more than 5%.

EXECUTIVES

Vice President, Mel Jackson
Senior Vice President Information Technology, Bill Aslin
Assistant Vice President, Patricia A Price
Vice President And Loan Officer, Jon Holman
Vice President, Don Hastings
Vice President Credit Admin, Burke Craver
Auditors: BKDLLP

LOCATIONS

HQ: Southern Missouri Bancorp, Inc.
531 Vine Street, Poplar Bluff, MO 63901
Phone: 573 778-1800   **Fax:** 573 686-2920
Web: www.bankwithsouthern.com

COMPETITORS

Bank of America	Regions Financial
Commerce Bancshares	U.S. Bancorp
IBERIABANK	UMB Financial

HISTORICAL FINANCIALS

Company Type: Public

Income Statement

FYE: June 30

	ASSETS ($ mil.)	NET INCOME ($ mil.)	INCOME AS % OF ASSETS	EMPLOYEES
06/14	1,021.4	10.0	1.0%	247
06/13	796.3	10.0	1.3%	181
06/12	739.1	10.1	1.4%	179
06/11	688.2	11.4	1.7%	174
06/10	552.0	4.6	0.8%	144
Annual Growth	**16.6%**	**21.5%**	**—**	**14.4%**

2014 Year-End Financials

Return on assets: 1.1%
Return on equity: 9.4%
Long-term debt ($ mil.): —
No. of shares (mil.): 6
Sales ($ mil): 46

Dividends
Yield: 3.5%
Payout: 43.9%
Market value ($ mil.): 238

	STOCK PRICE ($) FY Close	P/E High/Low	PER SHARE ($) Earnings	Dividends	Book Value
06/14	35.69	25 17	1.46	0.64	16.63
06/13	25.67	18 15	1.44	0.60	15.46
06/12	21.50	15 12	1.66	0.48	14.57
06/11	20.78	10 6	2.56	0.48	13.28
06/10	15.01	17 9	0.99	0.48	10.93
Annual Growth	**24.2%**	**— —**	**10.1%**	**7.5%**	**11.1%**

SP Plus Corp

SP Plus (formerly Standard Parking) wants to be the driving force in the parking industry —and it likely is. The parking behemoth manages about 4200 surface and multilevel parking facilities for airports hospitals hotels local governments office buildings retail centers sports venues and universities in more than 400 cities throughout the US and Canada. Its airport facilities consist of parking and shuttle bus operations at more than 75 airports including Chicago O'Hare and Dallas/Fort Worth International. Overall SP Plus provides more than 2.1 million parking spaces. In a sweeping move for the parking industry it acquired Central Parking Corporation one of its biggest rivals in 2012.

Mergers and Acquisitions

Merging with Central Parking essentially doubled SP Plus' operations in size adding more than 2200 locations and 1 million parking spaces to its portfolio across the country. After the deal closed in October 2012 SP Plus assumed $210 million of Central Parking's debt and Central Parking shareholders retained about 28% of the combined company. The new company is led by SP Plus' CEO and continues to operate under the existing Standard Parking and Central Parking brands.

Geographic Reach

Chicago-based SP Plus has parking facilities in 46 US states the District of Columbia Puerto Rico and Canada.

Operations

SP Plus manages about 4200 parking facilities containing some 2.1 million parking spaces in about 420 cities. The company also operates 30 parking-related service centers serving 75 airports ground transportation through its fleet of about 730 shuttle buses and 136 valet locations. USA Parking System acquired along with Central Parking is now a wholly owned subsidiary of SP Plus and ranks among the premier valet operators in the nation.

Financial Performance

Buoyed by the purchase of Central Parking in late 2012 SP Plus reported a revenue gain of 54% in 2013 versus 2012 to $1.47 billion. Gross profit rose 61% over the same period to $107.1 million driven primarily by the addition of CPC. Net income for the year was $12.1 million versus $1.3 million in 2012.

Strategy

Acquisitions have consistently been a key element of the company's growth. The purchase of Central Parking Corp. (CPC) broadened SP Plus's range of services by adding among other things valet parking to its menu. USA Parking one of the subsidiaries acquired in the CPC purchase is a leader in the valet industry and is the springboard from which SP Plus plans to build a national valet business. Other key markets for development include airport services and the university markets.

SP Plus is also looking to expand in its core markets with the aim of being #1 or #2 in each. A contract to operate and maintain approximately 1300 parking spaces in 17 facilities throughout the Manhattan Bronx Queens and Brooklyn boroughs of New York City further that aim. The multi-year deal which began in October of 2013 also includes responsibility for general maintenance painting restriping cleaning and snow removal.

Company Background

Standard Parking Corp. changed its name to SP Plus Corp. in December 2013.

HISTORY

In need of parking spaces for their rental-car business Alva "Ted" Bonda and Howard Metzenbaum founded Airport Parking Company of America (APCOA) in 1949. At the time airport parking was unorganized but free. Metzenbaum and Bonda changed all that garnering a contract in 1951 to manage paid parking facilities at Cleveland Hopkins International Airport.

APCOA's guarded well-lit parking lots were a hit and the company soon became the preeminent airport parking manager in the US. Metzenbaum and Bonda sold their venture to conglomerate International Telephone & Telegraph (ITT) in 1966. Metzenbaum went on to serve three terms in the US Senate.

Under ITT's reign APCOA expanded into Europe in 1970. Buffalo-based holding company Delaware North acquired APCOA in 1981 only to sell the company's North American operations to Holberg Industries and APCOA managers including Walter Stuelpe in 1989.

By 1998 APCOA had 700 parking lots in 30 cities. That year it bought privately held Chicago-based Standard Parking which operated 380 garages in 29 cities. Founded in 1929 at a Standard Oil gas station Standard had made its mark in parking management by playing music in theme garages to help patrons remember where they parked.

Myron Warshauer grandson of Standard's founder took the wheel of the combined company APCOA/Standard Parking. Acquisitions of several small parking firms in 1998 gave the company control of more than 400 lots in the Los Angeles area. APCOA/Standard continued its lot purchases in 1999 while selling its Graelic parking consulting subsidiary to that unit's managers. In 2000 APCOA/Standard gained rights to manage parking at airports in Flint Michigan and Eugene Oregon.

President James Wilhelm added the CEO position to his title after Myron Warshauer resigned as CEO in 2001 and was named the company's vice chairman emeritus. That year the company announced that Holberg Industries exposed to a possible takeover by creditors was no longer its indirect parent. In 2002 a company owned by chairman John Holten took control of 84% of Apcoa/Standard Parking. In 2003 the company changed its name to Standard Parking Corporation; it filed to go public a year later.

Standard Parking acquired Seattle's Sound Parking in 2005 gaining some 55 parking locations and 2 shuttle operations. The company expanded its reach into sports and event parking when it bought Gameday Management Group in 2009 and in late 2010 Standard Parking acquired Philadelphia's Expert Parking.

In its most historic acquisition to date in October 2012 Standard Parking snapped up Central Parking Corporation one of its biggest rivals. The company changed its name to SP Plus Corp. in December 2013.

EXECUTIVES

Senior Vice President Administrative, Michael Schwartz
EVP General Counsel and Secretary, Robert N. Sacks, age 61, $271,491 total compensation
Exec V Pres-mkt & Business Dev, Douglas R Warshauer, age 83
EVP Operations, Edward E. (Ed) Simmons, age 64
EVP Operations, Steven A. Warshauer, age 59, $469,280 total compensation
EVP Chief Administrative Officer and Associate General Counsel, Michael K. Wolf, age 64, $392,186 total compensation
EVP and Chief Human Resource Officer, Gerard M. Klaisle, age 60
President and CEO, G. Marc Baumann, age 58, $550,021 total compensation
EVP Operations, John Ricchiuto, age 57
EVP and Chief Business Development Officer, Thomas L. Hagerman, age 53, $411,767 total compensation
EVP New York Tri-State Division, Hector O. Chevalier
EVP Strategy and Technology, Keith Evans
EVP Hospitality Division; President and CEO USA Parking System, William H. Bodenhamer
EVP Operations, Robert Toy, $374,414 total compensation
EVP CFO and Treasurer, Vance C. Johnston
Vice President Infrastructure, Chris Rothbauer
Vice President Client Reporting, Rich Kapper
Vice President, Shevket Dardovski
Svp-standard Parking Of Canada, Bryan Wallner
Regional Vice President, Bill Kepp
Vice President Strategic Planning And Analysis, Connie Kim
Vice President Human Resources, Michael Machi
Vice President, Dave Lombardi
Vice President Associate Counsel, Jerry Pate
Senior Vice President Of Finance, Mark Janek
Vice President Benefits Comp And Er, Libby Redmon
Vice President National Accounts, Jeffrey Okyle
Vice President General Counsel, Jim Burdett
Vice President Regional Manager, Charles J Voase
Senior Vice President, Steven Aiello
Senior Vice President, Mike Tepper
Vice President Maintenance Services, Jim Kaster
Senior Vice President, Randall Ely
Vice President Claims Management, Jim Ostling
Vice President, Peter Thorson
Chairman, James A. (Jim) Wilhelm, age 60
Senior Treasury Analyst, Eric Clough
Senior Treasury Analyst, Matthew Smaizys
Senior Treasury Analyst, Matt Smaizys
Auditors: Ernst&YoungLLP

LOCATIONS

HQ: SP Plus Corp
200 E Randolph Street, Suite 7700, Chicago, IL 60601-7702
Phone: 312 274-2000
Web: www.spplus.com

PRODUCTS/OPERATIONS

2013 Sales

	$ mil.	% of total
Lease contracts	489.6	33
Management contracts	347.3	24
Reimbursement of management contract expense	629.9	43
Total	**1466.8**	**100**

COMPETITORS

ABM Industries
Ace Parking
Diamond Parking

Impark
VINCI Park

HISTORICAL FINANCIALS

Company Type: Public

Income Statement

FYE: December 31

	REVENUE ($ mil.)	NET INCOME ($ mil.)	NET PROFIT MARGIN	EMPLOYEES
12/13	1,466.8	12.0	0.8%	23,937
12/12	953.9	3.1	0.3%	25,011
12/11	729.6	17.9	2.5%	11,914
12/10	721.1	16.8	2.3%	11,971
12/09	695.4	14.0	2.0%	11,970
Annual Growth	20.5%	(3.8%)	—	18.9%

2013 Year-End Financials

Debt ratio: 33.4%
Return on equity: 6.0%
Cash ($ mil.): 23
Current ratio: 0.70
Long-term debt ($ mil.): 264

No. of shares (mil.): 21
Dividends
  Yield: —
  Payout: —
Market value ($ mil.): 572

	STOCK PRICE ($) FY Close	P/E High/Low		PER SHARE ($) Earnings	Dividends	Book Value
12/13	26.04	50	36	0.54	0.00	9.24
12/12	21.99	135	94	0.18	0.00	8.98
12/11	17.87	17	13	1.12	0.00	3.22
12/10	18.98	19	14	1.06	0.00	2.34
12/09	15.88	22	15	0.90	0.00	0.96
Annual Growth	13.2%	—	—	(12.0%)	—	76.2%

Sparton Corp.

This Sparton requires more than 300 people to defend its turf. Tracing its roots back to 1900 the company provides contract electronics manufacturing services primarily the design and production of electronic and electromechanical devices for aerospace defense and medical companies. Its products include printed circuit boards sensors and electromechanical components as well as fully built systems and devices. The company also manufactures an anti-submarine warfare device called a sonobuoy for the US Navy and foreign governments. It generates most of its sales in the US.

Operations The company is organized around three segments —medical devices defense and security systems and complex systems. It generates nearly half its sales from medical devices and subassemblies for the diagnostic therapeutic and surgical markets. Defense and security systems which includes the manufacturing of sonobuoys accounts for nearly a third of sales and complex systems (detection systems flight controls lighting security systems) brings in about 20%.

Geographic Reach Sparton operates from four factories in the US and one in Vietnam. The US accounts for about 80% of sales; Ireland the only other specific country highlighted generates about 5%. Sales to Ireland fell more than 50% year-over-year

Sales and Marketing The company markets its non-sonobuoy products and services directly to customers; sonobuoys are distributed through a joint venture subcontractor ERAPSCO. The US Navy is Sparton's top customer accounting for about 20% of revenue. Other major clients include Fenwal Blood Technologies (15%) and Siemens (11%).

Financial Performance The company has reported three consecutive years of revenue and net income growth since struggling with declines during the worst of the economic recession. In fiscal 2012 (ended June) it saw revenue jump 10% to $224 million and net income rise more than a quarter to nearly $10 million. Sparton saw growth across all three of its segments including double-digit growth in medical sales. Its medical segment was negatively impacted however by a decline in sales to one of its largest customers –industrial engineering firm Siemens adopted a dual sourcing strategy in 2012 that resulted in a loss of nearly $13 million.

Mergers and Acquisitions Sparton in late 2012 acquired medical device manufacturer Onyx EMS for about $43 million. The move expands the company's reach in the healthcare market and brings it into the Minneapolis area. It has made several medical acquisitions in recent years including two in Denver in 2010: Delphi Medical Systems (for about $8 million) and Byers Peak (for more than $4 million).

HISTORY

Founded in 1900 Sparks-Withington originally made agricultural equipment components. In 1911 it introduced the world's first electric car horn. In the 1920s the company moved into radios; over the years it introduced a number of firsts including the first radio to operate on household current. Sparks-Withington went public in 1926. In 1950 it began making submarine detection devices called sonobuoys which would become a primary business. That year longtime director John Smith became chairman and CEO; he would head the company for 40 years. The company changed its name to Sparton (a shortened version of the original) in 1957.

Sparton's sales were buoyant during the 1980s thanks to a military buildup that emphasized antisubmarine warfare. However the end of the Cold War dropped the company's sonobuoy business from 61% of sales in 1991 to 17% in 1995. In an effort to get back above water Sparton shifted its focus to contract electronics manufacturing. In 1996 the company sold its KPI Automotive Group to Dura Automotive Systems for about $100 million leading to a strong gain in fiscal 1997. Also in 1997 Sparton won a contract for 55% of the US Navy's sonobuoy requirements.

In 1998 the company closed its remaining auto operation a car horn plant after failing to find a buyer. That year Sparton began expanding globally through pacts with foreign contract manufacturers. It sold its acoustics line in 1999. Costs associated with a legal tussle against the EPA regarding cleanup at one of its New Mexico facilities pumped up losses for fiscal 1999. In 2000 Sparton settled the case and agreed to pay more than $1.6 million in fines and clean up soil and groundwater which it had contaminated. That year Smith died; his nephew Bradley Smith took over as chairman and president David Hockenbrocht added CEO to his title.

By mid-2005 Sparton agreed to acquire HDJ Company and its Specialized Medical Devices subsidiary. HDJ made medical products requiring precise machining including orthopedic plates and screws implanted in the human body by surgeons. Sparton later called off the acquisition however. HDJ sold its assets to Teleflex in 2007. Sparton opened its manufacturing facility in Vietnam in 2005.

In 2006 Sparton acquired Astro Instrumentation which made products involving medical laboratory test equipment. The purchase price was around $26 million with nearly $19 million in cash and the remainder covered by a note. The company made Astro a wholly owned subsidiary retaining existing management.

David Hockenbrocht retired as president and CEO in early 2008 a few weeks after he had been briefly hospitalized; he also resigned from the board of directors ending a career of 30 years with the company. SVP/CFO Richard Langley was named interim president and CEO to succeed him.

In late 2008 Citation Corp. COO Cary Wood was tapped as Sparton's CEO. Richard Langley remained president of the company until his resignation in 2009. Former Chairman Bradley O. Smith had been the largest individual shareholder controlling more than 27% of the company through shares he owned and shares held by the John J. Smith Trust before he stepped down in 2009 and sold 21% of his shares.

EXECUTIVES

President CEO and Director, Cary B. Wood, age 46, $443,333 total compensation
SVP Operations, Gordon B. Madlock, age 56, $224,000 total compensation
CFO, Donald W. (Don) Pearson, age 52
Senior Vice President - Quality; Engineering and Information Systems, Steven M. (Steve) Korwin, $198,000 total compensation
Vice President Sales And Marketing, James M (Jim) Lackemacher, age 52
Vice-president, Mike Davis
Senior Vice President Quality, Frank Weintraub
Vice President Of Program Management, Dan Rukavina
Group Vice President Quality, Steve Kozak
Vice-president, Christopher Ratliff
Vice President Of Engineering, Clark Briggs
Vice President Of Supply Chain, Leroy Broesder
Chairman, James R. (Jim) Swartwout, age 67
President CEO and Director, Cary B. Wood, age 46
Auditors: BDOSeidmanLLP

LOCATIONS

HQ: Sparton Corp.
425 N. Martingale Road, Suite 2050, Schaumburg, IL 60173-2213
Phone: 847 762-5800
Web: www.sparton.com

2012 Sales

	$ mil.	% of total
US	179.7	80
Ireland	10.9	5
Other countries	33.0	15
Total	**223.6**	**100**

PRODUCTS/OPERATIONS

2012 Sales

	$ mil.	% of total
Medical devices	110.9	47
Defense & security systems	74.1	31
Complex systems	53.6	22
Adjustments	(15.0)	-
Total	**223.6**	**100**

Selected Services and Products

Battery monitoring systems
Cable air pressure monitoring systems
Cable and wire harness assembly
Electronics manufacturing
Intrusion detection systems
Medical product design
Power monitoring systems
Power products
Sonobuoys
Strategic materials logistics

COMPETITORS

API Technologies	Magal
AeroVironment	Nortech Systems
Analogic	Northrop Grumman
Astronics	Plexus
Benchmark Electronics	Raven Industries
CTS Corp.	SMTC Corp.
Celestica	Sanmina
Ducommun	SigmaTron
Flextronics	Simclar
HEI	Sypris Solutions
IEC Electronics	Viasystems
Jabil	

HISTORICAL FINANCIALS

Company Type: Public

Income Statement

FYE: June 30

	REVENUE ($ mil.)	NET INCOME ($ mil.)	NET PROFIT MARGIN	EMPLOYEES
06/14	336.1	12.9	3.9%	1,483
06/13	266.0	13.6	5.1%	1,375
06/12	223.5	9.5	4.3%	950
06/11	203.3	7.4	3.7%	1,013
06/10	173.9	7.4	4.3%	703
Annual Growth	**17.9%**	**14.9%**	**—**	**20.5%**

2014 Year-End Financials

Debt ratio: 20.6%
Return on equity: 12.6%
Cash ($ mil.): 8
Current ratio: 2.83
Long-term debt ($ mil.): 40
No. of shares (mil.): 10
Dividends
 Yield: —
 Payout: —
Market value ($ mil.): 281

	STOCK PRICE ($) FY Close	P/E High/Low		PER SHARE ($) Earnings	Dividends	Book Value
06/14	27.74	26	14	1.28	0.00	10.87
06/13	17.24	13	7	1.33	0.00	9.48
06/12	9.90	11	6	0.93	0.00	8.16
06/11	10.22	14	7	0.73	0.00	7.33
06/10	5.03	9	3	0.75	0.00	6.30
Annual Growth	**53.2%**			**14.3%**	**—**	**14.6%**

Spectra Energy Partners LP

When you take one company's energy holdings and splinter them you get Spectra Energy Partners. Formed by Spectra Energy out of the former natural gas holdings of Duke Energy the company is a natural gas pipeline and storage facility operator. Its assets include a liquefied natural gas storage location in Tennessee 50% of Market Hub (two natural gas storage facilities in Texas and Louisiana) and 49% of Gulfstream Natural Gas System. All told Spectra Energy Partners has 3200 miles of natural gas transmission and gathering pipelines capable of moving about 3.6 billion cu. ft. per day. It also has 57 billion cu. ft. of gas storage capacity.

The company's core customers include distribution companies and utilities natural gas producers in Appalachia the Gulf Coast and the Mid-Continent power plants and major industrial companies. Major customers include EQT and the Tennessee Valley Authority.

Spectra Energy Partners' growth plans include expanding its pipeline and storage facilities (both by acquisitions and organic growth) to meet increased demand. In this regard in 2009 the company acquired Ozark Gas Transmission and Ozark Gas Gathering Systems from Atlas Pipeline Partners for $300 million.

In 2010 it acquired an additional 24.5% of a 745-mile interstate natural gas transportation system (Gulfstream Natural Gas System) from Spectra Energy for $330 million. The deal boosted Spectra Energy Partners' holdings to 49%.

Further expanding its Appalachian pipeline assets in 2011 the company bought a 70-mile natural gas pipeline (Big Sandy Pipeline) in eastern Kentucky from EQT Corp. for $390 million. That year the company also completed organinc expansion projects on the Gulfstream pipeline and at the Market Hub salt cavern storage complex.

The Big Sandy acquisition increased production and lifted the company's revenues and net income in 2011 offsetting decreased contract revenue (due to lower wholesale prices) from its Ozark Gas Transmission segment.

Expanding its Northeast pipeline operations in 2012 the company agreed to buy 39% of Maritimes & Northeast Pipeline L.L.C. from Spectra Energy for $319 million in cash and $56 million in newly issued partnership units.

EXECUTIVES

Vice President Marketing And Customer, Mel Ydreos
Vice President Executive Us Benefits, Charlotte Wayland
Group Vice President, Greg Rizzo
Auditors: Deloitte&ToucheLLP

LOCATIONS

HQ: Spectra Energy Partners LP
5400 Westheimer Court, Houston, TX 77056
Phone: 713 627-5400
Web: www.spectraenergypartners.com

PRODUCTS/OPERATIONS

2011 Sales

	$ mil.	% of total
Transportation of natural gas	182.4	89
Storage of natural gas & other	22.6	11
Total	**205.0**	**100**

COMPETITORS

AGL Resources	Florida Gas
CenterPoint Energy	Transmission
Crestwood Midstream	Occidental Petroleum
Partners LP	Texas Gas Transmission
DCP Midstream Partners	Transcontinental Gas
Enterprise Products	Pipe Line
Exxon Mobil	Williams Companies

HISTORICAL FINANCIALS

Company Type: Public

Income Statement

FYE: December 31

	REVENUE ($ mil.)	NET INCOME ($ mil.)	NET PROFIT MARGIN	EMPLOYEES
12/13	1,965.0	1,070.0	54.5%	0
12/12	236.8	193.5	81.7%	0
12/11	205.0	172.0	83.9%	0
12/10	197.7	147.9	74.8%	0
12/09	178.9	135.9	76.0%	0
Annual Growth	**82.0%**	**67.5%**	**—**	**—**

2013 Year-End Financials

Debt ratio: 35.4%
Return on equity: —
Cash ($ mil.): 121
Current ratio: 0.42
Long-term debt ($ mil.): 5,178

No. of shares (mil.): 289
Dividends
Yield: 4.4%
Payout: 124.7%
Market value ($ mil.): 13,147

	STOCK PRICE ($) FY Close	P/E High/Low		PER SHARE ($) Earnings	Dividends	Book Value
12/13	45.35	7	4	7.15	2.02	34.54
12/12	31.23	20	16	1.69	1.93	16.14
12/11	31.96	21	16	1.63	1.85	17.27
12/10	32.85	21	16	1.70	1.70	16.42
12/09	29.57	17	11	1.71	1.51	16.47
Annual Growth	**11.3%**		**—**	**43.0%**	**7.6%**	**20.4%**

Spirit Airlines Inc

Spirit Airlines can lift the spirits of people seeking sunshine. The ultra low-cost carrier (ULCC) operates more than 280 daily flights between major US cities and popular vacation spots in South Florida the Caribbean and Latin America serving nearly 50 destinations. It operates an all Airbus fleet of nearly 55 single-aisle aircraft including A319s A320s and A321s. Spirit capitalizes on an ancillary service model charging separately for baggage advance seat selection and other travel-related upgrades. In addition to scheduled service the company partners with third-party vendors to offer a slate of vacation packages via its website.

Geographic Reach

Spirit's largest maintenance facility is stationed in a leased facility at FLL under a lease that expires in January 2015. It also conducts additional maintenance operations in leased facilities in Detroit; Chicago; Atlantic City New Jersey; Dallas; and Las Vegas. Revenue generated from the US accounts for nearly 90% of Spirit's revenue.

Sales and MarketingSpirit Airlines sells through its website an outsourced call center and third-party travel agents. Its spirit.com site accounts for about two-thirds of sales.

Financial PerformanceWith the Great Recession that decimated the airline industry far behind it Spirit is enjoying uncharted growth over the years. Revenues jumped 25% from $1.32 billion in 2012 to $1.65 in 2013 a historic milestone for the company. The spike in revenue in 2013 was driven by a 26% increase in passenger revenue. Non-ticket revenue also climbed by 25% due to a 24% increase in traffic and an increase in baggage revenue per passenger flight segment.

Profits also surged 63% from $108 million in 2012 to peak at a record-shattering $177 million

in 2013 due to the higher revenue and decreased increase expenses. While its cash flow from operations has fluctuated a bit over the last few years it increased by $82 million in 2013 due to larger operating profits and a slightly higher air traffic liability driven by higher capacity and future bookings.

StrategyTo maintain its impressive growth trajectory Spirit is expanding its city destination network while also concentrating its resources on the growing Caribbean and Latin American markets. Like most carriers within its industry Spirit's top issue is controlling costs in order sustain a profit from its low fares.

To this end the company has moved to an aggressive unbundling strategy to stimulate passenger demand and revenues. Unbundling allows passengers to pay separately for products and services that they want to use. Charging for such extras as onboard beverages and snacks enables Spirit to offset its low ticket prices as well as maintain its competitive market presence.

EXECUTIVES

Senior Vice President Of Customer Service, Tony Lefebvre
Vp And Cio, Scott M Allard, age 47
President and CEO, B. Ben Baldanza, age 52, $479,987 total compensation
SVP Network and Revenue Management, Ted Botimer
VP Supply Chain and Operations Support, Charlie Rue, age 43
SVP and CRO, Edward Christie
VP Airport and Inflight Services, Jake Filene
VP Technical Operations, Joe Resnik
SVP and COO, John Bendoraitis, $64,410 total compensation
VP and CIO, Hilton Sturisky
SVP and CFO, Ted Christie
Vice President Technical Operations, Guy Borowski
Vice President And Controller, Edmundo Miranda
Vp And Treasurer, Jose Arrellaga
Vice President Flight Operations, Jyri Strandman
Senior Vice President Flight Operations, Scott Justman
Vice President Customer Service, Carol Fischer
Chief Marketing Off Senior Vp, Tom Anderson
Interim Chief Information Officer And Vice President Information Technology, Todd Andaya
Vice President Customer Service, Kent Hansen
Vice President Operations, Chris Grazel
Vice President Revenue Management, Roger Morech
Vp-pricing & Revenue Mgmnt, Eric Netland
Board Member, Barclay G Jones, age 54
Chairman, H. McIntyre (Mac) Gardner, age 53
Board Member, Horacio Scapparone, age 63
Auditors: Ernst&YoungLLP

LOCATIONS

HQ: Spirit Airlines Inc
2800 Executive Way, Miramar, FL 33025
Phone: 954 447-7920
Web: www.spirit.com

2013 Sales

	$ mil.	% of total
Domestic	1467.5	89
Latin America	186.9	11
Total	**1654.4**	**100**

PRODUCTS/OPERATIONS

2013 Sales

	$ mil.	% of total
Passenger	986.0	60
Non-ticket	668.4	40
Total	**1654.4**	**100**

COMPETITORS

AirTran Airways	JetBlue
Allegiant Travel	Southwest Airlines
American Airlines Group	US Airways
	United Continental
Delta Air Lines	Virgin America

HISTORICAL FINANCIALS

Company Type: Public

Income Statement

FYE: December 31

	REVENUE ($ mil.)	NET INCOME ($ mil.)	NET PROFIT MARGIN	EMPLOYEES
12/13	1,654.3	176.9	10.7%	3,619
12/12	1,318.3	108.4	8.2%	3,033
12/11	1,071.1	76.4	7.1%	2,580
12/10	781.2	72.4	9.3%	2,385
12/09	700.0	83.6	12.0%	0
Annual Growth	**24.0%**	**20.6%**	—	—

2013 Year-End Financials

Debt ratio: —
Return on equity: 26.1%
Cash ($ mil.): 530
Current ratio: 1.93
Long-term debt ($ mil.): —

No. of shares (mil.): 72
Dividends
Yield: —
Payout: —
Market value ($ mil.): 3,295

	STOCK PRICE ($) FY Close	P/E High/Low		PER SHARE ($) Earnings	Dividends	Book Value
12/13	45.41	19	7	2.42	0.00	10.60
12/12	17.73	16	9	1.49	0.00	8.04
12/11	15.60	12	7	1.43	0.00	6.44
Annual Growth	**70.6%**	—	—	**30.1%**	—	**28.3%**

SS&C Technologies Holdings, Inc.

SS&C Technologies helps its clients buy low and sell high. The company develops software for managing financial portfolios loans real estate equity back-office processing and securities trading and it provides consulting and outsourcing services. Its applications automate investment portfolio management asset and liability management for actuaries property and casualty insurance risk management trade ordering and financial modeling. SS&C serves asset managers insurance companies banks corporate treasuries hedge funds and government agencies among others. Clients have included Middlebury College and Monro Muffler Brake. It has offices in North America Europe and Asia.

Geographic Reach
SS&C Technologies has about two dozen offices across the US. It has international offices in Australia Canada the Cayman Islands Hong Kong India Ireland Malaysia Singapore The Netherlands and the UK.

Sales and Marketing
The company counts a diverse customer base of 5500 clients in the financial services industry. It uses a direct sales force given the complexity of the industry and its extensive regulatory and reporting requirements. For its property management software however it does use a telemarketing staff.

Financial Performance
Overall sales grew 29% to $712 million in 2013 primarily as a result of acquisitions it made in 2012 as well as a continued increase in demand for hedge fund and private equity services from alternative investment managers. Profits more than doubled to $117 million.

Strategy
Acquisitions play a key role in the company's strategy resulting in some 40 purchases since 1995. SS&C typically pursues companies that either expand its product and service offerings into new markets or increase its client base within the financial services industry.

Mergers and Acquisitions
Recent acquisitions include Prime Management Limited a fund administrator with offices in Bermuda and Canada. The 2013 acquisition furthers SS&C's ability to administer insurance linked securities and the funds which invest in them. In 2012 the company bought GlobeOp Financial Services a provider of middle and back-office services and integrated risk reporting to hedge fund and account managers and Thomson Reuters' PORTIA business a developer of middle-to-back office investment operations software for $170 million. Also that year it bought HedgeMetrix and Gravity Financial.

In 2011 it bought Connecticut-based benefits administration software developer BenefitsXML to expand its line of products for enterprise human resources management and BDO Simpson Xavier Fund Administration Services the Dublin-based division of BDO.

HISTORY

Former KPMG Peat Marwick (now KPMG International) executive William Stone founded Securities Software & Consulting in 1986. The company produced its first product in 1989 — a DOS-based portfolio management program geared toward large and medium-sized institutional investors — and called it CAMRA (complete asset management reporting and accounting).

SS&C introduced a Windows-based version of CAMRA in 1993. That year the company also introduced its first loan portfolio management product. SS&C acquired Chalke Inc. in 1995 and with it Chalke's PTS (profit testing system) economic modeling software for insurance companies.

The company went public as SS&C Technologies in 1996. The next year groups from New York and Connecticut filed a class-action suit claiming the company made misrepresentations in its prospectus (the case was dismissed in 1999). Also in 1997 SS&C acquired Dutch financial software company Mabel Systems and Shepro Braun Systems.

1998 purchases included software firms Quantra and Savid International. SS&C continued the trend in 1999 with the purchase of hedge fund software specialist HedgeWare. But the acquisition-fueled growth and a drop in software sales helped cause losses for 1999. In 2000 the company made its applications available for outsourcing on the Internet. The next year moving away from development and toward marketing of new projects SS&C cut 6% of its workforce.

In 2002 the company acquired finance applications service provider Real-Time USA and later that year it bought Thomson subsidiary DBC a provider of financial software for fixed-income analysis. In 2004 SS&C bought Automatic Data Processing subsidiary OMR Systems a provider of treasury processing software and the following year it acquired Eisnerfast a provider of services for hedge funds.

SS&C was acquired by Sunshine Acquisition Corporation an affiliate of private equity firm The Carlyle Group in 2005.

In 2006 and 2007 the company continued its acquisitive ways purchasing Cogent Management Zoologic and Northport. In 2008 it bought the assets of Micro Design Services a developer of investment and financial management software in a bid to increase its presence in the securities industry and to boost its mobile capabilities.

In 2009 SS&C purchased Unisys' MAXIMIS business line which provided institutional asset management applications and services. It also bought Evare a managed utility service provider for financial data acquisition enrichment transformation and delivery and TheNextRound a provider of software for the alternative investment and private equity sectors. Also that year the company bought Tradeware Global a provider of financial information exchange services to brokers and financial institutions for around $21.5 million.

SS&C went public again in 2010 raising nearly $161 million in the offering.

The company's acquisitions that year included the purchase of Geller Investment Partnership Services a provider of accounting reporting tax and investor services to private equity funds and hedge funds among others. It also bought TD AMERITRADE's thinklink business to expand its front office software and services and building its list of sell-side institutional clients. thinklink specialized in Web-based software used to enable trade order management among other functions. SS&C also bought Utah-based TimeShareWare a provider of software to shared-ownership properties such as condominium hotels timeshare vacation resorts and others.

EXECUTIVES

Managing Director SS&C Asia Pacific, Thanendra (Tee) Arasoo
President; Chief Operating Officer; Director, Normand A. (Norm) Boulanger, age 52, $450,000 total compensation
Chairman and CEO, William C. (Bill) Stone, age 59, $750,000 total compensation
SVP and CFO, Patrick J. Pedonti, age 63, $260,000 total compensation
SVP and Chief Development Officer, Steve H. Kremidas
SVP and General Manager Treasury Banks and Credit Unions Business, Colleen Nelsen
SVP and General Manager, Thomas (Tom) McMackin
SVP and Managing Director International, David N. (Dave) Reid
SVP and Managing Director Alternative Assets, Rahul Kanwar
Managing Director SS&C Fund Services, Henry Toy
Managing Director SS&C Technologies Australia, Phil Banas
SVP Enterprise Risk, James (Jim) Ramenda
SVP and General Manager Financial Markets Division, Bob Moitoso

SVP and General Manager SS&C PORTIA, Christy Bremner
SVP and General Manager Asset Management Division, Alex Marasco
SVP Institutional Outsourcing, Tim Reilly
Svp-institutional Outsourcing, Timothy Reilly
Vp Commercial Lending Ss&c Technology, John F Stone
Vice President Product Development, Stephen Cadmus
Vice President Software Development, Eric Rocks
Vice President Derivative Products, Seth Singer
Vice President Software Development, Joseph Genautis
Senior Vice President Of Development, David Varsano
Vice President Of Product Technology, Elad Pimenta
Alliances Vice President, Bob Millar
Vice President, Christine Egbert
Vice President Business Solutions, Mike Doyle
Chairman and CEO, William C. (Bill) Stone, age 59
Treasurer, William Waters
Auditors: PricewaterhouseCoopersLLP

LOCATIONS

HQ: SS&C Technologies Holdings, Inc.
80 Lamberton Road, Windsor, CT 06095
Phone: 860 298-4500
Web: www.ssctech.com

2013 Sales

	$ mil.	% of total
Americas		
US	466.7	65
Canada	61.0	9
Other countries	16.8	2
Europe	148.6	21
Asia/Pacific & Japan	19.6	3
Total	**712.7**	**100**

PRODUCTS/OPERATIONS

2013 Sales by Product Group

	$ mil.	% of total
Portfolio management/accounting	640.1	90
Trading/treasury operations	32.9	5
Property management	14.6	2
Financial modeling	8.4	2
Money market processing	8.3	1
Loan management/accounting	6.7	-
Training	1.7	-
Total	**712.7**	**100**

Selected Services

Application outsourcing and hosting
Consulting
Data conversion
Installation
Maintenance
Technical support
Training

Selected Software

AdvisorWare (portfolio management and investment accounting)
Altair (asset management for hedge funds and family offices)
AnalyticsExpress (financial modeling)
Antares (trade order management)
The BANC Mall (Internet-based lending and leasing tool)
CAMRA (asset management reporting and accounting)
DBC (financial modeling)
Debt & Derivatives (comprehensive derivative and debt portfolio analysis)
Finesse (dynamic financial analysis and simulation)
Lightning (office processing management and automation)
LMS (loan management)
PALMS (alternative investment managers)

PortPro (balance sheet and investment portfolio analysis and management)
PTS (life insurance modeling and decision support)
SamTrak (property management for real estate leasing agents and property managers)
SKYLINE II (property management accounting and reporting)
SS&C Wealth Management (wealth management)
TradeDesk (fixed-income transaction processing automation)
TradeThru (trading and treasury operations)

COMPETITORS

ADP	Intuit
Advent Software	Liquid Holdings
Algorithmics	McCracken Financial
Bank of New York	Solutions
Mellon	Misys
Bloomberg L.P.	Neovest
Charles River Systems	PNC Financial
Citigroup	StatPro Group
DST Systems	State Street
Eze Software Group LLC	SunGard
Fidessa	TradeStation
Frontline Technologies	Triple Point
HP Enterprise Services	Yardi Systems

HISTORICAL FINANCIALS

Company Type: Public

Income Statement

FYE: December 31

	REVENUE ($ mil.)	NET INCOME ($ mil.)	NET PROFIT MARGIN	EMPLOYEES
12/13	712.7	117.9	16.5%	4,194
12/12	551.8	45.8	8.3%	4,086
12/11	370.8	51.0	13.8%	1,484
12/10	328.9	32.4	9.9%	1,399
12/09	270.9	19.0	7.0%	1,253
Annual Growth	**27.4%**	**57.8%**		**35.3%**

2013 Year-End Financials

Debt ratio: 34.0%
Return on equity: 10.2%
Cash ($ mil.): 84
Current ratio: 1.32
Long-term debt ($ mil.): 751
No. of shares (mil.): 82
Dividends
Yield: —
Payout: —
Market value ($ mil.): 3,659

	STOCK PRICE ($) FY Close	P/E High/Low		PER SHARE ($) Earnings	Dividends	Book Value
12/13	44.26	30	15	1.38	0.00	14.90
12/12	23.09	45	30	0.55	0.00	13.60
12/11	18.06	32	20	0.63	0.00	12.62
12/10	20.51	45	29	0.44	0.00	11.78
Annual Growth	**29.2%**	—		**46.4%**	—	**8.2%**

Stamps.com Inc.

Stamps.com hopes its customers keep putting letters in the mail. Its PC Postage Service lets registered users who have downloaded Stamps.com software buy stamps online and print the postage directly onto envelopes and labels. Customers can order US Postal Service options such as registered mail certified mail and delivery confirmation as well as print custom stamps using virtually any image through its PhotoStamps.com website. Stamps.com charges a monthly fee for its service which is aimed at consumers home offices and

small businesses. In addition customers can buy mailing labels scales and dedicated postage printers from Stamps.com. Postage fees are sent directly to the US Postal Service.

Operations

Stamps.com's PC Postage segment delivered 96% of 2013 revenue with services generating 77% products 13% and insurance 6%. Its PhotoStamps segment brings in the remaining 4%.

The Internet postage firm's PhotoStamps service is a form of postage that allows users to turn digital photos designs or other images into valid US postage. The product segment has contributed less revenue in recent years down from 2009's 10%. PhotoStamps are available under authorization of the US Postal Service. Rival Envelope Manager Software (aka Endicia.com) also operates a custom postage service called "PictureItPostage."

Sales and Marketing

Stamps.com taps several channels to market its business. It relies on affiliated channels direct mail direct sales offline marketing programs partnerships traditional media and online advertising.

Its target niche customer continues to be small businesses.

In recent years the company has been devoting more dollars to advertising logging $10.3 million in expenses in 2013 up from $8.7 million in 2012 and $7 million in 2011.

Strategy

The postage company has propelled its business through strategic partnerships. It works with Amazon.com having formed a partnership in 2010 with the online retail giant. As part of the agreement Stamps.com makes its domestic and international shipping labels available to Amazon.com Marketplace users. Additionally under a contract with the USPS inked in 2011 Stamps.com provides electronic postage for shipping transactions generated by the postal service's Click-N-Ship web-based service. Stamps.com partners with other companies such as the USPS Microsoft HP Avery Amazon.com and Intuit among others. In 2014 the company integrated with e-commerce platform Shopify.

Stamps.com also seeks add-on acquisitions to grow its business organically.

Mergers and Acquisitions

Adding both new customers and a couple of brand names to its portfolio Stamps.com in 2014 acquired Austin Texas-based ShipStation for about $50 million in cash. The business offers monthly subscription-based e-commerce shipping software primarily under the ShipStation and Auctane brands.

Financial Performance

Stamps.com in fiscal 2013 logged $127.8 million in revenue representing a 24% jump from 2012's $115.7 million. It points to a 12% increase in PC Postage revenue —across its service product and insurance businesses —for the gains offset by a 17% decrease in PhotoStamps revenue to $4.7 million in 2013 from $5.7 million in 2012. Stamps.com posted $44.2 million in net income in 2013 continuing a four-year upward trend which was driven by higher sales and a lower cost of sales. Cash flow from operations has also enjoyed an upward trajectory. Stamps.com reported $35.7 million in cash flow from operations during the reporting period up some $8.5 million.

Company Background

Stamps.com was founded as StampMaster in 1996. The company changed its name to Stamps.com in 1998 and went public the following year.

EXECUTIVES

Vice President Marketing, Mark Krojansky
Chairman and CEO, Kenneth (Ken) McBride, age 47, $443,000 total compensation
Co-President and CFO, Kyle Huebner, age 44, $304,000 total compensation
VP Postal Technology and Affairs, J.P. Leon, $185,691 total compensation
Chief Product and Strategy Officer, John Clem, age 43, $201,667 total compensation
CTO, Michael Biswas, age 37, $279,167 total compensation
Vice President Advertising Technology, J P Leon
Vice President Customer Care, Dawn Stevenson
Vice President, Leslie Loomans
Vice President Postal Affairs, Mike Boswell
Vice President, Liana Stuart
National Sales Manager, Michael Mosher
Vice President Customer Services, Michelle Gardner
Chairman and CEO, Kenneth (Ken) McBride, age 47
Auditors: Ernst&YoungLLP

LOCATIONS

HQ: Stamps.com Inc.
1990 E. Grand Avenue, El Segundo, CA 90245
Phone: 310 482-5800
Web: www.stamps.com

PRODUCTS/OPERATIONS

2013 Sales

	$ mil.	% of total
Service	99.0	77
Product	16.6	13
Insurance	7.5	6
PhotoStamps	4.7	4
Total	**127.8**	**100**

COMPETITORS

Endicia	Pitney Bowes
FedEx	UPS
Neopost USA	US Postal Service
Newell Rubbermaid	eBay

HISTORICAL FINANCIALS

Company Type: Public

Income Statement

FYE: December 31

	REVENUE ($ mil.)	NET INCOME ($ mil.)	NET PROFIT MARGIN	EMPLOYEES
12/13	127.8	44.1	34.5%	250
12/12	115.6	38.5	33.3%	233
12/11	101.5	26.2	25.9%	226
12/10	85.5	5.5	6.5%	220
12/09	82.1	6.1	7.5%	210
Annual Growth	**11.7%**	**63.5%**	**—**	**4.5%**

2013 Year-End Financials

Debt ratio: —
Return on equity: 31.0%
Cash ($ mil.): 66
Current ratio: 6.33
Long-term debt ($ mil.): —
No. of shares (mil.): 16
Dividends
Yield: —
Payout: —
Market value ($ mil.): 681

	STOCK PRICE ($) FY Close	P/E High/Low		PER SHARE ($) Earnings	Dividends	Book Value
12/13	42.10	17	8	2.71	0.00	10.61
12/12	25.20	14	8	2.30	0.00	7.37
12/11	26.13	18	6	1.73	0.00	5.82
12/10	13.25	42	23	0.38	2.00	3.05
12/09	9.00	27	21	0.38	0.00	4.82
Annual Growth	**47.1%**	**—**	**—**	**63.4%**	**—**	**21.8%**

Standard Pacific Corp.

Standard Pacific's foundation is built on single-family homes. Active in Arizona California the Carolinas Colorado Florida and Texas the company constructs homes that typically range in size from 1500 sq. ft. to more than 3500 sq. ft. and prices up to more than $560000 (in California). The company also builds townhomes and condominiums and buys and develops tracts of land (both alone and through joint ventures). It offers home loans to its customers in all of its markets through subsidiary Standard Pacific Mortgage and title services in Texas through SPH Title.

Geographic Reach

Standard Pacific based in California builds single-family homes townhomes and condominiums across Arizona Colorado Florida North Carolina South Carolina Texas and its own Golden State.

Operations

For those who financed their Standard Pacific home in 2013 some 81% of consumers chose the company's mortgage financing subsidiary. Loans funded by the firm's mortgage unit are generally sold in the secondary mortgage market. In 2013 Standard Pacific controlled 35175 homesites (including joint ventures) and boasted 180 active selling communities. Some 79% of its deliveries in 2013 were single-family detached homes.

Sales and Marketing

Standard Pacific markets its home through a variety of channels including individual communities via local sales teams. The homebuilder leverages its Artistry of Home marketing message to attract move-up buyers.

Strategy

Underscoring its move-up strategy Standard Pacific in 2014 acquired the homebuilding operations of Austin Texas-based Streetman Homes. The move gave Standard Pacific control of some 850 additional homesites in bustling Austin across about 10 current and future communities (of which five are actively selling). The purchase follows Standard Pacific's Centerline Homes buy in 2013 which supplemented its move-up position in Florida and the Carolinas with control of about 3000 homesites.

With many other homebuilders focusing on lower priced homes including short-sells and foreclosures Standard Pacific instead is concentrating on luxury and move-up homes. It had also turned to belt-tightening by slashing inventories reducing construction costs and consolidating divisions that were located outside of its core geographic areas. California is its primary market accounting for about 52% of homebuilding revenues. Standard Pacific wants to take advantage of the depressed real estate market to acquire land for future developments in areas with high growth potential particularly in California.

Financial Performance

Standard Pacific logged $1.94 billion in revenue in fiscal 2013 a $681.3 million increase as compared to $1.26 billion in 2012. The homebuilder points to a 40% increase in new home deliveries and a 14% rise in consolidated average home price to $413000 for the gains in 2013. Company profits slipped 64% however to $188.7 million in 2013 from $531.4 million in 2012 due to the rising cost of sales and provision for income tax. A $77.4 million increase in cash land purchases and development costs caused Standard Pacific to post a $154.2 million cash outflow in 2013 despite a 55% rise in homebuilding revenues.

Company Background

Standard Pacific was founded in 1965 by Arthur Svendsen and Ronald Foell. MatlinPatterson an investment firm led by David Matlin who also holds a seat on Standard Pacific's board of directors controls 49% of the company.

EXECUTIVES

Vp Human Resources, Heather Breidenthal
Regional President Northern California Texas and Colorado, Todd J. Palmaer, age 56, $365,000 total compensation
President and CEO, Scott D. Stowell, age 57, $887,500 total compensation
Regional President Southeast, David Pelletz
EVP and CFO, Jeffrey J. (Jeff) McCall, $625,000 total compensation
EVP General Counsel and Secretary, John P. Babel, age 44, $462,500 total compensation
Regional President Southern California Arizona and Nevada, Edward T. McKibbin
EVP and Chief Marketing Officer, Wendy L. Marlett, $536,813 total compensation
Vice President Sales And Marketing, April Solimine
Vice President Operations, Dave Bulloch
Vice President Marketing Online, Stephanie Ayres
Vice President Construction, Dave James
Vice President Operations, Ram Fullen
Vice President Of Corporate Operations, Bruce Torkelson
Vice President Nation Director Of Arch, Jeff Lake
Regional Vice President Purchasing, Alan Willingham
Vice President Purchasing, Brian Bencz
Vice President Construction, Shawn Patterson
Vice President Construction, Chuck Bolen
Vice President Operations, Nathan Hawkins
Senior Vice-president, Peter Kiesecker
Vice President Corporate Tax, Alan Vitug
Chairman, Ronald R. Foell, age 84
Auditors: Ernst&YoungLLP

LOCATIONS

HQ: Standard Pacific Corp.
15360 Barranca Parkway, Irvine, CA 92618-2215
Phone: 949 789-1600

2013 Sales by Segment

	$ mil.	% of total
Homebuilding		
California	1006.6	52
Southeast	496.1	26
Southwest	411.9	21
Financial services	24.9	1
Total	**1939.5**	**100**

2013 Homes Delivered

	% of total
California	38
Florida	22
Carolinas	16
Texas	14
Arizona	6
Colorado	4
Total	**100**

PRODUCTS/OPERATIONS

2013 Sales

	$ mil.	% of total
Home sales	1899.0	98
Financial services	24.9	1
Land sales	15.6	1
Total	**1939.5**	**100**

COMPETITORS

Beazer Homes	M.D.C.
Corky McMillin	PulteGroup
D.R. Horton	The Ryland Group
David Weekley Homes	Toll Brothers
Hovnanian Enterprises	WCI Communities
KB Home	Warmington Group
Lennar	William Lyon Homes

HISTORICAL FINANCIALS

Company Type: Public

Income Statement

FYE: December 31

	REVENUE ($ mil.)	NET INCOME ($ mil.)	NET PROFIT MARGIN	EMPLOYEES
12/13	1,939.5	188.7	9.7%	1,115
12/12	1,258.2	531.4	42.2%	820
12/11	893.9	(16.4)	—	750
12/10	924.8	(11.7)	—	775
12/09	1,179.5	(13.7)	—	800
Annual Growth	13.2%	—	—	8.7%

2013 Year-End Financials

Debt ratio: 52.9%
Return on equity: 13.8%
Cash ($ mil.): 363
Current ratio: 12.14
Long-term debt ($ mil.): 1,940

No. of shares (mil.): 277
Dividends
  Yield: —
  Payout: —
Market value ($ mil.): 2,512

	STOCK PRICE ($) FY Close	P/E High/Low		PER SHARE ($) Earnings	Dividends	Book Value
12/13	9.05	19	14	0.47	0.00	5.29
12/12	7.35	5	2	1.44	0.00	5.89
12/11	3.18	—	—	(0.05)	0.00	3.14
12/10	4.60	—	—	(0.05)	0.00	3.16
12/09	3.74	—	—	(0.06)	0.00	4.14
Annual Growth	24.7%	—	—	—	—	6.3%

Star Gas Partners L.P.

Those who wish for heat and power can wish upon a star —Star Gas Partners. The company is the nation's largest retail distributor of home heating oil. Its Petro Holdings subsidiary provides heating oil and propane to 416000 customers in the US Northeast and Mid-Atlantic. The company sells home heating oil gasoline and diesel fuel to 48000 customers on a delivery only basis and provides HVAC and ancillary home services including home security and plumbing to 11500 customers. Investment firm Kestrel Energy Partners controls the general partner of Star Gas Partners.

Geographic Reach

The company has operations in Connecticut Maine Maryland Massachusetts New Hampshire New Jersey New York North Carolina Rhode Island Pennsylvania South Carolina Vermont Virginia and Washington DC.

Operations

Star Gas Partners' primary business is to provide services to residential and commercial customers to heat homes and buildings. Its operations are conducted through Petro Holdings. Other activities include the installation maintenance and repair of heating and air conditioning equipment and ancillary home services (home security and plumbing).

Star Gas Finance Company serves as the co-issuer jointly and severally with Star Gas Partners of the company's $125.0 million 8.875% Senior Notes (excluding discounts) which are due in December 2017.

Financial Performance

Revenues decreased by 6% in fiscal year 2012 due to a 7% drop in product sales as the decline in total volumes of 17.1% exceeded the lift of higher product selling prices. Selling prices increased in response to higher wholesale product costs of $0.4465 per gallon. This was offset by 1.9% increase in installation and service sales because of the additional revenues from acquisitions of $9.3 million.

The slump of revenues is attributable to the decrease in home heating oil volume and a decline in sales of other petroleum products and the residual conditions of high unemployment reduced home equity loans and consumer credit and reduced consumer confidence which helped to cause a decline in the demand for new heating systems.

Star Gas Partners' net income increased by 7% in fiscal year 2012 due to a decrease in interest expense largely because of lower bank fees of $1 million resulting from lower rates on letters of credit and lower unused commitment fees a decrease in pretax income of $4.5 million (which was less than the decrease in income tax expense of $6.1 million) and a decrease in Amortization of Debt Issuance Costs due to an increase in the number of years over which such costs are amortized due to the extension in June 2011 of the Partnership's revolving credit facility termination date from July 2012 to June 2016.

Strategy

The company seeks to grow its business by making selected acquisitions to increase its presence in some of its existing geographic markets and selectively expanding into new markets and broadenening its products and services by marketing related and complementary products and services.

During fiscal 2012 Star Gas Partners completed seven acquisitions and added 41000 home heating oil and propane accounts (for $39.2 million reduced by working capital credits of $1.2 million). In fiscal 2011 it acquired four retail heating oil dealers with 8800 home heating oil and propane accounts for $9.7 million including working capital of $1.9 million.

Ownership

Kestrel Energy Partners owns about 23% of the company.

EXECUTIVES

EVP CFO Secretary and Treasurer, Richard F. Ambury, age 58, $331,500 total compensation
Vice President, Charles M Lynch
President CEO and Director, Daniel P. Donovan, age 69, $413,100 total compensation
EVP and COO, Steven J. Goldman, age 55, $321,300 total compensation
Senior Vice President Operations, Steve Goldman, age 55
Vice President Of Operations, Jeff Woosnam
Vice President Business Development, Dan Birchmyer
Vice President Operations, David Eastin
Chairman, Paul A. Vermylen, age 68
EVP CFO Secretary and Treasurer, Richard F. Ambury, age 58
President CEO and Director, Daniel P. Donovan, age 69
Assistant Treasurer, Jay Palma
Secretary, Thomas Brady
Auditors: KPMGLLP

LOCATIONS

HQ: Star Gas Partners L.P.
9 West Broad Street, Stamford, CT 06902
Phone: 203 328-7310   **Fax:** 203 328-7393
Web: www.star-gas.com

PRODUCTS/OPERATIONS

2012 Sales

	$ mil.	% of total
Product	1295.4	86
Installations & service	202.2	14
Total	**1497.6**	**100**

COMPETITORS

AmeriGas Partners	Global Partners
Benit Fuel	Meenan Oil
Castle Oil	NOCO
Connecticut Light and Power	Rice Cos.
Crestwood Equity	Superior Plus
Energy Transfer Equity	Woodfin Oil
Ferrellgas Partners	richland partners
Getty Petroleum Marketing	

HISTORICAL FINANCIALS

Company Type: Public

Income Statement

FYE: September 30

	REVENUE ($ mil.)	NET INCOME ($ mil.)	NET PROFIT MARGIN	EMPLOYEES
09/14	1,961.7	36.0	1.8%	2,958
09/13	1,741.8	29.9	1.7%	2,577
09/12	1,497.5	25.9	1.7%	2,582
09/11	1,591.3	24.3	1.5%	2,677
09/10	1,212.7	28.3	2.3%	2,729
Annual Growth	12.8%	6.2%	—	2.0%

2014 Year-End Financials

Debt ratio: 18.1%
Return on equity: —
Cash ($ mil.): 49
Current ratio: 1.17
Long-term debt ($ mil.): 124

No. of shares (mil.): 57
Dividends
  Yield: 5.9%
  Payout: 47.8%
Market value ($ mil.): 330

	STOCK PRICE ($) FY Close	P/E High/Low		PER SHARE ($) Earnings	Dividends	Book Value
09/14	5.71	12	9	0.57	0.34	4.73
09/13	4.92	11	8	0.47	0.32	4.47
09/12	4.32	13	9	0.40	0.31	4.24
09/11	4.90	17	13	0.35	0.31	4.18
09/10	4.74	12	9	0.38	0.29	4.15
Annual Growth	4.8%	—	—	10.7%	4.5%	3.3%

Starwood Property Trust Inc.

Starwood Property Trust hopes to shine brightly in the world of mortgages. A real estate investment trust (REIT) the company originates finances and manages US commercial and residential mortgage loans commercial mortgage-backed securities and other commercial real estate debt investments. It acquires discounted loans from failed banks and financial institutions some through the FDIC which typically auctions off large pools of loan portfolios. Starwood Property Trust is externally managed by SPT Management LLC an affiliate of Starwood Capital Group. As a REIT the trust is exempt from paying federal income tax so long as it distributes quarterly dividends to shareholders.

Financial Performance

Overall revenues grew 63% in 2012 to $327 million up from $201 million in 2011. The trust primarily earns money on interest income from mortgage-backed securities and loans.

Mergers and Acquisitions

In 2013 Starwood Property Trust bought LNR Property LLC a real estate investment finance management and development firm. The trust paid $862 million for LNR's US special servicer the US investment securities portfolio Archetype Mortgage Capital (now Starwood Mortgage Capital) Archetype Financial Institution Services LNR Europe and 50% of LNR's interest in Auction.com.

Later that year it moved to spin off its single-family residential business as a new REIT named Starwood Waypoint Residential Trust. The trust which will be affiliated with Waypoint Homes will invest own and operate single-family rental homes and non-performing residential mortgage loans in the US.

EXECUTIVES

Executive Vice President, Jerome C (Jerry) Silvey, age 57
President, Jeffrey DiModica, age 48
Chief Credit Officer And Managing Director, Chris Tokarski
Vice President Loan Servicing, Mary Carlin
Auditors: Deloitte&ToucheLLP

LOCATIONS

HQ: Starwood Property Trust Inc.
591 West Putnam Avenue, Greenwich, CT 06830
Phone: 203 422-8100
Web: www.starwoodpropertytrust.com

2012 Sales

	% of total
Western US	24
Northeastern US	23
Southeastern US	16
Mid-Atlantic US	13
Midwest US	9
International	9
Southwestern US	6
Total	**100**

PRODUCTS/OPERATIONS

2012 Sales by Collateral Property Type

	% of total
Hospitality	45
Office	17
Retail	15
Residential	9
Mixed-Use	4
Industrial	3
Multifamily	2
Other	5
Total	**100**

COMPETITORS

American Capital Agency Corp.	Newcastle Investment
Annaly Capital Management	NorthStar Realty
Arbor Realty Trust	PennyMac Mortgage
	Petra Real Estate
	RAIT Financial Trust

CYS Investments	Realty Finance Corporation
Hatteras Financial	Redwood Trust
Invesco Mortgage Capital	Two Harbors
JER Investors Trust	iStar Financial Inc
MFA Financial	

HISTORICAL FINANCIALS

Company Type: Public

Income Statement

FYE: December 31

	REVENUE ($ mil.)	NET INCOME ($ mil.)	NET PROFIT MARGIN	EMPLOYEES
12/13	565.7	305.0	53.9%	2
12/12	306.9	201.2	65.5%	2
12/11	204.9	119.3	58.2%	2
12/10	93.5	57.0	61.0%	1
12/09	6.9	(3.0)	—	4
Annual Growth	**200.6%**	—	—	**(15.9%)**

2013 Year-End Financials

Debt ratio: 3.1%
Return on equity: 8.7%
Cash ($ mil.): 317
Current ratio: 1.21
Long-term debt ($ mil.): 3,436
No. of shares (mil.): 195
Dividends
Yield: 6.5%
Payout: 102.2%
Market value ($ mil.): 5,416

	STOCK PRICE ($) FY Close	P/E High/Low		PER SHARE ($) Earnings	Dividends	Book Value
12/13	27.70	16	13	1.82	1.82	21.90
12/12	22.96	14	11	1.76	1.86	20.07
12/11	18.51	17	12	1.38	1.74	18.88
12/10	21.48	19	14	1.14	1.20	18.69
12/09	18.89	—	—	(0.06)	0.11	18.66
Annual Growth	**10.0%**			—	**—101.7%**	**4.1%**

State Bank Financial Corp

State Bank Financial Corp. aspires to one day live in the center of central Georgia's banking world. A holding company State Bank Financial operates through subsidiary State Bank and Trust Company a state-charted commercial bank that serves individuals and businesses throughout central Georgia and in the Atlanta metropolitan area. Through some two dozen branches the bank offers traditional checking and savings accounts as well as commercial and residential real estate mortgages construction and commercial loans and consumer loans. Formed in 2010 State Bank Financial holds more than $2.8 billion in assets.

The holding company was formed to acquire the assets of distressed banks many of which fell victim to the 2008 credit crisis and ensuing recession. With the assistance of the FDIC and proceeds raised in a private offering of common stock State Bank Financial acquired seven community banks between 2009 and 2011 and re-branded them as State Bank and Trust Co. The acquisitions expanded the bank's presence in its core central Georgia and metro Atlanta markets. State Bank Financial intends to continue leveraging such acquisitions to strengthen its presence in these markets.

EXECUTIVES

Chairman and CEO State Bank Financial Corporation, Joseph W. (Joe) Evans, age 64, $415,000 total compensation
Vice Chairman and COO, J. Daniel (Dan) Speight, $365,000 total compensation
Vice Chairman and CEO State Bank and Trust Company, J. Thomas Wiley, $365,000 total compensation
EVP and Chief Credit Officer, David F. Black
EVP and CIO, David W. Cline
EVP and Enterprise Risk Officer, Steven G. Deaton
EVP and Chief Revenue and Deposit Officer, Michael R. Fitzgerald
EVP and Senior Banking Officer, Michael S. Sims
EVP and Director Real Estate Banking, Bradford Watkins
Assistant Vice President, Tracy McSwain
Assistant Vice President, Bradford Bagwell
Evp Corporate Development, David C Brown
Chairman and CEO State Bank Financial Corporation, Joseph W. (Joe) Evans, age 64
Vice Chairman and COO, J. Daniel (Dan) Speight
Vice Chairman and Executive Risk Officer, Kim Childers
Vice Chairman and Corporate Development Officer, Stephen W. Doughty
Vice Chairman and CEO State Bank and Trust Company, J. Thomas Wiley
Auditors: DixonHughesGoodmanLLP

LOCATIONS

HQ: State Bank Financial Corp
3399 Peachtree Road, N.E., Suite 1900, Atlanta, GA 30326
Phone: 404 475-6599

PRODUCTS/OPERATIONS

2013 Sales

	$ in mil.	% of total
Interest and dividend income		
Loans receivable	183.6	87
Investment securities	9.0	4
Deposits in other banks and other	1.2	1
Noninterest income		
Service charges on deposit accounts	5.2	2
Payroll fee income	3.1	2
Others	8.5	4
Amortization of FDIC receivable for loss sharing agreements	(87.9)	-
Total	**122.7**	**100**

COMPETITORS

BB&T	SunTrust
Bank of America	Synovus
Citizens Bancshares	Wells Fargo
Regions Financial	

HISTORICAL FINANCIALS

Company Type: Public

Income Statement

FYE: December 31

	ASSETS ($ mil.)	NET INCOME ($ mil.)	INCOME AS % OF ASSETS	EMPLOYEES
12/13	2,600.7	12.7	0.5%	577
12/12	2,662.9	22.7	0.9%	605
12/11	2,746.9	43.0	1.6%	605
12/10	2,828.5	45.5	1.6%	495
12/09	2,497.9	18.0	0.7%	0
Annual Growth	**1.0%**	**(8.3%)**	—	—

2013 Year-End Financials

Return on assets: 0.4%
Return on equity: 2.9%
Long-term debt ($ mil.): —
No. of shares (mil.): 32
Sales ($ mil): 122

Dividends
Yield: 0.6%
Payout: 31.5%
Market value ($ mil.): 584

	STOCK PRICE ($) FY Close	P/E High/Low	PER SHARE ($) Earnings	Dividends	Book Value
12/13	18.19	46 36	0.38	0.12	13.62
12/12	15.88	25 20	0.69	0.06	13.48
12/11	15.11	13 9	1.32	0.00	12.52
12/10	14.50	11 10	1.40	0.00	11.37
12/09	14.00	24 24	0.58	0.00	9.85
Annual Growth	**6.8%**	**— —**	**(10.0%)**	**—**	**8.4%**

Stepan Co.

Company secrets aside makers of laundry detergents shampoos toothpaste and other personal care products can come clean with Stepan Company. Surfactants the company's largest sector by far are chemicals most commonly used as cleaning agents used in consumer products like detergents toothpastes and cosmetics. Stepan's surfactants are also used in commercial and industrial applications ranging from emulsifiers for agricultural insecticides to agents used in oil recovery. The company also makes phthalic anhydride (an acid used in making polyester resins) and other polymers as well as specialty chemicals for food and pharmaceutical uses.

Geographic Reach

The company has plants in Anaheim California; Bauan Batangas Philippines; Fieldsboro New Jersey; Longford Mills Ontario Canada; Manizales Colombia; Matamoros Mexico; Maywood New Jersey; Millsdale (Joliet) Illinois; Nanjing China; Stalybridge UK; Voreppe (Grenoble) France; Wesseling (Cologne) Germany; Winder Georgia. It also has plants in Brazil Poland and Singapore. In 2012 the US accounted for 60% of Stepan's revenues.

Financial Performance

Stepan's revenues decreased by 2% in 2012 due to lower Surfactants revenues as the result of lower prices caused by a drop in raw material costs and foreign currency effects. Specialty Products revenues grew by 24% due to the addition of the Lipid Nutrition product lines (acquired in June 2011). Excluding the new Lipid Nutrition business year-over-year net sales and sales volume were down 5% and 13% respectively primarily due to losing a customer in the legacy multi-chain triglyceride product lines.Despite lower revenues and an increase in operating expenses in 2012 the company's net income grew by 10% due to lower costs of sales mainly stemming from higher unit profit margins and sales volumes.

Strategy

The company expands through acquiring surfactants polyols and urethane assets establishing manufacturing plants and sales office close to its expanding global markets focusing on new product development and forming strategic alliances with other chemical companies to add know-how technology capital and customers.

Mergers and Acquisitions

Diversifying its polyol offering (used in rigid insulation foam) in 2013 Stepan acquired Bayer MaterialScience's North American Polyester Resins business for about $64 million.

In 2011 the company acquired the Clarinol Marinol and PinnoThin product lines of Lipid Nutrition B.V. for about $13.6 million. The acquired products was integrated into Stepan's Food and Health Specialties business which was renamed Stepan Lipid Nutrition. The new lines greatly expand Stepan's health and nutrition product offerings.

Ownership

Chairman F. Quinn Stepan and his family own about 14% of the company.

Company Background

The family-owned business was founded in 1932 by Alfred C. Stepan Jr. It was incorporated in 1959.

In 2010 Stepan acquired the manufacturing assets of Peter Cremer GmbH's 100000 ton per year methyl ester plant located on Singapore's Jurong Island.

Later that year in a major expansion into eastern Europe Stepan's European subsidiary acquired Alfa Systems Sp. z o.o. from Chemitex Holding Limited and Chemovil Holdings Limited. Poland-based Alfa Systems manufactures aromatic polyester polyols from recycled polyethylene terephthalate.

EXECUTIVES

Vice President Human Resources, Greg Servatius
Vice President Corporate Development, James Pall
President CEO and Director, F. Quinn Stepan, age 53, $736,667 total compensation
VP and General Manager Polymers, Robert J. Wood, age 57, $292,500 total compensation
VP and General Manager Surfactants, John V. Venegoni, age 56, $401,833 total compensation
VP Supply Chain, Scott C. Mason, age 55, $313,083 total compensation
VP Europe, Anthony Martin
VP Manufacturing and Engineering, Robert S. Mangold
VP Latin America, Charles A. Brown
VP Plant Operations The Americas, Kyle Montgomery
VP Specialty Products, James M. Butterwick
VP North America Polymers, Kevin J. Knutsen
VP Consumer Products, Sean T. Moriarty
Chief Financial Officer; Vice President, Scott Beamer
Vice President Product Management, Jeff Grahn
Vice President Strategic Purchasing, Wehman Richard
Vice President Marketing, Bridget Weir
National Account Manager, Karl Hipchen
Vice President Procurement, Arthur Mergner
Vice President Europe, Tony Martin
Vice President Business Management, Scott Behrens
Vice President Surfactant Product Development, Robert Slone
Chairman, F. Quinn Stepan, age 76
Board Member, Anatoly Dameshek
Auditors: Deloitte&ToucheLLP

LOCATIONS

HQ: Stepan Co.
Edens & Winnetka Road, Northfield, IL 60093
Phone: 847 446-7500
Web: www.stepan.com

2012 Sales

	$ mil.	% of total
US	1076.2	60
France	298.2	17
UK	103.5	5
Other countries	325.8	18
Total	**1803.7**	**100**

PRODUCTS/OPERATIONS

2012 Sales

	$ mil.	% of total
Surfactants	1305.8	72
Polymers	423.9	24
Specialty products	74.0	4
Total	**1803.7**	**100**

COMPETITORS

Air Products	Henkel
Akzo Nobel	Huntsman Corp
Clariant	Koppers Holdings
Croda	Rhodia
Eastman Chemical	

HISTORICAL FINANCIALS

Company Type: Public

Income Statement

FYE: December 31

	REVENUE ($ mil.)	NET INCOME ($ mil.)	NET PROFIT MARGIN	EMPLOYEES
12/13	1,880.7	72.8	3.9%	2,015
12/12	1,803.7	79.4	4.4%	1,920
12/11	1,843.0	71.9	3.9%	1,848
12/10	1,431.1	65.4	4.6%	1,768
12/09	1,276.3	63.0	4.9%	1,594
Annual Growth	**10.2%**	**3.7%**	**—**	**6.0%**

2013 Year-End Financials

Debt ratio: 23.1%
Return on equity: 14.1%
Cash ($ mil.): 133
Current ratio: 2.26
Long-term debt ($ mil.): 235

No. of shares (mil.): 22
Dividends
Yield: 0.9%
Payout: 19.1%
Market value ($ mil.): 1,466

	STOCK PRICE ($) FY Close	P/E High/Low	PER SHARE ($) Earnings	Dividends	Book Value
12/13	65.63	21 16	3.18	0.65	24.73
12/12	55.54	28 14	3.49	0.58	21.81
12/11	80.16	12 9	6.42	0.53	39.16
12/10	76.27	12 7	5.90	0.49	34.58
12/09	64.81	11 4	5.84	0.45	29.08
Annual Growth	**0.3%**	**— —**	**(14.1%)**	**9.6%**	**(4.0%)**

Stericycle Inc.

A leading medical and pharmaceutical waste management company Stericycle serves some 541000 clients worldwide: 16500 large waste generators (pharmaceutical manufacturers hospitals and blood banks) and 524500 small waste generators (dental and medical offices veterinary offices pharmacies and municipalities). Services include disposing of used needles and expired drugs. Through 153 processing and collection sites and 154 transfer sites and 64 recall and returns or communication services facilities Stericycle treats waste through incineration autoclaving (using high temperature and pressure to kill pathogens) and electro-thermal-deactivation (using low-frequency radio waves to kill pathogens).

Geographic ReachThe company operates regulated waste management networks in Argentina Brazil Canada Chile Ireland Japan Mexico Portugal Romania Spain the UK and the US.OperationsStericycle's operating segments are International Waste Management Services and Domestic Regulated Waste Management Services/Domestic Regulated Recall and Returns Management Services (which operate together as the US reporting segment).Sales and MarketingThe company obtains new customers through direct sales and telemarketing activities.Financial PerformanceStericycle's revenues grew by 14% in 2012 primarily due to 17% increase in revenues from international operations due to internal growth and currency rate fluctuations as well as acquisitions. US sales increased by 13% due to the growth of Steri-Safe revenues and stronger sales to large account customers (which increased the total number of accounts and expanded their reusable services and pharmaceutical waste disposal programs).Net income increased by 14% in 2012 thanks to higher revenues and reduced acquisition expenses offset by a loss on the sale of business assets.A steady increase in both US and international customers has enabled revenue growth each year from 2008 to 2012.StrategyStericycle holds about 12% of the $15 billion global regulated waste market. Growth in that sector is driven by several factors including the aging of the world's population pressure to reduce health costs expanding environmental and safety regulations and a shift to off-site treatment in the health care industry. The company has shaped its operations to leverage these trends and maintain its leading position in the medical waste industry.Key to Stericycle's growth has been its targeted "tuck-in" acquisitions completing more than 270 acquisitions since 1993. In addition to expanding the range of services and products it provides Stericycle seeks to grow internationally. Its strategy calls for organically expanding its operations including its Steri-Safe safety and compliance program sharps (needles) management service program pharmaceutical waste disposal regulated returns and recall management services (for expired or recalled products) and recently acquired patient communication services.Stericycle also wants to focus on small account customers as part of its growth strategy. Because most of its customers use only one of its current service offerings the company believes its revenues will increase as they adopt more services.The strategy has been successful so far for Stericycle which has been growing steadily for several years. In 2012 the company completed 41 acquisitions 17 in the US and 24 international (in Latin America Europe and Japan). That year Stericycle increased its majority share in previous acquisitions in Brazil to 100% and Chile to 90%.In 2011 it continued to expand both in service offerings and with 45 acquisitions in the US and 11 other countries. That year the company completed 21 domestic acquisitions including the integration of Healthcare Waste Solutions (HWS) which has about 20000 customers an promises to add $45 million in annual revenues. It enhanced its position internationally as well with 24 acquisitions and moved into Spain for the first time. Stericycle also rolled out its clinical services business in select international markets for medical and dental practices.Mergers and AcquisitionsIn 2014 the company purchased PSC Environmental Services LLC a provider of environmental and regulated waste management services for $275 million.

EXECUTIVES

Executive Vice President And Chief, Frank T Brink
SVP International, Richard T. Kogler, $307,269 total compensation

EVP; President Recall and Return Management Services, Michael J. Collins, $272,115 total compensation
President and CEO, Charles A. (Charlie) Alutto, $348,077 total compensation
EVP and COO, Brent Arnold
EVP and CFO, Daniel V. Ginnetti
Vp Mergers & Acquisitions, Mike Mamaux
Vice President International Finance, Elizabeth Brandel
Vice President Customer Service, Arden Parchois
Vice President Operations, Lisa Ellis
Sales And Marketing Vp, Dan King
Vice President Continuous Improvement, John Blaseos
Vice President Corporate It, Gene Golden
Cls Executive Vice President, Rich Fanning
Vice President General Manager Intl, Mike Goonewardene
Vp Sales, John Kenny
Vice President Commercial Operations, Abdulmassih Ellen
National Account Manager, Kendran Gattuso
Chairman, Mark C. Miller
Board Member, Jonathan T (Jack) Lord
Auditors: Ernst&YoungLLP

LOCATIONS

HQ: Stericycle Inc.
28161 North Keith Drive, Lake Forest, IL 60045
Phone: 847 367-5910
Web: www.stericycle.com

2013 Sales

	$ mil.	% of total
US	1506.6	70
Europe	341.4	16
Other regions	294.8	14
Total	**2142.8**	**100**

PRODUCTS/OPERATIONS

Selected Subsidiaries

Ambiface & Buffer SGPS Lda (Portugal)
BFI Medical Waste Inc.
Consenur SA (Spain)
Healthcare Waste Solutions Inc.
MedServe Inc.
MedSolutions Inc.
Notify MD Inc.
SRCL Ireland Limited
SRCL Limited (Ireland)
Stericare Romania
Stericycle Brazil Ltd.
Stericycle Chile S.A.
Stericycle Co. Ltd. (Japan)
Stericycle Espania Srl (Spain)
Stericycle Europe Limited (UK)
Stericycle International Ltd (UK)
Stericycle Mexico
Stericycle Operations Srl (Spain)
Stericycle UK Limited
Stericlce ULC CANADA
White Rose Environmental (UK)
ZooMed - Gestao Lda (Portugal)

COMPETITORS

Ascent Healthcare Solutions	Republic Services
BioMedical Technology Solutions	Shanks
	US Ecology
Ecolab UK	Waste Connections
Mercury Waste Solutions	Waste Industries USA
	Waste Management

HISTORICAL FINANCIALS

Company Type: Public

Income Statement

FYE: December 31

	REVENUE ($ mil.)	NET INCOME ($ mil.)	NET PROFIT MARGIN	EMPLOYEES
12/13	2,142.8	311.3	14.5%	14,924
12/12	1,913.1	268.0	14.0%	13,245
12/11	1,676.0	234.7	14.0%	11,122
12/10	1,439.3	207.8	14.4%	9,715
12/09	1,177.7	175.6	14.9%	8,199
Annual Growth	16.1%	15.4%	—	16.2%

2013 Year-End Financials

Debt ratio: 36.8%
Return on equity: 18.9%
Cash ($ mil.): 61
Current ratio: 1.30
Long-term debt ($ mil.): 1,280
No. of shares (mil.): 85
Dividends
Yield: —
Payout: —
Market value ($ mil.): 9,933

	STOCK PRICE ($) FY Close	P/E High/Low	Earnings	Dividends	Book Value
12/13	116.17	33 26	3.56	0.00	20.47
12/12	93.28	30 24	3.08	0.00	17.93
12/11	77.92	34 27	2.69	0.00	14.15
12/10	80.92	34 21	2.39	0.00	12.30
12/09	55.17	28 22	2.03	0.00	9.98
Annual Growth	20.5%	— —	15.1%	—	19.7%

Sterling Bancorp (DE)

Sterling Bancorp is the holding company for Sterling National Bank a community-based thrift operating dozens of offices in New York's Hudson Valley region and Greater New York City area. Founded in 1888 the bank attracts consumers and business clients by offering traditional deposit products such as checking and savings accounts and CDs. It uses funds from deposits to originate primarily real estate loans and mortgages. Sterling Bancorp which has assets of more than $7 billion was formerly Provident New York Bancorp; Provident acquired the former Sterling Bancorp in late 2013 and changed its name as well as the name of its banking subsidiary to Sterling.

Financial Performance

In fiscal 2013 Sterling Bancorp reported revenue of about $160 million up 9% from the prior year. The increase was primarily because of an 18% jump in loans that year (powered by commercial real estate and commercial and industrial loans) offset slightly by a decline in noninterest income.

Net income was also up in 2013 rising 27% to $25 million. Net cash from operations was down about 10% to $22.6 million.

Mergers and Acquisitions

Sterling is focused on expanding in the greater New York metropolitan region and increasing the importance of its commercial banking operations. To that end in late 2013 it acquired the former Sterling Bancorp and took its name. The acquisition added the former Sterling's varied commercial and consumer lending products as well as its presence in the New York City area.

EXECUTIVES

Executive Vice President; Chief Risk Officer; General Counsel, Daniel G Rothstein, age 67
President CEO and Director, Jack L. Kopnisky, age 58
EVP and COO, Rodney Whitwell
EVP and CFO, Luis Massiani
Vp It, Katharine Brown
Vice President Finance, Vincent Delucia
Associate Vice President Information Technology Services, Pietro Bertoni
Vice President Finance, George Cardona
Vp And Director Of Marketing, Rita Champ
Senior Executive Vice President, Jeanne Uphouse
Avp Marketing, Stephanie Yaniga
Vice President Information Technology, James Florian
Assistant Vice President Risk Management, Helen Runchey
Assistant Vice President, Joan Norwin
Vice President Commercial Lending Offi, John Willis
Senior Executive Vice President, Stephen Heine
Vice President, Anthony Palmesi
Vice President And Operational Risk Manager, James Lee
Vice President, Kristen Santos
Vice President, Anthony Monti
Assistant Vice President Research And Database Marketing Manager, David Gerbino
Board Member, Gary Zeh
Board Member, William Sichol
Auditors: CroweHorwathLLP

LOCATIONS

HQ: Sterling Bancorp (DE)
400 Rella Boulevard, Montebello, NY 10901
Phone: 845 369-8040
Web: www.sterlingbancorp.com

PRODUCTS/OPERATIONS

2013 Sales

	$ mil.	% of total
Interest		
Loans including fees	107.8	67
Securities	23.2	14
Other	1.1	1
Noninterest		
Deposit fees & service charges	11.0	7
Net gain on sale of securities	7.4	5
Investment management fees	2.4	2
Other	7.0	4
Adjustments	(0.1)	-
Total	**159.8**	**100**

COMPETITORS

Capital One	JPMorgan Chase
Citibank	KeyCorp
HSBC USA	M&T Bank

HISTORICAL FINANCIALS

Company Type: Public

Income Statement

FYE: September 30

	ASSETS ($ mil.)	NET INCOME ($ mil.)	INCOME AS % OF ASSETS	EMPLOYEES
09/14	7,337.3	27.6	0.4%	836
09/13	4,049.1	25.2	0.6%	543
09/12	4,022.9	19.8	0.5%	522
09/11	3,137.4	11.7	0.4%	550
09/10	3,021.0	20.4	0.7%	603
Annual Growth	**24.8%**	**7.8%**	**—**	**8.5%**

2014 Year-End Financials

Return on assets: 0.4%	Dividends
Return on equity: 3.8%	Yield: 2.1%
Long-term debt ($ mil.): —	Payout: 117.3%
No. of shares (mil.): 83	Market value ($ mil.): 1,070
Sales ($ mil.): 294	

	STOCK PRICE ($) FY Close	P/E High/Low		PER SHARE ($) Earnings	Dividends	Book Value
09/14	12.79	40	32	0.34	0.27	11.49
09/13	10.89	20	15	0.58	0.24	10.89
09/12	9.41	19	11	0.52	0.24	11.12
09/11	5.82	35	19	0.31	0.24	11.39
09/10	8.39	19	15	0.54	0.24	11.26
Annual Growth	**11.1%**	**—**	**—**	**(10.9%)**	**3.0%**	**0.5%**

Stifel Financial Corp.

Stifel Financial doesn't repress investors. The company serves individual corporate municipal and institutional clients through nearly 315 offices in the US with a concentration in the Midwest and mid-Atlantic regions. It also has locations in Canada and Europe. Through subsidiaries Stifel Nicolaus (founded 1890) Thomas Weisel Century Securities Associates Stifel Bank & Trust and others the company provides asset management financial advice and banking services for private clients. Stifel also offers brokerage and mergers and acquisitions advisory services for corporate clients underwrites debt and equity and provides research on more than 1000 US and European equities.

Geographic Reach

The company headquartered in Missouri with about 315 branch offices in 45 states and the District of Columbia.

Financial Performance

Stifel has enjoyed two straight years of unprecedented growth. Revenues jumped around 20% to peak at the $2 billion mark in 2013 a company milestone. Profits also surged 17% from $139 million in 2012 to a record-setting $162 million in 2013. (Note: the company's 2012 financials were restated due to divestitures it made.)

The historic growth in 2013 was driven by growth in its Global Wealth Management segment due to higher commission revenues and growth in asset management and service fees as a result of an increase in assets under management through market performance and increase in client assets. Stifel was also helped by additional net interest revenues as a result of the growth of net interest-earning assets at Stifel Bank. Institutional Group segment revenue jumped in 2013 due to an increase in advisory fees; higher equity institutional brokerage revenues; an increase in equity capital raising revenues; and higher fixed income institutional brokerage revenues.

Stifel posted negative operating cash flow of $264 million in 2012. However in 2013 it posted $702 million in positive operating cash flow due to the additional net income recognized in 2013 the net effect of non-cash items and a decrease in operating assets.

Mergers and Acquisitions

Stifel has fortified its operations and extended its international footprint through the use of acquisitions. In 2014 it purchased Oriel Securities a

London-based stockbroking and investment banking firm. Stifel made the deal to create a larger middle market investment banking group in London with broad research coverage across most sectors of the economy equity and debt sales and trading and investment banking services.

In 2014 Stifel bought 1919 Investment Counsel & Trust Company (formerly Legg Mason Investment Counsel & Trust Co.) from rival financial services firm Legg Mason. 1919 provides customized investment advisory and trust services on a discretionary basis to individuals families and institutions throughout the country. Its portfolio managers manage more than $9 billion in assets. 1919 is part of Stifel's Global Wealth Management segment and should be an ideal complement to its existing wealth management platform.

In mid-2013 Stifel obtained KCG Holdings' US institutional fixed income sales and trading business. Altogether Stifel's and KCG's combined teams boast some 90 sales and trading professionals across the US and Europe. The team covers high-yield and investment-grade corporate bonds asset-backed and mortgage-based securities loan trading and fixed income research in certain sectors and companies.

EXECUTIVES

Senior Vice President, David D Sliney, age 45
Co-Chairman President and CEO, Ronald J. (Ron) Kruszewski, age 55, $200,000 total compensation
SVP CFO and Director, James M. Zemlyak, age 54, $175,000 total compensation
EVP and Director Capital Markets Stifel Nicolaus, Thomas P. Mulroy, age 52, $250,000 total compensation
Senior Vice President Director Denver Municipal Trading, Michael F. Imhoff
Senior Vice President Co-Director Institutional Group Director, Victor J. Nesi, age 54, $250,000 total compensation
Vice President Of Listed Trading, Weston Boone
Vice President, Todd Krentz
Cert Finc Planner Vice President Invsts, James A Fuente
Vice President And Investments, Daniel P Divine
Vice President Employee Rel Mgr Sphr, Robin Corey
Vice President Investments, Ellen J Liss
Vice President Senior Equity Analyst, Greg Mason
Vice President, Jeff Borgert
Senior Vice President And Investments, Steven Danieli
Vice President And Investments, David Bizjak
Vice President, Adam Chewning
Vice President Municipal Trading, Andy Theisen
Vice President Information Technology, Katy Watchka
Sp Vice President, David Born
Senior Vice President Investments, Rick Johnson
Vice President Investments Stifel, Michael Hordy
First Vice President, Jim Daly
First Vice President, Cheryl Strickland
Associate Vice President, Rob Andresen
Vice President Investments Stifel, Brenda Bell
Vice President Investment Analyst, Nathan Isbee
Vice President, Kenneth Christman
Vp R&d, Alexander Reiss
Vice President Investments Stifel, Greg Swanson
Senior Vice President, David Campbell
Vice President Of Energy Operations, Mark Manning
Senior Vice President, Kevin S Fitzpatrick
Vice President And Investments, John Fuger
Vice President And Investments, Julian Lively

Senior Vice President And Investments, Manuel Palan
Senior Vice President, Lorenzo Boyd
Senior Vice President For Public, Anne Noble
Vice President, Michael Cox
Senior Vice President Of Investments, Peter Meizels
Vice President, Keith Lister
First Vice President Investments Stifel, Christopher Larkey
Vice President, Rob Buttarazzi
Vice President Investment Banking, Grant Hosking
Vice President Research Analyst, Kevin Cassidy
First Vice President Operations, Douglas W Noll
Vice President, Lee Papania
Vice President Investment Banking, Chad Gorsuch
Senior Vice President And Investments, Kenneth Reeves
Senior Vice President Investments, William Hadden
Vice President, Judy Petrik
Vice President Investment Banking, Chen Xue
Vice President Investments, Robert Johnson
First Vice President Mgr Qualified, Mary Voss
Vice President, Michael Carr
Vice President, Patrick Ho
Senior Vice President Finc, Ed Valdettaro
Vice President, Michael Belloli
Vice President Investments Kalas Keeley, Mike Kalas
Senior Vice President Invsts Finc Advs, Eric Robb
Vice President Of Investments, William Omalley
Vice President, Vickie Miller
Senior Vice President And Director, Rick Maples
Vice Chairman, Richard J. Himelfarb, age 73
Co-Chairman President and CEO, Ronald J. (Ron) Kruszewski, age 55
SVP CFO and Director, James M. Zemlyak, age 54
Vice Chairman, Ben A. Plotkin, age 58
Co-Chairman, Thomas W. (Thom) Weisel, age 73
EVP and Director Capital Markets Stifel Nicolaus, Thomas P. Mulroy, age 52
Senior Vice President Co-Director Institutional Group Director, Victor J. Nesi, age 54
Board Member, Daniel Dileva
Auditors: Ernst&YoungLLP

LOCATIONS

HQ: Stifel Financial Corp.
501 North Broadway, St. Louis, MO 63102-2188
Phone: 314 342-2000
Web: www.stifel.com

PRODUCTS/OPERATIONS

2013 Sales

	$ mil.	% of total
Commissions	598.9	30
Principal transactions	460.0	23
Investment banking	448.1	22
Asset management & service fees	305.6	15
Interest	142.5	7
Others	64.7	3
Total	**2019.8**	**100**

Selected Subsidiaries

Broadway Air Corp.
Butler Wick & Co. Inc.
Century Securities Associates Inc.
CSA Insurance Agency Incorporated
Choice Financial Partners Inc.
First Service Financial Company
Stifel Bank & Trust
Hanifen Imhoff Inc.
Missouri Valley Partners
Stifel Asset Management Corp.
Stifel Nicolaus Limited (UK)
Stifel Nicolaus & Company Incorporated
Ryan Beck Holdings LLC

Stifel Nicolaus Insurance Agency Incorporated
Stifel Nicholas Limited (UK)
Thomas Weisel Partners Group Inc.

COMPETITORS

Bank of America
Cowen Group
Edward Jones
Goldman Sachs
JMP Group
Jefferies Group
Lazard
Morgan Stanley
Oppenheimer Holdings
Piper Jaffray
Raymond James Financial
Robert W. Baird & Co.
SWS Group
Wells Fargo Advisors

HISTORICAL FINANCIALS

Company Type: Public

Income Statement

FYE: December 31

	ASSETS ($ mil.)	NET INCOME ($ mil.)	INCOME AS % OF ASSETS	EMPLOYEES
12/13	9,008.8	162.0	1.8%	5,862
12/12	6,966.1	138.5	2.0%	5,343
12/11	4,951.9	84.1	1.7%	5,097
12/10	4,213.1	1.9	0.0%	4,906
12/09	3,167.3	75.8	2.4%	4,434
Annual Growth	**29.9%**	**20.9%**	**—**	**7.2%**

2013 Year-End Financials

Return on assets: 2.0%	Dividends
Return on equity: 9.1%	Yield: —
Long-term debt ($ mil.): —	Payout: —
No. of shares (mil.): 63	Market value ($ mil.): 3,055
Sales ($ mil: 2,019	

	STOCK PRICE ($) FY Close	P/E High/Low		PER SHARE ($) Earnings	Dividends	Book Value
12/13	47.92	19 12		2.20	0.00	32.30
12/12	31.97	15 11		2.20	0.00	27.23
12/11	32.05	46 15		1.33	0.00	25.15
12/10	62.04	1571 1080		0.03	0.00	24.79
12/09	59.24	33 17		1.57	0.00	19.16
Annual Growth	**(5.2%)**	**— —**		**8.9%**	**—**	**13.9%**

Stoneridge Inc.

Stoneridge makes sure your vehicle's electrical system can send power to all the places where it needs to go —whether it's an automobile medium- or heavy-duty truck or agricultural/off-highway vehicle. The company's wiring segment makes wiring harnesses and connectors and its electronics unit makes electronic control units instrumentation displays and driver information and electrical distribution systems. Its control devices segment products monitor and measure specific functions of a vehicle using switches control actuation devices and sensors. Stonebridge also has a PST segment that makes vehicle security alarms and tracking devices.

Geographic Reach

Stonebridge has more than 25 locations in 15 countries including joint ventures. North America is the company's largest segment contributing 65% of sales; South America follows with 19% while Europe and other markets represent the remainder of sales.

Operations

Sales to commercial vehicle makers account for 40% of the company's sales while automotive vehicle makers account for 22%. Agriculture vehicle makers generate 19% of sales and aftermarket distributors and mass merchandisers contribute the remaining 19%.

Stonebridge divides its operations across several segments. Wiring is its largest generating 33% of sales while control devices brings in 27%. The other two segments electronics and PST (a Brazil-based subsidiary that makes eletronic vehicle security alarms and tracking devices) generate 22% and 18% respectively.

Sales and Marketing

Stonebridge's major clients include Navistar International (18% of sales in 2012) Deere (13%) Ford (5%) General Motors (4%) and Scania (4%).

Financial Performance

As the automotive sector gradually moves away from the painful effects of the recession Stoneridge has seen significant revenue growth for three straight years. Its net revenues surged by 23% from $765 million in 2011 to $938 million in 2012.

The bump in revenue for 2012 was the result of an increase in wiring segment sales within the North American agriculture vehicles market. Stoneridge was also aided by higher control device segment sales within the North American automotive vehicle and commercial vehicle sectors.

The bad news for Stoneridge was that its profits nosedived by nearly 90% from $49 million in 2011 to $5 million in 2012. The decrease was primarily due to a 53% spike in selling general and administrative expenses related to the consolidation and majority share acquisition of PST Eletr´nica its former joint venture in Brazil.

Strategy

In addition to acquisitions Stoneridge partners with companies to gain access to new product and geographic markets and to exchange technologies. Its joint venture in India is Minda Stoneridge Instruments. In 2011 the company increased its stake in a former joint venture PST Eletr´nica (Brazil) to 74%; PST is now a subsidiary and contributed 18% of total sales in 2012. To stay competitive Stoneridge is also increasing its manufacturing footprint in China India and South America.

Ownership

Wellington Management Company owns 10% of Stoneridge.

EXECUTIVES

Vp; President Global Sales, Thomas A Beaver, age 62
Vp; President Stoneridge Electronics, Mark J Tervalon, age 49
VP Operations, Richard P. (Rick) Adante, $236,250 total compensation
EVP CFO and Treasurer, George E. Strickler, age 67, $357,500 total compensation
President and CEO, Jonathan B. DeGaynor, age 47
VP; President Control Devices Division, Michael D. Sloan, age 57, $243,400 total compensation
CEO of PST Eletronica Ltda, Sergio Leite
President Stoneridge Electronics Division, Peter Kruk
CIO, Richard E. Maus
President PST Eletr Â´nica Ltda.; Director, S Ærgio de Cerqueira Leite
V Pres Human Resources, Charles A Distaulo
Vice President Of Organizational Development Training Department, Roger Cyr
Regional Vice President, Miguel Valadez
Vice President, Gil Lopez
Vice President, Linda Allison
Vice President Operations, Mike Seely

Board Member, Jeffrey P Draime, age 48
Chairman, William M. (Bill) Lasky, age 66
Board Member, Al Ryan
Board Member, Elise Yanez
Treasury Manager, Marie Dawson
Auditors: Ernst&YoungLLP

LOCATIONS

HQ: Stoneridge Inc.
  9400 East Market Street, Warren, OH 44484
Phone: 330 856-2443
Web: www.stoneridge.com

2012 Sales

	$ mil.	% of total
North America	611.8	65
South America	180.4	19
Europe & other regions	146.3	16
Total	**938.5**	**100**

PRODUCTS/OPERATIONS

2012 Sales by Customer

	% of total
Navistar	18
Deere & Company	13
Ford	5
General Motors	4
Scania Group	4
Other	56
Total	**100**

2012 Sales

	$ mil.	% of total
Wiring	329.8	33
Control devices	271.8	27
Electronics	216.0	22
PST	180.4	18
Eliminations	(59.5)	-
Total	**938.5**	**100**

Selected Products

Electronics
  Driver information systems
  Electronic control units
  Electronic instrument clusters
Control Devices
  Control actuation devices
  Electronic and electromechanical switches
  Sensors

COMPETITORS

AMETEK	LEONI
Accuride	Lear Corp
American Axle &	Littelfuse
Manufacturing	Meritor
Aura Systems	Methode Electronics
CTS Corp.	Modine Manufacturing
Commercial Vehicle	Molex
Continental AG	Optek Technology
DENSO	Robert Bosch
Delphi Automotive	Sensata
Systems	Standard Motor
EnPro	Products
Esterline	Sumitomo Electric
Furukawa Electric	Superior Industries
Gentex	TRW Automotive
Graco	Texas Instruments
Hella Corporate Center	Titan International
USA	Visteon
Honeywell	Yazaki
International	ZF Electronics
Johnson Controls	

HISTORICAL FINANCIALS

Company Type: Public

Income Statement

FYE: December 31

	REVENUE ($ mil.)	NET INCOME ($ mil.)	NET PROFIT MARGIN	EMPLOYEES
12/13	947.8	15.1	1.6%	9,300
12/12	938.5	5.3	0.6%	8,700
12/11	765.3	49.3	6.4%	10,800
12/10	635.2	10.8	1.7%	6,800
12/09	475.1	(32.4)	—	5,200
Annual Growth	**18.8%**	**—**	**—**	**15.6%**

2013 Year-End Financials

Debt ratio: 33.5%
Return on equity: 10.1%
Cash ($ mil.): 62
Current ratio: 2.21
Long-term debt ($ mil.): 185
No. of shares (mil.): 28
Dividends
  Yield: —
  Payout: —
Market value ($ mil.): 363

	STOCK PRICE ($) FY Close	P/E High	P/E Low	PER SHARE ($) Earnings	PER SHARE ($) Dividends	PER SHARE ($) Book Value
12/13	12.75	24	9	0.56	0.00	5.23
12/12	5.12	54	23	0.20	0.00	5.36
12/11	8.43	8	2	2.00	0.00	5.00
12/10	15.79	38	14	0.44	0.00	3.30
12/09	9.01	—	—	(1.37)	0.00	2.78
Annual Growth	**9.1%**			**—**	**—**	**17.1%**

Strattec Security Corp.

STRATTEC SECURITY has your car under lock and key. The company designs and makes mechanical security locks electro-mechanical locks and keys and ignition lock housings primarily for global automakers. It also makes access control products including door handles latches power sliding doors and power lift gates. Chrysler Ford and General Motors account for the majority of STRATTEC's sales. In addition to cars and light trucks its products are used in the heavy truck and recreational vehicle markets as well as in precision die castings. With facilities in the US and Mexico STRATTEC delivers products mainly in North America but also abroad in Asia Europe and South America.

Geographic Reach

The company ships its products throughout the US Canada Mexico Europe South America Korea and China.

Operations

The company is expanding its geographic footprint with a third plant in Juarez Mexico and a sales and engineering facility in Southeastern Michigan.

STRATTEC along with fellow automotive product suppliers WIITE Automotive and ADAC Automotive is a member of the Vehicle Access Systems Technology (VAST) Alliance which allows members to act as each others' sales marketing manufacturing and support representatives in North America and Europe. Members also own a joint venture Vehicle Access Systems Technology LLC which operates manufacturing facilities in China and Brazil and supports sales in the Asia/Pacific and Latin America regions.

STRATTEC Power Access LLC a subsidiary formed alongside WIITE Automotive produces power access systems for sliding doors lift gates and trunk lids for the likes of Chrysler Ford GM and Taiwan-based Yulon.

Sales and Marketing

STRATTEC generated some 74% of its fiscal 2014 sales via direct sales to various OEMs. It taps about 50 authorized wholesale distributors as well as other marketers and users of component parts (including export customers) to distribute its components and security products to the automotive aftermarket.

As part of its business STRATTEC also provides its customers with full-service aftermarket support.

Strategy

STRATTEC in 2013 partnered with Actuator Systems to design and produce next-generation biometric security products. Known as NextLock the new joint venture leverages STRATTEC's North American engineering manufacturing and locksmith expertise with Actuator's technology to enhance overall electronics capabilities.

STRATTEC's moving beyond its traditional lock and key products and diversifying with a more sophisticated set of power access control products as purely mechanical devices are growing stale. The company views electro-mechanical devices for vehicles —mechanical locks keys housings and latches that are enhanced by built-in electronics —as the future. These include devices that incorporate user bio-identification systems keys with remote entry capabilities and ignition interfaces with passive start capabilities among other technologies.

Financial Performance

A boost in sales to Chrysler GM and Ford bolstered STRATTEC's bottom line in fiscal 2014. Revenue spiked by some 216% to $348 million in 2014 thanks to increased customer vehicle production volumes and more car models incorporating the components supplied by STRATTEC. Additionally one of GM's recalls spurred an $11 million sales increase for STRATTEC. Reduced sales to Hyundai/Kia tempered the company's positive results. Net income reached $16 million during the reporting period a 75% jump from 2013's $9 million. STRATTEC points to an increase in interest income and equity earnings of joint ventures as contributing to the gained ground.

EXECUTIVES

Senior Vice President - Chief Financial Officer Treasurer and Secretary, Patrick J. Hansen, age 55, $241,917 total compensation
President and Chief Executive Officer, Frank J. Krejci, age 64, $330,917 total compensation
Vice President - Marketing and Sales, Dennis A. Kazmierski, age 63, $211,741 total compensation
Vice President of Mexican Operations, Rolando J. Guillot, age 46, $203,833 total compensation
Vice President - Security Products, Brian J. Reetz, age 56
Vice President - Access Control Products, Richard P. Messina, age 48
Vice President, Guillermo Villa
Vice President Operations, Javier Diaz
Vice President Engineering, Omar Arras
Chairman, Harold M. Stratton, age 66
Board Member, Michael J Koss, age 61
Auditors: GrantThorntonLLP

LOCATIONS

HQ: Strattec Security Corp.
  3333 West Good Hope Road, Milwaukee, WI 53209
Phone: 414 247-3333   **Fax:** 414 247-3329
Web: www.strattec.com

PRODUCTS/OPERATIONS

2014 Sales by Customer

	$ mil.	% of total
Chrysler Group	117.5	34
General Motors	79.5	23
Ford Motor	46.6	13
Other customers	104.8	30
Total	**348.4**	**100**

2014 Sales

	$ mil.	% of total
Keys & locksets	115.4	34
Power access	60.1	17
Driver controls	53.7	15
Aftermarket & OE service	49.6	14
Door handles & exterior trim	48.0	14
Latches	14.7	4
Other	6.9	2
Total	**348.4**	**100**

COMPETITORS

AISIN World Corp.
Huf North America Automotive
Magna International
Tokai Rika
Valeo
Visteon

HISTORICAL FINANCIALS

Company Type: Public

Income Statement

FYE: June 29

	REVENUE ($ mil.)	NET INCOME ($ mil.)	NET PROFIT MARGIN	EMPLOYEES
06/14	348.4	16.4	4.7%	3,276
06/13*	298.1	9.3	3.1%	2,670
07/12	279.2	8.7	3.1%	2,507
07/11	260.9	5.4	2.1%	2,556
06/10	207.9	3.4	1.6%	2,280
Annual Growth	**13.8%**	**48.0%**	**—**	**9.5%**

*Fiscal year change

2014 Year-End Financials

Debt ratio: 1.1%
Return on equity: 14.3%
Cash ($ mil.): 19
Current ratio: 2.08
Long-term debt ($ mil.): 2

No. of shares (mil.): 3
Dividends
Yield: 0.0%
Payout: 9.5%
Market value ($ mil.): 230

	STOCK PRICE ($) FY Close	P/E High/Low	PER SHARE ($) Earnings	Dividends	Book Value
06/14	66.06	17 8	4.59	0.44	36.02
06/13*	37.36	15 7	2.72	0.40	30.91
07/12	21.04	10 7	2.64	0.40	24.38
07/11	21.13	23 12	1.63	1.20	26.21
06/10	22.01	26 13	1.04	0.00	22.63
Annual Growth	**31.6%**	**— —**	**44.9%**	**—**	**12.3%**

*Fiscal year change

Sturm, Ruger & Co., Inc.

Whether you like to shoot birdies or bogeys Sturm Ruger & Company can accommodate you. The company also called Ruger is one of the nation's biggest gun makers and produces all four categories of firearms: pistols revolvers rifles and shotguns. Models include hunting and target rifles single- and double-action revolvers muzzleloading guns and double-barreled shotguns. Its guns are sold by independent wholesale distributors to independent firearms retailers and chains including Academy Sports and Cabelas. Ruger also makes metal products –known as castings –for the commercial and military markets. Sturm Ruger & Company was founded in 1949 by William Ruger and Alexander Sturm.

Geographic Reach

Connecticut-based Sturm Ruger & Company makes all of its products in the US and sells most of them here as well. Foreign sales primarily to law enforcement and government agencies accounted for only 3% of 2012 sales.

Sales and Marketing

Four top customers account for more than half of Ruger's sales. They are Davidson's (17%) Jerry's/Ellett Brothers (15%) Lipsey's (13%) and Sports South (12%).

Operations

Ruger manufactures all of its rifles and revolvers in Newport New Hampshire. All pistols (except for one model) are produced in Prescott Arizona.

Investment castings accounted for 1% of the firearms maker's 2012 sales. Ruger's Pine Tree Castings (PTC) division makes and sells castings made from steel alloys for both its own use and for use outside customers. PTC supplies the architectural hardware sporting goods marine hardware firearms precision machinery pneumatic and hand tools industries among others. The company stopped manufacturing titanium castings in 2007 and consolidated its Arizona casting operations into its New Hampshire facilities. Following the move Ruger produces only castings made from steel alloys.

Financial Performance

The company's firearm sales increased nearly 50% in 2012 vs. 2011 closing in on the $500 million mark. Net income rose 76% over the same period. Sales are soaring driven by extraordinary retail demand for its firearms beginning in late 2008. (Units ordered increased by 107% in 2012 vs. 2011 while the number of units on backorder more than tripled.) Ruger attributes the high demand to politics and the economy. Also sales of handguns –purchased for self defense –have been particularly strong. To keep pace Ruger has increased production and even temporarily stopped taking orders for several months in 2012.

Profits are on the rise as well climbing steadily since 2008. The company's shares soared in 2012 and Ruger declared a special dividend of $4.50 per share in late 2012. While the renewed debate over gun control in the US following the tragedy in Newtown Connecticut could cast a shadow over the outlook for firearms sales in the short-term it has spurred sales.

Strategy

In 2011 Ruger became the first commercial firearms company to produce a million firearms in a single year. By August of 2012 it easily surpassed that milestone. While struggling to meet demand for its guns the company is also chasing after one of the faster-growing segments of the hunting market and working to expand its products portfolio. To that end in mid-2012 Ruger acquired a minority stake in crossbow manufacturer Kodabow. The company hopes the crossbow manufacturer based in West Chester Pennsylvania will boost sales and broaden its customer base. Ruger plans to continue to look for acquisition opportunities and work to expand manufacturing capacity in 2013.

HISTORY

Sturm Ruger & Company was founded in 1949 by William Ruger who designed a notable machine gun used by the military during WWII and Alexander Sturm who backed the production of a new Ruger design by investing $50000. Sturm died of hepatitis in 1951 at age 28 and after a battle with Sturm's family Ruger took control of the company.

The gun maker's growth during the 1960s and 1970s was driven by demand for single-action revolvers and .22-caliber autoloading pistols produced at its original plant in Southport Connecticut. Ruger went public in 1969 still the only American gun company to do so.

In 1986 the company forced its distributors to choose between it and archrival Smith & Wesson; about half chose to stay with Ruger. By streamlining its distribution channels the manufacturer made its products more difficult to find thus increasing their prestige.

Decreasing firearms sales prompted the company to expand its castings operations. Ruger bought Callaway Golf's share in their joint foundry to become its sole owner in 1997. In 1998 Ruger unveiled its first muzzleloader the Ruger 77/50 to capitalize on the growing popularity of muzzleloading rifles. Later that year New Orleans became the first municipality to sue gun makers including Ruger in an effort to recover the cost of gun violence. Other local governments followed suit.

In 2000 the company sent letters to gun distributors asking that its guns be sold at regular places of business not trade shows. In 2001 the Louisiana Supreme Court threw out New Orleans' suit but remained a defendant in some 37 lawsuits at the end of 2001.

Co-founder William Ruger died in July 2002. In early 2003 after 2 years of pretrial discovery the consolidated California cities suit against almost all firearms manufacturers (including Ruger) was dismissed.

EXECUTIVES

President CEO and Director, Michael O. Fifer, age 57, $400,000 total compensation
VP Prescott Firearms, Mark T. Lang, age 58, $196,154 total compensation
VP CFO and Treasurer, Thomas A. Dineen, age 45, $225,000 total compensation
VP Sales and Marketing, Christopher J. Killoy, age 55, $235,000 total compensation
VP Newport Operations, Thomas P. (Tom) Sullivan, age 53, $235,000 total compensation
President CEO and Director, Michael O. Fifer, age 57
VP CFO and Treasurer, Thomas A. Dineen, age 45
Auditors: McGladreyLLP

LOCATIONS

HQ: Sturm, Ruger & Co., Inc.
Lacey Place, Southport, CT 06890
Phone: 203 259-7843 **Fax:** 203 256-3367
Web: www.ruger.com

PRODUCTS/OPERATIONS

2012 Sales

	$ mil.	% of total
Firearms	484.9	99
Castings	6.9	1
Total	**491.8**	**100**

Selected Products
Firearms

Pistols
P-Series (centerfire)
Ruger 22/45 (rimfire)
Ruger Mark II (rimfire)
Revolvers
Single-action
Birds Head Vaquero
Bisley Hunter
New Bearcat
New Model Blackhawk
New Model Single Six
New Model .32 Magnum Super Single-Six
New Model Super Blackhawk
Old Army Cap & Ball
Ruger Bisley
Single-Six
Super Blackhawk
Vaquero
Double-action
GP100
SP101
Redhawk
Super Redhawk
Rifles
10/22
77/17
77/22
77/44
77/50 Muzzle Loader
96/17
96/22
96/44
Deerfield Carbine
M-77 Mark II
M-77 Mark II Magnum
Mini-14
Mini Thirty
Model 96 Rimfire
No.1 Single Shot
Ruger Carbine
Shotguns
Gold Label (side-by-side 12 gauge)
Red Label (12 20 28 gauge)
Woodside (12 gauge)
Castings
Aluminum
Chrome-molybdenum
Cobalt
Nickel
Stainless steel

COMPETITORS

A. Finkl & Sons	Gibbs Die Casting
Beretta USA	Glock
Browning Arms	Marlin Firearms
Colt Defense	Mossberg
Colt' s	Remington Arms
Fabbrica D' Armi Pietro	SIG SAUER
Beretta	Savage Arms
Freedom Group	Smith & Wesson Holding
GKN Sinter Metals	Springfield Armory

HISTORICAL FINANCIALS

Company Type: Public

Income Statement

FYE: December 31

	REVENUE ($ mil.)	NET INCOME ($ mil.)	NET PROFIT MARGIN	EMPLOYEES
12/13	688.2	111.2	16.2%	2,380
12/12	491.8	70.6	14.4%	2,040
12/11	328.8	40.0	12.2%	1,540
12/10	255.2	28.2	11.1%	1,160
12/09	270.9	27.5	10.1%	1,150
Annual Growth	26.2%	41.8%	—	19.9%

2013 Year-End Financials

Debt ratio: —	No. of shares (mil.): 19
Return on equity: 81.1%	Dividends
Cash ($ mil.): 55	Yield: 9.0%
Current ratio: 1.79	Payout: 125.2%
Long-term debt ($ mil.): —	Market value ($ mil.): 1,414

	STOCK PRICE ($) FY Close	P/E High/Low		PER SHARE ($) Earnings	Dividends	Book Value
12/13	73.09	14	8	5.58	6.62	9.26
12/12	45.40	16	9	3.60	5.80	4.93
12/11	33.46	17	7	2.09	0.43	7.20
12/10	15.29	12	7	1.46	0.33	6.08
12/09	9.70	10	4	1.42	0.31	5.01
Annual Growth	65.7%			— 40.8%	115.9%	16.6%

Suburban Propane Partners L.P.

Ranch-style homes are heated and backyard barbecues fueled by Suburban Propane Partners a leading US retail propane marketer which competes with Energy Transfer Partners AmeriGas Ferrellgas and other propane providers. With more than 300 service centers in 30 states Suburban Propane serves some 608000 retail customers. It annually sells about 300 million gallons of propane and more than 37 million gallons of fuel oil and refined petroleum products to wholesale and large end-users. It also sells natural gas and electricity and installs HVAC systems. In a major expansion in 2012 the company acquired Inergy's propane assets for $1.8 billion.

Before the acquisition Inergy operated in 33 states from 338 customer service centers. Inergy's propane assets added 600000 propane customers and 325 million retail propane gallons to Suburban Propane's total assets.

Suburban Propane's business segments include propane; fuel oil and residual fuels; natural gas and electricity; and services. Through its fuel oil and refined fuels segment Suburban Propane distributes fuel oil diesel kerosene and gasoline to about 48000 residential and commercial customers in the northeast of the US.

Through its natural gas and electricity segment (Agway Energy Services) Suburban Propane offers gas and electric utility services to almost 87000 residential and commercial customers in New York and Pennsylvania.

In addition to the sale and installation of heating and air conditioning units the company also provides air cleaners humidifiers de-humidifiers as well as air duct cleaning and energy audit services.

Suburban Propane's growth strategy includes complementary acquisitions customer maintenance and growth and the selective selling of non-core assets.

Fiscal 2010 saw the company posting weaker revenues and income as the recession dragged down demand. However with the economy pulling out of the recession during the fiscal year Suburban Propane resumed its acquisitive ways buying four mid-sized propane operations that complement its existing businesses including Lyles's Propane of Nevada.

In 2011 the company reported an almost 5% jump in revenues primarily due to higher prices offsetting lower volumes sold. Net income was essentially flat. Suburban Propane made one acquisition that year buying a medium-sized propane business in a market where it already had a major presence.

EXECUTIVES

Vice President Operational Planning, Mark Wienberg
Auditors: PricewaterhouseCoopersLLP

LOCATIONS

HQ: Suburban Propane Partners L.P.
240 Route 10 West, Whippany, NJ 07981
Phone: 973 887-5300
Web: www.suburbanpropane.com

PRODUCTS/OPERATIONS

2013 Sales

	$ mil.	% of total
Propane	1357.1	80
Fuel oil & refined fuels	209.0	12
Natural gas & electricity	79.4	5
Other	58.1	3
Total	1703.6	100

COMPETITORS

AmeriGas Partners	Piedmont Natural Gas
Energy Transfer	Southern States
Ferrellgas Partners	Star Gas Partners

HISTORICAL FINANCIALS

Company Type: Public

Income Statement

FYE: September 27

	REVENUE ($ mil.)	NET INCOME ($ mil.)	NET PROFIT MARGIN	EMPLOYEES
09/14	1,938.2	94.5	4.9%	3,796
09/13	1,703.6	78.8	4.6%	3,933
09/12	1,063.4	1.8	0.2%	4,144
09/11	1,190.5	114.9	9.7%	2,385
09/10	1,136.6	115.3	10.1%	2,598
Annual Growth	14.3%	(4.9%)	—	9.9%

2014 Year-End Financials

Debt ratio: 47.6%	No. of shares (mil.): 60
Return on equity: —	Dividends
Cash ($ mil.): 92	Yield: 0.0%
Current ratio: 1.33	Payout: 224.3%
Long-term debt ($ mil.): 1,242	Market value ($ mil.): 2,697

	STOCK PRICE ($) FY Close	P/E High/Low		PER SHARE ($) Earnings	Dividends	Book Value
09/14	44.72	31	26	1.56	3.50	16.93
09/13	46.33	37	28	1.34	3.48	18.75
09/12	41.36	968	696	0.05	3.41	19.15
09/11	46.41	18	13	3.22	3.41	10.11
09/10	53.70	17	13	3.24	3.35	10.33
Annual Growth	(4.5%)			— (16.7%)	1.1%	13.2%

Summit Hotel Properties Inc

From the southern states to the Mountain States Summit Hotel Properties has plenty of room for US travelers. Operating through its subsidiaries Summit Hotel is a self-advised real estate investment trust (REIT) that holds a portfolio of more than 80 midscale and upscale hotels in about 21 states including major markets in western and southern states like Arizona Colorado Idaho and Texas. Its hotels which comprise more than 7500 rooms operate primarily under brands owned by Marriott International as well as Hilton Hyatt and ICH. Formed in 2010 Summit Hotel went public via a 2011 IPO.

The company and its operating company Summit Hotel OP were formed to acquire and operate the hotel portfolio of predecessor company Summit Hotel Properties LLC. It plans to use the more than $250 million that it raised in its IPO to repay debt fund capital improvements at its properties and for general corporate purposes.

A significant part of Summit Hotel's growth strategy centers on expanding its portfolio through acquisitions. The company will likely also use some of its IPO proceeds to acquire properties that are similar in type and market location to those in its current portfolio. It will also take steps to bolster its portfolio's value through property renovation repositioning and asset management efforts.

Summit Hotel timed its IPO with its assessment that the hotel industry is in the process of recovering from the 2008 downturn in the US real estate sector. The company contends that because its properties operate under multiple leading hotel brands in markets suited to the hospitality industry (near tourist attractions corporate headquarters conventions centers etc.) it is well-positioned to capitalize on the anticipated rebound in the hotel industry.

EXECUTIVES

EVP CFO and Treasurer, Greg A. Dowell, age 51
President and CEO, Daniel P. Hansen, age 45, $400,000 total compensation
EVP and COO, Craig J. Aniszewski, age 51, $325,000 total compensation
Vice President Asset Mgmt Management, Greg James
Vice President Of Asset Management, Trent Peterson
Evp General Counsel Secretary, Christopher Eng
EVP CFO and Treasurer, Greg A. Dowell, age 51
Chairman, Kerry W. Boekelheide, age 60
Auditors: KPMGLLP

LOCATIONS

HQ: Summit Hotel Properties Inc
12600 Hill Country Boulevard, Suite R-100, Austin, TX 78738
Phone: 512 538-2300
Web: www.shpreit.com

COMPETITORS

Ashford Hospitality Trust	Host Hotels & Resorts
FelCor	LaSalle Hotel Properties
Hospitality Properties Trust	

HISTORICAL FINANCIALS

Company Type: Public

Income Statement

FYE: December 31

	REVENUE ($ mil.)	NET INCOME ($ mil.)	NET PROFIT MARGIN	EMPLOYEES
12/13	298.9	5.8	2.0%	33
12/12	189.5	(1.0)	—	25
12/11*	134.2	(2.9)	—	18
02/11	14.6	(6.2)	—	0
12/10	135.6	(20.9)	—	18
Annual Growth 21.8%		—	—	16.4%

*Fiscal year change

2013 Year-End Financials

Debt ratio: 33.6%	No. of shares (mil.): 85
Return on equity: 0.9%	Dividends
Cash ($ mil.): 46	Yield: 5.0%
Current ratio: 2.92	Payout: —
Long-term debt ($ mil.): 435	Market value ($ mil.): 769

	STOCK PRICE ($) FY Close	P/E High/Low		PER SHARE ($) Earnings	Dividends	Book Value
12/13	9.00	—	—	(0.12)	0.45	9.48
12/12	9.50	—	—	(0.17)	0.45	9.46
12/11*	9.44	—	—	(0.12)	0.28	10.20
02/11	9.80	—	—	(0.00)	0.00	(0.00)
Annual Growth	(2.8%)	—	—	—	—	—

*Fiscal year change

Sun Communities, Inc.

Sun Communities helps residents in the Sunshine State and around the US. The self-managed real estate investment trust (REIT) owns develops and operates manufactured housing communities (trailer and recreation vehicle parks) in 25 states. Its portfolio in May 2013 included about 185 properties with 67700 developed manufactured home and RV sites. Its Sun Home Services unit sells new and used homes for placement on its properties the majority of which are in Michigan Florida Indiana Texas and Ohio. Sun Communities also acquires at a discount and resells mobile homes that have been repossessed by lenders in its communities.

Geographic Reach

Sun Communities has properties in Arizona Colorado Connecticut Delaware Florida Georgia Illinois Indiana Iowa Kansas Maine Massachusetts Michigan Missouri Nevada New Jersey New York North Carolina Ohio Oregon Pennsylvania Tennessee Texas Virginia and Wisconsin.

Operations

Sun Communities operates two lines of business: Real property and homes sales and rentals.

The company's properties have trained on-site property managers and maintenance personnel as well as such amenities as clubhouses laundry facilities and swimming pools. At the end of 2012 the company owned and operated 182 properties in 19 states including 149 manufactured housing communities 13 RV communities and 11 properties containing both manufactured housing and RV sites. That year the average renewal rate for residents in Sun Communities' rental program was about 61%.

Financial Performance

The company's revenues grew by 17% in 2012 thanks to a 40% increase in revenues from home sales and a 14% increase in income from real property partially offset by decline in ancillary revenues. Sun Communities' manufactured home and RV portfolio increased by $9.5 million due to average rental rate increases of 2.8% and the growth in occupied home sites offset by rent concessions offered to residents who convert from home renters to home owners. The growth in home sales revenues was due to a hike in the sales volume of new home and pre-owned homes.The higher revenues allowed Sun Communities to post a net income of $5 million in 2012 as compared to a net loss in 2011 despite an increase in expenses. The company has seen an increase in revenues between 2010 and 2012 due to organic growth. Burdened by heavy debt from the collapse of the housing market and its equity investments in that market the company has steadily chipped away at its debt. Sun Communities saw a continuous decline in net loss from 2001 to 2011 and finally posted a net income figure in 2012.

Strategy

Sun Communities' solid performance is in part due to increased demand from retiring adults a growing demographic. The company also points to its rental program as key to its success during the recession. Home rentals have become a popular and affordable alternative to customers. The company is focusing on its growth strategy through acquisitions and expansion of its properties.

Mergers and Acquisitions

Expanding its geographic coverage in early 2013 the company acquired ten RV communities (Gwynns Island RV Resort LLC Indian Creek RV Resort LLC Lake Laurie RV Resort LLC Newpoint RV Resort LLC Peters Pond RV Resort Inc. Seaport LLC Virginia Tent LLC Wagon Wheel Maine LLC Westward Ho RV Resort LLC and Wild Acres LLC) with 3700 sites in Connecticut Maine Massachusetts New Jersey Ohio Virginia and Wisconsin for $112.8 million.In 2012 Sun Communities made seven acquisitions (which included 14 properties in total seven manufactured housing communities five RV communities and two communities containing both manufactured housing and RV communities. The acquisitions included Three Lakes RV Resort Blueberry Hill RV Resort and Grand Lake Estates located in Florida; Blazing Star RV Resort (260 sites located in San Antonio Texas); Northville Crossing Manufactured Home Community (756 sites in Northville Michigan); Rainbow RV Resort (500 sites in Frostproof Florida); four manufactured home communities (the Rudgate Acquisition Properties) in southeast Michigan and Palm Creek Golf & RV Resort (283 manufactured home sites 1580 RV sites and the expansion potential of 550 manufactured housing or 990 RV sites) in Casa Grande Arizona.

In 2011 Sun Communities grew its portfolio when it acquired 17 manufactured housing communities and one RV community in western Michigan from Kentland Corporation. That year Sun Communities also bought a RV resort in Florida for more than $6 million.

Ownership

FMR LLC and Edward C. Johnson III (the chairman of FMR LLC) own more than 12% of Sun Communities.

EXECUTIVES

EVP, Jonathan M. Colman, age 58, $75,000 total compensation
Chairman and CEO, Gary A. Shiffman, age 60, $671,111 total compensation

President and COO, John B. McLaren, $400,000 total compensation
EVP Treasurer CFO and Secretary, Karen J. Dearing, $352,980 total compensation
Senior Vice President Of Rv Operations, Tom O'Branovic
Auditors: GrantThorntonLLP

LOCATIONS

HQ: Sun Communities, Inc.
27777 Franklin Rd., Suite 200, Southfield, MI 48034
Phone: 248 208-2500
Web: www.suncommunities.com

2012 Properties

	% of total
Michigan	72
Florida	32
Texas	21
Indiana	18
Ohio	11
Other states	28
Total	**182**

PRODUCTS/OPERATIONS

2012 Sales

	$ mil.	% of total
Real property income	255.8	75
Home sales	45.1	13
Home rentals	26.6	8
Interest and other	12.1	4
Total	**339.6**	**100**

Selected Mergers and Acquisitions

2013
Gwynns Island RV Resort LLC Indian Creek RV Resort LLC Lake Laurie RV Resort LLC Newpoint RV Resort LLC Peters Pond RV Resort Inc. Seaport LLC Virginia Tent LLC Wagon Wheel Maine LLC Westward Ho RV Resort LLC and Wild Acres LLC (Connecticut Maine Massach
2012
Three Lakes RV Resort Blueberry Hill RV Resort and Grand Lake Estates; Florida
Blazing Star RV Resort; San Antonio Texas
Northville Crossing Manufactured Home Community; Michigan

COMPETITORS

American Land Lease	Nobility Homes
Equity Lifestyle Properties	Outdoor Resorts
Hometown America	UMH Properties

HISTORICAL FINANCIALS

Company Type: Public

Income Statement
FYE: December 31

	REVENUE ($ mil.)	NET INCOME ($ mil.)	NET PROFIT MARGIN	EMPLOYEES
12/13	415.2	20.1	4.9%	1,236
12/12	339.6	8.0	2.4%	915
12/11	289.1	(0.5)	—	775
12/10	263.1	(3.5)	—	747
12/09	256.6	(7.3)	—	664
Annual Growth	12.8%	—	—	16.8%

2013 Year-End Financials

Debt ratio: 74.6%
Return on equity: 7.0%
Cash ($ mil.): 4
Current ratio: 0.03
Long-term debt ($ mil.): 1,311
No. of shares (mil.): 36
Dividends
Yield: 5.9%
Payout: 969.2%
Market value ($ mil.): 1,541

	STOCK PRICE ($) FY Close	P/E High/Low	PER SHARE ($) Earnings	Dividends	Book Value
12/13	42.64	184 129	0.31	2.52	10.53
12/12	39.89	263 201	0.18	2.52	6.47
12/11	36.53	— —	(0.05)	3.15	(5.81)
12/10	33.31	— —	(0.15)	2.52	(6.02)
12/09	19.75	— —	(0.34)	2.52	(5.57)
Annual Growth	21.2%	— —	—	(0.0%)	—

Sun Hydraulics Corp.

It's not solar power that Sun Hydraulics delivers but fluid power. The company makes screw-in hydraulic cartridge valves and custom manifolds used to control speed force and motion in fluid power systems. Cartridge valves offer a general purpose floating design that is unique in pressure capacity reliability reduced size and installation. Sun Hydraulics' valves and manifolds are used in myriad industrial and mobile products including construction agricultural and utility equipment and to a lesser extent in machine tools and material handling equipment. The company operates through subsidiaries and distributors in the US UK Germany Korea China and India. The Americas represents 45% of sales.

Geographic Reach
Its products' worldwide manufacture and availability fuels the Floridian company's performance. Approximately 60% of sales are to customers outside of the US. About 20% of sales are buoyed by customers in the Asia/Pacific region.

Strategy
The company maintains a strategy of selectively expanding its core product two-thirds of which are sold for breadth of mobile equipment applications and the remainder for fixed-in-place or automation machinery applications. Emerging end markets include nontraditional sectors such as animatronics wind power solar power and amusement park rides. Products launched within the last five years generate between 10% and 15% of sales.

EXECUTIVES

President CEO and Director, Allen J. Carlson, age 59, $369,557 total compensation
CFO, Tricia L. Fulton, age 48, $138,708 total compensation
Officer Operations, Tim A. Twitty, age 47, $140,689 total compensation
Chairman, Philippe J. Lemaitre, age 64
Auditors: KirklandRussMurphy&Tapp

LOCATIONS

HQ: Sun Hydraulics Corp.
1500 West University Parkway, Sarasota, FL 34243
Phone: 941 362-1200
Web: www.sunhydraulics.com

2010 Sales

	$ mil.	% of total
US	94.0	62
UK	20.6	14
Germany	19.8	13
Korea	16.3	11
Total	**150.7**	**100**

PRODUCTS/OPERATIONS

2010 Sales

Customers	% of total
Mobile applications (construction agricultural mining & fire & rescue & other utility equipment)	66
Industrial applications (automation machinery presses plastics machinery machine tools)	34
New applications (animatronics wind power wave power solar power & amusement park rides)	
Total	**100**

Selected Products

Integrated packages (using custom designed manifolds)
Screw-in hydraulic cartridge valves (electrically actuated and non-electrically actuated)
Standard manifolds

COMPETITORS

Actuant	Koch Enterprises
Bosch Rexroth Corp.	Parker-Hannifin
Dayco Products	Sauer-Danfoss
Jet Research Development	Servotronics
	Textron

HISTORICAL FINANCIALS

Company Type: Public

Income Statement
FYE: December 28

	REVENUE ($ mil.)	NET INCOME ($ mil.)	NET PROFIT MARGIN	EMPLOYEES
12/13	205.2	37.9	18.5%	684
12/12	204.3	37.4	18.3%	903
12/11*	204.1	37.6	18.5%	717
01/11	150.7	21.4	14.2%	618
01/10	97.3	1.8	1.9%	633
Annual Growth	20.5%	112.7%		2.0%

*Fiscal year change

2013 Year-End Financials

Debt ratio: —
Return on equity: 21.9%
Cash ($ mil.): 54
Current ratio: 9.21
Long-term debt ($ mil.): —
No. of shares (mil.): 26
Dividends
Yield: 0.0%
Payout: 31.0%
Market value ($ mil.): 1,082

	STOCK PRICE ($) FY Close	P/E High/Low	PER SHARE ($) Earnings	Dividends	Book Value
12/13	41.06	30 17	1.45	0.45	7.26
12/12	24.97	23 15	1.44	1.48	5.95
12/11*	23.43	36 13	1.47	0.40	5.64
01/11	37.80	46 25	0.84	0.57	4.51
01/10	26.25	380 144	0.07	0.30	4.24
Annual Growth	11.8%	— —	110.9%	10.7%	14.4%

*Fiscal year change

Super Micro Computer Inc

Super Micro Computer manufactures high-performance server products based on open standard components (including Intel AMD and NVIDIA processors). Its nearly 7000 offerings include motherboards and serverboards blade servers rackmounts GPU systems chassis and Ethernet switches and network adaptors. The company also sells a host of subsystems and accessories. Super Micro markets its products –primarily through distributors and resellers such as Ingram Micro and Arrow Electronics –to customers in some 90 countries; nearly half its sales are generated outside the US.

Geographic Reach The company generates nearly 60% of its sales from the US with Europe and Asia contributing 22% and 17% respectively. All of these regions saw solid year-over-year growth in fiscal 2012. Super Micro has operations in The Netherlands and Taiwan that support its international customers.

Sales and Marketing The company sells primarily through distributors resellers and systems integrators (about 55% of sales) but it also markets to OEMs and directly to end users. Leading distributors and resellers include Ingram Micro Avnet MA Labs Tech Data and ASI.

Financial Performance Super Micro has seen strong revenue growth over the past decade with the exception of 2009 when the recession led to a small decline. In fiscal 2012 (ended June) it reported sales of $1 billion up 8% from 2011. The growth in 2012 was primarily the result of increased server system sales and a jump of nearly 20% in the average selling price for server systems. Net income in fiscal 2012 fell about a quarter to nearly $30 million as expenses rose by double digits driven by personnel growth.

Strategy Key to Super Micro's strategy is the expansion of its product portfolio as technology evolves. The company works closely with AMD Intel and others to make sure its offerings are compatible with the standards. In addition it puts a special focus on energy efficient products such as its SuperBlade line of blade server products. The company also wants to further expand into Asia and Europe. In 2012 it opened the Science and Technology Park in Taiwan to increase capacity and better serves its customers in the Asia-Pacific region.

Ownership CEO Charles Liang and his wife VP Sara Liang together own about 22% of Super Micro Computer.

EXECUTIVES

Vp Worldwide Sales, Phidias Chou, age 57
VP Operations Treasurer and Director, Chiu-Chu Liu (Sara) Liang, age 52, $188,723 total compensation
Chairman President and CEO, Charles Liang, age 56, $303,682 total compensation
CFO, Howard Hideshima, age 55, $271,325 total compensation
Senior Vice President Investor Relations, Perry Hayes
Vice President Of International Sales, Yih-shyan W Liaw
Vice President Operations, Jason Wang
Vice President Gen Counsel Legal Dept, Robert Aeschliman
Chief Technology Officer Vice President Of Engineering, Jeff Chen
Vp Engineering, Ryan Yang
Vice President Business Development, Gianluca Degliesposti
Chairman President and CEO, Charles Liang, age 56
Auditors: Deloitte&ToucheLLP

LOCATIONS

HQ: Super Micro Computer Inc
980 Rock Avenue, San Jose, CA 95131
Phone: 408 503-8000
Web: www.supermicro.com

2012 Sales

	$ mil.	% of total
US	589.7	58
Europe	221.4	22
Asia	176.0	17
Other regions	26.8	3
Total	**1013.9**	**100**

PRODUCTS/OPERATIONS

2012 Sales

	$ mil.	% of total
Server systems	447.0	44
Subsystems & accessories	566.9	56
Total	**1013.9**	**100**

Selected Products

Chassis enclosures (pedestal rack-mount tower)
Motherboards (desktop server workstation)
Power supplies
Serverboards
Servers (rack-mount tower)

COMPETITORS

Celestica	IBM
Cisco Systems	Intel
Dell	Quanta Computer
Flextronics	Silicon Graphics
Hewlett-Packard	International
Hon Hai	Wistron

HISTORICAL FINANCIALS

Company Type: Public

Income Statement

FYE: June 30

	REVENUE ($ mil.)	NET INCOME ($ mil.)	NET PROFIT MARGIN	EMPLOYEES
06/14	1,467.2	54.1	3.7%	1,869
06/13	1,162.5	21.2	1.8%	1,595
06/12	1,013.8	29.8	2.9%	1,503
06/11	942.5	40.2	4.3%	499
06/10	721.4	26.9	3.7%	1,012
Annual Growth	**19.4%**	**19.1%**	**—**	**16.6%**

2014 Year-End Financials

Debt ratio: 5.8%
Return on equity: 12.8%
Cash ($ mil.): 96
Current ratio: 2.10
Long-term debt ($ mil.): 3
No. of shares (mil.): 45
Dividends
  Yield: —
  Payout: —
Market value ($ mil.): 1,145

	STOCK PRICE ($) FY Close	P/E High/Low		PER SHARE ($) Earnings	Dividends	Book Value
06/14	25.27	21	9	1.16	0.00	10.36
06/13	10.64	33	16	0.48	0.00	8.83
06/12	15.86	25	16	0.67	0.00	8.14
06/11	16.09	18	8	0.93	0.00	7.13
06/10	13.50	26	10	0.65	0.00	6.07
Annual Growth	**17.0%**	**—**	**—**	**15.6%**	**—**	**14.3%**

Superior Industries International, Inc.

Superior Industries International is one of the world's largest makers of aluminum road wheels for passenger cars and light trucks. It sells roughly 80% of its wheels to OEMs General Motors Ford Motor and Chrysler for factory installation or as optional or standard items on some models. Other customers include BMW Nissan and Toyota. North America is its core market; sales to international OEMs supply assembly plants mainly in the US. Superior Industries operates five manufacturing facilities; nearly 65% of Superior Industries' wheels are made in Mexico. Remaining production is primarily in the US and to a small extent through an investment in India.

Geographic Reach

The company's largest market is Mexico which generates nearly 65% of total sales; the US accounts for the remainder. It operates a total of five facilities that produce aluminum wheels for the automotive industry located in Arkansas and Chihuahua Mexico.

Sales and Marketing

Superior Industries' main customers include Ford (45% of total sales) General Motors (24%) Toyota (12%) and Chrysler (10%).

Financial Performance

Superior Industries' revenues declined 4% from $821 million in 2012 to $790 million in 2013. The revenue decline was fueled by lower overall volumes sold resulting in about $38 million in lower sales compared to 2012. It experienced a 9% drop in sales from the US in 2013 and it was also impacted by a decline in the value of the aluminum component of sales which it generally passes through to its customers.

The company's profits fell 26% from $31 million in 2012 to $23 million in 2013. This was due to higher selling general and administrative expenses as a result of a rise in executive severance related costs higher medical self-insurance costs and higher taxes. Superior Industries' operating cash flow has fluctuated over the last five years. In 2103 cash flow increased by $3 million due to cash generated from tax liabilities non-cash changes depreciation and inventories.

Strategy

Superior Industries' strategy for growth includes keeping a tight lid on costs and optimizing its operating structure. In 2014 it announced plans to close its manufacturing facility in Rogers Arkansas.

Due to the anticipation of continued growth in demand for aluminum wheels in the North American market in 2013 the company began construction of a new manufacturing facility in Mexico with an estimated cost of $125 million to $135 million. It projects that the new facility will be operational in late 2014 with commercial production beginning towards the middle of 2015.

EXECUTIVES

President and CEO, Donald J. (Don) Stebbins, age 55
EVP and CFO, Kerry A. Shiba, age 60, $71,250 total compensation
SVP Sales Marketing and Product Development, Parveen Kakar, age 48, $208,077 total compensation
SVP Project Management, Robert Bracy, age 67
VP Mexico Operations, Gabriel Soto, age 66

VP Supply Chain Management, Cameron Toyne, age 56
VP Midwest Operations, Michael N. Bakaric
EVP Operations, Michael J. O'Rourke
Vice President And Corporate Controller, Mike Nelson
Vice President And Scientific Director, Guillermo Chacon
Svp-business Operations, James F Sistek
Chairman, Margaret S. Dano, age 54
Treasury Manager, Lars Morgan
Auditors: Deloitte&ToucheLLP

LOCATIONS

HQ: Superior Industries International, Inc.
7800 Woodley Avenue, Van Nuys, CA 91406
Phone: 818 781-4973   **Fax:** 818 780-3500
Web: www.supind.com

2013 Sales

	$ mil.	% of total
Mexico	503.2	64
US	286.4	36
Total	**789.6**	**100**

PRODUCTS/OPERATIONS

2013 Sales

	% of total
Ford	45
General Motors	24
Chrysler	10
International customers	21
Total	**100**

COMPETITORS

Accuride	Meritor
Alcoa	NGK INSULATORS
American Eagle Wheel	Topy
CRAGAR	YHI
Carlisle Tire & Wheel	wheel pros
Hayes Lemmerz	

HISTORICAL FINANCIALS

Company Type: Public

Income Statement

FYE: December 29

	REVENUE ($ mil.)	NET INCOME ($ mil.)	NET PROFIT MARGIN	EMPLOYEES
12/13	789.5	22.8	2.9%	3,700
12/12	821.4	30.8	3.8%	3,900
12/11	822.1	67.1	8.2%	3,800
12/10	719.5	51.6	7.2%	3,500
12/09	418.8	(94.1)	—	3,500
Annual Growth	**17.2%**	**—**	**—**	**1.4%**

2013 Year-End Financials

Debt ratio: —	No. of shares (mil.): 27
Return on equity: 4.8%	Dividends
Cash ($ mil.): 199	Yield: 0.0%
Current ratio: 3.86	Payout: 2.4%
Long-term debt ($ mil.): —	Market value ($ mil.): 559

	STOCK PRICE ($) FY Close	P/E High/Low		PER SHARE ($) Earnings	Dividends	Book Value
12/13	20.60	26	21	0.83	0.02	17.79
12/12	20.40	18	14	1.13	1.12	17.11
12/11	16.54	10	6	2.46	0.48	16.95
12/10	21.22	11	7	1.93	0.64	15.40
12/09	15.30	—		(3.53)	0.64	14.00
Annual Growth	**7.7%**	**—**		**—**	**(58.0%)**	**6.2%**

Superior Uniform Group, Inc.

Superior Uniform Group works to keep its business all sewn up. The company makes work clothing and accessories for US employees in several industries. The apparel firm designs makes and markets uniforms for employees in the medical and health fields as well as those who work in hotels fast food joints and other restaurants and public safety industrial and commercial markets. About half of its products are sold under the Fashion Seal brand. The company also makes and distributes specialty labels such as Martin's Worklon Blade and UniVogue. Chairman Gerald Benstock and his son CEO Michael run company which began as Superior Surgical Mfg. Co. in 1920.

Geographic Reach

From its headquarters in Florida Superior Uniform serves to outfit companies and customers nationwide boasting manufacturing operations overseas. Suppliers in Central American typically produce more than 50% of the company's products. It operates in El Salvador Costa Rica and the US through its The Office Gurus businesses and an affiliate entity in Belize added to its operations at the end of 2012.

Operations

The company operates its business through two reportable segments: Uniforms and Related Products (97% of sales) and Remote Staffing Solutions which includes The Office Gurus and TOG an affiliate firm that offers cost effective bilingual telemarketing and office support services.

Strategy

Demand for Superior's uniforms and service apparel largely depends on the health of the economy. The economic downturn in the US negatively impacted the uniform supplier's customers who closed locations reduced headcounts or eliminated uniforms to save money.

In addition to the challenging economic climate the dramatic rise in cotton prices has the potential to pinch Superior Uniform's profit margin. While the company has been able to compensate for its higher materials costs by raising prices it warns at times that gross margins could be negatively impacted.

Financial Performance

Due to a boost in market penetration Superior Uniform logged a 6% net sales increase in fiscal 2012 as compared to 2011 across its Uniforms and Related Products unit and 9% from its Remote Staffing Solutions. Net income for the same reporting period declined 27% due to the rising cost of goods sold —primarily related to cotton shortages in the Uniforms and Related Products business — and increasing payroll-related costs across the Remote Staffing Solutions segment.

Company Ownership

The Benstock family owns nearly 23% of the company's shares. Mochelle Stettner holds another 10% stake.

EXECUTIVES

Evp, Peter Benstock, age 53
Vice President Marketing, Ron Klepner
Vice President Operations, Jordan M Alpert
Vice President Design And Merchandising, Lisa Stewart
National Sales Manager, Denise Heinen

Vice President Supply Chain, Charles Sheppard
Assistant Treasurer, Jerry Chiovaro
Auditors: GrantThorntonLLP

LOCATIONS

HQ: Superior Uniform Group, Inc.
10055 Seminole Boulevard, Seminole, FL 33772-2539
Phone: 727 397-9611
Web: www.superioruniform.com

PRODUCTS/OPERATIONS

2012 Sales

	% of total
Uniforms and Related Products	97
Remote Staffing Solutions	6
Net intersegment eliminations	(3)
Total	**100**

Selected Brands

Blade
Fashion Seal
Fashion Seal Healthcare
Martin' s
Worklon
UniVogue

COMPETITORS

ARAMARK	Convergys
Accenture	Fujitsu America
Alsco	G&K Services
Angelica Corporation	Sitel Worldwide
Broder Bros.	StarTek
Capgemini North	Sykes Enterprises
America	TeleTech
Cintas	UniFirst

HISTORICAL FINANCIALS

Company Type: Public

Income Statement

FYE: December 31

	REVENUE ($ mil.)	NET INCOME ($ mil.)	NET PROFIT MARGIN	EMPLOYEES
12/13	151.5	5.8	3.9%	973
12/12	119.4	3.0	2.5%	690
12/11	112.3	4.1	3.7%	647
12/10	105.8	3.8	3.6%	630
12/09	102.8	1.9	1.9%	564
Annual Growth	**10.2%**	**31.3%**	**—**	**14.6%**

2013 Year-End Financials

Debt ratio: 20.9%	No. of shares (mil.): 13
Return on equity: 9.0%	Dividends
Cash ($ mil.): 5	Yield: 4.3%
Current ratio: 4.90	Payout: 73.3%
Long-term debt ($ mil.): 24	Market value ($ mil.): 202

	STOCK PRICE ($) FY Close	P/E High/Low		PER SHARE ($) Earnings	Dividends	Book Value
12/13	15.48	35	22	0.46	0.34	5.52
12/12	11.45	53	42	0.25	0.54	4.72
12/11	12.27	37	30	0.34	0.27	5.09
12/10	11.00	35	27	0.32	0.27	5.13
12/09	9.75	65	31	0.17	0.27	5.08
Annual Growth	**12.3%**	**—**		**29.2%**	**5.7%**	**2.1%**

support.com, Inc.

Support.com wants to be a pillar of tech support. The company's cloud-based Nexus platform proactively identifies and repairs hardware and software problems reducing the need for technical support staffing. It also specializes in phone and Web support for a wide variety of technology issues related to computer security data recovery networking file management and software installation. Support.com serves consumers and small businesses with its offerings available through its website and through partners such as retailers broadband providers and anti-virus software providers. Nearly all sales come from customers in the Americas.

Geographic Reach

Support.com has locations in California Oregon and Washington. It also has an international location in India. Most of its staff work from home rather than in company facilities.

Sales and Marketing

Support.com markets its services primarily through channel partners. Its partners include communications providers retailers technology companies and others. It markets its end-user software products directly principally online and through partners. Its sales and marketing efforts are primarily focused in North America.

The company depends upon a concentrated amount of customers. In 2012 its four biggest customers included Comcast (35% of total revenue) OfficeMax (12%) Office Depot (12%) and Staples (10%).

Financial Performance

In spite of significant sales growth the company has been unprofitable since inception. Revenues jumped 34% from $54 million in 2011 to reach a historical high of $72 million in 2012. The company posted a net loss of $5 million in 2012 which was noticeably less than the $19 million net loss it posted the previous year.

The exceptional growth for 2012 was driven by a 55% surge in services revenue due to growth in its channel programs and the continued expansion of its Comcast program.

Strategy

Support.com's strategies for achieving growth include expanding its existing service programs launching new programs growing small business revenue increasing SaaS revenue from its Nexus product and improving service delivery efficiency.

To achieve these goals the company is partnering with other companies and using acquisitions. In 2012 it deepened its small business expertise through the purchase of RightHand IT Corporation a managed service provider for small businesses. In 2011 Support.com picked up consumer-focused software developer SUPERAntiSpyware for $8.5 million. SUPERAntiSpyware's namesake application is used to detect and remove adware Trojans worms keyloggers root-kits hijackers parasites dialers and other mal-ware from PC's.

Ownership

RGM Capital and its affiliates own 14% of Support.com.

EXECUTIVES

Vp Marketing, Amy Millard
Vice President Contact Center, Ernest Carapetian
Vp Associate General Counsel, Maurice Leibenstern
Vice President Of Engineering, Doug Collier
Vice President Corporate Developeent, Eleanor Lacey
Vice President, Mark Forrest
Auditors: Ernst&YoungLLP

LOCATIONS

HQ: support.com, Inc.
900 Chesapeake Drive, 2nd Floor, Redwood City, CA 94063
Phone: 650 556-9440
Web: www.support.com

PRODUCTS/OPERATIONS

2012 Sales

	$ mil.	% of total
Services	57.6	80
Software & other	14.4	20
Total	**72.0**	**100**

Selected Software

Broadband service and installation support (Broadband Resolution Suite)
Self-service customer support (Satisfaction Suite)
Technical support (Resolution Suite)

Selected Services

Consulting
Installation and deployment
Technical support
Training

COMPETITORS

Alcatel-Lucent	Motive Inc.
BMC Software	Noble Iron
CA Inc.	Symantec
Hewlett-Packard	TriActive
KANA	eGain

HISTORICAL FINANCIALS

Company Type: Public

Income Statement

FYE: December 31

	REVENUE ($ mil.)	NET INCOME ($ mil.)	NET PROFIT MARGIN	EMPLOYEES
12/13	88.1	10.3	11.8%	1,344
12/12	71.9	(5.4)	—	877
12/11	53.8	(18.6)	—	1,137
12/10	44.1	(18.0)	—	761
12/09	17.5	(14.5)	—	420
Annual Growth	**49.8%**	**—**	**—**	**33.7%**

2013 Year-End Financials

Debt ratio: —
Return on equity: 12.2%
Cash ($ mil.): 28
Current ratio: 9.04
Long-term debt ($ mil.): —
No. of shares (mil.): 53
Dividends
Yield: —
Payout: —
Market value ($ mil.): 202

	STOCK PRICE ($) FY Close	P/E High/Low		PER SHARE ($) Earnings	Dividends	Book Value
12/13	3.79	31 17		0.19	0.00	1.79
12/12	4.17	— —		(0.11)	0.00	1.49
12/11	2.25	— —		(0.39)	0.00	1.47
12/10	6.48	— —		(0.39)	0.00	1.79
12/09	2.64	— —		(0.31)	0.00	2.07
Annual Growth	**9.5%**	**— —**		**—**	**—**	**(3.6%)**

Supreme Industries, Inc.

Supreme Industries keeps businesses rolling on the road. The company builds and distributes specialized commercial truck bodies and buses such as armored trucks dry-freight and insulated cargo vans service vans shuttle buses and trolleys. Its custom-made options include cargo-handling devices lift gates refrigeration equipment and special doors and bumpers. Supreme Industries sells its lineup under the Kold King Iner-City Spartan StarTrans and other brand names. In addition to vehicle bodies which represent most sales the company makes Fuel Shark branded fiberglass wind deflectors. Supreme Industries' customers are truck distributors commercial dealers and end-users mainly in the US.

Geographic Reach

Headquartered at Goshen Indiana Supreme Industries has service centers in Rhode Island and Colorado. Its manufacturing facilities are located in Indiana (Goshen and Ligonier) Georgia Texas California and Pennsylvania.

Operations

The company has two operating segments: specialized vehicles (99% of sales) and fiberglass products (1%). Specialized vehicles is operated by Supreme Corporation a wholly-owned subsidiary that makes customized truck bodies buses and other specialty vehicles such as customized armored vehicles and homeland response vehicles. The other segment sells fiberglass reinforced plywood to Supreme for use in the production of certain of its truck bodies and to third parties.

Sales and Marketing

Supreme Industries uses a nationwide direct sales and distribution network consisting of approximately 25 bus distributors a limited number of truck equipment distributors and approximately 1000 commercial truck dealers in order to sell its products throughout North America.Its major customers include Penske (accounted for 20% of revenue in 2012) Budget GE Fleet Service Rent-A-Center Safeway Scotts and Tru Green.

Financial Performance

After experiencing two straight years of growth Supreme Industries saw its revenues fall 5% from $300 million in 2011 to $286 million in 2012. The decline was driven by drops in sales for trucks (3%) buses (9%) and armored vehicles (13%). The decreases stemmed from lower sales from armored vehicles as a result of lower government procurements. Bus division sales also decreased in 2012 as the core market continued to feel the effects of tightened municipal and state budgets.

Despite the revenue dip Supreme Industries saw its profits skyrocket from less than $1 million in 2011 to nearly $12 million in 2012. This huge increase was due to a decrease in interest expenses resulted from a combination of lower average bank borrowings and lower (performance-based) borrowing rates during 2012. The company was also helped by no legal settlement and related costs.

Strategy

Supreme Industries is focusing on new product offerings technology and sales force development to help refill its coffers. It has expanded and streamlined production of truck bodies for shuttle buses commercial dry-freight vans and armored suburban vehicles. Company R&D is emphasizing green materials too. Supreme Industries launched

Aero-Body a van body used with Isuzu's ECO-MAX chassis touted as functional more fuel efficient yet durable. In addition sales also are buoyed by a five-year contract awarded by the US State Department to produce up to $100 million armor-plated vehicles.

In late 2013 Supreme Industries announced plans to divest its shuttle-bus business. As a proportion of revenue mix bus products have represented a declining percentage of sales for the company and divesting the operations will allow it to concentrate on more profitable markets with on-going opportunities for growth.

EXECUTIVES

Vice President Human Resources, Brad Karch
Vice President And General Counsel, John Dorbin
Chief Financial Officer And Vice President, Jeff Mowery
Vice President, Rick Pippenger
Auditors: CroweHorwathLLP

LOCATIONS

HQ: Supreme Industries, Inc.
2581 E. Kercher Road, Goshen, IN 46528
Phone: 574 642-3070   **Fax:** 574 642-3208
Web: www.supremeind.com

PRODUCTS/OPERATIONS

2012 Sales

	$ mil.	% of total
Trucks	212.0	74
Buses	55.0	19
Armored vehicles	16.1	6
Composites	3.0	1
Total	**286.1**	**100**

Selected Products

Armored SUVs
Armored trucks and specialty vehicles
Iner-City cutaway van bodies
Kold King insulated van bodies
Mid-size buses
Shuttle buses
Signature Van bodies
Spartan cargo vans
Spartan service bodies
Stake bodies
Trolleys

COMPETITORS

All American Group	Oshkosh Truck
Collins Industries	Thor Industries
Daimler Buses	Utilimaster

HISTORICAL FINANCIALS

Company Type: Public

Income Statement

FYE: December 28

	REVENUE ($ mil.)	NET INCOME ($ mil.)	NET PROFIT MARGIN	EMPLOYEES
12/13	282.2	6.4	2.3%	1,700
12/12	286.1	11.8	4.1%	1,500
12/11	300.8	0.6	0.2%	1,700
12/10	220.8	(11.5)	—	1,700
12/09	192.0	(8.7)	—	1,400
Annual Growth	**10.1%**	**—**	**—**	**5.0%**

2013 Year-End Financials

Debt ratio: 8.5%
Return on equity: 9.1%
Cash ($ mil.): 3
Current ratio: 2.33
Long-term debt ($ mil.): 9

No. of shares (mil.): 16
Dividends
    Yield: —
    Payout: 51.5%
Market value ($ mil.): 90

	STOCK PRICE ($) FY Close	P/E High/Low		PER SHARE ($) Earnings	Dividends	Book Value
12/13	5.59	17	8	0.39	0.00	4.59
12/12	3.43	6	3	0.73	0.00	4.20
12/11	2.51	73	39	0.05	0.00	3.56
12/10	2.75	—	—	(0.77)	0.00	3.45
12/09	1.86	—	—	(0.59)	0.00	4.19
Annual Growth	**31.7%**			**—**	**—**	**2.3%**

SVB Financial Group

SVB Financial Group is the holding company for Silicon Valley Bank which serves emerging and established companies involved in technology life sciences and private equity and provides customized financing to entrepreneurs executives and investors in such industries. It also offers deposit accounts loans and international banking and plays matchmaker for young firms and private investors. SVB Financial also provides investment advisory brokerage and asset management services; and provides credit and banking services to wealthy individuals.

Geographic Reach
SVB Financial has 28 offices in the US as well as seven branches in China India Israel and the UK.

Operations
The company operates in three segments: Global Commercial Bank SVB Private Bank and SVB Capital.

Global Commercial Bank segment is comprised of Commercial Bank SVB Specialty Lending SVB Analytics and Debt Fund Investments. Commercial Bank serves commercial clients in the technology venture capital/private equity life science and cleantech industries. SVB Analytics provides equity valuation services to private companies and venture capital/private equity firms while Debt Fund Investments has investments in debt funds.

SVB Private Bank provides personal financial solutions for consumers.

SVB Capital SVB Financial's capital arm focuses primarily on funds management.

Sales and Marketing
SVB Financial's clients are primarily venture capital and private equity professionals. Its customers include Active Power Coskata EnerNOC Joule and Solexant.

Financial Performance
The company's revenues grew by 4% in 2012 due to a rise in total interest income (stemming from an increase in loans and an increase in taxable available-for-sale securities) partially offset by decline in total non-interest income. SVB Financial's net income increased by 2% as the result of a decrease in interest expenses attributed to decline in deposits and borrowings expenses partially offset by higher non-interest income costs.

Strategy
Looking to grow via international expansion in 2012 the company opened a banking branch in the UK as well as a joint venture bank in China.

Greg Becker who joined SVB Financial in 1993 was named the company's CEO in 2011. He succeeded Ken Wilcox who became chairman and is focused on the company's efforts to expand in China including a joint venture with Shanghai Pudong Development Bank.

As part of its lending activities Silicon Valley Bank sometimes pursues warrants to purchase equity stakes in its clients. About 80% of the bank's loan portfolio is dedicated to business loans. Traditionally focused on up-and-coming firms the bank has implemented a strategy of courting larger later-stage clients.

Company Background
The company was established in 1983.

HISTORY

Silicon Valley Bank was founded in 1983 by Roger Smith to provide banking services to tech startups in San Jose. The bank boomed along with tech companies during the 1980s lending to the likes of Cisco Systems.

In 1990 the bank spread east to Boston's burgeoning technology alley. It also expanded into residential and commercial real estate lending. The recession of 1989 to 1991 found Silicon Valley Bancshares with an overextended loan portfolio and in 1992 the bank booked a loss due to nonperforming loans; the next year it was put under federal supervision.

To rally stockholder confidence the company brought in new management and demoted Smith from chairman to vice chairman; he left the in 1995. The bank reduced its real estate lending and diversified into factoring foreign exchange and executive banking for venture capitalists and clients' upper management.

The 1995 IPO frenzy aided the company's turnaround. Silicon Valley cashed in on warrants it had taken as collateral from young companies. Regulatory supervision was lifted in 1996 and the bank soon opened offices in the Atlanta; Austin Texas; Boulder Colorado; Phoenix; and Seattle areas.

In 1999 Silicon Valley Bancshares created a website targeted at technology firms in need of financing employees office space and equipment. However nonperforming loans began to dog the bank once again affecting profits and bringing a regulatory request to boost capital reserves.

In 2000 despite being hammered by the high-tech stock selloff the company continued to expand opening offices in West Palm Beach Florida and North Carolina's Research Triangle and successfully capitalizing its first venture fund. The following year it bought tech-focused investment bank Alliant Partners (later renamed SVB Alliant) to broaden its service offerings.

Still licking its wounds from the tech bust the company ceased lending to the entertainment industry and to churches in 2002. Silicon Valley Bancshares changed its name to SVB Financial Services in 2005.

SVB Alliant struggled with losses for years and SVB Financial explored its options including spinning the unit off to management. It ultimately decided to shut down the division which ceased operations in 2008.

EXECUTIVES

Chief Strategy and Risk Officer, Marc J. Verissimo, age 59, $310,679 total compensation
President Asia, David A. Jones, age 56, $431,447 total compensation
COO and Principal Operating Officer, Bruce Wallace, $398,113 total compensation
President and CEO Silicon Valley Bank, Gregory W. (Greg) Becker, age 47, $835,613 total compensation

Chief Banking Officer Commercial Banking Silicon Valley Bank, Joan Parsons, $399,780 total compensation

CFO, Michael (Mike) Descheneaux, age 47, $499,780 total compensation

Head Relationship Management, John D. China, $373,113 total compensation

Head EMEA and India; President UK Branch, Phil Cox

Chief Credit Officer Silicon Valley Bank, Marc Cadieux

CIO, Beth Devin

Senior Vice President And Senior, Dan Aguilar

Vice President Relationship Manager Co, Ray Aguilar

Assistant Vice President Letter Of Credit Consultant Senior, John Dossantos

Executive Vice President Information Systems, Robert Potts

Senior Vice President Svb Financial Group Uk, Andy Tsao

Vice President, Arman Zand

Vice President, Rob Freelen

Vice President, Rick Shuttleworth

Vice President, Nick Honigman

Vice President, Steven Reel

Assistant Vice President Director Cmpl, Karen Murray

Senior Vice President, Dave Bhagat

Vice President, Christopher Leary

Executive Vice President, Win Bear

Vice President, Jocelyn Hartmann

Senior Vice President Senior Loan Workout Advisor, Brian Bell

Vice President Relationship Manager, Anthony Raley

Vice President, Kyle Swan

Vice President, Thomas Armstrong

Vice President, Patrick Scheper

Vice President, Suzann Russell

Vice President Manager Of Sales And Business Product Management, Dennis Corbett

Vice President Relationship Manager Corporate Technology, Phil Silvia

Senior Vice President Producer, Joe Wolf

Vice President, Reisa Babic

Vice President, Alex McCracken

Vice President Product Management, Susan Merrill

Senior Vice President And Senior Relationship Manager, Matt Maloney

Vice President, Joe Werner

Vice President, Damarie Rodriguez

Vice President, Amber Scarchilli

Vice President Of Information Technology, Derrick Ponugoti

Vice President Vcrm, Sam Warburg

Vice President Relationship Manager, Bret Turner

Vice President And Relationship Manager, Adam Millsom

Vice President Relationship Manager, Mimi Stover

Vice President And Relationship Manage, Julia Bobrovich

Vice President, Brad Miller

Executive Vice President Producer, Blaine Trunnell

Vice President Executive Banking, Connie English

Vice President, Katrina Young

Vice President Regional Director, Carmella Montesdeoca

Vice President Operations, Julie Robertson

Vice President Svb Mezzanine Finance, Brendan Quinn

Vice President Relationship Manager, John Peck

Senior Vice President, Laura Scott

Vice President Portfolio Manager, Jay Tracy

Vice President, Josh Dorsey

Vice President Compliance Manager, Mary McGuirk

First Vice President Account Executive, Marilyn Schley

Senior Vice President, Michael Tramack

Vice President Manager Def, Kathleen Monahan

Vice President Employee Benefits Group, Chris Reynen

Vice President Regional Market Manager, John Atanasoff

Vice President, Lauren Cole

Vp, Shawn Parry

Vice President Relationship Manager, Erin Broderick

Deal Team Leader Senior Vice President, Blake English

Vice President ?? Sponsor Finance, Mounir Gad

Vice President Structured Finance, Michael Kalicak

Vice President I Cfd, Ashlee Kaji

Vice President, Donna Kelley

Vice President, Dan Hardman

Vice President I Corporate Fin, Alina Zinchik

Vice President, Gregory Peterson

Vice President I Corporate Fin, Andrea Jones

Vice President, Nicholas Currie

Vice President Global Markets, Kristina Oliver

Assistant Vice President, Brian Harrison

Chairman, Roger F. Dunbar, age 68

Credit Risk Officer, Derek Ridgley

Assistant Secretary And Treasurer, Lori De Leon

Senior Treasury Analyst, Logan Hurst

Auditors: KPMGLLP

LOCATIONS

HQ: SVB Financial Group
3003 Tasman Drive, Santa Clara, CA 95054-1191
Phone: 408 654-7400
Web: www.svb.com
US
  Atlanta
  Austin TX
  Broomfield CO
  Chicago
  Dallas
  Irvine CA
  Menlo Park CA
  Minnetonka MN
  New York
  Newton MA
  Palo Alto CA
  Philadelphia
  Phoenix
  Pleasanton CA
  Portland OR
  Raleigh NC
  Salt Lake City
  San Diego
  San Francisco
  Santa Rosa CA
  Seattle
  St. Helena CA
  Tysons Corner VA
International
  Bangalore India
  Beijing
  Herzliya Pituach Israel
  London
  Mumbai India
  Shanghai

PRODUCTS/OPERATIONS

2012 Sales

	$ mil.	% of total
Interest		
Loans	469.2	48
Taxable securities	171.9	18
Other	7.7	—
Noninterest		
Net gains on investment securities	122.1	12
Foreign exchange fees	49.0	5
Deposit service charges	33.4	3
Credit card fees	24.8	3
Net gains on derivative instruments	22.1	2
Letters of credit	15.2	2
Client investment fees	14.5	1
Other	54.4	6
Total	**984.3**	**100**

Selected Subsidiaries and Affiliates

Silicon Valley Bank
SVB Analytics Inc.
SVB Asset Management
SVB Business Partners (Beijing) Co. Ltd.
SVB Business Partners (Shanghai) Co. Ltd.
SVB Global Financial Inc.
SVB Global Investors LLC
SVB Growth Investors LLC
SVB India Advisors Pvt. Ltd.
SVB Israel Advisors Ltd.
SVB Qualified Investors Fund LLC
SVB Real Estate Investment Trust
SVB Securities
SVB Strategic Investors LLC
SVB Strategic Investors Fund L.P.
Venture Investment Managers L.P.

COMPETITORS

BancWest	City National
Bank of America	Comerica
Bridge Capital	Heritage Commerce
Holdings	MUFG Americas Holdings
Citigroup	U.S. Bancorp

HISTORICAL FINANCIALS

Company Type: Public

Income Statement

FYE: December 31

	ASSETS ($ mil.)	NET INCOME ($ mil.)	INCOME AS % OF ASSETS	EMPLOYEES
12/13	26,417.1	546.1	2.1%	1,704
12/12	22,766.1	175.1	0.8%	1,615
12/11	19,968.8	171.9	0.9%	1,526
12/10	17,527.7	94.9	0.5%	1,357
12/09	12,841.4	48.0	0.4%	1,258
Annual Growth	19.8%	83.6%	—	7.9%

2013 Year-End Financials

Return on assets: 2.2%
Return on equity: 28.7%
Long-term debt ($ mil.): —
No. of shares (mil.): 45
Sales ($ mil): 1,402
Dividends
  Yield: —
  Payout: —
Market value ($ mil.): 4,803

	STOCK PRICE ($) FY Close	P/E High/Low	PER SHARE ($) Earnings	Dividends	Book Value
12/13	104.86	22 12	4.70	0.00	42.93
12/12	55.97	17 12	3.91	0.00	41.02
12/11	47.69	16 9	3.94	0.00	36.07
12/10	53.05	24 16	2.24	0.00	30.15
12/09	41.66	68 18	0.66	0.00	27.30
Annual Growth	26.0%	— —	63.4%	—	12.0%

Sykes Enterprises, Inc.

When that software won't install Sykes can take your call. Sykes Enterprises operates more than 80 technical help and customer support centers in 24 countries across Africa the Americas Asia and Europe that use phone e-mail and chat to serve those in need of help. Sykes specializes in customer service and inbound technical support and also provides large corporations with technical staffing and consulting relating to customer relationship management. Sykes predominantly serves the communications consumer financial services and technology industries.

Geographic Reach

Sykes is very international in its scope. The company operates in 24 countries around the world with facilities in North America South America Africa Asia Australia and Europe. The Americas segment contributed 84% of total revenue while the EMEA segment contributed 16% of total revenue in 2012.

Operations

The company has operations in two reportable segments. The Americas segment includes the US Canada Latin America India and the Asia Pacific Rim. The company's EMEA segment includes Europe the Middle East and Africa.

Sales from the communications industry account for 31% of revenue while financial services generates 30%. Other markets include technology and consumer (16%) transportation and leisure (9%) health care (8%) retail (2%) and others (4%).

Sales and Marketing

Sykes' experience and depth in international operations serves the company well as customers worldwide continue to shift outsourced CRM teleservices overseas to markets with cheaper labor pools. AT&T accounted for $133.1 million or 12% of its consolidated revenue for 2012.

Financial Performance

After experiencing an upward trend in revenue the year before Sykes saw its revenues fall by 4% from $1.17 billion in 2011 to $1.13 billion in 2012. Its profits also declined by 41% from $48.3 million in 2011 to $28.4 million in 2012.

The company was stung by a 12% drop in sales from its EMEA segment and a 2% decline in sales from the Americas during 2012. This was due to the ending of client contracts and lower volumes of existing contracts. The profit erosion was attributed to a loss from discontinued operations and a loss on the disposal of property and equipment.

Strategy

Like most companies in the industry Sykes' efforts to cut costs have included layoffs and call center closures. In 2012 it sold its Spanish operations to Iberphone S.A.U. (It suffered a loss on the sale of nearly $11 million.)

However the company's overall growth strategy includes adding to its call center seat capacity and expanding the number of service lines and markets it serves internationally. Sykes recently entered the market in Brazil Romania Egypt and El Salvador.

The company hopes to nurture long-term client relationships as it expands both organically and through acquisitions. Sykes has also been seeking to establish strategic technology partnerships with other organizations.Mergers and Acquisitions

The company completed its $150 million acquisition of Alpine Access in August 2012. The deal fit in with company's strategy of staying focused within the core customer contact management industry. The acquisition bolstered the company's service portfolio and go-to-market offering.

Company Background

Former chairman and CEO John Sykes founded the company in 1977. His son Charles Sykes now leads the company as president and CEO.

HISTORY

Originally based in North Carolina Sykes Enterprises was founded in 1977 to provide design and engineering services; it often acted as a temp agency for technical professionals. In 1992 Sykes' merger with programming firm Forrest Ford Consultants boosted the company's software services division. The big shift came in 1993 when Sykes moved its headquarters to Florida and refocused its operations on information technology outsourcing services. The company opened two call centers in 1994 and added two more the following year. It went public in 1996.

Targeting Europe as a market for growth Sykes acquired Scotland's McQueen International Limited Germany's Telcare and TAS —all technical support companies —in 1997. In 1998 the company started its employee benefits administration joint venture with HealthPlan Services and soon bought out its partner's interest (it sold all but 7% in 2000 to investment firm Welsh Carson Anderson & Stowe).

In early 2000 the company restated 1999 second and third quarter earnings due to irregularities related to delays in the recognition of software revenues. A class-action shareholder lawsuit followed the announcement. In 2001 Iain Macdonald resigned from the board of directors. Founder chairman and CEO John Sykes retired from the company in 2004; his son Charles Sykes was appointed president and CEO.

Sykes acquired an Argentina-based operator of call centers Centro de Interaccion Multimedia SA (known as Apex) for $27 million in 2006. It also sold its SHPS subsidiary which provided employee benefits administration services to health care industry investment firm Welsh Carson Anderson & Stowe.

After years of focusing on its core business and reducing costs the company acquired rival ICT Group in early 2010.

EXECUTIVES

EVP General Counsel and Corporate Secretary, James T. Holder, age 55, $306,342 total compensation

EVP Human Resources, Jenna R. Nelson, age 50

EVP and CFO, W. Michael Kipphut, age 60, $413,210 total compensation

President and CEO, Charles E. (Chuck) Sykes, age 51, $624,998 total compensation

EVP of Global Strategy, Daniel L. Hernandez, age 47

EVP and CIO, David L. Pearson, age 55, $234,765 total compensation

EVP and GM, Lawrence R. (Lance) Zingale, age 58, $306,342 total compensation

CEO, Christopher Carrington

EVP and CFO, John Chapman

Vice President Global Account, Wendi Summers

Vice President President, Flora Solera

Vice President Client Services, Chris Monnette

Vice President Operations, Pat Magee

Vice President Finance, Leah Miele

Senior Vice President Regional Ops Apac, Mike Henderson

Vice President Of Call Center, Denis Thibodeau

Senior Vice President Global Sales And Client Management, Lance Zingale

Vice President Of Sales And Client Management, Pat Mallon

Executive Assistant To Executive Vice President And General Counsel, Ronda Parris

Senior Vice President Global Payroll, Judi Plumley

Vice President Asia Pacific Sales, Sal Giordano

Vice President Of Marketing, Michael Clarkin

Gvp Learning And Platforms, John Kruper

Executive Assistant To Executive Vice President And General Manager Major Markets, Judi McKenna

Vice President Global Operations, Lynn Loefgren

Global Vice President Strategy, Charles Callari

Senior Vice President And General Manager C And I Services, Mark Sobieski

Vice President Sales And Operations, Todd Aldrich

Executive Vice President Global Human Resources, Caleb Christy

Chairman, Paul L. Whiting, age 70

CEO, Christopher Carrington

Advisory Board Member, Jennifer Grant

Auditors: Deloitte&ToucheLLP

LOCATIONS

HQ: Sykes Enterprises, Inc.
400 North Ashley Drive, Suite 2800, Tampa, FL 33602
Phone: 813 274-1000   **Fax:** 813 273-0148
Web: www.sykes.com

PRODUCTS/OPERATIONS

2012 Sales

	$ mil.	% of total
Americas	947.1	84
EMEA	180.6	16
Total	**1127.7**	**100**

Selected Mergers and Acquisitions

FY2012
   Alpine Access ($150 million; Denver CO; call center service)
FY2010
   ICT Group ($263 million; Newtown PA; call centers)

COMPETITORS

24/7 Customer	HP Enterprise Services
APAC Customer Services	IBM
Accenture	Infosys
Aegis Communications	NTT Data
Amdocs	Sitel Worldwide
Arise Virtual Solutions	StarTek
	Stefanini
Atento Brasil	Stream Global Services
Atos	Sutherland Global Services
Computer Generated Solutions	TRG Customer Solutions
Computer Sciences Corp.	TeleTech
Concentrix	Teleperformance
Convergys	West Corporation
DecisionOne	Wipro Infotech
Expert Global Solutions	vCustomer

HISTORICAL FINANCIALS

Company Type: Public

Income Statement

FYE: December 31

	REVENUE ($ mil.)	NET INCOME ($ mil.)	NET PROFIT MARGIN	EMPLOYEES
12/13	1,263.4	37.2	2.9%	47,900
12/12	1,127.7	28.4	2.5%	46,200
12/11	1,169.2	48.3	4.1%	41,000
12/10	1,158.7	(10.2)	—	43,400
12/09	846.0	43.2	5.1%	49,200
Annual Growth	**10.5%**	**(3.6%)**	**—**	**(0.7%)**

2013 Year-End Financials

Debt ratio: 10.3%	No. of shares (mil.): 43
Return on equity: 6.0%	Dividends
Cash ($ mil.): 211	Yield: —
Current ratio: 2.96	Payout: —
Long-term debt ($ mil.): 98	Market value ($ mil.): 957

STOCK PRICE ($)		P/E		PER SHARE ($)		
	FY Close	High/Low		Earnings	Dividends	Book Value
12/13	21.81	25	16	0.87	0.00	14.49
12/12	15.22	28	20	0.66	0.00	13.88
12/11	15.66	21	11	1.06	0.00	13.03
12/10	20.26	—	—	(0.22)	0.00	12.41
12/09	25.47	25	13	1.05	0.00	10.86
Annual Growth	(3.8%)	—	—	(4.6%)	—	7.5%

Synaptics Inc

Synaptics keeps you in touch with your electronics. The company's human interface products are sold to contract manufacturers for use in mobile phones (more than half of sales) notebook and handheld computers and other mobile electronic devices. Its TouchPad product can be used in peripherals such as monitors and remote controls; ClickPad replaces a mouse for notebook PCs and netbooks; and ClearPad provides touchscreen control for various mobile devices. Synaptics also relies on contract manufacturers to make its products. Most sales go to manufacturers in Asia more than two thirds in China. US customers provide 10% of sales.

Geographic Reach

Based in the US the company also operates in Hong Kong India China Taiwan and Japan.

Operations

Synaptics' technology engineering and product design functions in the US Taiwan Hong Kong Korea Japan India and China incurred $192.7 million of expenses in fiscal 2014.

Sales and Marketing

As consumers shift to mobile computing products used in PCs have been edged out as Synaptics' largest source of revenues. End users of its products include OEM customers such as Dell Hewlett-Packard Lenovo and Toshiba. Some of its contract manufacturing customers include Compal Electronics Flextronics and Wistron.

Financial Performance

Synaptics' reported its highest revenues in fiscal 2014 (some 43% up on 2013) driven by higher sales in its Mobile product applications (up 63% over fiscal 2013 together with increase of 8% in its PC product applications revenues.Net income fell by $52.2 million to $46.7 million in fiscal 2014 due to an increase in operating expenses including Selling general and administrative (which increased by $20 million) while its contingent consideration grew $68.5 million thanks to the increase in the estimated fair value of the contingent consideration liability related to the Validity acquisition. These were partially offset by an increase in sales.Synaptics' cash flow in operating activities in fiscal 2014 was $131.6 million a $29.4 million increase on 2013 driven by net income of $46.7 million plus adjustments for non-cash charges including accretion and re-measurement of the contingent consideration liability of $69.9 million share-based compensation costs of $32.8 million depreciation and amortization of $14.2 million other non-cash adjustments of $18.6 million and a net change in operating assets and liabilities of $50.8 million.

Strategy

Synaptics is expanding by adding applications such as home appliances for its touchpads as well as developing interface technologies such as proximity sensing which uses sensors to detect the presence of a user and activate certain functions.

During 2014 the company partnered with Microsoft to bring precision TouchPad technology to the Surface Pro 3 Tablet.

Mergers and Acquisitions

In 2014 the company announced plans to acquire Renesas SP Drivers the industry leader in small and medium-sized display driver ICs for smart phones and tablets to increase its addressable market opportunity by 1.5X and to accelerate its product roadmap for touch-and-display driver integration.

To gain access to the fast-growing biometrics market in 2013 Synaptics acquired Validity Sensors (a leading provider of biometric fingerprint authentication solutions for smartphones tablets and notebook PCs) for $127.8 million.

Company Background

The company is a founding member of the Open Handset Alliance an industry group utilizing the Android mobile device operating system software created by Google. The Nexus One smartphone unveiled by Google in 2010 used a ClearPad 2000 capacitive touchscreen sensor supplied by Synaptics.

EXECUTIVES

Senior Vice President Worldwide Sales, Scott Deutsch
Senior Vice President, Kathleen Bayless
Senior Vice President and General Manager Smart Display Division (SDD), Kevin D. Barber, age 54, $300,000 total compensation
Senior Vice President of Advanced Development and CTO, Stanley (Stan) Swearingen, age 55
Senior Vice President of Worldwide Operations, Alex H.C. Wong, age 59, $190,000 total compensation
President CEO and Director, Richard A. (Rick) Bergman, age 50, $600,000 total compensation
Senior Vice President of Silicon Engineering, David Wang, $247,884 total compensation
Vice President Of Operations, Hing Wong
Vice President Marketing, Brian Daly
Vice President Thintouch, Shawn Liu
Vice President Marketing And Product Management, Art Stewart
Vice President Engineering Desktop, Nuri Dagdeviren
Vice President General Manager Pc, Donald Kirby
Senior Vice President General Counsel Secretary, John McFarland
Chairman, Francis F. Lee, age 62
President CEO and Director, Richard A. (Rick) Bergman, age 50
Board Member, James Whims
Board Member, Nelson Chan
Board Member, Jeffrey Buchanan
Board Member, Richard Sanquini
Board Member, Keith B Geeslin
Auditors: KPMGLLP

LOCATIONS

HQ: Synaptics Inc
1251 McKay Drive, San Jose, CA 95131
Phone: 408 904-1100
Web: www.synaptics.com

2014 Sales

	$ mil.	% of total
China	449.4	47
South Korea	233.9	25
Taiwan	118.8	12
United States	93.8	10
Japan	45	5
Other	6.6	1
Total	**947.5**	**100**

PRODUCTS/OPERATIONS

2014 Sales

	$ mil.	% of total
Mobile product applications	689.9	73
PC applications	257.6	27
Total	**947.5**	**100**

Selected Products

ClearButtons (Sensor for scrolling and buttons)
ClearPad (Touch sensor for displays)
ClickPad (Click-enabled notebook computer cursor control pad)
Dual Pointing (Notebook computer cursor control stick and pad)
FlexPad (TouchPad functionality for conventional keyboards)
NavPoint (TouchPad functionality for handheld form factors)
OneTouch (Enablement of technology at customer level)
TouchPad (Notebook computer cursor control pad)
TouchStyk (Notebook computer cursor control stick)
TouchButtons (Capacitive alternative to mechanical button and scrolling controls)

COMPETITORS

Alps Electric	Interlink Electronics
Atmel	Key Tronic
CTS Corp.	Logitech
Communication	Microsoft
Intelligence Corp.	Panasonic Corp
Cypress Semiconductor	Wacom
Elo Touch Solutions	

HISTORICAL FINANCIALS

Company Type: Public

Income Statement

FYE: June 28

	REVENUE ($ mil.)	NET INCOME ($ mil.)	NET PROFIT MARGIN	EMPLOYEES
06/14	947.5	46.6	4.9%	1,230
06/13	663.5	98.9	14.9%	852
06/12	548.2	54.1	9.9%	697
06/11	598.5	63.8	10.7%	676
06/10	514.8	52.9	10.3%	586
Annual Growth	**16.5%**	**(3.1%)**	**—**	**20.4%**

2014 Year-End Financials

Debt ratio: —
Return on equity: 7.6%
Cash ($ mil.): 447
Current ratio: 2.92
Long-term debt ($ mil.): —
No. of shares (mil.): 36
Dividends
  Yield: —
  Payout: —
Market value ($ mil.): 3,295

	STOCK PRICE ($)	P/E		PER SHARE ($)		
	FY Close	High/Low		Earnings	Dividends	Book Value
06/14	89.38	68	29	1.26	0.00	19.02
06/13	38.56	15	7	2.89	0.00	15.68
06/12	28.63	24	14	1.57	0.00	12.06
06/11	25.02	18	13	1.80	0.00	10.16
06/10	28.28	25	13	1.50	0.00	8.42
Annual Growth	**33.3%**	**—**	**—**	**(4.3%)**	**—**	**22.6%**

Synchronoss Technologies Inc

Synchronoss Technologies helps telephone companies synch up a variety of customer service efforts. The company provides hosted software and services that communications service providers use to manage tasks such as phone service activation account changes and customer transactions including credit card billing inventory management and trouble ticketing. Customers include service providers such as AT&T Mobility Level 3 Time Warner Cable Verizon and Vodafone as well as equipment manufacturers such as Apple Dell and Sony. Synchronoss was founded in 2001.

Geographic Reach

The company is headquartered in Bridgewater New Jersey and operates research and development facilities in Bethlehem Pennsylvania and Galway Ireland. It also has regional US offices in Chicago Denver Tucson Arizona; Fairpoint New York; Bellevue and Seattle Washington; and San Jose California as well as international offices in Germany the UK India and Australia.

Sales and Marketing

Synchronoss is heavily dependent on its largest customer AT&T which accounted for 46% of the company's sales in 2012. The company's five largest customers (AT&T Level 3 Time Warner Cable Verizon and Vodafone) combined accounted for about 76% of its total revenues the same year. Reliance on a relatively small number of customers for a majority of sales can be risky for companies such as Synchronoss as the loss of a single customer can dramatically impact sales. To that end Synchronoss has in recent years been working to diversify its customer base which has grown past its core base of telecom service providers to include mobile device makers like Apple and Nokia.

Financial Performance

The company's revenue was up 19% in 2012 driven by the expansion of its professional services to existing customers and an increase in licensing revenue for the company's cloud-based services. Higher revenues that year also helped drive Synchronoss' net income up 79%.

Strategy

While the majority of its sales come from North America Synchronoss has announced strategic plans to expand its international sales with a focus on Europe Latin America and Asia-Pacific. In early 2012 the company paid more than $45 million for France-based Miyowa which provides social network and messaging software for mobile devices. Miyowa's customers include Orange and ZTE. The company also made a handful of other acquisitions in 2012 —including SpeechCycle Spatial Systems Nominees PTY Ltd. and Newbay Software —that bolstered its operations in Europe and the Asia-Pacific region.

Mergers and Acquisitions

In 2012 Synchronoss acquired France-based Miyowa a provider of social network and messaging software for mobile devices for $45 million. The same year Synchronoss acquired SpeechCycle Spatial Systems Nominees PTY Ltd. and Newbay Software which together bolstered the company's presence in Europe and the Asia-Pacific region.

EXECUTIVES

Vice President Marketing Commnications, Stacie Hiras
EVP InterconnectNow, Mark A. Mendes, age 51, $350,000 total compensation
Founder Chairman and CEO, Stephen G. Waldis, age 46, $557,230 total compensation
President and COO, Robert E. (Bob) Garcia, age 46, $412,000 total compensation
EVP and General Counsel, Ronald J. Prague, age 51
EVP Product Management and Business Development, Daniel Rizer, age 50
EVP and President International, Chris Halbard
EVP Research and Development and CTO, Patrick J. (Pat) Doran, age 40
EVP Human Resources, PJ Hilbert
EVP CFO and Treasurer, Karen Rosenberger
EVP; President Emerging Markets, Nick Lazzaro, $262,182 total compensation
EVP and Chief Innovation Officer, David Berry
Vice President, Pamela Oraschin
Vice President, Chuck Machlin
Vice President Corporate Development, Raj Arur
Vice President Sales, Sean Sullivan
Executive Vice President Operations, Peter Halis
Vice President Sales Emea, Anthony Manning
Vice President And General Manager Asia, Mike Maben
Vice President Product Management, Sanida Bratt
Vice President Of Business Development, Brent Wilkins
Founder Chairman and CEO, Stephen G. Waldis, age 46
Auditors: Ernst&YoungLLP

LOCATIONS

HQ: Synchronoss Technologies Inc
200 Crossing Boulevard, 8th Floor, Bridgewater, NJ 08807
Phone: 866 620-3940
Web: www.synchronoss.com

COMPETITORS

Amdocs	Intec Telecom
CSG Systems	Motive Inc.
International	NeuStar
Comptel	Syniverse
Evolving Systems	VeriSign

HISTORICAL FINANCIALS

Company Type: Public

Income Statement

FYE: December 31

	REVENUE ($ mil.)	NET INCOME ($ mil.)	NET PROFIT MARGIN	EMPLOYEES
12/13	349.0	23.3	6.7%	1,401
12/12	273.6	27.0	9.9%	1,340
12/11	229.0	15.1	6.6%	970
12/10	165.9	3.8	2.3%	758
12/09	128.8	12.3	9.5%	511
Annual Growth	**28.3%**	**17.4%**	**—**	**28.7%**

2013 Year-End Financials

Debt ratio: 1.7%
Return on equity: 5.6%
Cash ($ mil.): 63
Current ratio: 2.57
Long-term debt ($ mil.): 9

No. of shares (mil.): 40
Dividends
  Yield: —
  Payout: —
Market value ($ mil.): 1,263

STOCK PRICE ($) FY Close	P/E High/Low	PER SHARE ($) Earnings	Dividends	Book Value
12/13	31.07	65 35	0.58	0.00	11.01
12/12	21.09	50 24	0.69	0.00	9.69
12/11	30.21	80 52	0.43	0.00	8.71
12/10	26.71	246125	0.12	0.00	7.81
12/09	15.81	40 21	0.39	0.00	4.71
Annual Growth 18.4%		**— 10.4%**	**—**	**23.7%**

Synergy Resources Corp

Synergy Resources is on a quest to "synergize" the natural resources found in the Denver-Julesburg Basin (D-J Basin) which spans Colorado Kansas Nebraska and Wyoming. The company is exploring the Wattenberg Field a 50-mile area north of Denver rich with oil and gas deposits. Synergy Resources reports proved reserves of about 41 billion cu. ft. of natural gas and 7 million barrels of oil and condensate. It has about 245000 net acres under lease with 290 producing wells. The company was founded in 2005 and began operations three years later.

Geographic Reach

All of the company's developed acreage is located in Colorado but it has substantial undeveloped acreage in Nebraska and a smaller holding in Wyoming.

Financial Performance

As Synergy has increased its producing wells revenue has surged. After more than doubling in 2012 revenue jumped about 85% in fiscal 2013 (ended August) to $46 million. Oil revenues jumped some 75% while gas revenues more than doubled. Net income fell 20% in 2013 to $9.5 million after showing significant improvement the prior year. The decline is primarily because of non-cash charges related to a loss on commodity derivatives and a provision for deferred income taxes of nearly $7 million.

Cash provided by operations has been on a significant upswing along with revenue and net income. In 2013 it hit $32 million up more than 50% over 2012 and more than 300% over 2011.

Strategy

Synergy Resources plans to continue its focus on the D-J Basin. All its current wells are in the Basin and its undeveloped holdings are either in or adjacent to the Basin. The company has identified more than 600 development and extension drilling locations. In fiscal 2013 it also started transitioning from vertical to horizontal drilling. Its fiscal 2014 plans call for drilling or participating in about two dozen horizontal wells.

Mergers and Acquisitions

Also in fiscal 2013 Synergy Resources acquired about 35 wells in the Wattenberg Field from Orr Energy in a deal valued at about $42 million.

EXECUTIVES

CFO, Frank L. Jennings, $180,000 total compensation
President and Co-CEO, Edward Holloway, $300,000 total compensation

Co-CEO and Treasurer, William E. Scaff, $300,000 total compensation
COO, Craig D. Rasmuson
VP Land and Business Development, Ronald K. Morgenstern
Auditors: EhrhardtKeefeSteiner&HottmanPC

LOCATIONS

HQ: Synergy Resources Corp
20203 Highway 60, Platteville, CO 80651
Phone: 970 737-1073   **Fax:** 970 737-1045
Web: www.syrginfo.com

PRODUCTS/OPERATIONS

2013 Sales

	$ mil.	% of total
Oil	36.2	78
Gas	10.0	22
Total	**46.2**	**100**

COMPETITORS

Bill Barrett	PDC Energy
Cimarex	Par Petroleum
Double Eagle Petroleum	Resolute Energy
Earthstone Energy	Whiting Petroleum
Gasco Energy	

HISTORICAL FINANCIALS

Company Type: Public

Income Statement

FYE: August 31

	REVENUE ($ mil.)	NET INCOME ($ mil.)	NET PROFIT MARGIN	EMPLOYEES
08/14	104.2	28.8	27.7%	29
08/13	46.2	9.5	20.7%	16
08/12	24.9	12.1	48.6%	11
08/11	10.0	(11.6)	—	11
08/10	2.1	(10.7)	—	7
Annual Growth	163.6%	—		42.7%

2014 Year-End Financials

Debt ratio: 8.2%	No. of shares (mil.): 78
Return on equity: 11.9%	Dividends
Cash ($ mil.): 34	Yield: —
Current ratio: 0.66	Payout: —
Long-term debt ($ mil.): 37	Market value ($ mil.): 1,050

	STOCK PRICE ($) FY Close	P/E High/Low	PER SHARE ($) Earnings	Dividends	Book Value
08/14	13.46	36 22	0.37	0.00	3.61
08/13	9.36	55 16	0.16	0.00	2.88
08/12	2.80	14 9	0.25	0.00	1.97
08/11	3.11	— —	(0.45)	0.00	1.36
08/10	2.25	— —	(0.88)	0.00	(0.08)
Annual Growth	56.4%				

Synopsys Inc

To sum up Synopsys is a leading provider of electronic design automation (EDA) software and services. Its products are used by designers of integrated circuits (ICs) to develop simulate and test the physical design of ICs before production and then to test finished products. The company also provides semiconductor intellectual property (SIP) pre-designed circuits used as part of larger chips. Customers come from a variety of markets but particularly the semiconductor and electronics manufacturing industries. (Intel is its top customer.) Synopsys offers time-based software licenses where customers make yearly payments for use and support. It generates about half its sales outside the US.

Geographic Reach The company has about 25 offices in the US. International offices are located in another 25 countries with major operations in China France Germany India and Taiwan.

The US represents Synopsys' largest market accounting for nearly half of sales. Japan and Europe contributed 13% and 14% respectively. All regions except Japan reported year-over-year growth in fiscal 2013 (year-end October).

Sales and Marketing Synopsys markets its products primarily to semiconductor and electronics systems companies through direct sales efforts in the US and in select international markets.

Financial Performance

Overall sales rose 12% in 2013 to $1.9 billion. Synopsys saw growth in all areas of its business but results were driven primarily by upfront license revenue which jumped 25% year-over-year due to acquisitions. Profits grew 36% to $247 million in line with the increased revenue.

Cash provided by operating activities increased slightly to $496 million due to an increase in collections from customers and a decrease in tax payments which was offset by higher vendor payments and higher personnel-related costs due to increased headcount.

Strategy

The company has had success growing through acquisitions and by expanding its operations outside the US.

Mergers and Acquisitions Synopsys has used acquisitions to expand its product lines and it bought six companies in 2012. ExpertIO strengthened the delivery of its line of verification IP with a new collection of storage protocols while RSoft Design provides software used for design optimization and simulation in telecommunications components systems and networks. Ciranova added EDA technology used to cut the time required to design transistor-level layouts for nanometer-scale and other advanced nodes.

Additionally Synopsys paid $426 million for Taiwan-based SpringSoft a developer of IC design software. It also paid $550 million for Magma Design Automation and $213 million for Emulation & Verification Engineering S.A. (EVE).

In 2011 Synopsys bought nSys Design Systems as part of an effort to address the system-on-a-chip (SoCs) verification market. Also that year the company acquired Extreme DA a maker of software used to improve circuit design performance power consumption and manufacturing output.

HISTORY

Aart de Geus founded Optimal Solutions in 1986 with funding from General Electric where he had been a manager in the company's Advanced Computer-Aided Engineering Group. The group built the prototype of a product that saved chip designers time by automating much of the design work.

In 1987 the company changed its name to Synopsys (an abbreviation of "synthesis and optimization systems") and moved to California. It went public in 1992 and two years later it introduced software that engineers used to design chips by function rather than structure.

As chips grew more complicated Synopsys bolstered its product development efforts through acquisitions. In 1995 the company purchased hardware emulation developer Silicon Architects. Synopsys bought transistor-level tool specialist EPIC Design Technology in 1997 to improve its submicron-level design capabilities. It acquired Viewlogic Systems to increase its design automation prowess. (Synopsys later sold Viewlogic's printed circuit board design software segment.)

Synopsys' acquisitions continued in 1998 with the purchase of Radiant Design Tools a supplier of technology for designing simulation performance and Everest Design Automation which specialized in system-on-a-chip devices. In 1999 Synopsys bought Stanza Systems which developed physical layout products; Smartech a developer of wireless market design products; and several others. It also introduced several products including one that combined design and physical layout of system-on-a-chip devices in one package.

In 2001 the company sold its Silicon Library Business. Synopsys' attempt to acquire IKOS Systems in 2002 was stymied by Mentor Graphics. However Synopsys did acquire troubled software developer Avant! for nearly $730 million and purchased inSilicon for $64 million.

In 2003 Synopsys acquired Numerical Technologies whose software helped prepare chip designs for manufacturing for about $250 million. Looking to beef up its design capabilities for analog and mixed-signal chips Synopsys in 2004 purchased the assets of Analog Design Automation (ADA) a company founded in 1999. Also in 2004 Synopsys bought Accelerant Networks Inc. of Beaverton Oregon a fabless semiconductor company. The purchase price was $22.5 million in cash. Later that year Synopsys acquired Integrated Systems Engineering AG (ISE) of Zurich Switzerland for about $95 million in cash plus another $20 million in future earnout payments. At the same time Synopsys acquired the assets of Monterey Design Systems and hired most of the engineers working in Armenia for Monterey. Synopsys did not acquire Monterey's software products. Synopsys added even more Armenian engineers with its 2004 asset acquisition of LEDA Design which had more than 80 people working in Yerevan Armenia.

Synopsys agreed to acquire Monolithic System Technology (now MoSys) for about $432 million in cash but called off the deal in 2004. MoSys sued; the companies settled the case after the trial began a few months later. Synopsys also agreed in 2004 to acquire rival Nassda for around $192 million in cash. The acquisition was completed in 2005.

In 2008 the company purchased Synplicity a provider of field programmable gate array (FPGA) IC design and verification software. Later that year the company also bought the CHIPit business unit of ProDesign. The move boosted Synopsys' aim to provide end-to-end products for the design and verification markets enhancing its system validation and embedded software development capabilities.

In 2010 the company made several acquisitions. It extended its virtual prototyping portfolio into automotive and consumer applications through the acquisition of VaST Systems Technology a developer of models and tools for designing embedded electronics. It acquired CoWare a provider of software and services for electronic systems design. Synopsys expanded its portfolio of high-level synthesis tools through the purchase of Synfora. In September 2010 Synopsys expanded its SIP portfolio with the acquisition Virage Logic.

EXECUTIVES

SVP; General Manager Implementation, Antun Domic, age 63, $390,000 total compensation

Sr Vice President Human Resrcs, Jan Collinson

President and Co-CEO, Chi-Foon Chan, age 65, $450,000 total compensation

CFO, Brian M. Beattie, age 61, $400,000 total compensation

SVP Global Technical Services, Deirdre Hanford, age 52, $300,000 total compensation

SVP; General Manager Verification Group, Manoj Gandhi, age 54

SVP; General Manager Silicon Engineering Group, Howard Ko, age 58

SVP; General Manager Solutions Group, Joachim Kunkel

General Counsel and Corporate Secretary; Chief Ethics and Compliance Officer, Brian E. Cabrera, age 49, $353,000 total compensation

SVP Worldwide Sales and Corporate Marketing, Joseph W. (Joe) Logan, age 55, $357,200 total compensation

Chairman and Co-CEO, Aart de Geus, $500,000 total compensation

Vice President Strategic Market Development, Rich Goldman

Sr V Pres, David P Burow

Senior Vice President General Manager Analog Mixed Signal Group, Paul Lo

Vice President, Robert Genco

Vice President It, Debra Martucci

Vice President, Janick Bergeron

Vice President Marketing Implementation Group, Thomas Ferry

Vp Of Engineering, Ahsan Bootehsaz

Vice President Director Engineering, Jyh Chwen Lee

Corporate Vice President And Managing, Pradip Dutta

Vice President Of Sales, Jian Yue Pandry

Vp Marketing, Bijan Kiani

Vice President And General Manager, Yankin Tanurhan

Senior Vice President And Chief, Steven Shevick

Vice President Of North American Sales, Jason Niatas

Hr Director & Vp, Shelley Smith

Vice President Engineering Asic And Fp, Michael Jackson

Senior Vice President, Raul Camposano

Vice President Business Development, Robert Dahlberg

Vice President Corporate Finance, Karen Christensen

Vice President Finance Planning, Michael Armsby

Vice President Engineering Synplicity Business Gro, Andrew Dauman

Vp Of Marketing, Farhad Hayat

Vice President Engineering Director Engineer, Tzyh Wuu

Vice President, Kalpana Singh

Vice President Engineering, Dan Page

Regional Vice President, Linda Xu

Vice President Strategy And Corporate Development, Cynthia Fontenot

Vice President Engineering Director, Ravindra Tembhekar

Executive Assistant To Vice President, Anna Marano

Vice President Technology Support, Ken Nelsen

Vice President Engineering, Eshel Haritan

Vice President Of Marketing Ip, John Koeter

Vice President Western Area Sales, Brian Gregory

Vice President, Kevin Brelsford

Vice President Ir, Lisa Ewbank

Vice President Engineering, Naji Bekhazi

Vice President Engineering, Eyal Odiz

Vice President Engineering Director, Baribrata Biswas

Vice President Of Engineering Silicon Engineering Group, Fabio Angelillis

Vice President, John Ellis

Sales And Marketing Vp, Glenn Dukes

Vice President Of Marketing, Paul Lai

Vice President And General Manager, George Bayz

Svp Worldwide Sales, Joe Logan

General Counsel and Corporate Secretary; Chief Ethics and Compliance Officer, Brian E. Cabrera, age 49

Chairman and Co-CEO, Aart de Geus

Board Member, Irene Economou

Auditors: KPMGLLP

LOCATIONS

HQ: Synopsys Inc
700 East Middlefield Road, Mountain View, CA 94043
Phone: 650 584-5000   **Fax:** 650 965-8637
Web: www.synopsys.com

2013 Sales

	$ mil.	% of total
US	939.7	48
Europe	273.1	14
Japan	264.1	13
Asia-Pacific & other	485.3	25
Total	**1962.2**	**100**

PRODUCTS/OPERATIONS

2013 Sales

	$ mil.	% of total
Time-based license	1599.5	81
Maintenance & service	230.7	7
Upfront license	132.0	12
Total	**1962.2**	**100**

Selected Products

Astro (place and route)
Chip Architect (planning and analysis of various design phases)
coreBuilder (reusable design data)
CoCentric System Studio (system-level design and verification)
Coverity (quality and testing tools)
Design Compiler (logic synthesis)
Design Vision (design management and analysis)
DesignWare (implementation and verification design library)
Hercules (physical verification)
Module Compiler (synthesis of data paths)
NanoSim (memory and mixed-signal verification)
PathMill (static timing analysis)
Physical Compiler (physical synthesis)
PowerMill (circuit simulation and design)
Scirocco (VHDL-based simulation)
VCS (Verilog language-based simulation)

Selected Services

Tool & Methodology Consulting
Design Flow Deployment
IP Integration & SoC Verification
Core Optimization
Physical Design Assistance
FPGA-based Prototyping

Selected Acquisitions

2014
Coverity (quality and testing tools)
Target Compiler Technologies (tools for designing ASIP chips)
2012
EVE (emulation software)
Ciranova (EDA software for transistor-level design of nanometer-scale nodes)
RSoft Design (software used in telecom product and network design and simulation)
ExpertIO (intellectual property for storage protocol verification)
Magma Design Automation (chip design software)

2011
Extreme DA (software used to improve chip performance power consumption and manufacturing output)
nSys Design Systems (system-on-chip verification software)
2010
VaST Systems Technology (models and tools used to design embedded electronics)

COMPETITORS

ANSYS	Mentor Graphics
Agilent EESof	MoSys
Altium	PDF Solutions
CEVA	Rambus
Cadence Design	Silvaco
Intrinsix	SynTest

HISTORICAL FINANCIALS

Company Type: Public

Income Statement

FYE: October 31

	REVENUE ($ mil.)	NET INCOME ($ mil.)	NET PROFIT MARGIN	EMPLOYEES
10/14	2,057.4	259.1	12.6%	9,436
10/13	1,962.2	247.8	12.6%	8,573
10/12	1,756.0	182.4	10.4%	8,138
10/11	1,535.6	221.3	14.4%	6,803
10/10	1,380.6	237.0	17.2%	6,707
Annual Growth	10.5%	2.2%	—	8.9%

2014 Year-End Financials

Debt ratio: 1.5%
Return on equity: 8.8%
Cash ($ mil.): 985
Current ratio: 1.09
Long-term debt ($ mil.): 45
No. of shares (mil.): 155
Dividends
  Yield: —
  Payout: —
Market value ($ mil.): 6,391

	STOCK PRICE ($) FY Close	P/E High/Low	PER SHARE ($) Earnings	Dividends	Book Value
10/14	40.98	25 21	1.64	0.00	19.60
10/13	36.42	24 19	1.58	0.00	18.09
10/12	32.20	28 21	1.21	0.00	16.58
10/11	26.81	19 14	1.47	0.00	14.66
10/10	25.58	16 13	1.56	0.00	14.14
Annual Growth	12.5%	—	—	1.3%	— 8.5%

Syntel Inc.

Syntel is in the know about information technology. The IT services provider offers outsourced applications development knowledge process outsourcing (KPO) and IT consulting and staffing for global corporate client list. Its largest segment applications outsourcing focuses on the development management and maintenance of business software. Syntel offers KPO services for middle and back-office functions such as transaction processing and loan servicing to financial services health care and insurance companies. Its top clients include American Express and State Street. Co-founding spouses Bharat Desai and Neerja Sethi are the company's biggest shareholders.

Operations

Syntel is focused on its growing applications outsourcing business which accounted for three-quarters of sales in 2012 and KPO operations which accounted for 15%. Its traditional strengths include serving clients in banking financial services insurance and health care where outsourcing of business functions like claims processing commonly occurs. Other key markets include telecommunications automotive logistics and travel.

The company has all but transitioned away from its IT staffing roots. Overseen by its TeamSourcing division that business has accounted for only 2% of revenue in recent years. Syntel's e-Business division which specializes in Web applications and data warehousing accounted for 8% of revenue.

Geographic Reach

The company's application development centers and other facilities are located in India. The company also has about 20 sales offices worldwide. Although headquartered in the US 80% of the company's employees were based in India in 2012.

Sales and Marketing

Syntel markets and sells its services through sales teams operating throughout the US Canada Europe and Australia. Its two top clients American Express and State Street together accounted for just under half of the company's total revenue in 2012. American Express accounted for 27% while State Street accounted for 17%. The company served about 135 customers in 2012 most of which were in the US.

Financial Performance

With more than $720 million in revenues Syntel makes nowhere near the multibillion-dollar sales of its top Indian outsourcing rivals Infosys Tata Consultancy and Wipro. The company's sales continue to grow however and its average annual profit margin for the past five years is about 40%. Revenues grew by about 13% in 2012 driven by strong global demand for the offshore IT services. As in previous years Syntel also attributed the jump in sales for the year to the expansion of its workforce which enabled the company to scale up capacity. The company's cost of sales rose slightly for the year.

Ownership

Founder Bharat Desai holds a 38% stake in the company while co-founder Neerja Sethi holds 29%. Besides Desai and Sethi Syntel has a third major stakeholder Rakesh Vij who owns a household products trading company RK International Inc. in Houston. Vij controls 23% of the company.

Company Background

Desai and Sethi founded the company in 1980 while Desai was earning his Master's degree from the University of Michigan. The couple moved to the US in 1976 when Desai took a job with Tata Consultancy one of the top India-based IT outsourcing companies.

EXECUTIVES

Vp Corporate Communications, Neerja Sethi, age 60
CFO and Chief Information Security Officer, Arvind S. Godbole, age 56, $112,992 total compensation
COO, Rakesh Khanna, age 51, $200,689 total compensation
SVP Insurance Business Unit Head, Anil Jain, age 55, $238,201 total compensation
President and CEO, Nitin Rakesh, age 42, $286,750 total compensation
SVP Healthcare and Life Sciences Business Unit Head, Murlidhar Reddy, age 44
SVP Banking and Financial Services Business Unit Head, V. S. Raj, age 50
SVP Retail Logistics and Telecom Business Unit, Raja Ray, age 51, $262,306 total compensation
SVP and Head Europe, Amit Chatterjee, age 47
VP Manufacturing PLM & ES Business Unit Head, Avinash Salelkar, age 51

Vice President Global Marketing, Jonathan James
Vice President Of Strategic Programs, Andy Sivaraman
Former Executive Vice President, Raj Mashruwala, age 63
Vice President Banking And Financial, Stephen Brown
Hr Director & Vp, Sandra Kinter
Vp Of Finance, R Ramdas
Regional Vice President Business, Abhishek Gupta
Vice President And Escrow Manager, Kunal Agashe
Vp Of Finance, Kunal Waradkar
Chairman, Bharat Desai, age 61
Executive Vice Chairman, Prashant Ranade, age 62
Auditors: CroweHorwathLLP

LOCATIONS

HQ: Syntel Inc.
525 E. Big Beaver Road, Suite 300, Troy, MI 48083
Phone: 248 619-2800 **Fax:** 248 619-2888
Web: www.syntelinc.com

2011 Sales

	$ mil.	% of total
North America	594.4	92
Europe	43.3	7
Other countries	4.7	1
Total	**642.4**	**100**

PRODUCTS/OPERATIONS

2012 Sales

	$ mil.	% of total
Applications outsourcing	544.7	75
Knowledge process outsourcing	110.5	15
e-Business	54.4	8
TeamSourcing	14.3	2
Total	**723.9**	**100**

Selected Services

Applications outsourcing
  Applications development
  Applications maintenance
  Applications management
  Platforms conversion
Knowledge process outsourcing
e-Business
  Customer relationship management services
  Data warehousing and business intelligence
  E-business design development implementation and maintenance
  Enterprise applications outsourcing
  Web architecture
  Web-enablement of legacy applications
  Web portal design
TeamSourcing
  Design
  Development
  Implementation
  Information technology staffing
  Maintenance
  Systems specification
  Technical services

COMPETITORS

Accenture	HCL Technologies
Capgemini	HP Enterprise Services
Cognizant Tech Solutions	IBM Global Services
Computer Sciences Corp.	Infosys
Datacraft Asia	NTT Data
Deloitte	PricewaterhouseCoopers
First Data	TCS America
Getronics	Unisys
	WNS (Holdings)
	Wipro

HISTORICAL FINANCIALS

Company Type: Public

Income Statement

FYE: December 31

	REVENUE ($ mil.)	NET INCOME ($ mil.)	NET PROFIT MARGIN	EMPLOYEES
12/13	824.7	219.6	26.6%	23,652
12/12	723.9	185.5	25.6%	21,407
12/11	642.4	122.8	19.1%	19,484
12/10	532.1	113.5	21.3%	17,383
12/09	419.0	118.5	28.3%	12,567
Annual Growth	**18.4%**	**16.7%**	**—**	**17.1%**

2013 Year-End Financials

Debt ratio: 14.6%
Return on equity: 34.1%
Cash ($ mil.): 178
Current ratio: 6.78
Long-term debt ($ mil.): 138
No. of shares (mil.): 83
Dividends
  Yield: 5.3%
  Payout: 92.7%
Market value ($ mil.): 7,596

	STOCK PRICE ($) FY Close	P/E High/Low		PER SHARE ($)		
			Earnings	Dividends	Book Value
12/13	90.95	35 20	2.62	2.43	8.65
12/12	53.63	29 20	2.22	2.49	6.79
12/11	46.77	41 26	1.47	0.24	5.93
12/10	47.80	39 23	1.37	0.74	5.44
12/09	38.03	34 12	1.43	0.24	4.23
Annual Growth	**24.4%**		**16.3%**	**78.4%**	**19.6%**

Take-Two Interactive Software, Inc.

Crime might not pay in the real world but in the gaming universe it means big money for Take-Two. The company's popular mature-rated Grand Theft Auto series and other games are developed by subsidiary Rockstar Games. Its 2K Games subsidiary publishes franchises such as BioShock Borderlands and Sid Meier's Civilization; the 2K Sports unit carries titles such as Major League Baseball 2K and "NBA 2K". Take-Two's games are played on Microsoft Sony and Nintendo game consoles but also on PCs and handheld devices. Its products are sold through outlets including retail chains such as GameStop (20% of sales) Wal-Mart Best Buy and Amazon and as digital downloads. About half of its sales comes from the US.

Geographic Reach

Like most western game companies Take-Two's success in Asia/Pacific has historically been limited with the region bringing in less than 10% of sales. With more than 14 studios around the world The company does however maintain sales operations in Asia Canada Japan Singapore Australia South Korea Taiwan and New Zealand along with a handful of European countries including France Germany the Netherlands Spain Switzerland and the UK.

Operations

Take-Two's Rockstar Games subsidiary is aptly named having racked up sales game-of-the-year awards and controversy to back up the moniker. Focused on hardcore action games its other titles alongside golden child GTA include open-world racing game Midnight Club the Wild West-themed

Red Dead series 1940s-era action-detective game L.A. Noire and gritty action shooter Max Payne.

Although sister company 2K Games doesn't have as unruly a reputation it still maintains the action focus of the group. While intense titles geared toward adults and seasoned gamers have been Take-Two's bread and butter it hedges its bets by also pursuing projects that appeal to children and casual gamers. As part of that push Take-Two established the 2K Play label for its casual gaming and family-oriented efforts offering titles such as Dora the Explorer Deal or No Deal and its most successful release to date Carnival Games.

Sales and Marketing

The company spent $153.7 million $185.2 million and $122.9 million on advertising expenses in fiscal years 2014 2013 and 2012 respectively.

Financial Performance

Take-Two experiences volatility in its year-to-year revenues and income due to the uncertainty of the estimated popularity (sales) of its annual game releases. In fiscal 2014 Take-Two reported an increase of 94% in revenues driven by increase of $1481.5 million sales from its Grand Theft Auto franchise (related to the releases of Grand Theft Auto V); higher sales of $139.5 million (driven by the WWE 2K14 together with higher sales of its NBA 2K franchise); partially offset by a $446 million decrease in net sales due to prior year releases of Borderlands 2 Max Payne 3 BioShock Infinite XCOM: Enemy Unknown and Spec Ops: The Line.

In fiscal 2014 Take-Two reported a 1325% increase in net income driven by higher sales and lower selling and marketing expenses partially offset by an increase in research and development and general and administrative expenses.Cash flow in operating activities has been following Take-Two's net income trend reporting $700.3 million during fiscal 2014 compared to $704.8 million during 2013 which was a result cash generated from the release of Grand Theft Auto V and the collection of accounts receivable balances primarily attributable to the release of Bioshock Infinite near the end of the previous fiscal year. This was partially offset by cash used in financing and investing activities.

Strategy

The company grows organically but is open to making acquisitions for its product delivery or future product sales.

Take-Two parts company with most of its major competitors in strategy around the inexorable growth of mobile and casual games. While others scramble to make mobile and casual a major pillar in their future plans Take-Two remains focused on consoles and hard-core gamers. The company's games are dominated by cutting-edge home consoles (Sony's PlayStation 3 and Microsoft's Xbox 360) with PC titles being the third-largest contributor at around 10%. Take-Two hasn't however ignored the newly-burgeoning space altogether. It releases titles such as Max Payne Mobile for Apple and Android devices as well as for social networking sites such as Facebook. It also realizes that digital distribution represents a lucrative avenue for growth. That distribution is focused on games that it develops or publishes.

Although western video game companies have found it difficult to penetrate the Asian market the blossoming of online gaming has begun to open up the region especially in China and South Korea and Take-Two wants a part. Its strategy in that market includes expanding the distribution of existing products developing a presence in Japan and pursuing online gaming opportunities.

While in 2013 its 2K unit and WWE entered an agreement granting 2K the exclusive worldwide rights to publish the WWE video game franchise across all major platforms and distribution channels. It launched WWE 2K15 in 2014.

Company Background

Take-Two exited the third-party distribution business in 2010.

EXECUTIVES

CFO, Lainie J. Goldstein, age 47, $625,000 total compensation

Chairman and CEO, Strauss Zelnick, age 56

President, Karl Slatoff, age 44, $1 total compensation

EVP and General Counsel, Seth Krauss, age 44, $552,292 total compensation

Senior Vice President Of Human Resources, David Messenger

Vice President And Counsel, Matt Britton

Vice President Head Of Risk Management, Jonathan Washburn

Vice President Sales And Distribution Americas, David Cox

Vice President And Agc Litigation And Corporate Secretary, Linda Zabriskie

Vice President Global Tax, Stephen Vassallo

Chairman and CEO, Strauss Zelnick, age 56

Auditors: Ernst&YoungLLP

LOCATIONS

HQ: Take-Two Interactive Software, Inc.
622 Broadway, New York, NY 10012
Phone: 646 536-2842
Web: www.take2games.com

2012 Sales

	$ mil.	% of total
US	449.2	54
Europe	246.2	30
Asia Pacific	68.6	8
Canada & Latin America	61.8	8
Total	**825.8**	**100**

PRODUCTS/OPERATIONS

2012 Sales

	$ mil.	% of total
Microsoft Xbox 360	370.0	45
Sony PlayStation 3	300.6	36
PC & other	87.3	11
Nintendo Wii	19.7	2
Sony PlayStation Portable	18.5	2
Nintendo DS	16.8	2
Sony PlayStation 2	12.9	2
Total	**825.8**	**100**

Selected Titles

Rockstar Games
  Beaterator
  Bully
  Grand Theft Auto
  L.A. Noire
  Manhunt
  Max Payne
  Midnight Club
  Red Dead Redemption
2K Games
  The Bigs
  Bioshock
  Borderlands
  The Darkness
  Duke Nukem Forever
  Mafia
  Sid Meier' s Civilization
  Sid Meier' s Pirates!
2K Play
  Carnival Games
  Deal or No Deal
  Dora the Explorer
  Family Feud
  Go Diego Go!
2K Sports

Major League Baseball 2K
NBA 2K
NHL 2K
Top Spin

Selected Customers

GameStop
Wal-Mart
Best Buy
Game (UK)
GEM Distribution
Media Market
Toys "R" Us

COMPETITORS

Activision Blizzard	Nintendo
Atari	SEGA
Capcom	Sony USA
Electronic Arts	Square Enix
Konami	Ubisoft
Microsoft	Valve Corporation
Namco Bandai	

HISTORICAL FINANCIALS

Company Type: Public

Income Statement

FYE: March 31

	REVENUE ($ mil.)	NET INCOME ($ mil.)	NET PROFIT MARGIN	EMPLOYEES
03/14	2,350.5	361.6	15.4%	2,530
03/13	1,214.4	(29.4)	—	2,440
03/12	825.8	(108.8)	—	2,235
03/11	1,136.8	48.4	4.3%	2,118
03/10	359.2	(28.8)	—	2,202
Annual Growth	**59.9%**	**—**		**3.5%**

2014 Year-End Financials

Debt ratio: 25.2%
Return on equity: 52.0%
Cash ($ mil.): 1,129
Current ratio: 2.95
Long-term debt ($ mil.): 454

No. of shares (mil.): 88
Dividends
  Yield: —
  Payout: —
Market value ($ mil.): 1,950

	STOCK PRICE ($) FY Close	P/E High/Low		Earnings	PER SHARE ($) Dividends	Book Value
03/14	21.93	6	4	3.20	0.00	9.02
03/13	16.15	—	—	(0.34)	0.00	6.27
03/12	15.39	—	—	(1.31)	0.00	6.60
03/11	15.37	30	15	0.56	0.00	7.14
03/10	9.87	—	—	(0.37)	0.00	6.20
Annual Growth	**22.1%**	**—**	**—**	**—**	**—**	**9.8%**

Tal International Group Inc

If your freight is going by truck train or ship tall odds are it might be going in a container owned by TAL International Group. The company is a leading lessor of intermodal freight containers — steel boxes that come in standard sizes and can be used to move goods over the road over the rails or over the water. Marine shipping lines are among the company's top customers. TAL maintains a fleet of more than 1250000 containers or about 2.1 million 20-foot equivalent units (TEUs) of capacity. Besides its leasing operations TAL International sells used containers. Investment firm Jordan Company through its Resolute Fund affiliate and other entities controls about a 40% stake in TAL.

Geographic Reach

The company operates through nearly 20 leasing offices in over 10 countries. It has a geographically diverse revenue base with more than 200 container depot facilities in some 40 countries worldwide.

Operations

Through its equipment trading segment the company buys containers from its shipping line customers and resells the containers to traders. TAL handles about 40000 TEUs per year for resale.

Financial Performance

The company's revenue increased by 14% in fiscal 2012 compared to fiscal 2011 mainly due to an increase in its leasing revenues.

Its net income increased by 19% in fiscal 2012 compared to the previous fiscal year primarily due to the decrease of write-off of deferred financing costs and net loss on interest rate swaps. TAL's cash flow decreased by $153 million in fiscal 2012 compared to fiscal 2011 primarily due to a decrease in net borrowings.

Strategy

TAL constantly invests in maintaining its equipment and expanding its fleet to keep up with demand and customer expectations.

EXECUTIVES

Chairman President and CEO, Brian M. Sondey, age 45, $672,525 total compensation
SVP and CFO, John Burns, age 52, $320,000 total compensation
Board Of Directors, Claude Germain
Auditors: Ernst&YoungLLP

LOCATIONS

HQ: Tal International Group Inc
100 Manhattanville Road, Purchase, NY 10577-2135
Phone: 914 251-9000   **Fax:** 914 697-2549
Web: www.talinternational.com

2012 Sales

	$ mil.	% of total
Europe	260.2	44
Asia	252.1	43
US	43.9	7
Other regions	33.0	6
Total	**589.2**	**100**

PRODUCTS/OPERATIONS

2012 Sales

	$ mil.	% of total
Leasing revenues	525.0	89
Equipment trading revenue	60.9	10
Management fee income	3.1	1
Other	0.2	-
Total	**589.2**	**100**

Selected Products

Chassis
Flat racks
Generator sets
High cube dry containers
Open tops
Refrigerated containers
Standard dry containers
Tank containers

Selected Services

Chassis (leasing)
Container (leasing)
Container sales (trader)

GreySlot (logistic services)
SpaceWise (UK container rentals)
Tank container (leasing)

COMPETITORS

CAI International	SeaCube Container
COSCO Pacific	Seacastle
Chicago Freight Car Leasing	Seaco
	Union Tank Car
GATX	XTRA Corp.

HISTORICAL FINANCIALS

Company Type: Public

Income Statement

FYE: December 31

	REVENUE ($ mil.)	NET INCOME ($ mil.)	NET PROFIT MARGIN	EMPLOYEES
12/13	642.8	143.1	22.3%	172
12/12	589.1	130.1	22.1%	173
12/11	516.6	109.7	21.2%	174
12/10	366.8	57.7	15.7%	172
12/09	352.5	71.5	20.3%	184
Annual Growth	**16.2%**	**18.9%**	**—**	**(1.7%)**

2013 Year-End Financials

Debt ratio: 69.6%
Return on equity: 21.8%
Cash ($ mil.): 98
Current ratio: 0.32
Long-term debt ($ mil.): 2,817

No. of shares (mil.): 33
Dividends
Yield: 4.6%
Payout: 61.4%
Market value ($ mil.): 1,941

	STOCK PRICE ($) FY Close	P/E High/Low		PER SHARE ($) Earnings	Dividends	Book Value
12/13	57.35	13	9	4.25	2.68	20.44
12/12	36.38	11	8	3.87	2.35	18.29
12/11	28.79	11	7	3.34	1.99	16.85
12/10	30.87	17	7	1.88	1.30	13.95
12/09	13.23	6	2	2.30	0.04	13.69
Annual Growth	**44.3%**			**16.6%**	**186.1%**	**10.5%**

Team Health Holdings Inc

Team Health keeps its cool in an emergency room and it runs a smooth back office. The company is a leading provider of clinical outsourcing services across the US. It provides physician staffing and administrative services to hospital emergency rooms and handles everything from doctor recruitment to billing payroll and claims management. The company provides similar services for anesthesiology inpatient care (hospitalist) and pediatric programs. Team Health contracts with civilian and military hospitals clinics and physician groups across the US.

Operations

More than 70% of Team Health's revenues are earned on a fee-for-service basis where it receives payments for services provided at hospitals from private insurers Medicare and Medicaid individuals and other health payers. The rest of its sales come through flat-rate or hourly contracts with government agencies for the management of health care facilities as well as certain hospitals.

Its largest service category is health care staffing which accounts for more than 80% of revenue. The staffing segment includes emergency anesthesia surgery and temporary worker placement and comprehensive health care services.

The remainder of revenue comes from hospital medicine clinical services government staffing call center operations after-hours pediatric clinics and billing services. Temporary staffing placement of doctors (locum tenens) is provided through subsidiary Daniel & Yeager while military facility staffing and management services are offered through its Spectrum Healthcare Resources unit.

Geographic Reach

Team Health operates through a regional structure with about 20 management sites across the country that deliver services locally but are supported by integrated information systems and procedures. Its 9800 health care professionals serve more than 860 civilian and military hospitals and clinics in about 47 states. Florida and Tennessee are its largest markets accounting for about 15% and 12% of sales respectively.

Sales and Marketing

The company serves more than 850 community and military hospitals across the US. Reimbursements from Medicare and Medicaid plans accounted for more than 50% of sales in 2013 while revenue from commercial plans accounted for 27%.

Team Health uses an inside sales force to promote its offerings. Marketing efforts include online telephone social media publication and trade show advertisements; direct mail campaigns; and lead referral programs.

Financial Performance

Keeping its pace on a steady growth trend over the past five years Team Health reported a 15% jump in revenue to nearly $2.4 billion in 2013 primarily due to increased fee-for-service revenue of $475.3. Contract and other revenue also increased.

Profits have fluctuated in recent years however and Team Health reported a 37% increase in net income to $87 million compared to $63.8 million in 2012. The increase was due to higher professional service expenses related to acquisitions new contract growth and professional wage increases.

Cash from operations increased in 2013 after a couple years of decline. It more than doubled from $71.5 million to $154.4 million due to cash generated from provisions for noncollectable accounts.

Strategy

The company sees growth opportunities in the pressures that hospitals are currently facing to control costs (while keeping service quality high). It intends to capitalize on those pressures by adding new outsourcing clients and providing new services to existing customers. It is also using its established market position in emergency room management to grow its business in other clinical areas such as anesthesia and pediatrics.

Additionally the company looks to increase market share by continuing to acquire (or form partnerships with) complementary businesses in the fragmented clinical outsourcing industry. At the same time Team Health controls risks by occasionally exiting noncore operations; for instance it stopped providing radiology staffing services in 2010.

Mergers and Acquisitions

Acquisitions of smaller regional groups have helped Team Health bulk up its roster of emergency physicians over the years. In 2013 it purchased nine businesses for a total of $159.1 million. The moves expanded ERs in New Jersey Wisconsin and Ohio and increased the number of ER staff in Arizona Florida Michigan Kentucky Indiana Ohio and West Virginia as well as anesthia personnel in Florida and Nebraska.

By mid-2014 Team Health had purchased two more companies adding an ER department in Tennessee and a West-Virginia-based manager of Berkeley Medical Center.

Company Background

The company was founded in 1979. Investment firm Blackstone Group owned nearly all of Team Health Holdings prior to the company's 2009 IPO. Blackstone's stake was reduced from 90% to about 68% through the IPO and Blackstone gradually sold off the rest of its shares through 2013. Proceeds from the public offering went toward Team Health's corporate expenses and debt repayment efforts.

EXECUTIVES

EVP and CFO, David P. Jones, $445,923 total compensation
Chief Medical Officer; Executive Director TeamHealth Patient Safety Organization, Gar LaSalle
President Physician Recruitment and Retention, John R. Staley
President TeamHealth East, James George
President CEO and Director, Michael D. (Mike) Snow, $392,308 total compensation
SVP Operations, Kent Bristow
President and Chief Medical Officer TeamHealth Midsouth, Randal L. Dabbs
COO Hospital Based Services, Barbara Blevins
President Northeast Group, Stephen G. Holtzclaw
CEO TeamHealth Southeast, Oliver Rogers
President Northwest, Mark W. Harris
President Mid-Atlantic Group, Roger Brooksbank
President Hospital Medicine, Jasen Gundersen
President Central Group, John Proctor
President Great Lakes, Saif Nazir
President Southeast Group, Steve Schwartz
President West Group, Robert R. Frantz
President Anesthesia East Division, Jeffrey A. Weiss
President Anesthesia West Division, Elliott (Skip) Wohlner
President Urgent Care, Joseph Chow
Svp And General Counsel, Heidi S Allen, age 61
Chairman, H. Lynn Massingale
President CEO and Director, Michael D. (Mike) Snow
Auditors: Ernst&YoungLLP

LOCATIONS

HQ: Team Health Holdings Inc
265 Brookview Centre Way, Suite 400, Knoxville, TN 37919
Phone: 865 693-1000
Web: www.teamhealth.com

PRODUCTS/OPERATIONS

2013 Sales

	$ mil.	% of total
Healthcare staffing	1986.5	83
Other services	397.1	17
Total	**2383.6**	**100**

2013 Sales

	$ mil.	% of total
Fee-for-service	1708.3	72
Contract & other	675.3	28
Total	**2383.6**	**100**

Selected Services

Coding and billing services
Collections
Continuing medical education
Contract management
Credentials
Employee benefits
Information systems
Locum tenens (temporary physician placement)
Medical call center services
Military treatment facilities management
Operations consulting
Patient safety
Payroll administration
Program management services
  Anesthesiologists
  Emergency medicine
  Hospitalists (coordination of care for hospitalized patients)
  Pediatrics
Recruitment
Risk management
Scheduling
Staffing

COMPETITORS

AMN Healthcare	Maxim Healthcare
CHG Healthcare	Services Inc.
Cogent HMG	McKesson
Envision Healthcare	Onward Healthcare
Hospital Physician	Orion HealthCorp
Partners	STGi
IPC The Hospitalist	Schumacher Group
Company	Sheridan Healthcare
MEDNAX	UCI

HISTORICAL FINANCIALS

Company Type: Public

Income Statement

FYE: December 31

	REVENUE ($ mil.)	NET INCOME ($ mil.)	NET PROFIT MARGIN	EMPLOYEES
12/13	2,383.6	87.4	3.7%	9,000
12/12	2,069.0	63.7	3.1%	8,500
12/11	1,745.3	65.5	3.8%	6,800
12/10	1,519.2	13.3	0.9%	5,700
12/09	1,423.4	40.7	2.9%	5,900
Annual Growth	**13.8%**	**21.1%**	**—**	**11.1%**

2013 Year-End Financials

Debt ratio: 36.8%	No. of shares (mil.): 70
Return on equity: 45.5%	Dividends
Cash ($ mil.): 32	Yield: —
Current ratio: 1.15	Payout: —
Long-term debt ($ mil.): 483	Market value ($ mil.): 3,189

	STOCK PRICE ($) FY Close	P/E High/Low		PER SHARE ($) Earnings	Dividends	Book Value
12/13	45.55	38	23	1.24	0.00	3.82
12/12	28.77	31	21	0.93	0.00	1.73
12/11	22.07	24	15	0.98	0.00	0.27
12/10	15.54	86	56	0.21	0.00	(0.80)
12/09	14.02	—	—	(0.00)	0.00	(1.48)
Annual Growth	**34.3%**	—	—	—	—	—

Team, Inc.

Consider it the A-Team for high-pressure situations. Team provides specialized maintenance services for piping systems including repairing leaks hot tapping (adding new connections to pressurized pipelines) and detecting escaping emissions. It also offers field heat treatment and testing and inspection services. The firm makes custom equipment clamps and enclosures to augment its standard materials and sealant products. Through two divisions TMS and TCM the company serves heavy industries including the chemical and petrochemical pulp and paper defense manufacturing and steel industries. Team operates from more than 125 locations worldwide but its largest markets are the US and Canada.

The company's TCM division provides inspections assessments and field heating treating. It accounts for nearly 60% of the group's revenues. Team's TMS division handles leak repair emissions control and other repair services. In addition to its traditional customer base Team serves clients in the aerospace and automotive sectors.

Sales and profits both grew by more than 20% in fiscal 2012 as both the TCM and TMS divisions increased earnings. Team's overall revenues grew 23% from the previous year to $623.7 million; the growth was solid across its customer and geographic bases. A joint venture to perform testing and inspection services in Alaska also saw growth that year. And although selling and administrative expenses rose (and the company paid a $0.8 million legal settlement related to a personal injury case) profits still grew 24% to $32.9 million.

Team has grown rapidly in the past decade increasing its revenues by more than sevenfold since 2000. It has acquired several competitors and expanded its presence internationally. In 2013 Team acquired industrial rope access service provider Global Ascent. In 2010 it bought Quest Integrity Group which performs inspection and engineering assessment services in markets around the globe. The acquired firm became part of Team's TCM division. In fiscal 2012 the company made two minor acquisitions further growing its operations.

EXECUTIVES

Senior Vice President - Operations Support And Technology Development, John P Kearns, age 59
Senior Vice President - Tms Division, David C Palmore, age 60
President and CEO, Ted W. Owen, age 62, $352,312 total compensation
EVP Administration Chief Legal Officer and Secretary, Andre C. (Butch) Bouchard, age 49
SVP CFO and Treasurer, Greg L. Boane, age 51
President Quest Integrity Group, Jeffrey L Ott, $259,637 total compensation
President Inspection and Heat Treating Services, Arthur F. (Art) Victorson, age 54, $340,090 total compensation
President Mechanical Services, Peter W. (Pete) Wallace, age 51, $337,090 total compensation
Vice President Human Resources, Mark Hinderliter
Vice President General Manager Tcm West, Kurt Hand
Vice President, Scott Powell
Vice President General Manager, Jim Campbell
Vice President Finance, Charles Slater
Se Vice President General Manager, Rob Hub
Solutions Vice President Of Sales And Marketing, Tom Rowland
Executive Chairman, Philip J. (Phil) Hawk, age 61
EVP Administration Chief Legal Officer and Secretary, Andre C. (Butch) Bouchard, age 49
SVP CFO and Treasurer, Greg L. Boane, age 51
Senior Vice President General Counsel Secretary, Butch Bouchard
Auditors: KPMGLLP

LOCATIONS

HQ: Team, Inc.
13131 Dairy Ashford, Suite 600, Sugar Land, TX 77478
Phone: 281 331-6154
Web: www.teamindustrialservices.com

2011 Sales

	$ mil.	% of total
US	438.4	70
Canada	121.9	20
Europe	36.4	6
Other	27.0	4
Total	**623.7**	**100**

PRODUCTS/OPERATIONS

2011 Sales

	$ mil.	% of total
TCM	354.8	57
TMS	268.9	43
Total	**623.7**	**100**

Selected Industrial Services

TCM
Field heat treating
Non-descriptive testing
TMS
Field machining
Fugitive emissions control
Field valve repair
Hot tapping
Leak repair
Technical bolting

COMPETITORS

APi Group	Mistras Group
Flowserve	Quality Inspection
Furmanite	Services
Halliburton	Schlumberger
Halma	T. D. Williamson
ITT Corp.	

HISTORICAL FINANCIALS

Company Type: Public

Income Statement

FYE: May 31

	REVENUE ($ mil.)	NET INCOME ($ mil.)	NET PROFIT MARGIN	EMPLOYEES
05/14	749.5	29.8	4.0%	4,300
05/13	714.3	32.4	4.5%	4,200
05/12	623.7	32.9	5.3%	3,800
05/11	508.0	26.5	5.2%	3,500
05/10	453.8	12.2	2.7%	3,100
Annual Growth	**13.4%**	**24.9%**	—	**8.5%**

2014 Year-End Financials

Debt ratio: 15.2%
Return on equity: 9.9%
Cash ($ mil.): 34
Current ratio: 3.31
Long-term debt ($ mil.): 73

No. of shares (mil.): 20
Dividends
  Yield: —
  Payout: —
Market value ($ mil.): 858

	STOCK PRICE ($) FY Close	P/E High/Low	PER SHARE ($) Earnings	Dividends	Book Value
05/14	41.92	33 22	1.40	0.00	15.21
05/13	36.07	29 16	1.53	0.00	13.99
05/12	26.68	20 12	1.59	0.00	12.08
05/11	23.00	21 9	1.32	0.00	10.50
05/10	15.04	32 21	0.63	0.00	8.70
Annual Growth	**29.2%**	—	**22.1%**	—	**15.0%**

Tempur Sealy International, Inc.

Tempur Sealy International's mattresses are made from material that is out of this world. Formerly Tempur-Pedic the company manufactures premium pressure-relieving temperature-sensitive mattresses pillows and other sleep products made from viscoelastic foam technology developed by NASA during the 1970s to help cushion astronauts during liftoff. Its TEMPUR Sealy and Tempur-Pedic brands are sold in more than 80 countries through four distribution channels: retail (furniture and department stores) direct (online and company-owned stores) health care (hospitals and medical retailers) and third-party distributors. Amid declining sales Tempur-Pedic acquired Sealy in 2013 in a deal valued at $1.3 billion.

Mergers and Acquisitions

Together Tempur-Pedic and former-rival Sealy create a $2.7 billion bedding company and give their iconic brands more traction globally. Following the deal which closed in March 2013 the company changed its name to Tempur Sealy International.

Operations

Tempur Sealy operates through two primary segments: domestic and international. The company's domestic segment comprises its US manufacturing facilities in Virginia and New Mexico which cater to its US distribution unit and certain third-party distributors in the Americas. Its domestic business accounts for about 70% of sales. Tempur Sealy's international segment which generates the remainder of sales boasts a manufacturing plant in Denmark that serves all of the company's distribution subsidiaries and third-party distributors outside North America. In 2010 Tempur Sealy bought out its Canadian distributor and made it a wholly owned subsidiary as the mattress maker works to gain market share in the country. It has inked similar deals during the past few years in Austria Australia China and New Zealand.

Financial Performance

Before hopping into bed with Sealy Tempur-Pedic International in 2012 rang up sales of $1.4 billion a 1% decline versus 2011. Net income of $106.8 million represented a 51% decline versus the prior year.

Strategy

Mattresses are the company's flagship product representing two-thirds of Tempur Sealy's total sales. The mattress maker isn't one to rest though. The company regularly rolls out new models of mattresses launches new products or updates existing mattresses globally. In summer 2012 it debuted two new mattresses featuring its new TEMPUR-Breeze technology designed to produce a cooling effect. On the retail front the company in 2012 opened its first flagship retail store in Natick Massachusetts near Boston. The 3500-square-foot store carries the company's full product line. Given its relatively small share of the mattress market Tempur Sealy believes it has plenty of room to steal market share away from spring mattress makers. In recent years Tempur Sealy has been mining the healthcare niche selling its products to hospitals nursing homes and healthcare professionals. The firm also partners with healthcare products makers to integrate its TEMPUR material into their products. Still the healthcare segment is a tiny part of the company's business accounting for just about 2% of 2011 sales. The company is also looking to increase its presence in furniture and bedding stores throughout North America and in international markets and increasing global awareness of its premium brand.

EXECUTIVES

Executive Vice President and President; North America, Richard W. (Rick) Anderson, age 54, $328,000 total compensation
Vice President Investor Relations, Barry Hytinen
President; Chief Executive Officer; Director, Mark A. Sarvary, age 55, $750,000 total compensation
COO, W. Timothy (Tim) Yaggi
Chief Financial Officer; Executive Vice President, Dale E. Williams, age 51, $340,000 total compensation
Executive Vice President; President - International Operations, David Montgomery, age 53, $371,067 total compensation
EVP Global Operations, Matthew D. (Matt) Clift, age 54, $360,000 total compensation
Vice President Information Systems, Stephanie Gaines
Executive Vice President General, Lou H Jones, age 64
Vice President Of Sales Operations, Lewis Grounds
Vice President Supply Chain, Scott Vollet
Vice President Of Sales North America, Todd Miller
Vice President Compensation Benefits, Kim McKendrick
Vice President Category Marketing, Doug McQuillan
Vice President Sales, Kent Hampton
Vice President New Product Development, Allen Platek
Vice President Direct Channels Tempur, Dan Fine
Vice President Human Resources, Glen Gilbertson
Vice President Sales, Rick Zander
Vp Labor And Employee Relations, Diana Strickland
Vice President Product Merchandising, Mike Brady
Vice President Of Marketing Tempur, Brent Pfister
Vice President Of Marketing Stearns, Dan Calderwood
Vp Global Product Engineering, Gary Ford
Evp Of Global Operations, Matt Clift
President; Chief Executive Officer; Director, Mark A. Sarvary, age 55
Chairman, P. Andrews McLane, age 67
Vice Chairman, Robert B. (Bob) Trussell, age 63
Auditors: Ernst&YoungLLP

LOCATIONS

HQ: Tempur Sealy International, Inc.
1000 Tempur Way, Lexington, KY 40511
Phone: 800 878-8889
Web: www.tempursealy.com

2012 Sales

	$ mil.	% of total
North American	964.3	69
International	438.6	31
Total	**1402.9**	**100**

PRODUCTS/OPERATIONS

2012 Sales

	$ mil.	% of total
Retail	1228.0	88
Direct	113.2	8
Healthcare	31.1	2
Third party	30.6	2
Total	**1402.9**	**100**

2012 Sales

	$ mil.	% of total
Mattresses	934.6	67
Pillows	158.3	11
Other	310.0	22
Total	**1402.9**	**100**

COMPETITORS

Select Comfort   Simmons
Serta   Spring Air

HISTORICAL FINANCIALS

Company Type: Public

Income Statement

FYE: December 31

	REVENUE ($ mil.)	NET INCOME ($ mil.)	NET PROFIT MARGIN	EMPLOYEES
12/13	2,464.3	78.6	3.2%	6,700
12/12	1,402.9	106.8	7.6%	1,950
12/11	1,417.9	219.6	15.5%	1,800
12/10	1,105.4	157.1	14.2%	1,500
12/09	831.1	84.9	10.2%	1,150
Annual Growth	**31.2%**	**(1.9%)**	**—**	**55.4%**

2013 Year-End Financials

Debt ratio: 67.2%
Return on equity: 111.5%
Cash ($ mil.): 81
Current ratio: 1.65
Long-term debt ($ mil.): 1,796

No. of shares (mil.): 60
Dividends
Yield: —
Payout: —
Market value ($ mil.): 3,270

	STOCK PRICE ($) FY Close	P/E High/Low	PER SHARE ($) Earnings	Dividends	Book Value
12/13	53.96	42 24	1.28	0.00	1.96
12/12	31.49	50 12	1.70	0.00	0.37
12/11	52.53	22 12	3.18	0.00	0.48
12/10	40.06	18 11	2.16	0.00	1.84
12/09	23.63	21 3	1.12	0.00	2.29
Annual Growth	**22.9%**	**— —**	**3.4%**	**—**	**(3.9%)**

Teradyne, Inc.

Teradyne has the anodyne for electronics makers concerned about quality and consistency. The company is a leading supplier of automated test equipment and a maker of systems for testing semiconductors. Teradyne caters to electronics manufacturing services suppliers as well as OEMs who use its test systems to analyze complex electronics used in the computing consumer electronics military/aerospace and telecommunications industries. Customers include Apple government contractors and the US government. Teradyne has operations in Asia Europe and the Americas; but it generates the majority of sales from customers in Asia.

HISTORY

College pals Nicholas DeWolf and Alexander d'Arbeloff (who met in an alphabetical ROTC lineup at MIT) founded Teradyne in 1960 to develop industrial-grade electronic test equipment. The name combines "tera" (10 to the 12th power) and "dyne" (a unit of force); to the founding duo it meant "rolling a 15000-ton boulder uphill." The company's first headquarters was a loft over Joe & Nemo's hot dog stand in downtown Boston. In 1961 the company sold its first product –an automatic tester for semiconductor diodes called a go/no-go diode tester –to Raytheon for $5000.

Teradyne grew rapidly during the 1960s as it introduced new products including testers for integrated circuits resistors transistors and diodes. In the latter part of the decade the company began using computers to speed up the testing process helping create the automatic test equipment (ATE) industry. It formed Teradyne Components (later Teradyne Connection Systems) in 1968 to produce electronics connection assemblies.

Teradyne went public in 1970. That year with the first slump in the semiconductor industry the company laid off 15% of its workforce and began diversifying its customer base. DeWolf departed Teradyne in 1971 leaving d'Arbeloff to run operations. The market quickly recovered and the company grew and prospered again. In 1972 it began working on a telephone system testing device the 4Tel. However the market slumped again and in 1975 Teradyne cut its staff by 15% a second time.

When trouble hit again in the mid-1980s Teradyne suffered back-to-back annual losses. Meanwhile Japanese companies overtook US semiconductor makers leaving Teradyne short of customers for its testers. Teradyne fought back in the late 1980s by lowering prices to undercut the competition and by pushing into the Japanese market. In addition the company formed a computer-aided engineering group by purchasing and combining Aida Corporation and Case Technologies.

The cycle continued in the early 1990s as military spending fell leading to further staff cuts salary freezes and even a temporary suspension of production. Through the mid-1990s a $63 million contract from the German national telephone system an upgrade in Teradyne's ATE line and a release of the TestMaster software development tool had Teradyne growing again.

High demand for PCs elevated sales of the company's semiconductor testing equipment helping it top $1 billion in sales for the first time in 1995. However the next year another semiconductor industry downturn caused a drop in profits and Teradyne laid off about 300 workers. In 1997 president George Chamillard succeeded d'Arbeloff as CEO. (D'Arbeloff remained chairman until 2000 when Chamillard succeeded him in that post as well.)

Teradyne turned a profit for 1998 despite one of the chip industry's worst-ever downturns. As chip sales and Asian economies rebounded Teradyne booked more than $2 billion in sales in 1999. Riding the crest of a chip industry boom Teradyne in 2000 posted record sales and its highest revenue growth in more than 25 years.

In the closing days of 2000 Teradyne sold its software testing division to a group of private investors led by Matrix Partners; that business became Empirix.

In 2001 Teradyne acquired GenRad for about $260 million in stock and debt assumption. GenRad was later renamed Teradyne Diagnostic Solutions. Also that year it laid off about 1000 employees (about 11% of its workforce) and reduced managerial salaries in response to a sharp downturn in the worldwide chip industry.

In 2004 George Chamillard stepped down as CEO (he remained chairman); president Michael Bradley took on the additional title of CEO.

To focus on its test systems business the company sold its Connection Systems division to Amphenol for about $390 million in 2005; Connection Systems accounted for about 20% of its revenue in 2004.

In 2006 the company moved out of its high-rise headquarters in downtown Boston relocating operations to its campus in suburban North Reading. Teradyne sold the HQ building to Nordic Properties for nearly $35 million. It sold another Boston building in 2006 to Millennium Partners.

Co-founder Nick DeWolf died in 2006 at the age of 77. At the end of 2006 George Chamillard retired from the board of directors after working at Teradyne for more than 35 years. Patricia Wolpert a director since 1996 and a retired IBM executive was named to succeed him as chairman.

In 2007 Teradyne acquired memory test assets from MOSAID Technologies a memory device testing technology developer for $17 million in cash. That same year it also sold its broadband test product line and related assets to competitor Tollgrade Communications for about $12 million.

Co-founder Alex d'Arbeloff died in 2008 at the age of 80.

Complementing its strength in SoC test the company moved into flash memory testing with the 2008 acquisition of Nextest Systems which got more than 80% of its sales from flash memory testers. Teradyne spent about $325 million to buy Nextest which became a business unit of the Semiconductor Test division. Also that year Teradyne purchased another competitor Eagle Test Systems which specialized in testing analog and power management chips. It became a business unit of the Semiconductor Test division. Teradyne spent about $250 million to acquire Eagle Test. Both deals were expected to help Teradyne compete against the combination of two leading test vendors Credence Systems and LTX which merged in 2008 to form LTX-Credence (later renamed Xcerra).

EXECUTIVES

Vice President Operations, James A Federico
President CEO and Director, Michael A. Bradley, age 66, $720,000 total compensation
Vice President And Treasurer, Stuart M Osattin
VP and CFO, Gregory R. (Greg) Beecher, age 56, $415,000 total compensation
President Semiconductor Test Division, Mark E. Jagiela, age 53, $405,000 total compensation
President Systems Test Group, Walter Vahey, age 49, $255,256 total compensation
President LitePoint, Benny Madsen
Vice President, Vickie Eckert
Vice President, James Prestridge
Vice President, Robert Copithorne
Vice President, Angie Dean
Vice President Regional Sales, Steven Moy
Vice President Of Engineering, Mike Malone
Vice President Global Services, Michael Luttati
Vice President Business Sales, Finlay Morrow
Vice President Of Marketing, Eric Kaled
Vice President Global Strateg, Paul Markham
Vice President Memory Division, Thomas Felding
Vice President Of Strategic Planning, Brad Robbins
Vice President Platform Engineering, Bradford Robbins
President CEO and Director, Michael A. Bradley, age 66
VP and CFO, Gregory R. (Greg) Beecher, age 56
Chairman, Albert Carnesale, age 77
Board Member, Daniel W Christman
Board Member, Timothy Guertin
Board Member, Kee Tay
Auditors: PricewaterhouseCoopersLLP

LOCATIONS

HQ: Teradyne, Inc.
  600 Riverpark Drive, North Reading, MA 01864
Phone: 978 370-2700
Web: www.teradyne.com

2012 Sales

	$ mil.	% of total
China	354.1	21
Taiwan	303.4	18
US	233.5	14
Korea	225.1	14
Philippines	106.7	6
Japan	106.0	6
Europe	84.5	5
Singapore	80.5	5
Thailand	76.1	5
Malaysia	71.2	4
Rest of world	15.7	1
Total	**1656.8**	**100**

PRODUCTS/OPERATIONS

2012 Sales

	$ mil.	% of total
Semiconductor test	1127.7	68
Wireless test	286.4	17
Systems test	242.7	15
Total	**1656.8**	**100**

2012 Sales

	$ mil.	% of total
Product	1383.6	84
Service	273.2	16
Total	**1656.8**	**100**

Selected Products

Semiconductor test systems
  Memory test
  Microcontroller test
  Mixed-signal test (A5 line)
  System-on-a-chip test
  Very large scale integration (VLSI) chip test
Circuit board test and inspection systems
  Automated optical inspection
  In-circuit and functional board test
  Software
Military and aerospace
  Spectrum CTS (avionics systems)
  VICTORY (boundary scan and fault diagnostic software)
Wireless test
  IQfact (chipset)
  IQflex (WLAN)
  IQxstream (multi-device tester for devices)

COMPETITORS

Advantest	KLA-Tencor
Aeroflex	Mitsui
Agilent Technologies	National Instruments
Anritsu	Orbotech
Camtek	Rohde & Schwarz
Cascade Microtech	Tektronix
FormFactor	Xcerra
Hitachi	Xyratex
High-Technologies	Yokogawa Electric

HISTORICAL FINANCIALS

Company Type: Public

Income Statement
FYE: December 31

	REVENUE ($ mil.)	NET INCOME ($ mil.)	NET PROFIT MARGIN	EMPLOYEES
12/13	1,427.9	164.9	11.6%	3,800
12/12	1,656.7	217.0	13.1%	3,600
12/11	1,429.0	373.8	26.2%	3,200
12/10	1,608.6	379.7	23.6%	3,000
12/09	819.4	(133.8)	—	2,900
Annual Growth	**14.9%**	—		**7.0%**

2013 Year-End Financials

Debt ratio: 7.1%	No. of shares (mil.): 191
Return on equity: 8.7%	Dividends
Cash ($ mil.): 341	Yield: —
Current ratio: 3.03	Payout: —
Long-term debt ($ mil.): —	Market value ($ mil.): 3,378

	STOCK PRICE ($) FY Close	P/E High/Low	PER SHARE ($) Earnings	Dividends	Book Value
12/13	17.62	22 17	0.70	0.00	10.35
12/12	16.89	15 11	0.94	0.00	9.46
12/11	13.63	9 5	1.65	0.00	8.20
12/10	14.04	7 4	1.73	0.00	6.16
12/09	10.73	— —	(0.77)	0.00	3.80
Annual Growth	**13.2%**	— —	—	—	**28.5%**

Tesoro Logistics LP

Tesoro Logistics was created to serve its parent. The company a spinoff of oil refiner Tesoro Corporation owns and operates crude oil gathering transportation and storage facilities in the US. Its trucks and 700 miles of Montana and North Dakota pipeline serve Tesoro's Mandan refinery while eight refined product terminals hold petroleum in California Utah Washington Alaska and North Dakota. Tesoro Logistics' primary storage facility in Salt Lake City holds nearly 880000 barrels of crude and refined petroleum. Most of the company's revenue comes from Tesoro and is evenly split between the gathering segment and the transporting and storing segment. It went public in 2011.

Though all of Tesoro Logistics' assets are on its parent company's land it plans to pursue business with and acquisitions from third-parties. The company used its $230 million in IPO proceeds for working capital and to pay down debt to Tesoro Corporation.

In 2013 the company acquired Chevron Pipe Line Company's Northwest Products System for $355 million and the first portion of integrated Carson logistics assets from Tesoro Corporation for $640 million.

Tesoro Logistics works within the volatile petroleum industry but because its business is fee-based and it doesn't actually own the petroleum it believes it is protected from the variations in the market.

EXECUTIVES

Vp General Counsel Secretary And Director,
  Charles S Parrish
Auditors: Ernst&YoungLLP

LOCATIONS

HQ: Tesoro Logistics LP
  19100 Ridgewood Parkway, San Antonio, TX 78259-1828
Phone: 210 626-6000
Web: www.tesorologistics.com

PRODUCTS/OPERATIONS

2009 Sales

	$ mil.	% of total
Gathering		
Affiliate	19.3	86
Third party	.1	—
Terminalling transportation & storage		
Third party	3.2	14
Total	**22.6**	**100**

COMPETITORS

EOG	Plains All American
Enbridge	Pipeline
Encana	TransCanada

HISTORICAL FINANCIALS

Company Type: Public

Income Statement
FYE: December 31

	REVENUE ($ mil.)	NET INCOME ($ mil.)	NET PROFIT MARGIN	EMPLOYEES
12/13	305.4	41.6	13.6%	470
12/12	156.8	55.5	35.4%	160
12/11	80.9	27.9	34.5%	114
12/10	23.3	(20.8)	—	0
12/09	22.6	(21.8)	—	0
Annual Growth	**91.6%**	—	—	—

2013 Year-End Financials

Debt ratio: 77.5%	No. of shares (mil.): 55
Return on equity: 27.1%	Dividends
Cash ($ mil.): 23	Yield: 3.8%
Current ratio: 1.10	Payout: 117.9%
Long-term debt ($ mil.): 1,164	Market value ($ mil.): 2,906

	STOCK PRICE ($) FY Close	P/E High/Low	PER SHARE ($) Earnings	Dividends	Book Value
12/13	52.34	46 28	1.47	2.02	4.42
12/12	43.80	25 16	1.89	1.61	(0.50)
12/11	32.90	30 19	1.11	0.59	3.50
Annual Growth	**26.1%**	— —	**15.1%**	**84.2%**	**12.4%**

Texas Capital Bancshares Inc

Texas Capital Bancshares is the parent company of Texas Capital Bank with more than 10 branches in Austin Dallas Fort Worth Houston and San Antonio. The bank targets high-net-worth individuals and Texas-based businesses with more than $5 million in annual revenue with a focus on the real estate financial services transportation communications petrochemicals and mining sectors. Striving for personalized services for its clients the bank offers deposit accounts Visa credit cards commercial loans and mortgages equipment leasing wealth management and trust services. Its BankDirect division provides online banking services. Founded in 1998 Texas Capital Bancshares has about $11.7 billion in assets.

Financial Performance

The bank reported $488.6 million in revenue in 2013 an nearly 11% increase versus 2012. Net income was flat at about $121 million after posting three consecutive years of gains. Cash flow from operations continued its steep three year decline. The bank's total assets increased 11% from about $10.5 billion in 2012 to $11.7 billion in 2013.

Total deposits increased 24% year over year to about $9.3 billion.

Strategy

Headquartered in Dallas Texas Capital Bank (TCB) believes that its Texas roots give it a competitive advantage over larger competitors that are headquartered out of state. Indeed TCB is gaining market share and is expanding by hiring experienced bankers and support staff. The bank is looking to grow within its main metropolitan markets but has also branched out beyond the borders of its home state. The bank has an Cayman Islands branch to offer offshore cash management and deposit products to it core clientele.

EXECUTIVES

President CEO and Director, George F. Jones, age 70, $585,000 total compensation
President and CEO Texas Capital Bancshares Inc. President and CEO Texas Capital Bank, C. Keith Cargill, age 61, $346,667 total compensation
President Texas; Chief Lending Officer Texas Capital Bank, Vince A. Ackerson, $297,500 total compensation
Regional President Texas Capital Bank Austin, Kerry L. Hall
Regional President Texas Capital Bank Dallas, Russell Hartsfield
CFO and COO Texas Capital Bancshares; COO Texas Capital Bank, Peter B. Bartholow, age 65, $361,667 total compensation
Chief Risk Officer and Chief Credit Officer Texas Capital Bank, John D. Hudgens, $316,667 total compensation
EVP and COO Texas Capital Bank, James C. (Jim) White
Regional President Texas Capital Bank Fort Worth, Jeff Moten
Regional President Texas Capital Bank San Antonio, David Pope
Regional President Texas Capital Bank Houston, John Sarvadi
Senior Vice President Dir Investor Rel, Heather Worley
Vice President Manager Credit Underwriting, Anthony Violi
Vice President, Robert Little
Senior Vice President Compensation Director, Chris Gullo
Assistant Vice President Lender Finance, Mike Ebrahim
Vice President Finance, Duff Mahan
Senior Vice President, Jennifer Poindexter
Vice President, Ramona Baker
Executive Vice President Corp Banking, Reed Allton
Senior Vice President, Bill Rolley
Vice President Fraud Investigator, Jamie Burud
Vice President, Lela Naggar
Executive Vice President, Carlos Munguia
Senior Vice President Director Of In, Paul Bowler
Executive Vice President, Brent Johnston
Vice President, Raul Cantu
Assistant Vice President Ck Prcsng Mgr, Olga Gutierrez
Vice President Deposit Operations, Leslie Marsh
Vice President In Commercial Banking Group, Guy Miller
Senior Vice President Risk Management Officer, Terry King
Vice President Security, Neal Baker
Senior Vice President Builder Finance, Melissa Hicks
Vice President Of Information Technology Infrastructure, Randy Tiegs

Vice President Project Management, Allen Baumbach
Senior Vice President, Stephanie Hopkins
Assistant Vice President Marketing, Tanya Williams
Senior Vice President Commercial Banking, Randall Lasley
Vice President Training Documenation, Rebecca Cams
Assistant Vice President Recruiting, Tiffany Haire
Senior Vice President Ops Recruiting, Jennifer Brungardt
Senior Vice President, Don Rosics
Senior Vice President And Deposit Operation, Connie Couch
Senior Vice President Product, Allen Curcio
Assistant Vice President Loan, Mary Frosto
Senior Vice President Wealth Management And Trust Services, Chip Glispin
Vice President Performance Rpt, Jeffrey Petty
Senior Vice President, Leslie Tieszen
Senior Vice President Builder Finance, Tuck Perkins
Vice President Business Solutions Group, David Leventhal
Vice President, Jenny Downey
Senior Vice President And Coml Lndr, Douglas Cotner
Senior Vice President In The Southwest Corporate Banking Division, Paul Howell
Senior Vice President Tream Leader, Scott Wiginton
Vice President Information Technology Systems Engineer, Keith Harber
Vice President, Jimmie Schellinger
Senior Vice President, Robin Hogan
Chairman, Larry L. Helm, age 67
Auditors: Ernst&YoungLLP

LOCATIONS

HQ: Texas Capital Bancshares Inc
2000 McKinney Avenue, Suite 700, Dallas, TX 75201
Phone: 214 932-6600
Web: www.texascapitalbank.com

COMPETITORS

Amegy	Cullen/Frost Bankers
BOK Financial	JPMorgan Chase
Bank of America	Prosperity Bancshares
Comerica	Wells Fargo
Compass Bancshares	

HISTORICAL FINANCIALS

Company Type: Public

Income Statement

FYE: December 31

	ASSETS ($ mil.)	NET INCOME ($ mil.)	INCOME AS % OF ASSETS	EMPLOYEES
12/13	11,714.6	121.0	1.0%	1,016
12/12	10,540.8	120.6	1.1%	881
12/11	8,137.6	75.9	0.9%	786
12/10	6,446.1	37.1	0.6%	699
12/09	5,698.9	24.1	0.4%	631
Annual Growth	19.7%	49.6%	—	12.6%

2013 Year-End Financials

Return on assets: 1.0%
Return on equity: 12.5%
Long-term debt ($ mil.): —
No. of shares (mil.): 41
Sales ($ mil): 488
Dividends
Yield: —
Payout: —
Market value ($ mil.): 2,552

STOCK PRICE ($) FY Close	P/E High/Low		PER SHARE ($) Earnings	Dividends	Book Value
12/13	62.20	22 14	2.72	0.00	26.72
12/12	44.82	17 10	3.00	0.00	20.53
12/11	30.61	15 10	1.98	0.00	16.36
12/10	21.34	22 13	1.00	0.00	14.30
12/09	13.96	33 12	0.55	0.00	13.40
Annual Growth	45.3%	— —	49.1%	—	18.8%

Texas Pacific Land Trust

Texas Pacific Land Trust was created to sell the Texas & Pacific Railway's land after its 1888 bankruptcy and yup they're still workin' on it. The trust began with the railroad's 3.5 million acres; today it is one of the largest private landowners in Texas with around 960000 acres in 20 counties. Texas Pacific Land Trust's sales come from oil and gas royalties (70% of sales) grazing leases easements and land sales. It has a perpetual oil and gas royalty interest under some 470000 acres in West Texas. About 8% of the trust's oil and gas royalties are from leases operated by Chevron U.S.A. Texas Pacific Land Trust uses the revenues from sales and royalties to buy and retire its own shares.

The trust sold about 2200 acres of land in 2008 compared to some 1500 acres in 2007. While Texas Pacific Land Trust sold more acreage in 2008 the price per acre was less than a third of the price in 2007.

Grazing leases are in effect on 99% of the trust's land.

EXECUTIVES

CEO Secretary and General Agent, Roy Thomas, age 68, $187,917 total compensation
CFO and Assistant General Agent, David M. Peterson, age 49, $127,833 total compensation
Chairman, Maurice Meyer III, age 79
Trustee, John R. Norris III, age 61
Trustee, James K. Norwood, age 73
Auditors: LaneGormanTrubittL.L.P.

LOCATIONS

HQ: Texas Pacific Land Trust
1700 Pacific Avenue, Suite 2770, Dallas, TX 75201
Phone: 214 969-5530 **Fax:** 214 871-7139
Web: www.TPLTrust.com

PRODUCTS/OPERATIONS

2008 Sales

	$ mil.	% of total
Oil & gas royalties	13.7	71
Interest	1.4	7
Land sales	0.8	4
Grazing leases	0.5	3
Easements & other	2.9	15
Total	**19.3**	**100**

COMPETITORS

American Realty Investors	Koch Industries Inc.
	Permian Basin

HISTORICAL FINANCIALS

Company Type: Public

Income Statement

FYE: December 31

	REVENUE ($ mil.)	NET INCOME ($ mil.)	NET PROFIT MARGIN	EMPLOYEES
12/13	44.1	27.2	61.7%	8
12/12	32.5	19.6	60.3%	9
12/11	34.3	20.5	60.0%	9
12/10	20.0	11.3	56.4%	8
12/09	13.0	6.9	52.8%	8
Annual Growth	35.5%	40.9%	—	0.0%

2013 Year-End Financials

Debt ratio: —
Return on equity: 162.3%
Cash ($ mil.): 13
Current ratio: 7.57
Long-term debt ($ mil.): —

No. of shares (mil.): 8
Dividends
Yield: 0.0%
Payout: —
Market value ($ mil.): 847

	STOCK PRICE ($) FY Close	P/E High/Low		PER SHARE ($) Earnings	Dividends	Book Value
12/13	99.99	32	16	3.16	0.00	2.12
12/12	53.43	28	18	2.20	0.48	1.77
12/11	40.69	22	16	2.21	0.21	2.24
12/10	36.48	37	22	1.17	0.20	1.92
12/09	30.05	54	24	0.69	0.19	1.99
Annual Growth	35.1%	—	—	46.3%	—	1.5%

Texas Roadhouse Inc

If people are getting rowdy at this roadhouse it must be because of the steaks ribs or the famous sweet yeast rolls. Texas Roadhouse operates a leading full-service restaurant chain with more than 400 company-owned and franchised locations in 48 states. The Southwest-themed eateries serve a variety of hand-cut steaks ribs chicken pork chops and seafood entrees along with sandwiches chili starters and a variety of side dishes. The company also operates a small number of restaurants under the name Aspen Creek that specialize in hamburgers pasta entrees and pizza.

Geographic Reach

Although the chain is essentially nationwide now the bulk of Texas Roadhouse restaurants are located in the Midwest and Southeast. More than 50 of the company's restaurants are located in Texas and many units are located near interstate highways.

Operations

About 320 Texas Roadhouse locations are company-owned while the rest are franchised. The company gets nearly all of its revenue (about 99% in fiscal 2011 and 2012) from company-owned and operated units.

Sales and Marketing

Targeting the casual dining sector the Texas Roadhouse concept focuses on offering mid-priced menu items and a family-friendly dining atmosphere. The chain is primarily interested in serving the dinner segment offering its lunch menu only during the weekends. Its over-the-top Texas d ©or including such down home touches as jukeboxes and complimentary in-the-shell peanuts helps the chain distinguish itself in a crowded field of competitors that includes Logan's Roadhouse (owned by LRI Holdings) and Lone Star Steakhouse.

Texas Roadhouse also faces stiff competition from industry heavyweights Chili's (Brinker International) and Outback Steakhouse (OSI Restaurant Partners).

Country singer Willie Nelson who is a partner in two restaurants located in Austin Texas serves as a celebrity spokesperson for Texas Roadhouse. The chain sponsors the popular artist's concert tours and each restaurant features "Willie's Corner" decorated with memorabilia.

Financial Performance

The company's revenue increased by 14% to $1.26 billion in fiscal 2012 compared to the $1.1 billion it reported bringing in during fiscal 2011 while its profit increased by 11% in fiscal 2012 compared to the previous year. The 2012 revenue spike was powered by double digit growth in both restaurant sales and franchise royalties and fees.

Restaurant sales increased by 14% due to the opening of new restaurants and an increase in average unit volumes from hikes in menu prices along with higher guest traffic counts. Franchise royalties and fees increased by 13% primarily due to an increase in average unit volumes increasing royalty rates and the opening of new franchise restaurants.

Strategy

The company is focused on ensuring quality and boosting traffic at its existing restaurants. The chain relies on specially-priced value menu items and targeted its marketing message toward cost-conscious families looking for affordable dining options.

Texas Roadhouse has taken steps to rein in development costs for new restaurents as it continues to expand. Its growth strategy includes expanding its restaurant base. In 2012 the chain opened 25 company-owned restaurants. The company plans to open about 28 company restaurants in 2013 all of which will be Texas Roadhouse restaurants. In addition it anticipates during 2013 its existing franchise partners will open as many as five Texas Roadhouse restaurants primarily in international markets.

Over the past several years the company has invested in improvements to its information systems real estate holdings human resources legal and marketing operations.

Company Background

Founder and chairman Kent Taylor opened the first Texas Roadhouse in 1993. A veteran of the restaurant business he previously served with such chains as Bennigan's (formerly owned by Metromedia Company) Hooters and KFC.

EXECUTIVES

President, Scott M. Colosi, age 49, $400,000 total compensation
Chairman and CEO, W. Kent Taylor, age 58, $525,000 total compensation
COO, Steven L. Ortiz, age 56, $480,000 total compensation
CFO, Price Cooper, $250,000 total compensation
Vice President Manager Director, Brian Wathen
Regional Vice President, Lus Goovaerts
Vice President Information Technology, Hernan Mujica
Corporate Human Resources Vice President, Jenn Pressner
Vice President Customer Development, David Willey
Vice President Of Operations, Ron Houser
Vice President Of Training And People, Juanita Ensminger
Corporate Human Resources Vice President, Laura Hoon

Vice President Of Food And Beverage, Jim Broyles
Chairman and CEO, W. Kent Taylor, age 58
Senior Treasury Analyst, Stephanie Faulkner
Auditors: KPMGLLP

LOCATIONS

HQ: Texas Roadhouse Inc
6040 Dutchmans Lane, Suite 200, Louisville, KY 40205
Phone: 502 426-9984
Web: www.texasroadhouse.com

PRODUCTS/OPERATIONS

2012 Sales

	$ mil.	% of total
Restaurants	1252.4	99
Franchising	10.9	1
Total	1263.3	100

2012 Locations

	No.
Company-owned	320
Franchised	72
Total	392

COMPETITORS

Applebee's International	LRI Holdings
Brinker	Landry's
Buffets Inc	Lone Star Steakhouse
Carlson Restaurants	O'Charley's
Cracker Barrel	OSI Restaurant Partners
Darden	P.F. Chang's
Golden Corral	Ruby Tuesday
Hooters	
Ignite Restaurant Group	

HISTORICAL FINANCIALS

Company Type: Public

Income Statement

FYE: December 31

	REVENUE ($ mil.)	NET INCOME ($ mil.)	NET PROFIT MARGIN	EMPLOYEES
12/13	1,422.5	80.4	5.7%	45,700
12/12	1,263.3	71.1	5.6%	40,000
12/11	1,109.2	63.9	5.8%	33,000
12/10	1,004.9	58.2	5.8%	32,000
12/09	942.3	47.4	5.0%	31,000
Annual Growth	10.8%	14.1%	—	10.2%

2013 Year-End Financials

Debt ratio: 5.8%
Return on equity: 14.2%
Cash ($ mil.): 94
Current ratio: 0.83
Long-term debt ($ mil.): 50

No. of shares (mil.): 70
Dividends
Yield: 1.7%
Payout: 44.0%
Market value ($ mil.): 1,956

	STOCK PRICE ($) FY Close	P/E High/Low		PER SHARE ($) Earnings	Dividends	Book Value
12/13	27.80	25	15	1.13	0.48	8.35
12/12	16.82	18	14	1.00	0.46	7.61
12/11	15.13	21	14	0.88	0.32	7.11
12/10	17.31	22	13	0.80	0.00	6.88
12/09	11.58	18	10	0.67	0.00	5.97
Annual Growth	24.5%	—	—	14.0%	—	8.7%

The Bancorp, Inc.

The Bancorp is —what else? —the holding company for The Bancorp Bank which provides financial services in the virtual world. On its home turf of the Philadelphia and Wilmington Delaware metropolitan areas The Bancorp Bank offers deposit lending and related services targeting wealthy individuals and small to midsized businesses it believes are underserved by larger banks in the market. Nationally The Bancorp provides private-label online banking services for some 300 affinity groups issues prepaid debit cards processes merchant credit card transactions and acts as a custodian for health savings accounts (HSAs).

As an online bank the company has no branches; however it does operate three loan production offices in the Philadelphia area. The company also operates vehicle fleet leasing businesses Jefferson Leasing and Mears Motor Leasing which are active in about 40 states. Commercial and constructin loans and commercial mortgages dominate The Bancorp's loan portfolio.

The company's strategies for growth include generating deposits through its prepaid card community banking merchant processing and wealth management operations the funds of which it will expand its lending operations. It also hopes to market its offerings to customers of its affinity groups and generally drive up business in its home region. The Bancorp has also explored the possibility of establishing a new savings bank in southern New Jersey adjacent to its primary market area; the move would add a thrift charter to help accelerate the bank's nationwide expansion.

The Bancorp's earnings have been growing since the company lost money in 2008. Revenues in 2011 grew 15% to $119 million while profits grew 70% to $8.9 million. The increases were buoyed by higher prepaid card fees resulting from higher transaction volumes. Additionally prepaid card wealth management health care and merchant processing deposits all grew that year. However the company increased its provision for loan losses in both 2010 and 2011 allowing for challenges in the economic climate.

EXECUTIVES

EVP Strategy CFO and Secretary, Paul Frenkiel, age 62, $310,805 total compensation

President CEO and COO, Frank M. Mastrangelo, age 46, $509,508 total compensation

EVP and Chief Credit Officer The Bancorp Inc. and The Bancorp Bank, Donald F. (Don) McGraw, age 57, $257,115 total compensation

EVP and Chief Lending Officer, Scott R. Megargee, age 62, $202,541 total compensation

EVP Commercial Lending, Arthur M. Birenbaum, age 57, $423,207 total compensation

EVP and CIO, Peter (Pete) Chiccino

SVP Affinity Banking, Jill E. Kelly

SVP Loan Operations and Administration, Sandra C. Reel

SVP and Chief Risk Officer, James D. (Jim) Hilty

SVP and Managing Director Payment Solutions Group, Jeremy Kuiper

EVP Commercial and Construction Real Estate Lending, Dan Sacho

Finance Senior Vice President, Terrence Crowley

Finance Vice President, Mark A Conners

Vice President Divisional Compliance, Nancy Sjogren

Executive Vice President Marketing, Barbara Capelli

Vice President Commercial Mortgage, Paul Schuler

First Vice President, Genevieve Johnson

Vice President Leasing Sales, Billy Stueber

Senior Vice President Director Of Communications, Maria Antonelli

Chairman The Bancorp Inc. and The Bancorp Bank, Daniel G. Cohen, age 44

Auditors: GrantThorntonLLP

LOCATIONS

HQ: The Bancorp, Inc.
409 Silverside Road, Wilmington, DE 19809
Phone: 302 385-5000
Web: www.thebancorp.com

PRODUCTS/OPERATIONS

2011 Sales

	$ mil.	% of total
Interest		
Loans including fees	74.6	63
Securities	12.4	10
Other	1.5	1
Noninterest		
Prepaid fees	18.7	16
Service fees on deposit accounts	2.9	2
Other	9.0	8
Adjustments	(0.1)	-
Total	**119.0**	**100**

COMPETITORS

Citizens Financial Group	Republic First Bank
E*TRADE Bank	Royal Bancshares
ING DIRECT USA	Sovereign Bank
M&T Bank	Sun Bancorp (NJ)
PNC Financial	TD Bank USA
	WSFS Financial

HISTORICAL FINANCIALS

Company Type: Public

Income Statement

FYE: December 31

	ASSETS ($ mil.)	NET INCOME ($ mil.)	INCOME AS % OF ASSETS	EMPLOYEES
12/13	4,706.0	25.1	0.5%	624
12/12	3,699.6	16.6	0.4%	532
12/11	3,010.6	8.9	0.3%	428
12/10	2,395.7	5.2	0.2%	373
12/09	2,043.5	4.1	0.2%	367
Annual Growth	**23.2%**	**57.3%**	**—**	**14.2%**

2013 Year-End Financials

Return on assets: 0.6%	Dividends
Return on equity: 7.2%	Yield: —
Long-term debt ($ mil.): —	Payout: —
No. of shares (mil.): 37	Market value ($ mil.): 674
Sales ($ mil): 189	

	STOCK PRICE ($) FY Close	P/E High/Low		PER SHARE ($) Earnings	Dividends	Book Value
12/13	17.91	28	16	0.66	0.00	9.56
12/12	10.97	25	15	0.50	0.00	9.06
12/11	7.23	38	23	0.28	0.00	8.20
12/10	10.17	—	—	(0.04)	0.00	7.60
12/09	6.86	397	129	0.02	0.00	9.37
Annual Growth	**27.1%**	**—**		**—139.7%**		**0.5%**

Thermon Group Holdings Inc

Thermon Group's heating products are not merely pipe dreams. Through its subsidiaries Thermon provides specialized cables tubes and control systems used in electric and steam "heat tracing" which involves externally applying heat to industrial-grade pipes tanks and instrumentation. Its core customers include energy chemical and power generation companies that use Thermon's products to maintain temperatures of materials transported or stored in pipes and vessels as well as for freeze protection in harsh environments. The company's customers have included dozens of multinational giants like Exxon Dow ConocoPhillips Procter and Gamble and Kellogg.

IPO

Founded in 1954 Thermon went public in 2011 and used the proceeds to repay debt and for general corporate purposes.

Geographic Reach

Thermon operates through a global network of some 30 sales engineering and other offices in cities across North America Europe Asia and Australia. It also operates four manufacturing facilities located in San Marcos Texas; Calgary Canada; Pijnacker the Netherlands; and Koregon Bhima India.

Canada generates 35% of its sales while the US accounts for nearly 30%. Europe and Asia bring in nearly 20% and 15% respectively.

Sales and Marketing

The company markets its products to customers around the world that are constructing brand new facilities as well as those performing maintenance on updating or expanding existing facilities. It has a team of nearly 100 direct sales agents and a network of over 100 independent sales agents and distributors in 30 countries.

Financial Performance

Thermon has successfully bounced back after suffering a net loss in 2011. Revenues were up nearly 5% from $271 million in 2012 to $284 million in 2013. Profits also more than doubled from $12 million in 2012 to $27 million in 2013 due to the higher revenues and the absence of loss on debt.

The company was helped by a 42% increase in sales from the important market of Asia and a 20% spike in sales from Canada during 2013. Its growth stemmed from an increased number of sales for the construction of new facilities as well as strong demand from maintenance and repair operations.

Strategy

As part of its growth strategy Thermon intends to expand its sales and marketing efforts into international growth markets like Russia China and India where the energy chemical and power generation sectors are expanding with economic and consumer demand. It will also use acquisitions and investments to complement its existing business lines.

In addition to geographic expansion other growth efforts include broadening its product and service lines to serve alternative energy companies that work in solar carbon capture and other areas.

Ownership

Eagle Asset Management owns about 10% of the company.

EXECUTIVES

SVP Finance; CFO and Secretary, Jay C. Peterson, age 57

president and CEO and Director, Rodney Bingham, age 63, $265,608 total compensation

EVP Global Sales, George P. Alexander, age 64, $220,578 total compensation

SVP Global Operations, Ren Aⁿvan (Johannes) der Salm

Sr V Pres Global Opr, Rene Van Der Salm

Svp Global Corp Development, Geoffrey Demartino

Chairman, Charles A. Sorrentino

Board Member, Richard E Goodrich, age 71

Board Member, Michael W Press

Auditors: Ernst&YoungLLP

LOCATIONS

HQ: Thermon Group Holdings Inc
100 Thermon Drive, San Marcos, TX 78666
Phone: 512 396-5801
Web: www.thermon.com

2013 Sales

	$ mil.	% of total
Canada	99.8	35
US	83.5	29
Europe	59.4	21
Asia	41.3	15
Total	**284.0**	**100**

COMPETITORS

Hammond Manufacturing	Schneider Electric
Honeywell ACS	Siemens Water
Interpump	Technologies
Pentair	

HISTORICAL FINANCIALS

Company Type: Public

Income Statement

FYE: March 31

	REVENUE ($ mil.)	NET INCOME ($ mil.)	NET PROFIT MARGIN	EMPLOYEES
03/14	277.3	25.8	9.3%	829
03/13	284.0	26.9	9.5%	821
03/12	270.5	12.0	4.4%	755
03/11*	225.7	(14.9)	—	658
12/10	165.9	(10.9)	—	640
Annual Growth	**13.7%**	—	—	**6.7%**

*Fiscal year change

2014 Year-End Financials

Debt ratio: 27.5%
Return on equity: 10.8%
Cash ($ mil.): 72
Current ratio: 4.03
Long-term debt ($ mil.): 108

No. of shares (mil.): 31
Dividends
Yield: —
Payout: —
Market value ($ mil.): 740

	STOCK PRICE ($) FY Close	P/E High/Low	Earnings	Dividends	Book Value
03/14	23.18	35 22	0.80	0.00	7.85
03/13	22.21	30 22	0.85	0.00	7.22
03/12	20.45	52 28	0.40	0.00	6.37
Annual Growth	**6.5%**	—	— **41.4%**	—	**11.0%**

Tiptree Financial Inc

Tiptree Financial is interested in health and wealth. The holding company operates through four divisions: insurance and insurance services specialty finance (including corporate consumer and tax-exempt credit) asset management and real estate. Its insurance subsidiaries include the Philadelphia Financial Group of companies. Specialty finance services are conducted through Muni Funding Company of America and Siena Capital Finance while a handful of other subsidiaries provide asset management. Real estate activities include Care Investment Trust a health care REIT that owns a portfolio of senior housing properties. Prior to mid-2013 the company's only operations consisted of Care Investment Trust's real estate portfolio.

EXECUTIVES

President and CEO, Geoffrey N. Kauffman, age 55

Chief Financial Officer and Secretary, Julia Wyatt, age 56

Vice President, Michael Goldberg

Learning Vice President, Patrick McInnis

Vice President Asset Management, Eric Fox

Chief Financial Officer and Secretary, Julia Wyatt, age 56

Executive Chairman, Michael G. Barnes, age 48

Board Member, William A Houlihan

Board Member, Jonathan Ilany, age 61

Board Member, Rainer J Twiford

Auditors: KPMGLLP

LOCATIONS

HQ: Tiptree Financial Inc
780 Third Avenue, 21st Floor, New York, NY 10017
Phone: 212 446-1400
Web: www.tiptreefinancial.com

PRODUCTS/OPERATIONS

2012 Sales

	% of total
Rental income	86
Reimbursable income	9
Income from loans & investments	5
Total	**100**

Selected Subsidiaries

Asset Management:
Muni Capital Management LLC
TAMCO
Telos
Tiptree Capital Management LLC
TREIT
Insurance:
Philadelphia Financial Administration Services Company
Philadelphia Financial Agency Inc.
Philadelphia Financial Distribution Company
Philadelphia Financial Life Assurance Company
Philadelphia Financial Life Assurance Company of New York
Real Estate:
Care Investment Trust LLC
Specialty Finance:
Muni Funding Company of America
Siena Capital Finance

COMPETITORS

AXA Financial	Omega Healthcare
Extendicare	Investors
HCP	Prudential
Health Care REIT	Senior Housing
Healthcare Realty Trust	Properties
MetLife	Ventas
National Health Investors	

HISTORICAL FINANCIALS

Company Type: Public

Income Statement

FYE: December 31

	REVENUE ($ mil.)	NET INCOME ($ mil.)	NET PROFIT MARGIN	EMPLOYEES
12/13	100.9	16.4	16.3%	250
12/12	15.9	(0.5)	—	4
12/11	14.4	16.5	114.2%	6
12/10*	5.6	(2.4)	—	5
08/10	9.2	(16.9)	—	0
Annual Growth	**81.8%**	—	—	—

*Fiscal year change

2013 Year-End Financials

Debt ratio: 5.2%
Return on equity: 15.7%
Cash ($ mil.): 146
Current ratio: 7.95
Long-term debt ($ mil.): 360

No. of shares (mil.): 41
Dividends
Yield: 2.3%
Payout: 11.6%
Market value ($ mil.): 305

	STOCK PRICE ($) FY Close	P/E High/Low	Earnings	Dividends	Book Value
12/13	7.34	9 7	0.86	0.18	4.92
12/12	7.50	— —	(0.05)	0.54	8.61
12/11	6.50	4 3	1.60	0.41	9.20
12/10*	4.75	— —	(0.24)	0.11	8.04
08/10	8.93	— —	(0.84)	0.23	(0.00)
Annual Growth	**(4.8%)**	— —	—	**(6.3%)**	—

*Fiscal year change

Titan International, Inc. (IL)

A colossus of off-roads Titan International makes off-highway steel wheels and tires for the agricultural construction mining and consumer markets. It assembles wheel-tire systems for original equipment manufacturers and aftermarket distributors of tractors cranes combines scrapers all-terrain vehicles golf carts and utility trailers. Other operations include the manufacture and distribution of wheels rims and tires to the military for trucks tanks and personnel carriers as well as boat and trailer wheels for the consumer. Titan sells its products directly to manufactures and through dealers distributors and at its own distribution centers.

Geographic ReachThe company has manufacturing facilities in Latin American North America South America Europe Australia Asia and Africa. The US accounted for more than 50% of its revenue in 2013.

Operations

Titan's agricultural wheels and rims range in diameter from 1 ft. to 7 ft. the latter being the largest agricultural wheel manufactured in North America. Agricultural accounts for nearly 55% of sales. Its earthmoving/construction (also known as OTR or off-the-road) rims wheels and tires range in outside diameter from 3 to 13 ft. and can weigh as much as 12500 lbs.

For its consumer segment Titan made the decision to exit the OEM business for lawn and garden equipment and all terrain vehicles (ATVs) and instead focus on aftermarket products for the consumer market including ATV golf cart and trailer applications. The company also provides wheels and tires as well as assembles brakes actuators and components for the domestic boat recreational and utility trailer markets.

Sales and Marketing

Deere & Company Titan's largest customer accounts for nearly 15% of sales; CNH Global N.V. (another maker of agricultural equipment) represents about 10% of Titan's sales. Other customers have included Liebherr Group Hitachi Construction Machinery Kubota Corporation and AGCO Corporation. It primarily targets the agriculture construction consumer forestry and mining sectors.

Financial Performance

Titan has experienced phenomenal growth over the last four years. Revenues jumped 19% from $1.8 billion in 2012 to $2.2 billion in 2013 a historic milestone for the company. Profits however fell 63% from a record-high $96 million in 2012 to $35 million in 2013. (Note: the company has restated its annual financials for 2012.)

The historic revenue growth for 2013 was attributed to a 49% rise in sales from its earthmoving/construction segment due to acquisitions. Titan was also helped by a 9% spike from its agricultural segment partially offset by a 3% decline from consumer.

Titan's profit decrease for 2013 was due to the absence of a supply agreement termination income higher interest expenses and a spike in selling general and administrative expenses at recently acquired facilities. After posting a massive rise in operating cash flow from $4 million in 2011 to $130 million in 2012 the company's cash flow dropped to $117 million in 2013 due to the decline in profits and a spike in cash used in inventories and prepaid and other current assets.

Strategy

With the mining industry showing promise the company has formed Titan Mining Services to build its presence in this sector around the globe. In 2012 it acquired a 56% interest in Planet Corporation an OTR tire and wheel specialist catering to mining agriculture and earthmoving companies based in Australia. Titan in late 2012 also acquired a 97% interest in Titan Europe which was founded by Titan in 1994 and spun off in 2004.

In partnership with One Equity Partners (OEP) and the Russian Direct Investment Fund (RDIF) Titan in 2013 acquired a 30% interest in Voltyre-Prom a producer of agricultural and industrial tires in Volgograd Russia for approximately $94 million. The purchase broadened Titan's scope across Eastern Europe.

EXECUTIVES

EVP Corporate Development, Kent W. Hackamack, age 56, $290,000 total compensation
Chairman and CEO, Maurice M. (Morry) Taylor, age 70, $1,000,000 total compensation
President, Paul G. Reitz, age 41, $350,000 total compensation
President Titan Tire, Steve Briggs
President Titan Wheel, Dave Salen
EVP; Chairman Titan Tire, William Campbell, $350,000 total compensation
CFO, John Hrudicka

Vice President Purchasing, Maryann Wray
Executive Vice President And Chief, Ernest Rodia
Vice President Of Manufacturing, Jeff Kramer
Vice President Compounding Materials, Marty Morrow
Executive Vice President, Paul Hawkins
Vice President Of Manufacturing, Dan Kayser
Vice President Investor Relations, Rochelle Bold
Senior Vice President Martime, Allen Branch
Vice President, Maureen Sredl
Vice President Technology, Gary Hemming
Chairman, Erwin H. (Bill) Billig, age 88
Chairman and CEO, Maurice M. (Morry) Taylor, age 70
Auditors: PricewaterhouseCoopersLLP

LOCATIONS

HQ: Titan International, Inc. (IL)
2701 Spruce Street, Quincy, IL 62301
Phone: 217 228-6011   **Fax:** 217 228-7499
Web: www.titan-intl.com

2013 Sales

	$ mil	% of total
US	1159.1	54
Brazil	397.4	18
Other countries	607.1	28
Total		**2163.6**
100		

PRODUCTS/OPERATIONS

2013 Sales

	$ mil.	% of total
Agricultural	1182.2	55
Earthmoving & construction	749.1	35
Consumer	232.3	10
Total	**2163.6**	**100**

Selected Products

Tires
Trailer components
   Brakes and actuators
Wheels

COMPETITORS

Bridgestone	Meritor
Carlisle Tire & Wheel	Michelin
Falken Tire	Nokian Tyres
GKN	Topy
Hayes Lemmerz	Trelleborg

HISTORICAL FINANCIALS

Company Type: Public

Income Statement

FYE: December 31

	REVENUE ($ mil.)	NET INCOME ($ mil.)	NET PROFIT MARGIN	EMPLOYEES
12/13	2,163.6	35.2	1.6%	8,500
12/12	1,820.6	95.5	5.2%	6,300
12/11	1,487.0	58.1	3.9%	3,600
12/10	881.5	0.3	0.0%	2,400
12/09	727.6	(24.6)	—	2,400
Annual Growth	**31.3%**	**—**	**—**	**37.2%**

2013 Year-End Financials

Debt ratio: 31.4%	No. of shares (mil.): 53
Return on equity: 5.4%	Dividends
Cash ($ mil.): 203	Yield: 0.1%
Current ratio: 2.61	Payout: 2.6%
Long-term debt ($ mil.): 497	Market value ($ mil.): 963

STOCK PRICE ($) FY Close	P/E High/Low		PER SHARE ($) Earnings	Dividends	Book Value
12/13	17.98	41	22	0.64	0.02	12.84
12/12	21.72	13	8	1.83	0.02	12.24
12/11	19.46	22	10	1.18	0.02	9.36
12/10	19.54	1976	738	0.01	0.02	7.87
12/09	8.11	—	—	(0.71)	0.02	7.43
Annual Growth	**22.0%**	—	—	—	**(0.0%)**	**14.7%**

Titan Machinery, Inc.

For getting the job done Titan Machinery is one titanic dealer. Titan owns one of North America's largest full-service networks that supply construction and agricultural equipment. Its more than 100 dealerships sell and rent new and used machinery and attachments parts as well as service equipment. It represents equipment by CNH's Case IH New Holland Agriculture Case Construction and New Holland Construction. Titan offers excavators seeders tillers and tractors to customers from large-scale farmers to home gardeners. Other products include earthmoving equipment and cranes used for heavy construction and light industrial jobs in commercial or residential building roadwork forestry and mining.

Geographic Reach

Based in North Dakota Titan operates a contiguous network of almost 100 North American dealerships in 11 states throughout the US including three outlet stores and 16 agriculture stores in Europe —located in Bulgaria Romania Serbia and Ukraine.

Operations

The company operates three primary business segments Agriculture (76% of sales) Construction (18%) and International (6%) within which the company sells and rents new and used equipment sell parts and service equipment.

Sales and Marketing

Titan continues to expand its network of independent stores supported by a centralized administrative finance and marketing management. In tandem the company's full-service multi-point dealership approach is designed to leverage cross-selling equipment opportunities to a diverse group of customers.

Financial Performance

Titan has enjoyed unprecedented growth over the last four years. Revenues grew 33% from $1.7 billion in 2012 to reach $2.2 billion in 2013 a historic milestone for the company. Its revenues remained flat for 2014; however its profits nosedived from $42 million in 2013 to $8 million in 2014.

The growth has been driven by a spike in International segment sales as a result of acquisitions and new store openings in addition to same-store sale growth of 18%. The Construction segment also grew 6% in 2014.

The drop in profits was the result of rising operating expenses. In addition Titan incurred impairment costs and an increase in interest expenses in 2014. Titan has also experienced negative cash flow over the course of the last five years due to the large sums of money it takes to maintain its inventory of equipment.

Strategy

In the midst of a profit downfall Titan is having to sell less successful units and streamline its operating structure. To better align its Construction business in certain markets in 2014 it reduced its Construction-related headcount by 12% primarily through the closing of seven underperforming Construction stores staff reductions at other dealerships and reductions in support staff at a resource center.

Mergers and Acquisitions

One component for Titan's blueprint for growth involves acquisitions. In 2013 the company acquired Tucson Tractor Company consisting of one construction equipment dealership located in Tucson Arizona to expand its construction equipment footprint in the Southwest. The company also picked up Adobe CE consisting of one construction equipment dealership located in Albuquerque New Mexico to expand its construction equipment footprint into New Mexico.

In early 2012 Titan acquired Adobe Truck & Equipment which operates three Case Construction dealerships in Colorado. Outside the US Titan also acquired a majority stake in Rimex which operates seven agriculture equipment dealerships in Bulgaria during that same time period.

Company Background

David Meyer founded Titan in 1980.

EXECUTIVES

Chairman and CEO, David J. Meyer, $500,000 total compensation
President and COO, Peter Christianson, $500,000 total compensation
CFO, Mark Kalvoda, $285,000 total compensation
Vice President, Bob Lamp
Vp Construction, Chuck Dull
Vice President Human Resources, Randy Johnson
Vice President Human Resources, Jason Anderson
Chairman and CEO, David J. Meyer
Treasurer, Carolyn Hess
Auditors: EideBaillyLLP

LOCATIONS

HQ: Titan Machinery, Inc.
644 East Beaton Drive, West Fargo, ND 58078-2648
Phone: 701 356-0130
Web: www.titanmachinery.com

PRODUCTS/OPERATIONS

2014 Sales

	$ mil.	% of total
Agriculture	1765.8	76
Construction	405.8	18
International	145.9	6
Eliminations	(91.1)	-
Total	**2226.4**	**100**

2014 Sales

	$ mil.	% of total
Equipment	1722.7	77
Parts	275.7	12
Service	149.1	7
Rental & other	78.9	4
Total	**2226.4**	**100**

Selected Products

Agricultural
  Application equipment
  Attachments
  Combines
  Forage equipment
  Hay equipment
  Planting equipment
  Precision farming technology
  Seeding
Sprayers
Tillage equipment
Tractors
Construction
  Articulated trucks
  Compact track loaders
  Compaction equipment
  Cranes
  Crawler dozers
  Excavators
  Forklifts
  Loader/backhoes
  Loader/tool carriers
  Motor graders
  Skid steer loaders
  Telehandlers
  Wheel loaders

COMPETITORS

AGCO
Briggs Equipment
Caterpillar
Deere
Mustang CAT
RDO Equipment
Scott Equipment
Ziegler inc

HISTORICAL FINANCIALS

Company Type: Public

Income Statement

FYE: January 31

	REVENUE ($ mil.)	NET INCOME ($ mil.)	NET PROFIT MARGIN	EMPLOYEES
01/14	2,226.4	8.8	0.4%	2,823
01/13	2,198.4	42.4	1.9%	2,813
01/12	1,658.9	44.1	2.7%	2,396
01/11	1,094.4	22.3	2.0%	1,874
01/10	838.7	15.7	1.9%	1,491
Annual Growth	**27.6%**	**(13.4%)**	**—**	**17.3%**

2014 Year-End Financials

Debt ratio: 62.4%
Return on equity: 2.2%
Cash ($ mil.): 74
Current ratio: 1.47
Long-term debt ($ mil.): 224
No. of shares (mil.): 21
Dividends
  Yield: —
  Payout: —
Market value ($ mil.): 347

	STOCK PRICE ($) FY Close	P/E High/Low		PER SHARE ($) Earnings	Dividends	Book Value
01/14	16.30	76	35	0.41	0.00	19.23
01/13	28.91	18	10	2.00	0.00	18.80
01/12	24.74	14	7	2.18	0.00	16.08
01/11	24.23	19	9	1.23	0.00	11.98
01/10	11.02	18	9	0.88	0.00	10.72
Annual Growth	**10.3%**	**—**	**—**	**(17.4%)**	**—**	**15.7%**

Titan Pharmaceuticals, Inc. (DE)

Titan Pharmaceuticals thinks big. The development-stage firm is working on drug treatments for large pharmaceutical markets including central nervous system disorders like chronic pain Parkinson's disease and schizophrenia. On its own the company is developing Probuphine which may treat opioid addiction; Probuphine combines an already-approved chemical compound with Titan's continuous-release drug delivery technology called ProNeura. Titan is working with Vanda Pharmaceuticals on late-stage compound Iloperidone a possible treatment for schizophrenia.

Probuphine using the ProNeura technology is a tiny rod containing the drug buprenorphine. The rod is implanted in the upper arm and releases the drug slowly and continuously into the patient's body.

In order to focus on development of Probuphine in 2006 the company ended trials of DITPA a possible treatment for congestive heart failure. Titan Pharmaceuticals has also ceased development of its portfolio of monoclonal antibodies including CeaVac TriAb TriGem and Pivanex all of which targeted various cancers.

In mid-2008 Vanda received a not approvable letter from the FDA and put the Iloperidone development program on hold. Titan Pharmaceuticals took another blow when Bayer Schering Pharma canceled further development of Spheramine a potential Parkinson's disease therapy licensed from Titan.

Later that year the company announced plans to cut its workforce by 40% to preserve capital and lower operating costs. Titan is looking to maximize the value of its Probuphine program by seeking a development partner or a buyer for the assets.

EXECUTIVES

Vice President Information Technology, Humberto Villarreal, age 46
Vice President, Sunil Sreedharan
Board Member, Michael Hsu
Auditors: OdenbergUllakkoMuranishi&Co.LLP

LOCATIONS

HQ: Titan Pharmaceuticals, Inc. (DE)
400 Oyster Point Blvd., Suite 505, South San Francisco, CA 94080
Phone: 650 244-4990
Web: www.titanpharm.com

PRODUCTS/OPERATIONS

Selected Product Candidates

Iloperidone (schizophrenia and psychosis with Vanda Pharmaceuticals)
Probuphine (opioid addiction)

COMPETITORS

Alseres Pharmaceuticals
Bristol-Myers Squibb
Cephalon
Eli Lilly
GlaxoSmithKline
H. Lundbeck
Johnson & Johnson
Merck
Mylan
Neurocrine Biosciences
Novartis
Pain Therapeutics
Pfizer
Progenics Pharmaceuticals
Raptor
Sanofi
Teva

HISTORICAL FINANCIALS

Company Type: Public

Income Statement

FYE: December 31

	REVENUE ($ mil.)	NET INCOME ($ mil.)	NET PROFIT MARGIN	EMPLOYEES
12/13	10.4	9.7	92.7%	13
12/12	7.1	(15.1)	—	15
12/11	4.0	(15.2)	—	12
12/10	10.0	(6.8)	—	11
12/09	0.0	(5.8)	—	0
Annual Growth	**239.4%**	**—**	**—**	**—**

Debt ratio: —		No. of shares (mil.): 88	
Return on equity: —		Dividends	
Cash ($ mil.): 11		Yield: —	
Current ratio: 1.55		Payout: —	
Long-term debt ($ mil.): —		Market value ($ mil.): 54	

	STOCK PRICE ($) FY Close	P/E High/Low		Earnings	PER SHARE ($) Dividends	Book Value
12/13	0.61	21	4	0.12	0.00	0.06
12/12	1.10	—	—	(0.23)	0.00	(0.31)
12/11	1.14	—	—	(0.26)	0.00	(0.34)
12/10	1.19	—	—	(0.09)	0.00	(0.10)
12/09	2.31	—	—	(0.10)	0.00	(0.02)
Annual Growth (28.5%)				—	—	—

TiVo Inc

Prime time is anytime with TiVo. That's the idea behind TiVo and its digital video recorder (DVR). The DVR (similar to a VCR but using a hard drive instead of videocassette) allows more than 4 million subscribers to record standard- and high-definition TV (broadcast cable or satellite). The company sells DVRs online and through electronics retailers such as Best Buy. In addition to buying a DVR customers pay for TiVo's subscription service which is essentially a high-tech TV listing. TiVo reaches cable and satellite viewers by licensing its technology to DIRECTV Comcast and other service providers worldwide. TiVo is evolving from an "anytime" to an "anywhere" service to stay relevant to mobile viewers.

Financial Performance

TiVo's sales increased 34% in fiscal 2014 (ended January) versus the prior year to $406.3 million. The double-digit increase was driven by a 63% uptick in technology revenue a 4% gain in service revenue and a 48% increase in hardware sales. The company swung from a loss in fiscal 2013 to a profit of $271.8 million for the year a record profit for the company. Indeed TiVo which generally has found profits hard to come by posted its second annual profit in three years. Cash flow from operations soared to $495 million more than ten times that of the prior year on $490 million received from Google and Cisco in connection with the Motorola/Cisco settlement. (Pursuant to the terms of the Motorola/Cisco settlement the parties agreed to settle and dismiss all outstanding litigation between them.)

Strategy

While TiVo got its start as an "anytime" DVR service the ongoing revolution in how people consumer video content it pushing it to become an "anywhere" cloud-based service. Indeed ToVo's set-top boxes (STBs) are giving way to an increasing variety of consumer electronic applications and services such as entertainment-oriented smartphones and tablets. TiVo Stream enables users to to transfer shows to their tablet or smartphone. To extend its cloud-based service TiVo recently acquired the video technology company Digitalsmiths (in 2014) enabling it to offer elements of its service through non-TiVo branded user experiences.

In addition to expanding from when to where in terms of devices the company is also looking to expand beyond the US market. TiVo currently has subscribers in the UK Australia New Zealand Mexico Spain Sweden and Taiwan.

Mergers and Acquisitions

In February 2014 TiVo's acquired privately-owned Digitalsmiths Corp. for $135 million in cash making the cloud-based content discovery service a wholly owned subsidiary. The purchase furthered TiVo's evolution to a device and UI (user interface) independent cloud-based Software-as-a-Service thereby expanding its market. Digitalsmiths' Seamless Discovery technology makes it easier for subscribers of video content to find what they want to watch on a wide variety of screen including TVs mobile phones PCs and tablets.

Company Background

In 2011 Dish reached a settlement with TiVo ending patent litigation with which the two companies had been embroiled for more than six years. Dish agreed to pay TiVo $500 million with an initial payment of $300 million and then six separate payments for the remainder between 2012 and 2017. As part of the settlement Dish Echostar and TiVo agreed to share DVR-related patent licenses with each other. TiVo also agreed to play a role helping Dish promote its acquisition of the Blockbuster video chain.

EXECUTIVES

Vp Product Marketing, Jim Denney
Vp Marketing And Product Management, David Sandford
Vp And General Manager International, Joshua Danovitz
President and CEO, Thomas S. (Tom) Rogers, age 59, $1,150,000 total compensation
SVP and COO, Dan Phillips, $450,000 total compensation
EVP General Manager of Products and Revenue, Jeffrey (Jeff) Klugman, age 53, $450,000 total compensation
SVP Corporate Development and Strategy; CFO, Naveen Chopra, $375,000 total compensation
SVP and General Manager Content and Media Sales, Tara Maitra
Vice President Of Marketing, Tony Lee
Vice President Corporate Controller And Treasurer, Pavel Kovar
Vice President Corporate Commo Pub Rel, Steve Wymer
Vice President Audience Research Meas, Jonathan Steuer
Vice President Software Engineering, Prem Kumar
Vice President Of Sales And Marketing, Joe Miller
Vice President Of Platform Engineering, Kurt Heaton
Vice President Corporate Development, Rajive Dhar
Auditors: KPMGLLP

LOCATIONS

HQ: TiVo Inc
2160 Gold Street, P.O. Box 2160, San Jose, CA 95002
Phone: 408 519-9100   **Fax:** 408 519-5330
Web: www.tivo.com

PRODUCTS/OPERATIONS

2014 Sales

	$ mil.	% of total
Technology	165.6	41
Service	138.8	34
Hardware	101.8	25
Total	**406.2**	**100**

COMPETITORS

AT&T	Motorola Solutions
Apple Inc.	NDS Group
Boxee	Nielsen
Cablevision Systems	OpenTV
Charter Communications	Panasonic Corp
Comcast	Panasonic Corporation
Concurrent Computer	of North America
Cox Communications	Pioneer Corporation
DIRECTV	Roku
DISH Network	SeaChange
Dell	Sony
Ericsson Inc.	Technicolor
Google	Time Warner Cable
Hewlett-Packard	Toshiba
Microsoft	Verizon

HISTORICAL FINANCIALS

Company Type: Public

Income Statement   FYE: January 31

	REVENUE ($ mil.)	NET INCOME ($ mil.)	NET PROFIT MARGIN	EMPLOYEES
01/14	406.2	271.8	66.9%	626
01/13	303.9	(5.2)	—	576
01/12	238.1	102.1	42.9%	631
01/11	219.6	(84.5)	—	611
01/10	237.5	(23.9)	—	509
Annual Growth	14.4%	—		5.3%

2014 Year-End Financials

Debt ratio: 13.2%		No. of shares (mil.): 120	
Return on equity: 61.0%		Dividends	
Cash ($ mil.): 253		Yield: —	
Current ratio: 4.82		Payout: —	
Long-term debt ($ mil.): 172		Market value ($ mil.): 1,494	

	STOCK PRICE ($) FY Close	P/E High/Low		Earnings	PER SHARE ($) Dividends	Book Value
01/14	12.39	6	5	1.99	0.00	4.55
01/13	13.34	—	—	(0.04)	0.00	2.71
01/12	10.38	13	8	0.80	0.00	2.57
01/11	9.67	—	—	(0.74)	0.00	1.45
01/10	9.02	—	—	(0.23)	0.00	1.78
Annual Growth	8.3%			—	—	26.4%

Transdigm Group Inc

TransDigm's aviation components transcend any single airframe. Operating through several subsidiaries TransDigm Group makes and distributes a wide range of components for commercial and military aircraft. Subsidiaries include Aero-Controlex (mechanical controls pumps valves) Adams Rite Aerospace (cockpit security products electromechanical controls interior latches and locks) Marathon Norco Aerospace (batteries connectors) and Champion Aerospace (ignition systems and components). TransDigm estimates that its products are installed on about 90000 transport military and general aviation aircraft.

Geographic Reach

TransDigm manufactures its products in Belgium China Malaysia Mexico Sri Lanka the UK and the US. Each year around 70% of its sales are generated from the US. It has almost 40 manufacturing facilities.

Operations

TransDigm operates through three segments: Airframe (50% of total sales) Power and Control (45%) and Non-aviation (5%). Other subsidiaries include ADS/Transcoil (LCDs clocks transducers brushless motors) Adel Wiggins (clamps connectors heaters refueling systems) and Avionic Instruments (power conversion equipment). Additional subsidiaries include Avtech which makes flight deck PA systems and cabin lighting and power products; Bruce Aerospace which offers aircraft interior exterior and emergency lighting; CDA InterCorp a maker of actuators motors and gears; and Skurka Aerospace which provides electric motors generators speed transducers and tachometers.

Sales and Marketing

Around 55% of TransDigm's sales come from aftermarket products mostly for commercial and military aircraft from manufacturers such as Boeing Bombardier and Cessna.

Financial Performance

TransDigm has enjoyed significant growth over the last three years. Revenues jumped 13% from $1.7 billion in 2012 to peak at $1.9 billion in 2013 a historic milestone for the company. The growth for 2013 was driven by increased sales across all its segments and by acquisitions.

Power and Control's growth was driven by a 6% spike in defense sales a 4% jump in commercial aftermarket sales and a 3% rise in commercial OEM sales. Airframe experienced growth through an increase in commercial OEM sales of 14% and an increase in defense sales of 14% offset by a decline in commercial aftermarket sales of 3%. Non-aviation growth was primarily driven by acquisitions made within this segment.

Profits for TransDigm dipped 7% from $325 million in 2012 to $302 million in 2013. This was primarily due to higher interest expenses and additional refinancing costs recorded during the year.

Strategy

Strategically TransDigm focuses on specialized products rather than commodities. Most of the company's sales come from proprietary products for which TransDigm owns the design and/or is the sole-source provider for a particular aircraft. And although the company grows organically through contracts for work on next-generation aircraft such as the Airbus A380 and the Boeing 787 the company's acquisitions have fueled its significant growth.

Mergers and Acquisitions

TransDigm acquires companies that offer niche products that fit well with other subsidiary operations or have significant aftermarket sales. In 2013 it acquired Airborne Systems for $250 million in cash. Airborne Systems is a designer and manufacturer of personnel parachutes cargo aerial delivery systems emergency escape systems naval decoys and other related products. The deal gave TransDigm access to that list of products as well as deeper penetration into servicing government agencies around the world.

Also that year one of its subsidiaries acquired assets from GE Aviation's Electromechanical Actuation Division for $150 million in cash. Whippany Actuation manufactures proprietary highly engineered aerospace electromechanical motion control subsystems for civil and military applications. Its product offerings include control electronics motors high power mechanical transmissions and actuators. Whippany operates within TransDigm's Power and Control segment.

TransDigm added to its Power and Control segment again in 2013 through the $286 million purchase of Arkwin Industries a maker of proprietary highly engineered aerospace hydraulic and fuel

system components for commercial and military aircraft helicopters and other specialty applications.

EXECUTIVES

President Elektro-Metall, Uwe Basler
Chairman and CEO, W. Nicholas (Nick) Howley, age 62, $973,375 total compensation
COO Airframe, Robert S. Henderson, age 58, $420,875 total compensation
EVP, John F. Leary, age 67, $172,125 total compensation
EVP CFO and Secretary, Gregory Rufus, age 58, $470,250 total compensation
EVP, Kevin R. L. Frailey, age 47
President Transicoil LLC, Jack Planchak
COO Power Group, Kevin M. Stein, age 48
President AeroControlex Group, Roger V. Jones, age 55
EVP, Jorge Valladares
EVP, Peter Palmer
President Whippany Actuation Systems, Jack Stiffler
EVP, James Skulina, age 55
EVP Mergers and Acquisitions, Bernt G. Iversen, age 57, $377,125 total compensation
President Adams Rite Aerospace Inc., John Schaefer
President AdelWiggins Group, Jeff Zielinski
President Aero Fluid Products, Paula Wheeler
President Airborne Systems Ltd., Chris Rowe
President Airborne Systems North America, Bryce Wiedeman
President AmSafe Commercial Products, Peter Miller
President AmSafe Passenger Restraints, Willard Hagan
President AmSafe Restraints and Specialty Devices, Ian Kentfield
President Arkwin Industries Inc., Frank Robilotto
President Avionic Instruments LLC, Rigo Cruz
President AvtechTyee, Herbert Mardany
President Aerosonic LLC and CDA Intercorp LLC, Joe Grote
President Champion Aerospace LLC, Jason Marlin
President Electromech Technologies, Chad Ohl
President Harco Labaratories Incorporated, Michael Milardo
President Hartwell Corporation, Joel Reiss
President MarathonNorco Aerospace Inc., Sergio Rodriguez
President Schneller LLC, Alex Feil
President Skurka Aerospace Inc., Michael Barnaba
President Technical Airborne Components Industries, Dirk Dhooge
Chairman and CEO, W. Nicholas (Nick) Howley, age 62
EVP CFO and Secretary, Gregory Rufus, age 58
Auditors: Ernst&YoungLLP

LOCATIONS

HQ: Transdigm Group Inc
1301 East 9th Street, Suite 3000, Cleveland, OH 44114
Phone: 216 706-2960
Web: www.transdigm.com

2013 Sales

	$ mil.	% of total
US	1352.4	70
Other countries	572.0	30
Total	**1924.4**	**100**

PRODUCTS/OPERATIONS

2013 Sales

	$ mil.	% of total
Airframe	951.5	50
Power & Control	872.3	45
Non-aviation	100.6	5
Total	**1924.4**	**100**

Selected Subsidiaries

Acme Aerospace Inc
Adams Rite Aerospace
Adel Wiggins Group
ADS/Transicoil
AeroControlex Group
Aero Fluid Products
AmSafe
Avionic Instruments Inc.
Avtech Corporation
Bruce Aerospace
CDA InterCorp
CEF Industries
Champion Aerospace
Dukes Aerospace Inc.
Electromech Technologies
HARCO
Hartwell Corporation
Marathon Norco
Schneller
Semco Instruments Inc
Skurka Aerospace Inc.
Technical Airborne Components
Tyee Aircraft

COMPETITORS

BAE Systems Inc.	Lockheed Martin
Boeing	United Technologies
GE Aviation	
Honeywell	
International	

HISTORICAL FINANCIALS

Company Type: Public

Income Statement

FYE: September 30

	REVENUE ($ mil.)	NET INCOME ($ mil.)	NET PROFIT MARGIN	EMPLOYEES
09/14	2,372.9	306.9	12.9%	7,300
09/13	1,924.4	302.7	15.7%	6,100
09/12	1,700.2	324.9	19.1%	5,400
09/11	1,206.0	172.1	14.3%	3,800
09/10	827.6	163.4	19.7%	2,400
Annual Growth	**30.1%**	**17.1%**	**—**	**32.1%**

2014 Year-End Financials

Debt ratio: 110.6%	No. of shares (mil.): 52
Return on equity: ***,***.*%	Dividends
Cash ($ mil.): 819	Yield: 25.5%
Current ratio: 2.88	Payout: 4,519.2%
Long-term debt ($ mil.): 7,233	Market value ($ mil.): 9,662

	STOCK PRICE ($) FY Close	P/E High/Low		PER SHARE ($) Earnings	Dividends	Book Value
09/14	184.33	62	44	3.16	47.00	(29.69)
09/13	138.70	68	53	2.39	34.85	(6.39)
09/12	141.87	24	13	5.97	0.00	23.60
09/11	81.67	30	19	3.17	0.00	16.11
09/10	62.05	25	16	2.52	7.65	12.00
Annual Growth	**31.3%**	**—**	**—**	**5.8%**	**57.4%**	**—**

TRC Companies, Inc.

If more people treated the environment with TLC TRC Companies would be less busy. Through its Environmental Energy and Infrastructure segments the firm provides engineering construction and remediation services for commercial industrial and governmental customers. Services include energy efficiency and solid- and hazardous-waste management consulting as well as infrastructure improvements and landfill cleanup. TRC's services also include remediation for brownfield sites discontinued industrial operations operating assets and Superfund sites. It offers an Exit Strategy Program in which it assumes complete responsibility —including liability —for a contaminated site's closure and cleanup.

HISTORY

TRC was born as Travelers Research Center a unit set up in 1953 by Travelers Insurance to do meteorological and industrial hygiene research. In 1969 Travelers (now part of Citigroup) spun off TRC Companies which prospered as government spending on the environment and pollution control increased. It became a free-standing public entity in 1976. When the government began cutting back during the 1980s TRC started courting the commercial market.

In 1994 TRC expanded acquiring Environmental Solutions and Mariah Associates. It increased its international interests forming joint ventures in 1995 and 1996 to help with the remediation of Poland's horrendous pollution.

Sales fell in 1996 and 1997 the result of a weak market and stiff competition in the environmental services industry. TRC responded with a major cost-cutting effort. In 1997 chairman and CEO Vincent Rocco and president Bruce Cowen resigned amid an investigation into options exercised by the two executives that the company's board had not authorized. Richard Ellison head of the TRC Environmental Solutions subsidiary was named chairman president and CEO.

Also in 1997 TRC teamed up with insurer American International Group to introduce a service called the Exit Strategy Program in which TRC is paid to take full responsibility —including liability risks —for a contaminated site's closure and remediation.

In 1998 the company sold its Monitoring Instruments for the Environment subsidiary for about $2.7 million. The next year TRC embarked on a major buying spree: It purchased Alton Geoscience which specialized in installation removal and replacement of fuel tanks; A&H Engineers a transportation consulting and engineering firm in New York City; and Vectre which provided brownfield remediation services in New Jersey. The company also landed an Exit Strategy contract to clean up a Superfund site in Maine.

Continuing to grow through acquisitions in 2000 TRC acquired Texas-based Hunter Associates North Carolina-based Triange Environmental and California-based Lowney Associates. Also that year the TRC twice scored big with its Exit Strategy product: a $103 million contract with Consolidated Edison to clean up a site in New York City and a $21 million contract with Lockheed Martin to clean up sites in California Massachusetts and New Jersey.

TRC kept on snapping up companies in 2001. The company bought Engineered Automation Systems which provided electrical mechanical and environmental controls and ECON a provider of environmental services to the oil and gas companies that was to take on Exit Strategy business in the Gulf Coast region. The company also bought two infrastructure engineering companies LandCon and CSM that were to be combined with Hunter Associates.

The next year eager to expand its outsourcing operations for the power industry TRC acquired engineering firm E/PRO which had experience in the US Northeast in the licensing of hydroelectric plants as well as in designing constructing and managing other power utilities. TRC also completed its acquisition of transportation infrastructure firm SITE-Blauvelt Engineers which targeted mid-Atlantic states.

In 2002 the group expanded westward by acquiring California-based environmental planning training and compliance management firm Essex Environmental. It also enhanced its Midwestern operations by buying Novak Engineering a power transmission and distribution planning and design firm. In 2004 the group won a contract from the Department of Defense to design an "intelligent building" system to optimize energy use and detect threats within the Pentagon.

Ellison retired as president and CEO effective January 1 2006 but remained chairman. Christopher Vincze who had been COO took over as president and CEO.

But TRC began to broaden its reach nationally in all segments of its business in 2010. Since 2010 the company has been marketing its energy and infrastructure services on a national basis and its environmental services are being integrated into its national platform. Its national platform is linked to TRC's corporate sales and marketing organization.

Pursuing strategic acquisitions in 2011 TRC continued acquired Alexander Utility Engineering a San Antonio-based engineering and design firm that specializes in services to the electric utility and communications utility markets. The deal for Alexander which posted earnings of about $3 million in 2010 expands TRC's engineering presence in the Texas market and advances its growth strategy. That same year TRC acquired the environmental business of RMT Inc. a subsidiary of Alliant Energy Corp. The deal expands TRC's growth in the solar wind and geothermal energy markets. The company also picked up environmental consulting company The Payne Firm.

On the heels of acquiring RMT and Payne the company formed a strategic partnership with California-based environmental consulting group EORM to acquire its eastern region operations based in Danvers Massachusetts. The deal enhances TRC's environmental management sustainability and safety operations as well as broadens its geographic reach.

Broadening its geographic coverage in 2012 the company opened an office in London.

EXECUTIVES

Chairman and CEO, Christopher P. (Chris) Vincze, age 52, $500,000 total compensation
SVP and CFO, Thomas W. Bennet, age 54, $302,501 total compensation
SVP and Director Environmental and Infrastructure Sector, Robert C. (Bob) Petersen, age 71, $302,501 total compensation
SVP and Lead Energy Sector, James Mayer, age 62, $328,878 total compensation
Vice President, Anthony Letizia
Senior Vice President Corporate Pln Dev, James Stephenson
Senior Vice President Business Sales, Carl Zoephel
Sr V Pres, John W Cowdery
Vice President Deputy General Counsel, Cynthia Retallick
Senior Vice President, Kenneth Mackiewicz
Vice President Of Marketing, William Weaver

Vice President And Assistant Corporate Controller, Michael Martino
Executive Vice President, Douglas Massih
Vice President Power Services, Tedd Southern
Vice President, Raymond Boyd
Assistant Vice President, Aditya Birla
Board Of Directors, Dennis E Welch, age 63
Svp And General Counsel Secretary, Martin H Dodd, age 62
Chairman and CEO, Christopher P. (Chris) Vincze, age 52
Board Of Directors, J McNealey
Board Member, Elisha Back
Auditors: Deloitte&ToucheLLP

LOCATIONS

HQ: TRC Companies, Inc.
21 Griffin Road North, Windsor, CT 06095
Phone: 860 298-9692
Web: www.trcsolutions.com

PRODUCTS/OPERATIONS

2013 Sales

	% of total
Environmental	52
Energy	34
Infrastructure	14
Total	**100**

2013 Sales

	$ mil.	% of total
Net services	355.0	95
Insurance recoverables and others	17.9	5
Total	**372.9**	**100**

Selected Customers

AES Enterprises
ASARCO
Burlington Northern Santa Fe (BNSF)
Connecticut Resources Recovery Authority
Consolidated Edison
Duke Energy
El Paso Energy
Environmental Protection Agency
Exxon Mobil
Goodyear Tire & Rubber
Kinder Morgan
PG&E Corporation
Sempra Energy
State Departments of Transportation/Power Authorities
  California
  Louisiana
  Massachusetts
  New Hampshire
  New Jersey
  New York
  Pennsylvania
  Texas
  West Virginia

Selected Subsidiaries

Alexander Utility Engineering
Center Avenue Holdings
Cubix Corporation
Environomics Southwest
Hunter Associates
Site-Blauvelt Engineers Inc.
Site Construction Services
TRC Engineers Inc.
TRC Environmental Corporation
TRC Solutions Inc.
Vectre Corporation

COMPETITORS

3E Company	CH2M HILL
ARCADIS	Clyde Bergemann EEC
ATC Associates	Fluor
Bechtel	Weston Solutions
Black & Veatch	

HISTORICAL FINANCIALS
Company Type: Public

Income Statement
FYE: June 30

	REVENUE ($ mil.)	NET INCOME ($ mil.)	NET PROFIT MARGIN	EMPLOYEES
06/14	372.8	12.0	3.2%	3,000
06/13	325.1	36.2	11.2%	2,800
06/12	302.6	33.5	11.1%	2,600
06/11	244.7	(9.3)	—	2,300
06/10	239.5	(16.4)	—	2,100
Annual Growth	11.7%	—	—	9.3%

2014 Year-End Financials

Debt ratio: 0.3%
Return on equity: 10.3%
Cash ($ mil.): 33
Current ratio: 1.67
Long-term debt ($ mil.): 0

No. of shares (mil.): 29
Dividends
  Yield: —
  Payout: —
Market value ($ mil.): 185

	STOCK PRICE ($) FY Close	P/E High/Low		PER SHARE ($) Earnings	Dividends	Book Value
06/14	6.22	23	11	0.40	0.00	4.21
06/13	7.00	7	4	1.23	0.00	3.69
06/12	6.08	6	2	1.16	0.00	2.43
06/11	6.25	—	—	(0.69)	0.00	1.09
06/10	3.09	—	—	(1.17)	0.00	1.85
Annual Growth	19.1%	—	—	—	—	22.8%

Trecora Resources

Trecora Resources (formerly Arabian American Development) is an independent refiner in Texas. Through US subsidiary Texas Oil and Chemical Co. II which owns South Hampton Resources it operates a specialty petrochemical product refinery that primarily produces high-purity solvents used in the plastics and foam industries. South Hampton subsidiary Gulf State Pipe Line owns and operates seven pipelines. It owns a minority stake in the Al Masane mineral ore project in Saudi Arabia and 55% of inactive Nevada-based mining company Pioche-Ely Valley Mines.

Geographic Reach

Trecora's primary operational asset is a specialty petrochemical facility near Silsbee Texas about 30 miles north of Beaumont and 90 miles east of Houston.

Operations

The company's petrochemical product refinery operates seven interconnected operating units which make distinct products: a Penhex unit a Reformer a Cyclo-pentane unit an Aromax unit an Aromatics Hydrogenation unit a White Oil Fractionation unit and a Hydrocarbon Processing Demonstration unit.

South Hampton owns 16 trucks and 23 trailers. Gulf State owns and operates three 8-inch diameter pipelines and five 4-inch diameter pipelines that connect South Hampton's facility to a natural gas line a truck and rail loading terminal and a major third-party-owned petroleum products pipeline system.

Financial Performance

Trecora's revenues grew by 11% in 2012 primarily due to an increase in sales volume offset by a decrease in selling prices and processing revenues. Sales of petrochemical products increased to 12%

due to higher sales volumes. Processing revenue dropped by11% due to a tolling customer's inability to obtain raw material that impacted their run rates.

Net income declined by 17% in 2012 thanks to increased general and administrative expenses and depreciation due to expenses recorded for administrative payroll costs officers' compensation directors' fees insurance premiums travel costs and other expenses (property taxes accounting fees investor relations' expenses and expenses in Saudi Arabia). A cost of living adjustment and an increase in management and officer compensation increased payroll costs.

Company Background

Arabian American Development was founded following former CEO Hatem El-Khalidi's 1967 discovery by air of the Al Masane project which El-Khalidi later mapped on camelback. The project contains extensive ancient minerals originally mined from 1000 BC to 700 AD. These undeveloped mineral interests will require a major capital investment to make them commercially viable. Hatem El-Khalidi stepped down as CEO in 2009.

To generate cash for its long term mineral ore project in Saudi Arabia in 2009 Arabian American transferred its mining lease (for copper gold silver and zinc) in the Al Masane area to Saudi Arabia-based Al Masane Al Kobra Mining in return for a 41% stake (37% in 2012).

EXECUTIVES

Chairman President and CEO, Nicholas N. Carter, age 67, $376,880 total compensation
CFO, Connie J. Cook, age 51, $176,015 total compensation
VP Manufacturing Petrochemical Company, Ronald (Ron) Franklin, $241,038 total compensation
CEO, Simon Upfill-Brown, $316,923 total compensation
Chairman President and CEO, Nicholas N. Carter, age 67
Auditors: MooreStephensTravisWolffLLP

LOCATIONS

HQ: Trecora Resources
1650 Hwy 6 South, Suite 190, Sugar Land, TX 77478
Phone: 409 385-8300
Web: www.trecora.com

PRODUCTS/OPERATIONS

2012 Sales

	$ mil.	% of total
Petrochemical product sales	218.5	98
Processing	4.4	2
Total	222.9	100

Subsidiaries and Affiliates
Al Masane Al Kobra Mining Company (37%)
Gulf State Pipe Line Company
Pioche-Ely Valley Mines Inc. (55%)
South Hampton Resources Inc.
Texas Oil and Chemical Co. II Inc.

COMPETITORS

ConocoPhillips
Dow Chemical
Equistar Chemicals
Formosa Plastics USA

HISTORICAL FINANCIALS
Company Type: Public

Income Statement
FYE: December 31

	REVENUE ($ mil.)	NET INCOME ($ mil.)	NET PROFIT MARGIN	EMPLOYEES
12/13	236.2	19.5	8.3%	166
12/12	222.8	11.4	5.1%	168
12/11	199.5	8.4	4.2%	160
12/10	139.1	2.6	1.9%	145
12/09	117.5	6.6	5.6%	140
Annual Growth	19.1%	31.0%	—	4.4%

2013 Year-End Financials

Debt ratio: 9.2%
Return on equity: 20.9%
Cash ($ mil.): 7
Current ratio: 3.24
Long-term debt ($ mil.): 11

No. of shares (mil.): 23
Dividends
  Yield: —
  Payout: —
Market value ($ mil.): 299

	STOCK PRICE ($) FY Close	P/E High/Low		PER SHARE ($) Earnings	Dividends	Book Value
12/13	12.55	16	9	0.79	0.00	4.32
12/12	8.31	23	15	0.46	0.00	3.49
12/11	8.48	29	9	0.35	0.00	2.78
12/10	4.42	39	16	0.11	0.00	2.39
12/09	2.40	14	3	0.28	0.00	2.23
Annual Growth	51.2%	—	—	29.6%	—	18.0%

TreeHouse Foods Inc

This TreeHouse is stocked. TreeHouse Foods is the nation's #1 manufacturer of non-dairy powdered creamer sold under the Cremora brand and pickles (Farman's Nalley's Peter Piper and Steinfeld). The company also makes private-label soups salad dressings and Mexican sauces drink mixes hot cereals macaroni and cheese skillet dinners and jams. TreeHouse makes private-label products for foodservice distributors and restaurant chains as well as for supermarkets and mass merchandisers –the company's largest market that also buys its own brands. TreeHouse also boasts co-pack business and industrial customers. Founded in 2005 TreeHouse Foods grows organically through acquisitions.

Geographic Reach

TreeHouse Foods rings up more than 85% of its sales in the US and Canada. Exports account for the rest.

Operations

TreeHouse Foods operates about 25 manufacturing facilities across North America. The company's wholly-owned subsidiary Bay Valley Foods LLC is a leading supplier of private-label foods to grocery stores and foodservice operators. In turn Bay Valley operates several of its own subsidiaries: ST Specialty Foods a maker of rice and pasta dishes as well as add-meat skillet dinners and potato side dishes; Sturm Foods a manufacturer of hot cereals and powdered drink mixes; and jam-and-spread maker E.D. Smith.

North American Retail Grocery accounted for 71% of the company's 2013 sales. Its Food Away From Home business brought in 16% followed by Industrial and Export with 13%.

Sales and Marketing

Retail giant Wal-Mart Stores is TreeHouse Foods' largest customer accounting for 19% of its annual sales in 2013.

Financial Performance

TreeHouse Foods' sales climbed some 5% in 2013 to $2.29 billion vs. the prior year while net income fell 2% to $86.9 million over the same period. 2013 marked the fifth consecutive year of rising sales for the company. The uptick in sales in 2013 was driven by the acquisitions of both Cains and Associated Brands as well as a full year of sales from previously purchased Naturally Fresh. In 2013 cash flow from operations reached $216.7 million from 2012's $204.6 million. TreeHouse Foods attributes the increase to changes in operating assets and liabilities.

Strategy

TreeHouse is looking to higher margin businesses. It launched a single-serve roast coffee product line and is working to increase its distribution points and product offerings. The rollout of the single-serve hot beverage line gained momentum throughout 2013.

With its profits under pressure the company has been restructuring to reduce manufacturing costs. To this end TreeHouse Foods in recent years shuttered a soup plant in Illinois and transferred production to another plant in Pennsylvania. The company also closed a salad dressing plant in Ontario Canada and transferred production to facilities with lower production costs.

TreeHouse has grown by strengthening ties with retail grocers who are demanding private-label food products as cash-strapped consumers seek goods with equivalent quality at a lower price. Well-positioned the company's largest customer is Wal-Mart. To maintain momentum the food maker focuses on the most-purchased categories of private-label products typically canned soup salad dressings powdered creamer and pickles. Acquisitions have enabled TreeHouse to expand its production capacity and breadth of food products capturing an ever greater amount of retail shelf space.

Mergers and Acquisitions

The food firm keeps an eye on industry acquisition targets.

In 2014 TreeHouse Foods bought Flagstone Foods a maker of healthy snacks. Flagstone reported 2013 sales of approximately $697 million. The company also bought Protenergy Natural Foods a manufacturer of private-label broth soups and gravies. TreeHouse paid C$170 million (approximately $150 million) in cash for the business.

To add to its largest segment TreeHouse Foods in 2013 purchased Associated Brands from TorQuest Partners LLC which specializes in making powdered drinks specialty teas and sweeteners for $187 million. Boosting its dressings business TreeHouse Foods also bought Massachusetts-based Cains maker of shelf stable mayonnaise dressings and sauces for $35 million.

These deals follow TreeHouse Foods' 2012 and 2010 acquisition sprees. The company bought Naturally Fresh a privately-owned maker of refrigerated dressings sauces dips and marinades in 2012 for $25 million. The deal took TreeHouse from the shelf-stable grocery aisle to the refrigerated produce section providing a premium presence. TreeHouse also acquired the Aseptic Cheese and Pudding business of the Minnesota-based diary cooperative Associated Milk Producers Inc. thereby strengthening Bay Valley's market-leading position in the two product categories. TreeHouse also bought Sturm Foods a maker of private-label hot cereal and powdered soft drink mixes from HM Capital Partners for $660 million in 2010. The move strengthened TreeHouse's private-label op-erations as well as its packaging mixing and flavoring capabilities. Extending its reach in shelf-stable foods TreeHouse bought out S.T. Specialty Foods from Windjammer Capital Investors in an all-cash deal valued at about $180 million. S.T. Specialty Foods primarily makes private-label macaroni and cheese and skillet dinners mainstream staples of the dine-at-home consumer.

HISTORY

Dean Foods combined the businesses of its specialty foods group and its foodservice salad-dressing business in 2005 in order to create publicly traded TreeHouse Foods.

In 2006 the company it purchased pickle-maker Oxford Foods. It paid $275 million for the private-label soup and baby food (Nature's Goodness) businesses of Del Monte Foods. The following year it acquired San Antonio Farms a private-label Mexican sauce maker for about $89 million in cash. That year it also purchased DeGraffenreid a processor and distributor of pickles and related products for the foodservice industry from Bell-Carter Foods for $10.8 million. Strengthening its Canadian footprint in 2007 the company acquired Ontario-based E.D. Smith & Sons a manufacturer of branded sauces jellies jams and pie fillings for $220 million in cash plus the assumption of $100 million in debt.

In November 2012 TreeHouse Foods acquired the assets of the Aseptic Cheese and Pudding business from Associated Milk Producers Inc. The business sells products to foodservice and retail customers and strengthens the TreeHouse's existing Bay Valley Foods aseptic operation.

EXECUTIVES

Senior Vice President Corporate Development, Erik T Kahler

Chairman President and CEO, Sam K. Reed, age 68, $956,833 total compensation

EVP CFO and Interim President Flagstone Foods, Dennis F. Riordan, age 57, $478,868 total compensation

EVP General Counsel and Chief Administrative Officer, Thomas E. O'Neill, age 59, $448,000 total compensation

EVP Acquisitions Integration, Harry J. Walsh, age 59, $448,000 total compensation

EVP and COO, Christopher D. Sliva, age 52, $511,667 total compensation

Vice President Assistant General, Jo Osborn

Chairman President and CEO, Sam K. Reed, age 68

Board Member, Gary D Smith

Auditors: Deloitte&ToucheLLP

LOCATIONS

HQ: TreeHouse Foods Inc
2021 Spring Road, Suite 600, Oak Brook, IL 60523
Phone: 708 483-1300
Web: www.treehousefoods.com

2013 Sales

	% of total
North America	87
Outside North America	13
Total	100

PRODUCTS/OPERATIONS

2013 Sales

	$ mil.	% of total
North American Retail Grocery	1642.2	71
Food Away From Home	360.9	16
Industrial & Export	290.8	13
Total	2293.9	100

2013 Sales

	$ mil.	% of total
Beverage enhancers	361.3	16
Beverages	341.5	15
Salad dressings	334.6	15
Pickles	297.9	13
Mexican & other sauces	245.2	11
Soup & infant feeding	219.4	10
Cereals	169.8	7
Dry dinners	124.1	5
Aseptic products	96.1	4
Jams	57.3	2
Other products	46.7	2
Total	2293.9	100

Selected Products & Brands

Food Away From Home (foodservice)
  Saucemaker
  Schwartz
Jams & jellies
  E.D. Smith
  Habitant
Liquid egg substitute
  Second Nature
Non-dairy creamer
  Cremora
Pickles
  Farman's
  Nalley's
  Peter Piper
  Steinfeld
Refrigerated
  Mocha Mix
Salad dressings sauces & marinades
  Private label
Sauces & syrups
  Bennett's
  Hoffman House
  Roddenberry's Northwoods
  San Antonio Farms
Soups broths & gravies
  Private label

COMPETITORS

Annie's Inc.
B&G Foods
Baldwin Richardson Foods
Beech-Nut
Big Heart Pet Brands
Campbell Soup
ConAgra
Gerber Products
Goya
Hain Celestial
Heinz
Kraft Foods Group Inc.
Lancaster Colony
Marzetti
McCormick & Company
Mondelez International
Monterey Gourmet Foods
Nestlé USA
Newman's Own
Pinnacle Foods
Reser's Fine Foods
Rich Products
Smucker

HISTORICAL FINANCIALS

Company Type: Public

Income Statement

FYE: December 31

	REVENUE ($ mil.)	NET INCOME ($ mil.)	NET PROFIT MARGIN	EMPLOYEES
12/13	2,293.9	86.9	3.8%	4,786
12/12	2,182.1	88.3	4.0%	4,300
12/11	2,049.9	94.4	4.6%	3,900
12/10	1,817.0	90.9	5.0%	4,000
12/09	1,511.6	81.3	5.4%	3,100
Annual Growth	11.0%	1.7%	—	11.5%

2013 Year-End Financials

Debt ratio: 34.5%
Return on equity: 7.0%
Cash ($ mil.): 55
Current ratio: 2.70
Long-term debt ($ mil.): 938

No. of shares (mil.): 36
Dividends
  Yield: —
  Payout: —
Market value ($ mil.): 2,515

STOCK PRICE ($) FY Close	P/E High/Low	Earnings	PER SHARE ($) Dividends	Book Value
12/13	68.92	31 22	2.33	0.00	34.89
12/12	52.13	27 20	2.38	0.00	32.58
12/11	65.38	25 18	2.56	0.00	29.89
12/10	51.09	20 14	2.51	0.00	27.60
12/09	38.86	16 10	2.48	0.00	23.63
Annual Growth 15.4%	— —	(1.5%)	—	10.2%

Triangle Capital Corp

Triangle Capital lends to companies but they must be of a certain shape and size. An internally managed business-development company Triangle provides loans to and invests in lower-middle-market US companies with annual revenues of $20 million-$100 million. The company which likes to partner with its portfolio companies' management prefers to invest in established businesses with stable financial histories. Triangle most often invests in senior and subordinated debt securities and usually takes a equity interest; it contributes between $5 million and $15 million per transaction. The company's portfolio includes some 50 manufacturers business services food services and other types of enterprises.

Its portfolio comprises a diverse spread of businesses ranging from Ann's House of Nuts to Great Expressions Dental Center. Many of its investments are in companies that manufacture food products or equipment chemicals industrial goods or textiles.

The company targets lower-midsized companies because it believes such businesses are underserved by the business lending industry (which generally tends to lend capital to larger commercial enterprises). Formed in 2006 Triangle Capital has grown over the years by serving smaller midsized enterprises.

Triangle Capital's investment activity reached record levels in 2010. The company funded more than $170 million in investments that year (compared to about $49 million the year before). Its number of portfolio companies also increased by about 30% in 2010. As the economy slowly recovers Triangle is looking to make more investments in new and existing portfolio companies.

EXECUTIVES

CFO Secretary Treasurer and Director, Steven C. Lilly, age 43
Chairman President and CEO, Garland S. Tucker III, age 65
Chief Investment Officer and Director, Brent P.W. Burgess, age 47
VP and Principal Accounting Officer, C. Robert Knox Jr.
VP, James J. Burke
VP Investor Relations, Sheri B. Colquitt
VP, Matthew A Young
Director, Simon B. Rich, age 69
CFO Secretary Treasurer and Director, Steven C. Lilly, age 43
Director, W. McComb Dunwoody, age 68
Director, Mark M. Gambill, age 63
Director, Sherwood H. Smith Jr., age 78

Chief Investment Officer and Director, Brent P.W. Burgess, age 47
Director, Benjamin S. Goldstein, age 57
Auditors: Ernst&YoungLLP

LOCATIONS

HQ: Triangle Capital Corp
3700 Glenwood Avenue, Suite 530, Raleigh, NC 27612
Phone: 919 719-4770

PRODUCTS/OPERATIONS

2010 Sales

	$ in mil.	% of total
Loan interest fee & dividend income	29.7	83
Total paid-in-kind interest income	6.0	17
Interest income from cash & cash equivalent investments	0.3	-
Total	**36.0**	**100**

Selected Portfolio Companies

Ambient Air Corporation
American De-Rosa Lamparts & Hallmark Lighting LLC
Ann' s House of Nuts Inc
AP Services
Art Headquarters Inc.
Botanical Laboratories
Brantley Transportation
Carolina Beer and Beverage
CRS Reprocessing Services
CV Holdings LLC
Cyrus Networks LLC
Dyson Corporation
Emerald Waste Services
Energy Solutions
Equisales LLC
ESP
Fire Sprinkler Systems
Fischbein LLC
Flint Acquisition
Garden Fresh Restaurant Corp.
Genapure (QC Labs)
Gerli & Company
Great Expressions Dental Center
Hatch
An Industrial Distributor
Inland Pipe Rehabilitation
Jenkins Restorations
Library Systems & Services
Media Temple
Minco Technology Labs
Syrgis Holdings Inc.
TrustHouse Services Group
Tulsa Inspection Resources
Twin Star International
Wholesale Floors Inc.
Yellowstone Landscape Group
Zoom Systems

COMPETITORS

American Capital	Gladstone Capital
Ares Management	MCG Capital
Fifth Street Finance	MVC Capital
Full Circle Capital	Solar Capital

HISTORICAL FINANCIALS

Company Type: Public

Income Statement

FYE: December 31

	ASSETS ($ mil.)	NET INCOME ($ mil.)	INCOME AS % OF ASSETS	EMPLOYEES
12/13	814.8	61.5	7.6%	25
12/12	794.5	57.6	7.3%	22
12/11	583.1	40.3	6.9%	19
12/10	388.0	20.1	5.2%	17
12/09	261.0	14.0	5.4%	14
Annual Growth	**32.9%**	**44.7%**	**—**	**15.6%**

STOCK PRICE ($) FY Close	P/E High/Low	Earnings	PER SHARE ($) Dividends	Book Value
12/13	27.65	14 11	2.23	2.16	16.10
12/12	25.49	12 9	2.16	2.02	15.30
12/11	19.12	10 7	2.06	1.77	14.68
12/10	19.00	13 7	1.58	1.65	12.09
12/09	12.09	8 3	1.63	1.67	11.03
Annual Growth 23.0%	— —	8.2%	6.6%	9.9%

Triangle Petroleum Corp

Triangle Petroleum has three business - oil and gas exploration and production oilfield services and midstream services. The company holds leasehold interests in about 94000 net acres in the Williston Basin approximately 45000 net acres are located in its core focus area in McKenzie and Williams Counties North Dakota. The assets are mainly unconventional (natural gas produced from shale deposits via hydraulic fracturing). Triangle had proved reserves of 40.3 million barrels of oil equivalent in fiscal 2014. Exploration and production accounted for 46% of the company's 2014 revenues; Oilfield services 54%. Sales of crude oil accounted for about 60% of the company's revenues in fiscal 2014.

Geographic Reach

The company has a strategic focus on developing the Bakken Shale and Three Forks formations in the Williston Basin of North Dakota and Montana. The company has about 2667 lease agreements representing 217377 gross (93552 net) acres in the Williston Basin.

Operations

Triangle has two reportable operating segments: exploration and production operating segment and oilfield services (pressure pumping) operating segment. It also provides midstream services through a joint venture.The company conducts its activities in the Williston Basin of North Dakota and Montana through two subsidiaries and a joint venture: Triangle USA Petroleum Company which conducts its exploration and production operations by acquiring and developing unconventional shale oil and natural gas resources; and RockPile Energy Services LLC a provider of hydraulic pressure pumping and complementary well completion and workover services. Its 30%-owned Caliber energy infrastructure joint venture provides a range of services (including fresh water delivery produced water transportation and disposal crude oil gathering and stabilization and natural gas gathering and processing) to Traingle and other operating exploration and production companies in the Williston Basin.The operations of its non-operated leasehold positions are conducted through agreements with major operators in the Williston Basin including Oasis Petroleum Hess Continental Resources Statoil Newfield Exploration EOG Resources XTO Energy Whiting Petroleum Slawson Exploration and Kodiak Oil & Gas.

Financial Performance

Triangles revenues increased by 300% in fiscal 2014 due to increased revenues from all segments. Production revenues increased due to a 295% increase in production volumes and a 3% increase in oil and natural gas prices. The company reported net income of $73.5 million in fiscal 2014 (compared to a loss of 413.8 million in fiscal 2013) thanks to higher increased revenues an increased gain on equity investment derivative and a gain from derivative activities.Cash flows provided by operating activities increased in fiscal 2014 primarily due to higher oil revenues driven by stronger sales volumes partially offset by increases in production expenses production taxes general and administrative expenses and other expenses associated with the growth of its operations.The company has seen growth in revenues since 2010 primarily due to increased volume fueled by capacity additions.

Strategy

The company is focused on accelerate drilling inventory and production growth in the Williston Basin; maximizing efficiencies and improving cost structure and returns through vertical integration; continuing to buy complementary assets and businesses at attractive costs; and continuing to focus leasehold efforts on converting non-operated acreage to operated acreage.

In fiscal 2014 the company drilled and completed 27 gross (20.1 net) operated wells and connected 31 new wells to the Caliber midstream system. That year the company's proved reserves grew 175% as the result of drilling and completion activity on the Bakken and Three Forks formations properties. Its average daily production increased by about 295% year-over-year.Moving into the midstream space in 2012 Triangle formed a joint venture named Caliber Midstream Partners LP with First Reserve Corporation's Energy Infrastructure Fund. Caliber offers pipeline services to producers for oil natural gas flow back and produced water and freshwater in the Williston Basin of North Dakota and Montana. It also planned to expand its Phase 1 system in McKenzie County and to build new infrastructure in other counties of North Dakota and Montana as needed by its customers. Its Expansion project includes a 50000 barrels a day pipeline from the Caliber Central Facility to Alexander North Dakota where Caliber plans to build 40000 barrels of crude oil storage and related infrastructure providing Triangle and other customers with access to multiple crude oil pipelines rail terminals and market centers in the Williston Basin.

In 2013 Triangle's exchanged oil and natural gas leasehold interests in Kodiak's operated units for approximately 600 net acres of leasehold interests held by Kodiak in units then operated by the Company.

Mergers and Acquisitions

In 2014 Triangle acquired Williston Basin properties through subsidiary Triangle USA Petroleum Corporation for $120 million. In 2013 its subsidiary RockPile bought Team Well Service Inc. an operator of well service rigs in North Dakota for about $9 million.

Company Background

In 2012 Triangle changed its state of incorporation from Nevada to Delaware by merging with and into its wholly-owned Delaware incorporated subsidiary with the same name.

That year Triangle announced an investment by Natural Gas Partners an Irving Texas based private equity firm a revised capital expenditure program and provided an operational update including operated well results and RockPile Energy Services developments.

Boosting its shale holdings in 2011 Triangle announced the acquisition of 42000 net acres in the Bakken and Three Forks formations in the Williston Basin.

The company was formed in 2003 as Peloton Resources and took its current name in 2005.

EXECUTIVES

President and CEO, Jonathan Samuels, age 34, $389,423 total compensation
CFO, Justin J. Bliffen
President and CEO Caliber Midstream, R. Poe Reed
EVP Operations Triangle USA Petroleum, Dominic Spencer
CEO RockPile Energy Services, Curt Dacar
Vice President Land With American Oil, Don Schroeder
Vice President Office Of The Chief, Bryan Gunderson
Chairman, Peter Hill, age 65
Auditors: KPMGLLP

LOCATIONS

HQ: Triangle Petroleum Corp
  1200 17th Street, Suite 2600, Denver, CO 80202
Phone: 303 260-7125   **Fax:** 303 260-5080
Web: www.trianglepetroleum.com

PRODUCTS/OPERATIONS

2014 Sales

	$ mil.	% of total
Oilfield services	193.6	54
Exploration & Production	160.5	46
Corporate & other	1.2	-
Eliminations	(96.6)	-
Total	**258.7**	**100**

COMPETITORS

Apache	Enerplus
Baker Hughes	Newfield Exploration
Continental Resources Inc.	Schlumberger
	Southwestern Energy
Corridor Resources	Whiting Petroleum

HISTORICAL FINANCIALS

Company Type: Public

Income Statement

FYE: January 31

	REVENUE ($ mil.)	NET INCOME ($ mil.)	NET PROFIT MARGIN	EMPLOYEES
01/14	258.7	73.4	28.4%	332
01/13	60.7	(13.7)	—	165
01/12	8.1	(23.8)	—	61
01/11	0.5	(20.2)	—	10
01/10	0.1	(2.1)	—	5
Annual Growth	**566.3%**	**—**		**185.5%**

2014 Year-End Financials

Debt ratio: 33.4%	No. of shares (mil.): 85
Return on equity: 20.2%	Dividends
Cash ($ mil.): 81	Yield: —
Current ratio: 1.22	Payout: —
Long-term debt ($ mil.): 334	Market value ($ mil.): 652

	STOCK PRICE ($) FY Close	P/E High/Low		Earnings	PER SHARE ($) Dividends	Book Value
01/14	7.61	10	5	0.91	0.00	6.10
01/13	6.29	—	—	(0.31)	0.00	4.31
01/12	6.84	—	—	(0.78)	0.00	4.74
01/11	7.79	—	—	(1.63)	0.00	3.37
01/10	0.33	—	—	(0.30)	0.00	3.22
Annual Growth	**119.1%**			**—**	**—**	**17.4%**

TriMas Corp (New)

Whether at work or play TriMas fits the niche. The company makes a diverse mix of products through several segments. Its Cequent division makes trailer hitches towing systems and accessories for cars and RVs as well as agricultural military and industrial vehicles. The Energy division makes seals bolts and gaskets used primarily in the oil and gas industry. TriMas' Packaging segment makes closures and dispensing systems for industrial and consumer packaging for customers in North America and Europe. Aerospace & Defense produces aerospace fasteners and military munitions components including shell casings. Engineered Components manufactures compressed gas pressure cylinders and precision tools.

Geographic Reach

TriMas makes 80% of its total sales from the US. However it takes advantage of the lower-costs of production in other countries. It has about 60 manufacturing plants in 17 countries.

Operations

TriMas divides its operations into five segments. Its Cequent division is separated into Cequent Americas (31% of total sales) and Cequent Adsia Pacific (10%). Other segments include Packaging (22%) Engineered Components (16%) Energy (15%) and Aerospace & Defense (6%).

Sales and Marketing

TriMas sells its products through a direct sales force independent sales representatives and networks of independent distributors. It spends about $8 million on advertising annually.

Customers include Costco Dial Corporation Ecolab Lyons Magnus McDonald's Pepsi Pharmacia Reckitt Benckiser Sherwin-Williams Schering-Plough and Starbucks.

Financial Performance

TriMas has enjoyed three straight years of impressive growth. Its revenues spiked by 17% from $1.03 billion in 2011 to nearly $1.3 billion in 2012 a historic milestone for the company. However its profits declined by 44% from $60 million in 2011 to nearly $34 million in 2012.

TriMas reached its milestone of $1.3 billion in sales by the help of a 36% increase in sales from its Cequent Asia Pacific operations. Packaging sales skyrocketed by nearly 49% in 2012 while Energy sales were up by 14%. Engineered Components also jumped by 14%. Growth in these segments was due to previous acquisitions along with expansion in international markets.

The company attributes its decline in profits to the $47 million it paid on its debt for 2012 compared to $4 million during 2011.

Strategy

As a means to expand its core businesses and reach new markets TriMas typically looks to acquire companies that can supplement existing product lines. In 2013 and 2012 it purchased two Brazil-based companies in Gasket Veda §ṭes T Ḡnicas and CIFAL Industrial e Comercial. Based in Rio de Janeiro Gasket Veda §ṭes T Ḡnicas makes ring joints and gaskets for the onshore and offshore drilling markets. CIFAL makes specialty fasteners and bolts.

Also in 2013 the company obtained Martinic Engineering a maker of parts for commercial and military aerospace applications (including auxiliary power units electrical hydraulic and pneumatic systems) for $19 million. Martinic was integrated into TriMas' Aerospace & Defense segment.

The year before TriMas acquired 70% of Arminak & Associates LLC a manufacturer and supplier of foamers lotion pumps fine mist sprayers and other packaging items. TriMas paid about $64 million in the deal and gained additional customers in the cosmetic personal care beauty aids and household product sectors.

Ownership

William Blair & Company LLC owns 10% of the company.

EXECUTIVES

President and CEO, David M. (Dave) Wathen, age 62, $683,400 total compensation
President Rieke Packaging Systems Click to collapse, Lynn A. Brooks, age 62, $424,800 total compensation
CFO, Robert J. Zalupski, age 54
Group President Cequent, A. Mark Zeffiro, age 47, $380,000 total compensation
President Aerospace and Defense, Tom Aepelbacher
President of Cequent Performance Products; Inc., Thomas Benson
President Arrow Engine Company Click to collapse, Len Turner
President Norris Cylinder Click to collapse, Jerry Auken
President Monogram Aerospace Fasteners and NI Industries Click to collapse, David Adler
President Lamons Click to collapse, Kurt Allen
President Cequent Asia Pacific Click to collapse, Carl Bizon
President Cequent Consumer Products Click to collapse, John Aleva
Vp Human Resources, Dwayne M Newcom, age 54
Vice President, Colin Hindman
Colin Hindman Vice President Of Human, Teresa White
Vice President Human Resources, Alexander Lucero
Vice President Finance Business, Dave Watza
Vice President Operations, Hank Gund
Exec Admin To Executive Vice President, Carolyn Grusnick
Vice President Business Planning, Laura Pecoraro
Board Member, Richard M (Dick) Gabrys, age 73
Chairman, Samuel (Sam) Valenti, age 69
President and CEO, David M. (Dave) Wathen, age 62
Treasury Manager, Mike Dewinter
Auditors: KPMGLLP

LOCATIONS

HQ: TriMas Corp (New)
39400 Woodward Avenue, Suite 130, Bloomfield Hills, MI 48304
Phone: 248 631-5450   **Fax:** 248 631-5455
Web: www.trimascorp.com

2012 Sales

	$ mil.	% of total
North America		
US	1039.4	82
Other countries	34.1	3
Australia	100.6	8
Europe	62.4	5
Asia	32.2	2
Africa	4.2	-
Total	**1272.9**	**100**

PRODUCTS/OPERATIONS

2012 Sales

	$ mil.	% of total
Cequent		
Cequent North Americas	400.4	31
Cequent Asia Pacific	128.6	10
Packaging	275.1	22
Engineered Components	200.0	16
Energy	190.2	15
Aerospace & Defense	78.6	6
Total	**1272.9**	**100**

Selected Divisions and Brands

Aerospace & Defense
  Monogram Aerospace Fasteners
  Composi-Lok
  Ti-OSI
  NI Industries
Cequent
  Bargman
  Bulldog
  Draw-Tite
  Fulton
  Hidden Hitch
  Highland
  Reese
  ROLA
  Tekonsha
  Tow Ready
  Wesbar
Energy
  Arrow Engine
  Lamons Casket
Engineered Components
  Hi-Vol Products
  Norris Cylinder
  Precision Tool Company
Packaging
  Englass
  Rieke
  Stolz

COMPETITORS

3M
Alcoa
AptarGroup
Atwood Mobile
Caterpillar
Chicago Rivet
Cummins
Dutton-Lainson
EnPro
General Dynamics Ordnance and Tactical Systems
Greif
Grote Industries
Harsco
Hayes Lemmerz
Johns Manville
Master Lock
Peterson Manufacturing
Scapa
Textron
Worthington Cylinder

HISTORICAL FINANCIALS

Company Type: Public

Income Statement

FYE: December 31

	REVENUE ($ mil.)	NET INCOME ($ mil.)	NET PROFIT MARGIN	EMPLOYEES
12/13	1,394.8	75.5	5.4%	6,000
12/12	1,272.9	33.8	2.7%	5,500
12/11	1,083.9	60.3	5.6%	4,100
12/10	942.6	45.2	4.8%	3,900
12/09	803.6	(0.2)	—	3,900
Annual Growth	**14.8%**	**—**	**—**	**11.4%**

2013 Year-End Financials

Debt ratio: 23.5%
Return on equity: 17.7%
Cash ($ mil.): 27
Current ratio: 1.97
Long-term debt ($ mil.): 295

No. of shares (mil.): 45
Dividends
  Yield: —
  Payout: —
Market value ($ mil.): 1,795

	STOCK PRICE ($) FY Close	P/E High/Low		PER SHARE ($) Earnings	Dividends	Book Value
12/13	39.89	23	15	1.83	0.00	12.21
12/12	28.01	30	20	0.89	0.00	7.71
12/11	17.95	15	8	1.73	0.00	5.02
12/10	20.46	17	4	1.31	0.00	3.30
12/09	6.77	—	—	(0.01)	0.00	1.83
Annual Growth	**55.8%**	**—**	**—**	**—**	**—**	**60.7%**

Trimble Navigation Ltd.

Those who fear not knowing their place in the world should Trimble. Trimble Navigation makes systems and software that combine global positioning technology with wireless communications to provide location and position data and make it actionable. Using GPS laser optical and other technologies the company's products target areas such as surveying construction site project management mapping mobile personnel management and mobile and fixed asset management. They are offered to end users such as government entities farmers engineering firms and public safety workers as well as equipment manufacturers (OEMs). About half of sales are made outside the US.

HISTORY

Charles Trimble founded Trimble Navigation in 1978 to design navigation products for recreational boating. In 1982 the company began developing devices using the Global Positioning System (GPS) satellite network; in 1984 Trimble introduced its first GPS product. The company went public in 1990 10 days before Saddam Hussein invaded Kuwait. Trimble gained worldwide recognition when allied troops used its GPS devices during the Persian Gulf War.

The war left Trimble expanding too quickly and overproducing. In 1992 Trimble rebounded after reorganizing to focus on nonmilitary products. Two years later it introduced a low-cost handheld unit that helped with utilities fieldwork. In 1998 Trimble ceased manufacturing products for general aviation and allied with Siemens to develop GPS products. That year Charles Trimble was named vice chairman after he stepped down as the company's CEO. The company in 1998 also launched a cost reduction plan that cut its workforce by 8%.

The next year Trimble sold its Sunnyvale California manufacturing operations to contract manufacturer Solectron which agreed to make Trimble's GPS and radio-frequency products for three years. Also in 1999 Steven Berglund a former president of a Spectra-Physics subsidiary was named CEO of Trimble.

In 2000 Trimble acquired the Spectra Precision businesses of Thermo Electron (which later became Thermo Fisher Scientific) for about $294 million. That year the US government stopped scrambling GPS signals opening the door for more precise devices. In 2001 the company formed a subsidiary Trimble Information Services to expand the company's wireless location-based services including fleet management.

The next year Trimble and Caterpillar formed a joint venture Caterpillar Trimble Control Technologies to develop advanced electronic guidance and control technologies for earth-moving construction and mining machines.

The company acquired Eleven Technology a mobile application software developer focused on the consumer packaged goods market in 2006. The company also expanded its laser scanning business by acquiring the assets —including software for engineering and construction plant design —of BitWyse Solutions. Later in 2006 it purchased Visual Statement a developer of crime and collision incident investigation software and XYZ Solutions a 3-D intelligence software provider. It also acquired Meridian Systems a provider of enterprise project management and lifecycle software. Still later in 2006 Trimble bought Spacient Technologies a privately held provider of field service management and mobile mapping software used by municipalities and utilities.

Trimble's buying spree continued in 2007 when it purchased @Road a developer of mobile resource management systems for about $493 million.

The company expanded its ability to serve the farming industry when it acquired NTech Industries in 2009. NTech developed optical crop-sensing technology that helps farmers reduce costs by managing the application of nitrogen herbicides and other crop inputs. Also that year Trimble purchased Accutest Engineering Solutions a UK-based maker of mobile resource management applications for trucking fleets.

In 2010 Trimble acquired Punch Telematix from majority shareholder Punch International for nearly Å14 million ($18 million) in cash and re-branded it as Trimble Transport and Logistics. Punch Telematix made onboard computers for trucks. That year the company also bought Thing-Magic a developer of radio frequency identification (RFID) products and RFID integration services for commercial clients in the construction and transportation industries and Cengea a provider of operations and supply chain management software for the forestry agriculture and natural resource industries.

Additionally Trimble bought Mumbai-based Tata AutoComp Mobility Telematics (TMT) in a move to expand its mobile resource management services business in India. TMT provided vehicle tracking and other telematics services to such customers as Bharat Petroleum and Tata Motors. Also that year expanding its engineering and construction portfolio for electrical and mechanical contractors Trimble bought the assets of Accubid a provider of estimating project management and service management software.

Trimble bought 3D modeling software maker Tekla in 2011 in a deal valued at nearly Å340 million ($485 million) to better equip building contractors and engineers to manage construction projects. The follow-up investment came in 2012 when Trimble completed the acquisition of the StruCad and StruEngineer business from AceCad Software. StruCad offers 3D structural detailing while Stru-Engineer provides engineering companies with 3D steelwork modeling and construction management.

The company acquired a line of software products in 2011 from Norway-based Mesta Entrepren r a subsidiary of road and highway construction contractor Mesta Konsern. The deal added office and field data collection applications and improved the company's ability to provide customized systems to construction clients particularly in the area of managing local application requirements compliance. Also in 2011 Trimble strengthened its portfolio and Asia presence with the purchase of China-based Yamei Electronics a manufacturer of electronic automotive products including anti-theft GPS monitoring and tracking systems RFID smart keys and diagnostics systems.

Also that year Trimble acquired the OmniSTAR satellite system assets of Dutch geological engineering company Fugro. The company was interested in OmniSTAR's GPS signal correction technology (used to improve the accuracy of satellite navigation devices) which it is using to expand the functionality of its mapping systems for agricultural and construction purposes among others. It also acquired France-based Ashtech to expand Garmin's selection of survey products including the flagship application Spectra Precision for construction clients. Ashtech became part of Trimble's engineering and construction division.

EXECUTIVES

Vice President Finance And Chief Accounting Officer, Julie Shepard

President CEO and Director, Steven W. Berglund, age 62, $791,250 total compensation

VP Agriculture Division, Joseph S. Denniston, age 52, $229,932 total compensation

CFO, Francois Delepine, age 52

VP Heavy and Highway Construction Division, Bryn A. Fosburgh, age 52, $392,758 total compensation

VP Agriculture Forestry Water and Energy Utilities and Public Safety, Mark A. Harrington, age 59, $392,758 total compensation

VP Advanced Devices, J Årgen Kliem, age 57

VP Mobile Solutions Data Services and Hosting Global Services, James M. Veneziano, $319,500 total compensation

VP Transportation & Logistics Division, Ron Konezny

VP Survey Geospatial Geographic Information System (GIS) Infrastructure Rail Land Administration and Environmental Solutions, Christopher W. Gibson, age 53, $315,733 total compensation

VP OEM Solutions & Mining, Christopher J. Shephard

VP Operations and CIO, Leah K. Lambertson

VP Geospatial Division, Erik J. Arvesen

National Accounts Manager Americas, Eric Carson

Vp Human Resources, Mary K Strangis

Vice President Supply Chain And Logistics, Martin Wagener

Vice President Federal Programs, Cyndee Hoagland

Vice President, Rahim Farzaie

Vice President Of Software Engineering, Maria Madlambayan

Vice President Of Operations, Phil Balsamo

Vice President Of Software Engineering, Windy Doan

Vice President Of Finance, Kathy Radley-timberlake

Vice President Marketing, Michael Muehlbauer

Vice President Sales And Customer Service, Mark Amiot

National Account Manager, Jason Zhou

Vice President Sales, Rocco Bognet

Tandl Business Area Vice President, Michel Maercke

Treasurer, John E Huey, age 64

Vice Chairman, Nickolas W. Vande Steeg, age 72

President CEO and Director, Steven W. Berglund, age 62

Chairman, Ulf J. Johansson, age 69

Board Member, Bill Pecknold

Board Member, Jonathan Moore

Auditors: Ernst&YoungLLP

LOCATIONS

HQ: Trimble Navigation Ltd.
935 Stewart Drive, Sunnyvale, CA 94085
Phone: 408 481-8000 **Fax:** 408 481-2218
Web: www.trimble.com

2014 Sales

	$ mil.	% of total
US	1147.7	48
Europe	581.7	24
Asia/Pacific	345.6	15
Other	320.5	13
Total	**2395.5**	**100**

PRODUCTS/OPERATIONS

2014 Sales

	$ mil.	% of total
Engineering & construction	1348.1	56
Mobile solutions	422.1	20
Field solutions	486.8	18
Advanced devices	138.5	6
Total	**2395.5**	**100**

2014 Sales

	$ mil.	% of total
Product	1713.6	71
Service	396.1	17
Subscription	285.9	12
Total	**2395.5**	**100**

Selected Products

Engineering and Construction
  Global positioning system (GPS) data collection systems (GPS Total Station)
  Grade control systems (SiteVision)
  Laser transmitters (Spectra)
  Optical surveying equipment
Field Solutions
  Agricultural information systems
  Automatic tractor steering systems (AgGPS Autopilot)
  Farm equipment guidance systems
  Laser-based water management systems
  Mapping equipment (AgGPS 132)
  Geographical information systems
  GPS data collection and maintenance systems (GeoExplorer)
Mobile Solutions
  Fleet management system hardware software and service (Telvisant)
  GPS vehicle module (CrossCheck)
Advanced Devices
  GPS chipsets for mobile communication and computing (FirstGPS)
  GPS clocks (Thunderbolt)
  GPS receiver cards/modules for military applications (Force 5)
  GPS receivers for battery powered applications (Lassen LP)
  Handheld GPS survey data collectors (Tripod Data Systems Ranger)

COMPETITORS

AirIQ	Navico
Deere	NovAtel
Garmin	Novariant
Hernisphere GPS	QUALCOMM
Hexagon AB	Raven Industries
L-3 Communications	Raytheon
Leica Geosystems	Rockwell Collins
MacDonald Dettwiler	TOPCON
MiTAC	Thales
Minorplanet	TomTom
Motorola Solutions	XRS

HISTORICAL FINANCIALS

Company Type: Public

Income Statement

FYE: January 3

	REVENUE ($ mil.)	NET INCOME ($ mil.)	NET PROFIT MARGIN	EMPLOYEES
01/14*	2,288.1	218.8	9.6%	7,086
12/12	2,040.1	191.0	9.4%	6,561
12/11	1,644.0	150.7	9.2%	5,301
12/10	1,293.9	103.6	8.0%	4,166
01/10	1,126.2	63.4	5.6%	3,794
Annual Growth	19.4%	36.3%	—	16.9%

*Fiscal year change

2014 Year-End Financials

Debt ratio: 20.4%
Return on equity: 10.4%
Cash ($ mil.): 147
Current ratio: 1.45
Long-term debt ($ mil.): 652

No. of shares (mil.): 258
Dividends
  Yield: —
  Payout: —
Market value ($ mil.): 8,944

	STOCK PRICE ($) FY Close	P/E High/Low	PER SHARE ($) Earnings	Dividends	Book Value
01/14*	34.57	75 29	0.84	0.00	8.58
12/12	58.60	79 53	0.75	0.00	7.46
12/11	43.40	84 53	0.60	0.00	6.35
12/10	39.93	97 53	0.42	0.00	5.65
01/10	25.20	98 46	0.26	0.00	5.23
Annual Growth	8.2%	— —	34.1%	—	13.2%

*Fiscal year change

Tripadvisor Inc

TripAdvisor is primed to give you advice. Formerly owned by online travel services provider ExpediaTripAdvisor offers a search engine and directory that matches hotels with flights and packages. The company provides more than 60 million consumer reviews to help travelers plan consumer-savvy trips. The global source strives to fine-tune search results to provide information that is free of bias and in a mobile format for smartphone use. TripAdvisor partners with top online travel businesses such as Hotwire Hotels.com and American Airlines and offers some 30 localized versions in France Germany Ireland Italy Spain the UK China and a growing list of other countries.

Change in Company Type

TripAdvisor was spun off by Expedia in late 2011. After the spin off Expedia continues to focus on travel transactions (including airline and hotel reservations) while TripAdvisor along with nearly 20 other media and advertising brands concentrates on providing travel-related media. As part of the business separation Expedia investors gained a stake in TripAdvisor and a tax-free windfall. The deal benefited stockholders as well as the fast-ascending TripAdvisor. TripAdvisor accounted for some 15% of Expedia's revenue at the time of the split.

Geographic Reach

Massachusetts-based TripAdvisor generates slightly more than half of its revenue in the US. The UK is another important market for the company contributing nearly 15% of sales. TripAdvisor has about 20 locations across North America Europe and the Asia-Pacific region.

Sales and Marketing

To drive traffic to its sites TripAdvisor promotes its services on search engines other Internet portals and online and off-line venues including Facebook and Twitter. In 2012 the company reported advertising expenses of $175 million up from about $135 million and $86 million in 2011 and 2010 respectively.

Financial Performance

TripAdvisor's ad-driven revenue increased 20% in 2012 versus 2011 to $763 million. Net income rose 9% over the same period to $194 million. 2012 marked the fourth consecutive year of increasing sales and profits for the company which is benefiting from improvement in the broader economy and travel industry in particular. TripAdvisor added $88 million in click-based ad revenue in 2012 driven mainly by increased traffic from hotel shoppers.

TripAdvisor's core markets —the US and UK — posted 11% sales gains in 2012 versus 2011 while revenue from other countries increased 40%.

Strategy

As a stand-alone public company TripAdvisor has retained its growth strategy. It generates more than three-quarters of its sales through click-based advertising. To maintain this momentum the company continues to invest in social mobile and global initiatives Indeed mobile downloads have risen dramatically in recent years as the use of smartphones and tablets skyrocket. TripAdvisor's launch of 20 free Mobile City Guides for Android and iOS and its development of a user-friendly interface have given the company's mobile strategy added traction. TripAdvisor's also mining sales among its 200000 vacation rental properties and its more than 35000 hotel business listings a product launched in 2010.

The company is extending its reach internationally by launching individual TripAdvisor sites for other countries in Europe including France Germany and Italy and farther afield in Argentina Brazil China India Japan Russia and South Korea to name just a few. While sales in the US declined from 61% of 2010 sales to 51% in 2012 and its business in the UK hovering at about 15% of sales growth in other foreign countries increased to 35% of sales in 2012.

Multiple acquisitions of online travel media content companies inked during the past few years have made TripAdvisor a dominant force in travel media and pits the online source squarely against the likes of HomeAway which caters to customers who rent vacation homes (or a temporary home away from home). The purchases also positively impact its growth strategy.

Mergers and Acquisitions

In October 2013 TripAdvisor acquired Oyster.com a hotel review site featuring reviews and photos of some 150 cities. In May it purchased Niumba.com a vacation rentals website featuring more than 230000 properties globally and bolstering TripAdvisor's collection of Spanish vacation rentals to more than 120000 properties in Spain. In April it purchased Jetsetter.com a members-only private sale site for hotel bookings. In March it bought Tiny Post an app that enables users to write over photos.

In March 2012 the company bought the travel inspiration site Wanderfly. In February 2011 TripAdvisor enhanced its mobile offering by purchasing EveryTrail based in California. Buying the company which has developed a GPS-enabled publishing platform allows TripAdvisor customers to access walking tours city guides and hiking trails from their smartphones. Also that year TripAdvisor acquired Chicago-based Where I've Been whose eponymous Facebook application allows

users to pinpoint their travels on an interactive map.

In June 2010 the travel company acquired Holiday Lettings (holidaylettings.co.uk) the UK's largest independent website for reserving vacation homes apartments and other rentals. The purchase was preceded by the acquisitions of online travel community virtualtourist.com UK's holidaywatchdog.com and travel booking comparison site onetime.com.

Ownership

TripAdvisor is controlled by Liberty Interactive Corp. which acquired a 57% stake in the firm in late 2012.

EXECUTIVES

SVP Engineering and Operations, Andy Gelfond
President and CEO, Stephen Kaufer, $469,231 total compensation
President Vacation Rentals, Dermot Halpin
CFO, Julie M.B. Bradley, $302,116 total compensation
President TripAdvisor for Business, Marc Charron
Vp Global Cpc Sales, Brian Schmidt
V Pres Global Communicatins, Desiree Fish

LOCATIONS

HQ: Tripadvisor Inc
141 Needham Street, Newton, MA 02464
Phone: 617 670-6300
Web: www.tripadvisor.com

2012 Sales

	$ mil.	% of total
US	386.2	51
UK	110.2	14
All other countries	266.6	35
Total	**763.0**	**100**

PRODUCTS/OPERATIONS

2012 Sales

	% of total
Click-based advertising	77
Display-based advertising	12
Subscription transaction & other	11
Total	**100**

Other Travel Brands & Websites
airfarewatchdog.com
bookingbuddy.com
cruisecritic.com
everytrail.com
flipkey.com
holidaylettings.co.uk
holidaywatchdog.com
independenttraveler.com
kusun.cn
onetime.com
seatguru.com
smarttravel.com
travelpod.com
travel-library.com
virtualtourist.com
whereivebeen.com

Selected TripAdvisor Sites

daodao.com
no.tripadvisor.com
pl.tripadvisor.com
th.tripadvisor.com
tripadvisor.com.eg
tripadvisor.com.my
tripadvisor.tw
tripadvisor.com.ar
tripadvisor.co.id
tripadvisor.gr
tripadvisor.ru
tripadvisor.co.kr
tripadvisor.com.sg
tripadvisor.com.au
tripadvisor.com.tr

tripadvisor.com.mx
tripadvisor.dk
tripadvisor.ca
tripadvisor.se
tripadvisor.nl
tripadvisor.com.br
tripadvisor.jp
tripadvisor.in
tripadvisor.es
tripadvisor.it
tripadvisor.de
tripadvisor.fr
tripadvisor.co.uk
tripadvisor.ie

COMPETITORS

Costamar	Sabre
HomeAway	SkyAuction.com
Lonely Planet	Travelzoo
Orbitz Worldwide	Yelp
Pegasus Solutions	ebookers.com
Priceline	

HISTORICAL FINANCIALS
Company Type: Public

Income Statement
FYE: December 31

	REVENUE ($ mil.)	NET INCOME ($ mil.)	NET PROFIT MARGIN	EMPLOYEES
12/14	1,246.0	226.0	18.1%	2,793
12/13	944.6	205.4	21.7%	2,017
12/12	762.9	194.0	25.4%	1,575
12/11	637.0	177.6	27.9%	1,250
12/10	484.6	138.7	28.6%	1,000
Annual Growth	26.6%	13.0%	—	29.3%

2014 Year-End Financials

Debt ratio: 17.2%
Return on equity: 22.7%
Cash ($ mil.): 455
Current ratio: 1.96
Long-term debt ($ mil.): 260

No. of shares (mil.): 142
Dividends
　Yield: —
　Payout: —
Market value ($ mil.): 10,671

	STOCK PRICE ($) FY Close	P/E High/Low		PER SHARE ($) Earnings	Dividends	Book Value
12/14	74.66	70	43	1.55	0.00	7.87
12/13	82.83	62	29	1.41	0.00	6.08
12/12	41.92	33	18	1.37	0.00	5.09
12/11	25.21	21	18	1.32	0.00	2.20
Annual Growth	43.6%	—	—	5.5%	—	53.0%

TrueBlue Inc

Another day another blue-collar dollar. Staffing firm TrueBlue specializes in providing general laborers on short notice for short-term jobs in fields such as construction hospitality landscaping and transportation. The company offers general labor staffing services from more than 700 branches throughout the US and Canada mostly under the Labor Ready brand. Other units operating through branches include Spartan Staffing (light industrial temporary services) CLP Resources (skilled construction trades) and Centerline Drivers (temporary and dedicated driver placement). TrueBlue mainly serves companies residing in the services construction transportation manufacturing retail and wholesale sectors.

The company changed its name from Labor Ready to TrueBlue in late 2007 to emphasize the blue-collar nature of its staffing services. TrueBlue continues to use the Labor Ready as its primary brand along with its other units.

As the economy has slowly improved TrueBlue has experienced rises in revenues and net income. Revenue increased to about $1.3 billion for 2011 (a nearly 15% increase compared to 2010). The company reported revenue of about $1 billion in 2009 and $1.15 billion in 2010.

TrueBlue has used acquisitions to diversify its mix of services particularly in the light industrial and skilled labor staffing sectors. In 2008 the company made a pair of purchases: TLC Services Group a truck-driver staffing company with operations in 10 states; and Personnel Management (PMI) which provided staffing services in the light industrial sector. In February 2009 TrueBlue folded PMI's operations and 44 offices into its Spartan Staffing unit.

HISTORY

Glenn Welstad having made his fortune as a franchisee of Hardee's fast food restaurants came out of early retirement in 1989 to start Labor Ready with $50000 in investment capital. With one dispatch office in Kent Washington the company focused strictly on blue-collar labor a segment most larger temporary agencies ignored.

Labor Ready opened a couple of offices each year and by 1993 it had grown to 17 offices in the Northwest. Then Welstad began focusing on expanding nationally. He sacrificed much of his profit and sank the company's earnings into expansion; Labor Ready increased its number of offices to 200 over the next three years. In 1996 the company went public.

In 1997 it added more than 100 new locations. Also that year Labor Ready established a Grand Cayman-based insurance company that reinsures domestic workers' compensation carriers. In 1998 the company began providing cash machines in each of its US offices offering employees a choice between a paycheck or cash. Labor Ready continued its rapid expansion by opening more than 150 dispatch offices in 1998. Also that year it eliminated its internal sales force and hired an outside telemarketing firm. (A decline in sales forced the company into the expensive position of having to rebuild its own sales force in 2000.)

The company made its first foray outside North America in 1999 opening an office in Manchester UK. The following year Welstad resigned as CEO and was replaced by Dick King a former executive with Albertson's grocery store chain. The company also came under fire that year from investors (the AFL-CIO's Building and Construction Trades Department sued Labor Ready for misleading statements in its SEC filings and for failing to convene a shareholders meetings) and employees (workers in Atlanta sued over the fee the company charges to dispense daily pay in cash). In addition Labor Ready revamped its Web site to allow clients to place orders and view invoices online and initiated Service Ready a test program providing employees to the hospitality industry.

Joseph Sambataro who had previously served as Labor Ready's CFO replaced King as CEO in 2001.

In its first acquisition the company bought Spartan Staffing for $9.5 million in 2004. The next year Labor Ready purchased CLP Resources a construction trades staffing company for $46 million.

Steve Cooper company president was named as CEO in early 2006 replacing Sambataro. The company changed its name from Labor Ready to TrueBlue in 2007. Also that year TrueBlue strengthened the operations of CLP Resources by buying Skilled Services Corp. a provider of construction trades staffing and it entered the aircraft maintenance staffing niche market with the purchase of PlaneTechs.

As with most companies in the staffing industry TrueBlue was stung by the effects of the recession in 2008 and posted a net loss for the year.

EXECUTIVES

Svp And Cio, William Otto, age 48
Vice President Strategic Planning Fina, Robert P (Bob) Breen, age 50
Vice President Deputy General Counsel, Joanna Monroe
CEO, Steven C. (Steve) Cooper, age 51, $600,001 total compensation
EVP and General Counsel, James E. (Jim) Defebaugh, age 59, $310,001 total compensation
EVP and CFO, Derrek L. Gafford, age 43, $350,002 total compensation
President and COO Staffing Solutions, Wayne Larkin, age 48, $330,000 total compensation
EVP Human Resources, Kimberly A. Cannon, $294,231 total compensation
President and COO Outsourcing Solutions, Patrick Beharelle
SVP and CIO, Jesus Unzueta
Vice President Of Finance Treasurer, Darren McCallon
Vice President Marketing Financial Advisor, Gary Sugai
Region Vice President, Tom Stonich
Senior Vice President Operations Labor, Jay Reid
Regional Vice President Labor Ready, Shannan Manix
Senior Vice President Operations, Chris Burger
Vice President Services, Rob Murphy
Vice President Operations, Joe Heaton
Regional Vice President, Jay Leger
Avp, Billy Hansen
Vice President On Sites, Jennifer Herrbach
Vice President Energy And Industrial, Eric Feinberg
Vice President Corporate Communications, Stacey Burke
National Sales Manager, Charlene Spradlin
Chairman, Joseph P. (Joe) Sambataro, age 63
Board Member, Gates McKibbin, age 68
Assistant Treasurer, Robert Sovern
Auditors: Deloitte&ToucheLLP

LOCATIONS

HQ: TrueBlue Inc
　1015 A Street, Tacoma, WA 98402
Phone: 253 383-9101　　　**Fax:** 253 383-9311
Web: www.trueblue.com

2013 Sales

	$ mil.	% of total
US & Puerto Rico	1617.0	97
Other countries	50.9	3
Total	**1668.9**	**100**

PRODUCTS/OPERATIONS

Selected Brands and Operations
Labor Ready
Spartan Staffing
CLP
PlaneTechs
Centerline

TrueBlue Energy & Industrial
TrueBlue Hospitality
Aviation mechanics
Residential carpenters
Disaster recovery specialists
Hospitality services workers
Warehouse foremen

Selected Industries Served

Aviation
Construction
Facilities
Hospitality
Landscaping
Light manufacturing
Retail
Sanitation
Transportation
Warehousing
Wholesale

COMPETITORS

Adecco	Randstad Holding
CTR	SOS Staffing
Command Center	Your Employment
Kelly Services	Solutions
ManpowerGroup	

HISTORICAL FINANCIALS

Company Type: Public

Income Statement

FYE: December 27

	REVENUE ($ mil.)	NET INCOME ($ mil.)	NET PROFIT MARGIN	EMPLOYEES
12/13	1,668.9	44.9	2.7%	3,200
12/12	1,389.5	33.6	2.4%	2,900
12/11	1,316.0	30.7	2.3%	2,700
12/10	1,149.3	19.8	1.7%	2,600
12/09	1,018.4	8.8	0.9%	2,500
Annual Growth	**13.1%**	**50.3%**	**—**	**6.4%**

2013 Year-End Financials

Debt ratio: 4.1%
Return on equity: 12.3%
Cash ($ mil.): 122
Current ratio: 2.94
Long-term debt ($ mil.): 29

No. of shares (mil.): 41
Dividends
  Yield: —
  Payout: —
Market value ($ mil.): 1,065

	STOCK PRICE ($) FY Close	P/E High/Low	PER SHARE ($) Earnings	Dividends	Book Value
12/13	25.92	25 14	1.11	0.00	9.57
12/12	15.54	21 15	0.84	0.00	8.30
12/11	13.88	26 14	0.73	0.00	7.35
12/10	17.99	42 22	0.46	0.00	7.09
12/09	14.97	73 29	0.20	0.00	6.51
Annual Growth	**14.7%**	**— —**	**53.5%**	**—**	**10.1%**

TTM Technologies Inc

At TTM Technologies it's Time To Market. TTM provides contract printed circuit board (PCB) manufacturing services primarily for the networking communications high-end computing aerospace and defense medical industrial and instrumentation markets as well as to electronics manufacturing service providers that serve those markets. In addition to prototyping TTM offers both quick-turn production —limited quantities delivered in a shortened timeframe —and standard volume production

services. Its top OEM customers include Cisco Systems Huawei Apple Ericsson and ZTE. TTM gets almost 60% of its sales from customers outside the US; 28% comes from China.

Geographic Reach

TTM operates seven PCB fabrication plants in California Connecticut Utah and Wisconsin and has primary customer inventory hubs in Connecticut New York Texas and Wisconsin. Its international footprint includes Asia Pacific operations with five PCB fabrication plants in Hong Kong Dongguan Guangzhou and Shanghai China; and inventory hubs in France Poland Hong Kong China Mexico Malaysia and Thailand.

Operations

The electronics industry provides the majority of TTM's business. That industry is characterized by intense price competition short product life-cycles and fluctuations in product demand. When TTM previously had only one plant in China TTM made boards for big suppliers of computers and networking equipment and shipped the boards to electronic manufacturing services (EMS) providers working under contract to those OEM customers. With five PCB fabrication plants in China it now competes as a one-stop shop for both standard and quick-turn volume contracts.

Sales and Marketing

TTM's largest EMS customers most of whom have significant Asian operations include Celestica Flextronics Hon Hai Jabil and Plexus.

Financial Performance

The company reported a 1.4% revenue increase in 2013 driven by higher sales in North America (up by 11% due to higher demand for Networking/Communications and Aerospace and Defense end markets) partially offset by lower sales in China and other countries. TTM's net income saw a huge drop in 2012 mainly due to increased goodwill and impairment charges. However the company quickly recovered in 2013 with a 133% increase in net income primarily due to higher sales and gains from the sale of assets adding about $18 million to its net income. It was also driven by the absence of impairment charges partially offset by an increase in general and administrative selling and marketing expenses and restructuring charges related to the shutdown of its Suzhou China facility. The company's cash flow from operating activities plummeted to $71.4 million in 2013 (from $111.2 million in 2012) due to increased payments for salaries wages and benefits and other accrued expenses which accounted for about $24.7 million.

Strategy

TTM expects high growth in the PCB market in China where it intends to pursue high-end commercial and defense customers that demand flexible and advanced manufacturing processes expertise with high-performance specialty materials assembly and testing capabilities and expertise in other high-mix and complex technologies. To rationalize production costs in 2014 the company announced plans to close its manufacturing facility at its Suzhou China. In 2013 TTM agreed with its minority partner Shengyi Technology Co. Ltd. (Sytech) to sell TTM's 70% of equity interest in the Dongguan Shengyi Electronics Ltd (SYE) plant to Sytech for $161 million and to acquire Sytech's 20% equity interest in the Dongguan Meadville Circuits Limited (DMC) plant located in Dongguan China for $145 million.

Company Background

The company benefited from its acquisition of Hong Kong-based PCB producer Meadville Holdings. For 2010 TTM's sales more than doubled on a year-over-year basis and the company reported record profits. The purchase boosted its reach in

the computing and cell phone communications markets. It also added significant manufacturing operations in China and Hong Kong where production costs are lower as well as an expanded customer base concentrated in the region.

Many of the company's competitors also have large operations in Asia which prior to the Meadville acquisition gave them an advantage in standard volume PCB production. To counteract this the company used its quick-turn and prototyping services to get involved in the product development process early giving it an advantage in becoming the preferred vendor for new and existing customers. It also gave customers the advantage of shortening the time required to develop and bring new products to market. The purchase of Meadville gave TTM the ability to

EXECUTIVES

President and Director, Thomas T. Edman, age 51
EVP and President TTM Asia Pacific, Canice T. K. Chung, age 56
CEO and Director, Kenton K. (Kent) Alder, age 64, $783,846 total compensation
EVP and COO, Shane S. Whiteside, age 48, $352,692 total compensation
EVP CFO and Secretary, Steven W. (Steve) Richards, age 49, $303,077 total compensation
VP Information Technology, Dale Knecht
EVP and President TTM North America, Douglas L. Soder, age 53, $399,231 total compensation
Executive Vice President & Chief Financial Officer, Todd B. Schull, age 55
Executive Vice President President Asia Pacific Business Unit, Chung Keung
Vice President Of Operations, Phil Titterton
Vice President Sales Los Angeles Ca, Dror Maier
Vice President, Curt Robinson
Vice President Internal Audit, Julie Insley
Vice President Of Product Development, John Carvana
Vice President Business Development, Peter Meisinger
Vice President Human Resources, Shawn Powers
Executive Vice President, D Soder
Vice President Marketing And Ir, Audrey Sim
Chairman of the Board, Robert E. Klatell, age 68
President and Director, Thomas T. Edman, age 51
CEO and Director, Kenton K. (Kent) Alder, age 64
EVP CFO and Secretary, Steven W. (Steve) Richards, age 49
Auditors: KPMGLLP

LOCATIONS

HQ: TTM Technologies Inc
1665 Scenic Avenue, Suite 250, Costa Mesa, CA 92626
Phone: 714 327-3000
Web: www.ttmtech.com

2013 Sales

	$ mil.	% of total
US	571.1	42
China	391.9	28
Other countries	405.2	30
Total	**1368.2**	**100**

PRODUCTS/OPERATIONS

2013 Sales

	% of total
Networking & communications	32
Computing storage & peripherals	20
Cellular phone	20
Aerospace & defense	15
Medical industrial & instrumentation	8
Other	5
Total	**100**

Selected Services

Backplanes
Commercial assembly (assembling backplanes into
  subassemblies and other devices)
Custom subsystem assemblies
Heat sink assemblies
Printed circuit board (PCB) fabrication
Prototype production
Radio-frequency (RF) and microwave interconnects
Quick-turn production
Standard volume production

COMPETITORS

Amphenol	Simclar Group
Benchmark Electronics	TT electronics
Celestica	UNIMICRON TECHNOLOGY
Elec & Eltek	CORP.
Flextronics	Viasystems
Foxconn Technology	WUS PRINTED CIRCUIT
IBIDEN	CO. LTD.
Multek Flexible	Zhen Ding Technology
Circuits	Holding Limited
Plexus	i3 Electronics Inc.
Sanmina	

HISTORICAL FINANCIALS

Company Type: Public

Income Statement
FYE: December 30

	REVENUE ($ mil.)	NET INCOME ($ mil.)	NET PROFIT MARGIN	EMPLOYEES
12/13	1,368.2	21.8	1.6%	16,290
12/12	1,348.6	(174.6)	—	19,934
12/11	1,428.6	41.8	2.9%	16,278
12/10	1,179.6	71.5	6.1%	17,448
12/09	582.4	4.8	0.8%	3,037
Annual Growth	23.8%	45.7%	—	52.2%

2013 Year-End Financials

Debt ratio: 34.2%
Return on equity: 3.2%
Cash ($ mil.): 330
Current ratio: 1.76
Long-term debt ($ mil.): 477

No. of shares (mil.): 82
Dividends
  Yield: —
  Payout: —
Market value ($ mil.): 710

	STOCK PRICE ($) FY Close	P/E High/Low		PER SHARE ($) Earnings	Dividends	Book Value
12/13	8.59	40	25	0.26	0.00	8.53
12/12	9.19	—	—	(2.13)	0.00	7.98
12/11	10.96	37	17	0.51	0.00	9.95
12/10	14.92	15	8	1.01	0.00	9.07
12/09	11.53	113	36	0.11	0.00	7.90
Annual Growth	(7.1%)	—	—	24.0%	—	2.0%

Two Harbors Investment Corp

Two Harbors Investment Corp. is ready to double its money. The real estate investment trust (REIT) is managed and advised by (and was founded by) PRCM Advisers a subsidiary of Pine River Capital Management. The trust primarily invests in agency residential mortgage-backed securities (RMBS) with fixed or adjustable interest rates that are backed by government-supported enterprises Fannie Mae Freddie Mac or Ginnie Mae.

About a quarter of its mortgage portfolio is made up of non-agency RMBS such as subprime mortgages which carry more risk than federally-backed securities but offer higher yields. Chairman (and Pine River CEO) Brian Taylor controls almost 20% of the trust's stock.

Pine River Capital Management set up Two Harbors in 2009 through a reverse merger with a blank-check company named Capitol Acquisition Corp. Since then the company has completed three follow-on public offerings that netted more than $520 million which it has used to invest in agency and non-agency RMBS and other financial assets. Two Harbors plans to continue to maintain its portfolio of agency RMBS sprinkled with riskier investments to boost yield.

EXECUTIVES

Vice Chairman, Mark D. Ein, age 49
Chairman, Brian C. Taylor, age 50
Chief Financial Officer Treasurer, Steven (Steve) Kuhn, age 45
Co-Chief Investment Officer, William (Bill) Roth, age 57
General Counsel and Secretary, Timothy (Tim) O?Brien, age 55
Controller, Brad Farrell
VP Business Development, Andrew Garcia
Investor Relations, Anh Huynh
Managing Director, Paul Richardson
General Counsel; Secretary, Timothy OBrien
Director, Stephen G. Kasnet, age 68
Director, Peter S. Niculescu, age 55
Vice Chairman, Mark D. Ein, age 49
Director, W. Reid Sanders, age 65
Director, William W. Johnson, age 52
Auditors: Ernst&YoungLLP

LOCATIONS

HQ: Two Harbors Investment Corp
  590 Madison Avenue, 36th Floor, New York, NY 10022
Phone: 612 629-2500
Web: www.twoharborsinvestment.com

COMPETITORS

American Capital	MFA Financial
Agency Corp.	New York Mortgage
Annaly Capital	Trust
Management	Newcastle Investment
Capstead Mortgage	Putnam Mortgage
Chimera	Redwood Trust
Gramercy	iStar Financial Inc
Invesco Mortgage	
Capital	

HISTORICAL FINANCIALS

Company Type: Public

Income Statement
FYE: December 31

	REVENUE ($ mil.)	NET INCOME ($ mil.)	NET PROFIT MARGIN	EMPLOYEES
12/13	746.3	579.0	77.6%	0
12/12	296.0	291.9	98.6%	0
12/11	150.3	127.4	84.8%	0
12/10	42.6	35.7	83.9%	0
12/09	3.4	(8.7)	—	0
Annual Growth	284.0%	—	—	—

2013 Year-End Financials

Debt ratio: 3.7%
Return on equity: 15.8%
Cash ($ mil.): 1,427
Current ratio: 0.23
Long-term debt ($ mil.): —

No. of shares (mil.): 364
Dividends
  Yield: 12.6%
  Payout: 67.2%
Market value ($ mil.): 3,387

	STOCK PRICE ($) FY Close	P/E High/Low		PER SHARE ($) Earnings	Dividends	Book Value
12/13	9.28	8	5	1.65	1.17	10.56
12/12	11.08	10	7	1.20	1.71	11.55
12/11	9.24	9	6	1.29	1.60	9.03
12/10	9.79	6	5	1.60	1.48	9.44
12/09	9.80	—	—	(0.39)	0.26	9.10
Annual Growth	(1.4%)	—	—	—	45.6%	3.8%

UIL Holding Corp

UIL Holdings parent of electric utility The United Illuminating Company (UI) hopes its well-regulated business will result in regular revenue growth. The public utility distributes electricity to 321000 customers in southwestern Connecticut. Its service area largely urban and suburban includes the principal cities of Bridgeport (population 146000) and New Haven (population 130000) and their surrounding areas. UIL Holdings has teamed up with NRG Energy to operate GenConn Energy LLC a joint venture that focuses on developing new power generation facilities in Connecticut. The company has also diversified through the acquisition of three gas utilities in New England from IBERDROLA USA for $1.3 billion.

Operations

The 2010 acquisition of Southern Connecticut Gas Connecticut Natural Gas and Berkshire Gas diversified the company's portfolio to include natural gas distribution operations in its core geographic area and boosted UIL Holdings' customer base (706000 in 2012).

UIL Holdings operates Electric Distribution and Transmission and Gas Distribution segments. UI is a regulated operating electric public utility engaged in the purchase transmission distribution and sale of electricity for residential commercial and industrial purposes in a service area in the southwestern part of Connecticut.

The holding company's gas companies engage in natural gas transportation distribution and sales operations in Connecticut and western Massachusetts.

Financial Performance

UIL Holding's revenues decreased by 5% in 2012 primarily due to 2% lower revenues from the electric distribution and transmission segment because of decreased retail revenues and distribution sales volumes resulting from warmer-than-normal winter temperatures in 2012. Gas distribution segment revenues decreased by 9% due to increased lower sales volume as a result of warmer weather.

The company's net income increased by 4% in 2012 due to lower purchases of natural gas and decreased operation and maintenance expense of electric distribution and transmission segment due to a drop in outside services expenses offset by increased operating and maintenance expenses of the gas distribution segment due to shared services costs and increased uncollectible expenses.

Strategy

In 2012 the company adopted a new comprehensive energy strategy focused on promoting energy efficiency and expanding the use of natural gas in order to make Connecticut more competitive as it the state seeks to attract and retain business and industry.

In 2011 GenConn Energy brought its 200 MW peaking power plant at NRG Energy's Middletown Station online to serve the ISO New England markets. The new unit will provide power to Connecticut homes and businesses during periods of peak demand such as severe weather conditions.

Company Background

UIL Holdings' non-regulated units (once a more significant part of its operations before it refocused on its regulated business in the mid-2000s) consist of an operating lease and passive minority ownership interests in two investment funds (collectively held by United Capital Investments Inc.) a heating and cooling facility and a unit that manages claims for Xcelecom a mechanical contracting business it divested in 2006.

UI was established as a regulated electric public utility in 1899.

EXECUTIVES

Vp And Controller Uil Holdings And Ui, Steven P (Steve) Favuzza, age 62

EVP and COO; President and COO United Illuminating, Anthony J. Vallillo, age 65, $400,275 total compensation

EVP and CFO, Richard J. Nicholas, age 59, $315,000 total compensation

President CEO and Director, James P. Torgerson, age 62, $625,000 total compensation

Chief Information Officer; Vice President - Information Technology, Joseph Santamaria

Vice President - Connecticut Gas Operations, Robert Allessio

Vice President Administrative Services, William Reis

Vice President Audit Services And Chief, Deborah Hoffman

President CEO and Director, James P. Torgerson, age 62

Board Of Directors, Betsy Cohn

Auditors: PricewaterhouseCoopersLLP

LOCATIONS

HQ: UIL Holding Corp
157 Church Street, New Haven, CT 06506
Phone: 203 499-2000
Web: www.uil.com

PRODUCTS/OPERATIONS

2012 Sales

	$ mil.	% of total
Utility		
Electric		
Distribution	561.2	38
Transmission	222.3	15
Gas		
Distribution	703.0	47
Total	**1486.5**	**100**

COMPETITORS

Columbia Gas of Massachusetts
Con Edison
Connecticut Light and Power
Eversource Energy
Green Mountain Energy
Green Mountain Power
Iberdrola USA
NSTAR Electric
National Grid USA
PPL Corporation
PPL Generation
Unitil
Wayne J. Griffin Electric
Western Massachusetts Electric
Yankee Gas

HISTORICAL FINANCIALS

Company Type: Public

Income Statement

FYE: December 31

	REVENUE ($ mil.)	NET INCOME ($ mil.)	NET PROFIT MARGIN	EMPLOYEES
12/13	1,618.7	115.3	7.1%	1,895
12/12	1,486.5	103.7	7.0%	1,865
12/11	1,570.4	99.7	6.3%	1,868
12/10	997.6	54.8	5.5%	1,824
12/09	896.5	54.3	6.1%	1,066
Annual Growth	**15.9%**	**20.7%**	**—**	**15.5%**

2013 Year-End Financials

Debt ratio: 33.7%
Return on equity: 9.3%
Cash ($ mil.): 69
Current ratio: 1.45
Long-term debt ($ mil.): 1,723
No. of shares (mil.): 56
Dividends
Yield: 4.4%
Payout: 85.5%
Market value ($ mil.): 2,199

	STOCK PRICE ($) FY Close	P/E High/Low		PER SHARE ($) Earnings	Dividends	Book Value
12/13	38.75	19	16	2.18	1.73	23.86
12/12	35.81	18	16	2.02	1.73	21.95
12/11	35.37	18	15	1.95	1.73	21.62
12/10	29.96	20	16	1.52	1.73	21.32
12/09	28.08	16	9	1.93	1.73	19.15
Annual Growth	**8.4%**	**—**	**—**	**3.1%**	**(0.0%)**	**5.6%**

Ultimate Software Group, Inc.

The Ultimate Software Group (USG) isn't timid about the benefits of its workforce management products. Businesses use its cloud-based UltiPro software suite to manage hiring human resources compliance benefits enrollment payroll appraisals and time and attendance. Primarily serving clients in the US the company offers UltiPro Enterprise for businesses with more than 1000 employees and UltiPro Workplace for those with fewer than 1000 employees. It targets the communications finance health care retail technology and transportation industries among others. Founded in 1990 USG has more than 15 million people records in its HCM (human capital management) cloud.

Geographic Reach

Florida-based Ultimate Software operates data centers in Arizona Georgia and near Toronto Canada.

Sales and MarketingThe company markets its software through direct sales teams organized by geographic region. It boasts aome 2700 customers across many industries including manufacturing food services sports technology finance and others. Clients include Adobe Systems Major League Baseball and The Pep Boys. Sales and marketing expenses rose 29% in 2013 versus 2012 to nearly $94 million.

Financial PerformanceUltimate Software has enjoyed a decade of consistent sales growth. In 2013 it reported revenue of $410.4 million up 24% versus 2012. Net income increased 74% over the same period to $25.5 million marking the fourth consecutive year of growth. Recurring revenues

which account for more than 80% of the company's total increased 26% year over year primarily due to an increase in cloud revenues partially offset by a decrease in maintenance revenues. Services revenue rose 16%.

Strategy

In the highly competitive market for human capital management (HCM) software Ultimate Software focuses on product enhancements (including add-ons) and customer satisfaction. The company is working to expand its offering to support a multinational client base. New capabilities for global HCM include the 2013 launch of 29 additional country localizations (including Brazil China and Korea) providing support for locally compliant payroll and relevant employee details while also enabling worldwide oversight and reporting capabilities for corporate leadership. Another 25 localizations are planned for 2014.

Alliances are another important element of the people management company's strategy. In February 2014 Ultimate Software announced that it is integrating LinkedIn and its UltiPro Recruiting cloud product. Currently Ultimate Software offers customers seamless integration between LinkedIn and UltiPro Recruiting with additional integration between the two platforms planned for later in 2014.

Mergers and Acquisitions

In November 2013 Ultimate Software acquired certain assets of Georgia-based Accel HR LLC a provider of outsourcing solutions and services for middle to large market companies ranging from 500 to more than 25000 employees. In October it purchased EmployTouch Inc. a developer of workforce management hardware and software products based in Toronto Canada.

EXECUTIVES

Vice President Software Engineering At Ultimate Software Group, Stephen M Reid

EVP CFO and Treasurer, Mitchell K. (Mitch) Dauerman, age 56, $525,000 total compensation

Chairman President and CEO, Scott Scherr, age 61, $700,000 total compensation

Vice Chairman, Marc D. Scherr, age 56, $625,000 total compensation

SVP and Chief Technology Officer, Adam Rogers, age 39, $571,000 total compensation

SVP Marketing, Jody Kaminsky, age 39

Vice President Of Finance, Felecia Alvaro

Vice President Payroll Tax Operations, John Stauffer

Human Resources Director And Vice President, Mabel Cabrera

Vice President And Chief Info Officer, James Jensen

Vice President And General Manager Workplace Operations, Julie Dodd

Vice President, Susan Romanick

Vice President, Michael Schaberl

Vice President Sales Midwest Division, Rick Torrence

Vice President Sales Operations, Sherry Stein

Vice President Marketing, Diane Alonso

Vice President Workplace Center, Marilyn Almanza

Gm Vice President Business Unit Manager, Lee McDermott

EVP CFO and Treasurer, Mitchell K. (Mitch) Dauerman, age 56

Chairman President and CEO, Scott Scherr, age 61

Vice Chairman, Marc D. Scherr, age 56

Auditors: KPMGLLP

LOCATIONS

HQ: Ultimate Software Group, Inc.
2000 Ultimate Way, Weston, FL 33326
Phone: 954 331-7000
Web: www.ultimatesoftware.com

PRODUCTS/OPERATIONS

2014 Sales

	$ mil.	% of total
Recurring	419.2	83
Services	86.2	17
Licenses	0.5	—
Total	**505.9**	**100**

COMPETITORS

ADP	Peoplefluent
Ceridian	SAP
Kronos	SPM Global Services
Oracle	Sage Software
Paychex	Workday Inc.
Paylocity	

HISTORICAL FINANCIALS

Company Type: Public

Income Statement   FYE: December 31

	REVENUE ($ mil.)	NET INCOME ($ mil.)	NET PROFIT MARGIN	EMPLOYEES
12/13	410.4	25.5	6.2%	1,913
12/12	332.2	14.6	4.4%	1,614
12/11	269.2	4.2	1.6%	1,328
12/10	227.8	2.1	0.9%	1,134
12/09	196.5	(1.1)	—	989
Annual Growth	**20.2%**	—	—	**17.9%**

2013 Year-End Financials

Debt ratio: 1.3%	No. of shares (mil.): 28
Return on equity: 16.8%	Dividends
Cash ($ mil.): 79	Yield: —
Current ratio: 1.16	Payout: —
Long-term debt ($ mil.): 2	Market value ($ mil.): 4,302

	STOCK PRICE ($) FY Close	P/E High/Low	PER SHARE ($) Earnings	Dividends	Book Value
12/13	153.22	173 101	0.88	0.00	6.70
12/12	94.41	191 117	0.52	0.00	4.19
12/11	65.12	413 267	0.15	0.00	3.26
12/10	48.63	550 308	0.08	0.00	2.87
12/09	29.37	— —	(0.05)	0.00	2.35
Annual Growth	**51.1%**	—	—	—	**30.0%**

Ultra Clean Holdings Inc

Ultra Clean Holdings helps computer chip makers handle gases key to the manufacturing process under the ultraclean conditions the process requires. The company which does business as Ultra Clean Technology (UCT) designs engineers manufactures and tests customized gas liquid and catalytic steam generation delivery systems used primarily in the production of semiconductors. The company's three biggest customers account for about 80% of revenue. In an effort to reach new markets UCT uses its expertise in the semiconductor industry to develop tools for the flat-panel display medical research and energy industries. By extending its reach the company looks to smooth the effects of the highly cyclical chip industry.

Operations

UCT functions through wholly owned subsidiaries: Ultra Clean Technology Systems and Service Inc. AIT LLC and Ultra Clean Technology (Shanghai). The company places its factories near its customers' plants in the US and Asia because of the tight coordination of UCT tools into its customers' products. The company intends to expand its operations in Asia principally in China and Singapore to reduce costs.

Geographic Reach

UCT has operations in China Singapore the Philippines and in California Arizona and Texas in the US. Manufacturing is done at all locations while engineering functions are also conducted in the headquarters in Hayward California South San Francisco California and Austin Texas. More than 70% of sales come from customers headquartered in the US. Most of the rest come from Asia which has accounted for a growing portion UCT's sales in the past three years reaching about 25% in 2013.

Sales and Marketing

The business of making semiconductors is highly technical so UCT relies on a direct sales force of more than 80 sales directors account managers and sales support staff. The sales staff includes technical sales support and engineers stationed at customers' factories. Three customers accounted for 81% of UCT's sales: Applied Materials 35% LAM Research 33% and ASM 13%. In the past three years Applied Materials and LAM have bought companies that were UCT customers.

Financial Performance

Revenue for fiscal year 2013 increased 10% to $444 million in 2013 from $403 million in 2012. Net income rose to $10 million in 2013 from $5 million in 2012. Cash from operating activities was $29.9 million in 2013 an increase from $27.3 million for fiscal 2012. The increases in sales and net income came through UCT's acquisition of Advanced Integration Technologies (AIT) a major supplier of equipment complementary to UCT's products in July 2012. AIT's sales in 2013 were $122.4 million up from $63.8 million in 2012.

Without AIT's contribution UCT's revenue dropped in 2013 from 2012 which UCT blamed on the impact of several factors that surfaced in 2012. In early 2012 UCT ended its manufacturing arrangement for FEI a maker of precision instruments. Later in the year one of UCT's larger semiconductor equipment customers took a portion of its gas panel work in-house. And an overall downturn in the semiconductor industry began in the 2012 third quarter.

Strategy

UCT is working on several fronts to expand work with current clients develop new clients and diversify beyond semiconductors. The company believes that it can pick up business from OEMs that outsource manufacturing processes. It also has placed factories in lower-cost regions in order to maintain competitive prices for its customers. The company seeks to parlay its experience in developing tools for semiconductor manufacturing to make equipment for companies in the flat panel display robotic surgery medical equipment industrial and energy industries. It will consider acquisitions that expand the company's geographic reach gain new customers increase expand market share and move into new markets.

Mergers and Acquisitions

UCT's acquisition of AIT in 2012 was the largest deal in UCT's history. UCT paid in cash and newly issued common stock totaling about $105 million. The acquisition was to increase UCT's competitive position and market share by diversifying and expanding its customer base and product and service portfolio.

EXECUTIVES

CEO, James P. (Jim) Scholhamer, age 48
EVP and CFO, Kevin C. (Casey) Eichler, age 54, $329,192 total compensation
SVP Asia, Lavi A. Lev, age 58, $244,274 total compensation
SVP Engineering, Bruce Wier, age 65, $223,872 total compensation
SVP Supply Chain Management, Mark G. Bingaman
Vice President Business Operations Erp Management, Joshua Kramer
Vice President Finance, Sheri Brumm
Chairman, Clarence L. Granger, age 66
Auditors: Deloitte&ToucheLLP

LOCATIONS

HQ: Ultra Clean Holdings Inc
26462 Corporate Avenue, Hayward, CA 94545
Phone: 510 576-4400
Web: www.uct.com

2011 Sales

	$ mil.	% of total
US	357.3	79
Other countries	95.3	21
Total	**452.6**	**100**

COMPETITORS

ATMI	L' Air Liquide
Air Products	Matheson Tri-Gas
Allegro MicroSystems	Praxair
Ebara	Sanmina
Flextronics	Wolfe Engineering

HISTORICAL FINANCIALS

Company Type: Public

Income Statement   FYE: December 27

	REVENUE ($ mil.)	NET INCOME ($ mil.)	NET PROFIT MARGIN	EMPLOYEES
12/13	444.0	10.4	2.3%	1,622
12/12	403.4	5.1	1.3%	1,506
12/11	452.6	23.7	5.2%	1,155
12/10*	443.1	20.1	4.5%	1,241
01/10	159.7	(20.0)	—	901
Annual Growth	**29.1%**	—	—	**15.8%**

*Fiscal year change

2013 Year-End Financials

Debt ratio: 18.8%	No. of shares (mil.): 28
Return on equity: 6.3%	Dividends
Cash ($ mil.): 60	Yield: —
Current ratio: 2.00	Payout: —
Long-term debt ($ mil.): 17	Market value ($ mil.): 288

	STOCK PRICE ($) FY Close	P/E High/Low	PER SHARE ($) Earnings	Dividends	Book Value
12/13	10.05	28 13	0.36	0.00	5.99
12/12	4.68	45 22	0.20	0.00	5.62
12/11	6.11	13 4	1.01	0.00	5.12
12/10*	9.31	12 7	0.87	0.00	3.92
01/10	6.99	— —	(0.94)	0.00	2.85
Annual Growth	**9.5%**	—	—	—	**20.4%**

*Fiscal year change

UMH Properties Inc

UMH Properties (formerly United Mobile Homes) is a real estate investment trust (REIT) that owns and manages more than 80 manufactured home communities containing approximately 14500 developed lots in New Jersey New York Ohio Pennsylvania and several other states. The company leases home sites to private homeowners on a monthly basis and rents a small number of homes to residents. Communities offer such amenities as swimming pools playgrounds and municipal water and sewer services. The REIT sells and finances manufactured homes through subsidiary UMH Sales and Finance and owns more than 800 acres of land for development. UMH Properties also invests in other REITs.

Geographic Reach

The New Jersey-based REIT owns lots in Indiana Michigan New Jersey New York Ohio Pennsylvania and Tennessee.

Financial Performance

The REIT's revenue has been growing along with its active acquisition schedule and swelling portfolio of properties. In 2013 revenue increased by nearly a third over 2012 to $62.2 million. Rental and related income increased 41% in 2013 to $53.5 million from about $38 million in 2012. The increase was due to acquisitions made in 2013 and 2012. UMH has been raising rental rates by approximately 2% to 6% annually at certain communities. Sales of manufactured homes fell from $8.8 million in 2012 to $8.7 million in 2013 on fewer homes sold.

Despite the substantial increase in revenue net income declined 10% in 2013 versus 2012 to $5.8 million on an increase in community operating expenses acquisition costs interest and other expenses. Cash flow from operations has been rising along with revenue.

Strategy

UMH has been growing by acquisitions and plans to continue making opportunistic investments particularly in energy-rich areas such as the Marcellus and Utica shale regions in the Northeast. In 2013 it acquired 10 manufactured home communities for a total of $67.5 million. The 10 all-age communities totaled 1854 sites and spanned approximately 400 acres. Five of the acquired properties are in Indiana four in Pennsylvania and one in Michigan. In 2012 the REIT bought more than 15 properties including 11 manufactured home communities from ARCPA Properties LLC for an aggregate purchase price of $28.3 million.

Mergers and Acquisitions

In March 2014 UMH closed on the purchase of eight Ohio manufactured home communities for about $25 million. The eight all-age communities contan a total of 1018 developed homesites situated on about 270 acres.

EXECUTIVES

President and Chief Executive Officer; Director, Samuel A. Landy, age 53, $300,000 total compensation

Chief Financial Officer & Vice President, Anna T. Chew, age 55, $248,208 total compensation

Executive Vice President; Director, Michael P. Landy, age 53

Vice President Communiations And Public Affairs, Susan Jordan

Vice President Of Sales Operations, Christine Lindsey

President and Chief Executive Officer; Director, Samuel A. Landy, age 53

Chief Financial Officer & Vice President, Anna T. Chew, age 55

Chairman, Eugene W. Landy, age 81

Executive Vice President; Director, Michael P. Landy, age 53

Auditors: PKF

LOCATIONS

HQ: UMH Properties Inc
Juniper Business Plaza, 3499 Route 9 North, Suite 3-C, Freehold, NJ 07728
Phone: 732 577-9997
Web: www.umh.com

Indiana
Michigan
New Jersey
New York
Ohio
Pennsylvania
Tennessee

PRODUCTS/OPERATIONS

2013 Sales

	$ mil.	% of total
Rental & related income	53.5	86
Sales of manufactured homes	8.7	14
Total	**62.2**	**100**

COMPETITORS

American Land Lease	Hometown America
Clayton Homes	Origen Financial
Equity Lifestyle Properties	Sun Communities

HISTORICAL FINANCIALS

Company Type: Public

Income Statement

FYE: December 31

	REVENUE ($ mil.)	NET INCOME ($ mil.)	NET PROFIT MARGIN	EMPLOYEES
12/13	62.2	5.8	9.4%	250
12/12	46.8	6.4	13.8%	210
12/11	39.3	3.7	9.4%	150
12/10	34.0	6.6	19.6%	130
12/09	32.0	3.6	11.5%	100
Annual Growth	**18.1%**	**12.2%**	**—**	**25.7%**

2013 Year-End Financials

Debt ratio: 51.4%
Return on equity: 3.1%
Cash ($ mil.): 7
Current ratio: 2.96
Long-term debt ($ mil.): 209
No. of shares (mil.): 20
Dividends
Yield: 7.6%
Payout: 300.0%
Market value ($ mil.): 196

	STOCK PRICE ($) FY Close	P/E High/Low	Earnings	Dividends	Book Value
12/13	9.42	37 29	0.31	0.72	9.18
12/12	10.33	30 23	0.40	0.72	10.23
12/11	9.31	45 35	0.25	0.72	6.94
12/10	10.20	23 15	0.52	0.72	5.25
12/09	8.48	28 16	0.32	0.72	4.63
Annual Growth	**2.7%**	**— —**	**(0.8%)**	**(0.0%)**	**18.6%**

Under Armour Inc

Under Armour is proving its mettle as an apparel warrior. Since its foray into the sports apparel market the maker of performance athletic undies and clothing has risen to the top of the industry pack boasting a big portion of the compression garment market. It is gaining a foothold in footwear too. Under Armour is the official footwear supplier of the NFL and MLB and partners with the NBA. Specializing in sport-specific garments it dresses its consumers from head to toe. Products are made from its moisture-wicking and heat-dispersing fabrics able to keep athletes dry during workouts. Under Armour sells its wares online by catalog through its own factory house stores and in more than 25000 retail stores worldwide.

Operations

Apparel designed for winter (COLDGEAR) summer (HEATGEAR) and year-round (ALLSEASONGEAR) wear accounts for about three-fourths of sales. Footwear and accessories such as hats bags and gloves contribute about 15% and 10% respectively.

Geographic Reach

Headquartered in Baltimore Under Armour operates its business globally. It has European and Asian subsidiaries and sources from suppliers worldwide. Besides North America where it generates about 95% of sales Under Armour's products are sold primarily in Austria France Germany Ireland and the UK. It sells its wares in Japan and Korea as well through a third-party licensee.

Sales and Marketing

Under Armour generates nearly 70% of its sales through its wholesale business. Its customers include the likes of Cabela's and the Army and Air Force Exchange as well as Dick's Sporting Goods and The Sports Authority which as a pair accounted for 22% of Under Armour's 2013 revenue. The company's direct-to-consumer business is also growing rapidly; Under Armour operates about 130 of its own factory house and specialty stores.

Financial Performance

Under Armour has shown strong growth in both revenue and net income over the past decade with 2013 sales of $2.3 billion 27% higher than the prior year. The company saw about 25%-30% growth in all categories (apparel footwear accessories) as well as in licensing. The results were powered by an increase in direct to consumer sales (Under Armour opened 18 new factory house stores in 2013) new product offerings and higher average selling prices. Net income that year rose a quarter to about $162 million on the strength of revenue.

After a huge jump to nearly $200 million in 2012 cash from operations fell to $120 million the following year as the company spent more than $160 million more in inventory to support its international and direct-to-consumer operations and deal with supplier delivery issues from the prior year.

Strategy

Under Armour is working to double its business by 2016 with more offices located outside North America than inside. In 2013 the company began selling directly in Mexico instead of through a distributor and it launched its products in Brazil and Chile. It also opened more stores in China and has entered into partnerships with sports teams across the globe including the Tottenham Hotspur Football Club in the UK the Welsh Rugby Union and

Chile's Corporacion Club Social y Deportivo Colo-Colo football club.

New products and product innovation is also a strategic focus for Under Armour. Recent product launches include COLDGEAR Infrared designed to help wearers stay warmer longer in cold weather and UA SpeedForm Apollo running shoes. In addition the company is looking to expand into wearable technology —what it is calling Connected Fitness.

Mergers and Acquisitions

In late 2013 Under Armour acquired fitness-tracking firm MapMyFitness for $150 million as it seeks to expand into the growing fitness technology market. It was the company's first acquisition.

EXECUTIVES

Senior Vice President Global Logistics, Mike Faful
Chairman and CEO, Kevin A. Plank, age 42, $26,000 total compensation
President North America, Matthew C. Mirchin, age 55, $260,000 total compensation
President Footwear and Innovation, Kip J. Fulks, age 42, $556,200 total compensation
Chief Supply Chain Officer, James H. (Jim) Hardy, age 55
Chief Merchandising Officer, Henry B. Stafford, age 39, $545,900 total compensation
COO and CFO, Brad Dickerson, age 50, $500,000 total compensation
EVP Global Marketing, Adam Peake, age 45
President International, Karl-Heinz (Charlie) Maurath, $116,666 total compensation
Vice President Of Business Intelligence, Shawn Herrin
Svp Global Retail, Susie McCabe
Svp Global E-commerce, Jason Larose
Vice President North American Sales, Wilma Peake
Vice President Strategy And Ecommerce, Bill Besselman
Vice President Retail Marketing, Carl Smit
Vice President Global Corporate Real, Neil Jurgens
Vice President Men's Youth, Glenn Silbert
Sr Vice President Exec Creative Dir, Leanne Fremar
Vice President Under Armour China, Kevin Eskridge
Principal And Senior Vice President, Jed Larkin
Vice President Global Brand Marketing, Steve Sommers
Vice President Footwear Sourcing, Keith Dunlap
Vice President Women's Marketing, Heidi Sandreuter
Executive Vice President, Lisa Struble
Executive Vice President And National Property Practice Leader, Carolyn Johnson
Chairman and CEO, Kevin A. Plank, age 42
Auditors: PricewaterhouseCoopersLLP

LOCATIONS

HQ: Under Armour Inc
  1020 Hull Street, Baltimore, MD 21230
Phone: 410 454-6428
Web: www.underarmour.com

2014 Sales

	$ mil.	% of total
North America	2796.4	91
Other countries	288	9
Total	**3084.4**	**100**

PRODUCTS/OPERATIONS

2014 Sales

	$ mil.	% of total
Apparel	2291.5	74
Footwear	431	14
Accessories	275.4	9
Licensing	86.5	3
Total	**3084.4**	**100**

Selected ProductsApparelAllseasongearColdgearHeatgearFootwearAccessoriesLicense and Other

COMPETITORS

Calvin Klein	North Face
Columbia Sportswear	Patagonia Inc.
Fruit of the Loom	Victoria' s Secret
Hanesbrands	Stores
Jockey International	Warnaco Swimwear
L.L. Bean	adidas
NIKE	

HISTORICAL FINANCIALS

Company Type: Public

Income Statement

FYE: December 31

	REVENUE ($ mil.)	NET INCOME ($ mil.)	NET PROFIT MARGIN	EMPLOYEES
12/13	2,332.0	162.3	7.0%	7,800
12/12	1,834.9	128.7	7.0%	5,900
12/11	1,472.6	96.9	6.6%	5,400
12/10	1,063.9	68.4	6.4%	3,900
12/09	856.4	46.7	5.5%	3,000
Annual Growth	**28.5%**	**36.5%**	**—**	**27.0%**

2013 Year-End Financials

Debt ratio: 9.6%	No. of shares (mil.): 211
Return on equity: 17.3%	Dividends
Cash ($ mil.): 347	Yield: —
Current ratio: 2.65	Payout: —
Long-term debt ($ mil.): 47	Market value ($ mil.): 18,475

	STOCK PRICE ($) FY Close	P/E High/Low		PER SHARE ($) Earnings	Dividends	Book Value
12/13	87.30	113	60	0.75	0.00	4.98
12/12	48.53	173	74	0.61	0.00	3.90
12/11	71.79	183	112	0.46	0.00	3.07
12/10	54.84	178	71	0.34	0.00	2.43
12/09	27.27	141	52	0.23	0.00	1.99
Annual Growth	**33.8%**	**—**	**—**	**34.4%**	**—**	**25.8%**

Unit Corp.

It's oil for one and one for oil. With a single-minded focus on hydrocarbons Unit conducts on-shore drilling of oil and natural gas wells for customers in the Gulf Coast Midcontinent and Rocky Mountain regions of the US. Through Unit Drilling it has a drilling fleet of almost 130 rigs. The company owns stakes in more than 8820 wells. Unit also has upstream and midstream businesses. Unit Petroleum explores for and produces oil and gas in the Anadarko and Arkoma basins of Oklahoma and Texas. In 2011 it reported proved reserves of 116 million barrels of oil equivalent (a 12% increase over the previous year). Its Superior Pipeline subsidiary buys sells gathers processes and treats natural gas.

Operations

This company's midstream unit owns three gas treatment plants 10 processing plants and 35 gas gathering systems.

Geographic Reach

Unit's producing oil and natural gas properties undeveloped leaseholds and related assets are located mainly in Louisiana North Dakota Oklahoma and Texas and to a lesser extent in Alabama Arkansas Colorado Kansas Michigan Mississippi Montana New Mexico Pennsylvania and Wyoming and in Canada. Its drilling operations are mainly located in Colorado Louisiana Montana North Dakota Oklahoma Texas Utah and Wyoming.

Sales and Marketing

In 2011 QEP Resources Unit's largest drilling customer accounted for about 22% of total contract drilling revenues. Valero Energy and Sunoco Partners Marketing accounted for 18% and 10% respectively of oil and natural gas revenues. ONEOK and Gavilon accounted for 54% and 19% respectively of midstream revenues.

Financial Analysis

Unit's revenues increased by 37% in 2011 as drilling revenues increased $168.3 million or 53% in 2011 primarily due to a 24% increase in the average number of drilling rigs in use during 2011 and a 22% higher average dayrate in 2011. Oil and natural gas revenues increased by $115.5 million or 29% due to an increase in equivalent production volumes of 23% and a rise in oil and NGL prices partially offset by decreases in prices for natural gas. Midstream revenues increased by $53.7 million or 35% primarily due to higher NGL volumes and prices.

Net income increased by 34% in 2011 due to higher revenues offset by a growth in total expenses.

Strategy

Unit pursues a balanced strategy of growing its production reserves primarily though internally generated prospects and complementary acquisitions while growing its market share in the contract drilling segment by maintaining a modern rig fleet that serves both established and new markets.

Adding to its asset portfolio in 2012 the company bought oil and natural gas assets in the Granite Wash Cleveland and Marmaton plays (western Oklahoma and the Texas Panhandle) from Noble Energy for $594 million. That year it sold some Bakken properties to QEP Energy for $228 million.

That year to free up cash Unit sold its interest in certain of its Bakken properties to QEP Energy a subsidiary of QEP Resources for $228 million.

Ownership

Royce & Associates LLC FMR LLC and George Kaiser Family Foundation own 15% 13% and 10% of the company respectively.

EXECUTIVES

Senior Vice President Operations Unit, Mark Colclasure
Vice President Land Production, Mike Fankhouser
President CEO and Director, Larry D. Pinkston, age 60, $760,000 total compensation
EVP Exploration Unit Petroleum Company, Bradford J. (Brad) Guidry, age 59, $400,000 total compensation
CFO and Treasurer, David T. Merrill, age 54, $400,000 total compensation
EVP Drilling Unit Drilling Company, John Cromling, age 67, $400,000 total compensation
President and Manager Superior Pipeline, Robert H. Parks, age 60
Vice President, Bill Ward

Vice President Safety Health And Environment, Rick Heck
Vice President East Division, Carl Hansen
Vice President, Mark Ingram
Chairman, John G. Nikkel, age 80
President CEO and Director, Larry D. Pinkston, age 60
CFO and Treasurer, David T. Merrill, age 54
Auditors: PricewaterhouseCoopersLLP

LOCATIONS

HQ: Unit Corp.
7130 South Lewis, Suite 1000, Tulsa, OK 74136
Phone: 918 493-7700
Web: www.unitcorp.com

PRODUCTS/OPERATIONS

2011 Sales

	$ mil.	% of total
Oil & natural gas	516.3	43
Contract drilling	484.7	40
Gas gathering & processing	208.2	17
Adjustment	0.8	-
Total	**1208.4**	**100**

Subsidiaries
Superior Pipeline Company L.L.C.
Unit Drilling Company
Unit Petroleum Company
Unit Texas Drilling Company L.L.C.

COMPETITORS

Abraxas Petroleum	Murphy Oil
Anadarko Petroleum	Nabors Industries
Apache	Noble
BP	Parker Drilling
Cabot Oil & Gas	Patterson-UTI Energy
Devon Energy	Pioneer Natural
Dorchester Minerals	Resources
Ensign Energy Services	Precision Drilling
Exxon Mobil	Range Resources
Imperial Oil	Suncor

HISTORICAL FINANCIALS

Company Type: Public

Income Statement   FYE: December 31

	REVENUE ($ mil.)	NET INCOME ($ mil.)	NET PROFIT MARGIN	EMPLOYEES
12/13	1,351.8	184.7	13.7%	2,463
12/12	1,315.1	23.1	1.8%	2,309
12/11	1,208.3	195.8	16.2%	2,674
12/10	881.8	146.4	16.6%	1,888
12/09	709.9	(55.5)	—	1,094
Annual Growth	**17.5%**	**—**	**—**	**22.5%**

2013 Year-End Financials

Debt ratio: 16.0%
Return on equity: 8.9%
Cash ($ mil.): 18
Current ratio: 0.87
Long-term debt ($ mil.): 645
No. of shares (mil.): 49
Dividends
  Yield: —
  Payout: —
Market value ($ mil.): 2,535

	STOCK PRICE ($) FY Close	P/E High/Low		PER SHARE ($) Earnings	Dividends	Book Value
12/13	51.62	14	11	3.80	0.00	44.26
12/12	45.05	105	68	0.48	0.00	40.64
12/11	46.40	15	8	4.08	0.00	40.44
12/10	46.48	16	11	3.09	0.00	35.70
12/09	42.50	—	—	(1.18)	0.00	32.94
Annual Growth	**5.0%**	**—**	**—**	**—**	**—**	**7.7%**

United Capital Corp.

Making a profit is a capital idea that unites United Capital. The company invests in and manages real estate properties as well as manufactures and sells engineered products using knitted wire. United Capital owns and oversees about 150 retail office hotel and day care properties across the US. Subsidiary Metal Textiles makes knitted wire products and parts for a range of sealing and filtering applications. Under the AFP Transformers brand the company makes transformers for switchgear to motor starters and inverters. The lines are sold to commercial and industrial customers in the automotive electronic aerospace and process and chemical market. CEO Attilio Petrocelli and his wife own 70% of the company.

EXECUTIVES

Vp Real Estate Operations And Director, Michael J Weinbaum, age 48
Auditors: HoltzRubensteinReminickLLP

LOCATIONS

HQ: United Capital Corp.
9 Park Place, Great Neck, NY 11021
Phone: 516 466-6464   **Fax:** 516 829-4301
Web: www.unitedcapitalcorp.net

PRODUCTS/OPERATIONS

2010 Sales

	$ mil.	% of total
Engineered products	31.9	40
Hotel operations	27.9	34
Real estate investment & management	20.9	26
Total	**60.1**	**100**

Selected Subsidiaries

AFP Hospitality Corp.
AFP Management Corp.
AFP Realty Corp.
AFP Transformers Corporation
Metal Textiles Corporation
Metex Mfg. Corporation

COMPETITORS

ACS Industries	Keystone Consolidated
Dana Holding	LeFrak Organization
Duke Realty	Siemens AG
G. Bopp USA	Tishman Construction
Helmsley Enterprises	

HISTORICAL FINANCIALS

Company Type: Public

Income Statement   FYE: December 31

	REVENUE ($ mil.)	NET INCOME ($ mil.)	NET PROFIT MARGIN	EMPLOYEES
12/13	119.1	12.4	10.5%	0
12/12	115.7	16.6	14.4%	630
12/11	90.1	17.4	19.4%	460
12/10	80.6	12.7	15.8%	470
12/09	60.1	5.6	9.5%	390
Annual Growth	**18.7%**	**21.7%**	**—**	**—**

2013 Year-End Financials

Debt ratio: 37.2%
Return on equity: 9.2%
Cash ($ mil.): 78
Current ratio: 4.83
Long-term debt ($ mil.): 104
No. of shares (mil.): 5
Dividends
  Yield: —
  Payout: —
Market value ($ mil.): 193

	STOCK PRICE ($) FY Close	P/E High/Low		PER SHARE ($) Earnings	Dividends	Book Value
12/13	33.00	17	13	2.13	0.00	24.22
12/12	27.50	13	9	2.37	0.00	21.87
12/11	21.50	16	9	2.03	0.00	21.06
12/10	32.50	23	15	1.31	0.00	24.01
12/09	23.82	39	22	0.58	0.00	23.12
Annual Growth	**8.5%**	**—**	**—**	**38.4%**	**—**	**1.2%**

United Fire Group, Inc.

The United Fire Group companies join together to offer a unified range of property/casualty and life insurance products. The group operates through its United Fire & Casualty subsidiary which in turn holds entities that carry a variety of property/casualty offerings including fidelity and surety bonds and fire auto employee liability homeowners and workers' compensation lines. More than 1300 independent agencies in some 45 states sell its property/casualty products to businesses and individuals. The United Life division of United Fire & Casualty sells life annuity and credit life products to individuals and groups through some 950 independent agents in more than 30 states.
Geographic Reach
The company markets its products from its headquarters in Iowa and from four regional offices in California Colorado New Jersey and Texas and it operates primarily in adjacent areas of the midwestern southern and western US.
Operations
United Fire's property/casualty insurance offerings account for more than 90% of its annual insurance premiums with a majority of those policies being written to commercial group customers. The company also offers certain personal policies to individual customers.
Sales and Marketing
In order to increase policy placement in its existing markets United Fire offers profit-sharing and commission programs to its independent agents. It also seeks to provide modern technological tools to best serve both its agents and its policyholders.
Financial Performance
The company's revenue has been growing year-over-year. It reported revenue of $877 million in fiscal 2013 up from $813.2 million in revenue for fiscal 2012.
Net income also increased in fiscal 2013 compared to the prior year. The company netted $76 million in fiscal 2013 after reporting net income of $40 million in fiscal 2012.
United Fire's cash flow decreased by about $11 million in fiscal 2013 compared to the previous fiscal period.
Strategy
United Fire looks to expand into new markets to reduce the risk potential in its concentrated areas of operation.

EXECUTIVES

Vice President Gulf Coast Regional Office, Joseph B Johnson, age 63
Vp Fidelity And Surety, Dennis Richmann, age 51
VP General Counsel and Secretary, Neal R. Scharmer, age 58, $250,000 total compensation

COO, Michael T. Wilkins, age 51, $388,600 total compensation
VP and Chief Investment Officer, Barrie W. Ernst, age 60, $305,000 total compensation
President and CEO, Randy A. Ramlo, age 53, $595,000 total compensation
VP and Chief Claims Officer, David E. Conner, age 56
VP Information Services, Scott A. Minkel, age 53
VP Corporate Marketing, Colleen R. Sova, age 61
Assistant Vice President Midwest Regional Office, Corey J. Ruehle
VP and COO United Life Insurance Company, Michael J. Sheeley
Assistant VP Controller and Interim CFO, Kevin W. Helbing
Assistant Vice President And Midwest Regional Claims Manager, Dean Walstrom
Assistant Vice President And Regional Claims Manager (Gulf Coast), Dewayne Mundell
VP General Counsel and Secretary, Neal R. Scharmer, age 58
Vice Chairman, John A. Rife, age 72
Chairman, Jack B. Evans, age 66
President and CEO, Randy A. Ramlo, age 53
Secretary, Maria Wollfarth
Auditors: Ernst&YoungLLP

LOCATIONS

HQ: United Fire Group, Inc.
118 Second Avenue S.E., Cedar Rapids, IA 52401
Phone: 319 399-5700
Web: www.unitedfiregroup.com

PRODUCTS/OPERATIONS

Selected Subsidiaries
United Fire & Casualty Company
 Addison Insurance Company
 American Indemnity Financial Corporation
 Texas General Indemnity Company
 Lafayette Insurance Company
 Mercer Insurance Group Inc.
 Financial Pacific Insurance Company
 Mercer Insurance Company
 Franklin Insurance Company
 Mercer Insurance Company of New Jersey Inc.
 United Fire & Indemnity Company
 United Fire Lloyds
 United Life Insurance Company

COMPETITORS

ACE Limited	GEICO
AIG	Hanover Insurance
Allstate	John Hancock Financial
American Family	Services
Insurance	Liberty Mutual
American Financial	MassMutual
Group	Progressive
Arrowpoint Capital	Corporation
Corp.	Prudential
CNA Surety	State Farm
Chubb Corp	The Hartford
Erie Indemnity	Travelers Companies
Farmers Group	White Mountains
Fireman' s Fund	Insurance Group
Insurance	

HISTORICAL FINANCIALS
Company Type: Public

Income Statement
FYE: December 31

	ASSETS ($ mil.)	NET INCOME ($ mil.)	INCOME AS % OF ASSETS	EMPLOYEES
12/13	3,720.6	76.1	2.0%	943
12/12	3,694.6	40.2	1.1%	909
12/11	3,618.9	0.0	0.0%	894
12/10	3,007.4	47.5	1.6%	654
12/09	2,902.5	(10.4)	—	673
Annual Growth	6.4%	—		8.8%

2013 Year-End Financials
Return on assets: 2.0%
Return on equity: 10.0%
Long-term debt ($ mil.): —
No. of shares (mil.): 25
Sales ($ mil): 877
Dividends
 Yield: 2.4%
 Payout: 37.3%
 Market value ($ mil.): 727

	STOCK PRICE ($) FY Close	P/E High/Low		PER SHARE ($) Earnings	Dividends	Book Value
12/13	28.66	11	7	2.98	0.69	30.87
12/12	21.84	17	10	1.58	0.60	28.90
12/11	20.18	—	—	(0.00)	0.60	27.29
12/10	22.32	13	9	1.80	0.60	27.35
12/09	18.23	—	—	(0.39)	0.60	25.35
Annual Growth	12.0%	—	—	—	3.6%	5.0%

United Insurance Holdings Corp

United Insurance Holdings insures homeowners in the Sunshine State throughout the seasons even hurricane season. The company underwrites flood fire and homeowners insurance policies in Florida and provides property insurance for automotive service companies. It distributes its products through independent agents. United Insurance was founded in 1999 then underwent a reverse merger in 2008 when it bought the OTC-listed FMG Acquisition Corp. for $95 million ($25 million in cash and 8.75 million shares of stock.) The newly merged company has listed on the NASDAQ exchange.

EXECUTIVES
CEO, John L. Forney, $489,432 total compensation
CFO, B. Bradford Martz, $222,726 total compensation
VP Operations and Business Development, Deepak Menon
CIO, Andy Swenson
Vp Of Marketing, Jay K Williams
Senior Vice President, Marcus Greene
Chairman, Gregory C. Branch

LOCATIONS
HQ: United Insurance Holdings Corp
360 Central Avenue, Suite 900, St. Petersburg, FL 33701
Phone: 727 895-7737

COMPETITORS
AAA Auto Club South   Federated National

Allstate	Holding
American National	HCI Group
Insurance	Liberty Mutual
Bankers Financial	State Farm
Citizens Property	Universal Insurance
Insurance	Holdings

HISTORICAL FINANCIALS
Company Type: Public

Income Statement
FYE: December 31

	ASSETS ($ mil.)	NET INCOME ($ mil.)	INCOME AS % OF ASSETS	EMPLOYEES
12/13	441.2	20.3	4.6%	90
12/12	313.6	9.7	3.1%	68
12/11	240.2	8.0	3.4%	50
12/10	213.6	(0.9)	—	46
12/09	247.7	4.0	1.6%	46
Annual Growth	15.5%	49.6%	—	18.3%

2013 Year-End Financials
Return on assets: 5.3%
Return on equity: 20.8%
Long-term debt ($ mil.): —
No. of shares (mil.): 16
Sales ($ mil): 208
Dividends
 Yield: 1.0%
 Payout: 17.0%
 Market value ($ mil.): 228

	STOCK PRICE ($) FY Close	P/E High/Low		PER SHARE ($) Earnings	Dividends	Book Value
12/13	14.08	11	4	1.26	0.15	6.64
12/12	6.01	7	5	0.91	0.08	5.70
12/11	4.40	6	4	0.77	0.05	5.31
12/10	3.10	—	—	(0.09)	0.05	4.28
12/09	3.80	13	7	0.38	0.15	4.55
Annual Growth	38.7%	—	—	34.9%	(0.0%)	9.9%

United Therapeutics Corp

United Therapeutics hopes its products will be in vein. Its injectable drug Remodulin treats pulmonary hypertension which affects the blood vessels between the heart and lungs. The product is marketed directly and through distributors in North America Europe and other regions. Other hypertension treatments include Adcirca and Tyvaso. The company's development pipeline includes additional treatments for cardiovascular disease as well as various cancers respiratory conditions and infectious diseases. United Therapeutics has divested its cardiac monitoring division.

Operations

Remodulin accounted for about half of United Therapeutics' 2012 sales.

The company's development pipeline includes an investigational cancer drug licensed from the Memorial Sloan-Kettering Cancer Center. The antibody candidates aim to treat metastatic brain cancer. A second candidate (for neuroblastoma) was returned to Memorial Sloan-Kettering when United Therapeutics partnered on a different neuroblastoma candidate with the National Cancer Institute. United Therapeutics also has antiviral agents under development for treatment of ailments including hepatitis C. The company has additional early stage research programs and it regularly evaluates opportunities to license additional compounds for development.

In 2012 United Therapeutics entered into a license agreement with Ascendis Pharma to develop a self-injectable therapeutic alternative for PAH patients by applying Ascendis Pharma's TransCon technology platform to its treprostinil molecule. The agreement also gives United Therapeutics exclusive rights to develop prostacyclin prostacyclin analog and prostacyclin-related products for treating PAH using the TransCon technology as well as rights to commercialize any products developed from the collaboration on a global basis.

Geographic Reach

Remodulin is approved for sale throughout North America and Europe as well as in nine other countries. Tyvaso and Adcirca are only approved in the US. The company's home country accounts for 90% of revenues.

Sales and Marketing

The company uses a direct sales force in the US and distributors abroad for Remodulin. It sells Tyvaso through pharma distributors and Adcira to pharma wholesalers.

Financial Performance

United Therapeutics' revenue increased 23% in 2012 due to higher prices improved sales and development contract payments. Net income jumped 40% on the increased revenue and $31 million in insurance proceeds. Cash flow followed the others and improved substantially.

Strategy

The company pursues growth by developing new drugs either through R&D or in partnership with other firms.

EXECUTIVES

Vice President, Alyssa Friedrich
Chairman and Co-CEO, Martine A. Rothblatt, age 59, $931,485 total compensation
President and Co-CEO, Roger Jeffs, age 52, $754,333 total compensation
CFO and Treasurer, John M. Ferrari, age 60, $463,128 total compensation
CIO, Shola Oyewole
EVP and COO, David Zaccardelli
Senior Vice President, Wayne Roe
Vice President Business Development, Auster Martin
Vice President, Alex Sapir
Vice President Medical Device, Doug Biette
Associate Vice President Trade And Patient Program Management, Kevin Gray
Pharmd, Allison Pecha
Sr Vice President Mfg Sterile Prods, Patrick Poisson
Vice President Facilities, Mike Camp
Vice President Validation, Christopher Benson
Vice President Of Production, Liang Guo
Executive Vice President Organizational, Michael Benkowitz
Senior Vice President Global Clinical Operations, Hassan Movahhad
Chairman and Co-CEO, Martine A. Rothblatt, age 59
CFO and Treasurer, John M. Ferrari, age 60
Vp Treasurer, James Edgemond
Auditors: Ernst&YoungLLP

LOCATIONS

HQ: United Therapeutics Corp
1040 Spring Street, Silver Spring, MD 20910
Phone: 301 608-9292
Web: www.unither.com

2012 Sales

	$ mil.	% of total
US	846.6	92
Other countries	69.5	8
Total	**916.1**	**100**

PRODUCTS/OPERATIONS

2012 Sales

	$ mil.	% of total
Cardiovascular products		
Remodulin	458.0	50
Tyvasco	325.6	36
Adcirca	122.5	13
Other	10.0	1
Total	**916.1**	**100**

Selected Products

Marketed
  Remodulin (pulmonary arterial hypertension)
  Tyvaso (pulmonary arterial hypertension)
  Adcirca (pulmonary arterial hypertension)
In Development
  8H9 MAb (metastatic brain cancer)
  Beraprost (cardiovascular disease)
  Ch14.18 (neuroblastoma)
  Miglustat and other Glycobiology Antiviral Agents (hepatitis C and other infectious diseases)
  IW001 (pulmonary disease)
  Treprostinil (oral form for pulmonary arterial hypertension and peripheral vascular disease)

Selected Subsidiaries

Lung Biotechnology Hong Kong Limited
Lung Biotechnology (Nanjing) Co. Ltd.
Lung LLC
Lung RX Ltd. (UK)
Revivicor Inc.
United Therapeutics Europe Ltd. (UK)
Unither Biotech Inc. (Canada)
Unither Pharma LLC
Unither Pharmaceuticals Inc.

COMPETITORS

Abbott Labs	Gilead Sciences
Actelion	GlaxoSmithKline
American HealthChoice	NIPPON SHINYAKU
Ark Therapeutics Group	CO.LTD.
AstraZeneca	Novartis
Bayer HealthCare	Pfizer
Pharmaceuticals	Sandoz
Eli Lilly	Teva

HISTORICAL FINANCIALS

Company Type: Public

Income Statement

FYE: December 31

	REVENUE ($ mil.)	NET INCOME ($ mil.)	NET PROFIT MARGIN	EMPLOYEES
12/13	1,116.9	174.5	15.6%	706
12/12	916.0	304.4	33.2%	623
12/11	743.1	217.8	29.3%	543
12/10	603.8	105.9	17.5%	520
12/09	369.8	19.4	5.3%	410
Annual Growth	**31.8%**	**73.1%**	**—**	**14.6%**

2013 Year-End Financials

Debt ratio: 13.7%	No. of shares (mil.): 50
Return on equity: 14.5%	Dividends
Cash ($ mil.): 278	Yield: —
Current ratio: 1.32	Payout: —
Long-term debt ($ mil.): 3	Market value ($ mil.): 5,698

STOCK PRICE ($) FY Close	P/E High/Low		PER SHARE ($) Earnings	Dividends	Book Value
12/13	113.08	33 15	3.28	0.00	25.89
12/12	53.42	10 7	5.71	0.00	21.82
12/11	47.25	19 10	3.67	0.00	17.90
12/10	63.22	34 24	1.78	0.00	15.55
12/09	52.65	272110	0.35	0.00	12.24
Annual Growth	**21.1%**	**— —**	**75.0%**	**—**	**20.6%**

Universal Display Corp

Universal Display is putting organic technology on display. The company through sponsored research agreements with Princeton University the University of Southern California and the University of Michigan is developing organic light-emitting diodes (OLEDs) for flat-panel displays solid-state lighting and other applications. Its OLED technologies use organic semiconductor materials to overcome limitations in LCDs such as poor image and color quality. Universal Display is licensing its technology to makers of televisions computer screens and consumer electronics devices. The company gets the majority of its revenues outside North America.

Universal Display is expanding through development and licensing agreements with partners such as Samsung Mobile Display and LG Display (together the two customers made up nearly 60% of sales). Other companies with licensing agreements include AU Optronics Moser Baer Seiko Epson Sony and the US government. The company is researching applications for the US Army that include head-mounted displays displays on durable metal foil and pen-like communication devices with roll-up displays. Universal Display owns exclusively licenses or has the sole right to sublicense more than 1000 issued and pending patents.

The company has expanded its portfolio with the acquisition of patents covering a wide array of OLED device designs architectures materials and processing technologies from Motorola Solutions. The purchase included applications ranging from stacked and flexible OLED technologies to phosphorescent transparent white and patterned technologies and materials.

Universal Display is also expanding its research efforts into related OLED display technologies such as phosphorescent OLEDs (PHOLEDs) printable PHOLEDs flexible OLEDs (FOLEDs) and transparent OLEDs (TOLEDs) as well as organic vapor phase deposition tools for manufacturing the displays. Universal Display is providing red PHOLED chemicals to Tohoku Pioneer a subsidiary of Pioneer Corp. for use in passive-matrix OLED cell phone displays.

Many applications for the company's products involve consumer electronics sales of which were severely depressed during the global recession. In addition the markets for flat-panel displays and lighting products are highly competitive. In 2010 sales were up more than 45% over 2009 primarily reflecting increased chemical sales and development revenues that doubled for the year. Universal Display continued to be unprofitable however in spite of increased sales

EXECUTIVES

President and CEO, Steven V. Abramson, age 62, $581,049 total compensation
EVP and CFO, Sidney D. Rosenblatt, age 66, $581,049 total compensation
Executive Vice President Universal, Rich Rollison
Vice President Intellectual Property, Ronald Campbell
Chairman, Sherwin I. Seligsohn, age 78
Secretary, Erica Diah
Auditors: KPMGLLP

LOCATIONS

HQ: Universal Display Corp
375 Phillips Boulevard, Ewing, NJ 08618
Phone: 609 671-0980   **Fax:** 609 671-0995
Web: www.udcoled.com

2010 Sales

	% of total
North America	18
Other regions	82
Total	**100**

PRODUCTS/OPERATIONS

2010 Sales

	$ mil.	% of total
Development revenue	19.4	64
Commercial revenue	11.1	36
Total	**30.5**	**100**

COMPETITORS

AU Optronics	Merck KGaA
BASF SE	Microvision
Dow Chemical	Pioneer Corporation
DuPont	Samsung Electronics
Eastman Kodak	Sony
Epson	Sumitomo Chemical
Fujitsu	Texas Instruments
Idemitsu Kosan	Toshiba
LG Display	eMagin

HISTORICAL FINANCIALS

Company Type: Public

Income Statement

FYE: December 31

	REVENUE ($ mil.)	NET INCOME ($ mil.)	NET PROFIT MARGIN	EMPLOYEES
12/13	146.6	74.0	50.5%	124
12/12	83.2	9.6	11.6%	117
12/11	61.2	3.1	5.1%	93
12/10	30.5	(19.9)	—	86
12/09	15.7	(20.5)	—	84
Annual Growth	**74.6%**	—	—	**10.2%**

2013 Year-End Financials

Debt ratio: —	No. of shares (mil.): 46
Return on equity: 19.0%	Dividends
Cash ($ mil.): 70	Yield: —
Current ratio: 14.08	Payout: —
Long-term debt ($ mil.): —	Market value ($ mil.): 1,595

	STOCK PRICE ($) FY Close	P/E High/Low	PER SHARE ($) Earnings	Dividends	Book Value
12/13	34.36	24 16	1.59	0.00	9.21
12/12	25.62	228 107	0.21	0.00	7.56
12/11	36.69	858 326	0.07	0.00	7.42
12/10	30.65	— —	(0.53)	0.00	1.47
12/09	12.36	— —	(0.56)	0.00	1.62
Annual Growth	**29.1%**	— —	—	—	**54.4%**

Universal Electronics Inc.

Universal Electronics can help couch potatoes and TV junkies end multiple remote madness. The company makes One For All-branded universal remote controls with preprogrammed infrared codes allowing them to operate virtually any remote-capable device including TVs DVD players digital video recorders and set-top boxes. Its One For All remotes are sold by retailers worldwide. Universal Electronics also markets audiovisual accessories under the One For All name outside North America and it develops Nevo-branded wireless networking products. The company sells and licenses its technologies to consumer electronics and computer manufacturers and cable companies including DIRECTV its largest customer.

Geographic Reach

Universal Electronics rings up almost two-thirds of its sales overseas. China is its largest foreign market accounting for about a quarter of the company's international sales. Europe contributes about 13% of sales with the remainder originating in Asia and Latin America.

Operations

Universal Electronics operates about two dozen subsidiaries located in Argentina Cayman Islands France Germany Hong Kong (6) India Italy the Netherlands Singapore Spain Brazil British Virgin Islands (3) China (4) and the UK.

Sales and Marketing

DIRECTV is Universal Electronics' largest customer representing 17% of its 2012 sales up from 12% in 2011.

Financial Performance

The company's sales declined by about 1% in 2012 versus the prior year while net income fell 17% over the same period. Net sales of the company's Business lines (subscription broadcasting OEM and computing companies) declined 2% in 2012 compared with 2011 while its smaller Consumer business posted more than a 10% increase in sales. The company blamed the prolonged sluggish global economy for depressing television sales which affects its sales to consumer electronics companies.

Strategy

Demand for Universal Electronics' products has increased even as tough economic conditions lingered worldwide. Indeed sales have grown steadily albeit gradually (with the exception of the big jump in 2011) throughout the global financial crisis. The firm attributes the growth (and banks its future advances) on the steady adoption of high-definition TV and digital video recording devices which have become less expensive and more widely available as well as by increased subscription broadcasting rates.

Universal Electronics is pursuing further penetration of the more traditional OEM consumer electronics markets while also looking to expand its sales and marketing efforts with subscription broadcasters and OEMs in Asia Latin America and Europe. Its purchase of Enson in late 2010 enhanced its ability to compete in the OEM and subscription broadcasting markets particularly in Asia. In 2010 it launched a new subsidiary in Brazil which has fostered business growth in Latin America.

Mergers and Acquisitions

In November 2010 subsidiary UEI Hong Kong Private Ltd. acquired Enson Assets Ltd. for about $126 million. Hong Kong-based Enson was a leading manufacturer of remote controls and was a big supplier to the company prior to its acquisition. Enson operated two factories in China. The deal fortified Universal's relationships with such key electronics firms as Sony Panasonic and Toshiba

Ownership

Eagle Asset Management owns more than 17% of Universal Electronics' shares.

EXECUTIVES

Chairman and CEO, Paul D. Arling, age 51, $550,000 total compensation
Executive Vice President; Managing Director; Europe, Paul J. M. Bennett, age 58, $355,000 total compensation
SVP and CFO, Bryan M. Hackworth, age 44, $310,000 total compensation
Executive Vice President General Manager US, Mark S. Kopaskie, age 56, $320,000 total compensation
Executive Vice President Asia, David C.H. Chong
Vice President Of Product Development, Ramzi S Ammari
Vice President Engineering, Graham S Williams
Vice President Program Management, Lee Haughawout
Senior Vice President And Chief, Bill Brown
Vice President Global Information Technology, Valerie Kwiatkowski
Senior Vice President Information Tech, Nom Sheridan
Vice President Of Finance, Eugene Kim
Vice President Cable Sales Americas, Steve Gutman
Vice President Of Global Information Technology, Doug Durrant
Senior Vice President General Counsel Secretary, Richard A Firehammer, age 57
Chairman and CEO, Paul D. Arling, age 51
Auditors: GrantThorntonLLP

LOCATIONS

HQ: Universal Electronics Inc.
201 E. Sandpointe Avenue, 8th Floor, Santa Ana, CA 92707
Phone: 714 918-9500
Web: www.uei.com

2012 Sales

	$ mil.	% of total
US	165.2	36
International		
China	76.9	17
Rest of Asia	109.0	24
Europe	61.6	13
Latin America	28.7	6
Other countries	21.7	4
Total	**463.1**	**100**

PRODUCTS/OPERATIONS

2012 Sales

	$ mil.	% of total
Business	410.9	89
Consumer	52.2	11
Total	**463.1**	**100**

COMPETITORS

AMX Corp.	Philips Consumer
Crestron Electronics	Lifestyle
Interlink Electronics	SMK
Logitech	Sony Electronics

HISTORICAL FINANCIALS

Company Type: Public

Income Statement

FYE: December 31

	REVENUE ($ mil.)	NET INCOME ($ mil.)	NET PROFIT MARGIN	EMPLOYEES
12/13	529.3	22.9	4.3%	8,505
12/12	463.0	16.5	3.6%	1,807
12/11	468.6	19.9	4.3%	9,803
12/10	331.7	15.0	4.5%	1,843
12/09	317.5	14.6	4.6%	565
Annual Growth	13.6%	11.8%	—	97.0%

2013 Year-End Financials

Debt ratio: —
Return on equity: 8.4%
Cash ($ mil.): 76
Current ratio: 2.32
Long-term debt ($ mil.): —

No. of shares (mil.): 15
Dividends
Yield: —
Payout: —
Market value ($ mil.): 599

	STOCK PRICE ($) FY Close	P/E High/Low		PER SHARE ($) Earnings	Dividends	Book Value
12/13	38.11	26	12	1.47	0.00	18.55
12/12	19.35	19	10	1.10	0.00	16.74
12/11	16.87	22	11	1.31	0.00	15.55
12/10	28.37	27	15	1.07	0.00	14.13
12/09	23.22	22	10	1.05	0.00	12.40
Annual Growth	13.2%	—	—	8.8%	—	10.6%

Universal Forest Products Inc.

Universal Forest Products has no trouble separating the trees from the forest. The company is a leading manufacturer and distributor of engineered wood and construction materials which it sells to do-it-yourself retail stores residential and mobile home builders and industrial customers. It also offers composite wood and plastic products. Universal Forest buys its wood from lumber mills and pressure-treats it to make such products as roof trusses wall panels flooring pallets and shipping crates. Founded in 1955 the company operates about 80 facilities in the US Canada and Mexico.

Geographic Reach

Michigan-based Universal Forest has facilities throughout the US Canada and Mexico. The US accounts for 98% of sales.

Operations

Beyond wood products Universal Forest's consumer products subsidiary offers a large portfolio of outdoor living products including wood composite decking decorative balusters post caps and plastic lattice. Universal Forest's lawn and garden group supplies trellises and arches to retailers nationwide. The firm also provides framing services to the residential market and forming products for concrete construction.

Universal Forest generates more than 35% of its revenue from its Retail Building Materials business. Its Industrial arm brings in about 30% of revenue while each of its Manufacturing Housing and Residential Construction units contribute 15% apiece.

Sales and Marketing

The Home Depot is the company's top customer accounting for more than 15% of sales.

Financial Performance

Universal Forest posted $2.47 billion in revenue in fiscal 2013 revenue up 20% from 2012's $2.1 billion. Driving sales were both lumber (with an 8% increase) and residential construction (up 33%). Net income during the reporting period jumped $19.1 million to $43.1 million thanks to a 20% sales boost paired with a decrease in charges associated with Anti-Dumping Duty Assessments. Cash flow from operations reached $53.4 million —an increase of $59.1 million —after years of a downward trend.

Strategy

When the economic downturn and housing crisis slowed Universal Forest's building products business the company shuttered about 20 facilities and eliminated thousands of jobs to better align its manufacturing capacity. Additionally Universal Forest's Atlantic division was absorbed into its Eastern division in 2011 to reduce the number of operating divisions from three to two.

Universal Forest is working to extend its reach into areas where there is potential for growth by diversifying through acquisitions. It's focused on such areas as industrial and agricultural packaging. The move it hopes will allow the company to endure future dips and downturns in homebuilding.

Universal Forest still embraces its construction roots. Although fewer manufactured homes are being built Universal Forest anticipates that by offering more products it can gain a larger share of the remaining market. Recent acquisitions include manufacturers of treated wood composite products engineered wood components millwork ornamental woodwork truss work and related construction materials.

Through all these strategies Universal Forest plans to reach $3 billion in sales by 2017.

Mergers and Acquisitions

With an eye on growing its Industrial business Universal Forest in 2014 acquired a 50% ownership interest in Upshur Forest Products LLC which owns sawmill operations in Gilmer Texas. It also purchased High Level Components LLC a North Carolina-based building component manufacturer.

In 2013 a subsidiary of Universal Forest acquired Minnesota-based Custom Caseworks a high-precision business-to-business manufacturer of engineered wood products for the commercial market. In late 2012 the company bought Washington-based Nepa Pallet and Container Co. which makes pallets containers and bins to supplement its agricultural and industrial business. In another move to increase capacity and reduce costs Universal Forest bought out Alabama-based MSR Forest Products in 2012. The deal gave Universal Forest a regional supplier of roof trusses and cut-to-size lumber used in manufactured housing. Universal Forest expanded its manufactured housing and RV market operations in 2010 with the acquisition of Shepherd Distribution.

EXECUTIVES

CEO, Matthew J. Missad, age 53, $514,925 total compensation
CFO, Michael R. Cole, age 47, $304,408 total compensation
EVP Marketing, C. Scott Greene, age 57, $333,467 total compensation
EVP National Sales, Donald L. (DJ) James, age 54
EVP Manufacturing, Robert D. Coleman, age 59
President and COO, Patrick M. Webster, age 54, $375,058 total compensation

EVP UFP Purchasing Inc., Michael F. Mordell
President Western Division, Allen T. Peters, age 46, $244,167 total compensation
EVP UFP Eastern Division -North, Patrick Benton
EVP UFP Eastern Division -South, Jonathan West
National Sales Manager, Sean Kenny
Vice President Human Resources, Patricia Ullrich
Vice-president Operations, Dick Bride
Vice-president, Fred Jones
Chairman, William G. Currie, age 66
Treasury Manager, Kristy Becker
Auditors: Ernst&YoungLLP

LOCATIONS

HQ: Universal Forest Products Inc.
2801 East Beltline NE., Grand Rapids, MI 49525
Phone: 616 364-6161 **Fax:** 616 361-7534
Web: www.ufpi.com

2013 Sales

	$ mil.	% of total
US	2410.3	98
Other countries	60.1	2
Total	2470.4	100

PRODUCTS/OPERATIONS

2013 Sales

	$ mil.	% of total
Retail building materials	936.6	37
Industrial	701.7	28
Manufactured housing	388.7	16
Residential construction	340.3	14
Commercial construction & concrete forming	136.6	5
Adjustment	(33.5)	
Total	2470.4	100

2013 Segment Sales

	% of total
Eastern & Western	80
Site-Build	11
Other	9
Total	100

Selected Products

Crates
Deck components
Dimension lumber
Fence panels
Floor systems
Gates
I-joists
Lattice
Pallets
Particle board
Plywood
Preservative-treated lumber
Pressure-treated wood
Roof trusses
Trim
Wall panels

COMPETITORS

BMC
BlueLinx
Builders FirstSource
Champion Home Builders
Commercial Metals

Great Southern Wood
Louisiana-Pacific
Pacific Coast Building Products
Weyerhaeuser

HISTORICAL FINANCIALS

Company Type: Public

Income Statement

FYE: December 28

	REVENUE ($ mil.)	NET INCOME ($ mil.)	NET PROFIT MARGIN	EMPLOYEES
12/13	2,470.4	43.0	1.7%	5,500
12/12	2,054.9	23.9	1.2%	5,200
12/11	1,822.3	4.5	0.2%	4,800
12/10	1,890.8	17.4	0.9%	5,100
12/09	1,673.0	24.2	1.5%	4,900
Annual Growth	10.2%	15.4%	—	2.9%

2013 Year-End Financials

Debt ratio: 9.2%
Return on equity: 6.9%
Cash ($ mil.): —
Current ratio: 3.57
Long-term debt ($ mil.): 84

No. of shares (mil.): 19
Dividends
Yield: 0.0%
Payout: 19.0%
Market value ($ mil.): 1,038

	STOCK PRICE ($) FY Close	P/E High/Low		PER SHARE ($) Earnings	Dividends	Book Value
12/13	52.03	25	16	2.15	0.41	32.11
12/12	37.81	35	24	1.21	0.40	30.29
12/11	30.87	173	101	0.23	0.40	29.39
12/10	37.96	50	28	0.89	0.40	29.72
12/09	38.22	37	15	1.25	0.26	29.21
Annual Growth	8.0%	—	—	14.5%	12.1%	2.4%

Universal Health Realty Income Trust

Universal Health Realty Income Trust (UHT) is a real estate investment trust (REIT) that primarily invests in healthcare facilities and human services. The REIT owns more than 55 facilities in 16 states including acute care hospitals behavioral healthcare facilities rehabilitation hospitals subacute facilities surgery centers childcare centers and medical office buildings. McAllen Medical Center in Texas is UHT's largest facility. Many properties are owned via limited liability companies in which the trust holds an equity interest. UHT's hospitals boast some 1000 beds. Subsidiaries of Universal Health Services lease most of UHT's hospitals and provide their own maintenance and renovation services.

Geographic Reach

UHT operates nationwide and has properties located in 15 states including Texas Florida California and Illinois.

Operations

The company's real estate investments include seven hospital facilities 43 medical office buildings and four preschool and childcare centers. Universal Health Services accounts for about 37% of its consolidated revenues.

Strategy

UHT focuses on expanding its geographic footprint and generating most of its revenue through third parties.

Financial Performance

UHT's revenue rose some 83% to $54 million in 2012 from $29 million in 2011 due to a 162% increase in base rent of non-related parties and a 17% boost in base rental UHS facilities. Net income during the same reporting period dropped 74% to $19 million from $74 million.

EXECUTIVES

VP and Controller; Assistant VP Corporate Accounting Universal Health Services, Charles F. Boyle, age 55

Chairman President and CEO, Alan B. Miller

Vp Secretary And Treasurer, Cheryl K Ramagano, age 52

Chairman President and CEO, Alan B. Miller

Auditors: KPMGLLP

LOCATIONS

HQ: Universal Health Realty Income Trust
Universal Corporate Center, 367 South Gulph Road,
P.O. Box 61558, King of Prussia, PA 19406-0958
Phone: 610 265-0688   Fax: 610 768-3336
Web: www.uhrit.com

PRODUCTS/OPERATIONS

Selected Subsidiaries

73 Medical Building LLC
653 Town Center Investments LLC
653 Town Center Phase II LLC
Auburn Medical Properties II LLC
ApaMed Properties LLC
Banburry Medical Properties LLC
BRB/E Building One LLC
Centennial Medical Properties LLC
Cimarron Medical Properties LLC

COMPETITORS

G&L Realty Properties
HCP
Healthcare Realty
Trust

Lend Lease (US)
Medical Properties
Trust
Ventas

HISTORICAL FINANCIALS

Company Type: Public

Income Statement

FYE: December 31

	REVENUE ($ mil.)	NET INCOME ($ mil.)	NET PROFIT MARGIN	EMPLOYEES
12/13	54.2	13.1	24.3%	0
12/12	53.9	19.4	36.1%	0
12/11	29.4	73.7	250.2%	0
12/10	28.8	16.3	56.5%	0
12/09	31.9	18.5	58.2%	0
Annual Growth	14.2%	(8.2%)	—	—

2013 Year-End Financials

Debt ratio: 53.6%
Return on equity: 7.6%
Cash ($ mil.): 3
Current ratio: 17.72
Long-term debt ($ mil.): 199

No. of shares (mil.): 12
Dividends
Yield: 6.2%
Payout: 222.7%
Market value ($ mil.): 515

	STOCK PRICE ($) FY Close	P/E High/Low		PER SHARE ($) Earnings	Dividends	Book Value
12/13	40.06	57	37	1.04	2.50	12.88
12/12	50.61	32	25	1.54	2.46	14.00
12/11	39.00	7	6	5.83	2.43	14.91
12/10	36.53	29	23	1.33	2.42	11.49
12/09	32.03	23	16	1.56	2.38	11.66
Annual Growth	5.8%	—	—	(9.6%)	1.2%	2.5%

Universal Truckload Services Inc

Universal Truckload Services (UTSI) hasn't hauled freight beyond its own galaxy but the company does cover the US and parts of Canada (Ontario and Quebec) and Mexico. As an "asset-light" provider of truckload freight transportation the company operates through a network of truck owner-operators rather than employing drivers and investing heavily in equipment. It can call upon a fleet of some 4100 tractors and 6200 trailers including standard dry vans and flatbeds; the majority of its tractors and trailers are owned by others. Its flagship transportation segment transports general commodities such as automotive parts building materials paper food consumer goods furniture steel and other metals.

Geographic Reach

UTSI operates 80 terminals with key locations in Dearborn Michigan; Columbus Reading Latty and Cleveland Ohio; Gary Indiana; Dallas; South Kearney New Jersey; Garden City Georgia; Millwood West Virgina; Monroeville Pennsylvania; Memphis; Tampa; and Houston. The US accounts for around 95% of its total revenue.

Operations

Besides its transportation business which generates about 70% of company revenues UTSI also serves customers through its intermodal and value-added services segments. Value-added services accounts for about 20% of the company's sales and matches customers' freight with carriers' capacity.

Intermodal support services (10%) involve picking up shipping containers at ports and railheads and delivering them by truck to customers. The company's intermodal support services is a key source of growth and is expanding its agent network as well as encouraging agents to promote the intermodal business line.

Financial Performance

Mostly as a result of a recent acquisition UTSI has enjoyed unprecedented growth over the years. Revenues jumped 48% from nearly $700 million to reach the $1 billion mark in 2012 for the first time in the company's history. Revenues remained flat at $1 billion in 2013.

The static revenue for 2013 was due to a $34.7 million decrease in transportation services as a result of underperforming sales channels and lower volumes in government services building products and metals. This was offset by increases of $20 million in its value-added services as a result of the launch of several new operations for existing automotive and industrial customers.

Profits jumped 6% from $48 million in 2012 to $51 million in 2013. This was driven by a decline in the rent for purchased transportation and equipment due to a combined increase in intermodal and value-added service revenues as a percentage of total revenues. After two straight years of increased cash flow from operations UTSI saw its cash flow drop by $13 million due to less cash provided by deferred income taxes and additional accrued expenses insurance claims and other current liabilities.

Strategy

The trucking industry has entered a phase of consolidation. Based on rising insurance costs scarcity of capital fuel prices and expensive regulatory environmental equipment smaller trucking firms are combining through merger or acquisition. However UTSI's size and its continuing organic and acquisitive growth gives it a competitive edge over smaller more vulnerable trucking companies.

To establish one of the largest full-service asset light logistics services in North America UTSI in late 2012 purchased LINC Logistics a third-party logistics company for about $350 million including the assumption of debt. In 2013 the company purchased Westport USA Holding LLC for $123 million in cash. Based in Louisville Kentucky Westport provides value-added warehousing and component distribution services to US manufacturers of Class 4-8 trucks RVs and super-duty trucks. The deal further enhanced UTSI's value-added service capabilities.

Now that the industry has made a comeback since the recession UTSI is once again targeting the automotive sector as it is one of the largest users of global outsourced logistics services. In 2013 it generated 34% of the company's revenues.

EXECUTIVES

Vice President Operations, Dona Wethy
CFO and Treasurer, David A. Crittenden, age 52, $268,516 total compensation
Vice Chairman and President, Donald B. Cochran, age 63, $402,168 total compensation
CEO, Jeffrey A. (Jeff) Rogers, age 51
Senior Vice President Information Technology, Mark Sokolowski
Vice President Safety, Kimberly Genovese
Vice President, Joe Goryl
Executive Vice President Sales And Marketing, Joe Rubino
Executive Vice President Business Development, Ralph Castille
Vice President Operations, Herb Rhode
Vice President Of Equipment Services, Bill Gale
Chairman, Matthew T. Moroun, age 41
CFO and Treasurer, David A. Crittenden, age 52
Vice Chairman and President, Donald B. Cochran, age 63
Auditors: KPMGLLP

LOCATIONS

HQ: Universal Truckload Services Inc
12755 E. Nine Mile Road, Warren, MI 48089
Phone: 586 920-0100

2013 Sales

	$ mil.	% of total
US	992.5	96
Mexico	23.5	2
Canada	14.0	2
Europe	2.3	-
Other	1.2	-
Total	**1033.5**	**100**

PRODUCTS/OPERATIONS

2013 Sales

	$ mil.	% of total
Transportation services	707.0	68
Value-added services	195.1	19
Intermodal services	131.4	13
Total	**1033.5**	**100**

Selected Services Transportation Services Flatbed-Specialized & Heavy Haul Oilfield Van Refrigerated-Shuttles Drive Away T/L Brokerage Switching and Yard Management Transportation Management Value Added Services Axle & Chassis Assembly Consolidation Cross-docks Kittin

Selected Subsidiaries
Cavalry Logistics

Great American Lines Inc.
LINC
Louisiana Transportation Inc.
Mason & Dixon Lines Inc.
Mason Dixon Intermodal Inc.
NYP of Michigan Inc.
Universal Am-Can Ltd.
Universal Logistics Inc.

COMPETITORS

C.H. Robinson Worldwide	Schneider National
Crete Carrier	Swift Transportation
Hub Group	U.S. Xpress
J.B. Hunt	USA Truck
Landstar System	Werner Enterprises

HISTORICAL FINANCIALS
Company Type: Public

Income Statement
FYE: December 31

	REVENUE ($ mil.)	NET INCOME ($ mil.)	NET PROFIT MARGIN	EMPLOYEES
12/13	1,033.4	50.5	4.9%	5,960
12/12	1,037.0	47.6	4.6%	4,701
12/11	699.7	15.8	2.3%	675
12/10	605.9	12.7	2.1%	714
12/09	503.2	4.9	1.0%	630
Annual Growth	**19.7%**	**79.2%**	**—**	**75.4%**

2013 Year-End Financials

Debt ratio: 49.4%
Return on equity: 62.0%
Cash ($ mil.): 10
Current ratio: 2.01
Long-term debt ($ mil.): 235

No. of shares (mil.): 30
Dividends
Yield: 0.4%
Payout: 7.0%
Market value ($ mil.): 919

	STOCK PRICE ($) FY Close	P/E High/Low	PER SHARE ($) Earnings	Dividends	Book Value
12/13	30.51	18 10	1.68	0.14	3.51
12/12	18.25	12 8	1.59	2.00	1.91
12/11	18.15	18 12	1.01	1.00	10.42
12/10	15.92	24 17	0.80	0.00	10.48
12/09	18.10	61 34	0.31	1.00	9.66
Annual Growth	**13.9% (22.4%)**	**— —**	**52.6%**	**(38.8%)**	

US Ecology, Inc.

US Ecology (formerly American Ecology) helps keep a lid on hazardous waste industrial waste and low-level radioactive waste. The company handles hazardous and nonhazardous waste at sites in Texas Michigan Nevada and Idaho and it operates a low-level radioactive waste facility in Washington state. The company does business with private waste companies state and federal agencies and a variety of industries. Customers include nuclear plants steel mills petrochemical facilities and academic and medical institutions. US Ecology retains interests in several non-operating waste-disposal facilities.

Geographic Reach
The company has operations in the US (Idaho Michigan Nevada Texas and Washington) and in Canada. The US accounted for 77% of revenues in 2012.

Operations

US Ecology operates in two segments: Operating Disposal Facilities and Non-Operating Disposal Facilities. The Operating Disposal Facility segment represents disposal facilities accepting hazardous and radioactive waste. The Non-Operating Disposal Facility segment represents facilities which do not.

Sales and Marketing
Brokers for its base business and large project customers accounted for 51% of sales in 2012; other industries (including electric chemical and steel mill customers 18%; and government customers 12%. The US Army Corps of Engineers accounted for 6% of US Ecology's revenues in 2012.

Financial Performance
The company's revenues increased by 9% in 2012 primarily due to a 13% increase in treatment and disposal revenues. The decrease in transportation service revenues was due to fewer Event Business projects using the company's transportation and logistics services.

Net income grew by 40% in 2012 due to increased revenues in 2012 and higher foreign currency gains reflecting changes in business activity conducted in a currency other than the US dollar. Other income increased due to the sale of an excess water right at the company's Grand View (Idaho) plant.

Strategy
To increase its services and expand its geographical reach US Ecology bought waste treatment and storage operator Dynecol from PVS Chemicals for $10.8 million in 2012. Dynecol (which was renamed US Ecology Michigan) operates a disposal facility in Detroit that provides hazardous liquid waste services to the Midwest US and Canadian industrial markets.

Ownership
The Killen Group Inc. owns about 9% of US Ecology.

EXECUTIVES

EVP Sales and Marketing, Steven D. (Steve) Welling, age 56, $255,923 total compensation
EVP Operations and Technology Development, Simon G. Bell, age 44, $207,989 total compensation
US Ecology Nevada General Manager, Robert (Bob) Marchand
Director Transportation, Chuck Overman
President and CEO, Jeffrey R. (Jeff) Feeler, age 45, $296,904 total compensation
US Ecology Idaho General Manager, Terry Andrew Geis
EVP CFO and Treasurer, Eric L. Gerratt, age 45, $198,662 total compensation
EVP Field and Industrial Services, Mario Romero
VP Information Technology, Thames Kral
VP Radiological Programs and Field Services, Joe Weismann
US Ecology Washington Facility Manager, Mike Ault
US Ecology Texas General Manager, Andrew McDaniel
US Ecology Michigan General Manager, Kevin Trader
Vice President Business Development, Matt Dahl
Chairman, Stephen A. Romano, age 60
Auditors: MossAdamsLLP

LOCATIONS

HQ: US Ecology, Inc.
251 E. Front Street, Suite 400, Boise, ID 83702
Phone: 208 331-8400
Web: www.usecology.com

2012 Sales

	$ mil.	% of total
US	130.9	77
Canada	38.2	23
Total	**169.1**	**100**

PRODUCTS/OPERATIONS

2012 Sales

	$ mil.	% of total
Treatment & disposal	145.7	86
Transportation services	23.4	14
Total	**169.1**	**100**

Selected Subsidiaries

Texas Ecologists inc.
US Ecology Inc.
US Ecology Idaho Inc.
US Ecology Michigan Inc.
US Ecology Nevada Inc.
US Ecology Texas L.P.
US Ecology Washington Inc.

COMPETITORS

Clean Harbors	Stericycle
EnergySolutions	Valhi
Heritage Environmental Services	Veolia ES Technical Solutions
Perma-Fix Environmental	Waste Control Specialists
Safety-Kleen	Waste Management

HISTORICAL FINANCIALS

Company Type: Public

Income Statement

FYE: December 31

	REVENUE ($ mil.)	NET INCOME ($ mil.)	NET PROFIT MARGIN	EMPLOYEES
12/13	201.1	32.1	16.0%	458
12/12	169.1	25.6	15.2%	425
12/11	154.9	18.3	11.9%	387
12/10	104.8	12.5	12.0%	372
12/09	132.5	13.9	10.5%	221
Annual Growth	11.0%	23.2%	—	20.0%

2013 Year-End Financials

Debt ratio: —
Return on equity: 18.7%
Cash ($ mil.): 73
Current ratio: 3.30
Long-term debt ($ mil.): —
No. of shares (mil.): 21
Dividends
  Yield: 1.9%
  Payout: 45.8%
Market value ($ mil.): 798

	STOCK PRICE ($) FY Close	P/E High/Low	PER SHARE ($) Earnings	Dividends	Book Value
12/13	37.10	22 13	1.72	0.72	10.76
12/12	23.54	17 12	1.40	0.90	6.12
12/11	18.78	19 15	1.01	0.72	5.50
12/10	17.38	25 19	0.69	0.72	5.21
12/09	17.04	27 18	0.77	0.72	5.15
Annual Growth	21.5%	— —	22.3%	(0.0%)	20.2%

US Silica Holdings, Inc.

Life's a beach for the sand-sellers at U.S. Silica. The industrial mineral company provides silica and aplite for the glass foundry chemical and construction industries; and fine ground silica and kaolin clay used to make paint plastics and ceramics. Its "frac sand" product —currently its fastest-growing offering —is used by natural gas and oil producers in hydraulic fracturing a process to boost oil and gas production. U.S. Silica also makes raw materials for solar panels. The company supplies customers in the US and Canada. In addition to its main facility in West Virginia U S. Silica also has 15 plants in the East. U.S. Silica went public in 2012 with an offering worth $200 million.

IPO

U.S. Silica in February 2012 sold 11.7 million shares at $17 per share the middle of the range estimated for the IPO. Golden Gate Capital which had acquired the mining firm in 2008 sold 8.8 million shares while U.S. Silica offered 2.9 million shares. The offering coincided with an increasing demand for frac sand. U.S. Silica used the proceeds to invest in its frac and resin-coated sands operations by upgrading its existing plants and building a new resin-coated sand facility in Illinois (completed in 2014).

Sales and Marketing

Sales to the oil and gas proppants end market comprised 64% of U.S. Silica's sales in 2013. Customers include Schlumberger Ltd. Nabors Industries Texas Specialty Sands Calfrac and C&J Energy Services among others. The mining company primarily sells its products under short-term price agreements or at prevailing market rates. Sales under long-term contracts collectively accounted for 40% of total sales in 2013.

Financial Performance

Buoyed by strong demand for "frac sand" which is in short supply U.S. Silica's sales grew 24% in 2013 versus 2012 to $546 million. Sales of oil and gas proppants increased by more than $100 million accounting for nearly all of the sales growth in 2013. Volume sales increased by 14% year over year while average prices increased 9%.

Net income fell 5% over the same period to $75.3 million. The decline followed three consecutive years of profit growth and was blamed primarily on increased operating costs and decreased other income.

Strategy

The company's fortunes are rising along with the sharp increase in domestic shale oil and gas production which uses sand to break up rock underground to free-up fossil fuel in the Hydraulic fracturing process (aka fracking). Another area of promise for U.S. Silica is resin-coated sand which is also used in hydraulic fracturing. In fact the company predicts a 15% increase in demand annually for its frac sands and resin-coated sands. The company has announced plans to add approximately 3.8 million tons of new capacity in response to surging demand for northern white frac sand. U.S. Silica is planning an 800000 ton-per-year expansion at its Pacific Missouri plant. The $33 million project also includes a new flagship transload to support the additional volume. Also in 2014 the company entered into an agreement with Union Pacific Railroad to build a new unit train capable silica storage facility in Odessa Texas.

U.S. Silica is the second-largest producer of silica used in hydraulic fracturing in the US behind Unimin a unit of Belgium's Sibelco Group.

Mergers and Acquisitions

In July 2014 U.S. Silica acquired Cadre Services a regional sand mining company in Voca Texas. The $98 million purchase expanded the company's geographic footprint and product offering in the fast-growing Permian Basin.

Company Background

U.S. Silica was formed by the merger of Pennsylvania Glass and Ottawa Silica in 1987.

HISTORY

ilica

EXECUTIVES

CFO, Donald A. Merril, age 49, $86,250 total compensation
VP and General Manager Oil & Gas, Don D. Weinheimer, $140,038 total compensation
President and CEO, Bryan A. Shinn, age 53, $383,333 total compensation
VP and General Manager Industrial and Specialties, John P. Blanchard
VP and COO, Mike Winkler
Vp Supply Chain, Jason Tedrow
V P Operations, George Didawick
Auditors: GrantThorntonLLP

LOCATIONS

HQ: US Silica Holdings, Inc.
  8490 Progress Drive, Suite 300, Frederick, MD 21701
Phone: 301 682-0600
Web: www.ussilica.com

PRODUCTS/OPERATIONS

2013 Sales

	$ mil.	% of total
Oil & gas Proppants	347.4	64
Industrial & specialty products	198.6	36
Total	**546**	**100**

Selected Products & Services

Aplite
Fine Ground Silica
FLORISIL®
Ground Silica
Hydrous Kaolin
Kaolin
Oil & Gas Proppants
Recreational Silica
Testing Silica
Whole Grain Silica

COMPETITORS

Carmeuse Lime & Stone Inc.	Martin Marietta Materials
Emerge Energy	Reserve Industries
Fairmount Minerals	Unimin
Hi-Crush	Vulcan Materials
Martin Marietta Aggregates	

HISTORICAL FINANCIALS

Company Type: Public

Income Statement

FYE: December 31

	REVENUE ($ mil.)	NET INCOME ($ mil.)	NET PROFIT MARGIN	EMPLOYEES
12/13	545.9	75.2	13.8%	844
12/12	441.9	79.1	17.9%	785
12/11	295.6	30.2	10.2%	701
12/10	244.9	11.3	4.7%	685
12/09	191.6	5.5	2.9%	0
Annual Growth	29.9%	92.0%	—	—

2013 Year-End Financials

Debt ratio: 43.0%
Return on equity: 27.8%
Cash ($ mil.): 78
Current ratio: 5.01
Long-term debt ($ mil.): 367
No. of shares (mil.): 53
Dividends
  Yield: 1.1%
  Payout: 24.8%
Market value ($ mil.): 1,825

STOCK PRICE ($)		P/E		PER SHARE ($)		
	FY Close	High/Low		Earnings	Dividends	Book Value
12/13	34.11	25	12	1.41	0.38	5.78
12/12	16.73	15	6	1.50	0.50	4.38
Annual Growth 32.1%	103.9%	—	—	(6.0%)	(25.0%)	

USA Technologies Inc

Since you can't get much from a vending machine with a quarter these days USA Technologies decided to make them take plastic. Its ePort device attaches onto vending machines and its eSuds works on washing machines and clothes dryers to allow them to accept debit and credit cards. With the Business Express device hotels libraries and universities can run their business centers as self-pay operations; customers simply swipe their cards to use a PC fax machine or copier. USA Technologies also sells energy-saving devices for such "always-on" appliances as vending machines and office equipment. Information from the company's remote devices is transmitted through the company's USALive network.

Thanks mainly to good results in the company's license and transaction fees segment especially of ePort units connected to the USALive network USA Technologies' revenue rose 45% in fiscal 2011 over the previous year. Connections to the USALive network grew from about 82000 in fiscal 2010 to some 119000 in 2011. USA Technologies has partnered with AT&T Mobility Verizon Wireless and Rogers Wireless to supply USALive services.

Besides card processing the company's ePort product also offers online sales reports machine-dysfunction alerts and other retail-related services. The company's ePort device can also be configured to work with contactless cards a type of debit or credit card with a microchip that allows transactions to be completed through wireless means rather than swiping a card through a magnetic-strip reader.

Customers have included Marriott International Sony Electronics ARAMARK and PepsiCo. USA Technologies has partnerships with Verizon Wireless Visa and VIVOtech.

The company holds more than 70 patents for its technology.

EXECUTIVES

Vice President Sales And Marketing, Michael Lawlor
Vp Global Sales & Bus Dev't, Len Crosson
V Prese-port Connect Services, Bruce Shirey
Vice President Chnl Mgr Hospitality Bus, Cecil Ledesma
Vice President Of Sales, Peter Cronin
Senior Vice President Product, Cary Garland
Vice President Marketing, Maeve Duska
Auditors: McGladreyLLP

LOCATIONS

HQ: USA Technologies Inc
100 Deerfield Lane, Suite 140, Malvern, PA 19355
Phone: 610 989-0340
Web: www.usatech.com

PRODUCTS/OPERATIONS

2011 Sales

	$ mil.	% of total
License & transaction fees	16.5	72
Equipment sales	6.4	28
Total	**22.9**	**100**

COMPETITORS

Crane Co.	TNS
Gemalto	TransAct Technologies
Ingenico	VeriFone
Mac-Gray	Wincor Nixdorf
NCR	

HISTORICAL FINANCIALS

Company Type: Public

Income Statement

FYE: June 30

	REVENUE ($ mil.)	NET INCOME ($ mil.)	NET PROFIT MARGIN	EMPLOYEES
06/14	42.3	27.5	65.0%	61
06/13	35.9	0.8	2.4%	54
06/12	29.0	(5.2)	—	47
06/11	22.8	(6.4)	—	45
06/10	15.7	(11.5)	—	41
Annual Growth	**28.0%**			**10.4%**

2014 Year-End Financials

Debt ratio: 7.6%	No. of shares (mil.): 35
Return on equity: 71.4%	Dividends
Cash ($ mil.): 9	Yield: —
Current ratio: 0.96	Payout: —
Long-term debt ($ mil.): 0	Market value ($ mil.): 75

STOCK PRICE ($)		P/E		PER SHARE ($)		
	FY Close	High/Low		Earnings	Dividends	Book Value
06/14	2.11	3	2	0.78	0.00	1.51
06/13	1.74	265	118	0.01	0.00	0.70
06/12	1.45	—	—	(0.18)	0.00	0.67
06/11	2.22	—	—	(0.26)	0.00	0.81
06/10	0.50	—	—	(0.55)	0.00	0.89
Annual Growth	**43.7%**	—	—	—	—	14.0%

USANA Health Sciences Inc

Health is a matter of science at USANA Health Sciences. The company makes nutritional personal care and weight management products selling them through a direct-sales network marketing system of more than 250000 independent distributors (or associates). USANA Health Sciences also sells directly to 64000 customers deemed preferred. USANA's associates operate throughout North America as well as the Asia/Pacific region. The company's products portfolio includes nutritional supplements (76% of sales) and foods (12%) sold under the USANA brand and a line of skin and hair care products (9%) marketed under the Sens © label. Chairman Myron Wentz owns more than 50% of the company he founded.

Operations

USANA operates its business through one reportable business segment. The direct seller which has operations in 20 markets worldwide makes the majority of its products at its facilities in Utah. It manufactures all of its tablet products and its beauty products in-house. It also develops capsules drink mixes nutrition bars and personal care items. Previously USANA served as a third-party manufacturer for a limited number of body care companies. At the time contract manufacturing accounted for a larger share of the company's sales. However once the Sens ©line took off USANA sold its third-party manufacturing business and devoted its manufacturing capacity to its own products. In keeping with its emphasis on developing science-based products the company has a collaboration with the Linus Pauling Institute at Oregon State University to research the role of vitamins and minerals in human health.

Geographic Reach

The company divides its operations into two regions: North America/Europe and Asia/Pacific. Together they cover about 15 countries. The latter accounts for more than 60% of revenue.

Sales and Marketing

USANA intends to fight sagging sales by increasing brand awareness and acquiring more associates and preferred customers in North America. Along with direct selling USANA sells its products in natural health food retailers via mail order and the Internet and in drug stores and supermarkets.

Financial Analysis

Sales growth in most countries where it operates helped USANA log an 11% increase in revenue in 2012. The results represented strong growth in the Phillipines China Mexico France and Belgium.The higher sales led to a 30% increase in net income; cash flow dipped slightly as the company bought back some of its stock.

Strategy

USANA looks to grow its business through efforts overseas. In 2012 it entered the Thailand market with a dozen products consisting of four key nutritional supplements and eight skin-care products. The company also expanded its operations into France and Belgium as well.

The company builds sales by getting its associates to manage their own business groups by recruiting and training others to sell the company's products. Sales associates are paid on sales generated by those groups. They might also receive compensation by purchasing products at wholesale prices and reselling them at retail prices. USANA attempts to recruit sales people who are looking for a second income and want to start a home-based business.

EXECUTIVES

Vice President Of Customer Service, Alan Bergstrom
CFO, Paul Jones
CEO, David A. (Dave) Wentz, age 43, $574,108 total compensation
Executive Vice President of North America, Mark H. Wilson, age 49, $502,462 total compensation
Chief Information Officer, Rick Stambaugh
President and COO, Fred W. Cooper, age 51, $559,846 total compensation
President of the Americas Europe and South Pacific, Kevin G. Guest, age 51, $547,089 total compensation
President Asia Pacific, Deborah Woo, age 60, $498,490 total compensation
Chief Production Officer, Jim Brown

Executive Vice President of Research and Development, Tim Wood
Vice President Marketing, Diane Leroy
Vice President Of Canada And North, Belynda Lee
Secretary, James H Bramble
Chairman, Myron W. Wentz, age 73
Auditors: PricewaterhouseCoopersLLP

LOCATIONS

HQ: USANA Health Sciences Inc
3838 West Parkway Blvd., Salt Lake City, UT 84120
Phone: 801 954-7100   **Fax:** 801 956-9486
Web: www.usanahealthsciences.com

2013 Sales

	$ mil.	% of total
North America/Europe	244.3	38
Asia/Pacific		
Greater China	235.6	36
Southeast Asia	139.6	22
North Asia	29.1	4
Total	**648.7**	**100**

PRODUCTS/OPERATIONS

COMPETITORS

AIM International	NAI
AMS Health Sciences	NBTY
Amazon Herb	Nature's Sunshine
Amway	Nu Skin
Avon	Perrigo
GNC	Reliv' International
Hain Celestial	Schiff Nutrition
Herbalife Ltd.	International
Lifeway Foods	Shaklee
Mannatech	Sunrider
Market America	ViSalus
Mary Kay	

HISTORICAL FINANCIALS

Company Type: Public

Income Statement
FYE: December 28

	REVENUE ($ mil.)	NET INCOME ($ mil.)	NET PROFIT MARGIN	EMPLOYEES
12/13	718.1	79.0	11.0%	1,480
12/12	648.7	66.4	10.2%	1,330
12/11*	581.9	50.7	8.7%	1,290
01/11	517.6	45.6	8.8%	1,240
01/10	436.9	33.5	7.7%	930
Annual Growth	**13.2%**	**23.9%**	—	**12.3%**

*Fiscal year change

2013 Year-End Financials

Debt ratio: —
Return on equity: 35.5%
Cash ($ mil.): 137
Current ratio: 2.39
Long-term debt ($ mil.): —

No. of shares (mil.): 13
Dividends
Yield: —
Payout: —
Market value ($ mil.): 1,079

	STOCK PRICE ($) FY Close	P/E High/Low		PER SHARE ($) Earnings	Dividends	Book Value
12/13	77.72	16	5	5.56	0.00	18.76
12/12	31.60	11	7	4.45	0.00	13.43
12/11*	30.37	13	7	3.26	0.00	11.64
01/11	43.45	15	8	2.86	0.00	9.08
01/10	31.90	17	8	2.17	0.00	4.86
Annual Growth	**24.9%**	—	—	**26.5%**	—	**40.2%**

*Fiscal year change

Utah Medical Products, Inc.

Utah Medical Products (UTMD) focuses on expectant moms new moms and newborns. The company designs and makes a variety of medical products used in labor and delivery and in neonatal intensive care as well as products for gynecological and female urinary problems. Products include disposable pressure transducers to monitor blood pressure intrauterine catheters used to monitor pressure in the womb during high-risk births and a device that clamps and cuts the umbilical cord and collects a blood sample from the cord. UTMD which has manufacturing facilities in the US and Ireland sells its products around the world through a domestic sales force and more than 100 international distributors.

Operations

More than two-thirds of the company's annual sales come from hospitals outpatient clinics and physicians' offices in the US. UTMD's neonatal intensive care products include oxygen hoods aspirators feeding tubes and chest-drainage tubes as well as peritoneal dialysis products for babies and children.

The company also makes products for assessment and treatment of cervical and uterine diseases and incontinence in women. For example UTMD's ENDOCURETTE allows tissue sampling in a doctor's office that can rule out precancerous or cancerous conditions while its LIBERTY System is a battery-operated system that women can use at home to treat and control urinary incontinence. In addition UTMD makes electrosurgical generators accessories and instruments such as speculas forceps and hands-free lights.

Geographic Reach

UTMD is headquartered in Utah with subsidiary FemCare in the UK and manufacturing facilities Ireland. This European base gives the company easier access to its customers throughout Europe and in the Middle East and Africa. International sales account for just over half of total revenue.

Sales and Marketing

In the US the company uses its own direct sales force as well as independent manufacturers reps to sell its wares. It sometimes uses specialty hospital distribution companies. In the UK and Australia UTMD sells directly to customers while it works through medical device and other distributors in the rest of the world.

Financial Performance

Revenue grew 10% in 2012 due to increased FemCare sales in the US and abroad and an increase in blood pressure monitoring sales. The growth was partially offset by drops in obstetrics and neonatal sales. Net income was up 37% as UTMD improved manufacturing efficiency in the US and Ireland. Cash flow held steady.

Strategy

To keep growing UTMD focuses on expanding and improving existing products based on customer requests developing new products and purchasing products to add to its lineup. Rather than breaking new ground or going through the cumbersome FDA approval process the company usually develops products with pre-marketing agreement among experts that it will be approved.

Mergers and Acquistions

The firm expanded its women's health offerings through the acquisition of Femcare in 2011. The

purchase added a tubal ligation product the Filshie Clip System.

HISTORY

Medical equipment maker Utah Medical (UM) was formed in 1978. In 1982 it went public and the next year bought Medicor (vital sign monitors). Medicor co-founder William Wallace —who was involved in developing many of of the company's patents —became president in 1987.

In 1992 Wallace was charged with breaking income tax and insider trading laws as a result of his 1987 purchase of UM shares acquired through a third party during negotiations for a supply contract with Baxter Healthcare. Despite his exoneration at trial Wallace was fired. He struck back with a wrongful termination suit and UM bought out his interest in 1993.

UM was disappointed by its 1995 launch of Cordguard which harvests umbilical cord cells for later therapeutic use. The next year UM lost its Baxter contract (and about half of its sales). In response UM opened facilities in Ireland and built its product line with the purchases of Columbia Medical (vacuum-assisted obstetrical delivery systems 1997) and C. R. Bard affiliate Gesco International (neonatal intensive care products 1998).

The company's R&D efforts were disappointing. Its Fowler EndoCurette endometrial tissue sampling device (developed with the Mayo Clinic) did not make it to market in 1999 and the company abandoned development of a fetal pH monitor.

In 1999 the company agreed to supply intrauterine pressure catheters to Novation LLC a purchaser serving 25% of US hospitals. But to escape from the pricing pressures of such contract sales the company revitalized its internal sales force to sell its products on the basis of quality. Continuing to enhance sales UM launched an online sales system in 2000. UM acquired Abcorp in 2004; the maker of fetal monitoring belts was a UM supplier prior to the acquisition.

EXECUTIVES

Chief Administrative Officer Treasurer Assistant Secretary and Director, Paul O. Richins, age 53, $102,649 total compensation
Executive Vice President And Chief, Gary Tobian
Chief Administrative Officer Treasurer Assistant Secretary and Director, Paul O. Richins, age 53
Auditors: JonesSimkinsPC

LOCATIONS

HQ: Utah Medical Products, Inc.
7043 South 300 West, Midvale, UT 84047
Phone: 801 566-1200   **Fax:** 801 566-7305
Web: www.utahmed.com

2012 Sales

	$ mil.	% of total
US	19.9	48
Europe	9.3	22
Other	12.3	30
Total	**41.5**	**100**

PRODUCTS/OPERATIONS

2012 Sales

	$ mil.	% of total
Gynecology electrosurgery & urology	23.1	56
Blood pressure monitoring & accessories	6.7	16
Neonatal	6.5	16
Obstetrics	5.2	12
Total	**41.5**	**100**

Selected Products

Cordguard (umbilical cord management tool)
Deltran (needleless blood pressure monitoring system)
Disposa-Hood (infant oxygen hood)
Epitome (electrosurgical scalpel)
Finesse (electrosurgical generators)
FILTRESSE (surgical smoke filtration system)
Hemo-Nate (blood filtration system)
Intran Plus (transducer-tipped catheter)
LETZ (electrosurgical system)
Liberty (electrical stimulation device for urinary incontinence)
Nutri-Cath (enteral feeding tubes)

COMPETITORS

Becton Dickinson	Ethicon
Boston Scientific	Kimberly-Clark Health
CONMED Corporation	Rochester Medical
Cook Incorporated	Teleflex

HISTORICAL FINANCIALS

Company Type: Public

Income Statement

FYE: December 31

	REVENUE ($ mil.)	NET INCOME ($ mil.)	NET PROFIT MARGIN	EMPLOYEES
12/13	40.4	11.4	28.2%	184
12/12	41.5	10.1	24.5%	189
12/11	37.8	7.4	19.6%	187
12/10	25.1	6.0	23.9%	172
12/09	25.9	6.2	24.1%	165
Annual Growth	11.8%	16.2%	—	2.8%

2013 Year-End Financials

Debt ratio: 11.3%
Return on equity: 20.4%
Cash ($ mil.): 14
Current ratio: 3.19
Long-term debt ($ mil.): 5

No. of shares (mil.): 3
Dividends
 Yield: 1.7%
 Payout: 36.2%
Market value ($ mil.): 214

	STOCK PRICE ($) FY Close	P/E High/Low		PER SHARE ($) Earnings	Dividends	Book Value
12/13	57.16	21	12	3.02	0.99	16.19
12/12	36.05	13	10	2.74	0.97	13.77
12/11	27.00	14	12	2.03	0.95	11.20
12/10	26.88	18	15	1.65	1.67	10.44
12/09	29.32	17	12	1.72	0.93	10.52
Annual Growth	18.2%	—	—	15.1%	1.6%	11.4%

VAALCO Energy, Inc.

VAALCO Energy valiantly pursues energy opportunities. The small independent is engaged in the acquisition exploration development and production of oil and gas. VAALCO Energy holds high-risk exploration assets in Angola and Gabon through participating in oil company consortia and has exploration assets in Gulf Coast of Texas and Louisiana and in Montana. VAALCO's near-term production strategy is to focus on developing its reserves in Gabon through the exploitation of the Etame Marin block (the Etame Avouma South Tchibala and Ebouri fields). In 2013 the company reported proved reserves of 7.2 million barrels of crude oil (46% developed); and 1.3 million cu ft. of natural gas located in the US).

Geographic Reach

VAALCO owns producing properties and conducts exploration activities as an operator in Gabon conducts exploration activities as an operator in Angola and conducts exploration activities as a non-operator in Equatorial Guinea. It also has assets in the US.

Operations

The company's primary source of revenues is from the Etame Production Sharing Contract related to the Etame Marin block located in offshore Gabon where it produces from the Etame Avouma South Tchibala and Ebouri fields. During 2013 these fields produced approximately 6.2 million barrels (1.8 million barrels net to the company). Gabon contributed about 99% of VAALCO's revenues in 2013.During 2013 VAALCO produced about 1.6 million barrels of oil equivalent; 1.6 million barrels of oil; and 325 million cu. ft. of gas. In the US the company had 8 gross productive gas wells (net 2.6) and 3 gross productive oil wells (net 0.4). Internationally the company had 11 gross productive oil wells (net 3.1) in 2013.In 2013 the company drilled 5 wells. and completed 1 well in 2012. It had 1 exploratory well in the Nisku formation of the East Poplar unit in Roosevelt County Montana (dry); 1 exploratory well in the Red River formation in Harding County South Dakota (dry); 3 exploratory wells offshore Gabon (2 dry 1 in-progress); and 1 development well offshore Gabon in the Avouma field.

Sales and Marketing

Nearly all of the company's oil and gas is sold at posted or indexed prices under short-term contracts. In Gabon the company sells oil under annual contracts with Mercuria Trading NV. Production in Texas is sold via 2 contracts 1 for oil and 1 for gas and natural gas liquids.

Financial Performance

The company saw revenue growth between 2009 and 2011 thanks to acquisition and the expansion of its operating areas. However VAALCO's revenues declined in 2012 and by 13% in 2013 due primarily to due to decreased volume of oil sold as the result of a natural decline in production and the loss of two wells in 2012 (due to the presence of hydrogen sulfide from two of the three producing wells in the Ebouri field). Natural gas revenues also decreased due to lower volumes partially offset by higher natural gas prices.VAALCO reported a net income of $43 million in 2013 (up from $0.6 million in 2012) due to lower exploration costs lower income tax expenses and no impairment charges of proved properties. The lower income tax expense in 2013 was the result of lower revenues due to lower sales volumes (and lower profit oil barrels subject to taxes) and a significant increase in costs incurred due to the construction of two new platforms and cost incurred associated with an active rig under contract for the majority of 2013 in the Etame Marin block. The company had seen a healthy growth in cash flow from operations between 2009 and 2011; it declined in 2012 and 2013. Net cash provided by operating activities for 2013 was $75.4 million (compared to $94 million in 2012). This was due to a decrease in working capital components and in non-cash adjustments to net income. The lower non-cash adjustments were the result of a decrease in depreciation lower in dry hole costs and a decline in the impairment of proved properties. This decrease was partially offset by an increase in net income.

Strategy

VAALCO's long-term strategy is to balance its higher-potential international prospects with lower-risk US-base assets. The company's future success depends upon its ability to find develop or acquire additional oil and gas reserves that are economically recoverable. Its overall strategy is to increase reserves and production through the exploration and exploitation of oil and natural gas properties with high emphasis on international opportunities. In 2013 the company spent about $81.4 million on exploration and development investments.The company's international strategy is to pursue selective opportunities with a focus on West Africa that are characterized by reasonable entry costs favorable economic terms high reserve potential relative to capital expenditures and the availability of existing technical data. Its US production strategy is to continue to produce from the two Granite Wash wells with minimal additional capital investment.

Mergers and Acquisitions

In 2012 VAALCO acquired a 31% non-operating working interest in a production and development area in Block P offshore Equatorial Guinea from PETRONAS CARIGALI OVERSEAS SDN BHD for $10 million. That year it also bought a 100% working interest in 10000 acres inHarding County South Dakota (Red River formation) for $1.5 million.

Company Background

Growing its US assets in 2011 the company acquired a 640-acre lease in the Granite Wash formation in Hemphill County Texas and secured a drilling rig to operate there. VAALCO also acquired a 70% stake in 5200 acres in the Bakken Shale asset in Montana.

The company merged with the 1818 Oil Corp. in a reverse acquisition in 1998. The 1818 Fund managed by Brown Brothers Harriman & Co. of New York then controlled 65% of VAALCO but sold its stake in 2005.

EXECUTIVES

CFO, Gregory R. (Greg) Hullinger, age 61, $333,829 total compensation
President and COO, W. Russell Scheirman, age 59, $486,722 total compensation
EVP and Corporate Secretary, Gayla M. Cutrer, age 72, $300,132 total compensation
Chairman and CEO, Steven P. Guidry, $100,641 total compensation
Vice President And Legal Counsel, Roland Sledge
Vice President Production, Lin Espey
Chairman and CEO, Steven P. Guidry
Auditors: Deloitte&ToucheLLP

LOCATIONS

HQ: VAALCO Energy, Inc.
 4600 Post Oak Place, Suite 300, Houston, TX 77027
Phone: 713 623-0801   **Fax:** 713 623-0982
Web: www.vaalco.com

2013 Sales

	$ mil.	% of total
Gabon	167.4	99
US	1.9	1
Total	**169.3**	**100**

PRODUCTS/OPERATIONS

Selected Subsidiaries

VAALCO Energy (Gabon) Inc.
VAALCO Energy (USA) Inc.
VAALCO Garbon (Etame) Inc. (90%)
VAALCO Production (Gabon) Inc.

COMPETITORS

Exxon Mobil	Pioneer Natural
Harvest Natural	Resources

Resources
Hess Corporation
Imperial Oil

Royal Dutch Shell
TOTAL

HISTORICAL FINANCIALS
Company Type: Public

Income Statement
FYE: December 31

	REVENUE ($ mil.)	NET INCOME ($ mil.)	NET PROFIT MARGIN	EMPLOYEES
12/13	169.2	43.0	25.4%	111
12/12	195.2	0.6	0.3%	103
12/11	210.4	34.1	16.2%	94
12/10	134.4	37.3	27.8%	89
12/09	115.3	(7.8)	—	77
Annual Growth	10.1%	—	—	9.6%

2013 Year-End Financials

Debt ratio: —
Return on equity: 18.5%
Cash ($ mil.): 130
Current ratio: 3.65
Long-term debt ($ mil.): —

No. of shares (mil.): 56
Dividends
Yield: —
Payout: —
Market value ($ mil.): 392

	STOCK PRICE ($) FY Close	P/E High/Low		PER SHARE ($) Earnings	Dividends	Book Value
12/13	6.89	13	7	0.74	0.00	4.41
12/12	8.65	1011567		0.01	0.00	3.67
12/11	6.04	14	8	0.59	0.00	4.01
12/10	7.16	12	6	0.65	0.00	3.37
12/09	4.55	—	—	(0.14)	0.00	2.69
Annual Growth	10.9%	—	—	—	—	13.2%

Vanguard Natural Resources LLC

Vanguard Natural Resources is at the forefront of oil and natural gas exploration in the Appalachian Basin the Rockies the Permian Basin and South Texas acquiring and developing oil and gas properties in these region. In 2013 Vanguard Natural Resources reported estimated proved reserves of 172.2 million barrels of oil equivalent and an interest in 2551 net and 7277 gross productive wells. The company also owns a 40% working interest in 797118 acres in Appalachia. Vinland Energy Eastern owns the remaining 60% working interest of the acreage. In 2013 the company had identified 386 proved undeveloped drilling locations.

Geographic Reach

The company works with Vinland to operate producing properties in the Appalachian region and to make acquisitions of mature natural gas and oil properties in other producing basins in the US. Vanguard Natural Resources' assets consist primarily of producing and non-producing oil and natural gas reserves located in the Green River Basin in Wyoming the Arkoma Basin in Arkansas and Oklahoma the Permian Basin in West Texas and New Mexico the Big Horn Basin in Wyoming and Montana the Piceance Basin in Colorado the Gulf Coast Basin in Texas and Mississippi the Williston Basin in North Dakota and Montana the Wind River Basin in Wyoming and the Powder River Basin in Wyoming.

Operations

Vanguard Natural Resources focuses on the acquisition production and development of oil and natural gas properties.

Sales and Marketing

The company's oil and natural gas production is principally sold to marketers processors refiners and other purchasers that have access to nearby pipeline processing and gathering facilities. In areas where there is no practical access to pipelines oil is trucked to central storage facilities where it is aggregated and sold to various markets and downstream purchasers.

In 2013 Vanguard Natural Resources' sales of oil natural gas and NGLs to Marathon Oil accounted for 14% of its total revenues; Plains Marketing 10%; JP Morgan Ventures Energy 6%; Bill Barrett 6%; and Shell Trading (US) Company 5%.

Financial Performance

In 2013 the company's revenues rose by 31% thanks to higher oil natural gas and NGLs sales as the result of the increase in production from acquisitions that were completed during 2012 and 2013. Natural gas revenues increased from $47.3 million in 2012 to $124.5 million in 2013 primarily as a result of a 30.6 billion cu. ft. surge in natural gas production volumes.Vanguard Natural Resources reported net income of $59.5 million in 2013 (compared to a net loss of $168.8 million in 2012) primarily due to higher sales and a decline in the operating expenses. In 2013 the company's operating cash inflow increased to $260.97 million (from $204.49 million in 2012) as the result of changes in working capital (which increased total cash flows by $13.8 million). Contributing to the increase was a $35.3 million increase in accounts payable and oil and natural gas revenue payable and accrued expenses and other current liabilities that resulted primarily from the timing effects of invoice payments offset by a $22.1 million increase in accounts receivable related to the timing of receipts from production from acquisitions.

Strategy

Vanguard Natural Resources faces the challenge of the natural decline of oil natural gas and NGLs production which the company attempts to overcome by drilling on its properties and acquiring additional reserves. To broaden its opportunities Vanguard Natural Resources has expanded its asset base to include properties in the Permian Basin South Texas and elsewhere.

Mergers and Acquisitions

In 2014 the company bought natural gas and oil properties in the Pinedale and Jonah fields of Southwestern Wyoming for $549.1 million. For the first time in its history Vanguard Natural Resources will be allocating capital to drilling wells on these acquired properties which is expected to not only maintain cash flow but grow cash flow.In 2013 acquired natural gas oil and NGLs properties in the Permian Basin in southeast New Mexico and West Texas from Range Resources for $266.2 million. It also bought certain natural gas oil and NGLs properties located in the San Juan Basin in New Mexico the D-J Basin in Colorado and the Permian Basin in West Texas for $29.5 million.

Company Background

In 2012 Vanguard Natural Resources bought natural gas and liquids assets in Colorado and Wyoming from Bill Barrett for $328.8 million.

It teamed up with Encore Energy Partners in 2011 in a property acquisition. Both parties bought 50% stakes in a Permian Basin asset purchase for $40.5 million a piece. In late 2011 it bought the remaining shares of Encore Energy Partners.

In 2010 it bought producing oil and gas assets in Mississippi Texas and New Mexico for $115 million. That year it also acquired Denbury Resources' 46% stake in Encore Energy Partners for $380 million. The deal gives Vanguard Natural Resources assets in the Arkoma Big Horn Permian and Williston basins.

In 2008 Vanguard Natural Resources bought oil and gas properties in New Mexico and West Texas from Apache. It also acquired natural gas properties in South Texas for $53.4 million from an affiliate of the Lewis Energy Group. In 2009 it made an additional purchase in the same area from the same company for $52.3 million.

EXECUTIVES

Vp Engineering, Britt Pence, age 54
Senior Vice President Operations, Robert Cornelius
Managing Director, W Anderson
Board Member, John R McGoldrick, age 57
Board Member, Loren Singletary, age 67
Board Member, Lasse Wagene
Auditors: UHYLLP

LOCATIONS

HQ: Vanguard Natural Resources LLC
5847 San Felipe, Suite 3000, Houston, TX 77057
Phone: 832 327-2255
Web: www.vnrllc.com

PRODUCTS/OPERATIONS

2013 Sales

	% of total
Oil Sales	60
Natural Gas Sales	27
NGLs Sales	11
Others	2
Total	**100**

COMPETITORS

Anadarko Petroleum	Occidental Permian
Belden & Blake	PDC Energy
Cabot Oil & Gas	Petrohawk Energy
Chesapeake Energy	Quicksilver Resources
Clayton Williams Energy	Range Resources
EQT Corporation	Royal Dutch Shell

HISTORICAL FINANCIALS
Company Type: Public

Income Statement
FYE: December 31

	REVENUE ($ mil.)	NET INCOME ($ mil.)	NET PROFIT MARGIN	EMPLOYEES
12/13	454.5	59.5	13.1%	172
12/12	347.2	(168.8)	—	122
12/11	319.5	62.0	19.4%	110
12/10	93.1	21.8	23.5%	83
12/09	54.6	(95.7)	—	12
Annual Growth	69.9%	—	—	94.6%

2013 Year-End Financials

Debt ratio: 40.4%
Return on equity: 5.7%
Cash ($ mil.): 11
Current ratio: 0.85
Long-term debt ($ mil.): 1,007

No. of shares (mil.): 78
Dividends
Yield: 8.3%
Payout: 319.8%
Market value ($ mil.): 2,325

	STOCK PRICE ($)	P/E		PER SHARE ($)		
	FY Close	High/Low	Earnings	Dividends	Book Value
12/13	29.52	38 33	0.77	2.46	16.10
12/12	26.00	— —	(3.11)	2.79	13.49
12/11	27.63	17 12	1.95	2.28	17.31
12/10	29.65	30 19	1.00	2.15	10.66
12/09	22.07	— —	(6.74)	2.00	3.20
Annual Growth	7.5%	— —	—	5.3%	49.8%

Vantiv Inc

You may not know it but every time you swipe your credit card a whole world of transactions takes place in the background. And Vantiv lives to rule that world. Operating through subsidiaries Vantiv is a merchant acquirer; that is a third-party payment processor operating between merchants (and their banks) and customers (and their banks). It is one of the largest merchant acquirers but it also handles PIN transactions fraud detection and management and credit card issuing for financials intuitions. Vantiv Caters to merchants of all sizes including top retailers grocers pharmacies and restaurants. It also serves small to midsized banks and credit unions. Vantiv formed in 1970 went public in 2012.

IPO

Vantiv initially aimed to raise about $100 million when it filed an IPO in November 2011 but the company increased its value to $500 million and raised that amount when it priced in March 2012. It planned to use the proceeds to pay down debt. (Prior to going public Vantiv was the Fifth Third Processing Solutions subsidiary of Fifth Third bank. Vantiv took its current name in mid-2011 to differentiate itself from Fifth Third.)

Geographic Reach

Vantiv serves the US market. It's based in Ohio and operates offices in Arizona Colorado Florida Kentucky Illinois Massachusetts and Texas.

Operations

The company operates through two business segments: Merchant Services and Financial Institution Services. Its Merchant Services segment accounted for more than three-quarters of its revenue in 2013 while Financial Intuition Services accounted for the rest.

Sales and Marketing

Vantiv's financial institution clients include regional and community banks credit unions and regional PIN debit networks. The payment processor focuses on small- to mid-sized institutions with less than $15 billion in assets. In 2013 Vantiv processed approximately 3.6 billion transactions for some 1400 financial institutions. On the merchant services side of the business Vantiv counts grocery and drug stores restaurants gaming companies and other retail chains among its clients.

Financial Performance

An 10% increase in transactions and the impact of recent acquisitions drove a 13% increase in Vantiv's overall revenue in 2013 versus 2012. Vantiv's Merchant Services business posted a 16% increase in revenue while financial institution services saw a more modest revenue gain of 3%. The company's profits rose 132% due in large part to increased income from operations and a decline in

operating expenses partially offset by higher income tax expenses.

Strategy

The company's growth strategy includes strengthening its capabilities through acquisitions and strategic partnerships. In 2014 Vantiv partnered with Comerica to provide payment processing products and services for the bank's Merchant Services customers. Adding to its mobile products offering in 2014 the company launched Mobi-Money a mobile payments app that provides cardholders with a secure and easy-to-use debit card management tool.

Mergers and Acquisitions

In June 2014 Vantiv acquired Mercury Payment Systems (MPS) a payment technology and service provider whose products are embedded into point-of-sale software applications. Vantiv paid $1.65 billion in cash to acquire MPS from tech investor Silver Lake Partners.

In late 2012 the company acquired e-commerce payment processor Litle for $361 million in cash. The transaction bolstered Vantiv's e-commerce payment processing services and broadened its online merchant customer base.

EXECUTIVES

President and CEO, Charles D. Drucker, age 51, $788,462 total compensation
CFO, Mark L. Heimbouch, age 50, $461,077 total compensation
President Financial Institution Services, Royal Cole, age 53, $385,560 total compensation
President Merchant Services, Donald Boeding, $363,462 total compensation
President eCommerce, William (Bill) Weingart, age 56
COO, Carlos Lima, $400,000 total compensation
President Integrated Payments, Matt Taylor
President Element Payment Services, Sean Kramer
Vice President Regional Sales, David Entler
Exec Vice President Acquisitions, Adam Coyle
Vice President Of Tax, Scott Wittman
Vice President Finance, Mark Suder
Assistant Vice President Sr Sales Engr, Julie Pifer
Senior Vice President And Deputy General Counsel, John Huber
Vice President, Joseph Coriaggio
Vice President Architecture Integration, Chris Beatty
Senior Vice President Corporate Cntrlr, Chris Thompson
Assistant Vice President Mgr Entp Tools, Eric Hysong
Senior Vice President, Jack Ondeck
Vice President Merchant Info Tech, Kelly Beatty
Vice President National Rela Mgmt, Ken Thorsen
Senior Vice President Financial Pln, Stephanie Ferris
Vice President Marketing, Kara Mangan
Vice President Entp Solutions Pln Cntrl, Stephanie Hall
Vice President Learning Management, James Kennedy
Senior Vice President Chief Lgl Counsel, David Herron
Vice President Marketing, Kathryn Kaporis
Vice President National Rm, Cari Carda
Vice President Strategic Business Dev, Michele Herron
Vice President, Allison Kurtz
Vice President Prepaid Product, Ed Paciolla
Senior Vice President Merchant Services, Tom Sheridan
Senior Vice President Of Sales, Bob Long
Senior Vice President Finance, Kevin McKeon

Senior Vice President Sales Program Management, Matt Downs
Vice President Identity Access Mgmt, Steve Ruggiero
Senior Vice President, Jamie Landheer
Vice President, Heidi Saba
Vice President Human Resources, Christa Titus
Executive Vice President, John Yarmy
Assistant Vice President Conversions, Sarah Curtsinger
Vice President Business Systems, Ron Aucoin
Senior Vice President Investor, Nathan Rozof
Vice President Training Manager, Elizabeth Horrigan
Vice President Client Portfolio Management, Stephanie Polen
Vice President Regl Sales Financial, Carrie Gautsche
Assistant Vice President Team Lead, Phil Hiett
Vice President National Business Development, Lisa Lane
Vice President Product Management, Kasturi Mudulodu
Vice President And Director Software, Steve Javery
Vice President Solutions Consultant, Christina Lohrer
Vice President Executivesales Manager, Keith Carman
Vice President Chief Counsel, Leigh Anne Patton
Vice President Product Engagement Marketing Solutions, Brent Badger
Vice President End User Support, Andy Taylor
Senior Vice President Enterprise Architecture And Strategy, Ravi Shah
Assistant Vice President Applications, Michael Curran
Vice President Financial Institution Services, Sam Merkle
Vice President Of Sales East Divison, Scott Knabusch
Vice President Alliance Partners And Business Development, Jovino Velazquez
Vice President Jeanie Network And Business Development, Gina Ruedebusch
Assistant Vice President Executive Consultant, Matt Fluegge
President and CEO, Charles D. Drucker, age 51
Chairman, Jeffrey E. (Jeff) Stiefler, age 67

LOCATIONS

HQ: Vantiv Inc
8500 Governor's Hill Drive, Symmes Township, OH 45249
Phone: 513 900-5250
Web: www.vantiv.com

PRODUCTS/OPERATIONS

2013 Sales

	$mil.	% of total
Merchant Services	1639.2	78
Financial Institution Services	468.9	22
Total	**2108.1**	**100**

2013 Sales

	$mil.	% of total
External customers	2028.7	96
Related party revenue	79.4	4
Total	**2108.1**	**100**

COMPETITORS

Banc of America Merchant Services	Fiserv
Chase Paymentech Solutions	Global Payments
Elavon	Heartland Payment Systems
	Payment Processing

Fidelity National
Information Services
First Data

Total System Services
WorldPay

HISTORICAL FINANCIALS
Company Type: Public

Income Statement
FYE: December 31

	REVENUE ($ mil.)	NET INCOME ($ mil.)	NET PROFIT MARGIN	EMPLOYEES
12/13	2,108.0	133.5	6.3%	2,791
12/12	1,863.2	57.6	3.1%	2,671
12/11	1,622.4	36.2	2.2%	2,455
12/10	1,162.1	21.9	1.9%	0
12/09	506.0	(2.1)	—	0
Annual Growth	42.9%	—	—	—

2013 Year-End Financials

Debt ratio: 43.4%
Return on equity: 16.8%
Cash ($ mil.): 171
Current ratio: 1.18
Long-term debt ($ mil.): 1,730

No. of shares (mil.): 190
Dividends
  Yield: —
  Payout: —
Market value ($ mil.): 6,215

	STOCK PRICE ($) FY Close	P/E High/Low		PER SHARE ($) Earnings	Dividends	Book Value
12/13	32.61	33	21	0.87	0.00	4.03
12/12	20.42	48	39	0.47	0.00	3.87
Annual Growth	59.7%	—	—	85.1%	—	4.2%

VASCO Data Security International Inc

VASCO Data Security International holds the key to electronic banking. Its hardware and software lines include authentication platforms security tokens handheld devices and related applications used for authenticating a person's identity on computer networks. The company's products incorporate authentication and digital signature security technologies and can be used to secure intranets extranets and LANs. In addition to banking VASCO's products are used to provide remote workers with secure access to corporate networks; other applications include e-commerce transactions. It counts more than 10000 customers including some 1700 financial institutions such as Citibank BNP-Paribas and HSBC.

Geographic Reach

The company has customers in more than 100 countries but its largest market is Europe which accounts for about 60% of sales. There it has R&D centers in Austria France the Netherlands and the UK. Asia accounts for about 20% of sales and the US less than 10%.

It has sales offices in Australia Belgium Brazil China Dubai India Japan Singapore the UK and the US (in Marlborough Massachusetts.)

Sales and Marketing

VASCO Data Security uses a direct sales force as well as a network of 55 distributors their resellers and systems integrators. While it has a large customer base its top 10 customers account for 40% of sales. Of that its largest client HBSC accounts for almost 20% of sales. Non-banking cus-

tomers include Blizzard Entertainment PartyGaming and Konami Digital.

Financial Performance

The company has experienced up-and-down revenues over the past decade but has always been profitable. In 2013 revenue grew 1% to $155 million primarily due to the strength of the euro (the currency most of its customers pay in) over the dollar (the currency it reports in). Profits fell 28% to $11 million due to increased operating costs (sales and marketing R&D etc.)

Strategy

Banks and other financial institutions remain VASCO's bread-and-butter customer base but the company is expanding its enterprise security business. It serves the enterprise market exclusively through indirect marketing channels. VASCO has also made some of its products available under the Software-as-a-Service model.

VASCO has developed a clear strategy of using mobile applications to move beyond pure authentication services to more risk-based services based on a scoring mechanism. At the core is DIGIPASS for Application Perimeter Protection SDK (DIGIPASS for APPS) on the client side and VACMAN Controller on the server side.

Mergers and Acquisitions

In a move to expand the functionality of its product line VASCO bought Netherlands-based DigiNotarfor about $12.9 million in cash in 2011. DigiNotar developed a complementary electronic consumer identity authentication application known as EazyID which incorporates VASCO's technology. In 2013 it paid $22 million for Cronto which provides secure visual transaction authentication services for online banking.

EXECUTIVES

Chairman and CEO, T. Kendall (Ken) Hunt, age 70, $375,000 total compensation
President and COO, Jan Valcke, age 59, $425,376 total compensation
EVP and CFO, Clifford K. (Cliff) Bown, age 63, $340,000 total compensation
Chief Information Officer, Victor Hoogland
Vice President Mdp Business Unit, Martin Ahlers
Chairman and CEO, T. Kendall (Ken) Hunt, age 70
Auditors: KPMGLLP

LOCATIONS

HQ: VASCO Data Security International Inc
  1901 South Meyers Road, Suite 210, Oakbrook Terrace, IL 60181
Phone: 630 932-8844   **Fax:** 630 932-8852
Web: www.vasco.com

2013 Sales

	$ mil.	% of total
Europe Middle East & Africa	95.8	62
Asia/Pacific	27.3	17
US	11.8	8
Other countries	20.1	13
Total	**155.0**	**100**

PRODUCTS/OPERATIONS

2013 Sales

	$ mil.	% of total
Banking	126.8	82
Enterprise & Application Security	28.2	18
Total	**155.0**	**100**

COMPETITORS

ActivIdentity
Check Point Software

RSA Security
SafeNet

Entrust
IBM Internet Security Systems

VeriSign

HISTORICAL FINANCIALS
Company Type: Public

Income Statement
FYE: December 31

	REVENUE ($ mil.)	NET INCOME ($ mil.)	NET PROFIT MARGIN	EMPLOYEES
12/13	155.0	11.1	7.2%	396
12/12	154.0	15.6	10.1%	374
12/11	168.0	18.1	10.8%	358
12/10	107.9	10.8	10.0%	325
12/09	101.7	11.8	11.7%	294
Annual Growth	11.1%	(1.5%)	—	7.7%

2013 Year-End Financials

Debt ratio: —
Return on equity: 6.7%
Cash ($ mil.): 98
Current ratio: 4.36
Long-term debt ($ mil.): —

No. of shares (mil.): 39
Dividends
  Yield: —
  Payout: —
Market value ($ mil.): 306

	STOCK PRICE ($) FY Close	P/E High/Low		PER SHARE ($) Earnings	Dividends	Book Value
12/13	7.73	32	26	0.28	0.00	4.40
12/12	8.16	27	16	0.40	0.00	3.99
12/11	6.52	29	10	0.47	0.00	3.56
12/10	8.13	31	20	0.28	0.00	3.09
12/09	6.28	33	12	0.31	0.00	2.89
Annual Growth	5.3%	—	—	(2.5%)	—	11.1%

Vascular Solutions Inc

Vascular Solutions helps interventional cardiologists intervene into veins. The company develops manufactures and markets catheters used during treatment of vascular conditions. Its product line includes the Pronto extraction catheter which removes arterial clots and other tools used to get under the skin and into blood vessels. Its hemostat products include the D-Stat a thrombin-infused bandage used to control bleeding following catheterization. It also makes the Vari-Lase a laser system for treating varicose veins. Vascular Solutions markets the devices to interventional cardiologists and radiologists through its own sales team in the US; it uses independent distributors overseas.

Operations

Vascular Solutions' three product categories include catheter hemostat and vein products. Catheter products 63% of sales include the Pronto extraction catheters along with GuideLiner catheter and other minimally invasive devices. Hemostat products 22% include D-Stat as well as D-Stat Flowable splints and compression bands. Vein products 15% are mainly the Vari-Lase but also a reprocessing service for the ClosureFAST vein ablation catheter.

The company manufactures its products at its main facility in Minnesota. It maintains manufacturing and supply agreement with King Pharmaceuticalsgiving King marketing rights to the company's ThrombiGel hemostat products in non-interventional cardiology markets. In exchange King supplies Vascular Solutions with thrombin (a coagulation protein) for use in devices that aren't in competition with King's products. The company also purchases thrombin from Sigma-Aldrich Fine Chemicals for its international products.

Geographic Reach

The company has manufacturing facilities in Minnesota and in Ireland. About 85% of its sales come from the US.

Sales and Marketing

Vascular Solutions has about 90 direct sales agents in the US and an independent distributor network in 50 countries.

Financial Performance

Revenue grew about 12% in 2013 as product sales increased across the board lead by a 22% increase in Hemostat Products. Net income moved up about 9% due to increased revenue and a decline in income tax expenses as the company exercised stock options. Cash from operations also moved up slightly as revenue rose.

Strategy

Vascular Solutions' growth strategy is a mix of new product development and acquisitions to extend its product line. It develops new products and next-generation versions of its existing medical devices through its own research and development efforts and by partnering with other medical device makers through marketing and licensing deals.

In 2013 it launched new catheter products and extended it thrombin products for the hemostat line the following year. Also in 2014 Vascular Solutions entered an R&D agreement with the US Army to develop freeze-dried plasma for battlefield treatment of hemorrhages.

EXECUTIVES

Senior Vice President Of Worldwide, William (Bill) Rutstein
SVP Operations, Charmaine Sutton, $325,000 total compensation
CEO, Howard C. Root, $465,000 total compensation
SVP Finance CFO and Corporate Secretary, James Hennen, $250,000 total compensation
VP Manufacturing Engineering, Jonathan (Jon) Hammond
Chairman, John Erb
Auditors: BakerTillyVirchowKrauseLLP

LOCATIONS

HQ: Vascular Solutions Inc
6464 Sycamore Court North, Minneapolis, MN 55369
Phone: 763 656-4300   **Fax:** 877 656-4251
Web: www.vasc.com

PRODUCTS/OPERATIONS

2013 Sales

	$ mil.	% of total
Products		
Catheter products	69.9	63
Hemostat products	23.8	22
Vein products	16.5	15
License & collaboration	0.3	—
Total	**110.5**	**100**

Selected Products

Catheter products
  Elite Snares
  Gopher Cold catheter
  GuideLiner
  Guardian II hemostasis valve
  Langston catheter
  Minnie support catheter
  Pronto Extraction catheters
  SmartNeedle Vascular Access System

SuperCross microcatheter
  VSI guidewires micro-HV introducer kit
Hemostat products
  D-Stat Dry hemostat bandage
  D-Stat Flowable topical hemostat
  D-Stat Rad Band
Vein products
  Auto-Fill anesthetic syringe
  Klein infiltration pump
  Vari-Lase procedure kit
Other products
  Acolysis ultrasound thrombolysis system

COMPETITORS

Abbott Labs	Johnson & Johnson
AngioDynamics	Medtronic
Bard	Merit Medical Systems
Boston Scientific	Spectranetics
Cook Incorporated	St. Jude Medical
HemCon Medical Technologies	Terumo

HISTORICAL FINANCIALS

Company Type: Public

Income Statement

FYE: December 31

	REVENUE ($ mil.)	NET INCOME ($ mil.)	NET PROFIT MARGIN	EMPLOYEES
12/14	126.1	12.7	10.1%	485
12/13	110.5	11.1	10.1%	406
12/12	98.3	9.9	10.1%	377
12/11	89.9	9.7	10.8%	355
12/10	78.4	21.3	27.3%	296
Annual Growth	**12.6%**	**(12.1%)**	**—**	**13.1%**

2014 Year-End Financials

Debt ratio: —	No. of shares (mil.): 17
Return on equity: 12.1%	Dividends
Cash ($ mil.): 36	Yield: —
Current ratio: 6.02	Payout: —
Long-term debt ($ mil.): —	Market value ($ mil.): 467

	STOCK PRICE ($) FY Close	P/E High/Low		PER SHARE ($) Earnings	Dividends	Book Value
12/14	27.16	41	25	0.72	0.00	6.59
12/13	23.15	34	21	0.65	0.00	5.68
12/12	15.80	25	16	0.60	0.00	4.69
12/11	11.13	23	17	0.57	0.00	4.07
12/10	11.72	10	6	1.26	0.00	3.80
Annual Growth	**23.4%**	**—**	**—**	**(13.1%)**	**—**	**14.8%**

Verisign Inc

VeriSign helps companies and consumers connect the dots. The company is a big part of what makes the Internet work. It operates two of the world's 13 root nameservers which assign Internet protocol (IP) addresses to devices communicating across the Internet. VeriSign is also the only issuer of the .com and .net domain names that are sold to users by companies such as domain registrars Go Daddy and Register.com. The company also provides network infrastructure services providing hosted cyber intelligence managed domain name systems (DNS) availability and resolution and hosted monitoring and mitigation against the dreaded Distributed Denial of Service (DDoS) attacks. More than 60% of sales are from the US.

HISTORY

VeriSign was founded by Stratton Sclavos and Jim Bidzos in 1995. Sclavos a veteran of MIPS Computer Systems and two failed Silicon Valley startups ran the company as RSA's digital certification division until it was spun off in 1995. Its early backers included Ameritech Mitsubishi and Visa. Apple and Netscape were among its first customers.

VeriSign formed a Japanese subsidiary in 1996. The next year the company debuted its Financial Server ID a digital certificate for use with the Open Financial Exchange a home banking standard backed by Microsoft. VeriSign went public in early 1998 and added Sumitomo Bank and UPS as customers. Also in 1998 the company bought Secure It (Internet security consulting services).

In early 2000 the company stepped up expansion efforts buying South Africa-based Thawte Consulting (digital certification products) and Signio (Internet payment services). Later that year VeriSign acquired Internet domain registrar Network Solutions for about $20 billion.

Looking to expand its communications service offerings in 2001 the company acquired network service provider Illuminet Holdings for $1.3 billion. Also that year VeriSign reached an agreement with ICANN to become the exclusive operator of the top level .com domain registry until 2007.

The company continued its acquisitive ways in 2002 and 2003 purchasing H.O. Systems ($350 million) and UNC-Embratel ($16 million). In late 2003 it sold the portion of Network Solutions that sells domain names and provides Web-hosting services to Pivotal Private Equity for about $100 million.

In 2004 VeriSign acquired managed security services provider Guardent for about $140 million and later that year purchased Germany-based wireless content service provider Jamba! for about $273 million.

The company moved beyond its legacy encryption and digital certificate products with a string of purchases in 2005. Verisign bought LightSurf a provider of multimedia messaging and interoperability solutions for the wireless market for $270 million. Later that year Verisign purchased Authorize.Net Holdings' PrePay INS business (wireless phone rate plan and calling plan tracking products) for about $17 million. Quick on the heels of the PrePay INS deal came VeriSign's purchase of iDEFENSE for $40 million in cash. Other 2005 purchases included Moreover Technologies (news aggregation) Weblogs.com (blog tracking) and Retail Solutions (point-of-sale tracking). The company sold its payment gateway business to Pay Pal a subsidiary of eBay for $370 million in 2005.

VeriSign's acquisition tear continued in 2006. It purchased Web-based billing and client management software company CallVision for $30 million in cash as well as m-Qube a developer of software for delivering content and connectivity services to wireless subscribers. It acquired Internet transaction security specialist GeoTrust for $125 million in cash.

Also in 2006 VeriSign renewed its contract with ICANN extending its rights to the .com registry until 2012. It also bought Kontiki a developer of technology for speeding up large downloads on the Internet for $62 million.

News Corporation acquired a majority stake that year in VeriSign's Jamba unit which provides ring tones and other mobile phone content for $188 million. (Jamba also known as Jamster operated as a joint venture between the two companies until

2008 when VeriSign sold its remaining stake to News Corp for $200 million.)

In 2007 Sclavos resigned and director William Roper was named president and CEO.

Formerly organized around its business units VeriSign restructured its operations into functional groups in 2007; it formed a combined worldwide sales and services team and an integrated marketing and product development organization.

After only about a year on the job Roper resigned in 2008. He was replaced by company founder Jim Bidzos on an interim basis. Early the following year VeriSign named Mark McLaughlin as president and COO; he was widely seen as the most viable candidate to take on the CEO job. McLaughlin had been heavily involved in the company's strategy to focus on its core Internet infrastructure business during Roper's tenure; while he ran the Naming Services business he led contract negotiations that successfully extended VeriSign's hold on the .com and .net registries.

McLaughlin was named president and CEO in August 2009 and joined the board of directors; Bidzos remained chairman.

Also in 2009 VeriSign divested all of its business lines in the Communications Services Group encompassing connectivity and interoperability services billing and mobile commerce. The company sold the unit to Transaction Network Services for $230 million in 2009. The sale was part of a restructuring announced in 2007.

Continuing to hone its focus on Internet naming services in 2009 the company sold its Managed Security Services business to security services company SecureWorks and its Real-Time Publisher Services (RTP) business which provided content aggregation and business intelligence services. Later the same year it sold its Messaging Business to network engineering services firm Syniverse Holdings for $175 million in cash. It also sold its global security consulting business to AT&T.

In 2010 VeriSign sold its Identity and Authentication Services business to Symantec for about $1.28 billion in cash. The business included the VeriSign Trust Seal —a widely recognized symbol of online security —along with its secure sockets layer (SSL) and code signing certificate services managed public key infrastructure (MPKI) and its VeriSign Identity Protection (VIP) authentication and fraud detection services. The sale essentially completed VeriSign's withdrawal from all but its more lucrative (and less competitive) Naming Services business.

In 2010 VeriSign negotiated with ICANN for a fee increase for .com and .net domain registration resulting in increases from $6.86 to $7.34 and $4.23 to $4.65 respectively. In 2011 the company again increased fees to $7.85 for .com and to $5.11 for .net. These fees are paid by the domain name registrars.

VeriSign is not itself a registrar —it exited that business with the sale of Network Solutions in 2003.) In 2011 VeriSign was selected by the General Services Administration to operate the .gov and fed.us domain name registries..

EXECUTIVES

Vice President Chief Security Officer, Danny McPherson

Chairman President and CEO, D. James (Jim) Bidzos, age 58, $752,885 total compensation

SVP and CFO, George E. Kilguss, age 53, $232,212 total compensation

SVP and CTO, Burt Kaliski

Svp And General Manager Naming Services, Patrick (Pat) Kane

Senior Vice President Of Marketing Strategy And Business Development, Scott Schnell

Vice President Tax, Mitch Greenhill

Vp Of Mkt, Rob Nunes

Vice President Technical Operations, Tim Roe

Vice President Operations, Mike Giroux

Senior Vice President, Scott Crenshaw

Vice President Of Human Resources, Ellen Petrocci

Vice President Global Sales Planning, Brian Lillie

Chairman President and CEO, D. James (Jim) Bidzos, age 58

Assistant Treasurer, Tim Muindi

Auditors: KPMGLLP

LOCATIONS

HQ: Verisign Inc
12061 Bluemont Way, Reston, VA 20190
Phone: 703 948-3200
Web: www.verisign.com

2013 Sales

	$ mil.	% of total
US	585.2	61
Europe Middle East & Africa	169.8	18
Asia/Pacific	129.7	13
Ohter regions	80.4	8
Total	**965.1**	**100**

PRODUCTS/OPERATIONS

Selected Services

Network Intelligence and Availability Services
  Distributed Denial of Service mitigation (hosted monitoring and protection services against DDoS attacks)
  iDefense Security Intelligence Services (access to cyber intelligence)
  Managed Domain Name System services (hosting service for DNS resolution)
Registry Services
  Domain name registration (for .com .net .cc .tv and .name domain names)
  Internationalized domain name services
  Back-end system operation (for .jobs .gov and .edu domain names)

COMPETITORS

AT&T	Nominum
GoDaddy	Register.com
Google	SecureWorks
Infoblox	Tucows
McAfee	Verio
Microsoft	Verizon
Network Solutions	WorldSite.ws
NeuStar	Yahoo!

HISTORICAL FINANCIALS

Company Type: Public

Income Statement

FYE: December 31

	REVENUE ($ mil.)	NET INCOME ($ mil.)	NET PROFIT MARGIN	EMPLOYEES
12/14	1,010.1	355.2	35.2%	1,061
12/13	965.0	544.4	56.4%	1,079
12/12	873.5	320.0	36.6%	1,099
12/11	771.9	142.8	18.5%	1,009
12/10	680.5	830.9	122.1%	1,048
Annual Growth	**10.4%**	**(19.1%)**	**—**	**0.3%**

2014 Year-End Financials

Debt ratio: 64.1%
Return on equity: ***,***.*%
Cash ($ mil.): 191
Current ratio: 0.78
Long-term debt ($ mil.): 750

No. of shares (mil.): 118
Dividends
  Yield: —
  Payout: —
Market value ($ mil.): 6,752

	STOCK PRICE ($) FY Close	P/E High/Low	PER SHARE ($) Earnings	Dividends	Book Value
12/14	57.00	22 17	2.52	0.00	(7.46)
12/13	59.78	16 10	3.49	0.00	(3.17)
12/12	38.82	24 17	1.95	0.00	(0.06)
12/11	35.72	43 32	0.86	2.75	(0.55)
12/10	32.67	8 5	4.64	3.00	3.92
Annual Growth	**14.9%**	**— —**	**(14.2%)**	**—**	**—**

Verisk Analytics Inc

Insurance is a risky business and Verisk Analytics is in the business of helping to manage that risk. The company compiles data designed to detect fraud and predict loss for customers in the US property and casualty insurance health care and mortgage industries. Its Decision Analytics unit provides health care claim payers and mortgage lenders with predictive models loss estimation tools and fraud ID applications. Its Risk Assessment unit runs databases that hold billions of records containing statistical and underwriting data used to price insurance policies and write policy language. Verisk was created by subsidiary Insurance Services Office (ISO) as a means of going public; Verisk completed its IPO in 2009.

Geographic Reach

Verisk has offices in more than 20 US states as well as international locations in countries including Canada China Denmark Germany India Israel Japan Nepal Singapore and the UK.

Operations

The company is experiencing steady revenue growth in both of its main business segments —Decision Analytics and Risk Assessment —as businesses pay ever-increasing attention to risk management and loss control. The Decision Analytics division (which accounts for more than 60% of revenues) is seeing growth in its main insurance division as well as from customers in finance and other industries. The division's health care business is booming growing more than 100% in 2012 as medical firms adjust to changing industry laws. Within the Risk Assessment segment the primary industry-standard insurance program business continues to grow; however the smaller property rating business saw some decline in 2012.

The company aggregates data about premiums and losses throughout the US and internationally to help firms standardize coverage assess future potential risks and losses and comply with insurance regulators. Verisk's databases hold more than 500 terabytes of data on property/casualty insurance including catastrophe models for more than 50 countries fire-suppression capabilities for 47000 US communities 700 million claims records and more than 60 million residential and commercial properties.

Sales and Marketing

A majority of Verisk's revenue is generated through annual subscriptions and long-term agreements within the US property/casualty insurance industry. Major customers in this category include AIG Allstate Hartford and Liberty Mutual. It sells its products and services through a direct sales force. Customers in the health care mortgage lending and government categories include numerous Blue Cross and Blue Shield plans Wells Fargo and

FEMA. Verisk also serves select clients in the supply chain human resources and risk management industries.

Advertising costs from branding and promotional activities totaled some $7455 in 2012 up from $7065 in 2011.

Financial Performance

In fiscal 2012 Verisk achieved revenues of more than $1.5 billion a 15% increase over 2011 results. Through organic revenue growth new product development and selected acquisitions the company has been able to grow its revenues at a steady rate over the past five years. Net income also increased 16% to some $ in 2012 following profit growth in both 2010 and 2011.

Strategy

Verisk's strategy for further growth includes increasing sales to insurance customers developing proprietary data sets and predictive analytics continuing to acquire complementary businesses and leveraging its intellectual property into new markets.

Verisk is working to widen its offerings for players in the insurance market as catastrophic events and other market developments increase the demand for the company's services. In 2010 the firm launched its QuickFill analytics solution which provides auto and property databases to insurers at their point-of-service. The company has also integrated weather and climate risks into its predictive models. Verisk Analytics is also expanding rapidly in the health care and financial services segments and it is working to enter new markets and additional customer sectors through both acquisitive and organic growth strategies.

On the organic growth side Verisk Analytics conducts internal programs to create new and enhanced products. Its product development process incorporates market research internal software development and alliances with other information providers and technology companies. For instance the company formed a partnership with loan registry provider MERSCORP (2009) to develop a fraud-prevention database for the US mortgage lending industry.

Mergers and Acquisitions

To expand in the insurance market in 2012 the company acquired Minneapolis-based Aspect Loss Prevention a leading provider of loss prevention software for $8 million to gain its analytic solutions to the retail entertainment and food industries. Verisk Analytics further enhanced its health care solution set by paying about $349 million for MediConnect Global a large cloud-based health information exchange with proprietary systems and services to help aggregate and analyze medical records. The company then positioned MediConnect Global under its Verisk Health umbrella.

On the financial services side the company paid $425 million to acquire New York-based Argus Information & Advisory Services LLC in 2012. The purchase bolstered Verisk Analytics' service capabilities to the financial services industry by adding Argus' information analytics benchmarking scoring and customized services in the Americas and Europe.

Ownership

GreatBanc Trust which serves as trustee of the ISO employee stock ownership trust owns more than 10% of Verisk.

Company Background

The company traces its roots back to 1971 when ISO was created by an association of insurance companies. Verisk went public in 2009 in one of the largest offerings of the year raising almost $2 billion.

EXECUTIVES

Vice President Human Resources, Marlene Reisman
Chairman and CEO, Frank J. Coyne, age 65, $1,000,000 total compensation
President and COO, Scott G. Stephenson, age 57, $495,385 total compensation
EVP and CFO, Mark V. Anquillare, age 48, $414,252 total compensation
Senior Vice President President Xactware Solutions, Jim Loveland
President ‚Â— Verisk Insurance Solutions ‚Â— Claims and Crime Analytics, Vincent Cialdella, age 63
Vice President Chief Marketing Officer, Christopher H. Perini
President ISO Innovative Analytics, Marty Ellingsworth
President ‚Â— Verisk Insurance Solutions ‚Â— Commercial Property, William M. Raichle
President ‚Â— Verisk Insurance Solutions ‚Â— Underwriting, Neil Spector
President - Interthin, Kevin Coop
President AIR Worldwide, S. Ming Lee
CIO, Perry Blogs
EVP Client Development MediConnect Global, Kim Bresnan
President Interthin, Jeff Moyer
President Verisk, Joel Portice
President Atmospheric and Environmental Research, Ron Isaacs
President Argus Information & Advisory Services, Michael Heller
President 3E Company, Robert S. Christie
President Verisk Climate, Kyle Beatty
President Verisk Insurance Solutions Claims and Crime Analytics, Richard Rocca
President ISO Insurance Programs and Analytic Services, Beth Fitzgerald
Assistant Vice President, Massood Abolfazli
Vice President Marketing Business Dev, John Cantwell
Vice President, Anthony Canale
Vice President Human Resources, Alex Korb
Vice President Medical Intelligence, Carl Smith
Vice President Strategy, Anu Karna
Vice President Med Affairs Chief Med, Jennifer Derfuss
Vice President, Rich Dibenedetto
Vice President Chief Internal Auditor, Mark S Magath
Vice President Human Resources Adm, Patricia Lloyd
Vice President Human Resources, Lissette Martinez
Sales Vice President Verisk Ins, Glen Brooks
Vice President Corporate Development, Ariel Boyman
Assistant Vice President Pca Platform, John Heffernan
Vice President, Mohana Lohani
Vice President Corporate Development, Yang Chen
Assistant Vice President, Joe Louwagie
Vice President And Chief Field Operations Officer, Robert Andrews
Vp Commercial Property, Jonathan Stein
Chairman and CEO, Frank J. Coyne, age 65
Treasurer, Dave Hansen
Auditors: Deloitte&ToucheLLP

LOCATIONS

HQ: Verisk Analytics Inc
545 Washington Boulevard, Jersey City, NJ 07310-1686
Phone: 201 469-2000
Web: www.verisk.com

PRODUCTS/OPERATIONS

2012 Revenues

	$ mil.	% of total
Decision Analytics		
Insurance	493.5	32
Healthcare	222.9	15
Financial Services	153.0	10
Specialized markets	85.4	6
Risk Assessment		
Industry-standard insurance programs	450.6	29
Property-specific rating & underwriting info	128.9	8
Total	**1534.3**	**100**

Selected Acquisitions

2012
Insurance Risk Management Solutions (IRMS property risk assessment technology)
MediConnect Global (about $349 million; cloud-based health information exchange; Sandy Utah)

2011
3E Co. ($110 million; environmental health and safety compliance management)
Bloodhound Technologies (ConVergence Point claims editing software used by commercial health plans state Medicaid agencies and others to detect and control health insurance fraud)
Health Risk Partners ($60 million; database of Medicare and Medicaid participants)

2010
Crowe Paradis Services (claims analysis and Medicare compliance solutions)
Strategic Analytics (credit risk management services for consumer and mortgage lenders)

2009
D2 Hawkeye (health care data management and analysis)
Enabl-u Technologies (loss-prevention service provider for banks and other retail clients)
TierMed Systems (health care data management and analysis)

COMPETITORS

Computer Sciences Corp.	LexisNexis
CoreLogic	MSCI
DMG Information	McKesson
Deloitte Consulting	OptumnInsight
FNC	Thomson Reuters
Fair Isaac	Towers Watson

HISTORICAL FINANCIALS

Company Type: Public

Income Statement

FYE: December 31

	REVENUE ($ mil.)	NET INCOME ($ mil.)	NET PROFIT MARGIN	EMPLOYEES
12/13	1,595.7	348.3	21.8%	7,095
12/12	1,534.3	329.1	21.5%	6,495
12/11	1,331.8	282.7	21.2%	5,401
12/10	1,138.3	242.5	21.3%	4,890
12/09	1,027.1	126.6	12.3%	4,253
Annual Growth	**11.6%**	**28.8%**	**—**	**13.6%**

2013 Year-End Financials

Debt ratio: 50.9%	No. of shares (mil.): 167
Return on equity: 86.7%	Dividends
Cash ($ mil.): 165	Yield: —
Current ratio: 1.10	Payout: —
Long-term debt ($ mil.): 1,271	Market value ($ mil.): 11,005

STOCK PRICE ($) FY Close	P/E High/Low	PER SHARE ($) Earnings	Dividends	Book Value
12/13 65.72	33 25	2.02	0.00	3.27
12/12 50.97	26 20	1.92	0.00	1.52
12/11 40.13	24 18	1.63	0.00	(0.60)
12/10 34.08	25 20	1.30	0.00	(0.67)
12/09 30.28	43 36	0.70	0.00	(0.19)
Annual Growth 21.4%	— —	—	30.3%	—

Vertex Energy Inc.

Electric services nsk

EXECUTIVES

Ceo, Benjamin P Cowart
Vice President Refining And Marketing, Greg Wallace

LOCATIONS

HQ: Vertex Energy Inc.
1331 Gemini Street, Suite 250, Houston, TX 77058
Phone: 866 660-8156
Web: www.vertexenergy.com

HISTORICAL FINANCIALS

Company Type: Public

Income Statement

FYE: December 31

	REVENUE ($ mil.)	NET INCOME ($ mil.)	NET PROFIT MARGIN	EMPLOYEES
12/13	161.9	7.8	4.9%	154
12/12	134.5	3.6	2.7%	102
12/11	109.7	5.7	5.2%	13
12/10	58.1	1.2	2.1%	13
12/09	38.7	(0.6)	—	14
Annual Growth	43.0%	—	—	82.1%

2013 Year-End Financials

Debt ratio: 13.1%
Return on equity: 27.3%
Cash ($ mil.): 2
Current ratio: 1.50
Long-term debt ($ mil.): 6
No. of shares (mil.): 21
Dividends
  Yield: —
  Payout: —
Market value ($ mil.): 71

STOCK PRICE ($) FY Close	P/E High/Low	PER SHARE ($) Earnings	Dividends	Book Value
12/13 3.35	9 6	0.39	0.00	1.75
12/12 3.16	12 4	0.25	0.00	1.20
12/11 2.05	6 1	0.39	0.00	0.99
12/10 0.68	8 2	0.09	0.00	0.30
12/09 0.48	— —	(0.08)	0.00	0.14
Annual Growth 62.5%	— —	—	—	89.3%

Virtus Investment Partners, Inc

Virtus Investment Partners provides investment management services to wealthy individuals corporations pension funds endowments and foundations and insurance companies. With more than $50 billion of assets under management it operates through affiliated advisors including Duff & Phelps Kayne Anderson Rudnick and Newfleet Asset Management as well as outside subadvisors. Virtus markets diverse investment products such as wrap fee programs open- and closed-end funds and managed account services to high-net-worth individuals. It also manages institutional accounts for corporations and other investors. The firm was formed in 1995 through a reverse merger with Duff & Phelps.

Geographic Reach

Hartford Connecticut-based Virtus has offices in California Illinois Massachusetts and New York.

Operations

The asset manager operates through its growing group of boutique investment firms including: Zweig/Euclid Advisors Newfound Investments (established in 2012) and recently-acquired Rampart Investment Management among other affiliated firms. Virtus offers investors a menu of investment products and services through its affiliates.

Financial Performance

The investment firm's revenue topped $280 million in 2012 an increase of 37% versus 2011. Net income fell 78% in 2012 to $37.7 million. Virtus's revenue has more more than doubled since 2009 as the firm's assets under management has grown and management fees and fee rates increased. Also driving revenue is market appreciation and the acquisition of Rampart Investment Management in 2012. The decline in net income was due primarily to income tax expenses in 2012 compared with benefits in 2011.

Strategy

Virtus has grown in scope and assets through the addition of investment partners. To strengthen its presence in the US Virtus in 2013 partnered with Kleinwort Benson Investors a provider of specialized equity strategies. The alliance is focused on developing business interests in the US retail marketplace.

Mergers and Acquisitions

Virtus in October 2012 acquired the business and assets of Boston-based Rampart Investment Management Co. a registered investment adviser specializing in customized options strategies for institutional and high-net-worth individuals for $700000 in cash. The Rampart purchase added $1.3 billion in assets under management and added another investment partner to Virtus' group of boutique investment managers.

Company Ownership

Bank of Montreal subsidiary BMO Bankcorp owns about 22% of Virtus.

EXECUTIVES

Svp Human Resources And Corporate Services, Bonnie J Malley, age 53
EVP Product Management, Francis G. (Frank) Waltman, $275,000 total compensation
EVP General Counsel and Corporate Secretary, Mark S. Flynn, $300,000 total compensation
SVP and COO, George R. Aylward, $491,667 total compensation
EVP and CFO, Michael A. (Mike) Angerthal, $350,000 total compensation
SVP Fund Services, W. Patrick Bradley
EVP Head of Distribution, Barry M. Mandinach
President Chief Investment Officer, David Albrycht
Senior Vice President Human Re, Mardelle Pena
Senior Vice President Fund Services, Patrick Bradley
Vice President Total Compensation And Benefits, Mark Hollertz
Assistant Vice President Infrastructure Services, Bernard Hoffman
National Sales Manager, John McCormack
Vice President, Heidi Griswold
Assistant Vice President Corporate, Christopher Galletta
Assistant Vice President, Janalynne Gius
Assistant Vice President Information Technology Infrastructure, Don King
Vice President Project Management, Kate Surber
Assistant Vice President Fund Administration, Suneeta Krishnan
Assistant Vice President, Lorraine Votta
Vice President Head Of Digital Marketing E Business, Tom Odonnell
Assistant Vice President, Ann Flood
Vice President, Emma Simon
Senior Vice President Human Resources, Mardelle Peria
Chairman, Mark C. Treanor
Auditors: PricewaterhouseCoopersLLP

LOCATIONS

HQ: Virtus Investment Partners, Inc
100 Pearl St., Hartford, CT 06103
Phone: 800 248-7971
Web: www.virtus.com

PRODUCTS/OPERATIONS

2012 Sales

	$ in mil.	% of total
Investment management fees	187.9	67
Distribution & service fees	56.9	20
Administration & transfer agent fees	33.8	12
Other	1.5	1
Total	**280.1**	**100**

Selected Subsidiaries & Affiliates

Duff & Phelps Investment Management (Chicago)
Kayne Anderson Rudnick Investment Management (Los Angeles)
Newfleet Asset Management (Hartford Connecticut)
Rampart Investment Management Company LLC (Boston)
Virtus Investment Advisers Inc. (Massachusetts)
Zweig/Euclid Advisors LLC (New York)

COMPETITORS

Affiliated Managers Group	GAMCO Investors
BlackRock	Invesco
Citigroup Global Markets	Janus Capital
Cohen & Steers	Legg Mason
Conning	Neuberger Berman
Diamond Hill Investment	Putnam
Eaton Vance	T. Rowe Price
Epoch	TCW
FMR	The Hartford
Federated Investors	The Vanguard Group
Franklin Templeton	US Global Investors
	Waddell & Reed
	Westwood Holdings

HISTORICAL FINANCIALS
Company Type: Public

Income Statement
FYE: December 31

	REVENUE ($ mil.)	NET INCOME ($ mil.)	NET PROFIT MARGIN	EMPLOYEES
12/13	389.2	77.1	19.8%	376
12/12	280.0	37.7	13.5%	336
12/11	204.6	145.4	71.1%	299
12/10	144.5	9.6	6.7%	273
12/09	117.1	(6.4)	—	278
Annual Growth	35.0%	—	—	7.8%

2013 Year-End Financials

Debt ratio: —	No. of shares (mil.): 9
Return on equity: 20.9%	Dividends
Cash ($ mil.): 271	Yield: —
Current ratio: 5.55	Payout: —
Long-term debt ($ mil.): —	Market value ($ mil.): 1,822

	STOCK PRICE ($) FY Close	P/E High/Low		PER SHARE ($) Earnings	Dividends	Book Value
12/13	200.05	27	13	8.92	0.00	54.14
12/12	120.94	25	14	4.66	0.00	31.24
12/11	76.01	4	2	16.34	0.00	35.29
12/10	45.37	58	18	0.81	0.00	13.47
12/09	15.90	—	—	(1.76)	0.00	12.99
Annual Growth	88.3%	—	—	—	—	42.9%

Virtusa Corp

Virtusa believes that virtually any business can improve its technology. Founded in 1996 the company provides a variety of software development and information technology services including software engineering application development application outsourcing maintenance systems integration and legacy system conversion. Virtusa's customers come from industries such as financial services insurance telecommunications and media and healthcare. Its top two customers JPMorgan Chase and insurance giant AIG together account for about 30% of sales.

Geographic Reach

Virtusa generates 75% of sales in North America and 20% of sales from customers located in Europe.

It has offices in Austria Germany Singapore The Netherlands the UK and the US. Its IT staff is located in Hungary India and Sri Lanka.

Sales and Marketing

The company's sales strategy involves developing long-term relationships with IT and business executives not just landing a short-term contract with no opportunity for recurring revenue.

Financial Performance

Overall sales grew 20% in fiscal 2013 (year-end March) to $333 million. That year Virtusa counted 92 active clients up from 89 in 2011. The company has also been profitable for years; in 2012 profits increased 42% to a record $28 million.

Strategy

The company's strategy for growth includes focusing on services for healthcare and developing more business for its customer relationship management and business process management services. Performing more than 80% of billable hours

at offshore sites the company is making significant investments in its Indian and Sri Lankan facilities.

EXECUTIVES

Chairman and CEO, Kris A. Canekeratne, age 48, $421,475 total compensation

Executive Vice President Chief Strategy Officer, Thomas R. (Tom) Holler, age 51, $309,487 total compensation

Executive Vice President Chief Operating Officer, Roger K. (Keith) Modder, age 50, $240,845 total compensation

President Business Development and Client Services, Raj Rajgopal, age 54, $334,648 total compensation

Executive Vice President - Strategic Business Development, Jim Francis

Executive Vice President Chief Financial Officer, Ranjan Kalia, age 54, $316,154 total compensation

EVP Chief Delivery Officer and Head of India Operations, Samir Dhir

Vice President Of Technology, Mark Smith

Executive Vice President, Doug Mow

Svp-banking & Fin Serv, Vasan Srinivasan

Vice President Head Of Operations Global Revenue And Us Center Head, Lasantha Jayasinghe

Senior Vice President Sales Cct, Jim Matteson

Vice President Insurance, Zlatan Lipovaca

Vice President And Head Of Business Consulting Practice, Tim Wright

Assistant Vice-president, Jayendranath Krishnamoorthy

Vice President Client Services, Madhukar Sharma

Senior Vice President And Global Head, Paul Hari

Vice President, Paul Tutun

Vice President & Global Head Of Human, Sundararajan Narayanan

Senior Vice President Media And Entertainment, Harsha Kumar

Senior Vice President Of Solutions, Frank Palermo

Senior Vice President Banking And Financial Servic, Bob Graham

Vice President, Behzad Ilchi

Executive Vice President Client Services And Business Development, John Gillis

Vp Sales For Strategic Global Account, Drew Scarano

Vice President Delivery, Prakash Arunachalam

Vice President Client Partner, Raymond Carlson

Senior Vice President Delivery, Pragash Krishnamoorthy

Vice President Client Services, Michael Picard

Vice President Client Services, Sumita Ohri

Vice President Sales And Business Unit Head, Michael Fleishman

Vice President Human Resources, Sundarajan Narayanan

Chairman and CEO, Kris A. Canekeratne, age 48

Executive Vice President Chief Financial Officer, Ranjan Kalia, age 54

Board Member, William K O'Brien

Board Of Directors, Naveen Das

Auditors: KPMGLLP

LOCATIONS

HQ: Virtusa Corp
2000 West Park Drive, Westborough, MA 01581
Phone: 508 389-7300
Web: www.virtusa.com

2013 Sales

	% of total
North America	75
Europe	20
Other	5
Total	**100**

COMPETITORS

Accenture	HP Enterprise Services
Capgemini	IBM Global Services
Cognizant Tech Solutions	Infosys
Computer Sciences Corp.	Sapient
Deloitte Consulting	Tata Consultancy
HCL Technologies	Tech Mahindra
	Wipro

HISTORICAL FINANCIALS
Company Type: Public

Income Statement
FYE: March 31

	REVENUE ($ mil.)	NET INCOME ($ mil.)	NET PROFIT MARGIN	EMPLOYEES
03/14	396.9	34.3	8.7%	8,054
03/13	333.1	28.4	8.5%	6,911
03/12	277.7	20.0	7.2%	5,672
03/11	217.9	16.2	7.4%	3,056
03/10	164.3	12.1	7.4%	4,038
Annual Growth	24.7%	29.7%	—	18.8%

2014 Year-End Financials

Debt ratio: 0.0%	No. of shares (mil.): 28
Return on equity: 10.9%	Dividends
Cash ($ mil.): 82	Yield: —
Current ratio: 3.90	Payout: —
Long-term debt ($ mil.): —	Market value ($ mil.): 952

	STOCK PRICE ($) FY Close	P/E High/Low		PER SHARE ($) Earnings	Dividends	Book Value
03/14	33.51	29	17	1.27	0.00	13.17
03/13	23.76	21	10	1.11	0.00	10.02
03/12	17.27	26	15	0.79	0.00	8.80
03/11	18.73	27	12	0.66	0.00	8.52
03/10	10.31	20	12	0.50	0.00	7.76
Annual Growth	34.3%	—	—	26.2%	—	14.1%

Vitamin Shoppe Inc

Vitamin Shoppe helps vitamin-takers meet their recommended daily requirements. The fast-growing company sells vitamins supplements and minerals as well as herbal homeopathic and sports nutrition and wellness products at more than 600 company-operated The Vitamin Shoppe stores located in some 45 US states the District of Columbia Puerto Rico and Canada. It also sells directly via catalog and the websites VitaminShoppe.com and BodyTech.com. Stores offer about 17500 items including food and beverages and pet products under more than 400 national and private-label brands. Founded in 1977 Vitamin Shoppe entered the Canadian market in 2012.

Geographic Reach

The New Jersey-based company's largest markets are California New York and Florida home to about a third of its stores. Vitamin Shoppe opened its first two stores in Canada in late 2012 and has plans to expand internationally through franchise and wholesale opportunities.

Operations

The company operates retail stores under the Vitamin Shoppe and Super Supplements banners. The retail segment accounted for 89% of sales in

2012 with the rest coming from the Internet and catalogs.

Sales and Marketing

Vitamin Shoppe relies on location location location! as a prime marketing tool adhering to the belief that situating its stores on prime real estate draws customers. It advertises in magazines and relies on radio and television ads to promote certain new stores. Direct mail is another avenue for promotion. The company reported $14.7 million in advertising and promotion costs in 2012 up 16% from 2011.

Financial Performance

The Vitamin Shoppe is full of vim and vigor having more than doubled its net sales from 2005 to 2012 and posting positive same-store sales for 19 consecutive years. Its sales increased 11% in 2012 versus 2011 to $951 million. Net income rose 36% to nearly $61 million over the same period. Driving the double-digit sales gain was the addition of about 50 new stores an 8% increase in same-store sales and rising direct sales partially offset by a $3 million reduction in sales as a result of Super Storm Sandy in October 2012. Specialty supplements sports nutrition products and vitamins minerals and herbs were all strong performers. Sports nutrition and weight management categories are among the chain's fastest-growing categories.

Strategy

Vitamin Shoppe is extending its retail reach through organic growth and acquisitions. After adding 50 stores in 2013 the chain looks to open another 60 in 2014. Its long-term goal is to operate more than 900 US stores. The retailer prefers to locate shops in freestanding buildings or corner locations in strip malls rather than traditional shopping malls. To supply its growing store base the company opened a distribution center in Ashland Virginia in 2013. The new 311740-square-foot facility began receiving inbound inventory in June 2013 and began outbound shipments to store in September.

Besides adding stores Vitamin Shoppe is experimenting with new store formats and products. Eco Shoppe —launched in Austin Texas in 2009 — as its name suggests sells green-living products including apparel home garden and gift items; office and pet supplies; baby and kids products; and yoga gear. Previously the company launched an e-commerce site called BodyTech.com devoted to products for bodybuilders and other athletes.

Mergers and Acquisitions

In February 2013 the company acquired the assets of Super Supplements Inc. (SSI) a specialty retailer of vitamins minerals and supplements for about $50 million. SSI operates about 30 stores in Washington Oregon and Idaho and extends Vitamin Shoppe's retail presence in the Pacific Northwest.

Ownership

Wells Fargo & Co. owns 12% of Vitamin Shoppe's shares. Eagle Asset Management owns about 10%.

IPO

Vitamin Shoppe raised about $155 million in its October 2009 initial public offering. Concurrent with its IPO the company changed its name from VS Holdings to the more familiar Vitamin Shoppe moniker. Proceeds from the offering went to the selling shareholders and not to the company.

EXECUTIVES

CEO and Director, Anthony N. (Tony) Truesdale, age 52, $677,110 total compensation

EVP and CFO, Brenda M. Galgano, age 45, $340,962 total compensation

VP and General Manager Direct, Louis H. Weiss, age 45, $382,500 total compensation

CEO, Colin F. Watts, age 49

VP Merchandising, Doug Jones

SVP Supply Chain Management, Richard Tannenbaum

SVP Retail, Douglas Henson

VP and CIO, John Kirk

Regional Vice President, James Chavarria

Vice President Marketing, Susan Zeitz

Senior Vice President Retail Operations, Doug Henson

CEO and Director, Anthony N. (Tony) Truesdale, age 52

Chairman, Richard L. Markee, age 61

Auditors: Deloitte&ToucheLLP

LOCATIONS

HQ: Vitamin Shoppe Inc
  2101 91st Street, North Bergen, NJ 07047
Phone: 201 868-5959
Web: www.vitaminshoppe.com

2012 Locations

	No.
California	71
New York	64
Florida	63
Texas	45
Illinois	33
New Jersey	27
Virginia	22
Ohio	19
Maryland	18
Pennsylvania	18
North Carolina	17
Georgia	16
Massachusetts	15
Michigan	12
Arizona	10
Washington	10
Connecticut	9
Indiana	9
Tennessee	9
Colorado	8
South Carolina	8
Minnesota	7
Hawaii	6
Oregon	6
Wisconsin	6
Kentucky	5
Missouri	5
Alabama	4
Louisiana	4
New Hampshire	4
Delaware	3
Iowa	3
Kansas	3
Nevada	3
New Mexico	3
Nebraska	2
Puerto Rico	2
Utah	2
District of Columbia	1
Idaho	1
Maine	1
Oklahoma	1
Rhode Island	1
Vermont	1
Canada	2
Total	**579**

PRODUCTS/OPERATIONS

2012 Sales

	$ mil.	% of total
Stores	849.8	89
Direct (catalog & Internet)	101.1	11
Total	**950.9**	**100**

2012 Sales

	$ mil.	% of total
Specialty supplements & sports nutrition	500.7	53
Vitamins minerals & herbs	366.8	39
Delivery revenue	2.2	—
Other	81.2	8
Total	**950.9**	**100**

Selected Products

Herbal products
Homeopathic products
Personal care products
  Foot care
  Hair care
  Mouth care
  Pet care
  Skin care
  Women's products
Supplements
Vitamins

COMPETITORS

CVS	Nature's Sunshine
Costco Wholesale	PureTek
Forever Living	Rite Aid
GNC	Safeway
Gaiam	Target Corporation
Herbalife Ltd.	Vitacost
Kmart	Vitamin World
Kroger	Wal-Mart
MotherNature.com	Walgreen
NBTY	Whole Foods

HISTORICAL FINANCIALS

Company Type: Public

Income Statement

FYE: December 28

	REVENUE ($ mil.)	NET INCOME ($ mil.)	NET PROFIT MARGIN	EMPLOYEES
12/13	1,087.4	66.5	6.1%	4,842
12/12	950.9	60.8	6.4%	4,247
12/11	856.5	44.8	5.2%	3,907
12/10	751.4	29.2	3.9%	3,581
12/09	674.5	12.6	1.9%	3,358
Annual Growth	12.7%	51.4%	—	9.6%

2013 Year-End Financials

Debt ratio: —
Return on equity: 13.6%
Cash ($ mil.): 74
Current ratio: 2.68
Long-term debt ($ mil.): —

No. of shares (mil.): 30
Dividends
  Yield: —
  Payout: —
Market value ($ mil.): 1,570

	STOCK PRICE ($) FY Close	P/E High/Low		PER SHARE ($) Earnings	Dividends	Book Value
12/13	51.44	29	18	2.18	0.00	17.31
12/12	55.98	30	19	2.02	0.00	14.83
12/11	39.88	31	20	1.52	0.00	12.18
12/10	33.74	32	18	1.03	0.00	10.40
12/09	22.63	73	57	0.28	0.00	8.76
Annual Growth	22.8%	—	—	67.0%	—	18.6%

W & T Offshore Inc

Offshore exploration suits independent oil and natural gas acquisition exploration and production company W&T Offshore to a T. Focusing on exploiting assets in the Gulf of Mexico in 2013 the company reported proved reserves of 705.9 billion cu. ft. of natural gas equivalent. It holds 1.1 million gross acres in the Gulf of Mexico and has working interests in more than 65 fields. The company hopes to parlay its successful track record in the Gulf to generate capital for more expensive projects in deepwater (water depths in excess of 500 feet) and deep shelf (well depths in excess of 15000 feet) areas of the Gulf of Mexico. Hedging its bets it also holds onshore fields in a handful of Gulf Coast states.

Geographic Reach

The company's onshore activities are the Permian Basin of West Texas. Offshore holds interests in leases covering 1.1 million gross acres spanning across the outer continental shelf off the coasts of Louisiana Texas Mississippi and Alabama.

Operations

W&T Offshore holds working interests in 66 offshore fields in federal and state waters (62 producing and four fields capable of producing). Under lease it has 1.2 million gross acres including 600000 gross acres on the Gulf of Mexico Shelf 600000 gross acre in the deepwater and 50000 gross acres onshore in Texas.

The company has two fields of major significance (having proved reserves which comprise 15% or more of the company's total proved reserves): The Ship Shoal 349 field on the conventional shelf in the Gulf of Mexico and the Spraberry field in the Permian Basin in West Texas.

Sales and Marketing

W&T sells oil NGLs and natural gas to third-party purchasers. In 2013 Shell Trading (US) accounted for about 48% of its total revenues.

Financial Performance

W&T Offshore's revenues grew by 13% in 2013 primarily due to an increase oil and natural gas revenues. The oil revenue increase was attributable to a 16.3% boost in sales volumes partially offset by lower prices. The natural gas revenue rise was due a 20.7% increase in natural gas sales prices which more than offset a 1.1% decrease in sales volumes.In 2013 the company's net income decreased by 29% primarily due to increased operating expenses as a result of higher depreciation depletion and amortization costs.W&T Offshore's operating cash inflow increased to $561.3 million (from $385.14 million in 2012) thanks to higher revenues associated with increased production volumes for oil increased realized prices for natural gas receipt of income tax refunds lower income tax payments and collections on joint interest receivables. These factors were partially offset by higher lease operating and interest expenses.

Strategy

The company's business strategy includes entering into oil and natural gas derivative contracts which are designed to mitigate price risk for a majority of our oil NGL and natural gas production over a three- to five-year period. In 2013 W&T Offshore had in place oil and natural gas derivatives covering significant portions of its estimated 2014 through 2018 oil and natural gas production.

Mergers and Acquisitions

Growing its portfolio of quality deepwater assets in 2014 W&T Offshore acquired exploration and production properties in the deepwater of the Gulf of Mexico from Woodside Energy(USA) Inc. The transaction included a 20% non-operated working interest in the producing Neptune Field.

In 2013 the company acquired oil and gas leasehold interests in the Gulf of Mexico from Callon Petroleum Operating Company. Estimates of proved developed reserves associated with the deal were approximately 2.1 million barrels of oil equivalent (67% oil and 33% natural gas) .

Company Background

Growing its Gulf of Mexico asset base in 2012 W&T Offshore agreed to buy 78 federal offshore lease blocks (432700 gross acres) from Newfield Exploration for $228 million. In 2010 it acquired stakes in three federal offshore lease blocks located in the Gulf from TOTAL for $150 million. It also acquired four blocks from Royal Dutch Shell for about $193 million.

The company is pursuing acquisitions and onshore opportunities in addition to exploration and development operations in the Gulf. Given the relatively short production life of its Gulf wells the company is constantly seeking new acreage in order to maintain its reserves and replenish its production.

Boosting its onshore holdings in 2011 W&T Offshore acquired 21900 gross leasehold acres in the West Texas Permian Basin for $366 million.

Chairman and CEO Tracy Krohn controls the company with a 53% voting block.

EXECUTIVES

SVP CFO and Chief Accounting Officer, John D. (Danny) Gibbons, age 60, $400,400 total compensation
Chairman and CEO, Tracy W. Krohn, age 60, $1,000,000 total compensation
VP Drilling and HR&E, Joseph P. Slattery, age 60, $260,000 total compensation
President, Jamie L. Vazquez, age 54, $530,400 total compensation
SVP and CTO, Stephen L. Schroeder, age 52, $340,000 total compensation
VP and General Manager Offshore, Clifford J. Williams, age 58
VP Marketing and Midstream, W. Allen Tate
VP Information Technology, Gregory E. Percival
VP and General Manager Onshore, Paul Baker
Vice President Land & Business Development, Steven M. Freeman
SVP and COO, Thomas P. Murphy
Vice President Marketing Midstream, Allen Tate
Vice President Production, Antoine Gautreaux
Vice President Shelf Operations, William Voss
Vice President Marketing And Midstream, Randy Still
Vice President Information Technology, Christopher Barron
Vice President General Counsel Secretary, Thomas F Getten, age 61
Chairman and CEO, Tracy W. Krohn, age 60
Auditors: Ernst&YoungLLP

LOCATIONS

HQ: W & T Offshore Inc
Nine Greenway Plaza, Suite 300, Houston, TX 77046-0908
Phone: 713 626-8525   **Fax:** 713 626-8527
Web: www.wtoffshore.com

PRODUCTS/OPERATIONS

2013 Sales

	$ mil.	% of total
Oil	718.9	73
Natutal Gas	189.3	19
NGLs	73.4	7
Others	2.5	1
Total	**984.1**	**100**

COMPETITORS

Abraxas Petroleum	Newfield Exploration
BP	Noble Energy
Cheniere Energy	Stone Energy

Forest Oil	Swift Energy
McMoRan Exploration	

HISTORICAL FINANCIALS
Company Type: Public

Income Statement
FYE: December 31

	REVENUE ($ mil.)	NET INCOME ($ mil.)	NET PROFIT MARGIN	EMPLOYEES
12/13	984.0	51.3	5.2%	333
12/12	874.4	71.9	8.2%	337
12/11	971.0	172.8	17.8%	310
12/10	705.7	117.8	16.7%	305
12/09	611.0	(187.9)	—	286
Annual Growth	**12.7%**	**—**	**—**	**3.9%**

2013 Year-End Financials

Debt ratio: 48.0%	No. of shares (mil.): 75
Return on equity: 9.4%	Dividends
Cash ($ mil.): 15	Yield: 4.8%
Current ratio: 0.59	Payout: 74.2%
Long-term debt ($ mil.): 1,205	Market value ($ mil.): 1,209

	STOCK PRICE ($) FY Close	P/E High/Low		PER SHARE ($) Earnings	Dividends	Book Value
12/13	16.00	29	16	0.68	0.78	7.15
12/12	16.03	28	14	0.95	1.11	7.19
12/11	21.21	13	6	2.29	0.79	7.32
12/10	17.87	12	5	1.58	0.80	5.66
12/09	11.70	—	—	(2.51)	0.12	4.80
Annual Growth	**8.1%**	**—**	**—**	**—**	**59.7%**	**10.5%**

W.P. Carey Inc

Need help managing your property portfolio? Keep calm and Carey on. W. P. Carey invests in and manages commercial real estate including office distribution retail and industrial facilities. The company owns more than 1000 properties mainly in the US and Europe and manages properties for several non-traded real estate investment trusts (REITs). Its management portfolio totals some $15 billion. W. P. Carey typically acquires properties and then leases them back to the sellers/occupants on a long-term basis. It also provides build-to-suit financing for investors worldwide. W. P. Carey is converting to a REIT a corporate structure that comes with tax benefits and more flexibilty in investing in real estate.

Geographic Reach

New York-based W. P. Carey owns some 1020 properties in 21 countries. The firm has offices in Dallas London Amsterdam Hong Kong and Shanghai. International investments account for about 31% of the REIT's annual revenue.

Financial Performance

Carey's revenue increased 31% in 2013 versus 2012 to $489.9 million. Revenue growth was spurred by additions to the firm's real estate portfolio made in 2012 including 19 self-storage properties. Net income rose 59% over the same period to $98.9 million due primarily to higher revenue and income from discontinued operations.

Strategy

Since 1979 the REIT has sponsored a series of 18 income-generating investment programs that invest primarily in commercial properties net leased to single tenants under the Corporate Property Associates or CPA brand name. In 2013 the firm managed four global active funds: CPA 16 CPA 17 and CPA 18. W.P. Carey looks to diversify its managed funds and make investments in properties that provide consistent long-term sources of income. Property diversity helps shield W.P. from being reliant on any single industry. A few of its recent investments include a hypermarket in Germany operated by Metro AG a newly-constructed office in Wales the new Siemens AS headquarters in Oslo Norway and a 302-room Hampton Inn & Suites/Homewood Suites by Hilton hotel in Denver's central business district.

In addition to making property investments the firm is focused on diversifying its asset management capabilities. W.P. Carey has launched a lodging-focused fund (Carey Watermark Investors). The new investment program is dedicated to investing in the lodging sector and made its first investments in 2011.

In late 2014 the firm made its first investment in Australia via a 20-year net-lease transaction with Inghams Enterprises Pty. Ltd. The $138 million deal included industrial and agricultural properties.

Ownership

The Vanguard Group is Carey's largest shareholder with 12% of the REIT's shares.

EXECUTIVES

President CEO and Director, Trevor P. Bond, age 52, $333,846 total compensation
CFO, Catherine Rice
Second Vice President, Elizabeth Raun
Vice President, Chad F Edmonson
Vice President, Brooks Gordon
Vice President Sales, Rebecca Reaves
First Vice President Finance, Singh Gagan
Senior Vice President, Donna Araki
Operations Risk Manager Second Vice President, Gseg Zemanek Bayse
Regionaf First Vice President, Craig Arsenault
Senior Vice President Finance, Sunny Holcomb
Second Vice President, Nicolas Pond
Vice President Asset Management, Darren Postel
Second Vice President, Wendy Chang
Senior Vice President, Craig Vachris
Senior Vice President, W Bigler
Vice President, Matthew Fisk
Vice President, Pam Gonzalez
Vice President, Yana Semiglazova
Vice President Assistant Controller, Brian Williams
Vice President, Michael Mayer
Second Vice President, Thomas Strand
Second Vice President, Andrs Dallal
Counsel Vice President, Christie Susi
Operations Risk Manager Second Vice President, Gsec Zemanek Bayse
Regional Vice President, Katie McGinty
Accounts Payable Supervisor Assistant Treasurer, Leela Pathak
Auditors: PricewaterhouseCoopersLLP

LOCATIONS

HQ: W.P. Carey Inc
50 Rockefeller Plaza, New York, NY 10020
Phone: 212 492-1100
Web: www.wpcarey.com

PRODUCTS/OPERATIONS

2013 Sales

	$ mil.	% of total
Lease revenue	299.6	61
Reimbursed costs from affiliates	73.6	15
Structuring revenue	46.6	10
Asset management revenue	42.7	9
Other real estate income	16.3	3
Dealer manager fees	10.9	2
Others	0.2	-
Total	**489.9**	**100**

COMPETITORS

Brandywine Realty
CNL Financial
Crescent Real Estate
Equity Office
First Industrial Realty
Inland Group
Jones Lang LaSalle
Lexington Realty Trust
Vornado Realty

HISTORICAL FINANCIALS

Company Type: Public

Income Statement

FYE: December 31

	REVENUE ($ mil.)	NET INCOME ($ mil.)	NET PROFIT MARGIN	EMPLOYEES
12/13	489.8	98.8	20.2%	251
12/12	374.0	62.1	16.6%	216
12/11	336.4	139.0	41.3%	212
12/10	273.9	73.9	27.0%	170
12/09	235.8	69.0	29.3%	156
Annual Growth	**20.0%**	**9.4%**	**—**	**12.6%**

2013 Year-End Financials

Debt ratio: 44.1%
Return on equity: 5.0%
Cash ($ mil.): 117
Current ratio: 0.55
Long-term debt ($ mil.): 2,067
No. of shares (mil.): 68
Dividends
  Yield: 5.7%
  Payout: 280.0%
Market value ($ mil.): 4,188

	STOCK PRICE ($) FY Close	P/E High/Low		PER SHARE ($) Earnings	Dividends	Book Value
12/13	61.35	55	36	1.41	3.50	27.90
12/12	52.15	42	32	1.28	0.66	29.60
12/11	40.94	13	9	3.42	2.19	17.18
12/10	31.29	17	13	1.86	2.03	15.84
12/09	27.68	17	10	1.74	2.00	15.96
Annual Growth	**22.0%**	**—**	**—**	**(5.1%)**	**15.0%**	**15.0%**

Wabash National Corp.

The teaser trailer for trailer industry giant Great Dane is Wabash National. Wabash is one of North America's top manufacturers of dry freight and refrigerated vans flatbed and drop deck trailers and intermodal equipment. The trailers are marketed under such brands as DuraPlate ArcticLite and RoadRailer via a network of factory-direct sales representatives independent dealers and factory-owned retail outlets. Customers have included Averitt Express FedEx and Swift. The company operates through subsidiaries Transcraft Corporation (flatbed and drop deck trailers) and Wabash National Trailer Centers (retail distributor of trailers and aftermarket parts). Wabash makes most of its sales in the US.

Geographic Reach

Wabash has facilities located in Mexico the UK and the US.

Operations

The company serves customers across three strategic segments: Commercial Trailer Products (60% of total sales) Diversified Products (30%) and Retail (10%).

Sales and Marketing

The company markets and distributes its products through factory direct accounts its company-owned distribution network and independent dealerships. For its van business the company utilizes more than 20 independent dealers spanning roughly 60 locations throughout North America to market and distribute its trailers. The company distributes its flatbed and dropdeck trailers through a network of some 75 independent dealers throughout 120 locations across North America. Customers include Averitt Express Celadon Group Cowan Systems and Crete Carrier Corporation.

Financial Performance

Wabash is enjoying unprecedented growth over the last few years. Revenues jumped 12% from $1.46 billion in 2012 to peak at $1.64 million a historical milestone for the company. Profits however were down 56% from $106 million in 2012 to $47 million in 2013 primarily due to a loss on debt payments.

The growth for 2013 was fueled by increased sales from its Diversified Products segment due to acquisitions which contributed $128 million more in sales. The Retail segment's sales grew 15% due to the addition of six tank trailer parts and service locations as a result of an acquisition. Wabash also experienced higher trailer sales during 2013.

Along with its revenue stream Wabash has seen strong growth from its operating cash flow year-over-year. For 2013 it surged by $53 million due to cash generated from deferred income taxes and accounts payable and accrued liabilities.

Strategy

Wabash has traditionally sold to the largest operators of trailer fleets. Although it preserves its core customer base the company is striving to diversify its offerings and win business from the next tier of trucking companies —carriers with fleets of between 250 and 7500 trailers.

Mergers and Acquisitions

Wabash has experienced uncharted revenue growth through the use of acquisitions. In 2013 it purchased certain assets of the tank and trailer business of Beall Corporation a manufacturer of aluminum tank trailers and related equipment based in Portland Oregon. The deal fortified its Diversified Products segment and expanded its tank trailer market geographically by adding manufacturing operations in the Western half of the US. In 2012 Wabash previously enhanced its Diversified Products segment through the purchase of Walker Group Holdings a manufacturer of liquid-transportation systems and engineered products.

HISTORY

Donald Ehrlich was president of trailer maker Monon when its parent company was purchased in 1983. Disillusioned by the new management Ehrlich took several key employees with him to create Wabash in 1985. The business got a jumpstart when Ehrlich's Sears contacts ordered 10 trailers. In 1991 Wabash bought the rights to RoadRailer (bimodal railcar construction technology developed in 1956) and went public.

Business boomed in 1993 and Wabash expanded facilities the next year. In 1995 it started shipping RoadRailer units to Germany and received its first order from the French National Railways. Wabash upped its annual production capacity to 70000 units that year.

In 1996 Wabash's sales dipped as many of its customers delayed advanced ordering of its innovative composite-plate trailers. Aggravating this problem was a nationwide slump in the trailer industry: Two of the top 10 trailer makers filed for bankruptcy.

Wabash bounced back in 1997 and acquired bankrupt Fruehauf. It also bought 25% of ETZ-Europaische Trailerzug Beteiligungsgesellschaft (RoadRailer service) of Germany —its first non-US purchase. In 1998 Wabash set up a joint venture to market RoadRailer bimodal technology in South America.

Wabash merged Wabash National Finance Corp into Apex Trailer Leasing and Rentals in 2000 to consolidate its rental leasing and finance activities. The next year Wabash continued restructuring in the face of poor market conditions. The company ceased exporting manufactured products outside North America and announced plans to cut its workforce by 18%. It closed two assembly plants and a distribution center.

Early in 2002 Wabash announced that it was laying off 480 workers. The job cuts reduced the company's workforce to about two-thirds of the size it was at the beginning of 2001. Wabash announced the sale of its financial operations to Milestone Capital Corporation and Cypress Leasing Corporation in early 2004.

In 2006 Wabash acquired Transcraft a maker of flatbed and drop deck trailers that posted sales of about $120 million in 2006 from private equity firm Lincolnshire Management.

In mid-2008 Wabash bought certain operating assets of Benson International a manufacturer of aluminum flatbeds dump trailers and other truck bodies for approximately $5 million.

In 2009 facing liquidity problems in the credit crunch and global economic downturn Wabash sold preferred and common shares of its stock to Trailer Investment (a Lincolnshire Investment afilitate) for $35 million giving Trailer Investment ownership of about 44% of the company. With the capital infusion Wabash was able to amend its existing credit agreement.

EXECUTIVES

SVP and CTO, Rodney P. (Rod) Ehrlich, age 68, $253,984 total compensation
Vp Of Tax And Treasurer, Don Hurtt
President and CEO, Richard J. Giromini, age 61, $699,346 total compensation
SVP Sales and Marketing, Bruce N. Ewald, age 63, $253,984 total compensation
VP Manufacturing Lafayette Operations, Brent Yeagy, $285,173 total compensation
SVP; Group President Diversified Products Group, Mark J. Weber, age 42, $337,385 total compensation
SVP and CFO, Jeffery L. Taylor, $209,523 total compensation
Vice President-industrial Eng, Wilfred E Lewallen
Vice President Business Development, Robert L Nida
Vice President Of Finance, Mark R Holden
Vp Of Sales Of Commercial Trai, Sean Kenney
Senior Vice President Marketing, Larry Grosse
Vp Manufacturing For Commerci, Dustin Smith
Vice President Marketing, Daniel Jarboe
Vice President Marketing, Mike Coppinger
Senior Vice President Operations, Ronald Klimara
Senior Vice President, Todd Houten
Senior Vice President Of Manufacturing, Jerry Linzey
Vice President Regional Sales Beall, Don Olson
Vice President Sales And Marketing, Rob Edstrom

Vice President Security, Jason Roth
Vice President Quality Control, Pat Williams
Vice President Of International Sales, Billy Hedrick
Vice President Management Information, Pat Dwyer
Vice President Of Purchasing, Jim Masters
Vice President Manufacturing, Joe Zachman
Chairman, Martin C. Jischke, age 72
Sr V Pres Hr-asst Sec, William D Pitchford
Auditors: Ernst&YoungLLP

LOCATIONS

HQ: Wabash National Corp.
1000 Sagamore Parkway South, Lafayette, IN 47905
Phone: 765 771-5300
Web: www.wabashnational.com

PRODUCTS/OPERATIONS

2013 Sales

	$ mil.	% of total
Commercial trailer	1009.6	62
Diversified	446.0	27
Retail	180.1	11
Total	**1635.7**	**100**

2013 Sales by Category

	$ mil.	% of total
New trailers	1246.9	76
Parts service & other	180.4	11
Equipment & other	159.0	10
Used trailers	49.4	3
Total	**1635.7**	**100**

Selected Products

Aviation Refuellers and Hydrant Carts
Composite Doors
Composite Panels
Converter Dollies
Downflow Booths and Isolator Systems
Dry Freight Vans
Frac Tanks
Intermodal Equipment
Liquid Tank Trailers
Mobile Shelters
Platform Trailers
Portable Storage Containers
Railcar Components
Refrigerated Vans
Stainless Steel Vessels
Trailer Parts and Service
Trailer Side Skirts
Truck Mounted Tanks
Used Trailers
Wood Flooring

COMPETITORS

Featherlite	Trinity Industries
Fontaine Trailer	Utility Trailer
Great Dane	Wells Cargo
Hyundai Translead	

HISTORICAL FINANCIALS

Company Type: Public

Income Statement

FYE: December 31

	REVENUE ($ mil.)	NET INCOME ($ mil.)	NET PROFIT MARGIN	EMPLOYEES
12/13	1,635.6	46.5	2.8%	4,400
12/12	1,461.8	105.6	7.2%	4,400
12/11	1,187.2	15.0	1.3%	2,600
12/10	640.3	(141.7)	—	1,800
12/09	337.8	(101.7)	—	1,600
Annual Growth	**48.3%**	**—**	**—**	**28.8%**

2013 Year-End Financials

Debt ratio: 40.1%
Return on equity: 15.7%
Cash ($ mil.): 113
Current ratio: 2.12
Long-term debt ($ mil.): 365
No. of shares (mil.): 68
Dividends
  Yield: —
  Payout: —
Market value ($ mil.): 846

	STOCK PRICE ($) FY Close	P/E High/Low		PER SHARE ($) Earnings	Dividends	Book Value
12/13	12.35	19	13	0.67	0.00	4.70
12/12	8.97	7	4	1.53	0.00	3.93
12/11	7.84	57	20	0.22	0.00	2.15
12/10	11.85	—	—	(3.36)	0.00	1.90
12/09	1.89	—	—	(3.48)	0.00	2.50
Annual Growth	**59.9%**	—	—	—	—	**17.2%**

Waddell & Reed Financial, Inc.

Waddell & Reed Financial is one of the oldest mutual fund managers in the US. Subsidiaries administer and distribute about 80 mutual funds under the names Waddell & Reed Advisors Funds (the company's longest-running and largest fund complex) Ivy Funds (administered by Ivy Investment Management) and Waddell & Reed InvestEd Portfolios; they also manage accounts for institutional investors and private clients. The firm sells annuities and insurance through agreements with third-party providers. Waddell & Reed has 160-plus registered offices nationwide usually in small cities and rural areas. Founded in 1937 the firm has more than $110 million of assets under management.

Sales and Marketing

The company sells its products through a network of about 1750 advisors as well as through third-party channels such as brokerages retirement and pension plans and independent investment advisors.

Financial Performance

Waddell & Reed reported revenue of $1.4 billion in 2013 an increase of 17% versus 2012. The double-digit gain reflected an increase in the firm's average managed assets of 19% and a net flow increase of 264% year over year. Average assets under management were $109.2 billion in 2013 compared to $91.7 billion in 2012. Income from continuing operations increased 31% year over year while the firm's operating margin improved from 25.8% to 28.1%.

Strategy

Waddell & Reed's investment management strategy is centered around fundamental research collaboration among portfolio managers and asset growth and retention. The company has more than $110 million of assets under management most of it invested in domestic equities with an eye toward long-term performance. The firm is focused on expanding distribution through its wholesale channel. In 2013 it sold its Legend group of subsidiaries that served employees of school districts and not-for-profit organizations.

Company Background

Founded in 1937 Waddell & Reed introduced its first family of mutual funds The Waddell & Reed

Advisors Group in 1940. The firm went public in 1998.

EXECUTIVES

Senior Vice President General Counsel, Daniel C Schulte, age 50

Sr V Pres-gen Counsel-chief Le, Wendy J Hills

Chairman and CEO, Henry J. (Hank) Herrmann, age 72, $1,000,000 total compensation

EVP and Chief Marketing Officer, Thomas W. Butch, age 58, $600,000 total compensation

SVP and CRO, Daniel P. Connealy, age 68, $400,000 total compensation

President, Michael L. Avery, age 60, $680,000 total compensation

SEVP and National Sales Manager Waddell & Reed Inc., Steven E. Anderson

EVP Advisor Services Waddell & Reed Inc., Bradley D. (Brad) Hofmeister

SVP Brokerage, Karen F. Lare

SVP and Chief Investment Officer, Philip J. (Phil) Sanders, age 54, $525,000 total compensation

Senior Regional Vice President, Stan Renskers

President and Division Executive, Reed May

Chief Financial Officer Senior Vp, John Sundeen

Vice President, Ronald Buckley

Chief Operations Officer; Senior Vice President, Michael D Strohm, age 64

Vice President Marketing, Michael Gerken

Assistant Vice President Of Bu, Diana Henderson

Senior Vice President Finance Principal Accounting Officer And Treasurer, Brent Bloss

Vice President, Andrew Hearne

Vice President Of Financial Planning Development, Neal Anderson

Senior Vice President, Andrew Thinnes

Vice President Data And Architecture, Dave Wakefield

Vice President, Denise Deleo

Vice President Enterprise Program Management Organization, Todd Becker

Vice President, Amy Rush

Vice President, Grant Brickley

Vice President, Lisa Dale

Vice President, Matthew Garot

Assistant Vice President, Kurt Sundeen

Vice President, Frank Dearden

Assistant Vice President Internal Sales Desk Manager, Kirby Demoss

Senior Vice President And Chief Procurement Officer, Jon Baker

Senior Vice President Southern Divisio, Jeff Place

Vice President Enterprise Solutions Delivery, Randy Bentele

Vice President, Liz Wainwright

Vice President And Portfolio Manager, Mira Stevovich

Vice President, Jeffrey Gerstenblatt

Chairman and CEO, Henry J. (Hank) Herrmann, age 72

Auditors: KPMGLLP

LOCATIONS

HQ: Waddell & Reed Financial, Inc.
6300 Lamar Avenue, Overland Park, KS 66202
Phone: 913 236-2000   **Fax:** 913 236-2010
Web: www.waddell.com

PRODUCTS/OPERATIONS

2013 Sales

	$ mil.	% of total
Investment management fees	650.5	47
Underwriting & distribution fees	582.8	43
Shareholder service fees	137.1	10
Total	**1370.4**	**100**

COMPETITORS

AllianceBernstein	Invesco
American Century	Janus Capital
BlackRock	Legg Mason
Capital Group	MFS
Charles Schwab	Raymond James
Eaton Vance	Financial
Edward Jones	T. Rowe Price
FMR	The Vanguard Group
Franklin Templeton	

HISTORICAL FINANCIALS

Company Type: Public

Income Statement

FYE: December 31

	REVENUE ($ mil.)	NET INCOME ($ mil.)	NET PROFIT MARGIN	EMPLOYEES
12/13	1,370.3	253.0	18.5%	1,525
12/12	1,173.8	150.9	12.9%	1,656
12/11	1,195.1	175.4	14.7%	1,616
12/10	1,044.8	156.9	15.0%	1,485
12/09	839.0	105.5	12.6%	1,462
Annual Growth	**13.0%**	**24.4%**	**—**	**1.1%**

2013 Year-End Financials

Debt ratio: 14.2%	No. of shares (mil.): 85
Return on equity: 42.2%	Dividends
Cash ($ mil.): 609	Yield: 3.2%
Current ratio: 2.40	Payout: 79.7%
Long-term debt ($ mil.): 190	Market value ($ mil.): 5,551

	STOCK PRICE ($) FY Close	P/E High/Low		PER SHARE ($) Earnings	Dividends	Book Value
12/13	65.12	22	12	2.96	2.12	8.06
12/12	34.82	20	14	1.76	2.00	5.96
12/11	24.77	21	11	2.05	0.85	6.12
12/10	35.29	21	12	1.83	0.77	5.33
12/09	30.54	25	10	1.23	0.76	4.30
Annual Growth	**20.8%**	**—**	**—**	**24.6%**	**29.2%**	**17.0%**

Walker & Dunlop Inc

When it comes to its commercial real estate loans Walker & Dunlop has the government on its side. The company provides commercial real estate financial services —mainly multifamily loans for apartments health care properties and student housing —to real estate owners and developers across the US. It originates and sells its products (e.g. mortgages supplemental financing construction loans and mezzanine loans) primarily through government-sponsored enterprises (GSEs) like Fannie Mae and Freddie Mac as well as through HUD. To a lesser extent the company originates loans for insurance companies banks and institutional investors.

IPO

Walker & Dunlop went public via a 2010 IPO and raised some $100 million from the offering. It used the proceeds for general corporate purposes and for acquisitions of complementary businesses and products.

Geographic Reach

Walker & Dunlop operates through 20 offices across the country with locations residing in Atlanta; Chicago; Dallas; Ft. Lauderdale Florida; Irvine California; Nashville Tennessee; New Or-

leans; New York; Seattle; San Francisco; Needham Massachusetts; and Walnut Creek California.

Operations

The company generates its revenue from five main revenue streams: mortgage banking (73% of total revenue) servicing fees (20%) warehouse interest (2%) escrow earnings (1%) and other (4%).

Sales and Marketing

Walker & Dunlop originates and sells loans through the programs of the Federal National Mortgage Association the Federal Home Loan Mortgage Corporation the Government National Mortgage Association and the Federal Housing Administration a division of the US Department of Housing and Urban Development.

Financial Performance

As the mortgage banking industry recovers from the devastating effects of the recession Walker & Dunlop has enjoyed record-setting revenue growth over the last few years. Revenues skyrocketed by nearly 70% from $152 million in 2011 to $257 million in 2012. Its profits also reached historic heights in 2011 and 2012 hovering around the $30 to $35 million mark.

The company has achieved exceptional growth from all its channels of revenue. Mortgage banking revenue rose 82% from 2011 to 2012 while revenues stemming from service fees jumped by 55%. Walker & Dunlop attributes the growth largely to an increase in the volume of loans in addition to a previous acquisition it made.

Strategy

Walker & Dunlop has shaped its growth strategy (and timed its IPO) around certain opportunities in the commercial real estate market on which it believes it can capitalize. It intends to invest in origination activities and products to meet the expected increase in demand for real estate financing. In addition Walker & Dunlop's focus on growing its services to health care facilities is centered on an expected rise in the demand for health care real estate loans. It hopes to serve an expected increased demand for such facilities as baby boomers reach retirement age. The company is also motivated by the fact that many commercial health care loans are sought after through GSE and HUD programs.

In 2012 the company bought rival lender CW-Capital from CW Financial Services in a $220 million cash-and-stock transaction. The deal gave Walker & Dunlop a combined portfolio of $7.7 billion of commercial real estate loan originations and an aggregate servicing portfolio of more than $35 billion. Funded through IPO funds the transaction should allow the company to further grow its lending operations.

Ownership

Fortress Investment Group owns about 43% of Walker & Dunlop.

Company Background

Walker & Dunlop's relationship with government-related housing finance companies began in the late 1980s after it started originating underwriting and selling loans through Fannie Mae. In 2008 it began working with Freddie Mac and HUD after acquiring a loan servicing portfolio worth $5 billion from Column Guaranteed LLC. The acquisition served to widen Walker & Dunlop's revenue base and increase its sales volume.

EXECUTIVES

Chairman President and CEO, William M. (Willy) Walker, age 48, $500,000 total compensation

EVP and COO, Howard W. Smith, age 55, $400,000 total compensation

EVP and Chief Credit Officer, Richard C. Warner, age 59, $300,000 total compensation
EVP and CFO, Stephen P. Theobald
EVP and Chief Production Officer, Donald P. King
EVP Proprietary Capital, Jeffrey M. (Jeff) Goodman
Director Information Technology, Bill Granger
Senior Vice President, Jeff Burns
Svp-multifamily Finance Div, Douglas L Taylor
Svp-capital Markets Group, David J Redmond
V Pres Fha Finance, Keith L Melton
Svp-cpo Capital Markets Dept, William F Wein
Assistant Vice President, Michael Liefer
Assistant Vice President, John Hinder
Vice President, Jillian Bernstein
Vice President, Shannon Chase
Vice President, Will Baker
Assistant Vice President, Josh West
Assistant Vice President Capital Markets, Mauricio Rodriguez
Senior Vice President Loan Production, Philip Brooks
Vice President, Paul Wallace
Vice President, Bill Battaglia
Assistant Vice President Team Leader, Kim Perrell
Assistant General Counsel Vice President, Skai Bateman
Assistant Vice President Senior Management, Schuyler Haynes
Assistant Vice President, Rhoda Newman
Assistant Vice President Accounting, Johnny Harris
Vice President, Christopher Davis
Vice President, Tom Meunier
Vice President, Jay Hansen
Vice President Deputy Chief Underwriter, Ernest Benjamin
Assistant Vice President Healthcare Fin, Russell Dey
Vice President Multifamily Finance, Charlie Mentzer
Vice President, Jeff Lawrence
Senior Vice President Multifamily Fin, Todd Trehubenko
Senior Vice President, Trevor Fase
Vice President Servicing, Teri Wenger
Vice President, Craig Russell
Senior Vice President Asset Management, Michael Palmer
Svp Capital Markets Division, Albert G Rex
Executive Vice President Proprietary Capital, Jeff Goodman
Assistant Vice President, Sandy Barlow
Senior Vice President Chief Peoduction Officer Capital Markets, Cliff Carnes
Vice President And Deputy Chief Underwriter, Christopher Forte
Senior Vice President, David Burt
Senior Vice President, Verne Murray
Chairman President and CEO, William M. (Willy) Walker, age 48
Auditors: KPMGLLP

LOCATIONS

HQ: Walker & Dunlop Inc
7501 Wisconsin Avenue, Suite 1200E, Bethesda, MD 20814
Phone: 301 215-5500
Web: www.walkerdunlop.com

PRODUCTS/OPERATIONS

2012 Sales

	% mil.	% of total
Gains from mortgage banking activities	186.5	73
Servicing fees	52.2	20
Net warehouse interest income	4.7	2
Escrow earnings & other interest income	3.0	1
Other	10.4	4
Total	**256.8**	**100**

Selected Products and Services

Capital Markets and Investment Services
Construction loans
Equity investments
FHA Finance
First mortgage loans
Healthcare Finance
Mezzanine loans
Multifamily Finance
Second trust loans
Supplemental financings
Underwriting

COMPETITORS

American Capital	MetLife
Arbor Commercial	NewStar Financial
CapitalSource	Ocwen Financial
Centerline Holding Co.	Pzena Investment
Deutsche Bank	Management
Deutsche Bank	Redwood Trust
Berkshire Mortgage	Walter Investment
Encore Capital Group	Management
HFF	Wells Fargo
Kennedy-Wilson	

HISTORICAL FINANCIALS

Company Type: Public

Income Statement

FYE: December 31

	REVENUE ($ mil.)	NET INCOME ($ mil.)	NET PROFIT MARGIN	EMPLOYEES
12/13	319.0	41.5	13.0%	402
12/12	256.7	33.7	13.2%	420
12/11	152.3	34.8	22.9%	189
12/10	121.8	8.2	6.8%	157
12/09	88.7	24.7	27.9%	150
Annual Growth	**37.7%**	**13.8%**	—	**27.9%**

2013 Year-End Financials

Debt ratio: 48.4%	No. of shares (mil.): 34
Return on equity: 10.9%	Dividends
Cash ($ mil.): 170	Yield: —
Current ratio: 2.36	Payout: —
Long-term debt ($ mil.): 546	Market value ($ mil.): 550

	STOCK PRICE ($) FY Close	P/E High/Low		PER SHARE ($) Earnings	Dividends	Book Value
12/13	16.17	18	10	1.21	0.00	11.85
12/12	16.66	13	8	1.31	0.00	10.52
12/11	12.56	9	6	1.60	0.00	7.52
12/10	10.09	18	18	0.55	0.00	5.82
Annual Growth	**17.0%**	—	—	**30.1%**	—	**26.7%**

Walter Investment Management Corp

Walter Investment Management deals with the credit-challenged. The company owns and services residential mortgages particularly those of the subprime and nonconforming variety. Walter Investment Management services one million accounts with an unpaid principal balance of $86 billion. It operates through subsidiaries: Walter Mortgage Company; Hanover Capital; Marix Servicing; and Best Insurors. In 2011 Walter Investment Management increased its loan portfolio and transformed into a fee-based service provider when it paid $1 billion for GTCS Holdings the parent of Green Tree Servicing. Green Tree specializes in high-touch third-party credit servicing.

Financial Performance
The Green Tree acquisition helped boost Walter Investment Management's sales in 2011. However the company reported a $69 million net loss due to income tax costs (related to its conversion from a REIT) and expenses related to the Green Tree acquisition.

Strategy
An increase in delinquencies and foreclosures during the recession has forced traditional loan servicers and owners such as banks to look for third party assistance. Walter Investment hopes to tap into growing demand from big lenders looking to shift its debt servicing functions to outside firms such as Green Tree. Taking advantage of the opportunity to further expand its servicing portfolio Walter in February 2013 the firm closed on two separate purchases (from Bank of America and Residential Capital LLC) of Fannie Mae mortgage serving rights for loans totaling $132 billion in unpaid principal balance.

Mergers and Acquisitions
Walter Investment Management has agreed to acquire a $12 billion reverse mortgage servicing portfolio from Wells Fargo. The portfolio with $12.2 billion in unpaid balance houses more than 76000 loans. The sale is expected to close in the third quarter of 2013. The portfolio will transfer to Walter's wholly-owned subsidiary Reverse Mortgage Solutions and will double the size of its serviced book.

As a result of the GTCS Holdings acquisition Walter Investment Management no longer qualified as a real estate investment trust (REIT). The Green Tree acquisition represented a dramatic increase the size and scope of Walter Investment Management's business. The company's servicing portfolio grew by 50% and nearly 2000 employees were added. Green Tree also increased Walter Investment Management's geographic footprint by adding 27 offices in the US.

The company diversified further in late 2012 with the purchase of Reverse Mortgage Solutions (RMS) for some $120 million. RMS provides servicing origination asset management and technology services to the fast-growing reverse mortgage industry.

Company Background
Walter Investment Management was created in 2009 when Hanover Capital Mortgage merged with the home financing business of Walter Industries (now Walter Energy). Walter Energy was spun off after the closure of troubled homebuilder Jim Walter Homes.

EXECUTIVES

Chairman and CEO, Mark J. O ‚ÄBrien, age 71, $515,000 total compensation
Chief Operating Officer and CEO Green Tree Servicing, Keith A. Anderson, age 52, $400,000 total compensation
Executive Vice President and Chief Financial Officer, Charles E. Cauthen, age 56, $412,000 total compensation
Chief Investment Officer, Denmar J. Dixon, age 51, $409,940 total compensation
EVP and CFO, Gary Tillett
President Jan, Robert C. Turnham
Executive Vice President Green Tree Inv Management, Jeffrey Hilligoss
Vice President Business Intelligence, Joseph Kelly

Assistant Vice President Accounting Controls, Ramy Wahba
Senior Vice President And Sales Manager, Anne Akers
Chairman and CEO, Mark J. O ,ÅBrien, age 71
Coo And Director; Vice Chairman And Senior Managing Director Hanover Capital Partners 2, Irma N Tavares, age 60
Auditors: GrantThorntonLLP

LOCATIONS

HQ: Walter Investment Management Corp
3000 Bayport Drive, Suite 1100, Tampa, FL 33607
Phone: 813 421-7600
Web: www.walterinvestment.com

PRODUCTS/OPERATIONS

2011 Sales

$ in mil.		% of total
Servicing revenue & fees	186.2	46
Interest income on loans	164.8	41
Insurance revenue	41.6	10
Other	9.9	3
Total	**402.5**	**100**

COMPETITORS

Annaly Capital Management	Nationstar Mortgage
CIFC	Newcastle Investment
Capstead Mortgage	Ocwen Financial
DVL	Redwood Trust
FirstCity Financial	Resource Capital

HISTORICAL FINANCIALS

Company Type: Public

Income Statement
FYE: December 31

	ASSETS ($ mil.)	NET INCOME ($ mil.)	INCOME AS % OF ASSETS	EMPLOYEES
12/13	17,387.5	253.4	1.5%	6,400
12/12	10,978.1	(22.1)	—	3,900
12/11	4,093.5	(69.3)	—	2,600
12/10	1,895.4	37.0	2.0%	349
12/09	1,887.6	113.7	6.0%	219
Annual Growth	**74.2%**	**22.2%**	**—**	**132.5%**

2013 Year-End Financials

Return on assets: 1.7%
Return on equity: 24.5%
Long-term debt ($ mil.): —
No. of shares (mil.): 37
Sales ($ mil): 1,802
Dividends
Yield: —
Payout: —
Market value ($ mil.): 1,322

	STOCK PRICE ($) FY Close	P/E High/Low		PER SHARE ($) Earnings	Dividends	Book Value
12/13	35.36	7	5	6.63	0.00	31.22
12/12	43.02	—	—	(0.73)	0.00	24.39
12/11	20.51	—	—	(2.51)	0.22	19.04
12/10	17.94	14	10	1.38	2.00	21.54
12/09	14.33	3	0	5.25	1.50	22.16
Annual Growth	**25.3%**			**6.0%**	**—**	**9.0%**

Warren Resources Inc (MD)

Warren Resources believes that its heavy investment in oil and gas is warranted. The independent exploration and production company is focused on waterflood oil recovery programs in tar fields in California's Los Angeles Basin and the development of coalbed methane natural gas properties located in the Washakie Basin in the Greater Green River Basin in southwestern Wyoming. Warren Resources also owns oil and gas properties in New Mexico and Texas. In 2012 the company reported proved reserves of 51.2 billion cu. ft. of natural gas ans 24.9 million barrels of oil.

Operations

The company's drilling completion production re-entry and land operations are conducted by subsidiary Warren E&P which is the operator of 92% of the wells in which Warren Resources holds stakes. In 2012 Warren Resources 's average daily production was 12000 barrels of oil equivalent per day.

Sales and Marketing

Phillips 66 accounted for 55% of Warren Resources' revenues in 2012; Anadarko Petroleum (Anadarko Energy Services) 38%.

Financial Performance

Warren Resources' revenues rose by 18% in 2012 thanks to higher oil and gas production and stronger oil prices partially offset by lower natural gas prices.However net income decreased by 28% in 2012 primarily due to increased depreciation depletion and amortization expenses due to a reduction in the company's proved undeveloped gas reserves (lower gas prices rendered development of these properties uneconomic); increased general and administrative expenses resulting from severance packages for three former executives; and higher lease operating expenses.

Strategy

Warren Resources is pursuing a strategy that combines internal growth with joint venture projects (Anadarko Petroleum in the Rockies and Phillips 66 in California) and acquisitions. While Warren Resources is investing heavily developing its tar well projects in California it is also focusing on coalbed methane operations in the Rockies (where it has more than 94000 net acres of undeveloped acreage).

The company's 2013 capital expenditure budget of $73 million included funds to drill 25 new coalbed methane wells in the Spyglass Hill Unit in the Washakie Basin.

Mergers and Acquisitions

In 2013 the company bought a 62.5% working interest in the Leroy Pine Project area consisting of various oil and gas leases covering 1610 acres in the Santa Maria Valley oil field in Santa Barbara County California.

In 2012 it acquired 79% of Anadarko Petroleum's 36.5% working interest in the Spyglass Hill Unit; 26.5% of Anadarko's interest in the Catalina Unit area; and 100% of Anadarko's 50% interest in the gas gathering compression and pipeline midstream assets within the Atlantic Rim Project for $16 million. The midstream assets include gathering and compression equipment and a 59-mile long pipeline that transports gas from the gathering systems in Spyglass Hill to the Wyoming Interstate interstate gas pipeline.

Company Background

In 2010 the company announced drilling of the first two of eight wells in its Wilmington Townlot Unit (the first wells drilled there since 2008).

The downturn in the economy and the slump in oil prices prompted Warren Resources to write down a number of undeveloped properties in 2009. It also led to a major decline in revenues. In 2010 the company was looking to rising oil prices and a recovering economy to lift its revenues and cash flow.

EXECUTIVES

Senior Vice President General Counsel, David Fleming
SVP Land Management and Regulatory Affairs, Ellis G. Vickers, age 56, $226,808 total compensation
EVP and CFO, Timothy A. Larkin, age 51, $317,315 total compensation
VP and CFO, Stewart P. Skelly, age 40, $246,348 total compensation
VP and General Manager California Operations, Robert M. Dowell, $238,766 total compensation
Director, Lance Peterson
VP Business Development and Marcellus Operations, Zach Waite
VP Marcellus Land, Dan Collins
Interim Chairman, Dominick D ,ÅAlleva
Auditors: GrantThorntonLLP

LOCATIONS

HQ: Warren Resources Inc (MD)
1114 Avenue of the Americas, New York, NY 10036
Phone: 212 697-9660
Web: www.warrenresources.com

COMPETITORS

Abraxas Petroleum	Pioneer Natural
Aera Energy	Resources
Berry Petroleum	SM Energy
Gastar Exploration	

HISTORICAL FINANCIALS

Company Type: Public

Income Statement
FYE: December 31

	REVENUE ($ mil.)	NET INCOME ($ mil.)	NET PROFIT MARGIN	EMPLOYEES
12/13	128.8	30.3	23.6%	62
12/12	121.8	15.5	12.7%	67
12/11	103.3	21.6	20.9%	57
12/10	88.2	20.3	23.1%	57
12/09	63.4	(13.7)	—	56
Annual Growth	**19.4%**	**—**	**—**	**2.6%**

2013 Year-End Financials

Debt ratio: 24.3%
Return on equity: 14.5%
Cash ($ mil.): 11
Current ratio: 0.80
Long-term debt ($ mil.): 95
No. of shares (mil.): 72
Dividends
Yield: —
Payout: —
Market value ($ mil.): 229

	STOCK PRICE ($) FY Close	P/E High/Low		PER SHARE ($) Earnings	Dividends	Book Value
12/13	3.14	8	6	0.42	0.00	3.10
12/12	2.81	20	10	0.22	0.00	2.69
12/11	3.26	19	7	0.30	0.00	2.46
12/10	4.52	16	8	0.29	0.00	2.13
12/09	2.45	—	—	(0.23)	0.00	1.84
Annual Growth	**6.4%**			**—**	**—**	**14.0%**

Waste Connections, Inc.

Waste Connections does the dirty work so you don't have to. It provides solid waste collection transfer disposal and recycling services to more than 2 million commercial industrial and residential customers in 31 states. The integrated solid waste services company does business mainly in smaller markets. Waste Connections owns or operates almost 150 solid waste collection operations 66 transfer stations 55 landfills and 36 recycling facilities. It operates 20 liquid exploration and production (E&P) waste injection wells 17 E&P waste treatment facilities and 20 oil recovery facilities. In addition Waste Connections offers intermodal logistics services (7 facilities) in the Pacific Northwest.

Geographic Reach

Through three geographic segments (Eastern Western and Central) Waste Connections serves commercial industrial and residential solid waste customers in 31 states. Its exploration and production segment serves oil and gas customers from locations in Louisiana New Mexico North Dakota Oklahoma Texas and Wyoming. Waste Connections' intermodal operations take place in the Pacific Northwest.

Operations

It manages its operations on a decentralized basis. In addition to providing solid waste collection transfer disposal and recycling services the company is a leading provider of non-hazardous exploration and production waste treatment recovery and disposal services in oil and gas patches across the US through R360 Environmental Solutions which operates 26 facilities in six states (including the active production areas in the Permian Bakken and Eagle Ford Basins). Waste Connections also provides intermodal services for the rail transportation of cargo and solid waste containers through a network of seven intermodal facilities.

It provides intermodal services for the rail haul movement of cargo and solid waste containers in the Pacific Northwest through a network of intermodal facilities in Washington and Oregon. It provides collection services to residential commercial industrial and E&P customers under governmental contracts; exclusive franchise and municipal agreements; residential subscriptions and contracts; and commercial industrial and E&P service agreements. It deploys gas recovery systems at 30 of its landfills to collect methane which can then be used to generate electricity. It offers residential commercial industrial and municipal customers recycling services for a variety of recyclable materials including compost cardboard office paper plastic containers glass bottles and ferrous and aluminum metals. (The bulk of the recyclables it are paper products which are shipped primarily to customers in Asia.)

Financial Performance

Waste Connections reported a 16% growth in revenues in 2013 primarily due to the R360 Environmental Solutions and other acquisitions partially offset by divested operations. Volume increases in existing businesses were due to increases in landfill volumes landfill special waste projects and roll off collection resulting from increased construction and general economic activity across all of its markets. This was partially offset by the loss of commercial and residential collection revenues under the terminated Madera County contract and by declines in commercial collection (as the result of service level declines

with existing customers and a lower customer counts due to competition).

Other revenues decreased due to a lower cargo volumes caused by the loss of a large intermodal customer.

Waste Connections' net income increased by 23% in 2013 primarily thanks to higher revenues. This was partially offset by increased loss related to the disposal of three operating locations; prior office leases; increased depreciation from acquisitions; increased depletion expenses due to higher volumes at its existing landfill operations; and higher depreciation expenses associated with additions to its fleet and equipment purchased to support its existing operations.

Strategy

By focusing on acquiring mom-and-pop operations in secondary markets rather than large urban areas the company has been able to continue riding the crest of a consolidation trend in the waste management industry that began in the 1990s. While other large waste management companies –including major players Waste Management and Republic Services –have slowed or halted their buying sprees Waste Connections has continued to acquire although selectively.

It targets markets where it can provide waste collection under franchises or exclusive contracts or where it can hold a leading market position and provide integrated collection and disposal services. More than half of its revenues come from market areas where it has franchise or exclusive arrangements. The company also intends to further expand its intermodal business through cross-selling efforts with its solid waste services operations. As a part of its growth strategy the company devotes significant resources to securing additional franchise agreements and municipal contracts through competitive bidding and by acquiring other companies. Its sales and marketing personnel also expand its presence into areas adjacent to or contiguous with its existing markets and market additional services to existing customers. To generate internal revenue growth its district management and sales and marketing personnel focus on increasing market penetration in the current and adjacent markets soliciting new customers in markets where such customers have the option to choose a particular waste collection service and marketing upgraded or additional services (such as compaction or automated collection) to existing customers. The company is also continuing to acquire municipal solid waste (MSW) and E&P waste facilities and companies in new markets and in existing or adjacent markets that are then combined with its existing operations. During 2013 the company completed eight acquisitions for a total value of $64 million.

In a major strategic shift in 2012 the company also expanded its business offerings by moving to the arena of oil field clean up services.

Mergers and Acquisitions

In 2012 Waste Connections bought R360 Environmental Solutions which treats recovers and disposes of nonhazardous wastes in oilfields for $1.3 billion.

Expanding its geographic coverage for solid waste services in 2012 the company bought Alaska Pacific Environmental Services Anchorage and Alaska Green Waste Solutions. It also purchased SKB Environmental a provider of solid waste transfer and disposal services in Minnesota.

HISTORY

When United Waste Systems and USA Waste Services merged in 1997 Ron Mittelstaedt who

was managing United's western operations at the time saw an opening for mid-market waste haulers created by that consolidation and others. Mittelstaedt put together a group of investors that acquired the Washington operations of Browning-Ferris Industries (BFI) in 1997 and named the firm Waste Connections of Washington. Mittelstaedt Bradford Bishop and James Cutler then formed Waste Connections of Idaho and bought BFI operations in eastern Idaho.

In early 1998 Waste Connections of Washington acquired Waste Connections of Idaho. The company expanded into California that year when it purchased Madera Disposal Systems and added Hunter Enterprises a solid-waste hauler in eastern Idaho. Waste Connections also purchased firms in such midwestern and western states as Kansas Montana Nebraska Oklahoma Oregon South Dakota Texas and Wyoming.

Waste Connections went public in 1998 and used the money raised to buy more than 75 waste management facilities and service companies. In 1999 it added the Denver area to its territory after the US Justice Department required merger partners Allied Waste Industries and BFI to sell off operations there. Waste Connections also moved into New Mexico by purchasing landfill and collection company International Environmental Industries — one of more than 35 acquisitions in 1999.

Waste Connections in 2000 swapped some holdings with Allied Waste. Waste Connections sold its Idaho operations to Allied which in turn sold its operations in Iowa Montana and Wyoming to Waste Connections. Later that year Waste Connections purchased some of Allied's Kansas operations.

Consolidation in the waste industry hadn't stopped by 2002. That year Waste Connections made various tuck-in acquisitions in Washington Oregon Texas Tennessee Oklahoma and Colorado. One of its largest deals that year was the acquisition of San Luis Garbage Co. of San Luis Obispo California.

In 2003 Waste Connections bought two companies in California that together annually generated about $29 million. Other purchases that year included two collection and landfill operating companies in Mississippi and tuck-in acquisitions in Iowa Nebraska and South Dakota. The company acquired nine nonhazardous solid waste collection and disposal businesses in 2004.

Also in 2004 Waste Connections and Waste Industries USA traded some assets in the southern US. Waste Connections bought Waste Industries' hauling and landfill operations in the greater Memphis market and its hauling and transfer station operation (including an early stage municipal solid waste landfill development project) in Crossville Tennessee and the company sold to Waste Industries its hauling transfer station and construction and demolition landfill operations in Atlanta's north and northwestern suburbs.

Waste Connections stepped outside the solid waste business for the first time in 2004 when it bought Northwest Container Services a provider of intermodal logistics services in Washington and Oregon. Intermodal logistics involves arranging freight transportation by multiple methods such as truck and train. The synergy between solid waste and intermodal logistics might not be obvious but Waste Connections uses its presence in both markets to gain a share of the market for transporting solid waste by rail from the Seattle area to landfills in eastern Washington and eastern Oregon.

In 2007 Waste Connections acquired 15 nonhazardous solid waste collection transfer disposal and recycling businesses. The following year it made one large acquisition of Harold LeMay Enterprises in Washington for more than $200 million and 14 other smaller deals.

The company acquired a number of operations in 2009 from Republic Services (which that company was required to sell to meet the regulatory requirements of its acquisition of Allied Waste Industries) for $377 million. Waste Connections also made six smaller acquisitions that year and only a couple of small acquisitions in 2010.

EXECUTIVES

Vice President Business Development Of Waste Connections, Richard K Wojahn, age 57
SVP Sales and Marketing, David M. Hall, age 57
EVP and COO, Darrell W. Chambliss, age 50, $420,688 total compensation
President, Steven F. (Steve) Bouck, age 57, $545,250 total compensation
Chairman and CEO, Ronald J. (Ron) Mittelstaedt, age 51, $828,050 total compensation
SVP Engineering and Disposal, James M. (Jim) Little, age 53, $330,423 total compensation
VP Disposal Operations, Scott I. Schreiber, age 58
VP Information Technology, Eric O. Hansen, age 49
EVP and CFO, Worthing F. Jackman, age 50, $436,392 total compensation
Vice President Finance, Mary Whitney
Western Region Vice President Of Government Affairs, Eddie Westmoreland
Vice President Training And Leadership, Hank Coles
Division Vice President, Bill Bestreich
Chairman and CEO, Ronald J. (Ron) Mittelstaedt, age 51
Auditors: PricewaterhouseCoopersLLP

LOCATIONS

HQ: Waste Connections, Inc.
3 Waterway Square Place, Suite 110, The Woodlands, TX 77380
Phone: 832 442-2200
Web: www.wasteconnections.com

2013 Sales

	$ mil.	% of total
Western	805.8	42
Central	510.9	27
Eastern	371.8	19
E&P	240.3	12
Total	**1928.8**	**100**

PRODUCTS/OPERATIONS

2013 Sales

	$ mil.	% of total
Solid waste collection	1219.1	56
Solid waste disposal & Transfer	579.4	27
E&P waste treatment disposal & recovery	262.3	12
Solid wast recycling	71.8	3
Intermodal & other	46.0	2
Adjustments	(249.8)	-
Total	**1928.8**	**100**

COMPETITORS

Casella Waste Systems	Progressive Waste
Clean Harbors	Recology
Hub Group	Republic Services
Newpark Resources	Waste Industries USA
Pacer International	Waste Management

HISTORICAL FINANCIALS
Company Type: Public

Income Statement
FYE: December 31

	REVENUE ($ mil.)	NET INCOME ($ mil.)	NET PROFIT MARGIN	EMPLOYEES
12/14	2,079.1	232.5	11.2%	6,777
12/13	1,928.8	195.6	10.1%	6,633
12/12	1,661.6	159.0	9.6%	6,606
12/11	1,505.3	165.2	11.0%	5,909
12/10	1,319.7	135.1	10.2%	5,510
Annual Growth	**12.0%**	**14.5%**	**—**	**5.3%**

2014 Year-End Financials

Debt ratio: 37.7%
Return on equity: 10.8%
Cash ($ mil.): 14
Current ratio: 1.02
Long-term debt ($ mil.): 1,975
No. of shares (mil.): 123
Dividends
  Yield: 1.0%
  Payout: 26.8%
Market value ($ mil.): 5,454

	STOCK PRICE ($) FY Close	P/E High/Low	PER SHARE ($) Earnings	Dividends	Book Value
12/14	43.99	27 21	1.86	0.48	17.97
12/13	43.63	29 21	1.58	0.42	16.53
12/12	33.79	26 22	1.31	0.37	15.27
12/11	33.14	24 18	1.45	0.32	12.58
12/10	27.53	35 22	1.16	0.08	11.99
Annual Growth	**12.4%**	**— —**	**12.5%**	**58.6%**	**10.6%**

Wayside Technology Group Inc

Wayside Technology connects developers with users of IT products. A leading reseller for software developers the firm's TechXtend (formerly Programmer's Paradise) business markets software hardware and services to IT professionals government agencies and educational institutions in the US and Canada. Wayside's Lifeboat Distribution subsidiary provides software to resellers consultants and systems integrators worldwide. (Software accounts for about 95% of the company's sales.) Wayside Technology sells products through its catalogs and e-commerce sites and its suppliers include Quest Software Intel Flexera TechSmith and Vmware among others.

Geographic Reach

New Jersey-based Wayside Technology rings up 85% of its sales in the US. Canada is its second-largest market accounting for about 7% of sales. The company has a European sales office in Almere Netherlands.

Sales and Marketing

Software House International CDW Corp. and Insight Enterprises are Wayside's largest customers generating about 13% 12% and 11% of its 2012 sales respectively. The company promotes its products through its web sites. local and online seminars and print and electronic catalogs.

Financial Performance

Wayside's sales topped $297 million in 2012 a 19% increase versus the prior year and an all-time high for the company. The double-digit increase was driven by higher sales by both the Lifeboat Distribution and TechXtend segments up 13% and

39% respectively. Sales in both the US and Canada rose approximately 20%. 2012 marked the third consecutive year of rising sales for the software reseller following three straight years of decline in 2007 thru 2009 during the financial crisis.

Net income of $5.5 million was essentially flat in 2012 versus 2011.

Strategy

Wayside purchases about 90% of its products directly from manufacturers and publishers and the balance from multiple distributors. As a relatively small player in software sales the company relies on a diverse vendor base and for its suppliers to develop new products to drive demand among its customers. Wayside seeks to profit by covering market niches that its larger competitors often ignore.

EXECUTIVES

Vice President Marketing, Richard J Bevis, age 65
Vice President Of Sales, Shawn J Giordano, age 45
Chairman President and CEO, Simon F. Nynens, age 42, $250,000 total compensation
Executive Vice President, Bill Botti
Chairman President and CEO, Simon F. Nynens, age 42
Board Member, Mike Faith

LOCATIONS

HQ: Wayside Technology Group Inc
1157 Shrewsbury Avenue, Shrewsbury, NJ 07702
Phone: 732 389-8950
Web: www.waysidetechnology.com

2012 Sales

	$ mil.	% of total
US	252.0	85
Canada	22.2	7
Other	22.8	8
Total	**297.1**	**100**

PRODUCTS/OPERATIONS

2012 Sales

	$ mil.	% of total
Lifeboat	217.4	73
TechXtend	79.7	27
Total	**297.1**	**100**

COMPETITORS

Best Buy	PC Connection
CDW	PC Mall
Dell	Systemax
Insight Enterprises	Zones
Newegg	genica corporation

HISTORICAL FINANCIALS
Company Type: Public

Income Statement
FYE: December 31

	REVENUE ($ mil.)	NET INCOME ($ mil.)	NET PROFIT MARGIN	EMPLOYEES
12/13	300.3	6.3	2.1%	123
12/12	297.0	5.4	1.8%	120
12/11	250.1	5.5	2.2%	112
12/10	206.7	4.4	2.1%	103
12/09	146.3	2.8	2.0%	92
Annual Growth	**19.7%**	**22.2%**	**—**	**7.5%**

2013 Year-End Financials

Debt ratio: —
Return on equity: 19.1%
Cash ($ mil.): 19
Current ratio: 1.40
Long-term debt ($ mil.): —

No. of shares (mil.): 4
Dividends
  Yield: 4.8%
  Payout: 52.4%
Market value ($ mil.): 63

	STOCK PRICE ($) FY Close	P/E High/Low		PER SHARE ($) Earnings	Dividends	Book Value
12/13	13.53	10	8	1.41	0.65	7.46
12/12	11.09	14	9	1.19	0.64	6.78
12/11	12.20	12	8	1.20	0.64	6.18
12/10	11.26	12	8	0.98	0.61	5.59
12/09	7.95	14	10	0.65	0.60	5.20
Annual Growth	**14.2%**	—	—	**21.4%**	**2.0%**	**9.5%**

Wesco Aircraft Holdings Inc.

Planes may fly around the world but they can't leave the ground without Wesco Aircraft Holdings. One of the largest logistics and supply chain companies serving the aerospace industry it provides distribution vendor relationship management just-in-time (JIT) delivery quality assurance and kitting. Operating through Wesco Aircraft Hardware and other subsidiaries the company stocks about 525000 different pieces of hardware bearings tools electronic components and machined parts from more than 1200 suppliers. Boeing Airbus and Bombardier are among its largest customers.

Geographic Reach

Headquartered at Valencia California the company operates its facilities and offices across nearly 40 locations in 12 countries including Canada Mexico the UK the US and in other European and Asian countries. The US accounts for 70% of sales and the UK generates 15%.

Operations

Wesco divides its operations across three main product lines: hardware (83% of total sales) electronic components (12%) bearings (4%) and other machined parts (1%).

The company sources its inventory from over 1200 suppliers including Precision Castparts Alcoa Fastening Systems Amphenol Corporation Lisi Aerospace and Monogram Aerospace Fasteners. During 2013 it purchased nearly 40% of its inventory from Precision Castparts and Alcoa Fastening Systems.

Sales and Marketing

Operations and maintenance subcontractors such as Boeing Airbus Bombardier Cessna Gulfstream Embraer and BAE Systems account for 88% of the company's sales. Other customers include distributors airlines and the US government. Its 7400 customers can choose from just-in-time or long-term contracts or ad hoc sales.

Financial Performance

The company has posted unprecedented revenue growth over the years. Revenues jumped 16% from $776 million in 2012 to peak at a record-setting $902 million in 2013. Profits also spiked 14% from $92 million to $105 million another historic milestone.

The growth for 2013 was driven by a 22% jump in bearing sales a 18% increase in hardware and a 16% rise in electronic components. By region Wesco enjoyed an 85% increase from European sales and a more than 150% surge in sales from Canada. It attributes a lot of this growth to previous acquisitions the maturity of existing contracts and the addition of new international locations.

Mergers and Acquisitions

To create a new MRO (maintenance repair overhaul) operation expand its global footprint and provide more service for several strategic customers Wesco acquired Canada-based Interfast in 2012 for about CDN$134 million (about $130.9 million). Interfast distributes specialty fasteners fastening systems and production installation tooling for the aerospace electronics and general industrial sectors.

It is targeting international airlines and aircraft maintenance centers that are assuming an expanded role within the MRO market. Wesco also recently established a presence in international locations such as China India Mexico and Saudi Arabia to support new and existing customers in emerging markets.

EXECUTIVES

Interim CEO, Hal Weinstein
EVP and CIO, Dave Currence
EVP and Chief Procurement Officer, Robert Hanley
EVP and CFO, Greg Hann
EVP and Chief Legal Officer, John Holland
EVP and COO, Alex Murray
EVP and Chief Commercial Officer, Todd Renehan
EVP and Chief Human Resources Officer, Felicia Williams
Auditors: PricewaterhouseCoopersLLP

LOCATIONS

HQ: Wesco Aircraft Holdings Inc.
 24911 Avenue Stanford, Valencia, CA 91355
Phone: 661 775-7200
Web: www.wescoair.com

2013 Sales

	$ mil.	% of total
North America		
US	628.2	70
Canada	73.4	8
Europe		
UK	135.0	15
Other	52.9	6
Asia/Pacific the Middle East & other	12.1	1
Total	**901.6**	**100**

PRODUCTS/OPERATIONS

2013 Sales

	$ mil.	% of total
Hardware	744.7	83
Electronic components	104.4	11
Bearings	32.2	4
Machined parts & other	20.3	2
Total	**901.6**	**100**

COMPETITORS

AAR Corp.	First Aviation
Align Aerospace	GECAS Asset Management
Aviall Services	Services
B/E Aerospace	Kellstrom Industries

HISTORICAL FINANCIALS

Company Type: Public

Income Statement

FYE: September 30

	REVENUE ($ mil.)	NET INCOME ($ mil.)	NET PROFIT MARGIN	EMPLOYEES
09/14	1,355.8	102.1	7.5%	2,785
09/13	901.6	104.8	11.6%	1,354
09/12	776.2	92.1	11.9%	1,218
09/11	710.8	75.6	10.6%	1,014
09/10	656.0	73.6	11.2%	1,021
Annual Growth	**19.9%**	**8.5%**	—	**28.5%**

2014 Year-End Financials

Debt ratio: 45.8%
Return on equity: 10.9%
Cash ($ mil.): 104
Current ratio: 5.57
Long-term debt ($ mil.): 1,081

No. of shares (mil.): 96
Dividends
  Yield: —
  Payout: —
Market value ($ mil.): 1,677

	STOCK PRICE ($) FY Close	P/E High/Low		PER SHARE ($) Earnings	Dividends	Book Value
09/14	17.40	21	16	1.05	0.00	10.30
09/13	20.93	19	11	1.09	0.00	9.13
09/12	13.66	17	9	0.96	0.00	8.09
09/11	10.93	18	13	0.81	0.00	7.33
Annual Growth	**16.8%**	—	—	**9.0%**	—	**12.0%**

Western Gas Partners LP

Western Gas Partners' style is to gather and go. The company gathers and transports natural gas for its largest customer and parent Anadarko Petroleum and delivers natural gas and natural gas liquids (NGLs) to end-users. It handles gathering processing and throughput of about 2.2 billion cu. ft. of gas a day through eleven natural gas gathering systems seven treating facilities one natural gas liquids pipeline and one interstate pipeline (totaling more than 8820 miles across Wyoming Utah Texas Oklahoma and Kansas). Operating principally under long-term contracts the company gathers natural gas from individual wells after which it is compressed treated and delivered to customers.

Western Gas Partners was formed to handle certain petroleum processing storage and transport operations for Anadarko and to make complementary acquisitions. Its partnership business structure allows it seek to increase its cash distribution per unit over time.

In 2009 the company made its first acquisition when it bought $210 million of midstream assets located in the Powder River Basin from its parent. It later acquired assets in the Uintah Basin in northeastern Utah for $107 million. In 2010 it acquired properties in southwest Wyoming from Anadarko for $254 million. That year Western Gas Partners also bought natural gas assets in northeastern Colorado from its parent for about $498 million. Making a complementary acquisition in 2011 it acquired a natural gas processing plant and other assets in Colorado from Encana Oil and Gas (USA) for $303 million.

That year Western Gas Partners also acquired the Bison gas treating facility and related assets in the Powder River Basin from Anadarko Petroleum for $130 million.

System capacity expansion increased throughput and higher NGL prices lifted Western Gas Partners' revenues and net income in 2011.

In 2012 the company bought midstream assets from Anadarko Petroleum for $483 million (Mountain Gas Resources which owns the Red Desert Complex a 22% stake in gas processor Rendezvous Gas Services). It also went public that year

Anadarko Petroleum spun off Western Gas Partners in 2008. In 2012 held a 44% stake in the company.

EXECUTIVES

Vice President; General Counsel; Corporate Secretary Of Western Gas Holdings; Llc, Philip H Peacock
Vice President, Lora W Mays
Auditors: KPMGLLLP

LOCATIONS

HQ: Western Gas Partners LP
1201 Lake Robbins Drive, The Woodlands, TX 77380
Phone: 832 636-6000   Fax: 832 636-6001
Web: www.westerngas.com

PRODUCTS/OPERATIONS

2011 Sales

	$ mil.	% of total
Natural gas natural gas liquids and condensate sales	361.6	55
Gathering processing & transportation of natural gas & NGLs	287.0	43
Equity income & other	15.1	2
Total	**664.1**	**100**

COMPETITORS

DCP Midstream Partners	Questar
Enbridge Energy	Tallgrass Energy
Kinder Morgan Energy Partners	Partners
ONEOK Partners	XTO Energy

HISTORICAL FINANCIALS

Company Type: Public

Income Statement

FYE: December 31

	REVENUE ($ mil.)	NET INCOME ($ mil.)	NET PROFIT MARGIN	EMPLOYEES
12/13	1,053.5	275.1	26.1%	0
12/12	849.4	106.9	12.6%	0
12/11	664.0	142.9	21.5%	0
12/10	503.3	126.0	25.0%	0
12/09	245.1	77.3	31.6%	0
Annual Growth	**44.0%**	**37.3%**	**—**	**—**

2013 Year-End Financials

Debt ratio: 33.2%	No. of shares (mil.): 119
Return on equity: —	Dividends
Cash ($ mil.): 100	Yield: 3.5%
Current ratio: 1.02	Payout: 231.5%
Long-term debt ($ mil.): 1,418	Market value ($ mil.): 7,385

STOCK PRICE ($) FY Close	P/E High/Low		PER SHARE ($) Earnings	Dividends	Book Value
12/13	61.69	35 26	1.83	2.20	20.96
12/12	47.63	63 47	0.84	1.88	18.82
12/11	41.27	25 18	1.64	1.60	16.60
12/10	30.30	19 12	1.64	1.39	14.08
12/09	19.49	16 10	1.24	1.23	12.27
Annual Growth	**33.4%**	**— —**	**10.2%**	**15.6%**	**14.3%**

Westwood Holdings Group, Inc.

Westwood Ho! Westwood Holdings Group provides investment management services to institutions mutual funds and high-net-worth clients. The asset management company operates through its subsidiaries. Westwood Trust handles trust custody and account management for companies institutions and high-net-worth individuals. Westwood Management is the group's institutional investment management unit overseeing accounts for corporations municipalities and charitable organizations with at least $10 million in investable assets. The firm is also the administrator of the Westwood family of mutual funds WHG Funds. Westwood Holdings Group has about $18.9 billion in assets under management.

Operations

Westwood operates in two segments: advisory and trust. Advisory which contributes about 82% of total revenue provides investment advisory services to individuals foundations corporate and public retirement plans endowments and the company's other divisions.

The Trust segment includes trust and custodial services for institutions and high net worth individuals. It accounts for nearly 20% of the Westwood's revenue.

Geographic Reach

Westwood is headquartered in Dallas with US operations in Nebraska and an office in Canada.

Sales and Marketing

Investment advisory firms and other third-party financial institutions offer Westwood's products to their clients.

Financial Performance

In 2013 Westwood reported $92 million in revenue an 18% increase from $77 million the year before. The improvement was due to higher fees in both its operating segments primarily from market appreciation of assets. Net income increased 48% from $12 million to $18 million as revenue gained; cash flow held steady.

Strategy

Over the years Westwood has grown from a small company to a firm that offers diverse products to a variety of clients. The company continuously looks for opportunities to grow in the institutional private wealth and mutual fund markets. While Westwood has only opened one office outside the US it has increased its international focus by adding three new funds in 2013 targeting global and emerging markets.

Company Background

Westwood was founded in 1983 by chairman and CEO Susan Byrne. The company was spun off

from investment bank and brokerage SWS Group in 2002.

EXECUTIVES

Svp, Richard D (Dick) Frazar
Vice President Marketing And Client Service, Jacqueline L Finley
President and Chief Executive Officer, Brian O. Casey, age 50, $600,000 total compensation
President of Westwood Trust Dallas, Randall L. Root, age 53, $237,500 total compensation
EVP and Chief Investment Officer, Mark R. Freeman, age 47, $500,000 total compensation
CFO, Tiffany B. Kice
Vice President Research Analyst And Portfolio Manager, Cory Roberts
Vice President, Kellie R Stark
Vice President, John Vandermosten
Senior Vice President Jpmorgan Chase, Gregg Ballew
Assistant Vice President, Laura Willmann
Associate Vice President, Nicholas English
Sr V Pres-gen Counsel-corp Sec, Julie K Gerron
Vice President, Grant Taber
Vice President, Nancy Price
Vice President Of Finance, Cyndi Nistico
Senior Vice President Director, Joyce Schaer
Vice President Compliance, Cindy Gedney
Vp Marketing And Communications Manager, Jamie Christensen
Regional Vice President Mutual Funds, Blake Harbour
Senior Vice President Director Of Sub, Mark Dunbar
Vice President, Blair Albert
Vice President Research Analyst, Corey Henegar
Executive Vice President Inst Sales, Patricia Fraze
Associate Vice President Research Analyst, Michael Wall
Chairman, Susan M. Byrne, age 67
President and Chief Executive Officer, Brian O. Casey, age 50
Auditors: GrantThorntonLLP

LOCATIONS

HQ: Westwood Holdings Group, Inc.
200 Crescent Court, Suite 1200, Dallas, TX 75201
Phone: 214 756-6900
Web: www.westwoodgroup.com

2013 sales

	$ in mil	% of total
US	83.6	91
Canada	5.6	6
Europe	1.8	2
Australia	0.8	1
Total	**91.8**	**100**

PRODUCTS/OPERATIONS

2013 Sales

	$ in mil	% of total
Advisory fees	72.6	79
Trust fees	18.3	20
Other	0.9	1
Total	**91.8**	**100**

2013 Assets under Management

	% of total
Institutional	64
Private Wealth	21
Mutual funds	15
Total	**100**

COMPETITORS

American Century	NFJ Investment

Atalanta Sosnoff
Duncan-Hurst
Eaton Vance
FMR
Franklin Templeton
Janus Capital
Martin Capital

Neuberger Berman
Nuveen
Oak Associates
Putnam
T. Rowe Price
US Global Investors
W.P. Stewart

HISTORICAL FINANCIALS

Company Type: Public

Income Statement

FYE: December 31

	REVENUE ($ mil.)	NET INCOME ($ mil.)	NET PROFIT MARGIN	EMPLOYEES
12/13	91.8	17.8	19.5%	106
12/12	77.5	12.0	15.6%	96
12/11	68.9	14.6	21.3%	80
12/10	55.3	11.2	20.4%	77
12/09	42.5	7.9	18.6%	64
Annual Growth	21.2%	22.7%	—	13.4%

2013 Year-End Financials

Debt ratio: —
Return on equity: 21.6%
Cash ($ mil.): 10
Current ratio: 3.87
Long-term debt ($ mil.): —

No. of shares (mil.): 8
Dividends
Yield: 2.6%
Payout: 78.4%
Market value ($ mil.): 506

	STOCK PRICE ($) FY Close	P/E High/Low		PER SHARE ($) Earnings	Dividends	Book Value
12/13	61.91	25	16	2.34	1.64	10.84
12/12	40.90	24	20	1.65	1.51	9.53
12/11	36.55	19	15	2.04	1.42	9.18
12/10	39.96	25	16	1.58	1.65	7.94
12/09	36.34	35	20	1.18	1.23	6.60
Annual Growth	14.2%	—	—	18.7%	7.5%	13.2%

Wex Inc

WEX (formerly Wright Express) provides payment processing and information management services to commercial and government vehicle fleets through a network that tracks purchases made on fleet charge cards at more than 190000 fuel and vehicle maintenance facilities throughout the US Canada Australia New Zealand and Europe. The company provides clients with transaction data analysis tools and purchase control capabilities for every vehicle in their fleets. Data collected at the point of sale include expenditures lists of items purchased odometer readings and driver vehicle and vendor identification. WEX serves some 350000 fleets that collectively have a total of approximately 7.7 million vehicles.

Geographic Reach

Maine-based WEX rings up more than 85% of its sales in the US. Australia accounts for nearly 10% of annual sales. The company also has operations in Brazil and the UK. WEX has fuel and vehicle maintenance facilities throughout the North America Australia and New Zealand and Europe.

Operations

The company's subsidiaries include fleet card provider Fleet One (acquired in 2012) Utah-based WEX Bank and Pacific Pride Services a fuel distributor network with more than 340 independent fuel franchisees. WEX also owns a majority stake (acquired in 2012) in UNIK S.A. a provider of payroll cards and processing services in Brazil.

Financial Performance

WEX derives a significant portion of its revenue from charging a fee each time each time a client's driver uses his or her fleet card; the company processes more than 250 million such transactions annually.

WEX's sales have climbed steadily in recent years rising 125% since 2009. In 2013 the firm reported sales of $717.5 million an increase of 15% versus 2012. Increased revenue from its Fleet Payment business which accounts for about three-quarters of its total revenue higher fees and the acquisition of Fleet One in 2012 helped drive revenue gains. While consistently profitable WEX's net income growth has been erratic. Indeed net income rose 54% in 2013 versus 2012 after falling 27% in the previous annual comparison.

Strategy

WEX's closed-loop card network allow it access to both sides of every card transaction which provides it with usage data for its cardholder customer base as well as revenues from merchant fees charged. Its cards are accepted at more than 90% of service stations in the US and Australia and the company enjoys a leading market share of nearly 10% of all the fleet vehicles in the US. What's more there is room for growth for the firm as WEX estimates that a majority of fleets don't use fleet cards to manage fuel costs.

The company's growth strategy includes diversifying beyond its traditional domestic markets through acquisitions. Recent acquisitions outside the US have included companies in Brazil Australia and the UK.

Mergers and Acquisitions

In October 2013 UNIK S.A. acquired FastCred a provider of fleet card services to heavy truck operators in Brazil. About a year earlier WEX purchased Fleet One a provider of fleet cards to operators of heavy duty trucks and cars or light duty vehicles in the US and Canada. Previously WEX acquired CorporatePay a provider of prepaid virtual cards to the corporate travel industry in the UK for $27.5 million in May 2012 . Also in 2012 the company entered Brazil by acquiring a 51% stake in payroll card provider UNIK S.A. for nearly $22 million. At home it purchased fuel card provider Fleet One in an all-cash deal that closed in late 2012. Previous purchases include the Australian fuel and prepaid card operations of Retail Decisions for $318 million in 2010 making it a major player in the fleet card sector there.

EXECUTIVES

Senior Vice President Human Resources, Robert Cornett
Senior Vice President Client Service Operations, Jamie Morin, age 50
Senior Vice President Corporate Payment Solutions, Richard K Stecklair, age 66
Chairman President and CEO, Michael E. Dubyak, age 63, $589,458 total compensation
President The Americas, Melissa D. Smith, age 45, $426,777 total compensation
President International, David D. Maxsimic, age 54, $359,451 total compensation
SVP and CFO, Steven A. Elder, age 45, $272,308 total compensation
SVP and CIO, George W. Hogan, age 53, $287,432 total compensation
Senior Vice President Of Acquisition, Greg Strzegowski
Vice President Technical Operations, Sally Emery

Vice President Corporate Development, Rick Pomerleau
Vice President Product Management And Marketing, Kenneth W Janosick
Vice President Small Bus Fleet Sales, Fred Madeira
Area Sales Vice President Western Region, Tim Fortson
Chief Information Officer And Senior Vice President Shared Services, Stephen Crowley
Vice President Finance, Micky Thomas
Vice President Human Resources, Diane Rogers
Vp Sales, Jim Pratt
Vice President Applications Development, Jim Glatiotis
Vice President Sales And Operations, Brian Slowik
Vice President, Paul Dioli
Area Sales Vice President, John Thompson
Vice President Product Development, John Sterling
Vice President Human Resources Strat Comp And Bene, Kelley Shimansky
Vice President And Chief Risk Officer, Kevin Dansie
Vice President Strategic Acquisitions, Gary Robbins
Divisional Vice President Sales, Clinton Biever
Vice President Early Stage Product, Barry Chrol
Vice President Integration, Jim Oconnell
Vice President Service Delivery, Jill Northrop
Senior Vice President Corporate Paymen, Rich Stecklair
Vice President Investor Relations And Treasurer, Michael Thomas
Vice Chairman, Rowland T. (Row) Moriarty, age 67
Chairman President and CEO, Michael E. Dubyak, age 63
Auditors: Deloitte&ToucheLLP

LOCATIONS

HQ: Wex Inc
97 Darling Avenue, South Portland, ME 04106
Phone: 207 773-8171
Web: www.wrightexpress.com

2013 Sales

	$ mil.	% of total
United States	627.3	87
Australia	61.6	9
Other international	28.6	4
Total	**717.5**	**100**

PRODUCTS/OPERATIONS

2013 Sales

	$ mil.	% of total
Fleet payment solutions	527.4	74
Other payment solutions	190.1	26
Total	**717.5**	**100**

COMPETITORS

Comdata
FleetCor
Multi Service

Retail Decisions
U.S. Bancorp

HISTORICAL FINANCIALS

Company Type: Public

Income Statement

FYE: December 31

	REVENUE ($ mil.)	NET INCOME ($ mil.)	NET PROFIT MARGIN	EMPLOYEES
12/13	717.4	149.2	20.8%	1,431
12/12	623.1	96.9	15.6%	1,302
12/11	553.0	133.6	24.2%	899
12/10	390.4	87.6	22.4%	881
12/09	318.2	139.6	43.9%	725
Annual Growth	22.5%	1.7%	—	18.5%

2013 Year-End Financials

Debt ratio: 19.9%
Return on equity: 17.3%
Cash ($ mil.): 361
Current ratio: 1.21
Long-term debt ($ mil.): 685

No. of shares (mil.): 38
Dividends
 Yield: —
 Payout: —
Market value ($ mil.): 3,861

	STOCK PRICE ($) FY Close	P/E High/Low	PER SHARE ($) Earnings	Dividends	Book Value
12/13	99.03	26 18	3.82	0.00	23.16
12/12	75.37	30 21	2.48	0.00	21.02
12/11	54.28	17 11	3.43	0.00	18.30
12/10	46.00	20 12	2.25	0.00	14.54
12/09	31.86	9 3	3.55	0.00	11.55
Annual Growth	32.8%	— —	1.8%	—	19.0%

Williams Partners LP (New)

Access Midstream Partners (formerly Chesapeake Midstream Partners) is a midstream gathering company that owns operates develops and acquires natural gas natural gas liquids (NGLs) and oil gathering assets in the US. It gathers about 3.9 billion cu. ft. of natural gas per day via some 5800 miles of gathering and transmission lines. The company also has processing facilities that provide services to thousands of wells. Its assets are located in a dozen states with operations in the Barnett Eagle Ford Haynesville Marcellus Niobrara and Utica shales and several unconventional plays in the Mid-Continent region.

Geographic Reach

The company's pipelines are located in Arkansas Kansas Louisiana Maryland New York Ohio Oklahoma Pennsylvania Texas Virginia West Virginia and Wyoming.

Sales and Marketing

Through long-term fixed-fee contracts Access Midstream Partners provides its midstream services to Chesapeake Energy Total Mitsui Anadarko Petroleum Statoil and other major producers.

Financial Performance

The company's revenues grew by 8% in 2012 as a result of higher throughput in its Barnett Shale segment and an increase in rates in its Mid-Continent segment. This was partially offset by lower revenues from its Springridge gathering system in the Haynesville Shale due to lower drilling activities and natural declines in production. The Chesapeake Midstream Operating acquisition also contributed to revenue growth.

Access Midstream Partners' net income decreased by 8% in 2012 due to the higher interest operating expenses partially offset by increased other income from unconsolidated affiliates. Increased throughput in the Barnett Shale region also led to higher operating expenses that year.

Strategy

The company grows through acquisitions of its former parent Chesapeake Energy's midstream assets and by organically expanding its midstream infrastructure.

Mergers and Acquisitions

In 2012 Access Midstream Partners acquired Chesapeake Midstream Operating from a Chesapeake Energy unit for $2.2 billion. The deal gave the partnership certain midstream assets in the Eagle Ford Utica and Niobrara shale plays and expanded the company's assets and operations in the Haynesville Marcellus and Mid-Continent regions by adding 1675 miles of pipeline and 4.3 million acres of land. It also allowed the company to move into a new business —processing gas to produce NGLs.

As part of the acquisition the company also acquired a 49% of Utica East Ohio Midstream LLC with M3 Midstream L.L.C. and EV Energy Partners L.P. to develop infrastructure for the gathering processing and fractionation of natural gas and NGLs in the Utica Shale play in Eastern Ohio and 33% of Ranch Westex JV LLC (with Regency Energy Partners LP and Anadarko Pecos Midstream LLC) to build a processing plant in Ward County Texas.

Company Background

Access Midstream Partners was formed under the name Chesapeake Midstream Partners in 2009 as a joint venture between Chesapeake Energy and private equity firm Global Infrastructure Partners. Chesapeake Midstream Partners went public in 2010 and changed its name to Access Midstream Partners in mid-2012.

In 2014 The Williams Companies agreed to agreed to buy the 50% general partner interest and 55.1 million limited partner units in Access Midstream Partners held by Global Infrastructure Partners II for about $6 billion.

In 2011 the company acquired Appalachia Midstream Services from a Chesapeake Energy unit for $879 million. Through the deal it operates 100% of and owns 47% of 10 gas gathering systems (549 miles of gas gathering pipeline in the Marcellus Shale). The remaining 53% stake in these assets is owned by Statoil Anadarko and Mitsui.

EXECUTIVES

COO and Director, Robert S. (Bob) Purgason, age 58, $448,269 total compensation
CEO and Director, J. Mike Stice, age 55, $747,115 total compensation
CFO, David C. Shiels, age 49, $398,462 total compensation
SVP Eastern Operations, John D. Seldenrust, $371,077 total compensation
Vice President - Western Operations, Walter Bennett, $311,385 total compensation
CIO and Corporate Services, Deanna Farmer
Vice President Operations, Rob Harmon
Vice President, Jim Webb
Chairman, David A. Daberko, age 69
COO and Director, Robert S. (Bob) Purgason, age 58
CEO and Director, J. Mike Stice, age 55
Treasurer, Michael Smith
Auditors: PricewaterhouseCoopersLLP

LOCATIONS

HQ: Williams Partners LP (New)
 525 Central Park Drive, Oklahoma City, OK 73105
Phone: 877 413-1023
Web: www.accessmidstream.com

2012 Sales

	% of total
Barnett Shale	65
Mid-Continent	22
Haynesville Shale	11
Chesapeake Midstream Operating	2
Total	100

COMPETITORS

Atlas Pipeline Partners	Magellan Midstream
Crestwood Midstream Partners LP	MarkWest Energy Partners
DCP Midstream Partners	Martin Midstream Partners
EOG	Regency Energy
EnLink Midstream LLC	SandRidge Energy
Enable Oklahoma	Tristream Energy
Energy Transfer	XTO Energy
Enterprise Products	

HISTORICAL FINANCIALS

Company Type: Public

Income Statement

FYE: December 31

	REVENUE ($ mil.)	NET INCOME ($ mil.)	NET PROFIT MARGIN	EMPLOYEES
12/13	1,073.2	336.0	31.3%	1,411
12/12	608.4	178.4	29.3%	1,255
12/11	565.9	194.3	34.3%	445
12/10	459.1	195.2	42.5%	285
Annual Growth	32.7%	19.8%	—	70.4%

2013 Year-End Financials

Debt ratio: 41.0%
Return on equity: —
Cash ($ mil.): 17
Current ratio: 0.84
Long-term debt ($ mil.): 3,249

No. of shares (mil.): 218
Dividends
 Yield: 0.0%
 Payout: 203.6%
Market value ($ mil.): 12,345

	STOCK PRICE ($) FY Close	P/E High/Low	PER SHARE ($) Earnings	Dividends	Book Value
12/13	56.58	60 35	0.95	1.94	18.79
12/12	33.54	36 22	1.05	1.65	17.96
12/11	29.00	22 19	1.29	1.43	15.43
12/10	28.77	39 30	0.73	0.22	14.66
/0.00	—	—	(0.00)	0.00	(0.00)
Annual Growth	—		—	—	—

Winmark Corp

Winmark Corporation loves recycling but it's not collecting cans and paper. Winmark franchises retail chains that buy sell and consign used goods (and some new items) at more than 965 stores. The chains sell sporting goods (Play It Again Sports) children's items (Once Upon A Child) teen apparel (Plato's Closet) women's apparel and accessories (Style Encore) and musical instruments and electronics (Music Go Round). Most operations are in the US but it does have about 70 stores in Canada. In addition the company leases IT equipment to midsized and large businesses through its Winmark Capital unit and it offers financing services to small businesses through its Wirth Business Credit subsidiary.

Geographic Reach

Winmark's retail franchises number about 900 stores across the US and nearly 70 locations in Canada.

Operations

Winmark operates two primary businesses. The franchising of its value-oriented retail stores accounts for about three-quarters of its total sales while equipment leasing through Winmark Capital Corp. (WCC) makes up the rest. WCC targets businesses with annual sales between $30 million and several billion dollars. It provides high-tech and business equipment including computers telecommunications equipment point-of-sales systems and more. Also the firm operates a small-ticket (typically $5000 to $100000) financing business through subsidiary Wirth Business Credit.

Financial Performance

Winmark reported about $52 million in revenue in 2012 an increase of just 1% versus 2011. Net income fell 8% over the same period. The slight uptick in revenue was due to an increase in royalties franchise fees and merchandise sales offset by a drop off in leasing income. The expansion of its Plato's Closet and Once Upon a Child franchises and accompanying increase in merchandise sales boosted revenue in 2012. Franchise fees increased 19% as a result of the addition of 11 more franchises in 2012 compared with 2011. The company blamed the decline in profits on increased cost of merchandise sold provisions for credit losses among other rising costs.

Strategy

One of the keys to Winmark's revenue growth has been retail network expansion. In 2012 the company signed 65 retail franchise agreements for stores expected to open in 2013. Also in 2013 the company added a new women's apparel and accessories resale concept called Style Encore a reseller of women's apparel shoes and accessories.

The company markets franchises to individuals with sufficient net worth prior retail management and operations experience and intentions of being involved in running the business. To ensure success Winmark provides a mandatory training program for franchisees and field support to assist with operational issues. Franchisees also have the option to transfer their franchise agreements to new owners or close their stores altogether.

Ownership

Chairman and CEO John Morgan owns more than a third of Winmark's shares. Bares Capital Management holds about 17% of the stock while Ronald Olson the company's founder and former CEO holds about 12%.

HISTORY

Jeffrey Dahlberg (son of the founder of Dahlberg maker of Miracle Ear hearing aids) and Ron Olson started a consulting firm in 1986. Martha Morris their third client and the founder of Play It Again Sports showed them how profitable used goods could be. In 1989 the pair bought out Morris and Olson was named CEO; by 1992 they had built the concept into a chain of 281 stores. The company started franchising stores internationally in 1991.

The firm expanded by acquiring Once Upon a Child (1992); Hi Tech Consignments which became Music Go Round (1993); and Computer Renaissance (1993). Named Grow Biz International the company went public in 1993. The following year it acquired CDX Audio changing the name to

Disc Go Round. By the end of 1994 Grow Biz had 765 stores.

By capitalizing on consumers' desire for value and on the growing market trend for recycled goods the company built its sales from $2.3 million in 1991 to over $100 million in 1995 making it #1 on both the "FORTUNE" and "Inc." lists of fastest-growing US companies.

Grow Biz opened its 1000th store in 1996. The next year it bought 40 Video Game Exchange stores which became the nucleus of what was then its sixth franchise It's About Games.

In 1998 Grow Biz sold the Disc Go Round franchise and purchased Tool Traders (renaming it ReTool) and the franchise rights to Plato's Closet sellers of new and used clothing for teens. In late 1998 Dahlberg and Olson offered to take the company private by purchasing the 33% of its stock they didn't already own for about $24 million. They shelved their offer in 1999 after shareholder protests and soon thereafter Dahlberg took the CEO reigns from Olson. Also in 1999 the company closed It's About Games chain resulting in a loss for the year.

Dahlberg and Olson left the company in May 2000 retaining 50%. John Morgan who sold his successful equipment leasing firm to retire took over as chairman president and CEO and soon inducted a new board and shuffled management vowing to focus the company on stabilizing cash flow. In August 2000 the company sold its Computer Renaissance franchise to Hollis Technologies for $3 million.

In November 2001 the company changed its name to Winmark Corporation. It also ceased franchising its ReTool brand and subsequently terminated relationships with ReTool franchisees.

In late 2002 Winmark formed Winmark Business Solutions to provide more in-depth support to its franchisees. Services include detailed information services training and other products and services that are not typically part of a franchise agreement. The company also offers these services to other small businesses.

On December 2 2003 the company's stock moved from the Nasdaq small cap market to the Nasdaq national market.

Winmark launched its business equipment (computers POS systems telecom) leasing services in 2004 and business financing services in 2005.

The company's retail footprint has steadily grown over the years even amid the deep recession in the US. Its network included about 800 stores in 2005 and by the end of 2009 that figure grew to nearly 880.

EXECUTIVES

Vice President - Human Resources, Leah A Goff, age 53
President, Brett D. Heffes, age 47, $242,500 total compensation
Director of Play It Again Sports, Steven A. (Steve) Murphy, age 48, $242,500 total compensation
CFO and Treasurer, Anthony D. (Tony) Ishaug, age 42, $154,200 total compensation
VP Marketing, Merry Beth Hovey, age 50
President Winmark Capital Corporation, Steven C. Zola, age 53, $242,500 total compensation
CEO, Lawrence A. Barbetta
Vice President Of Finance, Charles Kanan
Vice President Of Quality Control, Joe Yashari
Senior Vice President Finance Chief, David Osdoba
Auditors: GrantThorntonLLP

LOCATIONS

HQ: Winmark Corp
605 Highway 169 North, Suite 400, Minneapolis, MN 55441
Phone: 763 520-8500
Web: www.winmarkcorporation.com

2010 Franchised Stores

	No.
Play It Again Sports	328
Plato's Closet	301
Once Upon A Child	241
Music Go Round	33
Total	**903**

PRODUCTS/OPERATIONS

2012 Sales

	$ mil.	% of total
Royalties	33.8	65
Leasing	13.2	25
Merchandise	2.7	5
Franchise fees	1.3	3
Other	0.9	2
Total	**51.9**	**100**

2012 Stores

	No.
Play It Again Sports	325
Plato's Closet	324
Once Upon A Child	247
Music Go Round	24
Total	**930**

Selected Franchise Brands

Music Go Round (used and new musical instruments speakers amplifiers music-related electronics and related accessories)
Once Upon a Child (used and new clothing toys furniture and accessories for infants and children up to 10 years of age)
Plato's Closet (used and new clothing and accessories for teenagers)
Play It Again Sports (used and new sporting goods equipment and accessories)
Style Encore (used women's apparel and accessories)

COMPETITORS

Abercrombie & Fitch	Hibbett Sports
Academy Sports	Kmart
Amazon.com	Salvation Army
Babies "R" Us	Sam Ash Music
Cash America	Sears
Costco Wholesale	Sports Authority
Dick's Sporting Goods	Target Corporation
Forever 21	The Gap
Goodwill Industries	Wal-Mart
Guitar Center	craigslist
Gymboree	eBay

HISTORICAL FINANCIALS

Company Type: Public

Income Statement

FYE: December 28

	REVENUE ($ mil.)	NET INCOME ($ mil.)	NET PROFIT MARGIN	EMPLOYEES
12/13	55.7	18.2	32.7%	109
12/12	51.9	12.9	24.9%	103
12/11	51.3	14.1	27.5%	103
12/10	41.2	10.3	25.1%	100
12/09	37.3	5.8	15.7%	106
Annual Growth	**10.6%**	**32.9%**	**—**	**0.7%**

2013 Year-End Financials

Debt ratio: —	No. of shares (mil.): 5
Return on equity: 65.2%	Dividends
Cash ($ mil.): 10	Yield: 0.0%
Current ratio: 2.92	Payout: 5.4%
Long-term debt ($ mil.): —	Market value ($ mil.): 479

	STOCK PRICE ($) FY Close	P/E High/Low		PER SHARE ($) Earnings	Dividends	Book Value
12/13	93.08	26	16	3.48	0.19	7.42
12/12	57.55	28	19	2.47	5.15	3.59
12/11	57.37	21	11	2.69	0.11	7.04
12/10	32.15	17	10	1.98	0.06	4.58
12/09	21.91	21	8	1.10	0.00	2.99
Annual Growth 43.6%		—	—	33.4%	—	25.5%

Winnebago Industries, Inc.

A pioneer in the world of recreational vehicles Winnebago Industries makes products intended to encourage exploration and outdoor escape. Almost all of the company's sales come from its motor homes and towables which are sold via independent dealers throughout the US and Canada under the Winnebago Itasca SunnyBrook and ERA brands. Winnebago Industries also sells RV parts and provides related services; in addition the company produces OEM parts such as extruded aluminum components for other RV manufacturers and for use in commercial vehicles. In mid-2012 Winnebago Industries received a $322 million bid to be bought by private equity firm North Street Capital but deemed the offer untenable.

Strategy

North Street placed its bid for Winnebago in May 2012 but Winnebago has stated further negotiations need to take place before any serious consideration for the proposal can be made.

HISTORY

During a mid-1950s economic downturn furniture store owner John Hanson convinced Forest City officials to welcome a local subsidiary of California trailer maker Modernistic Industries. The company's first trailer rolled off the line in 1958. Hanson later bought the plant and in 1960 named the business Winnebago Industries after Forest City's home county. Winnebago Industries went public in 1966. Sales took off when the company offered less-expensive RVs than its competitors.

The 1970s energy crisis and increased competition eroded the company's sales prompting it to make lower-cost more fuel-efficient motor homes. Hanson retired in 1972; he returned in 1979 and in 1986 diversified Winnebago Industries by buying Cycle Video (renamed Cycle-Sat; operations discontinued beginning in 1996) for distributing TV and radio commercials via satellite.

Winnebago Industries' sales suffered again during the early 1990s when recession hit and gas prices increased in response to the Gulf War. Sales rebounded in 1992 but remained stagnant for several years. Hanson died in 1996. That year and the next the company divested non-RV assets and sold its European operations.

During an industry-wide slump Winnebago Industries and other RV makers formed the Go RVing Coalition (1997) targeting baby boomers with a $15 million ad campaign. Lower gas prices and interest rates fed RV demand in 1998 and 1999. In 2000 the company spent $14.5 million on upgrading its equipment and expanding its manufacturing facilities.

In 2003 Winnebago ceased manufacturing its EuroVan RV. Also that year the company sold its dealer financing business to GE Commercial Distribution Finance. A new shipping facility located at its Charles City Iowa Class C motor home manufacturing plant was opened in 2004.

Winnebago weathered the economic crisis in 2008 and 2009 and managed to get on a positive trajectory in 2010 as demand for big-ticket items slowly returned.

EXECUTIVES

VP and CFO, Sarah N. Nielsen, age 41, $221,364 total compensation
Chairman President and CEO, Randy J. Potts, age 55
VP Manufacturing, Daryl W. Krieger, age 51
Vice President Product Development, William J Oleary
Chairman President and CEO, Randy J. Potts, age 55
Auditors: Deloitte&ToucheLLP

LOCATIONS

HQ: Winnebago Industries, Inc.
P.O. Box 152, Forest City, IA 50436
Phone: 641 585-3535   **Fax:** 641 585-6966
Web: www.winnebagoind.com

PRODUCTS/OPERATIONS

Selected Products
ERA
  ERA
Itasca
  Cambria
  Ellipse
  Impulse
  Impulse Silver
  Meridian
  Meridian V Class
  Navion
  Navion IQ
  Reyo
  Suncruiser
  Sunova
  Sunstar
Winnebago
  Access
  Access Premier
  Adventurer
  Aspect
  Journey
  Journey Express
  Sightseer
  Tour
  Via
  View
  View Profile
  Vista

COMPETITORS

Airstream	Patrick Industries
Elixir Industries	Prevost Car
Featherlite	Rexhall Industries
Forest River	Skyline
Gulf Stream Coach	Supreme Industries
Jayco Inc.	TRIGANO
Keystone RV	Thor Industries
Motor Coach Industries	Tiffin Motorhomes
Newmar Corporation	

HISTORICAL FINANCIALS

Company Type: Public

Income Statement

FYE: August 30

	REVENUE ($ mil.)	NET INCOME ($ mil.)	NET PROFIT MARGIN	EMPLOYEES
08/14	945.1	45.0	4.8%	2,850
08/13	803.1	31.9	4.0%	2,680
08/12	581.6	44.9	7.7%	2,380
08/11	496.4	11.8	2.4%	2,130
08/10	449.4	10.2	2.3%	1,950
Annual Growth 20.4%		44.8%	—	10.0%

2014 Year-End Financials

Debt ratio: —	No. of shares (mil.): 27
Return on equity: 24.8%	Dividends
Cash ($ mil.): 57	Yield: —
Current ratio: 2.72	Payout: —
Long-term debt ($ mil.): —	Market value ($ mil.): 669

	STOCK PRICE ($) FY Close	P/E High/Low		PER SHARE ($) Earnings	Dividends	Book Value
08/14	24.73	20	13	1.64	0.00	7.13
08/13	22.27	23	10	1.13	0.00	6.13
08/12	11.01	7	4	1.54	0.00	5.05
08/11	7.14	40	16	0.41	0.00	3.73
08/10	9.05	49	24	0.35	0.00	3.35
Annual Growth 28.6%		—	—	47.1%	—	20.8%

Winthrop Realty Trust

Winthrop Realty Trust thinks real estate loans can be just as profitable as the real thing. The externally managed real estate investment trust (REIT) invests in property real estate-related collateralized debt and other REITs. Its property portfolio consists of more than a dozen office buildings a handful of retail properties and seven apartment buildings across 15 states totaling 3.5 million square feet. Top commercial tenants include Spectra Energy's Houston headquarters grocer Kroger and e-tailer Football Fanatics' 500000-sq.-ft. distribution center. As a REIT the trust is exempt from paying federal income tax so long as it makes quarterly dividends to shareholders.

Operations

The trust's bread and butter come from rental payments on its real estate which account for 70% of revenues. Interest and dividends from its loans account for the other 30%.

Strategy

The trust's loan investment strategy focuses on acquiring loans at a discount or with the expectation of a borrower default or recapitalization that will lead to an equity ownership interest. For example it bought the first mortgage loan on an office building in downtown Philadelphia that was in maturity default. After restructuring the loan and paying $10000 for an indirect 49% interest Winthrop became the general partner of the property owner.

As for tangible property the trust periodically acquires new buildings to add to its portfolio. In 2013 it bought four apartment buildings in four different states for a combined $246 million. Three of the buildings are mixed use with retail space on the ground floor and luxury apartments on the upper floors. The year before it paid $21 million for a foreclosure apartment complex in suburban Memphis.

Also in 2013 the trust sold a medical office building in Arizona for a $10 million profit. The trust originally bought the building for $10.6 million in 2010 and sold it for $20.5 million.

EXECUTIVES

Chairman and CEO, Michael L. Ashner, age 62
President; Trustee, Carolyn Tiffany, age 48
CFO, John Garilli
Chairman and CEO, Michael L. Ashner, age 62
Vice Chairman, Peter Braverman, age 63
Auditors: PricewaterhouseCoopersLLP

LOCATIONS

HQ: Winthrop Realty Trust
7 Bulfinch Place, Suite 500, Boston, MA 02114
Phone: 617 570-4614
Web: www.winthropreit.com

PRODUCTS/OPERATIONS

2012 Sales

	$ mil.	% of total
Rents & reimbursements	51.4	71
Interest & dividends	21.1	29
Total	**72.5**	**100**

COMPETITORS

Boston Properties	Glimcher Realty
Brandywine Realty	Highwoods Properties
Cousins Properties	Liberty Property Trust
Douglas Emmett	Mack-Cali
Duke Realty	Pennsylvania Real
Equity Commonwealth	Estate
Equity Office	Piedmont Office Realty
Franklin Street	Trust
Properties	SL Green Realty

HISTORICAL FINANCIALS

Company Type: Public

Income Statement
FYE: December 31

	REVENUE ($ mil.)	NET INCOME ($ mil.)	NET PROFIT MARGIN	EMPLOYEES
12/13	79.5	28.7	36.2%	0
12/12	72.5	24.6	34.0%	0
12/11	70.0	10.9	15.6%	0
12/10	55.3	16.4	29.8%	0
12/09	47.9	(84.3)	—	0
Annual Growth	**13.5%**	**—**	**—**	**—**

2013 Year-End Financials

Debt ratio: 49.6%	No. of shares (mil.): 36
Return on equity: 6.1%	Dividends
Cash ($ mil.): 125	Yield: 5.8%
Current ratio: 5.07	Payout: 104.8%
Long-term debt ($ mil.): 562	Market value ($ mil.): 402

	STOCK PRICE ($) FY Close	P/E High/Low	PER SHARE ($) Earnings	Dividends	Book Value
12/13	11.05	27 21	0.51	0.65	13.21
12/12	11.05	27 22	0.46	0.65	13.77
12/11	10.17	41 26	0.32	0.65	11.74
12/10	12.79	20 15	0.72	0.65	10.94
12/09	10.86	— —	(5.19)	0.91	10.65
Annual Growth	**0.4%**	**— —**	**—**	**(8.1%)**	**5.5%**

Zix Corp

Zix wants to nix the idea of unsavory characters reading your e-mail. The company offers secure e-mail encryption data loss prevention and transmission services. Its technology enables users to transmit encrypted e-mail and documents to any address in the world; recipients who are not service subscribers can access the messages through the company's Web-based portal. Zix targets customers in the health care financial services insurance and government sectors and it has an e-mail encryption community with tens of millions of members growing by 100000 members per week. Trademarks and brand names for its products include ZixCorp. ZixGateway ZixDirectory ZixIT ZixPort and PocketScript.

Operations

ZixCorp. Email Encryption is a Software-as-a-Service (SaaS) offering that allows customers to pay an annual subscription fee to have access to ZixDirectory the company's e-mail encryption community. Within the community the company offers ZixGateway a gateway that decrypts messages. In early 2013 Zix launched ZixDLPTM (DLP) a data loss prevention product catering to enterprise customers. DLP is available as a bundle to ZixCorp. Email Encryption for new customers and is also available as a standalone offering.

Geographic Reach

Zix operates through leased properties in Dallas and Austin Texas; Dallas; Burlington Massachusetts; Ottawa and Ontario Canada; and the UK. Almost all of its total sales derive from US customers.

Sales and Marketing

Zix sells its Email Encryption SaaS through a direct sales for that zeroes in on larger business while a telesales force caters to small and midsized accounts. It also uses a network of 200 value-added resellers and other distribution partners including service clients needing encryption offerings. Google is its largest third party reseller and represented 6% of its first year orders in 2013.

As the company pursues multi-year subscription contracts a high percentage of customers subscribe to its Email Encryption SaaS for a three-year term versus a one-year term.

Financial Performance

Zix has enjoyed steady revenue growth over the last four years; however its profits have sharply decreased over the last three. Revenues were up by 11% from $43 million in 2012 to peak at $48 million in 2013. Profits dropped 51% from nearly $23 million in 2011 to $11 million in 2012 and in 2013 profits decreased 5% to $10.5 million.

Zix attributes the revenue growth to higher demand for its subscriptions coupled with a high rate of renewing existing customers. It experienced growth in 2013 across its three main verticals: health care finance and government. New orders from its value-added reseller OEM and third party distribution channels for 2013 was 59% of its total new orders compared to 63% in 2012.

Its erosion of profits from 2012 to 2013 was mainly due to a spike in research and development expenses in addition to higher selling general and administrative costs.

Strategy

Zix plans to focus on core vertical markets: health care finance and government. It is looking to add new customers through an enlarged distribution network value-added retailers and a existing base of customers who continue to renew their subscriptions.

The company is also looking to offer new tools and service upgrades to its existing customer base. Along these lines Zix launched ZixDLPTM (DLP) a data loss prevention product catering to enterprise customers in early 2013. DLP is available as a bundle to ZixCorp. Email Encryption for new customers and is also sold as a standalone offering.

In 2014 Zix broadened its customer reach when it launched Google Apps Message Encryption (GAME). GAME was designed at the request of Google for the Google Apps infrastructure and provides secure email to Google Apps users when communicating outside Google's cloud to all other email users.

HISTORY

Zix Corporation traces its circuitous history back to five scientists from Los Alamos National Laboratory who in 1983 took possession of the patents on a system used by the Department of Agriculture to track livestock. Working to develop commercial applications for the technology their enterprise called Amtech gained the attention of David Cook the co-founder of Blockbuster Entertainment as well as Ross Perot.

Work progressed slowly and Cook brought in Dallas attorney Russell Mortenson to lead the company. In 1988 Amtech struck a deal to develop a toll collection system for the Lincoln Tunnel in New York. Its system proved successful and was chosen for the Dallas North Tollway the next year. The company reported its first profit in 1992. The Union Internationale des Chemins de fer adopted Amtech's toll system technology in 1993 as the standard for European railroads.

Diminishing sales to the rail industry spurred the firm to expand its market base. Amtech acquired Swedish firm Cardkey Systems (electronic access systems) in 1995 and later became involved in radio-frequency (RF) security systems and wireless LAN equipment (WaveNet). Its acquisitions could not help stabilize Amtech's roller coaster financial position however and in 1997 the company agreed to shed its WaveNet unit. That year the company won a $39 million contract to create a statewide electronic road toll system for Florida. Cost overruns led to a loss on the project further straining an already divided board and in 1998 Cook returned as CEO.

With interest in the Internet heating up Amtech sold its Transportation Systems Group for $31 million and announced it would shift its business to digital content distribution. Changing its name to CustomTracks and selling Cardkey Systems to Johnson Controls for $41 million the company began developing a secure system for downloading encrypted digital music files called ZixMail. CustomTracks also developed a system for collecting money for the music called ZixCharge.

While the music industry failed to adopt CustomTracks's technology customers in need of secure e-mail applications such as law firms did. In 1999 the company changed its name to ZixIt to focus on encrypted messaging. The next year the company received some real tech cache when former Lotus CEO Jeff Papows joined as chairman.

Developing and marketing its new product proved costly and ZixIt ran deep into the red. Its business was further hurt in 2001 when a security breach at its Anacom credit card processing subsidiary allowed credit card accounts to be illegally accessed. (Anacom was subsequently shut down.) Later that year Cook and Papows stepped aside as former Entrust CEO John Ryan took over as chairman and CEO.

In 2002 the company changed its name to Zix Corporation.

Zix acquired electronic prescription company PocketScript for $1.5 million in July 2003. PocketScript allows for doctors to file prescriptions using a BlackBerry PDA or regular computer connected to the Internet and is affiliated with various pharmaceutical benefit management firms.

Also in 2003 Zix acquired Elron Software a maker of spam email and online filtering software for $7 million.

Early in 2005 Ryan resigned as CEO remaining chairman; president and COO Rick Spurr stepped in as CEO.

EXECUTIVES

Vice President Business Operations, William J Kadonsky

Vp Sales Amd Marketing, James J (Jim) Lesniak

Chairman CEO and COO, Richard D. (Rick) Spurr, age 60, $300,000 total compensation

VP Engineering, David J. Robertson, age 55, $215,000 total compensation

VP Business Development and Product Management, Nigel P. Johnson

VP Corporate Marketing, Geoffrey R. (Geoff) Bibby

CFO, Michael W. English, age 58, $162,691 total compensation

VP Corporate Sales Channels and Marketing, Steven D. Irons

Vice President Operations And Chief Engineer, John Kalan

Vice President Technology Planning, Donald Druckenbrodt

Vp Of Marketing, Geoff Bibby

Legal Secretary, Betty McKeown

Vice President Care Coordination, Gerri Randazzo

Chairman CEO and COO, Richard D. (Rick) Spurr, age 60

Auditors: WhitleyPenn

LOCATIONS

HQ: Zix Corp
2711 North Haskell Avenue, Suite 2200, LB 36, Dallas, TX 75204-2960
Phone: 214 370-2000   **Fax:** 214 370-2070
Web: www.zixcorp.com

PRODUCTS/OPERATIONS

Selected Products and Services

Receivers
  Secure Compose
  ZixDirect
  ZixMobility
  ZixPort
Senders
  Cloud Hosted Email
  Reporting
  Superior TLS
  Transparency
  ZixGateway
  ZixMail
Other Services
  ZixAuditor
  ZixConnect
  ZixEnable
  ZixGateway Inbound

COMPETITORS

Barracuda Networks	Sophos
Cisco Systems	Symantec
Citrix Systems	Trend Micro
EMC	VMware
McAfee	Voltage Security
Proofpoint	

HISTORICAL FINANCIALS

Company Type: Public

Income Statement

FYE: December 31

	REVENUE ($ mil.)	NET INCOME ($ mil.)	NET PROFIT MARGIN	EMPLOYEES
12/13	48.1	10.4	21.7%	162
12/12	43.3	11.0	25.4%	144
12/11	38.1	22.5	59.1%	127
12/10	33.0	41.2	124.6%	123
12/09	30.6	(4.4)	—	136
Annual Growth	**11.9%**	**—**	**—**	**4.5%**

2013 Year-End Financials

Debt ratio: —
Return on equity: 16.4%
Cash ($ mil.): 27
Current ratio: 1.56
Long-term debt ($ mil.): —

No. of shares (mil.): 60
Dividends
  Yield: —
  Payout: —
Market value ($ mil.): 276

	STOCK PRICE ($) FY Close	P/E High/Low	PER SHARE ($) Earnings	Dividends	Book Value
12/13	4.56	29 16	0.17	0.00	1.09
12/12	2.79	19 13	0.17	0.00	1.00
12/11	2.82	14 6	0.34	0.00	0.91
12/10	4.27	7 3	0.62	0.00	0.70
12/09	1.71	— —	(0.07)	0.00	(0.03)
Annual Growth	**27.8%**	**— —**	**—**	**—**	**—**

Zumiez Inc

Zumiez's young customers like to zoom. The fast-growing retailer outfits action sports enthusiasts offering apparel footwear accessories and sports equipment for 12- to 24-year-olds who enjoy board sports BMX biking and surfing. It stocks such brands as Billabong Burton Quiksilver Vans and Spy Optic as well as private-label goods. Zumiez operates about 500 mall-based stores across North America and in Europe as well as an online store. Aside from the usual action sports merchandise (hoodies and puffy skater shoes) stores also feature couches video games and sales clerks who really use the gear —all designed to encourage shoppers to chill. Zumiez was founded in 1978 by chairman Thomas Campion.

Geographic Reach

Zumiez operates about 475 stores in some 40 US states and another 20 stores in Canada (seven in Ontario three in British Columbia). California Texas and New York are the retailer's largest market accounting for about a third of its stores. In Europe a new market for the retailer the company operates stores under the name Blue Tomato.

Operations

In addition to its fast-growing retail store chain Zumiez sells merchandise online and provides content and community for its young customers. E-commerce sales accounted for more than 7% of the company's sales in fiscal 2012 (ends January).

Sales and Marketing

To increase brand awareness and strengthen its connection to its customers Zumiez participates in various music and local sporting events that embody the action sports lifestyle. The Zumiez Couch Tour is a series of entertainment events that includes skateboarding demonstrations from top professionals autograph sessions competitions and

live music. In fiscal 2012 (ends January) the Couch Tour completed a 12-city tour of the US. Zumiez also advertises in magazines popular with its target market and sponsors interactive contests and maintains a presence on various social network channels such as Facebook and Twitter.

Financial Performance

Zumiez's fiscal 2012 (ends January) sales increased 16% vs. the prior year while net income grew by 54% over the same period. The double-digit uptick in sales and profits was driven by the addition of more than 40 new stores including the retailer's first in Canada and a 9% rise in sales at stores open more than one year. Footwear men's apparel accessories and junior's apparel posted increases in same-store sales while hardgoods and boy's apparel declined.

Indeed thanks to its rapidly-expanding retail store network Zumiez's sales have quintupled over the past decade and the chain is consistently profitable.

Strategy

Growth is the mantra at Zumiez. The company has made great strides in extending its retail network adding about 250 stores since the end of fiscal 2005 (ends January). In fiscal 2012 the chain entered the Canadian market and has since made an acquisition in Europe. Going forward the chain plans to open about 50 new stores including 10 more in Canada in fiscal 2013 and grow its online sales. In the US the chain is adding stores in existing and new markets.

To that end in mid-2012 the company acquired Blue Tomato a multi-channel action sports retailer based in Austria for E59.5 million ($78 million). Blue Tomato operates five stores in Austria as well as an e-commerce site serving the broader European market.

Ownership

Founder Campion owns about a 16% stake in Zumiez while CEO Richard Brooks holds 12% of the shares. The investment firm T. Rowe Price Associates owns about 16% while Waddell & Reed Financial Services owns 8% of the company.

EXECUTIVES

CEO, Richard M. Brooks, $631,324 total compensation

President and General Merchandising Manager, Lynn K. Kilbourne, $489,113 total compensation

EVP Stores, Ford K. Wright, $278,172 total compensation

CFO, Christopher C. Work, $158,265 total compensation

EVP E-commerce and Omni-channel, Troy R. Brown

Vice President Purchasing, Jim Hume

Vice President Marketing, Mark Georges

Chairman, Thomas D. Campion

Auditors: MossAdamsLLP

LOCATIONS

HQ: Zumiez Inc
4001 204th Street SW, Lynnwood, WA 98036
Phone: 425 551-1500
Web: www.zumiez.com

2012 Stores

	No.
California	77
Texas	45
New York	30
Washington	24
Colorado	18
Florida	18
New Jersey	18
Pennsylvania	18

Illinois	16
Arizona	13
Wisconsin	13
Oregon	12
Utah	12
Minnesota	11
Maryland	9
Nevada	9
Connecticut	8
Indiana	8
Massachusetts	8
Virginia	7
Idaho	6
Michigan	6
Oklahoma	6
New Mexico	5
Montana	4
New Hampshire	4
North Carolina	4
Alaska	3
Delaware	3
Georgia	3
Kansas	3
Hawaii	2
Iowa	2
Maine	2
Missouri	2
South Dakota	2
Wyoming	2
Rhode Island	1
Canada	10
Total	**444**

PRODUCTS/OPERATIONS

2012 Sales

	% of total
Men's apparel	33
Footwear	24
Accessories	20
Hardgoods	11
Junior's apparel	10
Other	2
Total	**100**

COMPETITORS

Abercrombie & Fitch	Hot Topic
American Apparel	Old Navy
American Eagle	Pacific Sunwear
Outfitters	Sport Chalet
Aeropostale	Sports Authority
Big 5	The Buckle
Dick's Sporting Goods	Urban Outfitters
Forever 21	Wet Seal

HISTORICAL FINANCIALS

Company Type: Public

Income Statement

	REVENUE ($ mil.)	NET INCOME ($ mil.)	NET PROFIT MARGIN	EMPLOYEES
				FYE: February 1
02/14	724.3	45.9	6.3%	5,600
02/13*	669.3	42.1	6.3%	5,300
01/12	555.8	37.3	6.7%	4,680
01/11	478.8	24.2	5.1%	4,840
01/10	407.6	9.1	2.2%	4,330
Annual Growth	**15.5%**	**49.8%**	—	**6.6%**

*Fiscal year change

2014 Year-End Financials

Debt ratio: —
Return on equity: 14.4%
Cash ($ mil.): 19
Current ratio: 3.75
Long-term debt ($ mil.): —

No. of shares (mil.): 29
Dividends
  Yield: —
  Payout: —
Market value ($ mil.): 637

STOCK PRICE ($)		P/E		PER SHARE ($)		
	FY Close	High/Low		Earnings	Dividends	Book Value
02/14	21.52	22	13	1.52	0.00	11.33
02/13*	21.11	30	14	1.35	0.00	10.08
01/12	28.33	26	14	1.20	0.00	8.74
01/11	22.31	39	16	0.79	0.00	7.35
01/10	12.73	55	21	0.30	0.00	6.37
Annual Growth	**14.0%**	—	—	**50.0%**	—	**15.5%**

*Fiscal year change

Hoover's Handbook of

Emerging Companies

Master Index for all
2015 Hoover's Handbooks

Index by Headquarters

ARE

Abu Dhabi
Aabar Petroleum Investments Co
P.J.S.C. W2
National Bank of Abu Dhabi W242
First Gulf Bank W148

AUS

Melbourne
BHP Billiton Ltd. W68

Sydney
Woolworths Ltd. W389

Perth
Wesfarmers Ltd. W384

Melbourne
Rio Tinto Ltd W292

Sydney
Commonwealth Bank of Australia
W105

Melbourne
National Australia Bank Ltd. W241

Sydney
Westpac Banking Corp W387

Melbourne
Australia and New Zealand Banking
Group Ltd W32

Sydney
AMP Ltd. W24

Brisbane
Suncorp Group Ltd. W341

Sydney
Macquarie Group Ltd W217

AUT

Vienna
Allianz Elementar
Lebensversicherungs-AG (Austria)
W19
OMV AG (Austria) W266
Erste Group Bank AG W143
Raiffeisen Zentralbank Oesterreich AG
(Austria) W286
Bank fur Arbeit und Wirtschaft AG
(Austria) W47
Oesterreichische Nationalbank W263

BEL

Leuven
Anheuser-Busch Inbev SA W27

Brussels
Etablissements Delhaize Freres et Cie
Le Lion S.A. (Belgium) W145
Dexia S.A. W131
KBC Group NV W199
Dexia Bank Belgium S.A. (Belgium)
W131
AXA Banque Europe SA W35
Banque Nationale de Belgique
(National Bank of Belgium) W56

BMU

Hamilton
Jardine Matheson Holdings Ltd. W194
Jardine Strategic Holdings Ltd
(Bermuda) W194

BRA

Rio de Janeiro
Petroleo Brasileiro S.A. W275

Sao Paulo
Itau Unibanco Holding S.A. W190

Brasilia
Banco do Brasil S.A. W43

Rio de Janeiro
Vale S.A. W372

Sao Paulo
JBS SA W195

CAN

Laval
Alimentation-Couche Tard, Inc. W18

Calgary
Suncor Energy Inc. W340

Toronto
Royal Bank of Canada W298

Aurora
Magna International Inc. W218

Winnipeg
Great-West Lifeco Inc. W159

Toronto
Toronto Dominion Bank W357
Weston (George) Limited W386

Calgary
Imperial Oil Ltd. W182
Enbridge Inc W137

Brampton
Loblaw Cos. Ltd. W215

Montreal
Power Corp. of Canada W282

Halifax
Bank of Nova Scotia Halifax W54

Toronto
Onex Corp. W268

Montreal
Power Financial Corp W283

Toronto
Sun Life Financial Inc W339

Montreal
Bank of Montreal W53

Toronto
Canadian Imperial Bank of Commerce
W83
Manulife Financial Corp. W221

London
London Life Insurance Co. W215

Toronto
Sun Life Assurance Company of
Canada W339

Montreal
National Bank of Canada W242

Vancouver
HSBC Bank Canada W173

Ottawa
Bank of Canada (Ottawa) W49

CHE

Baar
Glencore PLC W159

Vevey
Nestle S.A. W248

Zurich
Zurich Insurance Group Ltd W391

Basel
Novartis AG Basel W259
Roche Holding Ltd. W295

Zurich
Asea Brown Boveri AG (Austria) W30
ABB Ltd W3
UBS AG (Switzerland) W366
Swiss Re Ltd. W344

Basel
Coop Switzerland (Switzerland) W113

Zurich
Credit Suisse Group W114
ACE, Ltd. W7

Basel
Baloise Holding AG W39

CHL

Santiago
Banco Santander Chile W45

CHN

Beijing
China Petroleum & Chemical Corp.
Inc W96
PetroChina Co Ltd W274
Industrial and Commercial Bank of
China Ltd W186
China Construction Bank Corp W94
Agricultural Bank of China W13
Bank of China Ltd W50
China Railway Construction Corp Ltd
W97

Shanghai
SAIC Motor Corp Ltd W306

Beijing
China Railway Group Ltd W97

Shenzhen
Ping An Insurance (Group) Co of
China Ltd. W279

Beijing
China Life Insurance Co Ltd W94
China Communications Constructions
Group Ltd W93
China Telecom Corp Ltd W98

Shanghai
China United Network
Communications Ltd W99
Bank of Communications Co., Ltd.
W51

Beijing
China Shenhua Energy Co., Ltd. W98
China Minsheng Banking Corp Ltd
W95

Shenzhen
China Merchants Bank Co Ltd W95

Beijing
Minmetals Development Co Ltd W228
Metallurgical Corp China Ltd W226
PICC Property and Casualty Co Ltd
W278

Shanghai
China Pacific Insurance (Group) Co.,
Ltd. W96
Baoshan Iron & Steel Co Ltd W57

A = AMERICAN BUSINESS
E = EMERGING COMPANIES
P = PRIVATE COMPANIES
W = WORLD BUSINESS

Beijing
China Citic Bank Corp Ltd W93

Guixi City
Jiangxi Copper Co., Ltd. W197

Beijing
Aluminum Corp of China Ltd. W23

Shanghai
Sinopharm Group Co., Ltd. W321

Fuzhou
Industrial Bank Co., Ltd. W186

Shenzhen
Ping An Bank Co Ltd W278

COL

Bogota
Ecopetrol SA W135

CSK

Praha 5
Ceskoslovenska Obchodni Banka A.S.
(Czech Republic) W92

DEU

Wolfsburg
Volkswagen A.G. (Germany, Fed. Rep.)
W380

Duesseldorf
E.ON SE W133

Stuttgart
Daimler AG W117

Munich
Allianz SE W19

Munchen
Bayer Motoren WK W64

Munich
Bayerische Motoren Werke AG W65

Ludwigshafen
BASF SE W60

Munich
Siemens AG (Germany) W318
Muenchener Rueckversicherungs-
Gesellschaft AG (Germany) W239

Bonn
Deutsche Telekom AG W129
Deutsche Post AG W128
Deutsche Post RG W128

Essen
RWE AG W304

Ingolstadt
AUDI AG Vormals Audi-NSU Auto
Union AG W32

Stuttgart
Bosch (Robert) GmbH (Germany Fed.
Rep.) W72

Duesseldorf
Metro AG W226

Cologne
Rewe-Zentral AG (Germany, Fed. Rep.)
W291

Frankfurt am Main
Deutsche Bank AG W125

Berlin
Deutscher Sparkassen-und
Giroverband e.V. (Germany, Fed.
Rep.) W130
Deutsche Bahn AG W125

Leverkusen
Bayer AG W62

Essen
ThyssenKrupp AG W353
Thyssen Krupp Steel AG (Germany)
W353

Hanover
Continental AG (Germany, Fed. Rep.)
W111

Frankfurt
Deutsche Lufthansa AG (Germany,
Fed. Rep.) W126

Hannover
Talanx AG W346

Frankfurt am Main
DZ Bank AG Deutsche Zentral-
Genossenschaftsbank W132

Essen
Hochtief AG W167

Stuttgart
Landesbank Baden-Wurttemberg
W207
Celesio AG W90

Karlsruhe
ENBW Energie Baden-Wuerttemberg
AG W138

Bad Homburg
Fresenius SE & Co KGaA W148

Frankfurt am Main
Commerzbank AG (Germany, Fed.
Rep.) W104

Zurich
Swiss Life (UK) plc (United Kingdom)
W344

Hannover
Hannover Rueckversicherung SE
W162

Frankfurt am Main
Kreditanstalt Fuer Wiederaufbau
(Germany, Fed. Rep.) W206

Munich
Bayerische Landesbank (Germany)
W64

Frankfurt am Main
Deutsche Bundesbank (Germany, Fed.
Rep.) W126

Bonn
Deutsche Postbank AG W128

Frankfurt am Main
Landesbank Hessen-Thueringen
Girozentrale (Helaba) (Germany,
Fed. Rep.) W209

Frankfurt
Dekabank Deutsche Girozentrale
W123

Berlin
Landesbank Berlin Holding AG
(Berlin) W208

Frankfurt am Main
Landwirtschaftliche Rentenbank
(Germany, Fed. Rep.) W209

Duesseldorf
Westdeutsche Genossenschafts-
Zentralbank EG (Germany, Fed.
Rep.) W385

Hamburg
Deutsche Genossenschafts-
Hypothekenbank (Germany, Fed.
Rep.) W126
Hamburger Sparkasse (Germany, Fed.
Rep.) W162

Wiesbaden
Aareal Bank AG W2

DNK

Copenhagen K
A.P. Moller - Maersk A/S W1

Copenhagen C
Nordea Bank Denmark A/S W259

Copenhagen K
Danske Bank AS (Denmark) W121

Copenhagen
PFA Pension Forsikringsaktieselskab
(Denmark) W278

ESP

Madrid
Banco Santander SA W45
Telefonica, S.A. W349
Repsol S.A. W289
ACS Actividades de Construccion y
Servicios, S.A. W8

Bilbao
Banco Bilbao Vizcaya Argentaria SA
(BBVA) W41

Madrid
Iberdrola SA W180
Endesa S.A. W138

Barcelona
Gas Natural SDG, S.A. W152

Madrid
Mapfre SA W222

Barcelona
Banco De Sabadell SA W43

Madrid
Banco Popular Espanol, S.A. W44
Bankinter, S.A. W55

FRA

Courbevoie
Total S.A. W361

Paris
AXA S.A. W35
Societe Generale W323
BNP Paribas (France) W71

Courbevoie
GDF SUEZ W155

Boulogne-Billancourt
Carrefour S.A. W86

Paris
Electricite de France W136

Montrouge
Credit Agricole SA W114

Paris
Peugeot S.A. W276
Rallye S.A. Neuilly-Sur-Seine W287

Saint-Etienne
Casino Guichard Perrachon S.A. W88

Paris
CNP Assurances S.A. W103

Courbevoie
Compagnie de Saint-Gobain W106

Rueil-Malmaison
Vinci SA W375

Boulogne-Billancourt
Renault S.A. (France) W288

Paris
Orange W268
Schlumberger Ltd. W311
Bouygues S.A. W73
Sanofi W308
Societe Nationale des Chemins de Fer
Francais (SNCF) (France) W324
Christian Dior SA W99
LVMH Moet Hennessy Louis Vuitton
W215
Air France-KLM W13

Rueil-Malmaison
Schneider Electric SE W311

Clichy
L'Oreal S.A. (France) W

Paris
Veolia Environnement W373
Vivendi W377
P.T. Aqua Golden Mississippi
(Indonesia) W271
Danone W120

Levallois-Perret
Alstom W22

Clermont-Ferrand
Compagnie Generale des
Etablissements Michelin (France)
W108

Paris
NATIXIS SA W245
BRED Banque Populaire (France)
W77

GBR

London
BP p.l.c. W75
Fiat Chrysler Automobiles NV W148

Cheshunt
Tesco PLC (United Kingdom) W351

London
HSBC Holdings Plc W173
Lloyds Banking Group Plc W213
Prudential Plc W283
Unilever Plc (United Kingdom) W370

Victoria
BHP Billiton Plc W70

London
Legal & General Group PLC (United
Kingdom) W210

Newbury
Vodafone Group Plc W378

ALASKA

ANCHORAGE
Arctic Slope Regional Corporation P28
Chenega Corporation P107
Petro Star Inc. P382
Chugach Alaska Corporation P114
Alaska Native Tribal Health Consortium P9

FAIRBANKS
Golden Valley Electric Association Inc. P208

JUNEAU
Sealaska Corporation P440

ARIZONA

CHANDLER
Microchip Technology, Inc. E312

MESA
Empire Southwest Llc P175

PHOENIX
Avnet Inc A90
Freeport-mcmoran Inc A362
Republic Services, Inc. A696
Petsmart, Inc A639
Southern Copper Corp A738
Western Alliance Bancorporation A865
Banner Health A101 P41
Kitchell Corporation P272
Core Construction Inc. P136
Roofing Wholesale Co. Inc. P422
Banner Health A101 P41
Southwest Catholic Health Network Corporation P462
Blue Cross And Blue Shield Of Arizona Inc. P69
Shamrock Foods Company P447
John C. Lincoln Health Network P258
Phoenix Children's Hospital Inc. P384
Ewing Irrigation Products Inc. P177
Best Western International Inc. P60
Knight Transportation Inc. E267
Grand Canyon Education Inc E208
Cavco Industries Inc (de) E82
Inventure Foods Inc. E249

PRESCOTT
Davidson's Inc. P148

SCOTTSDALE
Blood Systems Inc. P67
Scottsdale Healthcare Corp. P439
Meritage Homes Corp E309

TEMPE
Insight Enterprises Inc. A447
Northern Tier Energy Lp A598
United Dairymen Of Arizona P561
Sonora Quest Laboratories Llc. P457

TOLLESON
County Of Maricopa P138
Russell Sigler Inc. P424

TUCSON
The University Of Arizona Medical Center P534
Muscular Dystrophy Association Inc. P333

YUMA
Yuma Regional Medical Center Inc P621

ARKANSAS

BENTONVILLE
Wal-mart Stores, Inc. A852

BLYTHEVILLE
Mississippi County Electric Cooperative Inc. P324

CONWAY
Home Bancshares, Inc. A420

EL DORADO
Murphy Usa Inc A572
Murphy Oil Corp A571
Deltic Timber Corp. E121

FAYETTEVILLE
Ozarks Electric Cooperative Corporation P373
Washington Regional Medical Center P597

FORT SMITH
Arcbest Corp E38

HARRISON
Community First Bank P126

JONESBORO
E. C. Barton & Company P160

LITTLE ROCK
Windstream Holdings Inc A876
Bank Of The Ozarks, Inc. A104
Baptist Health P42
Arkansas Children's Hospital P29
Replacement Parts Inc. P412

LOWELL
Hunt (j.b.) Transport Services, Inc. A435

NORTH LITTLE ROCK
Bruce Oakley Inc. P80

PINE BLUFF
Simmons First National Corp. A729
Jefferson Hospital Association Inc. P256

SEARCY
White County Medical Center P607

SPRINGDALE
Tyson Foods, Inc. A817

STUTTGART
Riceland Foods Inc. P414
Producers Rice Mill Inc. P396

CALIFORNIA

ALAMEDA
Insite Vision Inc. E246

ALISO VIEJO
Microsemi Corp. E314

ANAHEIM
Keenan Hopkins Suder & Stowell Contractors Inc. P267

ARCADIA
Methodist Hospital Of Southern California P315

AZUSA
Azusa Pacific University P38

BAKERSFIELD
Calcot Ltd. P86
Jaco Oil Company P254
San Joaquin Refining Co. Inc. P433

BEVERLY HILLS
Live Nation Entertainment, Inc. A515

BRISBANE
Bi-rite Restaurant Supply Co. Inc. P62

BURBANK
Disney (walt) Co. (the) A259

BURLINGAME
Mills-peninsula Health Services P323

CALABASAS
On Assignment, Inc. E361
Ixia E256
Dts Inc E130

CARLSBAD
Homefed Corp. E231

CARSON
Ducommun Inc. E131

CHICO
Trico Bancshares (chico, Ca) A811

CITY OF INDUSTRY
America Chung Nam (group) Holdings Inc. P15
Morrow-meadows Corporation P329

CLAREMONT
Claremont Mckenna College Foundation P117

COLTON
Arrow Head Regional Medical Center P31

CONCORD
Bay Cities Paving & Grading Inc. P49

CORONA
Monster Beverage Corp E325

COSTA MESA
Ttm Technologies Inc E485

CUPERTINO
Apple Inc A67

DOWNEY
Rockview Dairies Inc. P420

DUARTE
Beckman Research Institute Of The City Of Hope P56

DUBLIN
Ross Stores, Inc. A708

EL MONTE
M. C. Gill Corporation P292

EL SEGUNDO
Directv A254
Mattel Inc A537
The Aerospace Corporation P502
Stamps.com Inc. E438

ESCONDIDO
Realty Income Corp. E394

FOLSOM
California Independent System Operator Corporation P87

FOSTER CITY
Gilead Sciences, Inc. A381
Guidewire Software Inc E211
Sciclone Pharmaceuticals, Inc. E414

FREMONT
Synnex Corp A774
Lam Research Corp A500
Teamster Benefit Trust P497
Electronics For Imaging, Inc. E143

FRESNO
Saint Agnes Medical Center P427

FULLERTON
St. Jude Hospital P475

GARDEN GROVE
Southland Industries P462

GARDENA
Z Gallerie P622

GLENDALE
Avery Dennison Corp. A87
Glendale Adventist Medical Center Inc P207

GOLETA
Direct Relief International Inc P154

HAWTHORNE
Osi Systems, Inc. (de) E362

HAYWARD
Ultra Clean Holdings Inc E488

HUNTINGTON BEACH
Bj's Restaurants Inc

IMPERIAL
Imperial Irrigation District P244

INGLEWOOD
Marvin Engineering Co. Inc. P302

IRVINE
Western Digital Corp. A866
Broadcom Corp. A135
Spectrum Group International Inc A743
Allergan, Inc A32
Banc Of California, Inc. A96
World Of Jeans & Tops P616
Prudential Overall Supply Inc. P399
St. Joseph Health System P472
Vizio Inc. P589
Humax Usa Inc P241
Arbitech Llc P28
Hcp, Inc. E218
Edwards Lifesciences Corp E141
Standard Pacific Corp. E439
Newport Corp. E349
Masimo Corp. E293
Quality Systems, Inc. E387
Sabra Health Care Reit Inc E409
Autobytel Inc. E45
Pacific Premier Bancorp Inc E365

KINGSBURG
Sun-maid Growers Of California P490

LA CANADA FLINTRIDGE
Allen Lund Company Inc. P13

LA JOLLA
Sanford-burnham Medical Research Institute P433
The Scripps Research Institute P530
National University P338

LA MESA
Grossmont Hospital Corporation P213

LAGUNA HILLS
Saddleback Memorial Medical Center P426

LODI
Pacific Coast Producers P374

LONG BEACH
Molina Healthcare Inc A562
California State University Long Beach Research Foundation P88
Long Beach Memorial Medical Center P287

LOS ALTOS
The David And Lucile Packard Foundation P511

WOODLAND HILLS
Health Net, Inc. A410

YUBA CITY
Sunsweet Growers Inc. P491

COLORADO

AURORA
Graebel Companies Inc. P210

BOULDER
Amg National Trust Bank P23
University Corporation For
  Atmospheric Research P567
Boulder Brands Inc E63

BROOMFIELD
Ball Corp A95
Level 3 Communications, Inc. A508
Mwh Global Inc. P334

CENTENNIAL
Arrow Electronics, Inc. A74
Western States Fire Protection
  Company Inc P604
Penford Corp. E373

COLORADO SPRINGS
Academy School District 20 P2
Young Life P621
Intelligent Software Solutions
  Inc. P247
Century Casinos Inc. E83

DENVER
Davita Healthcare Partners Inc A242
Cobiz Financial Inc A196
Summit Materials Llc P489
Colorado Seminary P122
Pcl Construction Enterprises
  Inc P378
Exempla Inc. P177
Sm Energy Co. E426
Cimarex Energy Co E89
M.d.c. Holdings, Inc. E286
Markwest Energy Partners L.p. E293
Bonanza Creek Energy, Inc. E61
Triangle Petroleum Corp E479
Royal Gold, Inc. E404
Coresite Realty Corp. E107

EATON
Agfinity Inc. P8

ENGLEWOOD
Dish Network Corp A258
Liberty Interactive Corp A510
Western Union Co. A868
Ch2m Hill Companies Ltd. P104
Ihs Inc E238
Air Methods Corp. E18
Csg Systems International Inc. E114

EVERGREEN
Catamount Constructors Inc. P96

FORT COLLINS
Colorado State University P123
Otter Products Llc P371
Advanced Energy Industries Inc. E12

GRAND JUNCTION
Fci Constructors Inc. P184

GREELEY
Pilgrims Pride Corp. A646
Hensel Phelps Construction Co P229

GREENWOOD VILLAGE
Newmont Mining Corp. (holding
  Co.) A585
Great-west Life & Annuity Insurance
  Co. A393
Xanterra Inc. P619

Gerald H. Phipps Inc. P206
Madison Capital Management
  Llc P293

LAKEWOOD
Mesa Laboratories, Inc. E310

NIWOT
Crocs Inc E113

PLATTEVILLE
Synergy Resources Corp E458

SEDALIA
Intermountain Rural Electric
  Association P250

CONNECTICUT

BLOOMFIELD
Cigna Corp A179
Metlife Insurance Company Of
  Connecticut A553
Kaman Corp. E260

BRIDGEPORT
Bridgeport Hospital & Healthcare
  Services Inc P76

CHESHIRE
The Lane Construction
  Corporation P518
Alexion Pharmaceuticals Inc. E21

CLINTON
Connecticut Water Service, Inc. E101

DANBURY
Praxair, Inc. A655

DARIEN
Genesee & Wyoming Inc. E199

FAIRFIELD
General Electric Co A372
Fairfield University P178

FARMINGTON
Phalcon Ltd. P383

GREENWICH
Berkley (w. R.) Corp. A115
Greenwich Hospital Association
  Inc P213
Starwood Property Trust Inc. E440
Fifth Street Finance Corp E167

HAMDEN
Quinnipiac University P403

HARTFORD
Hartford Financial Services Group
  Inc. A405
United Technologies Corp. A835
Aetna Inc. A14
Phoenix Companies, Inc. (the) A646
Connecticut State University
  System P130
Saint Francis Hospital And Medical
  Center P428
Connecticut Children's Medical
  Center P129
Virtus Investment Partners, Inc E508

LITCHFIELD
Litchfield Bancorp P286

MANCHESTER
Lydall, Inc. E284

MIDDLETOWN
Wesleyan University P603

MILFORD
Eastern Bag And Paper Company
  Incorporated P162
Doctor's Associates Inc. P155

Ebp Supply Solutions P163

NEW BRITAIN
Stanley Black & Decker, Inc. A750
Hospital Of Central Connecticut P239

NEW HAVEN
Knights Of Columbus P272
Uil Holding Corp E486
Higher One Holdings Inc. E225

NEW LONDON
Lawrence & Memorial Hospital
  Inc. P278

NORWALK
Xerox Corp A884
Priceline Group Inc. (the) A658
Emcor Group, Inc. A287

OLD GREENWICH
Ellington Financial Llc E145

OXFORD
Rbc Bearings Inc E391

RIDGEFIELD
Chefs' Warehouse Inc (the)

ROGERS
Rogers Corp. E401

SHELTON
Prudential Annuities Life Assurance
  Corp A669

SIMSBURY
Hartford Life Insurance Co A406

SOUTHPORT
Sturm, Ruger & Co., Inc. E447

STAMFORD
Synchrony Financial A774
Charter Communications Inc A172
Starwood Hotels & Resorts Worldwide
  Inc A754
United Rentals, Inc. A831
Harman International Industries,
  Inc. A402
Frontier Communications Corp A364
Navigators Group, Inc. (the) A576
Lexa International Corporation P284
Americares Foundation Inc. P22
Star Gas Partners L.p. E440
Gartner, Inc. E194
Hexcel Corp. E223
Independence Holding Co. E244

WALLINGFORD
Amphenol Corp. A57

WATERBURY
Webster Financial Corp (waterbury,
  Conn) A858
Saint Mary's Hospital Inc. P430
The Waterbury Hospital P539

WEST HARTFORD
Keystone Equipment Finance
  Corp. P270
The University Of Hartford P536

WESTPORT
Terex Corp. A790
Save The Children Federation
  Inc. P435

WINDSOR
Ss&c Technologies Holdings,
  Inc. E437
Trc Companies, Inc. E475

DELAWARE

DOVER
Chesapeake Utilities Corp. E87

LEWES
Beebe Medical Center Inc. P56

NEW CASTLE
United Electric Supply Company
  Inc. P561

NEWARK
Slm Corp. A731

WILMINGTON
Du Pont (e.i.) De Nemours & Co A274
Wsfs Financial Corp. A880
The Bancorp, Inc. A797

DISTRICT OF COLUMBIA

WASHINGTON
Fannie Mae A315
Federal Reserve System A321
Danaher Corp. A239
Pepco Holdings Inc. A636
Carlyle Group, L.p. (the) A154
Federal Agricultural Mortgage
  Corp A317
Gavi Fund P202
Gallaudet University P201
Washington Hospital Center
  Corporation P597
Financial Industry Regulatory
  Authority Inc. P185
Howard University Inc. P240
Medstar-georgetown Medical Center
  Inc. P309
Children's National Medical
  Center P110
American University P22
Securities Investor Protection
  Corporation P442
American Chemical Society P16
National Education Association Of The
  United States P335
Patton Boggs Llp P377
American Institutes For Research In
  The Behavioral Sciences P19
Neighborhood Reinvestment
  Corporation P340
Gallup Inc. P202
The Catholic University Of
  America P505
Association Of Universities For
  Research In Astronomy Inc. P34
World Wildlife Fund Inc. P616
United Negro College Fund Inc. P563
American Petroleum Institute
  Inc P20
John F Kennedy Center For The
  Performing Arts P259
International Brotherhood Of
  Teamsters P250
American Federation Of Labor &
  Congress Of Industrial
  Organzatio P16
Communications Workers Of America
  Afl-cio Clc P125
Advisory Board Company (the) E14
Liquidity Services Inc E277
Costar Group, Inc. E109
Dupont Fabros Technology Inc E132
Cogent Communications Holdings,
  Inc. E93

FLORIDA

BOCA RATON
Office Depot, Inc. A608
Jarden Corp. A467
Boca Raton Regional Hospital
  Inc. P71
Applied Card Systems Inc. P27

A = AMERICAN BUSINESS
E = EMERGING COMPANIES
P = PRIVATE COMPANIES
W = WORLD BUSINESS

Columbia Banking System, Inc. E96

VANCOUVER
Peacehealth P379
Barrett Business Services, Inc. E49

WALLA WALLA
Banner Corp. A105

WENATCHEE
Goodfellow Bros. Inc. P209

YAKIMA
Yakima Valley Memorial Hospital
Association Inc P620

WEST VIRGINIA

CHARLES TOWN
American Public Education Inc E31

CHARLESTON
United Bankshares, Inc. A825
City Holding Co. A187
Charleston Area Medical Center
Inc. P106

ELKINS
Woodford Oil Company P615

FOLLANSBEE
Wheeling-nisshin Inc. P607

HUNTINGTON
St. Mary's Medical Center P477
Marshall University P301

WHEELING
Wesbanco, Inc. A862

WISCONSIN

APPLETON
U.s. Venture Inc. P559
Great Northern Corporation P211

BEAVER DAM
United Cooperative P561

BROOKFIELD
Fiserv, Inc. A347

CLINTON
The Delong Co Inc P511

CUDAHY
Roadrunner Transportation Systems
Inc E400

DURAND
Bauer Built Inc. P49

EAU CLAIRE
Market & Johnson Inc. P299
Sacred Heart Hospital Inc. P426

ELLSWORTH
Ellsworth Cooperative Creamery P172

FITCHBURG
Certco Inc. P103

FOND DU LAC
C.d. Smith Construction Inc. P84

FRANKLIN
Krones Inc. P274

GREEN BAY
Associated Banc-corp A77
Pomp's Tire Service Inc.. P390
Paper Converting Machine
Company P376
Krueger International Inc. P274

HARTFORD
Hartford Savings Bank P221

KENOSHA
United Hospital System Inc. P563

LA CROSSE
Kwik Trip Inc. P275
Gundersen Lutheran Medical Center
Inc. P215

LA FARGE
Cooperative Regions Of Organic
Producer Pools P135

MADISON
J. H. Findorff & Son Inc. P252
The Douglas Stewart Company
Inc P511
Vp Holdings Corporation P591
University Of Wisconsin System P580
Meriter Health Services Inc. P315
University Of Wisconsin
Foundation P579

MARSHFIELD
Security Health Plan Of Wisconsin
Inc. P442

MAYVILLE
Mayville Engineering Co Inc P305

MENASHA
Faith Technologies Inc. P181

MEQUON
Charter Manufacturing Company
Inc. P106

MIDDLETON
Spectrum Brands Holdings Inc A741
University Of Wisconsin Medical
Foundation Inc. P580

MILWAUKEE
Johnson Controls Inc A471
Manpowergroup A525
Rockwell Automation, Inc. A706
Harley-davidson Inc A401
Wisconsin Energy Corp. A877
Mgic Investment Corp. (wi) A554
Marquette University P300
Goodwill Industries Of Southeastern
Wisconsin Inc. P210
Astronautics Corporation Of
America P34
Froedtert Memorial Lutheran Hospital
Inc P199
Strattec Security Corp. E446

MOUNT HOREB
Premier West Companies Llc P394

NEENAH
Bemis Co Inc A114

OSHKOSH
Oshkosh Corp (new) A619

SUSSEX
Quad/graphics, Inc. A677

WAUKESHA
American Transmission Company
Llc P21
Waukesha Memorial Hospital
Inc. P598
Generac Holdings Inc E199

WAUSAU
Aspirus Inc. P31

WISCONSIN DELLS
Holiday Wholesale Inc. P235

WYOMING

CASPER
Wyoming Medical Center Inc. P618

LARAMIE
University Of Wyoming P581

SUNDANCE
Powder River Energy
Corporation P391

A

Index of Executives

A

A-nanthothai, Thongchai W47
Aa, Terry L. Van Der P535
Aagaard-Svendsen, Birgit W122
Aagard, Tammy P581
Aaholm, Sherry A. A233
Aaholm, Sherry A. A324
Aaker, Tom W332
Aakre, D. Scott A426
Aamodt, Patsy P29
Aanensen, Theodore J. A480
Aanestad, Ola M. W334
Aardsma, David A. (Dave) A858
Aardsma, Wayne P454
Aaron, Henry E130
Aaron, Sammy E192
Aaron, Carol P379
Aaron, Clay M. P481
Aaron, Todd S. P481
Aaron, Steven L. P481
Aaron, Todd S. P481
Aarsvold, Bruce P215
Aaserude, Robert P334
Aasheim, Kristine M. P577
Aasnaes, Hans W335
Aasved, Craig P469
AbaalKhail, Faris Abdullah W295
Abad, Alfredo Saenz W46
Abadessa, Virginia P367
Abadie, Laurent W273
Abadir, Nabil P218
Aballo, Paul G P153
Abanumay, Mohammed S. W310
Abate, Carl E172
Abate, Rene W87
Abbasi, Sohaib E245
Abbasi, Sohaib E246
Abbasi, Osama W116
Abbate, Mark L. E307
Abbate, Mark L. A551
Abbeele, Annick D. Van den P146
Abbey, Richard E. A778
Abbey, Ellen P540
Abbott, Gary R. E89
Abbott, Gardner E172
Abbott, James A. A555
Abbott, Mark A687
Abbott, Dean A692
Abbott, Frederick C. (Fred) A828
Abbott, James R. A891
Abbott, Jon P400
Abbott, Cal P501
Abbott, John W302
Abboud, Ali El A758
Abdalla, Zein A638
Abdalla, Zein A804
Abdel, Raouf F. E156
Abdelnour, Gaby A. A476
Abdo, Hatem P196
Abdoo, Richard A. (Dick) A26
Abdoo, Elizabeth A. A430
Abdoo, Richard A. A594
Abdul-Latif, Saad A638
Abe, Takashi W232

Abe, Takashi W233
Abe, Ken W236
Abe, Yasushi W247
Abe, Yasuyuki W336
Abe, Yasuyuki W337
Abe, Kensuke W354
Abe, Ken W373
Abel, Gregory E. (Greg) A117
Abel, Leonard L. A279
Abel, Virginia K. A620
Abel, Gregory E. (Greg) A626
Abel, James E. A654
Abel, Bob P406
Abel, Dawn P598
Abele, John E. A133
Abell, Elaine D. A440
Abelli, Donna L. A444
Abello, Vincent W87
Abelson, Sigmund H. P578
Abely, Susan Cerrone P421
Abendschein, Robert D. A60
Abendschein, Ken P299
Aber, Suzanne (Sue) P586
Aberdeen, Jeffery D. A208
Aberdeen, Joy P612
Aberle, Derek K. A680
Aberle, Jim P620
Abernathy, Kathleen Q. A365
Abernathy, Robert E. A488
Abernethy, Janet D. A332
Abinson, Terry P602
Abizaid, Gen. John P. A711
Abji, Minaz B. A430
Able, Michael W240
Ables, Mona D. E101
Ables, Dorothy M. A741
Abney, David P. A472
Abney, David P. A831
Abney, Donna A. P317
Abogado, Scott E77
Abolfazli, Massood E507
Abols, Tate A. M. W268
Abood, Steve A692
Aboodi, Henry J. P76
Aboulafia, Itzhak W49
Aboujoud, Marwan S. P228
Aboumrad, Daniel Hajj W24
Abraham, Cecelia M. A291
Abraham, Spencer A608
Abraham, William J. A678
Abraham, Karen P70
Abraham, Leopold W267
Abrahamowicz, Dan P617
Abrahamsson, Jonas W134
Abramowicz, Daniel A. A230
Abrams, Ian J. E198
Abrams, Robin E273
Abrams, Bruce R. A51
Abrams, David C. A442
Abrams, George S. A847
Abrams, Jon F. P253
Abrams, Jim P253
Abrams, David P350
Abramson, Steven V. E494
Abramson, Joel A14
Abramson, Andrew B. A842

Abramson, Richard P465
Abramson, Morrie K. P519
Abreu, Steven M. (Steve) A37
Abriola, Linda M. P556
Abruzzese, Albert E200
Abruzzese, Joseph (Joe) A257
Abston, Larry J. A60
Abts, Douglas C. E65
Abu-Hadba, Walid E37
Abu-Nasrah, Khaled A479
Aburatani, Yoshihiro Yoshihiro
  Aburatani W360
Abutaleb, Sam P540
Abzug, Barry M. A708
Accum, Claude A. W339
Ace, Brian R. A210
Acerra, Peggie P606
Acevedo, Jorge A. A305
Acevedo, Cecilia A535
Acevedo, Sylvia P206
Aceves, Salvador P575
Ach, J. Wickliffe A337
Ach, A N P29
Achar, Sumana E315
Achary, Michael M. E216
Achary, Michael M. A396
Acharya, Sanjay E19
Acharya, Ramesh E20
Achatz, Reinhold W320
ACHE, Jennifer Weiss Wilkerson P514
Achleitner, Paul W63
Achleitner, Paul W119
Achleitner, Paul W305
Achurra, Emiliano W152
Ackart, Jennifer C. A687
Acker, David E177
Acker, Robert A403
Acker, Laurens G. van den W289
Ackerley, Margaret L. P616
Ackerman, Dennis E51
Ackerman, Jeffrey (Jeff) E188
Ackerman, F. Duane A37
Ackerman, Paul R. A318
Ackerman, F. Duane A422
Ackerman, Joel A491
Ackerman, F. Duane A831
Ackerman, Jeff P3
Ackerman, Denise P45
Ackermann, Bryan E268
Ackermann, Josef W303
Ackermann, Josef W320
Ackermann, Josef W392
Ackerson, Vince A. E468
Ackerson, Vince A. A793
Ackman, William A. A634
Acosta, Fernando J. A92
Acosta, Arcilia C. A294
Acquaviva, John E9
Acranis, Tina W221
Acton, Roger E196
Acuff, A. Marshall A621
Acuna, Richard E139
Adachi, Barbara P. P206
Adachi, Yoroku (Joe) W85
Adachi, Michio W124
Adachi, Toshio W315

Adachi, Takemi Takemi Adachi W360
Adachi, Seiichiro W364
Adair, A. Jayson E106
Adair, Graham E182
Adair, Claudia E219
Adair, James R. A554
Adair, Charles E. (Eddie) A784
Adair, Charles E. (Eddie) A806
Adair, Don P494
Adair-Potts, Janna A781
Adali, Erhan W365
Adam, Deborah J. A856
Adam, Herve W376
Adamczyk, Marilyn P179
Adamicki, Bob E11
Adamo, Jane E422
Adamo, Nicholas A. (Nick) A182
Adamo, Victor T. A663
Adamo, Jennifer Gilmore P551
Adams, Phil E4
Adams, Dana E124
Adams, Casey E158
Adams, Joseph P. E181
Adams, Robbin B. E203
Adams, Robin E245
Adams, Stephanie E300
Adams, W. Andrew (Andy) E333
Adams, Cathy E388
Adams, Joe E425
Adams, Kelly A21
Adams, Rex D. A32
Adams, Diana A44
Adams, Robert D. A106
Adams, Robin J. A130
Adams, Robin J. A131
Adams, John A144
Adams, Kent M. A157
Adams, Tom A172
Adams, Thomas E. A172
Adams, Harold L. A209
Adams, John L. A272
Adams, Richard L. A292
Adams, Craig L. A305
Adams, Thomas C. A339
Adams, Joseph P. A359
Adams, John L. A394
Adams, Milburn A421
Adams, Katherine L. (Kate) A424
Adams, John B. A459
Adams, Angela S. A472
Adams, Ted A496
Adams, Mark W. A558
Adams, Lisa A588
Adams, Michael A660
Adams, Alan S. (Al) A662
Adams, Scott A669
Adams, Thomas R. (Tom) A700
Adams, Austin A. A741
Adams, Patricia A781
Adams, Tim A786
Adams, John C. (John) A808
Adams, John L. A812
Adams, Joe A825
Adams, Richard M. A826
Adams, Paul A836
Adams, John D. A845

A = AMERICAN BUSINESS
E = EMERGING COMPANIES
P = PRIVATE COMPANIES
W = WORLD BUSINESS

Alperin, Barry J. A719
Alperin, Thomas M. (Tom) P556
Alpern, Josh E246
Alpern, Robert J. A5
Alpern, Robert J. A6
Alperstein, Leslie M. A279
Alpert, Bruce N E194
Alpert, Jordan M E452
Alpert, Lee K. P288
Alpert, Chuck P517
Alpert, Charles S. P517
Alpert-Romm, Adria A257
Alphandery, Edmond W156
Alphonso, Mervyn L E399
Alsborg, Thomas C. A774
Alsobrooks, Glen P614
Alsowaidi, Nasser A. W113
Alspaugh, Robert W. (Bob) A96
Alstead, Troy A754
Alston, Jeremy E69
Alston, James N. P564
Alstrom, Ray P10
Alsup, Bill P233
Alt, Mark P299
Alt, Susan P328
Altamari, Jeffrey G. (Jeff) A147
Altaras, June P494
Altenburg, Rana H. P300
Altenschmidt, Hans-Hermann W105
Alter, Sarah A256
Alter, Wayne E. A769
Alter, Allen B. P76
Alters, Alan E258
Altes, Wallace W. A118
Althann, Natica von A654
Althann, Natica A654
Althoff, Judson A618
Althoff, Eric W261
Altholz, Robert N. (Rob) P287
Althouse, Joel P66
Altieri, Gina P341
Altig, David E. A319
Altman, Roger C. E159
Altman, Amy L. E283
Altman, William M. A490
Altman, Steven R. (Steve) A680
Altman, Richard I. (Rick) A684
Altman, Stanley J. (Stan) A694
Altman, Dara P409
Altman, Gideon W49
Altmann, Butch P562
Altmann, Ryan P562
Altmiller, Steve P351
Altmiller, Steve P352
Alton, Gregg H. A383
Alton, Steve W80
Altozano, Angel Manuel Garcia W9
Altozano, Angel Garcia W168
Aluisi, Andrea P537
Aluko, Olu E389
Alumni, Young P510
Alutto, Charles A. (Charlie) E443
Alva, Danny P361
Alvanos, Costa E301
Alvarado, Linda G. A2
Alvarado, Joseph (Joe) A209
Alvarado, Donna M. A231
Alvarado, Joseph (Joe) A741
Alvarado, Peter J. A833
Alvarado, Cristobal Valderas W9
Alvarez, Dawn E77
Alvarez, Cesar L. E306
Alvarez, Alex E326
Alvarez, Pedro E339
Alvarez, Alex C. De A67
Alvarez, Carlos E. A232
Alvarez, Raul A513
Alvarez, Raul A523
Alvarez, Pablo A. A535

Alvarez, Tony A549
Alvarez, Ignacio A651
Alvarez, Jose B. A804
Alvarez, Jose B. A832
Alvarez, Maria Luisa P46
Alvarez, Fernando de Asua W46
Alvarez, Jose Antonio Alvarez W46
Alvarez, Fernando de Asua W46
Alvarez, Luis W81
Alvarez, Manuel W152
Alvaro, Felecia E487
Alvather, Jay P497
Alvera, Marco W141
Alvera, Marco W153
Alves, David A804
Alvin, William R. (Bill) P227
Alving, Amy E. A505
Alvino, Alissa E28
Alvino, Kathleen P398
Alworth, Dave E27
Alyea, Mark P14
Alzamora, Mike A788
Alziari, Lucien A92
Amado, Joseph S. (Joe) A41
Amado, Nuno W46
Aman, Franz E246
Aman, Kris A592
Aman, Alfred C. P487
Amano, Hollie A168
Amano, Tsugunobu W354
Amante, Jerry P367
Amaral, Donald J. A811
Amaral, Carl M. A856
Amaral, Ev P284
Amaral, Horace J. P574
Amaral, Mario Mosqueira do W145
Amarel, Robert P492
Amaro, Fernando Rodriguez A331
Amat, Leonardo A173
Amat, Len A173
Amato, Lou E156
Amato, Albert L. A52
Amato, Anthony (Tony) A257
Amato, Frank C. A379
Amato, Alfonse A729
Amato, Len A801
Amato, Elizabeth B. A836
Amato, Frank C. P127
Amato, Louis J. P374
Amato-ferri, Maryann E54
Ambani, Mukesh D. A100
Ambani, Mukesh D. W287
Ambani, Ramniklal H. W287
Ambe, Shintaro W236
Ambler, John O. A139
Ambrecht, Kenneth C. A49
Ambrecht, Kenneth C. A742
Ambrogi, John E402
Ambrogio, Ronald S. A103
Ambrose, Steve A248
Ambrose, Steven B. A273
Ambrose, Joseph M. A334
Ambrose, Richard E. (Rich) A479
Ambrose, Richard F. (Rick) A518
Ambrose, Adele D. A549
Ambrose, Kathleen A. W320
Ambrosio, Anthony G. A161
Ambrosio, Anthony P180
Ambury, Richard F. E440
Amdur, Henry P279
Amelio, Gilbert F. (Gil) A81
Amemiya, Hiroshi W355
Amendola, Patricia A365
Amendola, Alma P445
Amerie, Abraham A. A344
Ames, Jacqueline E136
Ames, Thomas A73
Ames, Joel A81
Ames, Carmen Holding A335
Ames, Marshall H. A506
Ames, Pamela P105
Ames, Eugene L. P463
Amick, Amy D. E300
Amick, Rebecca K. A117
Amick, Bill L. A718

Amig, Eric P. A318
Amin, Neha E167
Amin, A. Salman A638
Amin, Devang (Dave) P61
Amin, Pamela Al P612
Amine, Ali Al W212
Amino, Yutaka W337
Amiot, Mark E482
Amir, Ariel E46
Amler, Robert W. P344
Ammann, Daniel (Dan) A377
Ammar, Tarak Ben W225
Ammar, Tarak Ben W349
Ammar, Tarak Tarak Ben Ammar W349
Ammari, Ramzi S E494
Ammerman, Douglas K. (Doug) A326
Ammirato, Nancy E103
Ammons, Steve E46
Amoh, Minoru A275
Amon, Michael E174
Amon, Cristiano A680
Amonette, Alison P609
Amore, Robert A636
Amore, John W392
Amoriell, Dave A885
Amorim, Americo Ferreira de W45
Amoroso, Alfred J. (Fred) A886
Amoroso, Edward G. P481
Amoroso, Greg W146
Amos, Daniel P. (Dan) A17
Amos, Paul S. A17
Amos, John Shelby A17
Amos, Paul S. A17
Amos, Daniel P. (Dan) A776
Amos, Richard P124
Amos, Harold P412
Amos, Louise W106
Amouriaux, Emmanuelle E71
Amozeg, Gilad E204
Amprey, Walter G. P285
Amrod, Alan E257
Amster, John A. E406
Amundson, Bruce A870
Amundson, Jennifer P181
Amundson, Olin P188
Amy, David B. E423
Amyot, Maribeth P619
Amyot, Lise-Anne W243
An, In K. A398
Anagnost, John A459
Anand, Siddharth (Sid) A583
Anand, V. W67
Anandan, Rajan A389
Ananenkov, Alexander G. W154
Anarde, Russ A602
Anastasio, Lance W. P613
Anastassov, Stassi A665
Ancelin, Bruno W289
Ancell, Christopher K. (Chris) A170
Ancher-Jensen, Henrik A20
Anchondo, Mark A. P115
Anda, Jacqueline E. (Jackie) De A344
Andarza, Ivan A. P501
Andaya, Todd E436
Andeberhan, Michael E328
Andelman, David R. A162
Anderman, Sig E144
Anders, Caren B. A277
Andersen, Niles E29
Andersen, Barry E119
Andersen, Lars A126
Andersen, Jesper A182
Andersen, Stacia J. A781
Andersen, G. Chris A791
Andersen, Peter P114
Andersen, Judith A. P281
Andersen, Tonny Thierry W122
Andersen, Ole Gjesso W122
Andersen, Thomas Thune W329
Anderskouv, Niels A794
Anderson, Ted E4
Anderson, Chad E57
Anderson, Diane E60
Anderson, Chad E68

Anderson, Christopher E73
Anderson, Mike E89
Anderson, Scott A E91
Anderson, Elizabeth E97
Anderson, Dean E162
Anderson, Mark E163
Anderson, Michael E180
Anderson, Maurus E188
Anderson, Robert E197
Anderson, Bob E267
Anderson, Diego B. E284
Anderson, David J. (Dave) E330
Anderson, Gary E. E383
Anderson, Tom E436
Anderson, Richard W. (Rick) E465
Anderson, Jason E473
Anderson, W E502
Anderson, Steven E. E514
Anderson, Neal E514
Anderson, Keith A. E515
Anderson, Bruce K. A35
Anderson, David J. (Dave) A47
Anderson, Gary A. A58
Anderson, Daniel T. A61
Anderson, Michael J. (Mike) A61
Anderson, Richard P. (Dick) A61
Anderson, Gerard M. A62
Anderson, Richard P. (Dick) A62
Anderson, Reuben V. A81
Anderson, Basil L. A112
Anderson, Grantly A116
Anderson, William (Bill) A119
Anderson, Timothy C. A141
Anderson, William A. A145
Anderson, Gary E. A173
Anderson, Bruce A177
Anderson, James A193
Anderson, Harry L. A198
Anderson, Lars C. A207
Anderson, Richard H. A248
Anderson, Le-Ha A264
Anderson, Melissa H. A265
Anderson, Gerard M. A273
Anderson, Gary E. A281
Anderson, Fred D. A283
Anderson, Karie A305
Anderson, Andre T. A319
Anderson, Karl V. A330
Anderson, Michael J. (Mike) A345
Anderson, Bradbury H. (Brad) A376
Anderson, R. John A402
Anderson, David G. A407
Anderson, Lynn A418
Anderson, David J. (Dave) A424
Anderson, Bradley S. A428
Anderson, Gary A435
Anderson, David S. (Dave) A437
Anderson, Richard S. A444
Anderson, Paul G. (Pete) A460
Anderson, Ian D. A489
Anderson, Reuben V. A495
Anderson, Steven M. A498
Anderson, Kerrii B. A498
Anderson, James M. (Jamie) A525
Anderson, Daniel F. A525
Anderson, James A537
Anderson, Karli A586
Anderson, Sheldon T. A600
Anderson, B. Chuck A608
Anderson, David C. A625
Anderson, Douglas L. A626
Anderson, Diane C. A629
Anderson, Brian P. A676
Anderson, Sarah A694
Anderson, Joseph B. A701
Anderson, Steven H. A720
Anderson, Allen H. A725
Anderson, Bryan A737
Anderson, Laurence A738
Anderson, Paul M. A741
Anderson, Philip D. A744
Anderson, Virginia L. A750
Anderson, Basil L. A753
Anderson, Kyle A756
Anderson, Jim A759

A = AMERICAN BUSINESS
E = EMERGING COMPANIES
P = PRIVATE COMPANIES
W = WORLD BUSINESS

A = AMERICAN BUSINESS
E = EMERGING COMPANIES
P = PRIVATE COMPANIES
W = WORLD BUSINESS

Boor, Anthony W. (Tony) E57
Boor, William C. (Bill) E83
Boor, William C. (Bill) A189
Boor, David A. A231
Boos, Brad P26
Boot, Arnoud W. A. A693
Boothsaz, Ahsan E460
Booth, Kenneth S. E111
Booth, Daniel J. E357
Booth, Courtney E432
Booth, Stuart W. A224
Booth, Richard H. A303
Booth, Cynthia A337
Booth, George H. A695
Booth, Joseph W. P56
Booth, Kathryn Ryan P244
Booth, Scott P300
Booth, Otis P507
Booth, Clement B. W20
Booth, David W58
Booth, David W60
Booth, Richard W340
Boothe, Timothy W. (Tim) E64
Boothman, Paula P485
Bootsma, Pieter W13
Boozer, Jim E41
Bopp, Anne E97
Boran, Pat P350
Boratto, Eva C. A237
Borba, George A. A235
Borba, John A. A235
Borcherding, Tricia L. A194
Borchers, Susan C. A694
Borchers, Patrick J. P140
Borda, Fina E273
Bordas, Stephen P192
Bordelon, John W. E229
Bordenave, Philippe W71
Border, Ted P540
Borders, Carolynne A719
Borders, Denise Glyn P465
Bordes, Michael P. (Mike) A288
Bordes, Constance A455
Bordner, Dave E200
Borel, James C. A274
Borel, Daniel V. W249
Boren, Jim E206
Boren, Laurasusana E329
Boren, Robin B. A22
Boren, Caroline A28
Boren, David L. A794
Boren, David L. A806
Boren, Kevin P315
Boretz, J. Craig A216
Borgard, Lawrence T. (Larry) A449
Borgen, Thomas F. W122
Borgert, Jeff E444
Borggaard, Jennifer E16
Borghgraef, Paul W199
Borghoff, Rosemary P139
Borgklint, Per G. W143
Borgman, Robert M. A627
Borgmann, Kevin A151
Borgstrom, Robert C. A782
Bori, Carlos E425
Borich, Joseph J. E269
Borig, Klaus G. W133
Borja, Paul D. A349
Borjesson, Rolf A88
Borkar, Rani N. A451
Borkar, Shekhar Y. A452
Borkovich, Kris D. A84
Borkowski, Maureen A. A45
Borkowski, Ellen P557
Borland, Alisa P509
Borman, J. Richard A379
Bormuth, John P66
Born, David E444
Born, John R. P100
Born, Jorge W82
Born, Ulrika W344
Borneman, J. Ralph A301
Bornmann, David E. A674
Bornstein, Ethan S E232
Bornstein, Jeffrey S. (Jeff) A373

Borodovsky, Yan A. A451
Boroff, Karen P445
Borofsky, Gary M. A253
Borok, Gil A159
Boroughs, Rev Philip L. P122
Boroughs, Rev Philip L. P575
Boroughs, Timothy A. W7
Borowicz, Klaus W90
Borowski, Guy E436
Borowsky, Kurt T. P446
Borowy, Michael E173
Boroyevich, Dushan P515
Borr, Craig A. P614
Borras, Maria Claudia A95
Borras, Michelle P272
Borrelli, Bill E118
Borrelli, Jerry G. A32
Borrini, Amerigo W31
Borsig, Clemens A. H. A290
Borsig, Clemens A. H. W63
Borsig, Clemens A. H. W119
Borst, Walter G. A578
Borst, George E. A807
Borth, Randi P37
Bortner, Andrea R. A404
Borton, Craig S. P614
Boruch, Robert F. P19
Boruch, James P515
Borus, David M. P586
Borwankar, Satish B. W347
Bos, Hans P19
Boscan, Mauricio A203
Bosch, Joe E327
Bosch, Joseph A. (Joe) A255
Bosch, Jose W43
Bosch, Dina W240
Boschelli, John M. A484
Boschetto, Laurence J. A459
Boschini, Victor J. P500
Boschmans, Didier E195
Boschulte, Alfred F. (Al) P525
Boscia, Jon A. A738
Boscia, Jon A. P498
Boscia, Jon A. W339
Bosco, S. Y. A290
Bosco, John P196
Bosco, Pat P266
Bosco, John P353
Bose, Michael A67
Bose, Supratim A133
Bose, Henry P575
Bose, U N W264
Boser, Ron E215
Bosio, Lori A455
Bosio, Amy P158
Bosken, Sean P347
Boskin, Michael J. A311
Boskin, Michael J. A618
Bosma, Brad E201
Bosma, Roger A499
Bospflug, Lance F. E377
Boss, Robert E. A629
Bosscher, James W. P549
Bosse, Pascal A265
Bosse, Jeffrey A. (Jeff) P273
Bosse, Shawna P364
Bosse, Christine (Stine) W258
Bossert, Terry E390
Bossh, Andi A212
Bossick, Jerry A538
Bossidy, Lawrence A. (Larry) A118
Bossina, Bruno W190
Bosso, Edward (Ed) P201
Bost, Melton S. A451
Bost, Glenn E. A653
Boster, David P67
Bostick, Mark P613
Bostock, Roy J. A248
Bostock, Roy J. A568
Bostock, Zachary P339
Bostock, Nathan W300
Bostoen, Paul W199
Boston, Wallace E. (Wally) E31
Boston, Byron L. E135
Boston, Bradford J. (Brad) A182

Boston, Joseph G. P350
Boston, Joe P350
Boston, W. Terry P388
Bostrom, Susan L (Sue) E71
Bostrom, Brent P213
Bosway, W. T. A290
Boswell, Mike E439
Boswell, Scott A208
Boswell, Gina R. A526
Boswell, Justin C. A697
Boswell, Justin C. A751
Boswell, Thomas W. P150
Boswell, Stephen T. P481
Bosworth, Stephen W. P556
Bot, Tim E385
Botes, Hermien W26
Bothmann, Larry P489
Botimer, Ted E436
Botin, Ana P. W46
Botin, Javier A46
Botkins, David B. A264
Botman, Selma P570
Botstein, Leon P45
Botta, G. Andrea A390
Bottaro, Drew J. A857
Bottcher, Sharon P533
Bottegbelz, Botteghelz Canga W9
Botteghelz, Alejandro Canga W9
Bottger, Graeme W. A30
Botti, Bill E518
Botti, Jean J. W15
Bottin, Ron P325
Bottini, Mark A107
Bottino, Lou P527
Bottomley, Steven A. A431
Bottoms, William (Bill) P243
Bottrill, Lorry P463
Botts, Larry P450
Boubel, Gary A416
Bouc, Herve Le W74
Bouchard, Andre C. (Butch) E464
Bouchard, Butch E464
Bouchard, Angelee F. A411
Bouchard, Jose A698
Bouchard, Robert P18
Bouchard, Father Charles E. P113
Bouchard, Alain W18
Bouchard, Francis W392
Boucher, Doug E34
Boucher, Robert A697
Boucher, Mary E. P129
Boucher, David P539
Boucher, Chris P571
Boucher, Richie W52
Boucher, Richie W53
Boucher, Sylvain Sylvain
    Boucher W374
Bouchut, Pierre B. W146
Bouck, Steven F. (Steve) E518
Bouckaert, Alfred W37
Boud, Janet P155
Boudreau, Kenneth A (Ken) E365
Boudreau, Donald L. P374
Boudreaux, Gail K. A838
Boudreaux, Gail A883
Boudreaux, Allen R. P325
Boudreaux, Gerald P372
Boudreaux, Carolyn P496
Boufidis, Dimitrios P158
Boughton, Keith E327
Bougon, Philippe W312
Bouhara, Yassine W367
Bouillion, Harold J. A767
Bouillot, Isabelle W108
Bouknight, Jacob A. (Lon) A673
Boulanger, Normand A. (Norm) E437
Boulet, Virginia A170
Bouligny, James A. A668
Boulos, Paul F. P334
Boultbee, Paula E376
Boulter, Brian A616
Boulter, Philip P129
Bouman, Rosemarie A539
Bounds, Patricia E301
Bounds, Barry P406

Bourdeau, Denis P213
Bourdon, Lynn L. A299
Bourez, Veronique A199
Bourgeois, Sheryl A. P105
Bourgeois, Gene P502
Bourges, Olivier W156
Bourgie, Pierre W243
Bourgoine, Michael C. (Mike) P32
Bourgoyne, Patrick A489
Bourke, Neville W53
Bourla, Albert A641
Bourland, Don P379
Bourne, Jeffrey T. P255
Bourque, Michael P555
Bourque, Daniel P555
Bourque, Mike P555
Bousbib, Ari A422
Boushey, Richard A. P336
Bousquet, Lisa P398
Bousquet, Gilles P581
Boustead, Rebecca A481
Boustridge, Michael W80
Boutchard, Brian A665
Bouton, Daniel W362
Bouton, Daniel W374
Boutros, Akram P467
Boutross, Joseph P. (Joe) A517
Bouts, Erik A624
Boutwell, Jim P134
Bouvier, Robert P251
Bouvier, Dominique W376
Bouygues, Olivier W23
Bouygues, Olivier W74
Bouygues, Martin W74
Bouygues, Olivier W74
Bouygues, Francis W75
Bova, Tiffani E196
Bovardi, Gerald A169
Bove, Elena M. (Lane) P289
Bovender, Jack O. A100
Bovey, Victor E36
Bowden, Cynthia E317
Bowden, Lloyd M. A876
Bowden, Murrae P480
Bowden, Andrew W388
Bowen, Robert L. (Bob) E5
Bowen, Bruce M. E154
Bowen, Kevin C. E226
Bowen, Brent E308
Bowen, Eric E397
Bowen, Rick A. A30
Bowen, Jeffrey A239
Bowen, Edward G. A327
Bowen, Nicholas S. (Nick) A455
Bowen, Lane M. A490
Bowen, Paul L. A494
Bowen, John A857
Bowen, Robert L. P74
Bowen, Kris L. P74
Bowen, Patricia P247
Bowen, John J. P261
Bowen, DeLyle P600
Bowen, Terry W385
Bower, John E338
Bower, Joseph L. A520
Bower, Charles P313
Bowerman, Laurel L. A856
Bowers, G. Thomas E173
Bowers, Chris A70
Bowers, William (Steve) A322
Bowers, G. Thomas A343
Bowers, W. Paul A381
Bowers, Paul A381
Bowers, W. Paul A381
Bowers, Elizabeth W. A605
Bowers, W. Paul A737
Bowers, Dan A786
Bowers, Kimberly S. (Kim) A841
Bowers, Rodney E P85
Bowers, Reveta P87
Bowers, Amy P159
Bowers, Brenda J. P606
Bowes, Patrick W266
Bowie, Arvelia A806

Bratt, Mikael W382
Bratton, William J. (Bill) A570
Braude, Michael A478
Brauer, Stephen F. A45
Brauer, Mark P242
Brauer-Rieke, David (Dave) P281
Braun, Michael H. E165
Braun, William (Bill) A176
Braun, Alan W. A611
Braun, Corey R. A620
Braun, Robert C. A671
Braun, Robert C. A673
Braun, Harland P221
Braun, Alan W. P273
Braun, Neil S. P373
Braun, Robert P516
Braun, Liz P532
Braun, David P562
Braunscheidel, Stephen J. A524
Braunstein, Douglas L. (Doug) A476
Brause, Kenneth A. (Ken) A184
Brautigan, Bernie A709
Braveman, Peter E. P98
Braverman, Peter E525
Braverman, Alan N. A260
Braverman, Joshua A314
Bravo, Rose Marie A874
Brawer, Michael E332
Brawley, S. Mark A45
Brawley, Kevin A702
Brawner, Paul B. A782
Braxton, Zach E337
Braxton, Charles R. (Chuck) P341
Bray, Jay E339
Bray, Jeffrey E384
Bray, John K. A587
Bray, Andrea P5
Bray, Robert J. P453
Brayboy, Regina P. P417
Brazaitis, Greg A295
Brazel, Darin E239
Brazil, John R. A157
Brazones, Steven E391
Brda, Bruce A570
Breach, Sue A270
Bready, Richard L. P261
Breaker, Imani A800
Breakiron-Evans, Maureen A201
Breault, Paul R E313
Breaux, John B. A231
Breaux, Ernest P. A440
Breaux, Lonnie P312
Breazeale, Tracey T E415
Brecher, Benjamin E215
Brecher, Todd A142
Brecher, Mark E. A498
Breda, Anita van P616
Bredimus, Andre W40
Breeden, Kenneth R. A789
Breeden, Susan D. P574
Breen, Robert P (Bob) E484
Breen, Edward D. (Ed) A205
Breen, Maura C. A309
Breen, Adrian O. A337
Breen, John G. A751
Breen, Patrick A881
Breen, Janice P102
Breen, Jennifer P621
Breene, R. Timothy S. (Tim) W6
Breetz, William H. (Bill) A494
Breffort, Jean-Claude W107
Brega, Jo?o C. A871
Bregier, Fabrice Fabrice Bregier W15
Bregman, Benjamin E77
Breheny, James J. P610
Brehm, John P115
Brehm, Laura P571
Brehm, Larry G. P578
Brehmer-Songer, Sina P541
Breid, Joe P299
Breidenbach, Fred A. A774
Breidenthal, Heather E439
Breier, Benjamin A. A490
Breier, Barbara P502
Breig, Geralyn R. A92

Breig, J P540
Breiling, Kurt J E85
Breitenfeldt, Steve P299
Breitenstein, Nancy E206
Brekke, Alice P573
Breland, Ron P243
Brelsford, Kevin E460
Brelsford, James F. (Jim) A714
Bremner, Christy E438
Brenden, Jon W258
Brennan, Shannon E47
Brennan, Gregory E91
Brennan, Pat E163
Brennan, Christine E346
Brennan, Troyen A. A237
Brennan, Joseph P. A252
Brennan, Jason A267
Brennan, John A375
Brennan, John J. (Jack) A399
Brennan, Kevin A460
Brennan, Donald A. (Don) A491
Brennan, Suzanne R. A627
Brennan, Donald G. (Don) P430
Brennan, James F. P505
Brennan, John A. P521
Brennan, Marty P526
Brennan, Donna P543
Brennan, Suzanne R. P550
Brennan, Richard P. P589
Brennan, Vincent W52
Brenneman, Gregory D. (Greg) A84
Brenneman, Gregory D. (Greg) A422
Brenneman, Konie P274
Brenneman, Dave P307
Brenneman, Cloyd E P449
Brenneman, Ronald A. (Ron) W54
Brenner, Janice E155
Brenner, Karen A32
Brenner, Willard C. (Bill) A412
Brenner, Timothy L. A579
Brenner, Victoria P. P187
Brenner, Michael P397
Brenner, Elizabeth (Betsy) P504
Brenner, Suzanne E. P522
Brenner, Catherine W25
Brentan, Andrea W139
Brenton, Rebecca E. (Beci) A438
Brenzia, John N. A713
Breon, Richard C. (Rick) P464
Bresch, Heather A573
Brescia, Franco R. W348
Breshears, Betty S. P283
Breskin, William A. P69
Bresky, Steven J. A722
Breslau, Robert (Bob) P483
Breslawski, James P. A719
Breslin, Sean J. E47
Breslin, Christopher (Chris) A553
Breslin, Susan P149
Breslin, Michael J. P347
Bresnahan, Ann W. A146
Bresnahan, Roger P406
Bresnan, Kim E507
Bresnan, Jennifer (Jen) A161
Bresney, John P. A725
Bresnick, Gerald I. A416
Bressler, Richard J. A442
Bressler, Gregory P329
Bressman, Michelle A823
Bretches, David C. A60
Bretl, Jim P140
Breton, Michele P363
Breton, Thierry W87
Breton, Claude W243
Brett, Anne Liners P283
Brett, Malcolm P400
Breukink, Henk W. W188
Breunig, Joseph C. (Joe) A94
Breunig, Debbie P275
Brew, Catherine A543
Brewer, Robert E172
Brewer, Keith E257
Brewer, David E318
Brewer, Ty E393
Brewer, Allen M. A353

Brewer, Rosalind G. A519
Brewer, John E. A535
Brewer, Mike A592
Brewer, Eric A765
Brewer, Rosalind G. A853
Brewer, Geoffrey P202
Brewer, Richard P413
Brewer, Richard B. P465
Brewster, David B. E148
Brewster, D Craig E625
Brewster, Vanta P212
Breya, Margaret E245
Breyer, James W. (Jim) A312
Breyer, James W. (Jim) A854
Brian, Linda Jean P51
Brian, Mark P66
Brian, Gerald P212
Briand, Remi P544
Brice, Todd D. A713
Brice, Thomas A. A713
Bricker, Jude E24
Bricker, Diane P141
Brickley, Liam E172
Brickley, Grant E514
Brickley, David P540
Brickman, David M. A362
Brickman, Christian A. (Chris) A488
Briddon, Bob A92
Bride, Tom E153
Bride, Dick E495
Bride, Tom P242
Bridge, Tracy A167
Bridge, Gary A182
Bridge, Anthony R. A833
Bridge, William P460
Bridge-Cook, Jeremy E283
Bridgecook, Jeremy E283
Bridgeford, Gregory M. (Greg) A523
Bridgeman, Bill E169
Bridgeman, Ulysses L. (Junior) A329
Bridges, Lindell E155
Bridges, Richard E185
Bridges, Rachel A234
Bridges, David E. A674
Bridges, Josh P222
Bridges, Robert D. P341
Bridges, Marty P375
Bridges, Scott P492
Bridgewater, Diane C. A156
Bridgewater, Ronald D. A615
Bridgman, Peter A. A638
Bridleman, Dan E263
Bridwell, Tucker S. A338
Brieck, John W. E356
Brien, Donna A354
Brien, Nick A459
Brien, William W. P98
Brien, Michael W340
Brier, Donald P. de A608
Brier, Kenneth P180
Brier, Pamela S. (Pam) P293
Briere, Martin A30
Briesemeister, Wayne P75
Briganti, Irena A816
Brigden, John F A772
Brigeman, Benjamin L. A720
Briger, Peter L. E181
Briger, Peter L. A359
Briggs, Jon E339
Briggs, Clark E435
Briggs, Steve E472
Briggs, Timothy W. A86
Briggs, Jack D. A332
Briggs, Robert W. A346
Briggs, Brandon P63
Briggs, Mary P111
Briggs, Steve P458
Bright, Justin E139
Bright, Brian N. A52
Bright, Mark A67
Brighton, W. Curtis A339
Brignano, Michel E156
Brillet, Rene W87
Brimhall, Craig A53
Brimner, Steven H. A262

Brin, Sergey A389
Brin, Jean-Francois W309
Brina, Cora A673
Brinded, Malcolm W303
Brines, Ned W. A235
Bringaze, Walter L. P372
Bringle, Charlie P102
Brink, Frank T E443
Brink, Greg A592
Brink, Edward M. P535
Brink, Brian W26
Brinkama, Susan P117
Brinker, Scott A407
Brinker, James E. A629
Brinker, Laura A664
Brinker, Mayleen P382
Brinker, Nancy G. P531
Brinker, Nancy G. P532
Brinker, Eric P532
Brinkerhoff, Joris W E227
Brinkley, Christine E297
Brinkley, Cynthia J. (Cindy) A377
Brinkley, Vernon N. P338
Brinkley, Amy W. W358
Brinkman, Noel E30
Brinton, Mark E294
Brinzo, John S. A26
Brinzo, John S. A248
Briquet, Claude W312
Briscoe, Julee P496
Brisebois, Alain W18
Briseno, Monica A782
Briskman, Louis J. A191
Brisnehan, Monica A587
Bristow, Derek R. E414
Bristow, Kent E464
Britain, James E98
Britanik, Thomas P. (Tom) A191
Britell, Jenne K. A230
Britell, Jenne K. A683
Britell, Jenne K. A832
Brito, Carlos W28
Britt, Irene Chang A149
Britt, Glenn A. A153
Britt, Chess A660
Britt, Glenn A. A800
Britt, Glenn A. A885
Britt, John M. P234
Brittain, Willard W. (Woody) A243
Brittain, Willard W. (Woody) A430
Brittain, Jeffrey C. P424
Britten, David L. A833
Britti, Michael E393
Brittin, Matthew (Matt) W194
Brittis, Julie P612
Britton, Matt E462
Britton, Betsy Noyes P259
Britz, Ronald L. A782
Brizius, Charles A. A442
Brlas, Laurie A189
Brlas, Laurie A586
Broach, Danny E60
Broad, Molly Corbett P400
Broad, M P413
Broadbent, Sir Richard W352
Broadbent, Jillian Jillian
　　Broadbent W390
Broaddus, J. Alfred A530
Broaddus, J. Alfred A621
Broader, Shelley G. A687
Broader, Shelley G. A853
Broadley, Philip W265
Broadman, Bart Joseph W123
Broadus, Charles E. (Chuck) A25
Broadus, Chuck A25
Broadwater, Tracy A281
Broadwell, Steve P459
Broback, Craig P210
Brochick, George A635
Brochu, David F. P261
Brock, Jeffrey E111
Brock, Anthony E160
Brock, Beth E317
Brock, John F. A200
Brock, Macon F. A263

A = AMERICAN BUSINESS
E = EMERGING COMPANIES
P = PRIVATE COMPANIES
W = WORLD BUSINESS

Chevalier, Hector O. E434
Chevalier, John T. A664
Chevallon, Sophie W107
Chevardiere, Patrick de La W362
Chevet, Pierre-Franck W156
Cheviron, Mark J. A72
Chevre, Claude W163
Chevrette, John P66
Chevrier, Robert W108
Chew, Andrew E384
Chew, Anna T. E489
Chew, Ching-Meng A284
Chew, Lee Fang (Sophia) A451
Chew, Lewis A643
Chew, Roy P269
Chew, Jeffrey S. T. W271
Chew, Paul W309
Chew, Mei Lee W371
Chewens, Michael J. A579
Chewning, Adam E444
Chey, Doug E258
Chey, Tae-Won W322
Chhibbar, Vishal E160
Chi, Gregory A555
Chi, Sung-Ha W306
Chia, Douglas K. A470
Chia-Wei, Prof Woo W212
Chiang, W. C. W. (Willie) A220
Chiang, Hai Hwai (HH) A465
Chiang, Willie C.W. A608
Chiappetta, Marco E344
Chiaramonte, Christina A770
Chiaravalle, Paul P125
Chiarelli, Peter A405
Chiarello, Guy A476
Chiaro, Preston W294
Chiaro, Preston W295
Chiasson, Glenn J. A147
Chiccino, Peter (Pete) E470
Chiccino, Peter (Pete) A797
Chicoine, Jerry L. A316
Chicoine, David L. A566
Chicoine, Michelle L. P129
Chidiac, Therese P445
Chidichimo, Pedro A723
Child, Martin E114
Child, George L. P5
Child-Villiers, Roddy W249
Childers, Steven L. (Steve) E103
Childers, Kim E441
Childers, Keith A606
Childers, Susan P10
Childress, Jeffrey E135
Childress, Jan C. A221
Childress, Aaron L. A235
Childress, Sabrina P369
Childress, Wade P492
Childs, Stephanie K. A218
Childs, Sarah B. P123
Childs, Joe P161
Childs, Alfred B. P297
Chillcott, John W39
Chillemi, John A603
Chilton, Randy E363
Chilton, Gen. Kevin P. A60
Chilton, Malcolm A229
Chilton, Kevin A508
Chilton, Penny P124
Chilton, Collette P394
Chin, Phillip E77
Chin, Dean A. A7
Chin, Woodrow A253
Chin, Michael Y. A782
Chin, Bobby W271
Chin, Elaine W332
Chin-Leong, Allison W367
China, John D. E455
China, John D. A770
Chinchilla, Randall A664
Chinchurreta, Tiffany E339
Ching, Christina A12
Ching, Glenn K.C. A168
Ching, David T. A804
Ching, Bob P222
Ching, Koh Ching W271

Ching, Man Kam W278
Ching, Sng W388
Chinn, Derek L. A856
Chinoy, Cyrus E240
Chiocchi, Frank A260
Chiodo, Deborah P198
Chiovari, Sal E141
Chiovaro, Jerry E452
Chipman, Ray P75
Chippendale, Ian A32
Chiquet, Maureen W377
Chirac, Bernadette W216
Chirico, Emanuel (Manny) A251
Chirico, Emanuel (Manny) A677
Chisholm, John W. E177
Chisholm, Rev Gregory P575
Chisholm, Bill Bill Chisholm W30
Chism, Jim P182
Chitwood, Deborah E93
Chiu, Thomas C. T. A158
Chiu, Amy H. A726
Chiu, Lisa P95
Chiu, Simon P357
Chiu, David P519
Chiu, Sung Hong W103
Chiuch, Robert A103
Chiwei, Wang W197
Chizak, Timothy E181
Chizen, Bruce R. A618
Chlebowski, John F. E416
Chlebowski, John F. A342
Chlebowski, John F. A603
Chmielewski, Stefano W382
Chmielinski, Jane A. A12
Chmura, Michael J. P39
Chny, Keith E91
Cho, SungHwan E32
Cho, Daniel E243
Cho, Sung Hwan A441
Cho, JeongHoon (Joseph) A698
Cho, Namju P87
Cho, Christine P221
Cho, Dam W198
Cho, In-Kook W205
Cho, Soon W322
Cho, Fujio W328
Cho, Fujio W363
Choate, Jerry D. A57
Choate, William Millard A327
Choate, Jerry D. A841
Choate, David P80
Choate, Ron P184
Chochoy, Gerard A322
Chodak, Paul A47
Chofuku, Yasuhiro Yasuhiro
    Chofuku W225
Choi, Justin C. A63
Choi, Sonia A135
Choi, Jack A875
Choi, Young Han W198
Choi, In Gyu W198
Choi, Gee-Sung W307
Choi, Buhmsoo W316
Choi, Myung-Hae W322
Chojnowski, Richard A579
Chokki, Morikazu W230
Choksi, Umesh E32
Choksi, Mary C. A89
Choksi, Mary C. A614
Cholmondeley, Paula H. J. A791
Chomet, Patrick W379
Chong, Dan E196
Chong, Ivan E245
Chong, David C.H. E494
Chong, Arthur A137
Chong, Boo Ching (BC) A275
Chong, Kie Cheong W371
Choo, Michael W200
Choo, Kangsoo W206
Choong, Cecilia E196
Chopra, Deepak E362
Chopra, Naveen E474
Chopra, Vivek A215
Chopra, Tejpreet S. A374
Choquette, Pierre A698

Chorosz, Gilbert C. A226
Chosy, James L. A819
Chou, Phidias E451
Chou, John G. A55
Chou, Shu-Chang W345
Chou, Chun-Lung W345
Chou, Chen-Tsai W345
Choudhury, S. Roy W164
Choufuku, Yasuhiro W225
Chouthai, Manoj S. A673
Choutka, Michael J. P229
Chow, Joseph E464
Chow, Henry W. K. A11
Chow, Joan K. A218
Chow, Wendy P232
Chow, Sir Chung-Kong (C.K.) W26
Chow, Kareen W221
Chowdhury, Ravneet W332
Choy, Lee Kok A558
Chresand, George P181
Chretien, Olivier W385
Chriatianson, Tony J E40
Chrin, John R. A79
Chrisman, Timothy R. A97
Chriss, Timothy D. A. P534
Christ, Robin E199
Christ, Carol T. P533
Christal, Nancy R. A237
Christatos, Steve S. A318
Christen, Dennis E3
Christen, Noel E3
Christensen, Christopher R. E150
Christensen, Roy E. E150
Christensen, Gus E159
Christensen, Kent W E162
Christensen, Karen E460
Christensen, Jamie E520
Christensen, Neil A253
Christensen, Jim A418
Christensen, Wesley J. A616
Christensen, Robert J. (Bob) A625
Christensen, Steven D. A782
Christensen, Jonna A850
Christensen, Joel G. P317
Christensen, Norman L. P509
Christensen, Claus W258
Christenson, Carl R. E26
Christensson, Anders W382
Christian, Wayne E209
Christian, David A. A264
Christian, Mark A627
Christian, Nathan E. A861
Christian, Brandy J. P432
Christian, A. Brooke P547
Christian, Brooke P547
Christian, Ralf W320
Christiansen, David A E79
Christiansen, John A60
Christiansen, Niels B. W122
Christianson, Jeffrey A. (Jeff) E163
Christianson, Peter E473
Christianson, Wei Sun A568
Christianson, Ron P361
Christie, Edward E436
Christie, Ted E436
Christie, Robert S. E507
Christie, Blair A182
Christie, William T. A320
Christie, Anthony A508
Christie, Tod S. A723
Christie, John S. P318
Christman, Kenneth E444
Christman, Daniel W E466
Christman, John A337
Christman, Peter C. A836
Christman, Peter P580
Christodolou, Michael N. E275
Christodoulou, Petros W244
Christodoulou, Nikos W244
Christoffersen, Tim P114
Christoffersen, Terri P566
Christofilis, Charles A. A344
Christon, Leslie P527
Christopher, Eric E93
Christopher, T E197

Christopher, Cynthia A311
Christopher, John Y. A416
Christopher, Norman C. P111
Christopher, Richard T. (Dick) P341
Christopherson, Matt P349
Christopoulou, Constantina A203
Christy, Caleb E456
Christy, James A. A667
Christy, James A669
Chrol, Barry E521
Chrominska, Sylvia D. W54
Chromy, Debra P303
Chronican, Philip (Phil) W33
Chronis, Damon N. P425
Chronis, Julie P425
Chrysler, L. Gage A811
Chryst, Dana A. A366
Chu, William A91
Chu, Chinh E. A105
Chu, Gary A376
Chu, Michael A723
Chu, Ron A807
Chu, Dan A851
Chu, David S.C. P247
Chu, Victor L.L. W392
Chuang, Alfred S. P575
Chuanzhi, Liu W212
Chubachi, Ryoji W328
Chuchottaworn, Pailin W285
Chugg, Juliana L. A376
Chugg, Juliana L. A846
Chugh, Davinder K. W30
Chulick, Tom A822
Chulos, Nicholas J. A342
Chumbley, Bud P31
Chun, Michael J. A101
Chung, Christopher E340
Chung, D. Christopher E340
Chung, Canice T. K. E485
Chung, Nelson A158
Chung, Michael H.K. A281
Chung, Yoon (Michael) A631
Chung, Paul W. A779
Chung, Madelene A792
Chung, Suk Soo W178
Chung, Dong-Rack W205
Chung, Hae-Joo W205
Chung, Joon-Yang W281
Chunguang, Li W97
Church, Steven C. (Steve) A91
Church, John R. A376
Church, Steve A. P206
Church, Steven A. P273
Church, Dean P389
Churchill, Andreah E317
Churchill, Clinton R. A101
Churchill, Bruce B. A255
Churchill, Gregory S. (Greg) A708
Churchill, Winston J. P192
Churchouse, Robin W390
Churchward, Guy A287
Churilla, Mark P444
Chye, Spencer Lee Tien W220
Ch'ien, Raymond K. F. W162
Ciaccia, Mario W189
Cialdella, Vincent E507
Ciampa, Dominick A583
Ciampa, Vicki P293
Ciancarelli, Lisa E28
Cianci, Tony E290
Cianci, Peter A273
Cianciaruso, Daniela A871
Cianciolo, Joseph M. A830
Ciancutti, John A583
Cianfrocca, Mike A720
Ciangi, Bob E167
Ciarrocchi, Michael A15
Ciavardone, John M. P347
Ciavarro, Domenic P129
Cibulka, Debbie E35
Ciccarello, Joe E430
Cicchinelli, Joleen E175
Cicchitelli, Allan H. P90
Cicco, Martin J. E159
Ciccone, Andy A391

A = AMERICAN BUSINESS
E = EMERGING COMPANIES
P = PRIVATE COMPANIES
W = WORLD BUSINESS

Cicconi, James W. (Jim) A80
Cicero, Kerry E220
Cicero, Richard P277
Cichocki, Andrew R. (Andy) A25
Cichowski, Lorraine P503
Cicurel, Michel W324
Cid, Manuel W41
Ciervo, Carman P268
Ciesinski, Stephen J. (Steve) P465
Cieslak, John B. W243
Cilia, Robert E114
Ciliberti, Connie A800
Cinar, Ali P243
Cindrich, Robert J. A573
Cinicola, John T. P585
Cinnamon, Todd E24
Cinotto, John A. P453
Cintron, Rocky D. P191
Ciocca, Arthur A. P575
Cioffi, Angela P192
Cioffi, George A. (Jack) P280
Cione, Todd E389
Ciongol, Adam G. A515
Cioppa, Joseph D. A167
Cipolla, Laine E77
Cipperly, Maryanne E3
Cipriano, Frank E172
Cipriano, Giovanna A356
Cipullo, Donald D. P329
Cirelli, Rosemary P190
Cirelli, Jean-Francois W156
Ciresi, Michael V. P577
Cirillo, Paulette P293
Cirillo-Goldberg, Mary A. W8
Cirksena, Mark P157
Cischke, Susan M. (Sue) A357
Cisel, Scott A. A45
Ciserani, Giovanni A664
Ciskowski, Michael S. (Mike) A841
Cisle, Donald M. A337
Cisne, Richard A104
Cisneros, Aurelio E360
Cisneros, Sharon P167
Cisneros, Henry G. P218
Citarella, Paul E176
Citarella, Claudia P133
Citrino, Mary Anne A263
Citrino, Mary Anne A411
Citron, Mark C E252
Cittadine, Steve A22
Ciulla, John R. A858
Ciurli, Stefano W348
Ciutiis, James E35
Civera, Edward S. (Ed) P308
Civgin, Don A36
Civil, Patricia T. A579
Civisca, Michael L. A577
Clack, Floyd P162
Cladouhos, Sherry L. A384
Claesson, Pehr W143
Claflin, Bruce L. A11
Claflin, Blair A234
Clair, Guillaume Saint E8
Clair, Keith E. St. A138
Clair, Vanja St. A329
Clair, Joyce St. A600
Clair, Joyce A600
Clair, Ronald A725
Clair, Mark St. P104
Claire, Wayne St. A138
Clairs, Reginald J. (Reg) W106
Clamen, Warren E235
Clamon, Jean W71
Clancey, John P. A25
Clancy, Shawn F. A121
Clancy, Paul J. A123
Clancy, Maureen E. A583
Clancy, Celia A804
Clancy, Robert G. (Rob) A876

Clancy, Mikki P319
Clancy, Maureen P597
Clancy, Maureen E. P613
Clanin, Robert J. (Bob) P75
Clapper, David M. A770
Clappin, James P. A225
Clappison, John H. W340
Clardy, Janet E268
Clare, Peter J. A129
Clare, Daniel G. A371
Clare, Peter W388
Clarey, Patricia T. (Pat) A411
Clarey, John P75
Clariond, Eugenio A578
Clark, Andrew S. E65
Clark, Todd E77
Clark, Alistair E97
Clark, Dennis M. E142
Clark, Jonathan E146
Clark, John H. E169
Clark, Kimberly E220
Clark, Jennifer B E232
Clark, Mary L E245
Clark, Ronald M E291
Clark, Kelly L. E298
Clark, James E306
Clark, Kevin E306
Clark, Mel E315
Clark, Doug E317
Clark, Scott E339
Clark, Craig E. E355
Clark, John E367
Clark, Karen E396
Clark, Robert E408
Clark, Jennifer B E417
Clark, Frank M. A15
Clark, Paul N. A20
Clark, Mayree C. A38
Clark, Alexander M. (Alex) A48
Clark, Gina K. A55
Clark, Stanley L. A58
Clark, John T. A90
Clark, Terrence A140
Clark, Wendy A198
Clark, J. David A210
Clark, Trippy A213
Clark, George L. A253
Clark, Frank M. A305
Clark, John J. A320
Clark, Thomas B. A341
Clark, Mark T. A345
Clark, David A376
Clark, R. Kerry A376
Clark, Celeste A. A481
Clark, Robert W. A495
Clark, Michael S. A517
Clark, Janet F. A527
Clark, Kevin A547
Clark, Simon A592
Clark, Robert C. A614
Clark, Ronald K. A637
Clark, Matt A680
Clark, Adm. Vernon E. (Vern) A689
Clark, Bernard J. A720
Clark, Randall L. A726
Clark, William E. (Bill) A729
Clark, Jonathan C. (Jon) A731
Clark, Henry A. A738
Clark, Carine A772
Clark, Andrew D. A782
Clark, R. Kerry A795
Clark, Robert C. A802
Clark, Howard L. A832
Clark, Chris A849
Clark, Frank M. A858
Clark, Shane P14
Clark, O. B. P32
Clark, Roger S. P32
Clark, Theodore A. P39
Clark, Sam P66
Clark, Max P75
Clark, Joan P80
Clark, Rodney L. P104
Clark, Julie P109
Clark, Robert G. (Bob) P118

Clark, Mary Jane P143
Clark, Monty P215
Clark, Laron P220
Clark, Kathy P222
Clark, Dirck P225
Clark, Edward B P249
Clark, Jeffrey P264
Clark, Wayne P280
Clark, Wayne L. P281
Clark, MaryAnn P287
Clark, Douglas R. (Doug) P317
Clark, Paul P332
Clark, Greg P334
Clark, Bernard J. P341
Clark, Carl E. P347
Clark, Matt P371
Clark, J. Daniel (Dan) P399
Clark, Terry P456
Clark, Adm. Vernon E. (Vern) P465
Clark, Charlotte P514
Clark, John B. P528
Clark, Frank M. P535
Clark, Michael P553
Clark, Paul G. P569
Clark, E. Culpepper (Cully) P569
Clark, Murray B. P570
Clark, Alice M. P571
Clark, Sandy P580
Clark, Kevin D. P589
Clark, Celeste P592
Clark, A. Bayard P600
Clark, Troy P601
Clark, J. R. P611
Clark, Richard P. W6
Clark, Brian W25
Clark, Gregory J. W33
Clark, Chris W72
Clark, Chris W80
Clark, Ian T. W297
Clark, W. Edmund (Ed) W358
Clark, Paul M. W358
Clark, W. Edmund (Ed) W358
Clarke, Boyd E119
Clarke, Terry E136
Clarke, Ronald F. (Ron) E176
Clarke, Loren E332
Clarke, Ian A63
Clarke, Janet M. A74
Clarke, Mark C. A285
Clarke, Peter J. A302
Clarke, Sheilagh M. A356
Clarke, Jeremy A572
Clarke, Troy A578
Clarke, Thomas E. A585
Clarke, Thomas E. A592
Clarke, Thomas E. A755
Clarke, Charles J. (Chuck) A810
Clarke, A. J. (Andy) A853
Clarke, Sean A853
Clarke, Stephen L. P25
Clarke, Richard L. (Dick) P112
Clarke, Chris P218
Clarke, David M. P332
Clarke, Jayne P490
Clarke, Charles W175
Clarke, Tracy J. W331
Clarke, Philip (Phil) W352
Clarkeson, John S. A303
Clarkin, Michael E456
Clarkson, Thomas F. A36
Clarkson, Lawrence W. P173
Clarkson, James R. P239
Clarkson, Jeff P306
Claros, Carlos P334
Clary, Thomas S. A339
Clary, James P413
Clatterbuck, Janice E. A320
Clau?en, Hans-Peter W240
Claudel, Shelley P127
Claudy, Frank P203
Claunch, Don P619
Claus, Gary A336
Clausen, Christian W258
Clauson, Cathy E14
Claussen, Hans Hans Claussen W240

Clavel, Pierre W156
Clavelle, Joanne P439
Clawson, Curtis J. A503
Clawson, Tom A716
Claxton, Robert C. A121
Clay, Shannon E339
Clay, Craig A267
Clay, Sheilah P. A319
Clay, Jason P616
Clayton, Lemuel E355
Clayton, John D. E404
Clayton, Joseph P. A258
Clayton, Janet A285
Clayton, R. Bruce A378
Clayton, Marvin A496
Clayton, Andrew R. (Andy) A600
Clayton, Kent A786
Clayton, Philip A. (Phil) P134
Clayton, Kevin L. P281
Clayton, Julie P373
Clayton, Rose P446
Clayton, Bret W294
Clayton, Bret W295
Clayton, Annette K. W312
Clear, Will E390
Clearman, John F. A856
Cleary, Philip E103
Cleary, Shaun E301
Cleary, Patricia K. A456
Cleary, Michael J. A475
Cleary, Dermott A592
Cleary, Anne M. A603
Cleary, Mike P170
Cleary, Charlie P549
Cleckley, Joan A. A630
Cleeland, Rev David W. P43
Clegg, Michael E150
Clegg, Michael P. E344
Clegg, Paul A689
Cleland, Jack H. A226
Cleland, Robert P290
Clem, Kerry E10
Clem, John E439
Clemans, Clint E41
Clemens, Quint E41
Clemens, Debbie E355
Clemens, Paul F. A342
Clemens, Bruce P29
Clemens, Jay W212
Clement, William (Bill) A231
Clement, Linda P10
Clement, Kim P125
Clement, Chris P582
Clement-Holmes, Linda W. A180
Clement-Holmes, Linda W. A664
Clemente, Serge W376
Clementi, Erich A455
Clementi, Michael S. A879
Clements, Dennis E. A74
Clements, James A786
Clements, Tim P7
Clements, Patricia L. P46
Clemins, Archie A508
Clemmens, Robert T. A587
Clemmensen, Larry P385
Clemments, Paul P407
Clemmer, Richard L. (Rick) A580
Clemmer, Terry P249
Clemons, Tanya A641
Clemson, Nigel W34
Clendenin, Phillip A. E35
Clendening, John S. A720
Clerico, John A. A212
Clerkin, Thomas A. (Tom) A633
Clerman, Robert J. P348
Cleveland, Allison E259
Cleveland, Todd M. E371
Cleveland, Ralph A21
Cleveland, Fred E. A46
Cleveland, Cotton M. A303
Cleveland, R. J. A311
Cleveland, Peter M. A451
Cleveland, Brian K. A694
Cleveland, Wade P194
Clevenger, Don J. A294

Cleves, Thomas A. A458
Click, Kevin A644
Click, Rick P326
Clifford, Melinda E64
Clifford, Timothy T. A84
Clifford, Scott A391
Clifford, Paul R. A727
Clifford, John P. A810
Clifford, Michael (Mike) A873
Clifford, R. Leigh W60
Clift, Matthew D. (Matt) E465
Clift, Matt E465
Clifton, David B. A436
Clifton, Rich A582
Clifton, Jim P202
Clifton, Mark A. P465
Clifton, Elwyn M. P504
Clinard, Michael H. (Mike) E77
Cline, David W. E441
Clineburg, Bernard H. A152
Clingan, Jamie L. E387
Clinton, John E373
Clinton, Stephen A362
Clinton, Malissia R. P502
Clipper, Chris A592
Clo, Alberto W141
Clonch, Hugh R. A187
Cloninger, Kriss A17
Cloninger, Charles A. (Chuck) A449
Cloninger, Kathy A206
Clonts, Terese P355
Clontz, Steven A508
Clopton, Ned P423
Clossin, Todd F. A329
Clothier, Kevin C. A230
Clothier, David P386
Clouatre, William P85
Cloud, Sanford (Sandy) A303
Cloud, Raymond J. P338
Clough, Eric E434
Clougher, John A873
Clouse, Mark A493
Cloutier, C. R. (Rusty) E319
Cloutier, Michele A496
Clouzard, Pascal W87
Clubb, Stacy A702
Clurman, Sally K. A369
Cluss, Robert (Bob) P395
Clutton, Stan A538
Clyde, Timothy S. A88
Clyde, R. Andrew A572
Clymer, Jamie E393
Clymer, John A. A855
Clymer, Byron P198
Clyne, Cameron A. W242
Coady, Roxanne E173
Coady, Roxanne J. A343
Coady, Shawn W. A590
Coady, Todd M. A590
Coady, Shawn W. A590
Coady, Linda W137
Coakley, Sheila E. P122
Coalson, James E118
Coalson, Mac A. A338
Coar, Mike E119
Coates, Robert S. A303
Coates, Janet P551
Coates, Julie W390
Coats, Jeffrey H. E46
Cobaleda, Manuel W152
Cobb, David R. E39
Cobb, Ron E181
Cobb, Renae E339
Cobb, D. Keith A35
Cobb, Sue M. A105
Cobb, Lori A234
Cobb, Steve P87
Cobb, William (Bill) P252
Cobb, Father Gerald T. P395
Cobb, Steven D. P535
Cobee, Vincent W255
Coben, Lawrence S. A603
Coble, Scott M. A861
Coblitz, Mark A. A205
Cobo, Santiago W152

Cobourn, Adam W268
Coburn, Gary A91
Coburn, Gordon J. A201
Coburn, John F. A592
Coburn, Gary N. P531
Coccari, Andrew S. E427
Cochell, Jana P63
Cochenour, David P199
Cochet, Philippe W23
Cochran, Chris E389
Cochran, George E421
Cochran, Shields E432
Cochran, Donald B. E497
Cochran, Phyllis E. A578
Cochran, Scott D. A693
Cochran, J. Scott A695
Cochran, Robert L. A826
Cochran, Jeffrey L. (Jeff) P96
Cochran, Clarke P138
Cochran, Dan P410
Cochran, Willie P462
Cochran, Robert W. P508
Cochrane, Collin A464
Cochrane, Luther A479
Cochrane, Bruce P318
Cochrane, Andy P350
Cock, Frans G. De A561
Cockcroft, Richard E196
Cockcroft, Adrian A583
Cocker, Tony W134
Cocklin, Kim R. A81
Cocklin, Kim R. A82
Cockrell, Tony P188
Coco, Cedric T. A523
Cocroft, Duncan H. A850
Codey, Lawrence R. (Larry) A723
Codina, Armando M. A46
Codina, Armando M. A422
Codron, Kris P283
Cody, Philip E331
Cody, Timothy E365
Cody, Derrill A167
Cody, John E. A369
Cody, Gen. Richard A. A497
Cody, William M. (Bill) A666
Cody, Kenneth B. P58
Cody, Jenny P74
Cody, Thomas G. P109
Coe, Jeffrey A. A274
Coe, Nicholas A496
Coe, Jason C. P5
Coel, Kevin S. A216
Coelho, Alexandre da Paix?o W145
Coen, Bill P318
Coen, Bill P578
Coffee, John P74
Coffey, Ryan A295
Coffey, Mark A. A426
Coffey, Marian A661
Coffey, Susan S. P18
Coffey, Kenneth P197
Coffey, Patrick P203
Coffey, Dick P369
Coffey, Charlie W299
Coffey, Philip (Phil) W388
Coffin, Mark W. P446
Coffing, Bridget A541
Coffman, Stephen O. E170
Coffman, Michael C. E368
Coffman, Vance D. A2
Coffman, Vance D. A57
Coffman, Vance D. A246
Coffman, Homer P577
Cogan, Gill E143
Cogan, John F. A383
Cogan, Andy P382
Cogan, Scott P488
Cogdill, William L. P375
Coggin, Michael E432
Cogswell, David A. (Dave) E39
Cohen, Ron E10
Cohen, Yuki E51
Cohen, Alan E131
Cohen, Jonathan Z. E398
Cohen, Daniel G. E470

Cohen, Betsy Zubrow A15
Cohen, Jay M. A78
Cohen, Gary M. A112
Cohen, Paul D. A160
Cohen, William S. A162
Cohen, David L. A205
Cohen, Peggy A267
Cohen, Kenneth P. (Ken) A310
Cohen, Alan M. A386
Cohen, Burton M. A556
Cohen, Martin M. A568
Cohen, Jon R. A683
Cohen, Irwin A768
Cohen, Eric I. A790
Cohen, Martin J. A796
Cohen, Betsy A797
Cohen, Daniel A797
Cohen, Larry P17
Cohen, Linda P19
Cohen, Jon P19
Cohen, Charles P57
Cohen, Richard P57
Cohen, Larry P57
Cohen, Marvin P125
Cohen, Howard P168
Cohen, Vicki P179
Cohen, Gary P212
Cohen, David P287
Cohen, David I P293
Cohen, Harvey P297
Cohen, Andrew P348
Cohen, Drew P348
Cohen, Joseph D. P532
Cohen, Gary M. P566
Cohen, Burton P577
Cohen, Tzahi W48
Cohen, Dan W49
Cohen, Doron W49
Cohen, Florence Baranes W87
Cohen, David W106
Cohilas, Terri A737
Cohn, Betsy E487
Cohn, Robert A172
Cohn, Steven D. A253
Cohn, Gary D. A386
Cohn, Kenneth P. A637
Cohn, Matthew A797
Cohn, Gerald P531
Cohn, Bruce M. P613
Cohodes, Jeffery D. A599
Cohon, Jared L. P93
Cohorst, Mary P114
Coia, Michael A. P288
Coiley, Michael A184
Coinaud, Ghislaine W269
Coker, Bill E432
Coker, Henry B. (Rusty) A25
Coker, R. Howard A734
Coker, James L. A735
Coker, David A. P248
Colacurto, Robert E181
Colafrancesco, Matteo W189
Colaguori, Ron A470
Colaluca, Anthony E300
Colan, Thomas A215
Colander, Charles P172
Colangelo, Eugene S. A132
Colao, Vittorio A. W379
Colarulli, Guy C. P536
Colas, Gilles W107
Colavecchio, William (Bill) P559
Colavita, Michael A764
Colbeck, Roger E379
Colberg, Alan B. A78
Colbert, Virgis W. A100
Colbert, Virgis W. A521
Colbert, Virgis W. A751
Colbert, Ray P548
Colburn, Martin P. A186
Colburn, Ken P341
Colburn, Kenneth P341
Colby, Jim P84
Colby, Ruth P454
Colby, William H. P554
Colclasure, Mark E490

Colcord, Dan P162
Colcord, Dan P163
Cole, Russell G. E66
Cole, Sue E167
Cole, Deborah E172
Cole, Neil E235
Cole, Peter E251
Cole, Phillip T. E321
Cole, Debi E393
Cole, Lauren E455
Cole, Michael R. E495
Cole, Royal E503
Cole, Daniel F. A45
Cole, Russell A138
Cole, David D. A170
Cole, Richard A. A391
Cole, Thomas W. A547
Cole, Gordon A698
Cole, Devin A818
Cole, Charles T. P90
Cole, Jerry P114
Cole, Billy P125
Cole, Stacy P243
Cole, Susan A. P329
Cole, Donald P571
Cole, Randy P598
Cole, Allen P619
Cole, Martin I. (Marty) W6
Cole, Robert W81
Cole-Fontayn, Michael A103
Coleal, David A744
Colecchi, Stephen P488
Colella, Gerald G. E321
Colella, Richard A346
Colella, Carmine A329
Coleman, Caryn E288
Coleman, Jon E294
Coleman, Robert D. E495
Coleman, Leonard S. A89
Coleman, Chris A103
Coleman, Donna A142
Coleman, Kenneth L. (Ken) A189
Coleman, William A267
Coleman, Scott A275
Coleman, Wade A348
Coleman, James D. A349
Coleman, Richard E. A363
Coleman, Mary Sue A470
Coleman, Eugene T. A572
Coleman, Lewis W. (Lew) A602
Coleman, Leonard S. A614
Coleman, Robert F. A662
Coleman, Charles A. (Charlie) A675
Coleman, Lawrence P. A681
Coleman, Kenneth E. A737
Coleman, William T. (Bill) A772
Coleman, Peter J. (Pete) A774
Coleman, Gary L. A806
Coleman, Scott H. A833
Coleman, David P73
Coleman, David P122
Coleman, Dan C. P258
Coleman, Mel P338
Coleman, Robert P445
Coleman, Robert P446
Coleman, Anne Marie P574
Coleman, Michael W218
Coles, Hank E518
Coley, Randolph C (Randy) E121
Coley, William A. (Bill) A633
Colfax, Paul P177
Colford, Paul P503
Colglazier, John A60
Colica, James A. (Jim) A374
Colindren, Jose E305
Colistra, David E304
Coll, Mario M. A60
Coll, Denise M. A755
Coll, Theresa P179
Collacchi, Frank P353
Collado, Shirley M. P395
Collar, Gary L. A18
Collar, Mark A. A337
Collazo, Francisco J. P124
Collazo, Jeannette P294

Dacey, John R. W37
Dach, Leslie A. A853
Dachille, Georgia P415
Dachman, Richard J. A777
Dachowski, Peter R. W107
Dacier, Paul T. A287
Dacus, Steve A853
DaDante, Mitch P119
Dadiseth, Keki B. W284
Dadlez, Christopher M. (Chris) P429
Dadon, Roni E169
Dadyburjor, Khush Khush
 Dadyburjor W387
Daffin, Mary A. P519
Daft, Douglas N. A854
Dagdeviren, Nuri E457
Dagenais, Katie P369
Dagenais, Jean W242
Dages, B. Gerard A320
Daggett, John A620
Daglio, Francesco E328
Dagnel, Bobby P51
Dagostino, Maureen P361
Dague, Brandi E221
Dague, David E346
Dahan, Rene W203
Dahanukar, Madhavi E160
Dahl, Stephen E234
Dahl, Matt E497
Dahl, Holly A365
Dahl, Carl A698
Dahl, Craig R. A782
Dahl, Cheri W. P108
Dahl, Mark P283
Dahl, Larry P299
Dahl, Jo Anna P391
Dahlback, Claes A386
Dahlberg, Robert E460
Dahlberg, Kenneth C. (Ken) A570
Dahlberg, Nancy P264
Dahlem, Andrew M. A513
Dahlen, Dennis P41
Dahlman, Cheryl P130
Dahlmann, David S. (Dave) A335
Dahltorp, Bruce L. P520
Dahnert, Stephen R. P586
Dahut, Karen A129
Dahya, Hanif W. (Wally) A583
Dai, Michael M. A2
Dai, Hai-Lung P498
Dai, Guoliang W50
Daichendt, Gary J. A580
Daido, Issei W53
Daigle, Robert C. (Bob) E402
Daigle, Donald H. P372
Dailey, Susan E360
Dailey, Marge E377
Dailey, Marlin A126
Dailey, Mark D. A351
Dailey, Keith A495
Dailey, Michael (Mike) P353
Dailey, Marianne P447
Dailey, Mike W. P533
Dailey, Jeffrey J. (Jeff) W392
Daily, Harry P. (Pete) A247
Daily, Calvin P136
Daiss, Ann P. A738
Daji, Swati V. A277
Dake, Stephan H. (Steve) P435
Dake, Gary C. P482
Dake, William (Bill) P482
Dakey, Alan W. E374
Dakolias, Constantine M. (Dean) E181
Dakolias, Constantine M. (Dean) A359
Dakovich, Bob P181
Dale, Lisa E514
Dale, David A582
Dale, Albert J. A695
Dale, Elizabeth A P158
Dale, Ken P504
Dale, Kameron E. P577
Dales, Chris A106
Daley, Leo H. (Toby) E187
Daley, Toby E187
Daley, Troy E328

Daley, James R. A188
Daley, Pamela A373
Daley, Kevin G. A416
Daley, Clayton C. A605
Daley, Dorian E. A618
Daley, Clayton C. A755
Daley, Pamela P616
Daley, Jeffrey W. W230
Dalgetty, Ruth P486
Dalhoff, John J. A245
Dalibard, Barbara M. W109
Dalibard, Yves-Marie W362
Dalibor, Ulrich W227
Dalibot, Denis W100
Dalke, Gary R. A868
Dall, Marcia A. A301
Dallaire, Andre A178
Dallaire, Daniel A379
Dallal, Andrs E512
Dallas, Wendell A21
Dallas, H. James A486
Dallavecchia, Enrico A651
Dalleur, Rene L.F. A322
Dallieres, Julie E197
Dallman, Laura E77
Dallman, Steven J. (Steve) A451
Dallmann, Jeff A792
Dalluge, Charles D. P282
Dally, Craig A. A366
Dally, Troy J. A523
DalPiaz, Derek A835
Dalrymple, Christopher K. A32
Dalrymple, Bob A789
Dalton, Nathaniel E16
Dalton, Kevin E124
Dalton, Grace E173
Dalton, Timothy G. (Tim) A132
Dalton, Richard J. A196
Dalton, William R. P. (Bill) A431
Dalton, David W. A756
Dalton, Andrew J. P170
Dalton, Robert P214
Dalton, Mark P227
Dalton, Susan P339
Dalton, William J. (Bill) P367
Dalton, Paul G. P424
Dalton, Sally P575
Dalvi, Ajit E258
dAlviella, Richard W121
Daly, Bob E3
Daly, Michael P. E51
Daly, Jim E181
Daly, James E181
Daly, Jim E444
Daly, Brian E457
Daly, James M. (Jim) A57
Daly, George G. A116
Daly, Michael P. A118
Daly, Mary C. A321
Daly, David M. A673
Daly, John P. A700
Daly, Ronald E. A768
Daly, Philip P167
Daly, Marilyn P340
Daly, Douglas P344
Daly, Carol Lynn P371
Daly, James J. P613
Daly, Mike W76
Daly, Andrea E. W268
Daly, Richard W379
Dalzell, Jane E120
Dam, Jan Van W203
Dambra, Barton P. A330
DAmbra, Diane H. P261
DAmbrosio, Ralph A497
DAmelio, Vincent J. A706
Dameris, Peter T. E362
Dameshek, Anatoly E442
Damesin, Marie-Francoise W289
Damhauser, Matthew E139
Damian, James M. E68
Damiano, Philip A585
Damico, Dave E234
Damico, Joseph F. A877
Damico, Joseph F. P255

Damilano, Susi E329
Damilatis, Chris A73
Damiris, George J. A420
Damme, Alexandre Van W28
Dammerman, Dennis D. A124
Dammon, Robert M. P93
Damon, Robert A. E268
Damon, Lisa J. P446
Damonti, John A135
DAmore, Robert A636
Damour, Regis A12
DAmours, Jacques W18
Dampierre, Olivier de P233
Damron, Rick D. A523
Damron, Ronnie E. A523
Damron, Ray P448
Dan, Michael T. A661
Dana, Charles E. (Chuck) A622
Dana, Donald E. A861
Dana, Michael P600
Dana, Michael W268
Danahy, John F. A693
Danahy, James M. A778
Dancausa, Maria Dolores W56
Dancho, Kyle A751
Dandini, Michael P. A116
Dandolph, John A564
DAndrea, Federico Federico
 DAndrea W348
Danella, James D. P589
Danforth, Michael E173
Danforth, Judy P472
Dang, Kimberly A. (Kim) A489
Dangeard, Frank E. A772
Dangoor, David E. R. A521
Danhan, Huang W50
Daniel, Carl E182
Daniel, John P Mc E305
Daniel, Laree R. A17
Daniel, James R. A97
Daniel, James R. A98
Daniel, Thomas O. (Tom) A164
Daniel, William K. (Dan) A240
Daniel, Patrick D. A292
Daniel, John N. A329
Daniel, John M. A339
Daniel, Dorothy A665
Daniel, Mary M P29
Daniel, Suzy P51
Daniel, Karen L. P66
Daniel, Bob P82
Daniel, Keith P205
Daniel, Joseph R. (Josh) P256
Daniel, William T. (Bill) P310
Daniel, June P446
Daniel, Wallace L. P510
Daniel, Wolfgang W62
Daniel, Patrick D. W84
Daniel, Patrick D. W137
Danieli, Steven E444
Danielian, Arsen P207
Daniels, Dean E196
Daniels, Gene E266
Daniels, Carl E282
Daniels, Robert P. (Bob) A60
Daniels, Brian A135
Daniels, Laird K. A237
Daniels, Bradley D. A451
Daniels, Michael E. (Mike) A454
Daniels, Donald (Don) A469
Daniels, Jennifer M. A580
Daniels, Gennaro A. P89
Daniels, W. Peter P172
Daniels, William P312
Daniels, Clifford R P316
Daniels, Rodney P320
Daniels, Amy P414
Daniels, Maurice C. P569
Daniels, J. Eric W81
Danielsen, John W122
Danielson, Lynn E239
Danielson, Charles P295
Danielson, Ronald P395
Danilek, Thomas (Tom) P233
Danilewitz, Dale A55

Danis, Gary E173
Danisewicz, Mark P21
Daniszewski, John P503
Dankenbrink, Kristine A. A205
Dankner, Wayne E369
Dankner, Dan (Danny) W48
Dann, Doreen P475
Danneman, Peggy J. P516
Dannewitz, Charles V. A784
Dannov, David M. A722
Dano, Margaret S. E452
Dano, Mary P172
Danon, Pierre Pierre Danon W333
Danos, Johnny A A156
Danos, Paul A376
Danovitz, Joshua E474
Danowski, Gary A653
Danowski, James P259
Dansby, Melanie E186
Dansie, Kevin E521
Dansie, Scott P63
Danyo, Joseph P40
Danzi, Christopher P413
Danziger, Eric A. A881
Daocheng, Wang W275
Daofu, Wang W275
Dapolito, Cheryl A677
Darbeau, Wayne K. P432
Darby, Jeff E127
Darby, Geannine P514
Darden, Tony E367
Darden, Calvin (Cal) A153
Darden, Calvin A200
Darden, Calvin (Cal) A781
Darden, T P414
Dardick, John E119
Darding, Jeffrey A. (Jeff) A629
Dardovski, Shevket E434
Dare, Dorothy P125
Darenberg, Rick E71
Darfoor, Andrew W266
Dargan, John A465
Darghous, Sam S P40
Dargie, John A345
Darin, Peter C. A782
Darkes, Maureen W137
Darling, Brad E40
Darling, Bradley D E40
Darling, Matt P488
Darmayan, Philippe W30
Darneille, Wallace L. (Wally) P389
Darnell, David C. A100
Darnell, Laurin J. A675
Darnell, Mike A801
Darnis, Geraud A836
Darragh, Michael E124
Darretta, Robert J. A838
Darricarrere, Yves-Louis W362
Darrington, Jim P249
Darsey, James R. A605
Darst, David M. P404
Dart, Stephen M. P127
Dart, Robert J. W387
Dartnall, William J. A41
Daruwala, Nik E197
Daruwala, Zarin W181
Darveaux, Robert E426
Darwall-smith, Donna E369
Darwin, Dean E163
Darwin, Jaime E175
Das, Naveen E509
Das, Sanjiv A186
Das, Ajay A803
Dasbach, Angie A236
Dasburg, John H. A810
Daschner, Georg W240
Dash, Gigi P89
Dash, Sujogya W30
Dasilva, Ronei E195
DaSilva, Jack P539
Dassance, Charles P332
Dassault, Laurent W282
Dassault, Thierry W374
Dastin, Richard M. (Rick) A885

Donovan, Peter F. A160
Donovan, Daniel E. (Dan) A264
Donovan, Shawn M. A348
Donovan, Michael J. A409
Donovan, Brian P. A600
Donovan, Ryan A714
Donovan, Jerry P205
Donovan, Susan P289
Donovan, Jennifer P344
Donovan, R. Nowell P500
Donovan, Denis W52
Doo, William W. H. W52
Doodian, Rob E27
Doody, Joseph G. (Joe) A753
Doohan, Kevin E131
Dooley, William N. (Bill) A51
Dooley, Greg A388
Dooley, William N. (Bill) A456
Dooley, Thomas E. (Tom) A847
Dooley, David M. P328
Dooley, Joanne P421
Doolittle, David A585
Doom, Elena A424
Dooner, Marlene S. A205
Doordan, Martin L. P25
Dop, Robert P364
Dopfner, Mathias A802
Doran, Peter E244
Doran, Patrick J. (Pat) E458
Doran, F. Michael A345
Doran, Walter F. A689
Doran, Richard P74
Doran, John P446
Dorange, Chantal A126
Dorazio, Tony A277
Dorbin, John E454
Dorchester, Wendy P287
Dordelman, William E. (Bill) A205
Dorduncu, Ahmet C. A458
Dore, Stacey A294
Dore, John W175
Doren, Jason A770
Dorer, Benno A191
Dorer, Thomas P536
Dorey, Gerard W87
Dorfman, Marc E328
Dorfman, Scott P453
Dorgan, David M. A707
Dorge, Philippe W277
Dorian, Carolyn P331
Doricko, Brian E124
Doris, Doug A786
Doris, Ennio W224
Dorman, Jodi A178
Dorman, David W. (Dave) A237
Dorman, David W. (Dave) A570
Dorman, David W. (Dave) A889
Dorman, H. Paul P153
Dorman, Rachel P549
Dorminey, O. Leonard (Len) E222
Dormo, Cindy P111
Dorn, Nancy P. A374
Dorn, Gail J. P577
Dorne, Eric A. A830
Dorner, Irene M. A431
Dorner, I. M. W175
Doros, Jonathan A140
Dorr, Jeff E107
Dorrance, Bennett A149
Dorrance, Bennett A448
Dorrance, Robert E. (Bob) W358
Dorrego, Joe A816
Dorris, Jim A832
Dorros, Chris E182
Dorsa, Caroline A123
Dorsa, Caroline A671
Dorsa, Caroline A673
Dorsa, Daniel M. P367
Dorsch, W. Gary E423
Dorsch, R. Michael A464
Dorsett, Kenneth A. A346
Dorsett, Richard P415
Dorsey, Josh E455
Dorsman, Peter A. A580
Dortch, Samuel W. E191

Dorward-King, Elaine A587
Dosal, Paul P576
Dosbrow, Jane E197
Dosch, Theodore A. (Ted) A63
Dosch, Theodore A. (Ted) P218
Doscher, Meggie P494
Dose, Angela L. A383
Doss, Michael P. A390
Doss, Andrea P29
Dossantos, John E455
Dostatni, Andrzej E239
Doster, Jeffrey S. E220
Doster, John A613
Doswell, Mary C. A264
Doti, Michael E421
Doti, James L. (Jim) A331
Doti, James L. (Jim) P105
Dotsch, Flip W369
Dotson, George S. E45
Dotson, J P75
Dotson, Darlene P226
Dotson, Pam P475
Dotson, Paul P540
Dotson, Orville W. (Pete) P596
Dottarelli, Marco E156
Dotter, Meghan A14
Doty, Jim E32
Doubleday, Matthew E. A877
Doucet, Cyril P433
Doucet, Michel W18
Doucette, James W. A211
Doucette, John J. A836
Doucette, Michael (Mike) P417
Doud, James J. (Jim) A856
Doud, Robert P78
Dougall, Dave A404
Dougan, Paul M. A507
Dougan, Matt P242
Dougan, Thomas R. P574
Dougan, Brady W. W115
Dougherty, Kevin E327
Dougherty, Robert A. A25
Dougherty, Kevin M. A494
Dougherty, Siiri A634
Dougherty, Lynne A755
Dougherty, James P92
Dougherty, Terry P295
Dougherty, Michael E. P577
Dougherty, Kevin P. W339
Doughtie, Chico E341
Doughty, Stephen W. E441
Douglas, J. Boyd E98
Douglas, Cory E303
Douglas, M. Cathy A60
Douglas, Elyse A78
Douglas, Richard W. A82
Douglas, Gregory A. A116
Douglas, J. Alexander M. (Sandy) A198
Douglas, William W. (Bill) A200
Douglas, Charlie A205
Douglas, Lewis W. A331
Douglas, Elyse A415
Douglas, Sean A439
Douglas, Dianne A538
Douglas, James H. (Jim) A579
Douglas, Laurie Z. A674
Douglas, Craig A A751
Douglas, J. William A776
Douglas, Ernie P111
Douglas, Bernadine P173
Douglas, Alison P210
Douglas, Walter E. P228
Douglas, Keith P540
Douglass, Roy E143
Douglass, Travis P568
Doukeris, Michel Dimitrios W28
Dourado, Carlos G. A549
Douro, Lord W309
Douroux, Lucien W75
Douty, Nathan P230
Douville, Jean A378
Douville, Jean A379
Douville, Alan A871
Douville, Jean W242
Dove, David E77

Dove, Michael A479
Dove, Reid P1
Dove, Kent P244
Dovey, John W80
Dovletian, Garineh E303
Dovrat, Moshe W49
Dow, Vincent G. A273
Dow, Laura P310
Dowd, Joseph P. A116
Dowd, James A235
Dowd, Thomas A525
Dowd, Kevin I. A850
Dowd, Tom P160
Dowd, Thomas F. P317
Dowd, Brian E. W8
Dowdie, George A149
Dowdle, Jeff A687
Dowdle, Deedie P318
Dowdle, Elizabeth B. P509
Dowdy, Amy P150
Dowdy, Robert L. P394
Dowell, Greg A. E449
Dowell, Robert M. E516
Dowell, Mark P619
Dowey, Ed P488
Dowidar, Hatem W379
Dowling, Michael J. (Mike) A345
Dowling, Bill P321
Dowling, Dennis P353
Dowling, Denise P571
Dowling, Dame Ann W76
Down, Philip B. P156
Downard, Tim A613
Downe, William A. (Bill) A526
Downe, Andrew J. W218
Downes, Terry P441
Downey, Jenny E468
Downey, Thomas J. (Tom) A126
Downey, Bruce L. A153
Downey, William H. (Bill) A298
Downey, David J. A334
Downey, John F. A880
Downey, William B. P417
Downey, A. W238
Downham, Keith A633
Downing, Jane E30
Downing, Steve E201
Downing, Max E273
Downing, David B. E275
Downing, John W E345
Downing, Patrick F. A613
Downing, Lee A808
Downing, Susan P125
Downing, Helen Dean P310
Downing, Walter D. P463
Downing, James P474
Downing, John W185
Downing, Wadham W210
Downs, Timothy J. E176
Downs, Matt E503
Downs, D. Michael A778
Downs, Barbara A. (Barb) P89
Downs, Kenneth E. P137
Downs, Katie P526
Downy, Thomas E34
Doye, Anthony P. (Tony) W150
Doyle, Chris E385
Doyle, Jason E393
Doyle, Bill E396
Doyle, Richard A. (Rick) E417
Doyle, Mike E438
Doyle, John Q. A51
Doyle, John J. A138
Doyle, M. Chris A174
Doyle, Donald J. A180
Doyle, Craig A207
Doyle, James D. A218
Doyle, Patrick T. (Pat) A255
Doyle, Marc A275
Doyle, Francis A303
Doyle, Charles J. A474
Doyle, Noreen A587
Doyle, Thomas P. (Tom) A603
Doyle, James J. A619
Doyle, Joseph W. A782

Doyle, Timothy G. A782
Doyle, Florence P97
Doyle, Julie P. P99
Doyle, James R. (Jim) P148
Doyle, Lori P158
Doyle, Jim P172
Doyle, James P172
Doyle, Debra B. P196
Doyle, Gerald P. P243
Doyle, Mark P317
Doyle, Noreen W116
Doyne, Diane P125
Dozier, R. Winston A332
Drablos, Craig A434
Draeger, Klaus W66
Draft, Howard A459
Draganza, Ernest J. A713
Dragas, Helen E. A264
Draghi, John E339
Drago, Dana A. A206
Drago, Linda S P159
Dragomanova, Dora E181
Draheim, John L. A404
Drahnak, Stephen A. (Steve) A713
Drahnak, Steve A713
Drahos, Gerard P. P528
Drahozal, Christopher R. A828
Draime, Jeffrey P E446
Draiss, Greg P4
Drake, Michael E97
Drake, Jon E430
Drake, Rodman L. A164
Drake, Timothy J. A598
Drake, Eileen P. A836
Drake, Miles P. A870
Drake, Linda C. A880
Drake, Julie P89
Drake, Gary P205
Drake, Denny P566
Drake, Tomas Alfaro W41
Drake, Tomas W42
Dralle, Laurie P464
Dranse, Phil W183
Drapeau, Robert F. P574
Draper, E. Linn A35
Draper, E. Linn A39
Draper, Milton Gray A224
Draper, Dan P453
Drass, M. Joy P308
Draughn, James B. (Jim) A213
Draughon, Don E60
Draxler, Helmut W267
Drees, David P511
Drees, Jeff W312
Dreher, Jed P162
Dreher, Sharon P321
Dreher, Melanie C. P550
Dreibelbis, David E. A706
Dreiling, Richard W. (Rick) A261
Dreiling, Richard W. (Rick) A523
Dreiling, Brian P321
Drelick, Robert E173
Drengler, Kathy P31
Drennan, Jerry M. (Mike) P502
Drennen, William (Bill) A416
Drerup, Jean P66
Drerup, Dale P299
Dresner, Joseph S. A546
Dressel, Melanie J. E97
Dressel, Melanie J. A204
Dresser, Jack P174
Dressman, Laura A665
Drew, Brian E37
Drew, J. Christopher (Chris) E360
Drew, Chris E360
Drew, J. Everitt A150
Drew, Pamela A. (Pam) A303
Drew, William E. A401
Drew, Ina R. A476
Drew, John J. P3
Drew, Terese A. P233
Drewry, Richard P45
Drews, Ralf E164
Drews, Chris A560
Drexler, Millard S. (Mickey) A68

A = AMERICAN BUSINESS
E = EMERGING COMPANIES
P = PRIVATE COMPANIES
W = WORLD BUSINESS

A = AMERICAN BUSINESS
E = EMERGING COMPANIES
P = PRIVATE COMPANIES
W = WORLD BUSINESS

Fuller, Lynn B. A412
Fuller, Wilford H. (Will) A514
Fuller, Joseph B. (Joe) A677
Fuller, Rodger D. A734
Fuller, Dan P143
Fuller, James (Jim) P147
Fuller, John D. (Jack) P342
Fuller, Eddie P391
Fuller, Jo Ann P444
Fuller, Regina P472
Fuller, Miranda P489
Fuller, Rev Jon D. P575
Fuller, Dale P583
Fuller-Stanley, Jean P541
Fullerton, Rob P609
Fullwood, Emerson U. A747
Fulman, Diane P39
Fulmer, James W. (Jim) A318
Fulmer, L. Craig A500
Fulmer, James W. (Jim) A805
Fulp, J. Raymond A54
Fulton, W. Groome E60
Fulton, Sandra E82
Fulton, Matt E139
Fulton, Tricia L. E450
Fulton, W. Groome A125
Fulton, J. Michael A206
Fulton, William D. A250
Fulton, Rufus A. A366
Fulton, Daniel S. (Dan) A870
Fulton, Tork A. P102
Fulton, Rufus A. P503
Funabashi, Haruo W117
Funasaki, Kiyohisa A807
Funato, Takashi W232
Funayama, Norio W317
Funck, Robert E. A4
Fundaro, Leo B. P184
Funderburg, Stuart E. (Stu) A73
Fung, David E106
Fung, Andrew H. C. W162
Fung, Anita Y. M. W175
Funk, Janice E150
Funk, Robert E. A145
Funk, James M. A767
Funk, Michael S. A830
Funke, Dick E391
Funkhouser, Joseph K. P255
Funo, Yukitoshi (Yuki) W363
Fuoss, Calvin E. A782
Furbacher, Stephen A. (Steve) A171
Furber, Julie A234
Furcolo, Mark E120
Furey, Tracy A135
Furihata, Toru W336
Furlan, Luiz Fernando A18
Furlan, Luiz Fernando W350
Furlano, Richard T. P517
Furlong, Kimberly E223
Furlong, Fred T. A321
Furlong, Leon P69
Furlonger, David E197
Furman, William A. (Bill) E210
Furman, John B E427
Furman, Matt A119
Furong, Zhang W186
Furrer, Roger A337
Furse, Dame Clara H. F. W210
Fursey, Victor E67
Furst, Thomas J. P465
Furst-Bowe, Julie P426
Furstein, Marc K. E181
Furstein, Marc K. A359
Furubayashi, Kiyoshi W364
Furuhashi, Mamoru W363
Furuichi, Takeshi W250
Furuichi, Takeshi W251
Furukawa, Toshimasa W236
Furusawa, Kiichiro W360

Furuta, Kei E156
Furuta, Takanobu W192
Furuya, Katsumasa W151
Fusaro, Michael J. A379
Fusco, Frank E. A79
Fusco, Jack A. A144
Fusco, Catherine R. A856
Fuseya, Noriaki W232
Fushen, Li W99
Fusilli, Roberto W40
Fussell, Stephen R. (Steve) A4
Futch, Dorinda A P384
Futrell, Mary Hatwood A425
Futter, Ellen V. A221
Futter, Ellen V. A476
Fuyao, Tong W212
Fuzy, Rea-ann E139
Fybel, Gary G. P440
Fyfe, Kristy E60
Fyffe, Robert E. P617
Fynan, Tamara A733
Fyodorov, Igor Y. W154
Fyrwald, J. Erik A284
Fyrwald, J. Erik A513

G

Gaalen, Jan Kees van A95
Gabas, Antonio W152
Gabbard, Robert D. A654
Gabel, Todd P321
Gabel, Timothy J. (Tim) P413
Gabel, Yadl W37
Gabelli, Mario J. E194
Gabelli, John D E194
Gabelli, Mario J. E194
Gaber, Sharon L. A729
Gable, Michelle E144
Gable, Debbie E432
Gable, Greg A720
Gable, Lisa Guillermin P206
Gaboury, David P499
Gabriel, Elin E189
Gabriel, James A. (Jim) A210
Gabriel, Clarence J. (Gabe) P220
Gabriel, Frank J. P528
Gabriel, Shirley P534
Gabriel, Laurie A. P556
Gabriel, Yves W74
Gabriel, Yves W75
Gabriele, Gary A. P589
Gabrys, Richard M (Dick) E481
Gabrys, Richard M. (Dick) A192
Gabrys, Richard M. (Dick) A223
Gachora, John W57
Gackstetter, Tom P288
Gad, Mounir E455
Gadbois, Ben A585
Gaddis, Byron J. A657
Gaddis, Glendi P283
Gaddy, Michael J. E362
Gadney, Oliver (Ollie) W367
Gaehwiler, Lukas W367
Gaemperle, Chantal W216
Gaer, Samuel H. P186
Gaertner, Frederick W. A178
Gaffigan, Joseph P. A782
Gaffner, Arlin E. A160
Gaffney, Mark T. A319
Gaffney, James A342
Gaffney, Michael S. A379
Gaffney, Carol L. P453
Gafford, Derrek L. E484
Gafford, Ronald J. (Ron) A812
Gagan, Singh E512
Gage, Shannon E385
Gage, Audrey A220
Gage, Douglas M. A245
Gage, Edwin C. (Skip) A768
Gage, Tim P7
Gage, John P17
Gage, Steve P160
Gage, Allen P548
Gage, Geoffrey C. P577

Gagle, Michael D. E248
Gagliano, Nancy J. A237
Gagliano, Gerald W. A833
Gaglione, Patricia J. A467
Gagne, Paul E. A795
Gagnon, Robert E. A123
Gagnon, Gary J. P522
Gaherity, James (Jim) E363
Gaherty, John B. A227
Gahr, Freddie P414
Gaidos, Rosemary A. (Rose) A858
Gaier, David A603
Gail, Lim E306
Gaillard, Clay A234
Gaillard, Charles W. A844
Gaines, Randy E113
Gaines, David L. E370
Gaines, Stephanie E465
Gaines, Brenda J. A315
Gaines, Bennett L. A345
Gaines, Jeremy A368
Gaines, Brenda J. A609
Gaines, Brenda J. A786
Gaines, Chinwe A602
Gains, Gary E190
Gaiter, Jatrice Martel P591
Gajan, J. U. P463
Gajdos, Ludovit A209
Gajecka, Marta W147
Gajjar, Amar P475
Gajos, Rachel A. P520
Gal, Shimon W48
Galanis, Peter E156
Galanis, Peter A418
Galanko, William A. A598
Galano, Robert E234
Galano, Raul I. A343
Galanski, Stanley A. (Stan) A577
Galante, Edward G. (Ed) A656
Galanti, Richard A. A227
Galarneau, Clayton P320
Galateri, Gabriele W31
Galateri, Gabriele W32
Galbo, Christina P258
Galbraith, Peggy P507
Galbraith, Steven M. (Steve) P556
Galbraith, Colin R. W106
Galbreath, Lizanne A755
Galdo, Julia Hunter P19
Gale, Dustin E139
Gale, Bill E497
Gale, William C. A181
Gale, Brent E. A626
Gale, Fournier J. (Boots) A691
Gale, Andrea P117
Gale, Donald P613
Galeazzi, Joe P312
Galen, Helene P167
Galen, Dean Van P581
Galenas, Gayle E251
Galetol, Fabiana Dos Santos A455
Galetto, Peter A763
Galetto, Rev Paul W. P589
Galey, Frank P581
Galgan, Priscilla P552
Galgano, Brenda M. E510
Galhau, Francois Villeroy de W72
Galifi, Vincent J. W219
Galik, Jeffrey A135
Galik, Barbara A. P75
Galin, Tomi A212
Galindo, Sergio A624
Galis, Aaron E16
Galla, Ronald M. E261
Gallacher, Steven A. (Steve) A116
Gallagher, John E15
Gallagher, Maurice J. (Maury) E24
Gallagher, James G. (Jamie) E27
Gallagher, David G. E76
Gallagher, Suzanne E119
Gallagher, Kevin F. E127
Gallagher, Timothy J. E200
Gallagher, Paul F. E219
Gallagher, Bill E355
Gallagher, Michael R. A34

Gallagher, Susan A45
Gallagher, Philip R. (Phil) A91
Gallagher, Phillip A. A169
Gallagher, Donald J. A189
Gallagher, William T. A230
Gallagher, Angela A246
Gallagher, Brian A287
Gallagher, Bryan A318
Gallagher, Thomas C. (Tom) A378
Gallagher, Steven A588
Gallagher, Marie T. A638
Gallagher, Terence (Terry) A669
Gallagher, Edward J. A782
Gallagher, Kevin C. A785
Gallagher, Hugh J. A821
Gallagher, Kevin C. A822
Gallagher, Duncan P. P14
Gallagher, Kelly P253
Gallagher, Arthur J. P261
Gallagher, Susan G. P313
Gallagher, Rick P343
Gallagher, Larry P359
Gallagher, Daniel G. P480
Gallagher, Stephen J. P575
Gallagher, Gerry W185
Gallagher, John W303
Gallaher, James P162
Gallamo, Jim P505
Gallant, John E196
Gallant, Michael J. A287
Gallardo, Juan A157
Gallardo, Gabriel E. P579
Gallas, Carla A. A555
Gallegos, Manuel A295
Gallegos, Chris P488
Gallery, Christine P174
Gallett, Scott D. A130
Galletta, Christopher E508
Gallia, Garrett P230
Gallia, Fabio W72
Gallia, Franco W189
Gallienne, Segolene W100
Galligan, Matt E98
Galligan, Matthew E. (Matt) A184
Galligan, Brendan J. A692
Gallina, John E. A65
Gallion, Diane A797
Gallitano, David J. A399
Gallitano, David J. A860
Gallivan, Matthew S. (Matt) A212
Gallo, Joseph A318
Gallo, Martha J. A475
Gallo, Joseph M. A499
Gallo, A. C. A873
Gallo, Robert (Bob) P224
Gallo, Kathleen P353
Gallo, Juan W290
Gallo, Juan Abello W290
Gallogly, Mark T. A239
Gallois, Louis W15
Gallois, Louis W109
Gallopoulos, Gregory S. (Greg) A371
Gallot, Jerome W312
Gallot, Jerome W374
Galloway, Brett D. A182
Galloway, Robert C. P236
Galloway, Jil W230
Galluccio, Nicholas F. E194
Gallup, George P202
Galmiche, Jack P400
Galovic, Scott L. A194
Galperin, Marcos E307
Galsky, Alan G. P75
Galt, Helen M. A671
Galt, Robert B. P46
Galt, Frederick P89
Galtman, Michael D. A763
Galvan, Martin P. E271
Galvan, Michael E297
Galvanoni, Matthew R. A305
Galvanoni, Matthew R. A306
Galvin, Walter J. A45
Galvin, Bill A63
Galvin, Walter J. A289
Galvin, Walter J. A290

Gevorkyan, Hakop E369
Gewanter, Robyn E181
Geyer, Paul R. A178
Geyer, Maria E. P401
Gfeller, Robert J. A523
Ghaffarian, Kam P447
Ghanbar, Ardy E17
Ghani, Tahir A452
Ghanim, Isam M. P108
Ghazali, Mohd Mohd Nazlan bin Mohd Ghazali W220
Ghidotti, Craig P277
Ghilardi, Emilio A11
Ghiradelli, John P75
Ghizzoni, Federico W368
Ghonim, Wael A389
Ghormley, Larry P27
Ghosh, Pallav W68
Ghosn, Carlos W255
Ghosn, Carlos W289
Ghuman, Sahil E195
Giacalone, Laura A257
Giacobbe, Ken A30
Giacomin, Jon A153
Giacomin, Francesco W368
Giacomini, Thomas W. (Tom) A268
Giacopelli, Ray E28
Giamalis, John N. P429
Giambastiani, Edmund P. A127
Giambastiani, Adm. Edmund P. (Ed) P523
Giambrone, Anna A226
Giammasi, Stella P542
Giammona, Laurie A643
Gianattasio, Chris E375
Giancarlo, Charles H. A583
Giancarlo, Charles H. W7
Gianchetta, Larry P571
Giancola, Jennifer P430
Giancursio, Michael E173
Giang, Vernon P493
Giangiordano, Stephen E407
Giangiuli, Jeffrey E. P86
Giangrande, Jocelyn P227
Giangrasso, Tina E18
Gianini, Elizabeth P433
Gianndrea, Joanne P371
Giannidis, Ioannis C. W244
Giannini, Richard P577
Giannini, Daniel J. P586
Gianno, Jean-Marie W72
Giannuzzi, Dan E173
Gianoni, Michael P. A348
Gianopulos, James N. (Jim) A816
Gianotti, Anthony W385
Giansante, Joseph P171
Giard, Diane W243
Giarda, Piero W40
Giardina, June Anne P179
Giardini, Anne A870
Giardino, Thomas F. P535
Giarrusso, Susan E. A32
Gibbel, Henry H. A769
Gibble, Robert J. P410
Gibbons, Lawrence E44
Gibbons, John D. (Danny) E511
Gibbons, Charles A84
Gibbons, Thomas P. (Todd) A102
Gibbons, Peter D. A538
Gibbons, Edward W. A703
Gibbons, Maritza A788
Gibbons, Dale M. A865
Gibbons, Michael J. P428
Gibbons, Michael P538
Gibbs, Rick E120
Gibbs, Jay A338
Gibbs, L. Martin A344
Gibbs, Barbara A. A629
Gibbs, Lawrence S. A839
Gibbs, H. Jarrell P500
Gibbs, Nelson F. P503
Giblett, Leslie P401
Giblin, Robert E. A275
Giblin, Vincent J. P17
Gibson, Paul E E64

Gibson, Mark D. E224
Gibson, Christina N E362
Gibson, James E365
Gibson, Christopher W. E482
Gibson, John W. A128
Gibson, Stacey A135
Gibson, James W. A210
Gibson, Charles S. A314
Gibson, Gregory L. A339
Gibson, Martin A344
Gibson, Terry A348
Gibson, Mark A444
Gibson, John W. A615
Gibson, John W. A616
Gibson, Lee R. A738
Gibson, Sandra Lee P70
Gibson, Ron P75
Gibson, Donald E. P178
Gibson, Richard (Dick) P280
Gibson, Elizabeth C. P343
Gibson, James J. (Jim) P413
Gibson, Bruce P425
Gibson, Brad P522
Gibson, Robert P575
Gibson, William M. P589
Gibson, Sir Ian W238
Gibson, Linda T. W266
Giddens, Thomas R. A17
Giddens, Bill P522
Giddiens, Ronald (Ron) A338
Gideon, Thomas F. A870
Gidley, Jodi A21
Gidwitz, Ralph W. P125
Giertz, James R. (Jim) E189
Giesinger, Jim W339
Giesler, Lisa A315
Giesler, Howard R. A449
Gieson, Michael P. Van A774
Giessman, Ulli E67
Giffin, Gordon D. W84
Gifford, William F. (Billy) A41
Gifford, Charles K. (Chad) A100
Gifford, Charles K. (Chad) A162
Gifford, Gerard H (Jerry) A230
Gifford, Charles A303
Gifford, Robert K. A445
Giftos, P. Michael A39
Giga, Aziz S. A653
Gigax, Lisa A393
Giglia, Charles E120
Giglio, Lawrence R. A391
Giglio, Lawrence R. (Larry) A391
Giglio, William P179
Gignac, Louis P. A265
Gijanto, Chuck P52
Gil, Elizabeth A. P574
Gilardeau, Jean-Pierre A30
Gilbane, Robert F. (Bob) E33
Gilbane, Thomas F. (Tom) P39
Gilbert, David E25
Gilbert, Carol S. E31
Gilbert, Todd E181
Gilbert, Walter E332
Gilbert, Jeffrey M. E421
Gilbert, Doug A7
Gilbert, Peter A265
Gilbert, Jarobin A356
Gilbert, Dean A389
Gilbert, E. Scott A532
Gilbert, Ben A535
Gilbert, Steven J. A540
Gilbert, Andrew M. A680
Gilbert, Jon A801
Gilbert, Tammy A812
Gilbert, William M. (Bill) A827
Gilbert, Steve A841
Gilbert, John O. P218
Gilbert, Andrea F. P294
Gilbert, Andrea F. P295
Gilbert, Durral R. P394
Gilbert, Ronnie P402
Gilbert, S. Parker P522
Gilbert, Ben P572
Gilbert, Jackson B. W145
Gilbert, Daniel T. (Danny) W242

Gilbert, Steffen W265
Gilbert, Malcolm W392
Gilberti, Lawrence P409
Gilbertson, Glen E465
Gilbertson, Richard J. P475
Gilbertson, Philip N. P578
Gilbreath, Reg P149
Gilbride, Cynthia P353
Gilbronson, David (Dave) A67
Gilchrist, Corydon A340
Gilchrist, M. Ian G. A511
Gilchrist, Andrew D. A700
Gilchrist, Sean W60
Gildersleeve, Debby E195
Gildred, George L. P622
Gile, Elizabeth R. A486
Gile, Charles P339
Gilead, Prof Israel W49
Giles, Jeremy E384
Giles, Susan K. A81
Giles, William T. (Bill) A86
Giles, Christopher J. A178
Giles, Johnnie A205
Giles, Alyson Pitman P98
Gilfeather, Michael J. A433
Gilibert, Pierluigi W147
Gilis, Kosty W268
Gilkey, Glenn C. A353
Gill, Tim E14
Gill, Sarah E64
Gill, Shelley E174
Gill, Darla R. E308
Gill, Julie A14
Gill, Tim H. A316
Gill, Phupinder S. A342
Gill, James A371
Gill, G. Andrew A720
Gill, Charles D. A836
Gill, Jack M. P244
Gill, Margaret (Maggie) P310
Gill, Harry P486
Gill, Jeff P522
Gill, Peter R. P603
Gillam, John W385
Gillani, Aleem A765
Gillard, William P179
Gillard, Ian Guy W47
Gillean, John P112
Gilleland, Diane Suitt A732
Gilleland, Gary P604
Gillen, Brent E339
Gillen, Peter P179
Gillern, Jeffry H. (Jeff) von A819
Gilles, Jean A245
Gillespie, Peter K. A346
Gillespie, Barry N. A653
Gillespie, Teca A664
Gillespie, Phillip S. A758
Gillespie, Alan R. W266
Gillespy, Clark S. A277
Gillet, Vincent A755
Gillett, Rick E163
Gillett, Stephen A119
Gillett, Stephen A772
Gillett, Yvette P330
Gillette, Alex E181
Gillette, Allen E199
Gilley, Paul A. A598
Gillham, Simon W377
Gilli, Erin A603
Gilliam, Amy E162
Gilliam, Clinton E369
Gilliam, Theron I. (Tig) A506
Gilliam, Craig P29
Gilliam, Dale P74
Gillian, Jay P453
Gilliand, Donna P553
Gillick, Megan P289
Gillies, Crawford W333
Gilligan, Kevin M E189
Gilligan, Bob A374
Gilligan, William P174
Gilligan, J P413
Gilligan, Don P561
Gillilan, Jay A675

Gilliland, Sam E389
Gilliland, Art A772
Gilliland, Martha W. P66
Gilliland, Lisa P413
Gilliland, Terry P444
Gillingham, Jim A841
Gillingwater, Richard D. W329
Gillion, Morgan E98
Gillion, Ron P159
Gillis, John E509
Gillis, S. Malcolm A12
Gillis, Michelle A. (Shelly) A49
Gillis, Colin A96
Gillis, Ruth Ann M. A305
Gillis, S. Malcolm A395
Gillis, Ruth Ann M. A486
Gillis, Lea P9
Gillis, Wayne P258
Gillis, Don P538
Gillman, David D. A785
Gillman, Joan H. A800
Gillman, Sarah P610
Gillon, Brian E306
Gillula, E. William (Bill) P143
Gillum, Donald E88
Gilman, Paul A229
Gilman, Alfred G. A513
Gilman, Robert W. P16
Gilman, Peter P34
Gilman, Fred P93
Gilmartin, Raymond V. A376
Gilmartin, Raymond V. A560
Gilmore, John E37
Gilmore, Barbara D E205
Gilmore, Dennis J. A331
Gilmore, Benjamin A. A444
Gilmore, Barbara D. A809
Gilmore, Grover (Cleve) P95
Gilmore, Ronald P580
Gilmour, Allan D. A273
Gilmour, Allan D. P228
Gilrain, Kevin R. P23
Gilreath, Donna P406
Gilsinger, Brett A365
Gilson, Sarah E173
Gilstrap, Douglas L. W143
Giltner, F. Phillips (Phil) P447
Gilvary, Brian W76
Gilyard, Reggie P105
Gim, Mark K. W. A856
Gimbel, Thomas W. A694
Gin, Sue L. A305
Gina, Jian W212
Ginac, Judy P534
Ginanni, Katy P551
Ginascol, John F. A4
Gincavage, Ray A385
Ginder, Keith E193
Gineris, Peter A160
Gingerich, Philip E. A311
Gingerich, Willard P. P329
Ginn, Dori A E390
Ginnetti, Daniel V. A443
Ginsberg, Errol E257
Ginsberg, Frank A459
Ginsberg, Gary L. A801
Ginsberg, Joshua R P610
Ginsburg, J. Lawrence P176
Gintzig, Donald R. P594
Ginzberg, Michael J. P620
Ginzburg, Assaf (Assi) A247
Gioffre, Kathleen E195
Gioia, Dante E288
Gioia, Nancy A358
Giordano, Joseph S. E128
Giordano, Sal E456
Giordano, Shawn J E518
Giordano, Donna F. A494
Giorondo, Ralph P423
Giovanni, Gianni Di W141
Giovannone, John P540
Giovinazzi, Brian A667
Giovinazzi, Brian A669
Gipp, David P19
Gipp, Clif P562

Golden, Michael L. A861
Golden, Charles E. P246
Golden, Robert P580
Golden, Charles E. W369
Golden, Charles E. W370
Goldenberg, Beena G. E215
Goldenberg, Harry E240
Goldenberg, Scott A804
Goldenberg, David H. P536
Goldenstein, Ihno W90
Goldfarb, Morris E192
Goldfarb, Michael P327
Goldfarb, Shlomo W49
Goldfein, Jocelyn A312
Goldfield, H. P. P66
Goldie, Hal J. A147
Golding, Sally E168
Golding, Cornelius E. (Neal) A432
Goldklang, Kenneth P480
Goldman, Barry E11
Goldman, Matthew E195
Goldman, Todd E246
Goldman, Steven L E306
Goldman, Steven J. E440
Goldman, Steve E440
Goldman, Rich E460
Goldman, Carol E. A165
Goldman, Marshall I. A169
Goldman, Jay C. A187
Goldman, Nathan A231
Goldman, Robert W. (Bob) A792
Goldman, Kenneth (Ken) A886
Goldman, Kenneth P158
Goldman, Ray P561
Goldman, Amy R. P577
Goldman, George P611
Goldman, Marc P620
Goldman, Yaacov W49
Goldsberry, John P. A716
Goldsberry, Ronald E. A840
Goldschmid, Steven P534
Goldschmidt, Pascal E306
Goldsmith, Joe E124
Goldsmith, Harry L. A86
Goldsmith, Russell D. A188
Goldsmith, Bram A188
Goldsmith, Russell D. A189
Goldsmith, Russell D. A321
Goldsmith, Russell D. A882
Goldstein, Michele E28
Goldstein, Joshua E257
Goldstein, Robert E301
Goldstein, Lainie J. E462
Goldstein, Benjamin S. E479
Goldstein, Rob L. A124
Goldstein, Donald B. (Don) A160
Goldstein, Kenneth T. A178
Goldstein, Gregg M. A205
Goldstein, Brooke A257
Goldstein, Robert B. A311
Goldstein, Adam A318
Goldstein, Richard A. A459
Goldstein, Robert G. (Rob) A502
Goldstein, Jeff A582
Goldstein, Bruce A677
Goldstein, David S. A773
Goldstein, Steven A827
Goldstein, Steve A. N. P76
Goldstein, Sydney P251
Goldstein, Paul P368
Goldstein, Cynthia Greer P374
Goldstein, Carla P390
Goldstein, Rodney L. (Rod) P535
Goldstein, Stuart P541
Goldstein, Steven A. P556
Goldstein, Brian P. P572
Goldsticker, Alan E408
Goldstone, Steven F. (Steve) A218
Goldstone, Steven F. (Steve) A549
Goldwasser, Mark A. E334
Goldwater, John K. A116
Golemis, Stilianos D. W279
Goler, Lori A312
Goler, Michael R. P277
Golestani, Clark A549

Goli, Shravan E123
Golitko, Andy E139
Golizio, Lisa P481
Golko, Yaroslav Y. W154
Golla, Linae A788
Golladay, Mark T E341
Golladay, Catherine A720
Golliher, Kristin P371
Gollogly, Kevin E196
Gollust, Allison A374
Golm, Louis C. A681
Golsby, Stephen W. (Steve) A135
Golston, Allan C. A762
Golten, Robert P123
Goltz, Frederick M. A294
Golub, Bennett W. A124
Golub, Neil M. P513
Golub, Jerel T. (Jerry) P513
Golub, Mona J. P513
Golub, David P513
Golub, Jane N. P513
Golubev, Valery W153
Golubev, Valery A. W154
Combos, Carrie P509
Gomersall, Sir Stephen W167
Gomes, Moacyr E195
Gomes, Joe E301
Gomes, Anita A680
Gomes, Sergio W4
Gomes, Renato W373
Gomes, Renato da Cruz W373
Gomez, Carlos E113
Gomez, Robert E251
Gomez, Michele Markham E263
Gomez, Henry A418
Gomez, Hernan P251
Gomez, Dolores P323
Gomez, Albert P401
Gomez, Genoveva G. P401
Gomez, Charley P438
Gomez, Sara P579
Gomez, Eugenio Llorente W9
Gomez, Jose Ramon Arce W56
Gomez, Hernando J. W135
Gomez-Lavin, Javier Polanco W9
Gomi, Kazuhiro W253
Gomo, Steven J. (Steve) A714
Gomulka, Robert P563
Gomwe, Godfrey G. W26
Gonabe, Steve E146
Goncalves, Armando F. A636
Gonclaves, Tony P353
Gonda, Leslie L. A456
Gonda, Louis L. P531
Gonda, Toshihiro W17
Gonensin, Turgay W365
Gong, Philip E28
Gong, Yu E429
Gong, Kevin A. A318
Gong, Jin P579
Gong, Huazhang W98
Gongsheng, Pan W186
Gonick, Lev S. P95
Gonsalkorale, Dinesh P602
Gonsoulin, Al A. E377
Gontarski, Gregory G. A629
Gontrum, John P196
Gonz?lez, JosT A318
Gonzales, Armando E232
Gonzales, Craig E339
Gonzales, David A379
Gonzales, Richard (Rick) P525
Gonzales, Miguel W146
Gonzales-Hurtado, Jose C. W87
Gonzalez, Chuy E132
Gonzalez, Iliana E146
Gonzalez, Mark E154
Gonzalez, Ramon E310
Gonzalez, Lupe E315
Gonzalez, Juan E339
Gonzalez, Pam E512
Gonzalez, Richard A. (Rick) A4
Gonzalez, Richard A. (Rick) A6
Gonzalez, Saul A216
Gonzalez, Jaime A227

Gonzalez, Rachel A. A244
Gonzalez, Carlos Fernandez A290
Gonzalez, Alexander A379
Gonzalez, Ileana A652
Gonzalez, Edward A. (Eddie) A722
Gonzalez, Aldo P133
Gonzalez, Francisco T. P535
Gonzalez, Jacqueline L. (Jackie) P585
Gonzalez, Juan Enrique Ruiz W9
Gonzalez, Jose Maria Aguirre W9
Gonzalez-Albo, Jose Romero de
 Avila W9
Gonzalez-Beltran, Ernesto A239
Gonzalez-Mendoza, Luis P585
Gonzalez-Vallina, Ruben P586
Gooch, Mark A. A213
Gooch, Cecily S. A294
Gooch, David J. A629
Gooch, Jay A664
Good, Richard E173
Good, Lynn J. A277
Good, Michael R. A690
Good, Katlyn E. P289
Goodall, David G. E174
Goodall, David C. A17
Goodall, David G. A346
Goodarzi, Sasan K. A462
Goodbarn, Steven R. A258
Goode, David R. A157
Goode, David R. A248
Goode, James A418
Goode, Earl A. A732
Goode, David R. A794
Goode, Jeff P106
Goodell, Timothy B. A416
Goodell, Jeffrey (Jeff) A469
Gooden, Linda R. A84
Gooden, Clarence W. A231
Goodenow, Linda R. A518
Goodenow, Stephen J. (Steve) A319
Gooderick, Nadine A693
Goodfellow, Thomas A. A629
Goodfliesh, Greg A693
Goodgion, Sean P104
Goodhue, John E135
Goodin, David L. A545
Gooding, Marie C. A319
Gooding, Yvonne P256
Gooding, Valerie F. (Val) W194
Gooding, Valerie F. (Val) W332
Goodlett, Walter P413
Goodman, Roy E8
Goodman, Gail F. E103
Goodman, Gail F. E104
Goodman, Ford E246
Goodman, Jeffrey M. (Jeff) E515
Goodman, Jeff E515
Goodman, Andrew (Andy) A140
Goodman, Shira D. A155
Goodman, Stacey A184
Goodman, Andrew A278
Goodman, Harvey M. A279
Goodman, Bruce J. A434
Goodman, Richard A. A472
Goodman, Patrick J. A626
Goodman, Cheryl A680
Goodman, Gregg M. A730
Goodman, Shira D. A753
Goodman, Richard A. A868
Goodman, Norman B. P77
Goodman, Phyllis P109
Goodman, Lawrence (Larry) P168
GOODMAN, ANDREW P366
Goodman, M. H. P502
Goodman, W. H. P502
Goodman, Wayne H. P502
Goodman, Alan P. P505
Goodmanson, Richard R. W294
Goodmanson, Richard R. W295
Goodner, Bob A338
Goodnight, Todd P256
Goodrich, Richard E E471
Goodrich, Donna C. A110
Goodrich, Carol A470
Goodrich, T. Michael (Mike) A776

Goodrich, Zane P161
Goodrich, David W. P246
Goodrich, John P262
Goodrich, Rev Richard W. P519
Goodrum, William E179
Goodson, Paul E65
Goodson, Robert H. (Bob) P348
Goodson, Charles T. P372
Goodspeed, Linda A. A47
Goodwin, Josh E123
Goodwin, Robert E196
Goodwin, John E (Buddy) E263
Goodwin, Daniel E298
Goodwin, Gary R. E359
Goodwin, Keith A182
Goodwin, Cynthia C. A319
Goodwin, William J. (Bill) A525
Goodwin, John P. A664
Goodwin, Michael P17
Goodwin, Tarina P29
Goodwin, Keith D. P161
Goodwin, Terry W. P403
Goodwyn, Bill A257
Goody, Cynthia M. A541
Goodyear, Jay E190
Goonewardene, Mike E443
Goorevich, Charlie P447
Goot, Stephen B. P451
Goovaerts, Lus E469
Gopal, Ajei S. A140
Gopalakrishnan, Karthik E316
Gopalakrishnan, Ravi A107
Gopinath, S. A351
Gora, Jo Ann M. A341
Gora, Jo Ann M. P40
Gorbach, Pat A387
Gorczynski, Ronald E60
Gorder, Joseph W. (Joe) A841
Gorder, Chrisoph P23
Gorder, Christopher D. Van P440
Gordillo, Rodrigo Echenique W46
Gordo, Juan Ignacio Apoita W41
Gordo, Juan W41
Gordon, Charles R. (Chuck) E15
Gordon, Crystal L E18
Gordon, Frank E220
Gordon, Doug E339
Gordon, Brooks E512
Gordon, Mary A. A40
Gordon, William B. (Bing) A42
Gordon, John R. A60
Gordon, Dennis A82
Gordon, Richard K. (Rick) A82
Gordon, Andrew M. A102
Gordon, Bruce S. A161
Gordon, Mary Winn A262
Gordon, Christopher R. (Chris) A407
Gordon, Ilene S. A447
Gordon, Ilene A458
Gordon, Bruce S. A602
Gordon, Tim A659
Gordon, Russell L. A711
Gordon, Barry A827
Gordon, Scott R. P29
Gordon, Robert S. (Bob) P45
Gordon, Thomas D. P98
Gordon, Sydney Smith P125
Gordon, Barbara P164
Gordon, Darryl P P230
Gordon, Jeffrey D. P281
Gordon, Mark P313
Gordon, Steven P506
Gordon, Ray W274
Gordon, Helen W300
Gordon-simet, Josette P139
Gore, Lisa E80
Gore, Doug A41
Gore, Albert A. (Al) A68
Gore, Judy P348
Gore, Millie P620
Gorel, Michelle A91
Gorelick, Jamie S. A836
Goren, Isabella D. (Bella) A46
Gorey, Christopher M. A499
Gorham, Roger B. A32

A =	**AMERICAN BUSINESS**
E =	**EMERGING COMPANIES**
P =	**PRIVATE COMPANIES**
W =	**WORLD BUSINESS**

Gorham, Doug P515
Gorjanc, Christine M. E344
Gorman, Jeffrey S. E204
Gorman, James C. E204
Gorman, Stephen E. (Steve) A248
Gorman, Christopher M. (Chris) A486
Gorman, James P. A568
Gorman, Mark J. A649
Gorman, Robert A824
Gorman, Mia P87
Gorman, Kathleen E. P110
Gorman, Kirk E. P255
Gorman, Alvin L. (Al) P392
Gorman, Raymond (Ray) W212
Gormley, Beth E339
Gormley, Aidan A631
Gormley, Kathleen K. P594
Gornall, Brad E210
Gorney, Len E263
Gorney, David J. P502
Gorny, David E172
Gorny, Bob P437
Gorrell, Jeffrey E173
Gorrell, Mark B. P52
Gorski, Robert (Bob) A493
Gorski, Al P367
Gorsky, Alex A470
Gorsky, Dan A541
Gorsuch, Chad E445
Goryl, Joe E497
Gosche, Kenneth G. A629
Goschl, Peter W240
Gosin, Barry M. P374
Gosling, Matthew M E122
Gosling, Lisa A169
Gosney, William Ray (Ray) P341
Gosney, Marion M. P505
Goss, Ray E200
Goss, Bill P188
Goss, Andreas J. W320
Gosse, David E416
Gosselin, Stephen A. (Steve) A157
Gosselin, Edward P25
Gosselin, Grant M. P39
Gossett, Mark C. A600
Gossin, Cheryl A222
Gossweiler, Albert E. A480
Goswitz, Joseph P14
Gosz, Michael R. P243
Gother, Ronald E. P507
Goto, Katsuhiro W313
Goto, Kazutoshi W315
Goto, Masahiro W317
Gotsch, Kenneth C. (Ken) P125
Gottesfeld, Stephen P. A586
Gottesman, David S. A117
Gottesmann, Patricia A142
Gottfried, P. Gene A346
Gottlieb, Tricia A665
Gottlieb, Katherine P10
Gottlieb, Tracy P445
Gottlob, Martin W122
Gottschalk, Sister M. Therese P471
Gottschalk, Helmut W133
Gottscho, Richard A. (Rick) A501
Gottsegen, Jonathan M. A832
Gottula, Todd E13
Gottung, Lizanne C. (Liz) A488
Gottuso, Vince L. A235
Gottwald, Thomas E. (Teddy) E348
Gotz, Gerd W204
Gou, Terry T.M. W170
Goudie, Tim A198
Goudsmit, Frank F. A178
Goudy, Gregg R. A782
Gouge, Molly P472
Gouge, Sandra P553
Gough, David P11
Gough, Patrick P367

Gough, Thomas J P518
Gouin, Serge W268
Goulart, Steven J. A553
Goulart, Steven J. P579
Gould, Joe E181
Gould, Donald E305
Gould, Lewis E386
Gould, Leonard E387
Gould, Chris A119
Gould, Paul A. A257
Gould, Christopher A305
Gould, Mark A. A321
Gould, Ted H. A344
Gould, Jay S. A436
Gould, John A613
Gould, Eric W. A842
Gould, Jean P16
Gould, Rob P41
Gould, Lewis F. P498
Gould, Jonathan W137
Gould, Andrew W294
Goulden, David I. A287
Goulden, David I. A851
Goulding, Gerald L. A383
Goulding, Richard F. W331
Gouldthorpe, Hugh F. A621
Goulet, Beverly K. A46
Goulet, Ken R. A65
Goundis, Dimitrios E303
Gouraige, Ghislain P585
Gouraige, Ghislain P586
Gourbin, Jean-Louis W82
Gourji, Sol P618
Gourley, Fletcher P393
Gouveia, Jeffrey A. P486
Gouw, Julia S. A280
Gouws, Francois W367
Gove, Sue E. A86
Gove, Prentice A804
Govindan, Indira P179
Govindarajan, M. P. W68
Govoni, David P362
Gow, Kay P339
Gow, Aileen P508
Gow, Joe P581
Gowa, Joanne S. P556
Gower, Scott P414
Gower, J. Michael P620
Goyal, Ambuj A455
Goyal, Naser P548
Goyanes, Everardo A650
Goyder, Richard J. Barr W385
Goza, Robert P159
Gozon, Richard C. A55
Gozon, Richard C. P543
Graaf, Raymond de E257
Graage, Eric P39
Graass, James H. (Jim) E137
Grabe, William O. W212
Graber, Al E34
Graber, Larry R. E244
Graber, Don R. A657
Grabicki, Michael W62
Grable, Robert C. A82
Grabow, Karen P181
Grace, Peter E76
Grace, Claire S. A870
Grace, Edward P. P261
Grace, Adrian W11
Grace, I. W238
Gracel, Tim A741
Gracey, Melissa A105
Grach, Maya P600
Gracian, Pablo Quiros W9
Graddick-Weir, Miriam M. A549
Graddick-Weir, Mirian A889
Graddy, Steve P198
Grade, Joel T. A778
Grady, Edward E12
Grady, Shawn E119
Grady, R. Paul A296
Grady, Kelley A. A514
Grady, Robert E. (Bob) A761
Grady, Lois W. A773
Grady, Shaun P316

Grady, Diane W218
Grady, Diane J. W390
Grady-Troia, Christopher (Chris) A107
Graebel, William (Bill) P210
Graebel, David (Dave) P210
Graeber, Juergen W163
Graef, Thorsten E376
Graef, Eric R. E380
Graef, Roger W305
Graefe, Beth E300
Graenicher, Walter W23
Graev, Lawrence G. A810
Graf, Jonathan A. E30
Graf, R. Mark A256
Graf, Alan B. A324
Graf, Alan B. A592
Graf, Anja W112
Grafe, Karl J. A49
Graff, Leslie J. A25
Graff, Lisa H. A452
Graff, F. T. A826
Graff, Pierre W156
Graffis, Richard P246
Grafton, Susan S. A119
Grafton, W. Robert (Bob) A155
Grafton, Daniel A. (Dan) A814
Gragg, Joel E64
Gragg, Gary S. A338
Gragg, Derrick P162
Gragg, Maria Vazquez P413
Gragnolati, Brian A. P260
Gragnolati, Brian A. P486
Graham, Michael E119
Graham, Martin E210
Graham, Nicol G. (Nic) E232
Graham, Linda H E405
Graham, Bob E509
Graham, Jon A67
Graham, Patricia A. A67
Graham, Patricia F. (Pat) A167
Graham, Jonathan P. A240
Graham, Kristiane C. A268
Graham, John G. A303
Graham, Donald E. (Don) A312
Graham, H. Devon A364
Graham, Roger D. A573
Graham, Stuart E. (Stu) A654
Graham, Jordan W. A702
Graham, Solomon A715
Graham, Chris A759
Graham, Gail A. A830
Graham, Ned A832
Graham, D. Robert (Bob) A860
Graham, Carol P29
Graham, Billy P75
Graham, Kristi P82
Graham, Karen R. P105
Graham, Mark P144
Graham, Rilus P177
Graham, Morris P239
Graham, Katie P242
Graham, Catherine P289
Graham, Randolph H. P336
Graham, Ron P393
Graham, Jack P423
Graham, Stephen A. P445
Graham, Kenneth A. P543
Graham, Rev Michael J. P619
Graham, John W76
Graham, Annie W194
Graham, Anthony R. W282
Graham, Anthony R. W283
Graham, James W385
Graham, Anthony R. W387
Grahn, Jeff E442
Grainge, Lucian A8
Grainge, Lucian W377
Grainger, Russell P239
Gralike, David M. P214
Gram, Franklin P413
Gram, Frank P413
Gram, Dwight P415
Gramaglia, Tom E255
Graman, Howard P379
Gramann, Margaret A676

Grambs, Peter A201
Grams, Dana A. A21
Granado, Ray A81
Granado-Villar, Deise P585
Granado-Villar, Deise P586
Granato, Ciro E243
Granato, John J. A62
Granberry, Jennifer E306
Grand, Patrice A135
Grandin, Michael A. W173
Grandinetti, Russell (Russ) A42
Grandis, Chris A215
Grandke, Gerhard W209
Grandmont, Alain A698
Grandstrand, Karen L. A783
Graner, James A. E206
Graner, Terry P14
Granfield, Stephen P69
Granger, Clarence L. E488
Granger, Bill E515
Granger, Barry M. A275
Granholm, Jennifer M. A270
Grani, Kevin E158
Granick, Mel P314
Granier, Jean-Laurent W37
Grannis, Roger E197
Gransee, David H. E291
Grant, Thomas E114
Grant, Reg E131
Grant, Joan E136
Grant, Anna E367
Grant, Jennifer E456
Grant, Joseph F. A52
Grant, W. Thomas A208
Grant, Joan M. A279
Grant, Martin C. A320
Grant, William J. A467
Grant, Hugh A566
Grant, Jeff A602
Grant, Hugh A653
Grant, Ruth M. A713
Grant, Joseph M. (Jody) A793
Grant, Thomas P5
Grant, Shaunette P46
Grant, Peyton P47
Grant, Roger P170
Grant, Barbara P256
Grant, Kenneth P260
Grant, Glen P334
Grant, Lee J. P463
Grant, Kim P494
Grantham, William C. (Bill) A737
Grappotte, Francois W109
Grapstein, Steven H. A792
Grass, Keith B. A605
Grass, Linda P498
Grassi, Louis C. (Lou) A354
Grassi, Massimo A751
Grasso, Michael A294
Grasso, Maria A. A353
Grasso, Davide A592
Grasso, Alfred P522
Grasso, Alfred P523
Grasso, Maureen P569
Grasso, Carla W373
Gratton, Robert W282
Gratton, Robert W283
Gratz, Gabriele W135
Grau, Bruce P318
Graue, Michael (Mike) A786
Grauer, Peter T. A243
Grauer, Steve P229
Graugnard, Milton P85
Graupman, Brandon P318
Graupmann, Claire M. A782
Gravel, Louis E200
Gravelle, Ralph E245
Gravelle, Michael L. A325
Graves, Adrienne E20
Graves, Jim E47
Graves, Kris M. E131
Graves, Gregory B. (Greg) E151
Graves, Greg E151
Graves, Jeffrey A. (Jeff) E330
Graves, Chris E380

Hikita, Fuminari W225
Hiland, Chris A459
Hilbert, PJ E458
Hildebrand, Philipp M. A124
Hildebrand, J. Bruce A338
Hildebrandt, Bernd D. A694
Hildebrandt, James P434
Hildenbrand, Wilton (Wilt) A142
Hildestad, Terry D. A545
Hildner, Rolf W133
Hildwein, Robin P71
Hile, W. Douglas (Doug) A318
Hileman, David A613
Hiler, Lawrence E. A1
Hilfman, Dave A828
Hilgen, David A178
Hilgendorf, Ellen P85
Hilger, James K. (Jim) A243
Hilger, Michael A687
Hilger, Randy P425
Hilk, Jane A493
Hilkemann, Brett E113
Hill, Paul E62
Hill, Richard T. E215
Hill, William E227
Hill, Kenneth E339
Hill, W. Bryan E393
Hill, Mike E421
Hill, Robert R. E432
Hill, Peter E480
Hill, Bonnie G. A26
Hill, W. Guy A36
Hill, Julie A. A65
Hill, Trey A81
Hill, Doug A82
Hill, Anne A88
Hill, Susan M. A118
Hill, Shepard W. (Shep) A126
Hill, John B. (Thad) A144
Hill, Edwin J. (Ed) A155
Hill, Kathryn M. (Kathy) A182
Hill, Stephen E. A235
Hill, V. Janet A244
Hill, John A. A250
Hill, Brian A273
Hill, Karen A305
Hill, Craig D. A316
Hill, Homer C. A320
Hill, Lori A338
Hill, Craig H. A366
Hill, Richard T. A396
Hill, Bonnie A402
Hill, James R. A412
Hill, Gregory P. A416
Hill, Gregory P. A417
Hill, Bonnie G. A422
Hill, Brice A. A452
Hill, Stephanie C. A519
Hill, Willard I. A540
Hill, Brian A. A586
Hill, Elliott A592
Hill, David R. A603
Hill, Charles H. (Chuck) A641
Hill, Andrew C. (Casey) A675
Hill, Robert R. A735
Hill, Barbara B. A749
Hill, Linda A. A758
Hill, David A816
Hill, C. Riley A883
Hill, Bonnie G. A889
Hill, Gregory P2
Hill, Edwin D. (Ed) P17
Hill, J P29
Hill, Marilyn P56
Hill, Janeen P105
Hill, Christopher R. P123
Hill, Annie P125
Hill, Keith P151
Hill, Terry P232
Hill, Bob P254
Hill, Tim P285
Hill, Nancy P313
Hill, Lyn S. P344
Hill, Cary P375
Hill, John P379

Hill, Sam P389
Hill, Rob P403
Hill, Craig P413
Hill, Nichole P459
Hill, Jennifer A. P535
Hill, Allen M. P535
Hill, Terri P560
Hill, Catharine B. (Cappy) P586
Hill, Douglas E. P600
Hill, Stuart P607
Hill, David W212
Hill, Richard W332
Hill, Thomas R. (Tom) W367
Hill-Miller, Katherine P287
Hille, James R. P500
Hillebrand, Wolf E369
Hillebrand, Lana L. A47
Hillebrand, Jeffrey H. P354
Hillegonds, Paul C. A273
Hillenius, Dorothy W188
Hiller, Norbert W.G. E112
Hiller, Russ P488
Hillered, Jan A868
Hillerud, Andrea P443
Hillery, Vincent E. A782
Hilliard, Chris E365
Hilliard, J. Robert (Bob) A25
Hilliard, Jean A329
Hilliard, Herbert H. (Herb) A339
Hilliard, Mary Anne P110
Hilligoss, Ken E263
Hilligoss, Jeffrey E515
Hilliker, D. James A437
Hillis, Nan C. P206
Hillman, John T. A66
Hillman, Elizabeth A257
Hillman, Jeanne A. A870
Hillman, Lisa P25
Hillman, Michael P488
Hillow, Michael E E12
Hills, Wendy J E514
Hills, Carla A. A383
Hills, Warren P185
Hillyer, Christopher D. P343
Hilse, Jurgen W209
Hilsenrath, Brian P415
Hilt, Angela C. A191
Hilton, Steven J. (Steve) E309
Hilton, Steven J. (Steve) E310
Hilton, Michael F. E351
Hilton, Robert L. A48
Hilton, Michael A712
Hilton, Steven J. (Steve) A865
Hilton, John P164
Hilton, Ralph W173
Hilty, James D. (Jim) E470
Hilty, James D. A797
Hilyard, Richard E321
Hilzinger, Matthew F. A305
Hilzinger, Kurt J. A434
Himebauch, Steven F. A555
Himelfarb, Richard J. E445
Himelfarb, Richard J. A761
Himes, Michael B. P382
Himes, Vicki L. P382
Himes, Geoffrey P521
Himpe, Robrecht W30
Hin, Wong Chung W177
Hinch, Marc A73
Hinchey, Kevin T. P53
Hinchey, Joseph M. P557
Hinckle, Robert D. E98
Hinckley, Robert C. A144
Hinckley, Robert R. P89
Hinder, John E515
Hinderer, John P284
Hinderliter, Mark E464
Hindle, Peter W107
Hindman, Colin E481
Hindman, James M. (Jim) A34
Hindman, Craig A. A443
Hindmarsh, James E310
Hinds, Aston A. P391
Hindt, Michael R. P518
Hine, Chris E290

Hines, D. J. A525
Hines, Michael F. A804
Hines, Joe P172
Hines, Gerald D. P233
Hines, Jeffery C. (Jeff) P233
Hines, Grace P444
Hiney, Robert A. P525
Hingson, Luke L. P505
Hingtgen, Tim A212
Hining, Greg A827
Hinkelman, Jon B. P336
Hinkle, Todd A. A309
Hinkle, James G. A421
Hinkle, Craig M P273
Hinkle, Judith P385
Hinkleman, Jon B. P336
Hinkley, Bill E162
Hinrichs, Joseph R. (Joe) A357
Hinsch, Christian W346
Hinshaw, John A126
Hinshaw, John A418
Hinsley, Ron A256
Hinsley, Ronald J. (Ron) P170
Hinson, Laura A258
Hinson, W. Ron A381
Hinson, Jeffrey T. A516
Hinson, Robert C. (Bob) A602
Hinson, Jeffrey T. A876
Hinson, Becket P184
Hinson, Dan P464
Hintlian, Varney J. P556
Hinton, Glenn J. A451
Hintz, Donald C. (Don) A297
Hinz, Bill E68
Hipchen, Karl E442
Hipp, Glenn A469
Hippe, Duane P217
Hippe, Alan W297
Hippeau, Eric A755
Hipple, Richard J. (Dick) E295
Hippler, Jon W. A383
Hirabayashi, Hiroshi W236
Hirabayashi, Hiroshi W360
Hirai, Yasufumi A183
Hirai, Kenji W151
Hirai, Toshifumi W255
Hirai, Kazuo (Kaz) W328
Hirakawa, Yoji W316
Hirakawa, Haruki Haruki
    Hirakawa W316
Hiramoto, Koji W232
Hirano, Eiji A807
Hirano, Hajime W230
Hirano, Nobuyuki W234
Hirano, Atsuhiko W318
Hiranuma, Yoshiyuki W55
Hirao, Kohei W336
Hiras, Stacie E458
Hirasawa, Toshio W225
Hirayama, Kizo W252
Hirdman-Ryrberg, Viveka W323
Hire, Steve E11
Hiremath, Nik A547
Hirji, Rahim W221
Hirji, Zabeen W299
Hirobe, Toshihiko W315
Hiroe, Mutsuo W232
Hiromoto, Yuichi W230
Hironaka, Kazuo W124
Hirose, Takahisa W17
Hirose, Atsushi W255
Hirose, Naomi W356
Hirsch, Laurence E. (Larry) E137
Hirsch, Jack E306
Hirsch, David E391
Hirsch, Didier A20
Hirsch, Thomas J. A348
Hirsch, Laurence E. (Larry) A362
Hirsch, Jeffrey A. (Jeff) A800
Hirsch, Ronnie P70
Hirsch, David R. W268
Hirschauer, Karl E394
Hirschbiel, Paul P108
Hirschfeld, Steven I. (Steve) E303
Hirschfield, Alan J. A507

Hirschhorn, Eric E53
Hirschhorn, Beth M. A553
Hirschman, Terry E387
Hirshberg, Eric A8
Hirshberg, Alan J. (Al) A220
Hirshberg, Gary W121
Hirshman, Brian K. A739
Hirst, Richard B. (Ben) A248
Hirst, Alistair A481
Hirst, Martha K. P467
Hirth, William P318
Hiruma, Masato W78
Hiruma, Takahisa W182
Hisco, David W33
Hiscoe, Les P449
Hiscox, Jeff E348
Hiser, Bob E289
Hisey, David C. E339
Hisey, Richard M. P59
Hisham, Muzaffar W220
Hishikawa, Akira W232
Hishikawa, Akira W233
Hiskey, Michael E316
Hita, Jean-Charles A585
Hitch, Lorraine A634
Hitchcock, Robert T. A165
Hitchcock, James A257
Hitchner, Ken A386
Hite, Kate E113
Hite, William H. A252
Hite, William P. P17
Hitel, Patricia P426
Hitosugi, Itsuro W317
Hitschel, Bonnie A792
Hitt, Russell A. P234
Hitt, Brett R. P234
Hitt, Teresa P527
Hittner, Barry G. A857
Hitz, David A581
Hix, Steve P401
Hixon, F. Perkins (Perk) E159
Hixon, James A. (Jim) A598
Hjelm, Christopher A491
Hjelm, Christopher T. (Chris) A494
Hladek, Keith M. A401
Hlavacek, James D. A605
Hnat, James G. (Jim) A469
Ho, Patrick E445
Ho, Peter S. A101
Ho, Raymond A203
Ho, Paul W. A354
Ho, David H. Y. A624
Ho, Stephen A755
Ho, Cynthia A781
Ho, Doreen A819
Ho, Brenda A. P221
Ho, Edith W173
Ho, Edwina W221
Hoadley, Garrick P366
Hoag, Jay C. A583
Hoag, Jo Ann P476
Hoagland, Cyndee E482
Hoagland, Joe A789
Hoaglin, Thomas E. (Tom) A47
Hoang, Minh A14
Hoar, Robert J. P481
Hoare, Rohan E117
Hoare, Graham A358
Hoban, Bill E162
Hobart, Lauren A251
Hobbis, Thomas R. (Tom) A184
Hobbs, Allen E362
Hobbs, Franklin W. (Fritz) A37
Hobbs, C. Scott A138
Hobbs, C. Scott A236
Hobbs, Nick A435
Hobbs, Helen A642
Hobbs, Timothy L. P127
Hobbs, John P358
Hobbs, John P359
Hobbs, Patrick E. P445
Hobbs, Keith M. P507
Hobbs, Marcia Wilson P507
Hobbs, Brian P604
Hobby, Paul W. A603

A = AMERICAN BUSINESS
E = EMERGING COMPANIES
P = PRIVATE COMPANIES
W = WORLD BUSINESS

A = AMERICAN BUSINESS
E = EMERGING COMPANIES
P = PRIVATE COMPANIES
W = WORLD BUSINESS

Juliber, Lois D. A275
Juliber, Lois D. A386
Julien, Jeffrey P. A687
Julius, DeAnne S. A474
Julius, DeAnne S. W297
Julow, Jim E46
Jumah, Abdallah A395
Jumper, Gen. John P. A466
Jumper, Gen. John P. A505
Jum'ah, Abdallah S. A395
Jun, Lei W51
Junck, Mary E. P503
Junco, Kirk D. P518
Juneau, Kenneth J. A52
Juneau, Courtney P2
Junek, John C. A53
Junemann, Gregory J. P17
Jung, Andrea A68
Jung, Andrea A92
Jung, Sonia A226
Jung, Andrea A374
Jung, Hak A398
Jung, Brian P221
Jung, Helga W20
Jung, David W213
Jung, Helga W368
Jungblut, Peter R. P453
Jungels, Pierre H. A95
Jungels, Pierre H. W185
Jungers, Mike P325
Junhui, Cui W275
Junio, Marc A388
Junior, Jose Batista A647
Junior, Wallim Cruz de
   Vasconcellos A647
Junkins, Lowell L. A317
Junquera, Jorge A. A651
Junyent, Miquel Roca i W9
Junyent, Miguel W43
Junyuan, Fu W95
Jura, Anton A833
Jura, James J. P32
Jura, Virginia Van P114
Jurado, Jose E251
Juranek, Herbert W144
Jurczak, Joe P382
Jurczyk, Andrew D. P446
Jurczyk, John A. P482
Jureller, John M. A365
Jurgens, Neil E490
Jurgensen, William G. (Jerry) A218
Jurgielewicz, Stanley R. P467
Juricic, Terri E343
Juris, Susan V. P569
Jurkowski, Jack P162
Jurkowski, Jack P163
Jury, David P375
Jury, Victor R. P488
Jury, Daniel J. (Dan) P606
Just, Scott E269
Juster, Kristine L. (Kristie) A585
Juster, Andrew A. (Andy) A730
Justice, Melissa E78
Justice, M L E370
Justice, Lonnie G. (Lon) A20
Justice, Kelly P. A25
Justice, John A789
Justice, Lorraine P419
Justin, David A. A763
Justiss, Donna A9
Justman, Scott E436
Justus, Ronald P75
Jutkiewicz, Chris E153
Juusela, Kari P59

K

K?nig, Elke A. W163
Ka-cheung, Li (Eric) W51
Ka-shing, Li W176
Kaay, Erik H. van der A96
Kaba, Franz W267
Kabat, Kevin T. A329
Kabat, Donald J. A719
Kabat, Kevin T. A840
Kabat, Richard H. P453
Kabata, Tsuyoshi W232
Kabbaz, Michael P318
Kablawi, Hani A103
Kabureck, Gary R. A885
Kacer, Edward J. E197
Kachavos, Peter P171
Kaczmar, Swiatoslav W P358
Kaden, Ellen Oran A149
Kaden, Lewis B. (Lew) W30
Kadenacy, Stephen M. (Steve) A12
Kadien, Thomas G. (Tom) A458
Kadien, Thomas G. (Tom) A728
Kadifa, George A418
Kadir, Rashid P26
Kadish, Ronald T. (Ron) A744
Kadish, Alan P546
Kadlec, Thomas R. A73
Kadokami, Ei W232
Kadonsky, William J E526
Kadoorie, Sir Michael D. W176
Kadowaki, Katsutoshi W270
Kadri, Ilham A723
Kadrnoska, Friedrich W368
Kaehr, Thomas R. (Tom) A194
Kaelberer, Darvin A106
Kaelin, Michael H. (Mike) P413
Kaelle, John E420
Kaemmerer, Peter A. W208
Kaerhoeg, Kenth A199
Kaeser, Joe W320
Kaeser, Christian W320
Kaferle, Daniel (Dan) A140
Kagan, Peter R. A779
Kagan, Julia P133
Kagawa, Shingo Shingo Kagawa W150
Kagawa, Akihiko W234
Kagay, Barry P318
Kagel, Kris W367
Kagen, Brian E305
Kagerer, Patricia P262
Kagermann, Henning Henning
   Kagermann W67
Kagermann, Henning W240
Kageyama, Sachio W85
Kagge, Gunnar A720
Kahan, James S. (Jim) A365
Kahan, James S. (Jim) A516
Kahanek, Sheila P489
Kahkedjian, George P130
Kahl, Kelly A161
Kahle, Shawn M. A78
Kahle, Charles F. A653
Kahle, David J. P556
Kahler, Erik T E478
Kahler, Harold A700
Kahly-McMahon, Heidi P203
Kahmann, Mike A184
Kahmer, Bob P353
Kahn, Karen A137
Kahn, Todd A196
Kahn, Robert E. A680
Kahn, Thomas G. A760
Kahn, Susan D. A780
Kahn, Maureen A. P67
Kaigelak, Bernice P10
Kail, Mike D. A583
Kailbourne, Erland E. (Erkie) A330
Kailbourne, Erland E. (Erkie) P525
Kaimer, Jason A344
Kain, Tommy A592
Kain, Dale P378
Kaiser, George B. A128
Kaiser, James G. A547

Kaiser, Laura S. P249
Kaiser, Michael M. P259
Kaiser, Ann P426
Kaiser, Larry R. P498
Kaiser, Ken P498
Kaiser, Sherif P611
Kaiser, Regine W240
Kaiserman, David J. A506
Kaisheng, Yang W186
Kaitson, E. Chris A292
Kaji, Ashlee E455
Kajiwara, Terufumi W232
Kakar, Parveen E451
Kakehi, Kazuo W78
Kakinoki, Masumi W223
Kakiuchi, Takehiko W230
Kakumu, Masakazu W360
Kakutani, Kazuki Kazuki
   Kakutani W225
Kalafatis, Lara P95
Kalaitzidakis, Nikos A199
Kalajainen, Kimberly P279
Kalamaras, Paul E251
Kalamaras, Paul A463
Kalan, Peter E. E114
Kalan, John E526
Kalaris, Thomas L. P153
Kalaris, Thomas L. (Tom) W58
Kalaris, Thomas L. (Tom) W60
Kalas, Mike E445
Kalathur, Rajesh (Raj) A246
Kalberer, Peter W40
Kalder, Christy P396
Kaled, Eric E466
Kalena, Maureen A318
Kalia, Kumud E19
Kalia, Ranjan E509
Kalicak, Michael E455
Kalidindi, Sunil E257
Kalikow, Theodora J. (Theo) P570
Kalil, Charles J. A270
Kalina, Michael E93
Kalina, Kyle P605
Kalinowski, Mitchell E118
Kalinsky, Jeffrey A596
Kalish, Robert (Bob) P366
Kaliski, Burt E506
Kalker, Ton E131
Kallas, Linda M. A449
Kallembach, Larry J. A539
Kalligher, Peter E196
Kallman, Todd J. A836
Kallmeier, Hans-Jurgen W130
Kalm, Stephen P571
Kalmanson, Steven R. A707
Kalmbach, J. Steven (Steve) A675
Kalodner, Liz A161
Kaloustian, Robert E97
Kalsbeek, David Van A556
Kalsbeek, David H. P148
Kalsi, Balvinder S. A275
Kalsu, J. Barton E430
Kaltenbach, Bryan H. A494
Kalumbu, Nathan A198
Kalvoda, Mark E473
Kam, Moshe P515
Kam, Kellee W292
Kamangar, Salar A389
Kamano, Hiroyuki W337
Kamari, Nass P167
Kamata, Hiroshi W1
Kamath, Kundapur V. (K. V.) W181
Kamau, Manasseh E339
Kamback, Eric D. A103
Kambe, Mitsutaka W1
Kambeitz, Stephen A630
Kamboj, Manju E64
Kambury, Stuart A. A379
Kameda, Shigeaki W318
Kamei, Clifton P76
Kamei, Katsunobu W270
Kamei, Atsushi W313
Kamel, G. Sam A445
Kamen, Hershel I. A828

Kamenz, Ina B. A799
Kameoka, Tsuyoshi W318
Kamerick, Eileen A. A77
Kamerick, Anthony J. (Tony) A637
Kamers, Todd P552
Kametz, William (Bill) A713
Kamholz, Stephan P294
Kamijo, Masahito W291
Kamimae, Osamu W182
Kamin, John R. A610
Kamin, Chester T. P125
Kaminski, Jeff E263
Kaminski, Jennifer A77
Kaminski, Paul G. A371
Kaminski, Mark V. A694
Kaminski, Stephen E. (Steve) P341
Kaminsky, Larry E272
Kaminsky, Jody E487
Kamlani, Suneel W300
Kamlet, Mark S. P93
Kamlet, Lee P404
Kammer, Ronald L. P233
Kammerman, Eli E294
Kammerman, Susan E369
Kamp, W. Taylor A184
Kamperschroer, George P315
Kampfe, Michael E254
Kampfe, Randall R. A73
Kamphuis, Robert P305
Kamsky, Virginia A. A239
Kamsky, Virginia A. A742
Kan, Tetsuya W291
Kana, Elizabeth P70
Kanada, Yoshihiko W17
Kanai, Hiroshi W117
Kanan, Charles E523
Kanarek, Robin P556
Kanas, John A. A105
Kanazawa, Suguru W171
Kanazawa, Kaoru W253
Kanda, Yoshifumi W166
Kandarian, Steven A. (Steve) A552
Kandula, Srinivas E238
Kane, Paul J. E357
Kane, Debra E396
Kane, Patrick (Pat) E506
Kane, Laura A17
Kane, Jacqueline P. (Jackie) A191
Kane, Jacqueline P. (Jackie) A207
Kane, Andrew S. A280
Kane, Michael A320
Kane, Dan A337
Kane, Terry A344
Kane, Jim A602
Kane, Nancy A669
Kane, Linda S. A674
Kane, Michael B. P19
Kane, Patrick P88
Kane, Patrick P89
Kane, Candace P166
Kane, Roger P179
Kane, John W. P234
Kane, David R. P234
Kane, Pamela P279
Kane, Marci P364
Kane, Addy P421
Kane, Chris P602
Kane, Archie W53
Kane, Julie W261
Kanegae, Michihiko W336
Kaneko, Walter P607
Kaner, Brian A751
Kang, Il-Hyung W179
Kang, Chan Soo W198
Kang, Seog-Hoon W205
Kang, Yu-Sig W213
Kang, T.H. W305
Kangas, Edward A. (Ed) A462
Kangas, Edward A. (Ed) A786
Kangas, Paul A804
Kangas, Edward A. (Ed) A836
Kangmin, Sun W98
Kani, Shigeru W317
Kania, Don R. E165
Kania, Don R. E166

A = AMERICAN BUSINESS
E = EMERGING COMPANIES
P = PRIVATE COMPANIES
W = WORLD BUSINESS

Kazah, Hernán E307
Kazel, Ronald A64
Kazmierski, Dennis A. E446
Kazunga, Mary P218
Ke, Nigel W221
Keables, Michael P123
Keady, Thomas R. A499
Keady, Thomas J P555
Keag, W. Ken P36
Kean, Thomas H. (Tom) A360
Kean, Thomas H. (Tom) A417
Kean, Steven J. (Steve) A489
Kean, Linda E. P39
Kean, Holly P82
Kean, Melissa C. P140
Kean, Sue W266
Keane, Kevin T. E42
Keane, Denise F. A41
Keane, Kathryn A. A121
Keane, John M. A371
Keane, Margaret M. A374
Keane, John M. A553
Keane, Peter J. A675
Keane, James P. (Jim) A707
Keane, Frances P102
Keaney, Timothy F. (Tim) A102
Keaney, Timothy F. (Tim) A103
Keanly, Rose W266
Kearney, Michael S. A74
Kearney, Daniel P. A348
Kearney, Daniel P. A540
Kearney, Daniel P. A555
Kearney, Christopher J. A605
Kearney, Christopher J. A747
Kearney, Thomas W. A880
Kearney, Joseph D. P300
Kearney, Stephanie P361
Kearney, Charles P583
Kearns, John P E464
Kearns, Christopher A103
Kearns, John F. A301
Kearns, Donald P405
Keating, Elizabeth E10
Keating, Larry E27
Keating, Stephen E114
Keating, Todd E139
Keating, John E139
Keating, Neal J. E261
Keating, Mary Ellen A107
Keating, Timothy J. (Tim) A126
Keating, Frank A174
Keating, Terrence J. (Terry) A239
Keating, M. J. A290
Keating, Peter M. A371
Keating, Catherine M. A475
Keating, Mark A758
Keating, Robert G. M. P373
Keating, Patrick J. P555
Keating, Catherine M. P589
Keating, J. Edmund (Ed) P613
Keating, Andrew W52
Keaton, Joel E115
Keaveney, Tony E308
Keaveny, Tom A257
Keck, Brian L. A218
Kedderis, Pamela J. (Pam) P130
Keddington, Lynn P. A420
Kedia, Gunjan A758
Keech, Brian P158
Keefe, Michael C E321
Keefe, R. E. A289
Keefe, Mary A661
Keefe, Paul P143
Keefe, Hugh F. P404
Keefer, Elizabeth J. P523
Keefover, Brian E400
Keegan, Gerard C. A79
Keegan, Peter W. A520
Keegan, Robert J. (Bob) A885

Keegan, James P407
Keegel, C. Thomas (Tom) P251
Keehan, Sister Carol P577
Keel, Alexander E181
Keel, Deborah C. (Debbie) A786
Keeler, Richard E162
Keeler, Robert N. A803
Keeler, Thomas C. P354
Keeler, Karl P428
Keeler, Diane Fishel P512
Keeley, Jim E219
Keeley, Brian E. P43
Keen, James F. (Jim) A339
Keen, Eric L. P217
Keen, Suzanne P. P538
Keenan, Timothy E189
Keenan, Kevin E326
Keenan, Greg E374
Keenan, Vincent (Vince) A91
Keenan, Brian P. A329
Keenan, Brian F. A505
Keenan, David R. (Dave) A691
Keenan, Karen C. A758
Keenan, James E. (Jim) A828
Keenan, Kathleen P24
Keenan, Paula P383
Keenan, Richard (Rich) P537
Keenan, Gerry W274
Keenan, Roy W274
Keene, Mark E18
Keene, Ian E196
Keene, Brooke A. P426
Keener, Gaither M. A523
Keeney, Andrew P243
Keep, Scott L. P317
Kees, Tom P406
Keesey, Dana P466
Keeth, M. Frances (Fran) A633
Keeth, M. Frances (Fran) A845
Keeton, Pamela V. (Pam) P502
Keffer, John R. A649
Keffer, Terry P504
Keglevic, Paul M. A294
Kehl, Thomas E226
Kehl, Richard R. P614
Kehler, Dean C. P135
Kehoe, Michael P. E233
Kehoe, Patty A562
Kehoe, Mary P82
Kehoe, John P. P192
Kehoe, Michael J. (Mike) P378
Kehua, Zhang W97
Kehui, Zhang W98
Keib, John A800
Keifer, Alan J. A95
Keightley, Rebecca P310
Keil, Jeffrey C. A507
Keim, Douglas B. P584
Keim, Marco W11
Keino, Antti E195
Keir, Alan M. W175
Keiser, Sue P571
Keisling, Jeffrey E. (Jeff) A641
Keister, Jane P749
Keister, Polly P485
Keita, Maghan P122
Keitel, William E. A680
Keitel, Prof Hans-Peter W105
Keitel, Hans-Peter W354
Keith, Jeffrey B. E77
Keith, Jeffery B. E77
Keith, Stephen C. P99
Kekedjian, Aris A373
Kelbel, Craig J. A409
Kelch, Mercedes P12
Kelderhouse, Robert J. A835
Kellar, Robert E. A321
Kellar, Justine P212
Kelleher, Dennis P. A171
Kelleher, Gregory T. A250
Kelleher, Michael J. A379
Kelleher, Patrick B. (Pat) A380
Kelleher, Ann B. A452
Kelleher, Colm A568
Kelleher, Kevin J. A690

Kelleher, Joe P184
Kelleher, Bruce M. P335
Kellems, Jackie S. A409
Kellenberger, Steve P214
Keller, Keith E11
Keller, Casey E14
Keller, Ken E15
Keller, Christoph E121
Keller, Joseph H E206
Keller, Dave E244
Keller, Michael D. A605
Keller, Kurt A. A631
Keller, Gregory S. A778
Keller, Dawnise P75
Keller, Frederick P. (Fred) P94
Keller, Neal P119
Keller, Chuck P127
Keller, David P174
Keller, Kevin P217
Keller, Clarence M. P338
Keller, Ray P548
Keller, Bethany P600
Keller, Gottlieb A. W297
Kelley, William E E44
Kelley, Glen E45
Kelley, Tania E222
Kelley, Joseph P. E295
Kelley, Tom E309
Kelley, Bruce E345
Kelley, Donna E455
Kelley, James Virgil (Jim) A98
Kelley, Brian P. A198
Kelley, Kathy A364
Kelley, Matt A365
Kelley, Jacki A459
Kelley, Brian P. A485
Kelley, Thomas M. (Tom) A528
Kelley, William N. A549
Kelley, James Virgil (Jim) A572
Kelley, Charles M. (Chuck) A615
Kelley, Clarence A634
Kelley, Ronald A725
Kelley, Peter D. A782
Kelley, Brien A800
Kelley, D. Lynn A825
Kelley, Thomas J. A856
Kelley, J. Mike A888
Kelley, James P6
Kelley, Benjamin S. P51
Kelley, Brian P208
Kelley, Daniel T. (Dan) P213
Kelley, Mark A. P227
Kelley, H. Lynn P283
Kelley, Richard G. P404
Kelley, Kimberly B. P505
Kelley, Robert O. P573
Kelley, Meera P594
Kelliher, Patrick E360
Kelliher, Joseph T. A589
Kellington, John S. A180
Kellis, Dana P386
Kellner, Lawrence W. (Larry) A178
Kellner, Lawrence W. (Larry) A531
Kellner, Kirk L. A861
Kellner, Lawrence W. (Larry) P519
Kellner, Petr W32
Kellogg, William S. (Bill) A492
Kellogg, Peter N. A549
Kellogg, James A. (Jim) A611
Kellogg, Harry W. A770
Kellogg, Susan A846
Kellogg, Don P75
Kellow, Glenn A633
Kellow, Glenn W70
Kelly, Declan E22
Kelly, Anne Gill E28
Kelly, Ashley E30
Kelly, Kimberly E30
Kelly, Maura E51
Kelly, Richard E93
Kelly, Gerald E158
Kelly, Kevin E232
Kelly, Michael J E261
Kelly, Patrick E266
Kelly, Hayes E287

Kelly, Brian E300
Kelly, Thomas J E325
Kelly, John E346
Kelly, Thomas E427
Kelly, Jill E. E470
Kelly, Joseph E515
Kelly, Michael A. A2
Kelly, Brian G. A8
Kelly, Thomas L. (Tom) A15
Kelly, Anne Gill A44
Kelly, Michael A. A57
Kelly, James P. (Jim) A81
Kelly, Edmund F. (Ted) A103
Kelly, Wally C. A161
Kelly, Kathleen A. A169
Kelly, Jackson A198
Kelly, Janet Langford A220
Kelly, Thomas A. A230
Kelly, Edward J. (Ned) A231
Kelly, Jim A234
Kelly, Michael A258
Kelly, Edmund F. (Ted) A287
Kelly, J.F. A290
Kelly, Scott M. A309
Kelly, Allan J. A311
Kelly, Theresa A354
Kelly, Thomas A368
Kelly, John E. A454
Kelly, Christie B. A474
Kelly, Tom A476
Kelly, Gary C. A515
Kelly, Alex A549
Kelly, Alfred F. (Al) A553
Kelly, Anastasia D. (Stasia) A624
Kelly, William A660
Kelly, Michael A677
Kelly, David N. A701
Kelly, Gary C. A739
Kelly, Michael A741
Kelly, Steve A792
Kelly, Jill E. A797
Kelly, Thomas A833
Kelly, John J. P1
Kelly, David L. P2
Kelly, Thomas B. (Tom) P7
Kelly, Stephen E. P48
Kelly, William M. P70
Kelly, Kim A. P102
Kelly, Sam P120
Kelly, Mark P125
Kelly, Annice M. P125
Kelly, Michael E. P140
Kelly, Jack L. P179
Kelly, Paul P201
Kelly, Jack P212
Kelly, Michael P230
Kelly, Timothy E. (Tim) P297
Kelly, Terri L. P341
Kelly, Kathryn P342
Kelly, Michael J. (Mike) P399
Kelly, Linda P406
Kelly, Alan B. P439
Kelly, John P443
Kelly, James P473
Kelly, Brian P485
Kelly, Robert E. P524
Kelly, Sister Mary P550
Kelly, Tom W81
Kelly, Greg W255
Kelly, Gail P. W388
Kelly-Ennis, Debra J. A676
Kelman, Naomi W261
Kelmar, Steven B. A15
Kelp, Mark P103
Kelp, Jamie P510
Kelsall, Bruce W333
Kelsheimer, Brad P151
Kelso, Matt E328
Kelso, J. Peter A17
Kelso, Harry B. A52
Kelso, David B. A78
Kelso, April D. A383
Kelso, Alan W. A777
Kelson, Richard E213
Kelson, Richard B. (Rick) A209

Kelson, Richard B. (Rick) A547
Kelson, Richard B. (Rick) A651
Keltner, Robert P279
Kelton, Justin P306
Kemerling, James L. (Jim) A449
Kemmel, Gerard Van W309
Kemmerer, Josh E139
Kemmerer, Janet E285
Kemmochi, Masatoshi W270
Kemp, Linda E175
Kemp, Roger E195
Kemp, Derek E238
Kemp, Michael A. E244
Kemp, Andy P353
Kemp, Steve P376
Kemp, Jacques P.M. W198
Kempe, Rick P67
Kempen, Wouter van A741
Kempen, Jake P31
Kemper, Jonathan M. A208
Kemper, David W. A208
Kemper, Jonathan M. A208
Kemper, Alexander C. (Sandy) A822
Kemper, J. Mariner A822
Kemper, Alexander C. (Sandy) A822
Kemper, Jonathan M. P332
Kemper, Jeffrey H. (Jeff) P364
Kemper, Nikola W240
Kempf, Karl G. A452
Kemppel, Denali P28
Kemps, Steven J. A244
Kempton, Will P367
Ken, Gumbiner E244
Kenagy, John P281
Kenan, Wilfred M. (Mills) A226
Kenard, Deanna P316
Kenchel, Kurt T. P96
Kendall, Sara S. A870
Kendall, Randy P502
Kendall-Rijos, Pamela P125
Kender, Joseph P P281
Kendle, Candace A831
Kendra, Thomas W. (Tom) A140
Kendrella, Brian A744
Kendrick, Robin A130
Kendrick, Lynn A648
Kendrick, Don C. A861
Kendrick, Ken P385
Kendricks, Samuel B. E216
Kendricks, Sam B. A396
Kendricks, Samuel A396
Keneally, Timothy P. E262
Kenefick, John E172
Kengeter, Carsten W367
Kenison, Tracy P198
KenKnight, Bruce H. E117
Kenley, William A. P317
Kenna, Tom Mc E362
Kenna, John A30
Kennan, Elizabeth T. A303
Kenne, Leslie F. A405
Kenne, Leslie F. A620
Kenne, Leslie F. P465
Kenneally, John E325
Kennedy, Ken E114
Kennedy, Barbara E146
Kennedy, Kitty E338
Kennedy, Jonathan A. E340
Kennedy, Tony E429
Kennedy, James E503
Kennedy, Bryan J. A35
Kennedy, Charles D. A65
Kennedy, Nicole A71
Kennedy, John J. A178
Kennedy, W. Keith A216
Kennedy, Maria A257
Kennedy, Parker S. A331
Kennedy, Rick A374
Kennedy, Kevin W. A386
Kennedy, Laura A505
Kennedy, Wendy S. A664
Kennedy, Thomas A. (Tom) A689
Kennedy, Daniel O. A702
Kennedy, R. Michael A760
Kennedy, Scott A781

Kennedy, Barbara J. A835
Kennedy, Michael J. A862
Kennedy, Brad P7
Kennedy, Raymond P30
Kennedy, Charles A P93
Kennedy, Robert T. (Bobby) P115
Kennedy, Ann P125
Kennedy, P. Todd P191
Kennedy, Henry P209
Kennedy, Leroy P243
Kennedy, Daniel E. P294
Kennedy, Terris P417
Kennedy, Bill P492
Kennedy, James M. (Jim) P503
Kennedy, Patrick T. W53
Kennedy, Jerome J. W53
Kennedy, Keith N. W266
Kennedy-Lahiff, Kristi P423
Kenner, Shane P213
Kenney, Don E186
Kenney, Sean E513
Kenney, Anthony R. (Tony) A528
Kenney, Thomas F. (Tom) A855
Kenney, Tom A855
Kenningham, Daryl A394
Kenny, Maria E133
Kenny, Steven E189
Kenny, John E443
Kenny, Sean E495
Kenny, Gregory B. A153
Kenny, Katharine A155
Kenny, Kate A157
Kenny, Gregory B. A370
Kenny, Gregory B. A447
Kenny, John J. A520
Kenny, Patrick J. A653
Kenny, Chris T. A828
Kenny, David W. A886
Kenny, Thomas P92
Kenny, Richard P133
Kenny, John R. P188
Kenny, Brian P510
Kenny, Shirley S. P528
Kenoyer, Jason W E60
Kent, Jesse E401
Kent, Lena A139
Kent, Muhtar A198
Kent, Mark A434
Kent, Robert N. (Bob) A629
Kent, Philip I. (Phil) A801
Kent, Robert R. A857
Kent, Evelyn P28
Kent, Patricia P167
Kent, Gregg P275
Kent, Robert P488
Kent, Thomas P503
Kent, K. Craig P580
Kent-Sheehan, Kate A344
Kentfield, Ian E475
Keny-Guyer, Neal L. P313
Kenyon, Norman M. P43
Kenyon, John P114
Kenyon-Slaney, Harry W295
Keogan, Janet M. P467
Keogh, Tracy P418
Keogh, John W. W8
Keohane, Ellen J. P122
Keon-Soo, Shin W200
Keough, Dan E18
Keough, Donald R. (Don) A117
Keough, Donald R. (Don) A199
Kephart, Bruce M. A346
Kephart, Bruce M. P277
Kephart, Kevin D. P458
Kepler, David E. (Dave) A270
Kepp, Bill E434
Keppler, Ed E69
Keprta, Nancy P406
Kerber, Mindy E430
Kerber, Lynn A173
Kerby, Brad P496
Kerckhove, Ghislaine Van W199
Kerek, W. Damain P488
Kergaravat, Charles E53
Kerger, Paula A. P400

Kerin, Matthew A. A349
Kerins, Ray A641
Kerins, Nancy P165
Kerkhoff, Guido W354
Kerley, Jay A70
Kern, Brad E246
Kern, Paul J. A304
Kern, Peter M. A307
Kern, Ric L. A585
Kern, Dave A587
Kern, Howard P. P444
Kern, Mark P478
Kern, Harald W320
Kernan, May P90
Kerner, John A. A309
Kerner, Douglas E. A538
Kerner, Michael G. (Mike) W392
Kerns, Mike A886
Keroack, Mark A. P52
Keroack, Mark A. P53
Kerr, Ronda E138
Kerr, Patrick E200
Kerr, Derek J. A46
Kerr, William A. (Woody) A103
Kerr, William T. (Bill) A459
Kerr, Thomas R. A587
Kerr, Thomas P. (Tom) A653
Kerr, William T. (Bill) A871
Kerr, Mary E. A95
Kerr, Theresa P125
Kerr, Laurie P130
Kerr, Howard J. P131
Kerr, Donald M. P523
Kerr, Janet E. P616
Kerr, John C. W54
Kerr, Graham W69
Kerr, Graham W70
Kerr, John W295
Kerr, David W. W339
Kerrey, J. Robert (Bob) A786
Kerrigan, John E369
Kerrigan, Sylvia J. A527
Kerrigan, Sandra A851
Kerrigan, John P395
Kerrigan, Adrian P467
Kerris, Robert F. (Bob) E138
Kerris, Richard A418
Kerrmann, Dirk-Uwe W90
Kerschbaum, Manfred A70
Kershaw, James B. P70
Kershaw, Ed P548
Kerstein, Todd E369
Kersten, Rebecca P29
Kerstetter, R.P. A290
Kersting, Matt P143
Kersting, Joan P143
Kerwin, Cornelius M. (Neil) P22
Kesavan, Sudhakar A7
Keskar, Dinesh A126
Kesler, D. Craig E137
Kesler, Robert M. A598
Kesler, Leslie P342
Kesler, Michael P517
Kesner, Prof Idalene F. (Idie) W339
Kessel, Steven A42
Kessler, Carl E172
Kessler, Pam E280
Kessler, Pamela Shelley E280
Kessler, Randy E383
Kessler, Steven J. E399
Kessler, John E. A173
Kessler, Murray S. A521
Kessler, Lisa A664
Kessler, Eric A801
Kessler, Robert D. P204
Kessler, Joseph (Joe) P265
Kessler, Bruce L. W7
Kessler, Denis W72
Kesteloot, Thomas M. A778
Kestenbaum, Alan E204
Kestenbaum, Jay A25
Kestenbaum, Jerry A25
Keswani, Sid A781
Keswick, Henry W194
Keswick, Simon L. W194

Ketcham, Henry H. W358
Ketchum, Mark D. A585
Ketchum, Richard G. P186
Ketelsen, Ron E379
Ketola, Todd P47
Ketron, Russ P75
Kettelle, John P534
Kettels, Janet A34
Ketterer, Douglas J. A568
Kettering, Karen E432
Kettering, Glen L. A594
Kettering, Susan P535
Ketterson, James B. A116
Kettig, David T. E244
Kettle, Charles E. A776
Keuer, Steven P. P551
Keulen, Sjoerd W188
Keung, Chung E485
Keup, Gregory J. (Greg) P26
Keuten, John P361
Kevelighan, Sean W392
Kever, Jim D. A818
Kever, Tom P116
Kevers, Charly A418
Kew, Steven E351
Key, Scott E239
Key, Janet P571
Keyes, Kevin A64
Keyes, Tony A215
Keyes, James H. (Jim) A578
Keyes, J. Patrick A878
Keyes, James R. P395
Keys, James E419
Keys, Bob P463
Keyser, Brian E124
Keyser, Dan E158
Keyser, Kate A85
Keyser, Richard L. (Dick) A661
Keyser, Richard L. (Dick) P354
Khaishgi, Mohammed E23
Khalaf, Michel A553
Khalaf, Randy P558
Khaldi, Anan A544
Khaleghi, Mehdi E301
Khalfa, Amin I. A640
Khalsa, Mahan E185
Khalsa, Sat Nirmal K. P8
Khalsa, Daya S. P8
Khalsa, Gurutej S. P8
Khalsa, Dev Suroop K. P8
Khamish, Yan E181
Khan, Najeeb A. A1
Khan, Mehmood A638
Khan, Fareed A. A835
Khan, Kamran P610
Khan, Afaq W332
Khandekar, Janardan D. P354
Khandelwa, Sachin W181
Khanna, Rakesh E461
Khanna, Tarun A14
Khanna, Chand P228
Khasbulatov, Khamzat A541
Khasis, Lev A853
Khatibi, Alex A E17
Khattri, Sanjiv A229
Khavkin, Evgeny W264
Khayat, Clark H. I. A486
Khazam, Jonathan (Jon) A451
Kheradpir, Shaygan W58
Kheradpir, Shaygan W60
Khoba, Lyubov W264
Khomyakov, Sergey F W154
Khoo, Ronald E156
Khoo, Kay E181
Khoo, Edwin W123
Khoo, Eddie Boo Jin W371
Khor, Jiak Woen A374
Khoshafian, Setrag E373
Khoshoo, Raj W320
Khosla, Sanjay A120
Khosravi, Behzad (Ben) A749
Khosrowshahi, Dara A307
Khouja, Mohamad E71
Khouri, Eli E265

A = AMERICAN BUSINESS
E = EMERGING COMPANIES
P = PRIVATE COMPANIES
W = WORLD BUSINESS

Kluever, Steve A406
Klug, Loren C. A431
Klug, Ken P598
Kluge, Holger W177
Klugman, Jeffrey (Jeff) E474
Kluhr, Thomas W127
Klunder, Sean E268
Kluse, Michael P48
Kluska, Margie P526
Klusmeyer, Roy P604
Kluth, Barbara A. A788
Klutts, Clayton E. A262
Kluver, Lynette P12
Kmetz, David C. A856
Knabel, Wayne L. E204
Knabusch, Scott E503
Knapke, Murph A337
Knapke, Amy P364
Knapp, Lisa E136
Knapp, Robert E350
Knapp, Charles B. A17
Knapp, Dennis E. A227
Knapp, Tracy W. A478
Knapp, Kevin A643
Knapp, Leah A666
Knapp, Amy A860
Knapp, Halsey G. P56
Knapp, Cheryl L. P78
Knapp, Paul R. P125
Knapp, Ralph P179
Knapp, Loey P571
Knarr, Lori P245
Knauf, Jason W300
Knaup, Carolyn P594
Knauss, Donald R. (Don) A191
Knauss, Donald R. (Don) A481
Knauss, Robert H. A821
Knavish, Timothy M. A653
Knecht, Dale E485
Knecht, Randy A177
Kneeland, Michael J. A832
Kneeland, Michael J. A888
Kneeley, Steve P574
Kneeshaw, Warren A680
Kneisel, Jan E384
Kneisel, Geoff P23
Knell, Michael E67
Knelly, Shirley J. P25
Knerr, Butch A730
Kneubuehl, Stephen A. (Steve) P59
Kneubuehl, Edward (Ed) P59
Knez, Debra S. P556
Knezevic, Bane A541
Knichel, Thomas P196
Knickrehm, Ashley E139
Kniering, John P536
Knifechief, Charles E239
Knight, Kevin E57
Knight, Craig A. E179
Knight, Frances E234
Knight, Eric E240
Knight, Gary J. E267
Knight, Kevin P. E267
Knight, Susan E. (Sue) E330
Knight, Jessie J. A28
Knight, James P. (Jim) A178
Knight, Linda K. A315
Knight, William C. (Bill) A379
Knight, George F. A564
Knight, Philip H. A592
Knight, Kevin T. A596
Knight, Jeffrey L. (Jeff) A610
Knight, Leo E. A611
Knight, Jessie J. A726
Knight, Timothy A. A727
Knight, Nancy Lopez A733
Knight, Nancy A733
Knight, Andrew S. B. A816
Knight, Robert M. A825

Knight, Napoleon B. P92
Knight, Sherry P102
Knight, Clif P127
Knight, Priscilla P353
Knight, Lester B. P354
Knight, Ellis M. (Mac) P375
Knight, Alfred B. P438
Knight, Deborah P472
Knight, Christopher W332
Knight, John W334
Knipple, Larry E119
Knittel, C. Jeffrey (Jeff) A184
Knitzer, Peter A278
Knizevski, Carson P. P234
Knobbe, Mike A460
Knobel, Jeff A. A96
Knoblich, Werner E396
Knoebel, Adam P306
Knoeppel, Chris P227
Knoll, Bill E77
Knoll, Thomas E. A245
Knoll, Rolf W. P429
Knop, Jacek E86
Knopf, William E303
Knopf, Ted F. A889
Knott, Kenneth E426
Knott, Liam P26
Knotts, Daniel L. (Dan) A266
Knotts, Chris P191
Knowles, Dennis R. A523
Knowles, Marie L. A544
Knowles, Dwight P170
Knowles, Kenneth A. (Ken) P366
Knowles, Wendy P367
Knowlton, Warren D. A54
Knowlton, Carla May P404
Knox, Kevin E195
Knox, Rita E196
Knox, William E300
Knox, Kent E339
Knox, C. Robert E479
Knox, Wyck A. A22
Knox, Lina S. A150
Knox, E. Phillips A334
Knox, Wendell J. A399
Knox, D. Bruce A862
Knox, D. L. (Pete) P456
Knox, Lesley W92
Knudsen, Douglas A. (Doug) A218
Knudsen, Mary F. A379
Knudsen, Jeannette L. A733
Knudson, Julie E139
Knudson, Tom E273
Knudson, Thomas C. (Tom) A545
Knudson, Kip A792
Knust, Susan L. A337
Knutel, Phillip G. P58
Knutsen, K E196
Knutsen, Kevin J. E442
Knutzen, Tom W258
Ko, Howard E460
Ko, Miguel A755
Ko, Gunho (Alex) A875
Ko, May W177
Koba, Fumihiro W336
Kobak, Bernard S. A796
Kobara, John E. P87
Kobayash, Hisashi W113
Kobayashi, Michael K. (Mike) A709
Kobayashi, Ryo W17
Kobayashi, Masayuki W53
Kobayashi, Kenji W85
Kobayashi, Hisashi W113
Kobayashi, Koji W124
Kobayashi, Hiroshi W171
Kobayashi, Hiroshi W172
Kobayashi, Kiyonobu W182
Kobayashi, Yoichi W192
Kobayashi, Eizo W192
Kobayashi, Yoichi W192
Kobayashi, Yoshimitsu W228
Kobayashi, Ken W230
Kobayashi, Takashi W232
Kobayashi, Kazuo W250
Kobayashi, Kenichi W250

Kobayashi, Kazuo W251
Kobayashi, Kenichi W251
Kobayashi, Toshio W253
Kobayashi, Yotaro W253
Kobayashi, Toshio W253
Kobayashi, Toru W262
Kobayashi, Toshiaki W273
Kobayashi, Tsuyoshi W313
Kobayashi, Masayuki W318
Kobayashi, Kiyoshi W360
Koberl, Josef A207
Kobliska, Peter E181
Kobrin, Harvey P369
Kobus, Karen P293
Koby, Chet P269
Koc, Elissa A578
Koch, Christian E40
Koch, C. James (Jim) E62
Koch, Tammy E79
Koch, Rob E188
Koch, Charles J. (Bud) A78
Koch, Philipp P. (Phil) A171
Koch, Mitchell L. (Mitch) A560
Koch, Stephen P. (Steve) A694
Koch, Albert A. (Al) A747
Koch, Gary P27
Koch, Amelia P59
Koch, David P66
Koch, Peter P109
Koch, Robert L. (Bob) P206
Koch, Kevin R. P206
Koch, Shari P266
Koch, Robert L. (Bob) P273
Koch, Kevin R. P273
Koch, David M. P273
Koch, Robert L. (Bob) P273
Koch, Kevin R. P273
Koch, David M. P273
Koch, Brice W4
Koch, Olaf W227
Koche, Gary P366
Kochendoerfer, Gerd E122
Kocher, Jeff A793
Kocher, Isabelle W37
Kocher, Prof Renate W67
Kocher, Isabelle W156
Kochevar, Deborah T. P556
Kochhar, Rakesh W255
Kochuparampil, Augustine W29
Kochvar, Mark A713
Kocsondy, Lou P396
Kocur, John A. A67
Kodaira, Nobuyori W363
Kodama, Toshio W232
Kodama, Yukio W233
Koder, Matthew W367
Kodesh, Harel A287
Koecher, Renate W20
Koecher, Renate Renate Koecher W67
Koehl, Dennis L. A883
Koehler, Michael F. (Mike) A415
Koehler, William R. (Bill) A486
Koehler, Peter A592
Koehler, Suzanne P407
Koehnen, Michael W. A811
Koelbl, Tom P42
Koelbl, Konrad W149
Koele, Chad P7
Koelemay, Brenda T. A53
Koelkebeck, Debi P198
Koelker, June P500
Koellner, Laurette T. A51
Koellner, Laurette T. A456
Koelmel, John R. A343
Koelmel, John R. P265
Koenen, Patrick F. P233
Koenig, Karl J. A378
Koenig, Steve P137
Koenigs, Todd P409
Koenigsberg, Steve P533
Koep, Michael J. W268
Koepfgen, Bruce L. A555
Koeppel, Holly K. A700
Koerber, Hans-Joachim A778
Koerner, John A440

Koerner, Judith P300
Koerner, Ulrich W367
Koerselman, Linda P166
Koessel, Kathryn C. A481
Koeter, John E460
Koezuka, Masahiro W150
Koezuka, Masahiro W151
Koff, Howard M. P579
Koffenberger, Harry P260
Kofman, Yale A344
Kofman, Clyde P559
Kogan, Richard J. A103
Kogan, Richard J. A203
Kogler, Richard T. E443
Kogod, Dennis L. A243
Koguchi, Shigeo W360
Kogure, Makoto W328
Koh, Philip E196
Koh, Lay-tin E268
Koh, Steven S. A875
Kohart-Kleine, Barbara L. P613
Kohl, Christopher D E300
Kohl, Joe P35
Kohle, Tommy W382
Kohler, Shane E139
Kohler, Mark L. E226
Kohler, Pete B. A131
Kohler, Diane A344
Kohler, Peter O. A750
Kohler, Fernando P155
Kohler, Alexis W289
Kohlhepp, Robert J. (Bob) A181
Kohlhepp, Robert J. (Bob) A631
Kohlhepp, Robert J. (Bob) P619
Kohli, Raj A203
Kohlinger, Jorg W112
Kohlligian, Ann Marie A321
Kohlmann, Thomas P259
Kohlruss, Chuck P235
Kohmann, Hugo E240
Kohn, Robert A. A14
Kohn, Thomas W. A173
Kohn, Scott A257
Kohn, Pamela K. (Pam) A853
Kohn, Larry P436
Kohnke, Matthew E127
Kohnke, Gilbert W271
Koide, Masatoshi A17
Koide, Thomas J. (Tom) A101
Koide, Sadayuki W161
Koike, Atsuyoshi A714
Koike, Tetsuya W92
Koike, Koh W263
Kois, John P57
Kojima, Keiji W166
Kojima, Yorihiko W230
Kojima, Nobuaki W230
Kojima, Yorihiko W233
Kojima, Kazuo W270
Kojima, Yorihiko W328
Kok, Wim W303
Kokas, Adam R. E44
Kokensparger, Thomas L. A629
Kokubu, Fumiya W223
Kokubun, Ryosei W151
Kolady, Ashok E E47
Kolakowska, Malgorzata W188
Kolanz, Marc E295
Kolarik, Tyler S. A400
Kolasa, Neta P46
Kolassa, Sean A643
Kolb, David L. A561
Kolb, Jurgen A759
Kolbeck, Steve A170
Kolberg, Robert (Bob) P492
Kolbl, Konrad W149
Kolbo, Stephanie E336
Kolcaba, Kathy P74
Kolding, Eivind W122
Kolesar, Robert J. A291
Koletsos, Alex E224
Kolkhorst, Mark L. A73
Kollar, Paul E273
Kollat, David T. A121
Kollat, David T. A496

Kulmann, Bjorn A96
Kulp, Bruce A367
Kulyagin, Sergey A456
Kumagai, Bill E195
Kumagai, Les A845
Kumagai, Bunya W262
Kumagai, Bunya W263
Kumagai, Osamu W328
Kumar, Vikas E71
Kumar, Kris E124
Kumar, Shailendra E146
Kumar, Rakesh E196
Kumar, Prem E474
Kumar, Harsha E509
Kumar, Devinder A11
Kumar, Aneish A103
Kumar, Suresh A103
Kumar, Gopa A321
Kumar, Rajesh A452
Kumar, Marise A523
Kumar, Jaya A638
Kumar, P.V. W67
Kumar, Rupesh W181
Kumarasamy, Sundar P535
Kumaraswamy, P. W68
Kumaresan, Bala E246
Kumasaki, Rodney D. A44
Kumbier, Michelle A402
Kume, Yuji W101
Kume, Shinsuke W117
Kumler, Alan H. A827
Kummer, Werner W40
Kummert, Ted A560
Kump, Traude E421
Kumura, Haruyoshi W255
Kun, Larry P475
Kunberger, George A. A466
Kuncl, James J. A782
Kuncl, Sharon P164
Kundich, Steve E124
Kundu, Kaushik E146
Kunesh, John C. P617
Kuneva, Meglena W72
Kung, Robert E5
Kung, Lin W47
Kung, Patrick S. W204
Kunibe, Takeshi W338
Kunicki, Walter J. A878
Kunieda, Toshinari W262
Kunio, Takemitsu W247
Kunk, James E. A436
Kunkel, Joachim E460
Kunkel, William A48
Kunkel, Jay A503
Kunkel, Grethel A751
Kunkel, Thomas M. A810
Kunkel, Louis M. P333
Kunkler, Kevin E243
Kunst, George P583
Kuntz, Edward L. (Eddie) A490
Kuntz, John F. A667
Kuntz, John F. A669
Kuntz, Thomas G. A765
Kuntz, Kevin P306
Kunz, Jonathan W. E197
Kunz, Thomas S. A651
Kunz, John E. A788
Kunz, Barbara L. P48
Kunz, Ricky W. P391
Kunz, Thomas W121
Kunze, Kenneth C (Kc) P602
Kuok, Khoon ean W52
Kupatt, Wolf F. A108
Kupec, Jess P429
Kupfer, Lawrence J. (Larry) P240
Kupfer, Peter W227
Kupferberg, Max L. A583
Kupper, Randy A54
Kurahara, Fumiaki W338
Kurahashi, Masatsugu W230
Kuraishi, Seiji W171
Kuraishi, Seiji W172
Kuramochi, Junjiro W182
Kurashige, Hideki W12
Kuri, Alejandro Soberon W24

Kurian, George A582
Kurian, Thomas A618
Kurihara, Kazuhiro W166
Kurilko, Dave P119
Kurisu, Duane K. A168
Kuritzkes, Andrew A758
Kurkcu, Cengiz S. A803
Kurlan, Norman J E334
Kurlander, Michael P445
Kurmas, Steven E. A248
Kurmas, Steven E. A273
Kurnick, Robert H. A635
Kuroda, Masami W250
Kuroda, Masami W251
Kurosawa, Tomohiro W263
Kuroyanagi, Nobuo W172
Kursman, Seth A698
Kurth, Jens A163
Kurtis, Bill P125
Kurtz, Christian E181
Kurtz, Allison E503
Kurtz, John E P358
Kuryak, Timothy A257
Kurz, Christian A257
Kurz, Thomas P. A777
Kurzweil, Eric H. E305
Kusakabe, Isao W113
Kuschewski, Rainer W227
Kuschman, Thomas A365
Kusek, David P59
Kush, Donna A825
Kushan, Ravi W106
Kushel, J. Richard A124
Kushi, Joe E431
Kushihashi, Yasuo W182
Kushiya, Shoichi W354
Kushner, Michael P585
Kusserow, Paul B. A434
Kuszyk, Cheryl E79
Kutateladze, Andrei P123
Kutchera, Kris M. A28
Kutey, Paul W. P528
Kutinsky, Pharm.D. Bruce E20
Kutner, Mark P19
Kutnick, Dale E195
Kutschke, Ed P11
Kutty, Madhu E181
Kuuskvere, Steven R. A577
Kuwaiti, Alyazia W267
Kuwaiti, Alyazia Ali Saleh Al W267
Kuwari, Jassim W381
Kuwayama, Shoji W223
Kux, Barbara W320
Kuykendall, Ronald E. A715
Kuyper, Ame E56
Kuzas, Betsy P384
Kuzdal, John L. E341
Kuzel, Russel J. (Russ) P443
Kuzevenkov, Dmitry A95
Kuziel, Robert C. A661
Kuzma, Thomas M. (Tom) A116
Kuzmitz, Joseph T. A1
Kuzovenkov, Dmitry A95
Kuzume, Kaoru W223
Kuzuoka, Toshiaki W166
Kvaal, Kim P575
Kvalheim, Grant P117
Kvam, Prof Robert P40
Kvamme, Mark E276
Kvamme, E. Floyd E379
Kvasnikoff, James P114
Kvello, Adrienne E339
Kverneland, Hege A574
Kvet, Edward J. P290
Kvilekval, Kara H.V. P259
Kvilhaug, J?rn O. W132
Kvistad, Gregg P123
Kwan, Judy E65
Kwan, Jenny E301
Kwan, Simon H. A321
Kwasniewski, Lance H. P57
Kwiatkowski, Thaddeus E300
Kwiatkowski, Valerie E494
Kwoh, Daniel E258

Kwok, Bernard A772
Kwok, Thomas P. K. W52
Kwon, Havis W213
Kwon, Oh-Hyun W307
Kwong, Kelvin W268
Kyhnell, Koreen P245
Kyle, Rex A104
Kyle, Richard G. A803
Kyle, Rick P393
Kyle, James P472
Kyle, Shelia P477
Kymes, Stacy C. A128
Kyncl, Robert A389
Kypta, Richard J. (Rich) A316
Kyriakidis, Alex A531
Kyriakopoulos, Ioannis W244
Kyriakos-Saad, Fawzi W116
Kyser, Kevin A885
Kysilka, Pavel W144

L

Laakso, William A449
Laan, Sander van der W203
Laasch, Jack P29
Labarge, Suzanne A200
LaBarrie, Ronald P45
Labat, Kristen A297
LaBato, Anthony P133
LaBauve, Randall R. (Randy) A349
LaBauve, Randall R. (Randy) A589
Labbie, Andrew P586
Labelle, Sue E172
Labelle, Debbie E423
LaBelle, James P440
Laben, Nancy A12
Laberge, Fred A15
Laberge, Daniel A698
Laberge, Pierre A698
Laberge, Alice D. W299
Labeyrie, Christian W376
Labiak, Eric E9
Labonte, Ralph W354
Labovites, Jim E163
Labrato, Ronnie R. A381
LaBrecque, Julie M. P606
Labree, Damian P570
Labriffe, Christian De W100
Labriola, Pietro A348
Lacaille, Rick A758
LaCalamito, William J. A432
Lacaze, Tony M. E305
Lacertosa, Marie A634
Lacey, Eleanor E453
Lacey, Roger H. D. A2
Lacey, David L. (Dave) A56
Lacey, Debra L. A472
Lacey, Mark A600
Lacey, John S. W387
Lach, Eileen M. P515
Lachance, Margaret P. (Meg) A677
Lacharriere, Marc Ladreit de W89
Lacharriere, Marc Ladreit de W289
Lachenmeyer, William M E285
Lachman, M. Leanne A515
Lachman, Leanne A515
Lachman, Henri W312
Lachs, Susanna E. P498
Lackemacher, James M (Jim) E435
Lacker, Jeffrey M. (Jeff) A320
Lackey, Stephen A103
Lackey, Bobby Lee A364
Lackey, Mary P578
Lacko, Andrew A119
LaClair, Robert W. A329
Lacombe, Martin D E200
Lacoste, Jonathan P555
LaCour, Kirk P2
LaCour, Nat P17
LaCour, George P137
Lacroix, Larry E64
Lacroix, Rob E243
LaCroix, Franck W374
Lacy, Stephen E119

Lacy, Alan J. A135
Lacy, Stephen A426
Lacy, William H. A472
Lacy, Joseph P375
Lacy, Robert P402
Ladany, Nicholas P395
Ladau, Drew T. A747
Ladd, Chris E114
Ladd, Susan P157
Ladda, A. Todd E181
Ladda, A. Todd A359
Lade, Herb E94
Ladell, Ron E47
Ladenburger, Robert W. (Bob) P550
Lader, Philip A14
Lader, Philip A527
Laderman, Gerald (Gerry) A828
Laderman, Gerry A828
Laderman, Michael S. P45
Laderoute, Keith P445
Ladiwala, Shiraz A799
Ladner, Trevor P10
Ladner, Clement P119
Ladnier, Mark E370
Ladone, Mary Kay A108
Ladonne, Dave E293
Laethem, Michael T. A173
Lafave, John A698
Laferriere, Dana P560
Laffaye, Ann E195
Laffer, Arthur E92
Lafferty, Mike P393
Lafferty, Jane P604
Laffin, Michael A573
Laffitte, Montague E432
Lafitte, Michael J. (Mike) A160
Laflamme, Yves A698
LaFlamme, Richard P536
Laflamme, Louise W243
Lafley, Alan G. (A. G.) A375
Lafley, Alan G. (A. G.) A664
LaFlure, Ernest J. A300
LaFollette, Julie L. A48
Lafond, Russell E373
Lafont, Bruno Bruno Lafont W30
LaFontaine, Michael S. A819
LaFontaine, Laurie M. P72
LaFonte, Joseph P. P234
LaForce, Colette A11
LaForest, Robert J. A871
Laforge, Brenda E300
LaFortune, Robert J. A128
Lafos, Hans-Peter W305
Lafrenaye, Ray P572
Lafuente, Francisco Fernandez W9
Lagacy, Julie A. A157
Lagard+?re, Arnaud W15
Lagardere, Arnaud Arnaud
   Lagardere W15
Lagardere, Arnaud W15
LaGarry, Claire F. A210
Lagasse, Emeril J. P261
Lagayette, Philippe W289
Lagemann, John D. A246
Laggini, Chris P154
Lagina-kleine, Marlena P453
Lagioia, Andrea A203
Lagomasino, Maria Elena (Mel) A92
Lagomasino, Maria Elena (Mel) A199
LaGosh, Dave P477
Lagreca, Carl E307
Laguarta, Ramon A638
Laguens, Dawn P390
Lagunes, Jose O. Reyes A198
Lagunes, Jose O. Reyes A537
Lagunes, Jose A537
Lahey, Richard T. P388
Lahey, John L. P403
Lahey, John L. P404
Lahmers, Graydon P29
Lahoud, Marwan W15
LaHowchic, Nicholas J. (Nick) A309
Lai, Paul E460
Lai, Dominic K. M. W176

A = AMERICAN BUSINESS
E = EMERGING COMPANIES
P = PRIVATE COMPANIES
W = WORLD BUSINESS

Laidlaw, W. Samuel H. (Sam) W92
Laidlaw, W. Samuel H. (Sam) W175
Laidlaw, Roy W218
Laidley, David H. A288
Lain, Frank B. P508
Laine, Sabrina P19
Laing, Phillip G. A356
Laing, Melanie W106
Lains, Steve P115
Laird, Robert E4
Laird, Gregory E119
Laird, James F. (Jim) E122
Laird, Thomas E. A432
Laird, David A. A478
Laird, Lisa P472
Laisathit, Kirati W47
Laisathit, Niraman W47
Laisure, James M. (Mike) A323
Laitem, Leo A202
LaJoie, Michael L. (Mike) A800
Lajous, Adrian A812
Lajoux, Christian W309
Lajtha, Adrian J. W6
Lake, Jeff E439
Lake, Charles D. A17
Lake, Marianne A476
Lake, Stephen W. (Steve) A615
Lake, Peter J. A815
Lake, Spencer W175
Lakshminarayanan, Ramesh E339
Laliberte, Maurice A. A262
Lalljie, Paul S. E346
Lally, Danielle E339
Lally, Austin A665
Lally, Kathleen A. A673
Lally, Bob P196
Lally, Mary M. P487
Lalor, Angela S. A2
Lalor, Angela A240
Lalwani, Ellen A499
Lam, Derek E344
Lam, Katty A638
Lam, Rachel A802
Lam, Yim Nam W72
Lam, Cheung Wing (Linus) W99
Lam, Kam Hing W176
LaMacchia, John T. A495
LaMacchia, Edmund A873
LaManna, Frank P4
LaMantia, Charles R. A758
Lamar, Ken A320
Lamarca, Christine P204
Lamarre, Jacques W299
Lamarre, Jacques W340
Lamb, Stan E60
Lamb, Jeffrey D. E176
Lamb, Dan E325
Lamb, Brian A329
Lamb, William G. (Bill) A346
Lamb, Thomas J. (Tom) A523
Lamb, Jeff A739
Lamb, William H. A797
Lamb, Michael G. A883
Lamb, Eric P157
Lamb, Connie R. P186
Lamb, John C. P300
Lamb, Kerry P342
Lambech, Arne W258
Lambert, Sandra E260
Lambert, J. Hamilton A152
Lambert, Lisa M. A452
Lambert, Ellen W. A549
Lambert, Phelps L. A611
Lambert, Beth A660
Lambert, Michael D. A867
Lambert, Chip P505
Lambert, Thierry W107
Lambert, Jean-Marie W374
Lambert, Nick W379

Lamberti, Jeffrey M. (Jeff) A156
Lamberti, Hermann-Josef W16
Lamberton, Michelle W39
Lambertson, Leah K. E482
Lambertson, Steve P540
Lambiase, Matthew J. A64
Lambiase, John A. A64
Lambkin, Charlotte W38
Lamboley, Harold J. A289
Lambrecht, Ben A200
Lambright, Dan A21
Lambright, Keith P290
Lamen, Drake M. P563
Lamere, David F. (Dave) P39
Laming, Michael S. A380
Lamkin, Martha D. P115
Lamm, Jacob A140
Lamm, Norman P620
Lamm-Tennant, Joan M. A725
Lammers, Jon A744
Lamneck, Kenneth T. (Ken) A448
Lamnin, Adam D. A78
Lamont, Andrew E2
Lamont, Ned P313
LaMontagne, Grant J. A191
Lamoreaux, Roy I. A649
Lamoure, Jean-Pierre W376
Lamp, Bob E473
Lamp, David L. A420
Lampe, Stephen T. A653
Lampert, Mark A106
Lampert, Gregory J. A370
Lampert, Joseph I. (Joe) A404
Lampert, Erin A544
Lampert, Edward S. (Eddie) A724
Lamphere, Gilbert H. A231
Lampiano, Lorenzo W368
Lampo, Craig A. A58
Lamppa, Zach E23
Lampropoulos, Fred P. E308
Lampropoulos, Justin E308
Lampropoulos, Fred P. E308
Lamptey, Peter R. P182
Lampton, Mason H. A776
Lamson, W. Scott A383
Lamutt, Marianne A188
Lan, Yan W95
Lancaster, Michael E301
Lancaster, Ronny B. A78
Lancaster, George C. P233
Lancaster, Bill P500
Lance, Thomas W. E62
Lance, Ryan M. A220
Lance, Howard L. A281
Lance, Cynthia A. A342
Lance, Howard L. A762
Lance, Dane L. P491
Lanchbury, Jerry S. E332
Lanci, Gianfranco W212
Lancia, Pete A680
Lancour, Greg A. A379
Land, Mark D. A233
Land, Robert A469
Land, Alison P190
Land, Edward J. P337
Land, Nick W379
Landahl, Susan A305
Landau, Jeffrey D. (Jeff) A103
Landau, Glenn A458
Landau, David A. A677
Landau, Igor W20
Landau, Igor W309
Landenwich, Joseph L. A490
Landers, James C E292
Landers, Scott E323
Landers, Debra S. (Debbie) A212
Landers, Pete P557
Landert, Karl W115
Landert, Karl W116
Landes, Charles E. (Chuck) P18
Landes, Mike P26
Landes, Michael D. P167
Landes, Barbara L. P400
Landgraf, John C. A4
Landgraf, Kurt M. A226

Landgraf, Kurt M. P165
Landgren, Dale P22
Landheer, Jamie E503
Landim, Rodolfo A147
Landini, Bruce W18
Landiribar, Javier Echenique W9
Landiribar, Javier W43
Landiribar, Javier Echenique W290
Landiribar, Javier W290
Landis, Tess P290
Landis, F. H. (Skip) P501
Landis, Katrina W76
Landman, John E3
Landol, Samuel (Sam) P441
Landolt, Pierre W261
Landon, R. Kirk A506
Landon, Allan P400
Landreaux, Susan P113
Landreth, Connie P540
Landrum, Brian A589
Landrum, James R. A605
Landrum, Tom S. P569
Landry, Erin E339
Landry, Joseph C. A300
Landry, Gregory J. A466
Landry, Stephen J. A527
Landry, Denise A749
Landry, Paul A797
Landry, Cathy P20
Landry, Steve P. P372
Landry, Stephen P445
Landsberg, Marc A459
Landsman, Liza K. A278
Landwehr, David E363
Landwirth, Michael A. P75
Landy, Samuel A. E489
Landy, Michael P. E489
Landy, Samuel A. E489
Landy, Eugene W. E489
Landy, Michael P. E489
Landy, James J. A433
Lane, Rachel E35
Lane, Jeffrey E174
Lane, James A. E292
Lane, Larry E300
Lane, Lawrence E310
Lane, Barbara N E322
Lane, Brad E334
Lane, Kevin E364
Lane, Lisa E503
Lane, Robert J. A106
Lane, Deanne A165
Lane, Daniel D. (Ron) A326
Lane, Robert W. (Bob) A375
Lane, Raymond J. (Ray) A418
Lane, Matt A459
Lane, Wendy E. A498
Lane, Jeffrey H. A555
Lane, Leslie A592
Lane, Robert W. (Bob) A600
Lane, Lawrence A675
Lane, Mark J. A776
Lane, Kathy S. A804
Lane, Amy B. A804
Lane, Robert W. (Bob) A845
Lane, John F. P33
Lane, Carol P34
Lane, Raymond J. (Ray) P93
Lane, Neil P122
Lane, Christopher T. (Chris) P265
Lane, Rick P329
Lane, Mark L. P346
Lane, Kevin P454
Lane, Eric P553
Lane, J. P611
Lane, John T. P613
Lane, Robert W. (Bob) W66
Lane, Jon W80
Lane, Melanie W303
Lanegran, Katie E28
Laney, Heather E30
Laney, Doug E197
Laney, Elizabeth A842
Laney, John B. P137
Lanfranchi, Peter T. P234

Lang, Steve E85
Lang, Anne E300
Lang, Timothy E E316
Lang, Kimberly E393
Lang, Mark T. E447
Lang, Belinda A15
Lang, Marshall A21
Lang, Mike A424
Lang, Lord Ian A532
Lang, Edward A. A697
Lang, Laura W. A801
Lang, Sherry A804
Lang, Roberta A873
Lang, Melissa P163
Lang, Larry P256
Lang, Wally P324
Lang, Tyler P406
Lang, Anita P480
Lang, Les P572
Lang, Teng Soon W271
Langa, James P (Jim) E216
Langan, Terence P577
Langberg, Michael L. P98
Langdon, Jerry J. A296
Lange, Norman E175
Lange, Michael J. E321
Lange, Tom A825
Lange, David A. A828
Lange, P P414
Lange, Patrice P488
Lange, Sheila E. P579
Lange, Titia de W249
Langebrake, Larry P465
Langel, Craig A. A384
Langemeyer, Gerhard W305
Langenberg, David P222
Langendonk, David A871
Langer, Carlton E174
Langer, Carlton A346
Langer, Jurgen W119
Langerot, Danny P142
Langerud, LaRae E. P166
Langevin, Eric T. E260
Langevin, David J. E291
Langford, John E160
Langhammer, Fred H. A260
Langlais, Maxime A698
Langland, R. Marc A28
Langley, George E. A627
Langley, Bill P203
Langley, W. John P304
Langley, Tim P329
Langlois, Robert E196
Langlois, Francois W340
Langman, Craig B. P24
Langmead, James H. E136
Langmead, James H. A279
Langner, Arne W30
Langone, Kenneth G. (Ken) A889
Langridge, Iain A257
Langsdorf, William (Bill) P616
Langston, Michael R. A681
Langston, Debra P264
Langwell, Kevin P499
Langworthy, Shawna P109
Lanier, Gayle S. A277
Lanier, J. Hicks A379
Lanier, J. Hicks A765
Lanier, Bo P105
Lanier, Elyse P391
Lanier, Lynn P568
Lanier, Jean W116
Lanigan, John P. A139
Lanigan, Susan S. A261
Lanigan, Tony P218
Laning, Steven A73
Lanius, Joe P397
Lankau, Maik E257
Lankford, William C. A327
Lankford, C. Frederick (Fred) A778
Lankin, Ron E152
Lankler, Douglas M. (Doug) A641
Lankton, Madelyn A810
Lankton, Gordon B. P358
Lanman, Mike A845

Macfarlane, Ian J. W390
MacGowan, William N. (Bill) A586
MacGowan, Bill A587
MacGregor, J. Scott A513
MacGregor, Alastair P317
Macgregor, Nancy P531
MacGuire, Mary P619
Machado, A. Ricardo A631
MacHale, Joseph P. (Joe) W300
Mache, John C E3
Mache, John C. P262
Machell, Simon W34
Macher, Erin K. A416
Macheras, Kostas W146
Machetti, Claudio W139
Machi, Michael E434
Machida, Kiyomi W336
Machlin, Chuck E458
Machon, Monika A51
Machones, Melinda P476
Macht, Michael W380
Machtolf, Paul A698
Machuca, Luis F. A823
Machuzick, John T. A376
Macias, Stephen A434
Maciel, Jason P589
Macilroy, Glenn E267
Macina, Robert P. P278
Macina, Lucy O. P613
MacInnes, Glenn I. A858
MacInnes, Frank T. A288
MacInnis, David G. (Dave) A782
MacInnis, G. Brian A782
MacIntyre, Sandy P503
MacIntyre, Gregg W266
Mack, Jim E10
Mack, Connie A241
Mack, Michael J. A245
Mack, Peter A329
Mack, Cary P. A865
Mack, Don P72
Mack, John J. P525
Mackay, Martin E22
Mackay, Leo S. A201
MacKay, Harold H. A265
Mackay, Michelle M. A464
Mackay, Leo S. A518
Mackay, E.A. G. (Graham) A645
Mackay, Iain J. W162
Mackay, Iain J. W175
MacKay, Harold H. W358
Mackay, Allan Allan Douglas
  Mackay W390
Macke, George A. A52
Macke, Fred A. P428
MacKeigan, John P464
Mackensen, Warren P341
Mackenty, Michael C P357
MacKenzie, Earle A. E418
MacKenzie, William R. A137
MacKenzie, George A808
Mackenzie, Robert D. P496
MacKenzie, John W26
Mackenzie, Amanda W34
Mackenzie, Andrew W69
Mackenzie, Andrew W70
Mackenzie, Andrew W92
MacKenzie, Jason W268
Mackerey, John A318
Mackesy, Richard P102
Mackey, James G. A37
Mackey, Lori R. A620
Mackey, John P. A873
Mackey, Neosha P325
Mackie, Spurgeon A440
Mackie, Bert H. A616
Mackie, Karen P212
Mackie, Jane W370
Mackiewicz, Kenneth E476
Mackin, H. Carroll A78
Mackin, Virginia S. (Ginny) A277
MacKinnon, Gail G. A800
Mackintosh, Drew E409
Mackleit, Duane D. E264
Macko, Jeffrey R. (Jeff) P430

Macko, Terry P616
Macksood, Dan A. P597
MacLaren, Scott P484
Maclean, Greg E156
MacLean, John R. A46
MacLean, Brian W. A810
Maclean, Tara P29
Maclean, Roger P571
MacLellan, Steve A600
MacLennan, James E237
MacLennan, David W. (Dave) A705
MacLennan, Mark A. A770
MacLeod, Ian R. A12
MacLeod, Amy A371
MacLeod, Donald J. A524
Maclin, Becky E300
Maclin, James E317
Maclin, Samuel Todd (Todd) A476
Maclin, Joan C. P530
MacLiver, Donald H. A60
MacMahon, John P. A225
MacMaster, Douglas J. P543
MacMillan, Mark D. A383
MacMillan, Stephen P. (Steve) A794
MacMillan, Michael A804
MacMillan, A. S. (Pat) A840
MacMillan, Catherine C. A865
MacMillan, David F. P575
MacMillen, Lisa B. A318
MacMullan, Barbara A. A856
Macnab, Craig E337
Macnamara, Brian G. A430
MacNamara, Caridad P45
MacNaughton, Michael G. P463
Macnee, Walter M. (Walt) A537
Macnee, Walt W. A537
Macnee, Walter M. (Walt) A537
MacNeil, Kevin A267
MacNicholas, Garry W160
MacPhail, Fiona P227
Macphee, Scott R E187
MacPherson, Bruce A110
Macpherson, David A309
Macpherson, Nina W143
Macris, Achilles O. A476
MacSharry, Ray W274
MacSwain, Claudia N. A320
MacSween, Mike W340
Mactas, Mark V. P435
Mactas, Mark V. P436
MacWillson, Alastair W6
Macy, Mike E51
Macy, Sydney S. P509
Madabhushi, V. Rajamannar A434
Madabhushi, Venkata Raja
  Rajamannar A654
Madaio, Biagio E251
Madan, Pradip A774
Madar, Gregory S. A858
Maddaluna, Anthony J. A641
Madden, Douglas M. (Doug) A163
Madden, Joe A553
Madden, Teresa S. A883
Madden, Sean P274
Madden, Terry P358
Madding, Kevin P86
Maddison, John E180
Maddison, Tom A885
Maddock, Ernest E. A501
Maddox, Fran E301
Maddox, Scott E. A21
Maddox, Matt A882
Maddox, Peter P112
Maddox, Paul W266
Maddrey, Willis E415
Maddy, Faith E. P600
Madeira, Fred E521
Maden, Tom P438
Mader, Donald A P559
Madere, Consuelo E. A566
Madge, David A744
Madigan, John W. A383
Madigan, James P145
Madison, Anne E408
Madison, Thomas F. A167

Madison, Sandra P46
Madison, Barbara E. P577
Madlambayan, Maria E482
Madlinger, Sukanya R. A494
Madlock, Gordon B. E435
Madoff, Mitchell A873
Madonia, Frank E320
Madonna, Jon C. A81
Madonna, Jon C. A364
Madrigal, Rackel E23
Madsen, Jennifer E138
Madsen, Benny E466
Madsen, Dennis F. A28
Madsen, C. Fred A115
Madsen, Andrew H. (Drew) A241
Madsen, Tammy P249
Madsen, Thomas E. P338
Maeda, Masaya W85
Maeda, Masaya W86
Maeda, Yasunori W182
Maeda, Kiyoshi W253
Maeda, Yoshihiro W360
Maeder, Jeff P540
Maekawa, Atsushi W232
Maekawa, Osamu Osamu
  Maekawa W360
Maekawa, Masamoto W363
Maercke, Michel E482
Maerki, Hans W4
Maero, Norman L. A605
Maerz, Michael O. (Mike) P313
Maes, Hedwig A707
Maesako, Shizumi W55
Maestas, Frank P27
Maestri, Bruno A598
Maestri, Luca A661
Maestri, Luca A885
Maestri, Adriano W189
Maeyama, Tadashige W161
Mafaher, Ziaeddin P505
Maffe, France W243
Maffei, Gregory B. (Greg) A107
Maffei, Gregory B. (Greg) A511
Maffeo, Vincent A. A505
Maffett, Randal E117
Maffett, Jeffrey A. A546
Maffucci, David A265
Mafie, Farhad E315
Magano, Basetsana W266
Maganov, Ravil U. W264
Magaro, Phill P243
Magath, Mark S E507
Magee, Pat E456
Magee, Michael M. A319
Magee, Chris P5
Magee, John P164
Magee, Richard S. P481
Magee, Becky P597
Magenheimer, Richard P247
Magers, Dakon E35
Maggart, Lon P413
Maggelakis, Sophia P419
Maggi, Colleen E244
Maggin, Bruce A677
Maggiotto, Michael P40
Maggs, Bruce A694
Maggs, Thomas O. A813
Magid, Hanoch E330
Magill, Paul A4
Magill, R. Hugh A600
Magill, Chuck A739
Maginley, Kenneth J. (Ken) P266
Maglaque, Neal A54
Magley, R S P583
Magnatta, JoAnn M. P294
Magner, Marjorie (Marge) A38
Magner, Marjorie (Marge) A368
Magner, Marjorie (Marge) W7
Magnesen, Larry S. A329
Magness, Bill P170
Magnini, Aldo E75
Magnone, Joseph B (Joe) A602
Magnus, George C. W176
Magnus, Birger W335
Magnusson, Bo W323

Magoon, Patrick M. P24
Magowan, Peter A. A157
Magrid, Bruce P76
Maguire, John P. A215
Maguire, Joanne M. A518
Maguire, Richard N. A781
Maguire, Kimberly A P219
Maguire, Mike P438
Maguire, Donald C. P611
Magyer, Denise W21
Mah, Paul E344
Mahabhashyam, Suresh E22
Mahaffee, Joseph W. (Joe) A129
Mahaffy, Denise A252
Mahajan, Raj E136
Mahajan, Puneet A374
Mahajan, Anand W107
Mahan, Duff E468
Mahan, Ann P179
Mahan, Michelle P197
Mahan, Stephen W. P462
Mahana, Brent P104
Maher, Sally E141
Maher, Thomas M. (Tom) A67
Maher, Melissa A307
Maher, Lee A. A379
Maher, Joelle A510
Maher, Peter A849
Maher, Sister Walter P113
Maher, Tom P378
Maher, James J. A467
Maher, Joseph P482
Maher, Dennis P493
Maher, Robert P585
Maher, Peter J. W218
Maher, Grahame W379
Maheras, Thomas G. (Tom) A256
Maheshwari, Amit E120
Maheshwari, Sudhir W30
Maheshwari, Sorabh W268
Mahfood, Robin G. P191
Mahindra, Anand G. W312
Mahler, Armando A364
Mahler, Christopher L. A432
Mahler, Carl P496
Mahlich, Ben P212
Mahlke, Thomas K. (Tom) A705
Mahmoud, Adel A. F. A112
Mahmoud, Ahmed A418
Mahon, Steve E81
Mahon, Steven G E330
Mahon, Kenneth J. A253
Mahon, Thomas P. Mac A309
Mahon, Thomas P. Mac A498
Mahon, Casey D. A828
Mahon, John P162
Mahon, John P163
Mahon, Paul A. W160
Mahoney, Cornelius D. A118
Mahoney, Michael F. (Mike) A133
Mahoney, George R. A314
Mahoney, Timothy O. (Tim) A424
Mahoney, Michael F. (Mike) A470
Mahoney, Michael J. (Mike) A508
Mahoney, James M. A546
Mahoney, James E. (Ed) A558
Mahoney, Thomas P. A586
Mahoney, Hugh J. A673
Mahoney, Colin A708
Mahoney, Dan A720
Mahoney, John J. A753
Mahoney, David L. A772
Mahoney, Patty P29
Mahoney, Thomas J. P251
Mahoney, David L. P313
Mahoney, Patrick D. P515
Mahony, A. M. W175
Mahoney, Tony W175
Mahony, Susan (Sue) A513
Mahowald, Douglass A. A545
Mahr, Wolfgang W90
Mahrer, William (Bill) P253
Mai, Cecily E268
Maia, Paulo W173
Maia, Paulo W175

A = AMERICAN BUSINESS
E = EMERGING COMPANIES
P = PRIVATE COMPANIES
W = WORLD BUSINESS

Maibach, Sheryl P47
Maibach, Doug P47
Maibach, Ben C. P47
Maibach, Ryan P47
Maibach, Doug P47
Maibach, Ben C. P47
Maiden, Janice A323
Maidlow, Spencer T. (Spence) P138
Maidment, Karen E. W358
Maiella, James E28
Maier, Stuart E213
Maier, Dror E485
Maier, Henry J. A324
Maier, Kelley P75
Maier, Joe P95
Maier, Kelley P560
Maier, Peter K. P575
Maile, Russ E329
Mailloux, J. Wayne A244
Maiman, Dana A459
Maiman, Janice M. P18
Main, Timothy L. A465
Mainardi, Carlo L P346
Mainardi-Rosenthal, Helen W348
Maingot, Rhonda P191
Mainka, Jeffrey E89
Mainous, Rosalie O'Dell P617
Mainwaring, Brenda A825
Maio, Di E196
Maio, Keith D. A891
Mair, Jim P579
Maire, Kathleen P97
Maissel, Gerda P53
Maisto, Mark A589
Maitland, James A103
Maitland, Alister Alister Maitland W220
Maitra, Tara E474
Maiz, Jose A. A452
Majeed, Ebony P220
Majernik, Matthew E175
Major, John E. A137
Major, William B. P584
Majoras, Deborah P. A664
Majors, Mike A806
Mak, Patrick P502
Makarem, Marc E385
Makarewicz, Joe E78
Maki, Craig A. E9
Maki, Mark A. A292
Maki, Mark A. W137
Makino, Fujiatsu W231
Makino, Masashi W273
Makoul, Gregory P429
Makovik, Valeri E152
Makovsky, Evan A197
Makowka, Vicki L. A782
Makowski, Rogean B. A856
Makridis, Alexandros W244
Makris, George A. A729
Maksymow, Michael J. P56
Malach, Itzhak W49
Malaise, Richard E. P335
Malandro, Edward (Ed) A763
Malangone, Frank E98
Malasto, Thomas A. P127
Malatesta, Matthew J. P557
Malavez, Patricia W373
Malavé, Andrés P357
Malchoff, Kevin R. P415
Malchuk, Daniel W69
Malchuk, Daniel W70
MalchukBE, Daniel W70
Malcolm, Steven J. (Steve) A128
Malcolm, Robert M. (Rob) A413
Malcolm, Steven A616
Malcolm, Andrew L. (Andy) A778
Maldonado, George E194
Maldonado, Bill W175
Male, John E198

Male, Jeremy J. A161
Malecky, Robert A. A138
Malehorn, Jeffrey (Jeff) A373
Malek, Frederic V. A160
Malek, Kamran P26
Malek, Tom P137
Malek, Philip G. (Phil) W339
Malempati, Krishna M. A213
Malerba, James J. A758
Malerba, Marilynn R. (Lynn) P279
Maleson, Diane P498
Maletira, Amar A418
Maletta, Matthew J. A34
Maley, Heather A181
Maley, Ernie A345
Maleyeva, Maria A246
Malfatti, Carole P622
Malgieri, James A103
Malhotra, Ajay E71
Malhotra, Ravi E411
Malhotra, Kanuj A107
Malik, Boz E34
Malik, Suvin E181
Malik, Harman E365
Malik, Irfan A2
Malik, Ashraf K. A171
Malik, Rajiv A573
Malik, Shahid A673
Malin, Clint B. E280
Malin, John P182
Malina, John A234
Malina, Brian C. A845
Malinoski, Steven P288
Malinowski, Rafal A714
Malinskas, Linda P344
Malisow, Jack E269
Maliszewski, Kenneth A760
Malkiel, Shahar W49
Malkiewicz, Steve A455
Malkoski, Thomas D. E374
Mall, Mike E108
Malleau, Anne A873
Mallery, Edwina P276
Mallesch, Eileen A. A756
Mallet, Karen P502
Mallett, Leonard W. A299
Mallett, Conrad L. A483
Mallett, Conrad L. A503
Mallett, Cynthia A553
Malley, Bonnie J E508
Malliet, Dan W320
Mallik, Amardeep E161
Mallinckrodt, Thomas von W346
Mallinder, Paul E257
Mallino, Sue A37
Mallon, Pat E456
Mallon, Gerry W122
Mallory, Steve E356
Mallory, Robin D. A555
Mallory, Kenny P234
Mallory, Susan H. P507
Mallott, Byron I. A28
Mallott, Philip E. A121
Mallott, Anthony P441
Mallott, Byron I. P441
Mallow, Matthew J. A124
Malloy, Kirk D E243
Malloy, Richard E384
Malloy, William A. P179
Malloy, Feng P222
Malloy, Cam P245
Malloy, Thomas E. P575
Malloy, Richard P576
Malloy, Rev Edward A. P577
Malloy, Dorothy A. P588
Malloy, Thomas K. P608
Mallozzi, Frank E143
Malnight, Steven A643
Malone, Dan E. A21
Malone, Mike E466
Malone, Mary Alice D. A149
Malone, Daniel J. (Dan) A223
Malone, John C. A257
Malone, John C. A307
Malone, Michael J. A309

Malone, David J. A311
Malone, Robert A. (Bob) A395
Malone, John C. A511
Malone, Evan D. A511
Malone, Robert A. (Bob) A633
Malone, James R. (Jim) A692
Malone, Michael P. P233
Malone, Terry P323
Malone, Thomas P488
Malone, Rev H.S. P520
Malone, Rev John M. P577
Maloney, Matthew E148
Maloney, Matt E455
Maloney, Drew A417
Maloney, Michael P. A433
Maloney, Sean M. A451
Maloney, Dan A613
Maloney, Matt A770
Maloney, Don P42
Maloney, Karen A. P206
Maloney, Kurt P591
Maloney, Bill W334
Mals, Deb P319
Malter, Kenneth M. (Kenny) A81
Maltsbarger, Richard D. A523
Malus, Alan J. A799
Malveaux, Floyd J. P140
Malveaux, Antoinette M. P575
Mamaux, Mike E443
Mamillapalle, Venkatram W347
Mammen, Timothy P. V. E253
Mammone, Christopher E209
Mamonov, Pavel A714
Manabe, Hiroshi W251
Manaf, Nora Nora Abd Manaf W220
Manager, Vada O. A76
Manahan, Vincent D. A463
Manas, Jean A716
Manaskie, Robert G. E261
Manber, Udi A389
Manca, Marcello P559
Manchanda, Mohit E160
Mancheski, Frederick J. P404
Mancho, Javier de Paz W350
Manchur, Fred P269
Mancinelli, Louis A203
Mancini, Louis J. (Lou) A126
Mancini, Lisa A. A231
Mancini, Joseph H. (Joe) A885
Mancino, Carol P507
Mancino, Joseph P613
Mancuso, Salvatore A41
Mancuso, Michael J. A747
Mandarich, David D. E286
Mandato, Joseph (Joe) P436
Mande, Sidharth A246
Mandekic, Anthony L. A556
Mandel, John E9
Mandel, Mary M. A319
Mandel, Joseph G. A466
Mandel, Gail A881
Mandel, Barbara A. P76
Mandelbaum, Jay A475
Mandelbaum, Richard P445
Mandelkern, Stanley E423
Mandell, James P506
Mandelup, Elana E28
Mandeng, Mathieu W332
Manderino, Louis A. A619
Manders, Carrie P464
Mandersson, Magnus W143
Mandil, Claude W362
Mandinach, Barry M. E508
Mandino, Matthew W. (Matt) A675
Mandle, Lynn E268
Mandraccia, Crocifissa (Croci) A73
Manduca, Paul W284
Maneker, Amy P111
Manemann, Kevin P472
Manera, Lisa P146
Manes, Gianna M. A277
Maness, Kathi E200
Maness, Terry S. P51
Manfredi, Steven P. P58
Mang, Thomas W209

Mangalaseril, Jasmine W221
Mangalindan, Mylene A418
Mangan, Kara E503
Mangan, Daniel A. A694
Manganello, Timothy M. (Tim) A115
Manganello, Ed P369
Mangel, Todd E181
Mangel, Allen W. P413
Mangel, Barry P602
Manger, Chris P166
Manger, Richard W133
Mangiagalli, Marco W190
Mangino, Lou P57
Mangione, Robert A. P467
Manglik, Harsh W6
Mangold, Robert S. E442
Mangold, Klaus J. W23
Mangold, Klaus W112
Mangold, Klaus J. W227
Mangone, Ken A634
Mangoni, Andrea W348
Manhas, Aneil W268
Manion, Doug A135
Manion, Mark D. A598
Manire, Ross W. A62
Manis, G. Scott A786
Maniscalco, Giuseppe P527
Manix, Shannan E484
Mank, Darrel E91
Mankin, Eric P498
Manky, Dave E264
Manley, Frederick E. (Fred) A25
Manley, Lisa A198
Manley, John L. A879
Manley, John P. W84
Manley, Patrick W392
Manly, Marc E. A277
Mann, Kenneth D. E121
Mann, Jeffrey E195
Mann, Irene E301
Mann, Timothy A94
Mann, Bill A140
Mann, Eric A582
Mann, Erica L. A641
Mann, Alejandro M. A647
Mann, Laurie A886
Mann, C. Randall P2
Mann, Dave P238
Mann, William N. P284
Mann, Lindsay W106
Mann, Trevor W255
Mann, Peter W266
Manna, Joe A516
Mannekens, Henk W80
Mannelly, Matthew M. (Matt) E381
Manners, Myrna A P524
Mannina, Kenneth (Ken) E64
Manning, Claire E16
Manning, David L. E35
Manning, W E175
Manning, Robert E306
Manning, Mark E444
Manning, Anthony E458
Manning, Bradley W. A52
Manning, Denise A81
Manning, Anna A693
Manning, Kenneth P. A723
Manning, Robin E. (Rob) A789
Manning, Peter J. A799
Manning, Stephanie P42
Manning, Kim B. P140
Manning, Bradley L. P315
Manning, MaryKay P426
Manning, Danielle P487
Manning, Lynn D. P528
Manning, Kenneth J P609
Manning, G. Andre W204
Manning, Robert J. (Rob) W339
Mannis, Avi A E218
Mannis, Raymond P80
Manno, Eralba A619
Mannschatz, Hermann E261
Manny, Manuel E306
Manny, Roger S. E390
Manoogian, Richard A. A358

Manoogian, Richard A. A534
Manos, Kristen L. A486
Manos, Steven S. P76
Manos, Kristen P235
Manos, Alexandros S. W279
Manqueros, Marlo P49
Manring, Lewis E. A275
Mansel, David E239
Mansell, Kevin B. A491
Mansfield, Robert (Bob) A68
Mansfield, John C. A391
Mansfield, Stephen L. (Steve) P316
Mansh, Steven H P152
Mansoor, Allan P367
Mansour, Peter E58
Mansouri, Manoocher E362
Mantakas, Georgios W279
Mantega, Guido W276
Mantel, Timothy A. A781
Mantel, Ellen P130
Manternach, Jacquie M. A412
Manti?an, Jose Manuel Loureda W290
Mantilla, Luis Suarez de Lezo W290
Mantilla, Luis W290
Mantilla, Luis Suarez de Lezo W290
Mantovani, Massimo W141
Mantua, Philip J. A715
Manty, Adam P22
Manuel, Penny M. A737
Manuel, Gerdenio P192
Manville, John A182
Manwani, Harish A871
Manwani, Harish W369
Manwani, Harish W370
Manyari, Patricia P226
Manzano, Wilhelmina P524
Manzi, Jim P. A799
Manzini, Aldo A556
Manzione, Louis P536
Manzo, Robert A850
Manzo, Leslie P277
Manzoni, Federico W371
Manzotti, Maurizio W189
Mao, Frank E426
Mao, Matthew A23
Mao, Bill P367
Maouche, Marc W269
Mapel, Bill E58
Maples, Rick E445
Maples, Timothy S. A332
Maples, DeAnna P283
Maquet, Alain A445
Mara, Bernard E79
Mara, Paul E81
Mara, Shaun P. A244
Mara, Thomas E. A507
Marabito, Richard T. E356
Marable, Jan P621
Maradiaga, Rev Oscar Andres
    Rodriguez P191
Maramotti, Luigi W368
Marano, Anna E460
Marano, Thomas (Tom) A37
Marano, Joe A876
Maranto, Tony C. A300
Maranuk, Leigh E181
Marasco, Alex E438
Marbach, Joseph P445
Marbach, Alain W72
Marbaugh, David J. A513
Marbut, Bob A841
Marc, Jean E151
Marc, Burnstein E263
Marc, J P473
Marcantano, Mark P506
MarcAurele, Joseph J. (Joe) A856
March, Kevin P. A794
March, Bruce H. W183
Marchand, Robert (Bob) E497
Marchand, Thomas (Tom) P292
Marchant, Ronnie F. A54
Marchant, Ian W329
Marcheschi, Michael P291
Marchesini, Gianni W190
Marchetti, Stefano W189

Marchi, Michael E97
Marchi, Dennis P195
Marchiando, John E232
Marchido, William F. (Bill) P59
Marchik, Katie P566
Marchilena, Frank E46
Marchioni, John J. A725
Marchioni, Paolo W141
Marchionne, Sergio A645
Marchiony, Brian J. A476
Marchiori, Dave P537
Marchis, Ranieri W368
Marchuk, Neil E. A815
Marciano, Karol P398
Marcinelli, Ronald P. A206
Marcinowski, Stefan W62
Marco, Lori J. A426
Marco, Rafael W152
Marco, Rafael Villaseca W152
Marcon, Martha E. A551
Marcondes, Sandro Kohler W373
Marcone, Rock P26
Marconi, Luis G. A426
Marcotte, Gary A85
Marcotte, Rick P154
Marcoux, Daniel A698
Marcoux, Isabelle W282
Marcoux, Isabelle W387
Marcucci, Richard P171
Marcuccilli, James C. (Jim) A759
Marcum, R. Alan A250
Marcum, Kenny P553
Marcus, George M. E158
Marcus, Steven B. A121
Marcus, Jeffrey A. (Jeff) A172
Marcus, David A283
Marcus, Robert D. (Rob) A800
Marcus, Bernie P451
Marcy, Mike A792
Mardany, Herbert E475
Marden, William W. (Bill) A344
Marden, Robert P295
Mardock, Mark P306
Mardrus, Christian W289
Mardy, Michael J. A485
Mareburger, Robert S. (Bob) A615
Mareburger, Robert S. (Bob) A616
Marek, Todd P437
Marek, Don P527
Mares, Mike P488
Maressa, Joseph A. P268
Mareuse, Olivier Olivier Mareuse W374
Marfone, Patrick (Pat) A95
Margaritis, William G. A324
Margerie, Christophe de W362
Margerie, Christophe Christophe de
    Margerie W377
Margerie, Christophe de W377
Margetts, Sir Robert J. (Rob) A439
Margolian, Beverly S. W221
Margolin, Eric M. A155
Margolis, Karyn A92
Margolis, Robert J. A243
Margolis, Robert A243
Margolis, Gail L. P507
Margolius, Philip N. A279
Margot, Skip P5
Margueron, Josiane E294
Margulis, Heidi S. A434
Margulis, Richard T. P79
Mariani, Pedro Henrique A96
Mariani, Henry A104
Mariani, John K. P268
Marican, Tan Sri Mohammed H. A220
Marie, Bruce P119
Marien, Philippe W23
Marien, Philippe W74
Marilley, Leanne D. A598
Marin, Gerardo P575
Marin, Javier W46
Marine, Terri E119
Marine, Jay A42
Marineau, Philip A. (Phil) E420
Marineau, Susan G. P575
Marinelli, Steve A25

Marinello, Kathryn V. (Kathy) A377
Marinello, Charles A689
Marinello, Anthony J. A813
Marinescu, Alexandra A816
Marino, Sal E4
Marino, Robert E321
Marino, V. James A677
Marino, William J. (Bill) A723
Marino, William J. (Bill) A763
Marino, Alice P191
Marino, Tony P316
Marino, Ricardo Villela W191
Marinzel, Ron P447
Mario, Ernest A133
Mario, Ernest A164
Mario, Finis P334
Marion, Bob E92
Marion, Elaine D. E154
Maritz, Philip F. (Flip) A74
Maritz, Paul A. A851
Maritz, W. Stephen (Steve) P299
Marjoram, Chris A459
Mark, Struckman E197
Mark, Richard J. A45
Mark, Florine A546
Mark, Kelly S. A570
Mark, Richard A. P100
Mark, Grabitz P212
Mark, Rapoza P398
Mark, William P465
Mark, Joe P472
Mark, G P472
Markarian, James E245
Markasevic, John P612
Markee, Richard L. E510
Markel, Anthony F. A530
Markel, Steven A. A530
Markel, Anthony F. A530
Markel, Steven A. A530
Markel, Steven A. A824
Markel, Robinson A842
Markelonis, Don P591
Markelov, Vitaly W154
Markert, Thomas E. (Tom) A756
Markese, Bob E246
Market, Dan R. P299
Markey, Edward W. (Ed) A387
Markey, Dave P18
Markezin, Elaine T. P224
Markfield, Roger S E130
Markham, Andrew E163
Markham, Paul E466
Markham, Rudy H. P. A831
Markham, Rudy H. P. W210
Markham, Rudy H. P. W332
Markheim, Steven E142
Marki, Donna Del Prete P180
Marki, Hans Ulrich W4
Markiewicz, Ed E273
Markin, Rodney S. (Rod) P582
Markland, Ruth W332
Markle, Karen P347
Markley, John D. A173
Markley, William C. A466
Markley, Christopher P. P386
Marko, Paul P484
Markopoulos, Jody A374
Markov, Vladimir W154
Markovich, John E46
Marks, Seth E364
Marks, Dawn A63
Marks, Eugene A553
Marks, Michael E. A714
Marks, David B. A861
Marks, Alison W243
Marksberry, Annette P619
Marlett, Wendy L. A439
Marletta, Michael A. P531
Marlette, Tim G. A212
Marley, Robert E149
Marley, Bradley W. (Brad) A337
Marlin, Jason E475
Marlow, Geoffrey E11
Marlow, Jesse L. A629

Marlow, Larry P361
Marmer, Lynn A494
Marmo, Laura P612
Marmol, Guillermo G. (Gil) A356
Marner, Jeff P477
Marnick, Sam A744
Maroc, Genny P283
Marocco, Antonio M. W368
Marold, Paul E92
Maroon, Joseph C. A573
Maroone, Michael E. (Mike) A85
Marooney, Caryn A312
Marotta, Richard M. E51
Marotta, Richard M. A118
Marotta, Daniel A. (Dan) A136
Maroulis, Pam P247
Marple, Mark E. A555
Marples, Paul E109
Marples, Colleen A. A300
Marquardt, David F. A560
Marquardt, Robert P296
Marquardt, R. Scott P296
Marque, Jann A660
Marquez, Antonio A279
Marquez, Fidel A305
Marquez, Theresa P135
Marquez, Charee P445
Marquez, Byron J. P580
Marquez, Felipe W152
Marquis, Michael S. A53
Marr, Christopher P. (Chris) E115
Marr, Tommy P236
Marr, Ronda P578
Marra, Thomas M. (Tom) A773
Marram, Ellen R. A358
Marram, Ellen R. A513
Marrandette, Jennifer P482
Marrazzo, Ross E172
Marrella, John A. P272
Marren, Alexandra P. (Alex) A828
Marrion, Cy E94
Marriott, Richard E. A430
Marriott, J. W. (Bill) A531
Marriott, John W. A531
Marriott, Bernadette P413
Marrocco, John A337
Marrodan, Carlos W152
Marron, Mark P. E154
Marrotte, James E295
Marrs, Douglas W. (Doug) A392
Mars, Thomas A. (Tom) A853
Marsala, Donald P586
Marsan, Bill P22
Marsan, William P22
Marschilok, Stephen A404
Marsden, Craig P249
Marsden, Lorna R. W221
Marseilles, Bill A344
Marsh, Bryan E124
Marsh, Jenifer E181
Marsh, Chris E297
Marsh, Gary P E313
Marsh, Richard M. E332
Marsh, Leslie E468
Marsh, Lawrence C. A55
Marsh, Ryan T. A74
Marsh, William D. (Will) A95
Marsh, Brenda A107
Marsh, Nancy M. A169
Marsh, Andrew (Drew) A297
Marsh, Stephen P. (Steve) A298
Marsh, John T. A337
Marsh, Martha A621
Marsh, Matthew R. A629
Marsh, Anitra C. A664
Marsh, Kevin B. A717
Marsh, Miles L. A871
Marsh, Pete P74
Marsh, Allen P434
Marsh, Marcia P616
Marshall, Christopher P (Woody) E230
Marshall, Corby E246
Marshall, Siri S. A54
Marshall, Ruth Ann A218
Marshall, David A. A319

McClure, David P271
McClure, David P273
McClure, Ken P325
McClure, Kevin P347
McClure, Josh P403
McClure, Bonnie P507
McClurg, E. Vane A674
McCluskey, Carole E363
McClymont, Patrick S. E432
McColgan, Ellyn A. A660
McColgan, Ann M. P535
McCollam, Sharon L. A119
McCollough, Micheal E19
McCollough, W. Alan A388
McCollough, W. Alan A846
McCollum, Michael E339
McCollum, Mark A. A395
McCollum, L. Gwaltney A776
McCollum, William R. (Bill) A789
McComas, Randy P290
McComb, Lisa A541
McComb, Stanton A544
McCombe, Mark A124
McComish, Karen P63
McComish, Dick P458
McConnaughhay, Trudy P. E377
McConnell, Steven E3
McConnell, Rick M. E19
McConnell, Mac E133
McConnell, Jim E233
McConnell, Sarah H. A7
McConnell, John M. (Mike) A129
McConnell, Ian A549
McConnell, William T. (Bill) A630
McConnell, Arthur R. A669
McConnell, Michael W. (Mike) A825
McConnell, Ronald J. (Ron) P582
McConney, Ty A582
McConville, Richard A413
McConville, Ray A845
McConville, Susan P179
McConville, Dan P334
McCool, John F. A182
McCool, John G. A275
McCool, Robert J. A385
McCool, James D. A720
McCord, Patricia J. (Patty) A582
McCord, Scott W. A763
McCord, Michael A. P75
McCorkindale, Douglas H. A519
McCorkle, Frederick E44
McCormack, John E508
McCormack, Sean I. A126
McCormack, Robert C. (Bob) A443
McCormack, Robert C. (Bob) A547
McCormack, Robert C. (Bob) A600
McCormack, Mike P164
McCormack, Kerry P318
McCormack, Irene P432
McCormick, Randall E155
McCormick, Daniel C. (Dan) E420
McCormick, Brendan A41
McCormick, Stan A232
McCormick, Stephen A. A262
McCormick, Andy A413
McCormick, William T. A707
McCormick, John J. A789
McCormick, Robert J. A813
McCormick, Richard D. A836
McCormick, Brenda A. A844
McCormick, Bob P148
McCormick, Diane P240
McCormick, David P243
McCormick, Clair P278
McCormick, Beth P367
McCormick, Michael P383
McCormick, John W300
McCoskey, John P400
McCourt, Joseph E. E284
McCowan, Nathan P441
McCowen, Kerry E61
McCown, Michael E198
McCown, Steve E325
McCoy, Mike E69
McCoy, Michael A E69

McCoy, Alan H. A26
McCoy, John B. A81
McCoy, Sherilyn S. (Sheri) A92
McCoy, Glenn D. A335
McCoy, Dustan E. (Dusty) A364
McCoy, Mark A499
McCoy, Joe G. A792
McCoy, Carol A. A806
McCoy, John B. P48
McCoy, Michael J. P97
McCoy, Shawn P148
McCoy, Stephen P. P271
McCoy, Stephen P. P273
McCoy, Thomas P328
McCoy, Laura P364
McCoy, Craig P551
McCoy, John T. W268
McCoy, John B. W268
McCracken, Alex E455
McCracken, William E. (Bill) A140
McCracken, William E. (Bill) A141
McCracken, Amanda S. A348
McCracken, Robert E. A500
McCracken, Robert W. A605
McCracken, Dave A664
McCracken, Rosalie P165
McCracken, Dax P. W367
McCrackin, Bobbie H. A319
McCraight, Billy P361
McCrary, David E77
McCrary, Charles D. A27
McCrary, Charles D. A692
McCrary, Charles D. A737
McCrary, Scott A792
McCraven, Marcus R. P404
McCraw, Libby P93
McCray, Gregory J. A170
McCrea, Marshall S. (Mackie) A295
McCrea, Marshall S. (Mackie) A296
McCrea, Jeffrey P. (Jeff) A451
McCrea, Marshall A764
McCready, Daniel D. A588
McCreary, Ramsey E41
McCreary, Lynn S. A348
McCreary, R. Scott A485
McCree, Donald H. (Don) A476
McCreesh, Glenn P456
McCrone, Stewart W204
McCrory, K.C. A653
McCroskey, Michael W. A52
McCubbins, John T. A549
McCue, David A215
McCue, Thomas A. (Tom) W30
McCuean, Tavia E179
McCuistion, Randy E179
McCuistion, Tamika Davis E394
McCulley, Steven E. A434
McCulley, Tom A587
McCulloch, James L E182
McCulloh, Thayne M. P510
McCullouch, John M. A814
McCullough, Deborah A. A23
McCullough, Mark A47
McCullough, Bruce A. A527
McCullough, Robert F. A660
McCullough, Gary E. A728
McCullough, Theodore J. (Ted) A737
McCullough, Howell D. (Mac) A819
McCullough, Samuel A. P410
McCullough, Lauren P503
McCune, Scott K. A369
McCurdy, Michael W. E66
McCurdy, Sarah E196
McCurdy, Michael A138
McCurdy, Kay W. P75
McCure, Matt W18
McCurry, Michael P314
McCusker, John E89
McCutcheon, Stewart H. A284
McDade, Ralph L E283
McDade, Ralph L. E332
McDade, Sandy D. A870
McDaniel, Terry E250
McDaniel, Thomas R (Tom) E416
McDaniel, Andrew E497

McDaniel, Dennis E. A180
McDaniel, Connie D. A198
McDaniel, Ronald (Ron) A572
McDaniel, Liliana C. A776
McDaniel, Marvin E. A883
McDaniel, Matthew P. P114
McDaniel, Duane P256
McDaniel, Gordon L. P424
McDaniels, Charles P143
McDaris, Marv A675
McDarment, John A792
McDavid, William A362
McDavid, Lolita M. P318
McDearis, Kevin E57
McDermid, Margaret E. (Lyn) A264
McDermid, Margaret E. (Lyn) A320
McDermott, Carrie E130
McDermott, Richard E172
McDermott, Tonya E400
McDermott, Lee E487
McDermott, Robert D. (Bob) A206
McDermott, Michael P A523
McDermott, John P. A707
McDermott, Mary P383
McDevitt, Michael E. E112
McDevitt, William J. E383
McDevitt, John J. A831
McDill, John A82
McDonagh, Baroness Margaret J. W333
McDonald, Andrew L. (Andy) E97
McDonald, Wayne E179
McDonald, Michael E197
McDonald, Erik E223
McDonald, Robert E342
McDonald, Eugene E396
McDonald, Andrew N E421
McDonald, Pace A82
McDonald, John W. A176
McDonald, Andrew L. (Andy) A204
McDonald, Dick A235
McDonald, Adrian A287
McDonald, R.D. A289
McDonald, Hugh T. A297
McDonald, David W. A345
McDonald, William J. (Bill) A434
McDonald, Patricia A. A452
McDonald, Prof John G. (Jack) A464
McDonald, R. Bruce A472
McDonald, Wesley S. (Wes) A491
McDonald, Gillian A541
McDonald, Gwendolyn (Gwen) A582
McDonald, James D. (Jim) A600
McDonald, Robert A. (Bob) A664
McDonald, Peter D. (Pete) A827
McDonald, Mackey J. A862
McDonald, Robert A. (Bob) A885
McDonald, John P16
McDonald, Glen P27
McDonald, Vicki P69
McDonald, Bruce M. P77
McDonald, James P204
McDonald, Thomas P223
McDonald, Charles J. P241
McDonald, Celeste P296
McDonald, Joe P379
McDonald, Brenda P391
McDonald, Fredda P399
McDonald, John J. P404
McDonald, Dean P441
McDonald, Mark P519
McDonald, Gary P575
McDonald, David S. (Dave) P612
McDonald, Mike P614
McDonald, Stephen D. (Steve) W54
McDonie, Patrick J. (Pat) A615
McDonnell, John F. A127
McDonnell, Patrick J. A342
McDonnell, Paul I. A832
McDonnell, Timothy J. P568
McDonough, Todd A391
McDonough, Kevin A702
McDonough, Robert J. (Bob) A836
McDonough, Andrea P157
McDonough, H. R. P160
McDonough, Rev Kevin P577

McDorman, Thomas (Tom) A866
McDougal, Dan E206
McDougall, Duane C. A750
McDougall, Duane C. P281
McDowell, Ronald W. (Ron) A81
McDowell, Debra A. P522
McEachern, Doug P316
McElhattan, Kent P75
McElligott, Kathleen (Kathy) A290
McElmurray, Brannen E181
McElravy, Deborah P213
McElroy, Paul A28
McElroy, Michael E. A54
McElroy, Terry L. A628
McElwee, Arthur H. A611
McElwee, Jeremiah A873
McEniry, James B. A52
McEnroe, John A177
McEntee, Kevin A583
McEntee, Gerald W. P17
McEntee, Jeff P432
McEuen, Mary P299
McEuen, Lisa P575
McEvoy, Steve E5
McEvoy, Jim E172
McEwan, Ross W106
McEwan, Ross W300
McEwen, Tim E259
McEwen, William J. P202
McFadden, Bruce E81
McFadden, William J. (Bill) A190
McFadden, Howard D. A598
McFadden, Dean A678
McFadden, Charles B. A717
McFadden, Ed A845
McFadden, Mary Kay P441
McFadden, Ian E. P520
McFadden, Thomas P557
McFadyen, Michael A572
McFall, Thomas G. (Tom) A606
McFall, Don P249
McFarlan, Prof F. Warren A215
McFarland, John E457
McFarland, Mac A. A294
McFarland, Susan R. A315
McFarland, Duncan A. A369
McFarland, Joseph (Joe) A422
McFarland, Doug P226
McFarlane, Daniel E181
McFarlane, Bob E290
McFarlane, Roe J. A266
McFarlane, Sydney P191
McFarlane, Lawrence P443
McFarlane, John W34
McFarlane, John W35
McFarlane, John W300
McFarlin, Bruce E41
McFarlin, Willie P540
McFarling, Suellen E394
McFeetors, Raymond L. W160
McFeetors, Raymond L. W282
McFeetors, Raymond L. W283
McFeggan, Don E278
McGahren, John P377
McGain, Trevor R. P392
McGann, Sally P228
McGarey, Jennifer C. A601
McGarry, John E94
McGarry, Tom E346
McGarry, Paul A203
McGarry, Kimberly A342
McGarry, Sean C. A444
McGarry, Michael H. A653
McGarry, Steven A731
McGarry, John F. (Jack) A840
McGartoll, Paul A795
McGarvey, Vicki Lewis P498
McGarvie, Blythe A517
McGarvie, Blythe J. A847
McGarvie, Blythe J. W7
McGary, Skip A809
McGavick, Kathryn E363
McGeary, Roderick C. (Rod) A183
McGeary, Roderick C (Rod) A625
McGee, Ken E196

A = AMERICAN BUSINESS
E = EMERGING COMPANIES
P = PRIVATE COMPANIES
W = WORLD BUSINESS

A = AMERICAN BUSINESS
E = EMERGING COMPANIES
P = PRIVATE COMPANIES
W = WORLD BUSINESS

Mehnert, Dana A. A404
Mehr, Nicole A403
Mehra, Ajay E362
Mehra, Asit A614
Mehra, R. K. W67
Mehrabian, Robert A653
Mehrberg, Randall E. (Randy) A673
Mehrer, Edward W. (Ed) A316
Mehrotra, Louise A470
Mehrotra, Sanjay A714
Mehta, Mitesh E9
Mehta, Tirath E196
Mehta, Nishil E384
Mehta, Rajeev (Raj) A201
Mehta, Kavan J. P496
Mehta, Tarak W4
Mehta, Aman W188
Mei, Paul E267
Meibergen, J. L. (Lew) P261
Meibergen, J. L. (Butch) P261
Meibergen, Joey P261
Meier, Richard A. (Randy) A621
Meier, Steven A758
Meier, April A870
Meier, Kim P223
Meier, Castor P559
Meier, Lisa P560
Meiers, James R. (Jim) E215
Meignie, Yves W376
Meigs, Gen. Montgomery C. P523
Meijer, Hendrik G. (Hank) A329
Meijer, Gert W369
Meiklejohn, Mark J. E66
Meiklejohn, Mark A138
Meiklejohn, David E. W33
Mein, David P182
Meincke, Christina P192
Meindel, Nympha P270
Meine, Hartmut W112
Meine, Hartmut W381
Meinerding, James A. A341
Meinitz, Sabine A794
Meins, Dan P414
Meintjes, Charles F. A633
Meirvenne, Dirk Van W63
Meis, Tom P321
Meisenbach, John W. A228
Meisenbach, John W. A309
Meisenberg, Barry R. P25
Meisenheimer, Fred E. A81
Meisetschlaeger, Katherine S. A52
Meisinger, Peter E485
Meisler, Luiz A618
Meismer, Denise A329
Meisner, Nancy K. A792
Meissner, Doris P135
Meister, John M. E367
Meister, Kurt A309
Meister, Paul M. A517
Meister, Margaret A. A773
Meister, Edgar W105
Meister, Hans-Ulrich W115
Meitz, Mary P78
Meixelsperger, Mary E130
Meizels, Peter E445
Mejia, Brian E219
Mejia, Maria Fernanda A202
Mejia, Carols E. A481
Mejia, Maria F. A481
Meka, Venkata E369
Mekawi, Hesham W76
Melamed, A. Douglas (Doug) A452
Melancon, Barry C. P18
Meland, Greg R. E119
Melaragno, Tony P281
Melby, Randy R. A105
Melcher, David F. A303
Melcher, David F. A304
Melcher, Ray P74

Melching, Ed A578
Melchior, Thomas V. A383
Melchiorre, Joseph P453
Meldrum, Peter D. E332
Melendez, Yvette P130
Melendez, Nestor P180
Melendi, Robert J. A209
Meler, Suzanne P105
Melgar, Sergio P570
Meli, Salvatore W141
Melin, Olga P46
Meline, David W. A2
Melinson, Gregg R. A418
Melius, Jason J. A169
Melk, Bob E123
Mellbye, Peter W334
Melle, Ermia P95
Meller, Alex E329
Meller, Aleksandr E329
Meller, Craig W25
Mellink, Bart E197
Mello, Flavio A. C. A234
Mellody, Ellen A205
Mellody, James G. A345
Mellor, Patrick E367
Mellott, Steve P302
Mellowes, John A. P107
Mellowes, John W. P107
Mellowes, Charles P107
Melmed, Shlomo P98
Melo, Cesar A203
Melo, Murilo B. A656
Melonas, Gus A139
Meloni, Vittorio W189
Meloy, Mattthew J. (Matt) A779
Meloy, Catherine P308
Melson, Benjamin (Ben) P500
Melton, Keith L E515
Melton, Stephen A54
Melton, Darrell W. A629
Melton, Carol A. A801
Melton, William P531
Meltzer, Cliff A140
Meltzer, Carol A744
Meltzer, Neil M. P284
Melville, C. G. A170
Melvin, Mark C. E154
Melvin, Rosetta P618
Melzi, Bruno A. A890
Memis, Adnan W365
Menanteau, Jean-Pierre W34
Menard, Jayne E153
Menchel, Marc P186
Mencoff, Samuel M. P354
Mendelowitz, Lawrence P383
Mendelsohn, Karen R. A534
Mendelsohn, Robert V. (Bob) A577
Mendelsohn, Howard P125
Mendelson, Victor H. E221
Mendelson, Avner W49
Mendenhall, Kelley E. A345
Mendes, Mark A. A458
Mendez, Angel L. A182
Mendez, Roberto D. (Bobby) A284
Mendez, John M. A336
Mendez, Lincoln P43
Mendez, Fernando W8
Mendicino, Frank J. A71
Mendick, Kay P573
Mendiola, Sonia P261
Mendiola, Cristina Sanz W290
Mendiola, Cristina W290
Mendiratta, Sham P618
Mendis, Paul P340
Mendler, Frederick E389
Mendoza, Roberto G. A526
Mendoza, Eugenio A540
Mendoza, Thomas F. (Tom) A581
Mendoza, Thomas F. (Tom) A582
Mendoza, Roberto G. A868
Mendoza, Ted P488
Meneades, Mac Kenzie E315
Menear, Craig A402
Menear, Craig A. A422
Menell, Gregg E196

Menendez-Cortada, Jose A331
Mener, Richard A202
Menesee, Kim P602
Meneses, Alex P507
Menezes, Ivan M. A196
Menezes, Eduardo F. A656
Meng, Mark P467
Mengebier, David G. A192
Mengebier, David G. A223
Mengel, Tammi P231
Mengel, Tammi-Erving P231
Menges, Sascha A415
Menichini, Leslie P423
Menikoff, Peter W8
Menix, Karen P293
Menke, Sean E218
Menne, Michael L. A45
Mennel, Donald L. A62
Menning, J. Ron (Ron) A803
Meno, Philip F. A63
Menon, Suresh E273
Menon, Satish E420
Menon, Deepak E492
Menon, Raj A234
Mensah, Nana A700
Mensch, Mariana B. P587
Mense, D. Craig A193
Menser, Michael K. A523
Menten, Eric de W362
Mentesana, Beth K. A23
Mentle, Iris P102
Menton, Jason E173
Mentzer, Charlie E515
Mentzer, W. Eric A451
Menzel, David B. (Dave) E139
Menzel, Susan L. (Sue) A194
Menzer, John B. A290
Menzie, Anthony A252
Menzies, D. Stephen (Steve) A812
Menzies, John K. P445
Meo, Francesco De W149
Meo, Francesco W149
Merav, Avraham P383
Merbach, Dick P181
Mercado, Pablo G E183
Mercado, Luis A871
Mercer, James W. (Jim) E219
Mercier, Dianne M. A636
Mercier, Linda A786
Mercier, John M. P461
Mercier, Andrew B. (Andy) P519
Mercurio, Anthony J. (Tony) E336
Mercurio, Jospeh P A169
Mered, Saad W392
Meredith, Thomas C. A82
Meredith, Les A170
Meredith, Dru P186
Merelli, F. H. A67
Mereness, Scott T. E128
Mergelmeyer, Gene E. A78
Mergenthaler, Frank A309
Mergenthaler, Frank A459
Mergin, Murat M365
Mergler, Jeff E388
Mergner, Arthur E442
Merhra, Ajay E362
Meriano, John J. P404
Merican, Mohamed W220
Merican, Dato? Mohamed
   Khadar W292
Mericle, Jeff P208
Meriggioli, Nicholas A493
Merin, Mitchell M. (Mitch) W339
Merino, John L. A324
Merizalde, Luis G. A376
Merizzi, Robert W34
Merk, Gregory P. (Greg) E351
Merk, Teresa P109
Merkamp, Christine W305
Merkel, Stephen M. E53
Merkh, Kristen P472

Merkle, Sam E503
Merkley, Shirley P382
Merksamer, Samuel J. A323
Merli, Geno P543
Merlino, Bernadette P377
Merlis, Laurence M. P1
Merlo, Larry J. A237
Merlo, Michael J. A729
Merlo, Kathleen P430
Merlot, Thierry E224
Meroi, Stefano W31
Merrani, Anil A E175
Merrell, Capt. Thomas W. A371
Merrell, Scott P413
Merrell, Katie P532
Merrick, Aaron S. G. A67
Merrick, Garth A338
Merrick, Vicki A870
Merrick, Robert P67
Merril, Donald A. E498
Merrill, Gary A98
Merrill, Jeff E173
Merrill, Mark G. A344
Merrill, Susan E455
Merrill, David T. E490
Merrill, David T. E491
Merriman, Kati Copley P413
Merrin, Seth I. P556
Merritt, Greg E112
Merritt, Sarah A138
Merritt, David C. A144
Merritt, David C. A172
Merritt, Lynn A592
Merritt, Carrie A770
Merritt, Norman W. A891
Merritt, Jennifer P526
Merry, James R. A629
Merry, Laura P578
Merryman, Gregory A37
Merryman, Susan P364
Merryman, Andrew P383
Mershon, Brian A353
Mersky, Seth M. W268
Merszei, Geoffery E. (Geoff) A270
Merten, Alan G. A152
Merten, Jeffrey A. A402
Merten, Alan W221
Merton, Tracy P430
Mertzlufft, Douglas (Doug) P214
Mervin-blake, Sabrena P413
Merwin, Robert W. (Bob) P323
Merz, Mark A606
Merz, Albrecht W133
Mescal, Robert A115
Mesdag, T. Willem (Will) E146
Mesdag, Willem E146
Meserve, Richard A. A644
Meshel, Jeffrey W. (Jeff) A729
Mesick, Mike A127
Mesmer, Larry E263
Mesquita, Jorge S. A664
Mesrobian, Edmond A307
Mess, Charles F. A715
Messenger, David E462
Messer, Arnold W. A627
Messerich, John P530
Messersmith, Gary E134
Messier, Luc J. A220
Messina, Richard P. E446
Messina, Elizabeth A. P70
Messina, Jim P299
Messina, Carlo W189
Messman, Tom E172
Messman, Rick P232
Messmer, Harold M. A703
Mestrallet, Gerard W108
Mestrallet, Gerard W156
Mestre, Eduardo G. E159
Mestre, Eduardo G. A89
Mestre, Eduardo G. A205
Mestrio, Karen De E391
Meswani, Hital R. W287
Meswani, Nikhil R. W287
Meswani, Hital R. W287
Meswani, Nikhil R. W287

A = AMERICAN BUSINESS
E = EMERGING COMPANIES
P = PRIVATE COMPANIES
W = WORLD BUSINESS

Miller, Steven A. E197
Miller, Paul E215
Miller, Adam E267
Miller, Todd E287
Miller, Robert A E312
Miller, William G. E320
Miller, Donald E351
Miller, John E355
Miller, Ben E377
Miller, Gary E414
Miller, Mark C. E443
Miller, Vickie E445
Miller, Brad E455
Miller, Todd E465
Miller, Guy E468
Miller, Joe E474
Miller, Peter E475
Miller, Alan B. E496
Miller, Donald E. A1
Miller, Rosa M. A2
Miller, Brian A. A14
Miller, Mark A. A14
Miller, Ted B. A25
Miller, Melisa A35
Miller, Robert S. (Steve) A51
Miller, Henry S. A51
Miller, Jay J. A59
Miller, Susan C. A88
Miller, MaryAnn G. A91
Miller, Irene R. A107
Miller, Melanie E. R. A115
Miller, Catherine B. A118
Miller, Greg A143
Miller, W. Thaddeus A144
Miller, Debbie A161
Miller, John R. A172
Miller, Stephen W. A174
Miller, Merrill A. (Pete) A174
Miller, Thomas R. (Thom) A188
Miller, Gwen T. A188
Miller, Irene R. A196
Miller, David L. A211
Miller, Thomas D. (Tom) A212
Miller, Christopher M. (Chris) A224
Miller, Stephen P. A226
Miller, Russell D. (Russ) A227
Miller, James H. (Jim) A230
Miller, William I. (Will) A234
Miller, Pepe A257
Miller, James L. A262
Miller, Eugene A. (Gene) A273
Miller, David B. A275
Miller, Rik L. A275
Miller, James A. A284
Miller, Susan E. A292
Miller, Jill A300
Miller, Steven (Steve) A309
Miller, Kenneth C. A318
Miller, James B. A327
Miller, Jordan A. A329
Miller, David W. A339
Miller, Karen A365
Miller, Jamie S. A374
Miller, Heidi G. A376
Miller, Joseph A. (Buzz) A381
Miller, Anthony E. (Tony) A387
Miller, John R. A390
Miller, Scot A. A393
Miller, Jeffrey A. (Jeff) A395
Miller, Suzan A. A451
Miller, Jim A459
Miller, Robert A. A460
Miller, Heidi G. A475
Miller, Daniel A477
Miller, Cecil R. A478
Miller, Hinda A485
Miller, Michael A489
Miller, Gregory C. (Greg) A490
Miller, Brian F. A491

Miller, Stuart A. A506
Miller, Charles C. (Buddy) A508
Miller, Jonathan F. (Jon) A516
Miller, Ken A520
Miller, Merrill A. (Pete) A574
Miller, Robert G. (Bob) A596
Miller, Tomas A. A605
Miller, Mark A605
Miller, Lydia E. A629
Miller, Matthew R. A630
Miller, Dennis P. A633
Miller, Laurie Beja A634
Miller, Forrest E. A644
Miller, Kevin A647
Miller, Jocelyn A661
Miller, Brent A664
Miller, Heidi G. A666
Miller, Dan A701
Miller, John M. A707
Miller, Donald K. (Don) A711
Miller, James C. A713
Miller, Lynne M. A718
Miller, Norman L. (Norm) A724
Miller, Kenneth A. A733
Miller, Guy W. A769
Miller, Robert S. (Steve) A772
Miller, W. Keith A778
Miller, Annette A781
Miller, Charles F. A786
Miller, Richard A. (Rick) A811
Miller, Jody G. A815
Miller, Heather K. A822
Minale, Diane D. A823
Miller, Zell B. A827
Miller, Alan B. A839
Miller, Marc D. A839
Miller, Kate A840
Miller, Richard S. A842
Miller, Carl A. A861
Miller, Robert J. A882
Miller, William K. P5
Miller, Michael M. (Mike) P32
Miller, Richard K. P39
Miller, Adam P55
Miller, Thomas H. P67
Miller, Terry P74
Miller, Jeff P77
Miller, Kyle P82
Miller, Silvana P87
Miller, Mark P94
Miller, Kathleen J. (Kay) P97
Miller, Scott P116
Miller, Stan P124
Miller, John W. (Jack) P130
Miller, Richard P139
Miller, Linda P143
Miller, David P148
Miller, Denny P152
Miller, Jane E. P202
Miller, Maggie P206
Miller, Randy P213
Miller, John L. P223
Miller, Edwin (Glen) P229
Miller, Jeffrey S. (Jeff) P231
Miller, Gary P240
Miller, Robert (Bob) P246
Miller, Jesse P248
Miller, Jennie P258
Miller, Edward D. P260
Miller, Mike P262
Miller, P. Daniel (Dan) P273
Miller, Patricia P282
Miller, Rudy P284
Miller, Roy P295
Miller, Mark P300
Miller, L. Christopher P300
Miller, Brigid O'Brien P300
Miller, Edward D. P308
Miller, Hal P323
Miller, Lee P323
Miller, Marc J. P332
Miller, Tony P336
Miller, Michael L. P338
Miller, H. Gilbert P348
Miller, Todd P375

Miller, Charles P. (Charlie) P377
Miller, Michael C. P383
Miller, Michael H. P383
Miller, Keith P403
Miller, Nic P409
Miller, Marlin P410
Miller, Ethan P411
Miller, Alisa P413
Miller, Henry S. P436
Miller, Greg P448
Miller, James P459
Miller, Mike P462
Miller, Gary P. P469
Miller, Steve P490
Miller, Allan P490
Miller, Marty W. P507
Miller, Andy P514
Miller, Richard B. P535
Miller, Marc H. P547
Miller, Ben P559
Miller, Carol P563
Miller, Melissa P567
Miller, Janet L. P569
Miller, Pamela P575
Miller, Michelle P577
Miller, Diane D. P578
Miller, David P581
Miller, Rick P581
Miller, Brent P584
Miller, Gary P601
Miller, John D. P613
Miller, Julie P616
Miller, Clifford P618
Miller, Serge W29
Miller, Alexey B. W153
Miller, Alexey B. W154
Miller, Aleksey W154
Miller, Alexey B. W154
Miller, Klaus W171
Miller, Thomas (Tom) W320
Miller, Timothy J. (Tim) W331
Miller, Irene R. W358
Millerchip, Gary A495
Millet, Jose M. Mas W45
Millett, Mark D. A759
Millett, Simon J. W332
Millhollin, Jeff P375
Milliet, Ron E216
Milligan, John E339
Milligan, Peter J. A303
Milligan, John F. A383
Milligan, George D. A828
Milligan, Cynthia H. A862
Milligan, Stephen D. (Steve) A866
Milligan, Michael D. (Mike) P38
Millikan, J. Scott P63
Milliken, Paul W303
Millikin, Michael P. A377
Millikin, Tom M. A664
Milliner, Mark W341
Milling, King A396
Milling, David A. P265
Milliren, Carmen P188
Milliron, Joseph E. (Joe) E190
Millman, Chris W80
Millner, Ann P249
Millon, Jean-Pierre (JP) A237
Millones, Peter J. A659
Milloy, Robert W81
Mills, Robert E172
Mills, Jeannette E305
Mills, George Q E369
Mills, Steven R. (Steve) A72
Mills, Robert M. A145
Mills, William J. (Bill) A186
Mills, Vicki A291
Mills, Gary A336
Mills, Rick J. A351
Mills, Steven A. (Steve) A455
Mills, Steven A. (Steve) A532
Mills, Linda A. A602
Mills, Matthew A678
Mills, Gary M. A778
Mills, Bob A792
Mills, Scott M. A847

Mills, Craig N. P18
Mills, Bryan A. P127
Mills, Alice P179
Mills, Don P318
Mills, Galen P338
Mills, Andrew J. P354
Mills, Craig P379
Mills, J. William P498
Mills, Jim P522
Mills, Thomas L. P612
Mills, Christina W294
Mills-Sirois, Amanda A34
Millsom, Adam E455
Millstead, Bart A459
Millwood, John E421
Milne, Doug E315
Milne, Gordon A. E408
Milnesi, Carolina E196
Milos, Charles D. A576
Milstein, Ronald S. A521
Milstein, Michael P82
Milstein, Marc P620
Milstien, Kim P207
Milton, B.W. A311
Milton, Mark A. A478
Milton, Paul A. P171
Milton, Kerry P431
Milunovic, Michelle E360
Mims, Harry M. A735
Min, Scott E181
Min, Christina S. A452
Min, Jung Kee W316
Minale, Stefano S. A409
Minami, Nobuya W117
Minan, Peter A215
Minard, Timothy J. (Tim) A661
Minardi, Christina A873
Minardi, Eduardo W78
Minassian, Bryan E339
Minc, David C E414
Minehan, Cathy E. A849
Minehan, Cathy E. P523
Minekawa, Sho W171
Minekawa, Sho W172
Minella, Lynn C. A23
Mineno, Toshiyuki W247
Mineo, Michael C. P192
Miner, Emily B. A577
Miner, Steve P32
Miner, Lenny P33
Miner, Mark P182
Miner, James D. P517
Minerich, Phillip L. (Phil) A426
Mines, Timothy F. P122
Mineta, Norman Y. (Norm) E269
Minetti, Carlos A256
Ming, Liz A664
Ming, Wong Wai W99
Ming, Timpson Chung Shui W99
Mingay, Simon E197
Mingchao, Gu W51
Mingchun, Zhou W275
Minges, Tim A638
Mingle, Robyn E233
Mingle, Regina P278
Mingot, Antoni W152
Mingst, Caryll Sprague P507
Miniati, Peter J. A856
Minick, Russ E199
Minicucci, Benito (Ben) A28
Minicucci, Robert A. A35
Minieri, Mary B. A433
Minifie, C. David A165
Miniger, Robert T (Bob) E49
Mink, Victoria A141
Mink, Susan W. A320
Minkel, Scott A. E492
Minkel, Scott A. A828
Minnehan, Mike P598
Minnich, George E. A18
Minnich, Gene A395
Minnich, Brandt N. A551
Minnick, David M. A761
Minnick, Mary E. A781
Minnick, Paul P56

Nardone, Randal A.   A359
Nardone, Mary Kaye   A499
Nardone, Mary   P555
Narev, Ian   W106
Narla, Mohandas   P343
Narlow, Greg   P125
Naruke, Yasuo Yasuo Naruke   W360
Nascenzi, Robert   E346
Nascimben, Rob   E316
Nasella, Henry J.   A677
Naselow, Craig S.   A97
Nash, Tony   E240
Nash, William D. (Bill)   A155
Nash, Thomas M. (Tom)   A314
Nash, Cheryl   A348
Nash, David B.   A434
Nash, Patrick L.   A629
Nash, Ron   A789
Nash, Cynthia B. (Cindy)   A876
Nash, Bruce D.   P89
Nash, Dick   P227
Nash, James   P391
Nash, Glenn   W328
Nasir, Louis P.   A778
Naslund, Charles D.   A45
Naspinski, Ed   P496
Nasrallah, Lynne G.   P191
Nassar, Zeina T.   A253
Nasser, Joseph G.   A579
Nasser, Jacques A. (Jac)   W69
Nassner, Jeffrey   P301
Nastase, Dave   A602
Natale, Gail   E150
Natale, J. Peter   A112
Natale, Marina   W368
Natalia, Lily   P226
Natalucci, Gregory F.   A551
Natarajan, Sanjay   A452
Natarajan, Murali   A702
Natekar, R. P.   W68
Nathan, Don   A838
Nathan, James A.   P98
Nathan, Susan   P303
Nathanson, Jonathan   A520
Nathanson, Martha   P284
Nattrass, Kevin W.   A115
Natzke, David   E175
Nau, Gerald A.   A366
Naudon, Carlos P.   P80
Nauert, Gary   P157
Nauffal, Rafael   W43
Naughton, Timothy J. (Tim)   E47
Naughton, Eugene   E425
Naughton, Duncan C. Mac   A853
Naugle, Denny   P413
Naugle, Dave L.   P577
Naugler, David   A661
Nault, Raymond   E104
Nault, Kenneth   E310
Naumann, Steve   A305
Naumann, Susan   W90
Navarro, Salvadore A   E56
Navarro, Victor   E174
Navarro, Ricardo A. (Rick)   A404
Navarro, Mary W.   A436
Navarro, Imelda   A453
Navarro, Edgardo   A541
Navarro, Pedro Alfonso Rosales   W135
Navarro, Juan Villalonga   W145
Nave, Steve   A853
Nave, James E.   A865
Naveda, Marcelino Botin-Sanz de
   Sautola y   W56
Navetta, Marco   E303
Navez, Jean-Marc   A202
Navikas, David B.   A653
Navon, Adi   E71
Navran, Susan H.   P70
Nayak, Vinay   P7
Nayar, Deepak   E278
Nayer, Rosslyn   P283
Naylor, Joe   E258
Naylor, Jeffrey G. (Jeff)   A804
Naylor, David   P408
Naylor, Mary D.   P589

Nayyar, Sandeep   E379
Nayyar, Geeta   A81
Nazar, Manoochehr K. (Mano)   A589
Nazarian, Marita   P29
Nazarko, Michael   P224
Nazeer, Khalid   P335
Nazemetz, Patricia M.   P192
Nazir, Saif   E464
Nazmi, Nader   W72
Nazzaro, Stephen F. (Steve)   A758
Ndong, Juan A.   P36
Neal, Lisa   E154
Neal, Mark   E268
Neal, Greg   E339
Neal, Richard   E373
Neal, Michael W.   A290
Neal, Homer A.   A358
Neal, Michael A. (Mike)   A373
Neal, Stephen C.   A510
Neal, John C.   A824
Neal, Grant R.   P26
Neal, Jim   P526
Neal, Greg   P601
Neal-Graves, Anthony   A452
Nealon, Thomas M.   A739
Nealon, Jackie   P287
Neaman, Avery   P288
Neaman, Mark R.   P354
Nearhood, Richard   P426
Neary, Robert D.   A209
Neary, James C. (Jim)   A326
Neary, Daniel P.   P140
Neary, Francis   P413
Nease, Lin   A418
Neath, Gavin   W370
Nebab, Bianca G.   A845
Nebbia, Luciano   W189
Nebeker, Gil   E240
Nebel, Randy J.   E262
Nebergall, Donald C.   A785
Nechustan, Oded   P302
Neckmar, Thomas   W258
Neddenien, Karl R.   A264
Nee, William J   E40
Neeb, Marc J.   W219
Neece, Maria   E46
Need, Linda   A861
Needham, Floyd E.   E331
Needham, Wendy B.   A379
Needham, George M.   P363
Needleman, Scott   P243
Neegan, Leone   P621
Neely, Eddie W.   A39
Neely, Gregory W.   A778
Neely, Brian   P21
Neely, Denise J.   P78
Neely, Andrea   P564
Neely, Joe B.   P596
Neemeh, Alain P.   A693
Neeper, Jarral   P86
Neesam, Jaci   P575
Neeteson, Paul   W107
Neff, Tom   E241
Neff, Robert K.   A45
Neff, Nancy   P42
Neff, Thomas J. (Tom)   W8
Nefkens, Mike   A418
Negrete, Mary   P501
Negrini, Anton J.   A782
Negron, Eduardo J.   A651
Negroni, Peter   P122
Nehammer, Ulrik   A198
Nehra, John M.   A243
Nehs, Scott   P69
Nei, Yasushi   W124
Neidorff, Michael F.   A165
Neidorff, Michael F.   P600
Neigher, William D   P36
Neil, Sylvia   P125
Neild, Ian   W80
Neiles, Byron C.   A292
Neiles, Byron   W137
Neill, Peter   A508
Neill, John   A630
Neilson, John   W39

Neiman, Sioma   A453
Neira, Adriana Marcela   W135
Neis, Thomas J.   A877
Nejman, Edward   E251
Nekrasov, Vladimir I.   W264
Nel, Stanley D.   P575
Nell, Steven E.   A128
Nelles, Duane A.   A680
Nelles, Josef   W134
Nelligan, Annette   P571
Nelms, David W.   A256
Nels, Tiffany   E430
Nelsen, Ben   E68
Nelsen, Colleen   E437
Nelsen, Ken   E460
Nelsen, Keith J.   A119
Nelson, Dave   E11
Nelson, Gregory L   E28
Nelson, Thomas N   E60
Nelson, Kevin   E92
Nelson, Mark W.   E97
Nelson, Jack   E146
Nelson, Tom   E204
Nelson, Jannie   E240
Nelson, Arlin D.   E308
Nelson, Sven   E315
Nelson, Brian   E408
Nelson, Kimberly   E409
Nelson, Mike   E452
Nelson, Jenna R.   E456
Nelson, John R. (Jack)   A40
Nelson, Gregory L.   A45
Nelson, Ronald L. (Ron)   A89
Nelson, Georgia R.   A96
Nelson, Sandra C.   A115
Nelson, Douglas M.   A116
Nelson, Keith   A119
Nelson, Thomas N.   A125
Nelson, Mark A.   A176
Nelson, David   A201
Nelson, Rosemary   A203
Nelson, Mark W.   A204
Nelson, Georgia R.   A234
Nelson, Barry   A246
Nelson, Steven K.   A252
Nelson, Kathleen   A253
Nelson, Gregory W. (Greg)   A281
Nelson, Ann W.   A291
Nelson, John P.   A291
Nelson, Christopher   A298
Nelson, Marilyn Carlson   A311
Nelson, James W. (Jim)   A319
Nelson, Eric   A348
Nelson, Mike   A365
Nelson, Dan   A374
Nelson, Kimberly A. (Kim)   A376
Nelson, Glenn G.   A383
Nelson, Richard S.   A383
Nelson, Charles P.   A393
Nelson, Ronald L. (Ron)   A397
Nelson, James L.   A441
Nelson, Brandon   A469
Nelson, Debra   A556
Nelson, Jane   A587
Nelson, Brad   A620
Nelson, Gregory M.   A675
Nelson, Jeff   A696
Nelson, Scott   A781
Nelson, Richard J.   A782
Nelson, Bill   A801
Nelson, Diane   A801
Nelson, Brock   A825
Nelson, W. C.   A827
Nelson, Michael S.   A839
Nelson, F. Eric   A862
Nelson, Ronald A.   A865
Nelson, Thomas C.   A889
Nelson, Jean Delaney   P14
Nelson, Shelby   P41
Nelson, Scott M.   P68
Nelson, Donna   P170
Nelson, Sandra   P172
Nelson, Andrew   P179
Nelson, Rev Christopher   P181
Nelson, Rob   P203

Nelson, Rick   P213
Nelson, Jay F.   P262
Nelson, Kelly   P289
Nelson, Karen   P293
Nelson, Charles   P328
Nelson, William C.   P332
Nelson, Howard   P344
Nelson, Bruce   P356
Nelson, David R.   P404
Nelson, Brock D.   P411
Nelson, Mike   P422
Nelson, Bob   P432
Nelson, Bob   P433
Nelson, Joseph G.   P441
Nelson, Jacqueline   P458
Nelson, Bob   P481
Nelson, James (Jim)   P487
Nelson, Kyle   P490
Nelson, Elaine   P502
Nelson, Gregory V. (Greg)   P519
Nelson, Carrie   P526
Nelson, Todd   P562
Nelson, Diane   P573
Nelson, Fredric C.   P579
Nelson, Nancy (Nan)   P598
Nelson, David J.   W69
Nelson, Brendan   W76
Nelson, Brendan   W300
Nelson, Shayne K.   W331
Nemchev, Denise   A751
Nemec, Joseph   P66
Nemelka, Joseph   E350
Nemeroff, Wendy   E144
Nemerov, Jackwyn L. (Jacki)   A686
Nemesch, Ferdinand   W267
Nemeth, Andy L.   E371
Nemoto, Takehiko   W234
Nemoto, Shoji   W328
Nenaber, Pam   P41
Neoh, Anthony F.   W50
Nepper, Justin   P182
Neral, Samantha   P130
Nerbonne, Daniel J. (Dan)   A649
Nerenhausen, Frank R.   A620
Nergaard, Truls   W335
Nerkar, Hem   P18
Nersesian, Ronald S. (Ron)   A20
Nesbit, Robert F.   P522
Nesbitt, Martin H.   A474
Nesbitt, Douglas   A694
Nesbitt, Abigail R.   A782
Nesbitt, Richard L.   P394
Nesbitt, Richard W.   W84
Nesci, James D.   A667
Nesci, James D.   A669
Nesi, Victor J.   E444
Nesi, Victor J.   E445
Nesi, Victor J.   A761
Neske, Rainer   W129
Nesler, Fred J.   P140
Nesmith, William   P569
Ness, Trevor D   E254
Ness, J. Gregory (Greg)   A749
Ness, J. Greg   A750
Ness, Greg   A750
Nessel, Mark   P371
Nesselroad, Mark   A826
Nessler, Peter J. (Pete)   A460
Nestegard, Susan K.   A284
Nestegard, Susan K.   A426
Nester, Theresa   P401
Nestler, George   P344
Netherland, Joseph H.   A355
Netherland, Joseph H.   A741
Nethery, Regina C.   A434
Netland, Eric   E436
Neto, Antonio Maciel   A73
Neto, Alfredo Miguel   A246
Neto, Oscar de Paula Bernardes   A656
Neto, Mario Alves Barbosa   W373
Netravali, Arun N.   A508
Netska, Jim   A800
Nettles, Patrick H.   A666
Nettles, Michael T.   P165

Parker, John A341
Parker, Prof George G. C. A344
Parker, Herbert K. A403
Parker, Charles A. A425
Parker, Jefferson G. (Jeff) A440
Parker, Jeffrey A. (Jeff) A495
Parker, Ialantha A547
Parker, Jackie A585
Parker, Mark G. A592
Parker, Deborah S. A594
Parker, Teresa A. A599
Parker, Krystal J. A616
Parker, Gary D. A616
Parker, Kenneth J. (Ken) A637
Parker, Sean T. A664
Parker, Beau A751
Parker, Sandra A. A805
Parker, P. William (Bill) A819
Parker, David A841
Parker, James A873
Parker, Geoffrey P75
Parker, Bobby P75
Parker, Bill P76
Parker, Thomas A. (Tap) P137
Parker, Andy P153
Parker, Francine (Fran) P162
Parker, W. Scott P170
Parker, Connie P172
Parker, Tom P205
Parker, Jack C. P240
Parker, Frank P240
Parker, Liza P286
Parker, Robin Leigh P318
Parker, Ashley P397
Parker, Craig W. P505
Parker, Ralph P559
Parker, Elizabeth Rindskopf P578
Parker, Sir John W15
Parker, Sir John W26
Parker, Sue Graham W54
Parker, Sue W54
Parker, Andrew W80
Parker, Josh W300
Parker, Christine W388
Parker-Selby, Esthelda R. P56
Parkes, David W39
Parkhill, Karen L. A207
Parkhurst, Kleyton L (Kley) E154
Parkington, Richard J. P483
Parkins, Lorna P40
Parkinson, Robert L. A108
Parkinson, Jerry P581
Parks, James E336
Parks, Catherine E393
Parks, Delbert R. E423
Parks, Robert H. E490
Parks, David A207
Parks, Michael K. A278
Parks, Lawrence H. A318
Parks, Julie A538
Parks, Charles A792
Parks, Kenneth S. A864
Parks, Crockett P105
Parks, Richard H. P138
Parks, Richard H. P472
Parks, Carol Sawyer P487
Parlapiano, Donna A85
Parlett, Kristopher A665
Parlette, James S E83
Parman, Travis M. A676
Parman, John P613
Parmar, Rishabh E300
Parmele, Roxanne E215
Parmelee, Ferole P277
Parmenter, Darren E227
Parmiter, Ian A257
Parmley, Greg E11
Parnaby, Nathan W333
Parnell, Tim P477
Parneros, Demos A753
Parod, Richard W. (Rick) E275
Paroski, Margaret P265
Parr, Ross E355
Parr, Kevin C. A832
Parr, Stephen E. P266

Parr, Gary W P286
Parr, Nick W163
Parra, Rosendo G. (Ro) A591
Parra, Rosendo G. (Ro) A643
Parra, Alfred P381
Parrett, William G. (Bill) A799
Parrett, Chanda P473
Parrett, William G. (Bill) W367
Parris, Ronda E456
Parris, Lydia P5
Parris, Jill P127
Parrish, Mike E197
Parrish, Charles S E467
Parrish, Marc A107
Parrish, M. Lynn A213
Parrish, Mark W. A573
Parrish, Julie A582
Parrish, Charles S. (Chuck) A792
Parrish, Benjamin F. A808
Parrish, Martin A841
Parrish, Deborah P19
Parrish, Thomas (Tom) P19
Parrish, Mike P324
Parrish, Mike P350
Parrish, Brenda P565
Parrish, Bradford P602
Parrott, Cindy A212
Parrs, Marianne Miller A184
Parrs, Marianne Miller A751
Parry, Michelle E369
Parry, Shawn E455
Parry, Michael J. (Mike) A288
Parry, David C. A443
Parry, Robert T. A625
Parry, Susan P149
Parry, Lyle J. P296
Parsel, Lori P367
Parsley, E. William (Bill) A650
Parslow, Darren A849
Parsons, Mike E119
Parsons, Jerry E416
Parsons, Joan E455
Parsons, Kelli A315
Parsons, Joseph E. (Joe) A373
Parsons, Eric E. A750
Parsons, Joan A770
Parsons, Jim A770
Parsons, Stephen P43
Parsons, Abby P117
Parsons, Susan E. P206
Parsons, Susan E. P273
Parsons, Gary P339
Parsons, Bill P436
Parsons, Alex W185
ParT, David A267
Partch, Judy Gerrard P154
Partee, W. Cal A98
Partee, Terrell A203
Parthasarthy, Ashish W164
Parthemore, Eric A460
Partridge, Tom A329
Partridge, John M. A849
Partridge, Thomas L. P504
Parush, Ohad E19
Parvis, Sharon J. A813
Pascal, Amy W328
Pascale, John C P38
Pascall, Calvin E251
Pascavis, Roger E199
Pasch, Leo P212
Pasch, Reinhard W240
Paschalis, Konstantinos W279
Pascoe, Kevin E333
Pascoe, Ricardo W243
Pascualy, Ralph P494
Pascuzzi, Lori E172
Paseaur, Jeff P176
Pasha, Ahmed A14
Pashamova, Bistra A66
Pasiechnik, Alexander E50
Pasik, Alexander P515
Paskell, Rowena E108
Pasko, Thomas E54
Paskowski, Walt A405
Paslawsky, Olena P522

Pasley, Debi P427
Paslick, Marty A407
Pason, Leah P347
Pasquale, Mario E114
Pasquale, James F. P345
Pasquini, Fabio W190
Pasquinucci, Sarah A665
Pasquotto, Louis A234
Passa, Lester M. A231
Passarella, Michael J. A840
Passaro, John P445
Passerini, Filippo A664
Passerini, Filippo A832
Pastega, Kim A127
Pasterick, Robert J. (Rob) A126
Pastor, Slavo E239
Paszynsky, Michael S. A673
Pat, Mary E57
Pata, Jacqueline L. (Jackie)
  Johnson P441
Patankar, Manoj P430
Pate, Jerry E434
Pate, R. Hewitt (Hew) A176
Pate, William C. (Bill) A229
Pate, Ivy P113
Pate, Steve P485
Pate, Kevin P485
Pate, A. Cole P485
Pate-Cornell, M. Elisabeth P503
Pategas, Dianna P404
Patel, Dharmesh E3
Patel, Andy E108
Patel, Himat E234
Patel, Anil E238
Patel, Trusha E325
Patel, Amar R. E339
Patel, Sandip A15
Patel, Kalendu (Kal) A119
Patel, Pankaj S. A182
Patel, Jeetu A287
Patel, Kiran M. A462
Patel, Sunit S. A508
Patel, Manesh A716
Patel, Jay P61
Patel, Yogen R. P234
Patel, Margaret P438
Patel, Bipin P469
Patel, Harish P618
Patel, Sanjay P618
Patel, Krishna W174
Patenaude, Dean J E16
Paterno, Andrew J. A437
Paterra, Leo P500
Paterson, Robert G. E261
Paterson, Kenny A67
Paterson, Dorothy S. P532
Paterson, David W221
Patete, Daniel L. P214
Pathak, Leela E512
Pathela, Vivek E344
Patiri, Theresa E27
Patitucci, Ralph E190
Patkotak, Crawford P28
Patkotak, James P29
Patkotak, Crawford P29
Patla, Craig J. E101
Patmore, Jeff W81
Paton, Ann P45
Paton, John P404
Patrasso, Jamie E175
Patricelli, Robert E. A303
Patricio, Miguel W28
Patrick, Bart E373
Patrick, Michael E. A147
Patrick, Thomas H. (Tom) A215
Patrick, Thomas H. (Tom) A246
Patrick, Donna A677
Patrick, Christian C. (Chris) P45
Patrick, Thomas E. P115
Patrick, John J P239
Patrick, Wesley C. P463
Patrick, William F P495
Patrick, Christian C. P585
Patrick, Christian C. P586
Patricot, Hubert A200

Patrizi, Steve E276
Patron, Ricardo A233
Patrus, Rogerio A374
Patsalos-Fox, Michael A201
Patsley, Pamela H. (Pam) A272
Patsley, Pamela H. (Pam) A794
Pattarozzi, Richard A. (Rich) A355
Patterson, Tom E4
Patterson, W E91
Patterson, Albert E410
Patterson, Alex E431
Patterson, Shawn E439
Patterson, Frank J. A60
Patterson, William A73
Patterson, Linda A91
Patterson, Aubrey B. A98
Patterson, Suzanne D. A200
Patterson, David C. A210
Patterson, Robert T. A332
Patterson, Mark R. A349
Patterson, Samuel R. A650
Patterson, William R. A782
Patterson, Philip A. P72
Patterson, Cynthia B. P90
Patterson, Lori P161
Patterson, Grace P361
Patterson, Cecil P384
Patterson, Gary P455
Patterson, James P501
Patterson, Paul P526
Patterson, Bernie P581
Patterson, Gavin W80
Patterson, Gavin W81
Patti, Robert E153
Patti, Anthony C. (Tony) A215
Pattijn, Elbert W123
Pattis, Lisa J. A877
Patton, Mary E175
Patton, Jason E243
Patton, Chad E339
Patton, Leigh Anne E503
Patton, Charles R. A47
Patton, Cynthia A57
Patton, Rodman D. A67
Patton, Jamila A205
Patton, Roy A295
Patton, Meghan P1
Patton, Jeannie P19
Patton, Sheryl P38
Patton, Alton D. (Dee) P170
Patuano, Marco W348
Patullo, Robert F P358
Patz, Darren E306
Patzke, Pamela A620
Paugh, Lorna E46
Paul, Ronald D. E136
Paul, Barbara R. A212
Paul, Matt T. A273
Paul, Ronald D. (Ron) A279
Paul, Brian P3
Paul, Holley P68
Paul, Kathryn A. P178
Paul, Joseph S. (Joe) P577
Paul, George W67
Paul, Stuart W106
Paula, Julio C. de P283
Paula, Jefferson W30
Paule, David P. (Dave) A248
Paulett, Terence A796
Pauley, Gregory G. A47
Pauley, Lisa A. A96
Pauley, William E. (Bill) P512
Pauline, Greg E200
Pauling, Brian K. A590
Paulk, J P124
Paull, Matthew H. (Matt) A119
Pauls, Douglas J. (Doug) A105
Pauls, Louis E. A576
Paulsen, Teresa A218
Paulsen, Jeffrey B. A890
Paulus, Kenneth (Ken) P14
Pauly, David F. (Dave) A32
Pauly, John J. P300
Paus, William W323
Paustian, Dan P54

Piggott, Julie A. A139
Pignone, Marty F. A734
Pigott, Mikell J. (Jason) A174
Pigott, Mark A360
Pigott, Mark C. A625
Pigott, John M. A625
Pigott, Julie T. A737
Pigozzi, Lorenza W224
Pike, Mike P105
Pilachowski, Caty P34
Pilachowski, David M. P394
Piland, Terry P184
Pilarz, Rev Scott R. P300
Pilat, David A873
Pilates, Joseph P476
Pilaud, Eric W312
Pilgrim, Lonnie (Bo) A647
Pilipie, Deborah P179
Pilkington, Dale H. A115
Pilkington, John M. P517
Pilla, Domenic A543
Pilla, John A744
Pillai, Devadas D. (Dev) A451
PiLlanes, Tony P139
Pillard, Larry G. W82
Pillay, Indresen A12
Pille, Michael A. P140
Pillizzi, Brian E113
Pillote, Larry A723
Pillsbury, S. Gainer P287
Pillsbury, Marnie S. P529
Pilnick, Gary H. A481
Pilnock, Lanie E235
Piloti, Akbar E298
Pilz, Dale F. E264
Pimenta, Elad E438
Pimental, Marcello A591
Pimentel, Armando A589
Pina, Ruth A841
Pina, Christine E536
Pinault, Francois-Henri W75
Pinckney, Wendy E2
Pincu, David E315
Pincus, Robert P. E136
Pincus, Theodore E147
Pincus, Robert P. A279
Pineci, Roy A608
Pineda, Patricia Salas A510
Pinero, Diane P192
Pines, Doralynn P522
Pineta, Joe P357
Pingang, Wang W98
Pingel, Spencer A203
Pinger, Markus W90
Pink, Charles W106
Pinkelman, Jordan E139
Pinkerton, John H. E390
Pinkham, Gary W143
Pinkston, Larry D. E490
Pinkston, Larry D. E491
Pinkston, Arnold A. A34
Pinkston, Corey A37
Pinkston, Patrick A246
Pinner, Ernest S. (Ernie) A167
Pino, Jeffrey P. (Jeff) A836
Pinoncely, Gilles W89
Pinsky, Nicole E306
Pintchman, Lisa E373
Pintek, Michael F. E283
Pinter, David W. A345
Pinto, Mark R. A70
Pinto, Joe A182
Pinto, Tina A470
Pinto, Daniel E. A476
Pinto, Michael P. (Mike) A524
Pinto, John J. A583
Pinto, Alberto Alves de Oliveira W44
Pinto, Ari W48
Pinto, Francisco Eduardo de Almeida W191
Pinto, Eugenio W225
Pinto, Eduardo Fernando Jardim W373
Pinzer, Reinhard W320
Pion, Jeffrey S. A160
Pione, Jonathan E197

Piontek, Gregg E348
Piper, Krista P145
Piper, Daniel P187
Piper, Martha W303
Pipito, Frank A379
Pipitone, Ann E263
Pipoly, Ronald E. A59
Pippenger, Rick E454
Pippins, Dakota A. A426
Piraino, Thomas A. A631
Pirak, Jim A773
Piramal, Swati W181
Pires, Luciano W373
Pirih, Debbie P316
Pirjanian, Paolo E255
Pirraglia, Don P618
Pirtle, William L. (Willy) E418
Pirtle, John J. A855
Pisani, William P449
Pisano, Kerry L. P383
Pisano, Wayne F. W309
Pisarra, Drew E28
Pischetsrieder, Bernd W227
Pischetsrieder, Bernd W240
Pisciotta, Matteo R. A620
Piscopo, Vince P537
Pisharody, Ravindra W347
Pistacchio, Dave A142
Pistilli, Dale A866
Pistor, Robert L. A821
Pistulka, Damon P441
Pitaro, James A. (Jimmy) A260
Pitaro, Regina M. P192
Pitcher, Tracy A205
Pitchford, William D E513
Pitchford, E. Gail P106
Piteleski, Dan E189
Piterans, Marianne V. A796
Pitesa, John W. (Bill) A277
Pitfield, Robert H. (Rob) W54
Pitman, Charles J. A67
Pitman, Jonathan W. P424
Pitrone, Scott C E245
Pitt, William C. A826
Pitt, Stephen R P335
Pittard, Steve E233
Pittard, Patrick S. A515
Pittatore, Gianfranco W40
Pittman, Raymond E. A52
Pittman, Harris O. A54
Pittman, Robert W. (Bob) A441
Pittman, Robert W. (Bob) A442
Pittman, Cyndi P45
Pittman, Drew P51
Pittman, Jerry P145
Pittman, Charles V. P504
Pittner, Kurt P566
Pitts, David L. E80
Pitts, James (Jim) A21
Pitts, Gary L. A300
Pitts, James F. (Jim) A602
Pitts, Gregory C. A660
Pitts, Curtis H. P553
Pitzer, Steve P119
Pivato, Sergio W371
Pizarro, Pedro J. A285
Pizzini, Chris P105
Pizzini, Flavio W371
Pizzitola, Mickey E287
Pizzolatto, Jennifer P602
Pizzuto, Dave P539
Plaat, Mitchell E. (Mitch) A216
Placco, Christopher O. P261
Place, Jeff E514
Place, Best P507
Pladson, Dawn P573
Plaeger, Frederick J. (Rick) A300
Plaisance, Ric P226
Plake, Mark A. A420
Plamondon, Peter H. P5
Planchak, Jack E475
Plank, Kevin A. E490
Plank, Steve A34
Plank, Roger B. A67
Plank, Linda A. P156

Planque, E. Gail de A303
Plant, John C. A815
Plant, John C. P228
Planta, Andreas von W261
Plantamura, Mary L. P400
Plante, Dale N. A564
Plante, John P P159
Plante, Jason P299
Planz, John P234
Plassat, Georges W87
Platek, Allen E465
Platsch, Matthias W320
Platt, Melanie M. A21
Platt, Daniel B. A627
Platt, Andrew G. (Andy) A733
Platt, Daniel J. A763
Platt, Mary P105
Platz, John F. P277
Pleas, Charlie A86
Pleasance, P. J. W238
Pleasant, Ann P446
Pleasants, John F. A260
Plecenik, Jeanie P298
Plecki, Robert F. (Bob) A334
Pleines, Thomas W40
Plemmons, Gregory B E355
Plepler, Richard L. A801
Plessis, Jan P. du W294
Plessis, Jan du W295
Plessis-Belair, Michel W160
Plessis-Belair, Michel W282
Plessis-Belair, Michel W283
Pletcher, Richard L. A500
Pletrzak, Tim P26
Pleva, Karen P342
Plewa, Richard J. A207
Pliego, James E219
Plimpton, Frank E334
Plimpton, Hollis W. A138
Plischke, Wolfgang W63
Pliska, Bernard F. (Bernie) A592
Plochocki, Steven T. E388
Ploeg, Craig P74
Ploetz, Joanne Lofgren P181
Ploix, Helene W72
Ploof, Steve P357
Plotkin, Ben A. E445
Plotkin, Steven (Steve) A541
Plotkin, Chad A603
Plotkin, Ben A. A761
Plougmann, Carsten W2
Plourde, Real W18
Pluard, Dennis P434
Plucker, Ross P137
Plumb, Spencer G. E160
Plumb, Hudson A459
Plume, Cathy P616
Plumer, Christy P509
Plumley, Judi E456
Plummer, James D. A452
Plummer, William B. A832
Plummer, Bill P290
Plungis, Sheila P158
Plunkett, John P587
Plush, Gerald P. (Jerry) A858
Plush, Gerald P. (Jerry) A859
Plutzik, Jonathan A315
Po, Samantha E415
Poach, Jim P423
Pobjoy, Peter P462
Pochard, Shane A528
Pochop, Dawn P49
Pockett, Thomas (Tom) W390
Pocock, Dick A582
Poczekaj, Kenneth J. (Ken) A290
Podell, Shani E394
Podell, Tamar C P286
Podesta, Victoria A. A73
Podmore, Malcolm A103
Podolsky, Daniel K. W158
Podowski, Charles H. (Chuck) P228
Podsednik, J. Scott P496
Poduska, Martin P253
Podvin, Jean-Marc W309
Podyuk, Vasiliy W153

Poe, Dale P601
Poelvoorde, Geert Van W30
Poerschke, John D E17
Poferl, Judy M. A883
Poff, Jared A. A121
Pogharian, Mark K. A413
Pogue, Richard W. P569
Poh, Lai Teck W271
Poh, Tay W371
Pohl, Barby A392
Pohl, Ron P61
Pohl, Reinfried W32
Pohlad, Robert C. P573
Pohle, Klaus W309
Pohlig, Rolf W305
Pohlod, Marty E200
Pohlschroeder, Hans L. A202
Pohndorf, Michelle E156
Poindexter, Jennifer E468
Poirier, R. Scott A588
Poisson, Patrick E493
Poitou, Jean-Laurent W6
Poitras, Kevin A371
Poitras, Thomas M. A813
Pokerwinski, Deborah R. A524
Pokluda, James L. E232
Pol, Anne A821
Pol, Ramon W43
Pol, Chuck W379
Poladian, Avedick B. (Dick) A608
Polanco, Aida A318
Polanski, John J. P227
Polansky, Andy A459
Polansky, Burton J. P77
Polatajko, Mark P617
Polding, John P541
Polelle, Mike E211
Polen, Stephanie E503
Polen, Thomas A112
Polen, Michael (Mike) A860
Polep, Jeffrey M. (Jeff) P132
Polet, Robert A645
Polet, Roeland H. A843
Polett, Daniel H. P498
Polge, David P563
Polhamus, Arthur M. (Mac) E45
Polhemus, George P406
Polhill, Larry R. E250
Poli, Massimo A203
Policano, Andrew J. A708
Policinski, Christopher J. A883
Polignac, Nicole W54
Polignac, Francois Melchior de W87
Polinder, Sherman P355
Polino, Frank E172
Polistina, Terry L. A742
Politopoulou, Maria-Ioanna W244
Politopoulou, Marianna W244
Polizzi, John M. P426
Polizzotto, Paul A161
Polk, James C. (Jim) A101
Polk, Michael B. (Mike) A585
Polk, Dennis A774
Pollack, David A562
Pollack, Murray M. P384
Pollak, Joanne E. P260
Pollak, Georgia P620
Pollak, Andrea W163
Pollard, Tracey E173
Pollard, Ivan A199
Pollard, O. Miles A440
Pollard, C. William P100
Pollard, Dennis P199
Pollard, Rick P305
Pollauf, Laura A P111
Pollestad, Jan W258
Polley, Dale W. A648
Polley, Malcolm E. A713
Polley, Greg P190
Polley, Andrew P409
Pollitt, Byron H. A849
Pollock, Janet E21
Pollock, Roark E257
Pollock, Robert B. A78
Pollock, Robert B. (Rob) A78

Pragnell, Michael P. W376
Prague, Ronald J. E458
Prahl, Paula A119
Pramaggiore, Anne R. A305
Pramanik, Bhaskar A560
Prame, Thomas M. A342
Pranckevicius, John P303
Prange, Karen A133
Pranger, Judy P203
Prangley, Robert E. P619
Prantl, Jim E176
Pranzo, Jack E196
Prasad, Rama E106
Prasad, Ruchi E301
Prasad, P.M.S. W287
Prater, William L. (Bill) A98
Prater, John P17
Prater, Marita P485
Prather, Sharon P138
Pratt, Kyle E46
Pratt, Gregory A. E79
Pratt, Dan E240
Pratt, Elizabeth E255
Pratt, Brian E383
Pratt, Jim E521
Pratt, Michael J. (Mike) A119
Pratt, Timothy A. (Tim) A133
Pratt, John A. A433
Pratt, Jerry P73
Pratt, G. Michael P318
Pratt, Joseph P413
Pratt, Nancy P472
Pratt, Brett P565
Pratte, Gary S. A333
Pratts, Eric E332
Prausa, John W. P465
Praw, Albert Z. E263
Prebola, Donald J. (Don) A694
Predmore, Steve A469
Preesman, Pim W204
Preete, Kerry J. A566
Preiser, Douglas W. A486
Preissman, Ronald P507
Prelipp, Steven H. A273
Prelle, Hermann W367
Prendergast, Franklyn G. A513
Prendergast, George C. P294
Prendergast, E. James (Jim) P515
Prenger, Jeanette P74
Prenger, Ron P283
Prengler, Irving D. P51
Prentice, F. Sheldon A579
Prentice, Sheldon A579
Prentice, Rt. Hon. Jim W84
Presby, J. Thomas A879
Preschern, Matt A876
Prescott, Thomas M. E23
Prescott, John B. A587
Prescott, Thomas J. A776
Prescott, Dennis A. P51
Present, Randall C. (Randy) A427
President, Rocky Campbell ??????
  Vice P83
President, Christopher Bowe P471
Preska, Loretta A. P192
Preskenis, Donald A335
Preslar, Jimmy R. A332
Preslar, B. Clyde A628
Presley, Mike E18
Presley, Jim E119
Press, Michael W E471
Press, Eric L. A143
Press, Terry A161
Pressendo, Mike P108
Pressler, Paul S. A92
Pressler, Ginny P222
Pressley, W. Michael A806
Pressner, Jenn E469
Prestidge, James H. E69
Prestidge, D. Mark A494
Preston, Danny E167
Preston, James E. A356
Preston, Amie A496
Preston, Thomas P. A880
Prestridge, James E466

Pret, Comte Arnoud de W28
Pretorius, Craig A246
Pretorius, Brand S.G. W57
Prettejohn, Nicholas E. T. (Nick) W210
Pretto, Christina A51
Preuss, Michael W63
Prevaux, Steven D. P576
Previzo, Melissa E353
Prevost, Patrick M. A370
Prevoznik, Michael E. A683
Prewitt, Connie F. P63
Prezelj, Irene M. A345
Prezzano, Wilbur J. (Bill) W358
Pri-Zan, Hanna W48
Pribble, John E303
Pribilsky, Wilbur E. A106
Pribyl, Brian M. E338
Pribyl, Brian M. A576
Price, Keith E166
Price, Jillian E175
Price, Linda E196
Price, Charles E355
Price, Patricia A E433
Price, Nancy E520
Price, Tracy K. A7
Price, Ronald C. A52
Price, Quintin A124
Price, Thomas S. (Tom) A174
Price, Gretchen W. A180
Price, Duncan P. A190
Price, Robert A237
Price, Michael E. A252
Price, Ben A257
Price, T. Michael (Mike) A335
Price, Keith A387
Price, Michael A440
Price, Bill A470
Price, Patricia M. (Patti) A523
Price, Hugh B. A553
Price, Paul A568
Price, Wayne A606
Price, David B. A788
Price, Hugh B. A845
Price, Scott A853
Price, Rowe A880
Price, Bill P32
Price, David P47
Price, Jerry P105
Price, Michael C. P105
Price, Cynthia P108
Price, Jay P133
Price, Mary Jo P169
Price, Robert R. P182
Price, David T. P191
Price, David P258
Price, Michael O. (Mickey) P316
Price, Karen V. P329
Price, Diane Hartingh P348
Price, Adrian P391
Price, John P395
Price, Thomas H. P401
Price, Randy P456
Price, Roger P458
Price, Michael P496
Price, Otis G. P546
Price, Gary P548
Price, Greg P553
Price, Gary W34
Price, Jonathan W34
Price, Timothy R. (Tim) W173
Price, James D. (Jamie) W367
Prichard, Skip P363
Prichard, J. Robert S. W268
Prichard, J. Robert S. W387
Prickett, Charles (Charlie) P1
Prideaux, Nigel W34
Prideaux-Brune, D. P394
Pridgen, Daisy A264
Priebe, Cedric J. P90
Priem, Windle B. A287
Priest, John P142
Priest, Geoffrey P315
Priester, Barbara W105
Prietto, Rev Mario J. P575
Primelles, Oscar A535

Primoff, Mark P45
Prince, Ted E346
Prince, John A338
Prince, Larry L. A379
Prince, Charles O. (Chuck) A470
Prince, Charles O. (Chuck) A885
Prince, Martin P438
Pringle, Steven E41
Pringle, Mark E287
Pringle, David L. A17
Pringle, Susan A460
Pringle, Andrew A479
Pringle, Rebecca P335
Pringle, Curt P367
Printer, Hoshi E46
Printz, David (Dave) P100
Prioleau, Cornelius C. A169
Prior, Graham E138
Prior, Stephen E195
Prior, Jason A12
Prior, Matt A423
Prior, Lawrence B. (Larry) W38
Priori, Marcello W40
Prioux, Noel W87
Priselac, Thomas M. (Tom) P98
Prising, Jonas A526
Pritchard, Beth M. A284
Pritchard, Marc S. A664
Pritchard, Jane P348
Pritchett, Bill P353
Pritt, Sandra B. (Sandy) P430
Pritts, Jim E80
Pritzker, Karen M. P556
Privett, Rev Stephen A. P575
Probert, Timothy J. (Tim) A395
Probst, Marc P249
Probst, Larry A455
Procario, John C. P22
Proce, James P467
Prochaska, Joseph A776
Prochazka, Scott M. A167
Prock-Schauer, Wolfgang W127
Procopio, A. John A303
Procter-Rogers, Cheryl P148
Proctor, William E9
Proctor, H. Palmer E167
Proctor, Palmer E167
Proctor, Paul E196
Proctor, John E464
Proctor, Donald R. (Don) A182
Proctor, H. Palmer A327
Produoz, Stefanie A513
Proebstl, Siegmar W320
Proffitt, Julie P242
Profumo, Alessandro Alessandro
  Profumo W141
Profusek, Robert A. A841
Proglio, Henri W374
Prohaska, Maddalena E172
Proia, Gina A37
Prondzynski, Heino von A429
Prondzynski, Heino von W205
Prondzynski, Heino W205
Pronsati, Paul A140
Proost, Robert A104
Prophet, Anthony (Tony) A418
Propp, Brian P. P517
Propst, Beverly L. A391
Propst, Koger L. P177
Prorcelli, Christopher E365
Prosapio, Christy P552
Prosser, John W. A466
Prosser, Jim P154
Prosser, Joseph S. (Joe) P502
Prost, Ernst P461
Prost, Jacques W289
Prot, Baudouin W71
Prot, Baudouin W374
Prothro, Gerald D. P241
Proto, Joseph N. P4
Protz, William F. (Bill) A449
Proud, Danya E58
Proud, H. John (Jack) P535
Proujansky, Roy P341

Proulx, Jim A126
Proven, John E26
Provencal, Gerald (Jerry) P292
Provencher, Mike E155
Provencher, Robert P171
Provenzale, Peter E251
Provera, Marco T. W224
Provera, Marco T. W225
Providakes, Jason F. P522
Provine, Cathy P19
Provoost, Rudy S. W204
Provost, Deborah A. P52
Provost, Matthew P136
Provost, K-State P266
Provost, Joseph P289
Provost, Francois W289
Prowell, Bill P566
Prueher, Adm. Joseph W. (Joe) A290
Prueher, Adm. Joseph W. (Joe) A353
Pruellage, John K. P430
Pruessing, Peter P199
Pruett, Steven H E101
Pruett, Madonna E300
Pruett, David M. A110
Pruett, Steven D. A144
Pruett, Greg S. A643
Prufer, Hans W135
Pruitt, Kristin A500
Pruitt, George A. A763
Pruitt, Gary B. P503
Pruitt, Gary B. P504
Pruitt, Henry J. P541
Pruksakit, Parnsak W47
Prunchunas, Edward M. P98
Prune, Gabrielle W156
Prusiecki, David E3
Prutsman, James E153
Prygelski, Peter J. E165
Pryor, Bret E3
Pryor, Jay R. A176
Pryor, Charles W. A273
Pryor, Stephen D. (Steve) A310
Pryor, Vince P172
Pryor, Vikki L. P206
Pryor, Robert W. P438
Pryor, Robert D. W151
Przybocki, Kevin E257
Psillas, Ben E77
Pskowski, Edward Z. P282
Psotta, Joachim A644
Pua, Roger A374
Pucci, Roberto W309
Puccio, Shawn M. A821
Pucel, Kenneth J. (Ken) A133
Pucell, Wade E427
Pucella, Michael A253
Puchner, Alex E56
Puchtler, Julia P97
Puckett, Richard E262
Puckett, Jeff E339
Puckett, Steve E388
Puckett, Richard D. (Rick) E429
Puckett, Jon A163
Puckett, Karen A. A170
Puckett, Kerry C. A292
Puckett, Richard H. A814
Puckett, Richard D P89
Puckett, Jeff P112
Puckett, Jeffrey M. P113
Puckett, Carolyn P364
Puckett, Debbie P385
Puckhaber, Edmund P90
Puddy, Michael R. A236
Puddy, Mike A236
Pudlin, Helen P. A650
Puechl, Robert L. A734
Puente, Raul Llamazares de la W9
Puentes, George J. A750
Pugh, Mike E258
Pugh, David E268
Pugh, Spencer P48
Pugh, Frank P258
Pugh, Paul F. P588
Pugliese, Anthony J. P18
Puhy, Dorothy E. P146

Rafferty, Emily K. P522
Raffone, Lawrence M. (Larry) E168
Rafky, Janet P196
Raftery, Ellyn A326
Ragan, Joe E204
Ragan, Ashley E339
Ragan, John W. A603
Ragan, Albert J P257
Ragan, Michael E. P353
Ragauss, Peter A. A95
Ragen, York A. E199
Rager, R. Scott A611
Raggi, James E421
Raggi, Robert P618
Raghuram, Raghu A851
Ragland, David E. A98
Ragone, Daniel J. P268
Ragsdale, John P30
Ragsdale, Lyn P610
Ragusa, Elysia Holt A793
Ragusa, Frank P362
Raguz, Steven M. A189
Rahardja, Francisca A41
Rahe, Maribeth S. A337
Rahilly, Thomas F. (Tom) W387
Rahim, Frank E196
Rahim, Rami A477
Rahl, Leslie W84
Rahlf, Christine P181
Rahmberg, Lee A841
Rahming, Kelly P602
Rahn, Joel A173
Rai, Raj E20
Rai, Karan P35
Raia, Cathryn A600
Raichle, William M. E507
Raico, Nick D. P234
Raiden, Sally P613
Raiguel, Darren E154
Raikes, Jeffrey S. (Jeff) A227
Raikes, Deborah P298
Raimonde, Michael A. A669
Raina, Robin E138
Rainbolt, H. E. (Gene) A97
Rainbolt, David E. A97
Rainbolt, David E. A98
Rainer, Sallie A297
Rainer, Thom S. P285
Raines, J. Paul (Paul) A10
Raines, John D. A317
Raines, Ellen A345
Raines, J. Paul (Paul) A367
Raines, Marjorie D. A577
Rainey, Joseph D. (Joe) A395
Rainey, John A828
Rainey, James P80
Rainville, William A. (Bill) E260
Rainwater, Keith S E432
Rainwater, Tom P160
Raisbeck, David W. A153
Raisbeck, David W. A281
Raisl, Gary F. P433
Raiss, Sarah E. A209
Raj, V. S. E461
Raj, Raman P288
Raj, Niraj P374
Raja, Prabu A70
Rajagopal, Sukumar A201
Rajala, Mike P130
Rajamani, Sridhar P621
Rajamanickam, Ramachandran A4
Rajamannar, Venkata A654
Rajapakse, Suresh Suresh
  Rajapakse W30
Rajasigamany, Stephen A644
Rajavashisth, Tripathi P98
Rajczak, Daniel S. A664
Rajgopal, Raj E509
Rajkowski, E. Mark A547
Rajparia, Anish D. A84
Rakatansky, Carol R. A731
Rake, Sir Michael D. V. (Mike) W58
Rake, Sir Michael D. V. (Mike) W60
Rake, Sir Michael D. V. (Mike) W80
Rakes, Thomas A. P578

Rakesh, Nitin E461
Rakusin, Jeremy A687
Rales, Steven M. A240
Rales, Mitchell P. A240
Raley, James E. E126
Raley, Anthony E455
Raley, Zachary W. A58
Rall, Jeanmarie E181
Ralles, Mary A664
Ralli, Georges W374
Rallo, James M. (Jim) E277
Ralls, Matt A767
Ralph, Thomas A. A230
Ralph, Julie H. A629
Ralph, Steven A. P377
Ralph, James (Maggie) P395
Ralph, Jay W20
Ralston, Barry E245
Ralston, Joseph W. A519
Ralston, Joseph W. A803
Ralston, Douglas A814
Ramachandra, Sumant A429
Ramachandran, Ram E316
Ramachandran, M. S. W181
Ramagano, Cheryl K E496
Ramaker, David B. A173
Ramakrishnan, C. W347
Ramalho, Kimberly A518
Ramanathan, Ramaswami E67
Ramaswami, Rajiv A137
Rambler, Mark E181
Rambo, Amy A73
Rambo, Barbara L. A644
Ramchander, Pranill W26
Ramdas, R E461
Ramenda, James (Jim) E437
Rames, Jared E139
Ramesh, S. W67
Ramey, Diana M. P51
Ramirez, Robert A. E213
Ramirez, Rudy E365
Ramirez, Warren A138
Ramirez, Francisco Munoz A203
Ramirez, John A318
Ramirez, Raul A591
Ramirez, Jaime A. A751
Ramirez, Edith P288
Ramirez, Maria Fiorini P374
Ramirez, Gilda P391
Ramkissoon, Rev Gregory P191
Ramkumar, Krishnaswamy W181
Ramlau-Hansen, Henrik W122
Ramlo, Randy A. E492
Ramlo, Randy A. A828
Rammohan, Ashok A645
Ramo, Joshua A324
Ramo, Joshua C. A754
Ramonat, R. Whitfield A635
Ramoneda, Dede F. A335
Ramos, Marcos R. A30
Ramos, Ricardo (Ricky) A202
Ramos, William M. A292
Ramos, Anelsie A664
Ramos, Suzanne M. A861
Ramos, Rev Marcos A. P43
Ramos, Rick P299
Ramos, Jose Maldonado W41
Ramos, Maria W57
Ramos, Maria W58
Ramos, Maria W60
Rampacek, Charles M. (Charlie) A351
Rampalli, Prasad L. A287
Ramparas, Rhonda E181
Ramphele, Mamphela W26
Rampinelli, Audrey A. A520
Rampl, Dieter W224
Rampl, Dieter W368
Rampley, R. M. (Mike) P238
Rampone, Thomas A. (Tom) A451
Rampone, Thomas A714
Rampone, Wayne P259
Ramrath, Joseph R. A399
Ramsay, Paul D. A523
Ramsay, Brian G. P358
Ramsay, Brian G. P359

Ramsburg, Lara A573
Ramsburg, Kevin S. A619
Ramsey, Robert E412
Ramsey, James R. A213
Ramsey, Jane L. A496
Ramsey, David L. P106
Ramsey, Betsy P505
Ramsey, Beryl P519
Ramsey, Paul G. P579
Ramsower, Reagan M. P51
Ramstad, James A783
Ramundo, Katherine Hargrove A203
Rana, Basudev W67
Ranade, Prashant E461
Ranck, Bruce E. A681
Rand, A. Barry A20
Rand, A. Barry A149
Rand, Alison S. A660
Rand, Edward L. (Ned) A663
Rand, A. Barry P241
Rand, Barry S P293
Randall, John R E374
Randall, Carol A. A116
Randall, Heather P. A812
Randall, H. Douglas A857
Randall, Benny P459
Randall, Bryan J. P585
Randazzo, Gerri E526
Randel, Don M. A193
Randhawa, Sabah P368
Randich, Steven J. (Steve) P186
Randle, Erica E139
Randle, Lavance E430
Randolfi, Mike A248
Randolph, Mark E131
Randolph, James E. A844
Randolph, Michael P534
Randolph, Marcus P. W69
Randopoulos, Anthoula P154
Randt, Thomas P. A778
Randt, Clark T. (Sandy) A831
Rane, Keith P96
Raney, Steven M. A687
Raney, W. Grant A876
Raney, Carolyn P378
Raney, Marc P551
Ranganathan, Krishna E237
Rangen, Eric S. A838
Ranger, Michael W. A221
Rango, Robert A. (Bob) A136
Ranieri, John P. A275
Raniolo, Robert P383
Rankin, Norman J. (Norm) A121
Rankin, B. M. A363
Rankin, B. M. A364
Rankin, Kurt J. A651
Rankin, David A722
Rankin, Donald P210
Rankin, Mary Ann P463
Rankin, David J. P518
Rankin, Alfred M. P569
Rankin, Fred M. P596
Ranney, Christina P117
Ranney, George A. P509
Ranninger, Rebecca A. A772
Ranong, Chok W47
Ranque, Denis W108
Ransburg, David P. (Dave) P75
Ransier, Kathleen H. A437
Ransom, James W. (Jim) A115
Ranson, Brine A76
Ranspot, James A38
Rao, Janet E160
Rao, Pratap E161
Rao, Deepak E290
Rao, Shailesh A389
Rao, Valluri A452
Rao, Anand S. A514
Rao, Addagada C. P618
Rao, I. Srinivas W67
Rapanos, Prof Vassilios T. W244
Rapaport, Marc P98
Raper, Steve P254
Raphael, Joanne H. A654
Raphael, Carol P374

Raphaelson, Ira H. A502
Rapino, Michael (Mike) A516
Rapiya, Marshall W266
Rapley, David E. A511
Raposa, Sheila M. A857
Rapoza, Dean P130
Rapp, Edward J. (Ed) A6
Rapp, Edward J. (Ed) A157
Rapp, Peter F. P367
Rappaport, Felix A556
Rappe, Kristine A. A878
Rappe, Kristine A878
Rappe, Kristine P300
Rappo, Bruno W40
Raps, Jurgen W127
Rasalan, Maria P438
Rasband, Scott E294
Rasch, Carl P320
Rasche, Charlotte A668
Raschke, Klaus-Dieter W135
Rashbrooke, Ed E196
Rashid, Richard F. (Rick) A560
Rashkow, Ronald A607
Rasinger, Wilhelm G. W144
Raskas, Daniel A. A240
Raskind, Peter A151
Raskino, Mark E195
Rasky, Lawrence P174
Rasmuson, Craig D. E459
Rasmuson, Michael (Mike) A95
Rasmussen, Jennifer E350
Rasmussen, Dan E385
Rasmussen, Peter E421
Rasmussen, James W. A765
Rasmussen, Steven A. P90
Rasmussen, Kimball P151
Rasmussen, Dennis F. P196
Rasmussen, Heidi P249
Rasmussen, Erik P332
Rasmussen, Michael P. W2
Rasmussen, Michael W258
Rasmusson, Paul A538
Rassieur, Benjamin F. A208
Rassouli, Melody E252
Rastetter, William H. E243
Rastin, Ramin E228
Rasulo, James A. (Jay) A260
Ratcliff, Mary P396
Ratcliff, Karen P406
Ratcliff, Margaret P591
Ratcliff, David P597
Ratcliffe, David M. A231
Ratcliffe, David M. A381
Ratcliffe, David A765
Ratermann, Andrew P74
Rath, Connie P202
Rath, Tom P202
Rath, Connie P202
Rath, Cornelia W305
Rathbone, John P. A598
Rathbun, Dan A12
Rathbun, Robert A173
Rathbun, Elizabeth P445
Rathburn, Jim A693
Rathe, Bente W343
Rathgaber, Steven A. (Steve) E77
Rathgaber, Scott P215
Rathke, Frances G. (Fran) A485
Rathlev, Niels K. P52
Rathmann, Thomas W320
Rathsack, Dirk E94
Ratinoff, Edward A127
Ratledge, Ryan E200
Ratley, Warren P134
Ratliff, Christopher E435
Ratliff, Brent A296
Ratnathicam, Sanchayan (Chutta) A360
Ratner, Hank J. A142
Ratner, Charles A. A711
Ratner, Ronald A. P76
Rattanacharoensiri, Chaiyong W47
Ratti, Michela A664
Rattner, Justin R. A451
Ratts, Gary P490
Rau, Guy J. A782

Reid, Thomas G. W339
Reid-Anderson, James W. P. (Jim) E425
Reider, Rodney P428
Reidy, Christopher R. (Chris) A84
Reidy, Christopher R. (Chris) A112
Reidy, Carolyn K. A161
Reidy, M. Bridget A305
Reidy, Bridget A307
Reidy, Kara P377
Reif, David J E337
Reif, Richard A. P156
Reifeiss, Gary P396
Reifenheiser, Thomas V. A142
Reifer, William P383
Reifsteck, John P213
Reigle, Dennis P18
Reik, Timothy G. (Tim) A756
Reiley, Peggy J. P439
Reilley, Dennis H. A270
Reilley, Dennis H. A527
Reilley, Dennis H. P509
Reilly, Jim E156
Reilly, Michael E339
Reilly, Eugene F. (Gene) E383
Reilly, Tim E438
Reilly, Timothy E438
Reilly, Paul J. A78
Reilly, David A100
Reilly, William K. A220
Reilly, Bill A247
Reilly, William K. A275
Reilly, William K. A294
Reilly, Robert Q. (Rob) A651
Reilly, Paul C. A687
Reilly, Bernard A758
Reilly, John P. A803
Reilly, Joseph (Joe) A891
Reilly, Joe A891
Reilly, Bob P25
Reilly, Dan P28
Reilly, Joseph R. P446
Reilly, Lawrence P519
Reilly, Kevin P. P581
Reilly, Rev Donald F. P589
Reilly, Michael E. (Mike) W358
Reilly-White, Patti A241
Reiman, Eric (Bill) P42
Reimann, Simon W128
Reimer, Ronaldo E161
Reimer, Terry A. A48
Reimers, John P51
Rein, Catherine A. A103
Rein, Catherine A. A345
Rein, Laura P600
Reina, Ramon W43
Reinarts, Lorie P562
Reinbolt, Lynn C. A216
Reinbrecht, Jorg W20
Reinders, Tanneke A871
Reinemund, Steven S. (Steve) A311
Reinemund, Steven S. (Steve) A531
Reinemund, Steven S. (Steve) A854
Reiner, Gary M. A418
Reiner, Stephen R. P76
Reiner, Mark S P457
Reinerman, Alan J P555
Reiners, Cory E139
Reiners, Joseph E266
Reiners, Derek S. A616
Reiners, Hans W. W62
Reinhard, J. Pedro A203
Reinhard, J. Pedro W299
Reinhardsen, Jon E. A147
Reinhardt, Stefan E27
Reinhardt, Uwe E. A133
Reinhardt, Gerald W. A262
Reinhardt, Mark P85
Reinhardt, Alexander W15
Reinhardt, Jorg W63
Reinhart, Doris P5
Reinhart, Colleen P287
Reinhart, Darlene P379
Reinholtzen, Kristianne P215
Reiniche, Dominique A198
Reiniche, Dominique A200

Reiniche, Dominique W37
Reiniger, Wolfgang W305
Reinikkala, Veli-Matti W4
Reinke, Mary P315
Reinland, Andy E163
Reinmann, Adam W268
Reinoehl, Sue P78
Reinsch, E. James (Jim) A277
Reinsch, E. James P197
Reinstein, James E117
Reis, William E487
Reis, Julio dos A447
Reischlein, Greg R E349
Reising, Scott E64
Reising, Ronald R. A277
Reisinger, Mike P142
Reisman, Rachel E328
Reisman, Marlene E507
Reisman, Lonny A15
Reisman, Heather M. W268
Reiss, Alexander E444
Reiss, Joel E475
Reiss, Kenneth M. (Ken) A403
Reiss, Dale A. A464
Reiss, Richard P. P179
Reiss, Mary P413
Reitan, Torgrim W334
Reiten, R. Patrick (Pat) A626
Reiten, Richard G. (Dick) A819
Reiter, Donald W. (Don) P94
Reiterman, Michael W320
Reithofer, Norbert W66
Reitinger, Philip R. W328
Reitler, Walter W135
Reitz, Paul G. E472
Reitz, Brent P5
Reitz, Judy A. P260
Reitzes, Mark A437
Reitzle, Prof Wolfgang W112
Reizis, Rosa P293
Rekers, Hans A549
Rekhi, Taranjit E238
Relic, Zelko E23
Reller, Tami A560
Rellier, Huguette W103
Relling, Mary P475
Rembe, Ola W143
Remch, Patricia M. A318
Remedios, Alan A344
Remington, Eric B E261
Reminick, M. Scott P80
Remley, Micah E148
Remley, Abby A664
Remmell, Paul L. E105
Remondi, John F. (Jack) A731
Rempe, Ed P321
Remsperger, Prof Hermann W126
Ren, Alex H. C. W279
Renan, Van P596
Renard, Kerstin W383
Renaud, Robert P153
Renault, Philippe J. A456
Rendine, Robert J. (Bob) A374
Rendle, Steve A846
Rendon, Martin P566
Renduchintala, Murthy A680
Rendulic, Mark R. E172
Rendulic, Mark R. A343
Renehan, Todd E519
Renfrew, Brent P29
Renfro, John M. A12
Renfro, Larry C. A838
Renjel, Louis E. A231
Renjie, Li W186
Renken, Keith W. A280
Renken, Veronica P613
Renkowicz, Lisa F. P606
Renn, Christopher E195
Renna, Eugene A. (Gene) A712
Renna, James R. P482
Rennard, Marc W269
Rennemo, Svein W334
Renner, Michael J. P157
Renner, Elisabeth H. P232
Renner, Elisabeth P232

Renner, Julie P583
Rennie, William M. P467
Reno, Michael (Mike) P295
Renouard, Bruce E112
Renschler, Andreas W119
Renskers, Stan E514
Renta, Annette de la P522
Rentfrow, Robert P595
Rentler, Barbara A709
Rentschler, David E181
Rentz, Kim P137
Renwick, Glenn M. A348
Renwick, Scott A484
Renwick, Glenn M. A666
Renwick, Glen M. A838
Renwick, Richard A. P39
Reny, Luc W282
Reny, Luc W283
Renyi, Thomas A. A406
Renyi, Thomas A. A673
Renz, Gerhard W29
Renzi, Tony A747
Renzi, Pierluigi Pierluigi Renzi W141
Replogle, Mark E373
Replogle, Roger W. A321
Repp, Philip P40
Reppert, Joe P351
Reppert, Joe P352
Reppien, Gunter W305
Reppucci, Charles R. P90
Represas, Carlos E. A549
Repshas, Don E34
Requardt, Hermann W320
Resca, Mario W141
Resch, Edward J. A758
Resch, Richard J. P275
Rescorla, Charles L (Chuck) E206
Resendez, Edward (Ed) E145
Resera, Silvia A265
Reses, Jacqueline D A886
Resheske, Frances A. A221
Resinger, James E. (Jim) A420
Resler, Barclay T. A198
Resnick, Alice R. P465
Resnick, Donald W219
Resnik, Joe E436
Ressler, Richard S. E258
Rest, George B. P358
Restel, Anthony J. A440
Restrepo, Carlos E8
Restrepo, Claudia E. A591
Restrepo, Robert P. (Bob) A756
Resweber, Christopher P. A733
Resz, Greg E92
Retallick, Cynthia E476
Rethana, Carlos E27
Rethore, Bernard G. A268
Retsinas, Nicolas P. (Nic) A362
Rettig, Dwight W. A574
Rettig, Jim P574
Reu?, Dieter W149
Reuben, Meredith Baum P162
Reuben, Meredith Baum P163
Reum, James L E221
Reum, W. Robert A858
Reuss, John E92
Reuss, Mark L. A304
Reuss, Mark L. A377
Reuss, Dieter W149
Reusser, Curtis A836
Reuter, William J. A769
Reuter, Louis F P524
Reuter, Fritz P525
Reutersberg, Bernhard W134
Reuther, Michael W105
Revelle, Greg A85
Revels, Kathy E432
Reverman, Lisa P75
Revetria, Stephen P575
Revetta, Phil P493
Rewak, Father William P395
Rewick, Kenneth E E218
Rewick, Ken E218
Rex, Albert G E515
Rex, Anne G. A62

Rey, Bernard W289
Reyes, Nick E360
Reyes, Timothy D. (Tim) A30
Reyes, Jose Octavio A199
Reyes, Carolina P87
Reyes, M. Jude P354
Reyes, Cecilia W392
Reyes-Retana, Eugenio Clariond A472
Reyes-Retana, Eugenio A472
Reyna, Kathy P294
Reynen, Chris E455
Reynish, Steve D. L. W340
Reyno, Jorge P469
Reynolds, Ted E100
Reynolds, Ross E188
Reynolds, Liz E195
Reynolds, Martin E196
Reynolds, Ed E269
Reynolds, Thomas D. E312
Reynolds, Thomas E329
Reynolds, Natalie E389
Reynolds, Jenifer E411
Reynolds, Shelley L. A42
Reynolds, Paula R. A60
Reynolds, Stephen R. A71
Reynolds, F. Kevin A152
Reynolds, Catherine M. A192
Reynolds, Paula R. A248
Reynolds, Paul L. A329
Reynolds, Matt A338
Reynolds, Mark P. A409
Reynolds, Dave A434
Reynolds, Jean A756
Reynolds, Britt T. A786
Reynolds, Emily J. A789
Reynolds, Mary B. A804
Reynolds, Dave A860
Reynolds, John C. P38
Reynolds, Stephen C. P45
Reynolds, Joseph H. P86
Reynolds, Scott A. P96
Reynolds, Jennifer Ward P153
Reynolds, Laura P179
Reynolds, Beau P356
Reynolds, James C. P375
Reynolds, G. David P410
Reynolds, Paul P490
Reynolds, Shawn P497
Reynolds, Terry P517
Reynolds, Fredric G. P531
Reynolds, Thomas A. P535
Reynolds, James P535
Reynolds, Richard W. (Dick) P556
Reynolds, Maj. Jon W80
Reynolds, Robert L. (Bob) W159
Reynolds-Barnes, Deleca P305
Reznicek, Bernard W. (Bernie) A676
Rheaume, Alain A698
Rhein, Kevin A. A861
Rheney, Susan O. A167
Rhenman, Torkel A275
Rhind, Islay A199
Rhinehart, Mary K. A197
Rho, Joseph K. A398
Rhoades, Craig T. A47
Rhoades, M. Ann A469
Rhoads, Dennis E306
Rhoads, Barry A459
Rhoads, Rebecca B. A689
Rhode, Jason P. E91
Rhode, Herb E497
Rhodebeck, Lyle D. A756
Rhodes, Marie E195
Rhodes, Howard E. E360
Rhodes, Taylor E389
Rhodes, Graham M. A23
Rhodes, William C. (Bill) A86
Rhodes, William E. A112
Rhodes, David A161
Rhodes, William C. (Bill) A262
Rhodes, James T. A277
Rhodes, John A515
Rhodes, Simon V. A572
Rhodes, Blake M. A586
Rhodes, Gary L. A647

A = AMERICAN BUSINESS
E = EMERGING COMPANIES
P = PRIVATE COMPANIES
W = WORLD BUSINESS

Robin, Vincent A653
Robinov, Jeff A801
Robins, Scott P138
Robinson, Ray M E11
Robinson, Ronald A. (Ron) E21
Robinson, Chris E24
Robinson, Harriett J E43
Robinson, Scott D. E119
Robinson, Joe E119
Robinson, Braden E160
Robinson, Joseph E165
Robinson, Peter B E173
Robinson, Michael G. E174
Robinson, Lori E196
Robinson, Clifton C E227
Robinson, Ian E269
Robinson, Timothy E305
Robinson, Brian E329
Robinson, Earl E408
Robinson, Krista E416
Robinson, Curt E485
Robinson, Ray M. A46
Robinson, Ray M. A91
Robinson, Ryan D. A119
Robinson, Linda Gosden A124
Robinson, Kirk A125
Robinson, James D. A199
Robinson, Jon R. A223
Robinson, Joseph R. A329
Robinson, James L. A330
Robinson, Peter B. A343
Robinson, Michael G. A346
Robinson, Brian J. A370
Robinson, Lonny A398
Robinson, Andrew S. A399
Robinson, William D. (Doug) A523
Robinson, John A562
Robinson, Adrien T. A577
Robinson, Bruce E. A675
Robinson, Malcolm A677
Robinson, Mike A702
Robinson, Sonal P. A733
Robinson, John A770
Robinson, Bert A789
Robinson, Jon M. A822
Robinson, Michelle A. A845
Robinson, David L. A865
Robinson, Eileen A871
Robinson, Debb P89
Robinson, Nellie C. P110
Robinson, Lowry P137
Robinson, Wayne P171
Robinson, Patricia P176
Robinson, Dan P232
Robinson, Lynn M. P261
Robinson, Sylvia E. P261
Robinson, Gary P277
Robinson, Phillip D. P294
Robinson, Jan P305
Robinson, Karen Donahue P313
Robinov, James L. (Jay) P317
Robinson, John P334
Robinson, Kayne P337
Robinson, Rich P339
Robinson, Jo Nell P385
Robinson, Jay P412
Robinson, Phil P427
Robinson, Ted P428
Robinson, Larry A. P445
Robinson, Newell P467
Robinson, Shawn P535
Robinson, John G. P610
Robinson, David W8
Robinson, Sir Ian W110
Robinson, T. W238
Robinson, Thomas J. W339
Robison, Ronald O. A6
Robison, M. La Voy A257
Robison, Byron A392

Robison, M. La Voy A511
Robison, Chris J. A586
Robison, Andrea Lee A595
Robison, John E. A702
Robison, Bruce P283
Robison, Reid P360
Robison, Deborah P433
Robison, Les P475
Robison, Nancy P583
Robles, Mary Beth A203
Robles, Maj. Gen. Josue (Joe) A273
Robnett, Michael (Mike) A793
Robo, James L. (Jim) A435
Robo, James L. (Jim) A589
Robol, Calvin E172
Robottom, David T. W137
Robredo, Rafael Miranda W139
Robson, Glenn R. A12
Robson, K. Grant A116
Robusto, Dino E. A178
Roby, Lisa M. A253
Roby, Anne K. A656
Robyck, Bret A. A379
Roca, Robert P212
Rocca, Richard E507
Rocca, Michael S. (Mike) Della A12
Rocca, Michael A. A749
Rocchio, Leland P262
Rocchio, Leland P495
Roces, Santiago A768
Rocha, Robson W373
Roche, Michael J. A36
Roche, Joyce M. A81

Roche, Joyce A81
Roche, Joyce M. A272
Roche, Joyce A272
Roche, David A307
Roche, John C. (Jack) A399
Roche, Elaine A532
Roche, Collin E. A662
Roche, Patrick P117
Roche, Jerome J. P178
Roche, Kathleen M. (Kate) P429
Rochelle, Tia A665
Rochford, Brian E172
Rochon, Thomas R. A805
Rochow, Garrick J. A223
Rock, Douglas L. (Doug) A812
Rock, Michael (Mike) A825
Rock, Rex A. P28
Rock, Ann P476
Rock, Milton L. P498
Rock, David P618
Rocke, Elisabeth W382
Rockefeller, Sharon Percy A638
Rockefeller, Sharon Percy P400
Rocker, J. Thomas A167
Rockers, Thomas H. P471
Rockford, Marc A. A205
Rocks, Eric E438
Rocks, M. Joseph P347
Rockwood, Beth A257
Rockwood, Robin A. A321
Rockwood, John D. P308
Rocole, Therese M. (Terri) P606
Rocole, Terri P607
Roda, Craig A. A366
Rodato, Vadis A. E331
Roday, Leon E. A380
Roddenberry, Stephen K. A879
Roddy, Peter S. E366
Roden, John C. van A25
Roden, John A25
Roden, George P328
Roden, Neil W300
Rodeno, Michaela K. A770
Roder, Steve W221
Roder, Peter W240
Rodero, Vicente Rodero W41
Rodgers, Abby A199
Rodgers, Johnathan A205
Rodgers, Johnathan A. A592
Rodgers, Michael (Mike) A633
Rodgers, Johnathan A. A665

Rodgers, Ralph E. A789
Rodgers, Kent P245
Rodgers, Paige A. P262
Rodgers, Lanny P338
Rodgers, Robert P344
Rodgers, Mary Anne P511
Rodia, Ernest E472
Rodin, Judith (Judy) A46
Rodin, Judith (Judy) A186
Rodin, Judith (Judy) A205
Rodino, Jeffrey E371
Rodkin, Gary M. A92
Rodkin, Gary M. A218
Rodler, Friedrich W144
Rodman, Donald H. A204
Rodman, Leonard C. (Len) P66
Rodman, Steve P66
Rodman, Cynthia P360
Rodocanachi, Pierre W377
Rodocker, Julee M. P508
Rodrigues, Ron A176
Rodrigues, Joseph E. (Joe) A722
Rodriguez, John E163
Rodriguez, Daniel A181
Rodriguez, Mitch E306
Rodriguez, Damarie E455
Rodriguez, Sergio E475
Rodriguez, Mauricio E515
Rodriguez, Carlos A. A84
Rodriguez, Karyn E. A88
Rodriguez, Lawrence D. (Larry) A168
Rodriguez, Enrique A182
Rodriguez, Javier A243
Rodriguez, L. A. A290
Rodriguez, Sean A319
Rodriguez, Jose F. A331
Rodriguez, David A. A531
Rodriguez, Antonio A589
Rodriguez, Rita E. A616
Rodriguez, Eduardo A. (Eddie) A616
Rodriguez, Rita M. A677
Rodriguez, Ramon A. A697
Rodriguez, Armando G. A722
Rodriguez, Ben A. A786
Rodriguez, Richard P. P94
Rodriguez, Dora P179
Rodriguez, Jose P381
Rodriguez, Alex P428
Rodriguez, Alfred P551
Rodriguez, Holly P574
Rodriguez, Cecilia M. P578
Rodriguez, Ramon J. P618
Rodriguez, Florentino Perez W9
Rodriguez, Paul W18
Rodriguez, Jose W43
Rodriguez, Jose R. W45
Rodriguez, Julio W312
Rodriguez-Borjas, Carlos A694
Rodstrom, Daniel (Dan) A288
Rodstrom, Claudette P621
Rodwell, Peter A541
Roe, Wayne E493
Roe, Tim E506
Roe, Scott A846
Roe, Daniel P366
Roedel, Kathryn V. E415
Roedel, Richard W. (Rich) A521
Roeder, Dieter E278
Roeder, Kris P513
Roeder, Peter Peter Roeder W240
Roeglin, Ginnie M. A227
Roegner, Eric V. A30
Roehm, Arthur W. A451
Roehr, David E18
Roekel, Dennis Van P335
Roelandts, Willem P. (Wim) A70
Roell, Stephen A. A472
Roellgen, Andreas A803
Roellke, Prof Christopher F. P586
Roelofs, Nicholas H. (Nick) A20
Roelofs, Nicolas H. A20
Roemer, S. C. A289
Roenigk, Mark E389
Roenna, Joe P164
Roesch, Elaine E167

Roeschley, Steve P136
Roese, John A287
Roesel, Larry M. A86
Roeske, Richard A484
Roesler, Rick A680
Roessner, Martin E369
Roessner, Karl A. A278
Roeth, George C. A191
Roetzel, Frank M. P435
Roever, Carol P225
Roffler, Mike E174
Rogahn, Rod E199
Rogan, Brian G. A102
Rogan, Thomas I. A836
Roge, Carrol P161
Rogel, Steven R. (Steve) A495
Rogel, Steven R. (Steve) A825
Rogener, John E329
Roger, Robin A401
Roger, Robin A742
Rogers, Amy E8
Rogers, Michael W. E10
Rogers, Mark E30
Rogers, Tim E139
Rogers, Pete E139
Rogers, Joy E172
Rogers, Terry E174
Rogers, Ron E176
Rogers, Brittain E181
Rogers, Britt E181
Rogers, Sandy E185
Rogers, Steven E255
Rogers, Ronald E332
Rogers, Jim E346
Rogers, Oliver E464
Rogers, Thomas S. (Tom) E474
Rogers, Adam E487
Rogers, Jeffrey A. (Jeff) E497
Rogers, Diane E521
Rogers, James E. (Jim) A70
Rogers, J. Michael A97
Rogers, Michael D. (Mike) A144
Rogers, Ross E. A206
Rogers, Kenneth C. A248
Rogers, Steven A. A264
Rogers, Ronald G. (Ron) A272
Rogers, James E. (Jim) A277
Rogers, Donald R. A279
Rogers, James P. (Jim) A281
Rogers, John W. A305
Rogers, Kevin G. A316
Rogers, Karen A324
Rogers, John F. W. A386
Rogers, R. Scott A387
Rogers, R. Wade A439
Rogers, Eddy J. A491
Rogers, John W. A542
Rogers, Ronald A549
Rogers, Patrick A582
Rogers, Gerry A592
Rogers, James E. A621
Rogers, Ellen Sheriff A637
Rogers, Cynthia M. (Cindy) A691
Rogers, Michael F. A758
Rogers, William H. (Bill) A765
Rogers, Prof Steven S. A768
Rogers, Boyd A846
Rogers, Emma A851
Rogers, Jeffrey A. (Jeff) A888
Rogers, Sandy P74
Rogers, Brian P86
Rogers, Sam P148
Rogers, Julie P190
Rogers, Mark P203
Rogers, Rob P248
Rogers, Cynthia P262
Rogers, Mark P286
Rogers, Brian C. P289
Rogers, Malcolm P333
Rogers, Jane P360
Rogers, Erin P367
Rogers, Mary P473
Rogers, Russell P480
Rogers, Mike P578
Rogers, David W35

A = AMERICAN BUSINESS
E = EMERGING COMPANIES
P = PRIVATE COMPANIES
W = WORLD BUSINESS

Rosenthal, Monica P507
Rosenthal, Sheldon P618
Rosenthal, Terese W240
Rosenthaler, Albert E. A511
Rosevear, Kenneth (Ken) A556
Rosholt, Robert A. A409
Rosics, Don E468
Rosin, Bob E276
Roskovich, Charles B. A674
Roslin, Matthew I. A349
Rosman, Andrew J. P287
Rosner, Christine P514
Rospond, Raylene P157
Ross, Richard E44
Ross, Mark R E46
Ross, Deborah E158
Ross, Franz E173
Ross, Deborah E175
Ross, Daniel E181
Ross, Christina E316
Ross, Wil E338
Ross, Justin E396
Ross, Christopher J. A26
Ross, Kimberly A. A92
Ross, Cynthia A98
Ross, Mark A104
Ross, Wilbur L. A105
Ross, David A. A147
Ross, Mark A161
Ross, Jackie A182
Ross, Richard A. A190
Ross, Andrew A218
Ross, Rich A260
Ross, Rex A299
Ross, Steven D. A500
Ross, Kelly C. A523
Ross, A.J. A585
Ross, Andrew D. A631
Ross, Frank K. A637
Ross, Michael D. A695
Ross, Dennis E. A758
Ross, Wilbur L. A763
Ross, Michael P. A849
Ross, Donna J. P52
Ross, Samuel L. P72
Ross, Matthew P100
Ross, George E. P102
Ross, Henry J. P342
Ross, Terryl P368
Ross, Jerrold P467
Ross, Barry P475
Ross, Charles E. P488
Ross, Thomas L P518
Ross, Wilbur L. W30
Ross, Wayne W35
Ross, James H. W284
Ross, Tom W303
Ross-Dronzek, Nancy C. A63
Ross-Dulan, Brenda K. A861
Rossan, Paul P143
Rosseau, Jon B. A490
Rosser, Troy D E98
Rosser, Bill E195
Rosser, James M. A285
Rosser, James M. A736
Rosser, James M. P87
Rossetti, Carl U. J. A800
Rossetti, Eugenio W189
Rossetto, Ronald B. A728
Rossi, Dino A. E49
Rossi, Mark E78
Rossi, Alex E139
Rossi, Mark E299
Rossi, Carter E364
Rossi, Mark A. A101
Rossi, James L. A187
Rossi, Walter A251
Rossi, James P. Del A551
Rossi, Hugo A722

Rossi, Jerome A804
Rossi, Nicola A881
Rossi, Rev Philip J. P140
Rossi, Orazio W189
Rossi, Jean W376
Rossiter, Jay A886
Rossman, Bruce P464
Rossmann, Barbara W. P227
Rossmann, Martin W267
Rosso, Paul D. A2
Rosso, Clar P19
Rosson, Mark W81
Rossotti, Charles O. A14
Rossotti, Charles O. A100
Rossotti, Charles O. A129
Rossow, Ryan E209
Rossow, Kristin P330
Rossum, Anton Anton van
  Rossum W116
Rossum, Anton van W116
Rossum, Anton van W240
Rossum, Anton Anton van
  Rossum W240
Rostan, Richard H. A309
Rostiac, Sheila A673
Rostom, Rania A374
Rosty, Nicolas von W320
Rosumek, Anke W240
Roswell, Clint A455
Roszczyk, Al A337
Roszkowski, Joanne A619
Rotella, William (Bill) P572
Rotenberg, Lesli P400
Roth, Douglas E8
Roth, Heidi E265
Roth, Mark A E275
Roth, Brian E416
Roth, William (Bill) E486
Roth, Jason E513
Roth, Lance J. E. A21
Roth, Stanley O. A126
Roth, Michael I. A459
Roth, Tara A560
Roth, Donald C. A587
Roth, David E. A615
Roth, Steven A634
Roth, Renee S. A776
Roth, Peter A801
Roth, Ben P423
Roth, Adam P423
Roth, Brett P423
Roth, Shirley P513
Roth, Martin (Marty) P536
Roth, Michael S. P603
Roth, Martin W133
Roth, Jean-Pierre W249
Rothbauer, Chris E434
Rothberg, Jay P18
Rothberger, Richard K. P440
Rothblatt, Martine A. E493
Rothe, Christian E E206
Rothenberg, Mace L. A641
Rothermel, Elizabeth B. P410
Rothfeld, Jen E430
Rothfield, Jen E431
Rothkopf, Charlene E47
Rothman, Steven E219
Rothman, Noel N. A197
Rothman, Fred A506
Rothman, Paul B. P260
Rothmeier, Ross E304
Rothmeier, Steven G. (Steve) A657
Rothove, Robert P7
Rothschild, David de W89
Rothstein, Stuart A. E37
Rothstein, Daniel G E444
Rothstein, Sharon A754
Rothstein, Daniel G. A760
Rothstein, Fred C. P569
Rothweiler, Alan C. A629
Rothwell, Sharon J. A534
Rothwell, Dustin P157
Rotner, Phil P506
Rotolo, Chris P483
Rotsztain, Diego A. E193

Rotter, Jerome P98
Rotty, Dirk P145
Roty, Chris P44
Rotzien, Donald E173
Roualet, Mark C. A371
Roubos, Gary L. A614
Roudebush, Jenni A77
Roueche, John E. (Jay) A351
Rouf, Shah W34
Rougas, Tye P500
Roughead, Gary A602
Roulet, Marcel W269
Roulis, Eleni P577
Roumeliotis, Panagiotis W279
Round, Garry P426
Rountree, Gordon P276
Rouot, Mattieu W37
Rouquet, Jerome A323
Rouret, Hugues du A230
Rous, James E181
Roush, Robin S. A383
Roush, William R. P531
Roussat, Olivier W74
Rousseau, Michael S. (Mike) A698
Rousseau, Michael T. A749
Rousseau, Jeff P143
Rousseau, Henri-Paul W160
Rousseau, Henri-Paul W282
Rousseau, Henri-Paul W283
Rousseau, Luc W289
Roussel, Stephane A8
Roussel, Patrick W269
Roussel, Stephane W377
Roussis, Theodoros W199
Rousso, Doug A161
Rout, Robert E. (Bob) A335
Routh, Benton C. E176
Routs, Rob J. A12
Rouve, Andreas A742
Rouvillois, Patrick W87
Roux, Bob A516
Roux, Roger G. P405
Roux, Didier W107
Rovinsky, Michele P158
Rovit, Sam A493
Rovit, Hugh R. A742
Rovner, Robert A. P498
Rowan, Marc J. A143
Rowden, Diana P531
Rowe, Melissa E60
Rowe, Stanton J. E141
Rowe, Darin E310
Rowe, Chris E475
Rowe, John A37
Rowe, Zane C. A68
Rowe, R. Scott A147
Rowe, Robert C. A184
Rowe, Sharon H. A187
Rowe, John W. A305
Rowe, John W. A306
Rowe, John W. A600
Rowe, Michael A. A809
Rowe, Michael (Mike) P22
Rowe, Chris P111
Rowe, Rachel M. P129
Rowe, John W. P243
Rowe, Theresa M. (Terrie) P360
Rowe, Margie P456
Rowe, Patrick B. F. W6
Rowell, Christine A252
Rowerdink, Jeff S E158
Rowinsky, Eric K. A123
Rowlan, Steven J. A605
Rowland, Patrick E173
Rowland, Tom E464
Rowland, Tom A41
Rowland, G. Joyce A726
Rowland, Robert O. A795
Rowland, Amber A851
Rowland, David J. P446
Rowland, David P. W6
Rowlands, Sharon T. A84
Rowles, Michael G. A516
Rowley, Steven R. (Steve) E137

Rowley, Stuart A358
Rowley, Shannon P334
Rowlings, Jon E373
Rowsell-jones, Andrew E196
Roy, Indrajit E163
Roy, Christopher E172
Roy, G. Cayce (Cayce) E277
Roy, Sumit E394
Roy, Peter A. A830
Roy, Michael P395
Roy, Charles P527
Roy, Sumita Bose W67
Roy, Anami W164
Roy, Sylvie W243
Roy, Louise W283
Royal, Darrell E119
Royal, Kevin S. E299
Royal, Frank S. A264
Royal, Frank S. A765
Royal, Keli P582
Royce, Maria P621
Royce-Davis, Joanna P578
Roychowdhury, Debasish W309
Roycroft, Gary E139
Roye, Larry A776
Royeen, Charlotte B. P430
Royer, Raymond W160
Royer, Raymond W283
Royster, Maurice E155
Roza, Scott E211
Rozanski, Horacio D. A129
Rozansky, Kristen P516
Rozek, Robert P. E268
Rozek, Charles P95
Rozenblatt, Mike P334
Rozier, Monica P256
Roznowsky, Wayne A870
Rozof, Nathan E503
Rozon, James E207
Rozsa, Bette Jo A47
Rozwat, Charles A. (Chuck) A617
Rozwell, Carol E195
Rozzell, Scott E. A167
Ruane, Mike E139
Ruane, Frank E356
Ruane, Brian A. A103
Ruane, Mark P170
Rubart, Perry E. P337
Rubart, Perry E. P490
Rubel, Matthew E. (Matt) A768
Rubenstein, Allan E. E105
Rubenstein, Arthur H. A498
Rubenstein, David M. P259
Rubenzer, Kathy P446
Rubertone, Joseph D. P404
Rubin, Moshe E71
Rubin, Beverly E143
Rubin, Suzanne A46
Rubin, Shelley L. A121
Rubin, Jonathan M. (Jon) A255
Rubin, Andy A389
Rubin, Barbara (Barb) A464
Rubin, James S. A609
Rubin, Arlen P125
Rubin, Allan P243
Rubin, Bruce P544
Rubinfeld, Arthur A754
Rubino, Rob E28
Rubino, Steve E168
Rubino, Joe E497
Rubinstein, Jonathan J. (Jon) A42
Rubinstein, Jonathan J. (Jon) A418
Rubinstein, Pablo P343
Rubinstein, Mitchell A P537
Rubinstein, Jerold H. P616
Rubiola, Louie A792
Ruble, Joseph T. (Joe) E114
Ruble, Chris C. E183
Ruble, Doug A606
Rubright, James A. (Jim) A22
Rubright, James A. (Jim) A706
Rubritz, Timothy G. A311
Ruby, Terri E322
Ruccius, Frederick E. P543
Ruccolo, Domenic G. A245

A = AMERICAN BUSINESS
E = EMERGING COMPANIES
P = PRIVATE COMPANIES
W = WORLD BUSINESS

Sassin, Joseph E. P496
Sasso, Gary M. P281
Sasson, Brian J. A664
Sastre, Maria A. A241
Sastre, Maria A. A674
Sata, Chiyono P505
Satalic, John P535
Satcher, David A470
Satcher, David A553
Sateja, John J P133
Sato, Vicki L. A135
Sato, Reiichi W1
Sato, Yoichi W78
Sato, Masayuki W313
Sato, Hiroshi Hiroshi Sato W315
Sato, Hitomi W317
Sato, Yoshio W337
Sato, Hirofumi W364
Satomi, Kazuhiro W317
Satou, Hironobu W317
Satre, Paul E189
Satre, Philip G. (Phil) A596
Sattaur, Deena E251
Satterfield, William E412
Satterfield, Randy P22
Satterthwait, Dale P63
Satterthwaite, Livingston L.
(Tony) A233
Satterthwaite, Dale P63
Satterwhite, Michael P292
Sattler, Edward L. P75
Satydass, Lakshmi E160
Saucedo, Jesus P375
Saucier, John F. A447
Saucier, Grady P325
Saucier, Guylaine W121
Sauer, Brad T. A2
Sauer, Jon W. A67
Sauer, Brad T. A818
Sauerland, John P. A666
Sauers, Kyle E139
Saul, B. Francis P509
Saulnier, Charly A631
Saulsberry, Scott A873
Saun, Bruce W. Van W300
Saun, Bruce W300
Saun, Bruce W. Van W300
Saunders, Ryan E240
Saunders, James E310
Saunders, Charles E. (Chuck) A15
Saunders, Melodee J. A116
Saunders, Thomas A. A263
Saunders, Ken A455
Saunders, Jeff L. A577
Saunders, Barry L. A734
Saunders, Joseph W. (Joe) A849
Saunders, Paul C. P192
Saunders, Rosanne C P256
Saunders, Shelley P303
Saunders, Lloyd P391
Saunders, Colon L. P424
Saunders, Steven W P444
Saunders, Martha D. P577
Saunders, Candice P602
Saunders, J. W. P611
Saunders, Mark S. W339
Saupper, Eveline W40
Saura, Janet M. A523
Sauriol, Jean-Pierre W18
Sauter, Gregory A12
Sauter, Charles W. A629
Sauter, Dave P318
Sauter, Diane P587
Sauv+, Paul A693
Savage, Thomas E200
Savage, Stephen A140
Savage, Larry D. A434
Savage, William A. (Bill) A452
Savage, Joseph J. A858

Savage, Jeffrey S. (Jeff) A883
Savage, Stanley D. A891
Savage-Tracy, Elizabeth P611
Savart, Michel W89
Saven, Bjorn W258
Savin, Gary P559
Savino, Jeff E196
Savino, Eric E384
Savio, Kathleen W392
Savitt, Kathy A886
Savitz, Warren E35
Savoca, Ann C. A723
Savoff, Mark T. A297
Savoie, Dennis P272
Savoie, Michael J. P501
Savorelli, Lorenzo W31
Savoy, Chad E430
Saw, Chong Seong A23
Saw, Choon Seong A23
Saw, Daniel A149
Sawa, Akira W233
Sawall, Chris A45
Sawamoto, Kazuo W231
Sawayama, Hiroki W364
Sawchuk, Christopher (Chris) E213
Sawda, Mounir N (Mo) E68
Sawden, Angelina (Zippy) P114
Sawdon, Lori Best P579
Sawers, Rick W242
Sawhney, Ashwini (Ash) A264
Sawhney, Theresa P293
Sawicki, David S. P119
Sawicki, Robert P370
Sawin, Kerry P127
Sawyer, Robert M. E274
Sawyer, Dick E306
Sawyer, Margaret E355
Sawyer, Douglas A105
Sawyer, Robin A. A146
Sawyer, Linda A459
Sawyer, James S. (Jim) A656
Sawyer, Terrence P289
Sax, Elizabeth (Liz) Ryan A112
Sax, E P413
Saxe, Jon S. E415
Saxena, Sharad E372
Saxon, Michael J. A59
Saxton, Courtney P109
Saxton, Brad P404
Sayama, Mike K. A168
Sayato, Junichi W338
Saydack, Roger P379
Sayer, Susan A235
Sayler, Van C. A687
Sayles, Thomas S. (Tom) P288
Sayles, Andy P403
Saylor, Michael J. E316
Saylor, Steve A365
Saylors, Roy P453
Sayre, Debra E172
Sayre, Dan A198
Sblendorio, Glenn P. E303
Sbranti, Salvatore S. (Sal) P583
Scaccetti, Jane P498
Scaer, Robert M. P188
Scaff, William E. E459
Scaggiante, Michele P343
Scaglione, D. Anthony A7
Scagnetti, Paul E165
Scaife, Rodney H. P7
Scala, Laure A103
Scalet, J. Chris A549
Scalia, Chris E9
Scalia, Cecilia P69
Scalise, George M E71
Scalise, Kathy P239
Scalone, Edward L. P404
Scaminace, Joseph M. (Joe) A181
Scaminace, Joseph M. (Joe) A631
Scandrett, Hugh E148
Scangos, George A. A123
Scanio, Michael E430
Scanlan, John P293
Scanlon, Kevin E377
Scanlon, John J. A314

Scanlon, George P. A325
Scanlon, Sharon A515
Scanlon, John P. P99
Scanlon, Dennis P156
Scannapieco, Dario W147
Scannell, William F. (Bill) A287
Scannell, Timothy J. A762
Scapanski, Gene P577
Scapparone, Horacio E436
Scaramuzzo, John A714
Scarano, Drew E509
Scarborough, Dean A. A88
Scarborough, Dean A. A538
Scarborough, Fred P29
Scarborough, Ranulf W80
Scarbrough, Troy P373
Scarchilli, Amber E455
Scarciotta, Camille P293
Scardelletti, Robert A. (Bob) P17
Scardina, Frank E408
Scardina, John P164
Scaringi, Tony A678
Scarlata, John P. A671
Scarlett, Christine A544
Scarlett, Catherine M. A579
Scaroni, Paolo W31
Scaroni, Paolo W141
Scaroni, Paolo W374
Scarpello, Robert E173
Scarratt, Mary W81
Scarrozza, Claudio A177
Scarth, Susan C E144
Scattergood, Kelly E287
Scbula, Scott P472
Scelfo, John J. A416
Scerbo, Robert P133
Schaack, Greg Van P233
Schaarsmith, David P40
Schabel, Bill E353
Schabel, Tom P12
Schabel, Steve P12
Schabel, Joe P12
Schaber, Steven P481
Schaberl, Michael E487
Schachler, Juergen Juergen
Schachler W30
Schacht, David A730
Schack, Wesley W. von A103
Schacter, Phil E197
Schad, Martin W119
Schade, Brian E196
Schade, Michael W63
Schadee, Muriel D. P129
Schaefer, Jim E34
Schaefer, John E475
Schaefer, George A. A65
Schaefer, George A. A76
Schaefer, Barbara W. A825
Schaefer, John P102
Schaefer, Michele P314
Schaefer, Michael J. P316
Schaefer, Don P348
Schaefer, Phil P459
Schaefer, August (Gus) P559
Schaeffer, David (Dave) E93
Schaeffer, James E269
Schaeffer, Leonard D. A34
Schaeffer, Leonard D. A57
Schaeffer, Linda A797
Schaeffer, Gary P214
Schaeffer, William G. P467
Schaeffer, Paul P507
Schaeffer, Marc P541
Schaeffler, Georg F. W. W112
Schaeffler, Maria-Elisabeth W112
Schaekel, Julie W8
Schaer, Joyce E520
Schafer, Todd C. A170
Schafer, Lisa P91
Schafer, Chip P299
Schafer, Wolfgang W112
Schaffer, Greg A326
Schaffer, Rod P283
Schaffer, Gary G. P453
Schaffer, Thomas W320

Schaffner, Richard A. (Rick) P237
Schaffter, Barry W. A245
Schafmeister, Astrid A472
Schager, Marty P7
Schaitberger, Harold A. P17
Schak, Todd A680
Schalekamp, William A. (Bill) A478
Schall, Michael J. (Mike) E158
Schall, Martha E. P130
Schaller, Kim P230
Schallert, Ralph P318
Schalliol, Charles E. A341
Schanefelt, Rodney A73
Schapira, Daniel A619
Schapiro, Morton O. A532
Schapiro, Benjamin S. P284
Schapp, Paula P299
Schappert, Rich A156
Schaps, Oscar A460
Scharbauer, Clarence P500
Schardt, Fred A324
Scharf, David P. A108
Scharf, Charles W. (Charlie) A475
Scharf, Charles W. (Charlie) A849
Scharf, Charles W. A849
Scharf, Charles W. (Charlie) A849
Scharf, Charles W. A849
Scharmer, Neal R. E491
Scharmer, Neal R. E492
Scharmer, Neal R. A828
Scharneck, Colleen P258
Schassler, Bob A570
Schatzel, Kim P162
Schatzman, Andy P151
Schaub, Mary E286
Schaub, Carola A455
Schaudies, Jay P600
Schauenberg, Trevor A. A374
Schauer, Heidi A241
Schauer, Bob A702
Schauerman, John P. E383
Schaufelberger, John P579
Schaum, Richard O. A131
Schaumann, Hilmar A359
Schaumburg, Anne C. A603
Scheaffel, Margaret P236
Schechter, Jonathan E181
Schechter, David S. A323
Schechter, Adam H. A549
Scheck, John P347
Schecklman, Dave A620
Scheele, David (Dave) P170
Scheen, Benoit W269
Scheer, Geneie S. A629
Scheer, Todd P182
Scheessele, Jennifer P430
Scheetz, Chris E339
Schefer, Catherine P334
Scheffel, William N. A165
Scheffer, Henk W30
Schefft, Robert W. A53
Scheibenreif, Don E196
Scheible, David W. A390
Scheibye, Sten W122
Scheimreif, Scott T. E254
Scheinfein, Michael R. (Mike) E166
Scheinkestel, Nora L. W25
Scheinman, Steven J. P528
Scheirman, W. Russell E501
Scheirman, Scott T. A868
Scheitor, Dieter W320
Scheiwe, Paula P125
Schelbitzki, Clint A825
Scheler, Brad E. P281
Schell, Andrea A65
Schell, Michael J. A409
Schell, James A. P195
Schell, Tim P477
Schellekens, Ronald W379
Schellemans, Denise W62
Schellen, Mike E339
Scheller, Richard H. W297
Schellinger, Jimmie E468
Schelske, Beth P299

A = AMERICAN BUSINESS
E = EMERGING COMPANIES
P = PRIVATE COMPANIES
W = WORLD BUSINESS

Selser, John M. E198
Selter, Barbara E298
Seltz, Mike P591
Selus, Todd Van E114
Selvaraj, Saravanan P154
Selvas, Francesc W43
Selvidge, Jeff E289
Selwan, Fadi W376
Selwood, Robert C. A556
Selzer, Lawrence A. P509
Selzer, Larry P509
Semanie, Mark E355
Semaska, Victor P130
Semeneri, Alain A203
Semeraro, Michael P74
Semerdjian, Nancy P354
Semiglazova, Yana E512
Semmel, Christina W127
Semoff, Thierry E138
Semple, John P123
Sen, Pradipta A290
Sen, Ting Lee W212
Sen, Michael W320
Sen, Ranendra W347
Sena, Peter P. A345
Sena, Michael A401
Senackerib, Michael P. (Mike) A149
Senak, Brenda A857
Senanayake, Pramilla P182
Sendak, Michael P514
Sender, Mark P228
Senderovitz, Thomas E369
Sene, Guy A20
Senel, Aydin W365
Senequier, Dominique A418
Senequier, Dominique W313
Senf, J. Eduardo A585
Seng, Kwa Chong W123
Senge, Jim E138
Sengstack, Gregg C. E186
Senior, David M. A55
Senker, Thomas J. P513
Senn, Greta E15
Senn, Randal M. (Randy) A717
Senn, Martin W392
Senna, Joseph J. A169
Senne, Stacia P215
Sennish, James A. P186
Sennott, John L. (Jack) A32
Seno, Teruo E268
Seno, Louis C. P173
Sensabaugh, Karen A262
Sentell, Susan B. P354
Sentinelli, Mauro W349
Senyitko, Alissa P552
Seo, Sang-ju W306
Seong, Chan W371
Seow, Derek E195
Sephton, Brian T. A460
Sepull, Jennifer A488
Sepulveda, Eli A651
Seraceni, Robert E153
Serafini, Francesco A418
Serafini, Richard M. P72
Serafino, Mark P366
Seramur, John C. A77
Serbin, Daniel S. (Dan) A631
Serdar, Cenk W379
Sereda, Peter L. A785
Sereda, Mikhail L. W154
Sereno, Pete E167
Serfling, G. Aubrey P167
Serfontein, Deward W266
Sergel, Richard P. (Rick) A758
Sergesketter, Randal A. (Randy) A245
Sergi, Jane P612
Serianni, Charles F. A697
Serino, Joseph A. (Joe) A288
Serino, Joe A592

Serio, Gregory V. A684
Serjeant, Owen A. A147
Serluco, Michael A. A554
Serna, Angel W392
Serot, Debbie E389
Serota, Scott P. P69
Seroussi, Yair W48
Serra, Eileen M. A476
Serra, Andrea A544
Serra, Antonio A714
Serra, Andrea P93
Serrano, Manuel Soto W46
Serratelli, Rev Arthur J. P446
Serri, Andrew M. A45
Servatius, Greg E442
Servodidio, Mark J. A89
Seryak, Mark E175
Sescleifer, Daniel J. A292
Seshadri, K. V. W68
Sessions, Roy B. P61
Sessions, Judith A. P318
Sestini, Roberto W371
Sestric, Keiffer E201
Setbon, Philippe W31
Seth, Lokesh E152
Sethi, Neerja E461
Sethi, Kamlajit P399
Sethi, Satinder P413
Setliff, Will A241
Seto, Shinichirou W317
Seton, John W80
Setrakian, Berge W185
Setta, Salli A241
Setterdahl, Jon P182
Settle, Mark F. E239
Settle, Tom P242
Settle, Brian P339
Setubal, Roberto Egydio W191
Setubal, Alfredo Egydio W191
Setzer, Nikolai W112
Seuell, Jerry P301
Seung-Eun, Jeong W200
Sevaldsen, Erik W122
Sevang, Thomas W258
Sevcik, Kenneth J. (Ken) P492
Sever, Anna E298
Severance, Matthew P90
Severino, Michael A57
Severino, Jean W269
Severn, Colin T. E285
Severson, Sid P490
Sevilla, Vilma P432
Sewell, D. Bruce A68
Sewell, Michael J. (Mike) A180
Sewell, Gina E. A250
Sewell, David B. A728
Sewell, Phyllis S. A778
Sewill, Ann P87
Sexauer, Pam P423
Sexton, Andrew A323
Sexton, O. Griffith (Griff) A568
Sexton, David A763
Sexton, Dorothy P122
Sexton, James J. P227
Sexton, Lamar V P436
Sexton, Sandy P440
Sexton, Eric L. P540
Seya, Toshio W354
Seydel, J. Rutherford P509
Seyler, David E355
Seymour, Harlan F. E9
Seymour, Mark E224
Seymour, Bill A119
Seymour, Andrew W. A647
Seymour, Linda W173
Seze, Amaury-Daniel de W87
Seze, Amaury de W283
Sezer, Esat A200
Sfeir, Raymond P105
Sfeir, Nicolas P462
Sgarro, Douglas A. A237
Sgarzi, Richard H. A444
Sgoutas, Kostas E209
Sgroi, Rosemary J. P97
Shaak, Melissa P39

Shabelnik, Tatiana P117
Shabot, M. Michael P311
Shabshab, Nabil A112
Shackelford, Donald B. A329
Shackelford, Paul P387
Shackley, Nicholas E8
Shackley, Nick E8
Shackouls, Bobby S. A220
Shackouls, Bobby S. A495
Shada, Jeff P328
Shadduck, David A. (Dave) P553
Shade, David M. P318
Shadle, Mark P74
Shadley, Eric A365
Shaeffer, Carrie P47
Shafer, Walter F. A647
Shafer, Aida P43
Shaff, Karen E. A661
Shaffer, David M. E149
Shaffer, Robert A329
Shaffer, Eric N. A346
Shaffer, Bradley A. A379
Shaffer, Reuben A495
Shaffer, Michael A. (Mike) A677
Shaffer, Oren G. A791
Shaffner, George P. A528
Shafir, Robert S. (Rob) W115
Shafran, George P. A152
Shafter, A. James A73
Shah, Nancy E196
Shah, Dharmesh E196
Shah, Neil H. E223
Shah, Jay H. E223
Shah, Hasu P. E223
Shah, Mazhar E308
Shah, Scott E315
Shah, Amisha E332
Shah, Bhargav E364
Shah, Ravi E503
Shah, Rasesh H. A61
Shah, Neel A248
Shah, Mahesh A418
Shah, Raheel A. A452
Shah, Jai A534
Shah, Bhavi P68
Shah, Neha P103
Shah, Sanjay M. P517
Shah, Tushaar W181
Shaheen, George T. E268
Shaheen, Gerald L. (Gerry) A18
Shaheen, Gerald L. (Gerry) A358
Shaheen, Gabriel L. A425
Shaheen, George T. A582
Shaheen, Gabriel L. A759
Shaheen, Gerald L. (Gerry) P75
Shahkarami, Amir A305
Shahtaji, Eric E139
Shahudin, Ismail W220
Shaich, Ronald M. (Ron) E367
Shailubhai, Kunwar A144
Shainbrown, Ian E384
Shaked, Hezy P616
Shaked, Carol W175
Shakeel, Arif A867
Shakeel, Bassem A. W219
Shalala, Donna E E306
Shalala, Donna E. A506
Shalev, Prof Gabriela W49
Shalita, Steven E345
Shallash, Anthony P196
Shallcross, John P. A546
Shama, Robert A. (Rob) E348
Shamber, Mark E. A830
Shami, Eric E169
Shamieh, Charlie A51
Shamion, Vicki A492
Shammo, Francis J. (Fran) A845
Shamsuarov, Azat W264
Shamsudin, Mohaiyani Mohaiyani binti
  Shamsudin W220
Shamsy, Bejan E300
Shan, Tan Su W123
Shana, David Le P38
Shanahan, Patrick M. (Pat) A126
Shanahan, Teri A458

Shanahan, William S. (Bill) A849
Shanahan, Patrick J. A857
Shand, Lee P82
Shane, John E152
Shang, Stephen A424
Shang, Oliver W116
Shank, Leanne M. P538
Shank, Barbara P577
Shankar, Ramesh A789
Shankar, Uday A816
Shankar, Gita P465
Shankar, Viswanathan (Shankar) W332
Shanks, Robert L. (Bob) A357
Shanks, Eugene B. A362
Shanks, Eugene B. W8
Shankwiler, James P377
Shanley, Michael P. A694
Shanley, Linda P429
Shanley, Marlene W53
Shanmugam, Suresh A770
Shannahan, C. Kevin P233
Shannin, Pete E11
Shannon, Daniel E304
Shannon, C. Douglas (Doug) A94
Shannon, Holden A248
Shannon, R. Michael A629
Shannon, Mike A741
Shannon, John T. (Jack) P329
Shannon, Colleen P364
Shantz, Adam W268
Shao, Peter E415
Shao, Bo E415
Shaopeng, Chen W212
Shapard, Robert S. (Bob) A294
Shapazian, Carole J. A108
Shape, John P3
Shaper, Peter A404
Shaper, C. Park A489
Shapiro, Stephen E306
Shapiro, Dina A30
Shapiro, Mark L. A116
Shapiro, Mark S. A365
Shapiro, Neal B. A369
Shapiro, Marc J. A488
Shapiro, Mark S. A516
Shapiro, Steven L. A732
Shapiro, Benson P. A835
Shapiro, Alan A870
Shapiro, Philip N. (Phil) P39
Shapiro, Steven P90
Shapiro, E. Gary P101
Shapiro, Robert S. (Bob) P353
Shapiro, Ralph J. P531
Shapiro, Benjamin P535
Shapiro, Charlene P542
Shapiro, Neal B. P556
Shapland, George T. A334
Shapland, Darren W194
Shar, Jonathan A107
Shara, Thomas J. A499
Sharan, Kim A53
Sharbatly, Abdulrahman Hassan W295
Share, Scott P97
Sharer, Kevin W. A56
Sharer, Kevin W. A176
Sharer, Kevin W. A602
Sharif, Nawaz E314
Sharkey, Michael E421
Sharkey, Andrew G. A694
Sharkey, Michael A729
Sharkey, Gladys P97
Sharma, Madhukar E509
Sharma, Devesh A209
Sharma, Umesh P454
Sharma, Vipin P552
Sharma, Sharad K. W67
Sharma, Pramod W68
Sharma, Mahendra Kumar W181
Sharma, R. S. W263
Sharma, Vibhu R. W392
Sharman, Lord Colin M. W34
Sharnas, Michael K. A850
Sharon, Barbara E162
Sharp, David E119
Sharp, James T. E210

Sharp, Philip R. A277
Sharp, Erin A495
Sharp, Michael A507
Sharp, Edward A582
Sharp, Calvin C. A635
Sharp, M. Rust A846
Sharp, Joel H. P46
Sharp, Mike P203
Sharp, Myron P251
Sharp, Anita P296
Sharp, C. Brooks P338
Sharp, Robert P365
Sharp, Joseph P456
Sharp, Matthew D. (Matt) P511
Sharp, Aric P566
Sharp, Julie W53
Sharpe, David E181
Sharpe, Robert F. (Rob) A54
Sharpe, Kathryn A231
Sharpe, Matthew P. A425
Sharpe, Jeremy P576
Sharples, Brian H. E230
Sharr, Henry E328
Sharrett, Brandon A348
Sharum, Beth A367
Shashaguay, Mary Kate A63
Shaskey-Platek, Holly A314
Shaskey-Platek, Holly L. A314
Shassian, Donald R. (Don) A365
Shasta, Theodore E. (Ted) A540
Shasta, Theodore E. (Ted) W8
Shatteen, Westina Matthews P535
Shattenkirk, Darla P346
Shattuck, Mayo A. A151
Shattuck, Mayo A. A305
Shattuck, Steve A866
Shattuck, Carol P22
Shatzkin, Michael E11
Shaughnessy, Timothy S. A455
Shaukat, Tariq M. A143
Shaum, Claudia A92
Shaunnessy, Michael A556
Shaver, Tina E175
Shaver, Deb P533
Shavers, Cheryl L. A708
Shaw, Steve E116
Shaw, Janette E136
Shaw, Peter E195
Shaw, Bob E257
Shaw, Douglas J. (Doug) E323
Shaw, Terry L. A116
Shaw, Chris A257
Shaw, Ruth G. A270
Shaw, Ruth G. A273
Shaw, Francine C. A274
Shaw, Michael A. (Mike) A315
Shaw, Robert A393
Shaw, Bruce R. A420
Shaw, Jane E. A451
Shaw, Jane E. A544
Shaw, Frank X. A560
Shaw, Jeff M. A606
Shaw, Barbara E. A782
Shaw, Donald W. P32
Shaw, Don P47
Shaw, Milton P70
Shaw, Terri P122
Shaw, James C. P236
Shaw, Thomas L. P288
Shaw, Jack P409
Shaw, Randy P456
Shaw, Wiley P488
Shaw, Byers W. P582
Shaw, Cory D. P582
Shaw, Allan C. W54
Shaw, Peter W332
Shaw, Candace G. W339
Shawe, Phil P547
Shawi, Joseph P569
Shay, Brent P164
Shay, Heather P545
Shaykin, Katie A570
Shaz, Beth P343
Shea, Daniel E16
Shea, Keri E47

Shea, John E219
Shea, John T. E378
Shea, Brian T. A102
Shea, William J. (Bill) A132
Shea, Tammy A257
Shea, Peter O. A326
Shea, William J. A435
Shea, E. Stewart A440
Shea, K. Stuart (Stu) A505
Shea, Jody A681
Shea, Francis X. (Frank) A879
Shea, Thomas P179
Shea, Jerry P299
Shea-Ballay, Kathleen A763
Sheaffer, Hal D. A629
Sheagren, Craig P434
Sheahan, Denis K. A444
Shealer, Daniel G P260
Shean, Christopher W. (Chris) A511
Shean, Terry A678
Shear, Bruce A. E7
Shear, Neal W367
Shearan, Kevin W8
Shearer, Scott E376
Shearer, Grace O. A173
Shearer, R. Gordon A416
Shearer, Robert K. (Bob) A846
Shearer, Kevin A870
Shearer, James P144
Shearer, Alan P158
Shearer, Alan A418
Shearer, Brad P435
Shearer, Jim P451
Shearer, Craig W173
Sheares, Bradley T. A424
Sheares, Bradley T. A666
Sheares, Bradley T. A719
Shearman, Jennifer J. P522
Shearn, Jeremy E196
Shearrow, Brian E93
Shearrow, David P. A827
Shebik, Steve A36
Sheble, James A. A605
Shedd, Marelyn B. A338
Shedden, Jill W92
Shedlarz, David L. A413
Shedlin, Gary A124
Shedrick, Bobbi P498
Sheedy, Derek E3
Sheedy, Donna M. A449
Sheedy, William M. (Bill) A849
Sheehan, Edward E103
Sheehan, Dennis E243
Sheehan, Timothy R. (Tim) A119
Sheehan, Dennis E. A356
Sheehan, James N. A426
Sheehan, Mark W. A437
Sheehan, Mike A459

Sheehan, John D. A573
Sheehan, Peter A856
Sheehan, Terrence P5
Sheehan, Myles N. P72
Sheehan, Finbar M. W274
Sheehy, Eugene J. A524
Sheehy, William A738
Sheeley, Michael J. E492
Sheeley, Michael A828
Sheely, Thad P449
Sheen, Michael J. E203
Sheeran, Rev Michael J. P575
Sheerin, Rick P190
Sheets, John W. E36
Sheets, Jeffrey W. (Jeff) A220
Sheets, Cindy P331
Sheets, Wayne P337
Sheetz, Margaret E305
Sheetz, Guy E305
Sheetz, Stanton R. (Stan) A311
Sheetz-Zugmaier, Kim A365
Sheff, Paul E. P122
Sheffer, Gary A374
Sheffert, Mark W. P14
Sheffield, Martin P. A301
Sheffield, Peter A741

Sheffield, Angela P205
Sheffield, Vonne P510
Sheftel, David P6
Sheid, Mary P325
Sheil, Michael T. P606
Shein, Jeffries A669
Sheinbaum, Marc A476
Sheinbaum, Gary A677
Sheiness, Alan A84
Shekhter‎, Elaina E152
Sheldon, D. Scott E24
Sheldon, Brooks A54
Sheldon, Mike A459
Sheldon, Greg A573
Sheldon, Todd N. A768
Sheldon, Janet P334
Sheline, Douglas A. A524
Shell, Frederick E. (Fred) A273
Shell, Robin P141
Shelley, Pamela E280
Shelley, Debbie P249
Shelley, Tom P249
Shelley-Kessler, Pamela (Pam) E280
Shellman, Carolyn E. P116
Shelton, Charlita E65
Shelton, Henry H. (Hugh) E396
Shelton, Michael W. (Mike) A288
Shelton, Ralph K. A335
Shelton, Gen. Henry H. (Hugh) A497
Shelton, James D. (Denny) A613
Shelton, Todd A. A835
Shelton, John A. P149
Shelton, Scott P319
Shelton, Mark S. P442
Shelton, Jimmy P459
Shelton, Mark W367
Shelton-DeLapp, Marva P80
Shen, Simon P233
Shendell-Falik, Nancy P52
Sheng, Rodney T. (Rocky) E65
Shengchen, Guo W278
Shenk, Thomas E. (Tom) A549
Shennan, James G. (Jamie) A754
Shenoy, Navin A452
Shenoy, K. V. W68
Shepard, Julie E482
Shepard, Toya A67
Shepard, Donald J. A231
Shepard, Alfred A337
Shepard, Donald J. A651
Shepard, Donald J. A810
Shepard-lovell, J P63
Shepardson, J. Andrew P58
Shepardson, Karen P446
Shephard, Christopher J. E482
Shephard, John A304
Shepherd, Jim E309
Shepherd, Carl G. E230
Shepherd, Michelle E309
Shepherd, W. Clyde A327
Shepherd, Scott D. A616
Shepherd, Betty A702
Shepherd, Colin P233
Shepherd, James H. P451
Shepherd, Alana P451
Shepler, Christopher E328
Sheppard, Charles E452
Sheppard, Valarie L. A664
Sheppard, James J. A883
Sheppard, Mark P378
Sher, Susan S. P535
Sheraden, Tom E383
Sherbell, Stanley P344
Sherburne, Zachary E388
Sherburne, Jane C. A103
Sherer, Lance E181
Shergold, Peter W25
Sheridan, Nom E494
Sheridan, Tom E503
Sheridan, Diane L. A23
Sheridan, Jean E. A599
Sheridan, Jerry E. A821
Sheridan, Chris P95
Sheridan, Bert P212
Sheridan, Jason P242

Sheridan, Dennis P613
Sheridan, Ronan W21
Sherif, Tarek E303
Sherif, Tarek E304
Sherin, Keith S. A373
Sherin, Keith S. A375
Sherin, Jonathan P591
Sherland, Barbara C. P401
Sherlock, Peter P522
Sherman, Kevin E56
Sherman, Michael E95
Sherman, Jeffrey S. (Jeff) E227
Sherman, Jeffrey S. (Jeff) E228
Sherman, Neil E280
Sherman, George A10
Sherman, Scott D. A34
Sherman, Jeffrey S. A112
Sherman, George A119
Sherman, Patrick A. A341
Sherman, Belinda A437
Sherman, Malcolm L. P76
Sherman, Les P111
Sherman, Merrill W. P261
Sherman, Don P321
Sherman, Melanie P391
Sherman, Mark T. P444
Sherman, Glen P541
Sherman, Bruce P566
Shermetaro, Mark R E312
Shern, Stephanie M. A367
Shern, Stephanie M. W203
Sherr, Richard A804
Sherr, Charles P475
Sherrard, Roger S. A631
Sherrick, Bruce A317
Sherriff, Jim A182
Sherrill, Gregg M. A788
Sherringham, Philip R. A636
Sherry, Peter J. A358
Sherwell, Keith A724
Sherwin, Stephen A. (Steve) A123
Sherwood, Charles H. E36
Sherwood, David E273
Sherwood, Julie A47
Sherwood, Scott A203
Sherwood, Robert J. A284
Sherwood, Michael S. A386
Sherwood, Bill A459
Sherwood, William B. P566
Shetler, Charles P246
Shetty, Jyothsna E9
Shevchik, Joan O. A180
Shevick, Steven E460
Shevrin, Phil W326
Shewchuk, Darrin A403
Shewmake, Charles W. A139
Shewman, Teresa A513
Shi, S E369
Shi, Lili E430
Shi, Christiana A592
Shi, Zhenchun A633
Shiba, Kerry A. E451
Shibamiya, Masao W225
Shibata, Takumi A359
Shibata, Takumi W257
Shibata, Masaharu W257
Shiber, Wendy E263
Shickich, Mary Lynne P619
Shieh, Daniel E195
Shiel, James G. A115
Shields, Maria T. E37
Shields, Ian E46
Shields, Keith E111
Shields, Marcia E301
Shields, Lori E303
Shields, Joanna A312
Shields, Brian J. A558
Shields, Patrick P465
Shields, Kevin P540
Shields, Charlie P554
Shields, Dennis P581
Shiels, David C. E522
Shiely, John S. A620
Shiely, John S. A678
Shier, Richard A189

A = AMERICAN BUSINESS
E = EMERGING COMPANIES
P = PRIVATE COMPANIES
W = WORLD BUSINESS

Smithburg, William D. (Bill) A226
Smither, Nicholas J. (Nick) A358
Smithers, John A. P261
Smithmier, Matt P523
Smits, Peter W4
Smits, Didier W146
Smoak, Michelle E432
Smocer, Michael E37
Smoldt, Dave A460
Smolensky, Victor E299
Smolev, James K. P514
Smoot, Bill E18
Smoot, Dan A851
Smoot, JoAnn P289
Smoter, Jennifer A4
Smothers, Frederick W. A700
Smucker, Richard K. A728
Smucker, Richard K. A733
Smucker, Timothy P. (Tim) A733
Smucker, Mark T. A733
Smucker, Richard K. A733
Smucker, Mark T. A733
Smulders, Christopher E195
Smulevitz, Morry A513
Smullen, Richard (Dick) P240
Smyer, Michael A. P555
Smyley, Kevin P618
Smyth, Karen E308
Smyth, Thomas M. A25
Smyth, Robert E. (Bob) P506
Smythe, Barb P473
Smytka, Daniel (Dan) A388
Snake, Sarah P234
Snapper, Suzanne D. E150
Snarr, Trent A160
Snavely, Stephen V. P192
Snavely, Chris M. P192
Snayd, Michael P366
Snead, George A E251
Snead, Robert K. A621
Snead, Ronald P22
Snedaker, Dianne E174
Snedaker, Dianne A344
Snee, James P. A426
Sneed, Paula A. A25
Sneed, Thomas K. A527
Sneed, Paula A. A720
Snekvik, Rick P154
Snell, Richard S. A299
Snell, Mark A. A726
Snell, Scott P438
Snelwar, Dan E197
Snider, Rich E308
Sniderman, Howard D. P178
Snisarenko, Shawn P40
Snively, Joshua E177
Snively, David F. (Dave) A566
Snodgrass, John E369
Snodgrass, Steven T. A555
Snodgrass, John P105
Snodgres, Jon K. E397
Snook, Jonathan D. (Jon) A46
Snow, Brad E294
Snow, Michael D. (Mike) E464
Snow, Kristine A. (Kris) A182
Snow, John W. A527
Snow, John A528
Snow, John W. A845
Snow, Mike P366
Snow, Russell K. P507
Snow, Abby P570
Snow, Michael P591
Snow, Richard C. W379
Snowball, Patrick W341
Snowberger, Thomas D. P48
Snowberger, Tom P48
Snowden, Tamara A137
Snowden, Joseph I. A657
Snowden, Sandra Metts A696

Snowden, Sandra A696
Snowdon, Mark A600
Snyder, Marquietta E167
Snyder, Rowan E196
Snyder, Darrell E204
Snyder, Kim E384
Snyder, Window A68
Snyder, Jim A220
Snyder, Shea A250
Snyder, Andrew A257
Snyder, James C. (Jim) A314
Snyder, Matt A392
Snyder, Burton H. (Burt) A413
Snyder, William F. A426
Snyder, Judy A483
Snyder, Barbara R. A486
Snyder, Cheryl L. A629
Snyder, David A. A629
Snyder, Mark J. A. A758
Snyder, Stuart C. A801
Snyder, Donald D. (Don) A865
Snyder, Barbara R. P95
Snyder, Kristy P106
Snyder, Linda P556
Snyder, Dustin P164
Snyder, David H. P171
Snyder, John P180
Snyder, Donna L. P238
Snyder, Timothy Law P289
Snyder, Stephen D. P318
Snyder, Mary Beth P360
Snyder, Jodi P446
Snyder, Michael P469
Snyder, Linda P556
Snyder, Lori P583
Snyder, Arlene A. P597
So, Keith E269
Soanes, David W367
Soares, Carol E36
Soares, David S. E344
Soave, John S. E111
Sobey, Paul D. W54
Sobic, Daniel D. (Dan) A625
Sobieski, Mark E456
Sobin, Carole A221
Soboleff, Vicki P441
Sobolik, Kristin D. P617
Sobrato, John A. P395
Sobrinho, Jose Batista W195
Sobule, James A. A45
Soby, Lynn P413
Sock, Shannon P314
Sockolov, Alvin M. P232
Sockwell, Allen A11
Sockwell, Oliver R. A267
Sockwell, James P456
Sodaro, Frank J. A484
Sodeika, Lisa M. A431
Sodeika, Lisa M. W175
Soder, Douglas L. E485
Soder, D E485
Soder, Christopher L. (Chris) A659
Soderberg, Jan E196
Soderbery, Robert (Rob) A182
Sodha, Paresh W367
Sodhani, Arvind A451
Soellner, Kent A73
Soenderop, Susan J. W268
Soete, Hendrik W199
Soffen, Edward M P102
Sofio, Kenneth C. A226
Sofio, Monica L. A226
Sognefest, Peter E241
Sogofsky, Linda P130
Soh, Vincent W271
Soh, Jae Gwang W316
Sohn, Sung Won A865
Sohn, Jon W. P607
Sohn, Dale W307
Sohovich, JoAnna A751
Soich, Don P274
Soin, Rajesh K. (Raj) P75
Soistman, Fran S. A15
Sokol, Jim A739
Sokoloff, Jonathan D. (Jon) A873
Sokolov, Jacque J. A429

Sokolov, Richard S. (Rick) A730
Sokolov, Jacque J. P385
Sokolowski, Mark E497
Sokoly, Jim P305
Sokorai, Michael E223
Sol, Vincent P612
Sola, Jure A716
Solazzo, Steven C. A455
Solazzo, Mark J. P353
Solberg, John A816
Solberg, Jeff P213
Soldano, Candice A318
Soldo, Stephen P427
Soldoveri, Robert C. A842
Sole, Ian E34
Sole, Domenico De E432
Sole, Domenico De A585
Sole, Domenico A585
Solecki, Joe E37
Solera, Flora E456
Solferini, Fabio A460
Soliday, Lance A307
Solie, Carol P619
Soliman, Adam E199
Solimine, April E439
Soliman, Manuel Delgado W9
Solis, Miguel A. de W45
Solitaire, Diane P401
Solkema, Kevin J. Van A662
Solkema, Kevin A662
Solle, Chris E144
Sollecito, Larry A. A374
Sollmann, Justin P182
Solman, Patricia E330
Solmssen, Peter Y. W319
Sologaistua, Pedro W43
Solomon, Pam E117
Solomon, Mark T E426
Solomon, Darlene J. S. A20
Solomon, William B. A37
Solomon, J. Stuart A47
Solomon, Walter H. A76
Solomon, David M. A386
Solomon, B. Thad A605
Solomon, Fred A651
Solomon, Jay S. P102
Solomon, David S. P125
Solomon, Peter P167
Solomon, Brenda P330
Solomone, Jim E154
Solorzano, Jorge A4
Soloway, Marcella E314
Solso, Theodore M. (Tim) A76
Solso, Theodore M. (Tim) A96
Solt, Russell A121
Soluri, Tom E416
Soma, Kazuo W232
Somanath, T. W68
Somasegar, Sivaramakichenane
  (Soma) A560
Somasundaram, Sivasankaran
  (Soma) A268
Somavilla, Vania W373
Somaya, M. M. W68
Sombke, Bob P349
Somerhalder, Scott E350
Somerhalder, John W. A21
Somers, Jeffrey P E205
Somers, Daniel E. A178
Somers, Andreas A203
Somers, Richard D. P463
Somers, Michael W21
Somerville, Susan P353
Someson, George E77
Somireddy, Jyothi P406
Sommars, Barbara P612
Sommer, Oliver H. E172
Sommer, Alfred A112
Sommer, Oliver H. A343
Sommer, John L. A615
Sommer, Michael W130
Sommer, Ron W240
Sommer, Richard W240
Sommerauer, Thomas W144
Sommerfeld, Michael E175

Sommerhauser, Peter M. A492
Sommers, Steve E490
Sommers, Barry A476
Sommerville, William E267
Somsak, Marlene A418
Son, Jung Hak A398
Son, John P176
Son, Masayoshi W326
Sondej, John A. A78
Sondergaard, Peter E195
Sonders, Elizabeth (Liz Ann) A720
Sondey, Brian M. E463
Sondhi, Samrat E162
Sondhi, Vivek E238
Soneda, Mitsuru W182
Sones, Keith A681
Song, Qiao W212
Songer, Terri P29
Sonkin, Mitchell I. A540
Sonn, Crispin W266
Sonnabend, Stephanie A169
Sonnemaker, Scott A. A778
Sonnenberg, Steven A. (Steve) A290
Sonnenberg, Dean E. P558
Sonnenborn, Beverly E432
Sonnenfeld, Jeffrey A. (Jeff) A506
Sonnett, Judith A. (Judy) A564
Sonnino, Elvio W371
Sonshine, Edward W299
Sontheimer, Dan P283
Soo, Peggy E344
Sood, Arvind K. A56
Sood, Vijay K. A376
Sookoo, Suresh W299
Soon, Cham Tao W372
Soong, Raymond E125
Soong, Leo P400
Soong, Tham W371
Sophonpanich, Chartsiri W47
Sophonpanich, Charn W47
Sophonphanit, Chatri W47
Sopp, Mark W. A505
Sora, Riccardo W370
Soranno-Keating, Valerie (Val) W58
Soranno-Keating, Valerie (Val) W60
Sorbara, Nicole A218
Sordello, Steven J. (Steve) E276
Sordello, Giovanni W40
Sorelle, Richard D. (Rich) A304
Sorem, James R. P536
Sorensen, Jason E173
Sorensen, Susan E286
Sorensen, Mark R. A589
Sorensen, Allan C. (Al) A697
Sorensen, Brad A720
Sorensen, Roger T. A782
Sorensen, Don J. A792
Sorensen, Lars R. A799
Sorensen, Allen R. A828
Sorensen, Soren P151
Sorensen, Carl P574
Sorensen, Charles W. P581
Sorensen, Diane P612
Sorenson, Steven P. A36
Sorenson, Rob A155
Sorenson, Arne M. A531
Sorenson, Arne M. A854
Sorenson, Ralph Z. A873
Sorenson, Charles W. P249
Sorfleet, Diana A231
Sorgi, Vincent (Vince) A654
Soriano, Lidio V. A651
Sorkin, Michael A507
Sorrell, Martin A30
Sorrell, Jennifer P335
Sorrells, Michael A. A337
Sorrels, Hershel P603
Sorrentino, Charles A. E232
Sorrentino, Charles A. E471
Sorsby, J. Larry E233
Sorter, Michael T P109
Sorzano, Jose S. A535
Sosa, Enrique J. A600
Sosin, Jennifer A459
Sosland, L. Joshua A822

Steele, S. K. P502
Steele, Mark T. P554
Steele, David F. P577
Steelhammer, Robert A668
Steen, Michael T. E44
Steen, Andrew A116
Steen, Ida Clement A232
Steen, Ida A232
Steen, Bernie P522
Steenland, Douglas M. (Doug) A51
Steenland, Douglas M. (Doug) A456
Steenman, Bernard F. A356
Steenman, Ton H. A452
Steenrod, Mitchell D. A155
Steer, Robert L. A722
Steerman, John E46
Steerman, Katherine E46
Steers, Bill W30
Steeves, Frank L. A290
Stefani, Matthew E175
Stefani, Mark A374
Stefanik, Paul W. A796
Stefano, Julie de A664
Stefano, Christine M. De A673
Stefano, Ron A689
Stefano, Mariane P341
Stefano, George B. P528
Stefanski, Marc A. A796
Stefanski, Jodi P274
Steffen, Karl E113
Steffen, Carolyn P87
Steffens, Ray P213
Steffens, Earl P490
Steffensen, Dwight A774
Steffes, Jennifer E175
Steffes, James (Jim) A603
Steffes, Lorene K. A651
Steffl, Carol P562
Stegemann, Klaus P. W320
Steggert, Robert P364
Stegmann, Stefan von A245
Stegmayer, Joseph H. (Joe) E83
Stegner, Robert L. (Bob) A774
Steiger, Nancy P379
Steigerwald, Joseph M. (Joe) A452
Steil, Justin W E159
Steimel, Ron P314
Steimer, Olivier W8
Steimle, Kimberly P486
Stein, Scott E28
Stein, Richard M E67
Stein, Clint E. E97
Stein, A. William E124
Stein, Kevin M. E475
Stein, Sherry E487
Stein, Jonathan E507
Stein, David L. A77
Stein, Robert A78
Stein, Martin A. A101
Stein, Derek K. A124
Stein, Laura A191
Stein, Clint E. A204
Stein, William G. A224
Stein, Laura A360
Stein, Jonathan C. A416
Stein, Robin L. A630
Stein, Kevin M. A657
Stein, Michael S. A693
Stein, Theodore P98
Stein, John P344
Stein, Lisa P394
Stein, Eric L. P425
Stein, Rainer W149
Steinbach, Margaret E306
Steinback, Kenneth B. (Ken) P143
Steinbeck, Daryl P540
Steinbecker, Roger J. A425
Steinberg, Doug E133
Steinberg, Lee E306
Steinberg, Gregory (Greg) A15
Steinberg, Sandra A252
Steinberg, Stanley (Mickey) A367
Steinberg, Matt A497
Steinberg, Joseph S. A507
Steinberg, Paul A570

Steinberg, Burt A760
Steinberg, David J. P287
Steinberg, Scott A. W328
Steinberger, Georg A91
Steinborn, Birgit W320
Steinbrink, William H. A733
Steinbruck, Peer W354
Steiner, Judith A (Judy) E174
Steiner, Gregory L. (Greg) E261
Steiner, Janine E393
Steiner, James R. A225
Steiner, David P. A324
Steiner, Judith A. (Judy) A346
Steiner, Gerald A. (Jerry) A566
Steiner, Arnold L. A611
Steiner, Melanie A677
Steiner, David P. A858
Steiner, Kevin K P14
Steiner, Thomas K. P56
Steiner, Lara P93
Steinert, Earl A. A392
Steines, Robert J. E48
Steines, R J E48
Steines, Brian P439
Steingraber, Fred G. P244
Steinhafel, Gregg W. A780
Steinhart, Richard E246
Steinhart, Ronald G. (Ron) A635
Steinhoff, David E175
Steinhorn, Jeff L. A416
Steinike, Edmund R. (Ed) A198
Steinke, Bruce A45
Steinl, Greg E202
Steinle, Karl W163
Steinmetz, Edward J P576
Steinour, Stephen D. (Steve) A305
Steinour, Stephen D. (Steve) A436
Stel, David E431
Stella, Giovanni W348
Stellato, Louis E. A727
Stelling, Sandy A28
Stelling, James P. A52
Stelling, Kessel D. A776
Stelly, Berch P372
Stelnik, Jeff P70
Stelzer, John P208
Stemberg, Thomas G. (Tom) A155
Stemberg, Thomas G. (Tom) A640
Stemmer, Ralf W129
Stenberg, Patrik W382
Stenbit, John P. P523
Stendardi, Deborah P419
Stende, David L. (Dave) P166
Stengel, Steve A589
Stennes, Vicky A469
Stensgaard, Beth P68
Stenske, Douglas E. A708
Stenson, Tom D. A317
Stensrud, William R. (Bill) A477
Stenstadvold, Halvor W335
Stepan, F. Quinn E442
Stephan, Timothy A851
Stephen, Clarencia J. P5
Stephen, Emily P159
Stephens, Bob E124
Stephens, John M. E286
Stephens, Martin R. (Marty) E308
Stephens, John J. A80
Stephens, Danny A91
Stephens, Douglas A95
Stephens, Richard D. (Rick) A126
Stephens, Warren A. A253
Stephens, Keith A353
Stephens, Melvin L. (Mel) A503
Stephens, Cindy L. A630
Stephens, Jay B. A689
Stephens, John D. A827
Stephens, Burton R. A827
Stephens, John D. A827
Stephens, Steven D. A891
Stephens, Gary A. P80
Stephens, Shane P137
Stephens, James R. (Jim) P301
Stephens, Linda P382
Stephenson, Robert O. E357

Stephenson, Sandra E369
Stephenson, James E476
Stephenson, Scott G. E507
Stephenson, Randall L. A80
Stephenson, Vivian M. A155
Stephenson, Robert R. A262
Stephenson, Randall L. A290
Stephenson, Carol M. A377
Stephenson, Jack M. A476
Stephenson, Matt P40
Stephenson, Roland G. (Rollie) P181
Stephenson, Gordon P378
Stepic, Herbert W267
Stepp, E. Kay A750
Stepp, Lisa M. P498
Sterin, Steven M. (Steve) A163
Sterling, John F. E118
Sterling, Ingmar E365
Sterling, John E521
Sterling, John L. A342
Sterling, Steven (Steve) A481
Sterling, Dan A876
Sterling, Stephanie W302
Sterling, Eric W320
Stern, Alec E104
Stern, Neal E380
Stern, Gabrielle E421
Stern, Paula A92
Stern, Paul G. A270
Stern, Carl W. A348
Stern, Ronald A. A373
Stern, Rick A666
Stern, Peter C. A800
Stern, Paul G. A871
Stern, Holly P342
Stern, James A. (Jim) P556
Stern, Caryl M. P566
Sternberg, Seymour (Sy) A184
Sternberg, Seymour (Sy) A309
Sternberg, Elliot B P472
Sterner, Jeffrey L. P230
Sterner, Jeffery L. P231
Sternlicht, Leo P259
Sterrett, Stephen E. A730
Sterthous, Diane P347
Stesny, Anne P478
Stetz, Gary E50
Stetzer, Ed P285
Steuer, Jonathan E474
Steuer, Eric P514
Steuert, Michael A353
Steuert, D. Michael A870
Steur, Christine van der W80
Steuterman, Jim E41
Steven, Wayne P188
Steven, Anna W81
Stevens, Tara E10
Stevens, Terry E21
Stevens, Joe E77
Stevens, Glenn H. E193
Stevens, Curtis M. (Curt) E280
Stevens, Rick E287
Stevens, Brian E395
Stevens, Chip A17
Stevens, Michele P. A338
Stevens, William J. (Bill) A378
Stevens, Thomas C. (Tom) A486
Stevens, Robert J. (Bob) A518
Stevens, Anne L. A519
Stevens, Robert J. (Bob) A566
Stevens, Meredith A585
Stevens, Bert A592
Stevens, Todd A. A608
Stevens, Wayne A814
Stevens, Simon A838
Stevens, Lisa J. A861
Stevens, Jeff A. A868
Stevens, Chris P63
Stevens, Edward P74
Stevens, George Q. P184
Stevens, Amy P330
Stevens, Max P549
Stevens, Lori P549
Stevens, Jason W230

Stevenson, Eric E11
Stevenson, Whitney E62
Stevenson, Michael E360
Stevenson, Kevin P. E380
Stevenson, Heather E408
Stevenson, Dawn E439
Stevenson, Jennifer A4
Stevenson, Bruce A. A292
Stevenson, Kimberly S. (Kim) A451
Stevenson, Shannan A664
Stevenson, Lord Dennis A868
Stevenson, Tom A880
Stevenson, David A. P129
Stevenson, Jim P306
Stevenson, Leslie Williams P574
Stevenson, Sarah A. P577
Stevenson, Katharine B. (Kate) W84
Steverlynck, Juan A488
Steverson, Lewis A. A226
Steverson, Lewis A. A570
Stevick, Tom P162
Stevovich, Mira E514
Stew, Amy A318
Stew, Reed P379
Stew, Nicole P382
Steward, Michael E411
Steward, David L. A165
Steward, Larry E. A273
Steward, H. Leighton A300
Steward, David L. A333
Steward, Russ A789
Steward, David P600
Stewart, Eric E11
Stewart, Lacy E65
Stewart, Mary E119
Stewart, Robert S. (Bob) E137
Stewart, Chad E172
Stewart, Chris E183
Stewart, Heather E306
Stewart, Lisa E452
Stewart, Art E457
Stewart, Laurie K. A23
Stewart, David K. A53
Stewart, Julia A. A88
Stewart, J. W. A95
Stewart, Ian A103
Stewart, Beth A. A155
Stewart, Cecelia (Cece) A186
Stewart, David L. A262
Stewart, Shelley A275
Stewart, Tara A275
Stewart, Amy A318
Stewart, Michael J. (Mike) A341
Stewart, Gary A. A366
Stewart, James T. (Jim) A479
Stewart, Carol A481
Stewart, Ron A495
Stewart, Michael K. A527
Stewart, Derek M. A572
Stewart, Marta R. A598
Stewart, Scott D. A602
Stewart, John A692
Stewart, Jim A827
Stewart, Andrew P28
Stewart, Douglas S. P75
Stewart, Christopher P243
Stewart, David P243
Stewart, Milton R. (Milt) P244
Stewart, Concetta M. P312
Stewart, Nathaniel Johnson
    (John) P375
Stewart, Reed P379
Stewart, John P402
Stewart, D. Craig P482
Stewart, Mark A. P482
Stewart, Inez P506
Stewart, Henry R. P553
Stewart, John M. W210
Stewart-Jones, Priscilla A613
Stice, J. Mike E522
Stice, J. Michael (Mike) A174
Stice, D. Scott A316
Stichnoth, Roseann A320
Sticka, Travis P605
Stickler, Randy G. A437

Sykora, Sarah P39
Syler-Jones, Tracy P500
Sylvester, Todd E119
Sylvester, Maryrose T. A373
Sylvester, Edward B. A865
Symes, Connie A307
Symington, Margaret (Meg) P616
Symon, Carl G. W39
Symonds, Robert E195
Symonds, J. Taft A650
Symonds, Jonathan R. (Jon) W261
Symons, Robert A. A654
Syms, Marcy A701
Synek, Christopher R. A697
Syphax, Scott C. A318
Sypolt, Gary L. A264
Syriani, Aziz R.D. A608
Syriani, Aziz R.D. W116
Syverson, Cindra P472
Syverud, Kent P495
Syz, David W. W116
Szabados, Michael E345
Szabatin, Stephen J. A463
Szabo, Eric A64
Szabo, Eszter A374
Szabo, John P. A562
Szafraniec, Joe E295
Szarkowski, Lisa P566
Szathmary, Emoke J. E. W160
Szathmary, Emoke W160
Szathmary, Emoke J. E. W282
Szathmary, Emoke W282
Szathmary, Emoke J. E. W283
Szathmary, Emoke W283
Szatkiewicz, Cory P557
Szatkowski, Rick E46
Szatmary, David P579
Szczepanski, Adam E182
Szczepanski, Gerald R. (Jerry) A367
Szczesny, Jeffrey D P406
Szczsponik, John A794
Szczupak, David T. (Dave) A871
Szela, Mary T. A4
Szelagiewicz, Julius P557
Szenczy, Catherine P308
Szerlong, Timothy J. (Tim) A193
Szeto, Paul P38
Szews, Charles L. (Charlie) A619
Szews, Charles L. (Charlie) A620
Szilagyi, Stephen J. A523
Szkody, Paula P34
Szkutak, Thomas J. (Tom) A42
Szmurlo, Chuck J. W137
Sznewajs, John G. A534
Szokol, Joseph P354
Szostak, M. Anne A272
Sztraicher, Karen A. E55
Szubski, Michael A. (Mike) P569
Szuch, John S. A329
Szulc, Jaime C. A387
Szumski, Larry A449
Szwed, Stanley F. A345
Szydlowski, Norman J. (Norm) E403

T

T?pholm, Jan W2
Tabacco, Marina W189
Tabat, Dawn E199
Tabbutt, Mark A856
Taber, Grant E520
Tabernero, Jordi W152
Tabor, Coleen A744
Tabor, Jo P473
Taborga, Jorge E360
Tabron, La June Montgomery P592
Tabush, Eduardo P218
Tachibana-Fukushima, Sakie W78
Tachovsky, Barbara J. P294
Tacka, David W. A413
Tackett, Wayne E3
Tackett, David A213
Tackett, Brent P108
Tadaki, Keiichi W12

Taddeo, Ray E363
Tadeu, Ricardo W28
Tadie, Patrick A102
Taets, Joseph D. (Joe) A73
Taeuber, Annette W127
Taff, Katie E337
Taff, Michael S. A351
Taffe, Pat P350
Taffer, Lewis M E58
Tafoya, Debra (Debbie) P377
Taft, Dudley S. A329
Taft, Deb P206
Taft, David R. P287
Tagami, Minoru W255
Tagawa, Joji W255
Taggart, Julie A E301
Taggart, Gayle A82
Taggart, David M. A198
Taggart, Harriett (Tee) A399
Taggart, Richard (Rich) P452
Tagli, Larry M. A782
Tagliaferri, Mike P353
Taglieri, Lina W387
Tagomori, Satoshi W78
Taguchi, Yasuhiro W263
Tague, David P85
Tague, Carolyn P493
Tahir, Fahad P399
Tai, Pin A158
Tai, Luther A221
Tai, Jackson P. A537
Tai, Jackson P. W205
Tai, Ichiro W360
Taik, Joe E127
Tait, Steve E195
Tait, Joseph (Joe) E285
Tait, John H. A235
Tait, Steven A348
Tait, Bruce P26
Tait, Raymond P430
Tait, Duncan W150
Taitt, George E421
Taittinger, Anne-Claire W87
Tajima, Akio W124
Takaara, Toshikatsu W354
Takada, Katsumi Katsumi Takada W150
Takagi, Shigeo W169
Takagi, Shigeru W171
Takagi, Shigeru W172
Takaha, Yasuo W313
Takahara, Hirokazu W247
Takahashi, Seiichi W17
Takahashi, Atsushi W117
Takahashi, George W230
Takahashi, Hideaki W247
Takahashi, Yusuke W255
Takahashi, Kunio W313
Takahashi, Kozo W315
Takahashi, Hiroyuki W317
Takahashi, Katsunori W364
Takahata, Koichi W336
Takaki, Donald M. A101
Takamatsu, Norio W337
Takami, Kazunori W273
Takanabe, William E349
Takanashi, Kenji W364
Takano, Kengo W55
Takano, Hiroshi W364
Takao, Kazushi W225
Takasaki, Hideo W53
Takase, Susumu W17
Takase, Kenichi W225
Takasugi, Tadashi W230
Takata, Kiyota W254
Takayanagi, Koji W192
Takeda, Yukiko A851
Takeda, Kunitoshi W78
Takeda, Yoshiyuki W263
Takedagawa, Masahiro W171
Takeishi, Hiroaki W85
Takemura, Hideaki W225
Takenaka, Naoki Naoki Takenaka W360
Takenami, Yuichiro W78
Taketomi, Masao W117
Takeuchi, Mitsunobu A788

Takeuchi, Hirotaka W270
Takeuchi, Kazuhiro W336
Takeuchi, Akira W336
Takeuchi, Satoru W382
Takeyama, Yoshio W117
Takizawa, Soichiro W172
Talamas, Patrick E412
Talamonti, Mark S. P354
Talaulicar, Anant A233
Talbot, William E30
Talbot, David C. P341
Talbot, Graham W303
Talbott, Gail M. P207
Talento, Rick P398
Talhelm, Donald P281
Talhouet, Yves de A418
Taliaferro, Elizabeth W. (Coco) A370
Talka, Donald (Don) P559
Tallent, Jimmy C. A381
Tallent, Jimmy C. A826
Tallent, Jimmy C. A827
Tallent, William P481
Talles, Steven E. W268
Tallett, Elizabeth E. A661
Tallett-Williams, Michael A514
Talley, Robert F. A60
Talley, Tom P14
Talley, Linda P110
Talmor, Ron E163
Talone, Sister Alice M. P72
Talotta, Alessandro W348
Talwalkar, Abhi A501
Talwar, Vijay E59
Talwar, Harit A256
Tam, Alex E156
Tam, Frank P334
Tamagnini, Andrea W189
Tamai, Hiroto W318
Tamai, Takaaki W355
Tamayo, Cyndi E240
Tamba, Toshihito W192
Tambakeras, Markos I. A631
Tamberlane, John E421
Tamble, Joe P490
Tamburini, Jean-Jacques W40
Tamir, Rami E396
Tamke, George W. A415
Tamme, Susan Stout A696
Tamoney, Thomas H. A638
Tampa, Andy A391
Tampi, Pravin E348
Tamporello, Glenn P463
Tamura, Atsuto W113
Tamura, Minoru W342
Tamvakakis, Apostolos S. W244
Tan, Tze E53
Tan, Lip-Bu E71
Tan, Heow E376
Tan, John H. A207
Tan, Richard A265
Tan, Benjamin A318
Tan, Benjamin P547
Tan, Richard L. P608
Tan, Man-kou W52
Tan, Bernard W123
Tan, Tat Tat Wai Tan W220
Tan, Cynthia G. H. W271
Tanabe, Barbara J. A101
Tanabe, Yasuo W166
Tanabe, Eiichi W230
Tanabe, Kazuo W338
Tanai, Tsuneo W171
Tanai, Tsuneo W172
Tanaka, Harry E114
Tanaka, Takaaki E353
Tanaka, Masaaki (Masa) A568
Tanaka, Lance A792
Tanaka, Aaron P143
Tanaka, Toshizo W85
Tanaka, Akio W117
Tanaka, Koji W166
Tanaka, Kazuaki W223
Tanaka, Masaaki (Masa) W234
Tanaka, Tatsuo W234
Tanaka, Seiichi W236

Tanaka, Hiroshi W257
Tanaka, Takashi W262
Tanaka, Takashi W263
Tanaka, Yoshihiro W313
Tanaka, Hisao W360
Tanaka, Takaaki W360
Tanbourgi, Gabriel W62
Tande, Brett P100
Tandon, Mohit E160
Tandy, Karen P. A570
Taneda, Kyoko E195
Taneja, Sanjiv E71
Taneja, Raju E160
Taneya, Mototaka Mototaka
    Taneya W315
Tang, Francis E125
Tang, Cedric E328
Tang, David A11
Tang, K. P. A91
Tang, Anthony M. A158
Tang, Teller A455
Tang, Leona A720
Tang, Ryan P221
Tang, Paul C. P375
Tang, Michael P535
Tang, Yat Sun (Richard) W162
Tang, Bin W186
Tangeman, Amy J. A309
Tangen, Darren J. E96
Tangney, Michael J. A202
Tangney, Gene P352
Tangtatswas, Singh W47
Tani, Yasuhiro W85
Tani, Yasuhiro W86
Tani, Kenji W230
Tanigaki, Masahide W166
Tanigawa, Hiromichi W254
Tanigawa, Kazuo W360
Taniguchi, Norihiko W150
Taniguchi, Yuji W225
Taniguchi, Shinichi W252
Taniguchi, Nobuyuki W315
Tanimoto, Michihisa W337
Tanizawa, Fumihiko W338
Tankesley, B. Lynn A208
Tanking, Jim E429
Tannenbaum, Leonard M. E167
Tannenbaum, Richard E510
Tanner, Thomas E3
Tanner, Richard E162
Tanner, Krista E256
Tanner, Gregg A. A244
Tanner, Teresa J. A329
Tanner, Bruce L. A518
Tanner, Reed J. A862
Tanner, Allen P213
Tanner, Vickie P501
Tanner, Sharon P568
Tanner, Ernst W116
Tannuzzo, Leeann L. A353
Tanoue, Donna A. A101
Tanoue, Donna A. P400
Tanous, James J. A301
Tant, John P160
Tanurhan, Yankin E460
Taohai, Xue W96
Tapias, Alcides Lopes W191
Tapiero, Jacques A513
Tapling, Mark W262
Tapscott, Steven P323
Tarallo, Neil E11
Tarantini, Graziano W40
Taranto, Francesco W141
Tarapchak, Richard C. A578
Tarapor, Mahrukh P522
Tarbox, Andrea K. E262
Tarca, Fred P404
Tarchetti, Mark A585
Tardio, Vicente W45
Taresh, Carroll R. A811
Targetti, Ferdinando W190
Targhetta, Javier A363
Taride, Michel A415
Tarino, Gary E. A84
Tarle, Edward E141

Terashi, Shigeki W363
Terazawa, Tatsumaro W55
Teresi, Todd A68
Terisse, Pierre-Andre W121
Terium, Peter W305
Terkelsen, Franklin L. (Frank) A846
Terner, Franck W13
Ternowchek, Sam E321
Terpay, Susan A598
Terracciano, Anthony P. (Tony) A731
Terracciano, Paul P383
Terradas, Salvador W43
Terranova, Manuel A374
Terre, Jaon-David Grima i W9
Terrell, Daniel E. E282
Terrell, Dorothy A. A376
Terrell, Karenann K. A853
Terrell, Seth P402
Terrile, James P507
Terrinoni, Gary P268
Terrio, Kristine P129
Terrone, Michael R. A337
Terry, David A252
Terry, Hilliard C. A823
Terry, Paul P360
Terry, Steve P552
Terry, James W339
Terryn, Kristof W392
Teruel, Javier G. A634
Teruel, Javier G. A754
Tervalon, Mark J E445
Terwilliger, Roy P166
Terzano, Valerie P613
Tesciuba, Avi P233
Tese, Vincent S. A142
Tesija, Kathryn A. (Kathee) A781
Teslik, Sarah B. A67
Tessier, Drew A825
Tessier-Lavigne, Marc A642
Tessier-Lavigne, Marc P529
Tessler, Allan R. A496
Tessler, Herve A885
Tessmann, Patrick W209
Tessmar-Pfohl, Werner W144
Testa, Christopher P. A830
Testi, Paolo W40
Tetali, Rama E290
Tetreault, James P. A358
Tetreault, Patricia P576
Tetz, Warren P207
Teuber, William J. (Bill) A287
Teuber, William J. (Bill) A652
Teuber, Andrew (Andy) P10
Teulie, Pierre Alexandre W87
Teunis, Jon E98
Teuten, Thomas J. A444
Teuwsen, Bjorn W204
Tewell, Dennis W18
Textor, Donald F. A300
Teyssen, Johannes W134
Thabet, Pierre W243
Thacher, John P. P609
Thacker, Michael A418
Thaensathit, Suwan W47
Thaer, Lewis F. Von A371
Thaer, Lou F. Von A505
Thai-Tang, Hau A357
Thain, John A. A184
Thain, John A. P241
Thakur, Randhir A70
Thal, Bruce E. A546
Thal, Gayla L. A825
Thall, Martin T. A850
Tham, Ming Soong W371
Thaman, Michael H. (Mike) A589
Thaman, Michael H. (Mike) A622
Thames, Thomas P444
Thames, Robert P471
Than, Ralph A. A238
Thananithi, Piyaphan W47
Thanatsrang, Thawisak W47
Thangam, Prof Siva P480
Thani, Jassim Jassim Al Thani W116
Thansathit, Suvarn W47
Thanyasiri, Tharisa W47

Thareererg, Karen P221
Tharp, Beth P127
Tharp, Christy P184
Tharp, Eric P288
Tharp, Tom P438
Tharp, Jeffrey P602
Tharrington, Jeannie A664
Thatcher, Dale A. A725
Thatcher, Ed P151
Thaus, Kurt B. A785
Thawerbhoy, Nazim G. A466
Thaxton, Gregory A. E351
Thaxton, Kirk W. A338
Thayer, Jonathan W. (Jack) A305
Thayer, Charles J. A525
Thayer, Bud P54
Thayer, Harriette P. P613
Thebault, J. Brian A725
Thebeau, Steve E401
Theberg, LeeAna P549
Thede, Douglas K. E316
Thedford, Donald W. A738
Theile, Lindsay Lindsay A374
Theiler, Rick E98
Thein, Reggie W372
Theisen, Andy E444
Theisen, Henry J. A115
Theiss, Neil G. A778
Thekkekara, Ashley E176
Thelan, John D. A227
Thelen, Brian D. A377
Thelen, Gerhard A. A598
Thelmo, William P618
Themelis, Nicholas E292
Thene, Tony R. E79
Thene, Tony R. A30
Theobald, Stephen P. E515
Theobald, Thomas C. A44
Theobald, Thomas C. A474
Theobald, H. Scott A684
Theobald, Elizabeth P602
Theodorou, Andreas P534
Theodoru, Razvan L. A265
Theoklitos, Leonidas W244
Theoklitos, H. E. the Metropolitan of
   Ioannina W244
Theoklitos, Leonidas W244
Theophilus, Nicole B. A218
Theophilus, Don P494
Thernes, Dean P49
Therriault, Bridget P294
Thesing, Gregory P129
Thetge, Jeffrey D. A681
Theus, Caroline G. A572
Thiam, Tidjane C. W284
Thiara, Gary S. P491
Thibaud, Laure W309
Thibodeau, Denis E456
Thibodeaux, Benjy E167
Thibodeaux, Beth E177
Thibodeaux, Faron J. A67
Thiel, Peter A. A312
Thiel, Donald P94
Thielemann, Heather P240
Thienemann, Sabina Flaxa W9
Thiers, Bernard P. A561
Thies, Bradley J (Brad) E165
Thies, Jeff P472
Thiessen, Gordon G. W221
Thigpen, Jeremy A574
Thigpen, Carl S. A668
Thigpen, Richard T. A673
Thill, Howard J. A527
Thinnes, Andrew E514
Thirarotchanawong, Sa-ard W47
Thiratharathorn, Ratchada W47
Thirsk, William (Bill) P297
Thiruvengadam, Sridhar A201
Thiry, Kent J. A243
Thissen, Tom A95
Thixton, Laura A446
Thoder, Joseph J. P498
Thoene, Christie A680
Thoeresz, Johanna P313
Tholking, Ian A665

Thoma, Don L. E254
Thomae, Elizabeth E369
Thoman, Thomas S. A25
Thoman, Michele P339
Thoman, Gordon R. W312
Thomas, Martin E2
Thomas, Craig E47
Thomas, Samuel F. E85
Thomas, Stephanie E93
Thomas, Patrick E95
Thomas, Ogden U. E102
Thomas, Christopher E172
Thomas, Rob A E174
Thomas, Todd E186
Thomas, Chris E195
Thomas, Suzanne C. E216
Thomas, Bennett E223
Thomas, Del E237
Thomas, Guy E261
Thomas, James M E315
Thomas, Nancy E331
Thomas, Ron E339
Thomas, Andrew E344
Thomas, Roy E468
Thomas, Micky E521
Thomas, Michael E521
Thomas, John B. A4
Thomas, Lee M. A25
Thomas, Laura J. A47
Thomas, Dan A104
Thomas, Ian A126
Thomas, Chris A131
Thomas, Mary H. A143
Thomas, Tuesday N. A169
Thomas, Peter M. A189
Thomas, Eric A222
Thomas, Richard A235
Thomae, Kent B. A247
Thomas, Richard L. A265
Thomas, David J. A272
Thomas, Lee A275
Thomas, William R. A300
Thomas, Gary L. A300
Thomas, Vincent A303
Thomas, Robert W. A379
Thomas, Suzanne A396
Thomas, J. Darrell A402
Thomas, David M. A459
Thomas, Bruce V. A547
Thomas, Kurt J. A555
Thomas, Owen D. A568
Thomas, Geevy S. K. A596
Thomas, Paige L. A596
Thomas, Dan A613
Thomas, James A. (Jim) A636
Thomas, Timothy G. A647
Thomas, Darryl K. A663
Thomas, Martin (Marty) A707
Thomas, Randy A716
Thomas, John M. A789
Thomas, Matt A792
Thomas, W. Olen A824
Thomas, Cheryl A843
Thomas, Andrea A853
Thomas, Jesse L. A860
Thomas, Stephen F. St. A861
Thomas, Anthony W. (Tony) A876
Thomas, Arleen R. P18
Thomas, Brenda P87
Thomas, Darwin P117
Thomas, Kennon J. P127
Thomas, Stephen P149
Thomas, Mark F. P181
Thomas, Terry P188
Thomas, David B. P188
Thomas, Frank P249
Thomas, Karen P283
Thomas, Karen P294
Thomas, Karen P295
Thomas, Georgie A. P341
Thomas, J. Mikesell (Mike) P354
Thomas, Brian P371
Thomas, Dean P439
Thomas, Edward K. P441
Thomas, William (Bill) P441

Thomas, Brad P456
Thomas, Earl P496
Thomas, Christy P526
Thomas, Cary E. P531
Thomas, Mark P544
Thomas, Huw F. P556
Thomas, Ronald R. P573
Thomas, Linda L. P575
Thomas, Patrick R P610
Thomas, Edwin P610
Thomas, Glenda P612
Thomas, Chet P616
Thomas, Barbara S. W54
Thomas, Patrick W. W63
Thomas, Claire W158
Thomas, Ralf P. W320
Thomas, Geoff W390
Thomas-Graham, Pamela A. A191
Thomas-Graham, Pamela A. W115
Thomashauer, Robin P5
Thomason, Carl E179
Thomason, Linton J. (Lin) A392
Thomason, Shannon A392
Thomason, Joe A786
Thomason, Joel D P380
Thomasson, Virginia C. A332
Thomasson, Bob P604
Thome, Paul A731
Thoming, Christopher S. P281
Thomlinson, David C. W6
Thomopoulos, Anthimos C. W244
Thompsen, Kelvin P. P460
Thompson, Kevin E47
Thompson, Carleton K. (Tres) E77
Thompson, Jennifer E80
Thompson, Stephen C. (Steve) E88
Thompson, Ed E144
Thompson, Brett E186
Thompson, Jess E196
Thompson, Ewan E196
Thompson, Scott L. E232
Thompson, Peter R. (Pete) E233
Thompson, Michael E265
Thompson, Merryl Werber E265
Thompson, Harris E306
Thompson, Kevin B. E320
Thompson, Christine E432
Thompson, Chris E503
Thompson, John E521
Thompson, Connie A2
Thompson, James F. A12
Thompson, David G. A17
Thompson, J. Samuel (Sam) A25
Thompson, J. Kenneth A28
Thompson, Gregory C. (Greg) A93
Thompson, Bruce R. A100
Thompson, Shelley B. A101
Thompson, Theresa A107
Thompson, Thomas N. (Tommy) A110
Thompson, Bill A119
Thompson, Betty A129
Thompson, Mark D. A132
Thompson, Mark A140
Thompson, Mark A141
Thompson, Dale A. A150
Thompson, Tommy G. A165
Thompson, Mark W. A167
Thompson, Michael L. A181
Thompson, William S. (Bill) A186
Thompson, Delia H. (Bina) A202
Thompson, Neil A203
Thompson, Duanne A213
Thompson, Lori A234
Thompson, Bob A252
Thompson, Donald (Don) A305
Thompson, Cary H. A326
Thompson, D. Gary A381
Thompson, Laura K. A387
Thompson, G. Kennedy (Ken) A418
Thompson, William G. A421
Thompson, Craig S. A433
Thompson, Kirk A435
Thompson, Mark E. A436
Thompson, Christopher A466
Thompson, Donald (Don) A541

A = AMERICAN BUSINESS
E = EMERGING COMPANIES
P = PRIVATE COMPANIES
W = WORLD BUSINESS

Tivy, James W. A460
Tizzio, Vincent C. A577
Tjon, Karin-Joyce S.F. (KJ) E153
Tjosvold, Robert P440
Tkach, Douglas W160
Toal, Anne W160
Tobe, Michael (Mike) P66
Toben, Bradley J. B. P51
Tober, Stephen J E291
Tobian, Gary E500
Tobin, Jim E60
Tobin, Peter J. A184
Tobin, Bruce A730
Tobin, Lee A873
Tobin, Bill P151
Tobin, Greg P445
Tobin, John H. P539
Tobin, Graham P576
Toburen, Paul P410
Toczydlowski, Greg A810
Todd, Aaron D. E18
Todd, Charles T. E54
Todd, Greg E97
Todd, Stephen M. A268
Todd, Clarence B. (C. B.) A573
Todd, Janine P143
Todman, Michael A. A585
Todman, Michael A. A871
Todman, Michael A. (Mike) A871
Todoroff, Christopher M. (Chris) A434
Todt, Blair W. A860
Toevs, Alden W106
Tofani, Barbara P109
Toffey, Bryan P7
Toffler, Van A847
Togashi, Kazuhisa W336
Togher, Renee A539
Togneri, Gabriel B. (Gabe) A643
Togni, Alberto W50
Toit, Philippus Philippus du Toit W30
Toizer, Eric L. A184
Tokarczyk, Peter P23
Tokarski, Chris E441
Tokarz, Michael T. A194
Tokarz, Michael T. A855
Token, Eric P422
Tokubutsu, Fumio W337
Tokuda, Hiromi W124
Tokuhiro, Kiyoshi W262
Tokumitsu, Shigenori Shigenori
  Tokumitsu W360
Tokunari, Muneaki W234
Tolan, Julie P300
Tolbert, J. David A467
Toledano, Sidney W100
Toledo, Victor E263
Toledo, Laura P445
Toledo, Liz Gallegos P472
Toledo, Richard P578
Tolentino, Ryan P105
Toliver, Dennis P. A379
Tolley, Brad E419
Tollison, Michael E432
Tollison, D. Tip A379
Tolliver, Joseph P468
Tollkuehn, Julie E97
Tolman, Larry R E308
Tolosky, Mark R. P52
Tolot, Jerome W156
Tolstedt, Carrie L. A861
Tom, Baertlein E166
Tom, Walker P214
Toma, Shigeki W317
Toman, Nicholas E108
Toman, Troy E389
Tomarchio, Joseph E324
Tomaschefsky, Rick P353
Tomasek, Adam P616
Tomashewski, Dave E85
Tomasky, Susan A47
Tomasky, Susan A792
Tomason, Bruce P446
Tomassini, Luca W348
Tomasuolo, Henry P506
Tomb, David R. A335

Tomb, Matthew A335
Tomb, David R. A335
Tombaugh, Terry A82
Tomcsanyi, Pedro E301
Tomczyk, James E. A173
Tome, Carol B. A422
Tome, Lores A481
Tome, Carol B. A831
Tome, Carol A831
Tomecka, Anna P76
Tomich, Rosemary A608
Tomita, Hidetaka W101
Tomita, Kimio W255
Tomka, Dave P49
Tomkalski, Mark J. P518
Tomlin, John E379
Tomlin, Darcy A257
Tomlinson, Pam E298
Tomlinson, Janice C. A577
Tomlinson, Philip W. (Phil) A776
Tomlinson, Tommy P118
Tomlinson, Geoffrey A. (Geoff) W242
Tommiska, Kati W258
Tomnitz, Donald J. (Don) A427
Tomnitz, Donald J. (Don) A428
Tomono, Hiroshi W252
Tomozoe, Masanao W363
Tompkins, William E89
Tompkins, Cathlyn L. (Cathy) A174
Tompkins, P. Kelly A189
Tompkins, Paul A226
Tompkins, James A273
Tomson, Louis R. P528
Ton, Tony E400
Tonar, Bill E201
Tonarelli, Ed E394
Toner, Susan P52
Toney, Frederiek A358
Toney, Charles A551
Tong, Gary L. E261
Tong, Chris A779
Tong, William P66
Tong, Hon shing W52
Tong, Lim Khiang W271
Tonges, Mary P572
Tongson, Timothy J. (Tim) A194
Tonnison, John A784
Tonnu, DiemLan (Lannie) P507
Tonoike, Tohru A17
Toohey, Robert A. A845
Toohey, Robert A P36
Toohey, Garritt P422
Tooker, Gary L. A91
Tooker, Jean E. (Jeanie) P465
Tookes, Hansel E. A226
Tookes, Hansel E. A405
Tookes, Hansel E. A589
Tookes, Hansel E. A712
Toomajian, Marty P48
Toomajian, Charles R. P394
Toomey, James A206
Toomey, Rebecca J. A629
Toomey, John M. A785
Toomey, Roger P561
Toong, Yee Chek W388
Toot, Joseph F. W277
Toothaker, Ronald W E39
Toothaker, Bradley A500
Topalian, Elyse P522
Topazi, Anthony J. A396
Topazi, Anthony J. A737
Topham, H. Scott A538
Topham, Michael J. G. P233
Topjian, Diana P91
Topley, Silvia Merino E251
Topoluk, R. Elizabeth A782
Topp, Jerry A. P166
Topper, Joseph V. P589
Toppeta, William J. A552
Toppin, Richard T. A379
Toppin, Bruce P351
Toppin, Bruce P352
Topping, Scott E218
Topping, Linda A203
Torabi, Kamran E71

Torassian, Thomas K. A782
Torbert, Ellen A739
Torbert, Ronald J P47
Torborg, Jim P26
Torcom, Lance P444
Toretti, Christine J. A713
Torgersen, M. LaDon (Don) P338
Torgerson, James P. E487
Toriello, Edward P618
Torigian, Maria P446
Torii, Keizo W223
Torio, Livio W190
Toriumi, Chie W257
Torkelson, Bruce E439
Torma, Anna E E179
Tornbohm, Catherine E197
Torno, Arthur J. A46
Toro, Marilu Del A712
Toro, Gustavo P618
Torpey, Michael W52
Torre, Ralph de la P482
Torre, Alexis E. Rovzar de la W54
Torrego, Agustin Bateucas W9
Torrence, Rick E487
Torres, Francis E240
Torres, Denise A470
Torres, Manuel A570
Torres, Albert F. (Al) A643
Torres, Maria P446
Torres, Michelle P493
Torres, George P501
Torres, David S. P546
Torres, Antonio Escamez W46
Torres-Santos, Raymond P541
Torstendahl, Mats W323
Torto, Raymond (Ray) A160
Tortora, Robert D. P202
Toscano, Dan P143
Toselli, Damiano W348
Tosh, Kealani E153
Tostanoski, Jean P383
Tostivin, Jean-Claude W74
Totusek, Jeffrey P. A825
Totzke, Ned R. P336
Toubro, Per Alling W122
Touchton, David M. P576
Touff, Michael E286
Tougas, Roger C. P449
Tough, Mark C. E149
Tough, Steven D. (Steve) A411
Toulantis, Marie J. P374
Toulme, Patrick P353
Toulon, Rik A161
Toungette, Michele E35
Toups, Sharon A. P430
Tourek, Tim W18
Tourkaman, Ali P167
Tourkolias, Alexandros G. W244
Tourkolias, Alexandros W244
Tousi, Susan E243
Toutain, Henry P215
Toutant, Sylvain A485
Tov, Imri W48
Tovar, David (Dave) A853
Tow, Leonard A142
Towle, Ken W352
Towles, Stokley P. P333
Towne, Brian D. E131
Towne, Gary L. A72
Towne, Patrick P100
Townley, Nancy P564
Towns, Fred A774
Townsend, Sean E225
Townsend, James G E228
Townsend, Adam A161
Townsend, Jay C. A163
Townsend, Robert (Rob) A346
Townsend, John L. A458
Townsend, Christopher G. A552
Townsend, Thomas J. A763
Townsend, James M. A776
Townsend, Ronald D. (Ron) P48
Townsend, Joseph P109
Townsend, Craig K. P115
Townsend, Barbara P313

Townsend, John W379
Toy, Robert E434
Toy, Henry E437
Toyama, Takashi W273
Toyne, Cameron E452
Toyobe, Katsuyuki W53
Toyoda, Kanshiro W16
Toyoda, Shoichiro W17
Toyoda, Shoichiro W124
Toyoda, Akio W363
Toyohara, Masayasu Masayasu
  Toyohara W360
Toyohara, Yoji W364
Toyoki, Noriyuki W150
Toyomasu, Shunichi W255
Toyoshima, Masaaki W12
Tozzi, William A. A112
Traa, Richard L. P453
Trabulus, Joyce Bogart P507
Tracey, Patricia A. A833
Tracey, Jonathan W332
Trachtman, Les P191
Traci, Dana A256
Tract, Marc M. A577
Tracy, Jay E455
Tracy, John J. A126
Tracy, Ann A203
Tracy, Doug S. A215
Tracy, Mike A218
Tracy, Doug S. A239
Tracy, John M. A298
Tracy, Edward M. (Ed) A502
Tracy, James J. A568
Tracy, Joseph A810
Tracy, William A. (Bill) P115
Tracy, Doug P143
Tracy, Thomas (Tom) P356
Trader, Kevin E497
Tradewell, Thomas P587
Traenkle, Kevin P. E96
Traficant, James A. (Jim) A404
Traficant, Jim W7
Traficanti, Joseph J. (Joe) A830
Trager, A. Scott A695
Trager, Steven E. (Steve) A695
Trager, Bernard M. A695
Trahan, Kendall E80
Trahan, Sister Celeste P113
Traier, Kevin B P457
Trainer, Ken L E408
Trainer, Michael P111
Trainor, Edward J. (Ted) E357
Trainor, David P130
Tram, Phuong A275
Tramack, Michael E455
Trammell, Kenneth R. (Ken) A788
Tran, Duy E301
Tran, Dat T. A21
Tran, Thomas L. A860
Tranchon, Harold P259
Trani, John M. A697
Tranquillo, Stephen P543
Tranter, Gregory D. A399
Trapani, Francesco W216
Trapnell, Stephen (Steve) A769
Trapp, Paul P145
Trapp, Michael W. (Mike) P526
Traquina, Perry M. P76
Traub, Barbara P467
Traube, Joseph P440
Traugh, Cecilia P287
Trauth, Denise M. P502
Trautman, Tom E259
Trautman, David L. A629
Trautman, David L. A630
Trautmann, Robert E. A636
Travaglianti, Edward P287
Travaglianti, Edward P613
Travers, Martin G. P66
Traverso, Kenneth M. E340
Travis, Tracey A149
Travis, Timothy J. A197
Travis, Tom A365
Travis, Nigel A521
Travis, Nigel A609

Turek, Marty E98
Turek, Betsy P164
Turgeon, Mary K. A856
Turicchi, R. Scott E258
Turilli, M. Louise (Lou) A215
Turina, Mary P367
Turkovich, Joe P491
Turmel, Jean W18
Turnas, Jeff A873
Turnbull, Thomas P591
Turnbull, Lord Andrew W284
Turner, Scott E2
Turner, Brent E7
Turner, Lane E139
Turner, Douglas E175
Turner, Rick M. E210
Turner, Brad E239
Turner, Jane E251
Turner, Larissa E339
Turner, Herman E E351
Turner, Tracy E393
Turner, Bret E455
Turner, Len E481
Turner, John F. A47
Turner, William H. A54
Turner, John F. A76
Turner, Robb E. A138
Turner, John G. A194
Turner, Reginald M. (Reggie) A207
Turner, Kathryn C. A220
Turner, Jim L. A230
Turner, Jim L. A244
Turner, Dan A275
Turner, K. Rick A295
Turner, K. Rick A296
Turner, Scott C. A321
Turner, Joseph W. (Joe) A392
Turner, William V. A392
Turner, Joseph W. (Joe) A392
Turner, Brad A405
Turner, Leslie M. A413
Turner, Michael R. A416
Turner, John G. A426
Turner, Simon A439
Turner, John F. A458
Turner, Fred L. A541
Turner, Mervyn (Merv) A549
Turner, B. Kevin A560
Turner, John C. A561
Turner, B. Kevin A596
Turner, Michael L. (Mike) A616
Turner, Paul E. A629
Turner, John F. A633
Turner, R. Gerald A634
Turner, M. Terry A648
Turner, John M. A691
Turner, David J. A691
Turner, George W. A706
Turner, Jeffrey L. (Jeff) A708
Turner, Robyn P. A725
Turner, Jeffrey L. (Jeff) A744
Turner, Jeffrey L. (Jeff) A745
Turner, Simon M. A755
Turner, William B. (Brad) A776
Turner, Marlin E. A778
Turner, Robert W. A825
Turner, William R. (Rick) A825
Turner, Bobby A873
Turner, Mark A. A880
Turner, Margaret P75
Turner, Robert E. P75
Turner, Thomas S P111
Turner, Allen M. P125
Turner, Deborah M. P196
Turner, Kelly P207
Turner, Lynn H. P300
Turner, Skip P331
Turner, Kay P342
Turner, Tim P361
Turner, Mark J. P398
Turner, Rick P428
Turner, Jeffrey P511
Turner, Michael (Mike) P540
Turner, Howard P595
Turner, Cathy W58

Turner, Cathy W60
Turner, David J. W106
Turner, Nigel W127
Turney, Doug A459
Turney, Sharen J. A496
Turney, Sally W35
Turngren, Robert P315
Turnham, Robert C. E515
Turowski, Simon E373
Turpen, Kenneth M. P568
Turpin, Ian J. A793
Turpin, Jennifer E. P575
Turrini, Regis A8
Turrini, Regis W377
Tursi, Joan P345
Tursky, Martin P186
Turteltaub, Rhea P533
Turton, Daniel A297
Turton, Harry A. A824
Turver, John P508
Turvey, Lavona P477
Tury, Lee P390
Turza, Steve A797
Tusa, Andrew E432
Tuscai, T. J. A589
Tusher, Thomas W. P616
Tutcher, Dan C. W137
Tutelman, Betsy Leebron P498
Tuthill, Cynthia W. E415
Tutkovics, Julie C. E174
Tutkovics, Julie C. A346
Tutlis, Seth E384
Tutt, Brian E339
Tuttle, Chris E11
Tuttle, Robert H. (Bob) A189
Tuttle, Stephen D. A590
Tuttle, Marlene P66
Tuttle, Marlene P373
Tutun, Paul E509
Tutwiler, Margaret D. A184
Tuuk, Mary E. A329
Tuzun, Tayfun A329
Tveitnes, Tim P120
Tveten, Karen P245
Tvrdy, Pam J. A708
Tweed, Darell E387
Tweedy, Rusty A10
Tweeten, Donna P242
Twells, Katherine A198
Twembeke, Willem van W156
Twiford, Rainer J E471
Twigg, Bernard P. A862
Twiggs, Gary A. E305
Twillman, Shirley P18
Twinem, Mary J. E68
Twinem, Carita R. A742
Twining, John R. P404
Twinley, Ian A394
Twisdale, Lawrence A. P27
Twitchel, Sue P495
Twitty, Tim A. E450
Twomey, Chris E40
Twomey, Mike A297
Twomey, Bob A859
Twomey, Gerri P41
Twyman, Rob A873
Tyabji, Hatim A. A119
Tyburczy, Caroline E328
Tye, Christine P313
Tyers, Joseph A (Joe) E303
Tygart, Kathy P477
Tykocinski, Richard J. P543
Tyle, Craig S. A360
Tylee, Faye A881
Tyler, Anthony J. A305
Tyler, Brian S. A543
Tyler, Andrew A602
Tyler, Michael R. (Mike) A716
Tyler, Breck W. A814
Tyler, Robert J. A856
Tyler, Willis P160
Tyler, Linda P165
Tyler, Robert (Gene) P585
Tyler, David A. W194
Tyll, Michael A. (Mike) A751

Tymkiw, Andrew E141
Tynan, Matthew N. A659
Tynan, Robert P310
Tyndall, William F. (Bill) A277
Tyner, Herbert A546
Tyra, James A. A52
Tyre, Al E11
Tyree, James C. A662
Tyree, Tom P621
Tyrell, James E. P377
Tyrrell, Joseph E144
Tyrwhitt, Hamish G. W168
Tysen, Atticus A462
Tyser, Matthew C. A379
Tysoe, Ronald W. (Ron) A181
Tysoe, Ronald W. (Ron) W84
Tyson, Charles E. A10
Tyson, Laura D. A81
Tyson, Laura D. A160
Tyson, Laura D. A568
Tyson, Donald A797
Tyson, John H. A818
Tyson, Barbara A. A818
Tyson, George E. A883
Tytgadt, Alain W199
Tyus, Shaunna P205
Tywater, Ty A722
Tzaferos, Sandy P453
Tzakou-Lambropoulou, Nelly W244
Tzeng, Yun P293
Tzoulafis, Evangelos E193

U

Ubbing, Mina H. P178
Ubeda, Jose A. A309
Ubelaker, John P460
Ubell, Michelle P299
Ubell, Robert P480
Uber, Rick E3
Ucelay, Juan Manuel Eguiagaray W16
Uchida, Stanley A. A629
Uchida, Kozo W252
Uchimoto, Tsuneo W17
Uchin, Robert A. P357
Uchinaga, Yukako W328
Uchino, Shuma W230
Uchiyama, Tadashi W354
Uchiyamada, Takeshi W363
Udager, Mark P26
Uddenfeldt, Jan W143
Ude, Jeff E78
Udell, Bob E103
Udell, C. Robert (Bob) E103
Udovic, Rev Edward R. P148
Ueang-udomsin, Siridet W47
Uebber, Bodo W119
Ueberroth, Peter V. (Pete) A199
Ueberroth, Virginia M. A331
Ueda, Ryoichi W230
Uehara, Hirohisa W345
Uehira, Mitsuhiko W345
Uejima, Hirokazu W150
Uenishi, Kenji A374
Ueno, Satoru W117
Ueno, Yasuo W241
Uenoyama, Makoto W273
Ugarte, Ricardo P. P612
Uggla, Ane M?rsk Mc-Kinney W2
Ugwueke, Michael P317
Uhart, Barney P114
Uher, Cheryl E175
Uhl, Mike P453
Uhland, Gary E80
Uhlig, Richard A. A452
Uhlir, Jason W573
Uhlmann, Paul A822
Ui-yamaphan, Pratsani W47
Uible, John B. A629
Uji, Noritaka W253
Ujihara, Kiyoshi W251
Ujiie, Teruhiko W1
Ukrop, James E. (Jim) A621
Ukrop, James E. (Jim) A824

Ulbrandt, Laura E. A507
Ulbrich, Christian A474
Ulbricht, William (Bill) P470
Ulett, John W. A212
Ulett, John W. P102
Ulevitch, Chris E243
Ulicny, Gary R. P451
Ulissi, Roberto W141
Ullem, Scott B. E141
Ullem, Scott B. A115
Ullian, Elaine S. A799
Ullman, Myron E. (Mike) A633
Ullman, Myron E. (Mike) A754
Ullman, Donald L. P75
Ullman, David F. P342
Ullmann, Michael H. A470
Ullmer, Michael Michael Ullmer W390
Ullrich, Patricia E495
Ullrich, George P28
Ullyot, Theodore W. (Ted) A312
Ulmer, Dominik E110
Ulmer, Mark E239
Ulmer, R. Steve P26
Ulozas, Catherine P158
Ulreich, Shawn M. P464
Ulrich, Robert J. (Bob) A2
Ulrich, John C. A371
Ulrich, Paul S. A433
Ulrich, Clayton P233
Ulrich, Karl J. P443
Ulrich, Robert J. (Bob) P577
Ulrich, Fernando W42
Ulsh, James A. A769
Umaki, Tamio W270
Umemura, Hiroyuki W231
Umezawa, Toshinori W223
Umfress, Stephanie P544
Umland, Steve P364
Umpleby, D. James (Jim) A157
Unanue, Carlos A. A652
Underwood, Thomas A. A629
Underwood, M. List A691
Underwood, Galen E. A828
Underwood, William D. P510
Undis, Tom P562
Ung, Mark P316
Ungar, Stephen B. A59
Ungaro, Peter J. E110
Unger, Laura S. A44
Unger, Emerson V. A53
Unger, Laura S. A141
Unger, Laura S. A184
Unger, Donald L. A826
Unger, Catherine L. P87
Ungerleider, Howard A270
Ungerman, Bill P120
Uniat, Lois P439
Unkel, Craig P49
Unneland, Edmund A520
Uno, Ikuo W273
Uno, Ikuo W338
Unoura, Hiroo W253
Unruh, James A. A671
Unruh, V. Paul A772
Unruh, James A. A786
Unruh, Kay P321
Unruh, Todd P321
Unruh, David P498
Unsworth, John P76
Unterman, Tom P87
Unzueta, Jesus E484
Uotani, Masahiko A198
Upadhyay, Suketu A112
Upbin, Hal J. P374
Upchurch, W. Howard A397
Updegraff, Tom P74
Updike, James E. E267
Updyke, Rick E77
Upfill-Brown, Simon E477
Upham, Steadman P536
Uphouse, Jeanne M. E305
Uphouse, Jeanne E444
Upicksoun, Alma McClellan P28
Upton, Jerome T. A380
Upton, David M. A784

Vassall, John H. P494
Vassallo, Stephen E462
Vassallo, Susan A719
Vasseur, Denis Le W282
Vasseur, Denis W282
Vasseur, Denis Le W283
Vasseur, Denis W283
Vassiliadis, Michael W62
Vastrup, Prof Claus W122
Vasudev, C.M. W164
Vasudeva, Nishi W164
Vaswani, Ashok W58
Vaswani, Ashok W60
Vats, Trib P310
Vaucleroy, Jacques de W36
Vaucleroy, Jacques de W146
Vaughan, Bruce E373
Vaughan, Charles K. A82
Vaughan, Richard C. (Rich) A540
Vaughan, Curtis P463
Vaughn, Gregory R. (Greg) E49
Vaughn, Cless E121
Vaughn, Robert C. E126
Vaughn, Ann E240
Vaughn, Anthony D. (Tony) A250
Vaughn, Tony D. A250
Vaughn, Joe A698
Vaughn, Donnie P105
Vaughn-Furlow, Rebecca N. A814
Vaule, Rosamond B. A138
Vaux, Robert G. (Bob) W386
Vavalidis, Stefanos C. W244
Vavoso, Glenn E249
Vawdrey, Rod W150
Vayda, Joseph M. A486
Vazquez, Tanna E339
Vazquez, Jamie L. E511
Vazquez, John A553
Vazquez, Carlos J. A651
Vazquez, Margarita A660
Vazquez, Raul A853
Vazquez, Ronald O. P288
Vazquez, Diane P525
Veach, Shae C. P223
Veal, Jimmy D. A54
Veale, Dick P221
Veazey, Beth P47
Vecchio, Dale E196
Vecchio, Jules A. del A485
Vecchio, Jules A485
Vecchio, Mark Del A545
Vecchione, Kenneth A. (Ken) E146
Vecchione, Kenneth A. (Ken) A865
Vedak, Bharat S. A245
Vedrine, Hubert W216
Veer, Ben van der W11
Veer, Jeroen W188
Veer, Jeroen W205
Veer, Jeroen van der W303
Veeramraju, Jonathan E46
Veeranna, Nagendra E108
Veerasingham, Daisy P503
Vega, Gerard E162
Vega, Ralph de la A80
Vega, Ralph A81
Vega, Teresita P87
Vega, Sonia Marie De Leon de P87
Vega, Guadalupe P338
Vega, Elizabeth P525
Vega, Ruth P612
Vegas, Pablo A. A47
Vegas, Pablo A. A610
Veggeburg, Kurt E335
Veghte, Bill A418
Vehling, Timothy E421
Vehrkens, Kenneth P180
Veillette, Robert E E351
Veitia, Diego J. A460
Veksler, Angela D. A855
Vela, Manuel R. A786
Velarde, Georgia E. A855
Velarde, Randy E. P527
Velarde, Vicki P527
Velasco, Prof Guillermo Vasquez de P40

Velasco, Ernesto Vega W24
Velasco, Pedro W180
Velasco-Aznar, Whitney A426
Velasquez, Felipe E362
Velasquez, David R. A226
Velasquez, Maria E. W135
Velazquez, Jovino E503
Velazquez, David M. (Dave) A637
Velazquez, Victor P18
Velazquez, Ralph R. P370
Velden, Jan van der E118
Velden, Raymond van der A644
Veldman, Henry P379
Vella, James G. A358
Vella, Kimberly D. (Kim) A808
Vellaccio, Frank P122
Velli, Joseph M. A278
Veltmaat, Hans-Bernd A18
Veltre, Maria A329
Veltri, Enrico A549
Veltri, Gregg P106
Vemuri, Ashok E238
Ven, Kevin Van de A605
Ven, Michael G. (Mike) Van de A739
Venables, Thomas R. A444
Venancio, Matthew E186
Venberg, Bryan E. A314
Venean, Ann P183
Venegoni, Michael E401
Venegoni, John V. E442
Venenga, Steven J. A426
Venetos, Sophia A600
Venezia, Robert E194
Venezia, Joe A628
Veneziano, James M. E482
Vengco, Joel L. P52
Venick, Shelley J. A139
Venie, Evan P243
Venkataramanan, PS (Venkat) W30
Venkatesan, Ravi W383
Venn, Richard E. W84
Venner, Kenneth E. (Ken) A136
Venti, Gail P160
Venti, Jane P506
Ventola, Tony P557
Ventresca, Chris A476
Ventriglia, Bruce E195
Ventura, Daun E162
Ventura, Jeffrey L. (Jeff) E390
Ventura, Robert J. A335
Ventura, Carlotta Carlotta Ventura W348
Venturelli, Larry M. A871
Venturino, Philip T. P522
Venugopal, Rupak E160
Venugopal, Venu E230
Venza, James P5
Vepraskas, Nancy A379
Vera, Ronald T. P87
Vera, George A. P511
Verbanac, Daniel J. (Dan) A449
Verbeek, Dirk P. M. W11
Verbeten, Paul R. A115
Verbiest, Katrien A644
Verburgt, Linda A235
Vercruysse, Craig P493
Verdayes, Hilda E183
Verde, Peter J. (Pete) P149
Verde, Dora Ann P501
Verdes, Marcelino Fernandez W9
Verdes, Marcelino F. W168
Verdina, Ben E80
Verduin, Patricia A203
Vere, Phil E351
Vereecke, Marc Marc Vereecke W30
Vereker, William W257
Veres, Dave P7
Veres, Andrew F. P535
Vereschagin, Alex A. A811
Vergara, Michael J. P543
Vergauwen, Michael (Mike) P37
Verger, Carey M. A25
Verghese, Nishath E71
Vergin, Jim E189
Vergine, Umberto W141

Vergnano, Mark P. A275
Vergnano, Mark A472
Verguet, Patrick E141
VerHeul, Jeff A714
Verheyen, Mark A193
Verhoeven, Thomas A513
Verhoeven, Bernhard W. A555
Verhoeven, Brian P223
Verissimo, Marc J. E454
Verissimo, Marc J. A770
Verity, William W. (Will) A49
Verkleeren, Ronald L. A226
Verkuehlen, Brian P409
Vermeer, Kevin P566
Vermeersch, Frederick F. P614
Vermetti, Cindy P4
Vermeulen, Raymond W188
Vermeulen-Anastasi, Sara A73
Vermilya, Todd P. A629
Vermut, Leslie P98
Vermylen, Paul A. E440
Vernaleo, John P618
Verneray, Laurent W312
Vernerey, Laurent W312
Verney, Steve A36
Vernie, James E306
Vernieri, Marco W189
Vernon, W. Anthony (Tony) A493
Vernon, Cheryl P83
Vernoski, Barbara P448
Vero, Peter E173
Verplancke, Jan W332
Verrastro, Mike P229
Verrette, Paula P377
Verrier, James R. A131
Versaggi, Steven M. A178
Verschoyle-King, Alan A103
Verslues, Ernie P318
Verstraete, Pierre A549
Vertalino, Terri E172
Vertuno, Maria L. P75
Verwilghen, Etienne W199
Veryser, Dirk A198
Verzello, Bob P143
Vesey, Andrew M. A14
Vesey, James E. A856
Vesper, Christian E28
Vesper, Keith P364
Vespestad, Robert A460
Vespoli, Leila L. A345
Vessa, Michael J. A499
Vessely, Mark E76
Vestal, Allan P157
Vestberg, Hans W143
Vetch, Larry P349
Vetere, Colleen E300
Vetor, Duke D. A189
Vetter, Egon A116
Vetter, David R. (Dave) A784
Vetter, Joel P349
Veurink, Jon D. A594
Veurink, David J. A782
Vevers, Stuart A196
Vezina, Ann A885
Veziroglu, Mustafa E273
Vezzosi, Gregory M. (Greg) A193
VI, Edward (Ed) Day A737
Vial, Arnaud W282
Vial, Arnaud W283
Viall, Paul G. A500
Viano, Janet M. A342
Viator, Dionne E. P47
Viault, Raymond G. A585
Viault, Raymond G. A846
Vicaire, Guillaume W87
Vicary, John P621
Vice, Thomas E. (Tom) A602
Vicente, Joeseph P367
Vick, Kevan A E117
Vick, Cathleen A329
Vickerman, Pat P75
Vickers, Ellis G. E516
Vickery, Julie A329
Victor, Stan E91
Victor, Michael T. E198

Victor, Kathleen J. (Kathy) Higgins A120
Victor, Robert S. A205
Victor, Kathleen J. (Kathy) Higgins P577
Victor, Diane de Saint W4
Victoria, Alex E230
Victorson, Arthur F. (Art) E464
Vidacovich, Bill P2
Vidal, Joseph R. E359
Vidarte, Susana Rodriguez W41
Vidarte, Susana W42
Vidaurri, Tito A100
Videla, Christian E136
Vidman, Moshe W49
Vidutis, Diana P612
Vie, Richard C. A484
Viegas, Victor (Vic) E243
Viegas, Renzo W292
Viehbacher, Christopher A. (Chris) W309
Vielehr, Byron C. A348
Viens, Kenneth P295
Viera, John A358
Vierk, Richard J. P139
Vierra, Mark P127
Vietri, Dominick E305
Viets, Ryan E219
Viets, Robert O. A702
Vigan, Eric P413
Vigil, Czar E17
Vigil, David A680
Vigil, Henry P. P313
Vigneau, Dennis R. A484
Vigneron, Rev Allen H. P505
Vignial, Antoine W107
Viguri, Jose Maria Loizaga W9
Vijayakumar, S. W67
Vijayan, T. S. W181
Vila, Carlos Torres W41
Vilardo, Elizabeth P375
Vilhauer, Robert J. (Bob) A126
Villa, Laura E15
Villa, Rembert de E160
Villa, Guillermo E446
Villa, Gabriele W225
Villadiego, Oscar A. W135
Villafane, Julio A405
Villalon, Jose P616
Villani, Anthony W. E339
Villano, Maria P612
Villanueva, Robert L. A309
Villanueva, Daniel D. A739
Villanueva, Yvette P541
Villarreal, Humberto E473
Villarreal, Jose H. A825
Villasana, George A. A74
Villecco, Jody A873
Villela, Alfredo Egydio Arruda W191
Villeneuve, Andre-Francois H. A836
Villers, Benoit A73
Viloria, Glenn P604
Vincent, Doug E5
Vincent, Joe E175
Vincent, C. Alec A139
Vincent, Lucie Claire A203
Vincent, Anton A376
Vincent, Daniel L. (Dan) P374
Vincent, Nancy P429
Vincent, Mary P472
Vincent, Carmen R. P568
Vincent, Cecilia P602
Vincent, Ann P602
Vincent, Jacques W121
Vinci, Don A297
Vinci, Francesco Saverio W224
Vinciguerra, Bruno E432
Vincze, John E339
Vincze, Christopher P. (Chris) E476
Vinecombe, Nigel A. E331
Vineglas, Dorothy P583
Vineyard, Tim P285
Viniar, David A. A386
Viniar, David A. P557
Vining, Paul H. A39

Wakefield, Dave E514
Wakeley, Laura J. A366
Wakeman, David N. A45
Wakeman, Daniel P165
Wakie, Barbara P192
Wakulchik, Grace P111
Wal, Eric Van De E429
Walbaum, Jean-Pierre W103
Walburger, Corbin B. A751
Walch, Rob E163
Walchirk, Mark A543
Wald, Frederica N. (Freddi) P373
Waldbillig, Kurt P470
Waldbusser, Kendra A647
Waldeck, Daniel A175
Walden, Joshua M. A451
Walden, Dana A816
Walden, Michael P282
Waldenfels, Georg Freiherr von W135
Waldhauser, L. Lenny A702
Waldheim, Mark E196
Waldis, Stephen G. E458
Waldman, Mitchell B. (Mitch) A438
Waldmann, Daniel R. A786
Waldo, Kurt R. A30
Waldo, Dana E. A365
Waldron, John P. A578
Waldron, Michael A589
Waldron, Kelly P215
Waldron, Jay P367
Waldron, Patrick W53
Waldron, Jared W268
Waldrum, Michael P534
Wale, Michael A755
Walecko, Kathy P496
Walery, Debbie E246
Walesiewicz, Patricia A. A112
Waleski, Anne G. A530
Walia, Amit E246
Walje, A. Richard (Rich) A626
Walker, Winston E30
Walker, Ann E60
Walker, William E92
Walker, Philip E98
Walker, Mark S E98
Walker, Daniel H. (Danny) E150
Walker, A E156
Walker, Daniel C (Dan) E156
Walker, Richard G. (Rich) E239
Walker, David N. E298
Walker, Steve E331
Walker, Raymond E356
Walker, Gregory C. E372
Walker, Rob E373
Walker, Clifford J E379
Walker, Ray N. E390
Walker, William M. (Willy) E514
Walker, William M. (Willy) E515
Walker, Joan H. A36
Walker, R. A. (Al) A60
Walker, Mark A70
Walker, Andre K. A144
Walker, R. A. (Al) A167
Walker, Wendy A207
Walker, Kimberly G. A208
Walker, Andrew A215
Walker, Thomas K. A227
Walker, John E. (Ned) A248
Walker, John E. A316
Walker, Brian C. A319
Walker, David W. A321
Walker, Terry L. A341
Walker, Sean N. A376
Walker, F. Borden A416
Walker, F. Borden A417
Walker, Stanley L. A605
Walker, John H. A605
Walker, Cynthia L. A608
Walker, Steven R. A611
Walker, Daniel C. (Dan) A615
Walker, Daniel E. (Dan) A634
Walker, Wayne A636
Walker, Roberto A661
Walker, Steven G. A668
Walker, Kevin P. A735

Walker, H. David A744
Walker, Cindi A792
Walker, Donald L. A803
Walker, W. Virginia A811
Walker, LeRoy G. A814
Walker, Bryan J. A822
Walker, Brian A822
Walker, John H. A828
Walker, Lori A. A843
Walker, Terry P13
Walker, John A. P46
Walker, Claudia P129
Walker, Robert D. P140
Walker, LeRoy P149
Walker, Amy P150
Walker, Valaida S. P173
Walker, Tom P214
Walker, Randy D. P227
Walker, Bart P290
Walker, Tyree P387
Walker, Susan P401
Walker, H. Fred P419
Walker, Annette M. P472
Walker, Robert S. (Bob) P503
Walker, Tyree P568
Walker, Ashley P576
Walker, Scott P595
Walker, George H. P600
Walker, Jeffrey P602
Walker, Robert O. P607
Walker, Valerie P612
Walker, Janice P619
Walker, Mervyn W26
Walker, Sir David A. W58
Walker, Sir David A. W60
Walker, Donald J. W219
Walker, Bruce W251
Walker-Lee, Robin A. A815
Walkiewicz, Scott P44
Walkling, Adrian W332
Walkup, Gardner W. A14
Wall, David E111
Wall, Michael E520
Wall, Timothy O. (Tim) A67
Wall, John C. A233
Wall, Daniel R. A309
Wall, Barbara W. A368
Wall, Shane D. A451
Wall, Michael A459
Wall, Robert T. A582
Wall, John A793
Wall, Merrill S. A865
Wall, Kirk P300
Wall, Fred G. P318
Wall, Kelly C. P347
Wall, Barbara E. P588
Wall, Kathryn P596
Wallace, William H. E6
Wallace, Tim E69
Wallace, Timothy E69
Wallace, Joseph J. (Joe) E95
Wallace, John E97
Wallace, Robert E421
Wallace, Bruce E454
Wallace, Peter W. (Pete) E464
Wallace, Greg E508
Wallace, Paul E515
Wallace, Henry D. G. A44
Wallace, Karen A. A71
Wallace, Michael K. A98
Wallace, Noel R. A202
Wallace, Brian A215
Wallace, Mark E. A239
Wallace, Goldie H. A332
Wallace, Dan A374
Wallace, William S. A476
Wallace, Henry D. G. A503
Wallace, Richard P. (Rick) A582
Wallace, William Scott A620
Wallace, Sarah Reese A630
Wallace, Bruce A770
Wallace, Timothy R. A812
Wallace, Patrick S. A812
Wallace, Jon D. A824
Wallace, Jon R. P38

Wallace, Nancy P139
Wallace, Derek P162
Wallace, Derek P163
Wallace, Brent E. P249
Wallace, Patricia P268
Wallace, Eugene P300
Wallace, Robert C. P401
Wallace, Betsy P411
Wallace, Ina P413
Wallace, Mark A. P500
Wallace, Patrick P527
Wallace, Paula S. P529
Wallace, Terry P544
Wallace, Sean W332
Wallach, Russell A516
Wallander, Barbara B. A324
Wallen, Olle A415
Wallenberg, Jacob A199
Wallenberg, Jacob W4
Wallenberg, Jacob W143
Wallenberg, Marcus W143
Wallenberg, Jacob W143
Wallenberg, Marcus W143
Wallenberg, Jacob A323
Wallenberg, Marcus W323
Wallenberg, Jacob W323
Waller, Rodney L. E390
Waller, Kathy N. A198
Waller, Ken P242
Waller, Carl P355
Waller, John W242
Wallette, Donald E. (Don) A220
Wallette, Donald E. (Don) W264
Wallick, Kevin A365
Wallin, Anthony R P249
Wallin, Ulrich W163
Wallin, Ulrich W346
Walling, Kevin R. A413
Wallingford, Judy E. E101
Wallis, David W. A44
Wallis, Tim A827
Wallis-Lage, Cindy P66
Walljasper, William J. (Bill) A156
Wallman, Richard F. A239
Wallman, Amy A613
Wallner, Bryan E434
Wallpe, Gary E11
Walls, Robert H. A442
Walls, Gen. George H. A651
Walls, Russell F. W35
Walls, Lindsay W39
Walmsley, Sir Robert A371
Walmsley, Emma W158
Walprecht, Volker W320
Walsdorf, James K. P324
Walsdorf, Neil B. P324
Walser, W. Max P175
Walser, Jo Anne E. P358
Walsh, Kim E35
Walsh, Robert B. E159
Walsh, Erik E162
Walsh, Nick E172
Walsh, Daniel E260
Walsh, Paul E374
Walsh, Harry J. E478
Walsh, Nicholas C. (Nick) A51
Walsh, Timothy A. A52
Walsh, Dale A176
Walsh, Thomas J. A178
Walsh, Christopher L. A224
Walsh, J. Michael (Mike) A224
Walsh, Lydia Kenton A226
Walsh, Paul S. A324
Walsh, Laura A354
Walsh, Matt A360
Walsh, Jennifer A374
Walsh, Daniel P. A437
Walsh, Fionnuala A513
Walsh, Paul F. A753
Walsh, Brian J. A758
Walsh, Debbie L. A786
Walsh, John L. A821
Walsh, Michael A. A849
Walsh, Suzanne A856
Walsh, Michael P1

Walsh, Kate E. P73
Walsh, Marilyn J. P90
Walsh, Stephen J. P103
Walsh, Gerri P186
Walsh, Andrea P224
Walsh, Thomas P342
Walsh, James M. P481
Walsh, Katherine P519
Walsh, Laurie P525
Walsh, Matthew M. (Matt) P537
Walsh, Daniel J. P537
Walsh, Daniel P538
Walsh, Sean P538
Walsh, Joe W53
Walsh, Brian E. W160
Walsh, Imelda W194
Walsh, Paula W218
Walsh, Barry W274
Walsh, Sam W294
Walsh, Sam W295
Walsh, Pamela W329
Walsh, Paul S. W369
Walsh, Paul S. W370
Walsh, Adam W387
Walstrom, Dean E492
Walstrom, Kevin P379
Walter, Edward W E47
Walter, Kenneth E50
Walter, John R E139
Walter, Nikolai E181
Walter, Luc A58
Walter, Glenn A199
Walter, Frank A412
Walter, W. Edward (Ed) A430
Walter, William G. (Bill) A458
Walter, John R. A526
Walter, Jim A538
Walter, Robert D. (Bob) A596
Walter, Robert D. (Bob) A889
Walter, Robert D. (Bob) P48
Walter, John R. P354

Walter, Joseph C. (Rusty) P519
Walter, B. Oliver P581
Walter, Bernhard W119
Walter, Bernhard W130
Walter, Bernhard W208
Walters, Joyce E103
Walters, Marla E130
Walters, Brad E179
Walters, Farah M. A163
Walters, Christopher A. A235
Walters, Thomas R. (Tom) A311
Walters, Kathleen A. (Kathy) A465
Walters, Judy A. A551
Walters, Kirk W. A636
Walters, Cindy P86
Walters, Bayard H. P150
Walters, Rachael P255
Walters, Shawn P356
Walters, Bradford P413
Walters, Donna P448
Walther, Peter E251
Walther, Chris B. A8
Walther, Roger O. A720
Walther, Dale P238
Walther, Klaus W127
Waltman, Francis G. (Frank) E508
Walton, Mike E28
Walton, H. Richard E177
Walton, Deanna L. A53
Walton, S. Robson (Rob) A853
Walton, Aaron M. P39
Walton, Ferrell P393
Walton, Kevaan P445
Walton, D. Gibson P519
Walton, Susan P573
Waltz, Bradden E. A629
Waltzinger, G. William A113
Walz, Dan P551
Walz, Pat P621
Wambach, Karl P233
Wambold, Richard L. A657
Wambold, Richard A723
Wambold, Keith P290

A = AMERICAN BUSINESS
E = EMERGING COMPANIES
P = PRIVATE COMPANIES
W = WORLD BUSINESS

Zoller, Edgar W65
Zona, Richard A. A782
Zonio, Grace E379
Zonis, Prof Marvin A193
Zonneveld, Thomas E4
Zonouzi, Farideh P618
Zook, Dennis R. A227
Zook, Keith A664
Zorb, Maryjo P109
Zore, Edward J. A526
Zoretic, Richard C. A65
Zorkin, Melissa Waggener P313
Zorn, Eric S. A853
Zouzalik, Ervan E. A668
Zovko, Gregory A. A833
Zubeck, Barbara P554
Zuber, Patrick J. A767
Zuber, Jane P500
Zuber, Eugene P607
Zubiller, Matthew A544
Zubkov, Victor A. W154
Zubkov, Viktor W154
Zubkov, Victor A. W154
Zubretsky, Joseph M. A15
Zubrow, Barry L. A475
Zucaro, Aldo C. (Al) A611
Zuccarelli, Jennifer R. A476
Zuccaro, Robert S. E194
Zucconi, Paul J. A806
Zucker, Nehemia (Hemi) E258
Zucker, Scott A314
Zucker, Jeff A801
Zuckerberg, Mark A312
Zuckerbraun, David A856
Zuckerman, Mitchell E432
Zuckerman, Tom P578
Zuckerman, Gary W. P582
Zuel, Sally P560
Zuercher, Richard A264
Zuhlke, Dan P249
Zuhlke, Sue P367
Zuhlke, Oliver W64
Zuidema, Richard W. (Dick) E149
Zukauckas, Linda K. A37
Zulberti, Andrea M. A774
Zulim, Thomas M. A299
Zulla, Caitlin E300
Zulueta, Alfonso G. (Chito) A513
Zuna, Michael W. A17
Zunino, Luigi W225
Zupan, Mark A222
Zupan, Leon A. A292
Zupan, Leon W137
Zur, Noam E181
Zuraf, Frank P528
Zuraitis, Marita A399
Zurbay, Donald J. A749
Zurkow, Deborah A540
Zuschlag, Richard P2
Zuschlag, John P2
Zutz, Maureen P247
Zuzulo, Martin E369
Zviedris, Andrea W339
Zvonek, Daniel J. A768
Zwarenstein, Barry E120
Zweifach, Gerson A816
Zwerling, Gary P39
Zwickl, Franz W368
Zwiebler, Thomas W381
Zwiener, David K. A194
Zwirn, Randy H. W320
Zychlin, Claus P. von P331
Zygocki, Rhonda I. A176
Zyl, Adriaan A127
Zyl, Johan van W363
Zyskind, Barry D. A59